THE PRINCIPLES OF BACTERIOLOGY AND IMMUNITY

THE PRINCIPLES
OF BACTERIOLOGY AND
IMMUNITY

BY

W. W. C. TOPLEY, M.A., M.D., M.Sc., F.R.C.P., F.R.S.

PROFESSOR OF BACTERIOLOGY AND IMMUNOLOGY, UNIVERSITY OF LONDON,
DIRECTOR OF THE DIVISION OF BACTERIOLOGY AND IMMUNOLOGY,
LONDON SCHOOL OF HYGIENE AND TROPICAL MEDICINE

AND

G. S. WILSON, M.D., F.R.C.P., D.P.H.

PROFESSOR OF BACTERIOLOGY AS APPLIED TO HYGIENE, UNIVERSITY OF
LONDON, LONDON SCHOOL OF HYGIENE AND TROPICAL MEDICINE

SECOND EDITION

BALTIMORE
WILLIAM WOOD & COMPANY
MCMXXXVI

All Rights Reserved
First Published in . 1929
Reprinted 1931, 1932, 1934
Second Edition . . 1936

Printed in Great Britain by
Butler & Tanner Ltd., Frome and London

To

K. T. and J. W.

PREFACE TO THE SECOND EDITION

THE seven years that have elapsed since the publication of the first edition of this book have witnessed a rapid advance in the science of bacteriology—more rapid, perhaps, than any that has occurred since its early infancy. As a consequence, the task of revision has been peculiarly difficult. Adequate reference to all the new knowledge that has been acquired would have entailed expansion to a size altogether inappropriate to a textbook of this kind ; and we have been compelled to push selection very far. We have tried to give an account—full enough to be clear—of all those recent studies that have added significantly to our knowledge, particularly those that have an important bearing on the diagnosis, prevention, or treatment of infective disease. In certain cases, where recent work has greatly altered our conception of a particular bacterial group, or of the diseases caused by it, we have frankly adopted the style of an abbreviated monograph, or review, rather than of a section in a textbook, since the serious student would otherwise be forced to consult a scattered literature to obtain an understanding of important current problems. We have, on the other hand, omitted altogether many observations the significance of which is as yet difficult, or impossible, to assess ; and, where recent advances have solved long-standing problems, we have severely curtailed the account of earlier work, at some loss, perhaps, to historical perspective.

As in the first edition, we have dealt with the infective diseases of animals rather more fully than is usual in a textbook intended mainly for medical bacteriologists ; but the boundary between medical and veterinary science is becoming very indistinct, and this is as it should be. The importance of animal diseases to the public health is such that both the medical and veterinary bacteriologist will find themselves at a serious disadvantage, unless each has some familiarity with the territory covered by the other.

This has involved extensive alterations. Many of the chapters have been entirely re-written, and additional chapters have been introduced. We have, however, adhered to the original arrangement of the text, except that we have included, in the systematic description of bacteria, a fuller account of their pathogenicity for animals and man, transferring the relevant sections from later chapters.

The two volumes, in which the first edition was published, have been combined into one. This step has been taken in response to requests from many of those who have used the book in its original form ; and we hope that the change will be of assistance to readers.

In giving references to the literature we have adopted the abbreviations contained in the World List of Scientific Periodicals.

We should wish to take this opportunity of thanking those friendly critics who have pointed out to us various errors in the first edition. These we have tried to correct; but we cannot have avoided replacing them by others in the mass of new matter that has been included. We need not say that we shall welcome their detection and removal.

Finally, we should wish again to express our indebtedness to many colleagues and friends, in this School and elsewhere. To most of those who were mentioned by name in the first edition we owe a further debt. Among many others, from whom we have received help and advice in the revision of various parts of the text, we would acknowledge in particular our indebtedness to Dr. W. R. Wooldridge and Dr. B. C. J. G. Knight in connection with certain chemical problems, to Dr. A. B. Hill in relation to the chapter on elementary statistical methods, and to Dr. Leonard Colebrook, Dr. Dora Colebrook, Dr. R. Hare, Dr. F. C. Minett, Dr. A. W. Stableforth, Dr. W. M. Scott, Dr. A. A. Miles, and Dr. I. N. Asheshov who have helped us in a variety of ways.

We would also thank our colleagues Miss I. Maier, Miss H. A. Smith, Dr. J. C. Cruickshank, Dr. T. C. Stamp and Dr. P. H. Martin for their kindly assistance in the preparation of the manuscript for the press.

We are indebted to H.M. Stationery Office for permission to reproduce Figures 24, 59, 61, 62 and 63.

W. W. C. T.
G. S. W.

London School of Hygiene
and Tropical Medicine.

July, 1936.

PREFACE TO THE FIRST EDITION

It has become increasingly evident, during the past ten years, that there is a need for the provision of organized teaching in the principles and technique of bacteriology, of a far more detailed and extensive kind than can be included within the four corners of an overcrowded medical curriculum, or in the scarcely less crowded courses of post-graduate study which lead to a Diploma in Public Health, in Tropical Medicine and Hygiene, or in Veterinary State Medicine. There is an increasing demand, at home and abroad, for the services of the trained bacteriologist; and it is no longer possible, or justifiable, to meet this demand by trusting to the emergence of a certain number of bacteriologists, as a by-product of a training designed for those whose work in life will lie in the clinical or administrative field.

The demand for a separate and organized course of training has been met in various ways. We have, for some years past, been concerned in teaching post-graduate students taking a full-time course in bacteriology lasting over one academic year, and leading to a University Diploma. One of the main difficulties we have encountered has been the lack of a textbook covering the ground over which such students have to travel. The many admirable textbooks which are available for the ordinary medical student are designed to meet his needs. At the moment of writing we have no comprehensive handbook of bacteriology in the English language to which the student may turn for reference; though this long-felt want will shortly be supplied under the auspices of the Medical Research Council. Numerous monographs have been published within the last ten years, dealing with such aspects of bacteriology as classification and nomenclature, the chemical and physical behaviour of bacteria, infection and resistance, and a host of allied subjects; but even with these, some parts of the field are left untouched, and it is inconvenient for the student to have to rely on a multiplicity of textbooks reinforced by extensive reading of original papers in different languages. To consult different books, and to read and criticize a selection of the more important contributions to bacteriological literature, is of course an essential part of any sound academic training in this subject; but no student, at this stage in his career, can be expected to make himself familiar at first hand with the mass of controversial literature which forms the raw material on which any conclusions must be based.

We have attempted, on the basis of our personal experience in post-graduate and undergraduate teaching, to provide a textbook which will be of service to those students of medicine and biology who wish to make a serious study of bacteriology and its application to the problems of infection and resistance. The order of presentation is that which is followed in the course of study pursued in this School; and the matter contained in Parts I and II of this book

ix

is, we think, of a kind with which any bacteriologist should be familiar. The book, as a whole, has however a frank bias in the direction of the application of bacteriological principles to the study and control of infective disease ; and Parts III and IV deal entirely with general and particular problems of this nature. We have tried to present these problems in their general biological aspect, as instances of variations in the relations of living things to each other, and to their environment, rather than as isolated problems of diagnosis, treatment or prevention, centering round a sick man or animal. Only in this way, we believe, can bacteriology play its full part in the control of infective disease. For the same reason we have included, in Part IV, numerous instances of natural disease in live-stock, and descriptions in some detail of experimental infections in laboratory animals. The liaison between research workers in human and veterinary medicine —the need for which was so strongly stressed by the late Sir Clifford Allbut— is making rapid headway ; and in no branch of medical science is the sterilizing effect of the anthropocentric attitude more obvious than in the study of bacterial infection.

We are personally convinced that this order of presentation is sound—that the student should gain some knowledge of bacteria as a distinctive class of living things, and of their systematic relationships and ecology, before considering their reactions with more highly differentiated organisms, the characters of which he has learned while studying zoology, physiology, or clinical medicine. The formal separation of description which this treatment involves is, however, by no means easy ; nor can it be followed consistently. So many bacterial species have been studied almost entirely from the point of view of the pathologist that their systematic description is still impossible. It will, therefore, be found that there is considerable overlapping between Parts II and IV of this book, and an arbitrary allotment, based on convenience, of particular sections to one Part or the other. In compiling some of the descriptions contained in Part II, we have had to rely, in certain minor particulars, on our own observation of comparatively small samples of strains. The recorded descriptions of bacterial types or species are often incomplete ; and we have attempted, where possible, to fill in some of the more obvious lacunæ from our own experience and that of our colleagues.

To bring our material within a reasonable compass, we have been forced, in most instances, to omit all detailed descriptions of technique. We have done so with no great reluctance ; since the convention of mingling practical instructions for laboratory work with the discussion of general principles has obvious disadvantages, and the student must in any case learn this part of his work by practical experience at the bench. Moreover, bacteriological technique is susceptible to so many minor modifications, and the practice of different laboratories may differ so widely in its minutiæ, that the detailed description of a single method for carrying out each routine procedure would be of little service, while the presentation of a host of alternatives would clearly be impossible.

We have found our task peculiarly difficult. Any teacher of bacteriology, at the present time, will realize the impossibility of following the didactic method. Where so much is uncertain, one must be content to present the available evidence, suggest tentative conclusions necessarily affected by personal bias, and encourage the student to form his own opinions. A firm grasp of general scientific principles, and a well-developed critical faculty, are primary essentials in the intellectual equipment of any student in this field. We have, therefore, frankly abandoned any attempt to simplify the issues by limiting ourselves to well-attested facts, or to undisputed conclusions. To do so would be to neglect some of the most stimulating bacteriological problems. There is a considerable fascination in studying a branch of science which is growing so rapidly that the charting of its territories is in many places sketchy and uncertain. There are disadvantages. Every teacher and student of bacteriology would be happier if there were some stability in bacteriological nomenclature. So many problems are still in dispute that it is necessary to master the basis of an alarming number of conflicting hypotheses. But, at least, the bacteriologist has no lack of problems which invite attack.

In giving references to the literature, we have endeavoured to afford the reader the means of following up for himself any point in which he is interested. The selection we have made has, of necessity, been somewhat arbitrary. We have omitted many papers of the middle bacteriological period, which, though important in their day, have lost much of their significance at the present time. Among the mass of more recent publications, we have certainly omitted much that is important, and have probably included more than a little which future developments will show to be trivial or misleading. In the absence of historical perspective, personal judgments must exert an undue weight.

We would acknowledge our indebtedness to various monographs and reviews, too numerous to mention here. These have been referred to freely in the text. Among our colleagues and friends who have given us assistance in various ways, we should desire particularly to thank Professor Major Greenwood, F.R.S., and Miss Woods for providing us with certain statistical data, Mr. J. E. Barnard, F.R.S., for information on several points in connection with the application of optical methods, Dr. J. F. C. Haslam and Mr. R. L. Sheppard for tracing certain original papers, Professor Delafield and Miss M. Stephenson for their advice on certain chemical questions, and Mrs. Smith and Mr. R. Lovell for their help in many directions. We would also acknowledge our indebtedness to Mr. F. V. Welch and Mr. W. Bale, who have taken the photo-micrographs with which this book is illustrated. Finally, we would express our sense of gratitude to our past and present students, whose questions, answerable and unanswerable, have provided the stimulus for our work.

W. W. C. T.
G. S. W.

LONDON SCHOOL OF HYGIENE
    AND TROPICAL MEDICINE.

September, 1929.

CONTENTS

PART I

GENERAL BACTERIOLOGY

PART II

SYSTEMATIC BACTERIOLOGY

PART III

INFECTION AND RESISTANCE

PART IV

THE APPLICATION OF BACTERIOLOGY TO MEDICINE AND HYGIENE

PART I

GENERAL BACTERIOLOGY

CHAPTER I

HISTORICAL OUTLINE

In the study of any branch of science, an acquaintance with the historical development of knowledge is an important element in a clear understanding of our present
conceptions. To the student of bacteriology such a basis is essential. It is almost
true to say that the clue to the present position of bacteriology is the curious fact
that there have been no bacteriologists. From Pasteur onwards, the great majority
of investigators have been more interested in what bacteria do than in what they are,
and much more interested in the ways in which they interfere with man's health or
pursuits than in the ways in which they function as autonomous living beings. The
relations of bacteria to disease, to agriculture, and to various commercial processes,
have presented problems which pressed for solution ; and, as a result, we have
witnessed a reversal of the normal process. We have seen the development of an
applied science of bacteriology, or rather its application along many divergent
lines, without the provision of any general basis of purely scientific knowledge.
The essential interlocking of pure and applied science has, of course, been in
evidence here as elsewhere. The necessity for being able to recognize a bacterium,
which has been shown to be of importance in some province of human affairs,
or of determining the way in which its harmful or beneficial action is brought
about, has led to an intensive study of many aspects of bacterial morphology
and physiology ; but, in general, it may be said that the study of bacteria themselves has been carried out *en passant*, that amount of knowledge being acquired,
or searched for, which would afford adequate data for the solution of some problem
in applied bacteriology. Gradually the general structure of our knowledge has
been added to, and gaps have been filled. Many of those who have started from
some particular application have been led far afield by that desire for knowledge,
altogether apart from its technical application, which is the essence of science
itself. But this mode of construction has given to the general body of existing
bacteriological knowledge a curious patchiness and indefiniteness which are puzzling
to the student, and which must be realized and allowed for in any attempt to
present the subject as a whole. There can be no question of any future recon-
struction *ab initio*. The history of a science is largely a history of technique, and
the foundations of bacteriological technique, which presents many peculiar difficulties, have been well and truly laid by those who have worked in this field since

the middle of the nineteenth century. The pure bacteriologist of the future will owe a lasting debt to those who have worked on the applied side, and his investigations will necessarily be based upon the knowledge gained by the medical or agricultural bacteriologist. The study of immunology, for instance, has supplied a body of facts, and an armoury of technical methods, which no bacteriologist can neglect, and which will inevitably give to future bacteriological research certain peculiarities of outlook and special methods of attack.

It is customary, in summarizing the history of bacteriology, at least in relation to medicine, to refer to the conception advanced by Fracastorius of Verona (1546), concerning a *contagium vivum* as the possible cause of infective disease, and to the views advanced by von Plenciz (1762) on the specificity of disease, based on a belief in its microbial origin. A concrete science is, however, seldom advanced to any considerable extent by arguments, however ingenious, which are propounded without appeal to experiment, or to wide and detailed observation ; and the absence of all real progress until the middle of last century is sufficient evidence that the views of Fracastorius, von Plenciz and others have acquired their main significance from knowledge gathered by later generations, rather than from their inherent fertility. The construction and use of the compound microscope was an essential pre-requisite to the study of microbial forms, and the reported observation by Kircher (1659) of minute worms in the blood of plague patients forms, perhaps, the earliest attempt at direct microscopical observation in this field. It is, however, more than doubtful whether Kircher could have seen plague bacilli, or indeed any bacterial forms, with the apparatus which he had at his disposal. To van Leeuwenhoek (1683) must be ascribed the credit of placing the science of microbiology on the firm basis of direct observation (Dobell 1932). This Dutch maker of lenses developed an apparatus and technique which enabled him to observe and describe various microbial forms with an accuracy and care which still serve as a model for all workers in this field. He observed, drew, and measured with considerable approximation to truth large numbers of minute living organisms, including bacterial and protozoal forms. It is, perhaps, somewhat surprising that this marked advance was not followed by further rapid progress in our knowledge of bacteria and their activities. Such progress was, however, impossible without further developments in technique. The world of minute living things, opened to morphological study by van Leeuwenhoek, was seen to be peopled by a multitude of dissimilar forms, whose interrelationships it was impossible to determine without preliminary isolation ; and, so far as bacteria were concerned, this isolation was not accomplished until the problem of artificial cultivation was solved, almost two hundred years later.

The real development of bacteriology as a subject of scientific study dates from the middle of the nineteenth century, and is the direct outcome of the work of Louis Pasteur (1822–95). Isolated observations of microbial parasites, by Brassi, Pollender, Davaine and others, have priority in particular instances, just as Schultze, Schroeder and Dusch and others initiated technical methods which Pasteur applied to his own researches. But it was Pasteur and his pupils who settled the fundamental questions at issue, and developed a technique which made possible the cultivation and study of bacteria.

Trained as a chemist, Pasteur was led to the study of microscopic organisms by his observations on the phenomena of fermentation. His early studies on the structure of the tartrates, and on molecular asymmetry, had led him to believe that the property of optical activity, possessed by certain organic compounds, was characteristic of substances synthesized by living things, as contrasted with substances synthesized in the laboratory. It was known that small amounts of an optically active substance, amyl alcohol, were formed during the fermentation of sugar, especially in association with the lactic fermentation. Since it was impossible to regard the molecule of amyl alcohol as derived from the molecule of sugar by any simple break-down process, he was led to the conclusion that the optically active molecule of the sugar was first broken down to relatively simple substances, which experience had shown to be without optical activity,

FIG. 1.—LOUIS PASTEUR (1822–1895).

and that from such inactive substances the optically active amyl alcohol was synthesized. For Pasteur this was evidence of the presence and activity of living things, and he therefore started on his study of fermentation with a strong *a priori* leaning towards the microbial theory of fermentation, and away from the then dominant hypothesis of Liebig. He was prepared to adopt the theories already propounded by Caignard-Latour in 1836, and by Schwann in 1837, concerning the living nature of the yeast globules, which were always to be found in sugar solutions undergoing alcoholic fermentations, and which had been described by van Leeuwenhoek in 1680.

Since, however, it was in the lactic fermentation that the production of amyl alcohol had especially been noted, it was this reaction which Pasteur first selected for experimental study, though he had already made numerous observations on material from the vats of the breweries of Lille. He was probably influenced by the fact that the observations of van Helmholtz (1843) had already indicated that the alcoholic fermentation was due to the yeast itself or to some other organized material. Helmholtz had shown that the substance, whatever it might be, which was responsible for initiating alcoholic fermentation, would not pass through membranes, which allowed the passage of organic substances in solution but held back particles in suspension. This experiment, successful with alcoholic fermentation, failed with many other ferments and fermentable liquids. Pasteur's mind was naturally addicted to generalization, and his interest lay in the phenomenon of fermentation as a general type of reaction, rather than in one kind of fermentation in particular. It was therefore natural that he should at first neglect the field in which the battle was more evenly balanced between the purely chemical conceptions of Liebig, and the biological theories of Caignard-Latour, Schwann and Helmholtz, and turn to the field in which Liebig's views had never been successfully attacked. Pasteur's first memoir was published in 1857, and in it he declared the lactic ferment to be a living organism, far smaller than the yeast-cell, but which could be seen under the microscope, could be observed to increase in amount when transferred from one sugar solution to another, and had very decided preferences as regards the character of the medium in which it was allowed to develop ; so that, for instance, by altering the acidity of the medium one could inhibit or accelerate its growth and activity. In this memoir Pasteur laid the first foundations of our knowledge of the conditions which must be fulfilled for the cultivation of bacteria.

These studies on fermentation occupied Pasteur almost continuously from 1855 to 1860, and he returned to them again at intervals during later years. He was able to show that the fermentation of various organic fluids was always associated with the presence of living cells, and that different types of fermentation were associated with the presence of microscopic organisms which could be differentiated from one another by their morphology and by their cultural requirements. Thus, at this early stage, the idea of specificity entered into bacteriology.

It was impossible for Pasteur to pursue these studies without facing the problem of the origin of these minute living organisms, which he regarded as the essential agents of all fermentations. At this time (1859) there were two opposed schools of thought with regard to the genesis of microbial forms of life. One school, deriving their concepts from the great naturalists of antiquity, believed in the spontaneous generation of living things from dead, and especially from decomposing organic matter. It is of little interest to remember the vague terms in which such conceptions were clothed ; but one tendency may be noted, which did not escape the astute mind of Pasteur. The species of animals or plants believed to arise by spontaneous generation were diminishing in number, and the average size of those organisms still included in this category was getting smaller and smaller. In the beginning, the supporters of spontaneous generation were prepared to attribute this mode of origin to relatively large animals. Van Helmont, in the sixteenth century, offered a prescription for making mice. It needed the experiments of Redi (1688) to substitute, for the idea that worms were spontaneously generated in decomposing meat, the truth that these worms were the larvæ of flies, and that their appearance could be very simply prevented by protecting the meat with gauze, through which the flies could not pass to deposit their eggs. The discovery by Leeuwenhoek of the world of microbial organisms gave a powerful stimulus to the somewhat decadent theory. Here, at all events, were living things which obeyed no known law of reproduction, and whose existence seemed to lend support to a belief which had long been accepted by eminent authorities, and which had thereby acquired a natural prestige.

From the start of his inquiry, Pasteur leaned towards the opposing school of those who believed that spontaneous generation was a myth, that these microscopic organisms, like other living things, were reproduced in some way from similar pre-existing cells. He had already convinced himself that these organized cells were the active agents of fermentation. Clearly then they could not arise *de novo* during the changes for which they were themselves responsible, but must have been introduced from without. Their marked specificity, maintained through repeated transferences from one specimen of fermentable fluid to another of the same kind, was strong evidence in favour of their autonomous reproduction. Here again Pasteur had tentatively adopted the correct solution before starting his experimental inquiry, but the main interest of his part in the controversy lies in the consummate skill with which he developed methods which enabled him to give clear demonstrations where others had left doubt and confusion, and which determined the main rules of a technique which has made possible the cultivation and study of bacteria.

Neglecting for the moment the vaguer conceptions of the pre-experimental era, the position in 1859 was as follows. Needham, an Irish priest, had published in 1745 a memoir describing the spontaneous generation of microbial organisms in closed flasks of putrescible fluids, which had been heated to destroy pre-existing life. These views were strongly supported by the celebrated naturalist Buffon in 1749. An Italian abbot, Spallanzani, countered in 1769 with the publication of a series of admirable experiments in which he criticized Needham's results, and showed that, with longer heating, the fluid in such flasks remained clear and sterile. This controversy narrowed into a dispute as to the nature of the principle which survived short periods of heating, but was destroyed by long heating in flasks hermetically sealed. For Spallanzani the principle was a living germ, for Needham it was a " vegetative force," resident in the air, or perhaps in the putrescible fluid. In any case such argument was sterile, and although it was generally admitted that the honours remained with Spallanzani, no final judgment was pronounced.

At this time oxygen was regarded as an element of quite peculiar power and significance, and the experiments of Appert (1810) on the preservation of food-stuffs, by heating and hermetical closure of the containing vessels, followed by a weighty expression of opinion by Gay-Lussac, had led to a general belief that the exclusion of this gas was the essential factor in ensuring the absence of fermentation. Schwann (1837) showed that the air in a flask containing a putrescible fluid, which had been sterilized by boiling, could be renewed by drawing in air which had passed through a glass tube immersed in a bath of fusible alloy kept at high temperature, and by this means he demonstrated that the presence of oxygen alone would not cause the appearance of micro-organisms in the fluid. Unfortunately, in the same memoir, Schwann reported other experiments, in which he introduced heated and unheated air into flasks, containing a sterilized solution of sugar in a watery extract of yeast, by inverting the flasks over a mercury bath and admitting the air through the mercury seal. Here his results, as regards the occurrence of fermentation, were altogether uncertain, and his conclusions lost much of their force. Helmholtz (1844) confirmed certain of Schwann's observations. Schultze (1836) had already obtained similar results by admitting to his flasks air which had been drawn through strong potash solutions or through concentrated sulphuric acid. Schroeder and Dusch (1854) showed that the active principle could be removed from the air by drawing it through cotton-wool. This last method was a real advance, since the incoming air had not been subjected to high temperatures, nor to strong chemical reagents. Unfortunately another element of doubt was introduced. Schroeder and Dusch relied, for their preliminary sterilization, on a short period of heating to the boiling-point. They experimented with four kinds of material—water containing meat, malt of beer, milk, and meat without the addition of water. With the first two materials their results were quite uniform : the fluids remained unaltered. With the last two materials fermentation usually occurred. They concluded that there were two kinds of decomposition, associated with the presence of living organisms, the one spontaneous, needing only the presence of oxygen, the other requiring some additional principle, which could be removed from the air by filtration through cotton-wool.

This, then, was the position when Pasteur began his investigations in 1859. In a series of admirable memoirs, starting in 1860 and continuing for more than four years, he went over the ground already covered, added new and illuminating experiments of his own devising, and terminated the controversy by clear and decisive demonstrations. He showed that the material removed from air by passage through cotton-wool, or through similar filters, contained organized particles which were neither crystals nor starch granules, but which were similar in appearance to the spores of moulds. By introducing these particles into flasks of sterilized organic material, he demonstrated that they were capable of giving rise to the growth of numerous kinds of living organisms. Using other methods, he showed that the air in different situations differed in its content of these germs ; that they were numerous in the streets of cities, less numerous in the air of country uplands, rare in the quiet air of closed and uninhabited rooms or cellars, where the dust had deposited and remained undisturbed, and very rare in the pure air of the high Alps, above the level of human habitation. He showed that Schwann's failures were due to his use of mercury, from the surface of which his fluid had acquired the germs, which had settled on it from the air. He showed that the failures of Schroeder and Dusch were due to the inadequate sterilization of their material.

He also showed that certain animal fluids, such as blood or urine, known to be eminently liable to undergo putrefaction, could be collected in such a way as to remain permanently unaltered.

The controversy with Pouchet, Joly and Musset, which continued from 1860 to 1864, did not lead to the collection of many new facts, except those with regard to the unequal distribution of micro-organisms in the atmosphere ; but a later dispute with Bastian, who became a veteran in the dwindling army of the supporters of spontaneous generation, was more fertile, because it caused Pasteur to reconsider some of his ideas, and to elaborate the technical methods which he had partially developed during his re-investigation of the results obtained by Schroeder and

Dusch. In 1876 Bastian published a communication controverting an early statement by Pasteur that urine, sterilized by boiling, remained free from growth on subsequent incubation. Bastian declared that, if the urine were made alkaline at the start, growth often ensued. Pasteur, on repeating the experiment, was forced to admit the truth of Bastian's statement. A careful retracing of all his steps resulted in the demonstration that fluids with an acid reaction, after sterilization at 100° C., might remain apparently sterile because certain organisms, which remained alive, were unable to develop, while in an alkaline medium they might grow freely. It was found also that ordinary water frequently contained organisms which were not killed by heating to 100° C., and that organisms which had become deposited on the surface of glass-ware in the dry state might withstand far higher temperatures. We know now that it is especially for those bacteria which form spores that these conditions hold true. As a result of this controversy Pasteur established the practice of heating fluid material to 120° C. under pressure for the purpose of sterilization, thus introducing the autoclave into the laboratory, and the practice of sterilizing glass-ware by dry heat at 170° C. In this connection a very important advance was made by Tyndall who, observing that actively growing bacteria are easily destroyed by boiling, and that a certain amount of time is required for bacteria in the resistant, inactive phase to pass into the growing phase in which they are heat-sensitive, introduced the method of sterilization by repeated heatings, with appropriate intervals between them. This method is still known as Tyndallization. It was first described in a letter to Huxley in 1877 (see Bulloch 1930).

While investigating the phenomenon of fermentation, and the problem of spontaneous generation, Pasteur had studied the behaviour of very various kinds of natural organic fluids and solutions, and had succeeded in growing micro-organisms on simple synthetic media. As a result he had become assured of the fact that a medium, which is eminently suitable for the growth of one bacterium or mould, may be ill-adapted for the growth of another, and that one of the primary necessities for the successful cultivation of any species of micro-organism is the discovery of a suitable medium for its growth. Quick to grasp the general significance of isolated observations, he pointed out the decisive effect which must be exercised by the selective action of various environmental factors in determining the constitution of any naturally occurring bacterial flora ; and he later developed these ideas in connection with the problem of infection.

As the result of these studies Pasteur had collected a mass of data, which enabled him to deal successfully with bacteriological problems that could not previously have been attacked. He had learned the need for the scrupulous sterilization of everything that came into contact with material which was to be submitted to bacteriological examination. He had learned the necessary methods of sterilization, in the steamer, in the autoclave, in the hot-air oven, or by direct flaming, which enabled these conditions to be fulfilled. He had proved the serviceableness of the cotton-wool plug for protecting media in flasks or tubes. He had realized the importance of the constitution of the nutrient material offered to a given bacterium, of the acidity or alkalinity of that medium, and of the oxygen pressure to which it was subjected. Armed with this knowledge, he proceeded to break new ground.

Pasteur was before all else a scientist, intensely curious, and loving knowledge for its own sake, but he was also a convinced utilitarian, and a Frenchman. He desired greatly that his discoveries should benefit mankind in general, France in particular, and, if possible, his neighbours in the first place. Thus we find him investigating with enthusiastic care the troubles of the local vintners or brewers, or vinegar-makers, and many of his memoirs are devoted to the diseases of wines or of beers, and the methods of preventing them. It was in connection with these studies that Pasteur faced a new problem of fundamental importance. He had shown that ferments were living organisms, that they were specific, that they were reproduced from parent forms and not by spontaneous generation. He was now faced with the problem as to whether one species could change into another, in particular whether mycoderma vini could change into the ordinary yeast of wine. Deceived on this point at first, he resorted as usual to rigorous and repeated experiments, and not only demonstrated that this mutation did not occur, but indicated clearly the conditions which led to its apparent occurrence, and the care which must be exercised before accepting any reported variation of this kind.

Anyone who reads for himself the original memoirs on fermentation and spontaneous generation (see Vallery-Radot, P., 1922–1933) will realize that the possibility of applying this new knowledge to the elucidation of infective disease was already in Pasteur's mind. It needed only the spur of a request from Dumas to investigate the disease, which was then ruining the silkworm industry in the South of France, to turn his steps permanently towards the study of infective processes. We cannot follow here, even in outline, Pasteur's researches into pébrine, anthrax, chicken cholera, or hydrophobia. Some of them will be referred to in later chapters. We must, however, note certain contributions which Pasteur and his colleagues made to the fundamental data of bacterial infections. It was Pasteur who showed, in the case of anthrax, that a culture of a pathogenic organism could be passed through successive subcultures, in such a way as to dilute, beyond possibility of significant action, any other material introduced with it into the primary culture from the blood or tissues, and still produce the disease when inoculated into a susceptible animal ; though it is to Koch that priority must be given as regards many points in the demonstration of the nature and action of the anthrax bacillus. It was Pasteur who introduced into bacteriology the conception of virulence and of attenuation, and who demonstrated the fact that an attenuated bacterial culture will act as a vaccine, that is, will confer immunity against subsequent infection with a virulent strain of the same bacterium. For Pasteur, indeed, a vaccine was synonymous with an attenuated culture, as opposed to a virulent culture on the one hand and to a dead culture on the other. It was Pasteur who, in the case of rabies, showed that it was possible to study the virus of an infective disease by animal passage, when the organism could not be cultivated, and even to prepare a perfectly efficient vaccine by using suitably treated animal tissue.

Thus, throughout a long scientific life, Pasteur was largely concerned with the practical application of knowledge gained during his studies on fermentation. The correct procedure for preparing good wine, good beer, good vinegar, and the methods of preserving them, the control of pébrine, of anthrax, of chicken cholera, of hydrophobia, these were the problems which occupied the last thirty years of his life, and the solution of which made his name a household word. But we shall miss the real significance of his work if we fail to realize that his fertile generalizations were of infinitely more importance for the progress of science than were his successful attacks on these isolated problems.

He had learned how to isolate and cultivate bacteria, and how to study their effect on animals; but with the minutiæ of their morphology or physiology, apart from any significance these might have for the problem in hand, he was not greatly concerned. Duclaux relates that a clever and positive microscopist, who told Pasteur in very cautious language that a certain organism which he had taken for a coccus was in reality a very small bacillus, was much astonished to hear him reply : " If you only knew how little difference that makes to me ! "

One further point must be noted. Pasteur and his colleagues had shown how to obtain cultures of micro-organisms, and propagate them indefinitely in the

Fig. 2.—Robert Koch (1843–1910).

laboratory ; but the methods which they employed were not well suited to the isolation of pure strains of bacteria from an originally mixed culture, except in those relatively rare cases in which it was possible to employ a highly selective medium. Since all media were employed in the fluid state, the only method of purifying a culture was to make successive transfers with very small amounts of material, in the hope that only a few bacteria, all of one kind, would be carried over. Such a technique was very uncertain in its results.

Pasteur, starting as a chemist, founded bacteriology and revolutionized medicine. At about the time when he was propounding his germ theory of disease, a young German physician, some twenty years his junior, was turning from clinical medicine to bacteriology. Robert Koch (1843–1910), at that time a practising physician at Wollstein, attacked the problem of anthrax, and produced, as his first contribution to science, a demonstration of the character and mode of growth of the causative bacillus, which opened a new era in bacteriological technique. This memoir he published in 1876. In the following year he published his methods of preparing, fixing, and staining film-preparations of bacteria, using the aniline dyes introduced into histology by Weigert, and described his methods of photographing such preparations. In 1878 he published his memoir on traumatic infective diseases, which remains a classical example of the study of experimental infections in laboratory animals. In 1881 he described his method of preparing cultures on solid media, a technical advance of the first importance, since it made possible the isolation of pure strains of bacteria from single colonies. Solid media prepared from naturally occurring material such as pieces of potato, had previously been used for the isolation of micro-organisms, particularly by mycologists, and the general principles to be observed in the preparation of pure cultures had been clearly enunciated by Brefeld, who had suggested the solidification of a nutrient medium by the addition of gelatin. The media and methods available for the cultivation of fungi were not, however, well suited for bacteria ; and it was left for Koch to devise, in the form of his nutrient gelatin, and later, at the suggestion of Frau Hesse, of nutrient agar, a solid, transparent medium, easy to sterilize and handle, and thus admirably adapted for obtaining isolated colonies of bacteria (see Bulloch 1930). In 1882 and 1884 he published his classical papers on the bacillus of tuberculosis. In 1883 he discovered the vibrio of cholera. Already, Koch had enlisted the services of Loeffler and of Gaffky as his assistants. Later came Pfeiffer, Kitasato, Welch and many others, and, with his growing fame, he began to gather round him a group of keen and able young men, who were destined to introduce the methods he devised into the laboratories of many lands. In 1885 he was appointed Professor of Hygiene and Bacteriology in Berlin, and in 1891 he was made Director of the newly-founded Institute for Infective Diseases. His later years were devoted almost entirely to the investigation of bacteriological problems in their relation to the prevention and cure of disease, and many of his contributions to our knowledge will be considered in later chapters. Koch was, above all, an able and careful technician. He was greatly aided by the vigour and initiative of the great German chemical and optical firms, and the advances which he made in staining methods, in the use of the microscope for the observation of bacteriological preparations, and in the technique of cultivating bacteria, revolutionized this branch of science.

The fruits of this revolution appeared with surprising rapidity. During the last quarter of the nineteenth century a succession of discoveries was reported, bearing on the relation of bacteria to human and animal disease, which opened a new era in medicine.

In 1874 Hansen described the bacillus of leprosy, and Neisser, in 1879, the gonococcus. In 1880 Pasteur recorded the isolation of the bacillus of fowl cholera, and Eberth observed the bacillus of typhoid fever. In 1881 Ogston published an adequate description of the staphylococcus. In 1882 Koch discovered the tubercle bacillus, and Loeffler and Schütz the bacillus of glanders. In 1883 Koch discovered the cholera vibrio, Fehleisen isolated the streptococcus of erysipelas, and Klebs described, but did not isolate, the bacillus of diphtheria. In 1884 Loeffler isolated, and subjected to thorough study, the bacillus which Klebs had briefly described in the previous year, and Gaffky isolated and studied the typhoid bacillus, which

Eberth had observed four years previously. In 1885 Loeffler discovered the bacillus of swine-erysipelas, Kitt the bacillus of hæmorrhagic septicæmia of cattle, and Salmon and Smith the bacillus associated with hog cholera. In the same year Nicolaier observed the tetanus bacillus in soil, inoculation of which produced the disease in animals. In 1886 Fraenkel isolated the pneumococcus, Escherich the colon bacillus, and Loeffler the bacillus of swine-plague. In 1887 Weichselbaum discovered the meningococcus, and Bruce the micrococcus of Malta fever. In 1888 Gaertner described the bacillus which bears his name, and Schütz the strepto-coccus of equine strangles. In 1889 Kitasato cultivated the tetanus bacillus, which had been earlier observed by Nicolaier. In 1892 Pfeiffer isolated the bacillus which he believed to be the cause of influenza, and Welch and Nuttall described the anærobic bacillus now known as *Cl. welchii*. In 1894 Kitasato and Yersin independently discovered the bacillus of plague. In 1895 Moore isolated the bacillus of fowl typhoid. In 1896 van Ermengem described *Cl. botulinum* as the cause of a particular variety of food poisoning. In 1897 Bang discovered the bacillus of bovine abortion. In 1898 Shiga isolated the variety of dysentery bacillus which bears his name, and Nocard and Roux described the minute organism of infectious pleuro-pneumonia of cattle.

Thus, by the close of the nineteenth century a great variety of micro-organisms had been identified as occurring in definite association with human or animal disease. In many instances complete demonstration had been afforded that the relation was one of cause and effect. In others, this relation was rendered highly probable. In others, again, there remained good reason for doubting whether the bacterium, whose presence had been demonstrated, played any more important rôle than that of a secondary invader. Beyond dispute, however, the scientific investigation of infective disease had become the province of the bacteriologist.

Another incident had done much to emphasize the importance of bacteria as the cause of disease and death, although it had comparatively little influence on bacteriology itself. Joseph Lister (1827–1912), during his tenure of the Professor-ship of Surgery at Glasgow, was deeply interested in the post-operative sepsis, which exacted such a terrible toll on the lives of hospital patients. His attention was drawn to Pasteur's work on fermentation, and the analogy between the changes which occur in fermenting organic material and the putrefaction which occurs in wounds suggested to him that in the latter, as in the former, the underlying cause might be the activity of minute living organisms. This led directly to the intro-duction of his antiseptic technique in surgery, described in 1867, which opened the door to modern surgical methods. Lister's technique has since been replaced by aseptic measures, but this detracts in no way from the merit of his discovery, nor from the debt which we owe to him for fighting the usual battle against the forces of ignorance and prejudice. Nor should it be forgotten that Lister made important contributions to bacteriological technique as such. He devised a method for diluting a bacterial culture and preparing a series of subcultures with so small a volume of the original fluid that many of them remained sterile, the presump-tion being that those that grew had developed from a single bacterial cell. In this way he isolated, in 1878, a bacterium that caused the souring of milk ; and Bulloch (1930) expresses the view that he may perhaps have been the first bacteriologist to obtain a certainly pure culture.

But the revolution inaugurated by Pasteur and extended by Koch spread far beyond the field of medicine. Agriculturists had long been puzzling over the problem of soil fertility, without arriving at any very helpful conclusions. One curious phenomenon was the reaccumulation of nitrates in the soil, in spite of their constant removal by the washing action of the rain. It was suspected that these nitrates might be derived in some way from the decomposition of organic material, and in 1877 Schloesing and Müntz, acting on a suggestion made by Pasteur in 1862, showed by experiment that the formation of nitrates was due to the action of living organisms. Warington, at Rothamsted, confirmed these results in 1878 and 1879, and showed that two stages were involved, a preliminary conversion of ammonia to nitrites, and a subsequent oxidation of nitrites to nitrates. He believed that these two stages were carried out by different organisms, but failed to isolate or identify them. This problem was solved by Winogradsky in 1890, who isolated and described both the nitrite- and nitrate-forming organisms. In 1888 Hellriegel and Willfarth described the nitrogen-fixing bacteria which caused the formation of nodules on the roots of leguminous plants. Later Winogradsky described a free-living anaerobic organism which was able to fix atmospheric nitrogen, and Beijerinck, some ten years later, described a large, free-living, nitrogen-fixing aerobic bacterium, which he named *Azotobacter*, and which has since been extensively studied. The bacteriology of the soil thus became an important part of agricultural science.

In the early years of the bacteriological revolution it had been demonstrated that bacteria attacked plants, as well as animals. In 1878 Burrill described the organism of pear blight, and in 1883 Wakker discovered the bacillus which causes the " yellows " of the hyacinth. This branch of bacteriology has been pursued energetically during the last thirty years, especially by Erwin Smith and his colleagues in America.

The demonstration by Pasteur of the essential nature of fermentation led, as a natural consequence, to the entry of the bacteriologist into the commercial sphere. His help was required in dairy farming, in brewing, in the preservation of foods, and in all those commercial processes in which bacterial activity was desired or feared.

Fig. 3, which sets out in diagrammatic form the time relations of the more important discoveries associated with the work of Pasteur, Koch and Lister, may be of some service in enabling the student to follow the development of our knowledge down to the end of the nineteenth century.

This brief summary will indicate with sufficient clearness to how great an extent the bacteriologist has been occupied with applied problems. He has, by way of description, usually been satisfied if he could determine, for any given bacterium, a number of characters sufficient to differentiate it from the organisms with which he considered that it was most likely to be confused. It is in this way that our knowledge of bacterial characters has slowly grown and it is not surprising that the results should be an arbitrary and rather odd assortment of differential criteria. In such a bacterial group as that comprising the colon and typhoid bacilli, and certain nearly related organisms, it has been demonstrated that fermentation reactions form a reliable method of differentiation, and such reactions have been extensively studied. In another group morphological differences may be more distinctive, or the production of specific toxins may be a well-marked feature in certain species. The soil-bacteriologist employs methods which differ in important respects from those used by other workers. It is the inevitable result that systematic bacteriology has been very generally neglected, and it is only in recent years that any real attempt has been made to survey bacterial groups as a whole, and to bring some order out of our chaos.

The first two decades of the present century witnessed no such striking advances in our knowledge of the bacteriology of disease as occurred between 1875 and 1900, and the reason for this slower progress is obvious. The technique developed by Pasteur and Koch had been applied over a very wide field. Those problems which were susceptible of solution by the methods available had, to a great extent,

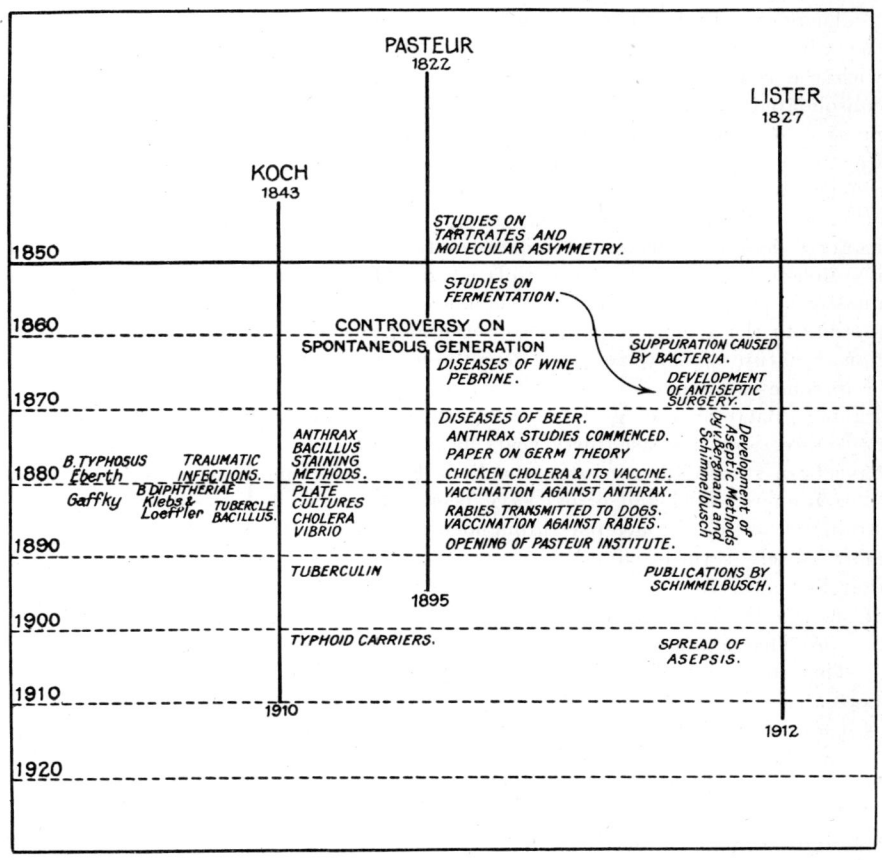

Fig. 3.

been solved, and those which remained unanswered appeared to demand new methods of attack, or at least attack along new lines.

The study of immunity has absorbed the interest and energies of a large number of bacteriologists during the past thirty years. This branch of bacteriology derives from Pasteur's studies on chicken cholera, anthrax and rabies, from Metchnikoff's investigations on the cellular reactions in infection, and from the work of Buchner, Nuttall, von Behring, Ehrlich, Bordet and others, who have investigated the reactions between the sera of artificially immunized animals and the bacteria, bacterial products, foreign cells, or foreign proteins with which they have been inoculated. The development of our knowledge of these phenomena will be discussed in Chapter VI.

The demonstration by Loeffler and Frosch, in 1898, that foot-and-mouth disease was caused by a virus which could pass through a porcelain filter, and was below the limits of direct microscopical observation, opened a new field for investigation. We now know many diseases which can be transmitted by filtered suspensions of material obtained from infected animals, and in which therefore a filter-passing virus is presumably concerned.

There is nothing surprising in the fact that the years from 1900 to 1920, or thereabouts, were for bacteriology a period of slower development as compared with the riotous growth of the eighteen-eighties. The ground won had to be consolidated. The previous advance had been a somewhat hasty affair ; and many secondary problems had been left for more leisurely solution. Many bacteria were very incompletely described. Many had been described independently by different investigators, so that the same bacterium was masquerading under several different names. Many of the earlier descriptions, especially of the anaerobic bacteria, had been based on impure cultures. Little notice had been taken of resemblances between bacteria, isolated at different times from different sources, unless the practical application of the knowledge gained brought such resemblances forcibly to the attention of some observer. Little was known about the distribution in nature of bacteria other than those concerned in the causation of disease, or in some commercial or agricultural process, and even here the data were very scanty. Bacterial ecology is, indeed, still almost an unexplored territory. In all these directions the past thirty years have seen a considerable advance. Bacteria have been studied more systematically. Fuller, and more accurate, descriptions have been recorded and errors have been corrected. The labelling of the stock strains of bacteria, scattered throughout the laboratories of the world, has been more closely scrutinized. Many synonyms have been suppressed, and species that had received several names have been shorn of all but one. The formation of such collections as the National Collection of Type Cultures in this country has provided a much-needed standard of reference.

This re-survey of the bacteriological field on its qualitative side has been associated with a great advance in our quantitative methods. The introduction of bacteriological methods of analysis in the control of water-supplies, milk, and so on, demanded standardized tests yielding numerical answers. Those first employed were in most cases very faulty. There was a failure to realize many of the technical sources of error ; and there was a still more general failure to take into account the statistical principles involved in any sampling of this kind. It is, indeed, only within recent years that a satisfactory liaison has been established between the bacteriologist and the statistician ; and, even now, it is not as general as it should be. It is not merely a question of the kind of analytical test referred to above. The vast literature of immunity contains record after record which is rendered meaningless by a neglect of the sampling errors involved in working with small groups of animals. Reference to Chapter XL will provide examples of the ways in which these errors may be avoided.

In the last ten years or so, there have been unmistakable signs that bacteriology is on the march again. As always in experimental science it has been a matter of technique. In this case the acceleration has followed the application to bacteriology of the more exact methods of analysis developed by the chemist and the physicist. The facts set out in Chapter III show clearly the rapid advance that has followed the incursion of the biochemist into the bacteriological domain. Those described in Chapter VI show the organic and physical chemist inaugurating a new era in immunology. The remarkable increase within quite recent years of our knowledge of the filtrable viruses (see Chapters XXXVIII and LXXXII–LXXXIV) has resulted in large part from improved methods of filtration, optical examination and high-speed centrifugation. It is not a rash prophecy that the years ahead of us will be the eighteen-eighties over again.

REFERENCES

BULLOCH, W. (1930) " A System of Bacteriology." *Med. Res. Coun.*, H.M. Stat. Office, London.

DOBELL, C. (1932) " Antony van Leeuwenhoek and his ' Little Animals.' " John Bale, Sons and Danielsson, London.

DUCLAUX, E. (1920) " Pasteur, the History of a Mind." Eng. Transl. by E. F. Smith and Florence Hedges. Saunders, Philadelphia and London.

VALLERY-RADOT, P. (1922–33) " Œuvres de Pasteur." 6 vols. Masson et Cie, Paris.

VALLERY-RADOT, R. (1919) " The Life of Pasteur." Eng. Transl. by Mrs. R. L. Devonshire. Constable, London.

CHAPTER II

THE BIOLOGICAL CHARACTERISTICS OF BACTERIA :
MORPHOLOGY

General Considerations.—With the exception of certain observations on the finer structure of the bacterial cell, which will be referred to later, our knowledge of bacterial morphology has been gained from the study of cells which have been cultivated in the laboratory under artificial conditions. The morphology of bacterial cells may be notably affected by the constitution of the medium on which the bacteria are grown, the temperature of incubation, and many other factors. In particular, the cells in a pure culture may show very striking changes with age. It is customary to regard the forms found in young cultures as typical of a given species, and the very different appearances, often met with in old cultures, as due to the occurrence of degenerative changes. How far we are justified in labelling all the morphologically atypical cells, which we meet with in old cultures, as degeneration or involution forms, is a controversial question which is discussed elsewhere. It must always be remembered, however, that when a description is given of the morphology of any bacterial species, such a description is supposed to apply to the cells found in a young, actively-growing culture, on a medium which is favourable to the growth of that particular species, and incubated at the optimum temperature, unless the contrary is specifically stated. Those who are for any purpose describing the appearances met with in preparations from bacterial cultures should always recollect that such descriptions have little value unless the exact conditions of cultivation are carefully noted.

Apart from variations associated with age, variations in form, sometimes of a very striking character, may occur in young cultures of a single bacterial species. Different forms of cell may be present in a single culture, or the cells may appear to alter their form in successive subcultures, or different strains of a single bacterial species may show morphological differences, which persist in successive subcultures carried on over a considerable period of time. A description of the morphology of a given bacterial species should include the characters displayed by the modal form, and the extent to which these characters vary. Variability of form is, in itself, very characteristic of certain bacterial species ; while other species show only minor differences in the shape and size of the bacterial cells.

The Size of Bacterial Cells.—Ignoring for the moment the very large bacteria which have been described by a few investigators, and those very minute organisms which will pass through a porcelain filter—the filtrable viruses—it may be said that the dimensions of most cultivable forms are of the order of low multiples or submultiples of μ, *i.e.* of 1/1000th of a millimetre. Among the spheroidal forms, the

16

parasitic staphylococci and streptococci usually measure between 0·75 μ and 1·25 μ in diameter. Some forms of micrococci or sarcinæ may show an average diameter of 1·5 to 2 μ. Among the rod-forms, a relatively large bacillus, such as *B. anthracis*, has a transverse diameter varying between 1 and 1·25 μ and a length varying between 3 and 8 μ. A medium-sized bacillus, such as *Bact. coli*, has a transverse diameter varying between 0·5 and 1 μ, and a length of 2 to 3 μ. A very small bacillus, such as the influenza bacillus, has an average diameter of 0·2 to 0·4 μ, and a length of 0·7 to 1·5 μ. Some bacilli, such as *Cl. tetani*, may combine a small transverse diameter, 0·3 to 0·4 μ, with considerable length, 3 to 5 μ. All such measurements must, of course, be taken as representing a modal size, corresponding to the modal form, and wide variations may occur. Some species of bacilli, for example, may show occasional filamentous forms, measuring 100 μ or more in length. It remains true that the modal size of a bacterium is one of its distinctive characteristics, and has the advantage that it can be stated in numerical terms. In such forms as the *Actinomyces*, which are normally filamentous, it is to the transverse diameter alone that we can assign a modal value.

The Shape of Bacterial Cells.—We can recognize three main types of bacterial cell—the coccal or spheroidal, the bacillary or cylindrical, and the spirillar.

The coccal form is distinguished by the fact that any one axis of the bacterial cell is approximately equal to any other. Many forms approximate to true spheres, although it is doubtful whether any living cell is truly spherical. In many cases the spherical form is widely departed from, and the individual cells may be ellipsoidal or show conical distortions, flattenings or indentations, which give the cells, when observed in film preparations, shapes which may be likened to a bean, or a kidney, or a lancet, as the case may be. Such cells, however, never undergo marked elongation in the direction of one axis, that is, they never become markedly cylindrical.

The bacillary form is distinguished by the fact that one axis of the cell is markedly longer than either of the others, which are themselves approximately equal. Since it is customary to examine bacteria in film preparations, and to describe them as though they were two-dimensional bodies, it is usual to refer to the long axis and the transverse axis, ignoring any possible departure from the circular form in the cross section of the cylinder. The ratio between the length of these cylindrical cells and their transverse diameter may vary over an enormous range ; so that, while some may be almost coccal in appearance, others may be filamentous. Certain modifications of the general cylindrical shape are characteristic of particular bacterial groups. The average ratio of the long axis to the transverse diameter, that is, the thinness or thickness of the cell, is one such character. The ends of the bacillus often show modifications of form which are of differential value. They may be square-cut, rounded, or acutely pointed, or may form definite clubs. Other irregularities in contour, due to the presence within the cell of structures which cause distortion of the cylindrical form, will be considered later.

The spirillar form is characterized by a bending or twisting of the cells, so that they assume curved or spiral shapes. It has become customary to speak of a bacterium which shows a single curve, thus assuming the so-called comma shape, as a vibrio, and of a bacterium which shows a series of curves or twists, thus assuming a corkscrew form, as a spirillum. Vibrios and spirilla are of necessity relatively elongated cells, and they always have rounded or pointed ends.

The study of the finer details of bacterial structure may be carried out in three different ways. Each of them is subject to the limitations imposed by the optical system employed.

Stained or unstained preparations may be examined under the microscope, using light transmitted through a sub-stage condenser of the ordinary type. The limit of resolution (that is, the shortest distance by which two particles must be separated in order that they may give distinct images) is determined by the wave-length of the light and the numerical aperture of the objective. It is given by the formula,

$$\frac{0.5\lambda}{N.A.}$$

where λ = wave-length of light used, and N.A. = numerical aperture of objective.

The possible range of λ is obviously limited to that part of the spectrum to which the human retina is sensitive, and the numerical aperture is subject to the technical limitations of the optical system employed. In practice, the highest N.A. that can be employed with transmitted light is about 1·4, and this, when used with monochromatic light with a wave-length of 546 $m\mu$, corresponding to the green mercury line, gives a resolving power of

$$\frac{546}{2} \times \frac{1}{1\cdot4} = 195 m\mu = 0\cdot2\mu \text{ (approximately)}$$

This degree of resolution is obtained only under optimal conditions, and in ordinary practice the limits of resolution are reached with particles that have a diameter of about 0·25 μ. Objects smaller than this can be " seen," in the sense of being visible ; but the image observed gives no accurate information in regard to the real size or shape of the particle.

Another method is that known as dark-ground illumination. The bacteria, or particles, are examined unstained, and the light passing through the special sub-stage condenser is directed along a path such that only those rays that are refracted, diffracted, or scattered by the object under examination reach the eye of the observer. Bacteria so examined appear as bright images on a dark background. This method is vastly superior to the former as a means of examining living, unstained organisms, but it is subject to the same limitations in regard to resolution ; and, since the highest N.A. at present available for use with illumination of this type is about 1·27, the smallest particle that can be resolved has a diameter of about 0·35 μ.

The third method, which has been developed particularly by Barnard (1919, 1925, 1930), extends the limits of resolution by decreasing the wave-length of the light used. Since the human retina is insensitive to light of a wave-length less than 397 $m\mu$, the full advantage of this procedure can be obtained only by substituting photography for direct observation. Using ultra-violet light with a wave-length of 257 $m\mu$ and an optical system of quartz lenses, Barnard has been able to photograph and resolve particles with a diameter of 0·075 μ. Beyond this point a limit is again reached, due to the lack of a refracting material that will transmit light of shorter wave-length. The degree of internal structure that may be revealed in certain bacteria by ultra-violet photography, combined with dark-ground illumination, is illustrated in Fig. 4, for which we are indebted to Mr. Barnard.

The great majority of the studies referred to in this section have, however, been carried out by the direct observation of stained preparations ; and have therefore been subject to the narrower optical limitations considered above. As against these limitations must be set the advantage that, in preparations of this kind, we can study the affinity of different cell constituents for certain special stains. In most, if not in all, instances, staining has been preceded by some form of fixation, so that the possibility of protoplasmic changes due to heat, or other fixing agents, must be borne in mind.

The Nuclear Apparatus.—One of the most controversial questions in regard to the structure of the bacterial cell is the presence or absence of a nucleus, and its nature if present.

It is impossible to discuss at all fully the many conflicting statements which have been made, and the evidence on which they have been based. Much of this evidence indeed is of little value since it has been obtained by faulty or inadequate technique. Those who desire fuller information on this subject may be referred to the papers of Dobell (1911), Guilliermond (1907) and Hollande (1934).

Briefly, four main interpretations have been given to the appearances observed.

The bacteria have been regarded as cells possessing no nuclei. Certain of the earlier workers held this view, but there has been a general tendency for more recent investigators to accept the presence of some kind of nuclear apparatus, though there is less agreement as to the exact form which it takes in particular cases.

The whole bacterial cell has been regarded as homologous with the cell-nucleus of more highly developed organisms. Růžička (1898, 1903, 1908, 1909) has strenuously advanced this view, and has received some support. In criticizing this interpretation, Dobell points out that to speak of a cell as being constituted of a nucleus without cytoplasm is in any event a misuse of terms, since a nucleus is, by definition, a morphologically and physiologically differentiated part of a cell.

Other observers have described structures which they regard as well-differentiated nuclei. Meyer (1897, 1899, 1908) has been a prominent exponent of this view, and has brought together the available evidence in his book on the bacterial cell (1912). His opinion as to the existence of such a nucleus has been shared by many other observers (Feinberg 1900, Nankanishi 1901, Ellis 1902–03, 1922, Grimme 1902, Swellengrebel 1906, Amato 1909, Vay 1909, 1910), but it is reasonably certain that the structures noted have differed in their nature, so that the observations cannot be regarded as confirmatory.

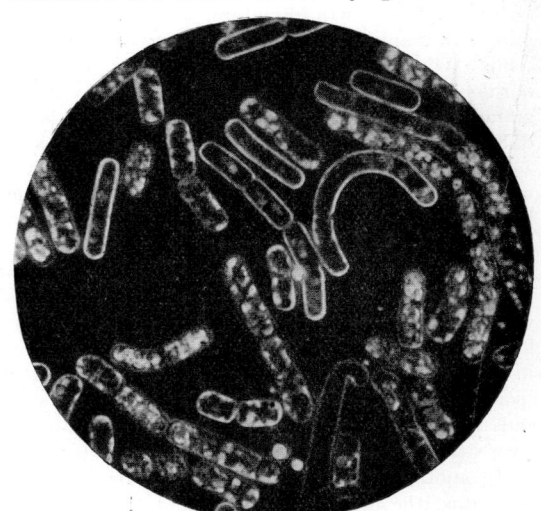

FIG. 4.—*B. megatherium.*
Unstained, dark-ground illumination, photographed with ultra-violet light [× 2,500].

Many of the papers referred to contain mutually destructive criticism, and it is clear from a study of the literature that the advance of our knowledge has tended to relegate to other categories most of the intracellular bodies which were regarded by the earlier workers as nuclear in character. Two series of observations by Mencl (1904, 1905, 1909, 1910), and by Rayman and Kruis (1904), have yielded results which strongly suggest the presence of a differentiated nucleus in the bacterial forms which they studied; but their conclusions are criticized by Guilliermond (1907), on the ground that the structures which they describe as nuclei are, in reality, stages in the formation of transverse septa. To this criticism Mencl has vigorously replied (1909). In one case, the observation by Vejdovský (1900, 1904) of a nucleus in the organism which he named *B. gammari*, there is a consensus of opinion that a true nucleus has been satisfactorily demonstrated, but there is good reason to believe that the organism itself is a fungus and not a bacterium. The recent studies of Stoughton (1929, 1932) on the cytology of a plant pathogen, *Bact. malvacearum*, would seem to provide an example of the clear demonstration of a nucleus in a cultivable bacterium.

A fourth view, which had been vaguely foreshadowed by many earlier workers, has been developed by Schaudinn (1902) in the case of *B. bütschlii*, by Guilliermond (1907) in the case of several cultivable spore-bearing bacilli, and by Dobell (1911) in the case of micrococci, bacilli and spirilla, parasitic in frogs, lizards, snakes and fishes.

Schaudinn found that in *B. bütschlii*, a large spore-bearing bacillus, the cytoplasm of the cell shows a finely alveolar structure, and that, scattered throughout the cytoplasmic net, are numerous small granules which have the same reactions as chromatin. At the commencement of sporulation these granules gather together in the centre of the cell, forming an axially situated spiral. The extremities of this spiral increase in size, apparently at the expense of the chromatin granules, and these granular, polar aggregates condense to form homogeneous masses which stain deeply with nuclear stains. Around each mass is formed a clear zone, beyond which a membrane appears to develop. As this process takes place, the developing spore gradually ceases to take up the nuclear stain, and finally appears as an unstained, highly refractile oval body.

Guilliermond (1907), in the spore-bearing bacilli studied by him, finds that, about the eighth hour of growth in culture, the bacterial cells become finely vacuolated and contain numerous granules of chromatin, giving a picture very similar to that observed by Schaudinn. When sporulation occurs, however, there is no development of an axial spiral, nor does the spore appear to be formed at the expense of the chromatin granules. A large granule, formed by the condensation of a few of the smaller ones, appears at one pole of the cell, and gradually increases in size, but the rest of the cytoplasm remains granular.

Dobell (1911) describes nuclear structures of very varying types in the different bacteria which he has studied. In certain large micrococci he has observed well-differentiated and homogeneous bodies, which take up nuclear stains, divide before cell-division occurs, and have the essential characters of nuclei. In cocco-bacillary organisms these bodies may assume the form of short rods, or short spirals. Dobell regards them as definite nuclei. In other cases, he finds a diffuse or chromidial nucleus of the type described by Schaudinn, which forms an axial spiral as a preliminary to spore-formation. In yet other bacilli, he finds a constantly present spiral filament, which has nuclear characters as judged by its staining reactions, its general morphology, and its behaviour during cell-division and sporulation. Dobell emphasizes the fact that the general morphology of a given structure, and the changes that it undergoes during cell-division, rather than any special affinity for particular stains, must be the ultimate test of its cytological significance.

In another species of bacillus he finds forms which show both varieties of nuclear apparatus, the diffusely granular and the spiral filamentous, and he has observed the breaking-up of the spiral filaments into irregular segments. Reviewing his own results, and those of other investigators, Dobell concludes that bacteria are nucleated cells, in which the nuclear apparatus is highly variable in form, appearing sometimes as granules scattered throughout the cytoplasm, sometimes as a spiral filament, and occasionally as a differentiated nuclear body of the type met with in the cells of higher organisms.

It will be noted that many of the forms in which satisfactory evidence has been obtained of the presence of a nuclear structure, are large bacterial cells, which have never been cultivated, while the bacteria studied by Guilliermond are all sporing species.

Recent studies by Hollande (1934) (see also Hollande and Hollande 1932) are in accord with the views of those authors who have reported the presence of a nuclear apparatus in non-sporing bacteria, such as staphylococci, the plague bacillus, bacilli of the typhoid-paratyphoid group, etc., though the apparatus he describes differs in many ways from that recorded by earlier workers. He differentiates three structures—the nucleosome, the paranucleosome and the metanucleosome. The nucleosome is described as a minute spherical granule, staining blue with eosinate of methylene blue. It divides by elongation, and the thread which at first joins the two daughter nucleosomes may attain great length. It is very inconspicuous except during cell-division, and is often obscured by the paranucleosome or the metanucleosome. The paranucleosome is described as an eosinophil granule, lying close to the nucleosome, and often embracing or obscuring it. It enlarges and divides into many small granules during certain types of cell-division. The metanucleosome is formed of basophil material. It is very irregular in form and is usually disposed round the paranucleosome. Hollande refrains from identifying the nucleosome, paranucleosome or metanucleosome with any particular component of a nuclear apparatus of the classical type, and inclines to the view that the bacterial nucleus is a structure *sui generis*. It may be noted in this connection that Wámoscher (1930), whose studies on the micromanipulation of the bacterial cell are referred to below, was unable to obtain any evidence of the existence of a nucleus sharply differentiated from the cell protoplasm.

Taking the evidence as a whole the most probable conclusion would appear to be that bacteria are nucleated cells, but that their nuclear apparatus differs in important aspects from that of other unicellular or multicellular organisms.

Other Intracellular Granules.

Nitrogenous Material—Volutin Granules.—In many species of bacteria there are found intracellular granules which possess a strong affinity for nuclear stains, and which are coloured a reddish purple with certain blue or violet stains, especially with polychrome methylene blue. These granules were first described by Ernst (1888, 1889, 1902) and by Babes (1889, 1895), and are frequently referred to as the Babes-Ernst granules. They have also been named volutin granules, and from their peculiar staining properties, metachromatic granules. These constituents of the bacterial cell have, from time to time, been credited with almost every conceivable function. There is now, however, very general agreement that they form no part of the living components of the cell. Using a cytological term, they are metaplasmatic granules, particles of some substance concerned in cell-metabolism. Their number and size vary according to the medium in which the bacterium is grown, and according to the period of growth. That they form no part of the nuclear apparatus is shown by the facts that they can be observed in yeasts and fungi, which possess well-differentiated nuclei, and that they take no active part in cell-division or sporulation. They contain a high proportion of nucleo-protein, and to this they probably owe their affinity for nuclear stains.

The rôle which they play in the chemistry of the bacterial cell is at present unknown; the suggestion of Marx and Woithe (1900), that the presence of these granules is correlated with the virulence of the bacterium, has been completely disproved by the work of several subsequent investigators (Ascoli 1901, Krompecher 1901, Gauss 1902, Ficker 1903, Guilliermond 1906).

Carbohydrates.—Glycogen granules and starch granules occur in many species of bacteria, and may be identified by staining with iodine.

Fats and Lipoids.—Fat globules are frequently found in bacterial cells, and may be stained by the usual fat-soluble dyes. Other lipoidal or waxy substances, which may be extracted by the usual solvents, are found in many bacteria, and are particularly abundant in certain species, such as the acid-fast bacilli.

These different forms of granular products of metabolism are by no means equally abundant in different bacterial species. In some, volutin granules tend to be numerous and of large size; in others, they are scanty or absent. Some species which seldom contain volutin granules frequently contain fat globules. In others the presence of glycogen or starch is a characteristic feature. The data available do not warrant us in saying that any one of these forms of granular material is the peculiar property of certain species or is uniformly absent from others, but their relative abundance or scarcity may be a striking characteristic of a particular bacterial species.

For a good and concise account of these intracellular granules see Zettnow (1918).

Endospores.—The formation of intracellular spores by bacteria was first observed by Cohn (1875), and first studied in detail by Koch (1876) in the case of *B. anthracis*. The fact that the existence of an endospore, and its significance in reproduction, had been clearly demonstrated in the case of one of the first bacteria to be identified as the cause of an important infective disease, led many observers to approach the study of new bacterial species with a bias towards identifying any morphologically differentiated element within the bacterial cell as a spore, or its equivalent. Much of the earlier literature is, for this reason, full of mistaken allusions to spores or sporogenous granules in various bacteria. We now know that the formation of endospores is an important distinguishing characteristic of certain bacterial groups.

The great majority of sporing bacteria which have been adequately studied are monosporous, that is only one spore occurs in any one cell. A few large forms which have been observed by cytologists are di-sporous.

The mode of formation of the spore has been briefly referred to in discussing the nuclear apparatus of the cell. There is general agreement that it is formed by a localized accumulation of chromatin, or of a chromatin-like substance, which at first stains deeply with nuclear stains, but which later becomes surrounded by a spore-wall or membrane, which is impervious to stains in the absence of special preliminary treatment; so that the ripe spore appears as an unstained, highly refractile body, spheroidal or ovoid in shape. As regards the finer details of spore-formation there is less agreement, and it would seem possible that the process differs to some extent in different bacterial species. Many observers have described the appearance, at the commencement of sporulation, of a clear vacuolar area, corresponding in size and shape to the space occupied by the ripe spore, and the subsequent accumulation, within this area, of the nuclear material of which the spore is formed. Meyer and his supporters lay great stress on the appearances seen during sporulation, as evidence for the existence of differentiated nuclei. Those who have studied the internal structure of bacterial cells have, for the most part, included the process of spore-formation in their observations, and the papers which have already been referred to contain full discussions of this question.

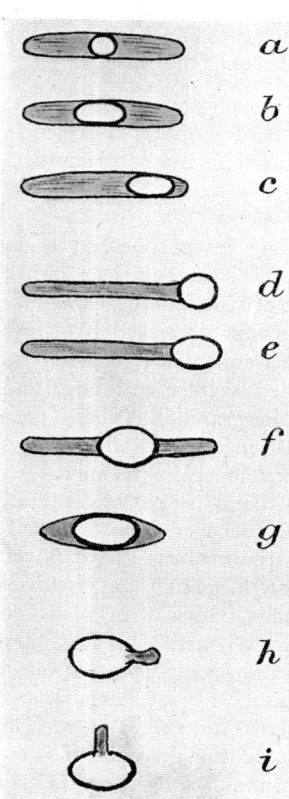

FIG. 5.

a–c. Without distortion of bacterial cell.
a. Spherical equatorial.
b. Oval equatorial.
c. Oval subterminal.
d–g. With distortion of bacterial cell.
d. Spherical terminal.
e. Oval terminal.
f. Oval equatorial.
g. Oval equatorial.
h and *i.* Germination of spores.
h. Polar germination.
i. Equatorial germination.

The situation of the spore within the bacterial cell, which may be terminal, sub-terminal, or approximately equatorial, gives a distinctive morphology to many bacterial species. In addition, the diameter of the ripe spore is often greater than that of the bacillus which contains it ; so that the cell is distorted and, according to the position of the spore, " drum-stick," " barrel," or other irregular forms may be presented (Fig. 5).

The germination of a spore, when placed under favourable conditions, may occur by simple enlargement of the spore without obvious rupture or shedding of the spore-envelope, though this is an unusual method. Far more frequently the spore-envelope ruptures, either at one pole or equatorially, and the spore as it develops into a bacillus sheds its enveloping membrane (Fig. 5).

All the available evidence indicates that the spore is simply a resting stage of the bacterial cell, in which it is far more resistant to adverse environmental conditions, than it is in the ordinary vegetative form. There is no good evidence that spore-formation is associated with any sexual reproductive process. Certain appearances which have been interpreted in this sense by Schaudinn (1902), and Růžička (1909), have been shown by Dobell (1911) to have no such significance.

The Cell Membrane.—Schaudinn, on the basis of the appearances seen in the large cells of *B. bütschlii* when these are immersed in hypertonic saline, has described a definite cell-membrane in this organism, with a relatively complex structure. Similar observations on the smaller cultivable bacteria are rendered very difficult by the optical limitations referred to above. There seems to be general agreement that bacterial cells may be differentiated, with very varying degrees of distinctness, into endoplasmic and ectoplasmic zones, but whether there is a differential membrane limiting the ectoplasm externally is a point on which there is some difference of opinion (Legroux 1925, Legroux and Margrou 1920). Wámoscher (1930) has studied the structure of various bacteria, including members of the coli-typhoid group, by needle-dissection with a micro-manipulation apparatus, using dark-ground illumination. His observations indicate that bacterial cells have a membrane, or outer layer, possessing great elasticity, and thus are able to resist pressure, tension or torsion. The interior of the cell is, he believes, normally composed of a colloidal sol which under certain conditions may assume the gel form.

Capsules.—Many species of bacteria, such as the pneumococcus, the pneumobacillus and the anthrax bacillus, are characterized by the ability to develop a well-marked capsule, which may be observable in stained or unstained preparations as a clear zone surrounding the bacterial cell or may, after suitable fixing and mordanting, be stained by various methods. The degree to which the capsule is developed is largely determined by the environmental conditions. Thus, the pathogenic capsulated bacteria show their maximal capsule formation when growing in the animal tissues (Babes 1895, Gruber and Futaki 1907, Preisz 1907, Bail 1908, Sauerbeck 1909 *a, b*, Eisenberg 1903, 1908, 1909). When such bacteria are grown in artificial culture there is usually a high correlation between the degree of capsulation and the content of the medium in unaltered, or slightly altered, animal protein.

The capsule is usually regarded as being formed by a thickening and alteration in consistency of the outer layer of the bacterial cell. It has however been held (Meyer 1912, Zettnow 1918) that the capsular substance should be regarded as an active secretion. Certain bacteria secrete a mucilaginous material in which large numbers of neighbouring cells are embedded ; and some organisms, such as the Type III pneumococcus, form this extracellular mucilaginous material in addition to possessing a well-marked capsule. It seems, however, more convenient to differentiate between the capsulated and the so-called " mucoid " types of bacteria (see Etinger-Tulczynska 1933), and the fact that capsular material may frequently become separated from the cell can hardly be taken as a proof that it is a secretion in the ordinary sense of that term. We may note that we have, within recent years, acquired a considerable knowledge of the chemical constitution of bacterial capsules. The capsules of the different types of pneumococci are for instance composed of complex polysaccharides (see p. 444), while the capsule of the anthrax bacillus appears to be composed of a protein material (see p. 658).

Whether the capacity to form a capsule is really confined to those species that are typically capsulated is very doubtful. Many observers have described capsule-formation by normally non-capsulated forms under particular environmental conditions ; and mucoid variants of normally non-mucoid species are of relatively common occurrence (see Chapter VIII).

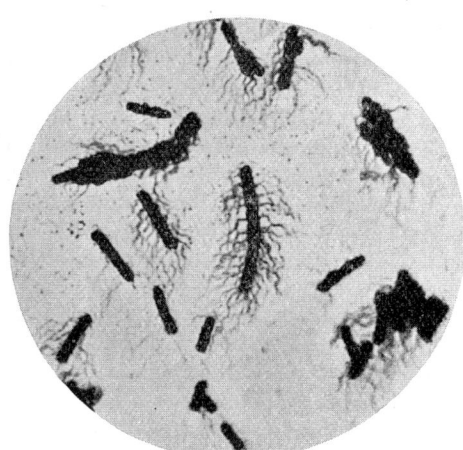

FIG. 6.—*Zopfius zenkeri.*
Stained to show flagella ($\times$ 1 : 1200).

Flagella.—A large number of bacteria, including a few coccal forms, many bacilli, and most known spirilla and vibrios, are more or less actively motile by means of flagella. These flagella are long, thread-like processes, arranged in various ways on the bacterial cell. They vary greatly in length, but are often longer than the organism to which they are attached. They are extremely slender ; but their average diameter has never been accurately measured. They were first effectively demonstrated by Loeffler (1890).

According to the observations of Trenkmann (1890), Ellis (1902–03), Fuhrmann (1910) and Meyer (1912), the central portion of the flagellar thread passes through the cell-membrane and is in direct connection with the cytoplasm, and Fuhrmann believes that the proximal extremity is connected with a granule of chromatin, which would then be analogous to the blepharoplast of protozoan flagellates. This conclusion is adversely criticized by Zettnow (1918). Whether the optical methods at present available allow any decision on such points as these seems very doubtful.

The arrangement of the flagella on the bacterial cell may take one of four forms. There may be a single flagellum at one pole, when the arrangement is called mono-trichate. There may be a single flagellum at each pole, the amphitrichate condition. There may be a bunch of flagella at one pole, or more rarely at each, an arrangement known as lophotrichate. The flagella may be arranged indiscriminately over the bacterial cell, when they are referred to as peritrichate (see Fig. 6).

The cells of any one flagellated species are characterized by one, and one only, of these possible arrangements (see Fig. 7).

The results that have been obtained in the detailed study of antigenic structure (see Chapter VII) have shown that the flagellar substance, or at least that portion of it which forms the flagellar surface, is chemically distinct from the substances forming the cell body.

Involution Forms.—In old cultures of many bacteria forms may be found which are quite unlike those seen in young and actively growing cultures. Some

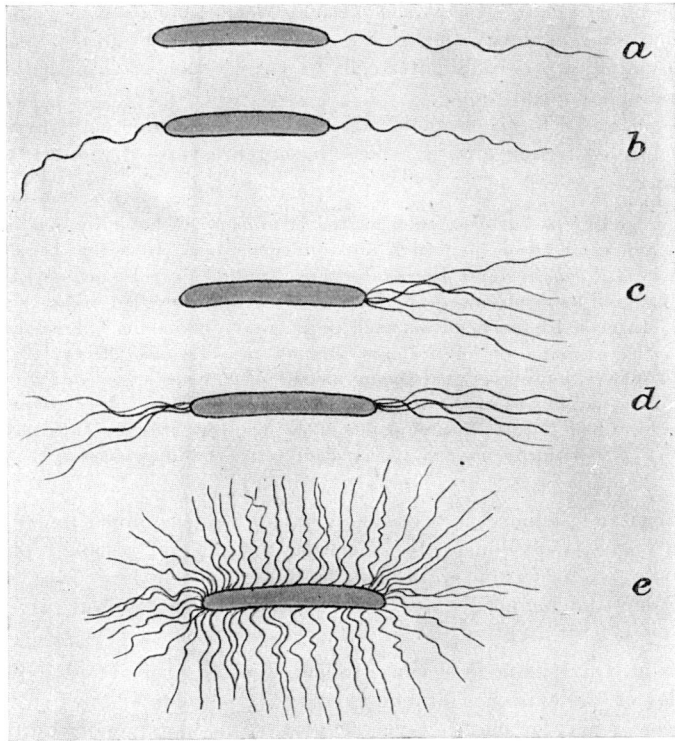

Fig. 7.—Diagram illustrating distribution of flagella.
a. Monotrichate.   *b*. Amphitrichate.   *c* and *d*. Lophotrichate.   *e*. Peritrichate.

of these forms are very typical of the bacterial species in which they occur, as is the case with the so-called involution forms of the plague bacillus, and of some other species of *Pasteurella*, and the giant forms which occur in cultures of the meningococcus. The existence of these and other abnormal forms has long been recognized, and they have been regarded as due to involution or degeneration following the ageing of the culture, and the consequent unfavourable environmental conditions. This view as to their nature has been generally adopted because of the undoubted fact that, under the conditions in which they usually occur, the majority of the organisms are non-viable ; while the extensive study of young actively growing cultures has, in general, shown no more striking departure from the normal form than the occurrence of unusually large cells, or occasionally in the rod forms, of very long, almost filamentous cells, due apparently to delay in cell division.

Reproduction.— Although a description of the method of reproduction in bacteria may be regarded as belonging more correctly to a discussion of their physiology than of their morphology, yet the question is so closely bound up with differences in form of the cells, and of the cell-aggregates which result from successive division, that there are many advantages in considering the question in the present chapter.

There is no doubt at all that the method of multiplication of bacteria, under optimal conditions of cultivation in the laboratory, is by simple binary fission, each cell dividing into two daughter cells by constriction, with or without a well-marked preliminary septation.

In the spheroidal forms division may occur in any diameter. In the ovoid or cylindrical forms division always occurs in the transverse diameter. It is never longitudinal.

In certain genera of bacteria, such as the *Actinomyces*, the formation of branching filaments is a normal phase of growth and multiplication. In a few bacillary species, and notably in *C. diphtheriæ* and *Myco. tuberculosis*, rudimentary branching has frequently been described, and its occurrence in actively growing cells observed under the microscope (Hill 1902). In most bacillary species such rudimentary branching is rare, and is seldom observed in the examination of ordinary stained preparations. Hort (1917*a*, *b*), and Gardner (1925) have, however, noted the occurrence of Y forms in actively growing microscopic cultures of organisms of the coli-typhoid group, and have observed multiplication by elongation and fission from all three points of the Y. (See also Wyckoff 1934.) Whether the occurrence of these forms has any special significance is a question that the future must determine.

Spore-formation, which has been described above, is confined to certain species of bacteria. The spore constitutes a special resting and resistant phase of the bacterial cell ; its formation appears to be determined in large part by environmental factors, and cannot be regarded as an integral part of any periodic or essential life-cycle.

A question still at issue is the occurrence of other forms of reproduction, and in particular of the existence or non-existence of a complex life-cycle, in which sexual processes may or may not play a part. It is not possible to discuss this problem at all fully. It must, however, be noted that there are those who believe that such a life-cycle is a natural characteristic of all bacterial species, and that multiplication by binary fission, which appears to be the only mode of reproduction in young, actively growing cultures, is only one phase of the cycle, which we encourage by the particular artificial conditions under which we choose to study bacterial cells.

Jones (1913, 1914, 1920) described reproduction by gonidia-like bodies in the case of *Azotobacter*. These observations were greatly extended by Löhnis and Smith (1916) who described a far more complex life-cycle in this, and in other, species, and applied their results to the reproduction of bacteria in general (Löhnis 1921). Stoughton (1929, 1932) in describing the morphology and cytology of *Bact. malvacearum*, an organism producing angular leaf-spot in the cotton plant, records the formation, by budding from the bacillary form, of coccus-like bodies that subsequently develop into bacilli, and also the fusion of bacillary cells with the formation of zygospores.

Almquist described various forms of reproductive bodies, mainly minute gonidial structures, in a wide range of bacteria (Almquist 1893–1924, Almquist and Koraen 1918, Koraen 1918). It may be noted that there was a general tendency for these appearances to be observed in old cultures, and sometimes in cultures which had been allowed to undergo a marked degree of drying. Mellon (1917–26) has described a variety of forms which he regards as stages in the complex life-cycle of various bacterial species. Enderlein (1925) upholds a similar thesis. Kuhn (1929, 1930) has described a remarkable series of morphological forms in common organisms, some of which are interpreted as evidence of a life-cycle, others of which—the so-called Pettenkofer bodies—are regarded as intracellular parasites. Hadley (1927), in a detailed review which should be consulted by those who desire further information on this subject, sets out the available data with regard to the occurrence and possible significance of these various forms, and seeks to relate them to the phenomenon of bacterial dissociation, which we shall discuss in a subsequent chapter. A shorter discussion of the possible modes of bacterial reproduction will be found in papers by Bergstrand (1920, 1921, 1923).

It is, we think, impossible on the evidence at present available to come to any conclusion on the general problem at issue. That a cycle of morphological changes may characterize the life-history of a particular bacterial species under natural conditions there can be no doubt. The detailed studies of Bewley and Hutchinson (1920) and of Thornton and Gangulee (1926) on *Rhizobium leguminosarum* provide a case in point. In regard to bacteria in general, there is clearly no justification for ignoring such observations as those recorded above; but the thesis, that the bacterial forms with which we are most familiar in artificial cultures are only stages in some more complex cycle of development, has not in our view been clearly and definitely established. All bacteriologists are familiar with the so-called " involution forms " to which we have already referred; and there is little doubt that many of these forms represent dead or dying cells. It may well be that we have been too ready to refer to this category every abnormal form encountered; and few would deny that some of the appearances that are met with are strongly suggestive of some more complex form than the simple bacillus. The problem is, however, beset with technical difficulties arising from the small size of the organisms concerned. The crucial test must remain the actual observation of the reproduction of typical bacterial cells from the granules, spheres, or syncytial masses which have been described as stages in the complete life-cycle; and the unequivocal demonstration of this cyclical development demands the isolation of single cells, not only at the commencement of the cycle, but at each successive stage. No harm will be done by maintaining a severely critical attitude at the present stage of the controversy, so long as each new piece of evidence is considered on its merits.

In this connection a recent paper by Klieneberger (1935) may be noted. She describes a minute pleuropneumonia-like organism in symbiosis with *Streptobacillus moniliformis*, and considers that many of the morphological peculiarities that are commonly regarded as characteristic of the bacillus are, in reality due to the presence of the symbiont. She suggests that some, at least, of the pleomorphic elements in bacterial cultures that have been described as belonging to a sexual or developmental cycle may have a similar origin.

We do not propose to enter into the vexed controversy over the existence of filtrable forms of bacteria. The whole crux of the question seems to us to lie in the definition of the term " filtrable," and in the properties of the filter-passing bodies. Bacteria of the same species are known to vary greatly in size under different environmental conditions and at different stages of growth. That certain forms may be small enough to pass through our relatively crude earthenware filters is hardly to be doubted, but whether these forms differ in any of their essential properties from larger members of the same species, and in particular whether they constitute some essential stage in the reproductive cycle of the organism, is still undecided. In our opinion the evidence that has so far been produced does not suggest that they are differentiated in any important respect other than size, and probably this differentiation is of a continuous rather than a discontinuous type.

The Formation of Cell-Aggregates.—When a bacterial cell divides, the two daughter cells may at once part company, or they may remain attached to one another by their cell-membranes. When this incomplete separation persists during many successive cell-divisions, cell-aggregates are produced, the form of which will depend upon the planes in which successive divisions take place, and upon the number of cell-divisions which occur before the cell-aggregate begins to separate. The aggregates which are formed in this way are often highly characteristic, and constitute an important factor in the identification of bacterial species. In the spheroidal forms division may occur in any plane, while in the cylindrical forms it always occurs in the transverse diameter. As a result the cocci may, and do, show a greater variety of groupings than the bacillary or spiral forms.

When the successive divisions, in a coccal bacterium, occur in such a way that the daughter cells remain united in pairs for a short period, but these pairs separate before a further division occurs, the organism in question is described as a diplococcus. When several successive divisions occur before separation of the resulting aggregate, and these divisions follow no ordered sequence as regards the planes in which they take place, irregular groups of cocci result, which have been compared to bunches of grapes. Organisms which form this type of cell-aggregate are known as staphylococci, and this term is used as a generic name. When such a series of divisions without separation occurs in planes parallel to one another, the aggregates so formed have the appearance of a chain or chaplet, and organisms which behave in this way are known as streptococci, and are usually classed in a single genus. In some species the cells remain attached while two divisions occur, the second at right angles to the first. The resulting aggregate is a group of four cocci ; such an organism is sometimes referred to as a tetracoccus. In some species the typical cell grouping is produced by three divisions, the plane of each being at right angles to the other two. In this way cubes, or packets, each of eight cocci, are produced. The species which form groupings of this type are classed in the genus *Sarcina*.

Among the cylindrical forms, the only possible departure from the single-cell formation is the adherence of two or more cells in pairs or chains. Such groupings may be referred to as diplobacilli or streptobacilli ; but they are not sufficiently constant in a particular bacterial species to be used for purposes of classification. They occur, however, far more often in some species than in others, and their relative frequency may be an important specific character.

Apart from the formation of such united cell-aggregates, the way in which a cell divides influences the grouping of the daughter cells. In certain bacillary forms, such as the diphtheria bacillus, division appears to occur asymmetrically, in the sense that the daughter cells remain attached at one side of the cylinder, after division has proceeded across the whole width of the organism from the opposite side. In the early stages of the subsequent growth of the daughter cells, this local attachment seems to act as a hinge, about which the elongating cells swing, so that they come to lie at varying angles to one another, depending on the period which elapses before division becomes complete. The groupings so formed, which have been compared to Chinese letters, or to cuneiform characters, are very characteristic of certain species.

Colony Formation.—When bacteria are grown on solid media, and care is taken to avoid too heavy an inoculation, the individual cells multiply and form isolated colonies. The appearance of these colonies is, in many cases, highly characteristic of the group or species to which a given bacterium belongs. We know little of the internal structure of bacterial colonies, but that little suggests that the structural differentiation is considerable (Legroux and Margrou 1920), and it is possible that much light may be thrown on bacterial morphology by further study along these lines.

The character of the colonies produced by a given bacterial species is of great importance in identification, and is, for this purpose, best considered in conjunction with other growth-characters, such as the appearances noted in cultures in liquid media, or in the so-called stab-cultures, in which inoculation is made by thrusting a platinum wire axially into a column of solid medium, such as agar or gelatin. Further description of colony structure is therefore deferred to Chapter XII.

Staining Reactions.—The staining reactions of bacteria, and particularly their response to certain differential stains, might well be regarded as more in the nature of microchemical tests, than methods of demonstrating structure. It would, therefore, be more logical to consider staining reactions in connection with the physiology of the cell than with its morphology, but the way in which a given bacterium reacts to special stains constitutes such an important part of the general picture which we form of it, that it is convenient to deal with this matter in the present chapter.

Reactions to General Bacterial Stains.—Quite apart from the presence of the metachromatic granules, or of other granular material, different bacterial cells may differ in the way in which they take up stains. In some cases the whole cell may be uniformly coloured. In some cylindrical forms the ends of the bacillus may be deeply stained, while the central portion may be almost colourless. This constitutes the so-called polar staining, which is very characteristic of the plague bacillus, and is found in many other bacterial species. Sometimes the cell may stain unevenly throughout its length, so that barred or beaded forms may occur, a feature which is very characteristic of the diphtheria bacillus and many allied organisms, and which occurs to a less marked extent with many acid-fast bacilli. In some cases, in which barred or beaded forms are found, these conditions are associated with the presence of metachromatic granules, but these granules are not the essential cause of such irregularities in staining. It seems clear that, in such forms, there is an unequal distribution throughout the cell of those constituents of the cytoplasm which take up the stain employed, and it has frequently been suggested that they are indicative of plasmolytic changes. It seems doubtful whether plasmolysis can be invoked as a general explanation of this phenomenon, though it is true that there is a general tendency for the frequency of granular and barred forms to increase with the age of the culture, and to be notably scanty in very young cultures. They are, however, so plentiful in young and actively growing cultures of certain species that it seems impossible to regard them as resulting entirely from degenerative changes.

The Differential Staining of Bacterial Species.—In the application of numerous stains, mordants, and differential decolorizing reagents to the study of bacteria, the empirical discovery has been made that certain staining reactions are highly characteristic of certain groups of bacteria. Two such staining reactions are especially important in this respect.

The Gram Stain.—Gram (1884) described a staining method which has been of the greatest service in differentiating bacterial groups, and which has been extensively studied, and frequently modified, by subsequent workers. This reaction depends on the fact that, when certain bacteria are stained with certain aniline dyes, such as gentian-violet, methyl-violet and others, and are subsequently treated with a solution of iodine in potassium iodide, a mordanting action occurs which prevents the subsequent decolorization of the bacteria on treatment with alcohol. Other bacteria, after similar treatment, are readily decolorized. This difference between the retention of the stain by Gram-positive bacteria and its loss by Gram-negative forms is correlated with certain other characters. Thus (Kruse 1910) Gram-negative organisms are more susceptible to solution in alkalies, or to digestion by enzymes, than are Gram-positive organisms; they are also more susceptible to lysis by an immune serum in the presence of complement. According to Stearn and Stearn (1930), they are more resistant to the lethal action of oxidizing, and perhaps of reducing, agents. Brudny (1908) and Eisenberg (1909) would ascribe the difference between Gram-positive-ness and Gram-negativeness to a difference in the permeability of the cell-membrane; while Sander (1935), who has been able to render Gram-positive bacteria Gram-negative by treatment with a variety of reagents and to demonstrate that this change is reversible, regards the determining factor as the state of dispersion of the bacterial protoplasm. Some observers, on the other hand, and notably Deussen (1918), incline towards a more purely chemical theory, and Stearn and Stearn (1928) regard differences in intracellular pH as the determining factor.

In employing Gram's method it must always be remembered that the differentiation is not absolutely sharp and specific as regards a given bacterium at all stages of its growth, or as regards all bacterial species. Those organisms which are completely Gram-negative never retain the stain, but those organisms which are Gram-positive frequently fail to retain the stain when preparations are made from old cultures. This is indeed easy to understand, since such cultures consist largely of dead, dying or degenerate cells, whose physical and chemical properties must be greatly altered. Certain bacterial species show reactions to this method of staining which are of an intermediate type, with the result that they are extremely sensitive to small changes in technique, sometimes appearing to be Gram-positive and at others Gram-negative. Due allowance must be made for all these points in determining the reaction of any given species.

Acid-fastness.—The fact that certain bacteria, after being stained with warm solutions of fuchsin, resist the decolorizing action of strong mineral acids was observed by Ehrlich (1882) and confirmed by Ziehl (1882, 1883) who modified the technique of staining. This reaction is highly characteristic of the tubercle bacillus, and of an allied group of organisms which are collectively known as the acid-fast bacilli. It is of interest to note that these bacilli are peculiarly resistant to the action of such solvents as strong solutions of alkalies, or mixtures of alkalies and sodium hypochlorite (antiformin), as also to the action of digestive ferments. In this connection it may be noted that acid-fast bacilli are also Gram-positive, though the majority of Gram-positive organisms are not acid-fast. The substance which confers this property of acid-fastness on the tubercle bacillus and allied forms has been studied by Klebs (1896), Koch (1897), Bulloch and Macleod (1904) and Tamura (1913). It was at first regarded as an unsaturated fat, but is now generally believed to be lipoidal or waxy in nature. Bulloch and Macleod state that it has the chemical properties of an alcohol, and Tamura isolated an alcohol which had the property of acid-fastness, and which he named " mykol." (For further details see Chapter XV.)

REFERENCES

ALMQUIST, A. and KORAEN, G. (1918) *Z. Hyg. InfektKr.*, **85**, 347.
ALMQUIST, E. (1893) *Z. Hyg. InfektKr.*, **15**, 283 ; (1904) *Zbl. Bakt.*, **37**, 18 ; (1905) *Z. Hyg. InfektKr.*, **52**, 179 ; (1907) *Zbl. Bakt.*, **45**, 491 ; (1911) *Ibid.*, **60**, 167 ; (1917) *Z. Hyg. InfektKr.*, **83**, 1 ; (1922) *J. infect. Dis.*, **31**, 483 ; (1924a) *Ibid.*, **35**, 341 ; (1924b) *Z. Hyg. InfektKr.*, **101**, 15.
AMATO, A. (1909) *Zbl. Bakt.*, **48**, 385.
ASCOLI. (1901) *Dtsch. med. Wschr.*, **20**, 313.
BABES, V. (1889) *Z. Hyg. InfektKr.*, **5**, 173 ; (1895) *Ibid.*, **20**, 412.
BAIL, O. (1908) *Zbl. Bakt.*, **46**, 488.
BARNARD, J. E. (1919) *J. R. micr. Soc.*, p. 1 ; (1925) *Lancet*, ii. 117 ; (1930) " A System of Bacteriology," Med. Res. Council London, **1**, 115.
BERGSTRAND, H. (1920) *J. infect. Dis.*, **27**, 1 ; (1921) *Bull. Johns Hopk. Hosp.*, **32**, 234 ; (1923) *J. Bact.*, **8**, 365.
BEWLEY, W. F. and HUTCHINSON, M. B. (1920) *J. agric. Sci.*, **10**, 144.
BRUDNY, V. (1908) *Zbl. Bakt.*, IIte Abt., **21**, 62.
BULLOCH, W. and MACLEOD, J. J. R. (1904) *J. Hyg., Camb.*, **4**, 1.
COHN, F. (1875) *Beitr. Biol. Pflanz.*, **1**, 2.
DEUSSEN, E. (1918) *Z. Hyg. InfektKr.*, **85**, 235.
DOBELL, C. (1911) *Quart. J. micr. Sci.*, **56**, 395.
EHRLICH, P. (1882) *Dtsch. med. Wschr.*, **8**, 269.
EISENBERG, P. (1903) *Zbl. Bakt.*, **34**, 739 ; (1908) *Ibid.*, **45**, 44, 134, 638 ; (1909) *Ibid.*, **49**, 465.
ELLIS, D. (1902–03) *Zbl. Bakt.*, **33**, 1, 81, 161 ; (1922) *Brit. med. J.*, ii. 731.
ENDERLEIN. (1925) " Bakterien-Cyclogenie, etc." Berlin.
ERNST, P. (1888) *Z. Hyg. InfektKr.*, **4**, 25 ; (1889) *Ibid.*, **5**, 428 ; (1902) *Zbl. Bakt.*, IIte Abt., **8**, 1, 34, 65, 97.
ETINGER-TULCZYNSKA, R. (1933) *Z. Hyg. InfektKr.*, **114**, 769.
FEINBERG. (1900) *Zbl. Bakt.*, **27**, 417.
FICKER, M. (1903) *Arch. Hyg.*, **46**, 171.
FUHRMANN, F. (1910) *Zbl. Bakt.*, IIte Abt., **25**, 129.
GARDNER, A. D. (1925) *J. Path. Bact.*, **27**, 189.
GAUSS, C. J. (1902) *Zbl. Bakt.*, **31**, 92.
GRAM, C. (1884) *Fortschr. Med.*, **2**, 185.
GRIMME, A. (1902) *Zbl. Bakt.*, **32**, 1, 81, 161, 241, 321.
GRUBER, M. and FUTAKI, K. (1907) *Münch. med. Wschr.*, **54**, 249.
GUILLIERMOND, A. (1906) *Bull. Inst. Pasteur*, **4**, 145 ; (1907) *Ibid.*, **5**, 273, 321.
HADLEY, P. (1927) *J. infect. Dis.*, **40**, 1.
HILL, H. W. (1902) *J. med. Res.*, **7**, 115, 202.
HOLLANDE, A. C. (1934) *Arch. Protistenk.*, **83**, 465.
HOLLANDE, A. C. and HOLLANDE, G. (1932) *Arch. Zool. exp. gén.*, **72**, No. 6.
HORT, E. C. (1917a) *Brit. med. J.*, i. 571 ; (1917b) *Ibid.*, ii. 377.
JONES, D. H. (1913) *Zbl. Bakt.*, IIte Abt., **38**, 14 ; (1914) *Ibid.*, **40**, 170 ; (1920) *J. Bact.*, **5**, 325.
KLEBS, E. (1896) *Zbl. Bakt.*, **20**, 488.
KLIENEBERGER, E. (1935) *J. Path. Bact.*, **40**, 93.
KOCH, R. (1876) *Cohns Beitr. Biol. Pflanz.*, **2**, 277 ; (1897) *Dtsch. med. Wschr.*, **23**, 209.
KORAEN, G. (1918) *Z. Hyg. InfektKr.*, **85**, 359.
KROMPECHER, E. (1901) *Zbl. Bakt.*, **30**, 385.
KRUSE, W. (1910) *Münch. med. Wschr.*, **57**, 685.
KUHN, P. (1929) *Med. Klin.*, **25**, 1351 ; (1930) *Ibid.*, **26**, 739.
LEGROUX, R. (1925) *Ann. Inst. Pasteur*, **39**, 382.
LEGROUX, R. and MARGROU, J. (1920) *Ann. Inst. Pasteur*, **34**, 417.
LOEFFLER, F. (1890) *Zbl. Bakt.*, **7**, 625.
LÖHNIS, F. (1921) *Mem. nat. Acad. Sci.*, **16**, 5.
LÖHNIS, F. and SMITH, N. R. (1916) *J. agric. Res.*, **6**, 675.
MARX, H. and WOITHE, F. (1900) *Zbl. Bakt.*, **28**, 1.
MELLON, R. R. (1917) *J. Bact.*, **2**, 81, 269 ; (1920) *J. med. Res.*, **42**, 61 ; (1921) *Ibid.*, **42**, 111 ; (1925a) *J. Bact.*, **10**, 481 ; (1925b) *Ibid.*, **10**, 579 ; (1926) *Ibid.*, **12**, 409.
MENCL, E. (1904) *Zbl. Bakt.*, IIte Abt., **12**, 559 ; (1905) *Ibid.*, **15**, 544 ; (1909) *Arch. Protistenk.*, **16**, 62 ; (1910) *Ibid.*, **19**, 127.
MEYER, A. (1897) *Flora*, **84**, 185 ; (1899) *Ibid.*, **86**, 428 ; (1908) *Ibid.*, **98**, 335 ; (1912) " Die Zelle der Bakterien." Jena.
NANKANISHI, K. (1901) *Zbl. Bakt.*, **30**, 97, 145, 193, 225.
PREISZ, H. (1907) *Zbl. Bakt.*, **44**, 209.

RAYMAN, B. and KRUIS, K. (1904) (see Guilliermond, 1907).
RŮŽIČKA, V. (1898) *Zbl. Bakt.*, **23**, 305 ; (1903) *Arch. Hyg.*, **46**, 337 ; (1908) *Ibid.*, **64**, 219 ; (1909) *Z. Bakt.*, IIte Abt., **23**, 289.
SANDER, F. (1935) *Zbl. Bakt.*, **133**, 385.
SAUERBECK, E. (1909a) *Zbl. Bakt.*, **50**, 289 ; (1909b) *Z. Hyg. InfektKr.*, **63**, 313.
SCHAUDINN, F. (1902) *Arch. Protistenk.*, **1**, 306.
STEARN, A. E. and STEARN, E. W. (1928) *Univ. Mo. Stud.*, **3**, No. 2, 1.
STEARN, E. W. and STEARN, A. E. (1930) *J. infect. Dis.*, **46**, 500.
STOUGHTON, R. H. (1929) *Proc. roy. Soc.*, B, **105**, 469 ; (1932) *Ibid.*, **111**, 46.
SWELLENGREBEL, N. H. (1906) *Zbl. Bakt.*, IIte Abt., **16**, 617, 673.
TAMURA, S. (1913) *Z. physiol. Chem.*, **87**, 85.
THORNTON, H. G. and GANGULEE, N. (1926) *Proc. roy. Soc.*, B, **99**, 427.
TRENKMANN. (1890) *Zbl. Bakt.*, **8**, 385.
VAY, F. (1909) *Zbl. Bakt.*, **52**, 305 ; (1910) *Ibid.*, **55**, 193.
VEJDOVSKÝ, F. (1900) *Zbl. Bakt.*, IIte Abt., **6**, 577 ; (1904) *Ibid.*, **11**, 481.
WÁMOSCHER, L. (1930) *Z. Hyg. InfektKr.*, **111**, 422.
WYCKOFF, R. W. G. (1934) *J. exp. Med.*, **59**, 381.
ZETTNOW. (1918) *Z. Hyg. InfektKr.*, **85**, 17.
ZIEHL, F. (1882) *Dtsch. med. Wschr.*, **8**, 451 ; (1883) *Ibid.*, **9**, 247.

CHAPTER III

THE BIOLOGICAL CHARACTERISTICS OF BACTERIA : METABOLISM

THE metabolic processes of the bacterial cell form so large a part of its total activities that any discussion of bacterial physiology must fall largely within the domain of microbiological chemistry. Before attempting to consider the nutritional requirements of bacteria, the chemical changes that they induce in the substances on which they act, and the mechanisms by which these changes are brought about, it will be well to set out very briefly such knowledge as we have in regard to the chemical constitution of the bacterial cells themselves.

The Chemical Constitution of Bacterial Cells.

It would seem that bacterial cells are formed on the same general chemical pattern as the cells of other living organisms, with certain characteristics that ally them closely to the fungi. The determination of the exact chemical composition of any given bacterial species or strain is rendered peculiarly difficult by variations induced by differences in the nutrient media in which they are grown. (See Cramer 1891–97, Nicolle and Alilaire 1909, Dawson 1919, Fulmer *et al.* 1921, Hunter 1923, Buchanan and Fulmer 1928–30, Eckstein and Soule 1931.) Apart from the variability induced by environmental factors, any bacterial species or strain may give rise to variants that differ sharply from the parental type in certain of their metabolic activities. When due allowance is made for these disturbing factors, the technical problem remains a difficult one. The collection of an adequate mass of bacterial cells for detailed chemical analysis makes large demands on time and apparatus ; and the use of the chemically complex media that are necessary to secure abundant growth of certain bacterial species greatly increases the difficulty of interpreting the analytical results, particularly in regard to any constituents that are present in small amount. It is not therefore surprising that our knowledge is as yet fragmentary.

The difference in chemical constitution between different bacterial genera or species are, as would be expected, wider than between different strains or variants belonging to a single species. In this section we may confine our attention in the main to those chemical constituents that are shared by bacterial cells in general, noting in passing certain divergencies that serve to illustrate the kind of differences in chemical structure that have been observed.

The Water Content of the Bacterial Cell.—In common with all living cells bacteria contain a high proportion of water ; but it seems likely that their protoplasm is rather denser than that of the higher plants and animals though less dense than that of the filtrable viruses. Estimations of the water content of different bacteria carried out by different observers have varied widely, and figures as high as 90 per cent. have sometimes been recorded ; but those given by Nicolle and Alilaire (1909) range, with few exceptions, from 73·35 per cent. (*Bact. coli*) to 79·99 per cent. (*Proteus vulgaris*).

The Ash Content of Bacteria.—The figures recorded for the ash content of bacteria vary very widely. Buchanan and Fulmer (1928–30) quote figures ranging from 2·0 to 13·94 per cent. of dry weight, omitting one widely discrepant figure. It seems probable that the ash content is particularly liable to be affected by the medium on which the bacterium is grown. Thus Fulmer and his colleagues (1921) record a reduction in the ash content of a yeast from 6·3 per cent. to 3·0 per cent. as the result of growing it in a medium free from magnesium and calcium salts.

There is general agreement that a high proportion of the total ash consists of phosphoric acid, 10–45 per cent. or more reckoned as P_2O_5 among most bacterial species, 40–70 per cent. or more among the acid-fast forms (see Tamura 1913*b*, Buchanan and Fulmer 1928–30). Among the mineral constituents that have been identified are Ca, Mg, Na, K and the Cl and SO_4 ions.

The Protein and other Nitrogenous Constituents of Bacteria.—The recorded figures for total nitrogen are widely discrepant. Buchanan and Fulmer quote figures varying between 1·8 and 15 per cent. of dry bacterial substance ; and the percentages recorded by different observers for the same bacterial species show little agreement. The usual range would appear to be from 8 to 15 per cent. Nicolle and Alilaire's figures vary only between 8·28 and 10·79 per cent., but recent determinations carried out by Linton, Mitra and Shrivastava (1934) on the cholera vibrio give values of 12·17–15·57 per cent.

In regard to the nature and amount of the coagulable proteins of bacterial cells our knowledge is curiously scanty. Boivin and Mesrobeanu (1934), who record a total N figure of 13·70 per cent. dry weight for *Bact. coli*, find that only 0·65 per cent. of this nitrogen, reckoned on the same basis, is soluble in trichloracetic acid, the remaining 13·05 per cent. being precipitated. Their figures for other organisms vary over a considerable range, but in every case the nitrogen precipitated by trichloracetic acid forms more than 80 per cent. of the total. Whether the coagulable protein is usually present in the form of globulin or albumin or both it is as yet impossible to say. Nicolle and Alilaire, in their résumé of the results of previous workers, state that albumins have been isolated from various bacterial species, globulins more doubtfully. Linton, Mitra and Shrivastava (1934), on the other hand, record in the case of *V. choleræ* that the coagulable protein is almost all in the form of globulin, *i.e.* is precipitated by half-saturation with ammonium sulphate. As regards the non-coagulable nitrogen, Boivin and Mesrobeanu calculate that about a quarter is present as polypeptides or amino-acids, and about another quarter as ammonium compounds. The percentages falling in these categories vary over a considerable range.

We have more information in regard to the units of which bacterial protein is built up ; and these seem, in general, to be the same as those that constitute proteins of other living cells. Numerous observers have carried out estimations by the methods of van Slyke, and the results show fair general agreement, though indicating significant differences in the proteins of different species. Thus, to take a few illustrative examples, in acid-fast bacilli, Tamura (1913*b*) has reported that 63·62–66·74 per cent. of the total nitrogen is present as mono-amino-acid-nitrogen, 13·71–15·21 per cent. as basic amino-acid-nitrogen, while Johnson and Coghill (1925) record 47·39–52·10 per cent. and 11·35–14·43 per cent.

for the tubercle bacillus. For the diphtheria bacillus Tamura (1914) gives corresponding figures of 54·62 per cent. and 16·89 per cent., Hirsch (1931) gives 44·80–47·41 per cent. and 16·67–17·67 per cent. For *Bact. coli*, Eckstein and Soule (1931) give 42·90–45·71 per cent. and 16·45–19·82 per cent., and for *V. choleræ*, Linton and Mitra (1934) give 54·84–57·11 per cent. and 24·08–26·03 per cent. These figures it should be noted refer to the total nitrogen present in the mono-amino and basic amino-acids, not to the nitrogen present in the amino form. Among the amino-acids that have been identified in bacterial proteins, arginine, histidine, lysine and tyrosine appear to be almost always present ; leucine and tryptophan have both been frequently demonstrated. The figures for cystine vary ; some observers have failed to demonstrate its presence, others have found it in relatively small amounts. There seems little doubt that the relative proportions of different amino-acids in different bacterial proteins vary significantly. Thus Tamura (1913*a*) records the presence of relatively large amounts of *l*-phenylalanine in the proteins of an acid-fast bacillus ; while (1914) he failed to identify this acid in the proteins of the diphtheria bacillus, which contained an unusually large amount of tyrosine. It would seem not un-likely that the presence of various amino-acids in detectable amounts, and still more that their quantitative relationships, might be largely influenced by the media employed for growth ; but Tamura (1913*b*) records closely similar figures for the mono-amino-nitrogen and basic amino-nitrogen in cultures of an acid-fast bacillus grown in nutrient broth and on a synthetic medium. In any case the findings recorded above give a very incomplete picture. Detailed and comprehensive analyses have, for the most part, still to be made.

There is one further point in connection with the nitrogenous constituents of bacterial cells, on which all observers are agreed—their high content in nucleo-proteins. (See Nishimura 1893, Galeotti 1898, Aronson 1900, Stoklasa 1908, Tamura 1913*a*, Schaffer *et al.* 1923, Buchanan and Fulmer 1928–30, Boivin and Mesrobeanu 1934.) The presence of nucleins had been suspected by many of the earlier bacteriologists because of the affinity of bacterial cells for nuclear stains ; and the work of the observers quoted above, and of others, has confirmed this conclusion by direct chemical analysis. Such substances as guanine, xanthine, hypoxanthine and adenine have frequently been demonstrated, and the high con-tent of phosphorus has been noted above. Boivin and Mesrobeanu (1934) report that the purine nitrogen, per cent. of undried bacterial cells, varied from 0·18 to 0·29 per cent. among six species examined, and of this purine nitrogen 73–94 per cent. was apparently in the form of nucleic acid.

Carbohydrate Constituents of Bacterial Cells.—Buchanan and Fulmer quote carbon figures ranging from a little below to a little above 50 per cent. dry weight for various bacterial species, with one widely discrepant finding.

There is very little evidence that bacteria share with the majority of vegetable cells the capacity of forming a cellulose envelope, or that cellulose enters in any way into their composition. (See Buchanan and Fulmer 1928–30.) They do, however, form a variety of polysaccharide gums ; and the studies of recent years have shown quite clearly that complex polysaccharides are of common occurrence in the surface layers of bacterial cells, and in their capsules when these are present. These polysaccharides play an important, often a dominant part in determining antigenic specificity (see Chapter VII).

We have noted in the preceding chapter that certain bacteria may contain granules that have been variously identified, on the basis of staining reactions, as starch or glycogen, but of the significance of these intracellular granules we know little, and their exact nature is still in dispute.

Bacterial Fats, Lipoids and Waxes.—Buchanan and Fulmer quote figures ranging from 1·56–40·8 per cent. dry weight for the ether-extractable substances in various species of bacteria. Nicolle and Alilaire record percentages of 6·31–15·77 for acetone-extractable substances, but the range of species covered is not the same. There is no doubt that the production of particular lipoids or waxes characterizes particular bacterial species. We have, for instance, noted in the previous chapter the production by the tubercle bacillus of a wax on which its acid-fastness depends (see also Chapter XV). We know so little of the part played by fats, lipoids and waxes in the economy of the bacterial cell that, for the moment, it will suffice to note their presence. For such data as are available in regard to their chemical constitution reference may be made to Buchanan and Fulmer (1928–30).

The Nutritional Requirements of Bacteria.

Perhaps the most striking feature of the nutritional activities of bacteria is their extreme diversity. It is possible to give a generalized description of plant nutrition that will apply, with minor modifications, to all flowering plants ; and the nutrition of the higher animals may be dealt with on the same broad basis. But in bacteria, as in certain other groups of unicellular or very simple organisms, the nutritional mechanisms have no common pattern. It is clear that they have been evolved by selective adaptation to the widest variety of environmental conditions ; so that one species or another can take advantage of almost any possible type of food-stuff, and any biologically supportable environment. This ubiquitous colonization by bacteria as a class has been made possible only by a correspondingly wide differentiation in their metabolic activities ; so that the nutritional needs of each bacterial group or species becomes a problem *sui generis*.

At one end of the scale we may note the existence of bacterial species that, in the use of a photosynthetic mechanism depending on the action of light on a cell pigment, form a link with the blue-green algæ, and with the higher plants. These photosynthetizing species include the blue and green sulphur bacteria (see van Niel 1931, 1933, Muller 1933, Roslofson 1934, 1935 and Gaffron 1934, 1935), and certain species of sulphur-free bacteria containing purple or brown pigments (Gaffron 1933, 1935). It may be noted that the purple sulphur bacteria contain two pigments, one red and one green, and that it is the green pigment alone that is concerned in photosynthesis. This pigment is related to chlorophyll (Noack and Schneider 1933, Schneider 1934, Fischer and Hasenkamp 1935) and is probably identical with, or of the same type as, the pigment of the green sulphur bacteria. For fuller details of the metabolic activities of this interesting bacterial group, with which we shall not be further concerned in this book, reference may be made to the papers quoted above or to the recently published monograph by Knight (1936), of which full use has been made in this and the following sections.

With the exception of this relatively small group, bacteria as a class do not employ any photosynthetic mechanism. The food with which they are supplied must provide for all their energy needs, as well as affording them the constituents they require for building up their cell protoplasm. Some species can live and multiply when provided only with very simple food materials. Others require far more complex substances. The classification of Orla-Jensen (1909) provides a convenient scheme for describing the main bacterial groups that can be differentiated on this basis. He recognizes three main groups ; though it is very doubtful, as will be seen in later sections, whether there is any real line of demarcation between his second and third groups. These groups are defined as follows :

(1) The autotrophic bacteria. These can obtain both their carbon and nitrogen from inorganic sources, such as CO_2, CH_4, NH_3, or atmospheric nitrogen itself.

(2) Bacteria that can obtain their nitrogen from inorganic sources, such as ammonium salts, but demand organic substances as a source of carbon.

(3) Bacteria that demand organic substances both for their carbon and nitrogen requirements.

The autotrophic bacteria are found mainly in the soil, and their activities are dealt with more fully in Chapter LXXXVII. Here we need only note that many of the reactions by which autotrophic bacteria utilize inorganic substances for synthetic purposes are endothermic, and that an associated source of energy must therefore be supplied by the simultaneous utilization of some other food-stuff (see Harden 1930). Thus, the synthesis of carbohydrates from CO_2 demands a considerable energy supply. The nitrosifying bacteria of the soil obtain this energy by oxidizing ammonia to nitrites, the nitrifying bacteria by oxidizing nitrites to nitrates. It can be shown (Winogradsky 1890*a, b, c*) that the relation between the ammonia or nitrite oxidized and the CO_2 assimilated is a quantitative one. It may be noted, too, that certain autotrophic bacteria, and also other organisms, are capable of oxidizing molecular hydrogen (Kaserer 1905, 1906, Niklewski 1908).

We may, for our present purposes, consider Jensen's second and third classes together. Most of the bacteria with which we are concerned in this book fall into one or other of them ; and though they are convenient for descriptive purposes there would seem to be no sharp line between them. A particular strain of a given bacterial species may, as we shall see, be transferred from the third to the second class. Detailed studies of the nutritional requirements of various pathogenic species of bacteria have been carried out within recent years by Fildes and his colleagues in this country and by Braun and his colleagues in Germany (1921–33). Braun and Cahn-Bronner (1921, 1922), for instance, record a series of experiments on the ability of *Bact. typhosum, Bact. paratyphosum B and Bact. enteritidis* (Gaertner) to grow in media containing only mineral salts together with ammonia as a source of nitrogen and various organic acids as a source of carbon. With formic acid as the source of carbon no strain grew. With acetic acid growth was obtained with three of five strains of *Bact. paratyphosum B* and a single strain of *Bact. enteritidis*, but with no typhoid strain. Succinic acid allowed growth of the paratyphoid and Gaertner bacilli but not the typhoid strains. Lactic and citric acid gave growth with all three species. One strain of *Bact. typhosum* was, however, unable to grow on any of these media, nor would it grow when provided with glucose as a source of carbon and an ammonium salt as the only source of nitrogen. With lactate as a source of carbon this strain failed to grow when provided with glycocoll, alanine, asparagine or leucine as a source of nitrogen, but grew when provided with tryptophan (see Braun and Cahn-Bronner 1922).

The problem of the rôle of tryptophan in bacterial nutrition has been studied in some detail by Fildes and his colleagues (Fildes, Gladstone and Knight 1933, Fildes and Knight 1933). Using a basal medium containing sodium citrate, magnesium sulphate, a phosphate buffer and glucose, they added the fourteen amino-acids : alanine, glycine, leucine, valine, glutamic acid, asparagine, tyrosine, phenyl-alanine, proline, histidine, arginine, lysine, cystine and tryptophan. In this medium the strains of *Bact. typhosum* studied grew well. They then tried the effect of omitting each amino-acid in turn. Only four affected the rate or degree of growth. The omission of leucine, lysine or cystine caused delay, but full growth eventually occurred. In the absence of tryptophan *Bact. typhosum* failed to multiply. Further experiments showed that, in the presence of other amino-acids or of ammonium chloride as a source of nitrogen, as little as 0·00064 per cent. of tryptophan in the medium sufficed to allow of growth. In further experiments it proved possible to train two strains of *Bact. typhosum* to grow in the absence of tryptophan with ammonium chloride as the sole source of nitrogen. The presence of tryptophan in the bacterial cells grown in this mixture was demonstrated by the glyoxylic reaction. It would seem therefore that tryptophan is an essential constituent of the typhoid bacillus ; that most strains are unable to synthesize it when first removed from media in which it is present ; but that they can be trained to do so by gradually accustoming them to a medium from which it is absent. Several other species were examined by the same methods and significant differences in behaviour were observed by Fildes and his colleagues. They conclude that bacteria may, on this basis, be divided into three groups : (1) Those that can synthesize tryptophan for themselves. These include the autotrophic bacteria and, among the pathogenic or potentially pathogenic organisms that have been examined, *Bact. coli, Ps. pyocyanea* and *Bact. typhi-murium* : (2) Those that cannot synthesize tryptophan for themselves, and hence will grow only when this amino-acid is provided in the medium. To this group belong the anaerobes *Cl. sporogenes, Cl. botulinum, Cl. tetani*, and the aerobe *B. anthracis* : (3) An intermediate group of organisms that are unable to synthesize tryptophan on first transference to a medium in which it is absent, but can be trained to do so by gradual deprivation. Examples of organisms that behave in this way are afforded by *Bact. typhosum, C. diphtheriæ, Staph. aureus* and probably *Myco. tuberculosis.*

The Vitamin Requirements of Bacteria.—The preceding sections illustrate the extreme diversity displayed by bacteria in regard to the food-stuffs they require for energy and for synthesis. We have also to consider whether all or any of them resemble more highly organized forms of life in demanding, in addition, the presence of vitamins—substances necessary for growth but active in concentrations so small that it seems impossible that their rôle should be to supply either energy or material for cell-synthesis. That vitamins are necessary for bacterial growth has often been asserted. It is impossible to review the relevant literature here ; but summaries will be found in papers by Knorr (1925), Sergent (1928) and Peskett (1933), and in the monograph by Knight (1936), which contains details of many very recent observations. The great difficulty of assessing the actual significance of many of the observations recorded is due to the relatively low concentrations in which substances that certainly are not vitamins are capable of promoting bacterial growth. Thus (see Knight and Fildes 1933), Hosoya and Kuroya (1923) record results which they regard as demonstrating a vitamin-demand by many different bacteria. They base this conclusion on the fact that the vitamin preparation selected for addition to the basal medium, when tested in the concentration employed (0·05 per cent.) gave negative colour tests for proteins and amino-acids, and was therefore, in their view, present in too small an amount to serve for energy or synthesis. It may well be that Hosoya and Kuroya were in fact observing a vitamin effect, but the particular argument on which they depend cannot be accepted as valid. Knight and Fildes, for instance, note that the amount of tryptophan present in a solution of gelatin is adequate for bacterial growth, though it is not demonstrable by the glyoxylic reaction until the mercury precipitate has been concentrated to an extent equivalent to a 100 per cent. solution of gelatin. A negative colour test cannot therefore be regarded as excluding the presence of an essential food-stuff in an amount that may be significant for bacterial growth. Mistakes of this kind have frequently been made. Thus, Broom (1929) has shown that the supposed vitamin effect of orange juice is due to its content in glucose and other fermentable carbohydrates.

Recent studies by Knight and Fildes (1933) have, however, placed the argument for a bacterial vitamin-demand on a firm basis. Working with *Cl. sporogenes*, they have been able to isolate from yeast, urine and other sources a substance necessary for bacterial growth, that is active in a concentration of 0·000,02 per cent., which would appear to remove it from the class of possible food-stuffs. This vitamin is also required by *Cl. botulinum* (Fildes 1935). It resembles in many respects the substance " auxin," described by Kögl and Haagen Smit (1931) as a stimulant of the elongation of plant cells, but Pappenheimer (1935), who has recently succeeded in obtaining very active preparations of the sporogenes vitamin in a state approaching chemical purity, finds that it differs from auxin in its sensitiveness to acid and alkali and in other ways. It appears to be very widely distributed in nature and is synthesized by many bacteria and moulds.

Knight (1935) has shown that a vitamin-like substance is required for the growth of *Staph. aureus*, a finding which confirms and greatly extends earlier observations by Hughes (1932) and by Hirsch and Muller (1933). This substance, which is in no way related to the sporogenes vitamin, can be extracted from marmite, and partially purified by solution in ethyl and butyl alcohols, precipitation with mercuric chloride, vacuum distillation of the free base, and removal of inactive material from the active distillate by extraction with chloroform. The material so prepared is active at a concentration of 1 mg. to 250 litres. It seems probable (Knight 1935) that this vitamin is also required for the growth of *B. anthracis*.

If we were to broaden our terms of reference to include substances that, though not vitamins in the usual sense, may reasonably be regarded as accessory growth factors, we should have to note here the growth requirements of the genus *Hæmophilus*, which are described on pp. 614–617. Thus *H. influenzæ* requires for its growth two factors in addition to the ordinary food-stuffs. One of these, the X factor, is supplied by hæmatin, or by certain other iron-containing organic compounds. The other, the V factor, is present in fresh animal or vegetable tissues, in yeast, and in most species of bacteria. It is less thermostable than the X factor and, partly for this reason, partly perhaps because of its source of origin, it has sometimes been regarded as a vitamin. It was, indeed, suggested that it might be identical with Vitamin C (ascorbic acid), but this has been disproved by Meyer (1934). We know too little as yet in regard to the real functions of these factors to assign them their correct place among the accessory factors required for bacterial growth.

The Gaseous Requirements of Bacteria.—Among the most important of the gaseous requirements of bacteria is the preference shown by many species for particular ranges of oxygen pressure, and the inability of certain species to multiply in the presence of this gas. It will, however, be more convenient to defer a discussion of aerobiosis and anaerobiosis, and to consider first the effect of another gas, CO_2.

The CO_2 Requirements of Bacteria.—Reference to Chapter XXXI will afford the most striking example of the growth-promoting properties of carbon dioxide,

Br. abortus, when freshly isolated from the tissues, often fails to grow when exposed to ordinary atmospheric conditions, but grows freely when the CO_2 content is raised to 10 per cent. Such strains can, however, usually be trained to grow at the ordinary atmospheric pressure of CO_2 after a few subcultures in the laboratory. Reference to Chapter XXIV affords an example in which the action of CO_2 is rather different, affecting not the power to grow but the capacity to produce a particular substance. *Staph. aureus* produces a characteristic toxin and some strains, though not all, produce this toxin in significant amount only when growing in the presence of an increased partial pressure of CO_2.

These are examples in which bacteria require an excess of carbon dioxide above the limits normally found when growing on solid or in liquid media. But it would seem that these species are peculiar only in respect of their quantitative demands, not in their need for gaseous carbon dioxide as such. There are many observations indicating that CO_2 is necessary for the growth of several, perhaps all, bacterial species including anaerobes (see, for instance, Rockwell and McKhann 1921, Rockwell 1921, 1923, 1924, Rockwell and Highberger 1926, 1927, Valley and Rettger 1927, Valley 1928).

More recent observations, carried out in synthetic media and by a different technique, have greatly extended our experimental data. Walker (1932), using a liquid synthetic medium, found that *Bact. coli* failed to grow when incubated for 24 hours in a current of CO_2-free air. After aeration was stopped growth occurred in a few hours. Walker concluded that CO_2 was necessary for growth, and that the lag phase represented the time taken by the organism to produce in its immediate vicinity a concentration of CO_2 sufficient to permit of multiplication. Gladstone, Fildes and Richardson (1935) have carried out far more detailed studies along somewhat similar lines. They found that the continuous passage of CO_2-free gases through cultures of *Bact. typhosum*, *Bact. coli*, *Ps. pyocyanea*, *Staph. aureus*, *B. subtilis*, *B. anthracis*, *C. diphtheriæ*, *Cl. sporogenes* and *Cl. welchii* often, but not always, prevented multiplication. The effect produced varied accordingly to the nature of the medium employed and certain other conditions. All the findings were compatible with the view that the occurrence or non-occurrence of growth depended on the relation between the rate at which CO_2 was being produced and the rate at which it was being removed by the stream of CO_2-free gas passing through the medium. If the former rate exceeded the latter, growth occurred. If CO_2 was removed as fast as it was produced, the bacteria failed to multiply. There is yet no sufficient evidence on which to base any conclusion as to how the CO_2 produces its essential effect.

Aerobiosis and Anaerobiosis.

The observations that certain bacteria would grow only in the absence of molecular oxygen was made by Pasteur in the very early days of bacteriology ; and since that time a wide variety of saprophytes and of pathogenic organisms have been isolated that show this distinctive physiological character.

It is customary to divide bacteria into three categories in regard to their behaviour towards molecular oxygen : (1) the *obligatory anaerobes*—or *anaerobes* without the qualifying adjective—which will grow only when oxygen is rigorously excluded, (2) the *facultative anaerobes*, which will grow both aerobically and anaerobically, *i.e.* in the presence or absence of oxygen, and (3) the *obligatory aerobes*, which will grow only when supplied with molecular oxygen.

Most of the organisms in Class (2)—to which incidentally the great majority of the bacteria with which we are concerned belong—are able to grow over a very wide range of oxygen pressures, but some species prefer a relatively restricted range, lying well below that of ordinary atmospheric conditions.

It may be noted here that the facultative anaerobes are by no means indifferent to variations in oxygen pressure. When deprived of oxygen they do not lose the capacity for growth, but their metabolic mechanisms change, with a consequent change in their nutritional requirements. It was Pasteur's observations on the different metabolic products associated with the aerobic and anaerobic growth of certain bacterial species that led him to place so great an emphasis on the absence of oxygen as a determinant factor in bacterial fermentations. An instance of changed nutritional requirements consequent on anaerobic growth is afforded by the observation of Pakes and Jollyman (1901) that *Ps. pyocyanea* will, under these conditions, no longer grow in an ordinary broth medium, but will do so if nitrate is added to the broth, the nitrate being reduced to nitrite and thus affording an alternative supply of oxygen. An example that has been studied in far greater detail is that of the aerobic and anaerobic growth of *Bact. coli* (Stephenson and Whetham 1924). When this organism is grown in a synthetic medium containing glucose, and afforded a free supply of air, the metabolic processes involved during the early stages of multiplication are almost anaerobic, as evidenced by the minimal uptake of oxygen ; the bacteria, during this period, are breaking down the glucose into lactic acid and other products by reactions of the hydrolytic oxidation-reduction type that yield free energy, though not in large amount. During later stages of aerobic growth, however, the atmospheric oxygen is freely utilized, and CO_2 is given off. During this period the products of the initial hydrolysis undergo more complete oxidation associated with a large energy output. When *Bact. coli* is supplied with glucose as a source of carbon, or with some other substance that yields energy on hydrolytic cleavage, it can grow under anaerobic conditions. If, however, its only source of carbon is one of the simpler organic acids, such as lactic, succinic, fumaric or pyruvic acid, it will not grow in the absence of air. If nitrate is added to the medium, anaerobic growth occurs in the presence of such organic acids, the nitrate again being reduced to nitrite. Thus the statements made above in regard to the possibility of bacterial growth when various simple substances are provided as the sole source of carbon, should, in many cases at least, be qualified by the proviso that either molecular oxygen or some other convenient source of oxygen, such as nitrate, must be assumed to be present.

Within recent years our conceptions of anaerobiosis have been rendered more precise by the introduction of electrical methods of measurement (see Clark *et al.* 1928, McLeod 1930, Hewitt 1935).

A complex system of interacting substances in solution, such as is provided by a bacterial culture, contains many substances that can undergo reversible oxidation or reduction. If an electrode of a noble metal, gold or iridium or platinum, is immersed in such a culture, a potential will be set up the value of which will depend on the concentration of oxidizable or reducible substances, the actual degree of their oxidation or reduction, and the pH of the system (see below). This potential can be compared with that of a normal hydrogen electrode, or more conveniently with a standard calomel electrode. The calomel electrode itself gives a potential of $+ 0.25$ volts when connected with a normal hydrogen electrode ; so that, when the former is used, 0.25 volts must be added to the reading obtained to give the potential in relation to the normal hydrogen electrode, which is the arbitrary standard of reference. The value so obtained is known as the Eh of the system and is a measure of its reducing or oxidizing capacity, *i.e.* of the concentration of electrons. Using this technique it has been possible to determine with considerable precision the limiting oxidizing or reducing potentials that will allow the growth of any particular bacterial species.

Thus, Knight and Fildes (1930) have shown that the limiting Eh, in the oxidizing direction, that will permit the germination of the spores of *Cl. tetani* is $+ 0.11$ volts. It may be noted (Lepper and Martin 1930*b*) that the actual growth of such anaerobes as *Cl. tetani* or *Cl. welchii* in a suitable medium causes a rapid drift of Eh in a negative *i.e.* reducing direction.

The oxidation-reduction potential, Eh, of any system may also be measured by the series of dyes introduced by Clark and his colleagues (1928) ; but the method gives less accurate results than those obtained by direct electrical measurement.

Other Factors Influencing the Growth of Bacteria.

Hydrogen-Ion Concentration (pH).—It will be convenient to consider the influence of hydrogen-ion concentration at this point, in order to bring it into relation with the conception of the oxidation-reduction potential set out above. Most students of bacteriology will have become familiar with the significance of hydrogen-ion concentration, and with the ways in which it may be measured and controlled, during earlier stages of their curriculum. For the benefit of any who happen not to have acquired this familiarity, or to have lost it, the following brief summary is inserted here. Since, however, this question is of great practical and theoretical importance to the bacteriologist, it will be advisable to consult a more detailed account either in a well-known monograph by Clark (1928) or in one of the chemical or biological text-books in which the subject is more fully treated.

Acids, as everyone knows, are substances that on dissociation yield a preponderance of hydrogen-ions, and bases are substances that yield a preponderance of hydroxyl-ions. The " strength " of an acid or of a base may be envisaged in two different ways. We may ask how much acid is present in a given volume, *i.e.* what is the total concentration or " normality " of the acid ? The answer to this question we obtain by titration against a standard solution of alkali, that is by adding alkali until all the acid is neutralized. The second way of viewing the " strength " of the acid solution is to think of it in terms of the existing concentration of free hydrogen-ions. This will depend not only on how much acid is present per unit volume, but also on how much of that acid is dissociated. Since different acids are dissociated to very different degrees, the hydrogen-ion concentration of, say, N/10 solutions of a number of different acids may vary over a very wide range. Bacterial cells are very sensitive to hydrogen-ions, and it is the concentration of these ions in any given medium at any given time, not the total acidity as measured by titration, that determines many bacterial reactions.

All the reactions with which we are here concerned take place in watery solutions. Water itself undergoes a very slight degree of dissociation into positively-charged hydrogen-ions and negatively-charged hydroxyl-ions ; and, as with other similar dissociation processes, the equilibrium between hydrogen-ions, hydroxyl-ions and undissociated water follows the mass-action equation :—

$$\frac{(H\cdot) \times (OH')}{(H\cdot OH)} = K$$

where the brackets denote ionic or molecular concentrations, and K is the dissociation constant.

Since, in this case, the concentration of undissociated water is enormously large in relation to the dissociated ions, no significant change will occur in the denominator of the fraction as the result of any ordinary alteration in the degree of dissociation, and

(H·OH) may itself be regarded as a constant. The equation may thus be re-written,

$$(H^{\cdot}) \times (OH') = K_w$$

where K_w is a new constant calculated on this basis.

This constant has been very carefully determined. Expressed in gram-ions per litre its value is approximately 10^{-14}. Since, in the case of pure water, the concentrations of hydrogen and hydroxyl-ions will be equal, the concentration of each will equal $\sqrt{10^{-14}} = 10^{-7}$. In any watery solution this concentration of hydrogen ions corresponds to neutrality.

It is inconvenient to employ numerical terms that involve decimal figures with long rows of noughts, or such expressions as $1 \cdot 36 \times 10^{-3}$, which happens to be the hydrogen-ion concentration of decinormal acetic acid. For this reason Sörensen (1909) suggested the use of an exponential scale, using the logarithm of the reciprocal of the hydrogen-ion concentration in order to obviate the constant use of the minus sign. To the value thus obtained he gave the name pH. Thus, at the neutral point, the hydrogen-ion concentration of a watery solution is approximately 10^{-7}. The reciprocal of this is 10^7. The logarithm of this, and the pH of the solution, is 7·0.

In using this scale there are two facts to remember. We are dealing with reciprocals and therefore the pH decreases as the hydrogen-ion concentration increases. We are using an exponential scale with 10 as a base, so that a change of one in our pH value corresponds to a ten-fold change in hydrogen-ion concentration. A solution that has ten times the hydrogen-ion concentration of pure water will therefore have a pH of 6·0, a solution that has one-tenth the hydrogen-ion concentration of pure water will have a pH of 8·0. The latter solution will, of course, be definitely alkaline, that is, it will have excess of OH'-ions. Since the product of the concentration of H· and OH'-ions will remain constant at 10^{-14} the OH'-ion concentration can always be derived from the pH value by simple subtraction of exponents ; but it is more convenient, and equally informative, to think of alkaline as well as acid solutions in terms of pH.

What will happen to the pH of pure water when we add to it any given amount of a particular acid ? If we add a strong acid, such as hydrochloric, or nitric, or sulphuric, that is almost completely dissociated in watery solution, the hydrogen-ion concentration will rise, and the pH will fall, approximately in direct proportion to the total amount of acid that we add. If, however, we add a weak acid, and it is with these that we are mainly concerned, we have to consider the degree of dissociation as well as the amount added. Here again the mass-action equation applies, and we shall have

$$\frac{(H^{\cdot}) \times (A')}{(HA)} = K$$

where (HA) is the concentration of the weak acid, (H·) the concentration of hydrogen-ions and (A') the concentration of the anions, say $CH_3 \cdot COO'$ ions.

Here, again, the concentration of hydrogen-ions and anions will be equal, so that we may write our equation

$$\frac{(H^{\cdot})^2}{(HA)} = K, \text{ or } (H^{\cdot})^2 = K(HA), \text{ or } (H^{\cdot}) = \sqrt{K(HA)}$$

We shall not, therefore, increase our hydrogen-ion concentration in direct proportion to the amount of acid that we add, but in proportion to the value $\sqrt{K(HA)}$. Since most weak acids are very slightly dissociated, the value (HA), the concentration of undissociated acid in solution, will not differ widely from the total concentration of acid, dissociated and undissociated together. The increase in the concentration of hydrogen-ions resulting from the addition to water of varying amounts of any weak acid will, therefore, be approximately, but only approximately, proportional to the square root of the amount of acid added. For equivalent amounts of different acids it will vary in proportion to the square root of the dissociation constant.

Suppose that, instead of pure water, we are dealing with a solution of the sodium or potassium salt of some weak acid. Such salts are almost completely dissociated in dilute watery solutions. If we add the same or another weak acid to such a solution there will be a momentary increase in the hydrogen-ion concentration, in accordance with the equation given above. But the added hydrogen-ions will at once combine with the anions of the salt to form the corresponding acid, and as the acid, as opposed to the salt, is very slightly dissociated the hydrogen-ions remaining free in the solution will be very slightly increased, and the pH will be very slightly lowered. The salts of weak acids have thus a pronounced stabilizing effect on pH, and for this reason they are known as *buffers*. Such substances, of which phosphates provide an important biological example, are of great importance in maintaining the correct hydrogen-ion concentration in the cells and tissue fluids of plants and animals, and they are of equal importance in bacterial cultures.

The measurement of pH.—As in the case of Eh, the oxidation-reduction potential, pH, the conventional measure of hydrogen-ion concentration, can be determined either by a colorimetric method (Clark 1928) or by the potentiometer, using a suitable arrangement of electric cells.

In the former case advantage is taken of the buffering effect of the salts of weak acids —phosphates, borates, phthalates, citrates, etc.—to prepare a series of standard solutions of known pH ; and to these are added suitable amounts of various dyes, selected to give various colour changes over the pH range caused by the solutions. The same indicator, in the same concentration, is added to the medium or culture under test, and is matched against the standard tubes in a suitable comparator.

In the potentiometer method a hydrogen electrode is immersed in the liquid to be tested, and the potential set up between the hydrogen-ions in solution and the hydrogen adsorbed on the electrode is measured by connection through a bridge to a standard cell.

The relations of pH to Eh.—It will be noted that both pH and Eh measure potentials depending on the concentrations of active substances, not the reserve acidity or reducing capacity. The pH value depends only on the concentration of hydrogen-ions, the Eh value on the concentration of electrons, *i.e.* the concentrations of all active substances that affect the oxidation-reduction balance of the system. Of these the hydrogen-ion is one, so that Eh is influenced by pH. A particular medium, which has a given Eh when its pH is adjusted to 7·0, will have a different Eh when its pH is altered to 6·0. In general the Eh decreases, *i.e.* the system becomes more actively reducing, as the pH rises, *i.e.* as the medium becomes more alkaline. Thus a system that at pH 2·0 gives an Eh of + 0·4 volts may, at pH 12, give an Eh of − 0·1 volts. Since the hydrogen-ion is positively charged, *i.e.* has lost the electron that is associated with it in the atomic state, and since the essence of reduction is the addition of one or more electrons, this general relation is to be expected ; but the relation is not usually linear, nor are different systems affected to the same degree by a change in hydrogen-ion concentration. In some cases changes in pH may produce relatively little alteration in Eh, in others the Eh value may vary widely when the pH is raised or lowered.

The Effect of pH on Bacterial Growth.

For any given species of bacterium there is an optimal, and relatively narrow range of pH allowing vigorous growth, and a wider range extending on each side of the optimum over which growth occurs less vigorously. For most of the bacteria with which we are concerned the optimal pH lies a little to the alkaline side of neutrality (pH 7·2–7·6). The range of pH over which growth is possible has not been accurately determined for many bacterial species, but for most pathogenic species it would appear to extend over some such range as pH 5·0–pH 8·0.

There are, however, species that show very distinctive variations from this modal range of sensitivity. *Azotobacter*, for instance, is very sensitive to acids, and will not grow in pure culture at a pH lower than 6·5 (Fred and Davenport 1918). The aciduric bacilli of the genus *Lactobacillus* are, on the other hand, highly resistant to acids, and will apparently grow to some extent at pH 4·0 or even less : though the power to grow has not, in this instance, been decisively differentiated from the power to resist the lethal action of the acid. (McIntosh *et al.* 1922, 1924.) The cholera vibrio is very tolerant of alkali, relatively sensitive to acid. Its optimum for growth is pH 7·6–8·0 and its limits for growth about pH 6·4–9·6.

It would seem, as is not surprising, that there is often a relation between the ability of an organism to grow under aerobic or anaerobic conditions and the pH of the medium on which it is growing. Thus it has been stated that *C. acnes* will grow aerobically only if the medium is adjusted to the range pH 6·2–6·8 ; and there is a suggestion that the microaerophilic species of *Lactobacilli* are less sensitive to oxygen when growing on an acid medium.

The Influence of Temperature on Bacterial Growth.

We need only note in this section that, for each species of bacterium, there is an optimal temperature for growth and a range of temperature over which growth is possible. For most pathogenic bacteria the optimal temperature for growth is in the neighbourhood of 37° C., and the range of temperature over which growth occurs is approximately 15°–40° C. Here as elsewhere, however, there are wide variations, especially when we include in our survey non-pathogens as well as pathogens. In their reactions to changes in temperature, bacteria as a whole display in a striking fashion their ability to colonize any biologically supportable environment.

To take a few illustrative examples among pathogenic and potentially pathogenic species, *Bact. coli* grows best at 37° C., but will grow at any temperature within the range of 15°–45° C. Among the Gram-negative cocci there are characteristic differences in reaction to temperature ; thus, *N. gonorrhœæ, N. meningitidis* and *N. catarrhalis* all show optima at about 37° C. ; but the range of growth of *N. catarrhalis* extends from approximately 18° to 42° C., while *N. gonorrhœæ* and *N. meningitidis* show a very restricted range of about 30° to 38° C. The different types of tubercle bacilli show temperature optima in conformity with the body-temperatures of the host-species that they infect ; thus the human and bovine types of tubercle bacillus grow best at 37° C. and fail to grow below 30° C. ; the avian type grows best at 40° C., and again fails to grow below 30° C., while the cold-blooded type grows freely at 22° C.

As examples of non-pathogenic species that depart widely from the temperature optima given above we may note (see Buchanan and Fulmer 1928–30) that bacteria have been isolated from fish, brine and similar sources that grow well at 0° C. ; while from a variety of natural sources (soil, excreta, silos and especially hot springs) thermophilic species have been isolated that have optima at 55° C. or over, and are able to multiply at a temperature of 75° C. These thermophiles are of considerable economic importance, since they are a source of difficulty when it is desired to sterilize any material at a relatively low temperature (see Chapter V).

The Chemical Changes produced by Bacteria in various Substrates.—In the preceding sections we have been concerned with the nutritional demands of bacteria, *i.e.* with the food-stuffs that must be supplied to them, and the environmental conditions that must be afforded in order that they may obtain the energy, and material for synthesis, that will enable them to multiply. We have not yet discussed, except incidentally, the chemical changes produced by the bacteria in these essential food-stuffs, or in other substrates that may be present in the medium in which they are growing. It would, indeed, be altogether impossible to deal in any detail with the wide variety of reactions that have been studied by workers in this field ; but a few illustrative examples may be given, confining our attention for the moment to the nature of the chemical changes that are brought about and leaving to a later section a consideration of the mechanisms involved.

We may note in passing that studies of the kind that here concern us have, for the most part, been carried out by biochemists, and mark the rapid development of microbiological chemistry as a distinctive branch of biological science. Although work in this field was initiated by Pasteur, and developed extensively by him within the limits of the chemical knowledge and technique of his time, it has been largely neglected by his bacteriological successors. These have, for the most part, been content to use the bacterial fermentation reactions as diagnostic tools, without inquiring in any systematic way into the actual chemical changes concerned. The common practice has been to map out the fermentative abilities of different bacterial species, using an arbitrarily selected series of carbohydrate and other substrates, which experience has shown to possess differential value, and noting the production of acid by a colour change in a suitable indicator, or the production of gas by observing its collection within a small inverted tube contained in the culture medium. The study of the changes produced in nitrogenous substrates has been even more limited and arbitrary—the production of indole from a tryptophan-containing substrate, the production of H_2S from sulphur-containing amino-acids, and so on. This neglect has been natural enough. The medical bacteriologist, at least, has been mainly interested in other bacterial activities ; but the time has quite clearly arrived when the chemical aspects of bacteriology and immunity must be mastered by all serious students of these branches of biology.

The Action of Bacteria on Carbohydrates and Allied Substances.—The majority of the bacteria with which we are concerned in this book are able to attack the simple hexose sugars. Occasionally the end result is complete oxidation to water and carbon dioxide. This is, however, an unusual type of reaction, limited to a few species and demanding a copious supply of oxygen. Various reactions leading to less complete oxidation are more common ; and one of the most characteristic types of bacterial fermentation is that in which molecular oxygen plays no direct part, the reaction consisting essentially in the splitting of a complex molecule, usually by hydrolysis, with a rearrangement of the oxygen atoms, so that one portion of the hydrolysed molecule is oxidized while the other is reduced. An example of this general type of reaction is afforded by the studies of Harden (1901, 1905) and of Harden and Walpole (1906) on the fermentation of dextrose by *Bact. coli*. The main products of fermentation are lactic acid, acetic acid, ethyl alcohol, carbon dioxide and hydrogen, and the reaction appears to be approximately represented by the formula,

$$2C_6H_{12}O_6 + H_2O = 2CH_3 \cdot CHOH \cdot COOH + CH_3 \cdot COOH + C_2H_5 \cdot OH + 2CO_2 + 2H_2$$

although small amounts of other substances, such as succinic acid, are produced.

In some instances, as in the fermentation of dextrose by the typhoid bacillus, no free gas is evolved. It was suggested by Harden that in this case that part of the reaction which, with such an organism as *Bact. coli*, leads to the evolution of equal parts of CO_2 and H_2, stops short at the formation of formic acid, $H \cdot COOH$ (see also Pakes and Jollyman 1901). This suggestion was strengthened by the observations of Sera (1910), while Grey (1913–14) has shown that formic acid can be identified as an intermediate product in the fermentation of dextrose by *Bact. coli*. (But see p. 59.)

This type of reaction is, however, by no means the only one that occurs during the cleavage of carbohydrates and allied substances by bacteria.

The existence of wide variations is well illustrated by the results recorded by Birkenshaw, Charles and Clutterbuck (1931). Using the carbon-balance-sheet method employed by Raistrick and his colleagues (1931) in their extensive studies on the metabolism of moulds, they determined the relative proportions of different metabolic products formed by twenty different bacterial species growing in a synthetic medium containing glucose. In the case of *Bact. coli* and of certain nearly related organisms, up to 30·4 per cent. of the carbon of the glucose was recovered, after fermentation, in the form of lactic acid, 5·0–14·4 per cent. was recovered in the form of volatile acids, while the amount present as butylene glycol ($CH_3 \cdot CHOH \cdot CHOH \cdot CH_3$) was negligible. On the other hand a coliform organism of a different type, *Bact. asiaticum mobile*, yielded 26·8–31·0 per cent. of the carbon as butylene glycol, but none as lactic acid. Two anaerobes (*Cl. saccharobutyricum* and *Cl. pasteurianum*) yielded a large proportion of carbon as volatile acids (34·8 per cent. and 37·8 per cent.) but formed little if any lactic acid or butylene glycol.

Among the many intermediate products that have been identified during the bacterial fermentation of carbohydrates and other carbon compounds, it seems possible that pyruvic acid ($CH_3 \cdot CO \cdot COOH$) holds an important place. Quastel (1925) has shown that, in the case at least of *Bact. coli*, those simple organic acids, such as succinic, that yield pyruvic acid on cleavage, serve as adequate sources of carbon for growth, while formic acid which on cleavage does not yield pyruvic acid will not function as the sole source of carbon. How far this applies to other bacterial species is, at the moment, impossible to say. It has been shown by Braun and his colleagues (see above) that many parasitic bacteria are unable to grow in the presence of formic acid as the sole source of carbon ; but some species, such as *Ps. pyocyanea*, are reported as able to utilize this acid, and there are in addition the autotrophic species to be considered.

The hexahydric alcohols, mannitol, dulcitol, and sorbitol, are fermented by many of the bacterial species that attack the hexose sugars, and are apparently broken down along very similar lines. The ability to utilize these substances is, however, more restricted, so that many species that ferment the sugars fail to ferment the corresponding alcohols.

As regards carbohydrates of more complex structure we find the widest differences between bacteria of different species. Some will attack complex polysaccharides, such as cellulose, starch, dextrin or complex glucosides. Other bacteria, which have no action on such polysaccharides as starch or dextrin, may cause the hydrolysis of the disaccharides, saccharose, lactose or maltose. Saccharose, under the influence of invertase, is hydrolysed to a mixture of dextrose and fructose ; lactose, under the influence of lactase, to dextrose and galactose ; maltose, under the influence of maltase, to two molecules of dextrose. When hydrolysis has reached this stage, the utilization of the hexose sugars proceeds along the lines indicated above.

The Action of Bacteria on Proteins and other Nitrogenous Substrates. The breakdown of complex proteins that occurs under natural conditions, and is known as putrefaction, has long been known to depend on the action of bacteria. This proteolytic activity is, however, confined to particular species, many of which are anaerobes ; and it is at least doubtful whether even these proteolytic species are able to utilize complex proteins for growth in the absence of other sources of nitrogen. Bainbridge (1911) found that many bacteria, including *Proteus vulgaris, Bact. coli* and staphylococci, were unable to grow in solutions of pure egg albumin, or of serum proteins, but that *Proteus vulgaris* was able to break down such complex proteins provided that a sufficient supply of nitrogen in an assimilable form was added to the medium. Similar results have been recorded by Rettger and his colleagues (Sperry and Rettger 1915, Rettger, Berman and Sturges 1916, Berman and Rettger 1918). Of several gelatin-liquefying bacteria studied by Berman and Rettger, none could utilize egg albumin in the absence of other sources of nitrogen. Only three species, *B. subtilis, Chr. prodigiosum* and *Proteus vulgaris* could break down peptone. With proteoses purified by precipitation, *B. subtilis* and *Chr. prodigiosum* caused complete breakdown. Only *B. subtilis, Chr. prodigiosum* and *Proteus vulgaris* could attack casein. *B. subtilis* and *Chr. prodigiosum* could not only liquefy gelatin, but could use it as a source of nitrogen ; but such organisms as *Staph. aureus* or *Bact. cloacæ*, although they caused rapid liquefaction of the gelatin when provided with another source of nitrogen for growth, showed no ability to utilize the liquefied substance.

Many of the anaerobes are conspicuous for their ability to break down complex proteins, and the method of cleavage has been studied by several workers (see Wolf and Harris 1918, Harris 1919, Wolf 1919*a*, *b*). It would seem, however, that the hydrolytic degradation of such protein material is in most, if not in all, cases due to the action of specialized enzymes, which are produced in adequate amount only when the bacteria concerned are supplied with other sources of nitrogen for direct utilization. Given such sources, the bacteria are able to grow and to increase their available nitrogen by protein cleavage.

In connection with the utilization of simple polypeptides and amino-acids by bacteria we may note the effect of the presence in the medium of a free supply of fermentable carbohydrate. Many workers have upheld the view that the addition of such carbohydrates to an ordinary nutrient medium, containing peptone or meat extract, exerts a " protein-sparing " effect, the carbohydrates being attacked in preference to the amino-acids or peptides (see Hirschler 1886, Smith 1897, Peckham 1897, Glenn 1911, Kendall, Day and Walker 1914, Kendall and Walker 1915, Jones 1916). This conclusion has been based in large part on the observation that the production of ammonia in the medium is largely inhibited when fermentable carbohydrates are present ; but Raistrick (1919) and Raistrick and Clark (1921) have shown that, in a medium containing known amino-acids, the decomposition of these acids is increased, not lessened, by the addition to the medium of another source of carbon, such as glycerol. The ammonia that is produced does not, under these conditions, accumulate in the medium, but is utilized by the bacteria for synthesis. It may be noted also that Berman and Rettger (1918) were unable to demonstrate any protein-sparing as the result of the addition of carbohydrates, except in those instances in which the rapid fall in pH resulting from carbohydrate breakdown caused an inhibition of further bacterial growth ; and that Heap and Cadness (1924) have shown that the presence of glucose greatly increases the rate of H_2S production from peptone by an organism that forms this gas during protein-cleavage. In regard to the cleavage of more complex protein molecules de Bord (1923) has shown that the addition of a fermentable carbohydrate to a protein-containing medium causes an increase in the concentration of amino-nitrogen induced by bacterial growth. These findings are in accord with later observations by Kendall (1922), which indicate that the effect of added carbohydrate is to lessen the utilization of proteins as a source of energy, not as material for synthesis.

The Action of Bacteria on Fats.—It has long been known that many bacteria are able to decompose fats (see von Sommaruga 1894, Rubner 1900, Eijkman 1901, Carrière 1901, Schreiber 1902, Orla-Jensen 1902, Huss 1908, Söhngen 1911, Wells and Corper 1912, Kendall *et al.* 1914, Avery and Cullen 1920, Stevens and West 1922, Michaelis and Nakahara 1923, Neill and Fleming 1927, van der Walle 1927, Collins and Hammer 1934). The bacterial lipase induces a simple hydrolysis into glycerol and fatty acid, and, under suitable conditions, the glycerol is further decomposed and the fatty acid oxidized (see Harden 1930).

Lipolytic activity is displayed by many parasitic and pathogenic species, such as *Bact. coli.*, *Staph. aureus*, streptococci, the pneumococcus and the tubercle bacillus, as well as by saprophytic organisms. But, here as elsewhere, there seem to be wide differences in activity between different bacteria. Many of the parasitic forms are feebly lipolytic, while certain saprophytic species, such as the bacterium isolated by Huss (1908) from milk, are extremely active.

The actively lipolytic bacteria are of considerable industrial importance, since they cause rancidity in butter and other fat-containing foods. It is possible, also, that such species play some part in sewage-purification.

It may be noted, in connection with the fat metabolism of bacteria, that one species, at least, can form fat from carbohydrate (Stephenson and Whetham, 1922, 1923).

The Mechanisms of Bacterial Metabolism

The metabolism of bacteria, as of other living cells, is dependent on, and regulated by, a complex system of enzymes and catalysts. The activity of these is conditioned by a variety of factors, such as the temperature of incubation, the pH and Eh of the medium, the presence or absence of molecular oxygen, and so on. In order that any given bacterium may grow and multiply it is necessary that these various conditioning factors should fall within a range limited by the requirements of the enzyme systems that must be brought into play. Many bacterial species, such as the facultative anaerobes, are, however, endowed with alternative enzyme systems that come into action under different environmental conditions ; and in this way the range of conditions under which they can multiply may be considerably extended.

Within recent years there has been a rapid advance in our knowledge of the action of various bacterial enzymes on different substrates ; and from these studies results of great interest and importance have emerged. We cannot here do more than attempt a short summary of some of the more important observations ; and in this summary it will be convenient to approach the problem by considering certain catalysed oxidation-reduction reactions, since the methods employed have, in the main, depended on the demonstration of reactions of this type. Viewed from this angle, our problem becomes cöextensive with that of bacterial respiration, using the latter term in the same sense as the physiologist speaks of tissue respiration. Although this term, so used, has the full sanction of current scientific literature, it is apt to be a little confusing to the student of bacteriology unless he realizes that it covers all those metabolic mechanisms that are employed in providing energy, as opposed to those that are concerned in synthesis. Before considering the observed reactions between bacteria and various substrates it will be convenient to outline very briefly the current views with regard to the mechanism by which oxidation and reduction are induced in any living cell.

The essential factor in any oxidation is the removal of electrons ; the essential factor in any reduction is their addition. In any oxidation-reduction process taking place in a watery solution we can view the action in terms of the transport of either oxygen or hydrogen. The addition of oxygen involves a relative decrease in electrons and is an oxidation. The withdrawal of hydrogen also involves a decrease in electrons, and is equally an oxidation. The withdrawal of oxygen, or the addition of hydrogen, involves a relative increase in electrons, and is a reduction. In either case at least two molecules must be involved. The oxygen, or hydrogen, must come from somewhere and must go to somewhere. The molecule from which they come is called the donator, the oxygen donator or hydrogen donator as the case may be. The molecule to which they go is called the acceptor. In donating oxygen a molecule is reduced, in accepting oxygen it is oxidized. In donating hydrogen a molecule is oxidized, in accepting hydrogen it is reduced. In either case the reaction is catalysed, and the catalyst is regarded as " activating " either oxygen or hydrogen.

The theory advanced by Wieland (1913, 1921, 1922) regards hydrogen activation, and consequent hydrogen transport, as the essential mechanism of cellular oxidations. The removal of hydrogen from a molecule may be preceded by the addition of a molecule of water, in which case oxygen is in fact added ; or there may be no preliminary addition of water, in which case the molecule is oxidized by the simple loss of hydrogen. In either case a suitable hydrogen acceptor must be provided. In general terms these reactions may be expressed as follows ;

(a) $X + H \cdot OH + A = XH \cdot OH + A = XO + AH_2.$
(b) $XH + A = X + AH$

In (a) X represents the substrate to be oxidized and A the hydrogen acceptor. Water is first added to X and the hydrogen of the compound XH·OH is then activated and passed on to A, leaving X oxidized. In (b) the compound XH is the substrate to be oxidized. Oxidation occurs by the activation of the hydrogen and its transference to A.

An example of the first type of reaction is afforded by the oxidation of an aldehyde to an acid with previous hydration,

$$CH_3 \cdot CHO + H_2O \rightarrow CH_3 \cdot C\overset{\displaystyle H}{\underset{\displaystyle OH}{\diagdown\!\!\!-OH}} \rightarrow CH_3 \cdot COOH + 2H.$$

An example of the second type of reaction is afforded by the oxidation of an alcohol to an aldehyde by removal of hydrogen,

$$CH_3 \cdot CH_2 \cdot OH = CH_3 \cdot CHO + 2H.$$

The hydrogen in such reactions is seldom liberated in the gaseous state. In almost all the reactions with which we are here concerned, a hydrogen acceptor must be provided. The enzyme that activates the hydrogen in the substrate to be oxidized, and so brings about its transport, is known as a dehydrogenase.

The theory advanced by Warburg (1925*a*, *b*) is concerned with the transport of oxygen, and lays stress on the essential part played by iron compounds in this process. In Warburg's view molecular oxygen unites in the cell with some substance containing iron in the reduced, or ferrous, state converting it into the oxidized, or ferric, state. In contact with an oxidizable organic molecule oxygen is transferred, and the iron returns to the ferrous, or divalent, condition. It is oxidized again by contact with molecular oxygen, and so the process goes on. This mechanism is, it may be noted, specifically inhibited by HCN.

There is another way in which oxygen may be transported in the living cell. Bach (see Oppenheimer 1926, Buchanan and Fulmer 1928-30) has shown that there are certain autoxidizable organic substances that readily take up oxygen without the aid of a catalyst ; such substances are said to be autoxidizable. Some of these unite with molecular oxygen to form peroxides, of the general form $A\begin{smallmatrix}O\\|\\O\end{smallmatrix}$. These organic peroxides may unite with water, and the hydrated compound may split with the formation of hydrogen peroxide ;

$$A\!\!<^O_O + H{\cdot}OH \longrightarrow A\!\!<^{OH}_{O-OH} \longrightarrow AO + \begin{smallmatrix}O{-}H\\|\\O{-}H\end{smallmatrix}$$

The hydrogen peroxide, or perhaps in some cases the organic peroxide itself, is acted on by an enzyme, a peroxidase, with the liberation of active oxygen which oxidizes substances that are not affected by molecular oxygen. It may be noted here that hydrogen peroxide is also acted upon by another enzyme, catalase. This enzyme, which is present in many bacteria, liberates oxygen in the molecular, not in the active form. Its action would seem, in many cases at least, to be protective (see p. 60).

There is yet another oxidation-reduction system that is of considerable importance from the bacteriological point of view. Hopkins (1921, 1923, 1929) has demonstrated the existence of a mechanism that involves only thermostable reagents of known chemical constitution, and that therefore functions without the intervention of an enzyme, in the usual sense of that term. The active substance, glutathione, is a tripeptide containing glutamic acid and cystein. It exists in two forms, the oxidized and the reduced. Ignoring its actual constitution, apart from the essential sulphur, or sulphydryl, groupings, we can represent these as follows :

$$\begin{matrix} G{-}S \\ | \\ G{-}S \end{matrix} \rightleftharpoons \begin{matrix} G{-}SH \\ \\ G{-}SH \end{matrix}$$
$$\textit{Oxidized} \qquad \textit{Reduced}$$

Both forms are freely soluble in water. The reduced form is autoxidizable in the presence of traces of iron or copper. The oxidized form is readily reduced by certain oxidizable organic substrates.

Adopting Wieland's hypothesis, and representing a cellular constituent that undergoes oxidation as $X\!\!<^H_H$, we have the following reactions, A being some suitable hydrogen acceptor :

$$X\!\!<^H_H + \begin{matrix}G{-}S\\|\\G{-}S\end{matrix} \longrightarrow X + \begin{matrix}G{-}SH\\\\G{-}SH\end{matrix}$$

$$\begin{matrix}G{-}SH\\\\G{-}SH\end{matrix} + A \longrightarrow \begin{matrix}G{-}S\\|\\G{-}S\end{matrix} + AH_2$$

Our knowledge of the way in which these reactions play their part in the life of bacterial cells is still very incomplete and fragmentary ; but the past ten years have seen a rapid advance, due in the main to the studies carried out by Quastel and his colleagues and successors at Cambridge. A technique that has played a major part in the elucidation of this problem consists in the observation of the behaviour of washed suspensions of bacterial cells, in an appropriate buffer solution, when incubated at 45° C. in evacuated Thunberg tubes in the presence of various substrates and of an indicator dye such as methylene blue. Before discussing the results obtained with this technique it will be well to note one point that might otherwise lead to some confusion. The washed bacterial suspensions used in these experiments have often been referred to as " resting bacteria." This term was used to denote bacteria placed under such conditions that active proliferation seemed very unlikely to occur. Actually it was recognized quite early in these studies (Quastel and Wooldridge 1927*a*, *b*) that a high proportion of the bacteria were dead, or at least non-viable when subcultured on a suitable medium. Later work (Cook and Stephenson 1928, Sandiford and Wooldridge 1931) has made it quite clear that many of the reactions observed can be catalysed by dead bacterial cells. It has also been shown that some degree of bacterial multiplication may occur, at least with certain bacteria, if the experiment is prolonged for several hours ; but the significance of this latter observation is lessened by the fact that the reactions under study are usually completed within 30 minutes or less. It would, however, probably be well to discard the term " resting bacteria," and to refer simply to washed bacterial cells, recognizing that the enzymic activities we are investigating are not necessarily dependent on the cells being alive. How far these activities are dependent on the integrity of the cell structure and how far they may be modified by acting on the cells with various physical and chemical reagents, we shall consider later.

The system substrate-bacterial cells-methylene blue, reacting in the absence of molecular oxygen, allows us to study hydrogen transport catalysed by dehydrogenases present in the bacterial cell. If a dehydrogenase is present which activates hydrogen in the substrate, the methylene blue will act as a hydrogen acceptor, and in so doing will be reduced to the colourless leuco-methylene blue.

In the earliest studies of this kind (Quastel and Whetham 1924, Quastel, Stephenson and Whetham 1925) it was shown that *Bact. coli* possesses an enzyme that is capable of oxidizing succinic acid in the presence of methylene blue, and that under these conditions a reversible equilibrium is set up.

Succinic acid + methylene blue ⇌ fumaric acid + leuco-methylene blue.

In later studies (Quastel and Whetham 1925*a*, *b*, Quastel and Wooldridge 1927*a*, *b*) experiments of this type, carried out with *Bact. coli*, were extended to cover a wide range of substrates. The hexose sugars, and the hexahydric alcohol mannitol, were found to donate hydrogen actively to methylene blue. Different fatty acids differed widely in activity. Formic acid was the most active, followed closely by acetic, while the higher members of the series, such as caprylic and nonylic, were almost inactive. Among the hydroxy-acids, lactic acid was found to be an active donator of hydrogen, while glyceric and glycollic acids were active only in high concentration. The saturated dibasic acids were relatively inert. The monohydric alcohols, from butyl alcohol upwards, had no power of hydrogen donation, and inhibited donation by other substrates. The lower members of the series, ethyl and propyl alcohol, had a similar inhibiting action, but donated hydrogen when present in very low concentrations. In regard to amino-acids not many figures are available. Of those examined glutamic acid proved the most active hydrogen donor. Alanine had some activity, as had histidine in relatively low concentrations. Tryptophan was active in high concentrations, but not in low. Leucine and glycine were quite inactive.

In regard to dehydrogenations induced by bacteria other than *Bact. coli*, we have as yet little information, except in the particular case of the anaerobes, which will be referred to later. The few data available are, however, amply sufficient to show that, here as elsewhere, one bacterial species may differ widely from another. Quastel and Wooldridge (1925) record the dehydrogenations induced by *Chromobacterium prodigiosum*, *Proteus vulgaris* and *Bact. fœcalis alkaligenes*. Among the main differences displayed by these organisms, as compared with *Bact. coli* or with one another, the following may be noted. *Bact. fœcalis alkaligenes* showed little power of activating hydrogen donation by the hexose sugars. *Chromobacterium prodigiosum* induced very active donation of hydrogen by glycine. *Bact. fœcalis alkaligenes* was less active in this respect, while *Proteus vulgaris* shared with *Bact. coli* an entire inability to activate hydrogen donation by this amino-acid.

Bacterial enzymes, or enzyme systems, in addition to activating hydrogen donation by various substrates, may activate other substrates to act as hydrogen acceptors or oxygen donors. Reference has already been made (p. 41) to the anaerobic growth of *Bact. coli* in the presence of nitrate, but not in its absence. The same was observed with chlorates. Stickland (1931) has studied the activation of nitrates by *Bact. coli* in greater detail, using a different technique. In some experiments the uptake of hydrogen was observed in a Barcroft differential manometer, in others the production of nitrite was estimated by a colorimetric method. He found that, under these conditions, a *Bact. coli* suspension can reduce nitrate quantitatively to nitrite. In the presence of nitrate this organism can oxidize formic acid to CO_2, lactic acid to pyruvic acid, or succinic acid to fumaric acid.

It would appear that certain of these dehydrogenating systems are dependent upon the presence of co-enzymes, as well as of the dehydrogenases themselves. Thus Yudkin (1933) found in the case of *Bact. coli* that progressive dilution of the bacterial suspension produced an increase in the reduction time of methylene blue, in the presence of formic or succinic acid, of the linear type that would be expected on the assumption that the dilution was affecting the specific dehydrogenase alone. With glucose as a substrate the activity of the bacterial suspension fell off far more rapidly on dilution ; and further experiments suggested that this phenomenon was due to the dependence of the glucose activation on a thermostable co-enzyme, which appeared to diffuse from the bacteria on excessive dilution. Further experiments (Yudkin 1934) indicated that this co-enzyme is probably identical with, or very similar to, the co-enzyme of yeast.

Summarizing the data that these and other similar studies have provided, it may be noted (see Green, Stickland and Tarr 1934) that :

(*a*) Substrates may be divided into those that act as hydrogen donators, and those that act as hydrogen acceptors.

(*b*) Reactions between these donators and acceptors are catalysed by certain bacterial cells. Thus *Bact. coli* activates the interactions of lactate and nitrate to form pyruvate and nitrite, or of lactate and fumarate to form pyruvate and succinate. In some cases a given substrate can act either as a donator or an acceptor of hydrogen according to the conditions of the experiments.

It would seem that the bacterial species in which mechanisms of this particular type are most highly and widely developed are those belonging to the class of facultative anaerobes, *i.e.* species that can grow either in the presence or absence of molecular oxygen.

It would accord well with their general behaviour if the obligatory aerobes were found to be lacking in these particular enzyme systems. Our knowledge of the way in which bacteria of this class obtain their energy is, however, at present very scanty. Quastel and Whetham (1924) note that *B. subtilis* fails to activate the oxidation of leuco-methylene blue by nitrates or by chlorates. Cook (1931) records that the vegetative forms of *B. subtilis* fail to reduce methylene blue under anaerobic conditions in the presence of formate, acetate, lactate or glucose, though a spore suspension will activate glucose, but not the other substrates. Vegetative cells, and to a less extent, spores, take up molecular oxygen, when examined in the Barcroft differential manometer ; and this uptake is greatly increased by the presence of glucose. These observations would clearly accord with the view that the vegetative cells of the obligatory aerobes lack the dehydrogenation systems required for obtaining energy under anaerobic conditions, and are dependent on a respiratory mechanism in which molecular oxygen plays an essential part. Direct observations by Tarr (1933), however, appear to tell against this view ; though he adopted modifications in technique that make his findings difficult to compare with those quoted above. The solution of this particular problem must clearly await the collection of further experimental data.

The case of the strict anaerobes presents features of peculiar interest. We have noted (p. 42) that organisms of this class fail to grow if the Eh rises above a low limit. Quastel and Stephenson (1926) have adduced evidence for believing that the inhibition of the growth of anaerobes by oxygen is due to the rise of Eh above this limiting value ; though other views have been advanced (see p. 60). A compound containing an —SH group, or one from which the —SH group can be produced, appears to be essential for growth ; and here again it seems likely that the function of the sulphydryl group is to maintain a sufficiently low Eh (see Quastel and Stephenson 1926, Lepper and Martin 1929, 1930*a*, Burrows 1933). Another feature of the anaerobes is that they require amino-acids for their growth. Carbohydrates, if present, may be fermented, but they seem to be neither necessary nor sufficient as a source of energy.

The recent studies of Stickland (1934, 1935) on the reactions by which *Cl. sporogenes* obtains its energy mark an important advance in the elucidation of this problem. He notes that it would be difficult to picture any reaction by which a single amino-acid could break down anaerobically to yield energy, and that the most probable reaction would involve two amino-acids, one acting as a hydrogen donator, the other as a hydrogen acceptor, the hydrogen transport being activated by the bacterial enzymes. The general type of such a reaction might be represented as,

$$R \cdot CHNH_2 \cdot COOH + R' \cdot CHNH_2 \cdot COOH + H_2O$$
$$\rightarrow R \cdot CO \cdot COOH + R' \cdot CH_2 \cdot COOH + 2NH_3$$

He was able to show that washed suspensions of *Cl. sporogenes* activate certain amino-acids (alanine, valine and leucine) as hydrogen donators, and others (glycine, proline and hydroxyproline) as hydrogen acceptors. It is of interest to note that, when using indicator dyes for the study of these reactions, it is necessary to select one, such as cresyl blue, that is oxidized at a very low Eh. In the particular pair of amino-acids alanine and proline, Stickland was able to show that while the alanine is deaminated during oxidation, the proline is not deaminated during reduction but is reduced to δ-amino-*n*-valeric acid ; so that, in this instance, the type of reaction differs a little from that given above.

The Nature and Integration of the Bacterial Enzymes or Enzyme Systems.— Enough has already been said to suggest that any given bacterial species must be endowed with a relatively complex equipment of enzymes, or catalysts. Quastel and Wooldridge (1927*a*, *b*) have examined the effect on the dehydrogenating systems of bacteria, of various physical and chemical agencies, many of which are lethal to the cells. When suspensions of *Bact. coli* are subjected to increasing temperatures before being tested by the Thunberg-tube-methylene-blue technique, the hydrogenating systems that are first inactivated are those acting on alanine, glycerol, glycol, the sugars and glutamic acid. Those acting on lactic, succinic and fumaric acid are next affected. Those acting on formic and acetic acid are most resistant, and remain active after the bacteria have been heated at 67° C. Various other physical and chemical agencies—changes in pH, variations in the salt concentration, exposure to nitrite, benzene, toluene, phenol, ether, chloroform and propyl alcohol—bring about the same step-by-step degradation in activity, and approximately in the same order. Bromine and iodine show minor differences in the order of inactivation. The enzyme systems acting on glycerol, glutamic acid and succinic acid are least resistant to these halogens, while the enzymes acting on sugars are more resistant. With strong solutions of KCN, on the other hand, the picture is reversed, the dehydrogenating systems acting on formic and acetic acid being least resistant. The effect of H_2O_2 is similar to that of KCN, but its action is more variable, perhaps as the result of a varying catalase content in the bacterial cells.

In a further series of experiments (Quastel and Wooldridge 1928) an attempt was made to study the specificity of the dehydrogenating enzyme systems by noting the degree of inhibition exerted by non-toxic, or relatively non-toxic, substances possessing chemical groupings of various kinds. The results indicated that the enzyme of *Bact. coli* that activates lactic acid as a hydrogen donator is specifically inhibited—presumably by specific adsorption at the enzymic surface—by compounds possessing the groups —CO—COOH, or —CHOH—COOH. The enzyme for succinic acid is inactivated by compounds possessing the groups

$$-\overset{|}{\underset{|}{C}}-CHOH-COOH, \text{ or } -\overset{|}{\underset{|}{C}}-CH_2-COOH.$$

The formic acid enzyme, on the other hand, was not inhibited by any substance tested, other than itself.

Although we have learned much in recent years of the ways in which bacterial enzymes act, we are still wholly ignorant as to what they are. Some of them are certainly separable from the fully organized bacterial cell ; since Stephenson (1928) has prepared a cell-free autolysate of lactic dehydrogenase, and Stickland (1929) a cell-free digest of formic dehydrogenase. The view that each different " enzyme " is a separate chemical entity is, however, not easy to reconcile with our knowledge of the size and structure of bacterial cells. There are many reasons for regarding the majority of " enzymes " as being composed of large organic molecules. To fit a multiplicity of these into the smaller bacteria, leaving room for the other cell constituents, would seem a difficult task. In the case of many of the filtrable viruses it would seem impossible even when allowance is made for the more limited range of enzyme activity with which they are probably endowed.

A conception has been advanced by Quastel (1926) and Quastel and Wooldridge (1927*a, b*) that presents a more intelligible picture. They suggest that the activation of substrate molecules, induced by bacterial cells, is primarily due to a polarization of these molecules by electric fields which characterize particular centres—the " active centres "—of cellular and intracellular surfaces. One of these active centres may activate a number of different substrates. The activation will depend on two conditions, both determined by the chemical structure of the substrate. The substrate molecule must have chemical groupings of such a nature, and so orientated, that it is able to come into intimate contact with the active centre. It must, that is to say, be specifically adsorbed. But adsorption will not necessarily be followed by activation. For this to occur the structure of the adsorbed molecule must be such as to render it susceptible, in this sense, to the electric field developed at the active centre.

The active centres themselves are conceived as being developed as the result of molecular strain, or distortion, brought about by the intermolecular or intramolecular forces that determine the formation of large colloidal aggregates. For example, a molecule or group that in isolation may have the configuration

$$
M-C \underset{C-C}{\overset{XY-C}{<}} C-M'
$$

may, under the stress of forces exerted by neighbouring groups at M and M', assume the form

$$
\begin{array}{cc}
 & Y \\
X & \backslash C \\
| & / \\
C & C \\
M \quad C-C \quad M' \\
\downarrow & \downarrow
\end{array}
$$

The pulling apart of the constituents X and Y will lead to the development of a new electrical field between them.

When the colloidal aggregates are broken down, as will occur to a greater or less extent in any physical or chemical disruption of the bacterial cell, certain of these active centres will disappear, though others, situated on the residual particles, may remain. Such a procedure might be regarded as the extraction of a soluble enzyme from the bacterial cell ; and the enzyme so extracted would have a more limited range of activity than the intact bacteria from which it was derived.

Certain observations by Penrose and Quastel (1930) are of interest from this point of view. There is an organism (*Micrococcus lysodeikticus*) that is peculiarly susceptible to lysis by an active substance (lysozyme) that is contained in various tissues and secretions (see p. 802). A suspension of this organism activates lactic acid, glucose, lævulose and glutamic acid, among other substances, as hydrogen donators. After dissolution by lysozyme the bacteria are found to have lost completely their power to activate the hexose sugars and glutamic acid, while retaining some 30 per cent. of their activity against lactic acid.

Accepting this hypothesis of Quastel and his colleagues as a convenient working picture, to be retained, modified, or discarded as future experimental evidence may demand, we may inquire whether other factors are concerned, in addition to these localized active centres. The evidence, much of which has again come from the Cambridge school, is that they are.

Green, Stickland and Tarr (1934) have educed evidence that the *in vitro* reactions between activated substrates demands the presence of some " carrier " having the general properties of one of the ordinary oxidation-reduction indicators, such as methylene blue. The systems examined included the following : (1) formate and nitrate, (2) lactate and nitrate, (3) succinate and nitrate, (4) lactate and fumarate, (5) glucose and nitrate. In each case the necessary enzymes were added in the form of solutions obtained from appropriate cells, formic dehydrogenase and nitratase, lactic dehydrogenase and nitratase, and so on. The reaction was followed by determining the concentration of one or other of the products. In no case did a reaction occur in the absence of a carrier ; but the addition of such indicator dyes as methylene blue or ethyl-capri blue at once brought the oxidation-reduction system into action. In addition to these indicator dyes many substances were tested that might reasonably be supposed to act as carriers in the living cell ; but, with the exception of pyocyanin, all gave negative results.

We must, however, suppose that natural carriers exist, and this brings us to the important studies of Keilin (1925, 1926, 1928–29, 1930) on cytochrome and its derivatives, and on the general mechanism of cell-respiration. These serve, it will be noted, to link Wieland's conception of hydrogen transport with Warburg's theory of oxidation by iron-containing compounds. Keilin's view of cellular oxidations may be briefly summarized as follows : Aerobic and facultatively anaerobic organisms contain a widely distributed respiratory pigment, cytochrome, which is composed of three hæmatin compounds (a', b' and c'), and an unbound hæmatin compound similar to the protohæmatin of hæmoglobin. Of these the b' component of cytochrome and the unbound hæmatin are autoxidizable. The cells also contain a hæmochromogen precursor of cytochrome, which is autoxidizable. Some cells, at least, also contain an insoluble, thermostable indophenol oxidase ; and all factors that inhibit, or destroy, this oxidase have a similar effect on the oxygen uptake of the cell, showing that the oxidase plays an important part in the cellular respiration. It would appear that the oxidase is responsible for the oxidation of cytochrome, especially for its non-autoxidizable components a' and c' ; since the oxidation of cytochrome is inhibited by the same factors that inactivate the oxidase. The oxidized cytochrome is reduced by various substrates that have been activated by the bacterial dehydrogenases, and have thus become hydrogen donators. All factors that inhibit the dehydrogenase systems of the cell also inhibit the reduction of oxidized cytochrome. Cytochrome therefore acts as a carrier between two activating mechanisms of the cell, the dehydrogenases activating the hydrogen of various organic substrates and the indophenol oxidase activating molecular oxygen.

The autoxidizable hæmatin compound b', the unbound hæmatin, and the hæmochromogen precursor of cytochrome, may also act as carriers between the hydrogen donators and molecular oxygen. They may also act as direct catalysts, promoting the oxidation of substrates that are not activated by specific dehydrogenases. The various hæmatin compounds of the cell are also responsible for the thermostable peroxidase reaction that occurs in the presence of H_2O_2.

These various catalysts are, it may be noted, inhibited or " poisoned " by different chemical substances. Thus, the dehydrogenases are inhibited by narcotics, while the indophenol oxidase is inhibited by KCN, by CO, or by H_2S.

The diagrammatic representation of these mechanisms in Fig. 8 has been taken with slight modifications, from that given by Keilin (1928–29).

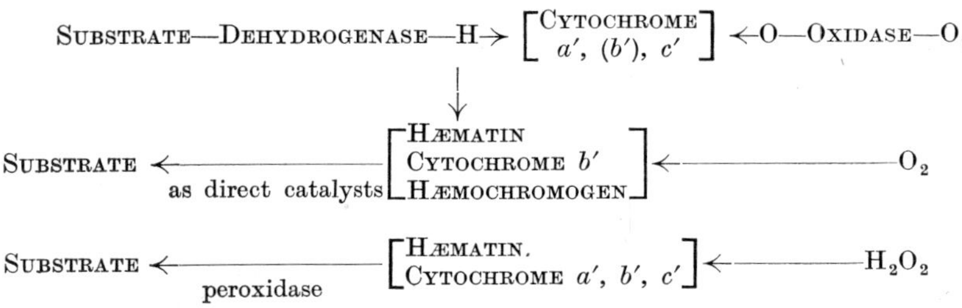

$$\text{Substrate—Dehydrogenase—H} \rightarrow \begin{bmatrix} \text{Cytochrome} \\ a',\ (b'),\ c' \end{bmatrix} \leftarrow \text{O—Oxidase—O}_2$$

$$\text{Substrate} \leftarrow \underset{\text{as direct catalysts}}{\underline{\hspace{3cm}}} \begin{bmatrix} \text{Hæmatin} \\ \text{Cytochrome } b' \\ \text{Hæmochromogen} \end{bmatrix} \leftarrow \underline{\hspace{3cm}} \text{O}_2$$

$$\text{Substrate} \leftarrow \underset{\text{peroxidase}}{\underline{\hspace{3cm}}} \begin{bmatrix} \text{Hæmatin.} \\ \text{Cytochrome } a',\ b',\ c' \end{bmatrix} \leftarrow \underline{\hspace{3cm}} \text{H}_2\text{O}_2$$

Fig. 8.

It will be noted that these mechanisms do not include all the respiratory mechanisms of the bacterial cell. They apply, in the form given, only to those reactions in which molecular oxygen, or H_2O_2, is the final hydrogen acceptor or oxygen donor. There is definite evidence (see above) that a carrier system is involved in the dehydrogenations carried out by facultative anaerobes under anaerobic conditions; but the nature of this carrier system we do not yet know. Among the substances tested by Green, Stickland, and Tarr (1934) that failed to act as carriers under these conditions were cytochrome c' and glutathione. Whether a carrier is involved in the dehydrogenation of amino-acids by the strict anaerobes is as yet uncertain, though analogy renders it very probable. The enzymes involved have not yet been isolated from the bacterial cells, so that experiments of the type recorded by Green, Stickland and Tarr cannot be made.

We should, then, think of bacterial cells as organisms possessing a respiratory mechanism in which a general pattern can be discerned, but differing from one another, even in regard to major elements of that pattern, far more widely than do the various species of more highly developed organisms. It is probable that the facultative anaerobes share a double series of mechanisms, including those described by Keilin, and those discussed earlier in this chapter. It is possible, at least, that the obligatory aerobes lack some of these mechanisms and, being dependent on the activity of the complete carrier system supplied by cytochrome and its associated enzymes, can obtain energy only when molecular oxygen is available as a hydrogen acceptor. It seems probable that the strict anaerobes rely for their energy on mechanisms of a very specialized kind. Certainly they do not require molecular oxygen as a hydrogen acceptor, and their inability to grow except at a very low Eh, combined with their dependence on the dehydrogenation of amino-acids, suggests a respiratory mechanism *sui generis*.

Within each of these great classes the range of enzymic activity varies widely, probably in relation to the structure of the dehydrogenating enzymes, which we may for convenience picture in the form of Quastel's active centres. Using the same general carrier mechanism, one facultative anaerobe will be able to act on a particular range of substrates, another on a wider, or a narrower, or perhaps an altogether different range, and so on.

We may in concluding our account of bacterial metabolism note a few other observations that, though not involved in our general picture, are of interest to the bacteriologist.

Other Bacterial Enzymes.

We have noted above that certain autotrophic bacteria are capable of utilizing molecular hydrogen. A recent study by Stephenson and Stickland (1931) has shown that this ability is due to the presence of a specific enzyme, hydrogenase, which activates molecular hydrogen. Suspensions of a non-sporing, Gram-negative bacillus, isolated from the mud of the River Ouse, were able to reduce methylene blue in the presence of molecular hydrogen. These suspensions also reduced nitrate and fumarate under the same conditions. A vibrio isolated from the mud of the same river also contained hydrogenase and, in addition, an enzyme activating sulphate as a hydrogen acceptor, so that suspensions of this vibrio, in the presence of molecular hydrogen, reduced sulphate quantitatively to sulphide in accordance with the equation $H_2SO_4 + 4H_2 = H_2S + 4H_2O$. A search was then made among various bacteria, not belonging to the autotrophic class, for the presence of this enzyme. It was found in *Bact. coli*, but not in *Ps. pyocyanea*, *Chr. prodigiosum*, *B. megatherium*, *B. subtilis* or *Cl. sporogenes*. It would appear therefore that the power of activating molecular hydrogen, although not widely generalized among bacteria as a whole, is not confined to the autotrophic species.

There is yet a third enzyme, or enzyme system, acting on hydrogen. Stephenson and Stickland (1932) have shown that a suspension of *Bact. coli* possesses an enzyme, hydrogenlyase, which liberates hydrogen in a molecular form from certain substrates. Their experiments indicated that formic hydrogenlyase and glucose hydrogenlyase were different enzymes. Moreover, the evidence obtained was definitely against the view that, under these experimental conditions, the molecular hydrogen produced from glucose was derived from formic acid as an intermediate product. The conventional scheme of the breakdown of glucose by bacteria producing acid and gas given on p. 47, must therefore be regarded with suspicion, at least as having a general application. It may be added that the formic hydrogenlyase belongs to the class of " adaptation enzymes " described by Karström (1930), *i.e.* it is produced by the organism in significant amount only when it has been growing in the presence of the substrate concerned, in this case a salt of formic acid. Yudkin (1932) has studied the formic and glucose hydrogenlyases of *Bact. coli*, *Bact. ærogenes* and *Bact. cloacæ* in somewhat more detail, particularly in regard to the factors that determine their adaptive development. He has also confirmed the interesting observation of Stephenson and Stickland that *Bact. dispar*, an organism that forms acid but no gas under the ordinary conditions of bacterial growth, produces no formic or glucose hydrogenlyase, on whatever medium it is grown. It does, however, contain a formic dehydrogenase, and so catalyses the reaction $H \cdot COOH \cdot + A \leftrightarrows AH_2 + CO_2$, where A is a hydrogen acceptor. Why no CO_2 is liberated in the gaseous form when the organism is grown under the usual test conditions with a Durham's tube is not yet clear.

We have referred above to the action of bacterial enzymes on H_2O_2. McLeod and Gordon (1922) have shown that the pneumococcus produces H_2O_2 during growth. The mechanism of this production has been studied by Avery, Morgan and Neill (Avery and Morgan 1924, Avery and Neill 1924*a*, *b*, *c*, Neill and Avery 1925). It appears to depend upon at least two factors, a thermolabile intracellular enzyme, which may be extracted in an active form from the pneumococcal cells, and an easily oxidizable substance, which may be replaced by yeast or muscle extract.

The production of H_2O_2 is not confined to the pneumococcus. It is shared by many streptococci, the lactic acid bacilli, certain sarcinæ, and probably by many other organisms. Its demonstration is often rendered difficult by the fact that an organism that produces H_2O_2 may also produce catalase (see McLeod and Gordon 1923a).

We have also referred to the part played by glutathione as an activator of hydrogen transport, and have noted the effectiveness of the sulphydryl group in producing and maintaining a low Eh in a fluid culture medium. It is of obvious interest to inquire whether bacteria themselves produce glutathione. McLeod and Gordon (1924) and Callow and Robinson (1925) have examined this point. McLeod and Gordon were unable to obtain any evidence of glutathione production by anaerobes; and the one anaerobic species studied by Callow gave negative results. It would seem therefore that while anaerobes utilize glutathione, and are indeed dependent on the presence of some such source of sulphydryl, they cannot produce this substance for themselves. Of the other species studied by Callow, *Bact. fœcalis alkaligenes*, *Proteus vulgaris*, *Ps. pyocyanea*, and *Chr. prodigiosum* showed the presence of glutathione in the washed bacterial cells, while *Bact. coli*, *Staph. aureus*, *Sarc. aurantiaca*, *Str. lactis* and the Timothy-grass bacillus gave negative results.

The Toxic Action of Certain Food Substances or Metabolic Products on Bacteria

The bactericidal or bacteriostatic action of various physical and chemical substances are considered in some detail in Chapter V. Here we are concerned only with the toxic action of certain potential food substances, or of the products of bacterial growth.

We have seen that parasitic bacteria, as a class, are able to utilize amino-acids, and that for many species certain amino-acids are essential for growth. It would appear, however, that certain of these acids may exert a toxic action. Koser and Rettger (1919) noted that solutions of pure amino-acids, while forming an excellent medium for certain species of bacteria, failed to support the growth of others. McLeod and Wyon (1921) and Wyon and McLeod (1923) have shown that certain of these acids exert a definitely inhibitory action on the growth of various bacterial species, including *B. subtilis*, staphylococci, *Str. pyogenes*, the pneumococcus and *C. diphtheriæ*.

Hydrogen peroxide provides an interesting example of the toxic action on bacterial cells of products of their own metabolism. It has long been known that certain bacteria are sensitive to hydrogen peroxide (Traugott 1893, Freer and Novy 1902), and the studies of McLeod and Gordon (1923a) have shown that this sensitiveness is associated with an absence of catalase production. The pneumococcus for instance, produces H_2O_2 but no catalase, and is sensitive, though not highly so, to the peroxide. Certain organisms such as *Bact. shigæ* and certain streptococci produce neither H_2O_2 nor catalase, and are moderately sensitive to the peroxide. Most bacterial species, as has long been known, produce catalase more or less actively (see Gottstein 1893, Löwenstein 1903, Rywosch and Rywosch 1907). Many of these species are moderately or slightly sensitive to added hydrogen peroxide, but there appears to be a negative correlation between the degree of sensitiveness and the activity of catalase production.

Among the bacteria that fail to produce catalase are the anaerobes (Löwenstein 1903, Rywosch and Rywosch 1907, McLeod and Gordon 1923a, Callow 1923), and these, as McLeod and Gordon have shown, are very sensitive to H_2O_2. These observers (McLeod and Gordon 1925*a*, *b*) have suggested that the great sensitiveness of anaerobes to oxygen is due to the formation of hydrogen peroxide. They record indirect evidence, based on the production of colour changes in blood medium, which they regard as supporting the view that anaerobes are, in fact, H_2O_2 producers. Against this indirect evidence must be set the results recorded by Cook and Stephenson (1928). Suspensions of *Cl. sporogenes* were found to be unable to take up any oxygen in the presence of glucose, lactate, pyruvate or formate. The addition of methylene blue, providing an alternative hydrogen acceptor, did not result in any oxygen uptake. As Cook and Stephenson point out, it would seem that the formation of H_2O_2 at the expense of molecular oxygen must result in a measurable oxygen uptake ; and an uptake equivalent to the production of H_2O_2 in a concentration of $1:50,000$ would be clearly demonstrable under the conditions of their experiments. We have seen, moreover (p. 54), that the inhibitory action of molecular oxygen on the growth of anaerobes is readily explicable on the view that the presence of this substance prevents the development of an Eh sufficiently low to permit the metabolic mechanisms of these organisms to come into play.

Kluyver (1924) has suggested that catalase production is limited to those bacterial species that utilize a respiratory mechanism involving the participation of molecular oxygen, and Callow (1923, 1924) has found that oxygen absorption is minimal in the case of those bacteria that produce no catalase.

Bacterial Pigments.

Many bacterial species produce a distinctive pigment, which sometimes, as with *Staphylococcus aureus*, *Chr. prodigiosum* or *Chr. violaceum* remains within the bacterial cells, sometimes, as with *Ps. pyocyanea*, diffuses throughout the medium. Particular bacterial pigments will be more conveniently dealt with in the systematic description of individual genera or species ; here we may confine our attention to a few notes on their possible physiological importance.

It has already been noted that, among the various organic substances tested by Green, Stickland and Tarr (1934), pyocyanin alone acted as an effective carrier between the oxidation-reduction systems that they were studying. This pigment has been shown by Friedheim and Michaelis (1931) to be reversibly oxidizable and reducible. At about pH 7 the potential range lies between that of methylene blue and indigo tetrasulphonate (see also Friedheim 1931).

It seems likely that other bacterial pigments may play an analogous rôle. *Chr. violaceum* frequently gives rise to non-pigmented variants. These variants, suspended in phosphate buffer solution, take up oxygen at a moderate rate. A solution of the pigment of *Chr. violaceum* in 6·6 per cent. glycerine takes up no oxygen, nor does the addition of a 6·6 per cent. glycerine solution to a suspension of the non-pigmented bacteria affect the oxygen uptake ; but the addition to such a suspension of the dissolved pigment results in an increase in the oxygen uptake amounting to 100–200 per cent. (Friedheim 1932).

It will be recalled that, in the photosynthetic bacteria (see p. 36), the bacterial pigments play a decisive rôle in cell metabolism.

Other Biochemical and Physiological Activities of Bacteria.

There are many other activities of bacteria—their action on blood cells and blood pigments, the production of various toxic substances, etc.—that might logically be included in this chapter. Many of these activities are, however, so specialized and are so characteristic of particular bacterial species, that it will be more convenient to consider them in later chapters.

REFERENCES

ARONSON, H. (1900) *Arch. Kinderheilk.*, **30**, 23.

AVERY, O. T. and CULLEN, G. E. (1920) *J. exp. Med.*, **32**, 571.

AVERY, O. T. and MORGAN, H. J. (1924) *J. exp. Med.*, **39**, 275, 289.

AVERY, O. T. and NEILL, J. M. (1924a) *J. exp. Med.*, **39**, 347 ; (1924b) *Ibid.*, **39**, 357 (1924c) *Ibid.*, **39**, 543.

BAINBRIDGE, F. A. (1911) *J. Hyg., Camb.*, **11**, 341.

BERMAN, N. and RETTGER, L. F. (1918) *J. Bact.*, **3**, 367, 389.

BIRKENSHAW, J. H., CHARLES, J. H. V., and CLUTTERBUCK, P. W. (1931) *Biochem. J.*, **25**, 1522.

BOIVIN, A. and MESROBEANU, L. (1934) *Arch. roum. Path. exp. Microbiol.*, **7**, 95.

BORD, G. DE. (1923) *J. Bact.*, **8**, 1.

BRAUN, H. (1931) *Zbl. Bakt.*, **122**, 5.

BRAUN, H. and CAHN-BRONNER, C. E. (1921) *Zbl. Bakt.*, **86**, 1, 196, 380 ; (1922) *Biochem. Z.*, **131**, 226, 272.

BRAUN, H. and GOLDSCHMIDT, R. (1924) *Biochem. Z.*, **146**, 573 ; (1927) *Zbl. Bakt.*, **101**, 283, 330 ; (1928a) *Ibid.*, **107**, 329 ; (1928b) *Ibid.*, **109**, 353.

BRAUN, H., HOFMEIER, K., and MÜNDEL, F. (1929) *Zbl. Bakt.*, **113**, 530.

BRAUN, H. and KONDO, S. (1924) *Klin. Wschr.*, **3**, 10.

BRAUN, H. and LISCH, H. (1928) *Zbl. Bakt.*, **107**, 35.

BRAUN, H. and MÜNDEL, F. (1927) *Zbl. Bakt.*, **103**, 182 ; (1929) *Ibid.*, **112**, 347.

BRAUN, H., STAMATELAKIS, A., and KONDO, S. (1924) *Biochem. Z.*, **145**, 381.

BRAUN, H. and VÁSÁRHELYI, J. VON. (1933) *Zbl. Bakt.*, **127**, 105.

BRAUN, H. and WÖRDEHOFF, P. (1933) *Zbl. Bakt.*, **128**, 50.

BROOM, J. C. (1929) *Brit. J. exp. Path.*, **10**, 71.

BUCHANAN, R. E. and FULMER, E. I. (1928–30) " Physiology and Biochemistry of Bacteria." (3 vols.) New York and London.

BURROWS, W. (1933) *J. infect. Dis.*, **52**, 126.

CALLOW, A. B. (1923) *J. Path. Bact.*, **26**, 320 ; (1924) *Biochem. J.*, **18**, 507.

CALLOW, A. B. and ROBINSON, M. E. (1925) *Biochem. J.*, **19**, 19.

CARRIÈRE, G. (1901) *C. R. Soc. Biol.*, **53**, 320.

CLARK, W. M. (1928) " The Determination of Hydrogen Ions." Baltimore and London.

CLARK, W. M., *et al.* (1928) *Bull. U.S. hyg. Lab.*, No. 151.

COLLINS, M. A. and HAMMER, B. W. (1934) *J. Bact.*, **27**, 473, 487.

COOK, R. P. (1931) *Zbl. Bakt.*, **122**, 329.

COOK, R. P. and STEPHENSON, M. (1928) *Biochem. J.*, **22**, 1368.

CRAMER, E. (1891) *Arch. Hyg.*, **13**, 71 ; (1893) *Ibid.*, **16**, 151 ; (1894) *Ibid.*, **20**, 197 ; (1895) *Ibid.*, **22**, 167 ; (1897) *Ibid.*, **28**, 1.

DAWSON, A. I. (1919) *J. Bact.*, **4**, 133.

ECKSTEIN, H. C. and SOULE, M. H. (1931) *J. biol. Chem.*, **91**, 395.

EIJKMAN, C. (1901) *Zbl. Bakt.*, **29**, 841.

FILDES, P. (1935) *Brit. J. exp. Path.*, **16**, 309.

FILDES, P., GLADSTONE, G. P., and KNIGHT, B. C. J. G. (1933) *Brit. J. exp. Path.*, **14**, 189.

FILDES, P. and KNIGHT, B. C. J. G. (1933) *Brit. J. exp. Path.*, **14**, 343.

FISCHER, H. and HASENKAMP, J. (1935) *Liebigs Ann.*, **515**, 148.

FRED, E. B. and DAVENPORT, A. (1918) *J. agric. Res.*, **14**, 317.

FREER and NOVY. (1902) *Amer. chem. J.*, **27**, 161.

FRIEDHEIM, E. A. H. (1931) *J. exp. Med.*, **54**, 207 ; (1932) *C. R. Soc. Biol.*, **110**, 353.

FRIEDHEIM, E. and MICHAELIS, L. (1931) *J. biol. Chem.*, **91**, 355.

FULMER, E. I., NELSON, V. E., and SHERWOOD, F. F. (1921) *J. Amer. chem. Soc.*, **43**, 191.

GAFFRON, H. (1933) *Biochem. Z.*, **260**, 1 ; (1934) *Ibid.*, **269**, 447 ; (1935) *Ibid.*, **275**, 301 ; (1935) **279**, 1.

GALEOTTI, G. (1898) *Z. physiol. Chem.*, **25**, 48.

GLADSTONE, G. P., FILDES, P., and RICHARDSON, G. M. (1935) *Brit. J. exp. Path.*, **16**, 335.

GLENN, T. H. (1911) *Zbl. Bakt.*, **58**, 481.

GOTTSTEIN, A. (1893) *Virchows Arch.*, **133**, 295.

GREEN, D. E., STICKLAND, L. H., and TARR, H. L. A. (1934) *Biochem. J.*, **28**, 1812.

GREY, E. C. (1913–14) *Proc. roy. Soc.*, B, **87**, 461.

HARDEN, A. (1901) *J. chem. Soc.*, **79**, 610 ; (1905) *J. Hyg., Camb.*, **5**, 488 ; (1930) " The Metabolism of Bacteria." " System of Bacteriology," **1**, 208. Med. Res. Coun. London.

HARDEN, A. and WALPOLE, G. S.   (1906) *Proc. roy. Soc., B,* **77,** 399.
HARRIS, J. E. G.   (1919) *J. Path. Bact.,* **23,** 30.
HEAP, H. and CADNESS, B.   (1924) *J. Hyg., Camb.,* **23,** 77.
HEWITT, L. F.   (1935) " Oxidation-Reduction Potentials in Bacteriology and Biochemistry."
   L.C.C., London.
HIRSCH, J.   (1931) *Z. Hyg. InfektKr.,* **112,** 660.
HIRSCH, J. and MÜLLER, A. W.   (1933) *Z. Hyg. InfektKr.,* **115,** 443.
HIRSCHLER.   (1886) *Z. physiol. Chem.,* **10,** 306.
HOPKINS, F. G.   (1921) *Biochem. J.,* **15,** 286 ; (1923) *Lancet,* i. 1251 ; (1929) *J. biol. Chem.,*
   84, 269.
HOSOYA, S. and KUROYA, M.   (1923) *Sci. Rep. Inst. infect. Dis. Tokyo. Univ.,* **2,** 233, 265.
HUGHES, T. P.   (1932) *J. Bact.,* **23,** 437.
HUNTER, O. W.   (1923) *J. agric. Res.,* **24,** 263.
HUSS, H.   (1908) *Zbl. Bakt.,* IIte Abt., **20,** 474.
JOHNSON, T. B. and COGHILL, R. D.   (1925) *J. biol. Chem.,* **63,** 225.
JONES, H. M.   (1916) *J. infect. Dis.,* **19,** 33.
KARSTRÖM.   (1930)   See Stephenson and Stickland (1932).
KASERER, H.   (1905) *Zbl. Bakt.,* IIte Abt., **15,** 573 ; (1906) *Ibid.,* IIte Abt., **16,** 681.
KEILIN, D.   (1925) *Proc. roy. Soc., B,* **98,** 312 ; (1926) *Ibid.,* **100,** 129 ; (1928–29) *Ibid.,*
   104, 206 ; (1930) *Ibid.,* **106,** 418.
KENDALL, A. I.   (1922) *J. infect. Dis.,* **30,** 211.
KENDALL, A. I., DAY, A. A., and WALKER, A. W.   (1914) *J. Amer. chem. Soc.,* **36,** 1962.
KENDALL, A. I. and WALKER, A. W.   (1915) *J. infect. Dis.,* **17,** 442.
KLUYVER, A. J.   (1924) *Z. physiol. Chem.,* **138,** 100.
KNIGHT, B. C. J. G.   (1935) *Brit. J. exp. Path.,* **16,** 315 ; (1936) *Spec. Rep. Ser. med. Res.*
   Coun. Lond., No. 210.
KNIGHT, B. C. J. G. and FILDES, P.   (1930) *Biochem. J.,* **24,** 1496 ; (1933) *Brit. J. exp. Path.,*
   14, 112.
KNORR, M.   (1925) *Ergebn. Hyg. Bakt.,* **7,** 641.
KÖGL, F. and HAAGEN SMIT, A. J.   (1931) *Proc. Acad. Sci. Amst.,* **34,** 1411.
KOSER, S. A. and RETTGER, L. F.   (1919) *J. infect. Dis.,* **24,** 301.
LEPPER, E. and MARTIN, C. J.   (1929) *Brit. J. exp. Path.,* **10,** 327 ; (1930a) *Ibid.,* **11,** 137 ;
   (1930b) *Ibid.,* **11,** 140.
LINTON, R. W., MITRA, B. N., and SHRIVASTAVA, D. L.   (1934) *Indian J. med. Res.,* **21,** 635.
LÖWENSTEIN.   (1903) *Wien. klin. Wschr.,* **16,** 1393.
MCINTOSH, J., JAMES, W. W., and LAZARUS-BARLOW, P.   (1922) *Brit. J. exp. Path.,* **3,** 138 ;
   (1924) *Ibid.,* **5,** 175.
MCLEOD, J. W.   (1930) *System of Bacteriology, Med. Res. Coun.,* London, **1,** 263.
MCLEOD, J. W. and GORDON, J.   (1922) *Biochem. J.,* **16,** 499 ; (1923a) *J. Path. Bact.,* **26,**
   326 ; (1923b) *Ibid.,* **26,** 332 ; (1924) *Biochem. J.,* **18,** 937 ; (1925a) *J. Path. Bact.,* **28,** 147 ;
   (1925b) *Ibid.,* **28,** 155.
MCLEOD, J. W. and WYON, G. A.   (1921) *J. Path. Bact.,* **24,** 205.
MEYER, K.   (1934) *Zbl. Bakt.,* **131,** 289, 291.
MICHAELIS, L. and NAKAHARA, Y.   (1923) *Z. ImmunForsch.,* **36,** 449.
MULLER, F. M.   (1933) *Arch. Mikrobiol.,* **4,** 131.
NEILL, J. M. and AVERY, O. T.   (1925) *J. exp. Med.,* **41,** 285.
NEILL, J. M. and FLEMING, W. L.   (1927) *J. exp. Med.,* **45,** 937.
NICOLLE, M. and ALILAIRE, E.   (1909) *Ann. Inst. Pasteur,* **23,** 547.
NIEL, C. B. VAN.   (1931) *Arch. Mikrobiol.,* **3,** 1 ; (1933) *Yearb. Carneg. Instn,* No. 32, 184.
NIKLEWSKI, B.   (1908) *Zbl. Bakt.,* IIte Abt., **20,** 469.
NISHIMURA, T.   (1893) *Arch. Hyg.,* **18,** 318.
NOACK, K. and SCHNEIDER, E.   (1933) *Naturwiss.,* **21,** 835.
OPPENHEIMER, C.   (1926) " Die Fermente und ihre Wirkung."   5th Edit., Leipzig.
ORLA-JENSEN.   (1902) *Zbl. Bakt.,* IIte Abt., **8,** 11 ; (1909) *Ibid.,* **22,** 305.
PAKES, W. C. C. and JOLLYMAN, W. H.   (1901) *J. chem. Soc.,* **79,** 322.
PAPPENHEIMER, A. M.   (1935) *Biochem. J.,* **29,** 2057.
PECKHAM, A. W.   (1897) *J. exp. Med.,* **2,** 549.
PENROSE, M. and QUASTEL, J. H.   (1930) *Proc. roy. Soc., B,* **107,** 168.
PESKETT, G. L.   (1933) *Biol. Rev.,* **8,** 1.
QUASTEL, J. H.   (1925) *Biochem. J.,* **19,** 641 ; (1926) *Ibid.,* **20,** 166.
QUASTEL, J. H. and STEPHENSON, M.   (1926) *Biochem. J.,* **20,** 1125.
QUASTEL, J. H., STEPHENSON, M., and WHETHAM, M. S.   (1925) *Biochem. J.,* **19,** 304.
QUASTEL, J. H. and WHETHAM, M. S.   (1924) *Biochem. J.,* **18,** 519 ; (1925a) *Ibid.,* **19,** 520 ;
   (1925b) *Ibid.,* **19,** 645.
QUASTEL, J. H. and WOOLDRIDGE, W. R.   (1925) *Biochem. J.,* **19,** 652 ; (1927a) *Ibid.,* **21,**
   148 ; (1927b) *Ibid.,* **21,** 1224 ; (1928) *Ibid.,* **22,** 689.
RAISTRICK, H.   (1919) *Biochem. J.,* **13,** 446.
RAISTRICK, H. and CLARK, A. B.   (1921) *Biochem. J.,* **15,** 76.

RAISTRICK, H., *et al.* (1931) *Philos. Trans. B*, **220**, 1.

RETTGER, L. F., BERMAN, N., and STURGES, W. S. (1916) *J. Bact.*, **1**, 15.

ROCKWELL, G. E. (1921) *J. infect. Dis.*, **28**, 352 ; (1923) *Ibid.*, **32**, 98 ; (1924) *Ibid.*, **35**, 381.

ROCKWELL, G. E. and HIGHBERGER, J. H. (1926) *J. infect. Dis.*, **38**, 92 ; (1927) *Ibid.*, **40**, 438.

ROCKWELL, G. E. and McKHANN, C. F. (1921) *J. infect. Dis.*, **28**, 249.

ROSLOFSON, P. A. (1934) *Proc. konink. Akad. Wetensch., Amsterdam*, **37**, 660 ; (1935) " On the Photosynthesis of the Thiorhodaceae." (Thesis.) Utrecht.

RUBNER, M. (1900) *Arch. Hyg.*, **38**, 67.

RYWOSCH, D. and RYWOSCH, M. (1907) *Zbl. Bakt.*, **44**, 295.

SANDIFORD, B. R. and WOOLDRIDGE, W. R. (1931) *Biochem. J.*, **25**, 2172.

SCHAFFER, A. J., FOLKOFF, C., and BAYNE-JONES, S. (1923) *Bull. Johns Hopk. Hosp.*, **33**, 151.

SCHNEIDER, E. (1934) *Z. physiol. Chem.*, **226**, 221.

SCHREIBER, K. (1902) *Arch. Hyg.*, **41**, 328.

SERA, Y. (1910) *Z. Hyg. InfektKr.*, **66**, 141, 162.

SERGENT, A. L. (1928) " Les facteurs de croissances des microbes sur milieux artificiels." Paris.

SMITH, T. (1897) *J. exp. Med.*, **2**, 543.

SÖHNGEN, N. L. (1911) *Jber. Fortschr. Chem.*, **41**, 788, 789.

SOMMARUGA, E. VON. (1894) *Z. Hyg. InfektKr.*, **18**, 441.

SÖRENSEN, S. P. L. (1909) *Biochem. Z.*, **21**, 131.

SPERRY, J. A. and RETTGER, L. F. (1915) *J. biol. Chem.*, **20**, 445.

STEPHENSON, M. (1928) *Biochem. J.*, **22**, 605.

STEPHENSON, M. and STICKLAND, L. H. (1931) *Biochem. J.*, **25**, 205, 215 ; (1932) *Ibid.*, **26**, 712.

STEPHENSON, M. and WHETHAM, M. S. (1922) *Proc. roy. Soc., B*, **93**, 262 ; (1923) *Ibid.*, **95**, 200 ; (1924) *Biochem. J.*, **18**, 498.

STEVENS, F. A. and WEST, R. (1922) *J. exp. Med.*, **35**, 823.

STICKLAND, L. H. (1929) *Biochem. J.*, **23**, 1187 ; (1931) *Ibid.*, **25**, 1543 ; (1934) *Ibid.*, **28**, 1746 ; (1935) *Ibid.*, **29**, 285.

STOKLASA, J. (1908) *Zbl. Bakt.*, IIte Abt., **21**, 620.

TAMURA, S. (1913a) *Z. physiol. Chem.*, **87**, 85 ; (1913b) *Ibid.*, **88**, 190 ; (1914) *Ibid.*, **89**, 289.

TARR, H. L. A. (1933) *Biochem. J.*, **27**, 136.

TRAUGOTT, R. (1893) *Z. Hyg. InfektKr.*, **14**, 427.

VALLEY, G. (1928) *Quart. Rev. Biol.*, **3**, 209.

VALLEY, G. and RETTGER, L. F. (1927) *J. Bact.*, **14**, 101.

WALKER, H. H. (1932) *Science*, **76**, 602.

WALLE, N. VAN DER. (1927) *Zbl. Bakt.*, IIte Abt., **70**, 369.

WARBURG, O. (1925a) *Ber. dtsch. chem. Ges.*, **58**, 1001 ; (1925b) *Science*, **61**, 575.

WELLS, H. G. and CORPER, H. J. (1912) *J. infect. Dis.*, **11**, 388.

WIELAND, (1913) *Ber. dtsch. chem. Ges.*, **46**, 3327 ; (1921) *Ibid.*, **54**, 2353 ; (1922) *Ergebn. Physiol.*, **20**, 477.

WINOGRADSKY, S. (1890a) *Ann. Inst. Pasteur*, **4**, 213 ; (1890b) *Ibid.*, **4**, 257 ; (1890c) *Ibid.*, **4**, 760.

WOLF, C. G. L. (1919a) *J. Path. Bact.*, **22**, 270 ; (1919b) *Ibid.*, **22**, 289.

WOLF, C. G. L. and HARRIS, J. E. G. (1918) *J. Path. Bact.*, **22**, 1.

WYON, G. A. and McLEOD, J. W. (1923) *J. Hyg., Camb.*, **21**, 376.

YUDKIN, J. (1932) *Biochem. J.*, **26**, 1859 ; (1933) *Ibid.*, **27**, 1849 ; (1934) *Ibid.*, **28**, 1463.

CHAPTER IV

THE GROWTH AND DEATH OF BACTERIA

LEST the title of this chapter should prove misleading, it may be pointed out that we are not here concerned with the broader aspects of growth, such as the temperature and food requirements of bacteria, or their metabolism and respiration. These have already been briefly dealt with in Chapter III. In the present chapter we restrict ourselves to what we may describe as the dynamic aspects of growth—a study that deals essentially with the rate of change in a bacterial population.

Technique of Counting Bacteria

Bacteria may be counted in such a way as to obtain an estimate either of the total number of organisms alive and dead, or of the number of living organisms only. The first we shall refer to as the *Total Count*, the second as the *Viable Count*. Each method is suited to various purposes, and the choice of which to employ must depend on the type of information desired. For many purposes, such as calculation of the generation time of bacteria, and the quantitative study of bacterial metabolism, both methods should be used in conjunction.

The general principles underlying the counting of bacteria may be briefly mentioned. [For further details the reader is referred to textbooks on practical bacteriology, and for a critical review of the different methods that may be employed, with the main sources of error involved, to articles by Wilson (1922) and Wilson *et al.* (1935).]

(1) Total Count.

(a) *Direct Counting under the Microscope of a Stained Preparation on a Slide.*—First described by Eberle (1896), this method has been used fairly extensively, and forms the basis of the Breed (1911) method for counting bacteria in milk. A drop of known volume is spread over a known area on a slide, dried, fixed, stained, and examined under a microscope. The organisms in a given number of fields are counted, and knowing the area of a given field with a particular combination of objective, tube length and ocular—this can be obtained by means of slide and eyepiece micrometers—it is possible to calculate the total number of organisms present in the original suspension. This method, though valuable for certain purposes, is open to a number of technical objections, one of the most important of which is that not all organisms—particularly when dead—stain sufficiently deeply to be visible under ordinary illuminating conditions. The method, therefore, affords an estimate of the number of stainable bacteria, not necessarily of the total bacteria.

(b) *Wright's Method* (1902).—A known volume of the bacterial suspension is mixed with a known volume of normal human blood. A smear preparation is made on a slide, dried, fixed, stained, examined under the microscope, and the number of bacteria and red cells in a given number of fields is counted. Since, in the blood of the normal adult male there are about 5·5 million red cells per c.mm., and since the numerical relationship of the bacteria to the red cells is known, it is easy to estimate the number of bacteria in the suspension. Owing mainly to the impossibility of obtaining a perfectly homogeneous distribution of the red cells and bacteria on the slide, this method is subject to a very considerable experimental error.

(c) *Microscopical Examination of the Organisms in a Counting Chamber.*—Though an ordinary hæmatocytometer may be used and the bacterial suspension stained with a suitable dye, it is much better to employ a Helber chamber (1904). The Helber slide itself should be 2 mm. thick, the depth of the chamber 0·02 mm., and the area of each small square 0·0025 sq. mm. ; it should be provided with a cover slip 1–2 mm. thick. The organisms are examined unstained, under dark-ground illumination, a special con- denser being provided for this purpose. A $\frac{2}{3}$ inch objective and a $\times 25$ compensating ocular afford a suitable combination for counting most organisms. This method is un- doubtedly the most accurate we possess. Provided a number of technical points are attended to, there is no reason why counts should vary by more than ± 10 per cent. from the real value.

(d) *The Opacity Method.*—This is essentially an indirect method of bacterial enumera- tion. The opacity of the suspension to be estimated is compared, either by the naked eye or by means of a nephelometer (see Liese 1926, Strausz 1930), photometer (Mestre 1935), or photo-electric cell (Pulvertaft and Lemon 1933, Alper and Sterne 1933), with a control suspension of standard opacity, the number of organisms in which has been counted by one of the direct methods just described. Though very rapid and of great value for many purposes, this method suffers from the disadvantage that the opacity to which bacteria give rise appears to be determined not only by their numbers, but also by their size and their optical density. Since different strains of the same species, and even organisms of the same strain at different periods of growth (Wilson 1926), vary in size, the opacity method cannot do more than afford an approximate estimate of the numbers of bacteria in a given suspension. According to Liese (1926), who worked with spherical organisms, the opacity is determined by the surface area of the organisms $(4 \pi r^2)$ and therefore varies with the square of the radius. Thus a suspension containing 500 million cocci per c.c. with an average diameter of 2μ would be four times as dense as that of a suspension containing the same number of cocci with an average diameter of 1μ. Accord- ing to Strausz (1930), however, it is doubtful whether the relationship is quite so simple as this. Considering that some of the light must pass through the organisms themselves, it is difficult to avoid the conclusion that volume and density probably play a part in determining the opacity of a bacterial suspension. Though unsatisfactory for the exact enumeration of bacteria, the opacity method is very useful, on account of its rapidity, for approximate estimations, and is peculiarly well adapted for the standardization of vaccines, in which the important factor is not the number of individual organisms, but the total amount of bacterial protoplasm per c.c. (For very useful information on the micrometric measurement of bacteria, and for tables giving the relationship of volume to surface area, see Skar 1934.)

(e) *The Centrifugal Method.*—This is again an indirect method. It consists briefly in centrifuging the suspension in a capillary tube, measuring the height of the column of deposited bacteria, and estimating their number by calculations based on their average diameter or their specific gravity (see Schmidt 1926, Schmidt and Fischer 1930). As an approximate method of ascertaining the bacterial content of a suspension, particularly when the organisms are clumped, this method is often useful, but the doubtful validity of some of the assumptions made in the calculations, and the various factors that may interfere with the sedimentation of the bacteria under a given centrifugal force, are such as to render the final result subject to a considerable error.

(2) Viable Count.

(a) *The Dilution Method.*—This method, which is based on Lister's original method of dilution to extinction, consists in diluting the suspension to a point beyond which unit quantities are sterile. In practice several consecutive dilutions are made, and from each of these a number of tubes of medium, usually liquid, are inoculated with suitable unit quantities. The tubes are incubated and from the number in which growth occurs, the probable number of bacteria in the original suspension may be calculated from formulæ such as those worked out by McCrady (1915), Stein (1917), and Greenwood and Yule (1917). (For useful tables see McCrady 1918, Hoskins 1934.) This method, or one of its numerous modifications, is frequently adopted when an approximate estimate of the numbers of living bacteria in a suspension is required. It has the great advantage of being applicable to organisms that cannot be counted by the ordinary plating method. It is used, for example, in the determination of coliform organisms in water, because no satisfactory plating medium has yet been devised for differentiating coliform bacilli in mixed culture from other bacteria, though several suitable liquid media are available. It is frequently used in filtrable virus work ; for this purpose quantities of the dilutions are inoculated into a susceptible animal, generally by the intradermal route, and the occurrence of a specific skin reaction is regarded as evidence of the presence of the organism in the corresponding dilution. As Halvorson and Ziegler (1933*a*, *b*) have pointed out, the method is subject to a very large experimental error, depending mainly on the numbers of tubes seeded from the different dilutions. Even with 40 tubes to each dilution the count is liable to vary between about 38 per cent. below and 47 per cent. above the true count, while with only 5 tubes to each dilution the corresponding figures are — 70 and + 260 per cent. The method is not therefore suitable for exact bacterial enumeration.

(*b*) *The Plating Method.*—This is generally performed by a modification of Koch's original plating method. It consists essentially in preliminary dilution, if necessary, of the suspension, the plating out of unit quantities of suitable dilutions into a suitable solid medium, and the counting of the number of colonies that develop after incubation. The average number of colonies per plate multiplied by the reciprocal of the dilution affords an estimate of the number of living organisms in the original suspension. Instead of plates, roll-tubes may be used. Provided that the bacteria are homogeneously distributed in the suspension, that not more than one species of organism is present, and that attention is paid to a large number of technical points, accurate counts may be obtained by this method. Departure from these provisos may often entail, however, experimental errors of considerable magnitude. (For sources and measurement of errors see Wilson *et al.* 1935.)

The Growth Curve

If a given bacterium is seeded into a liquid medium of suitable composition, and incubated at a suitable temperature, it will be found that its growth will follow a definite course. This course is most conveniently represented in graphical form (Fig. 9), the logarithms of the numbers of bacteria along the ordinates being plotted against the time in hours along the abscissæ.

The growth curve may be arbitrarily divided into four phases : (1) The lag phase, *a* to *b*, lasting for a few hours, during which multiplication is slow. In the early part of this phase there may be no apparent growth ; in fact many of the organisms may die, so that there is an actual diminution in their numbers. Within a short time, however, growth becomes apparent, and gradually increases in pace till the beginning of the next phase. (2) The logarithmic phase, *b* to *c*, in which regular division of the organisms occurs at maximum speed. Since their increase is in geometric progression, it follows that when the logarithms of their numbers are plotted against the time in hours they fall on an ascending straight line. (3) The stationary phase, *c* to *d*, during which the organisms cease to multiply at maximal rate, so that their increase in number becomes less and less, till ultimately it ceases ; the number present in a unit volume remains approximately constant for

an appreciable length of time.   During this phase the number of freshly formed
bacteria roughly counterbalances the number of those that are dying.   (4) The
phase of decline, *d* to *e*, during which the organisms gradually diminish in number,
till finally the culture becomes sterile.

So far we have been considering the viable bacteria only.   If, however, a count
is performed of the total number of organisms alive and dead in the culture, a
different curve is obtained.   It will be seen that this curve runs more or less
parallel to the curve of the viable bacilli till the period of decline sets in, after
which the two diverge, the total curve remaining practically stationary, or rising
very slightly.   It will be noticed, moreover, that the total curve is throughout

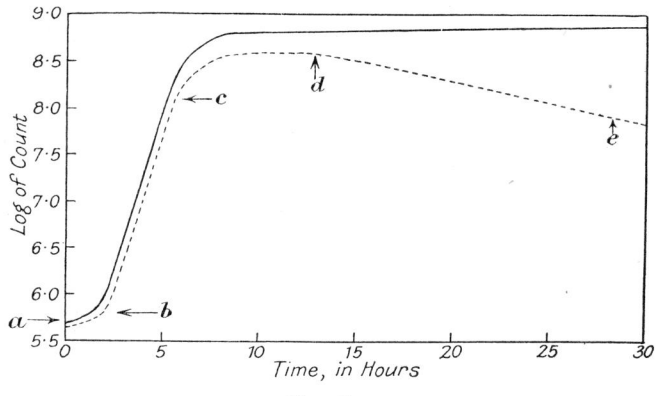

FIG. 9.
Continuous line = Total number of bacteria alive or dead.
Interrupted line = Number of living or viable bacteria.

somewhat higher than the viable curve.   The probable explanation of this will
be given later.

We must now consider each of the phases in detail.

The Lag Phase

The following observations have been made by various workers :

(1) Size of Inoculum.—The smaller the inoculum for a given volume of medium,
the longer is the lag phase.   Conversely, the larger the inoculum, the shorter is
the lag phase.   The important factor appears to be the ratio of the number of
bacteria to the volume of the fluid medium, or, in other words, the concentration
of the bacteria, assuming that the organisms are evenly dispersed throughout
the medium.   Herrington (1934), working on Ingraham's figures, found that the
length of the lag phase appeared to be a linear function of the logarithm of
the inoculum.

(2) Age of Inoculum.—Within certain limits, the younger the culture from which
the inoculum is taken, the shorter is the lag.   Thus Penfold (1914) found a shorter
lag when the inoculation was made from a culture which had been grown for 17
hours at 37° C. than from a 4-days' culture at 37° C.   Between a 4-days'
and a 12-days' culture there was very little difference.   Coplans (1910) also
found that the older the culture from which the inoculum was taken, the longer
was the lag period.

(3) **Frequency of Transplantation.**—Graham-Smith (1921) found that growth was more rapid when the inoculum was taken from a strain which had been sub-cultured frequently, than from one which was infrequently transplanted.

(4) **Stage of Growth of Inoculum.**—If the inoculum is taken from a culture in the lag phase, in the stationary phase, or in the decline phase of growth, lag is noticeable in the subculture ; if, however, it is taken from a culture in the logarith-mic phase of growth, there is no lag ; the organisms continue to multiply in the subculture at the same rate as that at which they had been growing in the parent culture. This important observation was first made by Müller in 1895, and has since been confirmed many times.

(5) **Temperature at which Culture is Incubated.**—The nearer the temperature of incubation approaches the optimum temperature of growth for the organism, the shorter is the duration of the lag phase. With *Bact. coli*, Penfold (1914) found that the lag phase lasted for 6 hours when the culture was incubated at 20° C., but only for 1–2 hours when incubated at 37° C.

(6) **Nature of the Organism.**—Some organisms show a longer lag period than others. With organisms of the coli-typhoid group, for example, the lag period is generally short, whereas organisms such as *Pf. mallei* or *Br. abortus* exhibit a pro-longed lag phase.

(7) **Nature of Medium.**—Generally speaking, the more suitable the medium is for a given organism, the shorter is the lag phase. As a rule an organism grows best in a medium to which it is accustomed. In a medium that is unfavourable —for example, one with too high a H-ion concentration—the lag phase is often greatly prolonged ; several hours may elapse before the organism begins to grow, but once it has started, it may grow as well as in a medium of optimum reaction. This statement is true only within certain limits ; if the medium is very acid, then the growth may not only be slow to begin, but may remain poor in its later stages. A similar observation has been made by Moore (1915), relative to the growth of pneumococci in a medium containing a high dilution of a disinfectant. In some media the lag is longer than in others, even though the organism is accustomed to both. Thus *Bact. coli* seeded from a peptone water culture into fresh peptone water is said to show a shorter lag phase than the same organism seeded from a dulcite peptone water culture into fresh dulcite peptone water (Penfold 1914, Coplans 1910).

Since the phenomenon of lag was first noticed by Müller in 1895, it has been studied by numerous workers (Rahn 1906, Lane-Claypon 1909, Coplans 1910, Penfold 1914, Ledingham and Penfold 1914, Chesney 1916, Slator 1917, Buchanan 1918), and several hypotheses have been put forward to account for it. A few of these may be briefly mentioned.

Rahn (1906) suggested that some essential substance or " bios " had to be excreted by the organisms into the medium before maximal growth could occur.

Penfold (1914) modified this hypothesis by supposing that certain bodies necessary for the synthesis of bacterial protoplasm had to accumulate within the bacteria themselves before rapid growth became possible. His suggestion was that in a bacterial culture these bodies tended to diffuse out into the medium, so that when the organisms were transferred to a fresh medium time had to elapse before they could be built up again.

Chesney (1916) regarded the phenomenon of lag as an expression of injury which the bacterial cell had sustained in its previous environment. Working with the pneumococcus, he found that toxic substances were formed during growth. These were present in maximum concentration at the end of the logarithmic phase and tended to decrease with subsequent incubation. They acted like a weak disinfectant, killing some bacteria and maiming others. The bacteria, in short, appeared to be poisoned by the products of their own metabolism. When inoculated into a fresh medium, a certain time had to elapse before they recovered sufficiently from the noxious effects of their previous environment to start growing. This time constituted the lag phase.

It is somewhat unfortunate that Chesney should have selected the pneumococcus for his test organism. Since the publication of his paper, our knowledge of the respiratory mechanism of this bacterium has greatly increased, and it has been shown that it produces hydrogen peroxide in sufficient concentration to exert a toxic action on other pneumococci added to the culture in which it has been growing. This peculiarity of the pneumococcus is not, so far as we know, shared by many other bacteria ; so that, on the assumption that H_2O_2 is the inhibitory substance in this case, the explanation afforded by Chesney would be particular and not general. That this assumption is not unjustifiable seems to be supported by the fact that H_2O_2 is not only highly toxic, but is also volatile, and possesses therefore the very properties which were attributed by Chesney to the toxic substances he described.

Ledingham and Penfold (1914) put forward a purely biological view. They supposed that in any given inoculum the organisms would have individually different powers of growth. During the lag phase a selection of the more rapidly growing cells would occur, so that during this period, although the total number of viable organisms would show only a slight increase, the number of those endowed with the power of active multiplication would increase rapidly. Attempts to verify this hypothesis by experimental methods have not proved very successful. Working with *Bact. typhi-murium*, we inoculated 20 broth tubes, each with a single organism, and measured the number of generations produced within 8 hours at 37° C. Several experiments of this type showed that most of the cells produced 15–16 generations, the extremes being 14 and 17. There was no suggestion that the progeny of any single cell greatly outnumbered the progeny of the other cells. Kelly and Rahn (1932) approached the problem in a different way. They made direct microscopical observations on individual cells of *Bact. ærogenes* inoculated on to a solid medium, following up the progeny of each cell for four generations. Considerable variation was observed in the rate of growth of individual cells, but this variation was not inheritable from one generation to the next. For example, the two cells arising from the division of one cell might have widely different generation times. On the average the progeny of any given rapidly dividing cell was found to multiply rather more slowly, and the progeny of any given slowly dividing cell was found to multiply rather more rapidly, than normal cells with an average rate of multiplication.

These are the various ways in which the lag phase has been explained. It will be observed that they are not mutually exclusive ; indeed, some of them are fundamentally similar. In reviewing them, we may note that the phenomenon of lag is manifested by bacteria in all stages of growth except the logarithmic stage. During this period the organisms are multiplying very rapidly—often dividing once in every 20 minutes—and as this stage, at 37° C. at least, does not last for more than a few hours, it follows that at this time the organisms must all be comparatively young. By the term " young " we mean an organism that has been generated within a comparatively recent time, from a few minutes to about an hour. The suggestion is that young organisms inoculated into a fresh medium grow without lag, and that old organisms inoculated into a fresh medium exhibit a lag phase before beginning to grow.

The old organisms must differ in some way therefore from the young organisms. Chesney believes that this difference is the result of the toxic substances formed in the medium. That toxic substances are in part responsible for the cessation of the logarithmic phase of growth is quite possible, but that lag can be entirely explained in terms of bacterial injury is very doubtful. Attempts made by Penfold (1914) to free the organisms from these hypothetical toxic substances by washing them in Ringer's solution proved a failure ; their lag period was increased rather than diminished by this procedure. Broom (1929) and Barnes (1931), who reinvestigated this question, have each failed to obtain evidence of any production of such toxic substances in cultures of *Staphylococcus* and bacilli of the coli-typhoid group.

These hypotheses need not be discussed further, because recent work has brought to light one supremely important fact of whose existence the earlier observers were ignorant, and which goes a long way towards explaining the difference in behaviour of young and old organisms. Briefly stated, the lag phase is not a phase of rest, as had been previously supposed, but a phase of intense growth activity, during which, however, little or no actual cell-division occurs. The evidence for this statement must now be considered in some detail.

Evidence of Growth without Multiplication during the Lag Phase.

(1) *Increase in Size.*—If a small number of organisms from a 24-hours' culture of *Bact. coli*, for example, are seeded into an agar medium, which is then spread between a slide and a cover glass and observed on a warm stage by dark-ground illumination, the first change observed is not division, but a gradual and progressive enlargement affecting a certain proportion of the organisms. This enlargement becomes visible shortly after the preparation has been put up and continues till the organisms reach a certain size, when they finally divide. The rate at which the enlargement occurs varies with the different organisms in the preparation. The time elapsing between the incubation of such a preparation and the first division varies from about $1\frac{1}{2}$ to 3 hours; but after the primary division has occurred, subsequent generations may be produced at the rate of about one in every 30 to 60 minutes. Examination of such a preparation at the end of about five hours will reveal a small proportion of cells that have apparently remained unaltered, and a large proportion that have divided ; amongst this latter group considerable variation will be found in the number of daughter cells produced, these varying in different micro-colonies from 2 to about 16 or even more. Measurements of the size of these daughter cells show that they are considerably larger than the original cells used for seeding the preparation. Clark and Ruehl (1919) were the first to draw attention to this increase in size of the bacterial cell during growth. Using a micrometer, they measured the size of seventy strains of organisms belonging to thirty-seven different species at intervals during their growth. With the exception of members of the diphtheria group, they found that the young organisms in cultures from 4 to 9 hours old were much larger than those in cultures 24 hours old. Henrici (1926, 1928), who largely confirmed their work, found in a culture of *B. megatherium*, that the average length of the original cells was 3·4 μ, but that during the phase of maximum multiplication the average length of the constituent organisms was about 15 μ. After this phase was over, the average length of the organisms decreased till in 10 hours it approximated to that of the organisms used for the original seeding. Similar observations on *Bact. typhi-murium* showed that the average size of the cells in a 4-hours' agar culture was 2·35 $\times$ 0·79 μ, whereas in the same

culture after 26 hours it was only 1·13 × 0·49 μ (Wilson 1926). Estimations made from these measurements showed that the cells from the young culture were nearly six times the volume of those from the older culture.

(2) *Increase in Respiratory Activity.*—Observations by various workers (for references see Walker *et al.* 1934) on the biochemical activity of the cells during the lag phase have shown that this phase is by no means a period of rest. Respiratory and metabolic processes, such as an increased oxygen uptake, a fall in oxidation-reduction potential, and a rise in the output of heat, of NH_3, and of CO_2, become detectable soon after the organisms have been inoculated into the medium. The rate at which these changes proceed increases till it reaches its culminating point during the first hour of the logarithmic phase of growth. These observations render it clear that, though the cells are not dividing, they are growing very actively during the so-called lag period. The plate count, it will be realized, gives a wholly erroneous idea of the amount of growth during this phase, and has in the past been responsible for the belief that the lag phase is a period of rest. We now know that, so far from its being a period of rest, it is a period of intensive activity in which increase in cell size and cell metabolism go on at an accelerating velocity.

(3) *Increase in Susceptibility to Disinfectants.*—Further evidence of change in the bacterial cells during the lag phase is afforded by a study of their resistance to disinfecting agencies. Schultz and Ritz (1910) showed that in young cultures of *Bact. coli*, 3 to 6 hours old, the organisms were heat-sensitive, whereas in older cultures, 8 to 24 hours, they were nearly all resistant, when tested at 53° C. for 25 minutes. Similarly Reichenbach (1911), working with *Bact. paratyphosum B*, found that the younger the cultures were, the higher was the proportion of heat-sensitive organisms. Sherman and Albus (1923) found that in a culture of *Bact. coli* the freshly formed bacteria are more susceptible to the action of inimical agents such as heat, cold, and disinfectants, than are the older bacteria. Taking advantage of these differences, they attempted (Sherman and Albus 1924) to study the relative numbers of the two kinds of bacteria present during the lag phase of growth. A 1 per cent. peptone water medium was inoculated from a culture of *Bact. coli* which had been grown in the same medium at room temperature for a week ; the inoculum consisted therefore of old bacteria. The culture was incubated at 37° C., and plate counts were made at intervals. At the same time 1 c.c. portions of the culture were transferred to 100 c.c. of 5 per cent. sodium chloride solution ; the mixture was allowed to stand for 1 hour at 20° C., after which a count was performed on it, the numbers being calculated in terms of the 1 c.c. of added broth culture. The results are given in Table I.

TABLE I

Time after Inoculation.	Original Culture.	After 1 hour in 5 per cent. NaCl.	Mortality, per cent.
0 hours	96,000	82,500	14·06
1 hour	80,500	60,500	24·82
1½ hours	90,500	41,000	54·70
2 hours	143,000	33,000	76·93
2½ hours	255,000	16,500	93·54

This table shows that the young bacilli, formed after the culture has entered on the logarithmic phase of growth, are very much more susceptible to the action of 5 per cent. NaCl solution than are the old bacilli inoculated at the start—a mortality of 93·54 per cent. as against 14·06 per cent. In addition it will be noticed that during the lag phase, lasting from 0 to $1\frac{1}{2}$ hours, though there is no increase in the number of bacteria, there is a progressive increase in their susceptibility to salt solution. Sherman and Albus interpret this as indicating that, during the lag phase, the old bacteria which have been inoculated are undergoing a process of rejuvenescence, which fits them for reproduction. Numerous instances are quoted from other fields of biology, such as the rejuvenescence of *Paramœcium*, the growth curves of colonies of fruit flies, etc., that may be regarded as exemplifying the same biological law of growth. Prior to active growth, there is a latent phase of preparation, during which the old cells are being rejuvenated, and fitted for reproduction.

Summarizing the data yielded by these observations and those recorded earlier in this chapter, we see that during the lag phase of growth there is (1) a variation in the proportion of cells that exhibit growth ; (2) a variation, probably not inheritable, between different cells in the same culture in the rate at which growth occurs ; (3) a progressive enlargement of the growing cells before actual division occurs ; (4) a rapid increase in the respiratory and metabolic activities of the growing cells ; (5) an increasing susceptibility of these cells to the bactericidal effect of heat and of various salts and disinfectants.

On the ground (a) that newly generated bacilli in the logarithmic phase, when transferred to a fresh medium, start multiplying without exhibiting any lag phase ; (b) that bacilli from cultures in all other stages show a lag phase before they start dividing ; and (c) that during this lag phase the cells are undergoing a rapid metamorphosis, similar perhaps to that described by Child (1915) in the rejuvenescence of infusoria, flat worms, and marine algæ, which renders them comparable to the young actively dividing bacilli of the logarithmic phase : it may be concluded that the lag phase is essentially a period in which the protoplasm of the old, but still viable, bacteria in the inoculum is acquiring the characteristics of young protoplasm. The lag phase appears to be essentially a phase of rejuvenescence.

Logarithmic Phase

The logarithmic phase is that period during which regular and maximum multiplication is occurring. Increase in the number of organisms is by geometrical progression, so that, if the logarithms of their numbers are plotted against time, they will fall along an ascending straight line. If counts are made at intervals, it is easy to calculate the number of generations during the phase, and the length of each generation.

Thus if $a =$ number of organisms at the beginning of a given time

and $b =$,,   ,,   ,,   ,,   ,, end   ,, ,,   ,,   ,,

then at the end of the first generation,

$$b = a \times 2$$

at the end of the second generation,

$$b = a \times 2 \times 2$$

at the end of n generations,

$$b = a \times 2^n$$

To find the value of n — $i.e.$ the number of generations, we may write

$$\log b = \log a + n \log 2$$

or

$$n = \frac{\log b - \log a}{\log 2} \quad . \quad . \quad . \quad . \quad . \quad . \quad . \quad (1)$$

Further, if there have been n generations in time T, the generation time G can be calculated from the formula

$$G = \frac{T}{n} \quad . \quad . \quad . \quad . \quad . \quad . \quad . \quad . \quad (2)$$

It has generally been held that during the logarithmic phase all the bacteria are alive and all are actively dividing. Thus, as represented in formula (1), 2 bacteria give rise to 4, 4 to 8, 8 to 16, and so on. If this assumption were correct, then all the organisms present during this phase should be viable, and the total count would be identical with the viable count.

This may be true when, as Kelly and Rahn (1932) have found, organisms are growing under optimal conditions and are followed for a few generations only. Observations, however on ordinary broth cultures have shown that the total number of organisms generally exceeds the number of viable organisms, even during the logarithmic phase (Wilson 1922, 1926, Régnier, David, and Kaplan 1932).

The most probable explanation of this fact is that during the period of maximum growth some of the organisms that are generated fail to survive. If, for example, 80 per cent. of the organisms produced during a given generation continued to live and divide, while 20 per cent. died, then at the end of the logarithmic phase the total number of organisms alive and dead would exceed the number of living. The increase in the living organisms would still occur by geometrical progression, and the resultant curve of plotting the logarithms against time would still fall on a straight line ; the only difference would be that instead of the number of organisms being doubled in each generation, their factor of increase, or *generation index*, would be 1·6.

Thus in Table II it is supposed that only 50 per cent. of the organisms inoculated are viable. The ratio of viable to total organisms, i.e $\frac{V}{T}$, increases with each generation. After about ten generations, it rapidly approaches the value $p - 1$, where $p =$ the generation index. The value of p can therefore be obtained with fair accuracy towards the end of the logarithmic phase by simply calculating the viable : total ratio and adding 1. In the example quoted it is approximately 1·6.

TABLE II

CALCULATIONS OF VIABLE AND TOTAL ORGANISMS WITH A 20 PER CENT. DEATH-RATE PER GENERATION

	No. of Viable Org. per c.c.	No. of Dead Org. per c.c.	Total No. of Org. per c.c.	Ratio Viable : Total.
At start	1,000	1,000	2,000	0·500
At end of 1st Gen. .	1,600	1,400(1,000 + 400)	3,000	0·533
At end of 2nd Gen. .	2,560	2,040(1,400 + 640)	4,600	0·557
At end of 3rd Gen. .	4,096	3,064(2,040 + 1,024)	7,160	0·572
At end of 4th Gen. .	6,554	4,702(3,064 + 1,638)	11,256	0·582

If the viable and total counts are known both at the start and at the end of x generations, then p can be ascertained at any time during the logarithmic phase, since

$$\frac{V_x - V_0}{T_x - T_0} = p - 1 \quad . \qquad . \qquad . \qquad . \qquad . \quad (3)$$

or

$$p = \frac{V_x - V_0}{T_x - T_0} + 1 \quad . \qquad . \qquad . \qquad . \quad (4)[1]$$

where V_0 and T_0 = number of viable and total organisms respectively at the start, and V_x and T_x = number of viable and total organisms respectively at the end of x generations.

Experiments on the growth of *Bact. typhi-murium* in broth have shown that the average ratio of viable to total organisms at the end of the logarithmic phase is about 0·8. This corresponds to a death-rate of about 10 per cent. per generation, and to a generation index of 1·8. Hence in calculating the generation time, formula (1) has to be changed to

$$n = \frac{\log b - \log a}{\log 1\cdot 8}$$

Employing this formula, the number of generations is greater than by the old formula, and the generation time necessarily shorter.

It must be understood that the factor of increase to be used in the formula may vary with each experiment, and can only be ascertained by the performance of a total and a viable count on each culture.

Instead of plotting the logarithms of the bacterial numbers against time, Lemon (1933) has pointed out that interesting information may be obtained by estimating the actual rate of growth in unit intervals of time.

If for each period of time T the count is N_0, N_1, N_2 . . . etc. at times t_0, t_1, t_2 . . . , the following formula may be used :

$$\frac{(N_1 - N_0)}{(t_1 - t_0)_{\frac{1}{2}(T_1)}} \text{ and } \frac{(N_2 - N_1)}{(t_2 - t_1)_{\frac{1}{2}(T_2 - T_1) + T_1}} \text{ and } \frac{(N_3 - N_2)}{(t_3 - t_2)_{\frac{1}{2}(T_3 - T_2) + T_2}}, \text{ etc.}$$

The results are plotted on a graph whose abscissæ represent T and whose ordinates indicate the rate of propagation. The numerator and the first term of the denominator

TABLE III
GROWTH OF *Bact. typhi-murium* IN BROTH (Wilson 1922)

Time in Minutes.	Viable Count per c.c.	Logarithms of Viable Count.	$N_1 - N_0$, $N_2 - N_1$, etc.	$t_1 - t_0$, $t_2 - t_1$, etc.	$N_1-N_0 \div t_1-t_0$, $N_2-N_1 \div t_2-t_1$, etc.	Mid-time Interval.
0	Not counted	—	—	—	—	—
40	828,800	5·9184	—	—	—	—
80	1,539,000	6·1872	710,200	40	17,755	60
120	4,363,000	6·6398	2,824,000	40	70,600	100
160	12,150,000	7·0845	7,787,000	40	194,675	140
200	32,490,000	7·5117	20,340,000	40	508,500	180
240	81,640,000	7·9119	49,150,000	40	1,228,750	220
280	155,900,000	8·1928	74,260,000	40	1,856,500	260
320	271,700,000	8·4341	115,800,000	40	2,895,000	300
370	334,300,000	8·5241	62,600,000	50	1,252,000	345
440	351,400,000	8·5458	17,100,000	70	244,286	405

[1] For this formula we are very much indebted to Dr. H. G. W. Hoare.

in the formula represent the arithmetic increase in the number of organisms in unit time. The second term or "suffix" of the denominator is not part of the divisor but indicates the mid-point of the period during which the actual increase has occurred. The use of the formula is exemplified in Table III and Fig. 10.

It will be observed that, while the curve of the logarithms indicates that a steady rate of multiplication is occurring during the 1–5 hour period, the curve given by Lemon's formula shows that the actual rate of arithmetic increase rises rapidly to reach a peak at 5 hours, after which it falls steeply. The reason for the rapid rise is, not that the organisms are dividing more rapidly at the end than at the beginning of the logarithmic phase, but that, owing to the fact that the actual numbers of bacteria are constantly

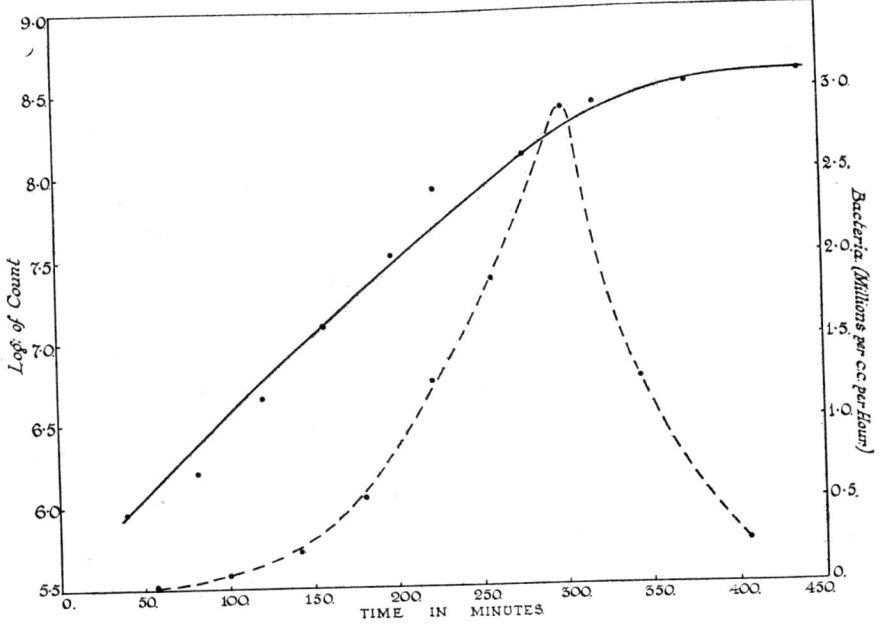

FIG. 10.—GROWTH OF *Bact. typhi-murium* IN BROTH, PLOTTED ACCORDING TO LEMON'S FORMULA.

Continuous line = Numbers plotted logarithmically against time.
Interrupted line = Rate of arithmetic increase plotted against time.

increasing throughout this phase, the progeny of any given generation expressed arithmetically must be greater than that of any previous generation. Lemon's method of calculating the growth rate is likely to be of advantage in physiological and biochemical problems when it is desired to study the rate of change in a chemical substrate in relation to the absolute numbers of organisms produced.

The generation time during the logarithmic phase is influenced by several factors.

(1) *Temperature of Incubation of Culture.*—The nearer the temperature is to the optimum for growth of the organism, the shorter is the generation time. Working with *Bact. coli*, Chick (1912) found that between 20° and 40° C., each rise of 1° C. increased the rate of growth 1·072 times; the temperature coefficient for every rise of 10° C. was $1·072^{10}$, i.e. 2·01. This agrees closely with Lane-Claypon's (1909)

figure of 2·2. Barber (1908), who made an exhaustive study of the rate of growth of *Bact. coli*, constructed the curve shown in Fig. 11. In this it will be seen that at a temperature of 15° C. the generation time is 180′, at 25° C. 44′, at 35° C. 22′, and at 40° C. 17′. The curve corresponds fairly closely to the quarter of an ellipse. Further, as the increase is geometrical, by plotting the logarithms of the generation times, we shall find that the points fall on a descending straight line. The maximum rate of growth of *Bact. coli* occurs at about 37° C., but between 37° and 46° C. there

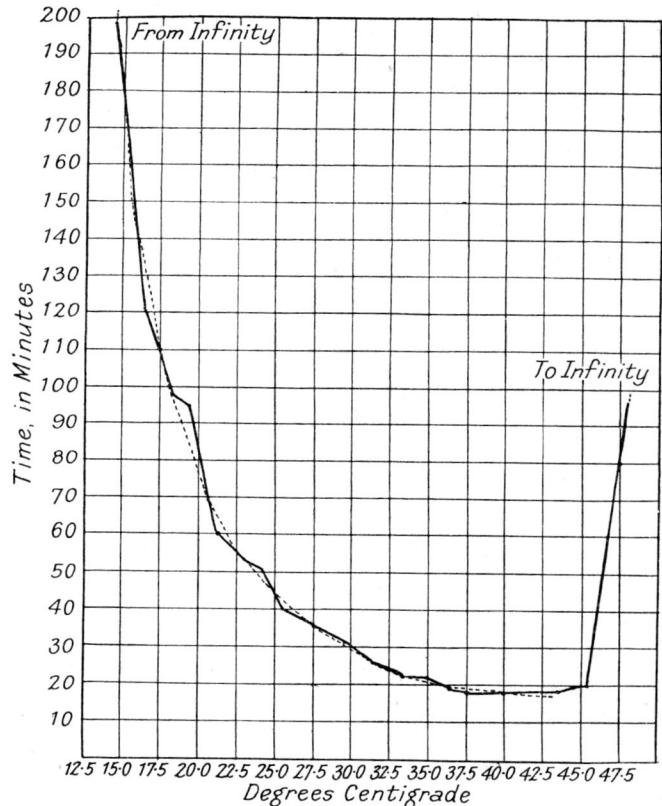

Fig. 11.—The Growth Rate of *Bact. coli* at different Temperatures.
Continuous line = Curve plotted from actual observations.
Interrupted line = Smoothed curve.
(After Barber.)

is little change in the generation time. For *Bact. typhosum*, Müller (1895) found the maximum rate of growth to be between 37° and 40·4° C. ; at a temperature of 44·5° C. the bacilli died rapidly.

(2) *Nature of Medium.*—The more favourable the medium, the more rapid is the growth. Penfold and Norris (1912) found that by increasing the concentration of peptone in a peptone water medium from 0·125 per cent. to 1 per cent., the generation time of *Bact. typhosum* was reduced from almost infinity to 40′. They likewise found that the addition of glucose to the medium further reduced the

generation time. Other workers have also commented on the beneficial effect of glucose ; thus Heap and Cadness (1924) found that the addition of 2 per cent. glucose to a 3 per cent. peptone water medium enormously increased the growth of *Bact. typhi-murium*. (Fig. 12.)

(3) *Nature of Organism.*—Some organisms appear to grow more rapidly than others. Mason (1935) has compiled from the literature the generation times of various species of bacteria growing under optimal conditions. Among the most rapidly growing organisms are the members of the coli-aerogenes group, with a generation time of less than 20 minutes. Some of the large spore-bearing bacilli grow at about the same rate, while the thermophilic species may grow even faster. Organisms of the Salmonella, *Proteus*, and probably *Vibrio*, groups have a genera-

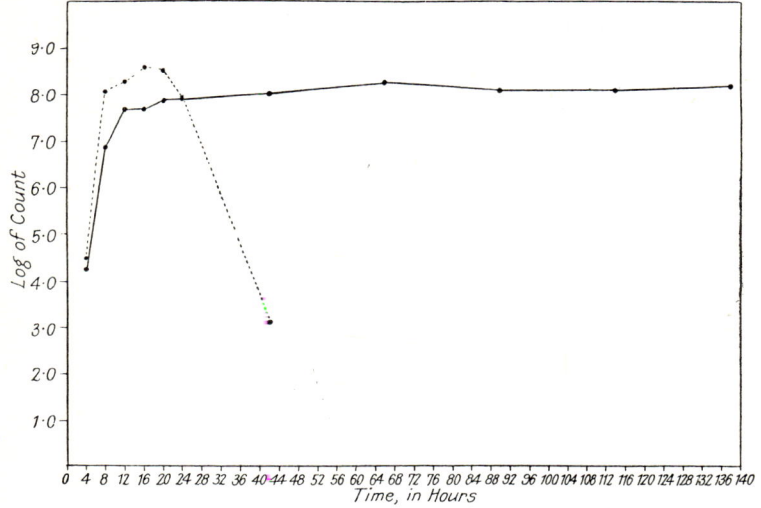

Fig. 12.

A. Continuous line = Viable count of *Bact. typhi-murium* in peptone water.
B. Interrupted line = Viable count of *Bact. typhi-murium* in peptone water + 2 per cent. glucose.
            (After Heap and Cadness.)

tion time of 20–30 minutes, *Staphylococcus* and *Streptococcus* of 25–35 minutes, *Pseudomonas* of 30–40 minutes, *Corynebacterium* of 35–40 minutes, *Clostridium* of 35–50 minutes, *Lactobacillus* of 40–80 minutes, *Rhizobium* of 100 minutes, *Azotobacter* of 30–240 minutes, and *Phytomonas* of 75–165 minutes. The *Mycobacteria* multiply very slowly, while the slowest of all appear to be *Nitrobacter* and *Nitrosococcus*.

Within certain limits definable for each organism, the duration of the logarithmic phase varies—

(1) inversely with the temperature. For example, Lane-Claypon (1909), and Jennison (1935), working with *Bact. coli*, made the following observations on the duration of the logarithmic phase at different temperatures :

$$6–7\tfrac{1}{2} \text{ hours at } 37° \text{ C.}$$
$$8–8\tfrac{1}{2} \text{ hours at } 30° \text{ C.}$$
$$11–15 \text{ hours at } 25° \text{ C.}$$
$$14–24 \text{ hours at } 20° \text{ C.}$$

(2) inversely with the size of the inoculum.

(3) directly with the quantity of culture medium.

If a flask of 50 c.c. of broth is seeded with one million living *Bact. coli*, then the logarithmic phase at 37° C. will last, generally, between 3 and 4 hours.

At the beginning of this section the logarithmic phase was defined as that period during which regular and maximal multiplication was occurring. Recent work, however, has cast some doubt on the accuracy of this definition. Rogers and Greenbank (1930) and Hirsch (1933), for example, have obtained evidence that the rate of growth during this phase is intermittent. Whether measured by the increase in numbers (*V. metchnikovi*) or by the oxygen consumption (mouse typhoid bacillus), Hirsch found that 3 or 4 peaks of growth occurred every hour. It is conceivable that these results may have been partly influenced by the periodic shaking of the culture, since the effect of aeration in stimulating growth is very marked. But this criticism does not apply to the results of Rogers and Green-bank, who inoculated their organisms (*Bact. coli* and *Str. lactis*) at one end of a tube 15 metres long and measured the rate of advancing growth by observing the decolorization of a dye in the medium. The rate of advance was intermittent, and the intermissions showed a striking degree of periodicity. When plotted against time, the curves depicting the rate of growth showed a moderate peak every 4–5 hours with a much higher peak every 15–20 hours throughout the 8 days required for the organisms to reach the distal end of the tube. It will be noted that the technique used by Rogers and Greenbank was very different from that of Hirsch, and it is by no means certain that the two sets of observers were dealing with the same phenomenon.

Further evidence that growth is not uniform throughout the logarithmic phase is afforded by the observations of Walker and his colleagues (1934) on the rate of CO_2 production by *Bact. coli* in a peptone water medium. It was found that the maximum output of CO_2 per unit volume of bacterial substance occurred during the third hour of growth, *i.e.* the first hour or so of the logarithmic phase, after which a progressive fall occurred.

Care must, of course, be exercised in drawing any conclusions on the rate of multiplication from the rate of growth, since it has already been pointed out that, owing to variations in cell size, increase in bacterial numbers may give a very fallacious idea of the true rate of growth, and the converse is equally true. Further observations at frequent intervals on the numerical increase occurring during the logarithmic phase, made with due attention to multiple small factors that may influence the result, are required before concluding that the rate of cell-division during this phase is discontinuous.

Stationary Phase

After multiplying at a maximum rate for a variable length of time during the logarithmic phase, the organisms become less active, and divide less frequently, till finally their numbers remain practically constant. What is responsible for this decrease in the reproduction rate ? The natural suggestion is that it results from an exhaustion of the food supply. Against this view, however, is the fact that if a culture that has reached the decline phase is sterilized by boiling, and then reinoculated with the same organism, growth occurs in the usual way, though the actual numbers attained may not be so great as in the primary culture (Graham-Smith 1921). The same result is obtained if the culture is sterilized by filtration instead of by boiling, provided that the organism has not produced some volatile substance which would be removed during boiling, as in the special case of the pneumococcus. Penfold (1914) found that if a 24-hours' culture of *Bact. coli* was centrifuged, and the supernatant fluid was incubated at 37° C., fresh growth took place. It is probable, therefore, that some other factor than exhaustion of the food supply is responsible for the cessation of maximal growth.

We have already discussed Chesney's hypothesis, that toxic substances are produced during the phase of multiplication, and that these so injure the bacteria as to delay their subsequent division when introduced into a fresh medium ; and we have seen that, although this explanation may hold good for the pneumococcus, it does not seem to be of more general applicability. We may similarly regard as special cases those instances in which the reaction of the medium is rendered acid during growth owing to the inclusion of a fermentable carbohydrate. In such cases neutralization of the acid by the addition of alkali often suffices to enable growth to occur (Kojima 1923).

Working with the fruit-fly *Drosophila melanogaster* Pearl and Parker (1922) found that the effective reproduction rate decreased as the population density became greater.

Following on these observations Bail (1929) carried out a number of experiments on different bacteria, from the results of which he concluded that in any fluid culture there was a limiting population density that could not be exceeded. This he referred to as the M-concentration. A few of his findings may be briefly recorded.

(1) Any given species of bacterium reaches in a fluid medium a particular and constant M-concentration of living organisms, the value of which differs with different species.

(2) With a large inoculum the M-concentration is reached rapidly, with a small inoculum more slowly.

(3) Living bacteria introduced into fresh broth in M-concentration are unable to multiply.

(4) Living bacteria introduced into fresh broth in a concentration greater than M die off until the M-concentration is reached.

(5) If a culture that has reached its M-concentration is centrifuged and then re-incubated, fresh growth will occur in the clear supernatant fluid till the M-concentration is reached. If, however, after centrifuging, the deposit is shaken up so that the organisms are distributed once more throughout the medium, no growth will occur. This seems to show that it is not the available physical space, but the available biological space, which is important for bacterial growth.

(6) If a culture that has reached its M-concentration is heated to 55° C. for a time sufficient to destroy the majority but not all of the living bacteria, and is then re-incubated, fresh growth will occur till the M-concentration is again reached. This seems to indicate that heat-killed bacteria do not appreciably interfere with the biological space available.

(7) Ordinary meat broth can be diluted 25 times or more without affecting the level of the M-concentration, showing that it is not due to exhaustion of the medium that growth ceases. In the diluted broth the turbidity, *i.e.* the total count, is much less, but the number of living bacteria, *i.e.* the M-concentration, is the same as in the undiluted broth.

(8) The addition of an enriching substance, such as glucose, to the broth increases

the total number of bacteria produced, but the M-concentration of viable organisms remains unchanged.

(9) Growth does not cease with the attainment of the M-concentration ; fresh organisms continue to be produced, but an equivalent number die off so that the M-value remains constant.

Many of these findings were confirmed by Fukuda (1929). This worker, however, pointed out that some of them, particularly Nos. 5, 7 and 8, held true only with certain organisms. He found moreover that, if broth cultures of *Ps. pyocyanea* were sterilized by heat and re-inoculated with fresh organisms, growth occurred till the original M-concentration was reached. This experiment could be repeated two or three times on the same culture, though with *Bact. gallinarum* only one quarter of the M-concentration was reached after the first heating.

von Wikullil (1932) brought further evidence in support of Bail's hypothesis. He found that, if two organisms A and B, each having the same M-concentration of 1,600 million per c.c., were inoculated simultaneously in the same numbers into a tube of broth, the final M-concentration of the mixed culture was still only 1,600 million per c.c., organism A constituting 800 million and organism B 800 million. The total biological space available had now to be shared between the two organisms. If two organisms, A and C, having respective M-concentrations of 1,600 million and 300 million per c.c., were inoculated simultaneously into the same tube of broth the final M-concentration was again 1,600 million per c.c., but this time the whole viable population consisted of organism A. The apparent explanation was that A grew more rapidly than C, and so monopolized the available biological space.

Bail and his followers were more interested in making observations than in explaining them. The problem still remains why it is that bacteria cease dividing at maximal speed when a certain population density is reached.

A suggestion, which we put forward quite tentatively, is that the progressive retardation in growth may often be due to a deficiency of oxygen in the culture. There are certain observations that seem to support this view. We have already seen that the addition of 2 per cent. glucose to a broth medium greatly increases the growth of *Bact. typhi-murium*. The mechanism by which this increase is brought about is unknown, but it is not unreasonable to suppose that the glucose provides a source of energy supply, which the organisms are able to utilize in the absence of readily available oxygen. In support of this we have found that the total number of organisms per c.c. in a given culture can be regulated by altering the available amount of oxygen. Thus, in a casein broth culture of *Bact. typhi-murium* incubated anaerobically, the total count after 24 hours is about 500 million organisms ; in a culture incubated aerobically it is about 2,000 million organisms ; and in a culture through which pure oxygen is bubbled continuously, it is about 8,000 million organisms. There seems to be no doubt that a liberal supply of oxygen does enable growth to be continued for some time after it has ceased in a culture incubated anaerobically or under ordinary aerobic conditions. The suggestion is that, in cultures incubated aerobically, growth continues until the increasing density of the organisms renders it impossible for each individual organism to obtain sufficient oxygen to meet its requirements. These findings apply, of course, only to aerobic and facultatively anaerobic bacteria.

This explanation, it will be observed, does not fit all of Bail's facts, though it explains many of them. The main discrepancy is in the effect on the

M-concentration of adding certain substrates. Bail found that the addition of glucose, for example, led to an increase in the total number of bacteria, while leaving the M-concentration of viable bacteria unaltered. Our experience, both with glucose and with increased aeration, entirely fails to support this finding. The more favourable the conditions for growth are, the higher is the viable population that the medium can support. It is true that in a medium containing a fermentable sugar the viable population may fall rapidly after having reached a height considerably greater than in the same medium without sugar (see Fig. 12), but this appears to be due to the disinfectant action of the acid produced, and not to any specific effect of bacterial density. That this is so is shown by the effect of continuous oxygen passage in the experiments quoted above, in enabling a broth medium to support four times its usual M-population.

Broom (1929) and Gildemeister and Neustat (1935) have brought evidence to show that the amount of growth of many organisms appears to depend to a considerable extent on the presence in the medium of easily assimilable carbon compounds, such as glucose. The addition of these to a culture in which growth has ceased may rapidly enable a fresh crop of organisms to be produced. The apparent ability of some organisms to inhibit the growth of others in mixed cultures seems to be due not only to their more rapid growth, but also to their more active fermentative power, which enables them to break down certain compounds more readily and so deprive the weaker organisms of their requisite nutritive materials.

The fact that mere aeration of a culture may enable fresh bacterial multiplication to occur suggests that there are at least two factors leading to cessation of growth. One is the exhaustion of easily assimilable food-stuffs; the other is oxygen starvation. It seems not improbable that, once the simpler food-stuffs have been broken down, the attack on the more complex compounds can be successful only in the presence of abundant oxygen.

It must not be thought that during the stationary phase all growth has ceased. In most cases multiplication continues for some time after the cessation of the logarithmic phase, but the rate of division progressively diminishes. The time taken to reach the maximum number varies. The temperature of incubation is important; thus, Graham-Smith (1921), working with *Staphylococcus aureus*, found that the maximum number of viable organisms was reached on the 2nd day at 37° C., on the 5th day at 27° C., and on the 8th day at 17° C. Much depends, too, on the nature of the medium.

Not only are fresh organisms being formed during the stationary phase, but large numbers are dying. Once the maximum number of organisms has been reached, and before the phase of decline, the multiplication rate just suffices to balance the death rate, so that the number of living bacteria remains constant.

Phase of Decline

After lasting for a variable time—from about an hour to several days—the stationary phase passes gradually into the phase of decline. The numbers decrease slowly over a period of days, weeks, or months, till all the organisms are dead. With some organisms, such as the pneumococcus, this phase is short, and the culture may be sterile in 2 to 3 days; with other organisms, such as *Bact. coli*, it may last for months. It is possible that growth is not entirely in abeyance during this stage, for if counts are performed at daily intervals, spasmodic rises are sometimes noticed, indicative of the production of fresh organisms. Moreover, there is a gradual rise in the total count, pointing to the same conclusion (Fig. 13).

This is the curve obtained for a culture of a coliform or similar organism in a nutrient broth medium. In a medium containing a fermentable sugar, such as glucose broth, the curve is very different. Instead of descending slowly and irregularly, it passes rapidly down in an oblique straight line, till it reaches the abscissa (Fig. 12).

This difference is almost certainly due to the disinfectant action of the acid

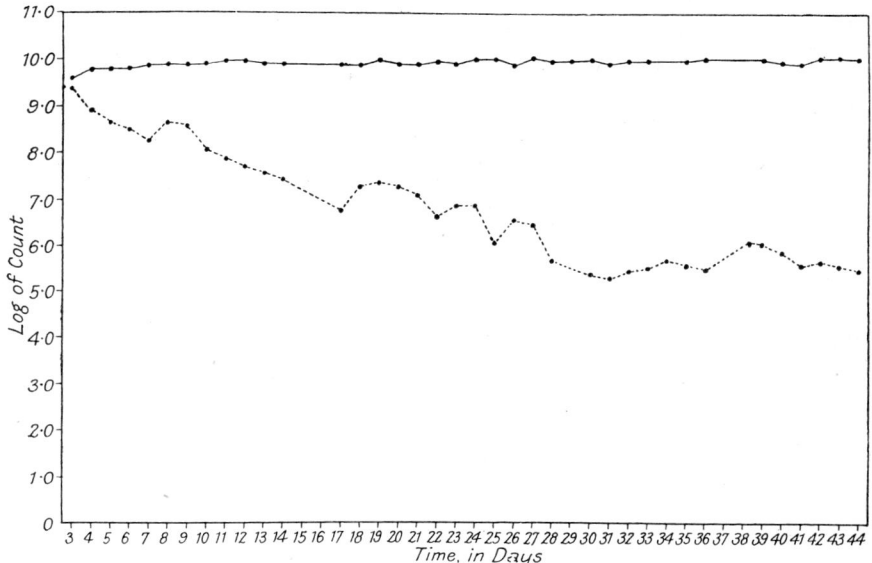

FIG. 13.—GROWTH OF *Bact. typhi-murium* IN BROTH, SHOWING THE PROLONGED DECLINE
PHASE.
Continuous line = Total number of bacteria alive and dead.
Interrupted line = Number of living or viable bacteria.

produced in the culture. The death of the organisms in Curve B is similar to the velocity of a unimolecular reaction, and can be represented by the formula

$$K = \frac{1}{t} \log \frac{n_1}{n_2}$$

where K is the velocity constant, t the interval of time between successive observations, n_1 the number of living bacteria present at the beginning, and n_2 the number present at the end of time t. This point will be more fully discussed in Chapter V. For further information on the growth phases of bacteria, the reader is referred to a detailed consideration of this subject by Buchanan and Fulmer (1928).

Dormancy of Bacteria.

G. S. Burke (1923) inoculated a series of tubes of glucose peptic digest agar and of glucose peptic digest broth with *Cl. botulinum*, seeding one spore into each tube. She sealed the tubes to prevent desiccation, incubated them at 37° C., and noted each day in how many tubes growth had occurred. In the agar medium the majority developed in 10 days, but occasional spores continued to germinate up till the 92nd day. In the broth the majority developed in 14 days, but one or two germinated daily until the 33rd day, and thereafter at intervals till the 144th day.

V. Burke, Sprague and Barnes (1925) obtained similar results with *B. subtilis*, *B. megatherium*, and *Bact. coli*, thus showing that the phenomenon is not confined to anaerobic bacteria or the germination of spores. It is clear from these experiments that bacteria may lie dormant for long periods without multiplying. Superficially, this resembles the phenomenon of lag, but it is possible that dormancy and lag are dependent on different factors. G. S. Burke (1923) draws attention to the similarity in behaviour of dormant spores and the seeds of certain of the higher plants. She suggests that in each instance the cause of the dormancy lies in the cell itself, and is connected with the degree of permeability of the wall.

It is this dormancy which appears to be responsible for the occasional failure of the intermittent process of sterilization. Probably owing to this, too, is the fact that a culture may be contaminated with an organism without signs of the contamination becoming evident till after three or four subcultures have been made.

Mitogenetic Rays.—The extensive work of Gurwitsch and his followers (for references see Bateman 1935) has suggested that certain plant and animal tissues under suitable conditions may emit so-called mitogenetic rays, which are able to stimulate growth in tissue cells placed in a position favourable for their absorption. According to some workers, the radiation is of the short ultra-violet type, but attempts to confirm this by physical methods have not so far been successful. The rays, if they exist at all, have therefore to be detected by biological means. So far as bacteria are concerned, the growth-stimulating effects that have been reported have usually been well within the limits of the experimental error of the technique. While not denying the existence of this effect, we feel bound to adopt a strictly sceptical attitude until quantitative results that will stand the usual tests of statistical significance are forthcoming.

REFERENCES

ALPER, T. and STERNE, M. (1933) *J. Hyg., Camb.*, **33**, 497.
BAIL, O. (1929) *Z. ImmunForsch.*, **60**, 1.
BARBER, M. A. (1908) *J. infect. Dis.*, **5**, 379.
BARNES, L. A. (1931) *J. Bact.*, **21**, 395.
BATEMAN, J. B. (1935) *Biol. Rev.*, **10**, 42.
BREED, R. S. (1911) *Zbl. Bakt.*, IIte Abt., **30**, 337.
BROOM, J. C. (1929) *Brit. J. exp. Path.*, **10**, 71.
BUCHANAN, R. E. (1918) *J. infect. Dis.*, **23**, 109.
BUCHANAN, R. E. and FULMER, E. I. (1928) " Physiology and Biochemistry of Bacteria."
    London.
BURKE, G. S. (1923) *J. infect. Dis.*, **33**, 274.
BURKE, V., SPRAGUE, A. and BARNES, L. V. (1925) *J. infect. Dis.*, **36**, 555.
CHESNEY, A. M. (1916) *J. exp. Med.*, **24**, 387.
CHICK, H. (1912) *J. Hyg., Camb.*, **12**, 414.
CHILD, C. M. (1915) " Individuality in Organisms." Chicago.
CLARK, P. F. and RUEHL, W. H. (1919) *J. Bact.*, **4**, 615.
COPLANS, M. (1910) *J. Path. Bact.*, **14**, 1.
EBERLE, R. (1896) *Zbl. Bakt.*, **19**, 2.
FUKUDA, Y. (1929) *Z. ImmunForsch.*, **60**, 88.

GILDEMEISTER, E. and NEUSTAT, M. (1935) *Zbl. Bakt.*, **133**, 101.

GRAHAM-SMITH, G. S. (1921) *J. Hyg.*, *Camb.*, **19**, 133.

GREENWOOD, M. and YULE, G. U. (1917) *J. Hyg.*, *Camb.*, **16**, 36.

HALVORSON, H. O. and ZIEGLER, N. R. (1933*a*) *J. Bact.*, **25**, 101 ; (1933*b*) *Ibid.*, **26**, 331, 559.

HEAP, H. and CADNESS, B. H. E. (1924) *J. Hyg.*, *Camb.*, **23**, 77.

HELBER, E. (1904) *Dtsch. Arch. klin. Med.*, **81**, 317.

HENRICI, A. T. (1926) *J. infect. Dis.*, **38**, 54 ; (1928) " Morphologic Variation and the Rate of Growth of Bacteria." London.

HERRINGTON, B. L. (1934) *J. Bact.*, **28**, 177.

HIRSCH, J. (1933) *Klin. Wschr.*, **12**, 191.

HOSKINS, J. K. (1934) *Publ. Hlth. Rep.*, *Wash.*, **49**, 393.

JENNISON, M. W. (1935) *J. Bact.*, **30**, 603.

KELLY, C. D. and RAHN, O. (1932) *J. Bact.*, **23**, 147.

KOJIMA, S. (1923) *Sci. Rep. Inst. infect. Dis. Tokyo Univ.*, **2**, 305.

LANE-CLAYPON, J. E. (1909) *J. Hyg.*, *Camb.*, **9**, 239.

LEDINGHAM, J. C. G. and PENFOLD, W. J. (1914) *J. Hyg.*, *Camb.*, **14**, 242.

LEMON, C. G. (1933) *J. Hyg.*, *Camb.*, **33**, 495.

LIESE, W. (1926) *Z. Hyg. InfektKr.*, **105**, 483.

MASON, M. M. (1935) *J. Bact.*, **29**, 103.

McCRADY, M. H. (1915) *J. infect. Dis.*, **17**, 183 ; (1918) *Canad. publ. Hlth. J.*, **9**, 201.

MESTRE, H. (1935) *J. Bact.*, **30**, 335.

MOORE, H. F. (1915) *J. exp. Med.*, **22**, 551.

MÜLLER, M. (1895) *Z. Hyg. InfektKr.*, **20**, 245.

PEARL, R. and PARKER, S. L. (1922) *Proc. nat. Acad. Sci. Wash.*, **8**, 212 ; quoted from Maclagan, D. S. (1932) *Proc. roy. Soc.*, *B*, **111**, 437.

PENFOLD, W. J. (1914) *J. Hyg.*, *Camb.*, **14**, 215.

PENFOLD, W. J. and NORRIS, D. (1912) *J. Hyg.*, *Camb.*, **12**, 527.

PULVERTAFT, R. J. V. and LEMON, C. G. (1933) *J. Hyg.*, *Camb.*, **33**, 245.

RAHN, O. (1906) *Zbl. Bakt.*, IIte Abt., **16**, 417.

RÉGNIER, J., DAVID, R., and KAPLAN, A. (1932) *C. R. Acad. Sci.*, **194**, 323.

REICHENBACH, H. (1911) *Z. Hyg. InfektKr.*, **69**, 171.

ROGERS, L. A. and GREENBANK, G. R. (1930) *J. Bact.*, **19**, 181.

SCHMIDT, H. (1926) *Z. Hyg. InfektKr.*, **106**, 314.

SCHMIDT, H. and FISCHER, E. (1930) *Z. Hyg. InfektKr.*, **111**, 542.

SCHULTZ, J. H. and RITZ, H. (1910) *Zbl. Bakt.*, **54**, 283.

SHERMAN, J. M. and ALBUS, W. R. (1923) *J. Bact.*, **8**, 127 ; (1924) *J. Bact.*, **9**, 303.

SKAR, O. (1934) *Z. InfektKr. Haustiere*, **46**, 110.

SLATOR, A. (1917) *J. Hyg.*, *Camb.*, **16**, 100.

STEIN. (1917) *Engng. News. Rec.*, **78**, No. 8, 391.

STRAUSZ, W. (1930) *Zbl. Bakt.*, **115**, 228.

WALKER, H. H., WINSLOW, C.-E. A., HUNTINGTON, E., and MOONEY, M. G. (1934) *J. Bact.*, **27**, 303.

WIKULLIL, L. v. (1932) *Zbl. Bakt.*, **126**, 488.

WILSON, G. S. (1922) *J. Bact.*, **7**, 405 ; (1926) *J. Hyg.*, *Camb.*, **25**, 150.

WILSON, G. S., TWIGG, R. S., WRIGHT, R. C., HENDRY, C. B., COWELL, M. P., and MAIER, I. (1935) *Spec. Rep. Ser. med. Res. Coun.*, *Lond.*, No. 206.

WRIGHT, A. E. (1902) *Lancet*, ii. 11.

CHAPTER V

THE RESISTANCE OF BACTERIA TO PHYSICAL AND CHEMICAL AGENTS: DISINFECTION

INTRODUCTORY

THE early investigations of the problem of disinfection, which may be said to have commenced with Pringle's observations in 1750, were largely concerned with a study of the efficacy of various substances in hindering putrefaction. A century and a quarter later Bucholtz (1875), using as his medium an infusion of tobacco leaves, conducted a series of investigations on disinfectants; and Baxter (1875), working with vaccine lymph and glanders nodules, showed the influence of organic matter in diminishing the activity of disinfectants.

The next advance, illustrating the importance of technique, was made by Koch in 1881, when he introduced an exact method of comparing the germicidal power of different substances. In place of fluids swarming with different organisms of varying resistance, he tested the action of disinfectants on pure cultures of bacteria of approximately equal resistance. By drying anthrax spores on silk threads of the same length, immersing them in a solution of the substance to be tested, and subsequently transferring them to a nutrient medium in order to ascertain if the bacteria were still alive, he collected a considerable quantity of information on the relative efficiency of different disinfectants. His work was criticized and his methods improved by Geppert (1889, 1891a, b). In 1897 Krönig and Paul published their classical paper, describing a new method for the quantitative study of disinfection, and demonstrating that the death of bacteria under the influence of a germicidal agent is a gradual process, the rapidity of which decreases with advancing time. To Madsen and Nyman (1907) and to Chick (1908, 1910, 1912) must be ascribed the merit of analysing the various factors upon which disinfection depends, and of showing that the law underlying the death of bacteria is similar to that underlying a simple unimolecular chemical reaction.

Starting from empirical observations on the preservation of dead human bodies, the study of disinfection has progressed through the qualitative stage to the quantitative stage, and has now reached a point when the ultimate solution of the problem lies in the domain of the physical chemist.

The subject of disinfection is large, and can be treated from different aspects. In the present chapter we shall make no attempt to deal with it exhaustively; on the contrary, we shall purposely neglect a considerable part of the subject dealing with the use of germicides in practice, as we consider this to fall within the province of the hygienist. Our main endeavour is to discover as far as possible the underlying principles of disinfection, to discuss the laws governing the killing of bacteria, and to point out the importance of a thorough knowledge of these laws and principles to any one who, whether engaged in medicine, hygiene, dairy-farming, food-preservation, or agriculture, is confronted with the problem of controlling bacterial activity.

Physical Agencies

Light.—Downes and Blunt in 1877 (1877, 1878) showed that exposure of a putrescible fluid to sunlight was sufficient to sterilize it. They observed that this effect was produced only in the presence of air, and were therefore led to regard the germicidal property of light as depending on oxidation. Duclaux (1887) in 1886 showed that in sunlight vegetative bacilli were killed more rapidly than spores. The following year Roux (1887) exposed anthrax spores in a nutrient medium to the sun. Some were contained in glass tubes with plenty of air above the level of the liquid, others in glass tubes containing no free air ; the former were destroyed in 29 hours, the latter survived longer than 83 hours. This was a confirmation of the work of Downes and Blunt, but Roux went further ; he found that if nutrient broth was exposed to the sun in a layer 5 mm. deep for 3 or 4 hours, it became changed in such a way as no longer to permit of the germination of anthrax spores, though still remaining suitable for the growth of the vegetative bacilli. This antiseptic property was lost after the broth had been allowed to stand for a time in the dark. Broth exposed to the sun in a sealed glass tube containing no free oxygen was unaffected. It was clear, therefore, that not only was sunlight in the presence of air able to destroy anthrax spores, but that it was able to produce an alteration in a nutrient medium—an alteration which was of a transient nature, suggestive of the activity of some volatile or unstable compound. Quite recently this action of sunlight has been reinvestigated by Burnet (1925) ; working with staphylococci, he found that they would not grow on agar plates that had been exposed to the sunlight, though growing quite satisfactorily on control plates that had been kept in the dark. He was able to show that the reason for this is that under the influence of sunlight hydrogen peroxide is produced, and that this substance is so powerful that its inhibitory effect is noticeable even in a dilution of 1–40,000 (see Chapter III).

To return to the action of light on the bacteria themselves : Ward in 1892 exposed gelatin and agar plates seeded with anthrax spores to the autumn sunlight for 6 hours, each plate being shaded in such a way that only part of it received the direct rays of the sun. After incubation, a growth of anthrax bacilli was found to have occurred in the protected but not in the exposed portion. The inhibitory action of the sun was not due to the heat rays, because the temperature of the plates at no time rose above 18° C. ; nor was it due to desiccation or other alteration of the medium, since exposed plates seeded with fresh spores proved quite suitable for growth. Ward therefore concluded that the germicidal effect of the sun was due to its actinic rays. Further work showed that if a spectrum was thrown across an agar plate, the inhibitory effect of the light was stronger at the blue than at the red end. This was the first demonstration of the selective action of violet light. Some years later Barnard and Morgan (1903), working with the arc spectrum of carbon and of various metals, made more extensive observations, which led them to conclude that the bactericidal action of light was almost entirely due to those radiations in the ultra-violet region which are included between the wave lengths 3287 and 2265 Å.U., that is, the light between the visible violet and the extreme ultra-violet. No other portion of the spectrum had any effect whatever. Their work has been confirmed by Browning and Russ (1917), who used a quartz spectrometer illuminated by an arc of pure tungsten, which is very rich in ultra-violet rays. The spectrum was thrown across a gelatin or agar plate seeded with staphylococci, the plate incubated after irradiation, and then used as an ordinary photographic negative for producing positive contact prints. An exposure of 6 minutes was sufficient to destroy the organisms in that region illuminated by rays of 2380 to 2940 Ångström units. (An Ångström unit is equal to 1×10^{-7} mm., *i.e.* 1/10,000,000th mm. One $m\mu$ is equal to 1×10^{-6} mm., *i.e.* 1/1,000,000th mm., or 1/1,000th μ, or 10 Ångström units.) There was a sharp line of demarcation at 2960 Å.U.; rays of a longer wave length than this were almost devoid of germicidal action. It was found that the rays between 2960 and 2100 Å.U. were highly germicidal, but that the most active were those between 2800 and 2540 Å.U. As the limit of retinal sensibility is reached when the wave length falls to 3970 Å.U., it follows that the most actively germicidal portion of the spectrum is in that part which is invisible to the human eye (Fig. 14). More recent work by Gates (1930), Ehrismann and Noethling (1932), and Buchholz and v. Jeney (1935), has shown that two of the most active wave lengths are 2650 and 2530 Å.U. Different organisms appear to vary in their susceptibility to different wave lengths.

Ultra-violet light is lethal, not only to bacteria, but to other unicellular organisms such as amœbæ (Barr 1923), and to the tissue cells of animals and plants. It is, in fact, a protoplasmic poison. Though the short rays are undoubtedly the most active, the other rays of sunlight are not completely devoid of germicidal power; they require, however, very much longer to produce their lethal effect (Thiele and Wolf 1907). Laroquette (1918) found that blue was more active than yellow, and yellow than red; green light was the poorest of all. The time necessary for destruc- tion of micro-organisms by ultra-violet light depends on the intensity of the light, the distance of the source of illumination, and the nature of the medium in which the organisms are exposed. In general, the Bunsen-Roscoe law holds true; that is, within given limits the product of the intensity of irradiation and the length of exposure is constant.

The germicidal effect of sunlight under natural conditions varies greatly. Its action is complex, due partly to the actinic and partly to the calorific rays, which act by dehydration. Apart from its action on the organisms themselves, it has an action on the medium in which they are growing. In Southern lands, the combined effect of the ultra-violet rays and the heat rays render sunlight highly efficient as a germicidal agent; thus Semple and Greig (see Hewlett 1909) in India found that *Bact. typhosum* exposed to the sun on pieces of white drill cloth were killed in 2 hours; controls kept in the dark were still alive after 6 days. In the civilized smoke-covered towns of the north, the ultra-violet rays are often very weak, being largely filtered off by the impurities in the atmosphere, thus depriving sunlight of most of its activity.

Ultra-violet light generated by a Cooper Hewitt Mercury vapour lamp has been used for the sterilization of drinking water. Foulds (1911) found that it was quite easy to ensure a 99 per cent. reduction in the bacterial count, including all *Bact. coli*, by this method. For further information, see Thresh and Beale (1910).

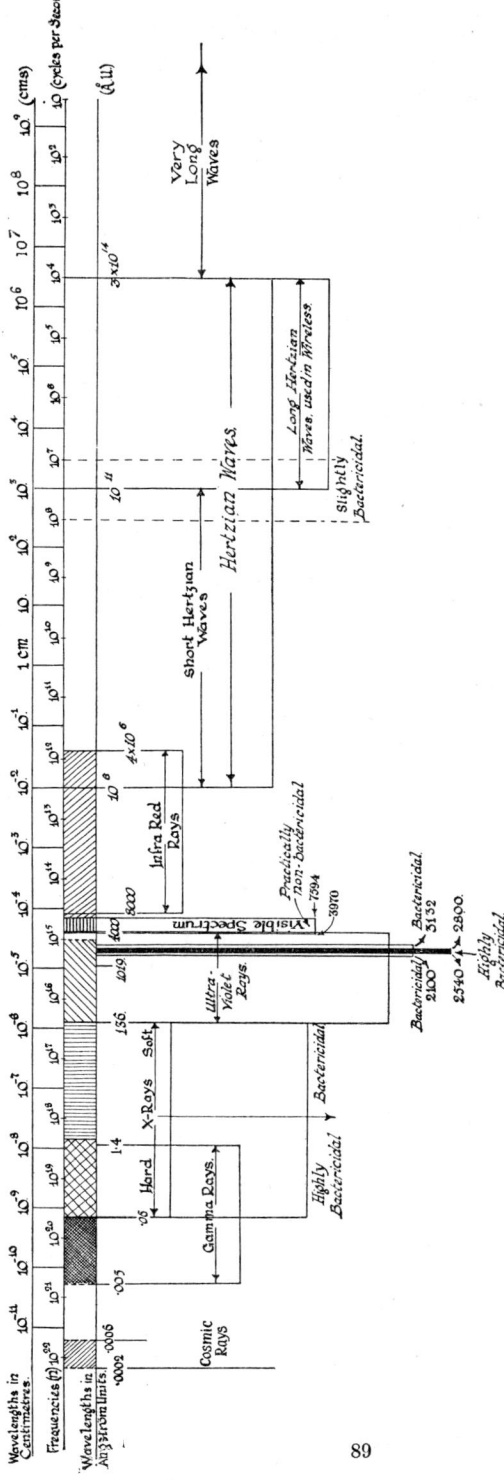

Range of Electromagnetic Waves.

Uniform Velocity of 30,000,000,000 Centimetres per Second.

Fig. 14.—Diagram showing the Range of Electromagnetic Waves with the Bactericidal Action of Rays of Different Wave-length.

Note.—Little work has been done on some parts of this range and none on others, so that the figure must be regarded as affording no more than an indication, incomplete and probably in part erroneous, of the bactericidal action of these waves.

The scale of this chart is taken from a diagram prepared by Vivian T. Saunders, M.A., of Uppingham School, and published by John Murray, London, W.1, to whom we are indebted for permission to reproduce it.

Mode of Action of Ultra-violet Light.—Ultra-violet light is peculiar in that its penetrating power is very low. Even a thin layer of glass, such as a cover slip, is able to filter off a large proportion of the rays. The same power is possessed by proteins. It follows therefore that its action must be chiefly on the surface of the body which it irradiates. Wesbrook (1896), by an ingenious series of experiments, showed that when tetanus or cholera cultures were irradiated by the sun in the presence of air, a consumption of oxygen took place. D'Arcy and Hardy (1894) came to the conclusion that under the influence of ultra-violet light, some oxidizing substance is produced—possibly ozone—which is responsible for its bactericidal effect. This is very doubtful. There seems to be no question that the destructive action of ultra-violet light is manifest in the absence of atmospheric oxygen (Thiele and Wolf 1906, 1907, Blum 1932, Buchholz and v. Jeney 1935), so that ozone can hardly be responsible. Nor does it seem likely that hydrogen peroxide is generated in sufficient quantities to prove lethal, since Ehrismann (1930) found that, to produce a destruction of bacteria similar to that caused by ultra-violet light, a concentration of 30 per cent. H_2O_2 was required.

There is evidence that the ultra-violet rays act by inducing some change in the protein molecule. Thus they are destructive, not only of organized cells, but of cellular products, such as tetanus toxin (Kitasato 1891, Fermi and Pernossi 1894, Wesbrook 1896), and serum complement (Sellards 1918, Brooks 1920). Dreyer and Hanssen (1907), working with solutions of various albumins and globulins, exposed in very thin layers, found that the rays caused a true coagulation of the proteins, which were no longer soluble in weak acids or alkalies. Corroboration of this view is found in the experiments of Tchahotine (1921). Working with the eggs of sea urchins, which are rich in lecithin, he found that if they were stained with neutral red and then irradiated with ultra-violet light, the colour changed after a time to yellow, indicating the presence of alkali within the cell. Further work seemed to show that the action of the rays was on the superficial membrane of the cell, which was rendered more permeable to the OH-ions of the medium ; these, on penetrating the cell, were responsible for the change of the neutral red to yellow. In support of this, it was found that if the eggs were irradiated in a neutral solution, no change in the colour of the dye took place. From these and further experiments he comes to the conclusion that the rays act primarily on the superficial layer of the cell, coagulating its colloids, and rendering it more permeable to the ions in the surrounding medium. Ehrismann (1930) exposed saline suspensions of various bacteria to ultra-violet irradiation for 6 hours, and observed that a decrease in the opacity occurred, accompanied by a fall in the total count. No change in pH, however, was noticed. Agencies such as increased acidity, higher temperatures, formol, and mercuric chloride, that tended to hasten the coagulation of protein, partly or completely inhibited the clearing effect of the rays. Analysis showed that the total nitrogen in the suspending fluid was increased, though the amino-nitrogen figure remained unaltered. The conclusion appears to be that the rays produce a colloidal change in the protoplasm leading to the solution of certain of its constituents. Whether true autolysis occurs in addition is still doubtful.

Buchholz and v. Jeney (1935) suggest that the reaction may possibly be of photo-electrical nature. These workers point out that the highly lethal waves 2650 and 2530 Å.U. correspond respectively to energy values of 4·6 and 4·8 volts, and conclude that this amount of energy is required to displace sufficient electrons from the bacterial protoplasm to give rise to irreversible photo-chemical alterations and thus bring about the death of the cell. Wyckoff (1932), who has studied this aspect of the problem in the light of the quantum theory, finds that about 4 million quanta of energy are required to kill a single coliform bacillus, showing that death is not due, as it appears to be with the cathode rays, to a single quantum absorption, but to some more generalized effect on the bacterial protoplasm.

The mode of action of ultra-violet light is still obscure, but the work of Gates (1930) and Ehrismann and Noethling (1932) renders it probable that it depends on the alteration of certain molecular groupings in the cell having high specific absorption spectra for these rays. The exact nature of the effect produced must await further observation.

Photodynamic Sensitization.—We have seen that the visible rays of the spectrum have only a weak germicidal action on bacteria. It has been found, however, by Raab (1900) and by v. Tappeiner (1900) that certain fluorescent dyes are able to sensitize infusoria to the action of these rays, so that they become almost as lethal as the ultra-violet rays. Thus it was shown that paramœcium suspended in a solution of acridin or eosin was killed very much more rapidly when exposed to diffuse sunlight, which was itself harmless, than when kept in the dark. Examining this phenomenon more closely, v. Tappeiner projected a spectrum across a table, and placed a culture of paramœcium, suspended in 1–800 solution of eosin, in the red, green, violet, and ultra-violet parts. The culture exposed to the green rays was killed in 2 to 4 hours, whereas the cultures exposed to the other rays appeared to be unharmed. This is of double interest ; firstly, because the green rays by themselves are the least active in germicidal power ; and, secondly, because it is in green light that eosin fluoresces most strongly. Similarly with acridin, death was most rapid when the suspension was exposed to the violet rays, these being the rays which cause acridin to fluoresce. For the sensitization to occur it was essential for the paramœcium to be in close contact with the fluorescing particles. When the cultures were exposed to light that was simply filtered through eosin, they remained unharmed ; the eosin had to be dissolved in the actual culture before its sensitizing action became apparent.

Later, v. Tappeiner and Jodlbauer (1904) and Jodlbauer and v. Tappeiner (1904) demonstrated that the photodynamic action of dyes is manifest not only in relation to infusoria, but in relation to bacteria, toxins, and to a less extent antitoxins, while more recently the bacteriophage (Clifton 1931) and filtrable viruses (Perdrau and Todd 1933b) have been found susceptible.

Burge and Neill (1915), exposing various micro-organisms to ultra-violet light, found that the non-fluorescent were killed more rapidly than the fluorescent bacteria ; their supposition is that the latter protect themselves from the coagulating effect of ultra-violet light by converting the short wave lengths into longer waves, and thus disposing of the energy of the absorbed short waves that would otherwise be spent in coagulating them. The non-fluorescent bacteria are unable to do this, and hence succumb. In this connection, it is interesting to note that fluorescent bacteria may themselves exercise a sensitizing action on infusoria, thus taking the place of complex dyes. Jodlbauer and v. Tappeiner (1904) found that paramœcium, suspended in a killed broth culture of *Ps. pyocyanea*, was killed in an hour if exposed to diffuse daylight, while surviving for 24 hours in the dark. Gram-negative organisms appear to be more resistant than Gram-positive ones (see T'ung 1935).

Later work by Schmidt and Norman (1920) suggests that the photodynamic effect of certain dyes is not dependent simply on their power of fluorescence. They showed that red blood cells mixed with eosin and exposed to sunlight were hæmolysed, even if the rays that cause eosin to fluoresce were filtered off before reaching the solution. Again, in a mixture of red cells, eosin, and a protective substance, such as tyrosine, exposed to sunlight, there was no hæmolysis even though the solution was fluorescing strongly. Clifton (1931) found that a staphylococcal bacteriophage suspended in 0·01 — 0·1 per cent. methylene blue solution was inactivated by exposure to sunlight for 5 minutes or more. The reaction did not occur *in vacuo*, or in the presence of an active reducing agent such as cysteine hydrochloride (0·01 per cent.). Perdrau and Todd (1933a), besides confirming these observations and finding that the optimal concentration of dye was about 1–100,000, showed that the interposition of a green screen prevented the reaction, while a red screen did not.

The mode of action of dyes, in causing sensitization to light that is not itself markedly germicidal, is not very clear, but it would appear that as the dye must be adsorbed on to the surface of the cell, and as oxygen is necessary for the effect to take place, the process is probably due to an activation of oxygen, or to an oxidation product of the dye (Bayliss 1924). (For a review of the whole subject see Blum 1932.)

Electricity.—(1) *Low-Frequency Currents.* Little work has been done. Prochownick and Spaeth (1890) passed a current through simple saline suspensions of *B. anthracis*, *B. subtilis*, and *Staphylococci* without much effect ; after 2 hours *B. subtilis* had lost its motility, but was quite capable of growth. In another experiment the electrodes were coated with agar, seeded with organisms, immersed in saline, and a current passed through. No effect was noticeable at the cathode, but around the anode the organisms were killed. Thus a 60 milliamp. current destroyed *Staphylococcus aureus* in 15 minutes, and a 230 M.A. current destroyed *B. anthracis* in 30 minutes. They concluded that the effect was due not to the electricity *per se*, but to the nascent chlorine which was evolved at the anode from the electrolytically dissociated saline. Similar results were obtained in the same year by Apostoli and Laquerrière (1890). They employed a constant galvanic current, which was passed through a broth culture of *B. anthracis* into which the electrodes, situated a short distance apart, had been inserted. A current of 300 M.A. was fatal in 5 minutes ; one of 200–250 M.A. failed to sterilize the culture in this time. They found that the action of the constant galvanic current was in direct relation to the intensity of the current, measured in milliampères ; that it depended far more on the intensity of the current than on the time for which it acted ; and that the lethal effect was confined to the positive pole. They excluded the effect of heat, and were able to show that the sterilizing action of the constant current was due to the liberation of acids and of nascent oxygen at the anode.

Beattie and Lewis (1920) were able to kill over 99·9 per cent. of organisms in milk by exposure for 4 minutes to an electric current, with a terminal voltage of about 4,000, and an amperage of about 2. Most of the sterilizing action appeared to be due to heat, as the temperature rose to between 60 and 64° C., but the authors considered that this alone was insufficient to account entirely for the effect.

(2) *High-Frequency Currents.* Apart from the early experiments of D'Arsonval and his colleagues in 1893 to 1896 (for references see Fabian and Graham 1933), little work has been carried out till recently on the action of high-frequency currents. During the past few years, however, a number of workers have made observations on the effect of these currents on bacteria, bacteriophage, toxins, and antibodies (Szymanowski and Hicks 1932, Hicks and Szymanowski 1932, Lentze 1932, Fabian and Graham 1933, Hasché and Leunig 1935, Gale and Miller 1935). The results are not easy to summarize, since the conditions of exposure used by different workers were often very different. In Fabian and Graham's experiments a gradual destruction of *Bact. coli* was brought about by exposure to a high-frequency displacement current of 10 megacycles per second and an intensity of 0·8 amps, but even after 8 hours the suspension was not sterile. The higher frequencies used by most of the other workers appeared to be less harmful. Whether the current acts mainly by generation of heat in the medium, or by setting up intense electronic and ionic linear agitation within the cells, is doubtful. [1 megacycle = 1,000 kilocycles = 1,000,000 alternating cycles. Since $V = n\lambda$, when V = velocity of travel (186,000 miles per second), n = frequency, or number of vibrations of the wave per second, and λ = the wave length, it can be calculated that a frequency of 10 megacycles corresponds approximately to a wave length of 30 metres.] Short-wave therapy, using radiations of 3 to 30 metres in wave length, is now on trial in clinical medicine for the treatment of certain inflammatory processes.

Cathode Rays.—Wyckoff and Rivers (1930), working with *Bact. coli*, *Bact. typhi-murium*, and *Staph. aureus*, bombarded single bacteria on the surface of an agar plate with a known number of cathode rays. The proportion of surviving organisms was estimated from colony counts made after incubation of the plates. The cathode rays were generated in a Coolidge type electron tube working at a voltage of approximately 155 kilovolt. Destruction of the organisms occurred in the usual semi-logarithmic fashion (see p. 118). After 20 seconds 83·1–93·9 per cent. of the organisms were dead. Quantitative analysis rendered it evident that the absorption of a single electron was generally sufficient to cause death.

The action of cathode rays seems to depend on the release of large numbers of ions consequent on the absorption of an electron. A single 150-kilovolt electron will liberate about 10^4 ions within less than 0·001 c.mm. The effect of such an ionic shower on organisms as small as those mentioned seems to be almost invariably lethal, though with yeast cells injury, and not death, may result (Wyckoff and Luyet 1931).

Röntgen Rays.—According to Rieder (1902) the cholera vibrio, when exposed on an agar plate at a distance of 10–12 cm. from the anti-cathode, is killed by Röntgen rays in 20 to 30 minutes. Feistmantel (1902) found that irradiation for 50 minutes of *Actinomyces farcinica*, exposed 10 cm. away from the anti-cathode, had apparently no effect. Wyckoff (1930a, b) exposed *Bact. coli* and *Bact. typhi-murium* on the surface of agar plates to soft X-rays, obtained either from a tungsten tube operated at low voltage, or by the characteristic K-radiation of copper. Destruction occurred semi-logarithmically, but less rapidly than with cathode rays (see above). Thus after 20 seconds' exposure to filtered copper radiation only 19·6–33·3 per cent. of organisms were dead. Analysis showed that only about one in twenty of the absorbed quanta of these radiations proved lethal.

According to Wyckoff, the X-rays incident upon a cell either pass through without altering it, or else give up one or more quanta whose energy content is connected with the wave-length λ of the rays through the relation

$$E = h\nu = h\frac{\lambda}{c}$$

where h is Planck's constant, ν is the frequency of the rays, and c is the velocity of light.

As the result of such an absorption a high-velocity electron is liberated. This electron gives rise to a chain of ions in the matter through which it passes and to X-rays which, in their turn, liberate more ions of less and less energy. The changes caused by X-rays in protoplasm are naturally identified with the physico-chemical changes induced by this ionic shower. The fact that only one in twenty of the absorbed quanta proves fatal suggests that the vital elements capable of being destroyed by a direct quantum hit occupy only about one-twentieth of the cell volume. This explanation, while possibly correct, must be accepted with caution, since similar reasoning applied to ultra-violet radiation leads to the almost certainly absurd conclusion that the " sensitive volume " within the cell is about the size of a single protein molecule. The harder the X-rays are, the nearer do they approach in their killing effect to the cathode rays. More recent work with *Bact. coli* by Pugsley, Oddie, and Eddie (1935) yielded results which seemed to show that, provided a correction factor was introduced for lack of uniformity of the X-ray beam, the organisms died in an exponential manner. Discussing these results, the authors came to the conclusion that the one-quantum-hit-to-kill explanation, first put forward by Crowther (1926), appeared to account most satisfactorily for the type of curve obtained.

Radium.—Bruynoghe and Dubois (1925) found that exposure of *Leptospira icterohæmorrhagiæ* for 26 hours to 8 mgr. of radium, enclosed in a platinum cell $\frac{1}{3}$ mm. in thickness, rendered the organism incapable of growing *in vitro* or of giving rise to disease in the guinea-pig, but did not interfere with its motility. Bruynoghe and Le Fèvre de Arric (1925) stated that they were able to deprive the viruses of rabies and of herpes of their virulence for rabbits, by exposure in fairly high dilution to radon, in a dose of 5 millicuries for 48 hours. Danysz (1906) failed to produce any attenuation of the rabic virus by exposure for 20 hours to the β- and γ-emanations from 20 mgr. of radium bromide. Bisceglie (1926) claims to have lowered the virulence for guinea-pigs of a human strain of tubercle bacillus, by exposure of three successive generations to 5 mgr. of radium bromide, the exposure being maintained for 5 days. Morphologically the bacilli of the third generation had lost their acid-fast properties to a considerable degree ; thread forms, occasionally showing branching, were numerous, and large numbers of Gram-positive Much granules were visible. According to Suess (1908), exposure of tubercle bacilli to highly active radium emanations for 2 days had apparently no effect on their morphology, growth, or pathogenicity. von Schroetter (1927) finds that bacilli and cocco-bacilli exposed to radon, in a dose varying for different organisms from 0·5 to 40·0 millicuries of an intensity of 5–250 microcuries, tend to elongate and become filamentous ; cocci, on the other hand, swell, increasing more or less equally in size in all diameters. Spirochætes do not change their size ; they are eventually killed by the rays, but they remain motile for a considerable time. Spencer (1934) implanted radium needles in tubes of broth inoculated with *Bact. typhosum*, *Proteus* X19, or *Str. hæmolyticus* and incubated at 37° C. There was at first a slight retardation of growth, but after 24 hours the growth was similar to that in control tubes. After 8–10 daily transfers the irradiated organisms sometimes grew more luxuriantly and tended to develop filamentous forms or, with streptococci, to grow in long chains. On the other hand irradiation at 0° C. proved fatal within a few days. Lea, Haines, and Coulson (1936) have recently studied the effect of α and β-rays on *Bact. coli*, *Staph. aureus*, and *B. mesentericus* exposed in very thin gelatin films. Death of the organisms occurred exponentially. The rate of disinfection was found to be independent of the temperature, and proportional to the intensity of the radiation. All three organisms were equally sensitive to α-rays, but towards β-rays *B. mesentericus* differed from the other two organisms. The authors conclude that the action of the radiation can be explained best on the " target " hypothesis.

Sonic and Supersonic Waves.—Starting with the experiments of Wood and Loomis in 1927, several observations have been made of recent years on the destruction of organized cells by high-frequency sound waves (for references up to 1932 see Chambers and Gaines 1932). Sonic waves, *i.e.* waves of audible frequency, of about 8,900 cycles per second, produced by a nickel tube vibrating in a strong electromagnetic field in resonance with a 2,000-volt oscillating power circuit, are said to be able to bring about a considerable destruction of coliform and certain other bacteria exposed to them for sufficient lengths of time. A reduction of over 99 per cent. in the plate count of milk submitted to the waves for 40–60 minutes has been reported.

Supersonic waves, *i.e.* waves above audible frequency, of 200,000 to 1,500,000 cycles per second, produced by connecting a piezo-electric crystal with a high-frequency oscillator, are also credited with bactericidal power. The observations of Beckwith and Olson (1932), Yen and Liu (1934), and Takahashi and Christensen (1934) suggest that a considerable destruction of bacteria, and even of filtrable viruses, may be brought about by exposure to these waves for an hour or so. Païc and his colleagues (1935*a*, *b*), however, found that ultrasonic waves of a frequency of 280,000 cycles per second had no destructive action in 2 hours on certain toxins, a *coli* bacteriophage, the herpes virus, or a number of different micro-organisms, while completely sterilizing a culture of *Paramœcium* in 5 minutes.

Too little work has yet been carried out to justify a critical discussion of the results. It is generally believed that the action of the waves, which are of course molecular and not electro-magnetic, is due to the disruption of the cell as a result of the violent agitation set up in its contents. According to Liu and Yen (1934) no effect is produced on cells exposed *in vacuo*, suggesting that cavitation of dissolved gases plays an important part in the disruption of the bacteria. Probably a relationship exists between the wave length and the size of the organism or molecule exposed. It is not clear that all workers have taken adequate precautions to guard against the effect of rise of temperature and of other disturbing factors, and the results so far recorded must be accepted with some reserve.

Desiccation.—If dried on silk threads or glass slips, the proportion of organisms surviving for any given length of time varies with a great number of factors, such as the species of bacterium, the initial numbers present, the nature of the suspending medium, the rapidity of drying, and the temperature and gaseous nature of the environment (see Ficker 1898). Anthrax spores dried on silk threads may survive for over 20 years, while many of the pathogenic non-sporing bacteria die in a few hours. Paul, Birstein, and Reusz (1910*a*), working with staphylococci dried on garnets, found that the velocity of disinfection was equal to the square root of the oxygen concentration. The lower the temperature at which the organisms were kept after being dried in this way, the smaller was the proportion that succumbed (Paul 1909).

More recent work (see Otten 1930, 1932, Elser, Thomas, and Steffen 1935, Flosdorf and Mudd 1935) has shown that even non-sporing pathogenic organisms are able to survive drying indefinitely, provided that desiccation is complete and that the dried organisms are maintained in a high vacuum (0·01 mm. Hg or less). Even such sensitive organisms as the meningococcus and the gonococcus remain alive and virulent for years under these conditions. The dried organisms are resistant to quite high temperatures. Typhoid bacilli, for example, dried and sealed *in vacuo*, are said to survive exposure to a temperature of 115° C. for over 30 minutes.

The method is now being used extensively for the preservation of stock cultures. In practice 0·5–1·0 c.c. quantities of a thick suspension of the organisms in broth are distributed into suitable tubes. Drying is carried out as rapidly as possible *in vacuo* in a desiccator over phosphorus pentoxide. The tubes are then evacuated individually with an efficient pump, and sealed off in the flame. To recover the organisms, an optimal medium is desirable for primary cultivation.

Dry Heat.—We have seen that disinfection by drying is influenced by numerous small factors ; in disinfection by heat, though numerous small factors may play a part, the one factor, heat, is so important that it overshadows them. We can therefore be more precise in our figures regarding this method of disinfection. Koch and Wolffhügel (1881) were the first to make exact measurements of the effect of heat on micro-organisms. They found that vegetative bacteria were killed by a temperature of just over 100° C. in 1½ hours ; many, of course, succumbed well within this interval, but this was the time necessary for complete sterilization. Spores, on the other hand, were much more resistant, requiring a temperature of 140° C. for 3 hours for destruction. On what this superior power of resistance of spores depends is not known. Probably it is related to their lower water content, since there is evidence to show that desiccation can raise the time-temperature limit necessary to cause coagulation of proteins (see Hewlett 1909, Cameron 1930). The resistance of both vegetative bacteria and of spores varies considerably with the different species, some being killed much more rapidly than others. The spores of moulds are intermediate in resistance between the vegetative and sporing bacteria ; they require a temperature of 110–115° C. for 1½ hours for their destruction.

As with desiccation, the higher the temperature, the shorter is the survival time. Thus, if the temperature is raised from 140° to 160° C. spores are killed in 1 to 1½ hours.

Koch did not regard dry heat as an efficient method of disinfection. Though satisfactory when dealing with naked bacteria, it is quite ineffectual within the times usually employed when the bacteria are protected by textile or other relatively non-conducting material ; this is due to the low power of penetration of hot air. Thus, when a bundle of tow measuring 55 × 50 cm. was exposed to a temperature of 140–150° C., the interior after 3 hours had only reached the temperature of 74·5° C.—a temperature quite inadequate to kill the spores enclosed in the bundle. Moreover a temperature of 140° C. is sufficient in a short time to ruin most cloth fabrics.

Flaming is a useful method of surface disinfection for non-inflammable substances; its efficacy appears to depend on the amount of heat generated (Mayser 1925).

Moist Heat.—Koch (Koch *et al.* 1881), in conjunction with Gaffky and Loeffler, was the first to make a quantitative study of the germicidal action of moist heat. He found that the temperature required for sterilization of spores was much lower than with dry heat. Thus anthrax spores were killed in 10 minutes at 95° C., and spores present in garden earth in less than 10 minutes at 105° C. He also showed that steam under pressure is more efficient than steam at atmospheric pressure. For the disinfection of clothes, too, he found moist heat to be preferable to dry heat, as it has a greater penetrating power. Thus after 4 hours' dry heat at 140–150° C. the temperature inside a roll of flannel was only 83° C., and the contained spores germinated freely, whereas after 1½ hours of moist heat at 120° C., the temperature inside was 117° C., and all the spores were dead. Koch was greatly impressed by the value of boiling water; from numerous experiments he concluded that even spores seldom survive its action for more than a few minutes. We now know that Koch rather over-estimated its efficiency, for there are certain bacteria the spores of which will resist the action of boiling water for hours. This is especially marked with the thermophilic bacteria; thus, Bigelow and Esty (1920) exposed the spores of thermophilic organisms, suspended in a nutrient medium of pH 6·1 in sealed glass tubes, to various temperatures in oil baths, with the following results:

Temperature.											
100° C.	.	.	.	.	.	.	.	.	.	1,320	minutes.
110° C.	.	.	.	.	.	.	.	.	.	225	,,
120° C.	.	.	.	.	.	.	.	.	.	23	,,
130° C.	.	.	.	.	.	.	.	.	.	3·5	,,
140° C.	.	.	.	.	.	.	.	.	.	1·0	,,

Thus at a temperature of 100° C. they remained viable for nearly a day.

It is on account of this resistance of spores to boiling water that the autoclave has largely displaced the steamer in laboratory practice. Steam is still employed at atmospheric pressure for the sterilization of certain media, the physical or chemical composition of which would be altered by steam under pressure, but where this is necessary we take advantage of Tyndall's observation, and submit the medium to steaming for 30 minutes on 3 successive days; any sporing organisms that have not been killed on the first day germinate, and thus become susceptible to exposure on the second day.

Steam under pressure, on the other hand, is so effective that a single sterilization usually suffices. In the autoclave the steam, while being submitted to pressure, still remains saturated with moisture. This is most important. Steam which is superheated behaves like a gas, and condenses very slowly on objects cooler than itself. Steam that remains saturated with moisture is much more effective, as it rapidly condenses on objects cooler than itself, and, by giving up its latent heat, quickly raises them to its own temperature. Though there are a few exceptions, it is safe to say that saturated steam under a pressure of 15 lbs. per square inch, *i.e.* with a temperature of about 120° C., is sufficient to sterilize any medium in 30 minutes. This is therefore the exposure to which the usual media are submitted.

The higher the temperature, provided the steam remains saturated, the more rapid is the sterilization.   This is clear from the results of Bigelow and Esty. But there are certain factors other than temperature that affect the time necessary for sterilization by steam.   One of the most important is the H-ion concentration of the medium.   It will be remembered that Pasteur in his experiments on spontaneous generation (see Chapter I) found that boiling was more lethal in an acid than in an alkaline medium.   This has since been confirmed repeatedly.   Bigelow and Esty (1920), for example, working with the spores of thermophilic organisms, found that when suspended in an acid medium of pH 4·6 they were destroyed by a temperature of 120° C. in 2 minutes, whereas in a less acid medium of pH 6·1 it required 9 minutes to destroy them.   Chick (1910) likewise found that minute quantities of acid or alkali, too small of themselves to produce any germicidal action, had a very marked influence on the power of disinfection by hot water.   With these substances the rate of disinfection was increased, but much more with the acid than with the alkali.   Thus, working with *Bact. typhosum* suspended in distilled water, she found that the addition of sufficient alkali to render the solution N/7,000 alkaline increased the mean rate of disinfection at 54° C. about 1·5 to 2-fold ; a similar addition of acid increased it 5 to 7-fold.   Further addition of alkali influenced the rate of disinfection but little, whereas further addition of acid rendered it too rapid for study.

Other factors are the age of the culture and the nature of the suspending medium.   Young organisms are generally more susceptible to the action of heat and of chemical disinfectants than old, while the presence of protein in the suspension, or of sugar in considerable concentration (Fay 1934), tends to protect the organisms to some extent.

Thermal Death Point of Bacteria.—The mode of action of heat on bacteria appears to be one of protein coagulation.   Chick and Martin (1910) showed that heat coagulation of proteins is an orderly process, the rate of which varies with the alteration of temperature, reaction of the medium, and other conditions.   The actual process of coagulation consists of two stages : in the first, known as denaturation, the water reacts with the protein ; in the second, known as agglutination, the altered protein separates out in a particulate form.   In the case of hæmoglobin the coagulation occurs logarithmically, the rate at any moment being proportional to the concentration of uncoagulated protein.   Very much the same law appears to be applicable to bacteria.   The higher the temperature to which they are submitted, the more rapidly is their cellular protein coagulated.   Between different organisms there are considerable variations ; thus some vegetative bacteria, such as the gonococcus, are destroyed by heat at 47° C. in a few minutes ; others, such as the enterococcus, withstand a temperature of 60° C. for nearly an hour.   It must not, however, be supposed that these temperatures are to be regarded as specific thermal death points, irrespective of the time of exposure.   Chick (1910) has shown that the death of bacteria under the influence of heat is due to a protein coagulation ; that this phenomenon occurs not at one definite point on the temperature scale, but over a considerable range of temperature ; and that therefore the death of bacteria within a given range is mainly a function of time.   To take for example *Bact. typhosum* : the thermal death point of this organism is usually given as 55° C.   In experiments carried out between 49° and 59° C. the temperature coefficient, *i.e.* the rise in the velocity of disinfection, was found to be 1·635 for 1° C.   Given a value for k (see p. 118) of 0·111, it can be calculated that a suspension containing 100,000 bacilli per c.c. would be sterilized in about 2 hours at 47° C., in 48 minutes at 49° C., in 18 minutes at 51° C., in 7 minutes at **53° C.**, in 2½ minutes at 55° C., and in 21 seconds at 59° C. If therefore a suspension was gradually heated, death might apparently take place suddenly at 55° C. But it is clear that this cannot be regarded as a point possessed of any special significance ; it is merely a point near the upper end of a series of temperatures, each of which in itself can legitimately be regarded as a thermal death point. It follows that for purposes of comparison of the heat susceptibility of organisms of different species, it is essential to use suspensions of equal numbers of bacteria, and to ascertain at what temperature complete sterilization is produced within a given time. Even with these precautions, as we shall see later, there is a certain inaccuracy, due to the apparent variation in susceptibility of organisms of the same species in the same suspension, resulting in the survival of some long after the majority have been killed.

Effect of Heat on Subsequent Multiplication.—In his studies on disinfection, Koch noticed that spores which had been heated but not quite killed required longer to germinate than unheated spores. Similar observations have been recorded by numerous workers both with spores and with vegetative bacteria. The conclusion usually drawn is that during the process of heating, the organisms are damaged in some way, so that their ability to multiply when subsequently transferred to suitable conditions is interfered with. Certain figures of Eijkman (1908) lend support to this view ; he heated a suspension of *Bact. coli* in saline at 52° C. and after varying intervals he made duplicate plates to ascertain the number of organisms remaining alive. One set of plates was counted after 3 days' incubation, and the other set after 15 days' incubation. The results are shown in Table IV.

TABLE IV

Length of heating at 52° C.	No. of organisms developing after incubation for :—	
	3 days.	15 days.
0 minutes	336,000,000	336,000,000
½ ,, ...	144,000,000	144,000,000
1 ,, ...	115,200,000	128,000,000
2 ,, ...	51,200,000	65,600,000
3 ,, ...	4,000,000	33,600,000
5 ,, ...	800,000	2,720,000
6 ,, ...	0	640,000
10 ,, ...	0	3,750
15 ,, ...	0	1,000
35 ,, ...	0	0

It will be noticed that during the first 30 seconds the heat, though killing over 50 per cent. of the organisms, does not interfere with the reproduction of the remainder. Subsequently, the longer the organisms are exposed, the greater is the difference between the results of the two series of plates. This suggests that a certain proportion of the remaining viable organisms are injured, and that the longer they are subjected to heat, the greater is the interference with their reproductive power.

Similar results have been obtained by Allen (1923), who, working with milk, found that the generation time of non-sporing organisms which had been pasteurized was longer than that of the untreated organisms, indicating an attenuation of the pasteurized organisms.

A different interpretation has, however, been proposed. Eckelmann (1917) suggests that the reason why a certain proportion of heated organisms require a long time to germinate is not because they are suffering from the effects of heat, but because they are provided with a more resistant cell membrane, which, while allowing them to withstand temperatures that prove lethal to their fellows, interferes with their rapid reproduction. According to her, heat would act as a selective agency, killing off all the bacteria with thin cell membranes and a power of rapid reproduction, and leaving intact the bacteria with thick, relatively impermeable cell membranes and a restricted power of reproduction. Burke (1923) adheres to the same view. She found that the spores of *Cl. botulinum* frequently took several days to germinate, even when placed under optimum conditions. When the spores were heated, the germination period was increased, generally in proportion to the length of exposure ; she found that they might lie dormant for as long as 426 days. Her conclusions are that the reason why the spores resist heat is because they are characterized by the possession of an impermeable membrane, which is also the cause of their delayed germination. The thicker the membrane, the more resistant is it to heat, and the longer does the organism take to develop.

The evidence of those in favour of the second view does not appear to us to be as strong as that in favour of the first. Eijkman's figures, given in Table IV, are very striking, and assuming their general validity, it is difficult to avoid concluding that the effect of heat is to increase the lag period of such organisms as remain viable. That the escape of the few is dependent on the possession of a relatively impermeable cell membrane is quite possible, but it fails to explain why in Eijkman's experiments before heating all organisms developed in 3 days, whereas after heating some failed to develop for 15 days.

Cold.—Very much less attention has been paid to the effect of cold on bacteria than to the effect of heat. This may undoubtedly be attributed to the fact that, although cold is an excellent means of preventing putrefaction, it has very little germicidal action. Macfadyen (1900) exposed cultures of *Bact. coli, Bact. typhosum, B. anthracis, V. choleræ, Proteus vulgaris*, and *Staphylococcus aureus* for 20 hours to liquid air at a temperature of $-182°$ to $-190°$ C. After exposure the organisms grew well on subculture, and manifested their usual biochemical activities. He noticed that photogenic bacteria, when frozen, became non-luminous, but, when re-thawed, their luminosity returned with unimpaired vigour. In another experiment he exposed the same organisms in broth suspensions enclosed in fine quill tubing for 7 days to liquid air ; subsequently no structural alteration could be detected in the bacteria, and all grew well on subculture. Macfadyen and Rowland (1900) found that the same organisms in sealed glass tubes withstood immersion for 10 hours in liquid hydrogen at a temperature of $-252°$ C. ; microscopically and culturally the bacteria appeared to be unaltered. Paul and Prall (1907) exposed staphylococci, which had been dried on garnets, to liquid air, and found that under these conditions they retained their viability for several months, and showed no appreciable alteration in their resistance to disinfectant agencies.

Nevertheless, though many organisms, such as those enumerated above, may withstand the enormous stresses set up by exposure to a temperature only 21° C.

above absolute, certain bacteria are readily affected by cold. Cultures of meningo-cocci and gonococci, for example, rapidly become sterile if placed in the ice-chest, though remaining viable for some days at a temperature of 37° C.

Chemical Agencies

Distilled Water.—The evidence concerning the action of distilled water on the viability of bacteria is most conflicting. Spores are undoubtedly able to survive for a long time ; thus Koch found that spores of the anthrax bacillus remained alive for more than 90 days. But with vegetative organisms it is otherwise. Some workers have found that they will survive for weeks, others that they are destroyed in a few hours. Such confusion can only be explained by differences in technique. One such difference of primary importance is the nature of the vessel from which the water is distilled. When a metallic still is used, traces of the metal are carried over into the distillate and undoubtedly exercise a deleterious effect on the bacteria. Ficker (1898) found, for instance, that water containing copper sulphate in a dilution of 1/50,000,000 was sufficient to kill cholera vibrios in 1 hour, while Hoder (1932) found that distilled water containing 1 part of copper in 10 million sterilized a suspension of *Ps. pyocyanea* in 2 hours.

But even those who have used pure glass-distilled water have obtained most varied results. One reason for this discrepancy may lie in the number of bacteria inoculated. In this connection some striking figures are reported by Ficker (1898). In one experiment he seeded pure glass-distilled water with 60,000,000 cholera vibrios per c.c., and found that they remained viable for several months. In another experiment, in which he reduced his inoculum to 10,000 per c.c., the organisms were nearly all dead in 2 hours. He explains such a difference on the assumption that the inoculation of large numbers of organisms into distilled water converts this into a dilute nutrient medium, no longer possessing the essential purity of the initial menstruum. The H-ion concentration of the water may also be an important factor. Thus Winslow and Falk (1923) give the following figures, compiled from no fewer than seventy-nine tests :

VIABILITY OF *Bact. coli* IN DISTILLED WATER AFTER 9 HOURS AT 37° C. *

pH	4·0	5·0	6·0	7·0	7·5	8·0
Percentage of organisms surviving	1	82	106†	54	35	12

* pH was adjusted by minute additions of acid or alkali.
† This figure suggests that a slight increase in the numbers of surviving organisms may have occurred.

The maximum viability occurs at pH 6·0. Cohen (1922) has likewise shown that when the pH of water is stabilized by the addition of buffer salts, the results are much more regular.

Other factors that may influence the action of distilled water on bacterial viability are traces of alkali absorbed from the glass, the amount of CO_2 absorbed from the air, the quantity of dissolved oxygen, and the temperature at which the suspension is maintained. Whipple and Mayer (1906), studying the length of life of *Bact. typhosum* in sterile tap water, showed that it remained viable for nearly 2 months when the water was exposed to the air, but died out in 4 days when the water was kept under anaerobic conditions. Houston (1914), likewise working with *Bact. typhosum*, found that, when suspended in water kept at 0° C., it lived for 8 weeks, at 18° C. for 3 weeks, and at 37° C. for only 1 week.

Summing up, we may say that the length of life of vegetative bacteria in distilled water is influenced by a large number of factors. When these factors are all favourable, the organisms may remain viable for considerable periods ; when unfavourable, they may die out in a very short time ; further, the effect varies greatly with different species of organisms. There is no evidence that distilled water acts by causing disruption of bacteria, as it does of many unicellular organisms ; bacteria are too resistant to changes in osmotic pressure for this to be probable.

Acids.—Krönig and Paul (1897) were the first to show that the disinfectant action of acids in general is proportional to their degree of electrolytic dissociation, *i.e.* to the H-ion concentration of their solutions. Some figures of Winslow and Lochridge (1906) will make this clear. Comparing the strengths of HCl and H_2SO_4 necessary to produce a 99 per cent. and a 100 per cent. reduction in the numbers of *Bact. coli* in 40 minutes, they observed that the disinfectant action of these two acids was in proportion to their degree of dissociation. Their results are given in Table V.

TABLE V

SHOWING PERCENTAGE REDUCTION OF *Bact. coli* IN 40 MINUTES BY ACIDS OF DIFFERENT STRENGTHS.

	99 per cent. Reduction.		100 per cent. Reduction.	
	HCl	H_2SO_4	HCl	H_2SO_4
Normality.	0·0077	0·0096	0·0123	0·0166
Degree of dissociation	97%	80%	96·4%	76%
Parts per million of dissociated hydrogen	7·49	7·68	12·8	12·6

It will be noticed that to cause a 99 per cent. reduction, the strength of HCl required was 0·0077 normal, whereas that of H_2SO_4 was rather greater, 0·0096 normal. But as the degree of dissociation was greater with HCl than with H_2SO_4, the final concentration of H-ions in the two solutions was practically identical. From this experiment we may, therefore, conclude that the disinfectant action of mineral acids in high dilution is a function of their degree of dissociation, and hence of their resulting H-ion concentration. Incidentally, we may notice that a considerably higher concentration of acid is necessary to sterilize a bacterial suspension completely than to reduce its numbers by 99 per cent. This point will be dealt with under the section dealing with the physical factors concerned in disinfection.

The effect of the H-ion concentration of the medium on bacteria suspended in it is rather complex. There is, first of all, an optimum concentration for growth ; for *Bact. coli* this is about pH 7·6. There is, secondly, an optimum concentration for survival ; for *Bact. coli* this is about pH 6·0. Thirdly, there is a point at which the acid-tolerance of the organism fails ; this for *Bact. coli* is about pH 4·6. During growth in a medium containing a fermentable carbohydrate, *Bact. coli* produces acid, which raises the H-ion concentration of the medium to about pH 5·0. This degree of acidity can be well tolerated, but if the acidity is increased beyond this point, instead of continuing to grow, the organisms cease multiplying and rapidly die. And lastly, there is evidence to suggest (Cohen and Clark 1919) that the H-ion concentration most suitable for certain fermentative processes is different from the optimum pH for growth.

Here, however, we are dealing with the acid-tolerance of micro-organisms, and this limit varies with different species. In Winslow and Lochridge's experiments, already referred to, the parts per million of dissociated hydrogen necessary to sterilize a suspension of *Bact. coli* in 40 minutes was 12·80 ; to sterilize a suspension of *Bact. typhosum* only 4·85 were required.

Apart, however, from the action of their free H-ions, certain acids have another disinfectant action on bacteria, which appears to be dependent on the nature of the molecule. To produce a 99 per cent. reduction in the number of *Bact. coli* in 40 minutes, Winslow and Lochridge (1906) found that a 0·0812 N solution of acetic acid, or an 0·0097 N solution of benzoic acid was required. The degree of dissociation of each acid at its respective concentration is only about 1 per cent., so that the amount of dissociated hydrogen in the acetic acid was 1·2 parts per million, and in the benzoic acid 0·1 parts per million. It will be remembered, however, that when HCl was used, 7·49 parts per million were necessary. From this it is evident that the toxic action of acetic and of benzoic acid depends on some other factor than their H-ion concentration. This other factor must be either the anion or the undissociated molecule. There is some evidence that the bactericidal activity of the monobasic series of organic acids increases with increase in molecular weight and decrease in surface tension, while with the dibasic organic acids the reverse holds true (Reid 1932). The subject, however, is complex, and no general statement can yet be made ; it will be discussed further in the section dealing with salt action.

SUMMARY.—(1) The disinfectant action of mineral acids is proportional, not to their normal strength, but to the number of free H-ions per unit volume.

(2) The organic acids are only slightly dissociated, so that their H-ion concentration is relatively low. As, however, they have a markedly germicidal effect, it must be concluded that this is a property of the whole molecule—or possibly to some extent of the anion—and is specific for each acid ; acetic acid has, for example, only 10–20 per cent. of the toxicity of benzoic acid.

(3) Certain other acids, such as fluoric acid and nitric acid, have a specific action, which is probably due to the anion.

Alkalies.—By similar experiments to those described in the section on acids, Krönig and Paul (1897) showed that the disinfectant action of alkalies was dependent on their degree of dissociation, and hence on their concentration of OH-ions.

Thus, of the bases KOH, NaOH, LiOH, and NH_4OH, KOH shows the highest degree of dissociation, and is hence the most actively germicidal ; NH_4OH is dissociated the least and is the least actively germicidal (Table VI, page 104).

When we turn to other bases, we find exceptions. Thus, $Ba(OH)_2$ is less dissociated than KOH, but is very much more toxic ; similarly with the hydroxides of the other alkaline earths. The reason for this, as we shall see in the section on salts, is that the metallic ion is frequently highly toxic, and assists the hydroxyl-ion in its germicidal activities.

Summarizing, we may say that unless a toxic metallic ion is present, the dis-

TABLE VI. (Krönig and Paul 1897.)

DISINFECTION OF ANTHRAX SPORES BY ALKALIES. Initial number of spores was about 6,800.

	Strength.	Percentage Degree of Dissociation.	No. surviving after :	
			3 hrs. 20 mins.	18 hrs.
KOH	M/1	77	585	31
NaOH	M/1	72	619	33
LiOH	M/1	64	778	44
$NH_4(OH)$	M/1	0·4	∞	∞

infectant action of an alkali is proportional to its degree of dissociation, and hence to its concentration of hydroxyl-ions.

Just as bacteria possess a limit of acid-tolerance, so they possess a limit of alkali-tolerance. Cohen (1922) found that for *Bact. typhosum* this was about pH 8·7. It is of interest to note that H-ions appear to be more toxic than OH-ions in similar concentration.

Salt Action.—Though this chapter primarily concerns the bactericidal action of various physical and chemical agencies, it is convenient to introduce here the subject of salt action in general.

We have seen that distilled water cannot be considered a satisfactory menstruum for bacteria. Many of the vegetative organisms die rapidly in it, and few survive for long. Ficker (1898) was the first to make direct observations on the action of physiological saline on bacteria. His results showed that instead of being harmless, it was actively bactericidal. Subsequent workers have confirmed his observations, and have demonstrated that the bactericidal effect is due to the toxicity of the sodium ion.

Delépine and Greenwood (1914), working with a number of heavy metals— copper, silver, zinc, cadmium, mercury—found that, though in certain concentrations they had a strong inhibitory action on bacterial growth, in lower concentrations they had the reverse effect, actually stimulating growth. Winslow and Hotchkiss (1922) found that the same held true for some of the lighter metals (Table VII).

TABLE VII

EFFECT OF DIFFERENT CONCENTRATIONS OF SALTS ON GROWTH OF *Bact. coli.*

	Stimulating.	Inhibiting.
$CaCl_2$.	0·01 M	0·5 M
$MgCl_2$	0·05 M	0·5 M
NH_4Cl	—	1·0 M
$SrCl_2$	0·1 M	1·0 M
NaCl	0·5 M	3·0 M
KCl	0·5 M	4·0 M

A further point of interest was brought out by Sherman and Holm (1922), who showed not only that NaCl stimulated growth in a concentration of 0·1 to 0·3 M, but that it widened the range of H-ion concentration within which *Bact. coli* would grow. Taking just visible turbidity of the culture as the sign of growth, they obtained results set out in Table VIII.

TABLE VIII.

GROWTH OF *Bact. coli* IN MEDIA OF DIFFERENT pH, IN THE PRESENCE AND ABSENCE OF NaCl.

Medium.	pH.	Turbidity appeared in:
P.W.	5·3	36 hours
P.W. 0·2 M NaCl . . .	5·3	4 ,,
P.W.	8·3	7 ,,
P.W. 0·2 M NaCl . . .	8·3	3½ ,,
P.W.	4·8	No growth
P.W. 0·2 M NaCl . . .	4·8	20 hours

Thus the addition of 0·2 M NaCl to a 1 per cent. solution of peptone in distilled water increased the rate of growth at unfavourable pH concentrations, and actually enabled the organisms to grow at pH 4·8—a concentration at which in plain peptone water they refused to grow at all.

It must be pointed out that a salt which is bactericidal in an aqueous solution may exert a stimulating effect when added in the same concentration to a nutrient medium.

Having referred to the favourable action of many weak solutions of salts on the growth and on the survival of bacteria, we must now pass on to consider their toxic action. This is the action which appealed particularly to the early workers. Koch in 1881 drew attention to the toxic action of salts, especially to the salts of the heavy metals, such as mercury and silver. Though his technique was criticized by Geppert (1889), who pointed out an important fallacy in his methods of determination of the toxicity of these salts, Koch's chief conclusions remain essentially true. Krönig and Paul (1897), and later Paul and Prall (1907), made the very important discovery that the toxicity of solutions of $HgCl_2$ depends not on the molecular concentration of the salt but on the concentration of free Hg-ions in the solution. Thus the halogen salts of mercury were found to be active in proportion to their degree of electrolytic dissociation,

$$HgCl_2 > HgBr_2 > HgI_2.$$

Solutions of salts in which the mercury was combined with a complex anion, and in which the degree of dissociation was poor, such as mercury acetate or cyanide, were found to be much weaker in germicidal power. The behaviour of the salts of the heavy metals is therefore analogous to that of the mineral acids, the toxicity being in proportion to the concentration of free metallic ions and of free H-ions respectively.

The mode of action of heavy metals themselves, as apart from their salts, is not clear. Their toxicity may be demonstrated either by adding them to distilled water, or by placing them, in the form of a bar or coin, on the surface of an inoculated agar plate. Kling (1932) believes that the pure metal goes into actual solution. On the other hand the experiments of Hofmann (1929) and Pilod and Codvelle (1932), both of whom found that oxygen was necessary for the manifestation of toxicity, suggest that an oxide of the metal is formed which then undergoes ionization. Pure metals, of course, cannot ionize, and their failure, whether in aqueous or colloidal solution, to prove toxic under anaerobic conditions, points strongly to the necessity of preliminary salt formation followed by their ionic dissociation.

A vast amount of work has been done on the effect of different salts on bacteria. As the salts of mineral acids are electrolytically dissociated, it is clear that their action may be due either to the undissociated molecule, to the anion, to the cation, or to all three in combination. To assess the importance of each of these factors, comparative tests have been made with salts of one metal combined with different anions, and of one anion combined with different metals. These tests have been conducted not only on various bacteria, but on protozoa, and on the eggs of certain fish. On the whole the results have been reasonably concordant, as may be seen from Table IX, in which the *cations* are arranged in order of ascending toxicity. It must be understood that strict comparison of the action of different salts can be undertaken only in media of the same H-ion concentration.

TABLE IX (modified from Falk 1923).
CATIONS IN SERIES OF INCREASING TOXICITY.

Eisenberg (1919). Bacteria.	Winslow and Hotchkiss (1922). *Bact. coli.*	Woodruff and Bunzel (1909). *Paramœcium.*	Mathews (1904). *Fundulus* Eggs.
Na	K	K	Sr
K	Na	Ca	Mg
NH₄	NH₄	Zn	Ba
Li	Li	Sr	K
Mg	Sr	Mg	NH₄
Sr	Mg	Mn	Al
Ca	Ca	Co	Ca
Ba	Ba	Ni	Na
Mn	Mn	Cd	Mn
Ce	Ti···	Cu	Li
Th	Sn	Ag	Fe··
Fe··	Ni	Pb	Ni
Yt	Ti·	Fe	Co
Cr	Zn	Hg	Zn
U	Cu		Au
Zn	Fe··		Cd
Fe···	Fe···		Cu
Ti	Co		Fe···
Be	Pb		
Al	Al		
Ne	Ce		
Pb	Cd		
Cu	Hg		
Tl			
Zr			
Ni			
Cd			
Co			
Au			
Pt			
Hg			
Ag			

From this table it will be seen that on the whole those metals of low atomic weight are less toxic than those of high atomic weight, though there are many exceptions.

To give some idea of the actual strengths necessary to cause inhibition of growth of *Bact. coli*, some results of Hotchkiss (1923) are given in Table X. She divides her salts into two groups, the more toxic ones comprising those of the heavy metals, and the less toxic, comprising those of the alkali metals and of the alkaline earth metals. The salts of Group I give neutral solutions; those of Group II, owing to hydrolysis, yield solutions with an acid reaction.

TABLE X

SALT CONCENTRATIONS THAT LIMIT GROWTH OF *Bact. coli* IN 1 PER CENT. PEPTONE WATER.
Incubation period, 3 days. Molar concentration.

GROUP I.			GROUP II.		
Salt.	No Growth.	Growth.	Salt.	No Growth.	Growth.
MnCl$_2$ . .	0·05	0·025	HgCl$_2$ . .	0·00001	0·000005
BaCl$_2$ . .	0·25	0·1	CdCl$_2$ . .	0·0001	0·00005
—	—	—	CeCl$_3$ . .	0·0005	0·0001
CaCl$_2$ . .	0·5	0·25	AlCl$_3$ . .	0·0005	0·0001
MgCl$_2$ . .	0·5	0·25	PbCl$_2$ . .	0·0005	0·001
SrCl$_2$ . .	1·0	0·25	CoCl$_2$ . .	0·0005	0·0001
—	—	—	FeCl$_2$ . .	0·001	0·0005
LiCl . .	0·75	0·5	FeCl$_3$ . .	0·001	0·0005
NH$_4$Cl . .	1·0	0·75	CuCl$_2$ . .	0·001	0·0005
NaCl . .	2·0	1·0	ZnCl$_2$ . .	0·001	0·0005
KCl . .	2·0	1·0	NiCl$_2$ . .	0·005	0·001
—	—	—	SnCl$_4$ . .	0·005	0·001
—	—	—	TiCl . . .	0·005	0·001
—	—	—	TiCl$_3$ . .	0·01	0·0025

A further point may be noted from this table, namely, that the bivalent cations tend to be more toxic than the monovalent cations.

Very much less work has been done on the effect of *anions* on the growth of bacteria. Falk (1923) points out that the anions play an essentially different part in metabolism from the cations. The former are intimately related to the nutritive metabolism—particularly the anions that contain carbon, sulphur, nitrogen or oxygen—whereas the latter are concerned with the regulative metabolism of the organism. Nevertheless, the anions in certain concentrations do undoubtedly possess a toxic action on bacteria. Some figures of Holm and Sherman's (1921) will exemplify this point. They grew *Bact. coli* in 1 per cent. peptone water, to which were added various sodium salts, the H-ion concentration being kept practically constant, and compared the rate of growth in the different tubes (Table XI).

TABLE XI

	pH	First Turbidity appeared in :
1 per cent. peptone	7·2	4½ hours.
,, ,, 0·2 M NaCl	7·3	3¼ ,,
,, ,, 0·2 M NaI	7·3	3½ ,,
,, ,, 0·2 M NaNO$_3$	7·3	3½ ,,
0·2 M Na$_2$SO$_4$	7·0	4 ,,
,, ,, 0·2 M (mixture of NaH$_2$PO$_4$ and Na$_2$HPO$_4$).	7·3	4¼ ,,
,, ,, 0·2 M Na lactate	7·0	4½ ,,
,, ,, 0·2 M Na oxalate	7·0	9½ ,,
,, ,, 0·2 M Na acetate	7·0	10¼ ,,
,, ,, 0·2 M Na citrate	7·3	10½ ,,
,, ,, 0·2 M NaF	7·4	48 ,,

From this it will be seen that the Cl-ion was the least, and the F-ion the most toxic.

One of the most extensive studies is that of Eisenberg (1919), who arranges the anions in order of toxicity thus : $SO_4 < S_2O_3 <$ Tartrate $< H_2PO_2 < MoO_4 < Cl < Br$; $NO_3 < SO_3 < Fe(CN)_6''''' <$ Acetate $< ClO_3 <$ Citrate $< HPO_3 <$ Oxalate $<$ Formate $<$ CNS $< ClO_4 < BrO_3 < I < H_2PO_4 <$ Benzoate $<$ Nitroprusside $< HAsO_4 < CrO_4 < P_2O_7 < NO_2 < F < BF_4 < HF_2 < BO_3 < B_4O_7 < Fe(CN)_6''' <$ Salicylate $< HSeO_3 < IO_3 < S_2O_8 < S_2O_7 < TeO_4 < SbS_4 < OsO_4 < IO_4 < Cr_2O_7 < TeO_3$.

The action of salts depends to a large extent on the medium in which they are dissolved ; thus they are more active when dissolved in distilled water than when dissolved in a medium containing protein. This is an observation that has been made frequently (Behring 1890, Krönig and Paul 1897, Chick and Martin 1908). Probably it is due to the fact that many cations combine with proteins to form an insoluble albuminate ; hence the concentration of free ions in the medium is diminished.

Another important observation is that different bacteria vary in susceptibility to the same salt. v. Eisler (1909) found that *B. subtilis* was killed by N/10 LiCl, whereas the El Tor vibrio was unharmed by N/5 LiCl. Eisenberg (1919) found that *B. anthracis* possesses more than the average resistance to fluorides, iodates and oxalates ; *C. diphtheriæ* to tellurates, tellurites, Ni and Cu ; *Bact. typhosum* to Sr salts ; the pneumococcus to ferricyanides and tellurites ; and *V. choleræ* to chlorates and perchlorates. Certain organisms may be grouped together as having a similar susceptibility to the action of salts ; thus, *Staphylococcus pyogenes* and *Staphylococcus candicans* ; *C. diphtheriæ* and the diphtheroid bacilli ; *Bact. typhosum* and *Bact. coli* ; *Chromo. prodigiosum* and *Chromo. kielense* are grouped in pairs, each member of the pair exhibiting a similar susceptibility to different salts.

As well as this relationship, however, there is another curious similarity in resistance exhibited between the members of the Gram-positive group of organisms, and between the members of the Gram-negative group. Eisenberg found that many salts are more toxic to the Gram-positive than to the Gram-negative bacteria. This holds not merely for particular salts, but for their constituent anions and cations. On the other hand, some salts, such as potassium tellurite (Fleming 1932), are more toxic to Gram-negative than to Gram-positive bacteria. This fact is made use of in the preparation of selective media.

The difference in susceptibility to sodium chloride has been suggested by Schoop (1935) as a criterion for bacterial classification. He divides bacteria into three classes : (1) those that grow in ordinary media, but not in media containing 10 per cent. NaCl—non-halophiles ; (2) those that grow in both media—facultative halophiles ; (3) those that grow only in media containing 10 per cent. NaCl—obligatory halophiles. The last group of organisms are found mainly in sea water, and in sand and mud adjacent to the sea.

Antagonistic Effect of Salts.—Hitherto we have been considering the effect on bacteria of solutions containing one salt ; we must now examine the effect of solutions containing more than one salt.

Flexner (1907) found that an 0·85 per cent. solution of NaCl caused rapid disintegration of the meningococcus ; but that when a calcium salt was added to the solution, this disintegration no longer occurred. The conclusion he drew was that NaCl by itself is toxic to the meningococcus, but that its toxic action can be neutralized by a salt of calcium. Students of physiology will recall the similar observations made by Ringer on heart muscle in 1880. Shearer (1919) found that living bacteria offered a considerable resistance to the passage of an electric current, depending apparently on the relative impermeability of the cell membrane. Using, therefore, electrical conductivity as his criterion of viability, he obtained evidence suggesting that a 0·85 per cent. solution of NaCl was toxic to the meningococcus, but that this toxic action could be neutralized by the addition of a trace of $CaCl_2$ or other bivalent salt. On the other hand, it appeared doubtful whether the toxic action of a bivalent could be neutralized by the addition of a monovalent salt.

Similar results have been obtained by other workers. v. Eisler (1909) found that the inhibitory action of LiCl on *B. subtilis* could be counteracted by the addition of a divalent, but not of a monovalent salt. Thus, N/10 LiCl was counteracted by N/20 $CaCl_2$, by N/200 $BaCl_2$, or by N/200 $MgSO_4$. Further, he showed that the inhibitory effect of a divalent salt could be counteracted by either a mono- or a divalent salt. Thus, N/750 $MnSO_4$ was counteracted by N/200 $Ca(NO_3)_2$ and by N/100 KCl. This latter conclusion differs from Shearer's.

It must not be thought that the mere addition of a divalent to a monovalent salt will render the solution favourable ; the two salts must be present in definite proportions. If not, instead of being harmless to the organism, the solution may be actively toxic. Thus Winslow and Falk (1923) found that 0·145 M solution of $CaCl_2$ mixed with a solution of NaCl of two or three times this strength was highly toxic to *Bact. coli*. As the proportion of NaCl was increased to four times the strength of the $CaCl_2$ solution, the toxicity of the solution diminished very markedly. That is, a solution of 0·145 M $CaCl_2$ + 0·290 M NaCl was toxic ; a solution of 0·145 M $CaCl_2$ + 0·680 M NaCl was non-toxic. A further increase of NaCl rendered the solution again toxic.

This antagonistic effect of salts brings us to the conception of a balanced solution. A balanced solution is one in which the proportions of the different salts is so ordered that their individually toxic effects are neutralized. In such a solution, bacteria are able to survive very much longer than in a solution of any one of the constituent salts. Ringer's solution is of this type, and has the following composition :

NaCl	0·9 grms.
KCl	0·042 grms.
$CaCl_2$	0·048 grms.
$NaHCO_3$	0·02 grms.
Glass-distilled water	100·000 c.c.

Winslow and Dolloff (1928) have recently drawn attention to a possible fallacy in the interpretation of the antagonistic effect of salts. According to them, all cations appear to stimulate growth in a certain low concentration and to inhibit it in a certain higher concentration. So far as viability is concerned, therefore, they would postulate an optimum ionic concentration for each organism, depending probably upon an alteration in the permeability of the cell wall. They would explain the apparently antagonistic effects of monovalent and divalent salts as being due not to a qualitative antagonism between the two cations, but to the production in the suspension of a more favourable ionic concentration for the survival of the bacteria. In support of this they quote experiments in which the toxic action of a given salt in dilute solution has been annulled by increasing the concentration of the same salt. How far this explanation is of general applicability, it is as yet impossible to say.

The interaction of various salts is of considerable importance in disinfection. The germicidal action of any one salt may be increased or diminished by the addition of any other. $HgCl_2$ is a powerful germicide ; the addition, however, to a solution of $HgCl_2$ of NaCl, or indeed of any of the halogen salts of the mineral acids, definitely lowers its toxicity. On the other hand, the germicidal activity of a solution of mercuric nitrate, sulphate, or acetate is increased by the moderate addition of NaCl. We therefore see the importance, in estimating the toxicity of a salt, of defining the saline constitution of the solution in which it is acting. Norton and Hsu (1916) showed that salts were able to modify the germicidal power of acids. When ammonium formate was added to formic acid, the H-ion concentration of the solution decreased as a result of an increase in the concentration of undissociated acid molecules, and its disinfectant power was lowered ; when sodium nitrate and sodium chloride were added in very small quantities to formic acid, the degree of dissociation of the acid was hardly affected, but its disinfectant power was considerably increased. They conclude therefore that the addition to an acid of a salt containing an anion common to this acid diminishes its disinfectant power ; the addition of a salt which does not have any appreciable effect on the dissociation of the acid greatly increases its disinfectant power.

Not only do salts assist or antagonize the action of each other ; they have a similar effect on disinfectants of quite different chemical constitution. Scheurlen (1895) showed, for instance, that the addition of sodium chloride in a concentration of 24 per cent. to a solution of phenol increased its disinfectant power. Beckman (1896) confirmed this, and found that with *Staphylococci* the addition of even 1 per cent. NaCl to 1 per cent. phenol apparently increased its activity. With anthrax spores, the addition of 6 per cent. NaCl to 1 per cent. phenol had no effect ; 12 per cent. NaCl increased its activity slightly, and 24 per cent. NaCl increased its activity very greatly. Thus 1 per cent. phenol alone failed to kill a suspension of 24,800,000 spores in 8 days ; 1 per cent. phenol + 24 per cent. NaCl killed them completely in between 5 and 24 hours. Römer (1898) confirmed the work of Beckman, showing that the greater the amount of salt added, the greater was the increase in disinfectant power. As a rule, the more toxic a salt is in itself, the more does it supplement the action of the disinfectant (Eisenberg and Okolska 1913).

Mode of Action of Salts.—In endeavouring to explain the action of salts on bacteria, we must remember that we are dealing with a complex problem of which there is no simple solution. Many factors are involved, and the most we can do here is to discuss the most important in turn.

(1) *The Osmotic Effect.*—It is extremely doubtful whether salts, except perhaps in very high concentrations, exert any influence on bacteria by virtue of their osmotic pressure. Bacteria differ from practically all other living cells in being profoundly indifferent to changes in osmotic pressure. Thus Fischer (1900) found that *B. subtilis* grows well in an infusion containing 9 per cent. NaCl, 11 per cent. KCl, or 10 per cent. KNO_3. Though salts have no direct action of this nature on bacteria, they may exert an indirect action by causing a dehydration of the proteins on which the organisms are growing. It is this dehydrating action of salts which is relied on in many processes of food preservation.

(2) *Oxidation.*—Salts and certain allied bodies that contain a high proportion of oxygen, or that are able to liberate oxygen from other compounds, have long been known to be highly germicidal. Krönig and Paul (1897) compared the disinfectant activity of certain oxidizing agents with their oxidative capacity, as measured by the method of electrical oxidation chains. According to this method, oxidizing agents are arranged in order of decreasing oxidizing capacity thus : HNO_3, dichromic acid, chloric acid, Cl_2, $H_2S_2O_8$, and permanganic acid. This order was, with the exception of chlorine, the same as that of the germicidal action of these substances. Chlorine, bromine and iodine were found to be germicidal in inverse order to their atomic weight. Their action appears to depend on the liberation of nascent oxygen. Ozone is another powerful oxidizing agent ; likewise H_2O_2, a 3 per cent. solution of which kills anthrax spores in an hour. One of the most commonly used of this group of chemical substances is $K_2Mn_2O_8$; like $(NH_4)_2S_2O_8$ its action is increased by the presence of HCl. Krönig and Paul prepared a mixture containing 1 per cent. $K_2Mn_2O_8$ and 1·1 per cent. HCl dissolved in water, and found that it would kill anthrax spores in 30 seconds. A similar mixture containing 3·7 per cent. $(NH_4)_2S_2O_8$, and 1·1 per cent. HCl was found by Andrewes and Orton (1904) to exercise an effect very nearly as powerful. Both these are extremely potent, but even more potent is HOCl, which in a concentration of 0·01 per cent. kills anthrax spores in 30 seconds. So far as activity is concerned, this is one of the most powerful germicides we know. Bleaching powder acts by virtue of its ability, when acted upon by weak acids such as H_2CO_3, to yield nascent oxygen, which then combines to form HOCl. HOCl combines with organic substances containing the $=NH$ group, to form substances that are known as chloramines.

$$\begin{matrix} R_1 \\ \diagdown NH + HOCl \rightarrow \\ R_2 \end{matrix} \begin{matrix} R_1 \\ \diagdown NCl + H_2O \\ R_2 \end{matrix}$$

It is found that all bodies containing the NCl group are strongly antiseptic (Dakin 1915).

(3) *Reduction.*—Certain salts, such as the sulphites and the ferrous compounds, appear to act by virtue of their reducing power. Apart from such salts there are other substances that act mainly as reducing agents—sulphurous acid and formaldehyde. A 5 per cent. solution of formaldehyde, *i.e.* a 1–8 dilution of the commercial formalin, kills anthrax spores in between 1 and 2 hours—in about the same time as a 0·2 per cent. solution of $HgCl_2$.

(4) *Molecular Action.*—In a previous section we saw that certain acids, such as acetic and benzoic, and in fact most of the organic acids, act not by virtue of their H-ion concentration but by virtue of the undissociated molecule. Benzoic acid is dissociated very slightly, and its strong disinfectant power must therefore be attributed to the benzoate anion or to the undissociated molecule. Probably the same explanation will account for the action of the salts of the organic acids.

(5) *Ionic Action.*—It is clear that salts which are freely dissociated in solution owe their germicidal power to the action of the ions into which they are dissociated. The way in which these ions act is a matter for speculation. Bayliss (1924) points out that there are three ways in which electrolytes may exert their influence on living matter. (*a*) They may produce effects through the electrical charges that they bear ; this is specially marked with ions with valencies above

one, and bears no relation to the chemical nature of the ions. Thus the effect of Ca·· cannot be distinguished from Ba··. These effects, especially in the case of the multivalent ions, are manifest even in very dilute solutions. (*b*) They may affect the nature of the solvent in which they are dissolved—the so-called lyotropic effect. This action has been studied by several workers, prominent among whom are Hofmeister (1888, 1889) and Freundlich (1903). Hofmeister, working with a number of neutral salts, found that these could be arranged in a definite order relative to their action on the coagulation of colloids, and on other physical properties of proteins. Freundlich, studying the effect of electrolytes on the compressibility, surface tension, solubility, viscosity, and other properties of proteins, was likewise able to arrange them in a definite order. He concluded that the main effect was exerted not on the proteins directly, but upon the solvent ; modifications in the solvent thus affected the proteins. For this reason he spoke of the salt effects as " lyotropic " effects ; his series of salts hence bears the name "lyotropic series" in distinction to the " Hofmeister series." Both series, however, are similar in many respects. Holm and Sherman (1921) and numerous other workers have found a general concordance between the ionic series of Hofmeister or of Freundlich and the stimulative or toxic action of the salts of these series. (*c*) They may operate through a specific influence, which is more intimately connected with the chemical properties of the ions. Thus sodium and potassium, though having the same electrical charge, and exercising very similar lyotropic effects, are yet totally different in their action on heart muscle. As this action is shown by solutions so dilute that undissociated molecules are nearly absent, we know that this difference must be attributed to some specific or chemical property of the ions.

Other explanations of ionic action have been put forward, some of them modifications of the ones already given. Amongst these may be mentioned Loeb's (1899, 1900) hypothesis of ion-protein combination, Mathews' (1904*a*, *b*, 1905, 1906) conception of ionic potential, and Zwaardemaker's (1918, 1919–20) radioactivity hypothesis. For these and for further information on this subject the reader is referred to an admirable summary by Falk (1923)—a summary which has been freely drawn on in this section.

There is one further point. We have treated the action of anions and of cations separately ; whether they act together is not at all clear. It seems probable that in a salt such as $HgCl_2$, in which a highly toxic cation is united to a weakly toxic anion, almost the entire action of the salt must be referred to the Hg-ion ; in a salt such as $K_2Mn_2O_8$, on the other hand, in which a weakly toxic cation is united to a powerful anion, the action must be referred to the permanganate ion.

SUMMARY OF SALT ACTION.

(1) There is a certain concentration for nearly all salts which stimulates bacterial growth ; this concentration is generally very low.

(2) There is, for nearly all salts, a limit beyond which the stimulating action passes over into a toxic action ; on the whole, the higher the concentration, the more evident does the toxic action become.

(3) The toxic effect of univalent salts can be neutralized by the addition in suitable proportions of a divalent salt. In most instances, too, it is possible for a univalent salt to neutralize the toxic action of a bivalent salt. This action is known as the antagonistic action of salts.

(4) Electrolytes with bivalent cations are generally more toxic than those with univalent cations. Thus Ba$\cdot\cdot$ is more powerful than Na$\cdot$.

(5) On the whole, the salts of the heavier metals are more toxic than those of the lighter metals ; thus $HgCl_2$ is more toxic than $CaCl_2$. But there is no strict quantitative relation between the atomic weight of a metal and its toxicity.

(6) On the other hand there is a fairly close relationship between the lyotropic and the toxic effects of a salt.

(7) The toxic action of salts is less marked in protein solutions than in distilled water. Thus the activity of $HgCl_2$ is decreased markedly in the presence of blood serum.

(8) The more favourable the nutrient qualities of the medium in which the bacteria are suspended, the less manifest is the toxic effect of salts, and of germicidal agents in general, upon them.

(9) Different organisms vary in their susceptibility to the disinfectant action of the same salt. Closely allied organisms respond in much the same way to the same salts.

(10) There is evidence that the Gram-positive organisms, with a few exceptions, are more susceptible to the disinfectant action of salts than the Gram-negative organisms.

(11) The addition of a salt to a solution of a germicide—whether itself a salt or not—may increase or decrease the action of the latter. This action may be due partly to the effect on the electrolytic dissociation of the germicide ; partly, in a colloidal solution, to an effect on the dispersion coefficient of the disinfectant ; and partly perhaps to the disinfectant action of the salt itself.

(12) There is little or no evidence to show that salts owe their germicidal action to the osmotic pressure that they exert, since bacteria are strongly resistant to variations of osmotic pressure, but they may act by dehydrating the proteins of the medium in which they are suspended.

(13) The action of salts is complex. It may be referred to an oxidation effect, a reduction effect, a molecular effect, or an ionic effect. Other effects, namely, the sensitization of organisms to CO_2, and their interference with proteolytic enzymes, have not been considered in this chapter ; for details of these the reader is referred to an article by Rockwell and Ebertz (1924).

Alcohols and Ethers.—Epstein (1897) found that absolute ethyl alcohol was not a germicide, but that when diluted it became germicidal. The optimum concentration was 50 per cent. ; in higher or lower concentrations its activity diminished. Minervini (1898) confirmed this, showing not only that anthrax spores would remain alive in absolute alcohol for more than 50 days, but that *Staphylococcus aureus* resisted the action of absolute alcohol under a pressure of 3 atmospheres at a temperature of 120–130° C. for at least an hour. Using the thread method, he worked out the lethal effect of different concentrations of alcohol on a number of organisms. These are given in Table XII.

Not only is absolute alcohol almost devoid of disinfectant action, but it lowers the germicidal effect of substances that are dissolved in it. This action was noticed by Koch (1881) and confirmed by Krönig and Paul (1897). $HgCl_2$ dissolved in water kills *B. subtilis* spores in 10 to 30 minutes ; dissolved in 99 per cent. alcohol, it fails to kill them in 24 hours. This retarding action of alcohol is not so manifest when it is diluted. Minervini stated that the disinfectant activity of alcoholic solutions of disinfectants is in inverse proportion to the per-

TABLE XII

Time in which Alcohol of Different Concentrations proved Fatal to Various Organisms.

Micro-organisms.	25%.	50%.	70%.	80%.	99%.
M. tetragenus	60 mins.	30 mins.	10 mins.	60 mins.	9 hrs.
Chromo. prodigiosum	60 ,,	30 ,,	30 ,,	9 hrs.	24 ,,
Staph. aureus	18 hrs.	60 ,,	60 ,,	>3 days	>3 days
Bact. coli	24 ,,	60 ,,	60 ,,	24 hrs.	12 hrs.
B. anthracis (three days' broth culture. 37° C.)	>50 days	>50 days	>50 days	>50 days	>50 days

centage of alcohol they contain ; but this is contrary to the findings of other workers. Thus Epstein showed that $HgCl_2$ was more active in a 50 per cent. solution of alcohol than in water. Krönig and Paul likewise found that a 1·69 per cent. solution of $HgCl_2$ in 30 per cent. ethyl alcohol was more active than a similar solution in water ; for $AgNO_3$, 50 per cent. alcohol appeared to be more satisfactory. With some germicides, however, such as formaldehyde and phenol, they found that every addition of alcohol decreased the activity of the solution.

Ritchie (1899) showed that the germicidal action of different alcohols increased with the molecular weight, ethyl alcohol being more potent than methyl, propyl than ethyl, and butyl than propyl alcohol.

The ethers are possessed of some degree of germicidal activity. Cultures of non-sporing bacteria incubated in an atmosphere saturated with the vapour of diethyl ether—$C_2H_5OC_2H_5$—exhibited no growth ; subcultures showed that the organisms had been killed in a period varying from about 1 to 48 hours (Topley 1915). Direct immersion of *Bact. coli* in 50 per cent. ether proved fatal in about 3 minutes at room temperature. On the other hand, exposure of *Cl. septique* to pure ether failed to destroy the spores in 24 hours. According to Krönig and Paul (1897) ethereal solutions of disinfectants are almost without effect on anthrax spores.

Phenols and Cresols.—Under this heading we shall consider the action of those bodies that are obtained from the destructive distillation of coal, and that pass over between the temperatures of 170° and 270° C. Phenol itself in certain proportions is able to pass into solution in water, but most of the bodies in this group do not do so ; when mixed with water they form emulsions of varying degrees of fineness. Their mode of action is therefore different from the action of the germicides which we have so far considered. The phenols and cresols have a fairly high germicidal activity when employed in solutions above a given concentration ; but it requires quite a low degree of dilution to deprive them entirely of this activity. In this respect they differ markedly from the saline disinfectants (see p. 123).

It has been supposed that phenol acts by its formation in contact with proteins of an insoluble albuminate and of other chemical compounds. Reichel (1909), however, who studied the dispersion phases of phenol between oil and water, brought evidence to suggest that the action is not so much chemical as physical, the phenol being capable of passing into solution in such substances as coagulated albumin, certain lipoids, and the cytoplasm of bacteria. He suggests, therefore, that its disinfectant action results from its penetration into the bacterial cell in the form of a colloidal solution.

The emulsified disinfectants, such as the cresols, probably act in much the same way as phenol, but their germicidal activity is usually somewhat higher. By virtue of their emulsoid state, their particles are adsorbed on to the surface of suspended matter, and hence their concentration is increased in the immediate neighbourhood of the bacteria. This action is interfered with by the presence of other suspended organic matter, which serves to adsorb the germicide, and thus lower its effective concentration around the bacteria. Emulsoids of the cresol group are generally most active when freshly made up in solution ; after a day or two, probably because of an alteration in their colloidal state, their activity diminishes.

According to Klarmann, Shternov, and Gates (1934*a*, *b*), the germicidal activity of phenol derivatives is increased by halogen substitution, and is still further intensified by the introduction of aliphatic or aromatic groups into the nucleus of these compounds. Their general formulæ are

Parachlorophenol Derivative.   Orthochlorophenol Derivative.

where R is an aliphatic or aromatic group. Some of the compounds tested by these workers, such as parachlorophenol or orthochlorophenol derivatives with *n*-butyl to *n*-octyl substituents, proved highly destructive to bacteria, while being comparatively non-toxic to mice on subcutaneous injection.

Dyes.—Though a few desultory observations had been made at various times on the effects of aniline dyes on bacteria, Churchman (1912) was the first to investigate them thoroughly. Working with gentian violet, he found that if 5 drops of a saturated aqueous solution of this dye were added to broth cultures of different organisms, the mixtures allowed to remain for an hour, and transplants then made on to agar, the Gram-negative organisms grew satisfactorily, but the Gram-positive organisms failed to develop. A similar selective property could be demonstrated by seeding the fresh unstained organisms on to plates, one-half of which contained plain nutrient agar, and the other half nutrient agar containing a dilution of about 1–100,000 gentian violet. A large number of different bacteria were tested to ascertain if there was a perfect correlation between Gram-positiveness and ability to grow in media containing gentian violet. This was found not to be the case ; about 90 per cent. of the Gram-positive organisms were killed by gentian violet and failed to grow on media containing it, but the remaining 10 per cent., comprising the acid-fast group in particular, were not affected. Similarly, though about 90 per cent. of the Gram-negative organisms were resistant, the remaining 10 per cent. were susceptible.

The difference between the Gram-positive and the Gram-negative organisms is merely one of degree. There is, moreover, a considerable variation in the susceptibility of different species of Gram-positive bacteria. Garrod (1933*a*) has shown, for example, that staphylococci are much less resistant to the violet dyes—crystal violet, methyl violet, Hofmann violet, gentian violet, Dahlia—than streptococci.   The presence of 1/1,000,000 gentian violet in nutrient broth or in 5 per cent. serum broth is sufficient to inhibit the growth of staphylococci, while strepto-cocci can grow in the presence of 1/250,000, and sometimes even stronger concentrations of this dye.

Churchman (1923*a*) stated that, just as gentian violet had a bacteriostatic effect on most Gram-positive organisms, so acid fuchsin had a similar effect on Gram-negative organisms.   Garrod (1933*b*) has recently examined this statement, and concluded that it is untrue.   He finds that aniline dyes generally, whether of the basic or acid type, destroy Gram-positive more readily than Gram-negative bacteria.   On the other hand, Churchman's results gain some support from the work of Stearn and Stearn (1926, 1928).   From a study of the reactions of different bacteria to different stains, these workers conclude that Gram-positive bacteria have a lower isoelectric point than Gram-negative bacteria.   Hence Gram-positive bacteria combine more actively with basic, and Gram-negative with acid dyes. The subject clearly needs further investigation.

The aniline dyes have, on account of their marked germicidal effect on bacteria, been used for the treatment of wounds.   Browning and his colleagues (1917) recommended flavine—diamino-methyl-acridinium chloride.   Though they found that brilliant green sulphate, malachite green, crystal violet, and flavine strongly inhibited the growth of staphylococci and *Bact. coli*, flavine was the only one that was more active in the presence of serum (Table XIII).   Churchman (1923*b*) used a mixture of gentian violet and acriflavine.

TABLE XIII (modified from Browning *et al.* 1917).

SHOWING CONCENTRATIONS OF DIFFERENT SUBSTANCES NECESSARY TO INHIBIT THE GROWTH OF *Staphylococcus aureus* AND *Bact. coli*.

Substance.	Staph. aureus.		Bact. coli.	
	Conc. in P.W.	Conc. in Serum.	Conc. in P.W.	Conc. in Serum.
Chloramine-T	1–2,000	1–250	1–2,000	1–250
Cl₂ water	1–2,500	>1–1,000 *	1–2,500	>1–1,000 *
Phenol	1–250	1–250	1–500	1–500
HgCl₂	1–1,000,000	1–10,000	1–1,000,000	1–10,000
Brilliant green sulphate . .	1–10,000,000	1–30,000	1–130,000	1–3,500
Malachite green	1–10,000,000	1–40,000	1–20,000	1–1,000
Crystal violet	1–4,000,000	1–400,000	1–8,000	1–8,000
Flavine	1–20,000	1–200,000	1–1,300	1–100,000

* These concentrations were insufficient to prevent growth.

Table XIII is of interest in showing not only that flavine is much stronger in its inhibiting action in ox serum than in peptone water, but that HgCl₂ and the chlorine group of germicides are markedly diminished in activity in the presence of serum, whereas phenol remains unaffected.   This diminution of activity in the presence of organic matter will be referred to later.

Hitherto, the dye treatment of wounds has not fulfilled the expectations of its advocates, probably because the dyes can seldom be present continuously in sufficient concentration in every part of the wound to inhibit bacterial growth completely. As Browning (1933) points out, the destruction of organisms in the centre of masses of necrotic tissue or blood clot is probably beyond the power of any disinfectant.

Essential Oils.—Chamberland (1887) tested the disinfectant action of a large number of essential oils, by exposing anthrax spores and anthrax bacilli to their vapours in closed tubes. After 4 days' exposure at 37° C. only one oil was successful in killing the spores—namely, oil of Ceylon cinnamon. Anthrax bacilli, contained in blood, were killed by oil of vespetro in 18 hours at 37° C., in 40 hours by oil of angelica, and in 65 hours by oil of Ceylon cinnamon. Other oils the vapours of which were germicidal, though less actively so, were oil of geranium and oil of marjoram.

He then tested the effect of the oils in a solution of alcohol and saponin. By this method he found the most active in killing anthrax bacilli were oils of marjoram, cinnamon, sandal-wood, clove, juniper, and *Artemesia annua*. He draws attention to the fact that cinnamon and marjoram oils are strongly active both in the gaseous and in the liquid state. Similar observations were made by Cadéac and Meunier (1889). They worked with *Bact. typhosum* and *Pf. mallei*, which were allowed to remain in contact with the pure oil for a given time, and then seeded on to agar. Table XIV shows some of their results.

TABLE XIV

TIME NECESSARY TO KILL *Bact. typhosum.*

HgCl$_2$ 1–1,000	10 minutes
Ceylon cinnamon oil	12 ,,
Clove oil	25 ,,
Wild thyme oil	35 ,,
Oil of geranium	50 ,,

Many other oils did not kill for 24 to 48 hours, some not for 4 to 10 days, and some not even in 10 days.

It will be seen that certain of the essential oils, if applied pure, are fairly active germicides. The majority, however, are more valued for their antiseptic than for their disinfectant action. For this purpose they were used extensively by the ancient Egyptians in the process of embalming, with results which can be seen at the present day.

Vegetable oils that have no germicidal action themselves deprive other germicides, which are dissolved in them, of most of their activity ; in this respect they resemble alcohol. Koch, for example, found that phenol dissolved in vegetable oils, such as olive or cotton-seed oil, was only slightly active. McMaster (1919) has since confirmed this, but has pointed out that mineral oils do not have this effect. Phenol dissolved in paraffin oil, for example, is nearly as active as when dissolved in water.

With regard to animal oils, Harris, Bunker, and Milas (1932) find that some, such as seal oil and tuna oil, give off vapours which are germicidal, while others, such as cod-liver oil and sardine oil, become germicidal only after exposure to sunlight or ultra-violet light. It is possible that H$_2$O$_2$ is given off by the animal oils, and that its rate of evolution is accelerated by irradiation.

The Dynamics of Disinfection

Reaction Velocity.—The figures obtained by Krönig and Paul (1897) in their work on the disinfection of anthrax spores by $HgCl_2$ were submitted by Madsen and Nyman (1907) to a mathematical analysis, with the result that the reaction velocity of disinfection was found to be similar to that obtaining in a unimolecular reaction. Madsen and Nyman themselves made fresh experiments, using the garnet method, and were able to confirm the findings of Krönig and Paul. In the following year Chick (1908), working independently, reached the same conclusions with regard to the analogy between disinfection and a unimolecular reaction (Fig. 15).

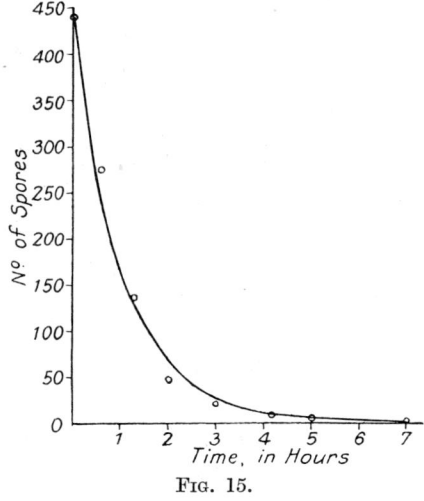

FIG. 15.

Disinfection of anthrax spores with 5 per cent. phenol at 33·3° C. The curve is drawn through a series of calculated points; the circles represent the experimental observations.
(After Chick.)

In a unimolecular reaction only one of the reacting substances need be regarded as undergoing change, the rate of change being proportional to the concentration of this substance. Examples in chemistry are the inversion of cane sugar by acids, the decomposition of AsH_3 into As and H_2, and the disintegration of radio-active substances. When only one of the reacting substances is undergoing change, the velocity of this change according to the Law of Mass Action will depend upon the concentration of this substance at any given moment, the temperature and other conditions remaining constant. This statement may be expressed by the relation

$$V = C.k$$

in which V represents the velocity of the reaction, C the concentration of the substance, and k a constant depending on the nature of the substance. The velocity may be expressed by $\dfrac{dx}{dt}$, in which x represents the amount of substance changed in time t; if the original amount of substance is designated by a, then $a-x$ will represent the amount remaining after time t. The equation may now be written :

$$\frac{dx}{dt} = k\,(a-x)$$

which, on integration, becomes :

$$k = \frac{1}{t} \log \frac{a}{a-x}$$

This is the equation representing the velocity of a unimolecular reaction and is often spoken of as the logarithmic law. If log $(a-x)$ be plotted against time in this equation, the resulting graph will be a straight line (Fig. 16).

We may adapt the unimolecular reaction definition to the process of disinfection by saying that at any moment the reaction velocity is proportional to the number

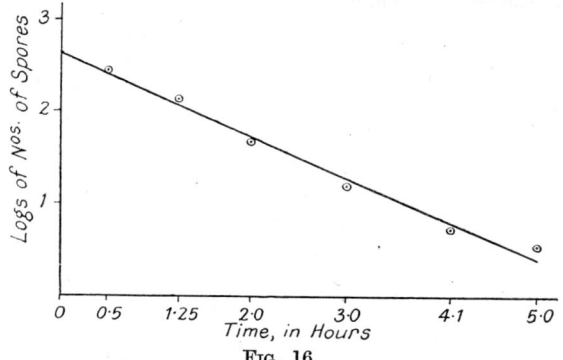

FIG. 16.

Disinfection of anthrax spores with 5 per cent. phenol at 33·3° C. The curve is drawn through a series of calculated points ; the circles represent the experimental observations. This curve is constructed from the same observations as those used for Fig. 15, but the numbers of organisms are expressed logarithmically.
(After Chick.)

of surviving bacteria per unit volume. For example, let us suppose that there are 100,000 organisms being submitted to disinfection, and that the rate is one at which 90 per cent. of the organisms are killed in each minute. Then :

	Time.		Nos. Surviving.
After 0 minutes	.		100,000
,, 1 ,,	.		1/10 × 100,000 or 10,000
,, 2 ,,	.		1/10 × 10,000 or 1,000
,, 3 ,,	.		1/10 × 1,000 or 100
,, 4 ,,	.		1/10 × 100 or 10

Supposing that B represents the initial number of living organisms, and b the final number, then the reaction velocity may be expressed by the equation :

$$k = \frac{1}{t} \log \frac{B}{b}$$

Chick, using the drop method, made experiments on the disinfection of anthrax spores by 5 per cent. phenol. Her results are given in Table XV and Figs. 15 and 16.

TABLE XV

ANTHRAX SPORES. 5 PER CENT. PHENOL. 33·3° C.

Time.					Mean No. of Bacteria per Drop.	Value of k.
0 hours	.	.	.	.	439·0	—
0·5 ,,	.	.	.	.	275·5	0·40
1·25 ,,	.	.	.	.	137·5	0·40
2·0 ,,	.	.	.	.	46·0	0·49
3·0 ,,	.	.	.	.	15·8	0·48
4·1 ,,	.	.	.	.	5·45	0·46
5·0 ,,	.	.	.	.	3·6	0·42
7·0 ,,	.	.	.	.	0·5	0·42

It will be seen from Table XV that k has a mean value of 0·44 ; from Fig. 15 that the velocity of the reaction becomes slower and slower, till it is almost negligible (in theory the reaction should go on to infinity), and from Fig. 16 that the logarithms of the numbers of surviving organisms plotted against time in hours fall along a descending straight line.

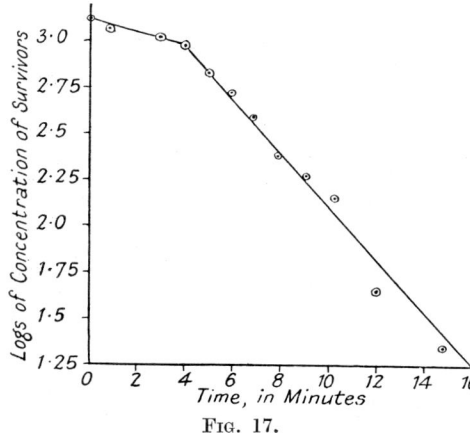

FIG. 17.

Disinfection of *Staph. aureus* with 0·6 per cent. phenol at 20° C. The numbers of organisms are expressed logarithmically.
(After Chick.)

In the case of vegetative bacteria, she (Chick 1908, 1910) found that though the disinfection of some organisms such as *Bact. typhosum* and *Bact. coli* conformed to the unimolecular reaction formula, with others there was a slight departure from it. Thus with *Staphylococcus aureus* exposed to 0·6 per cent. phenol at 20° C., there was invariably a lag period, lasting about 4 minutes before the rate became strictly proportional to the number of bacteria (Fig. 17). Paratyphoid bacilli behaved in the opposite way. Instead of there being a lag phase, there was a preliminary rush during which the rate of disinfection proceeded faster than it should have done according to the equation (Fig. 18).

Chick confirmed her work on disinfection by phenol by showing (1) that the death of *Bact. coli* under the influence of a bactericidal serum conforms to the unimolecular reaction law (Chick 1912) ; and (2) that the same law holds in the process of disinfection by hot water (Chick 1910) ; she pointed out the close parallel that exists between disinfection by hot water and the heat coagulation of proteins. Paul, Birstein and Reusz (1910*a*) found that the killing of *Staphylococcus aureus* by drying proceeds in accordance with the law of a unimolecular reaction. The results obtained by Clark and Gage (1903) in the study of disinfection by sunlight may also be interpreted in the same way. Robertson (1914) has adduced mathematical evidence in favour of this view.

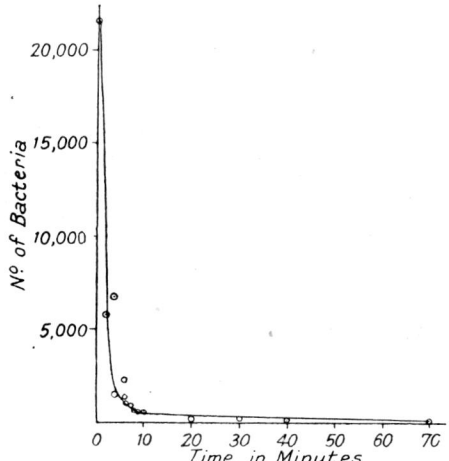

FIG. 18.

Disinfection of a 24-hours' culture of paratyphoid bacilli with 0·6 per cent. phenol at 20° C.
(After Chick.)

It does not, of course, follow from such results as these that a monomolecular reaction, in the chemical sense, is actually taking place ; the recorded observations merely show that a logarithmic curve describes the death of bacteria under the action of a disinfectant, just as it describes a chemical reaction whose rate is governed by the concentration at any moment of one of the reacting substances. Two alternative explanations have been offered to account for the form of the curves which Chick has described. The first of these suggests that the varying resistance of the bacteria in any given suspension can be described in the form of a frequency curve, as is almost certainly the case, and that the survival curves described by Chick are simply an expression of this difference in resistance. The obvious objection to this hypothesis, as Chick has pointed out, is that the form of the frequency curve describing the distribution of resistance must be supposed to be of the extreme skew form, if it is to account for the experimental results. It seems altogether unlikely that such a curve really represents the distribution of resistance among the bacterial population at risk.

A more probable explanation (Chick 1910) is that the death or survival of any given bacterium during any interval of time is determined by a multitude of small and independent causes—by "chance" in the statistical sense—the presence of the disinfectant weighting the chance of survival against each bacterium to a constant degree, for any given concentration of the disinfectant, and with other controllable conditions held constant. If the chance of each bacterium dying during any unit of time is x, and remains x over the whole period of the experiment, then the death rate will be the same during each unit of time ; the survivors at the end of any one time interval will suffer the same proportionate decrease in their numbers during the time interval which follows, and a logarithmic curve of decrease will result. This explanation does not, of course, mean that variations in resistance of individual bacteria play no part in disinfection. With vegetative bacteria, the rate of death is often represented by a sigmoid curve rather than by a straight line, suggesting that differences in resistance dependent on the age of the individual organisms are responsible for the deviation. The real question is whether, in the disinfection of spores which do not differ materially in age, the exponential type of curve is due to chance in the statistical sense, or to a frequency distribution of resistance of the extreme skew type. (For a further discussion of this subject see Eijkman 1908, Hewlett 1909, Reichel 1909, Reichenbach 1911, Loeb and Northrop 1917, Brooks 1919, Cohen 1922, Knaysi 1930, Knaysi and Gordon 1930, and Bancroft and Richter 1931.)

Concentration of Disinfectant.—Chick (1908) found that the relationship between the concentration of a disinfectant and the time taken for disinfection is not a simple but an exponential one, the exponent of the concentration being a factor varying with each disinfectant. That is to say, doubling the concentration of phenol does not halve the time necessary for the completion of the reaction as might be expected, but diminishes it to a far greater extent. Watson (1908), working on Chick's figures, found that the relation could be expressed by the formula

$$C^n t = \text{a constant}$$

where C is the concentration, n a constant varying with each disinfectant, and t the time necessary for disinfection. This equation represents the relation when one molecule of one substance reacts with n molecules of a second, the latter being in great excess. For purposes of calculation it may be written

$$n\log C + \log t = \text{a constant,}$$

that is, the relation between log C and log t is a linear one.

An example will make this clear (Table XVI).

TABLE XVI

DISINFECTION OF PARATYPHOID BACILLI BY PHENOL AT 20° C.

Parts of Phenol per 1,000.	Time taken for Disinfection.	$5 \cdot 5 \log C + \log t$.
8·0	45 minutes	6·62
7·5	75 ,,	6·69
7·0	105 ,,	6·67
6·5	125 ,,	6·58
6·0	225 ,,	6·64
5·5	440 ,,	6·71
5·0	690 ,,	6·68

In this table the value of n is taken as 5·5 ; the method of calculating this we shall consider presently. It will be seen that the values of the constant are closely similar. If the logarithms of the concentrations are plotted against the logarithms of time, the resulting curve is found to be linear (Fig. 19).

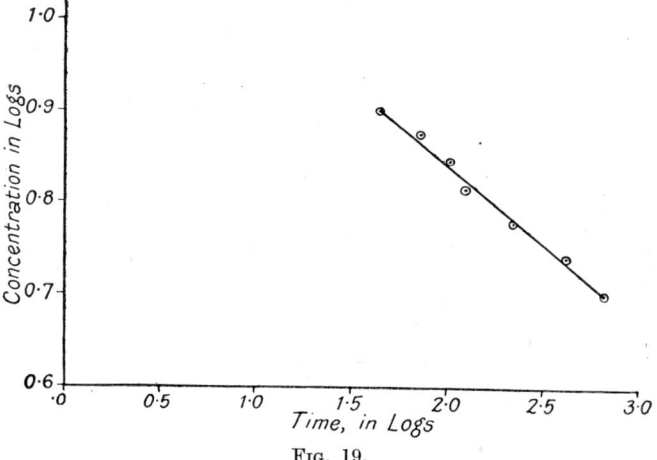

FIG. 19.

Disinfection of paratyphoid bacilli with varying concentrations of phenol. Both the numbers of the bacteria and time are expressed logarithmically.
(After Watson, from observations by Chick.)

For dealing with the salts of the heavy metals, a slight modification of the formula is required, due to the fact that these salts are dissociated in solution, and their action depends not on their molecular but on their ionic concentration. If the concentration of Hg-ions is substituted for concentration of $HgCl_2$, for example, then the formula holds good (see Table XVII opposite page).

Paul, Birstein and Reusz (1910*b*) found that the value of the velocity constant k for aqueous solutions of HCl was approximately proportional to the square root of its concentration.

TABLE XVII

DISINFECTION OF PARATYPHOID BACILLI BY $HgCl_2$ AT 20° C.

Parts of $HgCl_2$ per 1,000.	Conc. of Hg-ions.	Time taken for Disinfection.	$3.8 \log C + \log t$.
1·0	63·0	1·5 minutes	7·02
0·5	57·5	7·0 ,,	7·54
0·1	42·5	10·0 ,,	7·31
0·05	37·0	13·0 ,,	6·95
0·01	23·0	65·0 ,,	6·99
0·005	16·5	230·0 ,,	6·98

Calculation of Exponent n.—The exponent n may be regarded as a concentration coefficient varying with each disinfectant. To calculate its value, we have recourse to the formula representing the reaction velocity of disinfection. Taking the concentration into account we may say that

$$^1\ KC^n t = \log \frac{B}{b}$$

k_1 is determined for concentration C_1, and k_2 for concentration C_2 in a given experiment. Then

$$n = \log \frac{k_2}{k_1} \div \log \frac{C_2}{C_1}$$

Taking the figures in Table XVI,

let 7·0 parts of phenol per 1000 = C_2 and $t = 105'$
let 5·0 parts of phenol per 1000 = C_1 and $t = 690'$

$$k_2 = \frac{1}{t} \cdot \log \frac{B}{b}$$

B in this experiment was 30,000,000 ; b can be taken as 1. Then :

$$k_2 = \frac{1}{105} \cdot \log 30{,}000{,}000$$

$$= 0.0712$$

$$k_1 = \frac{1}{690} \cdot \log 30{,}000{,}000$$

$$= 0.0108$$

$$n = \log \frac{k_2}{k_1} \div \log \frac{C_2}{C_1}$$

$$= \log \frac{0.0712}{0.0108} \div \log \frac{7}{5}$$

$$= \log 6.5 \div \log 1.4$$

$$= 5.5$$

For $HgCl_2$, when the concentration of Hg-ions only was considered, the value of n was found to be 3·8 ; for the Ag-ions of $AgNO_3$, 0·86. If the molecular concentration of $HgCl_2$ is considered, then n is equal to about 1.

The value of n for any given disinfectant is very important, because it gives us

---

[1] K is the true velocity constant of the disinfectant, being independent of the concentration, and thus differing from k, which is constant only at a given concentration.

information that is not conveyed by the simple reaction velocity. For phenol let us take $n = 6$, and for $HgCl_2$ $n = 1$. Then a doubling of the concentration of $HgCl_2$, i.e. C^n or 2^1, will halve the time taken for completion of the reaction; doubling the concentration of phenol, i.e. C^n or 2^6, will diminish it 64 times. Conversely, halving the concentration of $HgCl_2$ doubles the time of the reaction; halving the concentration of phenol increases it 64 times.

A substance with a high value of n is actively germicidal above a given concentration; it requires, however, but a low degree of dilution to abolish its germicidal activity entirely. In contrast, a substance with a low value of n, while being actively germicidal in solutions above a given concentration, exercises an inhibiting effect on the growth of bacteria even when employed in high dilution.

One further point may be dealt with here, namely the question of whether the numbers of bacteria present in a suspension affect the reaction velocity. Working with $HgCl_2$ and anthrax spores, Madsen and Nyman (1907) found the numbers of spores to be of no importance; a suspension containing 124,800 was sterilized as rapidly as one containing only 7,750. Eisenberg and Okolska (1913), however, divided the disinfectants into 3 classes: in the first, comprising alcohol, phenol, and formaldehyde, the numbers of bacteria had but little effect, i.e. a concentration of disinfectant that would destroy a given number of bacteria would also destroy 100 times that number. In a second group, comprising acetone, $HgCl_2$ and $K_2Mn_2O_8$, the numbers of bacteria proved to be of importance; thus a concentration that destroyed a given number failed to destroy 10 times that number. A third group comprising HCl, H_2SO_4, oxalic acid, KOH, and other bodies, occupied an intermediate position between the first two classes.

Temperature Coefficient.—As the temperature increases in arithmetical progression, the velocity of the reaction increases in geometrical progression, or mathematically expressed

$$\frac{k'}{k} = \theta^{(T' - T)}$$

in which k' and k are the velocity constants of the reaction at temperatures T' and T respectively, and θ is the temperature coefficient.

In the disinfection of paratyphoid bacilli by 0·6 per cent. phenol at 20° and at 30° C., Chick (1908) obtained the following figures (Table XVIII):

TABLE XVIII
PARATYPHOID BACILLI. PHENOL 6 PER 1,000.

Time in Minutes.		Average No. of surviving Bacteria.	k.
At 20° C.	1	539	—
	2	276·6	0·29
	3	137·5	0·30
	4	80·1	0·28
	6	42	0·22
At 30° C.	1	1368	—
	2	162	0·93
	3	65·5	0·66
	4·1	15·1	0·63
	6	1·5	0·59

The mean value of k at 20° C. = 0·27.
The mean value of k' at 30° C. = 0·7.

To find the value of θ

$$\frac{k'}{k} = \theta^{(T'-T)}$$

$$\theta^{10} = \frac{0.7}{0.27}$$

$$= 2.592$$

$$\theta = 2.592^{0.1}$$

$$= 1.1$$

$$\theta = 1.1 \text{ for } 1° \text{ C.}$$
$$= 1.1^{10} \text{ or } 2.6 \text{ for } 10° \text{ C.}$$

A similar experiment is shown diagrammatically in Fig. 20.

Most observers have obtained higher values of θ for phenol—generally about 7 or 8 for each rise in temperature of 10° C. For $HgCl_2$ the temperature coefficient is lower, generally 2 to 4 for 10° C.

An alternative method of estimating the value of θ is to start with a suspension of organisms the number of which need not be estimated, and determine how long it takes for complete sterilization at two or more different temperatures. Since the time taken for the completion of a reaction may be considered as inversely proportional to the velocity, there is no need to estimate the value of k. Thus :

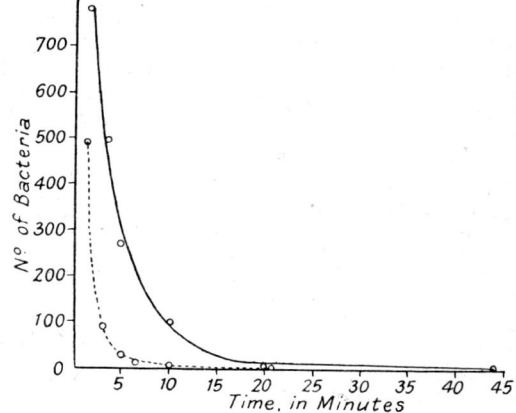

FIG. 20.

Disinfection of a 24-hours' culture of paratyphoid bacilli with 0·6 per cent. phenol at different temperatures.

Continuous curve = 11° C.
Interrupted curve = 21° C.
(After Chick.)

Phenol 6 per 1,000.	Paratyphoid bacilli. Time elapsing in minutes.
11° C.	2·2
21° C.	1·0

Then $\theta = \dfrac{2.2}{1.0} = 2.2$ for 10° C., or $2.2^{0.1} = 1.08$ for 1° C.

In disinfection by hot water a very much higher value is obtained for θ. Thus Chick (1910), working with *Bact. typhosum* at temperatures of 49° C. and 54·1° C., found that the velocity constant of the reaction was increased 13·1 times for the 5° C. rise in temperature, *i.e.* $\theta = 1.67$ for 1° C., or about 170 for 10° C.

The consistent effect of rise of temperature on the velocity of disinfection points to a close analogy with an ordinary chemical reaction. Arrhenius elaborated a formula, which has been found to be applicable to many chemical reactions, and it is interesting therefore to ascertain whether it applies also to the reaction of disinfection.   The formula is :

$$A = \frac{T_0 . T_n}{T_0 - T_n} . \log \frac{K_0}{K_n}$$

where K_0 and K_n are the velocity constants of the reaction in question corresponding to the absolute temperatures T_0 and T_n respectively, and A is a constant.   As the time taken for the completion of a reaction may be considered as inversely proportional to the velocity of the reaction, this equation may be re-written thus :

$$A = \frac{T_0 . T_n}{T_0 - T_n} . \log \frac{t_n}{t_0}$$

where t_n and t_0 are the times taken to complete the reaction at absolute temperatures T_n and T_0 respectively.

This formula was found by Madsen and Nyman to apply to the killing of anthrax spores by $HgCl_2$.   Chick showed that it was likewise applicable to the disinfection of paratyphoid bacilli by $HgCl_2$, $AgNO_3$ and phenol (Table XIX).

TABLE XIX
$HgCl_2$ 1/10,000.   Paratyphoid Bacilli.   (Modified from Chick 1908.)

Temperature.	Time taken for Disinfection.	Value of A.
30·7° C.	2·5 minutes	4580
19·8° C.	11·5 „	5010
13·9° C.	36·0 „	5480
6·8° C.	50·0 „	4610
0·0° C.	101·0 „	4390

For $AgNO_3$ the value of A was 5450, and for phenol 8430.

Whether rise of temperature affects the velocity of disinfection in a simple logarithmic manner or in accordance with the law of Arrhenius, it is impossible to say, for within a small range of temperature the two become almost identical (Chick 1910).   Bělehrádek (1926) brings evidence to suggest that Arrhenius' formula is not generally applicable to the influence of temperature on biological processes.

It must be pointed out that when an organism is suspended in a favourable medium, the effect of temperature on inhibition of growth may be the exact opposite of that on disinfection.   Thus Behring found that the growth of anthrax bacilli at room temperature was inhibited in the presence of 1/400,000 $HgCl_2$; at 37° C. a concentration of 1/100,000 was necessary to inhibit growth.   It appears that the rise of temperature favours the growth of the bacilli more than it does the action of the germicide.   Similar results were obtained by Chick (1908) with paratyphoid bacilli and phenol.

Standardization of Disinfectants.—In the practical application of disinfection, it is desirable to have some measure of the relative germicidal activity of different disinfectants.   The first method devised for this purpose was Koch's (1881) thread method.   Suitable organisms, such as anthrax spores, were dried on silk threads, submitted to the action of the disinfectant, and subsequently washed, and transferred to a solid medium in order to ascertain whether all the spores had been killed. This method is open to certain fallacies to which attention was first drawn by Geppert (1889, 1891a, b). Geppert found that if, after a short time in mercuric chloride solution, the spores were transferred to a culture medium, they failed to grow, but that if they were inoculated into a guinea-pig, they gave rise to anthrax. The reason for this appeared to be that sufficient $HgCl_2$ was carried over by the thread into the broth to prevent germination of the spores occurring; in the tissues of the guinea-pig, however, this quantity was neutralized, and the spores that were still alive were able to develop. The truth of this explanation was shown by the fact that cultivation of the spores proved successful, provided the threads were treated with ammonium sulphide to neutralize the mercury before being inoculated into the broth. The thread method, therefore, yielded higher values than the disinfectant actually possessed. Geppert's work was of considerable importance, particularly in relation to disinfection by salts of the heavy metals. These substances have a low concentration exponent, and therefore act as antiseptics even in high dilution. Since it is impossible by this method to remove all traces of the disinfectant from the interstices of the thread, Krönig and Paul (1897) replaced the threads by garnets; they introduced a further improvement, which rendered the test quantitative, by plating out the washings from the garnets, and counting the number of colonies that developed. The two tests that are chiefly used at the present time, either in their original or in a modified form, are the Rideal-Walker and the Chick-Martin methods.

The Rideal-Walker Drop Method (Rideal and Walker 1903).—In this method similar quantities of organisms are submitted to the action of varying concentrations of phenol and of the germicide to be tested. Subcultures are made into broth every $2\frac{1}{2}$ minutes up to 15 minutes and the tubes incubated at 37° C. for 3 days. That dilution of disinfectant X which sterilizes the suspension in a given time is divided by that dilution of phenol which sterilizes the suspension in the same time, and a phenol coefficient obtained. Thus:

TABLE XX

Bact. typhosum, 24 HOURS' BROTH CULTURE AT 37° C. TEMPERATURE AT WHICH TEST WAS CONDUCTED 60° F.

Disinfectant.	Dilution.	Time in minutes of exposure of suspension to disinfectant.					
		$2\frac{1}{2}'$	$5'$	$7\frac{1}{2}'$	$10'$	$12\frac{1}{2}'$	$15'$
Phenol . . .	1–110	+	—	—	—	—	—
,, . . .	1–120	+	+	—	—	—	—
,, . . .	1–130	+	+	+	—	—	—
,, . . .	1–140	+	+	+	+	—	—
X . . .	1–225	+	—	—	—	—	—
,, . . .	1–250	+	+	—	—	—	—
,, . . .	1–275	+	+	+	—	—	—
,, . . .	1–300	+	+	+	+	+	—

+ = growth.
— = no growth.

The phenol coefficient of X is therefore $\dfrac{275}{130} = 2\cdot1$.

(For a full discussion of the Rideal-Walker method see *Lancet*, 1909, ii, 1516.)

The Chick-Martin Test.—In the Rideal-Walker method the disinfectant acts in pure solution. But, in practice, disinfectants have usually to act in solutions containing organic matter. As the presence of organic matter seriously lessens the activity of most disinfectants, Chick and Martin (1908) suggested that the disinfectant should be tested on the organisms not in distilled water, but in water containing a suspension of 3 per cent. dried human fæces. Further, instead of allowing the time to vary, as in the Rideal-Walker method, they fix a time limit of 30 minutes for the action of the disinfectant, making subcultures at the end of this time. The phenol coefficient of disinfectants, especially those of the emulsified disinfectants, is distinctly lower by this method. Thus whereas the activity of phenol was reduced about 10 per cent. in the presence of 3 per cent. fæces, that of the commercial cresols was reduced 30–50 per cent.

There are certain general principles governing the estimation of disinfectant power that must be rigidly adhered to. Great care must be taken to use media that are alike in composition and in H-ion concentration. The organisms used for the test must always be grown and subcultured under exactly the same conditions. Disinfectants such as $HgCl_2$, which, as we have already seen, are antiseptic even in extremely high dilution, must be neutralized, preferably with a saturated solution of H_2S, at the termination of their action, before subcultures are made. With phenol this is unnecessary, as the dilution resulting on the inoculation of a loopful of culture into 5 c.c. of broth is sufficiently great to destroy its antiseptic action. In comparing salts, molar concentrations, either in their multiples or sub-multiples should be used. We have seen that the great majority of organisms are killed long before the culture is completely sterilized; there are always a few organisms that resist disinfection for a considerable period after the remainder are destroyed. Therefore any method that takes sterilization as its end-point is bound to be fallacious. This is one of the greatest objections to all the current methods. Similarly any method in which the time is fixed is unsatisfactory. The ideal method would be to take two or three points on the disinfection curve and ascertain the concentration of disinfectant necessary to bring about a given decrease in the number of viable bacteria (see Phelps, p. 129).

Even when the best available standard methods are employed, and the temperature is kept constant, there still remain very important theoretical objections. The present methods depend on the fixation of all but one variable, and the comparison of different disinfectants on this variable. Thus, under standard conditions we learn the concentrations necessary to kill a given organism in a given length of time. It is obvious that the results we obtain must vary with the conditions we lay down. Suppose the time taken be 2·5 minutes, as it sometimes is in the Rideal-Walker method, then for the sterilization of *Bact. paratyphosum* the phenol coefficient of $HgCl_2$ would work out at just over 2; but if the time taken is 30 minutes, as it is in the Chick-Martin test, the phenol coefficient works out at 550 (Chick 1908). This is an extreme instance, but it serves to show the importance of the time factor. Again, an increase in the concentration of phenol increases the rate of disinfection far more than a similar increase in the concentration of $HgCl_2$; doubling the concentration of the former shortens the reaction 64 times, of the latter only twice. Again, the effect of temperature is important, for a rise in temperature increases the rate of action with some disinfectants, such as phenol and the emulsified disinfectants, far more than with others, such as the salts of the heavy metals.

There are therefore three things we should desire to know about any disinfectant —its reaction velocity, its concentration exponent n, and its temperature coefficient θ. The Rideal-Walker method tells us only one of these, and that incompletely, namely the reaction velocity at a given concentration, and during a particular interval of time.

It must be admitted that the present tests are highly unsatisfactory. To remedy this, Phelps (1911) suggests that a method of standardization should comprise the determination of K, n, and θ for each disinfectant. Knowing these values, which can incidentally be worked out with relative accuracy even in a shorter time than is required for the performance of the Rideal-Walker test, by two equations we can determine the reaction velocity of a given disinfectant under any conditions desired. By the formula

$$KC^n t = \log \frac{B}{b}$$

we can calculate the reaction velocity at any concentration, and by the formula

$$K_{T_1} = K_{20°} \times \theta^{(T - 20°)}$$

where K_{T_1} represents the velocity to be calculated at the temperature desired, and $K_{20°}$ the velocity actually determined at a temperature of 20° C. (or any other convenient temperature), we can determine the value of the temperature coefficient θ.

The values of n and of θ do not appear to vary greatly for different organisms ; the value of K varies with each organism. Thus Chick and Martin (1908) found that phenol is more active against *Bact. typhosum* than against *Staphylococcus aureus* ; whereas chinosol has the reverse grade of activity. Further, they showed that a given disinfectant might vary in efficiency as much as 10 times, according to the organism it was tested on. Therefore it would be better, as Eisenberg (1919) suggests, to use several organisms for the test. For practical purposes, it would be sufficient to work out the values of K, n and θ for one organism, such as *Bact. typhosum*, and in addition the value of K only for a spore-bearing organism, such as *B. anthracis* or *B. subtilis*. In this way we should gain far more valuable information than is afforded by any of the present rather cumbersome, and distinctly unsatisfactory methods.

Practical Application of Germicides.—We shall not give more than a brief account of the use of germicides in practice, and shall confine ourselves to general remarks, illustrating the application of the principles that we have already considered.

Gaseous Disinfectants.—The gaseous disinfectants most commonly employed are sulphur dioxide, chlorine, and formaldehyde. The first two are active only in a moist atmosphere. Thus sulphur dioxide combines with water to form sulphurous acid, and chlorine to form hypochlorous acid. To be successful in the destruction of vegetative bacteria, sulphur dioxide should be present in a concentration of 2–3 per cent., chlorine of 1 per cent., and formaldehyde 1–2 per cent. of the atmosphere. Ozone is sometimes used for the sterilization of water and for meat preservation. Heise (1917) found that concentrations by volume of about 1/1000 destroyed 95 per cent. of coliform organisms on the surface of an agar plate in 1 minute, concentrations of about 1/270,000 in 1 hour, and concentrations of about 1/720,000 in 3–4 hours. The gas has little penetrating power, and is

P.B.   F of value only for the destruction of organisms unprotected by colloidal or other material.

Liquid Disinfectants.—In actual practice it is inevitable that disinfectants should be employed more or less empirically ; it is impossible, from knowledge gained in the laboratory, to predict exactly the length of time requisite for the complete sterilization of any material. Realizing this, we err on the safe side, and arrange our conditions so as to obtain sterilization in a time much shorter than that which is actually allowed. To do this, however, it is necessary to take into consideration the principles that we have already considered, so far as they are known, and pay particular attention to such variables as the nature of the organism, the material in which it is contained, the H-ion concentration, the salt content, and the temperature at which the reaction is to proceed. Having considered these, the disinfectant to be chosen, the concentration in which it shall be allowed to act, and the time for which its action shall continue, may be determined. For general purposes, we may lay down a few simple rules.

(1) Spores are more resistant than vegetative bacteria.

(2) Bacteria possessing a high content of lipoids, such as the acid-fast bacilli, are very resistant to liquid disinfectants. Tubercle bacilli in sputum may withstand 5 per cent. phenol for 24 hours, but they are killed by boiling in 1 minute.

(3) For the destruction of spores and acid-fast bacilli heat is preferable to chemical disinfectants.

(4) Bacteria suspended in a protein medium are more resistant than those in a non-protein medium.

(5) If the protein medium is also a good nutrient medium, the organisms are even more resistant.

(6) Disinfection by nearly all germicides proceeds more quickly in an acid than in an alkaline medium. There is evidence that a given concentration of H-ions is more bactericidal than of OH-ions.

(7) The effect of salts in the medium depends on their nature and on their concentration. In general, salts increase the action of phenol and of the emulsified disinfectants, but diminish that of $HgCl_2$.

(8) The higher the temperature at which a disinfectant is allowed to act, the more rapid is the process of sterilization.

(9) Germicides dissolved in alcohol or in vegetable oils are deprived of the greater part of their power.

(10) Doubling the concentration of $HgCl_2$ halves the time taken for sterilization ; doubling the concentration of phenol diminishes it about 64 times.

(11) For use in a protein medium, the acid disinfectants, such as hypochlorous acid, bleaching powder, and the disinfectants that can be employed combined with acids, such as $HgCl_2$, are most effective. The alkalies are also reliable.

(12) In the presence of organic matter, whether in solution or in suspension, the activity of certain disinfectants is markedly lowered, especially with the emulsified disinfectants, with oxidizing agents, and with the salts of the heavy metals. Phenol is much less affected, and likewise certain dyes, such as flavine.

Solid Disinfectants.—These are generally made up in the form of powders, with a basis of lime, silicious matter, or vegetable fibre. Phenol is the commonest disinfectant incorporated. To destroy bacteria they must pass into solution ; in the dry state they act merely as deodorants.

Below is a table (Table XXI) giving the action of some of the commoner disinfectants on anthrax spores, tested by the garnet method. It has been compiled mostly from Krönig and Paul (1897), but it must be emphasized that the figures are only relatively comparable, as they are the outcome of experiments made at different times with somewhat varying numbers of organisms. It is intended to give no more than a rough idea of the activity of some of the bodies that have been dealt with in this chapter.

TABLE XXI

TIME NECESSARY FOR STERILIZATION OF ANTHRAX SPORES BY VARIOUS SUBSTANCES IN AN AQUEOUS MEDIUM.

$HgCl_2$	$\dfrac{M}{64}$	0·42%	20 minutes.[1]
$HgCl_2$	$\dfrac{M}{256}$	0·11%	120 ,, [1]
$AgNO_3$	$\dfrac{M}{200}$	0·09%	12 hours.
$AgNO_3$	$\dfrac{M}{4}$	4·25%	40 minutes.
$CuSO_4$	$\dfrac{M}{1}$	15·95%	>10 days.
$ZnCl_2$	$\dfrac{M}{1}$	13·60%	>10 ,,
$BaCl_2$	$\dfrac{M}{1}$	20·85%	> 7 ,,
$KMnO_4$	$\dfrac{M}{4}$	3·95%	20 minutes.
$KMnO_4$	—	0·99% + HCl 0·91%	30 seconds.
$(NH_4)_2S_2O_8$	—	3·70% + HCl 1·1%	1 minute.
HF	$\dfrac{M}{1}$	2·00%	·60 minutes.
HNO_3	$\dfrac{M}{1}$	6·3%	70 ,,
HCl	$\dfrac{M}{1}$	3·65%	9 hours.
HOCl	—	0·01%	30 seconds.
Chlorine	$\dfrac{M}{256}$	0·03%	< 2 minutes.
Oxalic acid	$\dfrac{M}{2}$	4·50%	12 hours.
KOH	$\dfrac{M}{1}$	5·60%	10 ,,
$NH_4(OH)$	$\dfrac{M}{1}$	3·50%	>33 ,,
Alcohol	—	99·00%	>50 days.
HCHO	—	5·00% aqueous solution	90 minutes.
H_2O_2	—	3%	70 ,,
Phenol	—	5·00%	>24 hours.
Lysol	—	2·00%	>92 ,,

[1] It is doubtful how far these figures are correct. According to Poppe (1922), the time taken by a 1/1000 solution of $HgCl_2$ to destroy anthrax spores is recorded by different workers as 15 minutes to 70 hours. This variation probably depends on the degree of neutralization of the $HgCl_2$ which is practised after exposure.

REFERENCES

ALLEN, P. W. (1923) *J. Bact.*, **8**, 555.

ANDREWES, F. W. and ORTON, K. J. P. (1904) *Zbl. Bakt.*, **35**, 645, 811.

APOSTOLI, G. and LAQUERRIÈRE, A. (1890) *C. R. Acad. Sci.*, **105**, 918.

D'ARCY, R. F. and HARDY, W. B. (1894) *J. Physiol.*, **17**, 390.

BANCROFT, W. D. and RICHTER, G. H. (1931) *J. phys. Chem.*, **35**, 511.

BARNARD, J. E. and MORGAN, H. DE R. (1903) *Proc. roy. Soc.*, **72**, 126.

BARR, C. E. (1923) *J. med. Res.*, **44**, 79.

BAXTER. (1875) *Rep. loc. Govt. Bd. publ. Hlth.*, New Ser., No. 5, appendix p. 216.

BAYLISS, W. M. (1924) "Principles of General Physiology," 4th ed. London.

BEATTIE, J. M. and LEWIS F. C. (1920) *Spec. Rep. med. Res. Coun. Lond.*, Ser., No. 49.

BECKMAN, J. W. (1896) *Zbl. Bakt.*, **20**, 577.

BECKWITH, T. D. and OLSON, A. R. (1932) *Proc. Soc. exp. Biol., N.Y.*, **29**, 362.

BEHRING. (1890) *Z. Hyg. InfektKr.*, **9**, 395.

BÉLEHRÁDEK, J. (1926) *Nature*, **118**, 117.

BIGELOW, W. D. and ESTY, J. R. (1920) *J. infect. Dis.*, **27**, 602.

BISCEGLIE, V. (1926) *Z. ImmunForsch.*, **49**, 272.

BLUM, H. F. (1932) *Physiol. Rev.*, **12**, 23.

BROOKS, S. C. (1919) *J. gen. Physiol.*, **1**, 61 ; (1920) *J. med. Res.*, **41**, 411.

BROWNING, C. H. (1933) *Brit. dent. J.*, **54**, 389.

BROWNING, C. H. and RUSS, S. (1917) *Proc. roy. Soc.*, B, **90**, 33.

BROWNING, C. H., KENNAWAY, E. L., GULBRANSEN, R., and THORNTON, L. H. D. (1917) *Brit. med. J.*, i, 73.

BRUYNOGHE, R. and DUBOIS, A. (1925) *C. R. Soc. Biol.*, **93**, 849.

BRUYNOGHE, R. and LE FÈVRE DE ARRIC, M. (1925) *C. R. Soc. Biol.*, **93**, 852.

BUCHHOLZ, J. and JENEY, A. v. (1935) *Zbl. Bakt.*, **133**, 299.

BUCHOLTZ, L. (1875) *Arch. exp. Path. Pharmak.*, **4**, 1.

BURGE, W. E. and NEILL, A. J. (1915) *Amer. J. Physiol.*, **38**, 399.

BURKE, G. S. (1923) *J. infect. Dis.*, **33**, 274.

BURNET, F. M. (1925) *Aust. J. exp. Biol. med. Sci.*, **2**, 65.

CADÉAC and MEUNIER, A. (1889) *Ann. Inst. Pasteur*, **3**, 317.

CAMERON, A. T. (1930) *Trans. roy. Soc. Can.*, 3rd Series, **24**, Section V, 53.

CHAMBERLAND, M. (1887) *Ann. Inst. Pasteur*, **1**, 153.

CHAMBERS, L. A. and GAINES, N. (1932) *J. cell. comp. Physiol.*, **1**, 451.

CHICK, H. (1908) *J. Hyg., Camb.*, **8**, 92 ; (1910) *Ibid.*, **10**, 237 ; (1912) *Ibid.*, **12**, 414.

CHICK, H. and MARTIN, C. J. (1908) *J. Hyg., Camb.*, **8**, 698 ; (1910) *J. Physiol.*, **40**, 404.

CHURCHMAN, J. W. (1912) *J. exp. Med.*, **16**, 221 ; (1923a) *Ibid.*, **37**, 1 ; (1923b) *Ibid.*, **38**, 1.

CLARK and GAGE. (1903) *34th Rep. State Bd. Hlth., Mass.*

CLIFTON, C. E. (1931) *Proc. Soc. exp. Biol., N.Y.*, **28**, 745.

COHEN, B. (1922) *J. Bact.*, **1**, 183.

COHEN, B. and CLARK, W. M. (1919) *J. Bact.*, **4**, 409.

CROWTHER, J. A. (1926) *Nature*, **118**, 86.

DAKIN, H. D. (1915) *Brit. med. J.*, ii, 318.

DANYSZ, J. (1906) *Ann. Inst. Pasteur*, **20**, 206.

DELÉPINE, A. S. and GREENWOOD, A. (1914) *J. R. sanit. Inst.*, **35**, 317.

DOWNES, A. and BLUNT, T. P. (1877) *Proc. roy. Soc.*, **26**, 488 ; (1878) *Ibid.*, **28**, 199.

DREYER and HANSSEN. (1907) *C. R. Acad. Sci.*, **145**, 234.

DUCLAUX, E. (1887) *Ann. Inst. Pasteur*, **1**, 88.

ECKELMANN, E. (1917) *Zbl. Bakt.*, IIte Abt., **48**, 140.

EHRISMANN, O. (1930) *Z. Hyg. InfektKr.*, **111**, 618.

EHRISMANN, O. and NOETHLING, W. (1932) *Z. Hyg. InfektKr.*, **113**, 597.

EIJKMAN, C. (1908) *Biochem. Z.*, **11**, 12.

EISENBERG, P. (1919) *Zbl. Bakt.*, **82**, 69.

EISENBERG, P. and OKOLSKA M. (1913) *Zbl. Bakt.*, **69**, 312.

EISLER, M. v. (1909) *Zbl. Bakt.*, **51**, 546.

ELSER, W. J., THOMAS, R. A., and STEFFEN, G. I. (1935) *J. Immunol.*, **28**, 433.

EPSTEIN, F. (1897) *Z. Hyg. InfektKr.*, **24**, 1.

FABIAN, F. W. and GRAHAM, H. T. (1933) *J. infect. Dis.*, **53**, 76.

FALK, I. S. (1923) *Abst. Bact.*, **7**, 33, 87, 133.

FAY, A. C. (1934) *J. agric. Res.*, **48**, 453.

FEISTMANTEL, C. (1902) *Zbl. Bakt.*, **31**, 433.

FERMI, C. and PERNOSSI, L. (1894) *Z. Hyg. InfektKr.*, **16**, 385.

FICKER, M. (1898) *Z. Hyg. InfektKr.*, **29**, 1.

FISCHER. (1900) "The Structure and Functions of the Bacteria." Trans. by A. C. Jones. Oxford.

FLEMING, A. (1932) *J. Path. Bact.*, **35**, 831.

FLEXNER, S. (1907) *J. exp. Med.*, **9**, 105.
FLOSDORF, E. W. and MUDD, S. (1935) *J. Immunol.*, **29**, 389.
FOULDS, M. (1911) *J. R. Army. med. Cps.*, **16**, 167.
FREUNDLICH, H. (1903) *Z. phys. Chem.*, **44**, 129.
GALE, C. K. and MILLER, D. (1935) *J. lab. clin. Med.*, **21**, 31.
GARROD, L. P. (1933a) *St. Bart's Hosp. med. Rep.*, **66**, 203 ; (1933b) *Brit. J. exp. Path.*, **14**, 182.
GATES, F. L. (1930) *J. gen. Physiol.*, **14**, 31.
GEPPERT, J. (1889) *Berl. klin. Wschr.*, **26**, 789, 819 ; (1891a) *Dtsch. med. Wschr.*, **17**, 797, 825, 855 ; (1891b) *Ibid.*, **17**, 1065.
HARRIS, R. S., BUNKER, J. W. M., and MILAS, N. A. (1932) *J. Bact.*, **23**, 429.
HASCHÉ, E. and LEUNIG, H. (1935) *Dtsch. med. Wschr.*, **61**, 1193.
HEISE, R. (1917) *Arb. ReichsgesundhAmt.*, **50**, 204, 418.
HEWLETT, R. T. (1909) *Lancet*, i. 741, 815, 889.
HICKS, R. A. and SZYMANOWSKI, W. T. (1932) *J. infect. Dis.*, **50**, 466.
HODER, F. (1932) *Z. ImmunForsch.*, **74**, 455.
HOFMANN, P. (1929) *Zbl. Bakt.*, **114**, 216.
HOFMEISTER, F. (1888) *Arch. exp. Path. Pharmak.*, **24**, 247 ; (1889) *Ibid.*, **25**, 1.
HOLM, G. E. and SHERMAN, J. M. (1921) *J. Bact.*, **6**, 511.
HOTCHKISS, M. (1923) *J. Bact.*, **8**, 141.
HOUSTON, A. C. (1914) *10th Res. Rep. metrop. Wat. Bd.*
JODLBAUER, A. and TAPPEINER, H. v. (1904) *Münch. med. Wschr.*, **51**, 1096.
KITASATO, S. (1891) *Z. Hyg. InfektKr.*, **10**, 267.
KLARMANN, E., SHTERNOV, V. A., and GATES, L. W. (1934a) *J. Lab. clin. Med.*, **19**, 835 ; (1934b) *Ibid.*, **20**, 40.
KLING, A. (1932) *C. R. Acad. Sci.*, **194**, 1402.
KNAYSI, G. (1930) *J. infect. Dis.*, **47**, 293, 322, 328.
KNAYSI, G. and GORDON, M. (1930) *J. infect. Dis.*, **47**, 303, 318.
KOCH, R. (1881) *Mitt. ReichsgesundhAmt.*, **1**, 234.
KOCH, R. and WOLFFHÜGEL, G. (1881) *Mitt. ReichsgesundhAmt.*, **1**, 301.
KOCH, R., GAFFKY and LOEFFLER. (1881) *Mitt. ReichsgesundhAmt.*, **1**, 322.
KRÖNIG, B. and PAUL, T. (1897) *Z. Hyg. InfektKr.*, **25**, 1.
LAROQUETTE, M. DE. (1918) *Ann. Inst. Pasteur.*, **32**, 170.
LEA, D. E., HAINES, R. B., and COULSON, C. A. (1936) *Proc. roy. Soc.*, B, **120**, 47.
LENTZE, F.-A. (1932) *Zbl. Bakt.*, **126**, 508.
LIU, S. C. and YEN, A. C. H. (1934) *Proc. Soc. exp. Biol.*, N.Y., **32**, 485.
LOEB, J. (1899) *Pflüg. Arch. ges. Physiol.*, **75**, 303 ; (1900) *Amer. J. Physiol.*, **3**, 327.
LOEB, J. and NORTHROP, J. H. (1917) *J. biol. Chem.*, **32**, 103.
MACFADYEN, A. (1900) *Proc. roy. Soc.*, B., **66**, 180, 339.
MACFADYEN, A. and ROWLAND, S. D. (1900) *Proc. roy. Soc.*, B, **66**, 488.
MADSEN, T. and NYMAN, M. (1907) *Z. Hyg. InfektKr.*, **57**, 388.
MATHEWS, A. P. (1904a) *Amer. J. Physiol.*, **10**, 290 ; (1904b) *Ibid.*, **11**, 455 ; (1905) *Ibid.*, **12**, 419 ; (1906) *J. infect. Dis.*, **3**, 572.
MAYSER, H. (1925) *Zbl. Bakt.*, **94**, 238.
McMASTER, P. D. (1919) *J. infect. Dis.*, **24**, 378.
MINERVINI, R. (1898) *Z. Hyg. InfektKr.*, **29**, 117.
NORTON, J. F. and HSU, P. H. (1916) *Z. Hyg. InfektKr.*, **18**, 180.
OTTEN, L. (1930) *Zbl. Bakt.*, **116**, 199 ; (1932) *Trans. Far East. Ass. trop. Med. 8th Congr. Bangkok*, 1930, p. 89.
PAÏC, M., DEUTSCH, V., and BORCILA, I. (1935a) *C. R. Soc. Biol.*, **119**, 1063.
PAÏC, M., HABER, P., VOET, J., and ELIASZ, A. (1935b) *C. R. Soc. Biol.*, **119**, 1061.
PAUL, T. (1909) *Biochem. Z.*, **18**, 1.
PAUL, T. and PRALL, F. (1907) *Arb. ReichsgesundhAmt.*, **26**, 73.
PAUL, T., BIRSTEIN, G., and REUSZ, A. (1910a) *Biochem. Z.*, **25**, 367 ; (1910b) *Ibid.*, **29**, 202.
PERDRAU, J. R., and TODD, C. (1933a) *Proc. roy. Soc.*, B, **112**, 277 ; (1933b) *Ibid.*, **112**, 288.
PHELPS, E. B. (1911) *J. infect. Dis.*, **8**, 27.
PILOD and CODVELLE. (1932) *C. R. Acad. Sci.*, **194**, 497.
POPPE, K. (1922) *Ergebn. Hyg. Bakt.*, **5**, 597.
PRINGLE. (1750) *Philos. Trans.*, **46**, 480, 525.
PROCHOWNICK, L. and SPAETH, F. (1890) *Dtsch. med. Wschr.*, **16**, 564.
PUGSLEY, A. T., ODDIE, T. H., and EDDY, C. E. (1935) *Proc. roy. Soc.*, B, **118**, 276.
RAAB, O. (1900) *Z. Biol.*, **39**, 524.
REICHEL, H. (1909) *Biochem. Z.*, **22**, 149.
REICHENBACH, H. (1911) *Z. Hyg. InfektKr.*, **69**, 171.
REID, J. D. (1932) *Amer. J. Hyg.*, **16**, 540.
RIDEAL, S. and WALKER, J. T. A. (1903) *J. R. sanit. Inst.*, **24**, 424.
RIEDER, H. (1902) *Münch. med. Wschr.*, **49**, 402.
RITCHIE, J. (1899) *Trans. path. Soc. Lond.*, **50**, 256.

ROBERTSON, T. B. (1914) *J. Hyg., Camb.,* **14,** 143.
ROCKWELL, G. E. and EBERTZ, E. G. (1924) *J. infect. Dis.,* **35,** 573.
RÖMER, C. (1898) *Münch. med. Wschr.,* **45,** 298.
ROUX, E. (1887) *Ann. Inst. Pasteur,* **1,** 445.
SCHEURLEN, E. (1895) " Die Bedeutung des Molecularzustandes der wassergelösten
　　Desinfectionsmittel für ihren Wirkungswerth." Strassburg.
SCHMIDT, C. L. A. and NORMAN, G. F. (1920) *J. infect. Dis.,* **27,** 40.
SCHOOP, G. (1935) *Zbl. Bakt.,* **134,** 14.
SCHROETTER, H. v. (1927) *Zbl. Bakt.,* **104,** Beiheft. p. 205.
SELLARDS, A. W. (1918) *J. med. Res.,* **38,** 293.
SHEARER, C. (1919) *J. Hyg., Camb.,* **18,** 337.
SHERMAN, J. M. and HOLM, G. E. (1922) *J. Bact.,* **7,** 465.
SPENCER, R. R. (1934) *Publ. Hlth. Rep., Wash.,* **49,** 183 ; (1935) *Ibid.,* **50,** 1642.
STEARN, E. W. and STEARN, A. E. (1926) *J. Bact.,* **11,** 345 ; (1928) *Univ. Mo. Stud.,*
　　3, No. 2, 1.
SUESS, E. (1908) *Z. Tuberk.,* **12,** 480.
SZYMANOWSKI, W. T. and HICKS, R. A. (1932) *J. infect. Dis.,* **50,** 1.
TAKAHASHI, W. N. and CHRISTENSEN, R. J. (1934) *Science,* **79,** 415.
TAPPEINER, H. v. (1900) *Münch. med. Wschr.,* **47,** 5.
TAPPEINER, H. v. and JODLBAUER, A. (1904) *Münch. med. Wschr.,* **51,** 737.
TCHAHOTINE, S. (1921) *Ann. Inst. Pasteur,* **35,** 321.
THIELE, H. and WOLF, K. (1906) *Arch. Hyg.,* **57,** 29 ; (1907) *Ibid.,* **60,** 29.
THRESH, J. C. and BEALE, J. F. (1910) *Lancet,* ii. 1849.
TOPLEY, W. W. C. (1915) *Brit. med. J.,* i, 237.
T'UNG, T. (1935) *Proc. Soc. exp. Biol., N.Y.,* **33,** 328.
WARD, H. M. (1892) *Proc. roy. Soc.,* **52,** 393.
WATSON, H. E. (1908) *J. Hyg., Camb.,* **8,** 536.
WESBROOK, F. F. (1896) *J. Path. Bact.,* **3,** 70.
WHIPPLE, G. C. and MAYER, A. (1906) *J. infect. Dis., Supp.* 2, p. 76.
WINSLOW, C.-E. A. and DOLLOFF, A. F. (1928) *J. Bact.,* **15,** 67.
WINSLOW, C.-E. A. and FALK, I. S. (1923) *J. Bact.,* **8,** 237.
WINSLOW, C.-E. A. and HOTCHKISS, M. (1922) *Proc. Soc. exp. Biol., N.Y.,* **19,** 314.
WINSLOW, C.-E. A. and LOCHRIDGE, E. E. (1906) *J. infect. Dis.,* **3,** 547.
WOODRUFF, L. L. and BUNZEL, H. H. (1909) *Amer. J. Physiol.,* **25,** 190.
WYCKOFF, R. W. G. (1930*a*) *J. exp. Med.,* **52,** 435 ; (1930*b*) *Ibid.,* **52,** 769 ; (1932) *J. gen.*
　　Physiol., **15,** 351.
WYCKOFF, R. W. G. and LUYET, B. J. (1931) *Radiology,* **17,** 1171.
WYCKOFF, R. W. G. and RIVERS, T. M. (1930) *J. exp. Med.,* **51,** 921.
YEN, A. C. H. and LIU, S. C. (1934) *Proc. Soc. exp. Biol., N.Y.,* **31,** 1250.
ZWAARDEMAKER, H. (1918) *Amer. J. Physiol.,* **45,** 147 ; (1919–20) *J. Physiol.,* **53,** 273.

CHAPTER VI

THE ANTIGEN-ANTIBODY REACTIONS

THE problems of infection and resistance—the nature of the mechanisms which determine the course of events when a potentially pathogenic parasite gains access to an animal host—will be discussed in later chapters.

Very early in the development of this field of research investigators began to study the reactions which occur when blood, blood serum, or other body fluids are allowed to react in the test tube with bacteria, or with bacterial products. Almost from the first, the study of these reactions was pursued by many workers without particular reference to the rôle, if any, which they played in the combat between parasite and host; and it soon became clear that they provided a new technique, which could be applied to a variety of biological problems quite apart from the study of disease.

The development of our knowledge of the various reactions which may occur when the blood or serum of a given animal is mixed with various bacteria, bacterial products, foreign cells, or foreign proteins, may be briefly summarized as follows.

In 1888 Nuttall demonstrated that the defibrinated blood of certain animals had the power of killing certain bacteria. In 1889 Buchner showed that this bactericidal power was possessed by the cell-free serum, and that it was lost when the serum was heated to 55° C. for 1 hour.

In 1890 von Behring and Kitasato showed that the serum of animals which had received repeated injections of non-lethal doses of tetanus toxin, or of diphtheria toxin, had acquired the property of specifically neutralizing these toxins, and thus preventing their poisonous effect.

Between 1893 and 1895 Pfeiffer (see also Pfeiffer and Issaeff 1894) recorded the occurrence of bacteriolysis, or granular degeneration followed by partial dissolution, in cholera vibrios and some other bacteria, when these were introduced into the peritoneal cavity of guinea-pigs which had previously received inoculations of killed cultures of the particular bacteria in question. They showed, also, that the substances which determined this bacteriolysis were present in the blood serum, and in other body fluids.

In 1895 Bordet published his classical paper on the properties of the sera of immunized animals. We may note here that, although the idea of increased resistance to infection was implicit in the early conception of the process of immunization, this term soon came to possess a wider meaning. Any animal, into whose tissues has been introduced any antigenic foreign substance, dead or living, and whose serum has, in consequence, gained the property of reacting in some way with that particular substance, is spoken of as having been immunized against it; and such a serum is referred to as an *immune serum* or an *antiserum*. Bordet,

135

extending the observations of Buchner, showed that two different substances are involved in the phenomenon of bacteriolysis. One of these is present in any normal serum, is inactivated by heating to 55° C. for 1 hour, and is not increased in amount as the result of immunization. The other, if present in a normal serum, is seldom found in any considerable amount. It appears, or increases greatly in amount, in response to immunization with a particular bacterium, and is not inactivated by heating at 55° C. He noted in the same paper that, when cholera vibrios are subjected to the action of an immune serum, they often aggregate into clumps before lysis occurs, a phenomenon which had, indeed, been casually recorded by previous observers.

In 1896 Gruber and Durham published the first detailed studies of this aggregation, or agglutination, of bacteria.

In 1897 Kraus made the observation that the addition of filtrates of cultures of the plague bacillus, or of the cholera vibrio, to the serum of an immunized animal led to the formation of a precipitate, and that this reaction, like the reactions of bacteriolysis and agglutination, was specific ; that is, the filtrate of a cholera culture reacted with its own, or homologous antiserum, but not with the plague antiserum, and vice versa.

In 1898 Bordet described the appearance of lytic antibodies in the serum of animals which had been injected with the blood of an animal of some other species, and showed that the lysis of the red corpuscles, like the lysis of bacteria, depended upon the interaction of two distinct substances, the thermolabile, ferment-like body, present in normal serum, which he named *alexine*, but which is now generally known as *complement*, and a specific thermostable substance, developed as the result of immunization, which he referred to as the sensitizing substance. This paper of Bordet's had far-reaching results, for it substituted the simple technical procedure of observing the lysis of red cells in the test-tube for the more difficult process of determining the death of bacteria. The natural result was that many investigators in this field turned their attention to the phenomenon of hæmolysis, often with the tacit assumption that the data obtained could be transferred by analogy to the interaction of any serum with any bacterium, an assumption which now appears to be largely unwarranted.

In 1901 Bordet and Gengou showed that the absorption of complement by sensitized bacteria could be demonstrated without relying on the observation of lysis, or other change, in the bacteria themselves. Using many species of bacteria, they found that, if a suspension of a given organism were mixed with the corresponding immune serum in the presence of complement, the removal of complement from the fluid could be demonstrated by the addition of sensitized red cells, which failed to undergo hæmolysis. In the following year Gengou (1902) showed that the presence of organized material was unnecessary, and that the interaction of soluble proteins with antisera prepared against them was associated with a similar absorption of complement.

Denys and Leclef, in the course of experiments on antistreptococcal immunity, which were recorded in 1895, showed that the phagocytosis of bacteria by leucocytes was promoted by an action of the blood serum exerted on these bacteria, and Mennes (1897) confirmed and extended their observations. For some cause, which is difficult to assign in view of the inherent importance of these observations, little attention was paid to them by other workers during the years which immediately followed. In 1902 Leishman again, and independently, demonstrated the effect of serum in stimulating phagocytosis, but did not analyse the mechanism involved. In 1903 Wright and Douglas, in an extensive series of experiments, demonstrated that this action of normal serum was due to a thermolabile substance which acted directly upon the bacteria and not upon the leucocytes. To this substance they gave the name of *opsonin*. Neufeld and Rimpau (1904–5) demonstrated the presence of thermostable substances, in the blood serum of animals immunized against streptococci and pneumococci, which acted specifically on these bacteria in such a way as to increase the degree to which they were ingested by phagocytic cells. To these substances they gave the name of *bacteriotropins*.

Thus, in the earliest years of the present century, we had at our disposal a considerable body of facts with regard to the action of the sera of normal and of immunized animals on bacteria, foreign cells and foreign proteins. Little indeed has been added, during the intervening years, to our knowledge of what may happen when a normal or immune serum is mixed *in vitro* with the material against which it is active. Investigators during this period have been mainly engaged in trying to discover how these reactions are brought about. On this aspect of the problem a mass of information has been collected ; and, although the correlation of the ascertained facts has been a difficult matter, and our understanding of the underlying mechanism of the serum reactions is still far from complete, we seem during the last two decades to have made appreciable progress towards an orderly arrangement of evidence and a generalization of theory, which has resulted in a clearer conception of the processes involved.

Terminology.— With the gradual development of our knowledge of the serum reactions new names have been invented to describe the phenomenon observed and to designate the substances which are assumed to be the essential reagents. As in other terminologies which have grown naturally and have never yet been systematized, the terms employed are often ill-defined, and there is much overlapping. There has indeed been a riotous creation of hypothetical entities in the discussion of the available data, and this redundant growth is responsible for many of the obstacles encountered by the student in mastering the facts of a subject, which in its main outlines is not intrinsically difficult. It is, however, quite impossible to dispense with the use of some kind of scientific shorthand, and it is therefore necessary to gain an adequate acquaintance with the terms in common use, and especially to realize their limitations.

It is usual to refer to the substances which make their appearance in the blood serum, in response to the inoculation of foreign substances of various kinds, and which react with these substances, *in vitro* or *in vivo*, in some observable way, as *antibodies*. The foreign substances which, on inoculation into the tissues, stimulate the formation of these antibodies, are referred to as *antigens*. These two terms may be defined as follows.

An ANTIGEN *is any substance which, when introduced parenterally into the animal tissues, stimulates the production of an antibody, and which, when mixed with that antibody, reacts with it in some observable way.*

An ANTIBODY *is any substance which makes its appearance in the blood serum or body fluids of an animal, in response to the stimulus provided by the parenteral introduction of an antigen into the tissues, and reacts specifically with that antigen in some observable way.*

The term *parenteral* is introduced into this definition to emphasize the fact

P.B.   F * that the antigen must reach the tissues in an unaltered state, without preliminary disintegration by those digestive fluids which it would meet in the alimentary canal.

It will be noted that an antigen, as defined, has two essential attributes. It must react with the specific antibody, *i.e.* the antibody produced in response to its entrance into the tissues ; and it must have the power of stimulating the production of that antibody. Examples will later be noted of substances which react specifically with a given antibody, without possessing the power of stimulating its formation. Such substances are not true and complete antigens, though they are closely related to this class by the property of specific reaction.

The term antibody, as defined, has also two attributes, that of specific reaction with the antigen, and that of being produced in response to the stimulus provided by the access of that antigen to the tissues. In practice it is not customary to insist on the demonstration of the second attribute. When we prepare an anti-serum by inoculation, or find antibodies in the serum of a man or animal suffering from a particular bacterial infection, the condition of specific stimulation may be assumed to have been fulfilled. But there are numerous cases in which we find, in the blood of normal and untreated animals, substances which react with various foreign cells or bacteria in ways which are essentially similar to those observed when we mix an antigen with the specific antibody which has been produced by artificial immunization. It is usual to refer to these substances as " natural " or " normal " antibodies. They may, in many cases, have arisen as the result of natural infection ; in others they are probably an expression of the chemical interrelationships between living organisms, which have arisen during the long course of evolution (see Chapter XLVI).

Having decided upon a generic term for each of the two essential reagents, it became necessary to name in some way the particular substances which were assumed to be involved in the different reactions which were observed. Knowing little of their intimate nature, it was necessary to adopt the plan of naming them according to what they did, instead of according to what they were. Names were therefore given to the antibodies, describing the reaction which was observed when they were mixed with the corresponding antigens, the suffix *-in* being added to the descriptive term. Thus, an antibody which caused lysis was called a *lysin*, a *hæmolysin* if it acted upon red blood corpuscles, a *bacteriolysin* if it acted upon bacteria. An antibody which gave rise to agglutination was called an *agglutinin*, an antibody which caused precipitation a *precipitin*, and so on.

The actual material, organized or unorganized, with which these antibodies reacted, was in general provided with some well-recognized name ; so that one could speak of bacteria, or of red blood corpuscles, or of foreign proteins, as antigens. But it was clearly realized that many of these antigenic materials were highly complex, and that the antigenic property was almost certainly confined to some particular part of the material in question. It thus became customary to use a term, derived from the name of the antibody, to denote the essential part of the antigenic material which functioned as a stimulus to antibody production and reacted specifically with the antibody so formed. This was accomplished by adding the suffix *-ogen* to the name of the corresponding antibody.

Thus bacteria, when injected into the tissues, act as antigens and stimulate the production of agglutinins ; but the particular part of the bacterial substance which provides the specific stimulus is spoken of as an *agglutinogen* and one bacterium may possess several different agglutinogens.

Although the terms *agglutinogen, precipitinogen,* etc., were in common use until recent years they are now rarely employed. It is usually better, for reasons that are discussed in later sections of this chapter, to rely on the term *antigen,* allowing the context to make clear which particular antigen or antigenic component is indicated.

These general rules of nomenclature have certain exceptions. When the antigen itself possesses some well-marked biological activity, which is neutralized by the antibody, the antibody is named by adding the prefix *anti-* to the name of the antigen. Thus, the antibody which neutralizes a toxin is called an *antitoxin,* the antibody which neutralizes snake-venom is called *antivenin,* and so on. In many cases descriptive terms have been retained for the designation of antibodies, instead of coining new names, and this practice has much to recommend it in the present state of our ignorance.

It will be observed that the thermolabile substance, which is present in normal serum and which appears to be the active agent in bringing about the lysis of sensitized cells and the death of sensitized bacteria, demands a separate name. This substance is not an antibody, since it is not increased in amount as the result of immunization, and it must for the moment be regarded as in a class by itself. Its original name of alexine has become very generally replaced by the name complement, which was introduced by Ehrlich. It may be defined as follows.

COMPLEMENT (*or* ALEXINE) *is a thermolabile substance, or complex of substances, present in varying concentrations in the blood serum of most normal animals, which has the property of bringing about the lysis of certain cells and bacteria, in conjunction with certain antibodies which render the cells or bacteria sensitive to its action.*

This definition is incomplete, for it begs the question as to whether complement, acting by itself, produces any significant reaction whatever. It describes, however, with sufficient accuracy, the part which complement plays in the particular reactions with which we are concerned.

Theories of the Mechanism of the Serum Reactions.

Before entering on a detailed discussion of the various serum reactions, it is well to have a general idea of the theories which have been propounded to account for the phenomena observed.

One theory, which has played a prominent part in immunological studies, was propounded by Ehrlich (1898–1900). It has been developed and modified with extreme ingenuity by himself and by his colleagues to meet the demands made upon it by the continuous accumulation of new and often disconcerting facts, which had to be fitted into a structure growing more and more complex, and obviously becoming a little strained, as one new hypothesis after another was added to the central conception.

According to this " side-chain " theory we should regard the cell as being built up of highly complex chemical aggregates, which are provided with attached groupings, or side chains, the normal function of which is to anchor nutrient substances to the cell, and in some cases to act upon and modify them, as a preliminary to their incorporation into the essential cell substance. These side-chains, or *receptors,* thus form the point of contact between the cell substance and any other materials which gain access to the fluids in which the cell is bathed. It is only by gaining attachment to these receptors that substances of the class to which antigens belong can exert any action on the cell, and so stimulate it to activity. In Ehrlich's view the antigens, whatever their nature, attach themselves to these cell-receptors. Since they are in all cases foreign substances, which have no part in the normal economy of the cell, the receptors in question are diverted from their normal function. Stimulated by this derangement of its normal mechanism, the cell produces new receptors, of the same type as those thrown out of action ; and,

FIG. 21.—PAUL EHRLICH (1854–1915).

acting in accordance with a physiological habit which may frequently be observed in living things, the process is carried to excess. The superfluous receptors are shed by the cell into the surrounding fluids, and it is these shed receptors which constitute the specific antibodies. The essential feature of these antibodies is that they unite with the corresponding antigens. Ehrlich therefore endowed each of his receptors with a special chemical grouping, the *haptophore group*, which entered into chemical union with a corresponding group of the antigen. If neutralization alone resulted from the union, the requirements were met at this stage. If, however, the antigen became altered in some other recognizable way, as in agglutination or precipitation, Ehrlich postulated the existence of another grouping in the receptor, which determined the particular change in the condition of the antigen after the antibody was anchored by its haptophore group. This second, active, group was named by Ehrlich the *ergophore group*. In certain cases, which we discuss more fully below, it became necessary to postulate the existence of receptors which, while themselves inactive, served to unite an antigen to a second active substance, the complement or alexine to which we have referred above. To meet this case Ehrlich postulated the existence of receptors with two haptophore groups, one of which became attached to the antigen to be acted upon, and one to the complement which was the acting substance. Both these groups were to be regarded as strictly specific in their chemical affinities. The one which combined with the cell or other antigen to be acted upon was known as the *cytophilic group*, the one which combined with the complement was referred to as the *complementophilic group*. Ehrlich named this type of receptor an *amboceptor*, because both groups were supposed to be of the haptophore type. He also referred these three types of receptors to three orders, the first having a single haptophore group, the second one haptophore and one ergophore group, and the third two haptophore groups.

Fig. 22 gives a diagrammatic representation of Ehrlich's general conception.

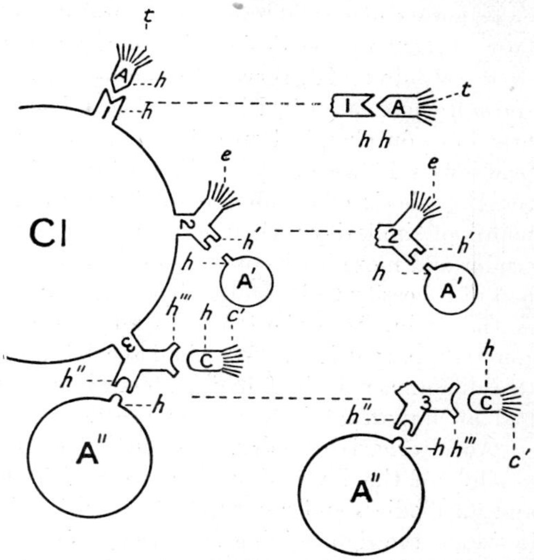

FIG. 22.

Cl. Cell.
1. Receptor of 1st order with its haptophore group h.
2. Receptor of 2nd order with its haptophore group h' and its ergophore group e.
3. Receptor of 3rd order with its two haptophore groups, h'' the cytophilic group, and h''' the complementophilic group.
A, A', A''. Various antigens, each with its haptophore group h; A has in addition an ergophore, or toxophore group t.
c. Complement, with its haptophore group h, and its ergophore group c'.

Ehrlich regarded these receptors as definite chemical entities which entered into firm union with antigens, or with complement, by linkage of the corresponding haptophore groups. When it was found that such antigens as the toxins could be so treated as to lose their toxicity without losing their power of combining with antitoxin, he assumed that the toxophore group had been altered or destroyed, while the haptophore group remained intact. Similarly he postulated the existence of a modified complement, in which an intact haptophore group was associated with an ergophore group which had lost its functioning power. It will be realized that such a theory lent itself readily to schematic representation of the various reacting substances, and their assumed modifications, and that there was a natural tendency to elaborate the assumed structure, and vary the functional activity of the various groups, to account for new phenomena not readily explicable by the unmodified hypothesis. This is in fact what happened.

As an instance we may cite the quantitative results obtained in the neutralization of toxin by antitoxin (see pp. 168–171). These could not be reconciled with the side-chain theory in its simple, unmodified form. In order to retain the conception of firm union between antigen and antibody in constant proportions, Ehrlich found it necessary to postulate the existence of a large number of different toxin components with varying degrees of affinity for antitoxin. Similarly, some of the results obtained in his studies on hæmolysins made it necessary to assume the intervention of receptors of considerable structural complexity. The consequent coining of a host of new terms, designating components the actual existence of which was extremely doubtful, served to confuse the problem rather than to clarify it. In spite of these failings, Ehrlich's theory has the outstanding merit that it has kept firm hold on chemical specificity as the essential feature of the antigen-antibody reactions. If we compare his picture of the activities of the living cell with the hypothesis of cellular metabolism referred to on p. 55 we shall note obvious points of similarity ; though the studies of recent years have largely modified the cruder and more hazy concepts of cellular processes on which the side-chain theory had of necessity to be built. The strains to which this theory was subjected arose, in the main, from the effort to retain the conception of firm chemical union in constant proportions. We shall see later the direction in which an escape from this dilemma may be found. Meanwhile we may turn to other theories that have had an important influence on the development of our present views.

An alternative theory, propounded by Bordet (1899, 1903), denies the applicability of the laws of ordinary chemical union to reactions between antigens and antibodies, and regards them as belonging to the class of colloidal reactions, in which the determining conditions are physical rather than chemical. On this view the laws which describe the phenomena associated with adsorption at surfaces and interfaces should be found to hold true, when antigens interact with antibodies. The supporters of this hypothesis have been energetic opponents of the view put forward by Ehrlich and his school, and the output of immunological literature during the twenty years which ended with the War was largely concerned with this controversy. Bordet's theory makes no attempt to present a complete picture of the mechanism underlying the serum reactions. He has himself insisted that his conclusions are so little removed from the facts observed, that they scarcely merit the name of hypotheses. He quite frankly leaves many observed phenomena unexplained, contenting himself with the claim that all the available data are consistent with the limited views he has expressed, while pointing out inconsistencies between these data and the more detailed conceptions of the supporters of the side-chain theory. The essential simplification introduced by Bordet's hypothesis was that, in bringing antigen-antibody reactions into the category of colloidal phenomena, it abandoned the necessity for assuming combination in constant proportions. One colloid may combine with another in proportions that vary over a wide range. This advantage was gained at the initial expense of leaving specificity out of account ; but more recent studies of the factors that determine adsorption at surfaces and interfaces (see pp. 183, 184) have gone far towards filling this very serious gap.

Arrhenius (1904, 1915), alone and in co-operation with Madsen (1902, 1904), has attempted to retain the advantages of the chemical basis of Ehrlich's theory, while avoiding the necessity of making a fresh assumption to meet each new fact observed. He has suggested that the reaction of an antigen with its antibody is not analogous to that between a strong acid and a strong base, but is a reversible action of the type which occurs between weak acids and weak bases, the equilibrium attained in any particular case being determined by the concentration of the reacting substances, in accordance with the law of mass action.

Our present concept of the mechanism of the antigen-antibody reactions is derived, in varying degree, from each of these three theories. Its essential core is provided by Ehrlich's classical hypothesis, simplified and made more precise by the pioneer chemical studies of Landsteiner and his colleagues (see pp. 177–183). It follows Bordet in postulating the union of antigen with antibody in varying proportions. It adopts the assumption of Arrhenius and Madsen that the antigen-antibody compound is dissociable, at least in some cases and under certain conditions.

Before discussing how this synthesis of conflicting theories has been brought about, it will be convenient to give a brief description of each of the antigen-antibody reactions in turn.

The Precipitin Reaction.

Our knowledge of the mechanism of this reaction has, in the main, been obtained during recent years ; but it forms so convenient a starting-point for a general description of the *in vitro* reactions between antigens and antibodies that we may with advantage ignore historical succession. In this reaction the antigen, as well as the antibody, is initially in a state of colloidal solution. We can therefore work with chemically purified antigens, such as crystalline egg albumin, or one of the bacterial polysaccharides that will be described in future chapters. In this way we can eliminate the complexities that are introduced by the presence in the reacting system of several different antigenic components. We can also, as Landsteiner and his colleagues have shown (see pp. 178–180), prepare synthetic antigens, the specificity of which is determined by known chemical groupings, and study their flocculation by antisera prepared against them. Moreover, in the precipitin reaction our data in regard to the quantitative relationships in our reacting system have attained their greatest precision.

Precipitation occurs when any antigen in solution is allowed to react with its corresponding antiserum in the presence of electrolytes, provided that the concentration of each of these reagents, and the experimental conditions, such as temperature of incubation and time of incubation, are suitably arranged.

The rate of formation of the antigen-antibody compound, and of its flocculation, varies according to the conditions of the experiment. It is hastened by any procedure that increases the frequency of impact between the molecules, or particles, of antigen and antibody, or between the first-formed particles of the antigen-antibody complex (see Eagle 1932). Such procedures include any decrease in the total volume of fluid in the reacting system, with a consequent decrease in the space between the reacting particles, and any factor that increases their rate of movement, such as shaking or convection currents in a tube partially immersed in a water bath. It is also hastened by increasing the concentration of electrolytes up to an optimal point, beyond which a further increase may cause a retardation. An increase in temperature up to an optimum also increases the speed of flocculation, and it seems doubtful whether this effect is wholly due to an increased frequency of impact. With some reacting systems the higher water-bath temperatures (37–55° C.) may be found unsuitable, since the antigen-antibody compound may be partly soluble in this range.

The Optimal Antigen-Antibody Ratio.

When we attempt to determine the quantitative relationships between antigen and antibody in a precipitating mixture, as in the titration of the antibody content of a particular serum, we encounter considerable difficulties. If we work to an end-point—the highest dilution of an antiserum that will give a visible precipitate in the presence of a constant amount of antigen under standard conditions of time, temperature, etc.—we obtain results that are difficult to interpret, partly because in diluting our antiserum we are diluting the amount of precipitable material, partly because the ratio of one reagent to the other profoundly affects both the speed and the completeness of precipitation. Analogous difficulties apply if, still working to an end-point, we reverse our procedure and titrate varying dilutions of antigen against a constant amount of antiserum.

This difficulty has been resolved by the studies of Dean and Webb (1926). The antigen they used was horse serum, and their antisera were prepared in rabbits. They kept the amount of antiserum constant and varied the amount of antigen from tube to tube, the total amount of fluid in each tube being kept constant by adding the requisite amount of saline. They noted, not the end-point of flocculation but the tube in which flocculation first occurred. Table XXII illustrates their results. It shows the state of affairs 32 minutes from the start of an experiment in which a 1 : 20 dilution of a particular antiserum was titrated against increasing dilutions of antigen.

TABLE XXII

Showing the State of reacting Mixtures 32 Minutes after mixing a 1 : 20 Dilution of Antiserum with increasing Dilutions of Antigen (Horse Serum)

Dilution of Antigen.	Appearance of Mixture.
1 : 10	Clear.
1 : 20	Clear.
1 : 40	Trace of opalescence.
1 : 80	Opalescence.
1 : 160	Opalescence.
1 : 320	Turbid : small particles.
1 : 640	Turbid.
1 : 1,280	Opalescence.
1 : 2,560	Trace of opalescence.
1 : 5,120	Trace of opalescence.
1 : 10,240	Trace of opalescence.
1 : 20,480	Clear.

Here flocculation is most advanced in the tube in which a 1 : 20 dilution of antiserum is reacting with an equal volume of a 1 : 320 dilution of antigen. The ratio of antigen to antibody in this tube is, in terms of *amounts* of the two reagents, 1 : 16. Mixtures in which this ratio is departed from, in the direction either of antigen or of antibody excess, flocculate more slowly. Great excess of either reagent results in a very marked retardation. When titrations of this kind were carried out with different dilutions of the same antiserum, it was found that the antigen-antibody ratio giving first flocculation was constant for all dilutions of antiserum. If a 1 : 20 dilution of antiserum flocculated most rapidly with a 1 : 320 dilution of antigen, then a 1 : 40 dilution of antiserum flocculated most rapidly with a 1 : 640 dilution of antigen, a 1 : 10 dilution of serum with a 1 : 160 dilution of antigen and so on.

Dean and Webb applied to the antigen-antibody ratio that gave most rapid flocculation the term *optimal proportions*, or *optimal ratio*. By titrations in which the dilutions of antigen were more closely spaced they were able to determine its value within a very small margin of error.

These observations have since been confirmed by many other workers, and with many different antigen-antibody systems. It may be accepted that the optimal ratio, determined by Dean and Webb's method, is constant for any given system, and thus affords a reliable method of comparing the antibody content of two or more solutions. If we wish to assign a definite value, a *titre*, to any single antiserum we can do so by taking as our standard of reference a fixed amount of antigen. If we happen to be working with a chemically pure antigen, and wish to determine the absolute amount by weight of this antigen in a given solution, or mixture, we can do so by first determining the optimal ratio of any given antiserum, using decreasing amounts of the pure antigen, and then titrating the antigen solution under test against the same antiserum. A few examples may make these points clear.

Dean and Webb titrated 33 samples of rabbit-v.-horse antisera, and found that the optimal antigen-antibody ratio varied from 1 : 177 to 1 : 14. A ratio of 1 : 177 indicates that one part by volume of antigen (horse serum) gives optimal flocculation with 177 parts by volume of antiserum ; similarly, in the second case, one volume of the same antigen gives optimal flocculation with 14 volumes of another antiserum. But the one part by volume of antigen requires a constant amount of antibody to give optimal flocculation. In one serum this amount of antibody is contained in 177 volumes, in the other it is contained in 14 volumes. The *concentration* of antibody is therefore $\frac{177}{14} = 12 \cdot 6$ times greater in the serum with the 1 : 14 ratio. By selecting any arbitrary unit in terms of antigen, we can, if we choose, assign a titre to any serum in terms of the number of such units with which a given volume of the serum, say 1 c.c., will give optimal flocculation.

Taylor, Adair and Adair (1932) have used this method to determine the amount of a given antigen in a naturally-occurring mixture. Thus, they have estimated the percentage of egg albumin in egg white, and the amount of globulin in horse serum, using in each case chemically purified antigens for their titrations. The results obtained were in close agreement with previous determinations, carried out by the usual methods of chemical analysis, as shown by the following comparative figures :

Percentage of crystalline egg albumin in egg white.	Per cent.
Hopkins (1900) .	6·0
Wu and Ling (1927) .	8·5
Optimal ratio method	7·29

Percentage of globulin in horse serum.	Per cent.
Hammarsten (1878) .	4·57
Gibson and Banzhaf (1910)	4·07
Optimal ratio method	4·46

It will be noted that Dean and Webb, in determining the optimal ratio for flocculation, kept the amount of antiserum constant, and varied the amount of antigen.   The ratio determined by this method may conveniently be referred to as the *constant-antibody optimal ratio*, or *constant-antibody O.R.*

Prior to these studies, Ramon (1922) had shown that diphtheria antitoxin could be titrated by mixing falling amounts of antitoxic serum with constant amounts of toxin, and noting which tube in such a series first showed flocculation.   The fact that this technique was introduced as a practical method of standardizing an important therapeutic reagent and that controversy centred round its relation to the current *in vivo* methods of standardization, probably delayed the recognition of its wider theoretical significance.   We may conveniently refer to the optimal antigen-antibody ratio, as determined by Ramon's technique, as the *constant-antigen optimal ratio*, or *constant-antigen O.R.*

What is the relation between the constant-antibody O.R. and the constant-antigen O.R. ?   The obvious expectation would be to find them identical ; but in fact they may be very different.

Duncan (1932*a*), working with a crude polysaccharide from a yeast-like fungus and the corresponding antiserum, records a constant-antibody O.R. of 1 : 8 and a constant-antigen O.R. of 1 : 64, the latter corresponding to a mixture containing a concentration of antibody eight times greater than the former.   Taylor (1933), working with crystalline egg albumin as an antigen, and a considerable number of different antisera prepared by the injection of rabbits, found that the antibody concentration at the constant-antigen O.R. was approximately 1·65 times the concentration at the constant-antibody O.R.   Moreover, ten antisera, tested by both methods, gave figures that did not fluctuate widely about this mean value. It would appear that, for any given system, the constant-antibody O.R., the constant-antigen O.R., and hence the ratio of one to the other, are constant values, though the constant-antibody O.R. may differ widely from the constant-antigen O.R.   In different systems, however, the relation of one optimal ratio to the other may vary over a considerable range.

To make the relation between the two optimal ratios quite clear, we may consider an actual titration, in which the times of first flocculation are recorded for a series of mixtures of antigen (horse serum) and antibody (rabbit-*v.*-horse antiserum). The figures, for which we are indebted to our colleague Dr. J. C. Cruickshank, are set out in Table XXIII.   Dilutions of antigen are given in the top row, dilutions of antiserum in the first column.   Times are recorded in minutes.   Each row corresponds to a constant-antibody titration, each column to a constant-antigen titration. The shortest time in each row which corresponds to the constant-antibody O.R. is underlined with a single line.   The shortest time recorded in any column corresponding to the constant-antigen O.R. is doubly underlined.   Where the shortest time in any column is the first recorded figure it is not underlined, since our antibody concentration has not been high enough to allow us to determine the optimal amount of antibody corresponding to the dilution of antigen concerned.   The blank spaces in the table correspond to tubes in which no visible flocculation occurred during the period of observation.   It will be noted that they fall in the zone of gross antigen excess.

If we take the rows of the table in turn, we see that the constant-antibody O.R. corresponds to a mixture containing a 1/200 dilution of antigen with a 1/5 dilution of antiserum, a 1/300 dilution of antigen with a 1/7·5 dilution of antiserum, and so on.   The flocculation in the row containing a 1/2·5 dilution of antiserum was so rapid that it was impossible to detect the small difference in time between the third and fourth tubes ; but in all higher dilutions the optimal ratio is quite clear.

TABLE XXIII

SHOWING THE FLOCCULATION TIME IN MINUTES OF DIFFERENT MIXTURES OF AN ANTIGEN (HORSE SERUM) WITH ITS HOMOLOGOUS ANTIBODY

Antibody Dilutions.	Antigen Dilutions.													
	1:50	1:75	1:100	1:150	1:200	1:300	1:400	1:600	1:800	1:1,200	1:1,600	1:2,400	1:3,200	1:4,800
1 : 2·5	2¾	2½	2¼	2¼	2½	2¾	3¼	5	6	10½	17	29	60	110
1 : 5	4	3¾	3½	3	2¾	3¼	3¾	5½	7	10	14	25	40	50
1 : 7·5	8	6½	6	5½	4¾	4½	5¼	6	7½	10½	12	20	33	45
1 : 10	14½	13	12	9½	8	6¼	6	6½	8½	11	13	16	28	40
1 : 15	53	27	23½	17	15	11½	8	7½	10	13	14½	18½	25	38
1 : 20	134	60	39	34	30	25	19	15½	13½	16	18½	22	28	35
1 : 30	—	—	102	62	55	50	35	28	22	20	23	25	30	41
1 : 40	—	—	—	120	83	72	65	60	50	40	38	42	45	55
1 : 60	—	—	—	—	—	125	100	93	85	68	52	51	65	80

Expressed in amounts instead of dilutions, the antigen-antibody ratio at the constant-antibody optimum is 1 : 40.

If, now, we take any of the columns in which the flocculation time is recorded for mixtures containing a concentration of antibody in excess of the constant-antibody O.R. falling in that column, we see that flocculation becomes more rapid as antibody is increased beyond this level. The constant-antigen optimum is not revealed until we reach the column corresponding to a 1/1,200 dilution of antigen. In that column we see that the flocculation time has been reduced from 20 to 10 minutes with an increase in antibody concentration to six times its value at the constant-antibody O.R., but begins to rise again as the concentration is still further increased. The last four columns of the table confirm this finding, and show that the antigen-antibody optimum is 1 : 240. Thus, in this instance, the mixture giving optimal flocculation in a constant-antigen titration contains, relatively, six times as much antibody as a mixture giving optimal flocculation in a constant-antibody titration.

The Two Optimal Ratios and Chemical Equivalence.

Before discussing the possible factors determining these relationships it will be convenient to deal with certain related problems. We may first inquire whether either optimal ratio, and if so which, corresponds to chemical equivalence between antigen and antibody. The method of attempting an answer to this question is to withdraw the supernatant fluid from each tube in a series, first separating the floccules by centrifugation if necessary, and to test it for the reagent likely to be present in excess by adding some of the other reagent, and noting whether a further precipitate develops. Thus, to take the example given in our table, if we found that we could detect an excess of antibody in the supernatant fluid from the nine tubes to the right of the second row by adding more antigen, that neither antigen nor antibody (or a mere trace of each) could be detected in the supernatant fluid from the optimal tube, and that an excess of antigen could be detected in the supernatant fluid from the tubes to the left of the optimal tube by adding further antibody, we should conclude that the constant-antibody optimal ratio corresponds to chemically equivalent amounts of antigen and antibody. This was, in fact, the conclusion reached by Dean and Webb (1926) and confirmatory results have been recorded by Taylor (1931, 1933), Smith (1932) and Duncan (1932a). It was also demonstrated by Duncan that the constant-antigen O.R. in the system with which he was working corresponded to a mixture that contained a gross excess of antibody. The accuracy of the Ramon method of titrating antitoxin was at first difficult to reconcile with these findings. It clearly gave the constant-antigen optimal ratio ; but it was equally clear from the close agreement between the *in vitro* and *in vivo* tests that this ratio corresponded to a mixture in which the toxin was just neutralized by antitoxin, and presumably therefore to chemical equivalence between these reagents. This apparent discrepancy has lost most of its significance since it has been shown (see Miles 1933) that the constant-antigen O.R. and the constant-antibody O.R. of toxin-antitoxin mixtures happen to differ very little from one another.

Do Antigen and Antibody Combine in Constant or Varying Proportions ?

The second problem that falls for discussion at this stage is that raised by Bordet's hypothesis. Do antigen and antibody combine in constant proportions, or may they combine in varying proportions, according to their relative concentrations in the reacting mixture ? The precipitin reaction affords particularly favourable opportunities for attacking this important problem.

Heidelberger and Kendall (1929) have thrown light on this question, using a technique that yields quantitative results. They used as their antigen the purified polysaccharide obtained from a Type III pneumococcus, a substance that contains no nitrogen. Their antibody was a solution of globulin obtained from a Type III antipneumococcal serum. In their tests they kept the amount of antibody constant and varied the amount of antigen. They determined, by micro-Kjeldahl tests, the concentration of nitrogen in the antibody solution, and in the supernatants from the various tubes after separation of the precipitate by centrifugation. Multiplying the nitrogen figure by the usual factor for protein they were thus able, on the well-justified assumption that antibody is a protein (see pp. 175, 176), to estimate by difference the amount by weight of antibody contained in the precipitate in each tube. The supernatant fluids were also tested for residual antigen or antibody. In those tubes in which no residual antigen could be detected in the supernatant fluid the relative amounts of antigen and antibody in the precipitate could be determined, since the amount of antigen present in the reacting mixture was known. The tube to which the smallest amount of antigen was added, and in which an excess of antibody remained in the supernatant fluid, gave a precipitate with an antigen-antibody ratio of 1 : 125. In the neighbouring tube, with proportionally more antigen in the reacting mixture, the antigen-antibody ratio in the precipitate was 1 : 106. In the tube that showed the first trace of antigen in the supernatant fluid it was 1 : 69. Although they had demonstrated the presence of varying proportions of antigen and antibody in the precipitate, in relation to varying proportions of these reagents in the reacting mixture, Heidelberger and Kendall at first attributed these findings, not to the union of antigen and antibody in varying proportions, but to the presence in the precipitates of a mixture of three different compounds, each formed by union of antigen and antibody in constant proportions. These compounds were assumed to have different degrees of solubility, and to be formed by reversible reactions. Marrack and Smith (1931b) have indicated objections to this view ; and in recording more recent experiments with the same system Heidelberger and Kendall (1935a, b, c) have adopted the conception of union in varying proportions, added a series of new observations to those previously recorded, and greatly elaborated the theoretical side of the problem. Working with an azo-protein antigen (see pp. 178–180), the concentration of which in the precipitate could be determined colorimetrically, the same workers (Heidelberger, Sia and Kendall 1930) found that the precipitate in the mixture that showed no excess of antigen or antibody in the supernatant fluid contained 13 per cent. of antigen. In the mixture containing the greatest antibody excess, the precipitate contained 6·7 per cent. of antigen ; in the mixture containing the greatest antigen excess about 33 per cent.

Marrack and Smith (1931b), working with azo-proteins and iodo-proteins as antigens, found that the proportion of antigens in the precipitate at the limit of antigen excess was about 1·5 times as great as at the constant-antibody optimal ratio. Breinl and Haurowitz (1930), working with hæmoglobin as an antigen, found that the precipitate might contain from 6 per cent. to 24 per cent. of antigen, according to the proportions present in the reacting mixture.

It is thus clear that the precipitate formed when a given antigen reacts with a homologous antibody may contain varying proportions of these reagents in accordance with variations in their proportions in the reacting mixture ; and it seems probable that this is due to the fact that antigen and antibody unite in varying not in constant proportions, though only one proportion gives optimal flocculation. Using the symbols A and G to represent antibody and antigen respectively, we should represent the antigen-antibody compound, not as AG, AG_2, or in any such numerical fashion, but as A_mG_n, where m and n may take any values within a certain range (Marrack and Smith 1931a, b, Marrack 1934). We should regard both antigen and antibody as possessing not one, but many specifically reacting groupings. In most, but not necessarily in all, instances it is probable that the antigen has more reactive groupings than the antibody. The actual nature of these active groupings, and the forces that determine antigen-antibody union, are considered on pp. 172, 183.

The Factors that Determine the Flocculation of the Antigen-Antibody Compound.

It has already been noted that, in the precipitin reaction, both antigen and antibody are in a state of colloidal solution. What are the factors that force the antigen-antibody compound out of solution, and thus lead to its appearance as a precipitate ?

Accepting the current views, we should class both antigen and antibody as hydrophile colloids, implying that they carry groups that have a considerable attraction for water, so that each molecule of antigen or antibody carries with it attached molecules of water that maintain it in solution. If some change occurs that renders these groupings inaccessible to the molecules of water, or causes them to lose their natural affinity for these molecules, the antibody or antigen or both may change from hydrophile to hydrophobe colloids, and will then appear as a precipitate. We must assume that such a change, from the hydrophile to the hydrophobe state, is associated with the formation of the antigen-antibody complex.

We have noted above that electrolytes play an essential part in the precipitin reaction. One effect that they produce is a lowering of the electric charge on the molecules of the antibody or of the antigen or of the antigen-antibody complex. The action of electrolytes has, however, been studied in much more detail in relation to agglutination, and will be more conveniently discussed when dealing with that reaction (see pp. 155, 156).

In most of the precipitating reactions that have been studied, by far the greater part of the precipitate is derived from the antibody (see above). There has, therefore, been a natural tendency to regard the flocculation of the antigen-antibody compound as due to some change in the antibody protein. It has been usual to picture the particles of antigen as becoming covered with antibody globulin, this globulin then undergoing a change—perhaps becoming " denatured "—that alters its condition from hydrophile to hydrophobe (see Dean 1917, Eagle 1930, 1932, Marrack 1934, Boyd and Hooker 1934).

That the condition of the antibody protein, or of the antigen when this is also of a protein nature, has an important effect on the occurrence, or non-occurrence, of precipitation has been shown by Hartley (1925) in an interesting series of experiments.

Horse serum was dried, and a portion of the dried serum was thoroughly extracted with ether. A rabbit-v.-horse antiserum was also dried, and a portion of the dried antiserum also extracted with ether. All these dried reagents, extracted and unextracted, were redissolved in saline, and a series of tests were put up in which each sample of antiserum was tested against each sample of antigen. The results were as follows:

Antiserum (unextracted) + Antigen (unextracted) $\rightarrow$ heavy precipitate.
Antiserum (unextracted) + Antigen (extracted) $\rightarrow$ heavy precipitate.
Antiserum (extracted)   + Antigen (unextracted) $\rightarrow$ slighter precipitate.
Antiserum (extracted)   + Antigen (extracted) $\rightarrow$ no precipitate.

It would seem that thorough extraction with ether prevents either antibody protein or antigen protein changing from the hydrophile to the hydrophobe state as the result of antigen-antibody union. The effect on the flocculation of the antigen-antibody complex varies according as the major component (antibody) or the minor component (antigen) has been submitted to this treatment. It may be noted that Hartley was able to exclude the possibility that the antigen-antibody union was itself inhibited, by showing that an ether-extracted antitoxic serum was able to neutralize diphtheria toxin, although it failed to give a precipitate with it.

The Inhibiting Effect on Precipitation of Antigen or Antibody Excess, and the Relation of the Two Optimal Ratios.

We may now return to the inhibitory effect exerted by antigen or antibody excess, and to the observed difference between the constant-antibody O.R. and the constant-antigen O.R.

Let us first adopt the view outlined above. The union between antigen and antibody we will assume to be specific—the mechanism of this specificity we will discuss later (see p. 183). As a result of this union each molecule or particle of antigen becomes coated with a varying number of molecules of antibody globulin. Some change occurs in this globulin which renders it, and hence the antigen-antibody of which it is a part, hydrophobe instead of hydrophile. Electrolytes are in some way concerned in the process. It is commonly stated that the antigen-antibody complex is " salt-sensitive." The antigen-antibody is thus forced out of solution. Its particles come in contact and, having more attraction for each other than the separate particles have for water, they cohere and form larger and larger particles, which eventually precipitate. The second stage of the reaction, as thus conceived, is, it will be noted, non-specific. Any antigen coated with antibody globulin will behave as a salt-sensitive colloid, and will be flocculated in an appropriate concentration of electrolyte. We will also adopt the view that antigen and antibody may combine in varying proportions, owing to the presence on the surface of each reagent of several combining groups, or sites, and accept a suggestion contained in a recent paper by Miles (1933) that differences in the composition and flocculability of the antigen-antibody compound, as well as differences in its concentration, are concerned in the velocity of precipitation.

We may, for simplicity, endow a hypothetical antigen and antibody with three combining groups apiece. Suppose we took six molecules of the form AG, where A represents antibody and G antigen. Suppose we kept the amount of antibody constant at 6 molecules, but increased or decreased the amount of antigen. When we increased it, adding say 12 or 18 G molecules instead of 6, we could not increase the number of AG molecules, since each must have one A ; but we might perhaps alter the type of compound formed. We might, when we added 12 G molecules, get 6 molecules of the form AG_2, or with 18 G molecules, 6 molecules of the form AG_3. Actually we should probably have to add many more than the equivalent number of G molecules to obtain any specified increase in the antigen content of the AG compound, since experience has shown that, in the zone of antigen excess, some of the antigen remains free in the supernatant fluid. Suppose that we decreased the G molecules, say to 5, 4, 3 and 2 in successive tubes. The number of AG molecules would of necessity decrease, *pari passu*. There might be 5, 4, 3 and 2 molecules of AG, with 1, 2, 3 and 4 molecules of A free in the supernatant fluid ; or, more probably, some of the molecules would be of the form A_2G or even A_3G.

What would be the effect of these changes on the velocity of flocculation ? As we decreased the number of G molecules from 6 to 5, to 4 and so on, the number of AG molecules per unit volume of fluid would decrease, since the total volume of the reacting mixture would, of course, be kept constant. The number of impacts per unit of time would also decrease, since the AG molecules would have further to go before they met each other. The rate of flocculation would clearly tend to decrease as a result. This might be offset to some extent if the A_2G or A_3G molecules were more flocculable than the AG molecules, as the result of being more strongly hydrophobe ; but in actual practice a limit would soon be reached at which all the combining sites on the G molecules would be occupied, and beyond which any further decrease in the concentration of these molecules would result in a slowing of flocculation. When we increased our G molecules beyond the six that we have assumed to be equivalent to our 6 A's, we should not affect the concentration of AG molecules, or the frequency of impact between them ; so that the rate of flocculation would not decrease from this cause. But if we were now getting molecules of the form AG_2 or AG_3 precipitation might well become slower, or cease, because the antigen would be incompletely covered with antibody globulin, and might be left with exposed chemical groupings that had a considerable attraction for water. Under such conditions the mixture 6A + 6G would represent the constant-antibody optimal ratio and this ratio would be, in terms of molecules, 1 : 1.

Suppose now that we kept the antigen constant at 6G and varied the amount of antibody. As we decreased it we should decrease the number of AG molecules ; and perhaps we should get a proportion of AG_2 or AG_3 molecules, which we are supposing to be less flocculable than the AG form. The rate of precipitation would therefore decrease. As we increased the amount of antibody we should not increase the amount of AG molecules or the frequency of impact between them ; but if A_2G or A_3G molecules were formed these might be more flocculable than the AG form. If so, the rate of flocculation would progressively increase. It is, however, possible that the A_2G molecules might be more flocculable than either the AG or the A_3G forms—more flocculable than the AG because each compound molecule would have relatively more antibody globulin that had lost its attraction for water, more flocculable than A_3G because, in the latter compound, the A molecules, with only one combining site attached to G, might retain more attraction for water. On this assumption the rate of flocculation would increase as more and more of the compound molecules assumed the A_2G form, and decrease when these began to change to A_3G. The constant-antigen optimal ratio would not be represented by the 6A plus 6G mixture, but by some mixture containing more A molecules and the antigen-antibody ratio would be less than 1 : 1.

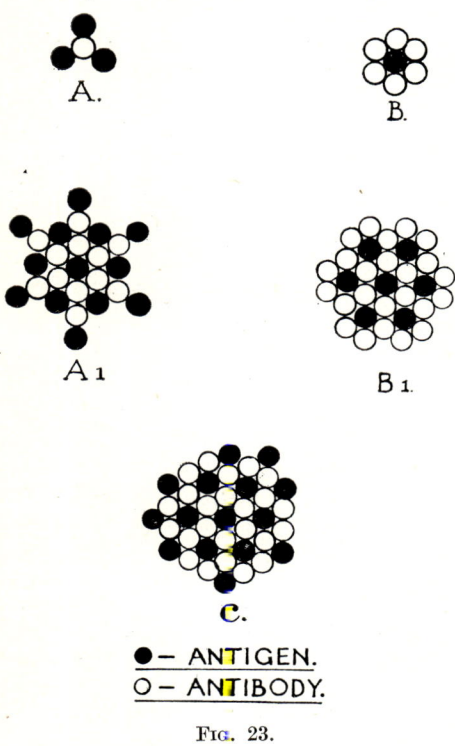

A.

B.

A 1

B 1.

C.

● − ANTIGEN.
O − ANTIBODY.

Fig. 23.

There is, however, no decisive evidence in favour of the view that the second stage of the precipitin reaction —the formation of large antigen-antibody aggregates—is non-specific, or, indeed, that we are dealing with a two-stage reaction at all ; and Marrack (1934) has put forward an alternative hypothesis based on different assumptions. He suggests that the larger antigen-antibody particles may consist, not of non-specifically aggregated molecules of a primary antigen-antibody compound, but of a lattice in which neighbouring antigen and antibody molecules, or particles, are bound together at their specific combining sites. On this view the hydrophobe character of the larger aggregates is ascribed not only to a loss of attraction for water, but also to a specific attraction between the particles or molecules of which the aggregates are composed. This conception, as Marrack points out, is entirely compatible with the dependence of flocculation on the presence of salt in moderate concentration. The action of the electrolyte, in reducing the negative charge on the molecules, or particles, will assist aggregation, whether this be due to a loss of attraction for water or to mutual attraction between one molecule, or particle, and another.

This hypothesis is illustrated diagrammatically in Fig. 23 which is slightly modified from a figure given by Marrack (1934). At A and A_1, the antigen is assumed to be in excess in the reacting mixture. With gross excess, as at A, very small particles of antigen-antibody compound are formed, because each combining site on each antibody molecule is rapidly occupied by a molecule of antigen. With a smaller excess of antigen, as at A_1, rather larger particles will be formed, but in each such particle all the combining sites on the antibody molecules are occupied before it attains a large size. B and B_1 illustrate particles formed in a mixture containing excess of antibody. All the combining sites on the antigen molecules are occupied before the aggregates have reached any considerable size. When particles such as A and A, A and A_1, A_1 and A_1, B and B, B and B_1 or B_1 and B_1 impinge on one another there will be no tendency for them to unite specifically, forming larger aggregates. C illustrates the particles formed in a mixture in optimal proportions, or in that neighbourhood. There are free combining sites on both antigen and antibody molecules at the surface. When such particles impinge on one another they will tend to unite specifically forming larger and larger aggregates, or, as Marrack expresses it, a continuous lattice. The ratio of the constant-antibody optimal ratio to the constant-antigen optimal ratio will on such a hypothesis clearly depend on the nature of the lattice formed.

Recent quantitative studies by Heidelberger and Kendall (1935*a*, *b*, *c*) accord well with Marrack's hypothesis. Boyd and Hooker (1934), on the other hand, in an interesting study of the influence of the molecular weight of an antigen on the antigen-antibody ratio in the precipitate, present a series of calculations, based on published experimental data, from which they conclude that the constant-antibody optimal ratio corresponds to a reaction system in which the antigen-antibody ratio is such that each molecule of antigen is completely covered by a layer of antibody globulin—a conclusion which is clearly not in accord with the lattice hypothesis. The calculation of the number of molecules of antibody globulin that would just cover a molecule of antigen involves a number of assumptions, and it seems scarcely possible to decide in favour of one hypothesis or the other on the basis of the quantitative data at present available.

There is certain ancillary evidence, to which some weight may reasonably be attached. As Marrack (1934) points out, the lattice hypothesis would account for the observed differences in the macroscopic appearance of the precipitates formed by different antigens. Polysaccharide antigens, for example, which probably form long-chain molecules, can bind together a large structure, giving a disc-like coherent precipitate, differing from the granular precipitate formed by most protein antigens. Certain observations on the nature of the aggregates formed in bacterial agglutination (see p. 157) also lend support to this view.

No final decision on this problem can, however, yet be reached. Nor need we regard the " lattice " and " two-stage " hypothesis as mutually exclusive. Both mechanisms may well be involved, and involved to a different degree under different experimental conditions. There is, as will be seen, no doubt at all that large particulate antigens, such as bacteria or red cells, show important changes in behaviour when antigen-antibody union occurs at their surface, quite apart from the tendency of such sensitized cells to adhere to one another.

The Agglutination Reaction.

The original description of the agglutination reaction by Gruber and Durham (1896) was concerned with the flocculation of bacteria ; but any foreign cells—yeasts and other fungi, red blood corpuscles coming from another species, etc.—will stimulate the formation of agglutinins when injected into the tissues, and will be specifically flocculated in the test tube under the influence of the antiserum so produced.

The reacting system differs from that involved in precipitation, in that the antigen is not in colloidal solution but forms part of the structure of an organized cell, usually part of its surface. It is the behaviour of the sensitized cells that we observe, not that of the isolated antigen-antibody compound. As a result, our system frequently becomes highly complex. It is not often that the surface of a bacterial cell is characterized by a single antigenic component. In many cases several different antigens are concerned; and the injection of the bacterial cells into a rabbit, or other animal, will induce the formation of a corresponding number of different antibodies. The problem of the antigenic structure of bacteria is, however, so important that it will be more convenient to deal with it in another chapter. For the moment we may confine our attention to the agglutination reaction as such, merely noting that the possible intervention of a multiplicity of antigens and antibodies is one of the factors that has to be allowed for when trying to interpret any experimental findings.

When observing agglutination we can, if we choose, watch the formation of bacterial aggregates under a microscope. This method was once commonly employed in diagnostic agglutination tests and still has its uses. But in quantitative titrations the macroscopic method, in which bacterial flocculation is observed with the naked eye, or with the aid of a hand lens, is greatly to be preferred.

The reactions that determine the agglutination of bacteria are essentially similar to those that determine the formation of a precipitate when a soluble antigen reacts with its homologous antibody. It was, indeed, in connection with agglutination that the essential rôle of electrolytes was first clearly demonstrated (Bordet 1899). If bacteria are allowed to react with an agglutinating antiserum in a salt-free medium there is usually no aggregation of the bacterial cells. That the antibody under these conditions unites with the antigen may, however, be shown by demonstrating its absence from the supernatant fluid after centrifugation of a mixture in which bacteria are present in excess, or by adding an electrolyte to the resuspended cells, when agglutination occurs (see also Joos 1901, 1902, Bechhold 1904, Porges 1906, Porges and Prantschoff 1906). It does not follow from these observations that the concentration of electrolytes is without effect on the *amount* of antibody absorbed by bacteria or other cells; indeed it seems improbable that this is so. In the analogous case of the binding of hæmolysin by red cells, or by red-cell stroma, there is evidence that the amount of antibody bound at or about neutrality (pH 7) is greatly reduced in the absence of electrolytes (Coulter 1920–21, von Euler and Brunius 1931). Changes in pH also affect the absorption of antibody by antigen, particularly in the absence of salts (Coulter 1920–21, von Euler and Brunius 1931, de Kruif and Northrop 1922–23). Many of these effects probably result from a change in the dissociation constant of the antigen-antibody compound; but it is possible that some of them, for instance the lessened absorption of agglutinins by typhoid bacilli at a pH below 4·0 observed by de Kruif and Northrop, may be due to the destruction or inactivation of the bacterial antigen concerned (see Duncan 1935).

We are, in the study of such reactions as these, dealing with systems of great physical and chemical complexity, about which we know relatively little. We should therefore be very cautious in ascribing any observed phenomenon to the influence of a particular physical or chemical factor until other possibilities have been satisfactorily excluded.

Before considering the effect of electrolytes, and other factors, on the actual flocculation of bacteria, it will be convenient to note certain quantitative data in regard to the absorption of agglutinins by bacterial cells, when these ancillary factors are kept constant. Here, as elsewhere, the observed relationships are inexplicable on the hypothesis of firm union in simple multiple proportions. For instance, Eisenberg and Volk (1902) showed that, when a constant amount of bacterial suspension was allowed to react with varying concentrations of an agglutinating serum, proportionately more agglutinin was absorbed from the more dilute serum, though absolutely more was absorbed from the more concentrated serum. When a constant dilution of antiserum was absorbed with varying amounts of bacteria, the amount of agglutinin bound did not bear a linear relation to the absorbing dose of bacterial cells. If a certain number of bacteria removed a certain amount of agglutinin, twice as many bacteria removed much less than twice that amount of agglutinin, and as the dose of absorbing bacteria was increased the proportionate increase in the amount of agglutinin bound became less and less ; so that, to remove all detectable agglutinin, it was necessary to add an absorbing dose of bacteria that was a high multiple of the amount required to remove, say, one-half of the total agglutinin originally present. Such a relationship is analogous to that observed in any adsorption process. Craw (1905) noted, in studying the absorption of agglutinin by bacteria, a phenomenon analogous to that described by Danysz in the toxin-antitoxin reaction (see p. 170).

Turning now to the mechanism involved in the actual flocculation of bacteria, we may consider first the rôle of electrolytes in this phase of the reaction. Bacteria carry a negative charge when suspended in a neutral solution of low salt content, and hence move towards the anode when observed in a cataphoretic cell (see Putter 1921, Northrop 1922, 1928, Winslow *et al.* 1923, and many subsequent observers). When various kations are added to the fluid in which the bacteria are suspended, or when the hydrogen-ion concentration is increased (the pH lowered), this negative charge is reduced, or in some cases replaced by a positive charge, movement in a cataphoretic cell being in consequence decreased in velocity or reversed in direction. So far as the effect of pH is concerned, many bacteria have an isoelectric point in the neighbourhood of pH 3·0.

It is clear that any procedure that reduces the surface charge on bacteria towards zero will increase their tendency to adhere to one another, and many observations have been made on the flocculating effect of salts and acids on bacteria, altogether apart from the action of agglutinating antibodies (Bechhold 1904, Michaelis 1911, Beniasch 1911). The range of pH over which acid agglutination occurs may vary considerably from one bacterial species to another, and has sometimes been employed as a differential criterion, but its usefulness in this respect would seem to be very limited (see Sgalitzer 1914, Buchanan 1919).

The relation of salt agglutination to agglutination by specific antisera has been studied in some detail by Northrop and de Kruif (1922*a*, *b*). Working with *Bact. typhosum*, they showed that with those kations that caused a great reduction in surface potential in low concentrations, flocculation either of sensitized or unsensitized bacteria tends to occur when the surface potential is reduced below about 15 mvt. With kations that reduce the surface potential only in higher concentrations unsensitized bacteria are not agglutinated, even when the surface potential is reduced to zero, while sensitized bacteria flocculate when the potential falls below 15 mvt. The effects produced on sensitized and unsensitized *Bact. typhosum* by the trivalent kation Al··· , the bivalent kation Ba·· , and the monovalent kation Na· , are shown in Fig. 24 (Northrop and de Kruif 1922*a*).

In an attempt to determine why unsensitized bacteria fail to agglutinate at relatively high salt concentrations, even when their surface potential is reduced to zero, Northrop and de Kruif (1922*a*) studied the effect of salt concentration on the " cohesive force " of bacterial cells, by measuring the forces required to separate two cover-slips coated with bacteria. They found that the mutual attraction of unsensitized bacterial cells was reduced with increasing salt concentration, whereas this effect was not produced when the bacteria had previously been covered with serum protein. It would seem then that one of the ways in which serum protein, or a specific antibody, exerts its effect is by so altering the bacterial surface that it reacts to a reduction of surface potential in relatively high salt concentrations in the same way as unsensitized bacteria react to an equal reduction of potential in very low salt concentrations.

Before leaving this question of the influence of electrolytes on agglutination, or on other

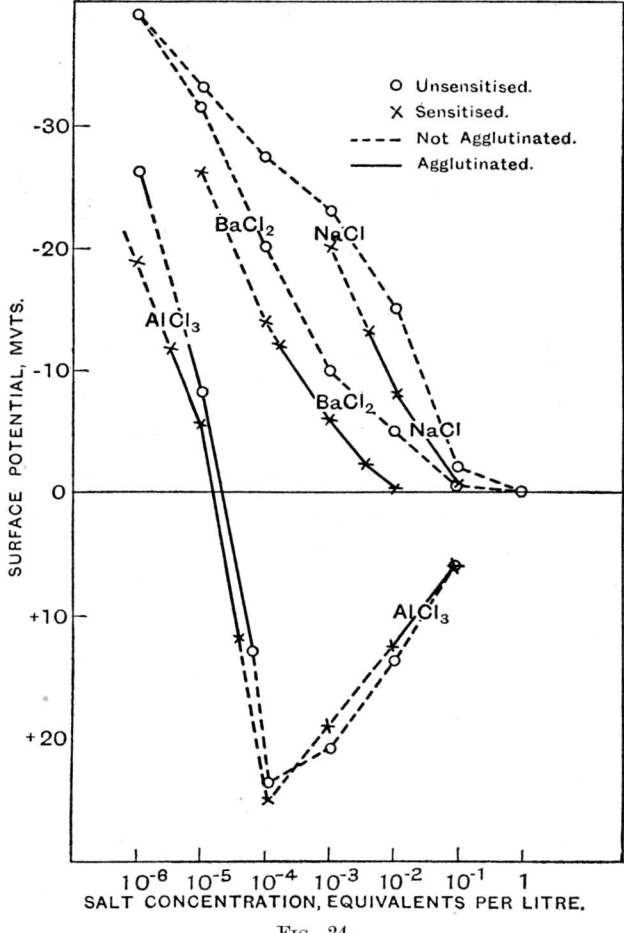

FIG. 24.

antigen-antibody reactions, we may note briefly the effect of salt concentrations higher than those that we have considered in the previous paragraphs. High concentrations of sodium chloride (2N or above) inhibit both precipitation and agglutination. These reactions may be delayed in concentrations of 0·2—0·5 N sodium chloride. (See Streng 1909, Friedberger and Goldschmidt 1910, Landsteiner and Welecki 1911, Eagle 1932.) Schmidt (1930) noted that the reaction was delayed in high concentrations of various salts, and that the order of activity of the anions was approximately that of the Hofmeister series,

namely $(ClO_4' > SCN' > ClO_3' > NO_3' > Br' > IO_3' > SO_4/2 > Cl' > NO_2' > F')$

and Marrack and Smith (1930) found that toxin-antitoxin floccules were dispersed by strong salt solutions, the order of activity being I′ > SCN′ > Br′ > NO_3′. (See also p. 164.) It is probable that the effect is due to a direct action of the salt on the serum proteins.

The effect of specific antibody itself on the surface charge of bacteria, at the pH (7–8) and the salt concentration (0·9 per cent. = 0·15 N NaCl) at which agglutination reactions are usually carried out, may be negligible (Shibley 1926, Marrack 1934) ; though some workers (see Brown and Broom 1929) have ascribed great importance to this effect.

There seems little doubt that the essential effect of sensitization is not its direct action on the surface charge, but the fact that sensitized bacteria react as hydrophobe colloids, even in moderately high salt concentrations, while unsensitized bacteria do not. These hydrophobe sensitized bacteria remain dispersed only when their surface potential is maintained at a level greater than about 13–15 mvt. When the charge is reduced below this level, by the action of electrolytes the bacteria flocculate. It may be noted (Streng 1909, Northrop and de Kruif 1922*b*) that when the amount of antibody combined with the bacteria is very small, agglutination may occur only over a very narrow range of salt concentration. The generally accepted view is that the bacteria, as the result of specific sensitization, are covered by a layer of denatured globulin and react to changes in salt concentration or changes in pH in the same way as denatured globulin itself (see Eagle 1930). This, of course, is the " two-stage " hypothesis. The actual agglutination following the specific antigen-antibody reaction union, is regarded as an example of the non-specific flocculation of a hydrophobe colloid by acids or salts.

It is possible, however, that Marrack's " lattice " hypothesis, with such modifications as would be necessitated by the fact that the antigen is here attached to a bacterial cell, may apply to agglutination as well as to precipitation. On this view the antibody molecules would act as specific linkages between adjacent bacterial cells ; and the inhibitory effect of antibody excess (see below) would be due to the rapid covering of all combining sites on the bacteria with antibody molecules, so that there would be no vacant sites for the attachment of specific linkages when sensitized bacteria came into contact with one another. On the " two-stage " view any one sensitized bacterium would be expected to adhere to any other sensitized bacterium, irrespective of the identity or non-identity of the antigens and antibodies concerned in sensitization. A sensitized pneumococcus, for example, would adhere to a sensitized typhoid bacillus as well as to another sensitized pneumococcus. On the " lattice " view the aggregation of sensitized bacteria, as well as the preliminary sensitization, is regarded as specific, and a sensitized pneumococcus will hence adhere to another sensitized pneumococcus of the same antigenic type, but not to a sensitized typhoid bacillus. In a small series of experiments (Topley, Wilson and Duncan 1935) the second type of reaction was observed. The formation of aggregates, when antigenically different bacteria were allowed to react in a mixture of the homologous antisera, appeared to be strictly specific, at least during the early stages of agglutination. Here, again, it is as yet too early to decide between these alternative hypotheses, nor need we retain one and altogether discard the other ; but it is beginning to seem doubtful whether we are justified in regarding a sensitized bacterium or other antigen as behaving in all essential respects as a particle covered with denatured serum globulin.

Of the other physical factors concerned in agglutination we need only note that their effect is similar to that exerted on precipitation. Anything—increased concentration of the sensitized bacteria, shaking, convection currents, increased temperature of incubation, etc.—that increases the frequency of impact between the sensitized cells will increase the velocity of the reaction. As in precipitation, there is an upper limit to the accelerating effect of a rise in temperature imposed by the direct action of high temperatures on the reagents concerned. It may be noted that different bacterial antigens may vary widely in their thermostability.

The system with which we are dealing in the agglutination reaction differs sharply from that concerned in precipitation in that the flocculi consist mainly of the antigen-carrying material—the bacterial cells. When, therefore, we progressively decrease the amount of antiserum, keeping the amount of bacteria constant, we do not appreciably diminish the amount of flocculable material.

The influence of changes in the antigen-antibody ratio may, however, be demonstrated as clearly in agglutination as in precipitation.

The occurrence of pro-zones in agglutination tests—the failure of agglutination in high concentrations of an antiserum that gives well-marked agglutination when highly diluted —has been noted by many workers. Heuer (1922) and da Costa Cruz (1929) have shown that this phenomenon can always be demonstrated when very light bacterial suspensions are titrated, in constant amount, against increasing dilutions of antiserum ; and they point out that it is possible, in a suitably graded series, to determine the amount of antiserum that gives most rapid flocculation. This, of course, corresponds to the constant-antigen optimal ratio. Duncan (1932b) and Miles (1933) have studied this problem in the light of our present knowledge of the significance of optimal proportions in antigen-antibody reactions in general. In one of the systems studied by Duncan the constant-antigen O.R. was 1 : 21·33, the constant-antibody ratio 1 : 3·55, the former corresponding to a mixture containing six times as much antibody as the latter. The limit of complete agglutination, taken in conjunction with the titration of residual agglutinin in the supernatant fluid, indicated that, as in precipitation, the constant-antigen O.R. was in the range of gross antibody excess. It is, however, doubtful whether we can justifiably apply these tests in the determination of equivalence when one of the reagents is attached to a relatively large particle, such as a bacterium.

The optimal proportions method is not, however, commonly employed in determining the antibody content of an agglutinating serum. In this case, the optimal ratios of any two sera bear the same relation to one another as do the end-points observed when increasing dilutions of the sera are titrated against a constant amount of bacterial suspension ; and the end-point is more easily determined.

In performing such titrations the experimental conditions, time and temperature of incubation and so on, must be so arranged that the true end-point is attained. If great accuracy is required, a definite degree of agglutination must be selected as marking this end-point, and this is usually taken to be the least degree of flocculation that can be easily observed by transmitted light against a dark background, when viewed by the naked eye, or with the aid of a hand lens. When the amount of antiserum in successive tubes is halved, as is commonly the case, it will often happen that no tube shows the standard degree of agglutination. When this is so a good approximation can usually be obtained by using an appropriate interpolation table based on a sufficient series of preliminary experiments (Dreyer and Inman 1917).

The Lysis of Red Blood Cells.

Although the original observations on the phenomenon of lysis were made on bacteria, Bordet's demonstration that a similar reaction could be obtained with red blood corpuscles, and the numerous and detailed investigations of Ehrlich and his school into the interactions between red cells and their corresponding antisera, turned the attention of the great majority of workers from bacteriolysis to hæmolysis ; and the greater part of our knowledge of the mechanism of lytic reactions in general is based on the data obtained in studying the lysis of red cells. For this reason we shall discuss hæmolysis, before considering the lysis of bacteria.

It is not possible, in the space at our disposal, to give any account of the historical development of our knowledge of this subject. Reference must be made to textbooks dealing particularly with immunological reactions, or to the collected papers of Bordet, and of Ehrlich, who have been the chief protagonists in this particular controversy. The main facts, which are not in dispute, are as follows :

The phenomenon of hæmolysis consists in a laking of the red blood corpuscles, that is, in a setting-free of their contained hæmoglobin, and not in a true solution. The cell stromata remain undissolved, though altered in size and shape, and probably in other physical and chemical characteristics.

As has already been noted, it was shown by Bordet (1898) that hæmolytic sera, like the bactericidal sera studied by Buchner, are inactivated by heating for 30 minutes at 56° C. He also showed that this inactivation concerned not the hæmolytic antibody itself but a second non-specific thermolabile factor, which caused the lysis of the red cells when these had been sensitized by the specific hæmolysin. This non-specific, thermolabile factor, which is present in all normal, fresh, unheated sera, was named *alexine* by Bordet. It is now generally known by the name *complement* employed by Ehrlich.

The fundamental reactions that demonstrate the nature of the lytic reaction may be briefly summarized as follows : The defibrinated or citrated blood of a suitable animal, such as the sheep, is centrifuged, and the deposited red cells are separated and washed several times in saline to free them from the last traces of serum. The washed cells are then made into a 5 per cent. suspension in saline. The serum from some convenient animal—usually a rabbit—that has received repeated injections of washed sheep corpuscles and has in consequence produced a specific hæmolysin to high titre, is heated at 56° C. for 30 minutes to inactivate the normal complement. The fresh, unheated serum of some other animal, usually the guinea-pig, is used as a source of complement. When these reagents are mixed in various combinations, and the mixtures incubated at 37° C., the following results are obtained :

    (1) Red cells + Hæmolysin   →   No hæmolysis.
    (2) Red cells + Complement   →   No hæmolysis.
    (3) Red cells + Hæmolysin + Complement → Complete hæmolysis.

If mixtures (1) and (2) are centrifuged, and the deposit and supernatant fluid examined separately for the presence of hæmolysin and complement, the following results will be noted, provided that the proportions of the reagents in the original mixtures have been suitably adjusted.

    (4) Deposit from (1) + Complement → Complete hæmolysis.
    (5) Supernatant from (1) + Red cells + Complement → No hæmolysis.
    (6) Deposit from (2) + Hæmolysin → No hæmolysis.
    (7) Supernatant from (2) + Red cells + Hæmolysin → Complete hæmolysis.

Reaction (4) shows that hæmolysin has combined with the red cells in (1) and sensitized them to the lytic action of complement. Reaction (5) confirms this by demonstrating the absence of hæmolysin from the supernatant fluid. Reaction (6) shows that complement has not combined directly with the red cells in (2). Reaction (7) confirms this by demonstrating the presence of complement in the supernatant fluid.

The controversy that arose between Bordet and his co-workers on the one hand, and Ehrlich and his school on the other, concerned the mode of union between the complement and the sensitized red cells. As already indicated, Ehrlich's conception of the hæmolytic antibody was that of a special type of side-chain, which he referred to as a receptor of the third order, or an amboceptor. He endowed this hypothetical receptor with two haptophore, or combining groups, one of which united with the red cell, and was named by him the cytophilic group, while the other united with the complement, and was named the complementophilic group. Ehrlich's conception of the structure and mode of action of an amboceptor may be represented as in Fig. 25A. In the diagram, R.C. represents the red cell, and R one of its receptors ; A the amboceptor, or hæmolysin, attached to the receptor of the red cell by its cytophilic haptophore group Cy, and to the complement by its complementophilic haptophore group Cm ; C repre-

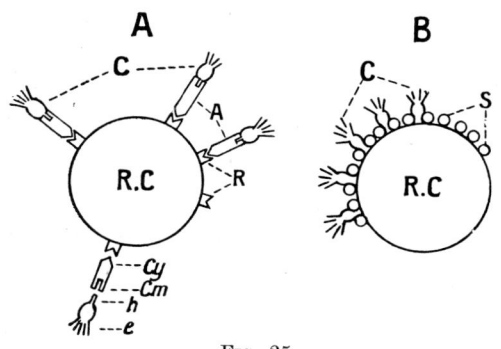

FIG. 25.

sents the complement, with its haptophore group h, by which it is attached to the complementophilic group of the amboceptor, and e its ergophore group, in virtue of which it brings about lysis of the red cell, when united to it by the hæmolytic amboceptor.

Bordet's conception of the action of the hæmolytic antibody, which he refers to as the "*substance sensibilisatrice*," or sensitizer, is essentially different. He denies that the sensitizer acts as a link between the red cell and the complement, or that the complement ever unites with the sensitizer as such. He regards the combining affinities of the hæmolysin as being directed entirely upon the red cell. The complement, in his view, unites not with the hæmolysin, but with the complex, red cell + hæmolysin, or, to put it in another way, with the red cell as altered by union with the hæmolysin. Bordet's conception may be represented diagrammatically in Fig. 25B. R.C. represents the red cell ; S the sensitizer or hæmolysin, which has united with the red cell, and altered the physical conditions at the surface ; and C the complement, uniting with the red cell which has been so altered.

It will be seen that the controversy can be narrowed down to the question : what evidence is there for the existence of a complementophilic group of the hæmolysin ? We have not space to present all the experimental data which have been advanced by each side in turn, nor the arguments which have been based upon them. It may, we think, be safely asserted that Ehrlich and his supporters have, in this respect, failed to substantiate their position, and that the weight of evidence strongly upholds Bordet's view.

The quantitative aspects of the union between red cells and hæmolysin have been studied by many observers, and the results recorded have been of the same general kind as those observed with mixtures of soluble antigens and the corresponding antibodies, or with bacteria and their homologous agglutinins. They are not compatible with the view that red cells and hæmolysin unite in constant proportions, in a firm chemical union. They are compatible with the view that the union obeys the laws of an adsorption process—for instance, Bordet was able to demonstrate a reaction analogous to the Danysz phenomenon. They show (see Muir 1909) that the red-cell-hæmolysin compound can be dissociated under certain conditions, though the dissociation is not of the type that occurs on simple dilution of a dissociable chemical compound. There is, indeed, no reason to suppose that the laws that determine the union of a hæmolysin with the specific antigenic components of a red cell differ in any way from those that determine the union of precipitins or agglutinins with their corresponding antigens.

The effect of electrolytes and hydrogen-ion concentration on the union of hæmolysin with red cells has been referred to on p. 154, in relation to the union of agglutinins with bacteria. It may be noted (see, for instance, Markl 1902, Topley 1915) that electrolytes in high concentration have an inhibitory effect on the union of complement with sensitized red cells, and on the resulting hæmolysis.

The effect of temperature on hæmolysis differs somewhat from its effect on precipitation and agglutination, because we have an additional reagent to consider—the complement— and this reagent is thermolabile. Union between red cells and hæmolysin occurs readily at 0° C. At this temperature complement may also unite with sensitized red cells, though very much more slowly, but lysis fails to occur over any ordinary period of observation. At room temperature lysis occurs, but so slowly that this temperature is quite unsuitable for experimental purposes. The optimal temperature for hæmolysis is in the neighbourhood of 37° C. At temperatures much above this the complement is inactivated, the rapidity of inactivation increasing as the temperature is raised.

The problem of the titration of a hæmolytic serum differs from that of titrating precipitins or agglutinins in that we are faced with three dependent variables instead of two. Our essential reagents are red cells, hæmolysin and complement. Of these reagents, it is natural to keep our red cells constant, regarding as our end-point the lysis of a specified quantity of red cells, in a specified time, under specified conditions. It is a common practice to use a 5 per cent. suspension of red cells in saline, and to employ some convenient volume of this suspension, such as 0·5 c.c, in our tests. We have two reagents left, hæmolysin and complement. The natural, and usual, plan is to vary the amount of the reagent that we want to measure— the hæmolysin—while keeping the complement constant. But here we meet a difficulty. We can only measure our reagents in terms of their activity, and they are dependent variables ; the more complement we add, up to a point, the less hæmolysin we need, and *vice versa*. We get out of our difficulty by making use of the kind of relation that exists between our variables. However much complement we add, we need a certain amount of hæmolysin. However much hæmolysin we add, we need a certain amount of complement. Moreover, the limit at which further additions of one reagent makes no appreciable difference to the required amount of the other is not a high multiple of the minimal dose. So we define our units of measurement as follows :

The Minimal Hæmolytic Dose (M.H.D.) of hæmolysin is the smallest amount that will cause complete lysis of an arbitrarily selected amount of red cells, in the presence of excess of complement, in 1 hour at 37° C.

The Minimal Hæmolytic Dose (M.H.D.) of complement is the smallest amount that will cause complete lysis of an arbitrarily selected amount of red cells, in the presence of excess of hæmolysin, in 1 hour at 37° C.

P.B.   G

In an actual titration we proceed as follows : We first titrate our complement, which must be used fresh, adding varying dilutions of our complement-containing serum to mixtures of red cells and a hæmolytic serum of known titre.   A hæmolytic serum, it may be noted, remains stable over a considerable period of time.   In this titration we use excess of hæmolysin say 5 or 6 M.H.D.   We note the last tube that shows complete hæmolysis, and this gives us the M.H.D. of our complement.   We now dilute our complement so that the volume we intend to use, commonly 0·5 c.c., contains 3–5 M.H.D., and to a series of tubes we add 0·5 c.c. of our red cell suspension, 0·5 c.c. of our diluted complement, and 0·5 c.c. of the hæmolysin under test, the dilution of the latter increasing from tube to tube.   After 1 hour at 37° C. we note the last tube that shows complete hæmolysis, and this gives us the M.H.D. of our hæmolysin.

The Lysis of Bacteria.

Although we talk of bacteriolysins, antibodies that lyse bacteria, and bactericidins, antibodies that kill them, the two effects are not differentiated in practice, and though we often talk of the bacteriolytic titre of a serum it is the bactericidal effect that we actually measure.   It is true that in many instances, as in Pfeiffer's classical experiments on the lysis of the cholera vibrio, gross degenerative changes in the bacteria have been observed, and there is no doubt that those bacteria that are susceptible to the lethal action of complement in the presence of a specific antibody undergo a change in structure that is analogous to the lysis of red blood corpuscles.   The change is not, however, of the same dramatic kind ; and the naked-eye observation of the changes in a turbid bacterial suspension is not a practical method of observing bacteriolysis.   The principles involved in the reaction do not differ from those concerned in hæmolysis, and the method employed in titration is essentially similar.

A very light bacterial suspension is employed, and the serum under test, after its natural complement has been inactivated by heat, is mixed in increasing dilution with a constant amount of the bacterial suspension and a constant amount of complement. The surviving bacteria in the mixtures are counted after varying intervals by some suitable cultural method, and the highest dilution of serum that produces a significant killing effect is noted.   The method contains many possible sources of technical error.   Gengou (1899), for instance, drew attention to the fact that bacteria are agglutinated as well as lysed by a specific antiserum, and that this effect may greatly reduce the number of colonies in a plate count, since a clump of bacteria will produce a single colony.   When the original mixtures are incubated for long periods before plating, this effect will be counterbalanced by the multiplication of those bacteria that have been agglutinated but not killed ; but this possible source of error must be considered in estimating the significance of any reduction of the viable count over a short period, and a control mixture containing the bacteriolytic serum without complement must always be included in the test.

It was noted by Neisser and Wechsberg (1901) that a marked pro-zone often occurred in tests of this kind.   A particular dilution of serum might exert no bactericidal action, while a much higher dilution resulted in a complete killing of the bacteria.   This phenomenon was seized on by the Ehrlich school as an example of the union of complement with free amboceptor, the hypothesis being that complement united indifferently with all the amboceptor present and that, when this was present in excess, chance would favour the union of all the complement, or the greater part of it, with the amboceptor that was not attached to bacteria.   We know, however, from our experience with precipitation and agglutination, that a similar inhibitory effect is produced by a great excess of antibody in reactions in which complement plays no part ; and it is clear that the use, in bactericidal tests, of very thin bacterial suspensions will favour the frequent occurrence of zones of gross antibody excess. The Neisser-Wechsberg phenomenon cannot, therefore, be regarded as affording any support to the view that complement combines directly with antibody.

A point of considerable importance in relation to the bactericidal, or bacteriolytic, reaction is that its occurrence depends in large part on the nature of the bacterial cell. Certain bacteria, such as the cholera vibrio, the typhoid bacillus, and most Gram-negative bacilli, are readily killed and lysed when acted on by complement after sensitization by a specific antibody. Other bacteria, such as the Gram-positive cocci, are insusceptible to the direct killing action of antibody and complement. And it should be noted that this insusceptibility is not due to any failure of the sensitized cell to combine with complement (see Buxton 1905*a*, *b*, *c*, Muir and Browning 1909).

The Nature of Complement.

We have seen that complement is a non-specific substance present in all normal sera, and not increased in amount as the result of immunization. It does not follow that complement is a single substance, or a single system. Different kinds of antibodies, for instance the antibodies acting on different species of red cells, might require different kinds of complement, all, or many of which, might be present in any specimen of normal serum. This question may be analysed into at least three components. (1) As regards one kind of lysis, for instance that of red cells, is the complement present in a given specimen of serum a single entity, or are there separate complements corresponding to the different hæmolytic antibodies ? (2) If only one kind of complement is concerned in hæmolysis, is it the same, or a different complement, which brings about the lysis of bacteria, or of other organized cells ? (3) If the complement in a given specimen of serum is one and the same, irrespective of the kind of cells which are lysed, or of the particular antibodies which are sensitizing them, is the complement in different sera, and particularly in sera from different animal species, always the same ?

This problem afforded one of the most closely debated points in the long controversy between Ehrlich and Bordet, and the question has been investigated by many other workers. Space does not allow us to reproduce the arguments employed, nor the experimental evidence on which these arguments were based. For this reference is best made to the original papers, which contain interesting examples of the complexity of the hypothetical receptor-apparatus employed by Ehrlich to describe his experimental results. The provisional answers to these questions which are, in our view, afforded by the available evidence, are as follows :

There is no evidence that more than one kind of complement is concerned in hæmolysis.

The evidence strongly suggests that the complement, in a given serum, which causes lysis of one type of cell, for instance the red cell, is identical with that which causes lysis of another type of cell, for instance a bacterium.

It seems clear that sera derived from different animal species may show qualitative differences in their complementary activities. It is difficult to determine whether such differences in behaviour depend on qualitative differences in the complements as such, or on other factors ; since we are always dealing with impure reagents.

Accepting the view that there is little, if any, evidence in favour of the existence of a multiplicity of complements in the sense employed above, it remains to inquire whether complement is a single chemical substance, or is a name for a property of normal serum that is dependent on a number of different factors. Here the answer is not in doubt. The complementary action of fresh, unheated serum depends on the interaction of a number of separate components.

Ferrata (1907) showed that complement lost its power of causing hæmolysis when placed in a salt-free medium. In such a case the euglobulins of the serum are precipitated ; and one fraction of the complement is carried down with the precipitate, while the other remains in solution. If the fluid is removed from the precipitate, and the latter is dissolved in normal saline, two solutions are obtained which together will cause the hæmolysis of sensitized red cells, though each is inactive alone. These observations were confirmed and extended by several subsequent workers (Brand 1907, Liefmann 1909, Skwirsky 1910, Amako 1911, Gengou 1911) and more satisfactory methods of complement-splitting were devised. That fraction of the complement which is precipitated with the globulin became known as " mid-piece," that fraction which remains in solution as " end-piece," because it was shown that the mid-piece united directly with the sensitized red cells while the end-piece only united with such cells in the presence of the mid-piece. The hypothetical structure of complement was represented diagrammatically according to the well-known convention introduced by Ehrlich, but this appears to us to offer no advantages, and to suggest more than our knowledge justifies. It was shown also that, in the various complement-fixation reactions, it is the mid-piece that is mainly adsorbed, the greater part of the end-piece being left free in solution. Both these factors are inactivated by heat.

It has long been known that if a serum is absorbed with yeast it loses its complementary action. It was shown by Coca (1914) that such a serum is rendered active again on the addition of serum which has been inactivated by heating to 56° C., a procedure which is known to destroy the activity both of the mid-piece and end-piece. Whitehead, Gordon and Wormall (1925) showed that this third, heat-stable complementary factor might be present both in the mid-piece and end-piece fractions, as prepared by Liefmann's method, though the greater bulk was usually found associated with the mid-piece. It may be noted (see Hyde 1923) that the absence of complementary action that has been observed in the serum of certain guinea-pigs, and is inherited as a recessive character, is apparently due to a lack of this third, heat-stable component. These naturally deficient sera could be activated by the addition of very small amounts of normal serum derived from certain animal species, but not from others, suggesting again the existence of certain qualitative differences in the complement derived from different species.

Gordon, Whitehead and Wormall (1926a, b) have demonstrated the presence of a fourth complementary factor, which is heat-stable, but is not absorbed by yeast. It is specifically inactivated by treating the serum with ammonia. It may be noted (see p. 168) that though this factor is essential for the causation of lysis, it is not necessary for the production of the complementary effect of normal serum in the opsonic reaction. The existence of this fourth component has been confirmed by Deissler (1932).

Strong and Culbertson (1934) have shown that the inactivation of a complementary serum that occurs on repeated filtration through a porcelain candle is due, in the first place, to the retention of the heat-labile mid-piece and end-piece. The heat-stable third and fourth factors require many more successive filtrations for this removal.

We have seen (p. 156) that various salts, in concentrations that affect the dispersion of the serum proteins, inhibit the normal activity of the serum antibodies, and the same holds true of serum complement. Gordon and Thompson (1933a, b) have studied the inactivation of complement by various salts, and find that the activity of the various anions falls in the general order of the Hofmeister series ($SCN' > I' > Br' = NO_3' > SO_4''/_2 > Cl'$). It would, however, appear that there is a qualitative difference in the mode of action of certain of these salts. The inactivating effect of Cl', Br' and NO_3' ions was found to be completely reversible on dilution, while the I′ and SCN′ ions produced an inactivation that was largely or entirely irreversible.

Complement Fixation.

We have noted that the absorption of complement is a general property of bacterial cells that have been sensitized by a specific antibody ; though some bacteria undergo lysis as a result of this absorption, while others do not. That complement fixation, apart from the observation of any resulting change in the bacterial cells, could be used as a general method for the detection and titration of specific antibodies was first demonstrated by Bordet and Gengou (1901). In these experiments a suspension of a given bacterium was allowed to react with a specific antiserum in the presence of complement. After time had been allowed for the reaction to take place, red cells and a suitable dilution of hæmolysin were added, and the mixture was incubated again for 1 hour at 37° C. It was found that in these circumstances no lysis took place, showing that no free complement was present, and it was reasonably inferred that it had been absorbed by the bacterium-sensitizer complex.

The reaction may be summarized as follows :

(*a*) Bacteria + Sensitizer + Complement = Fixation.
(*b*) (*a*) + Red Cells + Hæmolysin = No hæmolysis.

It will be noted that (*b*) is simply an indicator reaction. It has no connection with the fixation of complement by the sensitized bacteria. That reaction has already occurred in (*a*).

Using this technique Bordet and Gengou demonstrated sensitizers for *Past. pestis, B. anthracis, Bact. typhosum*, the bacillus of swine plague, and *Proteus vulgaris* in the corresponding antisera.

The following year Gengou showed that the same phenomenon occurs when soluble proteins are allowed to react with their specific antisera in the presence of complement. He demonstrated specific complement fixation, using as antigens cow's milk, egg-white, horse fibrinogen, and heated dog serum, and as antibody in each case the serum of a rabbit which had been immunized against the corresponding protein.

It thus became clear that complement fixation was a general reaction, liable to occur when any antigen was allowed to react with its specific antibody in the presence of complement.

The study of the relation between complement fixation and precipitation has yielded results of great theoretical importance. Gay (1905) showed that the precipitate formed by the interaction of an antiserum with the corresponding antigen frequently had the power of absorbing complement. This suggested that precipitation and complement fixation might be two aspects of a single reaction. Muir and Martin (1906*b*) found that, although there was a close correlation between precipitation and complement fixation, the correlation was not absolute. They showed that complement fixation might occur in the absence of precipitation, and that, in the presence of a constant amount of antiserum, there was a particular amount of antigen that gave maximal complement fixation, while amounts much greater, or much less, than this might fix little or no complement.

Dean (1912) made clear the cause of these earlier discrepancies. In a series of experiments in which varying amounts of antiserum were titrated against varying amounts of antigen he showed that for any given amount of antiserum two amounts of antigen could be determined, one that gave maximal precipitation and another that gave maximal complement fixation. In the particular system with which he was working and under the experimental conditions employed, maximal complement fixation occurred in a mixture in which precipitation was retarded by an excess of antiserum. With excess of antigen fixation was minimal. In a further series of experiments he showed that complement fixation occurred during the early stages of precipitation, before any flocculi were visible to the naked eye. He concluded that the best conditions for fixation were supplied when the proportions of antigen and antibody were such as to cause a slow aggregation of the antigen-antibody compound, so that the phase in which small particles were present, affording a very large total adsorbing surface, was relatively prolonged. He suggested that the lack of complete parallelism between the two phenomena was not due to the presence of two different antibodies, but to the fact that the two secondary results of a single antigen-antibody reaction were conditioned by different physical factors.

Goldsworthy (1928) has re-examined this problem in the light of the results obtained by Dean and Webb (1926). His results are in entire agreement with Dean's conclusion that precipitation and complement fixation depend on a single antigen-antibody reaction, and that complement fixation occurs during the early stage of precipitation, when the adsorbing surface is at its maximum. They indicate, however, that the maximal complement fixation observed by Dean in the presence of a slight excess of antibody, and the minimal fixation observed in the presence of excess of antigen, do not express a general relationship, but were determined by the particular antiserum with which Dean was working, and the conditions as regards time and temperature that he employed. The relation between the optimal antigen-antibody ratio for precipitation and the ratio giving maximal complement fixation depend on several factors, including the temperature at which the reaction is carried out, the exact moment at which the complement is added to the other reagents, and the length of time for which the reaction is allowed to proceed. In all cases, maximal complement fixation occurs with the antigen-antibody ratio that will, under the existing conditions, expose the complement to the maximal adsorbing surface of the antigen-antibody particles.

Opsonins and Bacteriotropins.

Wright and Douglas (1903, 1904) named and described the *opsonins*—thermolabile, relatively non specific substances, occurring in normal serum, acting on a variety of bacteria and rendering them liable to phagocytosis by leucocytes. Neufeld and Rimpau (1904, 1905) named and described the *bacteriotropins*—thermostable antibodies occurring in the serum of immunized animals, acting specifically on the bacteria against which the animals had been immunized, and rendering them liable to phagocytosis.

The mode of action of the bacteriotropins is clearly analogous to that of the precipitins, agglutinins and lysins. Like these antibodies they are relatively thermostable. Like them they unite specifically with an antigen carried by the bacterial cell. We can safely assume that the anchoring of the antibody globulin to the antigen alters the condition at the cell surface in such a way as to make it easier for the leucocytes to engulf the bacteria, just as it makes the bacteria salt-sensitive, and, in certain cases, renders the cell membrane more permeable. It would appear that one important factor is a lowering of the negative charge, and hence of the difference in electrical potential between the bacteria and the surrounding fluid.

Falk and Matsuda (1926) found that alterations in the charge carried by pneumococci induced by the addition of lanthanum nitrate or sodium oleate had a striking effect on the phagocytosis of these organisms, and Broom and Brown (1930) were able to decrease the phagocytosis of sensitized staphylococci from a high to a low level by preventing the usual reduction in surface charge by the addition of potassium ferrocyanide. Mudd and others (1929) studied the changes induced by specific antisera in four strains of acid-fast bacilli. They found that sensitization (a) increased the cohesiveness of the bacilli; (b) decreased the electric charge, as evidenced by a decrease in velocity of cataphoresis; (c) decreased the wettability of the bacilli by oil, as evidenced by their distribution at an interface between tricaprylin and normal saline, and (d) increased their susceptibility to phagocytosis.

There remains the problem of the relation of the normal opsonins of Wright and Douglas to the bacteriotropins of Neufeld and Rimpau. In their thermolability the opsonins resemble complement; and their identity with this serum constituent seemed at first to be rendered probable by the observation of Muir and Martin (1906a) that such complexes as red cells and hæmolysin, a protein antigen and its corresponding antibody, or bacteria and a specific antibacterial serum, all removed the opsonin from a normal serum, at the same time as they removed the complement. The observation of Neufeld and Hüne (1907), that absorbing a normal serum with yeast had a similar double effect, seemed to point in the same direction. But there were difficulties in this simple conception. The normal serum opsonins do not show the same strict specificity as the bacteriotropins—normal unheated serum promotes the phagocytosis of a wide variety of antigenically unrelated bacteria—but from the first there was evidence that suggested the presence of specific factors of one kind or another. Thus, it has been the general experience that the serum of any one person varies in its opsonic effect on different bacteria; that the sera of different individuals may show striking differences when tested against the same bacterium; and that any one person may show a variation in the opsonizing power of his serum for a particular bacterium, especially as the result of infection with that organism, or of artificial immunization. Variations of this kind have been studied extensively by Wright and his colleagues (see Wright 1909). Moreover, evidence pointing in the same direction was obtained by *in vitro* experiments. Bulloch and Western (1906) succeeded in removing the opsonic power of normal serum for particular bacteria by selective absorption. Other workers were unable to confirm these results, but the careful studies of Hektoen (1908) on the normal opsonins acting on the red blood corpuscles of different animal species afforded strong support for the correctness of Bulloch and Western's contention.

The explanation of these anomalous findings would appear to lie in the fact that the opsonic effect of normal serum resembles its hæmolytic and bacteriolytic effects in being dependent on both antibody and complement. Chapin and Cowie (1907) showed that normal serum may have its opsonic power for a staphylococcus removed by absorption with that organism in the cold, but that such absorbed serum may still have the power of reactivating normal serum that has been inactivated by heat. The cocci that have been used for absorption, when washed and resuspended in saline, show little if any increased susceptibility to phagocytosis in the absence of unheated serum. Later (Cowie and Chapin 1907) they showed that normal serum loses almost all its opsonic power when diluted fifteen times with saline. If, however, such diluted serum is added to another sample of serum that has been inactivated by heating at 55°–60° C. for 10 minutes the mixture is almost as active in promoting phagocytosis as was the original unheated, undiluted serum. It would appear that normal serum contains specific sensitizing antibodies, present in amounts so small that they are ineffective in a dilution of 1 : 15 or more.

Even in undiluted serum these antibodies are unable, by themselves, to alter the bacterial surface sufficiently to promote phagocytosis ; but when complement is adsorbed by the incompletely sensitized bacteria the necessary change in surface conditions is produced. It would seem, also, that complement is not without effect on the action of the bacteriotropins ; for G. Dean (1907) has shown that the action of a heated antiserum is increased by the addition of a little unheated normal serum. Sleeswijk (1908) has confirmed Dean's results, and concludes that sensitization, as a preliminary to phagocytosis, is primarily dependent on a specific antibody. When this antibody is present in adequate concentration it can produce its effect in the absence of complement, though added complement may enhance it. When the antibody is present in very small amount complement is necessary to induce adequate sensitization. (See also Ward and Enders 1933.)

It is of interest to note that the action of complement in opsonification appears to differ in some way from its action in hæmolysis ; since, as Gordon, Whitehead and Wormall (1926*b*) have shown, the addition of ammonia renders complement inactive as a hæmolytic agent, but removes none of its opsonic activity. More recently Gordon and Thompson (1935) have recorded a further series of experiments in which normal serum was treated with a variety of reagents—ammonia, congo red, acid, alkali and hypotonic solutions of certain sodium and potassium salts. The effect of storage at room temperature was also noted. In each case it was found possible to adjust the treatment of the serum so that opsonic activity was present in apparently undiminished degree when the capacity for causing the lysis of sensitized red cells had entirely disappeared ; though any of these treatments, if carried far enough, resulted in the loss of opsonic activity. Of the reagents employed only ammonia acts specifically on the fourth component. It would appear, therefore, that the system concerned in the opsonic effect differs from that concerned in the lysis of sensitized red cells in other ways.

The quantitative measurement of opsonic or bacteriotropic action is a technical problem of great difficulty. The system is a very complex one, including living phagocytic cells the uniform distribution of which is exceedingly difficult to ensure. It is impossible, even when the tubes are rotated by one of the various mechanisms that have been devised, to obtain results of the same order of accuracy as in the precipitin, agglutination or hæmolytic reactions.

In the method employed by Wright and his colleagues, serum, leucocytes and bacterial suspensions are mixed in capillary tubes and incubated at 37° C. for 15–30 minutes. Their contents are then expelled on to slides. Films are prepared and stained, and the bacteria contained in the first 50–100 leucocytes encountered are enumerated. The relative opsonic effect of two sera is expressed as the ratio between the numbers of bacteria taken up, under their influence, by the same number of leucocytes. As might be supposed, the experimental error is a high one (see Greenwood 1913). An alternative method, suggested by Klein (1907), is to fix on some particular degree of phagocytosis as an arbitrary end-point, and to dilute the serum under test until this end-point is reached ; but it seems probable that the experimental error will still be large.

The Toxin-Antitoxin Reaction.

This reaction hardly falls into the same category as those we have been considering, since the titrations are carried out *in vivo*. There is, however, no doubt at all that the neutralization of toxin by antitoxin depends on the same factors, and is governed by the same laws, as any other antigen-antibody reaction ; and we have seen that, when toxin and antitoxin are mixed in the test tube, specific precipitation occurs. It is convenient to discuss in this chapter some of the peculiarities recorded in the *in vivo* tests, since many of these were noted during the pioneer studies of Ehrlich (1897) on the standardization of diphtheria antitoxin, and so formed the basis of the controversy in regard to antigen-antibody reactions in general.

The starting-point of any method of standardization is the definition of units of measurement. When these units have to be defined in terms of some *in vivo* reaction, the resulting measurements are liable to errors of a kind different from those involved in *in vitro* titrations. These errors and the ways in which they can be avoided or allowed for are discussed in Chapter XL. For the moment we are concerned only with the general nature of the quantitative results that have been recorded.

The first reagent to which a unit was assigned was the toxin. This unit, the *Minimal Lethal Dose*, may be defined as follows :

The Minimal Lethal Dose (M.L.D.) of diphtheria toxin is the least amount that will, on the average, kill a guinea-pig of 250 gm. weight within 96 hours after subcutaneous inoculation.

Ehrlich (1897) defined the unit of antitoxin in terms of the M.L.D. as *the smallest amount of antitoxin that will neutralize* 100 *M.L.D. of toxin*. This left the M.L.D. as the fundamental unit ; but it was soon discarded. Toxin, on storage or on treatment with a variety of physical or chemical reagents, has a tendency to lose its toxicity while retaining its combining power for antitoxin. It is converted into *toxoid*. Under these conditions the definition of a unit of antitoxin, A.U., in terms of the number of M.L.D. of toxin that it will neutralize clearly becomes impossible, since no standard stable toxin can be preserved. An antitoxic serum, when dried *in vacuo* and stored at 0° C., remains stable over long periods of time, and hence provides an excellent standard of reference. Ehrlich's original antitoxin has been adopted as an international standard, and the correct definition of a unit of diphtheria antitoxin is as follows :

One unit of Diphtheria Antitoxin (1 A.U.) is contained in that amount of antitoxic serum that has the same total combining capacity, for toxin and toxoid together, as one unit of Ehrlich's original antitoxin.

The fact that one unit of Ehrlich's original antitoxin happened to neutralize 100 M.L.D. of the particular toxic filtrate with which he was working has now only a historical interest. The units of other antitoxins are defined in a similar way, some particular specimen of the antitoxic serum in question being selected as an arbitrary standard, against which all subsequent samples are measured.

The actual procedure consists in first determining the quantity of a given toxic filtrate that is neutralized, or nearly neutralized, by one unit of the standard antitoxin, and then determining the amount of the antitoxic serum under test that will neutralize, or nearly neutralize, this amount of toxic filtrate. This amount of the antitoxic serum will contain 1 A.U. Since the two tests are performed within a few days of one another there will be no significant change of toxin to toxoid during the interval, and the proportions of the two reagents in the toxic filtrates will remain constant.

This method of titration led to the definition of two other doses of toxin— " toxin " here, as in the case of the M.L.D., referring in practice to a toxic filtrate, containing both toxin and toxoid.

P.B.   G*

The Limes Nul (L_0) *dose of diphtheria toxin is the largest amount of toxin that, when mixed with one unit of antitoxin and injected subcutaneously into a guinea-pig of 250 gm. weight, will, on the average, give rise to no observed reaction.*

Actually, the L_0 dose is usually recorded as the dose that, when tested in this way, gives rise to a minimal local œdema.

The Limes Tod (L_+) *dose of diphtheria toxin is the smallest amount of toxin that, when mixed with one unit of antitoxin and injected subcutaneously into a guinea-pig of 250 gm. weight, will, on the average, kill that guinea-pig within ninety-six hours.*

Other doses of toxin, determined by other methods of testing, have been defined in terms of their combining power for antitoxin, and are now commonly employed for standardization purposes (see Chapter LVIII), but the relation between the L_0 and L_+ doses is the matter that concerns us here.

If toxin combined with antitoxin in constant proportions giving firm chemical union it would be expected that

$$L_+ \text{toxin} - L_0 \text{toxin} = 1 \text{ M.L.D.}$$

In fact it does not. The difference between the L_+ and the L_0 dose has been found, with different toxic filtrates, to vary from 10 M.L.D. to 100 M.L.D. or more.

Ehrlich attempted to account for this phenomenon, to which his name has often been attached, by postulating the existence, in toxic filtrates, of a special modification of toxoid, *epitoxoid*, having less affinity than toxin, or unmodified toxoid, for antitoxin. Over the range between L_0 and L_+ doses he assumed that the additional toxin added merely displaced epitoxoid, and that only when all epitoxoid had been displaced from its union with antitoxin did the added toxin remain free to exert its lethal effect. Whether toxoid differs from toxin in its affinity for antitoxin, or whether varieties of toxoid exist that differ from one another in this respect, we do not know with any certainty. Since we have many reasons other than the observed difference between the L_0 and the L_+ doses of toxic filtrates for discarding the hypothesis of chemical union in constant proportions between antigen and antibody, we are not faced with Ehrlich's dilemma, and have no need to postulate the existence of epitoxoid, or of any of the other special varieties of toxin and toxoid that he evolved to explain the results observed in his later studies on partial neutralization.

These studies, and those of many subsequent observers, made it clear that, when varying amounts of antitoxin are added to a constant amount of toxin, the curve of neutralization is not linear, as it would be if we were studying the neutralization of a strong acid by a strong base. (See Arrhenius and Madsen 1902, 1904, Arrhenius 1915, von Krogh 1911, Glenny *et al.* 1925.) The observed departure from linearity is not peculiar to diphtheria toxin and antitoxin, but is characteristic of toxin-antitoxin reactions in general (see, for instance, Burnet 1931); and, as we have seen, is equally well exemplified by the results obtained when studying the absorption of any antibody by any antigen.

Danysz (1902) recorded a phenomenon that has since been known by his name. He showed that, if a constant amount of toxin is added to a constant amount of antitoxin, the toxicity of the mixture varies according to the way in which the addition is made. If, for instance, the amounts of toxin and antitoxin are equivalent, and the toxin is added all at once to the antitoxin, the mixture is non-toxic. If, however, the same amount of toxin is added to the same amount of antitoxin in two or more fractions, an interval of 15 minutes or more being allowed to elapse between the successive additions of toxin, the mixture will usually be highly toxic.

Here again we have recorded analogous findings in the reactions of other antigens with other antibodies. This phenomenon is more readily explicable on the adsorption hypothesis than on the theories advanced by Ehrlich, or by Arrhenius and Madsen.

Before we discuss these general concepts in more detail, it will be convenient to deal with another problem which arises when we view the antigen-antibody reactions as a whole.

The Unity or Diversity of Antibodies.

In the preceding pages we have considered the effects produced by antibodies which we have named, in accord with the current terminology, precipitins, agglutinins, lysins, complement-fixing antibodies, opsonins, bacteriotropins and antitoxins. Are these different *kinds* of antibcdy, or are they the same kind of antibody doing different things ?

The former view held the field for many years ; but the latter—the unitarian hypothesis—has now gained almost universal acceptance. This has been due mainly to the work of Dean (1917) in this country, to that of Zinsser (1921) in America, and to Nicolle and Césari (1922) in France ; though a similar view had been adumbrated by Bail and Hoke (1908). We have seen how Dean established the essential identity of precipitation and complement fixation. We have noted that precipitation is a general form of reaction between all antigens and all antibodies, including toxin and antitoxin. And we have seen that the union of antigen and antibody at the surface of a bacterial cell sensitizes it alike to the flocculating action of electrolytes, to the lytic action of complement, and to the phagocytic action of leucocytes.

This conception of the serum reactions does not, of course, in any way modify our belief in a multiplicity of antibodies corresponding to a multiplicity of antigens. A red cell, a bacillus, a crude protein solution such as horse serum, contain many antigens and give rise to many antibodies. The unitarian hypothesis, as Zinsser (1921) has emphasized, implies simply that the injection into the tissues of a chemically pure antigen will lead to the formation of one antibody, and one only.

When we discuss, in the next chapter, the antigenic structure of bacteria, we shall see that there is a sense in which it would be correct to differentiate one antibody from another in terms of function—to say, for instance, that a particular antibody is an agglutinin but not a lysin. This difference in functional activity, however, is determined not by a difference in the nature of the antibody but by a difference in the structural position of the antigen to which it is attached.

THE QUANTITATIVE ASPECTS OF THE ANTIGEN-ANTIBODY REACTIONS

We are now in a position to summarize the quantitative observations on the reactions between antigens and antibodies and to attempt to assess their general significance.

If we abandon, as we must clearly do, the conception of firm union in constant proportions, are we to follow Arrhenius and Madsen, retaining the conception of union in constant proportions and invoking the mass-action law applied to a freely dissociable antigen-antibody compound to explain the departure from linearity in our neutralization curves ? Or are we to follow Bordet, and regard antigen-antibody union as governed by the quantitative laws that describe adsorption phenomena ?

In the formation of chemical compounds of the type involving intramolecular rearrangement of atoms, whether these compounds are freely dissociable or not, the forces that hold the constituent atoms of the compound together are, according to the electronic theory of valency, derived from a change in the distribution of the electrons (see Marrack 1934). In some cases one atom may simply give up one electron to another. Two oppositely charged ions are then produced which are held together only by the attraction between the opposite charges.

In other cases electrons are shared between the atoms concerned. Two shared electrons constitute a single bond, four a double bond and six a triple bond. The shared electrons may be contributed by one of the atoms concerned (co-valent bond) or by both atoms (co-ordinated bond). Combination of this kind must, of necessity, obey the law of simple multiple proportion.

Adsorption, on the other hand, depends primarily on intermolecular as opposed to intramolecular forces. The atoms in a chemical compound formed by an intramolecular redistribution of electrons are not electrically neutral ; and the surface of any large molecule, or aggregate of molecules, is characterized by electric fields distributed in a characteristic pattern. Other molecules, coming within these fields, will be held to the adsorbing molecule or particle if the conditions are such as to allow the mutual attractions to become effective. What these conditions are will be discussed more conveniently in a succeeding section. The consequence that concerns us for the moment is that combinations depending on these intermolecular attractions are not subject to the law of simple multiple proportions. Adsorption compounds may contain varying proportions of the two substances concerned, and the range of variation may be wide.

As Marrack points out, the existence of compounds showing varying proportions of two constituents is not an absolute criterion for the differentiation of adsorption compounds from those that are formed by the intramolecular union of atoms. If a molecule is very large, and contains numerous active groups, it may be very difficult to obtain a satisfactory differentiation on this basis. The nitro-compounds of cellulose, for instance, have a composition that varies over a wide range. Moreover, a compound that is formed as the result of intermolecular forces may undergo secondary changes in which intramolecular forces are involved. We may, however, take it as a safe guiding rule that a demonstration that the combination of two substances is subject to the law of simple multiple proportions is an indication that intramolecular forces are involved, while an apparent failure to obey this law suggests, though it does not prove, that we are dealing with an adsorption compound.

When we come to the results obtained in partial neutralization, or partial adsorption experiments, we find that they are not compatible with the concept of firm union in constant proportions ; but that they afford no secure basis for differentiating between an adsorption reaction and a combination due to intramolecular forces that is subject to the law of mass action.

The law which describes the relation between the amount of a given substance adsorbed from a solution, and the concentration of that substance remaining in solution when equilibrium has been reached, has been formulated by Freundlich (see Freundlich 1906, 1922, Freundlich and Neumann 1909), and expressed in the form of the following equation :

$$\frac{x}{m} = aC^n$$

where x is the amount of the substance adsorbed by the surface m, C is the final concentration of the substance in the fluid, a is a constant depending on the units of measurement, and n is a constant less than unity.

This may clearly be written:

$$\log \frac{x}{m} = \log a + n \log C.$$

If we let x represent the adsorption on unit surface, the equation will become:

$$x = aC^n$$

or

$$\log x = \log a + n \log C.$$

If the values given by the adsorption formula are plotted with concentrations as abscissæ, and amounts adsorbed as ordinates, we obtain a curve of the parabolic form (see Fig. 26). If the values obtained are plotted as logarithms, conveniently on double logarithmic paper, with the logarithms of the concentrations as abscissæ and the logarithms of the amounts adsorbed as ordinates, we obtain a straight line (see Fig. 27). The value of the

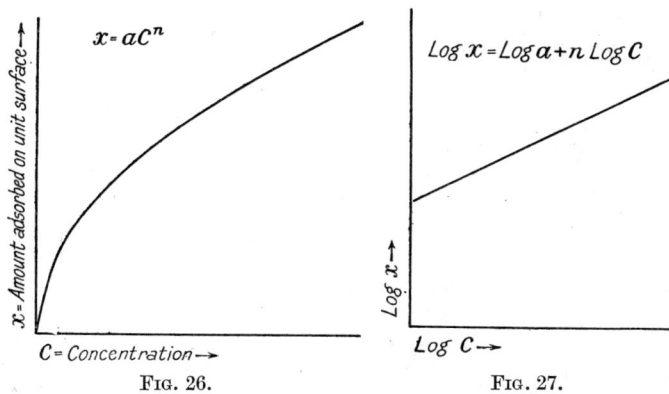

Fig. 26.　　　　　　　　Fig. 27.

constant n is given by the tangent of the angle made by the straight line with the axis of abscissæ. This line cuts the axis of ordinates at a point above the origin, which corresponds to the value of $\log a$.

It is clear that this formula expresses the fact that the amount of substance adsorbed by unit surface increases with increasing concentration, not in direct proportion to this increase, but to some root value of it. If, for instance, the value of n were 0·5, the amount adsorbed by unit surface would increase as the square-root of the concentration. It follows that proportionately more of a dissolved substance will be adsorbed from a weak solution than from a strong one.

The figures recorded in many antigen-antibody reactions, and particularly in the neutralization of toxin by antitoxin, have been found to fit a curve of this type very closely over a considerable part of their range, but the calculated and observed values usually depart significantly with a very great excess of either reagent (see, for instance, von Krogh 1911). This discrepancy is not surprising (see Marrack 1934). The Freundlich isotherm, in its classical form, does not asymptote to a maximum at high concentration of one reagent, but rises continuously, though at a decreasing rate. This seems very unlikely to describe the course of any antigen-antibody reaction. The adsorbing reagent would be expected to become fully saturated at some point. Modified equations have in fact been evolved that allow for such a saturation limit.

With this proviso, the demonstration that there is a close correspondence over most of the range between observed values and values calculated on the basis of Freundlich's isotherm, clearly suggests the possibility that antigen-antibody reactions are examples of adsorption phenomena. But an equation derived from the law of mass action gives a curve that has a close resemblance to the Freundlich isotherm over a great part of its range. It differs from it in rising rather less steeply at low concentrations of the reagent undergoing adsorption, and asymptoting towards a maximum at high concentrations. Arrhenius and Madsen (see Arrhenius 1915) give several examples in which there is a clear correspondence between the observed values and those calculated on the mass-action hypothesis over a considerable range of antigen-antibody reactions, though here again there are usually discrepancies at high concentrations of one or other reagent. Biltz (1910) found that the curve of neutralization of tetanolysin by an antitetanic serum would fit the Freundlich isotherm, but would also fit a curve based on the mass-action equation. It does not in fact seem possible, on the basis of the recorded data, to decide between adsorption and mass action by invoking the form of the neutralization curves obtained.

Even if the difficulty introduced by the partial similarity of the curves based on Freundlich's isotherm and on the mass-action law did not exist, the fact that a given reaction gave observed results in close agreement with those calculated from the adsorption equation would not justify any definite assumption as to the mechanism concerned. As Brownlee (1925) points out, this formula has been found to describe a number of different statistical phenomena. It gives a fair description of the association between death-rates and overcrowding, of the distribution of wealth, and so on. Freundlich's isotherm, in fact, describes the statistical behaviour of many complex systems of interrelated events, and the demonstration that any reaction obeys this " law " should probably be regarded as evidence of the complexity of that reaction, rather than as any indication of the nature of the factors to which that complexity is due.

We are on safe grounds in saying that all the quantitative data available are compatible with the view that adsorption phenomena—that is the formation of compounds as the result of intermolecular attractions—play an important part in antigen-antibody reactions. Some of the evidence seems to tell in favour of this view, and against those alternatives that have been considered. There is, on the other hand, no doubt that some at least of the antigen-antibody compounds formed dissociate fairly freely on simple dilution (see, for instance, the discussion on avid and non-avid diphtheria antitoxin on p. 810, and on antiviral antibodies on pp. 960, 961). In such cases the mass-action effect must come into play. There is, moreover, evidence that the union between antigen and antibody becomes firmer with the lapse of time, and this may well be due to intramolecular forces coming into action after the intermolecular forces have brought about the primary union. It would, however, be quite unjustifiable to dogmatize on any of these points on the basis of the evidence at present available ; nor does it seem likely, in view of the extreme complexity of the reagents with which we are concerned, that we shall, in any near future, be in a position to give an intellectually satisfying account of the kinetics of even the simplest of the antigen-antibody reactions. This does not greatly matter so far as the application of these reactions is concerned. We know approximately the actual quantitative relations involved, though we are largely ignorant of the factors on which these relations depend.

What concerns us much more closely is the nature of the mechanisms that determine immunological specificity ; and here, as we shall see in the following sections, our knowledge has advanced so greatly within recent years that we can give an account of the phenomena concerned that is far clearer and more precise than the hazy picture with which we had to be satisfied a decade or so ago. Those who desire a fuller and more detailed discussion of this important problem may be referred to the monograph by Landsteiner (1933) containing an account of his pioneer researches, and of related studies by other workers, and to the admirable review by Marrack (1934) which is freely quoted in this and the succeeding sections.

THE QUALITATIVE ASPECTS OF THE ANTIGEN-ANTIBODY REACTIONS—IMMUNOLOGICAL SPECIFICITY

This problem has been attacked mainly from the side of the antigens, but it will facilitate our discussion of the recorded data to deal first with the probable structure of the serum antibodies with which they react.

The Nature and Properties of the Serum Antibodies.

We have already made frequent references to the view that the serum antibodies are specialized globulins, using this term in its broadest sense to include the pseudo-globulin as well as the euglobulin fractions. We may now briefly summarize the evidence on which this view is based.

That antibodies are *associated with* the more readily precipitable serum proteins there can be no question. Precipitation of antisera with sodium or ammonium sulphate, with alcohol at various temperatures, or by dialysis, brings down the greater part of the contained antibody with the globulin fractions. (See Banzhaf and Gibson 1907, Gibson and Collins 1907, Ledingham 1907, Mellanby 1908, Hartley 1914, Felton 1926, 1928, 1932, Maitland and Burbury 1927, Barr, Glenny and Pope 1931, Barr and Glenny 1931, Laidlaw and Dunkin 1931, Barr 1932 and many others.) The antibody is not in general confined to any one globulin fraction, so that it cannot usually be separated from the non-specific globulins by fractional precipitation with any of the usual reagents ; but in two instances at least—the antibody to the Type I pneumococcus (Felton 1926, 1932) and the antibody to distemper virus (Laidlaw and Dunkin 1931)—the range over which it is precipitated is a narrow one, so that a very considerable degree of purification can be obtained. There are, it may be noted, other indications that different antibodies may be associated with different sub-fractions of the serum globulins.

The close association between antibodies and serum proteins is also attested by the general, though not complete, correspondence between the inactivation of antibodies and the denaturation of proteins by heat (see Streng 1909, Madsen and Streng 1910, Marrack 1934), and by the fact that the antibodies of a serum are precipitated when the serum proteins of an immunized animal are flocculated by a specific antiserum prepared in an animal of another species (Landsteiner and Prášek 1911, Eisler 1920, Smith and Marrack 1930).

This problem has also been attacked by studying the chemical properties of antibodies, not as they exist in the antiserum, but after they have combined with the corresponding antigens. It has been established that the antigen-antibody compounds so formed contain considerable quantities of protein derived from the antiserum, and that this protein has the general characters of serum globulin. Thus the precipitate formed, when 2·5 mg. of Type II pneumococcal polysaccharide, which contains no nitrogen and is therefore particularly suitable for work of this kind, reacts with its homologous antiserum, has been found to contain 37 mg. of serum protein (Felton and Bailey 1926) ; and the antibody titre of a given antiserum may be measured with considerable accuracy by determining the amount of protein that is removed by a soluble or particulate antigen (Heidelberger and Kendall 1929, Heidelberger *et al.* 1930, Heidelberger and Kabat 1934).

That the protein so bound has the general properties of globulin is attested by such observations as those of Marrack and Smith (1930, 1931*a*), who found that diphtheria toxin-antitoxin compound showed the same ultra-violet absorption spectrum as serum globulin, or those of Breinl and Haurowitz (1930), who found that a precipitate, containing about 10 per cent. of hæmoglobin and 90 per cent. of material derived from a homologous antiserum, showed the same proportions of tyrosine, cystine, histidine and arginine as did serum globulin when examined by the same technique. It has also been noted in earlier sections of this chapter that antigen-antibody compounds, or particulate antigens that have been allowed to combine with antibody, behave in respect to their migration in an electric field, and their precipitability by salts or acids, as does serum globulin.

All the available evidence, it may be noted, indicates that the serum protein that unites with antigen does so specifically. There is nothing to support the view that some non-protein antibody unites with the antigen, and that the complex so formed adsorbs serum protein non-specifically. Thus, Heidelberger and Landsteiner (1923), Marrack and Smith (1931*b*) and Haurowitz and Breinl (1933) have shown that recognizable coloured proteins are not carried down in the precipitate when an antigen reacts with its specific antibody ; and Dean, Taylor and Adair (1935), using the optimal proportions technique and examining a sample of antiserum containing antibodies to purified egg albumin and purified horse-serum albumin, found that either antibody could be specifically precipitated by the corresponding antigen without affecting the titre of the other. This does not, of course, mean that no protein constituents of the serum are ever non-specifically adsorbed by an antigen-antibody complex—we know that such adsorption does occur, as in complement fixation. The point at issue is whether the union between antigen and serum protein is specific or non-specific, and the evidence is clearly in favour of specificity.

We are, then, faced with the alternatives that antibodies *are* specialized globulins, or that they are associated with them in a curiously intimate way. There seems no valid reason for adopting the second hypothesis. Many attempts have been made to dissociate antibodies from an antigen-antibody complex in a protein-free condition. The dissociation of the antigen-antibody compound may be accomplished in a variety of ways, and certain of the antibody solutions so obtained have contained very little protein (see Landsteiner and Jagic 1903, Muir 1903, Bail and Tsuda 1909, Spät 1910, Kosaki 1918, Huntoon and Etris 1921, Huntoon *et al.* 1921, Locke and Hirsch 1925), but in none of these instances has it been satisfactorily demonstrated that the amount of protein present was insufficient to account for the antibody action observed (see Eagle 1930). Similar attempts have been made by adsorption on to various reagents other than the specific antigen, followed by elution with various fluids at different pH levels. Some of these attempts have been claimed as successful (see Frankel and Olitzki 1930, Olitzki and Frankel 1931,

Frankel 1932, Olitzki 1932), but these claims have not been confirmed by subsequent workers (see Marrack 1934, Rosenheim 1935).

We may then, for the purposes of our immediate discussion, adopt the view that antibodies are serum globulins, possessing specific chemical groupings that enable them to unite with the corresponding antigens. The possible mechanisms involved in the formation of these specified serum globulins will be discussed in Chapter XLVII.

The Structure and Properties of Antigens.

The *in vitro* reaction that has been most extensively employed in the detailed study of antigenic structure is that of precipitation. In the other reactions—agglutination, lysis, and so on—we are dealing with cells each of which may contain many different antigenic components, while what we require for such studies as these is a single antigen in a state of chemical purity. Such antigens will be in a state of molecular or colloidal solution, and the precipitin reaction is therefore the simplest and the most obvious to apply.

The study of native proteins, in the purest form available, has provided strong support for the view that immunological specificity is determined by chemical structure.

Thus, we can differentiate by immunological tests between serum albumin and serum globulin (Dale and Hartley 1916), between the egg albumin of the duck and of the hen (Dakin and Dale 1919), between the hæmoglobins of different animal species (Higashi 1922, Landsteiner and Heidelberger 1923, Hektoen and Schulhof 1923), and between different vegetable proteins (Wells and Osborne 1911, Wells 1915, Jones and Gersdorff 1923, Lewis and Wells 1925, Wells *et al.* 1927).

We know also that altering the complex protein molecule by heat, by racemization, or by hydrolysis, soon changes its antigenic behaviour ; though the exact relations between chemical and immunological changes are, under these conditions, very difficult to define (see Hartley 1931, Wells 1929).

Far more significant information has been gained by altering the chemical structure of proteins along certain limited and well-defined lines, and noting the resulting changes in their immunological reactions.

Obermayer and Pick (1906) (see also Pick 1912) showed that the nitration or halogenation of proteins—that is the introduction of the nitro-group or of a halogen element such as iodine—profoundly altered the antigenic reactions of the treated protein. Serum proteins so treated lost their species specificity, but they gained a new specificity, shared by normally unrelated serum proteins that had been chemically altered by the same procedure. Thus an antiserum prepared against the nitrated serum of a particular animal species failed to react with the unaltered serum of that species, but reacted with a wide range of nitrated sera from various animals. Since it was known that the nitro-group and the halogen elements entered into the benzene ring of certain of the amino-acids which build up the complex protein molecule, Obermayer and Pick were led to attach particular importance to these chemical groupings as factors determining immunological specificity. Wormall (1930) and Johnson and Wormall (1932) have recently carried out further studies along these lines.

Landsteiner and his colleagues, however, have shown that the salt-forming groups of the amino-acids (the carboxyl-, hydroxyl- and amino-groupings) play an equally important part. By esterification, methylation and acetylation, they have succeeded in altering the immunological specificity of proteins (see Landsteiner and Prášek 1914, Landsteiner and Lampl 1917a, Landsteiner 1917).

Hopkins and Wormall (1933a, b) have recently shown that the immunological reactions of a protein can be altered by allowing them to react with phenyl-isocyanate, which reacts with the free —NH_2 groups, forming a substituted urea.

All the procedures referred to above have this in common, they start with a protein that has a native specificity and seek to alter it by making particular changes in its chemical structure. Landsteiner and his colleagues (see Landsteiner 1930, 1933) have also approached the problem along other, and very fertile, lines. Starting with substances of known and relatively simple constitution, they have succeeded in building up synthetic antigens, the immunological specificity of which is in part determined by known chemical groupings.

The general method employed in the preparation of these synthetic antigens

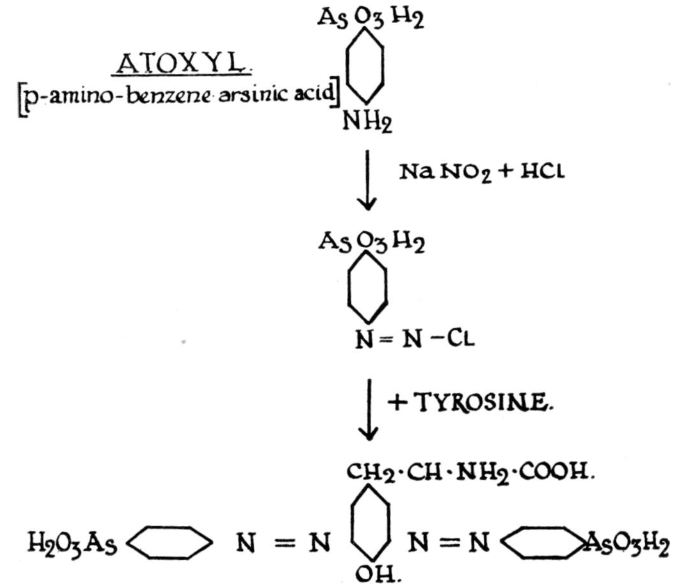

FIG. 28.

has been to utilize the diazo reaction. When a substance containing an —NH_2 group attached to a benzene ring, such as aniline, is treated with sodium nitrite and hydrochloric acid, a diazo compound 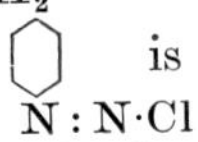 is formed. When this diazo compound is mixed with an aromatic compound having an —OH group in the benzene ring it couples with it, forming an azo-dye. Among the amino-acids that make up protein molecules there are two at least, tyrosine and histidine, that fulfil this condition. When, therefore, a diazo compound is mixed with a protein under suitable conditions it unites with it, and in this way a great variety of chemical groupings of known structure may be attached to the protein molecule. Fig. 28 illustrates the linkage of atoxyl (*p*-amino-benzene-arsinic acid) to a protein, on the assumption that it unites with the tyrosine in the protein molecule.

In general the protein to which such a grouping has been attached will retain its species specificity, though usually with some loss of potency. Thus an antigen prepared by coupling atoxyl to horse globulin will react with an antiserum prepared against any atoxyl-azo-protein, in virtue of the atoxyl grouping ; and with an antiserum prepared against horse globulin or against an azo-protein prepared from horse globulin, in virtue of the specific horse-globulin groupings. This difficulty is overcome by coupling any grouping that it is desired to study to two immunologically unrelated proteins. One of these is used as the antigen for the preparation of the antiserum, the other is used for the *in vitro* tests. Thus, atoxyl may be coupled with horse globulin, and the atoxyl-azo-protein so prepared may be used for the immunization of a rabbit. The serum so prepared will react with this antigen in the test tube in virtue of antibody groupings that unite specifically with unaltered horse globulin. But if atoxyl is also coupled to chicken globulin, and the atoxyl-azo-protein so prepared is used in the *in vitro* tests, the precipitation that occurs will depend solely on antibody groupings acting specifically on atoxyl, since horse globulin and chicken globulin show no antigenic relationship.

Using this method, it has been possible to prepare antisera that give specific precipitation with synthetic antigens in which the active groupings are provided by such substances as metanilic acid, atoxyl, lævo-, dextro- and meso-tartaric acid, glucosides, galactosides, and so on (Landsteiner and Lampl 1917*b*, Landsteiner 1919, 1930, Landsteiner and van der Scheer 1928, 1929, 1931, 1932*a*, *b*, 1934*a*, *b*, Avery and Goebel 1929, Avery, Goebel and Babers 1932). These results have afforded a clear-cut demonstration of an immunological specificity dependent on chemical groupings of known structure. In the case of the dextro-,

Fig. 29.—Precipitation.

lævo- and meso-tartaric acid antigens and in some other instances it has been shown that the difference in structure between optically active isomers is sufficient to confer specificity in the immunological sense.

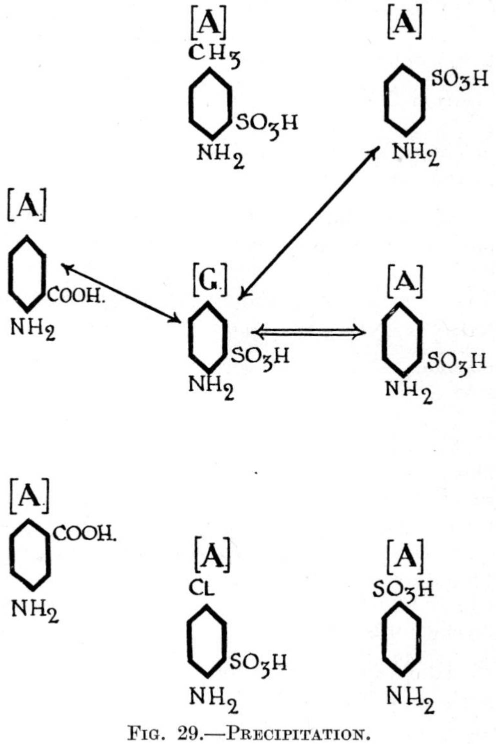

The extensive studies that Landsteiner and his colleagues have carried out along these lines have shown that specificity depends in part on the nature of any grouping that is attached to a complex organic molecule, such as a benzene compound, in part on the position in the molecule which the grouping occupies. Fig. 29 gives an example, the cross precipitations observed with an antigen prepared from *o*-amino-benzene-sulphonic acid (see Landsteiner 1919, Marrack 1934).

In the centre of the figure, labelled [G], is represented the active grouping of the azo-protein used as an antigen in the precipitation tests. Around it, labelled

[A], are placed antibodies prepared against antigens synthesized by coupling the groupings shown to some unrelated protein. The double-headed arrows indicate the instances in which precipitation occurs. The reaction is strongest with the homologous antigen, containing the ⬡—SO_3H group ; but precipitation occurs when the —SO_3H group is shifted to the meta position $\left(⬡^{-SO_3H}\right)$, or when it is replaced, in the ortho position, by —COOH $\left(⬡—COOH\right)$. It does not occur when the —SO_3H group is shifted to the para position $\left(\overset{SO_3H}{⬡}\right)$, or when the —$SO_3H$ group in the ortho position is replaced by a —COOH group in the meta position $\left(⬡^{-COOH}\right)$. The reaction is also abolished by introducing a methyl or chlorine group in the para position, even though the —SO_3H group is retained in the ortho position.

Another example, illustrating the importance of spatial configuration and the immunological equivalence of different chemical groups so long as this spatial configuration is maintained, is afforded by the studies of Erlenmeyer and Berger (1932). They found that azo-proteins prepared from the compounds NH_2⬡—O—⬡, NH_2⬡—NH—⬡ and NH_2⬡—CH_2—⬡ behaved similarly in precipitation reactions, though NH_2⬡—$\overset{\|}{\underset{O}{C}}$—⬡ reacted differently.

The effect on active groups of their relative position in a complex molecule is also illustrated by the recent studies of Landsteiner and van der Scheer (1932a, 1934b) on dipeptides. They prepared synthetic azo-proteins from the dipeptides glycyl-glycine, leucyl-leucine, glycyl-leucine and leucyl-glycine, It was found that the terminal amino-acid carrying the free carboxylic group had the greater influence on immunological specificity. Thus a glycyl-leucine antiserum reacted best with the corresponding antigen, less effectively with a leucyl-leucine antigen and much less effectively with a glycyl-glycine or leucyl-glycine antigen.

To obtain precipitation between these synthetic antigens and the corresponding antisera, it is in most cases necessary to employ the complete antigen, *i.e.* the active grouping coupled to a suitable protein. It is, however, possible to study the reaction in another way, by adding to the specific antisera the active grouping alone, or coupled to some simpler substance than protein, and noting whether it does or does not prevent the formation of a precipitate when a complete homologous antigen is added to the mixture. If such inhibition occurs, we may conclude that the simpler antigen, containing the active antigenic grouping, has combined with the antibody and so blocked its active groupings, though the compound so formed has not been precipitated.

When this procedure is adopted, it is found that relatively simple substances may function as incomplete, or partial antigens, in the sense that they combine specifically with corresponding antibodies. Thus, diazotized atoxyl coupled with tyrosine, instead of with an intact protein molecule, does not form a precipitate when mixed with the corresponding antiserum, but it inhibits the precipitation that would normally occur when this antiserum is mixed with an atoxyl-azo-protein. A similar inhibition may be demonstrated with atoxyl itself in higher concentrations, or even with arsinic acid when this is added in sufficient amount (Landsteiner 1920).

When the inhibition reaction is used to determine the immunological behaviour of non-identical but structurally related organic compounds, it is found that the specificity is less strict than that displayed in cross-protection tests. Fig. 30 illustrates the findings in relation to *o*-amino-benzoic acid (see Landsteiner and van der Scheer 1931, Marrack 1934). The antibody prepared against an azo-protein containing this grouping, indicated at the top of the figure, gives specific precipitation with another azo-protein, containing the same active grouping but a different protein-component, indicated at the bottom of the figure. Inhibition by various other groupings is indicated by the horizontal broken arrows. The reaction is inhibited not only by benzoic acid, or benzoic acid substituted either in the ortho or meta position by the methyl group, but by compounds showing considerable structural differences, such as thiophene carboxylic acid and naphthoic acid.

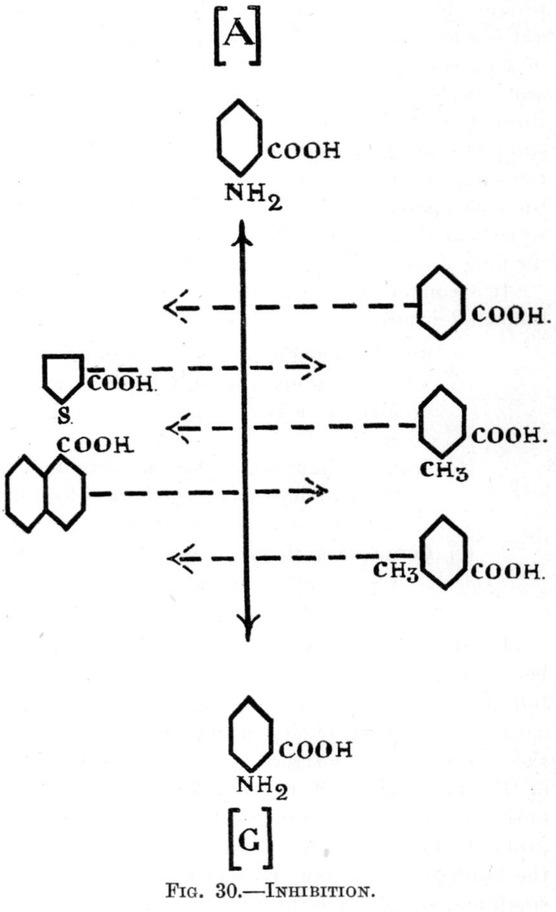

The specific combination of certain azo-dyes with the corresponding antibodies, without the formation of a precipitate, has also been demonstrated by Marrack and Smith (1932), using an ingenious colorimetric technique.

FIG. 30.—INHIBITION.

We have already noted that the partial antigens, or active groupings, that inhibit precipitation will not themselves yield a precipitate *in vitro*. Neither will they stimulate the production of precipitins *in vivo*. In the definition of an antigen that was given at the commencement of this chapter the capacity to act as a stimulant of antibody production was included among its essential properties—it is, indeed, the property from which its name is derived. The difference in behaviour between substances of varying complexity, all bearing the same active specific grouping, led Landsteiner to formulate the conception of the *hapten*, or partial antigen, which, while bearing the specific grouping and therefore combining with the homologous antibody, lacks certain of the properties of the complete antigen.

In subsequent chapters frequent reference will be made to various polysaccharide components derived from different types and species of bacteria. Many of these polysaccharides, from the immunological point of view, occupy a position intermediate between Landsteiner's simpler haptens and complete antigens. They react specifically with the homologous antisera *in vitro*, giving precipitation ; but they do not induce antibody formation *in vivo*, or, if they do so at all, the stimulus they provide is of an altogether different order from that provided by the complete antigen as it occurs in the bacterial cell. It seems likely that the range of activity of a partial antigen is determined in the main by its molecular size. Landsteiner and van der Scheer (1932*b*) have recently coupled succinic, adipic and suberic acids, through their aniline compounds, to proteins, and prepared antisera against the complete antigens so produced. Partial antigens were prepared by coupling the same compounds to resorcinol. These partial antigens gave precipitation with the corresponding antisera, and it was noted that the partial antigen derived from suberic acid gave particularly strong precipitin reactions, probably on account of its long aliphatic side chains.

It is convenient to classify the antigenic complexes we have described under the following headings :

(*a*) **Simple haptens,** possessing immunological specificity, combining with the homologous antibody and so preventing precipitation, but neither forming a precipitate *in vitro*, nor stimulating antibody production *in vivo*.

(*b*) **Complex haptens,** possessing immunological specificity, combining with the homologous antibody and forming a precipitate, but not stimulating antibody production *in vivo*.

(*c*) **Complete antigens,** possessing immunological specificity, combining with the homologous antibody and forming a precipitate, and stimulating antibody production *in vivo.*

It must not, however, be supposed that there is any sharp natural demarcation between our named classes. It seems likely that the characters that determine full antigenic potency are high molecular weight, associated with a large molecular surface and a multiplicity of active specific groupings, and the relative activity of these groupings themselves. If we were in a position to give a detailed description of the chemical structure and immunological properties of a very large number of antigenic substances, ranging from the simplest to the most complex, we should probably find that they formed a continuous rather than a discontinuous series, the falling-off in immunological activity as we passed from large and complex to small and simple molecules being marked by the gradual loss first of one immunological capacity, then of another, until we were left only with the ability to combine specifically with the antibody under optimal conditions of concentration and other relevant factors.

One factor that is commonly associated with full antigenic potency may be briefly noted here, though it is discussed more fully in Chapter XLVII in relation to the formation of antibodies. Complete antigens, possessing the power of stimulating antibody production *in vivo*, as well as that of reacting specifically *in vitro*, have, in the great majority of known instances, a protein component, if they are not themselves proteins. It has, until recently, been a widely accepted working hypothesis that the change from a complete antigen to a hapten is brought about by separating the portion of the antigen molecule that bears the specific grouping, or groupings, from the protein component to which it is normally attached. Recent work, however, has indicated that the unique efficacy of proteins in conferring full antigenicity cannot be upheld.

It is obvious that the work of Landsteiner and his colleagues constitutes an advance of the first importance. It has placed our study of the antigen-antibody reactions, and of the multitude of immunological problems that depend upon them, on a new and far more satisfactory basis. Taken in conjunction with the work of Avery and Heidelberger, and of all those who have followed them, on the chemical constitution of antigenic components derived from bacterial cells, it has definitely established the position of immunological specificity as a problem in the sphere of structural organic chemistry, using structure in the wide sense to include combinations due to intermolecular attractions as well as those induced by intramolecular forces. It is, therefore, worth while to consider briefly the analogies to our particular problems that are presented in other fields of chemical study. In doing so we shall draw freely on the account given by Marrack (1934) to which reference should be made for fuller details.

It has been noted in an earlier section that, when molecules are formed by the redistribution of electrons between their constituent atoms, many of these atoms may remain positively or negatively charged, although the molecule as a whole may be electrically neutral. This will result in the formation of localized electric fields in the immediate neighbourhood of the molecule, operative over a very short distance. When two molecules approach each other closely, these fields, if of opposite sign, will cause an attraction. In large molecules—and it will be remembered that it is with reactions between large molecules that we are mainly concerned—the electric fields set up may be very numerous, and they will have a quite definite spatial arrangement. Taken in conjunction with the shortness of the distance over which these intermolecular forces are operative, this complexity and constancy of pattern provide just the conditions required for specificity. Two molecules possessing at their surface electric fields so arranged that, when they come into close contact, there will be multiple points of attraction between them, will tend to adhere to one another. Two molecules possessing the same number of electric fields, but with these so arranged that close contact cannot be made at many points simultaneously, will show no tendency to adhere. The better the fit, in this specialized sense, the greater will be the total force of attraction.

One of the best available examples of the action of these intermolecular forces is the selective formation of mixed crystals. The molecules involved must conform to the required pattern in regard to their dimensions and the relative position of their active groupings, or atoms. As a result most crystals consist of one kind of molecule alone ; but molecules of different kinds may be built into a single crystal, provided that the structural differences between them do not exceed certain limits. Thus, for example, benzene ⬡ and thiophene ⌂ form mixed crystals, as do
S
azo-benzene ⬡—N=N—⬡ and stilbene ⬡—CH=CH—⬡.

The formation of mixed crystals might, perhaps, be regarded as analogous to the formation of a precipitable antigen-antibody compound, particularly if we adopt Marrack's lattice hypothesis. It is of interest to note that the phenomenon of crystallization also presents an analogy for the inhibition of precipitation by haptens. Many crystals will specifically adsorb on to their surfaces the molecules of another substance, with which they will not form mixed crystals. Such adsorption inhibits the growth of the crystal by the addition of further molecules of the substance of which the crystal is composed. The conditions, in regard to molecular size and position of active groupings, that determine the specificity of adsorption on the surface of a crystal, are less strict than those that determine availability for building into a complete crystal lattice. This would be expected, since only one aspect of the adsorbed molecule need conform to the distribution of active groupings on the surface of the molecule. Relatively small differences may, however, be sufficient to determine the occurrence or non-occurrence of adsorption. Thus (France 1930) the dye

is adsorbed on the cube faces of potash alum, while the dye

is not.

Clearly we must not press analogies too far, or accept uncritically the attractive but perhaps misleading resemblances that present themselves between certain of the concepts evolved by the organic or physical chemist and those to which our immunological studies have led us. But whatever the ultimate findings may be, the line of advance has been clearly laid down. So far as the antigen-antibody reactions are concerned, immunology has become a branch of chemistry.

REFERENCES

AMAKO, T. (1911) *Z. ImmunForsch.*, **8**, 168.
ARRHENIUS, S. (1904) *Arb. ReichsgesundhAmt.*, **20**, 559 ; (1915) " Quantitative Laws in Biological Chemistry." London.
ARRHENIUS, S. and MADSEN, T. (1902) *Festskrift Staatens Serum Inst.*, No. 3 ; (1904) *Zbl. Bakt.*, **36**, 612 ; (1904) *Ibid.*, **37**, 1.
AVERY, O. T. and GOEBEL, W. F. (1929) *J. exp. Med.*, **50**, 533.
AVERY, O. T., GOEBEL, W. F., and BABERS, F. H. (1932) *J. exp. Med.*, **55**, 769.
BAIL, O. and HOKE, E. (1908) *Arch. Hyg.*, **64**, 313.
BAIL, O. and TSUDA, K. (1909) *Z. ImmunForsch.*, **1**, 546.
BANZHAF, E. J. and GIBSON, R. B. (1907) *J. biol. Chem.*, **3**, 253.
BARR, M. (1932) *J. Path. Bact.*, **35**, 913.
BARR, M. and GLENNY, A. T. (1931) *J. Path. Bact.*, **34**, 539.
BARR, M., GLENNY, A. T., and POPE, C. G. (1931) *Brit. J. exp. Path.*, **12**, 217.
BECHHOLD, H. (1904) *Z. phys. Chem.*, **48**, 385.
BEHRING, VON and KITASATO. (1890) *Dtsch. med. Wschr.*, **16**, 1113.
BENIASCH, M. (1911) *Z. ImmunForsch.*, **12**, 268.
BILTZ, W. (1910) *Biochem. Z.*, **23**, 27.
BORDET, J. (1895) *Ann. Inst. Pasteur*, **9**, 462 ; (1898) *Ibid.*, **12**, 688 ; (1899) *Ibid.*, **13**, 225 ; (1903) *Ibid.*, **17**, 161.

BORDET, J. and GENGOU, O. (1901) *Ann. Inst. Pasteur*, **15**, 290.
BOYD, W. C. and HOOKER, S. B. (1934) *J. gen. Physiol.*, **17**, 341.
BRAND, E. (1907) *Berl. klin. Wschr.*, **44**, 1075.
BREINL, F. and HAUROWITZ, F. (1930) *Z. physiol. Chem.*, **192**, 45.
BROOM, J. C. and BROWN, H. C. (1930) *Brit. J. exp. Path.*, **11**, 305.
BROWN, H. C. and BROOM, J. L. (1929) *Brit. J. exp. Path.*, **10**, 387.
BROWNLEE, J. (1925) *J. Hyg., Camb.*, **23**, 437.
BUCHANAN, R. E. (1919) *J. Bact.*, **4**, 73.
BUCHNER, H. (1889*a*) *Zbl. Bakt.*, **5**, 817 ; (1889*b*) *Ibid.*, **6**, 1 ; (1889*c*) *Ibid.*, **6**, 561.
BULLOCH, W. B. and WESTERN, G. T. (1906) *Proc. roy. Soc.*, B, **77**, 531.
BURNET, F. M. (1931) *J. Path. Bact.*, **34**, 471.
BUXTON, B. H. (1905*a*) *J. med. Res.*, **13**, 305 ; (1905*b*) *Ibid.*, **13**, 431 ; (1905*c*) *Ibid.*, **13**, 461.
CHAPIN, W. S. and COWIE, D. M. (1907) *J. med. Res.*, **17**, 213.
COCA, A. F. (1914) *Z. ImmunForsch.*, **21**, 604.
COSTA CRUZ, J. DA. (1929) *C. R. Soc. Biol.*, **100**, 932.
COULTER, C. B. (1920–21) *J. gen. Physiol.*, **3**, 513.
COWIE, D. M. and CHAPIN, W. S. (1907) *J. med. Res.*, **17**, 57, 95.
CRAW, J. A. (1905) *J. Hyg., Camb.*, **5**, 113.
DAKIN, H. D. and DALE, H. H. (1919) *Biochem. J.*, **13**, 248.
DALE, H. H. and HARTLEY, P. (1916) *Biochem. J.*, **10**, 110.
DANYSZ, J. (1902) *Ann. Inst. Pasteur*, **16**, 331.
DEAN, G. (1907) *Proc. roy. Soc.*, B, **79**, 399.
DEAN, H. R. (1912) *Z. ImmunForsch.*, **13**, 84 ; (1917) *Lancet*, i. 45.
DEAN, H. R., TAYLOR, G. L., and ADAIR, M. E. (1935) *J. Hyg., Camb.*, **35**, 69.
DEAN, H. R. and WEBB, R. A. (1926) *J. Path. Bact.*, **29**, 473.
DEISSLER, K. (1932) *Z. ImmunForsch.*, **73**, 365.
DENYS, J. and LECLEF, J. (1895) *La Cellule*, **11**, 177.
DREYER, G. and INMAN, A. C. (1917) *Lancet*, i. 365.
DUNCAN, J. T. (1932*a*) *Brit. J. exp. Path.*, **13**, 489 ; (1932*b*) *Ibid.*, **13**, 498 ; (1935) *Ibid.*, **16**, 405.
EAGLE, H. (1930) *J. Immunol.*, **18**, 393 ; (1932) *Ibid.*, **23**, 153.
EHRLICH, P. (1897) *Klin. Jb.*, **6**, 299 ; (1898) *Dtsch. med. Wschr.*, **24**, 597 ; (1900) *Proc. roy. Soc.*, B, **66**, 424.
EISENBERG, P. and VOLK, R. (1902) *Z. Hyg. InfektKr.*, **40**, 155.
EISLER, M. (1920) *Zbl. Bakt.*, **84**, 43.
ERLENMEYER, H. and BERGER, E. (1932) *Biochem. Z.*, **252**, 22.
EULER, H. VON, and BRUNIUS, E. (1931) *Z. ImmunForsch.*, **72**, 65.
FALK, I. S. and MATSUDA, T. (1926) *Proc. Soc. exp. Biol., N.Y.*, **23**, 781.
FELTON, L. D. (1926) *Bull. Johns Hopk. Hosp.*, **38**, 33 ; (1928) *J. infect. Dis.*, **43**, 543 ; (1932) *J. Immunol.*, **22**, 453.
FELTON, L. D. and BAILEY, G. H. (1926) *J. infect. Dis.*, **38**, 131.
FERRATA, A. (1907) *Berl. klin. Wschr.*, **44**, 366.
FRANCE, W. G. (1930) *Coll. Symp. Monogr.*, **7**, 59. (See Marrack 1934.)
FRANKEL, M. (1932) *Proc. roy. Soc.*, B, **111**, 165.
FRANKEL, M. and OLITZKI, L. (1930) *Nature*, **126**, 723.
FREUNDLICH, H. (1906) *Z. phys. Chem.*, **57**, 385 ; (1922) " Kapillarchemie." Leipzig.
FREUNDLICH, H. and NEUMANN, W. (1909) *Z. phys. Chem.*, **67**, 538.
FRIEDBERGER, E. and GOLDSCHMIDT, E. (1910) *Z. ImmunForsch.*, **6**, 299.
GAY, F. P. (1905) *Zbl. Bakt.*, **29**, 603.
GENGOU, O. (1899) *Ann. Inst. Pasteur*, **13**, 642 ; (1902) *Ibid.*, **16**, 734 ; (1911) *Z. ImmunForsch.*, **11**, 143.
GIBSON, R. B. and BANZHAF, E. J. (1910) *J. exp. Med.*, **12**, 411.
GIBSON, R. B. and COLLINS, K. R. (1907) *J. biol. Chem.*, **3**, 233.
GLENNY, A. T., POPE, C. G., and WADDINGTON, H. (1925) *J. Path. Bact.*, **28**, 279.
GOLDSWORTHY, N. E. (1928) *J. Path. Bact.*, **31**, 220.
GORDON, J. and THOMPSON, F. C. (1933*a*) *Brit. J. exp. Path.*, **14**, 33 ; (1933*b*) *Ibid.*, **14**, 277 ; (1935) *Ibid.*, **16**, 101.
GORDON, J., WHITEHEAD, H. R., and WORMALL, A. (1926*a*) *Biochem. J.*, **20**, 1028 ; (1926*b*) *Ibid.*, **20**, 1036.
GREENWOOD, M. (1913) *Lancet*, i. 158.
GRUBER, M. and DURHAM, H. E. (1896) *Münch. med. Wschr.*, **43**, 285.
HAMMARSTEN, O. (1878) *Arch. ges. Physiol.*, **17**, 413.
HARTLEY, P. (1914) *Mem. Dept Agric. India*, **4**, 178 ; (1925) *Brit. J. exp. Path.*, **6**, 180 ; (1931) *Med. Res. Coun. Lond.* " System of Bacteriology," **6**, 224.
HAUROWITZ, F. and BREINL, F. (1933) *Hoppe-Seyl. Z.*, **214**, 111.
HEIDELBERGER, M. and KABAT, E. A. (1934) *J. exp. Med.*, **60**, 643.
HEIDELBERGER, M. and KENDALL, F. E. (1929) *J. exp. Med.*, **50**, 809 ; (1935*a*) *Ibid.*, **61**, 559, 563 ; (1935*b*) *Ibid.*, **62**, 467 ; (1935*c*) *Ibid.*, **62**, 697.

HEIDELBERGER, M. and LANDSTEINER, K. (1923) *J. exp. Med.*, **38**, 561.
HEIDELBERGER, M., SIA, R. H. P., and KENDALL, F. E. (1930) *J. exp. Med.*, **52**, 477.
HEKTOEN, L. (1908) *J. infect. Dis.*, **5**, 249.
HEKTOEN, L. and SCHULHOF, K. (1923) *J. infect. Dis.*, **5**, 249.
HEUER, G. (1922) *Z. Hyg. InfektKr.*, **95**, 100.
HIGASHI, S. (1922) *J. Biochem., Tokyo*, **2**, 315.
HOPKINS, F. G. (1900) *J. Physiol.*, **25**, 306.
HOPKINS, S. J. and WORMALL, A. (1933*a*) *Biochem. J.*, **27**, 740 ; (1933*b*) *Ibid.*, **27**, 1706.
HUNTOON, F. M. and ETRIS, S. (1921) *J. Immunol.*, **6**, 123.
HUNTOON, F. M., MASUCCI, R., and HANNUM, E. (1921) *J. Immunol.*, **6**, 185.
HYDE, R. R. (1923) *J. Immunol.*, **8**, 267.
JOHNSON, L. R. and WORMALL, A. (1932) *Biochem. J.*, **26**, 1202.
JONES, D. B. and GERSDORFF, C. E. F. (1923) *J. biol. Chem.*, **56**, 79.
JOOS, A. (1901) *Z. Hyg. InfektKr.*, **36**, 422 ; (1902) *Ibid.*, **40**, 203.
KLEIN, H. (1907) *Bull. Johns Hopk. Hosp.*, **18**, 245.
KOSAKI, M. (1918) *J. Immunol.*, **3**, 109.
KRAUS, R. (1897) *Wien. klin. Wschr.*, **10**, 736.
KROGH, M. VON. (1911) *Z. Hyg. InfektKr.*, **68**, 251.
KRUIF, P. H. DE and NORTHROP, J. H. (1922–23) *J. gen. Physiol.*, **5**, 127.
LAIDLAW, P. P. and DUNKIN, G. W. (1931) *J. comp. Path.*, **44**, 1.
LANDSTEINER, K. (1917) *Z. ImmunForsch.*, **26**, 122 ; (1919) *Biochem. Z.*, **93**, 108 ; (1920)
    Ibid., **104**, 280 ; (1930) *Naturwissenschaft.*, **18**, No. 29, 653 ; (1933) " Die Spezifizität
    der serologischen Reaktionen." Julius Springer, Berlin.
LANDSTEINER, K. and HEIDELBERGER, M. (1923) *J. gen. Physiol.*, **6**, 31.
LANDSTEINER, K. and JAGIC, N. (1903) *Münch. med. Wschr.*, **50**, 764.
LANDSTEINER, K. and LAMPL, H. (1917*a*) *Z. ImmunForsch.*, **26**, 133, 258 ; (1917*b*) *Biochem.
    Z.*, **86**, 343.
LANDSTEINER, K. and PRÁŠEK, E. (1911) *Z. ImmunForsch.*, **10**, 68 ; (1914) *Ibid.*, **20**, 211.
LANDSTEINER, K. and SCHEER, J. VAN DER. (1928) *J. exp. Med.*, **48**, 315 ; (1929) *Ibid.*, **50**,
    407 ; (1931) *Ibid.*, **54**, 295 ; (1932*a*) *Ibid.*, **55**, 781 ; (1932*b*) *Ibid.*, **56**, 399 ; (1934*a*) *Ibid.*,
    59, 751 ; (1934*b*) *Ibid.*, **59**, 769.
LANDSTEINER, K. and WELECKI, S. (1911) *Z. ImmunForsch.*, **8**, 395.
LEDINGHAM, J. C. G. (1907) *J. Hyg., Camb.*, **7**, 65.
LEISHMAN, W. B. (1902) *Brit. med. J.*, i. 73.
LEWIS, J. H. and WELLS, H. G. (1925) *J. biol. Chem.*, **66**, 37.
LIEFMANN, H. (1909) *Münch. med. Wschr.*, **56**, 2097.
LOCKE, A. and HIRSCH, E. F. (1925) *J. infect. Dis.*, **37**, 449.
MADSEN, T. and STRENG, O. (1910) *Z. phys. Chem.*, **70**, 263.
MAITLAND, H. B. and BURBURY, Y. M. (1927) *J. comp. Path.*, **40**, 93.
MARKL. (1902) *Z. Hyg. InfektKr.*, **39**, 86.
MARRACK, J. R. (1934) *Spec. Rep. Ser. med. Res. Coun. Lond.*, No. 194.
MARRACK, J. and SMITH, F. C. (1930) *Proc. roy. Soc., B*, **106**, 1 ; (1931*a*) *Brit. J. exp. Path.*,
    12, 30 ; (1931*b*) *Ibid.*, **12**, 182 ; (1932) *Ibid.*, **13**, 394.
MELLANBY, J. (1908) *Proc. roy. Soc., B*, **80**, 399.
MENNES, F. (1897) *Z. Hyg. InfektKr.*, **25**, 413.
MICHAELIS, L. (1911) *Dtsch. med. Wschr.*, **37**, 969.
MILES, A. A. (1933) *Brit. J. exp. Path.*, **14**, 43.
MUDD, S., LUCKÉ, B., MCCUTCHEON, M., and STRUMIA, M. (1929) *J. exp. Med.*, **49**, 779.
MUIR, R. (1903) *Lancet*, ii. 100, 446 ; (1909) " Studies on Immunity." London.
MUIR, R. and BROWNING, C. H. (1909) *J. Path. Bact.*, **13**, 76.
MUIR, R. and MARTIN, W. B. M. (1906*a*) *Brit. med. J.*, ii, 1783 ; (1906*b*) *J. Hyg., Camb.*, **6**,
    265.
NEISSER, M. and WECHSBERG, F. (1901) *Münch. med. Wschr.*, **48**, 697.
NEUFELD, F. and HÜNE. (1907) *Arb. ReichsgesundhAmt.*, **25**, 164.
NEUFELD, F. and RIMPAU, R. (1904) *Dtsch. med. Wschr.*, **11**, 1458 ; (1905) *Z. Hyg. InfektKr.*,
    51, 283.
NICOLLE, M. and CÉSARI, E. (1922) *Ann. Inst. Pasteur*, **36**, 463.
NORTHROP, J. H. (1922) *J. gen. Physiol.*, **4**, 629 ; (1928) " The Newer Knowledge of
    Bacteriology and Immunology." Jordan & Falk, Chicago, p. 782.
NORTHROP, J. H. and KRUIF, P. H. DE. (1922*a*) *J. gen. Physiol.*, **4**, 639 ; (1922*b*) *Ibid.*, **4**,
    655.
NUTTALL, G. (1888) *Z. Hyg. InfektKr.*, **4**, 353.
OBERMAYER, F. and PICK, E. P. (1906) *Wien. klin. Wschr.*, **19**, 327.
OLITZKI, L. (1932) *Z. ImmunForsch.*, **76**, 296.
OLITZKI, L. and FRANKEL, M. (1931) *Proc. Soc. exp. Biol., N.Y.*, **28**, 492.
PFEIFFER, R. (1893) *Z. Hyg. InfektKr.*, **11**, 393 ; (1894*a*) *Ibid.*, **16**, 268 ; (1894*b*) *Ibid.*,
    18, 1 ; (1895) *Ibid.*, **19**, 75.
PFEIFFER, R. and ISSAEFF. (1894) *Z. Hyg. InfektKr.*, **17**, 355.

PICK, E. P. (1912) *Kolle and Wassermanns Hdb. path. Mikroorg ;* IIte Aufl., **1,** 685.
PORGES, O. (1906) *Zbl. Bakt.,* **40,** 133.
PORGES, O. and PRANTSCHOFF, A. (1906) *Zbl. Bakt.,* **41,** 466, 546, 658.
PUTTER, E. (1921) *Z. ImmunForsch.,* **32,** 538.
RAMON, G. (1922) *C. R. Soc. Biol.,* **86,** 661, 711, 813.
ROSENHEIM, A. H. (1935) *J. Path. Bact.,* **40,** 75.
SCHMIDT, S. (1930) *C. R. Soc. Biol.,* **103,** 101.
SGALITZER, M. (1914) *Z. Hyg. InfektKr.,* **76,** 209.
SHIBLEY, G. S. (1926) *J. exp. Med.,* **44,** 667.
SKWIRSKY, P. (1910) *Z. ImmunForsch.,* **5,** 538.
SLEESWIJK, J. G. (1908) *Zbl. Bakt.,* **46,** 513.
SMITH, F. C. and MARRACK, J. (1930) *Brit. J. exp. Path.,* **11,** 494.
SMITH, W. (1932) *J. Path. Bact.,* **35,** 509.
SPÄT, W. (1910) *Z. ImmunForsch.,* **7,** 712.
STRENG, O. (1909) *Z. Hyg. InfektKr.,* **62,** 281.
STRONG, P. S. and CULBERTSON, J. T. (1934) *J. Hyg., Camb.,* **34,** 522.
TAYLOR, G. L. (1931) *J. Hyg., Camb.,* **31,** 56 ; (1933) *Ibid.,* **33,** 12.
TAYLOR, G. L., ADAIR, G. S., and ADAIR, M. E. (1932) *J. Hyg., Camb.,* **32,** 340.
TOPLEY, W. W. C. (1915) *Proc. roy. Soc., B,* **88,** 396.
TOPLEY, W. W. C., WILSON, J., and DUNCAN, J. T. (1935) *Brit. J. exp. Path.,* **16,** 116.
WARD, H. K. and ENDERS, J. F. (1933) *J. exp. Med.,* **57,** 527.
WELLS, H. G. (1915) *J. infect. Dis.,* **16,** 259 ; (1929) " The Chemical Aspects of Immunity."
2nd Edit. New York.
WELLS, H. G., LEWIS, J. H., and JONES, D. B. (1927) *J. infect. Dis.,* **40,** 326.
WELLS, H. G. and OSBORNE, T. B. (1911) *J. infect. Dis.,* **8,** 66.
WHITEHEAD, H. R., GORDON, J., and WORMALL, A. (1925) *Biochem. J.,* **19,** 618.
WINSLOW, C.-E. A., FALK, I. S., and CAULFIELD, M. F. (1923) *J. gen. Physiol.,* **6,** 177.
WORMALL, A. (1930) *J. exp. Med.,* **51,** 295.
WRIGHT, A. E. (1909) " Studies in Immunization." London.
WRIGHT, A. E. and DOUGLAS, S. R. (1903) *Proc. roy. Soc., B,* **72,** 364 ; (1904) *Ibid.,* **73,** 136.
WU, H. and LING, S. M. (1927) *Chin. J. Physiol.,* **1,** 431.
ZINSSER, H. (1921) *J. Immunol.,* **6,** 289.

CHAPTER VII

THE ANTIGENIC STRUCTURE OF BACTERIA

A COMPLETE description of the antigenic structure of a bacterial cell would include (a) the number and kind of different antigens present, (b) their relative proportions, and (c) their position in the cell or cell appendages.

Such a description is not yet possible in any instance. But our advance has been very rapid during the past decade, and we can now construct rough working models of the antigenic structure of certain bacterial species. With the aid of these we have already been able to solve many immunological puzzles ; and it seems certain that further advance along the same lines will enable us to solve many more.

We may start our discussion by considering the methods that are available for studies of this kind.

Antigenic Analysis by Selective Qualitative Absorption of Antibodies.

The fact that a single bacterial cell contains many antigens was established during the earliest studies on the agglutination reaction. The original observations of Gruber and Durham (1896) showed that the specificity of this reaction was not absolute in the biological sense. For instance, while the colon bacillus was sharply differentiated from the typhoid bacillus and both from certain vibrios, these vibrios were not so clearly differentiated from one another. Durham (1901) as the result of a more detailed study of these group agglutinations enunciated quite clearly the hypothesis of a multiplicity—as he called it, a *mosaic*—of antigens within a single bacterial cell. Employing small letters to denote the antigenic bacterial components, and capitals to denote the corresponding agglutinins in the antisera, he suggested that the actual agglutinins and agglutinogens involved might be represented as follows :

Agglutinogens.	Agglutinins.
Bacterium 1. *a, b, c, d, e.*	Serum 1. A, B, C, D, E.
Bacterium 2. *c, d, e, f, g, h.*	Serum 2. C, D, E, F, G, H.
Bacterium 3. *e, f, g, h, j, k.*	Serum 3. E, F, G, H, J, K.

The serum prepared against Bacterium 1 would contain the agglutinins A, B, C, D, E, and in virtue of the presence of each and all of these it would agglutinate the corresponding bacterium. It would also agglutinate Bacterium 2 in virtue of agglutinins C, D, and E, and Bacterium 3 in virtue of agglutinin E.

The method that has been employed in analysing the antigenic structure of a particular bacterial strain—the method of agglutinin absorption—was introduced by Castellani in 1902 ; though a precisely similar method had been previously employed by Ehrlich and his co-workers in demonstrating the multiplicity of hæmolytic antibodies. When an agglutinating serum is exposed to an excess of bacterial cells that contain some or all of the corresponding agglutinogens the agglutinins that find their counterparts in the antigenic structure of the bacteria are bound, or absorbed, and thus removed from the fluid in which the bacteria are suspended. If the bacteria are separated by centrifugation, the supernatant fluid can be tested as regards its remaining agglutinins. For instance, taking the illustrative example given above, if Serum 1 were absorbed with an excess of Bacterium 1 all the agglutinins A, B, C, D, and E would be removed and the super-natant fluid would have no agglutinating action. If it were absorbed with Bacte-rium 2, C, D and E would be removed, but A and B would remain. The supernatant fluid would not agglutinate Bacterium 2—the absorbing strain—nor Bacterium 3 (since that bacterium does not contain agglutinogens *a* or *b*) ; but it would still agglutinate Bacterium 1 in virtue of the remaining agglutinins A and B. If it were absorbed with Bacterium 3, the single common agglutinin E would be removed. The supernatant fluid would (as always) fail to agglutinate the absorbing strain ; but it would still agglutinate Bacterium 1 in virtue of agglutinins A, B, C, and D, and Bacterium 2 in virtue of agglutinins C and D.

This simple method has enabled us to study in considerable detail the antigenic make-up of the bacterial species with which we have been concerned, and to establish the existence within a single species of types or races which cannot be differentiated in any other way.

A note may be interpolated here with regard to two terms that are sometimes loosely applied. The antiserum that is produced by the inoculation into a suitable animal of a particular bacterium is frequently referred to as a *homologous* serum. A serum that agglutinates the same bacterium but has been produced by the inoculation of some other bacterium, differing in one or more of its antigenic components, is termed a *heterologous* serum. Used in this sense the terms are useful and logical, and may be applied either to an antiserum in relation to a bacterium, or to two antisera or two bacteria in relation to one another, implying in either case complete correspondence between active combining groups. Thus, a serum that contains the active antibody groupings A, B, C, D is homo-logous with a bacterium containing the active antigenic groupings *a, b, c, d* ; two bacteria each containing the active antigenic groupings *d, e, f, g* are homologous with one another, and so on. But an antiserum containing the active groupings A, B, C, D is not homo-logous, either with a bacterium containing the active groupings *a, b, c, e,* or *a, b, c, d, e,* or *a, b, c.* The terms cannot, logically, be applied to single antigens or single antibodies. They describe the relation between a group of different antibodies in a serum and a group of antigens attached to a bacterial cell, or between the group of antigens attached to one bacterial cell and the group attached to another. We are also, it should be noted, using the terms qualitatively, not quantitatively.

Suppose that we have an unknown bacterium *x*, which we suspect to be antigenically homologous with a known bacterium *y*, and suppose that we have available an anti-*y* serum. We absorb the anti-*y* serum with *x* and then test it against *y*. If it now fails to agglutinate *y* we may assume that all the active antigenic groupings in *y* are also present in *x*. But we have not excluded the possibility that *x* has additional active antigenic groupings, not present in *y*. So we prepare an anti-*x* serum, and then absorb it with *y*. If, after absorp-tion, it fails to agglutinate *x*, we assume that all the active antigenic groupings present in *x* are also present in *y*. That is, *x* and *y* are antigenically homologous. This double cross-absorption method is often spoken of as the " mirror test."

The Optimal Proportions Technique in Antigenic Analysis.

It will be obvious that the selection of the appropriate dose of bacteria for use in such differential absorptions as those we have described in the preceding section will be greatly facilitated by any technique that enables us to determine the equivalent proportions of a bacterial antigen and the corresponding antibody in an agglutinating serum.   We have seen that this can be done, approximately, by determining the constant-antibody optimum ; though, when groups of antigens and groups of antibodies are concerned, the problem may become extremely complex. Duncan (1932*a*, *b*) and Miles (1933) have demonstrated the utility of this method.

This leads us to the problem of differentiating two types of bacteria, both of which contain the same antigenic components, but in different proportions.   Using the qualitative differential absorption technique, with maximal absorbing doses of bacteria, the two types would appear identical, since each would absorb all the agglutinins from both the homologous and heterologous serum, using those terms in this case to include quantitative as well as qualitative relations.   By careful adjustment of the absorbing dose it is, however, sometimes possible to demonstrate a quantitative difference of this kind.   An example, dealing with the differentiation of *Br. melitensis* from *Br. abortus* will be found on p. 641.

The Study of Bacterial Variation as a Guide to Antigenic Structure.

Bacterial variation, as a general phenomenon, is dealt with in the succeeding chapter ; but the detailed study of the antigenic differences displayed by bacterial variants has played so large a part in the formation of our present views in regard to antigenic structure that we must anticipate a little and discuss in the present section certain examples that will help to illustrate the kind of antigenic changes that occur.

Smith and Reagh (1903) isolated a non-motile variant of the hog cholera bacillus, and compared its agglutination reactions with those of the normal, motile, flagellated type of this organism.   They found that a serum prepared against the motile strain agglutinated both the motile and the non-motile strains ; but the titre was much higher for the motile than for the non-motile, and the clumps formed by the motile strain were fluffy and formed rapidly, while the clumps formed by the non-motile strain were tight, small and granular, and formed far more slowly.   A serum prepared against the non-motile strain agglutinated the motile and non-motile strains to the same degree, giving in each case the slow, granular type of agglutination.   The serum prepared against the motile strain, when absorbed with the non-motile strain, lost its power of agglutinating the non-motile bacilli, but retained its power of agglutinating the motile strain.   The serum prepared against the non-motile strain lost its agglutinating power for both strains when absorbed with the motile strain.   Smith and Reagh concluded that the normal, motile hog cholera bacillus has two kinds of antigens, one contained in the flagella, the other in the cell body.   The non-motile type has lost the flagellar antigens and retains the body antigens only.   Beyer and Reagh (1904) extended these observations and showed that the flagellar antigens were so altered by heating to 70° C. for 15 minutes that the heated bacilli no longer gave the flagellar type of agglutination, but reacted like the non-motile strain.   The somatic, or body, antigens were not affected by this treatment and still gave the characteristic slow, granular agglutination (see also Orcutt 1924, Craigie 1931).

These observations of Smith and Reagh and of Beyer and Reagh demonstrated all the essential points of difference between the flagellar and somatic types of agglutination, but they passed almost unnoticed until similar findings were recorded by Weil and Felix (1917) in connection with their work on the diagnostic significance of the agglutination of a particular strain of proteus bacillus by the blood of a patient suffering from typhus fever. The proteus bacillus, in its normal, flagellated form, gives rise to a thin, widely spreading growth covering the surface of the agar medium on which it is grown. This was called by Weil and Felix the *Hauch* form—the " exhalation " form. A non-flagellated variant grew in isolated colonies with no thin, spreading growth between them ; this was the *Ohne Hauch* form—the form without an exhalation. As is the way in laboratory shorthand these soon became the " H " and " O " forms ; and so the thermolabile, flagellar antigens are now the H antigens, and the thermostable, somatic antigens are the O antigens.

Arkwright (1920, 1921, 1924), working with bacteria of the typhoid-paratyphoid-dysentery group, described a type of variation that has proved particularly instructive from this point of view. He noted that a particular type of variant was of relatively common occurrence among these bacilli ; and this variant differed from the parent form in several characteristic ways. Thus, the normal parent form gave smooth colonies on a solid medium and a diffuse growth in broth, and was not auto-agglutinable in normal saline (0·85 per cent.). The variant form gave rough or granular colonies on solid media and a granular growth in broth, and was auto-agglutinable in normal saline, though a stable suspension could usually be prepared in distilled water, or in a saline solution with a greatly decreased salt-content (0·2–0·4 per cent.). These differences in colony form, growth in broth, and salt-sensitiveness were associated with a profound change in antigenic structure. The normal parent form reacted specifically as regards its agglutinability by immune sera ; the variant was agglutinated not only by its own antiserum but by antisera prepared against many other bacteria in the rough state, some of which were only distantly related to the parent form according to the ordinarily accepted bacteriological criteria. By the usual transition—through shorthand to symbols—the normal form, giving smooth colonies, became the *Smooth* (or S) form ; the variant, giving rough colonies, became the *Rough* (or R) form. And here again we have become entangled in the web of our words, for we have never defined exactly the criteria of roughness and smoothness. The implicit meaning is certainly not the meaning we want ; since, as we shall see, the correlation between colonial form and antigenic structure is by no means constant. If we give *Smooth* and *Rough* their obvious or commonsense meaning, then we shall want new terms for the underlying changes that really interest us. If we employ the legitimate licence of scientific terminology, and say that by *Smooth* we mean one sort of antigenic structure and by *Rough* another, then we must at least define quite clearly what we mean. Up to the present we have evaded our difficulties, and so we find that the rough type of one species is recorded as having the more important characters of the smooth type of another species, as in the case of the anthrax bacillus (see Preisz 1904, Eisenberg 1912, Bordet and Renaux 1930, Tomcsik and Szongott 1932, 1933) ; or it becomes necessary to invent new descriptive terms, such as *matt* and *glossy*, as in the case of the hæmolytic streptococcus (see Todd 1928a, b, Todd and Lancefield 1928).

In most of the cases with which we are familiar the change from smoothness to roughness (the S → R variation) is associated with a loss of virulence—an association of obvious importance to the immunologist—as well as with a particular kind of change in antigenic structure. We have very good reasons for believing that the change in antigenic structure determines the loss of virulence, and it certainly determines the change in antigenic value of the variant strain regarded as an immunizing agent. We may, then, for our immediate purpose and to avoid confusion, explicitly limit ourselves to this antigenic variation and its consequences, noting that if we define the S——→R variation in this way we are acting in defiance of general usage.

In terms of antigenic structure we may say that this variation consists in the *loss of the heat-stable somatic antigen that characterizes the surface of the normal virulent bacterial cell.* This loss may be associated with an uncovering of some other somatic antigen, which then dominates the antigenic behaviour of the strain.

Variation of this type has now been described in a wide range of different bacterial species—in the *Pasteurella* Group (de Kruif 1921, Webster 1925), in pneumococci (Griffith 1923, Reimann 1925, 1927), in staphylococci (Bigger, Boland and O'Meara 1927), in streptococci (Todd 1928*a*) and in a host of other organisms. We are probably justified in regarding it as a type of variation to which pathogenic bacteria are inherently liable.

Sometimes (see White 1932, 1933) this variation may proceed still further, and another antigenic constituent may be lost. The antigenic behaviour of the organism may then be dominated by a component that, in the normal state, was altogether latent. It may be noted (*a*) that the S → R variation is quite independent of the H → O variation (rough variants are often flagellated), and (*b*) that loss variations of the S → R or more deeply seated types are often irreversible.

There is another kind of antigenic variation to which reference must be made before we pass to the next section of our discussion.

Andrewes (1922, 1925) described a curious *phasic variation* in the H antigens of certain flagellated species. Taking two bacteria, *x* and *y*, that showed the flagellar type of agglutination when tested either against an anti-*x* or against an anti-*y* serum, and therefore possessed at least one H antigen in common, he absorbed the anti-*x* serum with bacillus *y* and thus obtained a serum that agglutinated *x* but not *y*. He then took a broth culture of *x* and plated it on a solid medium, thus obtaining separate colonies. Subculturing from several of these, he obtained different cultures, each representing a single bacillus in the original broth culture. When he tested these different cultures against the anti-*x* serum, rendered specific by absorption, and against the anti-*y* serum, containing the common, or " group " antibody, he found that his subcultures fell sharply into two classes. Those of one class were agglutinated to titre by the specific anti-*x* serum, but not at all by the anti-*y* serum. Those of the other were agglutinated to titre by the anti-*y* serum, but not at all by the specific anti-*x* serum. The only possible conclusion would seem to be that the original culture of *x* showed cross-agglutination with the anti-*y* serum not because each bacillus in the culture possessed two antigenic components, say *a* and *b*, in their flagella, *a* being specific for *x* and *b* being shared by *y*, but because some of the bacilli possessed *a* alone, and others *b* alone. We need not, for the moment, worry as to whether the *a* bacilli do or do not possess a trace of *b* and *vice versa*. Similarly Andrewes was able to show that the *y* culture, that agglutinated with anti-*x* and anti-*y* sera, contained some bacilli possessing the common flagellar antigen *b* and others containing an antigen *c* specific for *y*. The bacilli that possessed the group antigen only were referred to as being in the *group phase* ; those that possessed the specific antigen only as being in the *specific phase*. If repeated plate cultures were prepared from a strain that was in the specific phase, bacilli in the group phase turned up sooner or later ; similarly a strain in the group phase gave rise to substrains in the specific phase. The variations might occur in either direction. Species or types of bacteria that show this curious variation in their flagellar antigens are termed *diphasic*. We do not know of any example of diphasic variation affecting the somatic antigens.

The Application of Chemical Methods in the Analysis of Antigenic Structure.

A few examples will suffice us here, since the chemical constitution of the antigenic components that characterize the various species of bacteria is described more fully, where it is known, in the chapters devoted to systematic bacteriology.

Zinsser and Parker (1923) isolated substances from pneumococci, staphylococci, the influenza bacillus, the typhoid bacillus and the tubercle bacillus, which gave none of the ordinary protein reactions, except a very weak xantho-protein reaction, but gave specific precipitation and complement fixation with the corresponding antisera prepared by the injection of whole organisms. These non-protein antigens failed to stimulate antibody production on injection.

In the same year Heidelberger and Avery published the first of a series of papers dealing with a chemical study of the antigenic constituents of the pneumococcus (Heidelberger and Avery 1923, 1924, Avery and Heidelberger 1923, 1925, Avery, Heidelberger and Goebel 1925, Avery and Morgan 1925, Avery and Neill 1925). From the three classical types of pneumococci, in their normal smooth form, partial antigens were separated, which were found to have the chemical structure of complex polysaccharides, failed to stimulate antibody production *in vivo*, but gave specific precipitation at extraordinarily high dilutions when mixed with antisera prepared by the inoculation of rabbits with the corresponding strains of pneumococci.

In rough variants, which are non-capsulated, these polysaccharide antigens are absent ; but there remains a protein antigenic component which is common to the rough variants of all types, and is also present in the smooth capsulated forms, though in these their presence is masked by the type-specific capsular polysaccharide.

Lancefield (1928) separated antigenic components from hæmolytic streptococci by chemical methods. She found that the component that confers type-specificity is acid-soluble and contains some 14 per cent. of protein nitrogen. In its purified state it is hapten-like, in that it gives specific precipitation in the test tube but fails to stimulate antibody-production *in vivo*. In addition to this type-specific antigen there is a polysaccharide component that is shared by many types of hæmolytic streptococci, but differentiates the species into large sub-groups (Lancefield 1933) ; and there is a nucleo-protein antigen that is shared by a wide variety of streptococci, hæmolytic and non-hæmolytic. Studies by Todd and Lancefield (1928) (see also Lancefield and Todd 1928) have shown that the change from the virulent matt to the avirulent glossy form is associated with the loss of the type-specific component, the polysaccharide component being retained.

The capsulated bacillus of Friedländer has given results entirely analogous to those obtained with the pneumococcus (Heidelberger, Goebel and Avery 1925, Julianelle 1926). The species may be divided into a number of sharply demarcated serological types. This type-specificity is conferred by a polysaccharide hapten present in the capsule. The body of the bacillus contains a nucleo-protein antigen that is shared by all types.

Polysaccharide haptens have also been isolated from the tubercle bacillus (Laidlaw and Dudley 1925, Enders 1929), from *Bact. lactis aerogenes* (Tomcsik and Kurotchkin 1928), from organisms of the Salmonella group (Furth and Landsteiner 1928, 1929), from cholera vibrios (Landsteiner and Levine 1927, Jermoljewa and Bujanowskaja 1930), from Shiga's dysentery bacillus (Meyer 1930, Morgan 1931), from the anthrax bacillus (Tomcsik 1930, Schockaert 1928, Tomcsik and Szongott 1932) and from yeasts (Mueller and Tomcsik 1924, Stone and Garrod 1931, Duncan 1932*a*).

The case of the anthrax bacillus presents points of interest. The normal virulent form of this bacillus is capsulated and gives a rough colony on agar ; the avirulent variant is non-capsulated and gives a smooth colony on agar (Preisz 1904, Eisenberg 1912). This, then, is

P.B.   H one of the cases in which the normal relation between smoothness and virulence is reversed. It was natural to suppose that the polysaccharide component isolated from *B. anthracis* was the capsular material; but Tomcsik and Szongott (1932, 1933) report that this is not the case. They state that the polysaccharide component is common to the virulent, capsulated, rough-colony-forming type and to the avirulent, non-capsulated, smooth-colony-forming type, and that the capsule is formed of a protein substance that is precipitated by copper sulphate, and has a nitrogen content of 10 per cent. It is of interest to compare these findings with those of Todd and Lancefield in the case of the hæmolytic streptococcus.

There is another way in which chemical methods may be applied in the investigation of antigenic structure. Bacteria may be treated with various chemical solvents, or other reagents, with or without heat, and the effect of this treatment on their immunological behaviour may be studied (see White 1927, 1928, 1929, 1932, 1933).

The Sharing of Antigenic Components between Unrelated Bacteria, or between Bacteria and Other Cells.

In the course of the numerous studies that have been made on antigenic structure, instances have come to light of the sharing of a particular antigenic component by bacteria that show no systematic relation to one another, or by bacteria on the one hand and plant and animal tissues on the other.

Thus (Avery *et al.* 1925, Julianelle 1926), the capsular polysaccharide of the Type II pneumococcus is closely similar to the capsular polysaccharide of the Type B pneumobacillus, and also to a polysaccharide isolated from a species of yeast (Sugg, Richardson and Neill 1929). And a polysaccharide obtained by the partial hydrolysis of gum arabic reacts with antisera prepared against Type II and Type III pneumococci (Heidelberger, Avery and Goebel 1929).

A still more curious example of this sharing of antigenic components is afforded by the presence in a wide variety of bacteria of Forssman's heterophile antigen (see p. 854), which is a constituent of the red blood corpuscles, and tissue cells of certain animal species (see Rothacker 1913, Iijima 1923, Schmidt 1925, Meyer 1926, 1930, 1931, Meyer and Morgan 1935, Powell 1926, Yasui 1929, Combiesco *et al.* 1930, Eisler 1931*a*, *b*, Eisler and Howard 1931, 1932, Bailey and Shorb 1931, Buchbinder 1935).

There is, of course, nothing very bizarre in the occurrence of identical, or closely similar, antigenic groupings in living cells that have no close systematic relationship. The specificity that antigen-antibody reactions detect is, as we have seen, a chemical one. The fact that it is also biological, in the systematic sense, depends on the way in which the chemical substances concerned are distributed in nature. It is very probable that, as our search extends, we shall come on one instance after another in which antigenically similar substances are found in entirely dissimilar biological situations.

The Localization of Antigenic Components in the Bacterial Cell.—The observations recorded above, and many others that will be referred to in subsequent chapters (see particularly the antigenic structure of the typhoid-paratyphoid group, pp. 546–551) not only tell us that there are many different antigens in bacterial cells, and that these antigens have different chemical constitutions; they give us some indication of whereabouts in the bacterial cell these different antigens are placed. They indicate also that this antigenic anatomy is a factor of primary importance in determining that cell's immunological behaviour. Our conception with regard to the way in which such components are actually arranged can be set out most easily in diagrammatic form. But it must be emphasized that our diagram is not a picture. By placing an antigen at the cell surface we are implying that it behaves as though it were there. By placing it beneath the surface we mean that it seems, in the normal form of the organism, to be overshadowed by some other bacterial component. How the components are really arranged we do not know, except that we can certainly allocate some to flagella or capsules, and are almost certainly right in supposing that changes in antigenic behaviour are associated with changes at the cell surface. It is quite likely that antigenic variation is associated with a change in the amount of a particular antigenic component, as well as a change in its situation. A component, for instance, that has been unmasked by the loss of another component may be produced in greater amount when it assumes a dominant position on the active surface of the cell. Perhaps in some cases it is only represented in the normal cell in a rudimentary form.

Bearing these caveats in mind we may consider the diagrammatic arrangements of antigens set out in Fig. 31.

At A is represented a portion of a flagellated bacillus in its normal, virulent, smooth form, with one antigen at the surface of its flagella, a second and a third antigen at the cell surface, a fourth antigen situated more deeply and masked by antigens two and three, a fifth antigen situated more deeply still, and a sixth antigen situated centrally in the cell body.

At B is a portion of a bacillus having the same antigens, but without flagella. We might regard it as an O variant derived from A. Alternatively we might alter the nature of the antigens, maintaining their arrangement, and regard it as the normal, smooth form of any non-flagellated organism.

At C is a rough variant from A. It has kept its flagella and its normal flagellar antigen ; but it has lost the antigenic components that determined the nature of the cell surface in the normal, smooth form. A deeper antigen has been unmasked. It will be noted that a few of the antigenic components that originally lay more deeply still are represented as having now found a place at the cell surface.

In some cases (see White 1933) antigenic variation by loss may proceed still further. The characteristic rough somatic antigen may disappear, and the bacterial surface may be dominated by components that lay very deeply in the normal, smooth form.

At D is an organism, such as the pneumococcus, having a capsule that consists mainly of one kind of antigen (or hapten). Beneath it, in the cell body, is another antigen which is entirely covered by the capsule.

At E is a rough variant from D. The capsule has gone, and with it the characteristic capsular antigen. The character of the cell surface is now determined by the antigen that before was hidden.

All these diagrams, and particularly D and E, are much too simple to be true. There are probably a very large number of antigens, or antigenic groupings, in any bacterial cell. But it *is* true that the character of the cell surface appears in most cases to be dominated by a few characteristic antigenic components, and that this surface may be profoundly altered by the replacement of these components by a few others. It is probable that the S → R variation is not a sudden, all-or-none mutation, but a more gradual or step-like process, with intermediate forms in which the normal surface antigens are still present, though in diminished amount (see, for instance, Wilson 1930).

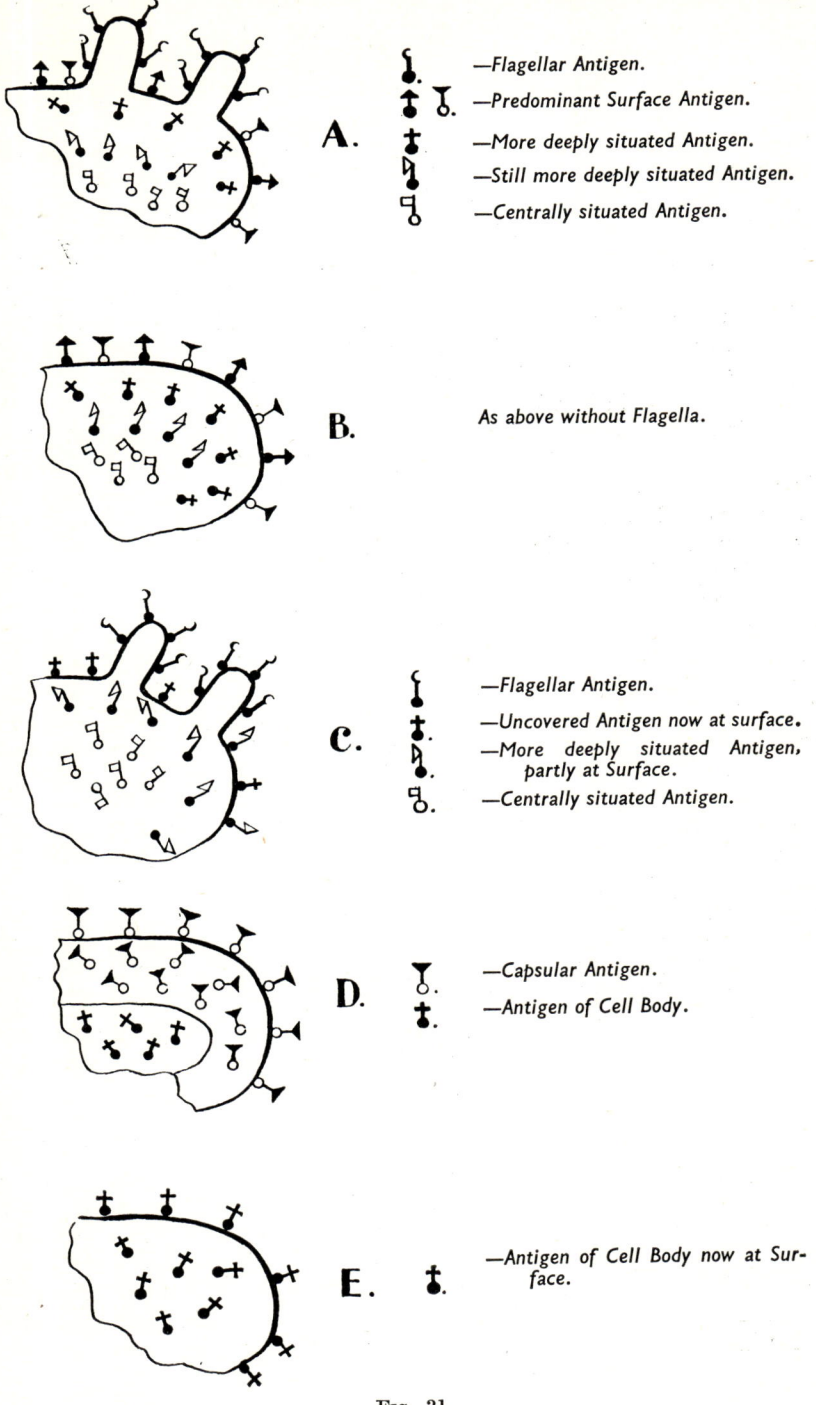

A.
—Flagellar Antigen.
—Predominant Surface Antigen.
—More deeply situated Antigen.
—Still more deeply situated Antigen.
—Centrally situated Antigen.

B.
As above without Flagella.

C.
—Flagellar Antigen.
—Uncovered Antigen now at surface.
—More deeply situated Antigen, partly at Surface.
—Centrally situated Antigen.

D.
—Capsular Antigen.
—Antigen of Cell Body.

E.
—Antigen of Cell Body now at Surface.

Fig. 31.

Antigenic Structure in Relation to the Different Antigen-Antibody Reactions.

When antibodies unite with antigens that form part of a bacterial cell, the effect on the cell will vary according to the position that the antigen occupies.

If the antigen is situated on the surface of the flagella the antigen-antibody compound will be formed in this situation, the usual change in the direction of salt-sensitiveness will occur, and, in the presence of electrolytes, the bacilli will flocculate in the large, loose clumps characteristic of flagellar agglutination.

Antigen-antibody union in this situation does not, however, render the bacterium sensitive to lysis by complement, and it is relatively ineffective in promoting phagocytosis (see Felix 1924, Braun and Nodake 1924, Felix and Robertson 1928). For sensitization of this type to occur antigen-antibody union must take place at the bacterial surface.

It would seem, also, that the aggregates formed in flagellar agglutination are not of the kind that readily fix complement; though there is some uncertainty on this point (see Hofmeier 1927, Springut 1927). It seems possible that the absence, or paucity, of complement fixation may be due simply to the physical character of the aggregates and the rapidity with which they are formed.

The more deeply seated antigens will play no part in the serological reactions of the intact cell in its normal smooth form. They are inaccessible to the antibody. In suspensions that have been allowed to autolyse, or that have been broken up in some other way, these antigens may be liberated. They will then unite with the corresponding antibody to form a precipitate, and if complement is present and the conditions favourable this complement will be fixed.

To revert for a moment to the problem of the unity or diversity of antibodies, it is logical to say that an antibody acting on a flagellar antigen is an agglutinin, but not a lysin; that an antibody acting on a surface antigen is an agglutinin and a lysin, and a complement-fixing antibody, and an opsonin; and that an antibody acting on an antigen that is normally situated below the bacterial surface is, when tested against bacterial extracts or autolysates, a precipitin and a complement-fixing antibody, but is not, so far as the normal cell is concerned, an agglutinin, or a lysin or a complement-fixing antibody or an opsonin. But none of these differences in reaction are determined by differences in the nature of the antibody, apart from its combining group; they depend on differences in the situation of the antigen with which it unites.

REFERENCES

ANDREWES, F. W. (1922) *J. Path. Bact.*, **25**, 505; (1925) *Ibid.*, **28**, 345.
ARKWRIGHT, J. (1920) *J. Path. Bact.*, **33**, 358; (1921) *Ibid.*, **34**, 36; (1924) *Brit. J. exp. Path.*, **5**, 23.
AVERY, O. T. and HEIDELBERGER, M. (1923) *J. exp. Med.*, **38**, 81; (1925) *Ibid.*, **42**, 367.
AVERY, O. T., HEIDELBERGER, M., and GOEBEL, W. F. (1925) *J. exp. Med.*, **42**, 709.
AVERY, O. T. and MORGAN, H. J. (1925) *J. exp. Med.*, **42**, 347.
AVERY, O. T. and NEILL, J. M. (1925) *J. exp. Med.*, **42**, 355.
BAILEY, G. H. and SHORB, M. S. (1931) *Amer. J. Hyg.*, **13**, 831.
BEYER, H. G. and REAGH, A. L. (1904) *J. med. Res.*, **12**, 313.
BIGGER, J. W., BOLAND, C. R., and O'MEARA, R. (1927) *J. Path. Bact.*, **30**, 261.
BORDET, J. and RENAUX, E. (1930) *Ann. Inst. Pasteur*, **45**, 1.
BRAUN, H. and NODAKE, R. (1924) *Zbl. Bakt.*, **92**, 429.
BUCHBINDER, L. (1935) *Arch. Path.*, **19**, 841.
CASTELLANI, A. (1902) *Z. Hyg. InfektKr.*, **40**, 1.
COMBIESCO, D., STATMATESCO, S., NESTORESCO, N., and ADAM, C. (1930) *Arch. roum. Path. exp. Microbiol.*, **3**, 241.

CRAIGIE, J. (1931) *J. Immunol.*, **21**, 417.

DUNCAN, J. T. (1932*a*) *Brit. J. exp. Path.*, **13**, 489 ; (1932*b*) *Ibid.*, **13**, 498.

DURHAM, H. E. (1901) *J. exp. Med.*, **5**, 353.

EISENBERG, P. (1912) *Zbl. Bakt.*, **63**, 305.

EISLER, M. (1931) *Z. ImmunForsch.*, **70**, 48 ; (1931) *Ibid.*, **73**, 37.

EISLER, M. and HOWARD, A. F. (1931) *Z. ImmunForsch.*, **71**, 473 ; (1932) *Ibid.*, **76**, 461.

ENDERS, J. F. (1929) *J. exp. Med.*, **50**, 777.

FELIX, A. (1924) *J. Immunol.*, **9**, 115.

FELIX, A. and ROBERTSON, M. (1928) *Brit. J. exp. Path.*, **9**, 6.

FURTH, J. and LANDSTEINER, K. (1928) *J. exp. Med.*, **47**, 171 ; (1929) *Ibid.*, **49**, 727.

GRIFFITH, F. (1923) *Rep. publ. Hlth. med. Subj., Lond.* No. 18.

GRUBER, M. and DURHAM, H. E. (1896) *Münch. med. Wschr.*, **43**, 285.

HEIDELBERGER, M. and AVERY, O. T. (1923) *J. exp. Med.*, **38**, 73 ; (1924) *Ibid.*, **40**, 301.

HEIDELBERGER, M., AVERY, O. T., and GOEBEL, W. F. (1929) *J. exp. Med.*, **49**, 847.

HEIDELBERGER, M., GOEBEL, W. F., and AVERY, O. T. (1925) *J. exp. Med.*, **42**, 701.

HOFMEIER, K. (1927) *Z. ImmunForsch.*, **50**, 71.

IIJIMA, T. (1923) *J. Path. Bact.*, **26**, 519.

JERMOLJEWA, Z. W. and BUJANOWSKAJA, I. S. (1930) *Z. ImmunForsch.*, **68**, 346.

JULIANELLE, L. A. (1926) *J. exp. Med.*, **44**, 113, 683, 735.

KRUIF, P. H. DE. (1921) *J. exp. Med.*, **33**, 773.

LAIDLAW, P. P. and DUDLEY, H. W. (1925) *Brit. J. exp. Path.*, **6**, 197.

LANCEFIELD, R. C. (1928) *J. exp. Med.*, **47**, 91, 469, 857 ; (1933) *Ibid.*, **57**, 571.

LANCEFIELD, R. C. and TODD, E. W. (1928) *J. exp. Med.*, **48**, 769.

LANDSTEINER, K. and LEVINE, P. (1927) *J. exp. Med.*, **46**, 213.

MEYER, K. (1926) *Z. ImmunForsch.*, **45**, 97 ; (1930) *Ibid.*, **68**, 98 ; (1931) *Ibid.*, **71**, 331.

MEYER, K. and MORGAN, W. T. J. (1935) *Brit. J. exp. Path.*, **16**, 476.

MILES, A. A. (1933) *Brit. J. exp. Path.*, **14**, 43.

MORGAN, W. T. J. (1931) *Brit. J. exp. Path.*, **12**, 62.

MUELLER, J. H. and TOMCSIK, J. (1924) *J. exp. Med.*, **40**, 343.

ORCUTT, M. L. (1924) *J. exp. Med.*, **40**, 43, 627.

POWELL, H. M. (1926) *J. Immunol.*, **12**, 1.

PREISZ, H. (1904) *Zbl. Bakt.*, **35**, 280, 416, 537, 657.

REIMANN, H. A. (1925) *J. exp. Med.*, **41**, 587 ; (1927) *Ibid.*, **45**, 1, 807.

ROTHACKER, A. (1913) *Z. ImmunForsch.*, **16**, 491.

SCHMIDT, H. (1925) *Z. ImmunForsch.*, **43**, 422.

SCHOCKAERT, J. (1928) *C. R. Soc. Biol.*, **99**, 1242.

SMITH, T. and REAGH, A. L. (1903) *J. med. Res.*, **10**, 89.

SPRINGUT, E. (1927) *Z. ImmunForsch.*, **52**, 25.

STONE, K. and GARROD, L. P. (1931) *J. Path. Bact.*, **34**, 429.

SUGG, J. Y., RICHARDSON, L. V., and NEILL, J. M. (1929) *J. exp. Med.*, **50**, 579.

TODD, E. W. (1928*a*) *Brit. J. exp. Path.*, **9**, 1 ; (1928*b*) *J. exp. Med.*, **48**, 493.

TODD, E. W. and LANCEFIELD, R. C. (1928) *J. exp. Med.*, **48**, 751.

TOMCSIK, J. (1930) *Z. Hyg. InfektKr.*, **111**, 119.

TOMCSIK, J. and KUROTCHKIN, T. J. (1928) *J. exp. Med.*, **47**, 379.

TOMCSIK, J. and SZONGOTT, H. (1932) *Z. ImmunForsch.*, **76**, 214 ; (1933) *Ibid.*, **78**, 86.

WEBSTER, L. T. (1925) *J. exp. Med.*, **41**, 571.

WEIL, E. and FELIX, A. (1917) *Wien. klin. Wschr.*, **30**, 1509.

WHITE, P. B. (1927) *J. Path. Bact.*, **30**, 113 ; (1928) *Ibid.*, **31**, 423 ; (1929) *Ibid.*, **32**, 85. (1932) *Ibid.*, **35**, 77 ; (1933) *Ibid.*, **36**, 65.

WILSON, G. S. (1930) *J. Hyg., Camb.*, **30**, 40.

YASUI, K. (1929) *Z. ImmunForsch.*, **63**, 440.

ZINSSER, H. and PARKER, J. T. (1923) *J. exp. Med.*, **37**, 275.

CHAPTER VIII

BACTERIAL VARIATION

In the earlier bacteriological writings, from the days of Pasteur and Koch onwards, there will be found scattered references to certain bacterial strains that have deviated, in one way or another, from the modal form of the particular species concerned. In the earliest days of all, when the doctrine of spontaneous generation was dying, but not yet dead, it was, indeed, the fixity rather than the variability of bacterial species that was in dispute. It was not, however, until the beginning of the present century that any serious attempt was made to study bacterial variation as a problem *sui generis*, or to apply to bacteria the concepts that had proved so fruitful in the study of the higher plants and animals. During the first decade or so of the present century these attempts were sporadic ; but during the last fifteen years an immense impetus has been given to this line of inquiry by a series of converging studies, and the relevant literature has expanded from a trickle to a flood.

The significance of many of the observations that have been recorded is at the moment exceedingly difficult to assess. Some of them serve to illustrate the wide range of variation that may occur within a single bacterial species, but tell us little or nothing in regard to the relative frequency of the different variants described, or the factors on which the variation depends. Others are concerned, at least in part, with problems that have been described in Chapter II—the existence of a complex bacterial life-cycle, of filtrable forms of bacteria, of some form of sexual reproduction and so on. In the present chapter we shall discuss the general problem of bacterial variation, as illustrated by a series of observations the selection of which must of necessity be to some extent arbitrary. A more detailed account of certain variants will be found in the systematic descriptions of the different genera and species given in later chapters.

Terminology.

The application to bacteria of terms that have been coined to express changes in form or function occurring in higher plants or animals, is not without its dangers ; and it is possible that there is little real justification for the use of such a term as mutation, in connection with the variations which bacteria may undergo. Some biologists would attach two implications to the use of this term : the suddenness of the change—the variation *per saltum*—and the permanency of the change, once it has occurred. Dobell (1913) regards as a mutation any permanent change, which is transmitted to subsequent generations of bacteria, without any implication in regard to the suddenness or gradualness of the change, or the manner of its acquisition. We must, at all events, remember that most of our conceptions

199

with regard to variation and heredity have been built up on data derived from observations and experiments on living things which pass through a sexual cycle ; and, so long as we regard bacteria as asexual organisms multiplying by simple binary fission, we must avoid the tendency to misapply formulæ which have their essential basis in the segregation, and conjugation, of a special system of reproductive cells.

Within recent years, the term " bacterial dissociation " has been frequently employed to denote a particular type of bacterial variation (see Hadley 1927 for a full and detailed review). This term, in its generally accepted sense, denotes the appearance, in a bacterial culture, of forms which differ sharply, in one or more characters, from the " normal " forms of the parent strain ; so that this strain may be said to have undergone dissociation into two types, differentiated from each other in colony-form, in antigenic structure, or in some other way. The variation must be discontinuous in type, even though there is some overlapping ; and the dissociated, or variant form, must be sufficiently stable to maintain its new characters over several generations, whether or not it eventually reverts, wholly or in part, to the normal form from which it was derived.

Those who uphold the view that bacteria pass through a complex life-cycle have naturally sought to relate the phenomenon of dissociation to the phases of this cyclical development (Hadley 1927) ; but the term may be employed in a purely descriptive sense, without any reference to the possible existence of modes of reproduction other than simple binary fission. It is, however, doubtful whether " dissociation " has any advantage over " variation " as a descriptive term ; and, since it is desirable, at the present stage, to avoid any implication in regard to the underlying mechanisms involved, it seems wiser to adhere to the older name, which serves our purpose well because of its very vagueness.

Correlated Variations.

An observed variation in any given bacterial character clearly gains in significance if it is found to be uniformly or frequently associated with a change in some other character, or characters. It is a fairly safe assumption that correlated variations of this kind indicate some relatively major change in genetic make-up. Whether the correlated character changes are different expressions of a single character factor, or are due to changes in two or more genetic factors that are themselves associated as a result of the reproductive mechanisms of the cell, we cannot tell ; but in a few instances, as in the smooth → rough variations to which we have already referred in Chapter VII, and which we shall shortly describe in more detail, we can relate many of the associated character changes to a loss of the ability to synthesize and store a particular chemical component of the bacterial cell.

Impressed Variations.

By an impressed variation is meant a variation that occurs in response to a particular environmental stimulus ; so that, by applying the stimulus, we can induce the variation at will. It should be noted that, if this term is to be applied in its strict sense, it is the genetic variation that must be impressed, not merely the character change by which this variation is recognized. We know, for instance, certain genetic variations in insects that lead to the appearance of well-defined character changes under particular environmental conditions. In the absence of these conditions the insects appear to conform to the normal type, though the genetic differences, which are themselves quite independent of these environmental factors, persist all the time. The criteria that justify the conclusion that a particular variation has been induced by a particular environmental stimulus are clearly that the application of the stimulus should regularly be followed by the appearance of the variation in question, and that the variant form should persist, over many generations at least, after the stimulus has been withdrawn. The appearance of a variant form in response to a given stimulus, followed by immediate reversion to the normal form when the stimulus is no longer applied, should be regarded as a temporary adaptation to a changed environment, rather than as a variation in the sense in which that term is used here. It is often extremely difficult, in the light of our present knowledge, to determine in which category a given change in bacterial form or function should be placed.

It will be convenient to discuss the variability of each of the more important bacterial characters in turn, indicating, where possible, whether the variation in question is correlated with others, and whether it occurs naturally or in response to any known change in environment.

Variations in Morphology.

There are innumerable accounts in the literature of changes in shape, size or structure of bacterial cells. Some of these, such as the involution forms that appear in cultures of the plague bacillus when that organism is grown on agar with a high salt-content, are clearly a direct response to an environmental stimulus, and are not inherited. In other instances it is very difficult to tell whether or not true variation has occurred. From among the many examples available, we may select the following as illustrating the kinds of variation that have significance from our present point of view.

Barber (1907), starting with a single strain of *Bact. coli*, selected and subcultured, by means of a micromanipulator, individual bacterial cells that had grown to an unusual length. In this way he was able to isolate three strains that grew in the form of long rods throughout many successive generations, showing no tendency to revert to the modal short bacillary form of the original parent strain. This would appear to afford an instance of the perpetuation of a natural heritable variation by simple selection.

We have already, in Chapter VII, noted the occurrence of the H $\longrightarrow$ O variation —the loss by a flagellated organism of the capacity to produce flagella, associated of course with a loss of motility. When this variation occurs naturally, the variant O form usually shows no tendency towards reversion. The importance of this change from the point of view of antigenic analysis led to a search for methods by which it could be induced at will. It has been found that growth on agar containing 0·1 per cent. phenol largely, or completely, suppresses the formation of flagella (Braun 1918) ; but the non-flagellated cells so obtained give rise to the normal flagellated form when subcultured on ordinary media ; so that we are here dealing not with an impressed variation but with a temporary adaptation to environment.

Another striking morphological variation is the occurrence of asporogenous variants of such spore-bearing bacilli as *B. anthracis* (Preisz 1904, Eisenberg 1912). Many of these naturally-occurring asporogenous variants have shown no tendency to revert to the normal spore-bearing form. Pasteur (1881*a*, *b*) found that the growth of *B. anthracis* at 42·5° C. for about a month resulted in a great decrease in the frequency of spore formation, as well as in a decrease in virulence ; and Roux (1890) obtained asporogenous strains of this organism by growing it in the presence of low concentrations of antiseptics. Whether the asporogenous strains obtained by these methods were examples of an impressed variation or of a temporary adaptation to environment is difficult to determine. Recent experiments by Bordet and Renaux (1930), however, strongly suggest the occurrence of an impressed variation of the genetic type. They found that certain strains of *B. anthracis*, yielding the normal, flat, filamentous colony when grown on solid media, gave rise on prolonged incubation to a characteristic type of papillary daughter colony consisting of asporogenous bacilli. By repeated subculture from these daughter colonies a completely asporogenous strain of *B. anthracis* could be isolated. When the medium on which these strains of *B. anthracis* were grown was deprived of its calcium by treatment with oxalate, spore formation was stimulated, and the papillary, asporogenous daughter colonies did not appear. When the calcium content of the medium was increased, by the addition of a little calcium chloride, the frequency of spore formation decreased and the papillary, asporogenous daughter colonies became very numerous. Repeated subcultures from these daughter colonies again produced a completely asporogenous strain (see also Bordet, P. 1930).

There would seem to be an interesting difference between the asporogenous strains of *B. anthracis* obtained by the method of Pasteur, and those obtained by the method of Bordet and Renaux. Although growth at 42·5° C. for several days leads to a decrease in the average virulence of a culture and to the appearance of various abnormal bacillary forms, many of which are non-spore-bearing, Preisz (1911) was unable to find any correlation between the capacity to form spores and virulence as tested by animal inoculation. Spore-bearing strains might be virulent or avirulent ; so might asporogenous strains. In Bordet and Renaux's experiments the actively sporogenous strains obtained by cultivation on oxalated media were highly virulent, while the asporogenous strains obtained by subculturing from the daughter colonies on media with a high calcium content were completely avirulent. It would seem, then, that loss of ability to form spores is sometimes, but not always, associated with loss of virulence. The most reasonable hypothesis would seem to be, either that asporogenous strains may be produced by different genetic mechanisms, or that the presence in a medium of excess of calcium stimulates some genetic change in addition to that on which the loss of spore-bearing capacity depends. We should not, it may be noted, on the basis of these divergent results, be justified in regarding this loss and the loss of virulence as correlated variations in the usually accepted sense.

There are many other ways in which bacterial variants may depart from the normal morphological type of the species to which they belong. A capsulated organism, such as the pneumococcus, may, for instance, give rise to a non-capsulated variant. This particular variation is, however, associated with other important changes in behaviour, and it will be more convenient to consider it in the section dealing with antigenic variation.

Variations in Biochemical Reactions.

Since the earliest days of bacteriology, differences in fermentation reactions have been extensively utilized in differentiating bacterial species or types that belong to the same genus or group, as judged by morphological or other criteria. To be of use from this point of view the fermentation reactions of any given species, or type, must, of course, be constant. This has been found to be the case, to the extent that it is usually possible to select empirically a number of substrates that a given organism, in its normal form, will consistently alter or leave unaltered. It has, however, been found that for any given bacterial species there are other substrates that are sometimes fermented, sometimes not ; from the systematic point of view we should say that those particular substrates, in relation to that particular organism, had little differential value. Similarly, some bacterial species vary more than others in their fermentative abilities ; and the differential value of fermentation tests therefore varies from one bacterial group to another.

In trying to assess the significance of the numberless recorded instances of variants that differ in their fermentation reactions from the parent strain from which they were derived, we must keep these facts constantly in mind. We may regard any given bacterial species as equipped with an armoury of enzymic mechanisms of the kind discussed in Chapter III. Some of these may perhaps readily be lost by disuse, and as readily regained if called into activity by appropriate stimuli. Others may, perhaps, be easily adapted to deal with some substrate that does not differ too greatly from that which the enzyme naturally attacks. Others, again, will depend on more constant and fundamental cell mechanisms ; these will be lost, regained, or altered only as the result of some deep-seated variation in cell structure.

It is indeed impossible to draw any hard and fast line between those changes in fermentative ability that arise as temporary adaptations to environment, and those that may be regarded as variations of a more permanent kind, though certain instances can be assigned with some confidence to one category or the other.

We have, for instance, noted in Chapter III that formic hydrogenlyase affords a typical example of an " adaptation enzyme " and, to take an illustration of a different kind, we have seen that the typhoid bacillus though normally dependent for its growth on the presence of tryptophan in the nutrient medium can be trained to synthesize this essential amino-acid from ammonium salts.

Whereas the typhoid bacillus appears to acquire the ability to synthesize tryptophan with relative ease, its normal inability to attack lactose seems to depend on a more fundamental peculiarity of cell organization, since it is extremely difficult to produce lactose-fermenting strains of this organism, even by prolonged " training " in media containing this substrate as the main available source of carbon. Twort (1907) has succeeded in producing one such strain ; and we may perhaps regard the extreme rarity with which this change has been induced as evidence that it depends on a major variation in cell organization, though it must be noted that Penfold (1910*a*) found a lactose-fermenting strain of this organism to be very unstable, with a marked tendency to revert to the non-lactose-fermenting form.

In this connection we may refer to an interesting type of variability in enzymic activity which was first demonstrated by Massini in 1907. This observer described a coliform bacillus which, on first isolation, failed to ferment lactose, and hence gave rise to colourless colonies on an agar medium, containing lactose and an indicator that gave a red colour in the presence of acid. From the third day of incubation onwards, small papillæ began to appear on these colonies, and took on a red tint, indicating that the bacilli composing them were breaking down the lactose with the formation of acid. Subcultures from these papillæ gave non-papillated red colonies, showing that the power to ferment lactose had been transmitted to the descendants of the bacilli which had originally formed the red papillæ ; and repeated subcultures showed that this power was not subsequently lost. Subcultures from the colourless parts of the original colonies, however, gave rise to colourless colonies on which red papillæ appeared after about 3 days, just as in the case of the original culture ; and repeated subcultures from the colourless portions of the colonies of successive generations gave similar results. Thus, the non-lactose-fermenting form of this organism showed a constant tendency, when grown on a lactose-containing medium, to give off lactose-fermenting variants in which the new character appeared to be permanent. To this organism Massini gave the name of *Bacterium coli mutabile*. Such a bacterial strain may, as Dobell has pointed out, be likened to the ever-sporting races of plants which have frequently been described. Massini's observations have been confirmed, in all essentials, by many subsequent workers (Burk 1908, Benecke 1909, Burri 1910, Kowalenko 1910, Baerthlein 1912*a*, *b*) ; while Benecke, and Kowalenko, added greatly to the significance of their results by starting with a culture obtained from a single bacterial cell, thus eliminating the possibility that the phenomena resulted from an original admixture of strains.

Experiments along similar lines, employing other species belonging to the same bacterial group, have been carried out by Penfold (1910*a* and *b*, 1911*a*, *b* and *c*, 1912) and Müller (1908, 1911). The observations recorded by these observers have made it clear that the behaviour of Massini's *Bact. coli mutabile* is by no means a bacteriological curiosity, but that, given a substrate appropriate to the particular species under investigation, many members of the coli-typhoid-dysentery group will adapt themselves to a particular nutrient material which they do not immediately attack by giving rise to variants endowed with the power of breaking down this particular substrate.

Thus, *Bact. typhosum* usually fails to ferment dulcitol ; but when grown on a medium containing that alcohol, it gives colonies which develop dulcitol-fermenting papillæ (Penfold 1910*a* and *b*, 1911) ; the same organism behaves similarly towards rhamnose (Müller 1911) ; while *Bact. paratyphosum B* behaves similarly towards raffinose. From Müller's account it would appear that the rhamnose-fermenting variants of *Bact. typhosum*, and the raffinose-fermenting variants of *Bact. paratyphosum B*, are non-reverting modifications of the parent strain. Apparently, also, subcultures from the non-fermenting portions of the colonies, in these two organisms, showed the same tendency to throw off fermenting variants in the form of papillæ, as was observed by Massini in the case of *Bact. coli mutabile*. Penfold's observations do not, however, confirm the absence of a tendency towards reversion. In connection with the appearance of dulcitol-fermenting forms of *Bact. typhosum*, in particular, he finds that subcultures from the dulcitol-fermenting papillæ, or from fermenting cultures in dulcitol peptone water, show a marked tendency to revert to the non-fermenting parent form during the earlier generations. If the selective process is continued through a long series of successive generations the tendency to reversion becomes less and less ; though it appears doubtful whether absolute permanency is ever attained. Penfold concludes from his results that the more rapidly a particular species acquires the ability to ferment a particular substrate, the less tendency is there for subsequent reversion ; while the longer and more rigorous is the training required to bring about the appearance of fermenting variants, the longer must that training be afterwards continued to make a lasting impression on that particular strain.

Certain experiments carried out by Penfold (1911*b, c*) and by Revis (1911, 1912) have brought to light a different type of impressed variation in bacteria. Penfold found that, by growing certain strains of *Bact. coli* on an agar medium containing sodium monochloracetate, he was able to isolate strains which retained the power of producing acid in all the usual carbohydrate media, but which had lost the power of producing gas in many of them. Moreover, he found that while the power to produce gas from sugars, or from substances giving rise to sugars on hydrolysis, was usually suppressed, the power of forming gas from alcohols, such as mannitol or dulcitol, was usually unaffected, or but slightly diminished. The only exception noted was in the case of rhamnose, a methyl pentose, which was fermented with gas formation by the variant strains.

Goodman (1908) obtained variants showing differences in fermentative ability by an essentially different technique. Starting with a particular strain of *C. diphtheriæ*, which produced a certain degree of acidity in dextrose broth, he inoculated 15 tubes of this medium from a single colony, and determined the degree of acidity attained after a few days. From the tube showing the highest acidity he inoculated 15 tubes of the same medium and a similar number from the tube showing the lowest acidity. This process he repeated through 36 successive subcultures. At the end of this series the high-acid strain produced a titratable acidity more than twice as great as the parent strain, while the low-acid strain produced no acidity at all. As would be expected this strain had also lost its power to produce acid from maltose, but it is of interest to note that its power to produce acid from dextrin was almost unaffected. These observations would appear to afford an example of the separation of a bacterial strain into a fermenting and a non-fermenting variant, by a simple process of selection without any modification of the environmental conditions ; for though it is true that the high-acid strain was in fact subjected to a high concentration of hydrogen-ions during its successive subcultures, while the low-acid strain was not, it is difficult to understand how the latter condition could lead to the production of a variant which had lost its power to ferment dextrose and maltose, while retaining its power to ferment dextrin.

Variations in Pigment Production.—It has long been recognized that different strains of a particular bacterial species, which gives rise to a coloured growth on the ordinary laboratory media, may vary widely in their power of pigment production ; and that any particular strain may lose this power as the result of repeated subculture, and may regain it for no apparent reason at some later period. In many cases it has been demonstrated that particular environmental conditions are favourable or unfavourable to pigment production, but there are many cases on record in which we cannot reasonably attribute the loss of pigmentation to such external influences.

An interesting series of observations have been recorded by Rettger and Sherrick (1911), who studied a strain of the red *Chromobacterium prodigiosum*, which had partially lost its pigment-producing capacity. By successive subcultures from growths on solid media, using in one series the most pigmented part of the growth and in another that part which showed least pigmentation, they were able to separate a strain which produced an intensely coloured growth, and a strain which gave almost colourless colonies. The segregation of these two types occurred early in the series of subcultures, and there appeared to be some tendency for the highly-pigmented variant to revert to the slightly pigmented type, though the property of intense pigmentation was successfully maintained by selection through a long series of subcultures. There was, however, no apparent tendency for the non-pigmented variant to acquire the property of pigment production. Within recent years there have been numerous records of colourless variants of species that are normally pigmented. In some cases, at least, these variants differ sharply from the parent strain in the form of colony produced, as well as in the absence of pigment, and in such instances the variation appears to have much in common with the type discussed in the succeeding section.

Antigenic Variations and the Changes in Colonial and other Characters Associated with Them : the Smooth-Rough Variation.

The Smooth → Rough (S → R) type of variation has already been referred to in our discussion of antigenic structure (pp. 191, 192), but it is of such fundamental importance in the general problem with which we are here concerned that it is necessary to consider it in considerably greater detail.

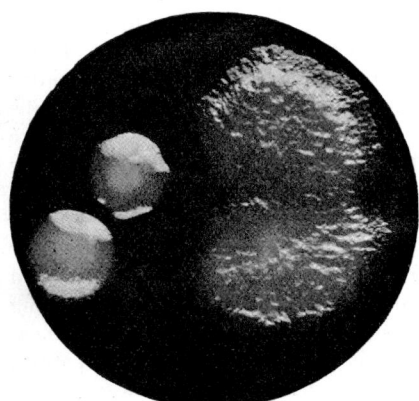

FIG. 32.—*Bact. typhosum.*
Smooth and rough colonies, 24-hours' growth on agar (× 8).

Arkwright (1920, 1921, 1924) described variants of bacteria belonging to the coli-typhoid-dysentery group which were characterized by the formation of rough or granular colonies on solid media (see Fig. 32), by giving granular growths in broth or peptone water, and in many cases by undergoing spontaneous agglutination in the presence of 0·85 per cent. sodium chloride.

These properties—colonial roughness, granular growth in fluid media, and instability in saline—are associated, in some species at least, with recognizable changes in morphology (Wilson 1930) and with an alteration in the method of cell division (Nutt 1927). If normal smooth strains of *Bact. typhi-murium* are grown in a thin layer of agar between a slide and a cover-slip and watched under the microscope, it will be noted that each cell division is soon followed by separation of the daughter cells, which slip past each other and come to lie side by side. In rough variants derived from these smooth strains, the daughter cells tend to adhere, end to end, for some time after division has occurred. Short chains are formed and angular bends develop at the junctions between adjacent cells. The tendency of rough bacilli to agglutinate spontaneously in normal saline appears to be due in many cases to the presence, at the bacterial surface, of some lipoidal substance, since extraction with alcohol at a temperature of 50–60° C. removes the salt-sensitiveness of many rough strains (White 1927). It seems probable that this alcohol-soluble constituent is present in the normal smooth form as well as in the rough variant, but in the former it does not determine the character of the cell surface.

In the organisms referred to above, and in many others, the S → R variation is associated with the loss of the polysaccharide antigen that characterizes the surface of the normal smooth form ; and, though the rough variant has a poly-saccharide constituent of its own, there seems little doubt that the change from smoothness to roughness is associated with a relative increase of lipoidal as compared with polysaccharide components at the cell surface, and a consequent change in colloidal behaviour from hydrophil to hydrophobe. There would also appear to be a laying-bare of protein constituents ; since rough variants of Salmonella bacilli, and certain other organisms, usually give a positive Millon reaction, while normal smooth strains do not (see White 1929*b*).

In the particular case of the pneumococcus the change from smoothness to roughness is associated with the loss of the characteristic capsule, and with it of the specific capsular polysaccharide that determines type-specificity. Among the antigenic components that are left are a nucleo-protein antigen and a minor poly-saccharide component that is common to all pneumococcal types (see Avery and Heidelberger 1923, Griffith 1923, Reimann 1925, Tillett, Goebel and Avery 1930).

In each of these instances the change from smoothness to roughness is also associated with a complete or partial loss of virulence, a factor which is clearly of the first importance from the point of view of the medical bacteriologist.

Again (see Chapter X) the S → R variation is usually associated with a change in sensitivity to the lytic action of various strains of bacteriophages, the filtrable viruses that propagate on, and at the expense of, the bacterial cells.

Changes that are exactly similar have been described in *Pasteurella* (de Kruif 1921, Webster 1925), many other bacilli of the coli-typhoid group (White 1926), *Staph. aureus* (Bigger *et al.* 1927), and in a large number of other species (see, for instance, Hadley 1927). We may, indeed, regard it as a variation to which most if not all bacteria are subject.

Clearly this affords an excellent example of a correlated variation. If we accepted the change in colony form as the essential criterion of the change from roughness to smoothness, we should note that the rough variant differed from the smooth form in the following characters :

(1) Roughness or granularity of colonies.

(2) Instability in saline.

(3) Loss of the antigenic component characterizing the surface of the bacterial cell in the normal smooth form, whether this component is normally present in the form of a definite capsule or not.

(4) Loss of virulence, partial or complete.

(5) Altered sensitivity to various bacteriophages.

In accepting such a list of correlated characters we are, however, met with the difficulty that the variations observed in certain bacterial species fail to fall into line.

We have already noted (p. 193) that the hæmolytic streptococci form an exception to our general rule. The colony given by the normal virulent form is finely granular, not smooth, and the virulent form that arises from it, and has lost its type-specific antigen, is smoother, not rougher, than the normal form. For this reason, Todd (1928), who first gave a detailed description of these variants, used the term " matt " to describe the normal colony form, and " glossy " to describe that of the avirulent variant. Similarly, the normal, virulent, capsulated form of the anthrax bacillus gives a flat, uneven, filamentous colony, while the avirulent, non-capsulated variant that arises from it is raised, circular and smooth (Preisz 1904, 1911, Eisenberg 1912). But clearly each of these variations is of the same essential character as those described above—loss of normal, type-specific, surface antigen associated with loss of virulence. The exact nature of the change in colony form, though it happened to give the conventional name to this particular kind of variation, is clearly of quite secondary importance. We have already noted as a point of interest that the two instances referred to above, in which the avirulent, non-specific variants happen to give smoother colonies than the normal, virulent forms, have protein instead of polysaccharide components as their dominant surface antigens when in the normal virulent state.

We can, if we wish, use some term other than Smooth → Rough to denote these particular variations, but it seems undesirable to do so, since they belong, in all essentials, to the same category. Alternatively we could abandon " smooth " and " rough " altogether as descriptive terms, and select some new name to describe the loss of the normal surface antigen that is the essential factor concerned. It seems simpler, as we have suggested in Chapter VII, to retain the terms that have now become so widespread in bacteriological literature, but to re-define them. We should then define the rough variant as differing from the normal smooth form in the following ways :

(1) Loss of the antigenic component characterizing the surface of the bacterial cell in the normal smooth form, whether this component is normally present in the form of a bacterial capsule or not.

(2) Loss of virulence, partial or complete.

(3) Altered sensitivity to various bacteriophages.

(4) A change in colony form, usually, but not always, in the direction of increased granularity or roughness.

(5) A change in the hydrophobe or hydrophile properties of the cell, usually but not always in the direction of a decreased affinity for water, and a consequently increased sensitivity to the flocculating action of electrolytes.

It must not be supposed that the S → R variation represents the limit of the loss of particular antigenic components that bacterial variants may display. An excellent example of this progressive variation by loss is provided by the detailed studies which White has carried out on members of the typhoid-paratyphoid group of bacteria (see White 1926, 1927, 1928, 1929a, b, 1931a, b, 1932, 1933). The polysaccharide components that characterize the surface of the bacterial cell in the normal smooth form are shared by *certain types*, which are further differentiated from one another by the antigenic components contained in the flagella (see Table XLI, p. 551). With these flagellar antigens we are not here concerned. When the normal smooth polysaccharide antigen is lost, the surface of the cell is dominated by antigenic components that are shared by all members of the typhoid-paratyphoid group, and by some related bacteria. These include a polysaccharide component that differs from that characterizing the normal smooth form, and another antigen, or pair of antigens, that are apparently protein in nature and have been named by White ρ_1 and ρ_2. As the result of further variation the rough or R form may lose its particular polysaccharide component and then give rise to a form, the antigenic behaviour of which is determined entirely by the components ρ_1 and ρ_2. Situated still more deeply in the bacterial cell is another antigen, which White has named T ; but it seems doubtful whether this component is ever exposed at the cell surface as the result of loss-variation.

It may be noted that the S → R variation, and still more the progressive loss-variations referred to in the preceding paragraph, are relatively irreversible. The S → R variation occurs frequently under ordinary laboratory conditions of cultivation, and may be readily induced by the methods that we shall shortly describe. The reverse change (R → S) seldom, if ever, occurs under the ordinary conditions of cultivation and it is very difficult, though not impossible, to induce it by any specific stimulus, when the original S → R change has been complete. The evidence indicates that this S → R variation is not a sudden "all-or-none" process, but a gradual or step-like change, so that intermediate SR forms appear between the typical S and the fully degraded R. In these partially degraded SR variants reversion to the normal S form may be more easily induced.

Prolonged growth of a normal smooth strain in any of the ordinary fluid media of the laboratory, followed by plating on ordinary agar, will usually result in the appearance of a proportion of rough, or partially rough, colonies. A bacteriophage that causes lysis of the normal smooth strain provides another, and very potent, method by which this change can be induced (see Chapter X). The contamination of a bacterial culture with a bacteriophage is not, however, an entirely desirable procedure for this particular purpose ; and the best method available is that introduced by Griffith (1923), who showed in the particular case of the pneumococcus, that rough variants could readily be produced by growing the normal smooth form in the presence of an antiserum acting on the type-specific capsular polysaccharide. This method, the efficacy of which has been repeatedly confirmed by other workers, appears to be of quite general applicability. We are then, in the change from smoothness to roughness, dealing with a striking example of a variation, of a very definite type, that can be induced at will by certain specific stimuli. It seems probable that bacteria afford particularly favourable material for this field of biological study.

Although the colonial changes associated with the S → R variation have been described in particular detail, it must not be supposed that they constitute the only variations in colony form to which bacteria are subject. Such is far from the case. An instance that certainly belongs to a different category is the occurrence of mucoid variants of a species that is normally non-mucoid. This type of variation is not infrequently stimulated when a non-mucoid bacterium is submitted to the action of a bacteriophage to which it is sensitive. It seems likely that most variations associated with a change in colony form will be found to be associated also with a change in the antigenic components at the bacterial surface, but not necessarily with that particular change on which the S → R variation depends.

The Transmutation of Antigenic Types.

The loss of a specific antigenic component in the S → R variation and its re-appearance when, as occasionally happens, the rough variant again gives rise to the normal smooth form, naturally raises the question as to whether it is possible for a rough strain to acquire the power of synthesizing, not the specific antigen that characterized the smooth strain from which it was derived, but some different antigen that is characteristic of another serological type belonging to the same species. Is it possible, for instance, to transmute a smooth Type I pneumococcus, *via* the non-capsulated rough variant, into a smooth Type II or Type III pneumococcus ? The problem is so important, in its biological interest and implications, that the evidence must be considered in some detail.

The pioneer experiments in this field were those of Griffith (1928). He injected mice subcutaneously with living cultures of rough avirulent pneumococci, mixed with large amounts of heat-killed smooth pneumococci belonging to the same or another type. From the animals so inoculated smooth virulent pneumococci were frequently recovered; not only was a rough strain induced to revert to the smooth type from which it was derived, but a rough variant from a Type II strain was changed to a smooth Type I strain, a rough variant from a Type I strain to a smooth Type II strain, rough variants of Type I or Type II strains to a smooth Type III strain, and so on.

These results were confirmed by Neufeld and Levinthal (1928), by Reimann (1929) and by Dawson (1930*a*, *b*). The study of this phenomenon was considerably advanced by the experiments of Dawson and Sia (1931), who were able to bring about a similar change *in vitro* by growing rough variants in a medium containing a heavy suspension of heat-killed smooth pneumococci of the type it was desired to produce. The addition of an anti-rough serum greatly assisted the transmutation, but was not an essential factor. In further experiments (Sia and Dawson 1931) it was found that the transmutation could not be induced by growing rough pneumococci in the presence of purified pneumococcal polysaccharide, and that heat-killed smooth pneumococci obtained from old autolysed cultures, or from suspensions that had been subjected to repeated freezing and thawing, were unsuitable for this purpose. These results clearly suggested (*a*) that the presence of the polysaccharide antigen belonging to a given type was not alone sufficient to induce a rough variant to manufacture that particular antigenic component, and pass on the capacity to synthesize it to subsequent generations, and (*b*) that some enzyme, readily liberated from the pneumococcal cells, destroys some substance that is an essential stimulant of this change. Alloway (1932) was able to change rough variants of Type II pneumococci to smooth Type III or smooth Type I, by growing the former on Berkefeld filtrates of extracts derived from the latter, together with normal pig serum, which contains anti-R agglutinins. In further experiments (Alloway 1933) he substituted, for the Berkefeld filtrate, a preparation obtained by dissolving pneumococci of the required type in a solution of sodium desoxycholate, and precipitating the extract so obtained with alcohol. When rough pneumococci were grown in serum broth to which a saline extract of such a precipitate was added they gave rise to smooth strains of the type from which the extract was derived.

In view of the somewhat startling nature of this phenomenon the suspicion inevitably arises that none of the procedures adopted sufficed to kill, or remove, all the living smooth pneumococci in the preparations employed to induce the transmutation of the rough variants. The sterility tests employed in the control of the experiments cited above were, however, very stringent; and it seems very unlikely that any smooth forms had in fact survived. With the proviso that this source of error is almost impossible to exclude with complete certainty, we must accept these results as provisional evidence that, under the action of a specific stimulus, a rough variant derived from one type of pneumococcus may acquire the power to synthesize the polysaccharide antigen characteristic of some other type. It should, however, be carefully noted that this is the only instance in which a transmutation of this kind has so far been demonstrated, and that there is nothing to suggest that any similar change occurs under natural conditions. All the available evidence supports the view that the different antigenic types within any species or genus of bacteria are very stable entities, in the sense that they have no natural tendency to change from one type to another, though any one of them may lose the antigenic component on which its type-specificity depends and become converted into the non-specific rough form.

Variations in Virulence or Toxigenicity.

Variations in the characters on which bacteria depend for the production of disease in man and animals are clearly of particular importance to the medical bacteriologist. It would, however, be altogether impossible in the course of a general survey to give illustrative instances of the innumerable types of variation that are associated with some change in virulence, or in toxigenicity. We may, however, note a few general principles, leaving particular instances to be dealt with in the systematic description of the different bacterial species, or in the chapters devoted to the diseases to which they give rise.

Taking *virulence* to mean the capacity for tissue invasion, and *toxigenicity* to mean the power to produce a soluble toxin (see Chapter XLI) we may note that these two characters depend on different factors, so that, where both are present in the same bacterial species, they may vary independently. A hæmolytic strepto-coccus, for instance, may lose its power of invading the tissues of a particular animal host without necessarily losing its power to produce a filtrable hæmolysin.

We have noted that a loss of virulence accompanies the S → R variation, but it must be emphasized that a loss, or a considerable decrease, of virulence may occur apart from the loss of the specific antigenic component that characterizes the normal smooth form, and that these avirulent smooth strains must be regarded as true variants, as judged by their failure to revert easily to the virulent parent type (see, for instance, Wilson 1928).

Non-toxigenic strains of *C. diphtheriæ*, *Cl. tetani* and other normally toxigenic species have been frequently described. There is no reason to suppose that this loss of toxigenicity is in any way related to the S → R variations, since there is no evidence that the production of a filtrable toxin is affected by the presence or absence of the smooth somatic antigen.

REFERENCES

Alloway, J. L. (1932) *J. exp. Med.*, **55**, 91 ; (1933) *Ibid.*, **57**, 265.
Arkwright, J. A. (1920) *J. Path. Bact.*, **23**, 358 ; (1921) *Ibid.*, **24**, 36 ; (1924) *Brit. J. exp. Path.*, **5**, 23.
Avery, O. T. and Heidelberger, M. (1923) *J. exp. Med.*, **38**, 81.
Baerthlein. (1912a) *Zbl. Bakt.*, **66**, 21 ; (1912b) *Ibid., Ref.*, **54**, 178.
Barber. (1907) *Kansas Univ. Sci. Bull.*, **4**, No. 3, 1.
Benecke, W. (1909) *Z. indukt. Abstamm. -u. VererbLehre*, **2**, 215.
Bigger, J. W., Boland, C. R., and O'Meara, R. A. Q. (1927) *J. Path. Bact.*, **30**, 261.
Bordet, J. and Renaux, E. (1930) *Ann. Inst. Pasteur*, **45**, 1.
Bordet, P. (1930) *Ann. Inst. Pasteur*, **45**, 26.
Braun, H. (1918) *Berl. klin. Wschr.*, **55**, 637.
Burk, A. (1908) *Arch. Hyg.*, **65**, 325.
Burri, R. (1910) *Zbl. Bakt.*, IIte Abt., **28**, 321.
Dawson, M. H. (1930a) *J. exp. Med.*, **51**, 99 ; (1930b) *Ibid.*, **51**, 123.
Dawson, M. H. and Sia, R. H. P. (1931) *J. exp. Med.*, **54**, 681.
Dobell, C. (1913) *J. Genetics*, **2**, 325.
Eisenberg, P. (1912) *Zbl. Bakt.*, **63**, 305.
Goodman, H. M. (1908) *J. infect. Dis.*, **5**, 421.
Griffith, F. (1923) *Min. Hlth., Rep. publ. Hlth. med. Subj.*, 18 ; (1928) *J. Hyg., Camb.*, **27**, 113.
Hadley, P. (1927) *J. infect. Dis.*, **40**, 1.
Kowalenko, A. (1910) *Z. Hyg. InfektKr.*, **66**, 277.
Kruif, P. de. (1921) *J. exp. Med.*, **33**, 773.
Massini, R. (1907) *Arch. Hyg.*, **61**, 250.
Müller, R. (1908) *Zbl. Bakt. Ref.*, **42**, Beitr., 57 ; (1911) *Zbl. Bakt.*, **58**, 97.
Neufeld, F. and Levinthal, W. (1928) *Z. ImmunForsch.*, **55**, 324.

NUTT, M. M. (1927) *J. Hyg., Camb.*, **26**, 44.
PASTEUR, L. (1881*a*) *C. R. Acad. Sci.*, **92**, 429 ; (1881*b*) *Ibid.*, **92**, 666.
PENFOLD, W. J. (1910*a*) *Brit. med. J.*, ii. 1672 ; (1910*b*) *J. Path. Bact.*, **14**, 406 ; (1911*a*)
    J. Hyg., Camb., **11**, 30 ; (1911*b*) *Proc. roy. Soc. Med.*, **4** (Path. Sec.), 97 ; (1911*c*) *J. Hyg.*,
    Camb., **11**, 487 ; (1912) *Ibid.*, **12**, 195.
PREISZ, H. (1904) *Zbl. Bakt.*, **35**, 280, 416, 537, 657 ; (1911) *Ibid.*, **58**, 510.
REIMANN, H. A. (1925) *J. exp. Med.*, **41**, 587 ; (1929) *Ibid.*, **49**, 237.
RETTGER, L. F. and SHERRICK, J. L. (1911) *J. med. Res.*, **24**, 265.
REVIS, C. (1911) *Zbl. Bakt.*, IIte Abt., **31**, 1 ; (1912) *Proc. roy. Soc.*, B, **85**, 192.
ROUX, E. (1890) *Ann. Inst. Pasteur*, **4**, 25.
SIA, R. H. P. and DAWSON, M. H. (1931) *J. exp. Med.*, **54**, 701.
TILLETT, W. S., GOEBEL, W. F., and AVERY, O. T. (1930) *J. exp. Med.*, **52**, 895.
TODD, E. W. (1928) *Brit. J. exp. Path.*, **9**, 1.
TWORT, F. W. (1907) *Proc. roy. Soc.*, B, **79**, 329.
WEBSTER, L. T. (1925) *J. exp. Med.*, **41**, 571.
WHITE, P. B. (1926) *Spec. Rep. Ser. med. Res. Coun., Lond.*, No. 103 ; (1927) *J. Path. Bact.*
    30, 113 ; (1928) *Ibid.*, **31**, 423 ; (1929*a*) *Ibid.*, **32**, 85 ; (1929*b*) *Med. Res. Coun.* "System
    of Bacteriology," **4**, 86 ; (1931*a*) *J. Path. Bact.*, **34**, 23 ; (1931*b*) *Ibid.*, **34**, 325 ; (1932),
    Ibid., **35**, 77 ; (1933) *Ibid.*, **36**, 65.
WILSON, G. S. (1928) *J. Hyg., Camb.*, **28**, 295 ; (1930) *Ibid.*, **30**, 40.

CHAPTER IX

THE CLASSIFICATION OF BACTERIA

As has been indicated in preceding chapters, it is the behaviour rather than the nature of bacteria which has interested the bacteriologist. It is not surprising, therefore, to find that the field of systematic bacteriology has been very largely neglected. The study of bacteria has indeed never passed through that phase of detailed and accurate description, which has formed so important a part of the foundations of botany and zoology.

This neglect is not entirely attributable to lack of interest. In dealing with the morphology of bacteria, we have pointed out the difficulties which are inherent in any study of bacterial structure. As a result of these difficulties, the bacteriologist has come to rely very largely on physiological characters in the differentiation of bacterial groups, and the study of the antigen-antibody reactions has led to the elaboration of a technique which is peculiar to this field of biology. In addition to these methods of studying bacteria in artificial culture, the medical bacteriologist, who is primarily interested in the rôle of micro-organisms in disease, has naturally developed the habit of testing the pathogenicity of the strains he has isolated by the experimental infection of laboratory animals.

Employing a combination of these methods, the bacteriologist has learned by experience to identify a large number of well-differentiated and stable bacterial types; and to these he has given names. The criteria that have determined the classification and nomenclature of bacteria are not, therefore, such as would be accepted by the systematist in any other branch of biology; and the bacteriologist himself has not in general troubled overmuch as to the validity of a system which has developed rather as the result of luck than of cunning.

The inconvenience of a total absence of classification, reflected in a chaotic nomenclature, has, however, been so great, that various attempts have been made to introduce some sort of order into the bacteriological household. We cannot here enter into any historical description of the various systems which have been propounded; except to note that a comparison of those suggested by Zopf (1885), Migula (1894), Kruse (1896), Lehmann and Neumann (1896) and Orla-Jensen (1909) will reveal how widely the lines of cleavage may differ, when a large biological group is viewed from different angles. Those who desire more detailed information on this aspect of the question are referred to the two reports of the Committee of the Society of American Bacteriologists on characterization and classification of bacterial types (1917, 1920); the monograph by Buchanan (1925); the manual by Bergey and his colleagues (1934); and to a paper by Buchanan and others (1928), which sets out in diagrammatic form the classifications suggested by Migula, Orla-Jensen, Buchanan, Castellani and Chalmers (1920), Lehmann and Neumann, Bergey and his colleagues, and the earlier Committee of the Society of American Bacteriologists which reported in 1917 and 1920.

As a result of the activities of the American Society, the whole question of bacteriological classification and nomenclature has been reopened during recent years. It cannot be said that the system propounded by the American Committee (1920) has met with the entire approval of bacteriologists in general ; while systematists in other biological sciences would probably question the validity of the whole basis upon which the classification is founded. There does not, however, appear to be any compelling reason for the bacteriologist to abandon, for purposes of classification, the criteria on which he has come to rely for purposes of identification ; and few of us would be willing to admit that our systematic grouping must have a purely morphological basis, simply because structural differences have been found to afford adequate classificatory criteria in the case of more highly differentiated plants and animals. While admitting that morphological differences must be given their full weight, and accepting them as the natural basis for our primary subdivisions, we might argue that our differential criteria, depending as they do on differences in chemical structure rather than on the gross architecture of the cell, come nearer to the heart of the matter than do those adopted by botanists or zoologists.

We may note that our assessment of the significance of any particular differential criterion rests largely on a statistical basis. Our first concern is to determine the variability of a given character within a particular bacterial strain. If it is constant, it may be of value for purposes of classification. If it varies, but in such a way that the variation is itself characteristic, it may still have classificatory value. If it varies in an entirely random and unpredictable fashion, it cannot be used for purposes of identification or classification. Once it has been shown that a given character is of service in identifying a particular strain, we can examine the distribution of this character among a sample of strains which possess other characters in common. In this way we gradually obtain a picture of the frequency distribution of many different characters among large samples of strains. The significance we attach to any particular character then depends in the main on its association with other characters. If we find that a particular group of strains resemble each other in several different characters, and differ in these same characters from all other groups, we feel justified in regarding the group as a biological entity and in attaching an added significance to each of the associated characters, as a differential criterion within the larger group of which our homogeneous group forms a part. If, on the other hand, one particular character varies independently of all other characters, within a group which has many other characters in common, we shall not in general attach the same significance to it, from the point of view of classification. In assessing characters in this way, we shall not of course accord all characters equal rank, *a priori*, and limit our consideration entirely to their frequency distribution and degree of association. The more striking structural differences will clearly be given most weight ; and we shall differentiate such groups as the spore-bearing bacilli, the non-sporing bacilli, the cocci, and many other groups or sub-groups, on morphological grounds alone. Similarly such differences in staining reaction as acid-fastness or its absence, or Gram-positiveness or negativeness, have as the result of experience been accorded a prominent place as differential criteria. It is in the subdivision of these large groups, based on differences in physiological behaviour, antigenic structure, pathogenicity, and ecology in general, that the principles outlined above come into play, because we cannot, on *a priori* grounds, form any hierarchy of such characters. We cannot, for instance, say that the ability or inability to ferment a particular carbohydrate is, on general biological grounds, a more important differential character than the possession of a particular antigenic structure, or the power of producing a characteristic toxin.

Our main trouble is that we have no rules, and the few conventions which take their place are honoured as much in the breach as in the observance. It seems quite clear that nothing but some form of international agreement with regard to classification and nomenclature will put an end to the existing state of chaos. Whether it will be possible to adopt, in their entirety, the rules of botanical nomenclature, is a problem which only the future can decide. There are obvious advantages in adopting the Linnæan binomial nomenclature, which has served the purposes of zoologists and botanists in general ; but it is doubtful whether the bacteriologist will not be forced to make frequent use of additional terms, designating races, varieties, or types. The frequent use of trinomial or quadrinomial names is, however, a cumbersome procedure ; and it may be found necessary to regularize the use of letters or numbers, which is a current convention in bacteriological terminology. The Linnæan admonition, "*varietates levissimas non curat botanicus*," may serve the turn of the systematic botanist, and the bacteriologist would probably be well advised to bow to it in naming those groups which he intends to regard as genera or species ; but he cannot ignore small differences, and he needs a vocabulary which will allow him to talk or write about the bacterial types which interest him.

This leads to the consideration of another difficulty, which has grown acute in the last ten years, and will clearly increase rather than diminish in the absence of some agreed international ruling. There is no agreement at all as to the end from which a bacteriological classification should start. Are we to begin by an intensive study of one or another relatively small group, seeking to differentiate within it all the identifiable and stable types, and giving names to these ? Or are we first to differentiate the larger groups, and only when these have been adequately demarcated seek to divide them into their constituent species, varieties or types ? As a method of mapping out the ground either approach will serve ; but they lead, unfortunately, to quite incompatible nomenclatures. The method of the intensive study of a small, or relatively small, bacterial group has been adopted by several groups of workers within recent years, and has resulted in such conspicuously successful systematic descriptions as those of the Salmonella group (see Chapter XXVII), or of the hæmolytic streptococci and the pneumococci (see Chapter XXIII). In each of these instances the final differentiation has depended, entirely or almost entirely, on an analysis of antigenic structure. The workers who have been engaged in the study of the Salmonella group have, however, adopted, at the extreme end of the scale, differentiable types listed as *Salmonella typhi*, *Salmonella dublin*, *Salmonella eastbourne*, and so on. Those who have studied the pneumococci and hæmolytic streptococci have, we think more wisely, labelled their recognizable types with numbers, or letters, or letters and numbers combined ; though, except in the case of the pneumococci, there is as yet no general agreement as to the lettering or the numbering.

We do not, ourselves, think that the agreed definition of species and genera, which has still to be achieved, should be prejudged by the results obtained by antigenic analysis. We have not, therefore, adopted *Salmonella* as a generic name, but have retained this group in the genus *Bacterium*, though in doing so we are ignoring a convention that is becoming extremely common in the literature.

While remaining convinced that, in naming genera and species, weight should be given to other criteria in addition to antigenic relationships, we should wish to record our entire agreement with those who hold that antigenic analysis affords the best available method of differentiating the ultimate types or varieties into which bacteria are divided, that the antigenic similarities and differences provide a most valuable clue to the natural relationships of these types and the lines along which they have probably been evolved, and that each type or variety so differentiated should be given a distinctive label. We may perhaps add that this distinctive labelling is of particular importance to the medical bacteriologist, since it is the antigenic make-up of a bacterium that determines all its immunological reactions, in the body as well as in the test tube. We must, however, be consistent. We cannot use letters and numbers for one set of labels, specific names for another ; and we have given our reasons for preferring the letters and numbers.

Apart from the increasing importance of antigenic analysis in the classification of bacteria, it may be noted that there is a growing tendency to enlarge the range of criteria employed in the differentiation of types and species, and to rely less exclusively on the somewhat crude series of fermentation reactions that played so large a part in earlier systematic studies. The reaction of an organism to variations in the partial pressure of carbon dioxide, its resistance to various dyes, its tolerance of a high concentration of hydrogen-ions, its more detailed nutritional requirements, all these and many other criteria are being increasingly employed in defining bacterial groups, and in tracing the relation of one group to another.

One essential character of any systematic nomenclature is stability ; and those who have to read or write about bacteria at the present time are in a singularly unhappy position in this respect. When the same organism is masquerading as *Bacillus typhosus*, *Bacterium typhosum*, *Salmonella typhi* or *Eberthella typhi*, while another answers with equal readiness to the names of *Micrococcus melitensis*, *Bacillus melitensis*, *Brucella melitensis* or *Alkaligenes melitensis*, all printed in italics with a capital letter to the generic name, the student, or even the more practised reader of bacteriological literature, may be excused some degree of confusion.

It would, perhaps, be simplest to await some agreed solution of our difficulties, and employ the moribund nomenclature which was current before the War, until some better system with authoritative support is offered in its stead. There are, however, very real disadvantages in such a course. It is desirable, especially from the student's point of view, that a name should be as informative as possible. The scientific name of a living organism should tell us as much as possible about that organism itself, and about its relation to other organisms with different names. The latter problem is the particular concern of the systematist ; and it may be many years before we know enough about the relationship of bacteria to evolve a system of classification in which those relationships can be adequately expressed. It is, however, possible to allot names to bacterial groups, which will give us a considerable amount of information with regard to the species, races, or types, of which they are constituted. In this respect the conventional bacteriological nomenclature of the past fifty years has been a conspicuous failure. Nothing could be less informative than the name *Bacillus*, when that name is applied to any rod-shaped bacterium ; and the student, who has memorized the names *B. typhosus, B. pestis, B. anthracis,* and *B. tuberculosis,* has obtained very poor value for his effort. If, adopting the nomenclature of the American Committee's Report, he memorizes the names *Bacterium typhosum, Pasteurella pestis, Bacillus anthracis,* and *Mycobacterium tuberculosis,* he will, when he has studied the groups concerned, have a very useful picture of each of these organisms as typifying a separate genus ; and the fact that some other organism is called *Bacterium enteritidis,* or *Pasteurella aviseptica,* or *Bacillus subtilis,* or *Mycobacterium phlei,* will convey to him some knowledge of its salient characteristics.

We are, ourselves, convinced that the correct approach to bacteriology, irrespective of the particular field in which the student intends ultimately to work, is to gain some knowledge of bacteria as living things ; and such knowledge can most easily be obtained by grouping like forms together for the purposes of study, comparing them with other groups, and noting the differences and resemblances. For these groups we need names, even if they must, for the moment, be regarded as provisional.

This requirement can be fulfilled by adopting one of the several systems of classification and nomenclature, which have been advocated within recent years. This is quite definitely a policy adopted *faute de mieux.* None of these systems has received any official or international sanction. As Buchanan, Breed and Rettger (1928) point out, neither of the systems drawn up by committees appointed by the Society of American Bacteriologists has been officially approved by that Society. The selection of one of the existing systems therefore remains a matter of personal choice ; and, whichever system is selected, there is no reason to suppose that it, or the nomenclature based upon it, will receive international sanction without modification.

The terms " genus " and " species," as applied to bacteria, seem to us to defy definition, except as designations for two convenient groupings, of which the genus is the larger including group, and the species the smaller included group. For this reason, and because of the absence of any form of international agreement, we doubt the usefulness, at the present time, of naming orders, families, subfamilies, and tribes. Nor do we feel that the time is ripe for the creation of large numbers of genera, or for the erection of an inelastic system into which all known varieties of bacteria are to be forced, each with its appropriate label.

It appears to us that the classification advocated in the final report of the first American Committee (1920) offers a carefully constructed scheme on which a useful nomenclature can be based, and that it has been designed on general lines which most bacteriologists would regard as sound ; moreover, the Committee themselves make no claim to finality, and are at pains to indicate the tentative nature of some of the groupings they suggest.

We have therefore adopted the system of nomenclature set out in the final report of the first American Committee (Winslow *et al.* 1920), with a few minor modifications. We have merged the genus *Diplococcus* in the genus *Streptococcus,* since it appears to us that the pneumococcus should be included in the latter group. We have adopted the genus *Brucella,* which has already received unofficial recognition from many bacteriologists ; since the group which contains the bacillus of Malta fever, and the bacillus of bovine abortion, appears to have as good a title to generic rank as the group which contains the plague bacillus and the bacilli causing hæmorrhagic septicæmia in animals, though we frankly admit that the content of the *Brucella* group is extremely difficult to define. We have combined the genera *Erythrobacillus* and *Chromobacterium* under the latter name, since it does not appear to us that the differences in morphology, physiological reactions or habitat between *Erythro. prodigiosus* and such species as *Chr. indicum ruber* merit separate generic rank. The final classification of these small saprophytic, chromogenic bacilli must await a more detailed study of the group; and it seems doubtful whether pigment formation should be accepted as a generic character. We have retained the genus *Erwinia* in the classification appended to this chapter; but we have not given any detailed description of this group. It seems doubtful whether the plant-pathogens should be segregated in this way, unless the associated characters are sufficiently distinctive as compared with those of other genera, and sufficiently homogeneous within the group, to justify the creation of one inclusive genus on general biological grounds.

We append to this chapter a diagrammatic representation (Fig. 33) of the classification given in the final report of the first American Committee (see Buchanan *et al.* 1928) with the modifications referred to above, noting that we are concerned with the list of genera, rather than with the grouping of these genera into tribes, families or orders.

We also include in this chapter a summarized description of the characters of each genus, taken from the final report of the first American Committee (Winslow *et al.* 1920), and emended in some cases in the light of more recent studies of the various groups.

In the remainder of this book we shall employ these generic names, when referring to any species which appears to be clearly assignable to one of the listed genera. In general, bacteria which can be so assigned are already provided with a specific name, which is not in dispute. Such binomial names will be printed in italics, the generic name being given a capital letter, and used in an abbreviated form.

Other well-recognized designations for various bacteria will, of course, be freely used, with the recognition that we are using the common name for a particular organism, instead of its scientific name—a practice universally followed in biological science. Such common names will be printed in ordinary type, and without a capital initial letter. For instance, the scientific name of the organism which causes tuberculosis will be written as: *Mycobacterium tuberculosis*, or more shortly as *Myco. tuberculosis*, but it will be generally referred to as the tubercle bacillus; similarly with *Corynebacterium diphtheriæ*, *C. diphtheriæ*, or the diphtheria bacillus; *Pasteurella pestis*, *Past. pestis* and the plague bacillus; *Brucella abortus*, *Br. abortus* or the bacillus of bovine abortion; *Neisseria gonorrhœæ*, *N. gonorrhœæ* or the gonococcus.

In this system two important names fill a dual rôle; and their meaning in any given case has to be defined by the use of appropriate type; *Bacillus* means an organism possessing the characters of that particular genus, but bacillus means any rod-shaped organism; *Bacterium* means an organism possessing the characters of that particular genus, but bacterium means any organism whatever which comes within the general class with which we are concerned, the scientific name of that class being *Schizomycetes*.

There remain a considerable number of bacteria, which cannot yet be accorded a scientific name: in some cases because the available descriptions are not sufficiently detailed to allow us to determine their systematic relationships;

in others, because the characters, as described, do not seem to warrant the inclusion of the organism in any of the recognized genera. No useful purpose would be served by suggesting new generic names, which would have no validity. As we have emphasized above, any system of nomenclature employed at the present time must be a temporary expedient, pending some form of international agreement, and it appears to us that our aim should be to use those names which seem most likely to be retained when such agreement is reached. When dealing with those organisms which, at present, defy classification, we have therefore frankly abandoned the use of a scientific name, with its conventional italics and capital letter, and have employed the most convenient designation available. It is unfortunate that many of these organisms have been given the generic name of *Bacillus*. As this name is reserved for the spore-bearing aerobes, it cannot be used, in the conventional form, for bacteria which do not in fact belong to that genus. We have, in general, adopted the expedient of referring to *Bacillus x* as " the x bacillus." In describing bacteria whose title to specific rank appears to us doubtful, though their generic position is not in doubt, we have in some cases employed a similar convention.

We would here add a protest against the habit, which is unfortunately frequent among medical bacteriologists, of coining new names for bacterial strains which they have isolated, without appending an adequate description of the organism or determining whether the organism in question corresponds with one that has already been described. This laxity has in the past led to much confusion ; and it would be greatly to the advantage of bacteriology in general if editorial authority could be exerted to prevent the publication in medical or scientific journals of descriptions of newly-named bacterial species, where these requirements are not properly fulfilled. The existence in this country, and in America, of adequate collections of type cultures provides the material for such comparisons as may be necessary.

Fig. 33 provides a summary, in chart form, of the American classification, with the minor modifications referred to above.

The following are the genera included in this classification, given in the order in which they are listed in the chart:

Actinobacillus.—Gram-negative, non-acid-fast rods, sometimes occurring in long chains or in unjointed filaments. In lesions in the animal body no mycelium is formed, but at the periphery finger-shaped cells or clubs may be visible.

Type species. *Actinobacillus lignieresi.*

Leptotrichia.—Thick, long, straight or curved threads, unbranched, frequently clubbed at one end and tapering to the other. Gram-positive when young. Threads fragment into short, thick rods. Anaerobic or facultative. Non-motile. Filaments sometimes granular. No aerial hyphæ or conidia. Parasites or facultative parasites.

Type species. *Leptotrichia buccalis.*

Actinomyces.—Organisms growing in the form of a much-branched mycelium, which may break up into segments or produce " spores." Aerial mycelium often formed under suitable conditions. Mainly aerobic, but may be microaerophilic or even anaerobic. Usually saprophytic, but some species are parasitic on plants or animals, and may give rise to disease. In animal body organisms are frequently arranged in colonies composed of radiating threads with clubbed ends. Non-motile. Some species are acid-fast.

Type species. *Actinomyces bovis* Harz.

Erysipelothrix.—Rod-shaped organisms with a tendency to the formation of long filaments, which may show branching.   The filaments may also thicken and show characteristic granules.   No spores.   Non-motile.   Gram-positive.   Slight fermentative activities.   Microaerophilic.   Usually parasitic.

Type species.   *Erysipelothrix rhusiopathiæ.*

Mycobacterium.—Slender rods which are stained with difficulty ; but, when once stained, are acid-fast.   Cells are sometimes swollen, clavate, cuneate, or even branched. Non-motile.   Gram-positive.   No endospores.   Growth on media slow.   Aerobic. Several species are pathogenic to animals.

Type species.   *Mycobacterium tuberculosis.*

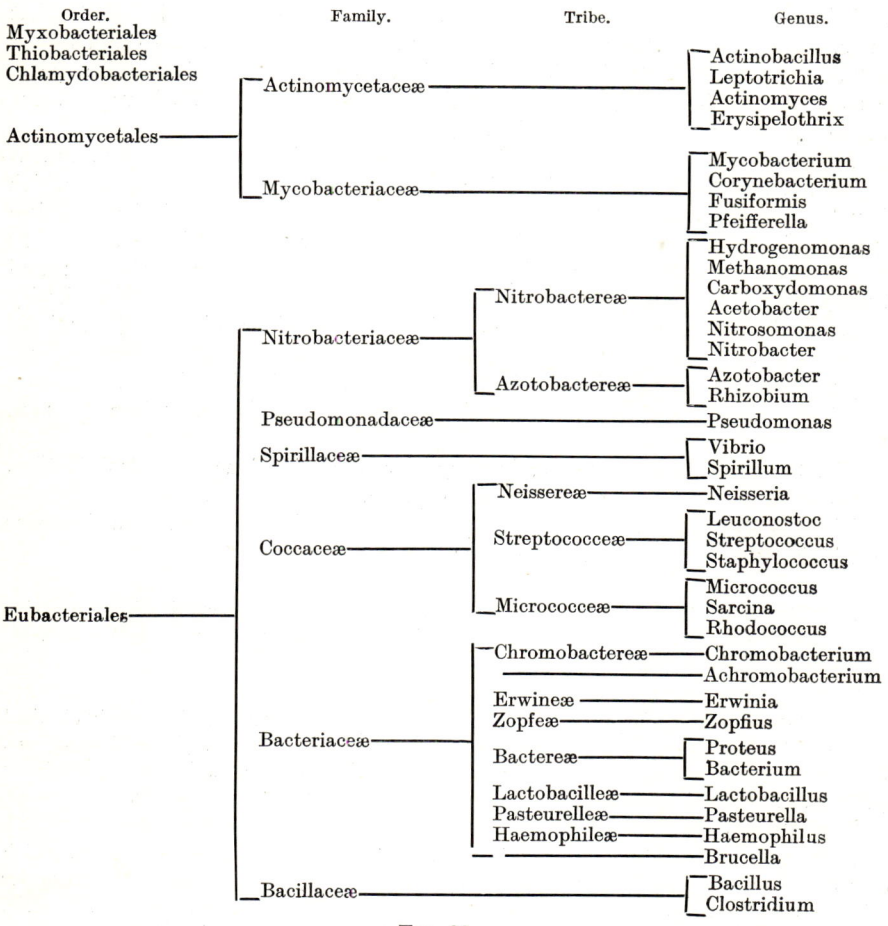

SCHIZOMYCETES.

Fig. 33.

Corynebacterium.—Gram-positive rod-like forms, arranged usually in a palisade.   Not acid-fast.   Often with club-shaped swellings at the poles, generally with irregularly staining segments or granules.   Non-motile, non-sporing.   Growing aerobically or under microaerophilic conditions, but often capable of anaerobic cultivation. Never forming gas in carbohydrate media, in which they may or may not produce acidity. They may or may not liquefy gelatin or serum. Some species produce a powerful exotoxin.

Type species. *Corynebacterium diphtheriæ.*

Fusiformis.—Obligate parasites. Anaerobic or microaerophilic. Cells frequently elongate and fusiform, staining somewhat unevenly. Filaments sometimes formed. Non-branching. Non-motile. No spores. Reaction to Gram's stain variable. Growth in laboratory media feeble.

Type species. *Fusiformis termitidis.*

Pfeifferella.—Small, slender, non-motile, Gram-negative rods, often staining irregularly, and sometimes forming threads or showing a tendency towards branching. Growth on all media is rather slow ; gelatin may be slowly liquefied ; fermentation of carbohydrates is very weak ; characteristic brown honey-like growth on potato.

Type species. *Pfeifferella mallei.*

Hydrogenomonas.—Monotrichate short rods capable of growing in the absence of organic matter, and securing growth energy by the oxidation of hydrogen (forming water).

Type species. *Hydrogenomonas pantotropha.*

Methanomonas.—Monotrichate short rods capable of growing in the absence of organic matter and securing growth energy by the oxidation of methane (forming carbon dioxide and water).

Type species. *Methanomonas methanica.*

Carboxydomonas.—Rod-shaped cells capable of securing growth energy by the oxidation of carbon monoxide (forming carbon dioxide).

Type species. *Carboxydomonas oligocarbophila.*

Acetobacter.—Cells rod-shaped, frequently in chains, non-motile. Cells grow usually on the surface of alcoholic solutions as obligate aerobes, securing growth energy by the oxidation of alcohol to acetic acid. Also capable of utilizing certain other carbonaceous compounds, as sugar and acetic acid. Elongated, filamentous, club-shaped, swollen and even branched cells may occur as involution forms.

Type species. *Acetobacter aceti.*

Nitrosomonas.—Cells rod-shaped or spherical ; motile or non-motile ; motile forms possess polar flagella. Capable of securing growth energy by the oxidation of ammonia to nitrites. Growth on media containing organic substances scanty or absent.

Type species. *Nitrosomonas europœa.*

Nitrobacter.—Cells rod-shaped, non-motile, not growing readily on organic media or in the presence of ammonia. Cells capable of securing growth energy by the oxidation of nitrites to nitrates.

Type species. *Nitrobacter winogradskyi.*

Azotobacter.—Relatively large rods, or even cocci, sometimes almost yeast-like in appearance, dependent primarily for growth energy upon the oxidation of carbohydrates. Motile or non-motile ; motile forms possess a tuft of polar flagella. Obligate aerobes ; usually growing in a film upon the surface of the culture medium. Capable of fixing atmospheric nitrogen when grown in solutions containing carbohydrates and deficient in combined nitrogen.

Type species. *Azotobacter chroococcum.*

Rhizobium.—Minute rods, motile when young. Specialized forms abundant and characteristic when grown under suitable conditions. Obligate aerobes, capable of fixing atmospheric nitrogen when grown in the presence of carbohydrates and in the absence of compounds of nitrogen. Produce nodules upon the roots of leguminous plants.

Type species. *Rhizobium leguminosarum.*

Pseudomonas.—Rod-shaped organisms, usually motile, by means of polar flagella. Generally Gram-negative. Non-sporing. Aerobic; some species are facultative anaerobes. Frequently produce a water-soluble pigment, which is yellow, green, blue, purple, or brown in colour, and which diffuses through the medium. Some species form a non-diffusible yellow pigment, and some species are photogenic. Fermentation of carbohydrates as a rule not active. Frequently gelatin-liquefiers, and active ammonifiers. Common in soil and water. Many yellow species are plant parasites.

Type species. *Pseudomonas pyocyanea.*

(On grounds of priority the American Committee recommend that this organism should be called *Ps. aeruginosa.*)

Vibrio.—Short, curved, rigid rods, arranged singly or united into S-forms or spirals. Motile by a single polar flagellum, which is usually relatively short. (Some species may have two or three polar flagella.) Non-sporing. Usually Gram-negative. Aerobic and facultatively anaerobic. Many species liquefy gelatin and are active ammonifiers. Commonly found in water. Most species are saprophytic; a few are pathogenic to man.

Type species. *Vibrio choleræ.*

Spirillum.—Rigid rods of spiral form, varying considerably in the number, length, and breadth of the spirals. Usually motile by means of a tuft of polar flagella (5 to 20). The flagella occur at one or both poles; their number varies greatly, and is difficult to determine, since in stained preparations several are often united into a common strand. Generally Gram-positive. Some species form a reddish-yellow or greenish-yellow pigment. Found in water or putrid infusions.

Type species. *Spirillum undula.*

Neisseria.—Gram-negative cocci, usually arranged in pairs. Strict parasites, often growing poorly on ordinary media, but growing well on serum media. Frequently pathogenic.

Type species. *Neisseria gonorrhœæ.*

Leuconostoc.—Spherical or ovoid cells, arranged in pairs and chains; the cocci are surrounded by a gelatinous envelope, which unites them into zooglœal masses. Usually Gram-positive, but decolorize easily. Saprophytes, usually growing in cane-sugar solutions.

Type species. *Leuconostoc mesenteroides.*

Streptococcus.—Spherical or ovoid cells, arranged in short or long chains, or in pairs. Non-sporing, usually non-motile. Most species Gram-positive. Some species form capsules. Growth tends to be relatively slight on artificial media, and some species grow poorly in the absence of added native protein. Several species produce characteristic changes in media containing blood. Various carbohydrates are fermented with the production of acid. Most species fail to liquefy gelatin. Most species are aerobic and facultatively anaerobic; some are anaerobic. Many species are normally parasitic on man or animals. Some species are highly pathogenic, and some produce soluble toxins.

Type species. *Streptococcus pyogenes.*

Staphylococcus.—Spherical or ovoid, non-motile, Gram-positive cells, arranged in grape-like clusters on solid media, and in pairs, small groups, or short chains in liquid media. On agar the growth is of a golden, white, or yellow colour. Great variation in biochemical activities, hæmolytic power, and pathogenicity. Actual or potential parasites.

Type species. *Staphylococcus aureus.*

Micrococcus.—Spherical or ovoid cells, non-motile, arranged in pairs, tetrads, or groups, but not in grape-like clusters or chains. Generally Gram-positive. Grow freely on ordinary media. Sometimes produce a yellowish pigment. Gelatin liquefaction is not constant, and is usually slow. Fermentative activities weak. Usually non-pathogenic to man or animals.

Type species. *Micrococcus luteus.*

Sarcina.—Has same characters as *Micrococcus*, except that cell division occurs, under favourable conditions, in three planes, so that cubical packets are formed.

Type species. *Sarcina ventriculi.*

Rhodococcus.—Spherical or ovoid cells occurring in groups or regular packets. Usually Gram-positive, but are easily decolorized. Growth on agar abundant with formation of red pigment. Weak fermentative powers. Gelatin rarely liquefied. Nitrates generally reduced. Saprophytes.

Type species. *Rhodococcus rhodochrous.*

Chromobacterium.—Small, non-sporing, aerobic rods, usually motile and usually Gram-negative, producing a yellow, red, or violet pigment, which is generally insoluble in water. Saprophytic; commonly found in water or soil.

Type species. *Chromobacterium violaceum.*

Achromobacterium.—Motile or non-motile, Gram-negative rods, usually small to medium in size, forming no pigment on agar, and varying in their fermentative ability. Optimum temperature for growth about 25° C; little or no growth at 37° C. Saprophytic; commonly found in water, soil, and milk.

Erwinia.—Plant pathogens. Growth usually whitish, often slimy. Indole generally not produced. Acid usually formed in certain carbohydrate media, but as a rule no gas.

Type species. *Erwinia amylovora.*

Zopfius.—Long rods, occurring in evenly curved chains. Gram-positive. Motile. Spider-web growth on solid media. Facultative anaerobes. Carbohydrates and gelatin not attacked; hydrogen sulphide not formed.

Type species. *Zopfius zopfii.*

Proteus.—Highly pleomorphic rods, filaments and curved cells being common in young cultures. Gram-negative. Actively motile. Characteristic spreading growth on moist media. Liquefy gelatin rapidly, and often produce vigorous decomposition of proteins. Ferment glucose and usually sucrose, but not mannitol or lactose, with fermentation of acid and gas.

Type species. *Proteus vulgaris.*

Bacterium.—Gram-negative, non-sporing rods : often motile, with peritrichate flagella : some species capsulated. Easily cultivable on ordinary laboratory media. Aerobic and facultatively anaerobic. All species ferment dextrose with the formation of acid, or acid and gas. Many species are active fermenters of a wide range of carbohydrates and allied substrates. Typically intestinal parasites of man and animals, although some species may occur in other parts of the body, on plants, or in the soil. Many species are pathogenic.

Type species. *Bacterium coli.*

Lactobacillus.—Rods, often long and slender. Gram-positive; non-motile; without endospores. Usually produce acid from carbohydrates, as a rule lactic. Some species grow best at 40° to 44° C., and some species are microaerophilic. Surface growth on media poor.

Type species. *Lactobacillus caucasicus.*

Pasteurella.—Small, Gram-negative, ovoid bacilli, showing bipolar staining. Aerobic and facultatively anaerobic. Powers of carbohydrate fermentation relatively slight; no gas produced. Gelatin not liquefied. Parasites in man and animals, producing characteristic infections.

Type species. *Pasteurella aviseptica.*

Hæmophilus.—Minute rods, sometimes almost coccal, sometimes thread-like; may be highly pleomorphic. Non-motile; non-sporing; Gram-negative; not acid-fast. Dependent for their growth on the presence of some factor, which is supplied by blood pigments, and by certain plant tissues. Some species require for their growth a second factor, which is present in blood, in most plant tissues, in yeast, or in the cells of other bacterial species. All known species appear to be obligatory parasites ; some are pathogenic.

Type species. *Hœmophilus influenzœ*.

Brucella.—Small, non-sporing, Gram-negative cocco-bacilli. Usually non-motile. Grow rather poorly on ordinary media or may require special media. Aerobic ; no growth under strict anaerobic conditions. Growth often improved by CO_2. Fail to ferment carbohydrates. Usually tend to produce alkali in litmus milk, and a brown pigmentation on potato. Strict parasites, occurring in man and animals, and producing characteristic infections.

Type species. *Brucella melitensis*.

Bacillus.—Aerobic, spore-bearing rods, usually Gram-positive. Often occur in long threads, and form rhizoid colonies. Form of rod not greatly changed at sporulation. Liquefy gelatin. Mostly saprophytes.

Type species. *Bacillus subtilis*.

Clostridium.—Anaerobic or microaerophilic rods, producing endospores, which are usually wider than the vegetative organisms in which they arise—so-called clostridium forms. Generally Gram-positive. In young cultures often decompose protein media through the agency of enzymes, and often ferment carbohydrates. Many species are pathogenic.

Type species. *Clostridium butyricum*.

REFERENCES

BERGEY, D. H., *et al.* (1934) "Manual of Determinative Bacteriology." 4th Edit. Baillière, Tindall and Cox, London.
BUCHANAN, R. E. (1925) "General Systematic Bacteriology." Baltimore.
BUCHANAN, R. E., BREED, R. S., and RETTGER, L. F. (1928) *J. Bact.*, **16**, 387.
CASTELLANI, A. and CHALMERS, A. J. (1920) *Ann. Inst. Pasteur*, **34**, 600.
KRUSE, W. (1896) " Die Mikroorganismen." Flügge, Leipzig.
LEHMANN, and NEUMANN. (1896) (See 1920) " Atlas u. Grundriss der Bakt. u. Lehrb., etc." 6th Edit. Munich.
MIGULA, W. (1894) (See 1900) "System der Bakterien," Bd. II, Jena.
ORLA-JENSEN, . (1909) *Zbl. Bakt.*, IIte Abt., **22**, 305.
Reports. Comm. Soc. Amer. Bacteriol. WINSLOW, C.-E. A., BROADHURST, J., BUCHANAN, R. E., KRUMWIEDE, C., ROGERS, L. A., and SMITH, G. H. (1917) *J. Bact.*, **2**, 505 ; (1920) *Ibid.*, **5**, 191.
ZOPF, W. (1885) " Die Spaltpilze." 3. Aufl. Breslau.

CHAPTER X

THE BACTERIOPHAGE

In 1915, Twort described a curious degenerative change that he had observed in cultures of a staphylococcus derived from calf-lymph. He was able to transmit this change from one culture of the susceptible organism to another, by placing on the surface of an inoculated agar slope a drop of a highly diluted filtrate from a suspension of an earlier growth that had undergone the degenerative change. In 1917 d'Herelle recorded his first series of observations on the lytic properties of filtrates of mixed cultures obtained from the fæces of patients suffering from bacillary dysentery. In these preliminary studies, he was able to demonstrate the occurrence of rapid and generalized lysis in a growing broth culture of a dysentery bacillus to which some of the filtrate from the original mixed culture had been added, and the transmission of the lytic agent in a prolonged series of cultures of the susceptible bacterium, by the addition to each new culture of a filtrate obtained from the preceding one after lysis had occurred.

There can be no doubt, though d'Herelle has strenuously opposed this view, that these two descriptions afford different examples of the same essential process. With our present knowledge, we are, indeed, able to identify earlier records of curious happenings and appearances in bacterial cultures as instances of this lytic change ; but in none of these cases was the nature of the process studied in any detail, nor was its transmission by bacteria-free filtrates demonstrated. Twort's original paper, on the other hand, contains a complete demonstration of all the essential features of this important and significant reaction ; and it has hence come to be generally known as the " Twort-d'Herelle phenomenon."

D'Herelle's observations, which he has recorded in numerous papers from 1917 onwards and collected in three monographs (d'Herelle 1921, 1926, 1930), have, however, been far more detailed and extensive, and have played a major part in the development of our present conceptions. The name that he applied to the lytic agent, *Bacteriophage*, has come into general use, familiarly shortened to the diminutive *phage* ; and the view, consistently maintained by him, that this agent is a filtrable virus, parasitic on bacterial cells, has won increasing support, particularly within recent years.

An extensive literature has grown around this subject ; but we can here do no more than summarize certain of the more important observations, and the conclusions that have been drawn from them. The results obtained in recent studies have, indeed, deprived many of the earlier records of all save historical interest.

The General Characters of Bacteriophage Lysis.

The observations of d'Herelle, of Twort, and of other early workers established the following facts in regard to the behaviour of the lytic agent.

(1) It will pass through filters that hold back all bacteria.

(2) It acts upon susceptible bacteria in such a way as to bring about their lysis during the phase of active bacterial growth. This lytic action may be demonstrated in several different ways.

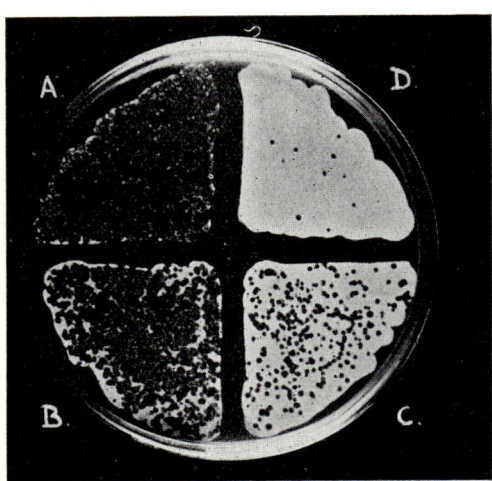

FIG. 34.

Effect of increasing dilutions of a phage on bacterial growth on an agar plate.

(a) A phage-containing filtrate may be added to a broth, or peptone-water, culture of a susceptible bacterium, the addition being made either at the time the broth is inoculated, or during the early stages of bacterial growth. The addition of an active filtrate will result, after a variable period, in a relatively sudden clearing of the turbid, growing culture. This clearing may be partial, or apparently complete ; but, even in the latter case, prolonged incubation usually results in renewed bacterial growth.

(b) The surface of an agar plate may be thickly inoculated with a susceptible bacterium, so as to give a confluent growth, and a few drops of a phage-containing filtrate may be spread over this inoculated surface before the plate is incubated. If the filtrate is very active, and has not been diluted, no growth may develop over the area on which it has been spread, or there may be a few " resistant " colonies (Fig. 34A). With a moderate dilution of the filtrate there will result irregular, confluent areas of clearing (Fig. 34B). With a still greater dilution there will be a number of well-separated clear areas, each of them circular, or roughly circular, in outline (Fig. 34c). These are the *tâches vierges*, or *plaques*, of the French authors, the *Löcher* of the German. As the phage filtrate is still further diluted, these plaques become fewer and fewer (Fig. 34D), a linear relation existing between the degree of dilution and the number of plaques, at least over a considerable range.

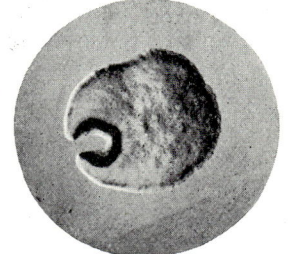

FIG. 35.

Colony of *Bact. coli* on agar, showing a " bitten " segment at the periphery, due to the action of a bacteriophage ($\times$ 8).

Phage action may also be demonstrated on a solid medium by the appearance of " bitten," or " nibbled " colonies, of the type shown in Fig. 35, or, in certain rather exceptional instances, by the occurrence of a vitreous, or granular, degeneration in colonies that have already attained a relatively advanced stage of growth.

(3) The lytic agent may be propagated indefinitely in association with growing cultures of the bacteria on which it acts. A few drops of a filtrate from the first culture in which lysis has occurred may be added to a second young, growing culture of the bacterium, this may be filtered after lysis and the filtrate added to a third freshly inoculated culture, and so on in series. A phage filtrate may be active in very high dilution (1×10^{-8} or higher), and in successive passages, carried out as above, the original titre is often increased during the earlier transfers, and is then maintained. It is clear, therefore, that the lytic agent, whatever it may be, is actively reproduced during the lytic process. There is no evidence that it can be reproduced in the absence of bacterial cells, or in the presence of dead bacterial cells, or even in the presence of bacterial cells that, though living, are not growing or dividing. There has been some controversy on the latter points; but the balance of evidence seems to be definitely in favour of the view that the presence of actively growing bacteria is necessary (see Otto and Munter 1923, Twort 1925, 1926, Gratia and Rhodes 1926, Gohs and Jacobsohn 1927, Bronfenbrenner and Muckenfuss 1927).

(4) Any given lytic agent will be found to be most active against one bacterial species or type, or against a few species or types that are known to be related to one another. Against unrelated species, or types, there is usually no action. The phage is, then, a highly specific agent.

(5) A secondary result of phage action is the appearance, in the bacterial culture that is undergoing lysis, of variants that are resistant to the action of the particular phage concerned. These variants are usually susceptible to the action of other phages.

(6) One of the commonest natural habitats of the phage is the intestinal tract of man and animals, and filtrates active against one or more bacteria can almost always be obtained from any specimen of fæces, or from material that has been subjected to fæcal pollution.

The Nature of the Bacteriophage.

As we have seen, d'Herelle has consistently maintained the view that the phage is a filtrable virus, parasitic on bacteria. This hypothesis has always been in accord with many of the most striking features of phage behaviour (see Flu 1923, Reichert 1924, Schuurman 1925). There can be little doubt that it would have gained early and general acceptance but for the fact that certain recorded observations seemed almost irreconcilable with it.

Because of these difficulties in accepting the virus hypothesis, various alternative theories have been propounded.

Kabéshima (1920) suggested that the phage was a catalyst, activating a pro-ferment present in the bacteria themselves. On this view the liberation of the ferment an active form would, of course, have to be regarded as an essential consequence of the lysis of the bacterial cells, the process, when once set going, being self-reproducing.

Bordet (see Bordet and Ciuca 1920, Bordet 1923, 1925) sought to reconcile the conception of an inanimate phage with its reproduction in an unlimited series in a rather different way. He suggested that the phenomenon was a true autolysis, the active agent being produced exclusively from the bacteria themselves. The origin of the autolysis he traced to a disturbance of the normal equilibrium between the assimilative and metabolic activities of the bacterial cell, adding the supposition that the substances set free during the autolysis of the cells initially affected were able to act in some way upon susceptible but hitherto unaffected cells, and to initiate in them the same series of autolytic changes. Once started, the process would thus be transmissible in series, provided that susceptible bacteria were present, and that these bacteria were metabolically active.

Another hypothesis, advanced by Hadley (1927, 1928), and since put forward in a rather different form by Wollman (1925, 1927, 1928, 1929, 1934, 1935) [see also Wollman and Wollman, 1932], assumes the phenomenon to be purely bacterial in origin, but relates it to the genetic, not to the metabolic activities of the bacterial cell. The phage, on this view, would be regarded as analogous to some gene-carrying constituent of the bacterial cell, or some filtrable phase in a complex life-cycle. It must, of course, be assumed that the addition of this cellular component, or bacterial phase, to a young culture of susceptible organisms, so alters their genetic behaviour that they undergo lysis during the process of multiplication, and, in so doing, reproduce the active agent in large amount.

None of these hypotheses can be regarded as intellectually attractive. To avoid certain difficulties they raise many others. They assume the presence of bacterial mechanisms the existence of which has not been established in any other way. And they suffer from a certain lack of clarity and precision. There are, we think, adequate reasons for accepting the virus hypothesis, at least as the most probable explanation of all the recorded facts. If new evidence should lead to its rejection, the void seems unlikely to be filled by any of the alternative views that have yet been propounded.

In setting out the evidence that seems to us to justify this conclusion, it will be convenient to discuss, *seriatim*, certain aspects of the nature and behaviour of the phage; but before doing so one point may be made clear, since it will be involved in our consideration of each other question in turn.

D'Herelle, for reasons that are not easy to appreciate, has upheld the view that the phage is a single living organism, *Protobios bacteriophagum*, which may adapt itself to live at the expense of a wide variety of different bacteria. The very extensive evidence that is now available is quite incompatible with this view. There is not one phage, but an enormous number of different phages; and in order to obtain constant and reproducible results it is as necessary to work with pure strains of phage as with pure cultures of bacteria. Neglect of this precaution has rendered many recorded studies of very doubtful value.

Pure strains of phage may be obtained in two ways. Since a given strain of bacterium will in many cases be susceptible to only one of the phages contained in a crude mixed filtrate, repeated transfer in growing cultures of this bacterium will often eliminate all phages except the one to which it is sensitive. This method is not, however, always reliable. A crude filtrate will often be found to contain more than one phage acting on the test bacterium selected. In such a case each of these phages may be propagated in successive transfers. It often happens that one or more are reproduced more rapidly than the others, and so have a better chance of transfer; but such phage cultures may remain mixed throughout a number of generations. An alternative, and better, method is to pick from isolated plaques on agar plates, just as we pick isolated colonies in attempting to purify a mixed bacterial culture. By a combination of these two methods it is usually possible to obtain phage strains of undoubted purity; but the procedure may be laborious, and contamination is very liable to occur. For these reasons strict attention to details of technique is required in any work of this kind (see Asheshov *et al.* 1933*a*).

The ways in which various strains of phage can be differentiated from one another will be considered in later sections of this chapter. At the moment we are concerned only with the point that such strains exist, and are identifiable.

The Physical State of the Phage. Is it Particulate or in Solution?

It might have been supposed that d'Herelle's demonstration of the occurrence of isolated plaques on an agar culture over which a high dilution of the phage had been spread would have sufficed to establish its particulate nature. This was not, indeed, the only observation pointing in this direction. D'Herelle noted that if a very high dilution of phage were distributed among a large number of tubes, each containing a young growing culture of a sensitive bacterium, lysis would occur in some tubes but not in others, indicating that the active agent was not dispersed in the form of a uniform solution, but in particles that were present in relatively small numbers in the high dilution employed, so that some of the tubes received no particle at all. This observation, it may be noted, has been confirmed by a number of subsequent observers (Bronfenbrenner and Korb 1925*b*, McKinley and Holden 1926, Bronfenbrenner 1927). Recently Feemster and Wells (1933), in a careful series of experiments, have shown that the proportion of tubes showing lysis, among large numbers inoculated with varying amounts of phage filtrate, are in exact accord with the statistical expectations based on the assumption that the agent is dispersed in a particulate form.

A possible escape from the obvious implication of these observations was provided by the assumption that only a few of the bacteria in any culture were susceptible to phage action. This assumption had little inherent probability and could hardly account for the test-tube experiments referred to above, but it was accepted by some observers, mainly on account of other observations that seemed to tell against a particulate structure. Thus Bordet (1925) stated that it was impossible to concentrate a phage filtrate by centrifugation at high speeds. We now know that this can readily be done if the speed is adequate. Olsen and Yasaki (1923) stated that the phage was volatile. This would have finally disposed of the view that it was particulate, or a living agent of any nature; but the results recorded were undoubtedly due to technical errors (Spät 1924, Borchardt 1924, Gildemeister and Herzberg 1924*b*, Meissner 1924*b*, Gercke 1925, Bronfenbrenner and Korb 1925*a*).

We may take it as beyond doubt that the phage is particulate, but the work of recent years has told us much more than this. It has given us an approximate measurement of the size of the particles, and has shown us that a particular strain of phage is characterized by a particular particle size.

Several early observers had noted the failure of the lytic agent to pass through fine collodion membranes (Doerr and Zdansky 1923, Biemond 1924, Ionesco-Mihiesti 1924); and some, using the method of ultrafiltration through membranes of approximately known pore size, had estimated the diameter of the phage particles to be of the order of 20–50 $m\mu$ (Stassano and de Beaufort 1925, Bechhold and Villa 1926, Zinsser and Tang 1927).

Elford and Andrewes (1932) made an important advance in our knowledge by showing that different pure-strain phages have a different particle size, and that this size is independent of the particular strain of bacterium on which they are being propagated. Working with carefully graded collodion membranes, they found that a particular phage had a mean diameter of about 8–12 $m\mu$. A group of phages showed a mean diameter of about 50–75 $m\mu$. Other strains gave intermediate values. By choosing strains with a sufficient difference in their mean diameters, it was possible to separate a mixture successfully by simple ultrafiltration. Yaoi and Sato (1935) have recently recorded similar results.

Schlesinger (1932–33a) has estimated the size of one of the larger phages by measuring its rate of sedimentation in a high-speed centrifuge. The mean calculated diameter was 79–90 $m\mu$, a figure that is in reasonable agreement with those obtained by Elford and Andrewes. More recent studies (Schlesinger 1933), while confirming the existence of a wide range of particle size among the series of phages measured by Elford and Andrewes, give higher individual values.

Reference to Chapters II and XXXVIII will show that these larger phages are of a size that renders possible their demonstration by modern microscopical methods. Barnard, using the technique of photography by monochromatic ultra-violet light, has obtained photographs of a phage of this type, which show it to be composed of uniformly sized particles with a diameter of about 50 $m\mu$ (see Burnet 1933e). These large phages produce in lysed broth cultures a turbidity that can be detected by its Tyndall effect, and the intensity of this effect has been found to provide an accurate measure of the concentration of the phage in the filtrate (Schlesinger 1932–33b).

The justifiable inferences from such observations as these take us far beyond the conclusion that the phage is particulate. They accord well with the view that phages are filtrable viruses. They accord very badly with any other hypothesis that has yet been propounded. A particulate lytic agent might conceivably consist of particles of bacterial protoplasm on to which some active principle had been adsorbed. But it is in the highest degree improbable that all the protoplasmic particles produced by the disruption of a particular species of bacterium would be of approximately the same size, or that the particles resulting from disruption by one type of phage would differ consistently in size from those produced by the action of another. The size of many of these phages (50–75 $m\mu$) is far too large to support the view that they are any type of molecular structure, or colloidal cell-constituent. The range of average diameters determined for those phages that have been measured is, on the other hand, almost exactly that of the known filtrable viruses (see Chapter XXXVIII).

Other Characters of the Phages.

Most phages, within the pH range over which they remain active, appear to carry a negative electric charge, in this way resembling bacteria and filtrable viruses (Todd 1927, Krueger *et al.* 1929, Burnet and McKie 1930a, Natarajan and Hyde 1930).

The fact that phages will grow only in the presence of living and multiplying bacteria renders the study of their metabolic activities exceedingly difficult. Apart from the work of Schüler (see Editorial 1935), which suggests that phosphatase is the only hydrolytic enzyme possessed by the bacteriophage, such studies as have been recorded have, in fact, yielded negative or ambiguous results (Bronfenbrenner 1924–25, 1926, Gózony and Surányi 1925, Kauffmann 1925–26, Bronfenbrenner and Reichert 1926–27, Schwartzman 1926–27, Bachmann and Wohlfeil 1927).

The resistance of various phages to heat and to other physical or chemical agents has been studied in some detail. Certain early statements ascribed to lytic filtrates a degree of resistance to heat, and to such chemical agents as chloroform, toluene, alcohol, acetone, etc., that seemed to place them in a category apart from other living things, except the spore-bearing bacteria (see Kabéshima 1920). These statements played a not-inconsiderable part in the controversy as to whether the phage was a living or non-living agent ; but they were not in accord with all the records existing at the time—Twort (1915), for instance, had stated that his lytic agent was inactivated by heating at 60° C. for 1 hour—and they have since been shown to have no general validity. All the evidence suggests that different strains of phage, like different species of bacteria differ from one another in their resistance to heat, to drying (see Knorr and Ruf 1935), and to various other physical and chemical reagents, and that the range of sensitivity, taken as a whole, is much the same in the two cases.

A few observations of general interest in regard to this particular problem may be briefly noted. Baker and Nanavutty (1929) found that the time relations of the inactivation of a Shiga phage by ultra-violet light were closely similar to the killing of *Bact. coli* by the same agent. The time required to inactivate the Shiga phage, or a staphylococcal phage, did not differ greatly from that required to kill *Bact. coli*; but the time required to inactivate trypsin was 20–30 times as long, and for the inactivation of diastase about 120 times as long. In this respect, therefore, the phages studied behaved as living things, not as ferments (see also Gates 1934).

Schultz and Krueger (1928) recorded the inactivation of a staphylococcus phage by methylene blue. Clifton (1931) found that this inactivation occurred when the mixture was exposed to sunlight, but not in the dark, and concluded that it was due to the oxidation of the phage by the photodynamically activated dye. Perdrau and Todd (1933), using more exact methods, record similar results. Different phages have been found to vary widely in their sensitiveness to this photodynamic action, though none are entirely resistant (Burnet 1933*b*, 1934).

A well-marked antagonistic action of Ca and Na ions on the viability of phages can be demonstrated (Burnet and McKie 1930*a*), which would seem to indicate that these ions are acting on the surface of a living cell, and to suggest the presence at that surface of a protein constituent. Some of the larger phages are rapidly inactivated by a strong urea solution, a reagent that acts similarly on many bacteria and viruses (Burnet 1933*b*, 1934).

It has been shown by several workers that some, but not all, phages are unable to produce lysis in bacterial cultures growing in a medium from which the calcium ions have been removed by previous treatment with citrate (Stassano and de Beaufort 1925, Bordet 1926, Asheshov 1926, Burnet 1933*b*). This fact allows a useful differentiation of phages into " citrate-sensitive " and " citrate-resistant " strains; but it should be noted that an initially citrate-sensitive phage may often be trained to produce lysis in a citrate-containing medium.

The Mechanism of Phage Lysis.

In considering the mechanism of phage lysis we may first deal with the phenomenon in a general sense, leaving the problem of specificity for later consideration.

D'Herelle's conception of the lytic process, based of course on the view that the phage is a parasitic virus, is simple and straightforward. He believes that a phage particle enters a growing bacterial cell, multiplies within it, and causes its more or less explosive disintegration when the limit of distension has been reached. This limit appears to vary over a considerable range; but disruption usually occurs when the number of particles in the cell have reached some figure between 6 and 60. In support of this view, d'Herelle states that the addition of very small amounts of phage to a growing culture is followed by a step-like increase in phage titre during the earlier stages of growth, successive sudden increases occurring at intervals of 20 to 30 minutes. After a few such jumps in titre the phage concentration rises logarithmically until lysis occurs. This change from a discontinuous to a continuous rise would, of course, be expected; since the successive increases would soon get out of step, and their combined effect would give a steady rise in titre.

Burnet (1929c) has recorded observations that are in entire accord with d'Herelle's view. To a number of small tubes, each containing a young, actively growing culture of a sensitive bacterium, he added a phage filtrate so highly diluted that, on the average, each tube received a single particle. At short intervals thereafter the whole contents of one of the tubes was spread on the surface of an agar plate, and the resulting plaques were counted. The results showed that there was no detectable increase during the first 20 minutes or so. After this time there was a sharp and sudden rise. Thus, a series of tubes plated at one-minute intervals, over the appropriate time range, gave 1, 0, 1, 2, 0, 1, 80, 0, 1, 120, 1, 230, 0 and 100 plaques. The absence of values intermediate between 1 and 80, makes it clear that the free phage in the culture was not increasing by twofold steps, as would occur during the early generations of a single bacterium multiplying by binary fission ; and the only obvious explanation of such findings is that the phage particles are dividing in, or on, a bacterium, and are suddenly liberated into the surrounding fluid when that bacterium disrupts.

Apart from these quantitative data, it is, of course, possible to observe the occurrence of phage lysis under the microscope, and this has in fact been done (see d'Herelle 1921, 1926, Twort 1922, Wollman 1925, Burnet 1925, v. Preisz 1925, Manninger 1926, da Costa Cruz 1926, Bronfenbrenner *et al.* 1927, Bronfenbrenner 1928, Bayne-Jones and Sandholzer 1933). Not all of these observations have been made under the best modern conditions of microscopy or microphotography, so that their value, particularly in regard to matters of detail, varies considerably. They differ, also, in certain particulars of the actual happenings that are described, and there can be little doubt that phage lysis may, in fact, occur in several different ways, according to the nature of the phage and bacterium involved. There is general agreement that the early stage of the process is associated with swelling of the affected bacterial cells, and this swelling may, or may not, be associated with an obvious granularity. The disruption of the swollen bacterial cell is usually very sudden. The cell may appear to explode, giving place to a cloud of granular debris, or it may suddenly lose its outline and disappear, without the liberation of the granular cloud. Bayne-Jones and Sandholzer (1933) give a series of cinematograph records of some of these events.

The process of phage lysis has also been studied quantitatively by observations carried out on a lysing culture as a whole (see for instance Lepper 1923). Curves have been plotted showing the relation between changes in the number of phage particles and changes in the number of viable bacteria. Krueger and Northrop (1931) record a very careful study of this kind. Their results allow the reaction to be expressed in a mathematical form, and show that massive lysis of the growing culture occurs when the ratio between the number of phage particles and of bacterial cells attains a limiting value. But such figures are clearly the expression of a statistical relationship, and afford no evidence in regard to the actual mechanism of phage multiplication, They are, as Burnet (1934) points out, entirely compatible with the conceptions derived from the observations recorded above.

It may be noted that phage particles, when present in adequate concentration, are able to kill bacteria without producing lysis. Andrewes and Elford (1932) have demonstrated this direct killing action by studies with a citrate-sensitive coli-phage. Mixtures of this phage with a sensitive *Bact. coli*, when plated on citrate agar gave normal growth, without lysis, so long as the phage concentration was below a certain limit. But when this limit was exceeded 95–99 per cent. of the *Bact. coli* were killed, in the sense that they failed to develop on the citrate agar, although there was, of course, still no lysis.

It should also be noted that, although the multiplication of phage particles and the characteristic lysis associated with it demand the presence of living and growing bacteria, the phage is readily absorbed by dead bacterial cells (see Krueger 1931). As we shall see in the following section, this absorption is specific.

The Factors that Determine Phage Specificity.

It has been well established, from the earliest days of bacteriophage study, that any given strain of phage has a relatively limited range of activity. A coli-phage, for instance, will not act on a staphylococcus, or on a diphtheria bacillus. It was soon found, however, that phage specificity, while varying widely in range with different strains of phage, might be much narrower than this. A coli-phage would act on some strains of *Bact. coli*, but not on others, and so on. The obvious assumption was that different strains of the same bacterial species differed in " phage sensitivity," but no attempt was made by the earlier workers to determine on what factors this sensitivity depended. A very significant advance in our knowledge of this problem has been made by the studies of Burnet and his colleagues.

In a study of the activity of different strains of phage on the species and types included within the Salmonella group of bacteria, it was found (Burnet 1927) that there was a close relation between the sensitiveness of different bacterial species, or types, to a particular phage, and the distribution of particular surface somatic antigens. Thus, a particular phage was active against *Bact. typhosum*, *Bact. enteritidis* and *Bact. pullorum*, all of which possess the somatic antigen IX, but was inactive against *Bact. paratyphosum A* and *Bact. choleræ-suis*, which do not possess this antigen. If, however, the normal smooth strains of these species were replaced by their rough variants, in which the smooth somatic antigens are lost, their place being taken by a common rough somatic antigen, then a phage that attacked one rough variant would attack all the others. Some phages were found to attack only the normal smooth forms, their range of activity then being determined by the distribution of the various smooth somatic antigens. Other phages attacked only rough forms. A few phages were able to attack both rough and smooth forms (Burnet 1929a).

Further studies revealed similar relationships between dysentery phages and the Flexner group of dysentery bacilli (Burnet and McKie 1930b), coli-phages and different strains of *Bact. coli* (Burnet and McKie 1933), and staphylococcal phages and different strains of staphylococci (Burnet and McKie 1929).

Analogous, though much less detailed, observations have been recorded by other workers. Thus Denys (1932) has noted that some strains of dysentery phage act only on smooth dysentery strains, others only on rough, others on both. Asheshov and his colleagues (Asheshov et al. 1930, 1933b) have recorded similar findings in relation to cholera phages. Clauberg and Marcuse (1932) note a general correspondence between sensitiveness to certain phages and antigenic structure as revealed by agglutination among four different antigenic types of dysentery bacilli, though the correspondence was not always exact; and Schmidt (1931) notes that different species of Salmonella bacilli can be differentiated by their sensitiveness to different selected phages, as well as by their response to specific antisera.

The intimate relationship between phage sensitivity and the nature of the surface bacterial antigens has been confirmed by observing the effects on phage lysis of different bacterial extracts. Levine and Frisch (1934) tested the fractions obtained by alcoholic precipitation of saline extracts prepared from bacteria of the Salmonella and dysentery groups, and found that they specifically inhibited the lysis of the homologous organisms by phage. Gough and Burnet (1934), working with more highly purified fractions, record similar results. The fractions obtained in this way were known to consist mainly of the specific polysaccharide somatic antigens. Still further confirmation has been obtained by the demonstration by Levine and his colleagues (Levine, Frisch and Cohen 1934, Levine and Frisch 1935), that heat-killed bacteria of the Salmonella group absorb phages specifically, in general accordance with their antigenic structure as revealed by agglutination tests.

There can, then, be no doubt at all that the antigenic structure of the bacterial surface is one of the main factors in determining the accessibility of the bacterial cell to a given strain of phage; and we must suppose the phage particles to be so constituted that those of one strain can find attachment, or entry, only at an area of bacterial surface that is characterized by a particular antigenic structure, while those of another strain have wider potentialities, and are able to attack a bacterium through more than one type of antigenic surface.

It should, however, be emphasized that this is not the only factor that determines phage sensitivity, or, at least, that there is not complete parallelism between sensitivity and antigenic structure as revealed by the available serological tests. Burnet (1929*b*), for instance, notes that a phage-resistant strain, appearing as the result of the lytic action of a particular phage on a particular sensitive bacterium, may show exactly the same antigenic structure, as revealed by serological tests, as the sensitive strain from which it was derived. He notes further that the resistant strain not only shows no lysis, but fails to adsorb the phage; so that some change in surface structure would appear to be concerned, though it is not detectable by the ordinary serological methods.

The Variations Induced in Bacteria in Response to Phage Lysis.

In an earlier section of this chapter, it was noted that a secondary bacterial growth usually appears in a culture that has undergone phage lysis. If this growth is further examined, it will be found to be composed of bacteria that are resistant to the strain of phage that caused the lysis, though they will usually be sensitive to other strains of phage.

Sometimes these resistant strains show a well-marked antigenic difference from the original sensitive strain; for instance, the lysis of a smooth strain of a dysentery bacillus by an anti-smooth phage is frequently followed by the appearance of characteristically rough resistant variants. But, as we have seen, resistant strains are not always of a recognizably different antigenic type from the original sensitive strain; and, in the great majority of cases, we have at present no evidence as to whether the change in phage sensitivity has, or has not, been accompanied by a change in antigenic structure. What we do know is that submission to the action of a phage is one of the most potent methods of inducing bacterial variation (see Arkwright 1924, Hadley 1927, 1928), that the variants so produced may be of many different kinds, that they share the character of resistance to the phage that induced the variation, and that some at least of them differ antigenically from the parent strain.

It is clear that the existence of these resistant strains of bacteria, and the possibility of producing them at will, affords a method of studying in greater detail the phages acting on single bacterial species.

Bail (1923) was the first to stress the importance of cross-resistance tests between different phages and different bacterial strains as a method of phage differentiation; and many others have since employed this method in the study of phages acting on particular groups or species of bacteria, such as the Salmonella group (Burnet 1929*b*), the dysentery group (Burnet and McKie 1930*b*, Morison 1932), or the cholera vibrios (Asheshov *et al.* 1930, 1933, Morison 1932). Many of these studies, however, were concerned with differences in phage sensitivity between different bacterial species or types, as well as between different variants derived by phage action from a single bacterial strain. It is with differences of the latter type, and their application as a method of separating and identifying different phages that are active against a single bacterial species or type, that we are here concerned. This method has been very extensively developed by Asheshov and his colleagues, and we may take an illustrative example of an experiment performed according to their technique (Asheshov *et al.* 1933*b*).

Suppose that we have three strains of phage, all acting on the same strain of a given bacterium, but which we suspect, for one reason or another, to belong to different types. We allow each of the three phages, which we may label I, II and III, and a mixture of them (I-II-III), to act on four separate cultures of our sensitive bacterium growing in a fluid medium. We allow lysis to occur, and a secondary growth of resistant bacteria to follow it. We take a large agar plate, and mark it off into 16 squares (4 × 4). Over each square in the first column of 4 squares we make a thick seeding from the secondary growth from our Type I phage, over each square in the second column we seed the secondary

growth from our Type II phage, over the squares in the third column the secondary growth from our Type III phage, and over the squares in the fourth and last column the secondary growth from the culture containing all three phages. Then we take a filtrate containing Type I phage, and spread a small drop of it over a circular area in the middle of the top square of each column (*i.e.* of each square of the first row). In each square of the second row we make a similar inoculation of Type II phage, in each square of the third row an inoculation of Type III phage, and in each square of the fourth and last row, an inoculation of phages I, II and III.

If the phages actually belong to different types, as judged by this test, the results will be as shown in Fig. 36, in which the dark circles indicate the occurrence of confluent lysis over the circular area inoculated with the phage.

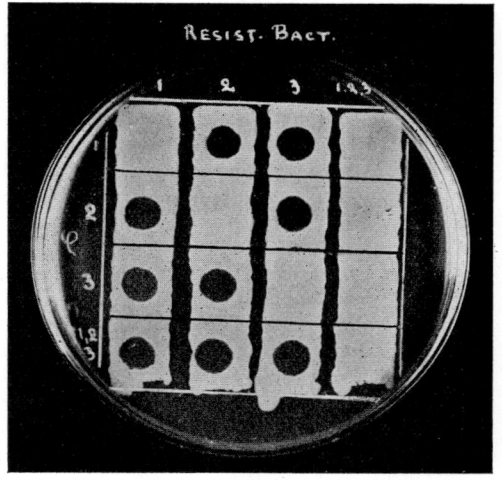

FIG. 36.

Differentiation of phage types by their action on resistant bacteria.

It will be noted that Phage I acts on the secondary growth from Phages II and III, but not on the secondary growth from Phage I, and so on. None of the three phages act on the secondary growth from the culture submitted to the action of all three phages. The mixture of three phages acts on the secondary growth from each of the three separate phages.

If we desire to test another phage, to see whether or not it is identical with any of our three Types I, II, or III, we include it in such a series of tests, adding the additional row and column to our squares. If it is identical with any of our three types it will behave as that type does. If it is a new type (say Type IV) then it will lyse the secondary growths from Types I, II and III, and its own secondary growth will be lysed by each of these types.

This leads us to a consideration of other ways in which phages may be differentiated from one another. One of these is the method of antigenic analysis, which has been so extensively employed in the identification and classification of bacteria.

The Antigenic Structure of Phages.

It was shown by Bordet and Ciuca (1921) that the phage is antigenic, and that an antiphage serum has the power of neutralizing the phage and so preventing its lytic action on bacteria.   Numerous workers have since studied this phenomenon, and it has been clearly shown (a) that the inhibition of phage lysis is due to antibodies acting on the phage itself, and not to the antibacterial antibodies that are usually present in an antiphage serum, and (b) that the antibodies are specific for particular types of phage, phages thus showing an antigenic specificity of exactly the same kind as that displayed by bacteria.   Many of the papers already referred to contain references to the antigenic behaviour of the phages studied, as well as to their other properties.

Three recent studies by Burnet are of considerable interest, as affording close analogies with the reactions that characterize bacterial antigens.   In the first (Burnet 1933c) bacteria were allowed to absorb large amounts of a particular phage, or sometimes of two antigenically unrelated phages, and were then tested against specific antiphage sera, from which all antibodies acting on the bacteria themselves had been removed.   The treated bacteria were agglutinated by the antiphage sera, and absorbed the antibodies from them, in accordance with the antigenic specificity conferred by the adsorbed phage particles.

In the second series of experiments Burnet (1933d) was able, by passing a lytic filtrate through a collodion membrane that held back all the phage particles, to demonstrate in this twice-filtered fluid, a substance that specifically inhibited the union between the phage concerned and the homologous antiphage serum.   It seems probable that this substance was a soluble antigenic constituent of the phage, analogous to the soluble antigens that have been separated from so many species and types of bacteria.

In the third series of experiments Burnet (1933e) was able to demonstrate the direct agglutination of a large-particle phage, freed from bacterial debris by ultra-filtration and washing.   The clumps so formed were photographed by Barnard, using ultra-violet light, and afforded the first ocular demonstration of the shape and size of the phage particles. It was also demonstrated that the results of direct agglutination ran parallel to those obtained in neutralization tests.   Eight phages, all belonging to the same serological group as judged by neutralization tests, were all agglutinated by the same antiserum, while ten other phages belonging to different neutralization groups, were not.

The quantitative relations existing between a phage and its homologous neutralizing serum have been studied by Andrewes and Elford (1933a, b).   Their results were curious, in suggesting that, over a considerable range of phage dilutions, a given amount of antiserum neutralized a constant percentage of the phage present, irrespective of the total number of phage particles exposed to its action (see also Clifton, Mueller and Rogers 1935).

Other Methods of Phage Differentiation, and the Identification and Classification of Phages.

The phage plaques that have so frequently been referred to in preceding sections have characters that are of great value in the differentiation of one phage from another.   For any one phage, acting on any one sensitive bacterium, the plaques formed on an agar plate are usually closely similar, both in size and in form.   But different phages acting on the same bacterium may give plaques that differ sharply and characteristically from one another.

To take first the character of plaque size, the existence of large-plaque-forming phages and small-plaque-forming phages has long been recognized, and used as a basis for differentiation (see Bail 1923).   Elford and Andrewes (1932) were able to show that there is an inverse relation between plaque size and phage size.   The small phages give big plaques, and *vice versa*. It is an obvious assumption that the small phages can diffuse more readily through the surface bacterial growth, and so extend over a larger radius. The probability of this assumption is increased by the demonstration by Andrewes and Elford (1933*b*) that a large-plaque-forming phage, incompletely neutralized by an antiphage serum and probably aggregated into small clumps, gives small instead of large plaques.

But size is not the only character that differentiates one phage plaque from another; there are often marked differences in the edge of the circular clearings. These may be entire or eroded, sharp or bevelled. They may, or may not, be surrounded by a halo in which the bacterial growth is altered in appearance, though not completely lysed. Phage plaques, indeed, present variations in morphology as distinctive as those shown by bacterial colonies, and have the same classificatory value. Asheshov (1924) (see also Asheshov *el al.* 1933*b*) has paid particular attention to these differences in plaque morphology, and Fig. 37 illustrates the differences, in size and form, that may be observed among the plaques produced by different phages acting on the same strain of a sensitive bacterium.

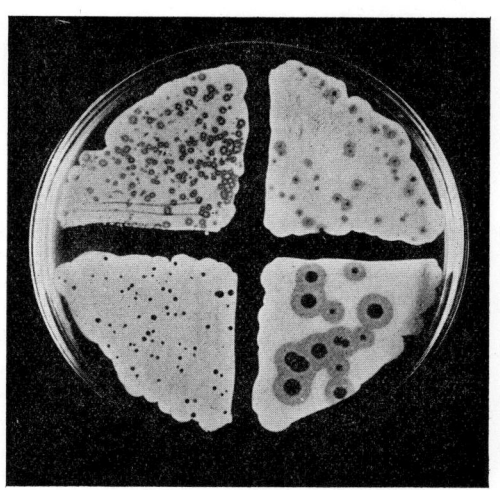

Fig. 37.

Different types of plaque produced by different phages acting on the same bacterial culture.

If, then, we seek to classify any particular group of phage strains, we can make use of the following series of tests.

(A) The determination of the species of bacteria against which each phage is active. This will enable us to differentiate broad groups — coli-phages, dysentery phages, Salmonella phages, staphylococcal phages, cholera phages, and so on.

(B) By more detailed tests of cross-resistance we can subdivide these broad groups, each into a number of different types—so many different types of dysentery phage, so many of cholera phage, and so on.

(C) We can apply to the same problem of the subdivision of our broad groups the method of antigenic analysis, using specific antiphage sera.

(D) We can study the size and morphology of the plaques formed, and divide our original groups of phages into large-plaque-forming strains, small-plaque-forming strains, and so on.

(E) We can also apply certain other biological tests, such as relative resistance to heat, or to the photodynamic action of methylene blue, or to the presence of citrate in a medium.

When, in fact, we apply several of these tests, our confidence in each of them is increased by finding that the results they give are highly correlated. The classification derived from detailed resistance tests corresponds closely with that derived from neutralization tests with antiphage sera. The phages producing a particular type of plaque, when acting on a particular sensitive bacterium, are usually found to fall into the same antigenic group. An admirable series of studies in which this correlation is brought out very clearly have been recorded by Burnet (1933*a*, *b*) ; and other evidence, all pointing in the same direction, will be found in the studies of Asheshov and his colleagues (1930, 1933*b*), in recent papers by Sertic and Boulgakov (1935*a*, *b*), and in many of the other records referred to above. The correspondence is not, of course, absolute. Just as some groups of bacterial strains would be divided into the same species or types, whether classified on the basis of fermentation tests or antigenic structure, while other groups that are identical in regard to their fermentation reactions may be divided into different types on the basis of serological tests, so one particular method of analysis may serve to separate strains of phage that would be grouped together when tested by another. But correlation of characters is as frequent among the phages as it is among the bacteria, and leaves no reasonable doubt that, by making full use of the methods now at our disposal we can separate and identify phage types that have just as much claim to be regarded as biological entities as have the various species or types of bacteria.

Variation and Adaptation in Phages.

The literature contains very numerous records of phage variation and phage adaptation. D'Herelle, as has been noted, regards the phage as a single virus, that may become adapted to attack a wide variety of bacterial species. Many of the earlier accounts of adaptation must be discounted, because the technique adopted did not ensure the purity of the original filtrates. There are, on the other hand, numerous observations which show quite clearly that adaptation occurs, though its range is probably more limited than was at one time supposed. Here, again, the evidence suggests that the phage behaves in the same way as other known micro-organisms.

The Ecology of Phages.

The problem of phage ecology raises points of the greatest biological interest and importance. We have already noted that phages acting on one or other of the normal or pathogenic intestinal bacteria can almost always be isolated from fæces, from sewage, or from polluted water supplies (see, for instance, Sonnenschein 1927, Stewart and Ghosal 1931, Gildemeister and Watanabe 1931, Schlossmann 1932, von Vagedes and Gildemeister 1934). This clearly suggests that wherever particular species of bacteria occur in nature, there also are likely to be found phages to which these bacteria are sensitive. But that is merely the first, and least interesting step in the problem.

Just as it was tacitly assumed, in the earliest days of medical bacteriology, that a pathogenic bacterium, when it became parasitic on its natural host would always, or almost always, cause the specific disease of which it was the causal agent, so it was assumed in the early days of bacteriophage studies that a phage, if it became attached to, and multiplied in association with, a particular bacterium would cause phage lysis. The conception of phage-carriers among bacteria, or of a normal phage flora living symbiotically with certain bacterial species, came relatively late.

The demonstration that a phage, active against a particular species of bacterium, could sometimes be isolated from an old laboratory culture of that organism by repeated filtration, and the addition of each successive filtrate to a fresh broth culture of the bacterium in question (Gildemeister and Herzberg 1923, Kuttner 1923, Kline 1927, Hadley 1928, Fukuda 1928, Klieneberger 1932) was at first regarded as a powerful argument against the virus theory, and in favour of the view that the phage was a product, enzymic or other, of the bacteria themselves. It was indeed the failure of many workers to confirm these findings (Ogata 1924, Reichert 1924, Meissner 1924*a*, Arkwright 1924, Sonnenschein 1927), rather than any realization that they were quite compatible with the virus theory, that deprived them of much of their force. It is quite probable (see Burnet 1934) that some, at least, of the positive findings were due to technical errors. But in the light of our present knowledge it would be by no means surprising if many of them were correct.

Our present conception of the real nature of phage-bacterium parasitism has been determined largely by the proved existence of what are known as " lysogenic strains " of bacteria.

The classical examples of these lysogenic strains are the *Bact. coli* strain, which was first described by Lisbonne and Carrère (1922) and later studied by Bordet and Renaux (1928), and another *Bact. coli* strain which was studied by Gildemeister and Herzberg (1924*a*). Both these strains, although they themselves show no evidence of phage lysis, regularly yield filtrates which lyse *Bact. shigæ*, *i.e.* they are permanent carriers of a phage to which they are themselves resistant, but to which *Bact. shigæ* is sensitive.

Such strains were, for a time, regarded as bacteriological anomalies, but such a view is no longer tenable. Here, again, our present concepts have been largely influenced by the studies of Burnet (1932, 1934).

In a careful study of 34 strains of *Bact. enteritidis* he found that 27 were lysogenic, in the sense that they yielded a phage to which they were themselves resistant, but which produced transmissible lysis in other, specially susceptible bacterial strains. From these 27 lysogenic strains three different types of phage were obtained, A, B, and D ; fourteen strains yielded phage B, seven phage D, two A and B, and one A and D. Phage A was also frequently isolated from lysogenic strains of *Bact. paratyphosum A*, *Bact. paratyphosum B* and *Bact. typhi-murium*, while phages B and D, and another phage N were sometimes present in strains belonging to these species. Such results as these, as Burnet points out, are incompatible with the view that the lytic agent in these lysogenic strains is some component of the genetic apparatus of the bacterial cell.

In the case of *Bact. paratyphosum C*, on the other hand, all strains examined, whether they had been isolated in Russia, South America, or the East Indies, were found to be carrying a single antigenic type of phage. A similar state of affairs may, as Burnet points out, exist in the case of *C. diphtheriæ*, since Smith and Jordan (1931) found that every strain examined was lysogenic when tested against a single, sensitive indicator strain of the same species. The occasional occurrence of " nibbled " colonies that have been noted by many workers in certain bacterial cultures represent, in Burnet's view, lysogenic strains in which the resistance of the carrying bacterium is slightly unstable.

We must then, if we are to accept the virus hypothesis, to which all other evidence clearly points, also accept the view that symbiosis between phage and bacterium is an exceedingly common event ; so common that it would at the moment be unwise to assert that any bacterial strain was certainly not carrying phage.

In such an association (see Burnet 1934) it is clear that the multiplication of phage and bacterium must be so co-ordinated that, when a bacterium divides, each daughter cell receives its phage quota. It has in fact been shown (den Dooren de Jong 1931, Cowles 1931) that, when a lysogenic strain is a spore-bearer, the phage is present in the spore and in the new generations that arise from it.

What place this symbiotic process will eventually take in our conceptions of bacterial structure, bacterial variation, antigenic behaviour, and other similar problems we cannot yet prophesy. It may be a relatively minor one ; but it may not.

The possible relation of phages to bacterial infections in man and animals is considered in Chapter LI.

REFERENCES

ANDREWES, C. H. and ELFORD, W. J. (1932) *Brit. J. exp. Path.*, **13,** 13 ; (1933a) *Ibid.,* **14,** 367 ; (1933b) *Ibid.,* **14,** 376.
ARKWRIGHT, J. A. (1924) *Brit. J. exp. Path.*, **5,** 23.
ASHESHOV, I. N. (1924) *J. infect. Dis.*, **34,** 536 ; (1926) *C. R. Soc. Biol.*, **94,** 687.
ASHESHOV, I. N., ASHESHOV, I., KHAN, S., and LAHIRI, M. N. (1930) *Indian J. med. Res.,* **17,** 971 ; (1933a) *Ibid.,* **20,** 1101.
ASHESHOV, I. N., ASHESHOV, I., KHAN, S., LAHIRI, M. N., and CHATTERJI, S. K. (1933b) *Indian J. med. Res.,* **20,** 1127.
BACHMANN, W. and WOHLFEIL, T. (1927) *Zbl. Bakt.*, **104,** 256.
BAIL, O. (1923) *Z. ImmunForsch.*, **38,** 57.
BAKER, S. L. and NANAVUTTY, S. H. (1929) *Brit. J. exp. Path.*, **10,** 45.
BAYNE-JONES, S. and SANDHOLZER, L. A. (1933) *J. exp. Med.*, **57,** 279.
BECHHOLD, H. and VILLA, L. (1926) *Z. Hyg. InfektKr.*, **105,** 601.
BIEMOND, A. G. (1924) *Z. Hyg. InfektKr.*, **103,** 681.
BORCHARDT, W. (1924) *Klin. Wschr.*, **3,** 278.
BORDET, J. (1923) *Brit. med. J.*, i. 175 ; (1925) *Ann. Inst. Pasteur*, **39,** 717 ; (1926) *C. R. Soc. Biol.*, **94,** 403.
BORDET, J. and CIUCA, M. (1920) *C. R. Soc. Biol.*, **83,** 1296 ; (1921) *Ibid.,* **84,** 280.
BORDET, J. and RENAUX, E. (1928) *Ann. Inst. Pasteur*, **42,** 1283.
BRONFENBRENNER, J. (1924–25) *Proc. Soc. exp. Biol., N.Y.*, **22,** 81 ; (1926) *Science,* **63,** 51 ; (1927) *J. exp. Med.*, **45,** 373 ; (1928) " Filterable Viruses " (Rivers) Baillière, Tindall and Cox, London, p. 373.
BRONFENBRENNER, J. J. and KORB, C. (1925a) *J. exp. Med.*, **41,** 73 ; (1925b) *Ibid.,* **42,** 483.
BRONFENBRENNER, J. and MUCKENFUSS, R. S. (1927) *J. exp. Med.*, **45,** 887.
BRONFENBRENNER, J., MUCKENFUSS, R. S., and HETLER, D. M. (1927) *Amer. J. Path.,* **3,** 562.
BRONFENBRENNER, J. J. and REICHERT, P. (1926–7) *Proc. Soc. exp. Biol., N.Y.*, **24,** 176.
BURNET, F. M. (1925) *J. Path. Bact.*, **28,** 407 ; (1927) *Brit. J. exp. Path.*, **8,** 121 ; (1929a) *J. Path. Bact.*, **32,** 15 ; (1929b) *Ibid.,* **32,** 349 ; (1929c) *Brit. J. exp. Path.*, **10,** 109 ; (1932) *J. Path. Bact.*, **35,** 851 ; (1933a) *Ibid.,* **36,** 307 ; (1933b) *Ibid.,* **37,** 179 ; (1933c) *Brit. J. exp. Path.*, **14,** 93 ; (1933d) *Ibid.,* **14,** 100 ; (1933e) *Ibid.,* **14,** 302 ; (1934) *Biol. Rev.,* **9,** 332.
BURNET, F. M. and MCKIE, M. (1929) *Aust. J. exp. Biol. med Sci.*, **6,** 21 ; (1930a) *Ibid.,* **7,** 183, 199 ; (1930b) *J. Path. Bact.*, **33,** 637 ; (1933) *Ibid.,* **36,** 299.
CLAUBERG, K. W. and MARCUSE, K. (1932) *Zbl. Bakt.*, **124,** 29.
CLIFTON, C. E. (1931) *Proc. Soc. exp. Biol., N.Y.*, **28,** 745.
CLIFTON, C. E., MUELLER, E., and ROGERS, W. (1935) *J. Immunol.*, **29,** 377.
COSTA CRUZ, J. DA. (1926) *C. R. Soc. Biol.*, **95,** 1501.
COWLES, P. B. (1931) *J. Bact.*, **22,** 119.
DENYS, P. (1932) *Ann. Inst. Pasteur*, **48,** 349.
DOERR, R. and ZDANSKY, E. (1923) *Z. Hyg. InfektKr.*, **100,** 79.
DOOREN DE JONG, L. E. DEN. (1931) *Zbl. Bakt.*, **120,** 1.
Editorial (1935) *Lancet,* i. 818.
ELFORD, W. J. and ANDREWES, C. H. (1932) *Brit. J. exp. Path.*, **13,** 446.
FEEMSTER, R. F. and WELLS, W. F. (1933) *J. exp. Med.*, **58,** 385.
FLU, P. C. (1923) *Zbl. Bakt.*, **90,** 362.
FUKUDA, Y. (1928) *Z. ImmunForsch.*, **54,** 369.
GATES, F. L. (1934) *J. exp. Med.*, **60,** 179.
GERCKE, A. (1925) *Zbl. Bakt.*, **94,** 387.
GILDEMEISTER, E. and HERZBERG, K. (1923) *Zbl. Bakt.*, **91,** 12 ; (1924a) *Ibid.,* **93,** 402 ; (1924b) *Klin. Wschr.*, **3,** 186.
GILDEMEISTER, E. and WATANABE, H. (1931) *Zbl. Bakt.*, **122,** 556.
GOHS, W. and JACOBSOHN, I. (1927) *Z. ImmunForsch.*, **53,** 12.
GOUGH, G. A. C. and BURNET, F. M. (1934) *J. Path. Bact.*, **38,** 301.
GÓZONY, L. and SURÁNYI, L. (1925) *Zbl. Bakt.*, **95,** 353.

GRATIA, A. and RHODES, B. (1926) *Lancet*, i. 204.

HADLEY, P. (1927) *J. infect. Dis.*, **40**, 1 ; (1928) *Ibid.*, **42**, 263.

D'HERELLE, F. (1917) *C. R. Acad. Sci.*, **165**, 373 ; (1921) " Le Bactériophage : son rôle dans l'immunité." Masson, Paris. Eng. transl., Baltimore and London, 1922. (1926) " Le Bactériophage et son Comportement." Masson, Paris. Eng. transl., Baltimore and London. (1930) " Bacteriophage and its clinical applications." Thomas, Springfield, Illinois.

IONESCO-MIHAIESTI, C. (1924) *J. exp. Med.*, **40**, 317.

KABÉSHIMA, T. (1920) *C. R. Soc. Biol.*, **83**, 219.

KAUFFMANN, F. (1925–26) *Z. Hyg. InfektKr.*, **105**, 594.

KLIENEBERGER, E. (1932) *Zbl. Bakt.*, **123**, 318.

KLINE, G. M. (1927) *J. Lab. clin. Med.*, **12**, 1074.

KNORR, M. and RUF, H. (1935) *Zbl. Bakt.*, **133**, 289.

KRUEGER, A. P. (1931) *J. gen. Physiol.*, **14**, 493.

KRUEGER, A. P. and NORTHROP, J. H. (1931) *J. gen. Physiol.*, **14**, 233.

KRUEGER, A. P., RITTER, R. C., and SMITH, S. P. (1929) *J. exp. Med.*, **50**, 739.

KUTTNER, A. G. (1923) *J. Bact.*, **7**, 49.

LEPPER, E. (1923) *Brit. J. exp. Path.*, **4**, 204.

LEVINE, P. and FRISCH, A. W. (1934) *J. exp. Med.*, **59**, 213 ; (1935) *J. infect. Dis.*, **57**, 104.

LEVINE, P., FRISCH, A. W., and COHEN, E. V. (1934) *J. Immunol.*, **26**, 321.

LISBONNE, M. and CARRÈRE, L. (1922) *C. R. Soc. Biol.*, **86**, 569.

McKINLEY, E. B. and HOLDEN, M. (1926) *J. infect. Dis.*, **39**, 451.

MANNINGER, R. (1926) *Zbl. Bakt.*, **99**, 203.

MEISSNER, G. (1924*a*) *Zbl. Bakt.*, **91**, 149 ; (1924*b*) *Ibid.*, **92**, 424.

MORISON, J. (1932) " Bacteriophage in the treatment and prevention of cholera." Lewis & Co., London.

NATARAJAN, C. V. and HYDE, R. R. (1930) *Amer. J. Hyg.*, **11**, 652.

OGATA, N. (1924) *Zbl. Bakt.*, **93**, 329.

OLSEN, O. and YASAKI, Y. (1923) *Klin. Wschr.*, **2**, 1879.

OTTO, R. and MUNTER, H. (1923) *Z. Hyg. InfektKr.*, **100**, 402.

PERDRAU, J. R. and TODD, C. (1933) *Proc. roy. Soc.*, B, **112**, 277.

PREISZ, H. VON. (1925) " Die Bakteriophagie, etc." Fischer, Jena.

REICHERT, F. (1924) *Zbl. Bakt.*, **91**, 235.

SCHLESINGER, M. (1932–33*a*) *Z. Hyg. InfektKr.*, **114**, 161 ; (1932–33*b*) *Ibid.*, **114**, 746; (1933) *Biochem. Z.*, **264**, 6.

SCHLOSSMANN, K. (1932) *Z. Hyg. InfektKr.*, **114**, 65.

SCHMIDT, A. (1931) *Zbl. Bakt.*, **123**, 202, 207.

SCHULTZ, E. W. and KRUEGER, A. P. (1928) *Proc. Soc. exp. Biol., N.Y.*, **26**, 97.

SCHUURMAN, C. J. (1925) *Zbl. Bakt.*, **95**, 97.

SCHWARTZMAN, G. (1926–27) *Zbl. Bakt.*, **101**, 62.

SERTIC, V. and BOULGAKOV, N. (1935*a*) *C. R. Soc. Biol.*, **119**, 983 ; (1935*b*) *Ibid.*, **119**, 985.

SMITH, G. F. and JORDAN, E. O. (1931) *J. Bact.*, **21**, 75.

SONNENSCHEIN, C. (1927) *G. Batt. Immun.*, **2**, 32.

SPÄT, W. (1924) *Med. Klin.*, **20**, 184.

STASSANO, H. and DE BEAUFORT, A.-C. (1925) *C. R. Soc. Biol.*, **93**, 1378.

STEWART, A. D. and GHOSAL, S. C. (1931) *Indian J. med. Res.*, **19**, 137.

TODD, C. (1927) *Brit. J. exp. Path.*, **8**, 369.

TWORT, F. W. (1915) *Lancet*, ii. 1241 ; (1922) *Brit. med. J.*, ii. 293 ; (1925) *Lancet*, ii. 642 ; (1926) *Ibid.*, i. 416.

VAGEDES, K. VON and GILDEMEISTER, E. (1934) *Zbl. Bakt.*, **131**, 414.

WOLLMAN, E. (1925) *Ann. Inst. Pasteur*, **39**, 789 ; (1927) *Ibid.*, **41**, 883 ; (1928) *Bull. Inst. Pasteur*, **26**, 1 ; (1929) *Ann. Inst. Pasteur*, **43**, 359 ; (1934) *Bull. Inst. Pasteur*, **32**, 945 ; (1935) *Lancet*, ii. 1312.

WOLLMAN, E. and WOLLMAN, E. (1932) *Ann. Inst. Pasteur*, **49**, 41.

YAOI, H. and SATO, K. (1935) *Jap. J. exp. Med.*, **13**, 565.

ZINSSER, H. and TANG, F. F. (1927) *J. exp. Med.*, **46**, 357.

PART II

SYSTEMATIC BACTERIOLOGY

CHAPTER XI

THE METHODS OF OBTAINING PURE CULTURES, AND THE IDENTIFICATION OF BACTERIA

METHODS OF OBTAINING PURE CULTURES OF BACTERIA

ONE of the first essentials in the study of bacteriology is the preparation and maintenance of pure cultures of bacteria. Neglect of this leads inevitably to confusion. During the sixties and seventies of last century, micro-organisms were perforce cultivated in liquid media ; and as the preparation of pure cultures in such media is often difficult and sometimes impossible relatively little progress in the identification of particular species was made in these years. It was the introduction of solid media by Robert Koch in 1881 that rendered possible the easy separation of different organisms from one another in a mixed culture, and provided a means for distinguishing macroscopically between different species of bacteria. Koch found that on a suitable solid medium, such as potato or gelatin, most organisms formed characteristic colonies by which they could be readily identified ; by inoculation of separate colonies into tubes of a liquid medium, pure cultures could be obtained. These could again be streaked on to a solid medium, and if the resulting colonies were all of the same appearance, it might be concluded that the liquid culture probably contained only one species of bacterium. This method—Koch's plating method—affords the simplest and most rapid means of separating one organism from another ; we shall later describe it more fully.

We have now at our command numerous methods of purifying cultures. Some are of limited utility, or are suited solely to certain organisms ; others are of wider applicability. Without discussing the technical details we shall give a brief description of the principles underlying the more important of these methods.

A. Dilution Method.—In point of time, this was the earliest method introduced for obtaining pure cultures of a bacterium, a method which we owe to Lister. The mixed culture is diluted with sterile tap water, or other suitable fluid, till there is only about one organism in every two drops of the mixture. A series of tubes containing broth is then seeded, each with one drop of the diluted culture. If the dilution has been correctly gauged, there should be a growth in approximately every alternate tube. This method affords one no certainty that the cultures obtained are pure; further study must be undertaken to ascertain this. The objections to the method are that too much guess-work is involved in judging the correct dilution, and that several tubes of medium are inevitably wasted. It is useful, however, in a modified form in conjunction with the plating method. That is to say, when the culture is thick, it is wise to dilute it considerably before plating out; in this way there is more likelihood of obtaining single colonies from single organisms.

B. Koch's Plating Method.—Originally the solid medium used was spread out in the melted state on microscopic slides and allowed to set; these were then streaked with a needle dipped in the culture, and incubated in a moist bell-jar. Later, large glass plates were used; these had to be specially levelled by means of adjustable screw supports, and covered with a bell-jar. The method now employed is to pour the melted medium into Petri dishes; each of these is provided with a cover, which protects the medium from contamination. The plating method may be employed in one of two ways. Either the culture material may be streaked on the surface of the solid medium, or it may be mixed with the medium in the melted state, poured out into Petri dishes, and allowed to set. The former method results in a surface growth, the latter in a growth throughout the whole thickness of the medium. As a rule the former method is the more useful. In streaking the surface of the medium, a drop of the fluid culture may be placed in the centre of the dish, and spread out in all directions by means of a sterile glass or metal rod bent at a right angle. This results in an even distribution of organisms over the plate. If, however, single colonies are particularly desired—and this is usual— it is best to make a series of streaks across the plate with a platinum loop dipped in the culture; the streaks should be about 10 mm. apart, and may be crossed at right angles; the platinum loop should not be re-charged with culture during the process. If preliminary dilution has not been performed, it is often advisable to continue the streaking over a second or even a third plate without re-charging the loop. On the first plate the growth may be entirely confluent; but on the second and third, single colonies will generally be obtained. These single colonies can then be examined with a hand lens, and picked off with a platinum needle into broth. Except with certain organisms, single colonies obtained in this way, especially if the culture has been previously diluted, are generally derived from single organisms, and are hence pure. The purity of colonies picked from over-crowded plates is less certain. In using the surface streak method it is important that the plates should be fairly dry; if there is a film of moisture on the medium— resulting partly from condensation and partly from expression—organisms, especially if motile, are apt to form a confluent growth over the whole surface. This point must always be borne in mind when attempting to isolate anaerobic bacteria. These organisms, instead of growing up from the medium, frequently spread in a thin layer over it; the edges of the colonies are difficult to define, and if there is a film of moisture over the medium, they coalesce, thus rendering their isolation impossible. The pour-plate method is, in general, of less value; the deep colonies are not usually as characteristic as the surface colonies, and to pick them off involves stabbing the medium with a platinum wire—a process that takes longer than the simple one of surface picking. In carrying out this method of plating, a tube containing 15 c.c. of the solid medium is heated in water till the medium is melted; for gelatin a temperature of 30° C. will suffice; for agar the water must be boiled.

The gelatin tube can be inoculated directly with a drop of the diluted culture ; the agar tube should be cooled to 45° C. before inoculation. The culture is then thoroughly mixed by rotation of the tube, and the mixture is poured out into a Petri dish and allowed to set. Gelatin sets at about 25° C., agar at 38° C. In warm weather the gelatin plates should be set on ice.

C. Shake-tube Method.—This is used chiefly for anaerobes. A test tube containing about 15 c.c. of solid medium, generally made up with a reducing agent such as glucose, is heated till the medium is melted ; a drop of culture is delivered into the medium, which has been cooled to a suitable temperature, and thoroughly mixed by gentle shaking and rotation. The medium is then allowed to set in the tube in a vertical position. Incubation is carried out aerobically or anaerobically. The great value of this method is that it affords a simple means of grading the oxygen pressure in the medium ; on the surface the pressure is atmospheric ; at the bottom of the tube, particularly if a reducing agent has been added, the conditions are completely anaerobic. Thus the aerobic bacteria grow at or just below the surface ; the anaerobic bacteria grow near the bottom ; and the facultative aerobes and anaerobes are distributed throughout the medium. The single colonies, which appear, are often fairly characteristic. To pick them off, the test tube is cut round with a diamond at the middle of the column of medium, the two halves of the tube drawn apart, and the medium allowed to fall gently into a sterile Petri dish. A stout platinum wire is then used to fish the colonies ; it is stabbed into the medium over the particular colony desired, taking care that no other colony is touched on the way ; and as soon as it has come into contact with the colony, it is withdrawn and inoculated into broth. Sometimes it is advisable to cut the medium into pieces with a sterile scalpel before attempting to pick off the colonies. This method was used at one time for purifying anaerobes ; but now that the technique of obtaining anaerobiosis has improved, it has been largely replaced by the more reliable surface plating method. In order to avoid breaking a test tube every time a colony has to be picked off, it is better to use a Veillon tube instead of the ordinary test tube. This consists of a piece of glass-tubing, about 1 cm. in diameter, and 8 or 10 inches long. One end is fitted with a rubber cork, the other with a cotton-wool plug. The medium is poured into the tube till it reaches about half or two-thirds of the way up. Inoculation is performed in the usual way. When it is desired to pick off a colony, the rubber cork and the woollen plug are removed, and the whole column of medium expelled by a stout glass rod into a Petri dish. The tubes and corks can be used over and over again.

Fig. 38.—
Veillon
Tube.

D. Motility.—Various methods have been devised for making use of motility to separate motile from non-motile organisms. These methods are of limited applicability, and in practice are seldom used. We mention them here for convenience. Rovida's (1925) tube, which is a modification of that invented by Carnot and Garnier (1902), may be used for this purpose. It consists of a large test tube to the bottom of which is fused a glass tube of 7 mm. internal diameter. This inner tube has a constriction near the lower end, below which are three small holes to afford a communication between the inside of the inner and the outer tubes. Above the constriction there is a plug of glass wool, which supports a layer of sand. Broth is poured into both tubes till it reaches the same level. The mixed culture is seeded into the broth of the outer tube, and the apparatus is put in the incubator. The organisms that are motile will pass through the holes into the inner tube, grow up through the wool and sand, and produce a turbidity in the broth of the inner tube; from this they may be recovered in pure culture. The non-motile organisms remain confined to the broth of the outer tube.

E. Optimum Temperature.—It is sometimes possible to make use of the optimum temperature of growth of an organism when it is desired to obtain it in pure culture, as for instance when one wants it to multiply freely in a mixed culture. The thermophilic bacteria may be separated from other organisms by incubating the medium at about 60° C.; none of the ordinary bacteria will grow at this temperature, so a pure growth of the thermophilic organisms is obtained. Again, certain bacteria will not grow at 22° C., whereas others will. If a mixture of the two is incubated at 22° C., only one type will develop; this may then be picked off pure. In this way *N. catarrhalis* may be separated from the meningococcus. In water analysis, when it is desired to know the numbers of potentially pathogenic bacteria in a given sample, the cultures are incubated at 37° C.; many of the saprophytic forms fail to grow at this temperature, and consequently the resulting growth consists largely of potential parasites.

F. Aerobic and Anaerobic Incubation.—This is a simple method of separating aerobes from anaerobes. Incubated aerobically, the strict anaerobes will not grow; incubated anaerobically, the strict aerobes will not grow. And as even the facultative anaerobes will rarely grow as well under anaerobic as under aerobic conditions, anaerobic incubation favours the strict anaerobes more than the facultative ones.

G. Heating.—Heating a mixed culture at 80° C. for 10 minutes will destroy all the vegetative non-sporing bacteria, while leaving the spores unaffected. This method is largely used in the preliminary purification of the anaerobes. In the body, most of the organisms with which the anaerobes are likely to be contaminated are non-sporing cocci and bacilli; all of these are destroyed at 80° C., and consequently the anaerobic organisms alone develop.

H. Selective Bactericidal Substances.—Certain substances with a germicidal action are useful in destroying susceptible organisms, while leaving the more resistant unaffected. One of the best examples of this method is the isolation of the tubercle bacillus from sputum by the use of antiformin. Tubercle bacilli are very resistant to chemical disinfectants, even though they are easily killed by heat. If the sputum, which generally contains numerous other organisms, is treated with 15 per cent. antiformin (equal parts of 15 per cent. NaOH and Liq. sodæ chlorinatæ B.P.), for a time varying from 5 to 60 minutes according to the thickness of the sputum, and inoculations are then made on to egg medium, the tubercle bacilli will develop in pure culture; without the antiformin they would be overgrown in 24 hours or less. Fifteen per cent. sulphuric acid is often used for the same purpose. Subcultures should be made at intervals of from 5 to 20 minutes.

I. Agglutinating Serum.—If it is suspected that relatively few organisms of a particular species are present in a bacterial culture or suspension, so that direct plating is unlikely to prove successful, it is sometimes possible to concentrate them by adding a specific high-titre agglutinating serum, incubating for 2 hours, and centrifuging. The organisms, which are clumped together, are easily thrown down, and are present almost exclusively in the deposit. Plates may then be streaked from this directly. This method is sometimes of value in isolating the typhoid bacillus from water.

J. Filtration.—This method may be used to separate the filtrable viruses from the ordinary bacteria, or if a fairly coarse candle is used, such as a Berkefeld N or V, it may be used to separate very small bacteria like *Bact. pneumosintes* from larger organisms. Many spirochætes will also pass through Berkefeld filters ; this property is made use of in separating them from the bacteria with which they are often contaminated.

K. Selective Media.—These are media that contain substances having a stimulating effect on the growth of the organism it is desired to cultivate, or an inhibitory effect on the growth of others. The result in either case is an enrichment of the particular organism that is being sought for. Blood, serum, and ascitic or hydrocele fluid are substances that are frequently used to stimulate the growth of certain organisms ; glucose and other sugars, extracts of vegetable and animal tissues, and certain salts such as potassium nitrate, are likewise used for the same purpose. On the other hand certain aniline dyes, phenol, telluric acid, bile salts, and numerous other substances are used for inhibiting the growth of certain organisms. Gentian violet, in a concentration of about 1–10,000, suppresses the growth of most Gram-positive organisms, while allowing most Gram-negative organisms to develop. Used at 1–500,000 it is of value in separating streptococci from staphylococci, since the latter organisms are inhibited by this concentration. Brilliant green is often used for preventing the growth of lactose-fermenting organisms in cultures from the stools. It is added to the fæcal suspension in broth in a concentration of about 1–150,000 ; the culture is incubated, and plated out on a suitable medium after 18 to 24 hours. Many Gram-negative bacteria are inhibited by potassium tellurite in a concentration of 1–80,000 or more, while penicillin—the name given to the filtrate of a broth culture of *Penicillium notatum*—exercises an inhibitory action mainly on Gram-positive bacteria (Fleming 1932). The use of selective media is of great importance in bacteriology. For the isolation and growth of any organism it is desirable to use the medium or media on which the best results are likely to be obtained. For the general bacteriologist therefore, a wide range of media is essential.

L. Indicator Media.—These are media that contain an indicator which changes colour when a certain organism or group of organisms develops. Thus, if it is known that the organism which it is desired to cultivate produces H_2S, lead acetate may be added to the medium ; the colonies of the organism are coloured brown, owing to the production of lead sulphide, and can be readily picked off for identification. The diphtheria bacillus reduces sodium tellurite, whereas many of the organisms likely to be associated with it in a throat swab do not. When this substance is added to the medium, the colonies of the diphtheria and of the diphtheroid bacilli are coloured black, whereas those of the streptococci and numerous other organisms are colourless. Litmus and neutral red are two dyes that are frequently used to indicate the production of acid from some carbohydrate incorporated in the medium. Colonies of organisms that ferment the sugar are coloured red owing to the production of acid, whereas those that do not do so take on the alkaline colour of the dye—blue and yellow respectively. Blood is a very useful indicator. Some organisms produce no alteration in it, others form from it a green pigment, while others lyse it completely. It is usually added to agar in a concentration of 5 per cent. The colonies of the first class leave the medium unchanged ; those of the second class are surrounded by a greenish ring ; those of the third class by a perfectly clear transparent ring. It is used particularly in the differentiation of the streptococci.

Selective and indicator media are frequently combined. Thus in MacConkey's medium, bile salts are added to inhibit the growth of non-intestinal organisms, and lactose and neutral red are added to distinguish the lactose fermenting coliform organisms from the non-lactose-fermenting group.

M. Pathogenicity Methods.—The introduction of the pathogenicity method of separating organisms from one another we owe to Koch (1880). By this means he succeeded in separating streptococci from *Erysipelothrix muriseptica*. When the mixed culture was injected into the ear of a *house* mouse, *Ery. muriseptica* proliferated, invaded the blood stream, and could be obtained in pure culture from the heart's blood after death ; the streptococcus proliferated locally but did not invade the blood stream. As it was mixed in the local lesion with *Ery. muriseptica* it could not be obtained in pure culture. But Koch found that if the mixed culture was injected into a *field* mouse, the streptococci proliferated, invaded the blood-stream, and caused death, while *Ery. muriseptica* did not grow at all ; the streptococcus was therefore obtained in pure culture from the blood. This principle is of wide application. It is used particularly to isolate organisms that are pathogenic to a certain laboratory animal from other closely similar organisms that are not pathogenic. Thus *B. anthracis* can easily be separated from *B. subtilis* or *B. megatherium* by the injection of a mouse or a guinea-pig. It is also used to isolate pathogenic organisms which are not easy to grow in culture, or which are readily over-grown by contaminating organisms. As examples, we may quote the tubercle bacillus in pus, or the pneumococcus in sputum. The contaminating organisms are rapidly killed in the animal body, whereas the pathogenic organism multiplies and can be recovered in pure culture from the tissues.

N. Single Cell Methods.—The aim of these methods is to obtain a culture of a given organism from a single bacterial cell. If this can be carried out successfully, then the resultant culture must obviously be pure. If the technique for single-cell isolation was simple and flawless, this would be the ideal method for the purification of cultures ; in fact, however, several of the methods advocated for this purpose suffer from optical or other defects, which seriously detract from their value. In Barber's (1908) method the culture is diluted, and a series of tiny droplets prepared. These are placed on the under surface of a cover-slip forming the roof of a special chamber, and examined under the microscope. When a drop is found containing only one organism, it is picked off with a special capillary pipette and transferred to a fluid medium. This method has been widely used, but it suffers from the defect that in viewing a spherical droplet the optical conditions are such as to render accurate observation of particles at the water-air interface very difficult or impossible. Hence there is no absolute certainty that a single cell has been picked. A method devised by Topley, Barnard and Wilson (1921) eliminates these particular optical defects. A loopful of a young gelatin culture at 37° C. is placed on a slide, and covered with a quartz cover-glass. Under dark-ground illumination a single organism is picked out which is well removed from any other organisms, and is covered with a minute droplet of mercury. The preparation is exposed for a short time to ultra-violet irradiation with the object of destroying all organisms except the single one that has been protected by the mercury droplet. After incubation overnight the preparation is again examined, and, if successful, a colony will be observed at the site previously occupied by the protected organism. This can then be transferred to a liquid medium. Adequate controls are necessary to prove that the irradiation was sufficient to kill all non-protected organisms.

THE IDENTIFICATION OF MICRO-ORGANISMS

Having once obtained a pure culture of a particular organism it is necessary to establish its identity by an appropriate series of tests. This may require a few weeks, or it may take several months to complete. Many of the reactions may have to be tested three or four times to make sure of their consistency. It is often desirable to prepare photographs of the morphology and of the colonial appearances on the most important media ; these will be found of great value for future comparison. For studying the properties of an organism the following scheme is suggested.

A. Morphology.—Under this heading we include the shape and size of the organism, its arrangement, motility, the number and distribution of flagella, the shape and situation of spores, and capsule formation. It is impossible to study all these properties on a single medium ; motility for example should be looked for in a young rapidly growing broth culture, preferably not more than 6 to 8 hours old ; flagella are sought for on a young agar culture ; spores in a culture that has been growing for some days ; capsules in a pathological exudate, and so on. The shape and size of the organisms are subject to considerable variation, and it is important to gain some idea of the extent of this variation. With a few exceptions, such as the diphtheria group, most organisms are larger in a young than in an old culture (Henrici 1926). Measurements, for example, of *Bact. typhi-murium* in a 4-hours' culture on agar showed that the average size was $2 \cdot 35 \ \mu \times 0 \cdot 79 \ \mu$; in the same culture after 26 hours the size was only $1 \cdot 13 \ \mu \times 0 \cdot 49 \ \mu$. In volume the organisms from the young culture were over five times that from the old. On further incubation the average size decreased still further (Wilson 1926). When taking measurements of a given strain it is therefore important to record the age of the culture from which they were taken. Even in one and the same preparation the individual organisms may vary considerably in size and shape ; this may be so marked as to justify the term " pleomorphic." Thus coccoid, bacillary, and filamentous forms may all be present together ; or besides the usual rods there may be club forms, navicular forms, granular forms, large bloated forms, shadow forms, and so on. Moreover, the appearance of the organisms is often considerably influenced by the type of medium on which they are grown. Chain formation, for example, is more evident in liquid media than on solid. The typical morphological appearance of the diphtheria bacillus is seen best on Loeffler's serum ; on agar the organisms tend to be more solid and less granular. The nature of the medium often influences the production of spores and of capsules. Some organisms, such as *B. anthracis,* form spores readily in artificial culture, but never do so in the animal body. On the other hand, capsules are quite frequently found in the body, but less often in artificial culture. The arrangement of the organisms should be carefully studied ; if they are cocci, they may be arranged singly, in pairs, tetrads, packets, clusters, or chains ; if bacilli, they may be arranged singly, in pairs end-to-end, in bundles, chains, clusters, or in Chinese-letter forms in which the individual bacilli lie more or less at right angles to each other ; if vibrios, they may be arranged singly, in S-forms, semicircles, in wavy chains composed of S-forms strung end-to-end, or they may present the fish-in-stream appearance. Though most organisms show two or three types of arrangement, it is usual for one of these to be predominant ; this comes to be regarded as the typical arrangement. It cannot be emphasized too strongly that the morphology of bacteria is subject to variation, depending on the age of the culture, the nature of the medium, the particular strain used, the temperature of incubation, and a number of other factors ; the extent of this variation can be learnt only by experience.

B. Staining Reactions.—The morphology of bacteria may be studied in a hanging-drop preparation, by dark-ground illumination, or in stained films. By each of these methods different information may be gained. Staining methods, in addition to revealing the morphology of the organism, may render evident differences in the chemical constitution of different organisms, or of different parts of the same organism. For studying the morphology, it is advisable to use a weak stain ; otherwise so much dye may be absorbed as to alter the appearance of the organism. Gram's stain is of great value, in that it serves to divide all bacteria into one or other of two classes—the Gram-positive and the Gram-negative. The Ziehl-Neelsen method of staining is likewise of value, since it serves to distinguish the acid-fast from the non-acid-fast bacilli. Numerous other stains are used for special purposes, such as the demonstration of flagella, capsules, spores, and meta-chromatic granules.

By a study of the morphology and the staining reactions, it is generally possible to identify the group to which a given organism belongs. In certain instances, when the origin of the organism is known, it is possible to make a presumptive diagnosis of its actual identity. Thus acid-fast bacilli in the cerebro-spinal fluid of a patient with clinical symptoms of meningitis may safely be identified as tubercle bacilli ; Gram-negative diplococci in the pus of an infant with ophthalmia neonatorum are almost certainly gonococci; and Gram-negative bipolar-staining ovoid bacilli in the gland-juice from a patient with an inguinal bubo, in an area where plague is prevalent, may safely be regarded as plague bacilli. As a rule, however, it is impossible to identify an organism by morphology and staining alone.

C. Cultural Reactions.—Under this heading must be included a study of the surface, and often of the deep, colonies formed on solid media, and of the type of growth in fluid media. Nutrient agar is the usual medium on which colony formation is studied, but if the organism fails to grow on agar, then some other medium must be chosen. The colonies are best examined after 24 hours' incubation at 37° C., and again at intervals for a week. In describing them, particular attention should be paid to their shape, size, elevation, structure, colour, transparency, surface, edge, consistency, and emulsifiability ; differentiation into central and peripheral areas should also be noted. The type of growth following a streak inoculation on an agar slope should be studied, attention being paid particularly to the profuseness of growth, to the elevation, colour, surface, and edge, and to any change in the medium itself. The type of growth in a gelatin stab culture should also be studied, and notes made of the degree and extent of the growth, the presence of a surface growth, the presence or absence of liquefaction, and if liquefaction occurs, of the particular type which it assumes (see Chapter XII). In any systematic examination, the growth should be studied on certain special media such as Loeffler's serum, glycerine potato, and coagulated egg.

The cultural reactions of the different groups of bacteria are fairly distinctive, and even within a given group there may be differences between the members. Some organisms moreover have a characteristic form of growth, which enables them to be distinguished from morphologically similar organisms. As a rule, however, a study of the cultural reactions merely indicates the group to which a given organism belongs ; it does not distinguish between the different members. It serves to confirm the conclusions reached from the examination of the morphology and staining reactions.

D. Resistance.—Organisms vary considerably in their resistance to inimical agencies. Roughly speaking, three classes may be distinguished :

(1) The bacteria that are susceptible to low degrees of heat, and low concentrations of chemical disinfectants ; this class includes the non-sporing bacteria and the vegetative forms of the spore-bearing bacteria. They are destroyed by moist heat at 60° C. in half an hour and by 1 per cent. phenol within an hour.

(2) The bacteria that are susceptible to low degrees of heat, but are resistant to low concentrations of disinfectants ; this class includes the acid-fast bacteria, which are killed at 60° C. in half an hour, but resist destruction by chemical agents in the cold often for several hours.

(3) The bacteria that are resistant both to low degrees of heat and low concentrations of disinfectants ; this class includes the sporing forms of the spore-bearing bacteria. To kill them with certainty, steam under pressure at a temperature of 120° C. for half an hour should be employed, or high concentrations of disinfectants, for example, 5 per cent. phenol, maintained for several hours.

A study of the resistance of a given bacterium will, as a rule, merely serve to confirm the conclusions already reached by the three previous methods of examination, but occasionally it is in itself of some diagnostic importance. Thus certain of the non-sporing vegetative bacteria, for example the enterococcus, are not destroyed at 60° C. in half an hour ; they require a temperature of 65° C. ; this abnormal heat resistance is of value in differentiating this species of streptococcus from other species, which are readily killed at the lower temperature. Whenever an organism is suspected of forming spores, the heat resistance must be tested, and not till the suspected spores have definitely been found to be resistant to heat should the conclusion be reached that they really are spores. Many forms have been interpreted in the past as being true spores, which on subsequent examination have been found to be devoid of the characteristic property of heat resistance.

E. Metabolism.—Under this heading is included a study of the oxygen pressure required for growth, the optimum temperature for growth, pigment formation, hæmolysin production, and the effect on growth of adding different substances to the medium. It is usual to divide bacteria into 3 classes according to their oxygen requirements : (1) Strict aerobes : these organisms will grow only in the presence of free oxygen. (2) Strict anaerobes : these will grow only in the absence of free oxygen. It must be noted, however, that growth will occur in the presence of molecular oxygen, provided the medium contains a reducing system capable of bringing about a sufficiently low O–R potential. (See Chapters III and XXXIII.) (3) Facultative anaerobes : these grow best under aerobic conditions, but are able to grow under anaerobic conditions. To these may be added a fourth class, the microaerophiles, comprising those organisms that grow best under a pressure of oxygen lower than that of the atmosphere. According to their temperature requirements bacteria may be divided into (1) the mesophilic, which have an optimum temperature between 20° and 40° C., and (2) the thermophilic, which have an optimum temperature between 60° C. and 70° C. In medical bacteriology, the important distinction lies between those organisms that will grow at room temperature as well as at 37° C., and those that will grow at 37° C. but not at room temperature. The latter class includes many of the highly parasitic organisms. The power to hæmolyse may be studied by growing the organism on blood agar plates, or by mixing varying dilutions of a broth culture with a suspension of washed red cells. This property is of considerable importance, and is employed as a primary criterion for differentiating between the members of the streptococcal group. The effect on growth of adding blood, serum, glucose, nitrates, and bile salts to the medium is important, since it is often of differential value. The formation of pigment should be studied on various media and at different temperatures ; as a rule it will be found that pigment is best formed on the surface of a solid medium at a temperature of 25–30° C. In liquid media, or in the depth of solid media, and at temperatures above 35° C., pigment is formed less abundantly ; under strict anaerobic conditions it is not formed at all.

A study of the salient metabolic functions of an organism as a rule adds considerably to the information derived from the previous methods of examination. Oxygen and temperature requirements, and pigment formation, especially are of great classificatory value, being frequently used for the differentiation of species.

F. Fermentation Reactions and Other Biochemical Properties.—Under this heading we include a study of the fermentative action on certain carbohydrates and alcohols (colloquially spoken of as " sugars ") ; of the proteolytic powers, especially the digestion of gelatin, egg, and serum ; of the fat-splitting powers ; of the power to reduce certain dyes such as methylene blue and litmus, or certain salts such as nitrate and tellurite ; of the production of catalase ; the production of indole from peptone ; the formation of NH_3 and H_2S ; the final hydrogen-ion concentration in glucose broth ; and the power to utilize certain salts such as tartrates and citrates.

As a rule the fermentation of sugars is observed qualitatively, the formation of acid being rendered evident by the inclusion in the medium of an indicator, and the liberation of gas by an inverted Durham tube, or by a special fermentation tube. For the testing of the other biochemical properties, certain fairly stereotyped methods have been evolved, which it is unnecessary to describe here.

In bacterial differentiation the biochemical reactions are often of the greatest importance ; in many groups of organisms the classification is made on the basis of sugar fermentation, of proteolytic power, or of both tests taken together. The sugar tests especially afford a means of bringing out the finer distinctions between closely allied organisms. The oxidation of tartrates and citrates is employed in the differentiation of the coliform group of bacteria.

G. Antigenic Structure.—For identifying bacteria, the serological reactions most frequently employed are agglutination and complement fixation. Provided that adequate controls are used, these reactions—particularly agglutination—afford the most rapid and reliable method of identifying a given bacterium. For the identification to be complete the organism should be agglutinated to titre by a serum prepared against the organism which it is supposed to resemble, and should absorb all the agglutinins from that serum ; moreover the type organism should be agglutinated to titre by a serum prepared against the unknown organism, and should likewise remove all agglutinins from it. That is to say, there should be complete cross-agglutination and cross-absorption between the two sera and the two organisms. In certain groups of bacteria, the serological method is found to be much the quickest and most satisfactory way of distinguishing between the different members, and it is therefore extensively used for rapid identification. In other groups the agglutination method is not of much help, either because there are numerous varieties within the species, or because the organisms are auto-agglutinable, or for some other reason. Apart from affording a rapid means of identification of certain bacteria, the serological method is as a rule the most delicate method available for bringing out the finer distinctions between closely allied organisms. In this respect it is more valuable even than the biochemical tests. It is often the only method available for differentiating between the sub-species or varieties of a given species of organism.

H. Pathogenicity.—The pathogenicity of bacteria is usually tested on laboratory animals, especially the guinea-pig, rabbit, rat, and mouse. It may be advisable to introduce the organism directly into the tissues by inoculation subcutaneously, intramuscularly, intraperitoneally, or intravenously ; or it may be given by the mouth, or in the form of a spray, which the animal is made to inhale. Pathogenicity tests are open to numerous errors, but provided these are adequately guarded against, they often afford very important information. This is limited, however, to certain groups of organisms. In the study of the purely saprophytic bacteria and of certain bacteria that are harmless to laboratory animals, the pathogenicity test is of no value except to establish the absence of virulence. It is used chiefly in distinguishing virulent from avirulent members of the same genus or species. But it is also used to distinguish between closely allied organisms, both of which are virulent to the same animal, but which produce in it lesions of varying extent or localization ; or which differ in their virulence to different species of animal.

For the complete identification of a pathogenic species, it may be necessary to determine whether or not it forms a soluble exotoxin ; that is to say, whether sterile filtrates of cultures grown for a suitable time in suitable fluid media produce death with characteristic lesions. In species which produce such exotoxins, neutralization with a specific antitoxin may play an important part in identification. In the description of any newly isolated pathogenic species a record of the toxicity or non-toxicity of filtrates should always be included.

It will be realized that the complete identification of an unknown organism is often a lengthy proceeding. As a rule it is easy to refer it to its proper genus ; this can be done by simple examination of the morphological and staining reactions, aided at times by the cultural reactions. But its more exact denomination requires the use of the most delicate tests at our disposal, namely the biochemical, serological, and pathogenicity tests. It is advisable never to place too much weight on any one test ; errors of technique or of interpretation are always liable to occur. If a large series of tests is carried out, and the organism is studied by several different methods, then the chances of being misled are very greatly reduced.

The complete identification of a given organism with any known type is not, of course, always possible ; within the type species there are often varieties differing in minor respects from the type organism. It is very important to realize this ; in any large collection of organisms of apparently the same species, there will almost invariably be found a number that differ from the rest in one or more of their properties ; sometimes these differences are so numerous, or a single one of them may be so important, that it is necessary to revise one's classification.

If the characters of the organism differ from those of any described species, and if it is desired to preserve or to publish a description of the new species or type, it is essential to make a full and careful record of all its characters and re-actions, so that they will be available for comparison with organisms isolated at a future date, or with organisms isolated by other observers. Such a record should always contain careful comparisons with those species or types which most nearly resemble the newly isolated organism.

REFERENCES

BARBER, M. A. (1908) *J. infect. Dis.*, **5,** 379.
CARNOT, P. and GARNIER, M. (1902) *C. R. Soc. Biol.*, **54,** 748.
FLEMING, A. (1932) *J. Path. Bact.*, **35,** 831.
HENRICI, A. T. (1926) *J. infect. Dis.*, **38,** 54.
KOCH, R. (1880) " Investigations into the Etiology of the Traumatic Infective Diseases."
    New Sydenham Soc., Lond. ; (1881) *Mitt. ReichsgesundhAmt.*, **1,** 1.
ROVIDA, G. (1925) *Sperimentale*, **79,** 1053.
TOPLEY, W. W. C., BARNARD, J. E., and WILSON, G. S. (1921) *J. Hyg., Camb.*, **20,** 221.
WILSON, G. S. (1926) *J. Hyg., Camb.*, **25,** 150.

CHAPTER XII

DESCRIPTION OF THE METHODS USED IN THE SYSTEMATIC EXAMINATION OF BACTERIA, AND A GLOSSARY OF THE TERMS EMPLOYED

WE have already dealt in Chapter XI with the methods of isolating pure cultures of bacteria, and with the various criteria that are employed in their identification. In the present chapter we describe a routine which may be used in examining the various morphological, cultural, and biochemical properties of bacteria, and define the terms which we shall employ in the description of these properties.

Morphological Appearance of Bacteria.—The chief points to be noted are the following :

Shape.—Spheres, short rods, long rods, filaments, commas, or spirals.

Axis.—Straight or curved.

Size.—Length and breadth.

Sides.—Parallel, bulging, concave, or irregular.

Ends.—Rounded, truncate, concave, or pointed.

Arrangement.—Singly, in pairs, in chains, in fours, in groups, in grape-like clusters, in cubical packets, in bundles, or in Chinese letters.

Irregular Forms.—Variations in shape and size ; club, filamentous, branched, navicular, citron, fusiform, and shadow forms.

Motility.—Motile or non-motile.

Flagella.—Monotrichate, amphitrichate, lophotrichate, peritrichate (Fig. 7).

Endospores.—Spherical, oval, or ellipsoidal ; equatorial, subterminal, or terminal ; single or multiple ; causing bulging of bacillus or not (Fig. 5).

Capsules.—Present or absent.

Staining.—Even, irregular, unipolar, bipolar, beaded, barred ; and variations in depth between different organisms. Presence of metachromatic granules ; reaction to Gram and to Ziehl-Neelsen stains.

Surface Colonies on Solid Media.

Shape.—Circular, irregular, radiate, rhizoid.

Size.—In millimetres.

Elevation.—Effuse, raised, low convex, convex or dome-shaped, umbonate ; with or without bevelled margin.

Structure.—Amorphous ; fine, medium, or coarsely granular ; filamentous, curled.

Surface.—Smooth ; contoured, beaten-copper ; rough ; fine, medium, or coarsely granular ; ringed ; papillate ; dull or glistening.

Edge.—Entire, undulate, lobate, crenated, erose, fimbriate, curled, effuse.

Colour.—Colour by reflected and transmitted light ; iridescent, fluorescent, opalescent, luminous.

Opacity.—Transparent, translucent, or opaque.

Consistency.—Butyrous, viscid, friable, membranous.

Emulsifiability.—Easy or difficult ; forms homogeneous, granular, or membranous emulsion when rubbed up in a drop of water with a platinum loop.

Differentiation.—Differentiated into a central and a peripheral portion (Fig. 39).

Growth on Stroke Culture.

Degree.—None, scanty, moderate, abundant, profuse ; discrete, or confluent.

Form.—Filiform, spreading, rhizoid.

Elevation.—Effuse or raised.

Surface.—Smooth ; contoured ; beaten-copper ; rough ; finely, moderately, or coarsely granular ; papillate ; heaped up ; dry or moist.

Edge.—Entire, undulate, lobate, crenated, erose, fimbriate ; curled, effuse.

Colour, Opacity, Consistency, and Emulsifiability.—As for colonies.

Odour.—Absent, decided, resembling——.

Medium.—Coloured ; digested ; crystal formation (Fig. 39).

Growth in Stab Culture.

Degree.—As for stroke culture. Also position of optimal growth.

Form.—Filiform, beaded, with or without branching.

Extent.—Depth in tube to which growth occurs.

Surface.—Surface growth present or absent ; if present, diameter, surface, and edge.

Colour and Opacity.—As for stroke culture.

Liquefaction.—Present or absent ; if present, crateriform, napiform, infundibuliform, saccate, or stratiform.

Medium.—As for stroke culture (Fig. 39).

Growth in Shake Culture.

Position.—Uniform growth throughout tube ; or position of optimal growth.

Surface.—Surface growth present or absent.

Colonies.—Size, shape, colour, opacity, outgrowths from periphery, if any.

Gas.—Present or absent ; medium disrupted.

Medium.—Coloured, digested, or rendered turbid.

Growth in Fluid Medium.

Degree.—None, scanty, moderate, abundant, or profuse.

Turbidity.—Present or absent ; if present, slight, moderate, or dense ; uniform, granular, or flocculent.

Deposit.—Present or absent ; if present, slight, moderate, or abundant ; powdery, granular, flocculent, membranous, or viscid ; disintegrating completely or incompletely on shaking.

Surface Growth.—Present or absent ; if present, ring growth around wall of tube ; or surface pellicle, which is thin or thick, with a smooth, granular, or rough surface, and which disintegrates completely or incompletely on shaking.

Odour.—Absent, decided, resembling——.

Growth in Blood Agar.

Colonies.—Description of surface colonies.

Hæmolysis.—Present or absent ; if present, of α- or β-type.

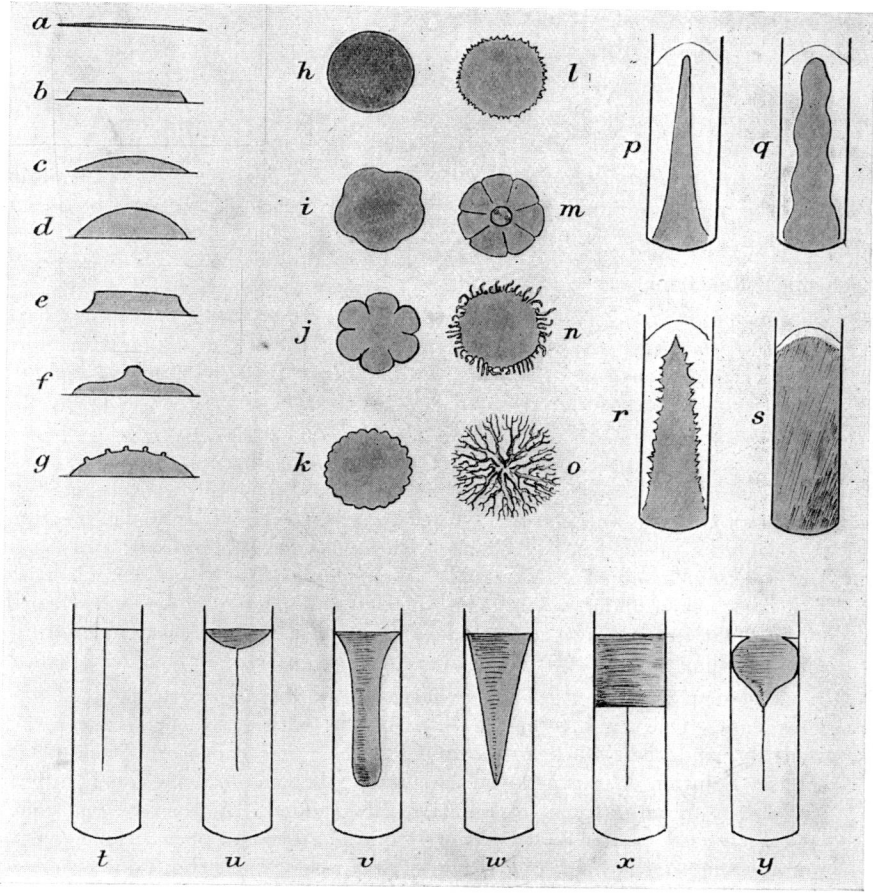

FIG. 39.

a–g. Elevation of colonies. *a.* Flat or effuse. *b.* Raised. *c.* Low convex. *d.* Convex or dome-shaped. *e.* Raised with concave bevelled edge. *f.* Umbonate. *g.* Convex with papillate surface. *h–o.* Edge of colonies. *h.* Entire. *i.* Undulate. *j.* Lobate. *k.* Crenated. *l.* Erose or dentate. *m.* Radially striated periphery with lobate edge. *n.* Fimbriate. *o.* Rhizoid or arborescent. *p–s.* Growth on agar stroke culture. *p.* Filiform. *q.* Slightly spreading with undulate edge. *r.* Slightly spreading with erose edge. *s.* Spreading. *t–y.* Growth in gelatin stab culture. *t.* Filiform growth without liquefaction. *u.* Crateriform liquefaction. *v.* Saccate liquefaction. *w.* Infundibuliform liquefaction. *x.* Stratiform liquefaction. *y.* Napiform liquefaction.

Resistance.—Tested usually by placing a 24-hours' broth culture, containing 5 c.c. of medium in a ⅝-inch test tube, in a water-bath at such temperatures as 55° C. for 1 hour, 60° C. for 1 hour, and 80° C. for half an hour, and subculturing into a favourable medium. This is, of course, merely a rough differential test.

Metabolic Properties.

Oxygen Pressure required for Growth.—Aerobic, facultatively anaerobic, obligatory anaerobic, microaerophilic.

Effect of Temperature on Growth.—Limits between which growth occurs ; optimal temperature for growth.

Pigment Formation.—Tested usually on an agar slope incubated at 22° C., or left at room temperature after preliminary incubation at 37° C.

Effect of Modifying the Constitution of the Medium.—Effect on growth of adding to the medium blood, serum, ascitic fluid, glucose, glycerine, potassium nitrate, bile salts, or other substances.

Biochemical Reactions.

Fermentation of Sugars.—Tested in 1 per cent. peptone water containing 1 per cent. of the sugar and Andrade's indicator. A Durham's tube is included. For certain groups of organisms, which do not grow well in this medium, 5 per cent. of horse serum is added. Production of acid, or of acid and gas, is noted.

Litmus Milk.—No change, acid or alkali ; clot ; clot disrupted by gas ; peptonization ; saponification. The term " clot " is unfortunately used for both an acid clot and a rennet clot. An acid clot results from the precipitation of the caseinogen ; it is soft, gelatinous, does not retract, and can be completely dissolved in alkali. A rennet clot is due to the coagulation of the caseinogen under the influence of bacterial enzymes. A few hours after its formation it retracts with the expression of a clear greyish-coloured fluid called whey ; the clot itself is firm and cannot be dissolved by alkali.

Indole.—Tested in 1 per cent. peptone water after 5 days' growth, using Böhme's reagents. One c.c. of ether is added to the culture, which is shaken thoroughly, and then allowed to stand till the ether collects on the surface. 1 c.c. Solution A is run down the side of the tube ; if no colour appears within a minute, 1 c.c. of Solution B is added. A positive reaction is characterized by a colour varying from a faint pink to a deep magenta. According to Happold and Hoyle (1934) xylene is better than ether.

> Solution A :
> | Paradimethylamidobenzaldehyde | 4 gms. |
> | 96 per cent. Alcohol . . | 380 ,, |
> | Concentrated HCl . . . | 80 ,, |
>
> Solution B :
> Saturated watery solution of potassium persulphate.

An alternative method, depending on the volatility of indole at 37° C., is recommended by Holman and Gonzales (1923). It consists in placing a strip of filter paper, soaked in a saturated watery solution of oxalic acid and subsequently dried between the cotton-wool plug and the tube. The paper should be carefully folded so as to present the maximum surface to the volatilizing indole, which turns it a pink colour.

Methyl-Red Test (M.R.).—Tested by adding 5 drops of an 0·04 per cent. solution of methyl red to a culture in glucose phosphate medium (peptone 0·5 gms., K_2HPO_4 0·5 gms., glucose 0·5 gms., water 100 c.c., pH 7·5). Culture grown for 5 days at 30° C or 3 days at 37° C.

> Red colour   = positive.
> Yellow colour = negative.

Voges-Proskauer Test (V.P.).—Tested by adding 1 c.c. of a 10 per cent. solution of KOH to a glucose phosphate culture grown for 5 days at 30° C. or 2 days at 37° C. The colour develops slowly, and the test should be read after 18 to 24 hours.

> Pink fluorescence = positive.
> No coloration   = negative.

A higher proportion of positive reactions is obtained by the use of O'Meara's (1931) modification. A knife point of creatin is added to the culture, followed by 5 c.c. of 40 per cent. sodium hydroxide. The tube is shaken thoroughly for 2 to 5 minutes. If acetoin is present, a pink colour appears within about 2 minutes, unaccompanied by fluorescence (see also Barritt 1936).

Nitrate Reduction.—Tested on a broth culture containing 0·1 per cent. KNO_3, grown for 5 days at 37° C., by the Griess-Ilosva method.

> Solution A :
> α-naphthylamine   .   .   .   1 gm.
> Water   .   .   .   .   .   22 c.c.
> Dissolve, filter, and then add 180 c.c. of dilute acetic acid (sp. gr. 1·04).
> Solution B :
> Sulphanilic acid   .   .   .   0·5 gm.
> Dilute acetic acid   .   .   .   150 c.c.
> Add 1 c.c. of Solution A, followed by 1 c.c. of Solution B.
> Pink, red, or maroon colour = positive.
> No coloration   = negative.

A negative reaction may sometimes be due to the reduction of the nitrite to gaseous nitrogen almost as rapidly as it is formed, or to the production of hydroxylamine. The first possibility may be examined by growth in a gas fermentation tube, or by chemical estimation of the nitrate, the second by testing for nitrite in the way just described, after preliminary oxidation of the hydroxylamine with iodine (see Lindsey and Rhines 1932, Conn 1936). A control tube should always be tested.

Ammonia.—Tested on a peptone water culture, grown for 5 days at 37° C., by adding Nessler's reagent.

> Brown colour   = positive.
> Faint yellow colour = negative.

Hydrogen Sulphide.—Tested on lead acetate medium (heart extract broth containing 4 per cent. peptone and 2·5 per cent. agar. Sterilize, and add an equal quantity of a sterile 0·1 per cent. solution of basic lead acetate.)

> Brown or black coloration = positive.
> No coloration   = negative.

The lead acetate may be replaced by 0·05 per cent. ferric ammonium citrate or 0·03 per cent. ferrous acetate (Zobell and Feltham 1934). A higher proportion of positive reactions is obtained with some organisms by incubating at 30° C. instead of 37° C. (Tittsler 1931). The most delicate method is to grow the organisms in a slope tube of liver extract agar, and to include between the cotton-wool plug and the tube a slip of filter paper soaked in 10 per cent. lead acetate solution and subsequently dried. The amount of browning or blackening of the paper is measured in millimetres. A fresh slip may be inserted daily.

Methylene Blue Reduction.—Tested on a 24-hours' broth culture at 37° C. Add 1 drop of 1 per cent. aqueous methylene blue, and incubate at 37° C.

> Complete decolorization = strong positive.
> Green coloration   = weak positive.
> No decolorization   = negative.

Catalase.—Tested on a 24-hours' agar slope culture at 37° C. One c.c. of H_2O_2 (10 vols.) is poured over the growth, and the tube is set in an inclined position.

> Gas bubbles produced = positive.
> No gas produced   = negative.

For an account of the methods of examining the antigenic structure and the pathogenicity of bacteria, reference must be made to the chapters dealing with the particular organism under consideration.

GLOSSARY OF DESCRIPTIVE TERMS

Aerobic : growing in the presence of free oxygen ; strictly *aerobic*, growing only in the presence of free oxygen.

Amorphous (colonies) : without visible differentiation in structure.

Amphitrichate : having a single flagellum at each pole.

Anaerobic : growing in the absence of free oxygen ; strictly *anaerobic*, growing only in the absence of free oxygen ; facultatively *anaerobic*, growing both in the presence of and in the absence of oxygen. It must be noted, however that growth of even strict anaerobes will occur in the presence of molecular oxygen, provided the medium contains a reducing system capable of bringing about a sufficiently low O–R potential (see Chapters III and XXXIII).

Beaded (stained bacteria) : deeply staining granules arranged at regular intervals along the course of the rod. (In stab or stroke culture) : disjointed or semi-confluent colonies along the line of inoculation.

Beaten-copper : multiple small crateriform depressions on the surface of a growth, resembling beaten copper.

Bipolar : at both ends or poles of the bacterial cell.

Butyrous : growth of butter-like consistency.

Chains : four or more bacterial cells attached end-to-end.

Chromogenesis : the production of colour.

Citron : shaped like a lemon, with a small knob at each end.

Clavate : club-shaped.

Coagulation : formation of a firm clot in milk with the subsequent separation of the casein from the whey.

Contoured : an irregular, smoothly undulating surface.

Convex : the segment of a sphere of short radius ; *Low convex*, the segment of a sphere of long radius.

Crateriform : a saucer-shaped liquefaction of the medium.

Crenated : small, shallow indentations of the edge, which has a scalloped appearance.

Cuneate : wedge-shaped.

Curled : composed of parallel chains in wavy strands, as in anthrax colonies.

Effuse : growth thin, hardly raised at all from the medium.

Endospores : thick-walled spores formed within the bacterial cell.

Entire : with an even margin.

Equatorial : situated about equidistant from each end.

Erose : border showing fine, pointed, tooth-like projections.

Filaments : applied to morphology of bacteria, refers to thread-like forms, generally unsegmented ; if segmented to be distinguished from chains (*q.v.*) by the absence of constrictions between the segments.

Filamentous : growth composed of long, often interwoven threads.

Filiform : in stroke or stab cultures, a uniform growth confined to the line of inoculation.

Fimbriate : fine, sometimes recurved, processes projecting from the edge of the colony or growth.

Flocculent : containing small adherent masses of bacteria of various shapes floating in the culture fluid, or deposited at the bottom.

Fluorescent : having one colour by transmitted light and another by reflected light.

Friable : growth dry and brittle, when touched with a platinum needle.

Granular : composed of granules ; fine, medium or coarse.

Hæmolysis : on blood agar plate. α-hæmolysis : colonies surrounded by a greenish ring. β-hæmolysis : colonies surrounded by an area of clearing, which is transparent (see Chapter XXIII).

Heaped-up : irregular, coarse processes projecting considerably above the level of the rest of the growth.

Infundibuliform : in form of a funnel or inverted cone.

Iridescent : exhibiting changing rainbow colours in reflected light.

Lenticular : surface colony, which is convex and translucent, and which acts like a plano-convex lens, giving an inverted image of an object viewed through it. Deep colony, which is shaped like a lentil.

Lobate : having the margin deeply undulate, producing lobes (see *Undulate*).

Lophotrichate : having a tuft of flagella at one or both poles.

Luminous : glowing in the dark, phosphorescent.

Maximum Temperature : temperature above which growth does not take place.

Membranous : growth thin, coherent, like a membrane.

Microaerophilic : growing best under a lowered oxygen pressure.

Minimum Temperature : temperature below which growth does not take place.

Mirror-like : having a smooth glistening surface, in which reflections of surrounding objects, *e.g.* window bars, can be seen.

Monotrichate : having a single flagellum at one pole.

Napiform : liquefaction in form of a turnip.

Navicular : shaped like a boat.

Opalescent : resembling the colour of an opal.

Opaque : objects, *e.g.* window bars, cannot be seen through growth.

Optimum Temperature : temperature at which growth is most rapid.

Papillate : growth beset with small nipple-like processes.

Pellicle : bacterial growth forming either a continuous or an interrupted sheet over the culture fluid.

Peptonization : rendering curdled milk soluble by the action of peptonizing enzymes.

Peritrichate : having flagella disposed around the organism.

Punctiform : very small, but visible to naked eye ; under 1 mm. in diameter.

Radiate : showing fissures or ridges arranged in a radial manner.

Raised : growth thick, with a comparatively flat surface, and with abrupt or terraced edges.

Rhizoid : growth of an irregular branched or root-like character, as in *B. mycoides.*

Ring : growth at the upper margin of a liquid culture, adhering to the glass.

Ringed : having one or more circular depressions or elevations on the surface, sometimes giving a draughtsman-like appearance.

Rough : general term for an irregular surface, the irregularity being of a coarsely granular type, or resembling morocco-leather or a relief map.

Saccate : liquefaction in form of an elongated sac, tubular, cylindrical.

Spreading : growth extending much beyond the line of inoculation, *i.e.* several millimetres or more ; sometimes over an entire tube or plate.

Stratiform : liquefying to the walls of the tube at the top and then proceeding downwards horizontally.

Subterminal : situated towards the end.

Terminal : situated at the extreme end.

Translucent : objects, *e.g.* window bars, are visible through growth, but growth is not water-clear.

Transparent : growth is water-clear.

Truncate : ends abrupt, square.

Turbid : cloudy ; may be a uniform, flocculent, or granular turbidity.

Umbonate : having a button-like, raised centre.

Undulate : border wavy, with shallow sinuses.

Unipolar : at one end only of the bacterial cell.

Viscid : sticky, semi-fluid ; on withdrawal of the needle, the growth follows it in the form of a thread ; sediment on shaking rises as a coherent swirl.

REFERENCES

Barritt, M. M. (1936) *J. Path. Bact.,* **42,** 441.
Conn, H. J. (1936) *J. Bact.,* **31,** 225.
Happold, F. C. and Hoyle, L. (1934) *Biochem. J.,* **28,** 1171.
Holman, W. H. and Gonzales, F. L. (1923) *J. Bact.,* **8,** 577.
Lindsey, G. A. and Rhines, C. M. (1932) *J. Bact.,* **24,** 489.
O'Meara, R. A. Q. (1931) *J. Path. Bact.,* **34,** 401.
Tittsler, R. P. (1931) *J. Bact.,* **21,** 111.
Zobell, C. E. and Feltham, C. B. (1934) *J. Bact.,* **28,** 169.

CHAPTER XIII

ACTINOMYCES AND ACTINOBACILLUS

ACTINOMYCES

DEFINITION. *Actinomyces*, Harz 1877.

> Organisms growing in the form of a much-branched mycelium, which may break up into segments or produce "spores." Aerial mycelium often formed under suitable conditions. Mainly aerobic, but may be microaerophilic or even anaerobic. Usually saprophytic, but some species are parasitic on plants or animals, and may give rise to disease. In animal body organisms are frequently arranged in colonies composed of radiating threads with clubbed ends. Non-motile. Some species are acid-fast. The type species is *Actinomyces bovis* Harz.

THE term *Actinomyces bovis* was originally given by Harz to a mould-like organism which was found by Bollinger (1877) in the lesions of cattle suffering from a peculiar disease of the tongue and jaw, now known as Actinomycosis. This organism was first cultivated by Wolff and Israel in 1891 under anaerobic conditions. An aerobic organism, which is occasionally present in actinomycotic lesions, but which is probably not ætiologically related to the disease, was isolated in the same year by Bostroem (1891). In order to avoid confusion with the anaerobic pathogenic type, we have suggested that Bostroem's organism should be called *Actinomyces graminis*. Since then a number of similar organisms have been recovered from a variety of diseases in man and animals, and from such situations as soil, grains, and grasses.

These organisms appear morphologically as jointed or unjointed filaments, which frequently show true branching. In culture, rod forms are not uncommon. In the animal body, many of the pathogenic species are characterized by the formation of granules of varying size, which are found to consist of a filamentous mycelium surrounded by radiating clubs—a picture which is responsible for the term "ray-fungus." (Botanically the term "ray" refers to the marginal portion of a composite flower, consisting of ligulate florets arranged radially.) In their staining reactions some species are acid-fast, though the majority are non-acid-fast. It is evident that these organisms bear some resemblance to the *Mycobacteria*, and in the classification furnished by the American Committee of Bacteriologists in 1917 (Report 1917), the *Actinomyces* and the *Mycobacteria* were included in a single family, known as the *Mycobacteriaceæ*. In the 1920 report (Report 1920), however, it was decided to create a separate family of *Actinomycetaceæ*, which should contain the genera *Actinobacillus*, *Leptothrix*, *Actinomyces*, and *Erysipelothrix*. For descriptive purposes it is convenient to consider these genera separately, and in the present chapter we shall confine ourselves to a description of *Actinomyces* and *Actinobacillus*.

263

Other terms such as *Streptothrix* or *Nocardia* have been applied to organisms of the *Actinomyces* group. Since the term *Streptothrix* was applied by Corda in 1839 to a genus of fungi belonging to the *Hyphomycetes*, quite different from the group that we are considering, this name is obviously inapplicable. The term *Nocardia* is antedated by *Actinomyces*, and is likewise inapplicable.

Ecology.—Many members of this group lead a saprophytic existence on grains and grasses, and in water. As these substances are widely used as foods, it is not unnatural that by their means the *Actinomyces* often gain access to the alimentary and respiratory tracts of man and other animals. They have been isolated chiefly from man and cattle, and also from pigs, chickens, rabbits, dogs, elephants, lizards, and oysters (Foulerton 1910). Most members live in the soil, where they play an important part in the biological processes that are occurring there (see Chapter LXXXVII). There is at least one species that appears to be a strict parasite in man and animals. Numerous members are pathogenic for plants, causing such diseases as potato scab.

Morphology.—On culture media the morphology is variable. In ordinary film preparations the anaerobic Wolff-Israel type occurs chiefly as rods, 3–4 μ long by 0·6 μ broad, which from their arrangement, their clubbed ends, and their irregular staining bear a resemblance to certain members of the *Corynebacteria*; careful search, however, will generally reveal a few

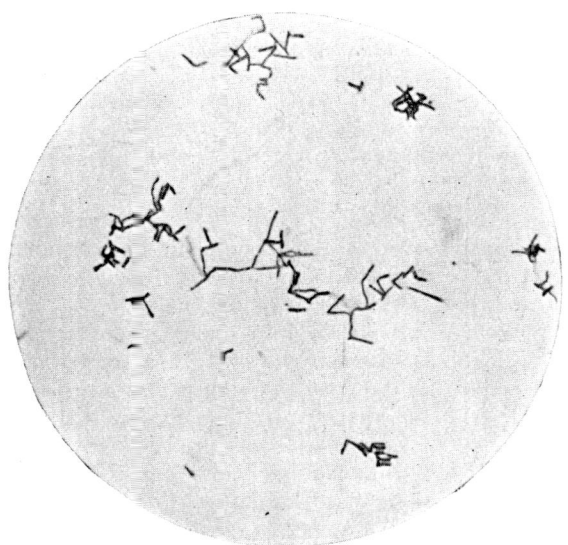

Fig. 40.—*Actinomyces bovis* × 1000.
From an agar slope culture, 14 days, 37° C. anaerobically.

definite filaments, some of which may show true branching (Fig. 40). The aerobic type in young cultures occurs chiefly as long unsegmented straight or wavy filaments, which show simple or dichotomous branching (Fig. 41), and which not infrequently grow upwards from the surface as aerial hyphæ. Later these filaments undergo segmentation, and break up into rod forms of varying length and oval coccoid bodies, which are usually referred to as spores. In some strains of the aerobic type segmentation is visible within 24 hours; in others it may not occur for 3 weeks or more. On solid media the filaments are arranged in loose groups or in a tangled mycelium, but in broth definite colonies occur consisting of a densely matted central core of filaments and a peripheral zone in which the filaments are more loosely disposed (Fig. 45). These colonies in liquid media are common to both the aerobic and the anaerobic types. The rods and filaments may stain evenly, but as a rule granular staining is evident. After growth for some time in liquid media both the aerobic and the anaerobic types may show involution forms, consisting mainly of spherical or club-shaped swellings on the ends of the filaments.

If, instead of making film preparations, the growth of the organisms is followed by Ørskov's (1923) agar-block technique, it will be seen that in some species the aerial mycelium gives rise, without preliminary segmentation, to circular or oval "spores." There is evidence that these "spores" are rather more resistant to inimical agencies generally than the plain mycelium. They may, for example, resist moist heat at 65° C. for as long as 3 hours. The segmented mycelium, observed in many species, is no more resistant, however, than the unicellular mycelium.

All members are non-motile and all, with a few possible exceptions, are Gram-positive. The anaerobic types are uniformly non-acid-fast. The aerobic types may be differentiated into : (1) acid-fast ; these resist decolorization with 1 per cent. sulphuric acid for 5 minutes, but are usually decolorized by the application of 25 per cent. H_2SO_4 for a similar length of time ; there is, however, a marked variation in the acid-fastness of different species. (2) Non-acid-fast.

In the animal body the morphology is often different from that on culture media. The anaerobic Wolff-Israel type grows in the form of definite colonies, which appear in the pus or in sections of the tissues as granules or "*Drusen*." When crushed and ex-

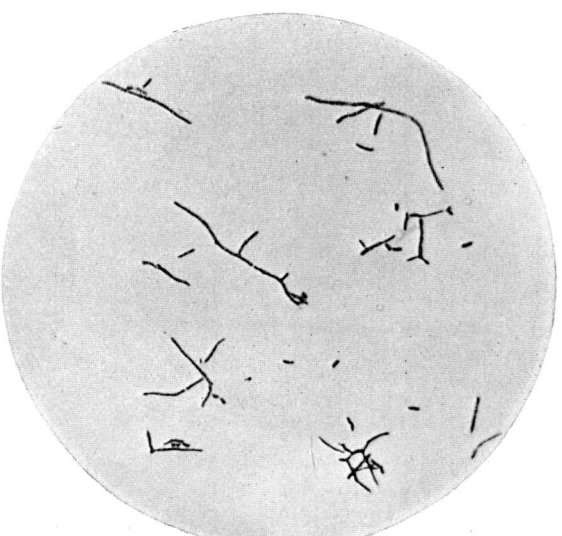

FIG. 41.—*Actinomyces graminis* × 1000.
From a broth culture, 24 hours, 37° C. aerobically.

amined microscopically these granules are seen to consist of a central fila-mentous Gram-positive mycelium surrounded by a peripheral zone of large, Gram-negative clubs. In old colonies the mycelium is replaced by a mass of short Gram-positive rods and coccoid bodies, which appear to have resulted from the disintegration of the filaments. The clubs vary in size, but may be as long as 10 μ and as broad as 5 μ. Their mode of origin has given rise to much dis-cussion. On the whole it seems probable that there are two entirely different types of club, one observed in artificial culture and derived from the organism itself, the other observed in the animal body and derived from the host. The first type, or "culture club" as Ørskov (1923) calls it, represents the swollen end of the mycelial filament. The second type or "tissue club," as we may call it, appears to be due to the deposition around the end of the filament of some material, probably rich in lipoid, by the tissues of the host. Tissue clubs are observed, not only in ray-fungus infections, but also in lesions caused by other

P.B. K*

organisms such as tubercle bacilli and staphylococci. Even dead tubercle bacilli are said to stimulate their production.

In sections of tissues the filaments may be differentiated from the clubs by a modified Ziehl-Neelsen stain. If a section is stained with carbol-fuchsin, decolorized for 20 to 30 seconds with 1 per cent. H_2SO_4, and counterstained with methylene blue, the clubs appear red and the filaments blue.

The aerobic types, when growing in the animal body, generally form a tangled mycelium without evidence of ray or of club formation ; but exceptions do occur, as with *Actinomyces maduræ*, which forms definite granules similar to those of the Wolff-Israel type.

The most striking feature of the *Actinomyces* is their pleomorphism. All forms may be seen—filaments, rods, cocci, and even spirilla. In the anaerobic type rod forms predominate in culture, in *Actinomyces maduræ* filaments. But in most of the aerobic types all forms are seen, coexisting in a single culture. For a detailed

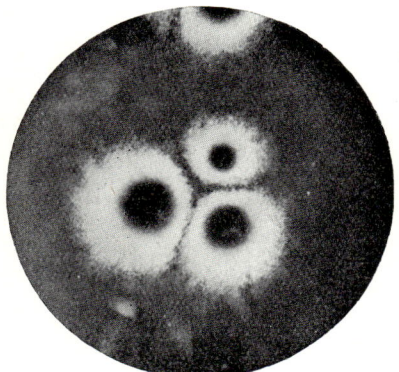

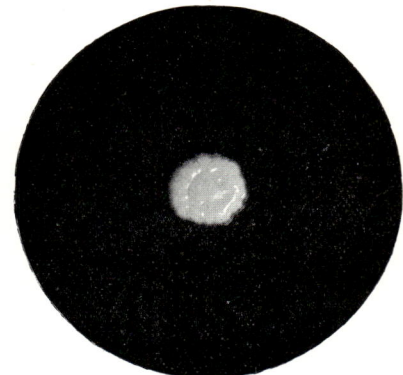

Fig. 42.—*Actinomyces graminis.*
Colonies on agar plate, 7 days, 37° C. aerobically : × 8.

Fig. 43.—*Actinomyces bovis.*
Colony on agar plate, 14 days, 37° C. anaerobically : × 8.

description of their morphology, the reader is referred to a monograph by Lieske (1921).

Cultural Reactions.—In general, growth on artificial media is readily obtained. The usual media suffice, but the addition of glucose or glycerol is beneficial. The aerobic types, with a few exceptions, multiply rapidly, so that in 24 hours definite evidence of growth is visible on agar. The anaerobic types, on the other hand, grow more slowly, taking 3 or 4 days to form macroscopic colonies. Great diversity of cultural appearance is noticeable, particularly in the aerobic species. The descriptions that follow refer only to some of the commoner types.

On an agar plate the aerobic types form round, low convex, opaque, finely granular colonies, which later undergo differentiation into a raised, knob-like, sometimes radially striated centre and an effuse, ground-glass-like periphery. The surface is finely granular and often has a " chalk powder " covering due to the formation of aerial spores ; the edge is rhizoid, indented, or feathery (Fig. 42). Most strains form pigment—yellowish, pink, or orange in colour—which becomes apparent after a few days' incubation, and which may show progressive alterations in tint. This is especially noticeable in cultures that have been incubated at 37° C., and subsequently left in the dark at room temperature. After a variable time under suitable conditions, aerial hyphæ may develop, giving rise to a characteristic bloom on the surface of the colony—the chalk powder appearance just described.

The anaerobic Wolff-Israel type forms smaller colonies, not apparent for 3 or 4 days ; they are more compact, greyish or porcelain white in colour, and have a nodular surface (Fig. 43).

On glycerol or glucose agar the aerobic types give a luxuriant, confluent, heaped-up, worm-cast, pigmented growth, adherent to the medium, of tough consistency, and difficult to emulsify (Fig. 44). The anaerobic type grows in the form of discrete colonies, which are only slightly adherent to the medium, and are much easier to emulsify.

In a glucose agar shake culture the aerobic types give a thick pigmented growth confined entirely or almost entirely to the surface. The anaerobic type gives a characteristic band-like growth situated about 0·5 to 1 cm. below the surface, with a few larger discrete colonies scattered throughout the medium below. No growth at all occurs in the upper few millimetres.

In broth the aerobic types often form a thick, dry, dull, scaly or nodular, pigmented surface pellicle, which may extend for some distance up the sides of the tube. A ropy or membranous, sometimes pigmented sediment

FIG. 44.—
Actinomyces graminis.
Culture, 14 days, 37° C.
glycerine agar slope,
aerobically.

forms, augmented by frequent deposits from the surface membrane. The broth remains clear, or at most shows a finely granular turbidity. Aerial hyphæ may sprout from the surface pellicle. Sometimes growth commences at the bottom, and characteristic fluff-balls, resembling the head of a seeding dandelion develop. The anaerobic type grows in the form of compact whitish granules with a nodular surface deposited at the bottom of the tube ; there is no turbidity and no surface growth. Nitrate broth is more favourable for growth than ordinary broth.

The cultural characteristics on other media can

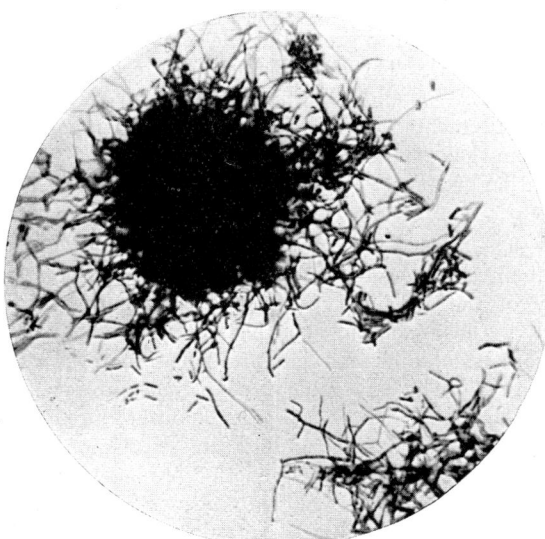

FIG. 45.—*Actinomyces graminis* × 1000.
A small granule composed of radiating filaments ; from a broth culture, 24 hours, 37° C. aerobically.

be ascertained from the descriptions of the individual species.

Resistance.—The members of this group show no special resistance to heat or disinfection. Most are killed in 15 minutes when exposed to moist heat at 60° C. Some attempts have been made to find whether filaments containing so-called spores are specially resistant. Vincent (1894), working with *Actinomyces maduræ,* stated that the spores were killed at 85° C. in 3 minutes, whereas the non-sporing forms were killed at 60° C. in 3 to 5 minutes. Ørskov (1923) has likewise found that the " spores " are more resistant than the plain mycelium ; they may survive exposure to moist heat for 3 hours at 65° C. There is, however, a great difference between the resistance of the *Actinomyces* " spores " and that of true bacterial spores.

Cultures of the aerobic type, if kept at room temperature, remain viable for months ; cultures of the anaerobic type usually die out in about 6 to 8 weeks. If kept in the incubator they die very much more quickly.

Growth Requirements.—There is a fairly sharp division between the aerobic and the anaerobic types. The aerobic types are unable to grow under strictly anaerobic conditions, while the anaerobic types are unable to grow, at any rate on solid media and when first isolated, in the presence of air. In liquid media, especially in nitrate broth, and in the depths of solid media, such as glucose agar, the anaerobic types may flourish when kept under aerobic conditions, showing that they are not strict anaerobes, but rather organisms having a preference for a low oxygen pressure—micro-aerophiles. Intermediate types are met with (Bruns 1899, Lignières and Spitz 1903), usually having a preference for anaerobic conditions (Naeslund 1925). The development of both aerobic and anaerobic types is favoured by the addition of 10 per cent. CO_2 to the atmosphere. The range of temperature over which the *aerobic* species are able to grow is very wide. Many of the water and soil strains multiply even at 3–6° C., while nearly all strains grow between 6° and 30° C. About 30° C. some strains fail to grow, but the majority have their optimum temperature round about 37° C. Thermophilic species are encountered with an optimum temperature between 40° and 70° C. The *anaerobic* strains are much more restricted in their requirements, and fail to grow if the temperature varies more than a few degrees from the optimum of 37° C. (Lieske 1921). Growth is improved as a rule by the addition of glucose or glycerol, sometimes by blood or serum.

Biochemical Characteristics.—The anaerobic type produces acid, but no gas, in glucose, maltose, lactose, and salicin ; the aerobic types, as a rule, have no action on these carbohydrates. Many of the aerobic types turn litmus milk slightly alkaline and peptonize it slowly ; the anaerobic type has no action on litmus milk. A few members are proteolytic, digesting gelatin and serum, but the majority have no proteolytic power. The anaerobic type cannot grow in the presence of bile salts ; some of the aerobic types are able to do so.

None of the strains that we have tested were hæmolytic, but Waksman (1918) has noted hæmolysis in certain strains, and has correlated this property with the power to digest proteins.

Pigment formation is characteristic of many of the aerobic species, the usual colour being some shade of pink or brown.

Antigenic Structure.—Very little work has been done on the serology of this group. Colebrook (1921), working with three strains of the Wolff-Israel type, found that their agglutination reactions differed. Claypole (1913), working with members of the aerobic type and with acid-fast bacilli, such as *Myco. tuberculosis* and *Myco. lepræ*, concluded from complement-fixation tests that there were two main antigens—one in the mycelial non-acid-fast types, another in the non-mycelial acid-fast types. Strains occupying an intermediate position often showed fixation with sera of both types. These results must await confirmation.

Pathogenicity.—The anaerobic Wolff-Israel type appears to be responsible for actinomycosis in man and cattle. The aerobic types are mostly saprophytic, but occasionally they are able to give rise to chronic granulomatous lesions in man and other animals.

For laboratory animals both types have a low pathogenicity. Intraperitoneal injection of the Wolff-Israel type into guinea-pigs and rabbits may give rise to small nodules containing typical granular pus, but the lesions are never extensive, and do not lead to the death of the animal. The aerobic types are as a rule even less pathogenic. An exception, however, must be made for the acid-fast members, such as *Actinomyces asteroides*. Injection of this strain by the subcutaneous, intravenous, or intraperitoneal route leads to a progressive fatal infection of guinea-pigs and rabbits in 5 days to 4 weeks. Post mortem, small tubercles are found scattered throughout the organs, being especially numerous in the lungs, liver, and spleen (Eppinger 1891, MacCallum 1902). Microscopically these nodules contain tangled filaments, sometimes arranged in the typical ray form.

CLASSIFICATION

Lieske (1921), who made an extensive study of the *Actinomyces* from the point of view of a botanist, found so much variation in the behaviour of individual strains that he was unable to arrive at any satisfactory classification. Subsequent workers, however, have felt that Lieske overestimated the difficulties of this task. Attempts at classification have been made along both morphological and physiological lines. The most prominent exponent of the former group during recent years is Ørskov (1923), who devised the following scheme :

Group I. " Spores " give rise to a unicellular branching mycelium. This affords the substratum for an aerial mycelium, which consists of rather thicker-branched filaments. " Spores " are formed from the aerial hyphæ without any previous segmentation of the cytoplasm. " Spore " formation commences at the tip of the thread and proceeds towards the base. " Spores " are more resistant to heat than the plain mycelia. Minor points are that the primary mycelium is of cartilaginous consistency, and often sends roots into the agar. The aerial mycelium may arise centrally or peripherally, and may not appear for a long time. Condensation of the cytoplasm occurs at regular intervals. Whole appearance of organism is fairly uniform. Gelatin is often liquefied. This group seems to include most of the non-acid-fast aerobic species.

Group IIA. Both the primary and the aerial mycelium are of the same diameter, and both undergo early segmentation into irregular fragments. The aerial mycelium arises very early in the culture. It starts at the centre of the primary mycelium and spreads concentrically towards the periphery. No " spore " formation occurs, and the segmented mycelial fragments are no more resistant to heat than the unicellular mycelium. The whole appearance is very pleomorphic ; coccoid, bacillary, filamentous, clubbed, and irregular-shaped forms are common. The growth is generally soft in consistency, and does not adhere to the medium. A reddish insoluble pigment is frequently formed. Gelatin is not usually liquefied.

This group includes many of the aerobic acid-fast species, such as *Actinomyces asteroides* and *Actinomyces farcinicus*.

Group IIB. Differs from Group IIA in forming no aerial mycelium. [Erikson (1935), however, denies this, and would do away with the distinction between the A and B groups.] Besides segmentation, the so-called angular division is common in this sub-group, and is responsible for the diphtheroid appearance of these organisms in film preparations. Group IIB comprises mainly the anaerobic species, of which the most important is the pathogenic organism described by Wolff and Israel.

Group III. The characteristic feature of this group is the formation of oval " spores " at the extreme tips of the mycelial branches. No aerial mycelium is produced. Only one species has so far been recognized—*Actinomyces chalceæ*.

Naeslund (1925) put forward a classification based primarily on physiological characteristics. We have modified it very slightly, and present it in the following form, paying attention mainly to the organisms that are parasites or potential parasites of animals.

Actinomyces.
    A. Predominantly anaerobic types.   *Actinomyces bovis* Harz.
    B. Predominantly aerobic types.
        (1) Non-acid-fast.   *Actinomyces graminis* Bostroem.
                            Actinomyces capræ.
                            Actinomyces maduræ.
                            Actinomyces somaliensis.
        (2) Acid-fast.   *Actinomyces farcinicus*.
                            Actinomyces asteroides.
                            Actinomyces gypsoides.
    C. Facultative aerobic types.   *Actinomyces muris*.

The creation of a special subdivision for the facultative aerobic types is dictated, partly by convenience, and partly by the differences of the main species *Actinomyces muris* from the anaerobic Wolff-Israel type. There seems little doubt that the organism *Streptothrix moniliformis*, to which so much attention has been called in recent years by Levaditi, Nicolau, and Poincloux (1925), Parker and Hudson (1926), Levaditi, Selbie and Schoen (1932), Strangeways (1933), and Mackie, van Rooyen, and Gilroy (1933), is the same as the organism isolated by Schottmüller (1914), Blake (1916), and Tileston (1916), from one type of rat-bite fever in human beings, and called *Streptothrix muris ratti*. Since the original name for this organism claims priority over *Streptobacillus moniliformis*, we propose to adopt it. Modification, however, is necessary, partly to suit the binomial nomenclature, and partly because the term *Streptothrix* is not valid. In its place we suggest the name *Actinomyces muris*. The members of the facultative aerobic sub-group grow better as a rule anaerobically than aerobically, though they are capable of developing under both sets of conditions.

Erikson (1935), who has recently studied a number of new parasitic species of *Actinomyces*, has suggested a scheme of classification containing both morphological and physiological characteristics. She accepts Ørskov's grouping, but does away with the distinction between his Groups IIA and IIB. She objects to the use of oxygen requirements as a basis of classification on the ground that the distinction between the aerobic and anaerobic species is not sufficiently sharp. Instead, she places reliance on pigment formation, and proteolytic action.

A detailed description of some of the more important members is appended, followed by notes on others that are of less importance. These descriptions are based in part on our own observations of relatively few strains. For a differential table see p. 280 (Table XXIV), and for a general description of different types see Lieske (1921), Naeslund (1925), and Setti (1929).

Actinomyces bovis Harz

Isolation.—Described by Bollinger in 1877, named *Actinomyces bovis* by Harz in 1877, and first isolated by Wolff and Israel in 1891.

Ecology.—Strict parasite found in lesions of actinomycosis in man and cattle.

Morphology.—*Glycerol agar, 7 days at 37° C.* Long and short rods predominate; long continuous or segmented threads with a straight or curved axis, showing simple or dichotomous branching; S-shaped or spiral organisms; coccoid forms. The rods resemble, and are arranged like, certain members of the *Corynebacteria*; sides parallel or irregular; ends rounded, clubbed or tapered; axis straight or curved; great variation in appearance; irregular staining is usual; granular and beaded forms are not uncommon. Non-motile. Non-sporing. Gram-positive. Non-acid-fast.

Agar Plate.—*7 days at 37° C. anaerobically.* Poor growth of round, 0·5–1·0 mm. in diameter, convex, opaque, amorphous colonies with smooth dull surface and entire edge; greyish-white by transmitted, porcelain white by reflected light; butyrous or friable consistency; emulsifiability not difficult as a rule. *21 days*, rather larger, 1–1·5 mm. in diameter, umbonate, with slightly irregular nodular surface and lobate edge; differentiated into a glistening raised centre and a dull shelving periphery resembling a rosette. Colonies may grow into medium.

Agar Slope.—*7 days at 37° C. anaerobically.* Moderate growth of discrete colonies similar to those described. Numerous greyish-white floccular masses of coarsely granular structure in water of condensation; they are irregular in shape, have an irregular edge, and are opaque. In the condensation water there is also a finely granular turbidity.

Gelatin Stab.—No growth at 23° C. After 12 days at 37° C., the culture shows, when cooled, a band of growth 4 mm. deep with its upper margin 1 mm. below the surface. Growth consists of very fine greyish-white interlacing filaments, looking like cotton-wool. No liquefaction.

Broth.—*5 days at 37° C. anaerobically.* Poor to moderate growth; deposit of compact, white, mulberry-like granules with nodular surface, often adherent to each other; not disintegrated on shaking. No turbidity; no surface growth; no odour.

Glucose Agar Shake.—*5 days at 37° C.* No growth for 1 cm. below surface. Then comes a turbid band, about 0·8 mm. deep, consisting of large numbers of tiny colonies. Throughout the rest of the medium are scattered discrete, irregularly round, opaque, greyish-white colonies, about 0·1–1·0 mm. in diameter, with smooth or slightly knobby surface.

Loeffler's Serum.—*7 days at 37° C. anaerobically.* Moderate, partly confluent, raised, shiny growth of low convex, rounded colonies about 0·5 mm. in diameter. No liquefaction.

Glycerol Egg.—*14 days at 37° C. anaerobically.* Poor, slightly raised, confluent growth with finely granular surface due to imperfect fusion of colonies. No liquefaction.

MacConkey.—No growth either in solid or liquid medium.

Potato.—*14 days at 37° C. anaerobically.* Very poor growth of discrete, round, 1 mm. in diameter, whitish low convex colonies with smooth glistening surface and entire edge.

Resistance.—At 37° C. cultures live for about 1 to 4 weeks, sometimes longer. Dried on glass and kept in the dark, organisms may live for 7 weeks or more. Killed by moist heat at 60° C. in 10 minutes.

Metabolism.—Anaerobe of the microaerophilic type. Will not grow on surface culture exposed to the air. Optimum temperature for growth 37° C. ; growth below 30° C. is either very slight or absent. Optimum pH 7·3–7·6. No hæmolysis of horse red cells. No pigment formation. Growth is improved by nitrates, glycerol, blood, and sometimes by glucose.

Biochemical.—Acid, no gas, in glucose, maltose, lactose and salicin within 21 days under anaerobic conditions. L.M. no change. Indole — ; M.R. — ; V.P. — ; Nitrate reduction + + ; H_2S — ; NH_3 + ; M.B. reduction — ; Catalase —.

Pathogenicity—Responsible for actinomycosis in man and cattle. Very slight pathogenicity for laboratory animals. Intraperitoneal inoculation of a broth culture into a rabbit or guinea-pig may be followed by appearance of small nodules, chiefly in the great omentum, containing the typical clubbed colonies of *Actinomyces*. The animals live indefinitely.

Actinomyces maduræ

Isolation.—Isolated from pale variety of Madura foot by Vincent in 1894. Called by him *Streptothrix maduræ*.

Ecology.—Found in pale variety of Madura foot. Saprophytic existence probable, but not demonstrated.

Morphology.—*Glycerol agar, 14 days at* 37° C. Long, non-segmented filaments, 0·4–0·6 μ thick, showing true and false branching ; sides parallel, ends often tapering. Arranged in a mycelium ; sometimes aggregated into dense masses. Stain evenly. Later fragmentation may occur with production of ovoid bodies. Non-motile. Gram-positive. Non-acid-fast.

Agar Plate.—*5 days at* 37° C. Small, round, convex colonies about 0·5 mm. in diameter. 14 *days*, larger, 1–3 mm. in diameter, greyish-yellow, opaque, irregularly heaped-up, nodular, umbonate colonies, resembling worm casts, which have a smooth glistening surface. Very adherent to medium ; consistency horny ; very difficult to emulsify. Whole colony looks like a rosette.

Agar Slope.—*7 days at* 37° C. Poor growth of discrete, dull, greyish-white opaque irregularly heaped-up colonies with nodular surface.

Gelatin Stab.—*14 days at* 20° C. Moderate, filiform growth consisting mostly of small, discrete, greyish-white colonies, having a darker centre and a lighter feathery periphery ; growth extends to bottom of tube. Slightly raised surface growth about 3 mm. in diameter. Slight liquefaction after 6 weeks.

Broth.—*7 days at* 37° C. Poor growth. Deposit of little greyish-white puff-balls, looking like colonies of moulds, and having a dense centre and a lighter periphery ; often cohering in groups of two or three. No turbidity ; no surface growth ; no odour. Later a white efflorescent surface growth may appear.

Loeffler's Serum.—*7 days at* 37° C. Poor growth of isolated colonies. 21 *days*, moderate growth of heaped-up nodular colonies. No liquefaction.

Glucose Agar Slope.—*7 days at* 37° C. Discrete colonies, raised, heaped-up, with worm-cast surface, moist and glistening.

Glycerol Agar Slope.—*12 days at* 37° C. Luxuriant, raised, confluent, greyish-white worm-cast growth, very tough, adherent to medium, and difficult to emulsify.

Glycerol Egg.—*7 days at* 37° C. Mostly confluent growth of rounded, dome-like colonies with dull nodular surface. Very tough, adherent to medium, and difficult to emulsify. No liquefaction.

Potato.—*7 days at* 37° C. Discrete, heaped-up, nodular, yellowish-brown colonies. 18 *days*, heaped-up dry, chalky-white and greyish-brown, worm-cast colonies. Later may take on a rose-red colour.

MacConkey.—No growth on solid or liquid media.

Resistance.—Destroyed by moist heat at 60° C. in 5 minutes.

Metabolism.—Aerobic ; very slight growth on glycerol agar anaerobically. Optimum temperature 37° C. ; grows at 20° C. Forms sometimes a rose-red pigment on potato. Growth improved by glycerol and glucose.

Biochemical.—Ferments no sugars. L.M. turned slightly alkaline ; may be peptonized. Indole — ; M.R. — ; V.P. — ; Nitrate reduction + ; H₂S — ; NH₃ sl. + ; Catalase v. sl. + ; M.B. reduction —.

Pathogenicity.—Subcutaneous inoculation into rabbits, guinea-pigs, mice, and cats causes a local nodule, which increases in size for a month and then retrogresses. Responsible for pale or ochroid variety of Madura disease in man.

Actinomyces graminis Bostroem

Isolation.—Isolated by Bostroem in 1891 from human actinomycosis. Subsequently isolated by numerous workers from different lesions in man and other animals.

Ecology.—Saprophyte living on grains and grasses. Often gains access to mouth and respiratory passages of man and other animals.

Morphology.—*Agar 24 hours at 37° C.* Long filaments, 0·6 μ wide, showing true and false branching ; long and short rods, and coccoid bodies. Sides parallel, ends rounded or tapering. Filaments are straight, wavy, or spirillar, and may or may not be segmented. Arranged in small loose groups, or in a mycelium. In broth ray forms are frequent, with compact centre and radiating filaments. Staining of rods and filaments is often irregular. Non-motile. Gram-positive. Non-acid-fast.

Agar Plate.—*24 hours at 37° C.* Round, greyish-white, low convex, dull, opaque colonies with finely granular surface and erose edge. *7 days,* rounded, up to 3 mm. in diameter, umbonate, granular colonies, with raised, opaque, primrose-yellow, radially striated centre, and effuse, greyish, ground-glass periphery. Surface granular, edge feathery or rhizoid. Generally tough and adherent to agar, and difficult to emulsify. Colonies may be folded on surface and coral-like, or they may be undifferentiated with a nodular surface and lobate edge. Colour may be chalky-white, yellow or brown.

Agar Slope.—*24 hours at 37° C.* Abundant, slightly raised, greyish-white, faintly translucent or opaque growth with dull, finely granular or mealy surface and entire or erose edge. *7 days,* surface is whitish and moderately granular ; growth may be heaped-up in places.

Gelatin Stab.—*7 days at 20° C.* Moderate filiform growth of confluent, greyish-white, feathery colonies ; extending to bottom of tube. Slightly raised surface growth, 3 mm. in diameter. After 3 weeks the growth near the surface is orange-pink. Liquefaction unusual.

Broth.—*24 hours at 37° C.* Moderate growth ; ropy or membranous sediment, not disintegrating on shaking ; ring growth and finely granular almost invisible surface pellicle ; turbidity absent, or slight and finely granular. *7 days,* thick surface pellicle, extending up sides of tube ; dry, dull, and scaly with pinkish-yellow or orange nodules in places : heavy floccular deposit, pinkish in colour. No odour.

Glucose Agar Shake.—*8 days at 37° C.* Good growth confined to surface, except for a few tiny colonies in upper 5 mm. of medium. Surface growth is thick, raised, confluent, dull, greyish-white with several secondary colonies developing on it. Sometimes surface growth is heaped-up, yellowish-brown, and of worm-cast type with no colonies below surface. *21 days,* growth is brick-red or yellowish-orange in colour.

Loeffler's Serum.—*24 hours at 37° C.* Good, raised, moist, glistening confluent growth with nodular surface and lobate edge. *24 days,* no liquefaction.

Dorset Egg.—10 *days at* 37° *C.* Good, confluent, raised, yellowish growth with nodular surface and edge formed of single colonies. 24 *days,* no liquefaction.

MacConkey's Agar.—6 *days at* 37° *C.* Growth of small, 0·1 mm. in diameter, pinkish, opaque colonies ; growth very poor compared to that on agar. In liquid medium there is good growth with a heavy granular deposit.

Potato.—24 *hours at* 37° *C.* Poor, slightly raised, chalky-white growth with powdery surface. Later, growth may turn yellowish-orange or ochre-brown.

Resistance.—Cultures remain viable for months.

Metabolism.—Aerobic. No growth under strict anaerobic conditions. Optimum temperature 37° C. ; grows at 20° C. No hæmolysin for horse red cells. Yellowish, orange, or pink pigment formed, particularly in old cultures stood at room temperature. Growth is improved by glucose, sometimes by serum.

Biochemical.—No fermentation of sugars. Litmus milk turned slightly alkaline in 6 days ; may be slowly peptonized. Indole — ; M.R. — ; V.P. — ; Nitrate reduction + ; NH_3 + ; H_2S very slight + ; Catalase + ; M.B. reduction —.

Pathogenicity.—Appears to be non-pathogenic.

Actinomyces muris

Synonyms.—*Streptothrix muris ratti* Schottmüller ; *Streptobacillus moniliformis* Levaditi

Isolation.—Isolated by Schottmüller (1914) from human patients bitten by rats.

Ecology.—Natural parasite inhabiting the nasopharynx of rats (Strangeways 1933).

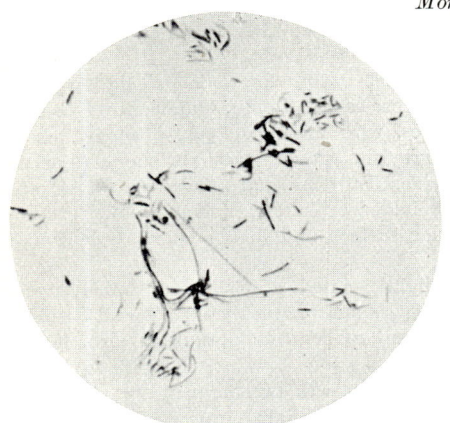

Morphology.—*Loeffler's serum at* 37° *C.* Slender branching filaments, 0·4–0·6 μ wide, growing in interwoven masses. After 18–24 hours fragmentation of the filaments sets in, and many of the filaments are replaced by chains of bacillary or coccoid bodies. Very marked pleomorphism. Occasional filaments show spherical, oval, fusiform or club-shaped swellings occurring terminally, sub-terminally, or in some other situation—hence the term "*moniliformis.*" These swellings may be 2–5 times the diameter of the filament, and may project from one side only. In the animal body the morphology is more regular and bacillary. Great irregularity in depth of staining. Non-motile. Usually described as Gram-negative, but may be Gram-positive in young cultures. Non-acid-fast (see Fig. 46).

FIG. 46.—*Actinomyces muris.* From a Loeffler slope, 2 days, 37° C. aerobically (× 1000).

Nutrient Agar at 37° *C.*—No growth.

Glucose Agar at 37° *C.*—No growth.

Serum Agar Plate.—2 *days at* 37° *C.* Circular, greyish-yellow, low convex, almost water clear, amorphous colonies, 0·2–0·3 mm. in diameter, with smooth glistening surface and entire edge ; butyrous in consistency and easily emulsifiable. No differentiation. Little or no increase in size on further incubation.

Gelatin Stab.—7 *days at* 20° *C.* No growth.

Nutrient Broth at 37° *C.* No growth.

Serum Broth.—2 *days at* 37° *C.* No turbidity. Abundant, greyish-white, coarsely granular sediment, looking like fluffy bread crumbs, miniature cotton balls, or tiny snow flakes, not disintegrating completely on shaking. No surface growth. No odour.

Glucose Agar Shake.—7 *days at* 37° *C.* No growth.

Loeffler's Serum.—*2 days at* 37° *C.* Discrete, circular, low convex colonies, similar to those on serum agar, but rather larger—0·5–0·7 mm. in diameter. *7 days ;* some colonies may show a differentiation into a slightly raised umbonate centre with a flatter periphery having an irregular or crenated edge ; surface appears finely granular and rather dull. Growth may be confluent from the start, and appear slightly raised, colourless, with a glistening beaten-copper surface and a more or less entire edge. No liquefaction, even after 3 weeks.

Dorset Egg.—*2 days at* 37° *C.* Similar to colonies on Loeffler's serum, but perhaps slightly smaller—0·3–0·6 mm. in diameter. No liquefaction, even after 3 weeks.

Horse Blood Agar.—*2 days* 37° *C.* Colonies resemble those on serum agar. No hæmolysis.

Potato.—*7 days at* 37° *C.* No growth.

MacConkey's Agar.—*7 days at* 37° *C.* No growth.

Resistance.—Destroyed in serum broth by heating to 55° C. for 30 minutes. Dies out in culture very readily. Serum broth cultures may remain viable at 37° C. for a week.

Metabolism.—Grows aerobically, but grows equally well or better under anaerobic conditions. Growth said to be improved by 10 per cent. CO_2. Optimum temperature 37° C. ; little or no growth at 22° C. No hæmolysin for horse red cells. No pigment formation. No growth on ordinary media, but growth occurs in presence of serum, ascitic fluid, or blood ; not improved by glucose or glycerol.

Biochemical.—Not thoroughly studied. In serum sugar media acid is produced within 3 days in glucose and salicin, sometimes in maltose and lactose. Litmus milk unchanged. Indole — ; M.R. — ; V.P. — ; Nitrate reduction — ; H_2S — ; catalase — ; M.B. reduction — .

Antigenic Structure.—Different strains appear to be antigenically homogeneous.

Pathogenicity.—Responsible in man for one type of rat-bite fever—sometimes described as infectious erythema or Haverhill fever. May give rise to an epizootic disease in mice characterized by œdematous swelling of the feet and legs, arthritis, conjunctivitis, and lymphadenitis. Intraperitoneal inoculation of mice with 0·5 c.c. of a serum broth culture is usually fatal in 1–2 days ; no characteristic post-mortem appearances visible. Subcutaneous inoculation into one of the hind feet often leads to a more or less perfect reproduction of the natural disease. Comparatively avirulent for rats, guinea-pigs, and rabbits, though intravenous inoculation of culture into rabbits may sometimes lead to arthritis.

Note.—Dick and Tunnicliff (1918) isolated a similar organism—*Actinomyces putorii*—from a boy bitten by a weasel.

A. Other Anaerobic Types.

Tunnicliff (1926) describes a weakly Gram-positive motile anaerobic organism, which she isolated from a tonsillar granule. Smear preparations of the granule showed thick bacilli with rounded ends, filaments, tightly waved spirilla, and cocci. Sections stained with Giemsa showed bundles of filaments with the bacillary forms radiating from them. In anaerobic culture on ascitic fluid tissue medium and sheep-blood agar, rosettes and test-tube-brush-like forms appeared, similar to those in the original material. It is very doubtful whether this organism should be included in the *Actinomyces* group (see also Tunnicliff and Jackson 1930).

B. Other Aerobic Types.

(1) Non-acid-fast Types

Actinomyces capræ.—Described by Silberschmidt (1899) in 1897. It was isolated from the lung of a goat supposed to be suffering from tuberculosis. Consists of very thin, wavy filaments, showing a varying degree of branching ; filaments segment into rod and coccoid forms. On agar, dry colonies, flattened in the centre with an irregular warty folded surface. In broth, surface growth of dry discoid colonies and a rough deposit.

No change in litmus milk. Abundant growth on potato of rose-red colonies, later becoming chalky-white. No liquefaction of gelatin. Aerobic. Subcutaneous injection into rabbits produces an abscess. Intravenous injection sometimes causes tubercles in various organs. Guinea-pigs are rather more susceptible than rabbits (see also Galli-Valerio 1912).

Actinomyces somaliensis.—Described by Brumpt in 1906 (see Brumpt 1927). Was first isolated by Bouffard in French Somaliland from patients affected with mycetoma. Consists of long branching filaments with truncate or sometimes tapering ends. Gram-positive. Grows on agar, but better on blood agar. On this medium colonies are at first small, circular, convex and translucent, but after a few days they become irregularly heaped up, nodular, worm-cast, or crateriform ; they are opaque, vary in colour from white, through yellowish-orange, to brown or black, often show radial segmentation which gives them a stellate appearance, are extremely tough in consistency and adherent to the medium, and have a peculiar odour. In broth no turbidity or surface growth, but a deposit of little greyish-white puff balls. On potato a white folded layer of growth, which in 5 to 6 days becomes yellow. Peptonizes milk. Ferments no sugars. Gives rise in man to mycetoma of the hand or foot. Lesions contain hard smooth yellowish-red granules, 1 mm. in diameter, not dissociated by caustic potash.

(2) Acid-fast Types

Actinomyces farcinicus.—Isolated by Nocard in 1888 from cattle suffering from farcy. Branching filaments growing in a mycelium. Gram-positive ; feebly acid-fast (see p. 265). On agar it forms small, irregular, raised, opaque, yellowish-white colonies with a dull mammilated powdery surface. Dry, scaly, pale yellow plaques on potato. Irregular whitish masses in broth, some of which remain at the surface and others fall to the bottom. No liquefaction of gelatin. No change in litmus milk. No growth anaerobically. In cultures, the organism forms filamentous felted masses and diphtheroid-like bacilli. Cultures remain viable for 4 months at 37° C. ; killed by heat at 70° C. in 10 minutes. Intraperitoneal injection is fatal to guinea-pigs in 9 to 20 days ; post mortem, miliary nodules over peritoneum, containing a little pus ; in the pus are masses of bacilli. Intravenous injection of guinea-pigs causes the formation of generalized miliary nodules, particularly abundant in the lungs, liver, and spleen. Miliary nodules follow intravenous injection of cows and sheep. Rabbits, dogs, cats, horses, and asses are resistant to intravenous or intraperitoneal injection. Subcutaneous injection causes a slowly progressive abscess, which ulcerates and heals.

Actinomyces asteroides.—Isolated by Eppinger in 1891 from a brain abscess in a glass-grinder. Consists of threads showing true and false branching ; threads may be long, or short and segmented ; tiny rod forms also seen. In the body it forms long, granular, interlacing filaments with no ray or club formation. Gram-positive. Acid-fast, though not so strongly as the tubercle bacillus. Aerobic ; no growth anaerobically. Destroyed by heat at 70° C. in 5 minutes. On agar—at first whitish, later ochre-coloured, umbonate colonies, having a raised, dry, wrinkled, opaque centre and a moist glistening more translucent periphery with a mycelioid edge ; whole colony star-shaped—hence the name *asteroides*—may be a central depressed crater ; later, colour deepens to orange, and the wrinkling of the surface becomes more marked. Agar slope—raised ochre growth with a mealy surface and entire edge. Gelatin—very slow growth without liquefaction. Potato —red raised growth with a granular, and later wrinkled, surface ; a chalk-white bloom may develop due to a velvet-like upgrowth of fine filaments into the air. These uplifted filaments have terminal chains of coccoid bodies or spores, which, when transferred to broth, sprout and give rise to long filaments or star-like clusters (MacCallum 1902). Broth—white surface pellicle, which falls to the bottom, and is renewed several times ; no turbidity. After subcutaneous, intraperitoneal, or intravenous injection, rabbits and guinea-pigs die in 5 days to 4 weeks. Post mortem, the viscera, especially lungs, liver, and spleen, are studded with small white nodules. Abscesses may develop in the muscles, kidneys, and other organs; these abscesses contain branching test-tube brush forms with laterally radiating clubs. An organism called *Actinomyces variabilis* with similar pathogenicity but different cultural reactions to Eppinger's strain was isolated by Cohn (1913) from the bladder of a man with pyuria.

Actinomyces gypsoides.—Isolated by Henrici and Gardner (1921) from the sputum of a woman. Acid-fast branching filaments were found in the sputum, sometimes in mycelial form. Agar slope—thin greyish veil, soon becoming thick, opaque, and chalky-white; surface dry and wrinkled; growth finely adherent to the medium and very brittle. Potato—growth similar to that on agar. Gelatin stab—surface growth only; liquefaction stratiform and complete in a week. Broth—small white flakes coalescing to form a thick, wrinkled, snow-white surface pellicle extending up sides of tube. Litmus milk—yellowish surface pellicle; milk is turned alkaline and curdled; litmus reduced; later digestion. Media containing peptone are darkened (tyrosinase). Growth improved by dextrose, maltose, and glycerol. No carbohydrates fermented. Intravenous injection into rabbits is fatal in 2 days; post mortem, minute abscesses in viscera, especially kidneys, which are studded with yellowish-white nodules. Intraperitoneal injection into guinea-pigs is fatal in 4 to 6 days; post mortem, small tubercle-like nodules over peritoneum; omentum shrunken and studded with nodules.

An acid-fast strain described by Birt and Leishman (1902) gave a snow-white growth on solid media, peptonized milk, but did not liquefy gelatin. Another acid-fast strain described by Berestnew (see Feistmantel 1902) gave a grey to whitish growth, liquefied gelatin, but was non-pathogenic to laboratory animals.

C. Other Facultative aerobic Types.

Described by Naeslund (1925), who isolated organisms of two different types from the human mouth.

Type I consists morphologically of branching, and often very sinuous, relatively short threads, usually arranged in a radiating fashion; rods and granules are also present. In old cultures there is marked pleomorphism. No aerial spores. Chiefly Gram-positive, non-acid-fast. Culturally, growth in dextrose broth occurs in the form of round, oval, or ovoid colonies, white to yellowish-grey in colour, which appear at the bottom in about a week. On saliva dextrose agar a slightly shiny colourless film appears, becoming granular after a few days; some of the granules may develop into small greyish-white nodular adherent colonies, having a narrow translucent, finely striated margin. Little or no growth on gelatin, potato or milk. Optimum temperature for growth 37° C.; no definite growth at 20° C.

Type II consists of very long threads of fairly even thickness, showing typical but infrequent branching. No definite aerial spores formed. Gram-positive, but the greater part of the mycelium consists of Gram-negative elements with occasional Gram-positive segments. Non-acid-fast. Culturally, in saliva dextrose broth round, greyish, more or less translucent colonies develop at the bottom in about a couple of weeks. On saliva glucose agar growth at first occurs in a thin film, but in 1 to 2 weeks isolated pinhead colonies appear, hard or soft in consistence, and surrounded by a narrow translucent border. No definite growth on gelatin, potato, or in milk.

ACTINOBACILLUS

Lignières and Spitz (1902) isolated a non-motile, non-branching, Gram-negative bacillus from the lesions of cattle suffering from a disease which in many respects resembled actinomycosis. They called the organism the actinobacillus, and the disease to which it gave rise actinobacillosis. Two other organisms have since been described, having some points of similarity with this bacillus, and it is therefore convenient to consider them as forming a group to which the generic name *Actinobacillus* may be applied.

DEFINITION. *Actinobacillus* Brumpt. (Emended from the American Committee's Report.)

Gram-negative, non-acid-fast rods, sometimes occurring in long chains or in unjointed filaments. In lesions in the animal body no mycelium is formed, but at the periphery finger-shaped cells or clubs may be visible.

Type species is *Actinobacillus lignieresi*, Brumpt.

The classification we suggest is as follows :
Actinobacillus.
    A. Aerobic and facultatively anaerobic. *Actinobacillus lignieresi.*
                                        Actinobacillus actinomycetem-comitans.
    B. Preferring raised CO_2 pressure. *Actinobacillus actinoides.*
A description follows of the separate organisms.

Actinobacillus lignieresi.—For isolation see above. Appears to be a strict parasite.

MORPHOLOGY.—In young cultures it is a small rod-shaped organism ; in older cultures it is cocco-bacillary, and various involution forms appear. In serum broth long strepto-bacillary forms are common. In glucose agar shake cultures long, tangled, unbranched filaments may be formed, accompanied by smaller bacilli and coccoid bodies (Griffith 1916). Dimensions of the bacilli are given by Lignières and Spitz (1902) as 1·15–1·25 μ long by 0·4 μ broad. Non-motile ; non-sporing ; non-acid-fast. Stains readily, especially with carbol fuchsin, and is Gram-negative ; frequently shows bipolar staining.

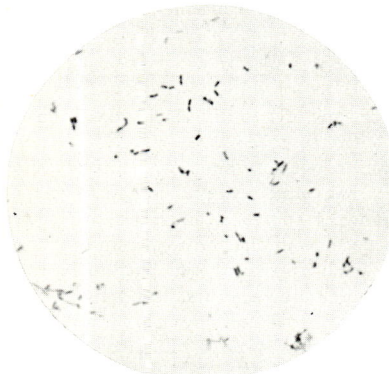

FIG. 47.—*Actinobacillus lignieresi.* From a liver agar slope, 2 days, 37° C. aerobically (× 1000).

In lesions in the animal body small granules are found, which consist of tufts of radially disposed clubs similar to those in actinomycosis. An important point of difference is that the centre of the granule is occupied not by a Gram-positive filamentous mycelium, such as is formed by *Actinomyces bovis*, but by minute Gram-negative bacilli, which may quite readily be overlooked. Though both the bacilli and the clubs formed by *Actinobacillus lignieresi* are Gram-negative, it is possible to differentiate between them by a modified Ziehl-Neelsen stain, as was pointed out by Bosworth (1923). If a section of affected tissue is stained with carbol fuchsin, decolorized for 20 to 30 seconds with 1 per cent. H_2SO_4, and counterstained with methylene blue, the clubs appear red and the bacilli blue. For pus, one of the best stains is glycerine picro-carmine, which stains the clubs yellow and the pus cells pink.

CULTIVATION.—Cultures are best obtained by grinding up infective pus in a mortar, and seeding on to agar. Growth occurs readily under aerobic conditions, and less readily under anaerobic conditions. The optimum temperature for growth is 37° C. ; very slight growth occurs at 20° C.

On agar in 24 hours at 37° C. small, circular, bluish-grey, translucent colonies with a smooth surface and an entire edge, up to 1·5 mm. in diameter, are formed ; further incubation results in a considerable increase in size—up to 4 mm.—due to peripheral extension of the colony. On an agar slope the growth of freshly isolated strains is poor, consisting of small, discrete, translucent bluish colonies, or of a thin, dry, confluent layer of growth adherent to the medium. After cultivation for some time in the laboratory, the organism grows more readily, giving a confluent, filiform, viscous growth with a thickened edge.

In stab agar there is a whitish opaque spot at the surface ; no growth occurs down the stab. In gelatin stab growth is very poor and is not visible for some days. A small opaque spot appears at the surface ; no growth occurs down the stab, and there is no liquefaction.

Coagulated serum is not a very favourable medium ; only a thin whitish growth is formed.

On acid potato there is no growth. On alkaline potato a slight, glistening, greyish-yellow growth appears.

In peptone broth there is a slight uniform turbidity. In old cultures, a surface film may develop, and an abundant deposit. Growth in broth is improved by serum.

RESISTANCE.—The organism is killed by heating to 62° C. in 10 minutes. It rapidly succumbs to drying. Cultures do not live long, and should be transplanted every few days. Infected pus preserved in sealed tubes may remain virulent for a month or two.

BIOCHEMICAL REACTIONS.—The fermentative ability of this organism is a little doubtful. Glucose, maltose, mannitol, and sucrose are generally rendered acid, though not markedly so, in a day, while lactose may be fermented later. Acid is produced in litmus milk, but no clot. Indole is formed, apparently in small quantity.

PATHOGENICITY.—No exotoxin is formed. The organism is responsible for Actinobacillosis in cattle. The virulence of different strains seems to vary considerably, and while cattle inoculation experiments are successful with some strains, they are completely negative with others (Magnusson 1928). Most workers, including ourselves, have been unable to produce any specific lesions in laboratory animals. The following statements, therefore, which are taken from Lignières and Spitz (1902), must be accepted with considerable reserve. Subcutaneous inoculation of pure cultures into cattle produces an abscess identical with those occurring spontaneously ; in the pus granules are found consisting of bacilli surrounded by clubs. Intraperitoneal inoculation of a whole agar culture is fatal to a guinea-pig in 12 to 24 hours. Post mortem there is an abundant turbid peritoneal exudate, rich in polymorphonuclear cells ; the organisms can be cultivated from the exudate, but rarely from the blood. Intraperitoneal injection of $\frac{1}{4}$–$\frac{1}{2}$ an agar culture into male guinea-pigs produces a typical Straus reaction. In 2 days the testicles are markedly inflamed, and the two layers of the tunica vaginalis are adherent ; the scrotum is red, swollen, and tender. The animal loses weight, and dies in 5 to 7 days. Post mortem small purulent granules, the size of a hemp seed, formed of a very thin membrane containing white or yellowish, thick, homogeneous pus, and scattered over the peritoneal serosa—particularly on the inferior surface of the diaphragm, the liver, spleen, and omentum. Around the testis there is a thick purulent exudate, gumming the two layers of the tunica vaginalis together. In the pus of these lesions tufts of clubs are found, though not in large numbers ; they are rather smaller than those seen in cattle. Subcutaneous inoculation of guinea-pigs causes a local abscess, which may resolve ; ulceration rarely occurs ; clubs are not usually demonstrable in the pus.

Rabbits, cats, and dogs are considerably more resistant than guinea-pigs, but succumb to intravenous inoculation. Small lesions may develop in mice or rats after subcutaneous inoculation. Pigeons and fowls are resistant.

Actinobacillus actinomycetem-comitans.—Described by Klinger in 1912 under the name *Bact. actinomycetem comitans.* Found in lesions caused by *Actinomyces bovis*, as densely packed Gram-negative cocco-bacilli (Colebrook 1920). In culture the rod forms are 1·0–1·5 μ long ; the coccoid forms are 0·6–0·8 μ in diameter. Intermediate forms are frequent. The organism is non-motile. In broth or liquid gelatin at 37° C. it forms iso-

TABLE XXIV

Organism.	Morphology in the Animal Body.	Morphology in Culture.	Staining.	Oxygen and Temperature Requirements.	Agar Colonies.	Broth.	Biochemical Reactions.	Pathogenicity.
Actinomyces bovis Harz	Mycelium of branching filaments with radiating clubs. Granules formed	Chiefly rod-shaped bacilli, like diphtherolds	Gram + Non-acid-fast	Anaerobe. No growth at 20° C.	Slow growth of small, white umbonate cols. with nodular centre and shelving periphery	Deposit of compact white granules with nodular surface. No turbidity. No surface growth	Acid in glucose, maltose, lactose and salicin. L.M. no change. Indole —	Causes actinomycosis in man and cattle. Localized nodule formation after ip. inoculation into guinea-pigs.
Actinomyces graminis Bostroem	Mycelium of branching filaments. No clubs, no ray formation, and no granules	Highly pleomorphic. Branching filaments, rods, and coccoid forms	Gram + Non-acid-fast	Aerobe. Growth at 20° C.	Rapid growth of fairly large, low convex cols. with finely granular pigmented centre and effuse periphery with rhizoid or feathery edge. Adherent to medium	Thick, dull, scaly surface pellicle, often pigmented, and heavy floccular deposit. No turbidity	No action on sugars. L.M. slight alkali and slow peptonization. Indole —	Pathogenicity to animals slight; may cause localized abscess formation. Non-pathogenic to laboratory animals.
Actinomyces madurae	Mycelium of branching filaments with radiating clubs. Fish-roe granules formed	Long, branching filaments forming a mycelium	Gram + Non-acid-fast	Aerobe. Growth at 20° C.	Rather slow growth of umbonate, heaped up, worm-cast cols. Very adherent to medium	Deposit of little puff balls. No turbidity. Sometimes late surface growth	No action on sugars. L.M. slight alkali and loose clot. Indole —	Causes Madura disease in man. Non-pathogenic for laboratory animals.
Actinomyces asteroides	Mycelium of branching filaments. No clubs, no ray formation. No granules	Branching filaments, rods, and coccoid forms	Gram + Acid-fast	Aerobe. Growth at 20° C.	Rapid growth of stellate cols., ochre-coloured, with dry, wrinkled, opaque centre and moist, glistening, translucent periphery with mycelioid edge	White surface pellicle, which deposits several times. No turbidity	No action on sugars. L.M. alkaline	Chiefly pulmonary infections in man. Causes pseudotuberculosis on injection into laboratory animals.
Actinobacillus lignieresi Brumpt	Very tiny bacilli with large radiating clubs. Granules formed	Small coccobacillus	Gram — Non-acid-fast	Facultative anaerobe. Very slight growth at 20° C.	Rapid growth of small, convex, translucent, bluish-grey cols. with smooth surface and entire edge	Slight uniform turbidity. Later surface film and deposit	Acid in glucose, maltose, mannitol, and sucrose. L.M. acid. Indole +	Causes actinobacillosis in cattle. Ip. injection of male guinea-pigs causes death in 7 days with orchitis.

lated, translucent granules, 0·5–1·0 mm. in diameter, along the sides of the tube, most numerous near the surface ; several hundreds of these colonies may develop. After some days they fuse into a greyish-white mass, forming a ring round the tube and a pellicle over the surface. The granules can be picked off the wall of the test tube with a loop, but are very difficult to break up. Later they may become opaque and greyish-white. On agar it gives rise to small tough colonies, not unlike those of streptococci, adherent to the medium. The organism flourishes under both aerobic and anaerobic conditions. There is no growth at room temperature. Cultures live for 4 weeks. It is toxic on injection into rabbits, but does not set up a true infection.

Actinobacillus actinoides.—This organism was isolated by Smith in 1918 from the lungs of calves suffering from epizootic pneumonia, and called by him *B. actinoides*. In the animal body it appears as a minute Gram-negative bacillus arranged in groups. In the condensation water of coagulated serum it forms minute whitish flocculi, which consist of a central mass of radiating non-branching filaments ending peripherally in clubs. In tissue-agar cultures the organism grows as aggregations of rounded, ring-like bodies, 2 μ in diameter, having a minute refringent speck on the periphery or near the centre. There are thus 3 distinct forms in which this bacillus occurs. Most strains are capsulated (Smith 1921*b*), but the capsule does not stain with the usual dyes. Growth occurs only under a raised pressure of CO_2—as in sealed tubes. On coagulated serum whitish flocculi appear in the condensation water in 3 days at 37° C. and after several weeks very tiny, elevated, pointed-like colonies may appear on the slant. Growth may be obtained on agar to which a piece of guinea-pig's spleen has been added. No growth on ordinary media or on ascitic fluid. Non-pathogenic for laboratory animals on experimental injection. Subcutaneous injection into calves causes a large necrotic swelling with caseous contents ; ulceration occurs in 4 weeks Intratracheal injection into calves causes small necrotic foci in the lungs, identical with those observed in the natural disease (Smith 1921*a*, see also Jones 1922). The fact that it has been isolated from the lungs of white rats suffering from pneumonia (Jones 1922) suggests that it may be a natural parasite of these animals. For further references to this organism see Smith (1921*a*, *b*). A similar organism, differing only in minor particulars has been isolated from the middle ear of white rats, in which it was causing suppuration (Nelson 1930, 1931).

REFERENCES

BIRT, C. and LEISHMAN, W. B. (1902) *J. Hyg., Camb.*, **2**, 120.
BLAKE, F. G. (1916) *J. exp. Med.*, **23**, 39.
BOLLINGER, O. (1877) *Zbl. med. Wiss.*, **15**, 481.
BOSTROEM, E. (1891) *Beitr. path. Anat.*, **9**, 1.
BOSWORTH, T. J. (1923) *J. comp. Path.*, **36**, 1.
BRUMPT, E. (1927) " Précis de Parasitologie." Masson et Cie, Paris, p. 1201
BRUNS, H. (1899) *Zbl. Bakt.*, **26**, 11.
CLAYPOLE, E. J. (1913) *J. exp. Med.*, **16**, 99.
COHN, T. (1913) *Zbl. Bakt.*, **70**, 290.
COLEBROOK, L. (1920) *Brit. J. exp. Path.*, **1**, 197 ; (1921) *Lancet*, i. 893.
DICK, G. F. and TUNNICLIFF, R. (1918) *J. infect. Dis.*, **23**, 183.
EPPINGER, H. (1891) *Beitr. path. Anat.*, **9**, 287.
ERIKSON, D. (1935) *Spec. Rep. Ser. med. Res. Coun., Lond.*, No. 203.
FEISTMANTEL, C. (1902) *Zbl. Bakt.*, **31**, 433.
FOULERTON, A. G. R. (1910) *Lancet*, i. 551, 626, 769.
GALLI-VALERIO, B. (1912) *Zbl. Bakt.*, **63**, 555.
GRIFFITH, F. (1916) *J. Hyg., Camb.*, **15**, 195.
HENRICI, A. T. and GARDNER, E. L. (1921) *J. infect. Dis.*, **28**, 232.
JONES, F. S. (1922) *J. exp. Med.*, **35**, 361.
KLINGER, R. (1912) *Zbl. Bakt.*, **62**, 191.
LEVADITI, C., NICOLAU, S., and POINCLOUX, P. (1925) *C. R. Acad. Sci.*, **180**, 1188.
LEVADITI, C., SELBIE, R.-F., and SCHOEN, R. (1932) *Ann. Inst. Pasteur.*, **48**, 308.

LIESKE, R. (1921) "Morphologie und Biologie der Strahlenpilze" (Actinomyceten). Gebrüler Borntraeger, Leipzig.

LIGNIÈRE, J. and SPITZ, G. (1902) *Bull. Soc. cent. Méd. Vét.*, **20**, 487, 546 ; (1903) *Arch. Parase.*, Paris, **7**, 428.

MacCULL M, W. G. (1902) *Zbl. Bakt.*, **31**, 529.

MACKIE, T. J., ROOYEN, C. E. VAN, and GILROY, E. (1933) *Brit. J. exp. Path.*, **14**, 132.

MAGNUSSON, H. (1928) *Acta. path. Microbiol. scand.*, **5**, 170.

NAESLUNE, C. (1925) *Acta. path. Microbiol. scand.*, **2**, 110.

NELSON, E. B. (1930) *J. infect. Dis.*, **46**, 64 ; (1931) *J. Bact.*, **21**, 183.

NOCARD, E. (1888) *Ann. Inst. Pasteur*, **2**, 293.

ØRSKOV, E. (1923) "Investigations into the Morphology of the Ray Fungi." Levin and Munkgaard, Copenhagen.

PARKER, R. and HUDSON, N. P. (1926) *Amer. J. Path.*, **2**, 357.

Report. 1917) *J. Bact.*, **2**, 505 ; (1920) *Ibid.*, **5**, 191.

SCHOTTMÜLLER, H. (1914) *Derm. Wschr.*, **58**, Supp., p. 77.

SETTI, C. (1929) *G. Batt. Immun.*, **4**, 585.

SILBERSCHMIDT. (1899) *Ann. Inst. Pasteur*, **8**, 841.

SMITH, T. (1918) *J. exp. Med.*, **28**, 333 ; (1921a) *Ibid.*, **33**, 441 ; (1921b) *Ibid.*, **34**, 593.

STRANGEWAYS, W. I. (1933) *J. Path. Bact.*, **37**, 45.

TILESTON, W. (1916) *J. Amer. med. Ass.*, **66**, 995.

TUNNICLIF, R. (1926) *J. infect. Dis.*, **38**, 366.

TUNNICLIF, R. and JACKSON, L. (1930) *J. infect. Dis.*, **46**, 12.

VINCENT, H. (1894) *Ann. Inst. Pasteur*, **8**, 129.

WAKSMAN S. A. (1918) *J. infect. Dis.*, **23**, 547.

WOLFF, M and ISRAEL, J. (1891) *Virchows Arch.*, **126**, 11.

CHAPTER XIV

ERYSIPELOTHRIX

DEFINITION.

Rod-shaped organisms with a tendency to the formation of long filaments, which may show branching. The filaments may also thicken and show characteristic granules. No spores. Non-motile. Gram-positive. Slight fermentative activities. Microaerophilic. Usually parasitic.

The type species is *Erysipelothrix rhusiopathiæ*, the causative organism of swine erysipelas.

The first member of this group to be described was the bacillus of mouse septicæmia, *Erysipelothrix muriseptica*; it was found by Koch in 1880 in the blood of mice that had been injected subcutaneously with putrefying blood. In 1882 Loeffler (1886) observed a similar bacillus in the blood vessels of the skin of a pig that had died of swine erysipelas. [It is possible that the bacillus observed four months previously by Thuillier (Pasteur and Thuillier 1883) in pigs dying of *rouget* was the same organism as that described by Loeffler, but this is not absolutely clear.] Another organism closely allied to *Ery. rhusiopathiæ* was found by Rosenbach in cases of human erysipeloid. He (1909) made a comparative study of these organisms, and came to the conclusion that they were different, although closely allied to each other; he suggested for them the names *Ery. muriseptica*, *Ery. porci*, and *Ery. erysipeloides* respectively. Rickmann (1909), on the other hand, pointed out that the morphological and cultural distinctions, on which Rosenbach relied for his differentiation, were not sufficiently definite or constant to serve as a means of classification; and since he found that all three organisms agglutinated to the same titre with immune sera, and exhibited the same pathogenicity to animals, he concluded that they were identical; the small morphological differences existing between them might well be ascribed to residence in the different animal hosts from which the three organisms were derived. Whether these organisms are identical or not is a question that still remains unsettled; since, however, there is no known method by which they can be separated with certainty, it seems probable that they should be regarded as variant members of the same species.

The work of Spryszak and Szymanowski (1929), Meyn (1931), and Redlich (1932) has rendered it clear that two fairly well-defined types of bacilli occur—a smooth and a rough. These types differ in morphological and cultural appearances as well as in virulence. The smooth type is generally responsible for acute disease, while in chronic forms of disease the rough type may predominate. Probably most of the apparent differences between the *rhusiopathiæ*, *muriseptica*, and *erysipeloides* types have been due to failure in the past to recognize the occurrence of these variations.

In culture all these organisms grow readily but poorly. The growth in gelatin stabs is one of the most characteristic features. Variant morphological and colonial types have recently been isolated by Sabella (1925) from old broth cultures.

Pathogenicity.—The mouse septicæmia bacillus causes a characteristic disease of mice (see Chapter LV). The swine erysipelas bacillus gives rise to swine erysipelas in pigs, and occasionally to disease in sheep and man ; it has moreover been isolated from the tonsils, gall-bladder, intestinal mucosa, and fæces of normal swine. Apparently it may live as a parasite in healthy pigs, and, under conditions of which we are at present ignorant, become actively pathogenic.

Reproduction of the Natural Disease in Animals

SWINE.—Loeffler (1886), who first isolated the swine erysipelas bacillus, failed to reproduce the disease in swine with pure cultures, but Schütz (1886) later succeeded in doing so. Broth cultures injected subcutaneously proved fatal to two pigs, one animal dying in 3, the other in 4 days ; there were typical findings at the necropsy, and the bacilli were recovered in pure culture from the blood and spleen, and from the pleural and peritoneal exudates. Artificial cultures rapidly lose their virulence for swine. The bacillus is pathogenic for mice, pigeons, and rabbits, but not for guinea-pigs.

MICE.—0·001–0·1 c.c. of a 24-hours' broth culture injected subcutaneously or intraperitoneally is usually fatal in 2 to 3 days. During life the mice develop conjunctivitis and their lids become glued together with a muco-purulent secretion ; arching of the back is very common, and constipation is usual. Post mortem, the vessels of the skin and subcutaneous tissue are congested, the spleen is enlarged, and the lungs are bright red and œdematous. Bacilli are usually abundant in the blood and viscera ; they are found particularly within the phagocytic cells, in which they appear to multiply (Tenbroeck 1920).

PIGEONS.—0·001–0·1 c.c. of a 24-hours' broth culture inoculated intramuscularly proves fatal in 3 or 4 days as a rule. Death is often preceded by paralysis of the legs, dyspnœa, and convulsions. Post mortem, there is a black hæmorrhagic mass in the muscle at the site of inoculation ; the spleen is enlarged ; there are often punctiform hæmorrhages in the mucosæ and viscera ; and there is almost constantly a clear lemon-yellow exudate in the pericardium (Crimi 1914). The bacilli are fairly numerous in the blood and organs.

RABBITS.—0·5 c.c. of a 24-hours' broth culture inoculated intravenously sometimes proves fatal in 2 to 3 days. A marked œdematous swelling or erysipelatous rash develops in the injected ear, and there is a rise in temperature and a loss in weight. Post mortem, besides the rosy skin lesion, there is congestion of the viscera, and often a clear lemon-yellow pericardial exudate ; there may be large hæmorrhages into the lungs. The bacilli are scarce. After subcutaneous inoculation death rarely occurs.

The virulence of the swine erysipelas bacillus is liable to fluctuation. Numerous statements have been made on the effect of passage through different animals on the virulence of this organism, but most of them rest on experiments in which comparatively few animals were employed, and no adequate controls were made. There is evidence, however, that artificial culture lowers the virulence for swine ; that passage from rabbit to rabbit lowers the virulence for other animals ; and that passage from pigeon to pigeon keeps the virulence in an exalted state (Kitt 1887, Deutsch 1903, Stickdorn, 1909).

Erysipelothrix rhusiopathiæ

Synonyms.—*B. rhusiopathiæ suis* Kitt ; *Erysipelothrix porci* Rosenbach ; *B. erysipelatis suis.*

Isolation.—Observed independently by Thuillier (Pasteur and Thuillier 1883) and Loeffler (1886) in 1882.

Habitat.—Found on the mucosæ and tonsils of swine.

Morphology.—*Smooth form.* Small, slender, straight or slightly curved rods, 0·8–2·0 μ long and 0·3–0·4 μ broad. Arranged singly, in small packets, in small groups, or in short chains. *Rough form.* Long chains of bacilli and interlaced filaments of

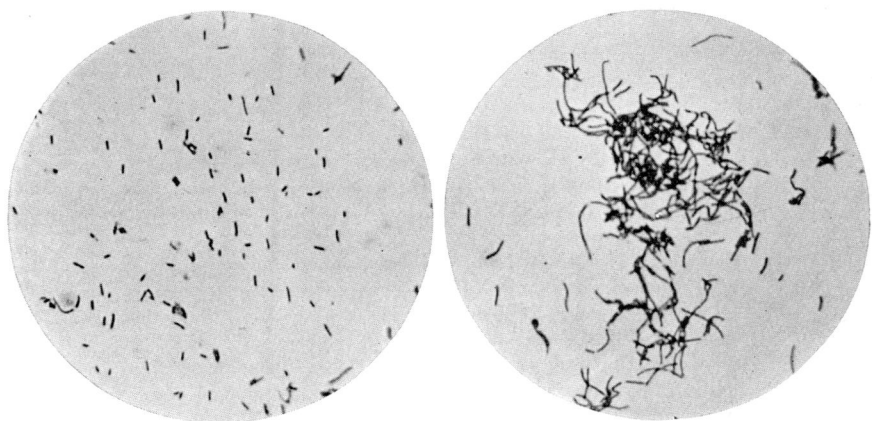

FIG. 48.—*Erysipelothrix muriseptica.*
Left : Smooth form. Right : Rough form. From a surface agar culture, 3 days, 37° C. (× 1000).

variable length. Staining is fairly regular, but sometimes deeply-stained granules may be seen. Non-motile. Non-sporing. Gram-positive.

Agar Plate.—24 *hours*, 37° C. *Smooth form.* Round, convex, tiny, amorphous, water-clear colonies, 0·1 mm. in diameter, with smooth glistening surface and entire edge ; butyrous and easily emulsifiable. No increase in size on further incubation. *Rough form.* Rather larger and flatter, 0·2–0·4 mm. in diameter, with a granular curled appearance and fimbriate edge ; resemble miniature anthrax colonies.

Agar Slope.—24 *hours*, 37° C. Very poor, partly confluent, slightly raised, colourless, transparent growth with an irregular surface due to imperfect fusion of indi- vidual colonies, and an edge which is very finely dentate or made up of single colonies. Practically no change on further incubation ; growth may become slightly viscous.

Gelatin Plates.—Deep colonies in 3 or 4 days resemble snow-flakes ; they are very small, but when magni- fied 50 times they are seen to consist of a granular centre with branching threads radiating outwards.

Gelatin Stab.—Growth occurs slowly and is subject to con- siderable variation, apparently depending to some extent on the reaction of the medium. May be a simple filiform growth extending to the bottom of the tube. Usually lateral outgrowths occur ; these may be ill-defined, looking like snow-flakes, nebulæ,

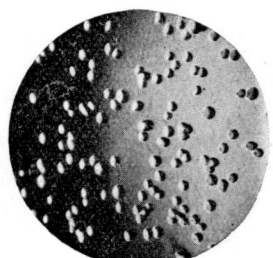

FIG. 49.—*Erysipelothrix muriseptica.*
Smooth form. Surface col- onies on agar, 24 hours, 37° C. (× 8).

or the conventional bursting bomb ; or they may be definite branches producing a lamp-brush appearance. The outgrowths may extend for a distance of only 2 or 3 mm. from the stab, or they may reach the sides of the tube. The smooth form tends to remain restricted to the line of inoculation, while the rough form grows out laterally. No liquefaction. The lamp-brush form may not be obtained till after 2 or 3 subcultures in gelatin.

Broth.—*24 hours*, 37° C. *Smooth form.* Slight uniform turbidity with very slight powdery deposit disintegrating on shaking. After a few days the broth may clear, and a viscous deposit become evident. *Rough form.* Little or no turbidity. Flocculi of varying size or tangled-hair-like masses of growth appear, and settle on the sides or bottom of the tube ; they are difficult to disintegrate by shaking.

Loeffler's Serum.—*7 days*, 37° C. Very poor, confluent, slightly raised, colourless growth, slightly better than on agar.

MacConkey's Agar.—No growth.

Potato.—No visible growth.

Resistance.—In broth cultures the bacilli are killed by moist heat at 55° C. in 5 minutes. In meat they are highly resistant to salting, pickling and smoking, surviving for 1 to 3 months ; they are likewise resistant to putrefaction, remaining alive and virulent for months in putrefying buried cadavers. Apparently succumb readily to drying, provided this is complete.

Metabolism.—Microaerophilic, but will grow under both aerobic and anaerobic conditions. Optimum temperature for growth is 30° C. ; grows between about 15° and 44° C. Growth favoured slightly by blood. Hæmolysis occurs round deep colonies in 10 per cent. horse blood agar plates.

Biochemical.—Sugar reactions are variable. Usually forms acid in dextrose and lactose, not in maltose, mannitol, sucrose, or salicin. L.M. no change or very slight acid. Indole negative. M.R. negative. V.P. negative. Nitrates slight reduction. Catalase +. M.B. reduction negative. NH_3 negative. H_2S +.

Antigenic Structure.—By agglutination *Ery. rhusiopathiæ*, *Ery. muriseptica*, and *Ery. erysipeloides* fall into a single homogeneous group.

Pathogenicity.—Causes swine erysipelas in swine, and occasionally in man. Experimentally it is pathogenic for mice, pigeons, and rabbits, but not for guinea-pigs. Virulence for swine is said to fall on artificial cultivation. No exotoxin is produced.

REFERENCES

CRIMI, P. (1914) *Ann. Staz. Mal. Best. Napoli*, **2**, 107.
DEUTSCH, L. (1903) *Zbl. Bakt.*, **33**, 214.
KITT, T. (1887) *Zbl. Bakt.*, **2**, 693.
KOCH, R. (1880) "Investigations into the Etiology of Traumatic Infective Diseases." New Sydenham Soc. London.
LOEFFLER. (1886) *Arb. ReichsgesundhAmt.*, **1**, 46.
MEYN, A. (1931) *Zbl. Bakt.*, **122**, 507.
PASTEUR and THUILLIER. (1883) *C. R. Acad. Sci.*, **97**, 1163.
REDLICH, E. (1932) *Z. InfektKr. Haustiere*, **42**, 300.
RICKMANN. (1909) *Z. Hyg. InfektKr.*, **64**, 362.
ROSENBACH, F. J. (1909) *Z. Hyg. InfektKr.*, **58**, 343.
SABELLA, A. (1925) *Zbl. Bakt.*, **94**, 411.
SCHÜTZ. (1886) *Arb. ReichsgesundhAmt.*, **1**, 56.
SPRYSZAK, A. and SZYMANOWSKI, Z. (1929) *C. R. Soc. Biol.*, **100**, 1151.
STICKDORN, W. (1909) *Zbl. Bakt.*, **50**, 5.
TENBROECK, C. (1920) *J. exp. Med.*, **32**, 331.

CHAPTER XV

MYCOBACTERIUM

DEFINITION. *Mycobacterium.*

Slender rods, which are stained with difficulty, but which, when once stained, are acid-fast. Cells are sometimes swollen, clavate, cuneate, or even branched. Non-motile. Gram-positive. No endospores. Growth on media slow. Aerobic. Several species are pathogenic to animals.

Type species is *Mycobacterium tuberculosis.*

The Acid-fast Bacteria.—The acid-fast bacteria are so called because of their ability, when once stained, to resist subsequent decolorization by mineral acids. The degree of acid-fastness varies with different members of the group, and in any single member is liable to alteration with changed environmental conditions ; these differences are never so distinct or so constant as to serve as a reliable means of differentiating between the members of the group.

The first member to be described was the *leprosy* bacillus, by Hansen in 1874. In 1882 came the discovery by Koch of the *mammalian tubercle* bacilli. The work of Smith (1898), Vagedes (1898), Ravenel (1901), Kossel, Weber and Heuss (1904, 1905), the English Royal Commission (Report 1911), and Park and Krumwiede (1910), during the years 1898–1910, showed that these mammalian bacilli could be divided into two types—the human and the bovine.

The discovery of the *avian* type of tubercle bacillus was due largely to the work of Rivolta (1889), Maffucci (1890, 1892), Cadiot, Gilbert and Roger (1890), Sibley (1890), and Straus and Gamaléia (1891), during the years 1889 to 1891. The work of Sibley (1889), Bataillon, Dubard and Terre (1897), Ledoux-Lebard (1898, 1900), Friedmann (1903), and Küster (1905) from 1889 to 1905 served to differentiate a fourth type of tubercle bacillus—the *cold-blooded* type. In 1895 Johne and Frothingham described the organism that is now known as *Johne's* bacillus, and in 1901 Stefansky (1903) described the *rat-leprosy* bacillus. And finally a number of workers during the years 1885 to 1906 demonstrated the existence of the *saprophytic acid-fast* bacilli—a group which, though able, under experimental conditions, to give rise in mammals to lesions closely simulating those of tuberculosis, does not appear capable of causing a definitely progressive disease. Amongst these bacilli the most important are (i) the butter bacillus *Myco. butyricum*—isolated by Rabinowitsch in 1897 from 23 out of 80 specimens of market butter examined in Germany, and since then by numerous other workers (Petri 1898, Korn 1899, 1900, Tobler 1901, Beck 1905, Pellegrino 1906) ; (ii) Moeller's Grass bacilli i and ii. Moeller isolated his first bacillus in 1898 from timothy-grass (*Phleum pratense*) ; hence it is generally referred to as *Mycobacterium phlei* i, or more familiarly as the timothy-grass bacillus ; his second bacillus

287

was isolated in 1899 from the dust of some plant material used as fodder ; (iii) the Mist bacillus or *Myco. stercusis* ; this was isolated by Moeller in 1901 from a dung-heap, and later from the fæces of cows, donkeys, and other herbivora ; it owes its name to the German term for manure (*Mist*) ; (iv) the Smegma bacillus, *Myco. smegmatis* ; this was first described by Alvarez and Tavel in 1885, but was not obtained in pure culture till 1897, when Laser (1897) and Czaplewski (1897) cultivated it independently. This organism is present in varying numbers in smegma of both males and females ; it has also been found in the smegma of dogs (Pellegrino 1906).

Saprophytic acid-fast bacilli are widely distributed in dust and water. The presence of metal seems to favour their growth, and they can almost invariably be found in scrapings from metal cold-water taps (Brem 1909, Beitzke 1910) and metal wind instruments (Jacobitz and Kayser 1910). They have also been reported in cultures made from a gangrenous lung (Rabinowitsch 1900), from human fæces (Mironescu 1901), from the tonsils (Marzinowsky 1900, Beck 1905), from the nasal secretion (Karlinski 1901, Marchoux and Halphen 1912), from the intestinal contents of insects (Pellegrino 1906), from cow's milk (Albiston 1930), from a pleural exudate (Beaven and Bayne-Jones 1931), from pus (Bruynoghe and Adant 1933), from sputum (Cummins and Williams 1933), and from blood (Tiedemann 1931, Schwabacher 1933*a*). In view, however, of the frequency of acid-fast bacilli in dust, it seems probable that some of these organisms gained access to the cultures by air contamination and were not necessarily present in the material from which they were apparently derived.

The leprosy bacillus, as already stated, was described in 1874. The bacillus of rat leprosy was discovered by Stefansky (1903) in 1901 at Odessa, while the organism responsible for Johne's disease was described by Johne and Frothingham in 1895 at Dresden. These three organisms differ in certain ways from the other members of the group of *Mycobacteria*, and will be described separately at the end of the chapter.

Habitat.—The tubercle bacilli are essentially pathogenic ; so far as we know they do not multiply naturally outside the animal body. The human and bovine bacilli give rise to mammalian tuberculosis (see Chapter LVI). The avian type is found chiefly in birds, though it often infects pigs and occasionally cattle. It is sometimes present in hens' eggs (see Gloyne 1933). The cold-blooded type is responsible for disease in cold-blooded animals and fish. The saprophytic acid-fast bacilli are found in such diverse surroundings as butter, milk, smegma, water, dust, grass, manure, and fæces. Though they have not infrequently been isolated from the animal body, they do not appear to give rise to actual disease. The leprosy bacillus is a specific parasite of man, and the rat-leprosy bacillus of rats. Johne's bacillus infects cattle, and to a less extent sheep, in both of which it causes a chronic enteritis.

Morphology and Staining.—The acid-fast bacilli are rod-shaped organisms, straight or slightly curved, with more or less parallel sides and rounded ends ; they are arranged either singly, in small groups or bundles, or in groups of three or four with the individual bacilli lying at acute angles to each other, resembling diphtheria bacilli. Their size varies considerably according to the medium on which they are grown. In the animal body they are generally longer and thinner than in culture. Their length is 1–4 μ, but occasional forms as long as 8 μ are seen ; in breadth they vary from about 0·3–0·6 μ. Long filamentous acid-fast bacilli have been described, but it is probable that these belong to the *Actinomyces* group (see Chapter XIII). Numerous authors, however, have stated that the tubercle bacilli are capable of producing filaments—particularly in liquid media —but these forms are not encountered under ordinary conditions. Clubbed forms, resembling the typical clubs of the diphtheria bacillus, are not uncommon in culture ; branched forms have been described by some authors, but are probably infrequent, except in the avian bacilli. Staining is either uniform or granular ; in the latter type the granules may be restricted to the poles, or they may be evenly distributed throughout the length of the bacillus—the so-called beaded form. In bacilli that appear to be undergoing degeneration, the staining is often irregular both in depth and in situation. In young cultures it is common to find a certain proportion of non-acid-fast forms.

On the average human bacilli tend to be long, thin, and curved, and to show granular staining, while bovine bacilli tend to be short, straight, and thick, and to show uniform staining. Their morphology, however, is so variable, and is so

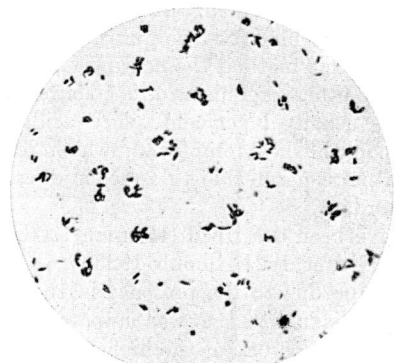

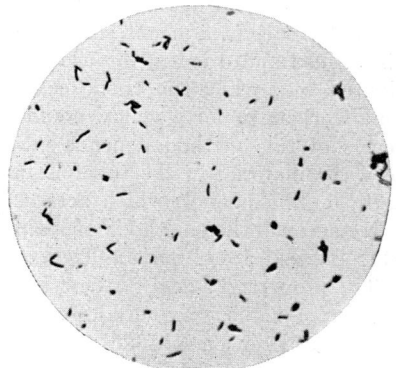

Fig. 50.—*Myco. tuberculosis.*
Glycerine egg-culture, 4 weeks, 37° C., showing short, straight forms of bacilli (× 1000).

Fig. 51.—*Myco. tuberculosis.*
Glycerine agar culture, 4 weeks, at 37° C., showing some short, straight forms, and some longer curved forms (× 1000).

dependent upon environmental factors, that no weight can be attached to these criteria in the identification of individual strains. The acid-fast bacilli are Gram-positive. Staining is not always easy, but with a 5 per cent. solution of gentian violet in alcohol and aniline oil, aided by gentle warming, it is usually possible to obtain satisfactory preparations. According to Kretschmer (1934), the Gram-positiveness is independent of treatment with iodine, and is closely bound up with the property of acid-fastness.

The organisms are resistant to simple solutions of the aniline dyes. To overcome this difficulty several methods of staining have been devised. Koch (1882) first stained the tubercle bacillus by immersion for 24 hours in an alkaline solution of methylene blue. Ehrlich (1882) improved on this by using aniline-oil-basic-fuchsin or aniline-oil-methyl-violet. By this means the bacilli were stained in 15 to 30 minutes and subsequently resisted decolorization with 33 per cent. HNO_3 for a few seconds. He believed that the reason why the bacilli were resistant to ordinary stains was that they were surrounded by a capsule which was permeable only to alkalies.   Ziehl (1882) showed that this conception was wrong ; the bacilli could be stained quite satisfactorily by a dye of acid reaction.   The stain he advocated was a 2 per cent. alcoholic methyl violet solution in carbolic acid water.   Later Ziehl employed carbol-fuchsin.   Neelsen increased the strength of phenol in the stain, and the Ziehl-Neelsen method is the one that is now usually employed.   It consists in covering the film with carbol-fuchsin (basic fuchsin 1 part, absolute alcohol 10 parts, and 5 per cent. phenol in water 100 parts), and gently heating till the steam rises ; heating is continued for 5 to 15 minutes, the water lost by evaporation being replaced by ordinary tap water.   The film is then washed thoroughly in water, and treated with a 15–20 per cent. solution of a mineral acid.   If the film is from a pure culture, the effect of the acid will be merely to dissolve the excess stain ; but if a film of tuberculous pus or a section of tuberculous tissue is being treated, the acid will turn the preparation yellow, indicating that the stain has been removed from the tissue cells, or from other organisms that may be present.   The treatment with acid is continued for 5 to 10 minutes as a rule, till subsequent washing with water causes no more than a faint pink tinge to reappear.   The film is then thoroughly washed in running water to remove all the acid.   It is counterstained with a 1 per cent. aqueous solution of methylene blue for 5 minutes, after which it is washed and dried in the usual way.   By this method the acid-fast bacilli are coloured red, while the tissue cells and all other organisms are coloured blue. Some workers prefer a yellow counterstain—usually 1 per cent. picric acid.   The success of this method depends partly upon the heat employed, which renders the waxy material in the tubercle bacillus more permeable to aqueous dyes, and partly on the phenol, which acts as a mordant.

Numerous other methods of staining have been described (Herman 1908, Mori 1911, Bozzelli 1914, Schulte-Tigges 1920, Kieffer 1921, Shoub 1923).

The property of acid-fastness appears to be due to the presence in the bacilli of unsaponifiable wax (Anderson 1932).   This substance was apparently first isolated by Aronson in 1898.   It was referred to as one of the higher alcohols by Bulloch and MacLeod (1904), and was termed " mykol " by Tamura (1913).   The larger the amount of chloroform-soluble wax, the greater is the resistance of the bacilli to decolorization (Darzine 1932).   The tubercle bacilli contain more of this substance than the saprophytic acid-fast bacilli (Table XXV), and are therefore usually more strongly acid-fast.   The degree of acid-fastness, however, is dependent on a number of factors, and no reliance should be placed on it in determining the particular type of organism under investigation.   Not all workers are agreed on the simple chemical explanation of acid-fastness just given.   Sordelli and Arena (1934), for example, state that it is a property of intact bacilli, and believe that it depends on the existence of a semi-permeable membrane around the organisms which allows fuchsin to diffuse in but does not allow acid fuchsin to diffuse out.

In formol-fixed tissue sections the bacilli often stain very poorly with Ziehl-Neelsen.   According to Fielding (1934), this is due to the development of an acid reaction following autolysis of the tissues, and can be overcome by fixing in a weakly alkaline solution of formol, or by staining with alkaline fuchsin.

Much (1907) brought evidence to show that under certain conditions the bacilli may be present in the tissues in the form of non-acid-fast granules.   Starting from the observation that in the *Perlsucht* nodules of cattle, and in cold abscesses of man, it was often impossible to find acid-fast bacilli in films, even though the presence of tubercle bacilli could be shown by culture and by pathogenicity experiments, he devised a number of different staining methods to determine whether bacilli of any sort could be demonstrated microscopically. The method that he found most successful was to stain for 24 to 48 hours in aniline gentian violet or carbol methyl violet at a temperature of 37° C., to treat with Lugol's iodine solution, and to decolorize by a mixture of absolute alcohol and clove oil, or by a dilute mineral acid, and a mixture of alcohol and acetone. Examining some miliary tubercles of a calf that had been injected with virulent bovine bacilli, he failed to find any bacilli in preparations stained with Ziehl-Neelsen ; but in preparations stained by his own method he found large numbers of fine rods in the tubercles, often accompanied by small rounded granules arranged singly, in pairs, or in short chains resembling beaded bacilli. The rods preponderated in the necrotic portions of the tubercles, the granules in the peripheral zones ; both were coloured violet, and both were numerous within the cells. Small pieces of the lung were seeded on to the serum slopes, and incubated at 37° C. ; smears were examined daily. In smears stained with Ziehl-Neelsen no bacilli were found for 6 days, when acid-fast rods appeared ; but in smears stained by Much's method fine granules and rods were visible after 3 days. Small pieces of the lung injected subcutaneously into guinea-pigs gave rise to generalized fatal tuberculosis in 8 weeks ; acid-fast bacilli were found in the tissues of the dead animals. Much obtained similar results with other tuberculous material. He concluded that—(i) There is a form of tubercle bacillus that is not stainable by Ziehl, but is stainable by Much's method ; it is granular. (ii) In tuberculous organs this granular form may be the only stainable form of bacillus present. (iii) The granular form may be accompanied by fine rods, which likewise do not stain with Ziehl. (iv) The granular forms are virulent. (v) There are transition forms between the Gram + granules, the fine Gram + rods, and the acid-fast rods and granules.

For a long time comparatively little attention was paid to Much's work, but of late years a number of observers have studied the growth of acid-fast bacilli in suitable culture preparations, and have demonstrated the presence of granular forms similar to those described by Much. The interpretation of these forms, however, has given rise to controversy. While Sweany (1928) and Kahn (1930) hold that they represent a stage in the life-cycle of the bacilli, Oerskov (1932) believes that they are products of degeneration. The bundles of extremely fine rods that Kahn described as forming part of the life-cycle are interpreted by Oerskov as crystals, formed partly from the medium and partly from bacillary products. The micro-motion pictures obtained by Wyckoff (1934) and Wyckoff and Smithburn (1933) show that the young bacilli increase in size before dividing, but that, as the culture ages, division continues without previous enlargement. The resulting organisms, therefore, become shorter and shorter, till true coccoid forms, staining intensely acid-fast, appear. Transplanted into a fresh medium, these short forms again give rise to typical bacilli. The sequence of events is so similar in general outline to the behaviour of non-acid-fast bacteria, that there seems no justification for postulating the existence of any special cycle of development. The combination in different proportions of highly refractile and poorly refractile forms, of rods, cocci, and granules with all variations in degree of acid-fastness, together with frank degeneration products, combine to yield a variety of pictures into which a subjective element is very easily projected by the observer.

Filtrable Forms of the Tubercle Bacillus.—Closely connected with the presence of Much granules is a subject that has recently come to the fore, namely, the existence of filtrable forms of the tubercle bacillus. In 1910 Fontès filtered some diluted caseous pus through a Berkefeld candle, and injected the filtrate subcutaneously into guinea-pigs. After a fortnight, one of these animals showed a swelling of the inguinal glands ; no acid-fast bacilli were visible microscopically. The spleen of this animal was inoculated into fresh guinea-pigs ; when these animals were killed 5 months later acid-fast bacilli were found in the glands and lungs. This observation has been confirmed by numerous workers. Generally, it may be said that if pure cultures of tubercle bacilli or tuberculous products are ground up and filtered through a Berkefeld or Chamberland candle, and the filtrate is injected in quantities of 2–10 c.c. subcutaneously into guinea-pigs, a peculiar disease is liable to follow, which differs widely from the usual type of experimental tuberculosis. The animals may survive indefinitely ; sometimes they die after 2 to 4 months. At necropsy there is no local lesion ; one or more groups of glands—especially the tracheo-bronchial glands—may be swollen, but rarely caseous ; and occasionally small —sometimes caseous—lesions may be found in the spleen or lungs. Careful examination with the microscope reveals a few acid-fast bacilli in the glands or other lesions. If the glands are injected into fresh guinea-pigs, the same type of disease follows ; that is to say, the acid-fast bacilli are not possessed of the normal virulence of tubercle bacilli. These are the observations quoted by numerous workers (Valtis 1924a, b, 1926a, b, 1927, Arloing and Dufourt 1925, Calmette *et al.* 1925, Durand and Charchanski 1925, Arloing, Dufourt and Malartre 1926, Bezançon and Philibert 1926, Boquet, Nègre and Valtis 1926, Veber 1926, Bernard and Nélis, 1927, Nélis 1927, Togounoff 1927a, b). The suggestion is that the tubercle bacillus passes through a stage in its developmental cycle characterized by the presence of minute bodies which are capable of traversing a porous filter and of giving rise to a modified form of tuberculosis in experimental animals.

We have no space to discuss these findings in detail. It may be pointed out, however, that work of this type is beset with possibilities of technical error. The ordinary Berkefeld and Chamberland candles cannot be properly standardized, and it is impossible to guard against the passage of a few bacilli through the filter. Some of the results in which definite caseation has been reported in the regional lymphatic glands appear to have been due to this cause. The presence of occasional acid-fast bacilli in the tracheo-bronchial glands is no evidence of tuberculosis. Cooper and Petroff (1928), for example, found such organisms in the glands of 5 out of 15 normal guinea-pigs. They apparently belong to the saprophytic acid-fast group and gain access to the glands by the inhalation or swallowing of dust. Spontaneous tuberculosis contracted from other guinea-pigs in the animal house is a further risk that has not always been adequately guarded against. Tuberculin has often been inoculated to follow the progress of the infection, and the numerous dead acid-fast bacilli in certain preparations of this substance may quite well have given rise to confusion on subsequent microscopical examination of the tissues. The cachectic symptoms that have so frequently been reported were found by Pinner and Voldrich (1931) to follow the inoculation of broth culture filtrates, but not filtrates of saline suspensions of cultures on solid media. These workers brought evidence to show that the symptoms were essentially due to tuberculin present in the broth cultures. The substance responsible for them resisted heating to 60°–65° C. for 1 hour, and was therefore almost certainly not a living organism. The disease, moreover, could not be transmitted by passage. In Schmidt's (1931a) series the cachexia was sometimes found to be due to scurvy. Finally, it is significant that those workers who have taken care to avoid the various technical errors common to this type of work have almost invariably obtained negative results (see Gloyne *et al.* 1929, Pinner and Voldrich 1931, Schmidt 1931*a, b*, Blumenberg 1931, Downie and Meiszner 1934). That small granular or coccal forms of the tubercle bacillus may pass through certain bacterial filters is not only possible but probable, but that these filtrable forms represent a special stage in the life-cycle of the tubercle bacillus, endowed with a degree of virulence far below that of the usual rod forms, remains unproven. The opinion of Calmette and his co-workers (1925, 1926) that filtrable forms of the tubercle bacillus pass through the placenta and infect the fœtus is at present quite unconfirmed.

Chemical Structure of Acid-fast Bacilli.—Largely owing to the work of Anderson and his colleagues (1927 *et seq.*) at Yale University, valuable information has been obtained in recent years on the chemical structure of the *Mycobacteria.* Large quantities of bacilli of different types, grown on Long's (1926) synthetic medium, were extracted with a mixture of alcohol and ether, and the resulting extract was treated with chloroform and with acetone. In this way the lipoid material was separated into three fractions, consisting of glycerides, phosphatides, and wax. The alcohol-ether extract also contained a considerable amount of polysaccharide, and some basic compounds that could be precipitated by $HgCl_2$ and by phosphotungstic acid. The results of the fractionations are given in Table XXV.

TABLE XXV

PERCENTAGE FRACTIONS OF LIPOID AND OTHER MATERIAL ISOLATED FROM ALCOHOL-ETHER AND CHLOROFORM EXTRACTS OF ACID-FAST BACILLI (Chargaff, Pangborn, and Anderson 1931).

	Type of Organism.			
	Human tubercle bacillus H 37.	Avian tubercle bacillus.	Bovine tubercle bacillus.	Timothy grass bacillus.
Phosphatide	6·54	2·26	1·53	0·59
Acetone-soluble fat . .	6·20	2·19	3·34	2·75
Chloroform-soluble wax . .	11·03	10·79	8·52	4·98
Total lipoids.	23·78	15·26	13·40	8·37
Polysaccharide	0·87	1·02	1·09	3·90
Dried bacterial residue . .	75·01	83·71	85·50	87·70

It will be observed that the total lipoid content was highest in the human type of bacillus and lowest in the saprophytic acid-fast bacillus. The polysaccharide content, on the other hand, was arranged in the reverse order. Further analysis showed that the phospholipids contained saturated and unsaturated fatty acids and glycerophosphoric acid; moreover, on hydrolysis they yielded large amounts of water-soluble carbohydrates, of which mannose and inositol seemed to be the two most important. Besides palmitic, linoleic, and linolenic acids, there were two fatty acids of special interest. One, which was optically active and isomeric with cerotic acid, was termed phthioic acid; the other, which was optically inactive and isomeric with stearic acid, was termed tuberculostearic acid. Of the waxy material, one portion was purified and found to be a white powder melting at 200°–205° C.; the remainder formed a yellowish salve-like mass which was called

" soft wax." The purified wax yielded on hydrolysis about 56 per cent. of unsaponifiable wax ; this corresponded to the higher alcohols of previous workers, and proved to be acid-fast. The purified wax also contained polysaccharides which on hydrolysis yielded a number of sugars including mannose, *d*-arabinose, and galactose. The " soft wax " appeared to be a complex glyceride. From the acetone-soluble fat of the human tubercle bacillus a yellow pigment was isolated. This pigment, to which the name phthiocol has been given, is one of the hydroxynaphthaquinones, and is the oxidant of a reversible oxidation-reduction system whose potential is among the lowest reported for systems of biological origin (Ball 1934). The polysaccharides in the ether extract were apparently different from those in the phosphatide or wax.

Biological examination of the various lipoid fractions by Sabin and her colleagues (1930) showed that the phosphatide was capable on repeated intraperitoneal injection into rabbits, of giving rise to massive tuberculous tissue containing epithelioid cells and epithelioid giant cells. Phthioic acid appeared to be one of the active constituents of the phosphatide fraction, while tuberculostearic acid was inert.

Besides the lipoid material and the polysaccharides, acid-fast bacilli also contain proteins that are soluble in water. From cultures of tubercle bacilli on synthetic media Long and Seibert and their colleagues (1926, 1928) have isolated various proteins, of which one appears to be the active principle of tuberculin. It is very toxic to tuberculous animals. The polysaccharide is non-toxic on intravenous inoculation into rabbits (Sabin *et al.* 1931), but like the protein it probably plays a part in the phenomenon of allergy. In this country, Gough (1932) has isolated a specific carbohydrate from cultures of human tubercle bacilli, which on hydrolysis yielded mannose, *d*-arabinose, and galactose. Gough (1933) also obtained evidence of the presence of two proteins showing different chemical and immunological characteristics.

There is evidence that both the phosphatide and the protein fractions are antigenic (Pedersen-Bjergaard 1934). The polysaccharide, though reacting with a precipitating serum, is incapable of calling forth the production of antibodies (Laidlaw and Dudley 1925, Mueller 1926). (See also Goris 1920, Remy 1932 ; for partial reviews see Anderson 1932, Sabin 1932 ; and for a full review see Wells and Long 1932.)

Cultural Reactions.

The acid-fast bacilli vary in the ease with which they grow under artificial conditions. At one end of the scale are the saprophytic acid-fast bacilli and the cold-blooded tubercle bacilli, which grow well in 2 or 3 days on ordinary media ; at the other end are the mammalian tubercle bacilli, which grow only on special media, and which may take a week or more to form a layer of growth visible to the naked eye ; in between come the avian bacilli, which grow poorly or not at all on ordinary media, but which give a good growth in a few days on glycerinated media. The most satisfactory media for cultivation of the tubercle bacilli are inspissated serum, coagulated egg, and potato. The addition of 5 per cent. glycerine to these media is of great value, enhancing the growth of all the acid-fast organisms, with the partial exception of the bovine tubercle bacilli. Its incorporation in nutrient agar or in broth renders these media suitable for the growth of both human and bovine bacilli, while it greatly improves the growth of the other members of the group.

One of the striking characteristics of the acid-fast group is the friable tenacious consistency of the growth, and its adhesiveness to the medium. This is evident not only in the process of subculturing the organisms, when a stout platinum loop has to be used, but particularly in endeavouring to form a suspension of the organisms in saline or other fluid. Instead of giving rise to a uniform turbidity, they settle in granules to the bottom and leave the supernatant fluid clear ; to produce a homogeneous suspension they must be ground up thoroughly in an agate mortar—a process that may take anything from half an hour to several days to complete. Similarly, it is difficult to make a uniform film of a culture for microscopic examination ; even with a stout platinum loop it is impossible to break up the growth completely, and the film remains granular. As a rule the most difficult growths to emulsify are those of the human and bovine types ; growths of the other types usually present less difficulty. Sometimes a creamy, almost butyrous, growth is formed by members of the avian and cold-blooded types, which can be emulsified rapidly ; but even with these suspensions the disintegration of the bacillary clumps is rarely complete ; against an illuminated dark-ground a fine granularity is visible, even to the naked eye.

Another feature that is common to all the tubercle bacilli, though not to the saprophytic acid-fast bacilli, is the rather pleasant, sweet, fruity odour of their cultures. This odour, so far as we know, is peculiar to the tubercle bacilli ; it is developed on all the usual media in which growth occurs, both solid and liquid ; and is most readily detected in tubes that have been corked during incubation.

In studying the cultural reactions of the acid-fast bacilli it is important to realize that, on first isolation, the reactions of a given organism may seem to be anomalous. It is often not till two or three generations, and sometimes more, have been spent in artificial media that the characteristic reactions of the type develop. Thus a cold-blooded bacillus, when first isolated, may grow very poorly —almost like a human strain—but in 3 or 6 months in the laboratory it will become accustomed to its new surroundings, and instead of giving a poor discrete growth on glycerine egg in 4 weeks it will give a profuse confluent growth in 5 or 6 days.

Cultural Differentiation between the Human and Bovine Tubercle Bacilli.—For differentiating between the human and bovine types of tubercle bacilli it is essential to seed a number of different media—serum, glycerine serum, egg, glycerine egg, glycerine agar, glycerine potato, and glycerine broth—with the organisms to be tested, preferably as soon after their isolation as possible. To obtain the maximum differentiation, the organisms used for seeding should never have been grown on a medium containing glycerine. It is advisable to inoculate two or three tubes of each medium, and to seal the tubes so as to prevent evaporation. For examining the growth in glycerine broth, flasks are most suitable, so that a large surface of medium is exposed to the air. Rapid methods of differentiating tubercle bacilli are to be regarded with caution. The method, for example, described by Jensen (1932), which claims to yield a result within 4 weeks, is open to several objections. Though possibly giving a high proportion of correct answers in experienced hands, it will not commend itself to those who realize how much bacteriology has suffered in the past from the use of faulty or inadequate technique.

On all media the growth of the human type is greater in amount than that of the bovine type ; for this reason the human type is called eugonic, the bovine type dysgonic. On media containing no glycerine, such as coagulated serum or egg, the superior growth of the human bacillus is barely evident, but on media

containing glycerine it is most striking. The effect of glycerine on growth is one of
the most important of the differential characteristics ; glycerine favours the growth
of the human type, but has little or no effect on that of the bovine type (Figs.
52 and 53). Thus on glycerine agar the human bacillus gives a thick, confluent,
wrinkled growth, while the bovine bacillus gives only a poor, effuse, ground-
glass growth, or may fail to grow at all. On glycerine potato again the human
bacillus gives a raised, confluent, wrinkled or warty growth, while the bovine
bacillus gives a poor, often discrete, effuse growth ; and similarly with the other
media.

Another point of distinction is that the human type often forms a yellowish or
orange pigment, whereas the bovine type never does. The pigment is noticeable

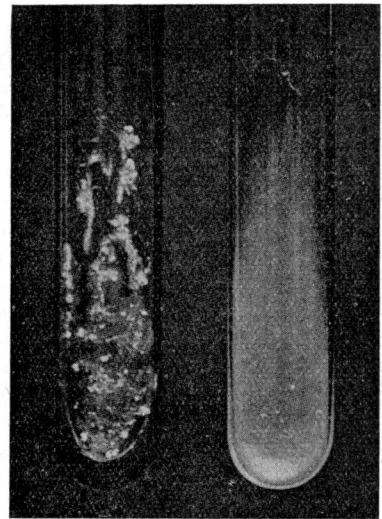

Fig. 52.—*Myco. tuberculosis.*

Human type. Left: Glycerine serum, 14
days, 37° C. Right: Plain serum, 14
days, 37° C., showing beneficial effect on
growth of addition of glycerine.

Fig. 53.—*Myco. tuberculosis.*

Left: Human type. Glycerine agar, 3 weeks,
37° C. Right: Bovine type. Glycerine
serum, 3 weeks, 37° C.

only on batches of serum that have a rich yellow colour. For this reason the serum
should come from an old cow; pale serum from a young cow, or from another species
of animal, is useless. On a golden-yellow serum the human type often produces
a rich yellow or orange-yellow growth ; the bovine type gives a non-pigmented
growth. On a serum coloured only slightly yellow the growth of the human type
is cream or light yellow in colour. The differentiation of the human and bovine
types may take months to complete ; often when the organisms are first isolated,
they grow very poorly, and it is not till they have become accustomed to saprophytic conditions that they give the best growths of which they are capable.

Cultural Differentiation between the Human and Avian Tubercle Bacilli.—
When first isolated from lesions in birds, the avian bacillus may closely resemble
the human bacillus, but as a rule after a few generations in the laboratory it takes
on a more rapid and luxuriant growth, so that differentiation on cultural grounds

alone is rendered possible. There are certain avian strains, however, that remain permanently like the human type ; on solid media these strains are indistinguishable from human strains, but differentiation is generally possible by the growth in glycerine broth ; in this medium the human bacillus forms a thick wrinkled surface pellicle (Fig. 54), whilst the avian bacillus grows at the bottom of the flask forming a granular deposit, or sometimes spreading out in a veil-like manner over the bottom, and part-way up the sides of the flask. Occasionally the avian bacilli give rise to a diffuse turbidity in broth. Why it is that some bacilli grow as a pellicle on the surface, others form a veil over the bottom, while still others grow diffusely, is

not known. It may depend on the oxygen pressure most suitable for growth, or, as some workers think, on the surface tension of the medium. By lowering the surface tension to below 42 dynes, Larson (1926) states that it is possible to induce organisms, which usually form a surface pellicle, to grow diffusely or at the bottom of the flask.

Most avian strains grow more rapidly and more profusely than human strains, and tend on solid media to give a more creamy, homogeneous, and less granular growth than that of the human bacillus (Fig. 55). Though growth is favoured by glycerine, it is possible to get the avian bacillus to grow on simple media like nutrient agar or broth without the addition of any glycerine ; this is more difficult with the human bacillus. Another point of difference is that the human strains do not grow at a temperature above 40° C., whereas the avian strains will grow up to 43° or 45° C. A point of not much importance is

Fig. 54.—*Myco. tuberculosis.*

Human type. Glycerine broth, 6 weeks, 37° C., showing thick, wrinkled, surface growth, spreading up the sides of the flask.

that avian cultures generally live longer than human ones ; they may be found viable after 1 or even 2 years ; human cultures are often dead in a couple of months, though occasionally they may survive for much longer. Another point of small importance is that a few avian strains when grown on glycerine egg medium give a faint pink-coloured growth ; human bacilli never give a pink coloration.

Cultural Differentiation between the Avian and Cold-blooded Tubercle Bacilli.—In culture the avian and the cold-blooded bacilli resemble each other closely. On first isolation they can easily be distinguished by the difference in their optimum temperatures of growth, the avian bacillus growing best at about 40° C., the cold-

P.B. L*

blooded at 25° C. After prolonged subculture in the laboratory this difference is partly obliterated; the cold-blooded bacillus comes to grow quite well at 37° C., though the avian bacillus will rarely grow below 30° C. Practical differentiation can therefore be made by growing the organisms at 25° C.; if growth is as good at this temperature as at 37° C., the strain is a cold-blooded one; if growth occurs freely at 37° C., but fails to occur at 25° C., the strain is an avian one. Apart from the differences in optimum temperature there are no definite cultural characteristics distinguishing the two types, except the pink coloration of certain avian strains when grown on glycerine egg. Minor differences such as the worm-cast growth of the cold-blooded type on glycerine potato, and the denser nature of the growth on the bottom of flasks of glycerine broth are not sufficiently constant to be

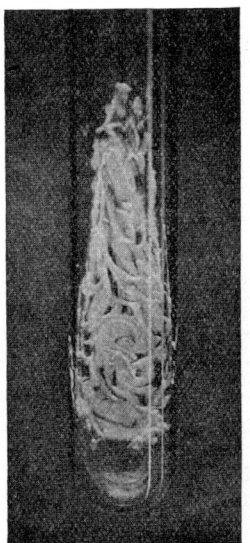 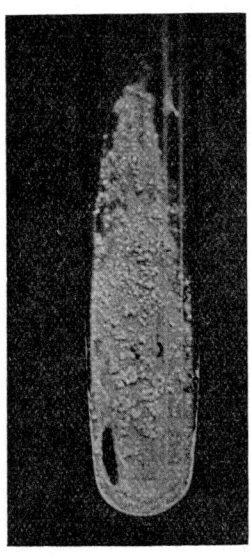 

FIG. 55. — *Myco. tuberculosis.*

Avian type. Glycerine agar, 3 weeks, 37° C., showing abundant growth of butter-cream type.

FIG. 56.—*Myco. stercusis* (Mist bacillus).

Glycerine agar, 3 weeks, 37° C., showing abundant heaped-up growth.

FIG. 57.—*Myco. phlei* I.

Glycerine agar, 3 weeks, 37° C., showing abundant growth with wrinkled surface.

reliable. As a rule the cold-blooded bacillus grows more rapidly than the avian bacillus; cold-blooded strains often give a definite layer of growth in 2 or 3 days: growth of avian strains is often not visible for 4 or 5 days.

Cultural Characteristics of the Saprophytic Acid-fast Bacilli.—These organisms grow rapidly at room temperature, giving rise in 2 or 3 days to a profuse confluent growth. Different strains vary in their cultural reactions, but on the whole their appearance on solid media is very characteristic. On glycerine agar there is a luxuriant, raised, dry growth, yellow, pink, or brick-red in colour, with a coarsely granular surface, resembling dry bread-crumbs (Figs. 56 and 57). This growth is unlike that of any of the tubercle bacilli. A few strains however are non-pigmented. In glycerine broth some strains give a turbidity, but most of them do not; there is generally a surface growth, which may be thick and wrinkled like the human tubercle bacillus, thick and coarsely granular, or more thin and delicate ; a deposit of granular material is usual. Growth occurs in gelatin, but no liquefaction is produced. The optimum temperature of growth varies, but is generally in the neighbourhood of 37° C. All strains grow freely at room temperature ; several grow at 45° C., while a few multiply even at 55° C. (see Schwabacher 1933*b*).

Variation.—The phenomenon of variation in acid-fast bacilli has occupied the attention of large numbers of workers in recent years. The field is a wide one, but so far the results of exploring it have not been fruitful. Many contributions to its study have been purely descriptive, and have been made without any apparent realization of its biological significance. The terms used by different workers to

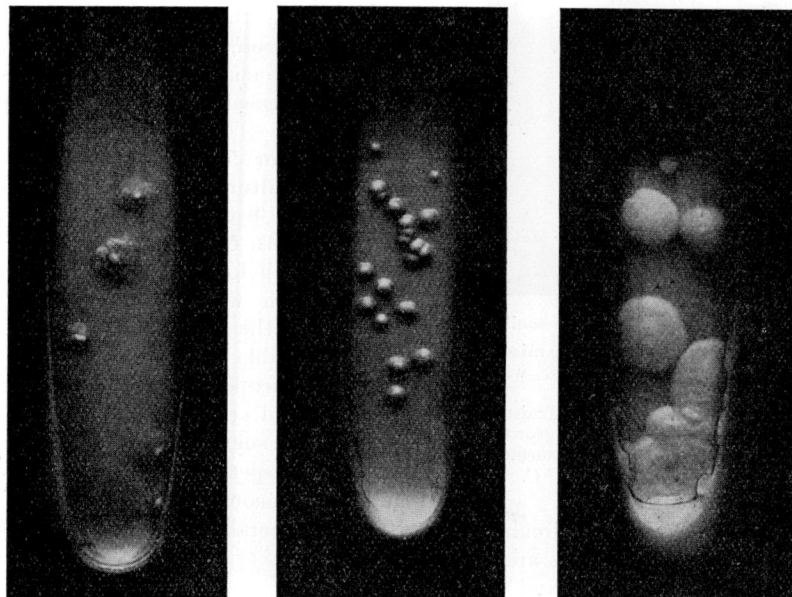

Fɪɢ. 58.—*Myco. tuberculosis*—bovine type.

Surface colonies on three different media, inoculated at the same time from the same suspension and incubated under identical conditions ; 37 days, 37° C. The figure illustrates the dependence of the colonial form on the nature of the medium.

Left : Modified Dorset egg medium. Middle : Egg yolk medium. Right : Egg yolk agar medium.

denote the variants they have observed have differed so widely that the nomenclature is in a state of the utmost confusion. Changes in virulence have been postulated on inadequate grounds, and attempts to measure small differences in virulence have often been confidently performed with numbers of animals quite insufficient to provide a definite answer.

One of the chief difficulties in work of this type lies in distinguishing between fixed and environmental variants. Our own experience suggests that a great many of the so-called variants are nothing more than adaptations to changed conditions. If, for example, a suspension of tubercle bacilli is inoculated simultaneously in equal quantities on to a number of different media, quite a variety of colonial types will develop (Fig. 58). If the different types are picked off and inoculated all on to the same medium, complete similarity of colonial appearance will often result, indicating that no fundamental biological change has been involved. What degree of fixity variant types may have, it is very difficult to ascertain, and we believe that before further progress is possible, a very careful study of the limits of transient environmental variation will have to be made. Without expressing any opinion on the degree of fixity of types, or of giving a critical review of the extensive bibliography that has grown up on the subject of variation, we shall confine ourselves to describing two main types possessing correlated morphological and cultural appearances.

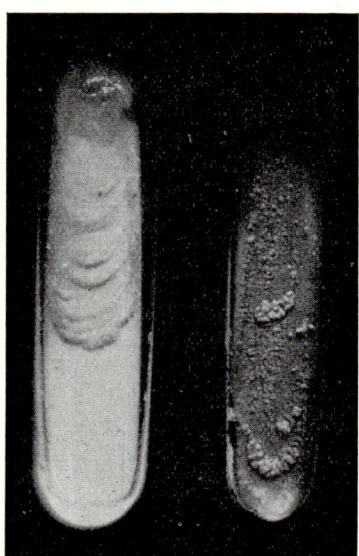

Fig. 59.—Saprophytic acid-fast bacilli.

Left : smooth strain, showing raised, confluent, butyrous growth, with smooth, glistening surface.
Right : rough strain, showing raised, confluent friable, heaped-up growth, with dry, dull, rough surface. Glycerol egg, 2 months, 37° C.

On Dorset or 5 per cent. glycerol egg medium many cultures of tubercle and saprophytic acid-fast bacilli produce colonies that are either smooth or rough. In stroke cultures the smooth forms give rise to a moist butyrous growth with a smooth glistening surface, while the rough forms produce a dry, rather friable growth, with a rough, dull, and often heaped-up surface, looking not unlike dry bread crumbs (Fig. 59). Rubbed up in water the smooth growth yields a fairly homogeneous suspension, the rough growth a granular suspension. Single colonies of the smooth form tend to be circular, convex, with a generally smooth surface and an entire edge ; rough colonies are irregular in outline, are often heaped-up and convoluted, have a roughish granular surface, and tend to be surrounded by a spreading veil-like peripheral extension (Fig. 60). In glycerol broth the smooth forms may grow diffusely throughout the medium, they may form a thin, smooth surface pellicle, or they may cover the bottom of the flask with a reticulated veil-like growth ; the rough forms usually grow as a thick wrinkled surface pellicle unaccompanied by turbidity. Morphologically, smooth strains consist of fairly long, curved, slender, sometimes beaded bacilli, lying more or less parallel to one another and occurring in bundles (Fig. 61) ; less often they are rather short, stout, or ovoid bacilli, staining evenly, and arranged singly or in groups (Fig. 62). Rough strains, on the other hand, consist

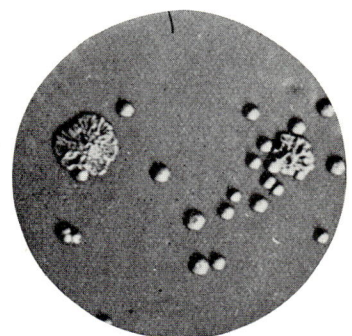

Fig. 60.—*Myco. tuberculosis*—avian type.

Surface colonies of smooth and rough forms. Petragnani medium, 7 weeks, 37° C.

of rather short, sometimes ovoid, bacilli or cocco-bacilli, arranged in Chinese letter forms and in dense masses (Fig. 63). This morphological difference in the arrangement of the smooth and rough types is similar to that described by Nutt (1927) and Wilson (1930) for *Bact. typhi-murium*, and by Soule (1928)

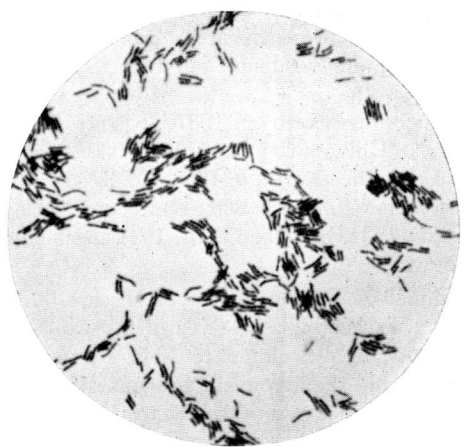

FIG. 61.—Glycerine egg, 1 month, 37° C., showing long curved bacilli arranged in bundles. Smooth type of morphology.

FIG. 62.—Glycerine egg, 1 month, 37° C., showing fat ovoid forms arranged individually and in groups. Smooth type of morphology.

for *B. anthracis* and *B. subtilis*. It has been well pictured by Schwabacher (1933b) and Wyckoff (1934) for saprophytic acid-fast and cold-blooded tubercle bacilli respectively. It depends essentially on the mode of division. The bacilli

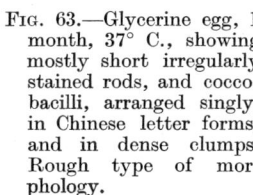

FIG. 63.—Glycerine egg, 1 month, 37° C., showing mostly short irregularly stained rods, and coccobacilli, arranged singly, in Chinese letter forms, and in dense clumps. Rough type of morphology.

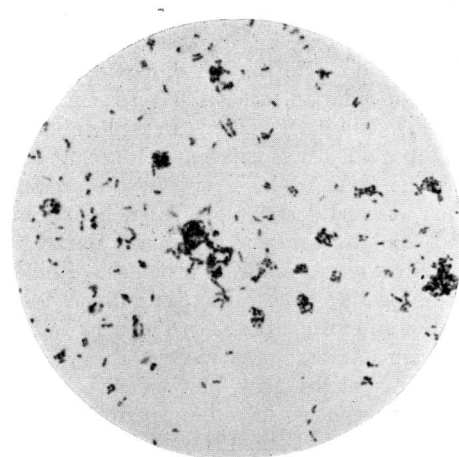

of the smooth type separate completely after division, and slip past each other so as to come to lie in parallel. The bacilli of the rough type exhibit an angular division, the organisms not separating completely but coming to lie at an obtuse angle to each other, resembling a green-stick fracture, or forming long tangled masses which become heaped-up and convoluted as growth continues. It is hardly necessary to add that many intermediate forms occur, partaking of some smooth and some rough characteristics.

Whether the smooth and rough types differ metabolically, antigenically, and in virulence, it is impossible to say definitely at present. Many workers assert that the smooth type of tubercle bacillus is more virulent than the rough, but further evidence is desirable on this point.

(References : Petroff 1927, Petroff, Branch, and Steenken 1927*a*, *b*, Petroff and Steenken 1930, 1935, Kraus and Gerlach 1929, Uhlenhuth and Seiffert 1930, Begbie 1930, 1931, Dreyer and Vollum 1931, Reed and Rice 1931*a*, *b*, Rice and Reed 1931, Rice 1931, Toda 1931, Seiffert 1932, Schwabacher 1933*b*, Seibert, Long, and Morley 1933, Wyckoff 1934, Meiszner and Prausnitz 1934, Steenken *et al*. 1934, Birkhaug 1935, Denys 1935, Shaffer 1935, Smithburn 1935.)

Resistance.—Acid-fast bacilli possess much the same degree of susceptibility to heat as other non-sporing bacteria, but a rather higher degree of resistance to chemical disinfectants. This behaviour is probably related to their content of waxy substances, which are less permeable to cold than to warm aqueous solutions. There is evidence that their resistance is more or less proportional to the amount of waxy material present (Shen 1934). Use is made of this differential susceptibility in isolating tubercle bacilli from contaminated material. Treatment of sputum, pus, or other products, with 15 per cent. antiformin or 15 per cent. sulphuric acid for 5 to 20 minutes is often sufficient to destroy contaminating non-sporing bacteria without killing the tubercle bacilli, which can then be cultivated on suitable media. For the effect of relatively concentrated solutions of disinfectants reference may be made to Calmette (1920). With regard to weaker solutions Douglas and Hartley (1934) found that a saline suspension containing 1 mgm. of moist bovine bacilli per c.c. was sterilized within 24 hours by exposure at room temperature to 0·5 per cent. phenol or 0·02 per cent. merthiolate. Phenol in 0·25 per cent. concentration failed to sterilize the suspension in 14 days, while 0·1 per cent. formol apparently just failed to do so. In our own experience, using the cultural instead of the animal inoculation method, 0·5 per cent. phenol cannot be relied on to destroy all tubercle bacilli in 24 hours. In milk tubercle bacilli are killed in 15–20 minutes at 60° C., provided it is contained in a closed vessel. In an open vessel a pellicle forms on the surface which protects the organisms to some extent, so that a few bacilli may escape destruction for an hour (Smith 1899, Oerskov 1925, Meanwell 1927). In polluted water kept in the dark at room temperature tubercle bacilli may remain alive for at least 3 months (Rhines 1935), while in soil or cow-dung exposed on pasture land during the summer and autumn in this country they may remain alive and virulent for 2 to 6 months (Williams and Hoy 1930, Maddock 1933). The organisms are comparatively resistant to drying, and provided they are protected from sunlight they may survive for months under suitable conditions. Numerous experiments have been performed to test the action of light on tubercle bacilli (Rochaix and Colin 1911, Mayer 1921, Caldwell 1925, Eidinow 1927, Mayer and Dworski 1932). Most workers have found that they are rapidly destroyed, if spread in a thin layer, by bright sunlight, or by ultra-violet rays from a mercury vapour lamp. The most effective appear to be the short ultra-violet rays. Thus bacilli suspended in saline, when exposed in quartz flasks to rays of 2300–7620 Å.U. were killed in 10 minutes ; those exposed to rays of 3300–5720 Å.U. were not completely killed even in 1 hour. Probably the rays shorter than 3300 Å.U. are the most lethal (Eidinow 1927). Blood, serum, and other proteins protect the bacilli against ultra-violet light.

Growth of tubercle bacilli in glycerine broth is inhibited by the addition of very small quantities of certain aniline dyes ; thus a concentration of 0·0004 per cent. thioflavine or 0·0002 per cent. methylene blue entirely prevents growth ; smaller quantities have little or no effect. This fact is taken advantage of in Petroff's medium, which consists of coagulated egg containing a 1–10,000 solution of gentian violet ; the dye inhibits the growth of most organisms, but does not interfere with the growth of tubercle bacilli. Thymol is active in a concentration of 0·004 per cent. ; but most metals in colloidal suspension are inactive even in a concentration of 10 per cent. (Karwacki and Biernacki 1925).

Metabolism.—The optimum hydrogen-ion concentration for growth in 4 per cent. glycerine broth is said by Ishimori (1924) to lie between the following points :

Human type of tubercle bacillus	pH 7·4–8·0
Bovine ,, ,, ,, ,, . . .	pH 5·8–6·9
Cold-blooded ,, ,, ,, . . .	pH 6·2–7·7
Rabinowitsch's butter bacillus	pH 5·7–8·5
Timothy grass bacillus	pH 7·5–9·1
Moeller's grass bacillus ii.	pH 7·4–7·7

Dernby and Näslund (1922) found that growth of human and bovine tubercle bacilli in 3 per cent. glycerine veal broth occurred between pH 4·5 and 8·0, the optimum being pH 6·0–6·5 ; their figures, it will be seen, do not agree with those of Ishimori, who found that the human preferred a more alkaline reaction than the bovine bacillus.

The optimum temperature of growth for the human, bovine, and, generally the saprophytic acid-fast bacilli, is 37° C. ; for the avian 40° C., and for the cold-blooded bacillus 25° C. The human, bovine, and avian types do not grow below 30° C., the cold-blooded and saprophytic acid-fast types grow freely at 20° C. Many saprophytic acid-fast bacilli grow at 45° C., and a few at 55° C.

The tubercle bacillus is an aerobe ; it will not grow under strictly anaerobic conditions. The optimum partial pressure of oxygen is said to be 40–50 per cent. for the human type (Novy and Soule 1925) and 60–70 per cent. for the avian and saprophytic acid-fast types (Uga 1935). Novy and Soule in their very careful study of the respiration of the tubercle bacillus found that CO_2 had little effect on growth, and no inhibition occurred till a partial pressure of 60 per cent. was reached. Subsequent observations, however, by Rockwell and Highberger (1926) and others have shown that CO_2 is beneficial for growth. For optimal development it is desirable to incubate cultures in a high partial pressure of oxygen and about 10 per cent. CO_2. A few measurements have been made on the oxygen uptake of the bacilli (Dieckmann and Menzel 1932), and on the oxidation-reduction potential established in phosphate buffer solutions (Aksianzew 1933).

Moisture is an essential requirement of the tubercle bacillus *in vitro*. For good growth to occur, plenty of condensation water—supplied best by passing steam into the tube before inoculation—and an abundance of air are essential. Growth does occur in sealed tubes provided plenty of moisture is present, but it ceases after 3 or 4 weeks.

The effect of glycerine on the growth of the tubercle bacillus has been the subject of much controversy. Nocard and Roux in 1887, working apparently with an avian strain, were the first to notice the beneficial action of this substance. Since then it has been found that the addition of glycerine, generally in a concentration of 5 per cent., greatly increases the growth of all acid-fast bacilli with the exception of the bovine tubercle bacillus. Even on this organism, however, glycerine is not without effect ; for it will enable it to grow—though very poorly—on agar, potato, or broth, on which no growth otherwise occurs. But the favourable action of glycerine on the bovine bacillus is not to be compared with that on other types ; the addition of glycerine, for example, to serum or egg medium, makes no difference to the growth of the bovine bacillus, whereas it greatly increases the growth of all the other acid-fast bacilli.

The difference in the effect of glycerine on growth was made use of by Smith (1904–05) in the elaboration of a test for distinguishing between the human and bovine types. He found that if bovine tubercle bacilli were grown in glycerine broth, which had an acid reaction to phenol-phthalein, the acidity gradually decreased, till after full growth had occurred the reaction was about neutral ; in cultures of human bacilli, on the other hand, after an initial production of alkali, the reaction gradually became acid again. That is to say, the final reaction of a bovine culture was about neutral, of a human culture decidedly acid. This difference in the reaction curve of the two types of mammalian bacilli has been investigated by numerous workers, some of whom have confirmed, and some of whom have not confirmed, Smith's observations. Undoubtedly one of the reasons for this discrepancy is that most of the work was done before the days of accurate determination of acidity by measurement of the H-ion concentration was possible. Smith's view, put briefly, was that the human bacillus was able to utilize glycerine with the consequent production of acid, whereas the bovine bacillus was unable to use it, and so caused an increased hydrolysis of protein and an alkaline reaction. Whether Smith's view is correct or not, it is still impossible to say. The reaction curve of broth cultures is determined by so many factors, such as the production of NH_3, CO_2, amino-acids, and other substances, some of which are volatile, and some of which are not, that it is almost impossible to determine whether the production of acid is due to disintegration of the glycerine by the bacilli, or to hydrolysis of the protein material. Harden (1913), who made a special investigation of this subject, failed to obtain evidence of any definite distinction in biochemical behaviour between the human and the bovine types. Kendall, Day and Walker (1920), who have examined the question more recently, conclude that glycerine probably exerts a sparing action on the protein constituents of the medium in cultures of the human, but not in cultures of the bovine type ; but, as noted elsewhere (p. 48), the existence of this protein-sparing effect is very doubtful. It is not possible to discuss this problem more fully (for a full discussion of the work up to 1917 see Cobbett 1917) ; but we may conclude that as a practical means of differentiating the human from the bovine bacillus, determination of the glycerine-broth reaction curve is too complex for routine use.

Glucose seems to act in much the same way as glycerol (see Kauffmann 1932). The growth of tubercle bacilli is likewise improved by the addition of extracts of acid-fast bacilli to the medium ; certain organisms, such as Johne's bacillus, will not grow at all unless such an extract is added (see pp. 322, 323). The tubercle bacillus has been grown in certain synthetic media (see Wells and Long 1932) ; its growth is said to be increased by the addition of 0·1 per cent. of boiled blood, of 0·01 per cent. of iron chloride (Schmidt 1925), of substances containing Vitamin B, such as yeast, and of orange, tomato, or cabbage juice (Uyei 1927) (but see p. 38). There is evidence that tubercle bacilli can oxidize certain fats, such as those of olive oil and butter (Sédyeh and Seliber 1927).

Pigment production is very variable. On deeply coloured batches of ox serum the human bacillus often forms a rich yellow or orange-yellow growth. A pink coloration on glycerol egg medium is not uncommon with avian strains, and according to Blacklock (1932) is sometimes given by rapidly growing bovine strains. Cold-blooded bacilli generally give colourless growths. On the other hand, the growth of nearly all the saprophytic acid-fast bacilli is accompanied by the production of a yellow, pink, orange, or brick-red pigment. On Sauton's medium a green coloration is not infrequently observed with cultures of *Mycobacteria* ; its intensity varies from strain to strain (Lange 1932, de Grolier 1933, Kraus and Koref 1933). Pigment formation seems to depend on a number of different environmental factors, particularly the composition of the medium and the oxygen supply. Reed and Rice (1929) found that the addition of iron favoured its formation. On a glycerol agar medium containing 0·02 per cent. of ferric citrate, human, bovine, and avian types of tubercle bacilli, and saprophytic acid-fast bacilli, all formed pigment of varying depth, whereas on the same medium without iron many strains formed no pigment at all. Pigment production is not well developed at 37° C. ; it is best seen in cultures that have been incubated for some time at 37° C., and then transferred to a dark cupboard at room temperature. In this respect the acid-fast bacilli resemble most other chromogenic bacteria.

The tubercle bacilli do not secrete a true exotoxin ; but endotoxins are liberated on autolysis of the bacilli in broth cultures ; these appear to be of complex constitution, and are more fully considered in the section on tuberculin (see Chapter LVI). There is evidence that the endotoxins of all the acid-fast bacilli are closely alike ; it is certainly possible to obtain positive tuberculin reactions with tuberculin, made from any of the four types of tubercle bacilli, in animals infected with the mammalian type (Ledoux-Lebard 1900, Wolbach and Ernst 1904). Intravenous injection of killed cultures of the mammalian, and especially of the avian tubercle bacilli, is often fatal to rabbits ; Twort and Craig (1913) state that the smegma, mist and timothy-grass bacilli are also toxic for rabbits, whereas the cold-blooded tubercle and the butter bacilli are relatively non-toxic.

Biochemical Reactions.—Very little work has been done on the biochemical reactions of the acid-fast bacilli. Frouin and Guillaumie (1923a, b) brought evidence to show that human and avian bacilli could break down glucose, maltose, glycerol, and trehalose with the production of acid. Merrill (1930), who worked with one human, one avian, three cold-blooded, and several saprophytic acid-fast strains, and who made quantitative estimations of the sugar content of the medium before and after growth, found that glucose was utilized by all the strains, arabinose by all but one, sucrose by some, and lactose by none. The reaction, however, did not become acid, nor did any acid cleavage products accumulate. Instead, the medium became more and more alkaline during growth, owing to the production of NH_3, though the rate at which it did so was less than in broth free from sugar. The conclusion was reached that the organisms oxidized the carbohydrates completely to CO_2 and water.

Our own observations, based on an incomplete study of 7 cold-blooded and 36 saprophytic acid-fast strains, showed that there was no detectable acid production in any of the usual sugar media. Litmus milk was turned alkaline by the saprophytic acid-fast, but usually acid by the cold-blooded strains. In peptone water ammonia was produced in considerable quantity. Indole production was uniformly negative, though Rabinowitsch (1897) stated that it was sometimes positive. Catalase production was always positive. H_2S was formed in variable amount. The reduction of methylene blue in broth was weak or absent. The methyl red and Voges-Proskauer reactions were consistently negative.

In milk tubercle bacilli are able to grow, but they produce in it no visible change.

Antigenic Structure.—By agglutination, absorption of agglutinins, and complement fixation, the acid-fast bacilli fall into four serological types—mammalian, avian, cold-blooded, and saprophytic acid-fast—the human and bovine types being indistinguishable (Tulloch *et al.* 1924, Cumming 1925, Wilson 1925, Griffith 1925, Furth 1926, Klopstock 1931, Kauffmann 1932). Direct agglutination is not sufficient to differentiate between the different types ; absorption of agglutinins is essential. By this means it appears that there is an antigen common to the human, bovine, and avian types, but that the avian type also possesses an antigen which is not present in the mammalian types (Wilson 1925). Grünberg (1935) has reached similar conclusions on the basis of the precipitin test. Furth (1926), using complement fixation, obtained evidence of a subdivision of the avian type into three sub-groups, and Schaefer (1935) into two sub-groups. It is possible that the cold-blooded and saprophytic acid-fast types are heterogeneous, but insufficient strains have as yet been examined to affirm this definitely.

It is a curious anomaly that serological methods are less delicate in classifying the tubercle bacilli than cultural methods ; the bovine and human bacilli can be easily separated by their cultural reactions, yet serologically they form a homogeneous group. This affords an exception to the rule that serological examination is a far more delicate method of differentiation than cultural examination.

Pathogenicity and Experimental Infection of Animals.—Under natural conditions the human tubercle bacillus gives rise to disease mainly in man, monkeys, pigs, and occasionally in dogs and parrots, the bovine bacillus to disease in cattle, pigs, horses, man, and occasionally dogs, cats, and sheep, the avian bacillus to disease in birds, and occasionally in sheep and cattle, and the cold-blooded bacillus to disease in cold-blooded animals and fish. Saprophytic acid-fast bacilli, though occasionally isolated from the tissues, rarely seem able to give rise to progressive disease (see also Chapter LVI).

The virulence of tubercle bacilli is subject to variation. Though usually virulent on isolation, they not infrequently become more or less avirulent during subculture in the laboratory. Very little exact information, however, based on an adequate number of animal tests, is available about the difference in virulence of freshly isolated strains of the same type, or about the factors that are responsible for changes in virulence occurring *in vitro* or *in vivo*.

The experiments of Villemin, recorded in 1868, furnished convincing proof of the transmissibility of human tuberculosis to animals. Material taken from different types of tuberculosis in man—catarrhal pneumonic forms, caseous pulmonary and chronic pulmonary tuberculosis, disseminated tuberculosis, scrofula, sputum, and the blood removed from a tuberculous patient after death—and introduced beneath the skin of rabbits, was successful in setting up the disease in 17 out of 21 animals ; 3 of the 4 animals that did not contract tuberculosis died within a week of erysipelas. Villemin also transmitted bovine tuberculosis to rabbits, and made the important observation that material from bovine tuberculosis set up a more rapid and more generalized disease than material from human tuberculosis, when inoculated into these animals. Convincing though Villemin's experiments were, the final proof of the transmissibility of the disease was not furnished till Koch in 1882 succeeded in producing tuberculosis in animals by injection of pure cultures of the tubercle bacillus. In 1898 Smith brought evidence to show that bovine tubercle bacilli were more virulent when injected into rabbits and calves than human bacilli. This difference was substantiated by other workers, in particular by Vagedes (1898), Ravenel (1901), the English Royal Commission on Tuberculosis (Report 1911*a*), Kossel, Weber and Heuss (1904, 1905), and Park and Krumwiede (1910).

CATTLE.—The subcutaneous injection of 50 mgm. of *bovine* bacilli from young serum cultures into calves sets up an acute, rapidly generalizing disease, proving fatal in about 6 weeks to 3 months. At necropsy the main features are a local lesion, focal glandular swelling and abscess formation, generalized glandular lesions, and lesions in the viscera, most extensive in the lungs and spleen, and less extensive in the liver and kidneys. Smaller doses give less constant results. The intravenous injection of even 1 mgm. of bovine bacilli produces a severe and fatal tuberculosis. Cattle may likewise be infected with bovine bacilli by inhalation and feeding.

The subcutaneous injection of calves with *human* bacilli, in no matter what dosage, never gives rise to a progressive disease. At most there is a local abscess and swelling of the focal glands; when the animals are killed after 4 or 5 months, the lesions are minimal, and are often calcified. The intravenous injection of human bacilli may cause death by toxæmia with acute infiltration and œdema of the lungs; but there is no true infection. The same toxæmia may be produced by the intravenous injection of avian bacilli, and even of the non-pathogenic saprophytic acid-fast bacilli.

The subcutaneous injection of calves with *avian* bacilli in a dose of 500 mgm. produces no more than a local lesion, with perhaps a caseous nodule in the nearest lymphatic gland. Intravenous inoculation, however, of even 5 mgm. may prove fatal in 2 to 3 weeks. Post mortem there are miliary tubercles in the lungs; the spleen, though showing no macroscopic tubercles, is enlarged and contains large numbers of tubercle bacilli visible microscopically.

GOATS.—*Bovine* bacilli inoculated subcutaneously in a dose of 1 mgm. give rise to a fatal, generalized disease. *Human* bacilli, even in a dose of 100 mgm., cause no more than small retrogressive lesions. *Avian* bacilli in a dose of 100 mgm. rarely give rise to progressive disease; on the other hand the animals may remain chronically infected and excrete the bacilli in the milk for a long time (Griffith 1931).

SHEEP resemble goats in being highly susceptible to infection with *bovine* bacilli, moderately susceptible to infection with avian bacilli, and resistant to infection with *human* bacilli.

PIGS.—Injected subcutaneously, the *bovine* type in a dose of 10 to 50 mgm. produces rapidly fatal miliary tuberculosis. The *human* type in a dose of 50 mgm. produces a local lesion with slight dissemination. *Avian* bacilli injected subcutaneously do not give rise to progressive disease, but they may multiply and be disseminated through the internal organs, where they remain alive for some considerable time. Young pigs fed with bovine bacilli develop widespread disease and generally die; when fed with human bacilli they may develop extensive glandular and pulmonary disease. Though the human bacilli cause less severe and less extensive tuberculosis than bacilli of the bovine type, they are more pathogenic for pigs than they are for cattle.

RABBITS.—*Bovine* bacilli injected subcutaneously in a dose of 0·1–1·0 mgm. produce a generalized disease, fatal in 2 to 3 months. At necropsy a local caseous lesion, caseous focal glands, innumerable little grey tubercles with caseating centres or larger irregular nodules in the lungs, numerous projecting hemispherical nodules in the cortex of the kidneys, and tubercles in the spleen and liver are found. Given intraperitoneally, even minute doses, such as 0·00,000,000,1 mgm. of bovine bacilli, are said to prove fatal in 2 to 3 months (Cobbett 1917). Intravenous injection of 0·01–0·1 mgm. of bovine bacilli proves fatal in 3 to 6 weeks.

The subcutaneous injection of *human* bacilli in a dose of 1–100 mgm. never causes fatal tuberculosis. Human bacilli may, however, give rise to lesions in the lungs and kidneys. Usually the lungs contain a few small grey tubercles or caseous nodules, and the kidneys show a few miliary tubercles in the cortex. But the acute fatal miliary tuberculosis seen after injection of bovine bacilli never results from the subcutaneous injection of human bacilli. Intravenous and intraperitoneal injections are less reliable for purposes of differentiation. 0·01 mgm. of human bacilli given intravenously rarely, if ever, proves fatal, but larger doses may give rise to a progressive fatal disease. Doses of 10–50 mgm. given intraperitoneally may likewise prove fatal on occasion. Extensive lesions in the lungs and kidneys are often seen both after intravenous and intraperitoneal injection (see Cobbett 1932). The rabbit, in fact, possesses a considerable resistance to the human type of bacillus, but not so great as the ox or the goat. The *avian* bacillus is less virulent for rabbits than the bovine, but more virulent than the human bacillus. Subcutaneous injection gives rise to a chronic disease; intraperitoneal injection of large doses to a rapidly fatal peritonitis; and intravenous injection to an acutely fatal infection. The macroscopic lesions caused by the avian bacillus are much less obvious than those caused by the bovine bacillus; sometimes no tubercles are visible. After intravenous inoculation Yersin (1888) found the spleen greatly enlarged and the liver enlarged to a less extent; no macroscopic tubercles were seen, but microscopically there were numerous small tuberculous nodules in the liver and spleen containing large numbers of tubercle bacilli; the kidneys and lungs appeared practically normal. This proliferation of the bacilli in the body without macroscopic tubercle formation is known as the *Yersin type of disease*; it is seen both in rabbits and guinea-pigs injected with avian bacilli, and in rats injected with both mammalian and avian types.

After injection of the bovine or human type of bacillus, no matter what route is chosen, the lesions in rabbits are most evident in the lungs and kidneys; the spleen and liver suffer less; the lymphatic glands, with the exception of the regional glands, hardly at all. Not infrequently the joints, mammary glands, and testes show lesions. For differentiating between bovine and human bacilli in the rabbit, the best doses to employ are 10 mgm. subcutaneously, 1 mgm. intraperitoneally, and 0·01 intravenously (Cobbett 1917).

Feeding the rabbit with 1–10 mgm. of *bovine* bacilli sets up a disease that proves fatal in 2 to 3 months.

GUINEA-PIGS.—The guinea-pig is highly susceptible to experimental infection with bacilli of the mammalian type. Indeed it has been stated that the subcutaneous injection of a single tubercle bacillus may succeed in producing disease—though only of a slow type showing little tendency to generalization (Wámoscher and Stoecklin 1927, Doerr and Gold 1932). Less than 10 living bacilli, even of virulent strains, cannot be relied upon to cause disease in every animal. With between 10 and 100 bacilli intramuscular inoculation into the thigh usually sets up a slowly progressive disease, often characterized in the later stages by healing of the initial lesions. The bovine bacillus is rather more virulent than the human bacillus; this can be demonstrated, however, only by a series of comparative experiments in which carefully measured doses are introduced. Table XXVI, from Griffith, quoted by Cobbett (1917), who gives an excellent review of the pathogenicity of tubercle bacilli to animals, illustrates this.

The subcutaneous injection—usually made in the left thigh—of either *human* or *bovine* bacilli, even in minute doses, is followed by death from generalized tuberculosis in about 6 to 15 weeks. At necropsy, there is a caseous local lesion; the superficial inguinal, and often the femoral, glands are much enlarged and caseous; the sublumbar, portal, mediastinal, and bronchial glands are enlarged and generally caseous; the spleen is greatly enlarged, and is beset with irregular necrotic areas, varying considerably in size, of a

TABLE XXVI

SHOWING GREATER VIRULENCE OF BOVINE THAN HUMAN BACILLI TO GUINEA-PIGS.

Method of Injection.	Dose of Bacilli.	Average Duration of Life in Days.	
		Bovine Type.	Human Type.
Intraperitoneal . . .	1·0 mgm. 0·1 mgm.	11·9 (15 animals) 16·4 (58 animals)	22·5 (17 animals). 27·9 (40 animals).
Subcutaneous . . .	1·0 mgm. 0·1 mgm.	49·6 (15 animals) 45·6 (58 animals)	80·9 (30 animals). 65·0 (40 animals).

yellowish-white waxy appearance ; the liver is enlarged and contains smaller necrotic areas of a yellow or greenish colour ; the lungs contain small numbers of rounded gelatinous tubercles. The most striking appearance is afforded by the necrotic areas in the spleen and liver ; these are peculiar to the guinea-pig. They are more marked after injection with bovine than with human bacilli. True tubercles are not often seen except in the very early stages of the disease, and in the lungs. It will be noted that the distribution of lesions is quite different in the guinea-pig from that in the rabbit. In the rabbit they are most marked in, and often confined to, the lungs and kidneys ; in the guinea-pig the lymphatic glands, spleen, and liver bear the brunt of the disease ; the lungs are but slightly affected, and the kidneys practically never.

Intraperitoneal injection of mammalian bacilli is followed by death in 2 or 3 weeks. Post mortem, there is a local caseous abscess in the abdominal wall ; the superficial inguinal glands are enlarged and caseous ; the omentum is rolled up, thickened, and caseous ; the portal and often the mediastinal glands are enlarged and caseous ; and the spleen and liver may show small foci of necrosis.

There is a disease that occurs naturally in guinea-pigs known as pseudotuberculosis ; it is caused by *Pasteurella pseudotuberculosis* (*B. pseudotuberculosis rodentium*). The lesions to which it gives rise include white rounded nodules in the spleen, liver, and mesenteric glands. These are unlike the necrotic lesions caused by the true tubercle bacillus, but may confuse those who are not well acquainted with the disease, especially since, when inoculated subcutaneously into normal guinea-pigs, the pseudotubercle bacillus gives rise to a local lesion and caseation of the focal lymphatic glands. The differential diagnosis can be made by microscopical and cultural examination. Microscopically, short, non-acid-fast, Gram-negative, bipolar-stained bacilli are seen, though often only in small numbers ; culturally these organisms grow readily on ordinary media within 24 hours (see Chapter XXIX).

Avian bacilli are very much less virulent for the guinea-pig than the mammalian type. Subcutaneous injection is followed by a local abscess and swelling of the regional glands ; death is unusual unless a large dose is given. Intraperitoneal injection of large doses is followed by death in a few weeks. Post mortem, the omentum is thickened, the spleen is large and red, there are minute grey points in the liver, and there may be fluid in the pleural cavities. Though neither after subcutaneous nor intraperitoneal injection are macroscopic tubercles visible, smears or cultures made from the spleen and liver will generally reveal the presence of tubercle bacilli—Yersin type of disease.

RATS AND MICE.—In the past these animals have been regarded as comparatively resistant to tuberculosis. More recent work, however, particularly with mice, seems to show that their resistance has been rather overestimated. Subcutaneous inoculation, except in large doses, seems to have little effect. Intraperitoneal inoculation of mice with

1 mgm. of human or bovine bacilli sets up a disease usually proving fatal in 3 to 4 weeks, while intravenous inoculation with 1 mgm. is often fatal in 2 to 3 weeks. Post mortem, the lungs are studded with translucent, gelatinous, miliary tubercles ; similar tubercles are sometimes present on the pericardium ; the spleen shows a variable degree of enlargement but no macroscopic tubercle formation. Microscopically, the lungs contain enormous numbers of bacilli, while in smears of the spleen, liver, and kidneys the organisms are usually plentiful but not abundant. Smaller doses give rise to a less rapidly fatal disease, in which there is time for the pulmonary tubercles to become partly aggregated into irregular, hard, caseous masses. Small doses cannot be relied upon to cause progressive infection when injected intraperitoneally, but intravenous inoculation with as few as 10–100 living bacilli has, in our experience, often been followed by chronic disease. If the animals are killed within 3 months after such small doses, no tubercles may be visible in the lungs, but quantitative bacteriological examination leaves no doubt that the bacilli are actively proliferating. The virulence of the human and bovine types for mice seems to be very much the same (Lange 1922). The avian type was found by Gunn and his colleagues (1934) never to cause fatal disease after intravenous inoculation of 0·25 mgm., but our experience does not bear this out. We do, however, find that the avian bacillus is less virulent than the mammalian types. According to Lange (1922), tuberculous mice appear to be relatively non-allergic. Field mice (*Arvicola arvalis*) were found by Koch (1886) to be more susceptible than house mice ; after subcutaneous inoculation they died in 4 to 6 weeks with extensive tuberculosis of the lungs, liver, and spleen.

OTHER ANIMALS.—The *dog* is relatively resistant to experimental tuberculosis, but young animals may be infected by intraperitoneal inoculation with the mammalian types. *Horses* and *asses* are also resistant ; subcutaneous injection sets up no more than a local lesion. *Cats* are highly susceptible to bovine bacilli, slightly susceptible to avian, and resistant to human bacilli. Subcutaneous injection of 0·1 mgm. of bovine bacilli sets up invariably a rapidly fatal generalized tuberculosis. *Monkeys* and *anthropoid apes* are easily infected either by subcutaneous inoculation or by feeding with the mammalian types, but are comparatively resistant to the avian type.

BIRDS.—With the exception of the parrot, and possibly certain birds of prey, which are susceptible to all three types, birds are resistant to infection with the mammalian bacilli. Subcutaneous, intraperitoneal, or intravenous injection of avian bacilli into fowls or pigeons gives rise to fatal tuberculosis. At necropsy, the main lesions are found in the liver and spleen, which contain rather hard caseous tubercles well differentiated from the surrounding tissue. After feeding experiments, tubercles are often seen projecting through the peritoneal covering of the intestine.

COLD-BLOODED ANIMALS.—The cold-blooded type of tubercle bacillus is unable to set up progressive disease in mammals or probably birds ; after subcutaneous injection of large doses a local lesion may result, but the disease does not spread. Frogs, turtles, lizards, snakes, fish and other cold-blooded animals are susceptible to experimental inoculation with the cold-blooded type, though not with the mammalian or avian types. After subcutaneous or intraperitoneal inoculation the lesions are often widely distributed throughout the viscera. Their nature depends on the site of inoculation and the time of survival. Soft, nodular lesions in the liver or lungs, filled with creamy or caseous material, are not uncommon. Sometimes the liver is studded with little greyish-white granules, almost confluent (see Ledoux-Lebard 1900, Friedmann 1903, Küster 1905). Whether cold-blooded bacilli are pathogenic for birds is not clear. Aronson (1926) states that he isolated a cold-blooded bacillus from certain salt-water fish—a sergeant-major (*Abudefduf mauritii*), three croakers (*Micropogon undulatus*), and two sea-bass (*Centropristes striatus*)—which proved pathogenic for pigeons.

Table XXVII, modified slightly from Cobbett (1932), summarizes the reaction of different animals to the three main types of tubercle bacilli.

TABLE XXVII

SHOWING THE SUSCEPTIBILITY OF CERTAIN ANIMALS TO EXPERIMENTAL INFECTION (IN ALL BUT MAN) WITH THE THREE MAIN TYPES OF TUBERCLE BACILLI.

Susceptible to	Species of Animal.	Severity of Disease caused by 3 Types of Tubercle Bacilli.		
		Human.	Bovine.	Avian.
General infection by bovine type	Ox, goat, cat	∓	+++	0
	Pig	±	+++	±
	Horse (a)	0	+	0
	Rabbit (b).	±	+++	+ Y
Infection by both bovine and human types	Guinea-pig (b)	+++	+++	+ Y
	Dog (a)	±	±	0
	Man	++	++	0
	Anthropoid apes and other monkeys	+++	+++	0
	Other wild animals in captivity	++	++	?
	Rat (c), mouse (c)	+ Y	+ Y	+ Y
	Parrot and cockatoo . . .	++	++	++
Insusceptible to mammalian types	Fowls and other domestic birds	0	0	++

∓ A local retrogressive lesion.
± Localized tuberculosis, with sometimes slight dissemination.
+, ++, +++ Various degrees of progressive tuberculosis.
+ Y Tuberculosis of the Yersin type.
(a) Spontaneous tuberculosis relatively uncommon ; difficult to infect experimentally.
(b) Extremely easy to infect experimentally, but seldom, if ever, contracts tuberculosis naturally.
(c) Spontaneous tuberculosis is rare. After very large intraperitoneal injections rats succumb slowly to a general infection approximating to the Yersin type of disease.

The *saprophytic acid-fast bacilli* are unable to set up a progressive infection in animals or birds. Nevertheless, when injected intraperitoneally in fairly large doses, especially together with some fatty protective substance such as butter, they may give rise to extensive lesions closely simulating those of true tuberculosis (see Rabinowitsch 1897, Grassberger 1899, Hagan and Levine 1932). This appears to result from the dissemination of the bacilli in the tissues by the lymph stream and leucocytes, and the subsequent focal reaction of the tissues around them. True nodule formation and caseation may occur, and acid-fast bacilli are found microscopically in the lesions. After subcutaneous or intramuscular inoculation the lesions are usually confined to the local site and the regional lymphatic glands. The disease may be distinguished, however, from tuberculosis by culture and by further inoculation. Cultures made from the lesions on to glycerine agar will reveal a growth of saprophytic acid-fast bacilli in 2 or 3 days ; while further inoculation into a guinea-pig, using a saline suspension of a small portion of one of the lesions, will prove innocuous. Histologically, the lesions caused by the saprophytic acid-fast bacilli show more exudation than proliferation ; there is less tendency to caseation and more to suppuration ; polymorphs are commoner than epithelioid cells ; and typical giant cells with peripheral nuclei are rare (Rabinowitsch 1897). Saprophytic acid-fast bacilli injected intravenously into laboratory animals, or even into larger animals such as calves, may give rise to severe illness, sometimes followed by death (Kossel *et al.* 1904, Twort and Craig 1913). The bacilli do not multiply in the tissues, and therefore no true infection is set up ; the symptoms appear to be due to toxæmia following the liberation of endotoxins from the bacilli in contact with the tissues. Similar results can be obtained with dead bacilli. This toxæmia following the intravenous injection of living or dead acid-fast bacilli, whether of the saprophytic acid-fast or the true tubercle type, into susceptible animals, is a phenomenon that may lead to confusion if differentiation of the various types is attempted by the intravenous route. For this reason the subcutaneous method of injection is generally to be preferred.

Type Differentiation by Pathogenicity.—At the risk of repetition we give for the sake of clearness the methods by which the three main types of tubercle bacilli may be differentiated.

The *human* and the *bovine* types of tubercle bacilli are able, when injected subcutaneously in minute doses, to give rise to a progressive and fatal disease in guinea-pigs. But whereas the bovine type is able likewise to produce a progressive, generalized, and fatal disease in rabbits, cats, goats, and calves, the human bacillus cannot do so. This fundamental distinction can be elicited in practice only by strict regard to certain factors, such as dosage and route of inoculation. The experience of the Royal Commission showed that the best differentiating dose for calves was 50 mgm. subcutaneously, and for rabbits 10 mgm. subcutaneously. The bacilli are taken from a 1 to 3-weeks old culture on inspissated serum and weighed moist. Under these conditions the bovine bacillus sets up a generalized fatal disease, while the human bacillus causes at most a localized and retrogressive disease, confined to the site of inoculation, and sometimes to one or more of the internal organs ; often no lesions are visible at all. Animals vary so much in their susceptibility to experimental inoculation that it is advisable to inject two or three simultaneously, and to repeat the test on a fresh series of animals if the results are not precise. The time taken to produce death is probably not of such importance as the extent of the lesions at necropsy (Park and Krumwiede 1910) ; but generally speaking calves inoculated with a bovine virus may be expected to die in about 6 to 8 weeks, and rabbits in 6 to 12 weeks.

The separation of the *avian* from the *mammalian* bacilli is generally quite straightforward. The avian bacillus is pathogenic for fowls and pigeons, but not for the guinea-pig ; the mammalian bacilli, on the contrary, are pathogenic for the guinea-pig, but not for fowls and pigeons. Cobbett (1917) recommends for differentiating purposes the injection of 10 mgm. of culture subcutaneously into guinea-pigs, and 10 mgm. intraperitoneally into fowls or pigeons. The mammalian bacilli prove fatal to guinea-pigs in about 4 to 8 weeks, and at necropsy there is generalized tuberculosis with extensive caseation of the glands and large necrotic areas in the spleen and liver. The avian bacilli often give rise to no lesions at all, or only to a slight local collection of caseous material ; but sometimes, if the animals are killed after a few weeks, the focal glands will be found to be hyperæmic, and the spleen enlarged and congested ; smears of the spleen, liver, and lungs from these cases may reveal a few acid-fast bacilli (Straus and Gamaléia 1891). After injection with avian bacilli, fowls and pigeons die in a variable time, often considerably emaciated ; if they are still alive at the end of 3 months they should be killed. Disease is most evident in the spleen, liver, and kidneys, which show numerous tubercles or hard caseous areas ; bacilli are abundant in smears of these organs.

The mammalian bacilli generally produce no recognizable lesions in fowls or pigeons, but occasionally a local abscess forms, which contains a few bacilli.

Lesions caused by the Injection of Dead Tubercle Bacilli.—The injection into animals of dead tubercle bacilli, preferably killed by heat, gives rise to lesions of varying degrees of severity. Subcutaneous injection provokes merely a local abscess, but after intravenous injection the dead bacilli are deposited in the viscera, where they give rise to small follicular lesions closely resembling true tubercles, and sometimes undergoing caseation. This disease is known as *Necro-tuberculosis* (Miller 1905). Apparently the dead bacilli are attacked and broken down by the cells of the body and their intracellular toxins liberated ; these toxins then act on the tissues, and give rise to the characteristic lesions of tuberculosis. For the production of necro-tuberculosis, virulent bacilli are not essential ; we have produced lesions in rabbits by the intravenous injection of dead avirulent bacilli, such as Calmette's B.C.G. strain.

Classification.—We have already indicated that the acid-fast bacilli may be divided into five types—human, bovine, avian, and cold-blooded tubercle bacilli, and the saprophytic acid-fast bacilli. The distinction between the types rests chiefly on cultural appearances and pathogenicity, aided when necessary by serological reactions. These types are remarkably constant ; so far as we are aware, no clear evidence has ever been produced to prove that one type may change into another. Numerous experiments have been made by different methods to bring this about, but no one has yet succeeded in doing so.

Nevertheless, the division of the mammalian tubercle bacilli is not always clearly defined. From time to time aberrant strains are encountered, which depart from the standard type either in cultural behaviour, in pathogenicity, or in both. The most fruitful source of these aberrant types is lupus ; thus from 140 cases of lupus examined by A. S. Griffith (1924), no fewer than 99 yielded strains of aberrant type. Apparently, when growing in the skin, tubercle bacilli are liable to undergo a modification in virulence, so that both human and bovine types become less pathogenic for experimental animals. Aberrant types are encountered in other lesions, though much less frequently ; thus Griffith (1916) found 4 aberrant strains amongst a total of 212 strains isolated from sputum, and 5 amongst 141 strains isolated from bone and joint disease (1916–17) ; Eastwood and F. Griffith (1916) likewise isolated 10 aberrant out of a total of 261 strains from cases of bone and joint disease. Aberrant strains have occasionally been found in animals, especially horses (A. S. Griffith 1924, Stableforth 1929).

The mammalian bacilli may be subdivided as follows (Table XXVIII, p. 314).

Of these various types the attenuated eugonic human and the attenuated dysgonic bovine are the ones usually found in lupus ; the attenuated dysgonic human and attenuated eugonic bovine are rare, and have been met with in lupus only. The dysgonic human type was the type isolated from sputum and from bone and joint disease, in the cases already referred to. On serum and glycerine serum it grows luxuriantly with the production of yellow pigment. But on glycerine agar and glycerine potato growth is very slow ; an effuse grey glazed layer of growth occurs, on which a few large isolated warty and pigmented colonies may eventually develop. Similarly on glycerine broth there is only a thin layer of growth with an occasional raised island of irregular appearance. In virulence this variety resembles the standard human type, being high for the guinea-pig and low for the rabbit. These dysgonic human strains are most likely to be confused with the attenuated

TABLE XXVIII.　(Modified from A. S. Griffith 1924.)

SHOWING THE DIFFERENTIAL CHARACTERISTICS OF MAMMALIAN TUBERCLE BACILLI.

Human.	Classification.	Cultural Characteristics.	Virulence.
1	Typical human .	Eugonic on all glycerine media. Pigmented growth on bovine serum	High for guinea-pig; low for rabbit (standard human virulence).
2	Dysgonic human	Dysgonic on glycerine agar, potato, and broth. Pigmented growth on bovine serum	Like (1).
3	Attenuated dysgonic human	Like (2)	Very low for rabbit, and lower for guinea-pigs and monkeys than standard human strains.
4	Attenuated eugonic human	Like (1)	Like (3).
Bovine.			
1	Typical bovine .	Dysgonic on all glycerine media; no pigment formation on bovine serum	High for guinea-pig and rabbit (standard bovine virulence).
2	Eugonic bovine .	Growth better than typical bovine strains, but not equal to human	Like (1).
3	Attenuated eugonic bovine	Like (2)	Less than standard bovine virulence for all animals, but higher for calf and rabbit than standard human.
4	Attenuated dysgonic bovine	Like (1)	Like (3).

bovine strains; differentiation can be effected by making a sufficiently wide and prolonged series of tests. The dysgonic bovine strains do not give a yellow pigmented growth on bovine serum; and their virulence is lowered not differentially but uniformly that is to say, their virulence is lowered not only for the more resistant calf and rabbit, but also for the highly susceptible guinea-pig and monkey.

Whenever an aberrant strain is encountered, the possibility of the cultures being impure must always be considered. Thus the Royal Commission (Report 1911) examined 2 cultures that were eugonic on glycerine media and were highly virulent to calves and rabbits. By plating out these cultures they were able to separate off a dysgonic virulent strain from a eugonic strain of slight virulence for the calf and rabbit; in other words, the original cultures contained a mixture of bovine and human types.

Considerable attention has been paid to these atypical strains, because they have been regarded by some workers as evidence of instability of type. Griffith, who has had the greatest experience of these atypical strains, is however firmly of the opinion that they represent no more than modifications of the fixed types; they do not represent transitional forms between the types. By passage through suitable animals it is often possible to restore the normal properties of their type to the e atypical strains; but it has never yet proved possible to modify them in such a way that they change into a different type. Thus an attenuated dysgonic bovine strain, if passed through a series of rabbits, will often regain the standard virulence of the bovine type ; it will not take on a eugonic growth and come to resemble the human type (Griffith 1924).

We may conclude therefore that the types of tubercle bacilli are fixed ; that occasionally modifications due to residence in a particular environment may result ; but that no alteration of environment or any other factor has yet been successful under experimental conditions of changing an organism of one type into that of another.

Classification of the saprophytic acid-fast strains is very unsatisfactory. Numerous types have been described, and have been differentiated on morphological and cultural appearances, the degree of acid-fastness, the formation of pigment, and the optimum temperature of growth (see Haag 1927, Pinner 1932, Thomson 1932, Schwabacher 1933*b*).

A large amount of detailed information, much of which has been overlooked by subsequent workers, on the various properties of the tubercle bacilli, is contained in the Reports (1907, 1909, 1911, 1913) of the Royal Commission on Tuberculosis. Those anxious to learn more about these organisms are advised to study these reports carefully, as well as the numerous subsequent publications of Dr. A. Stanley Griffith, many of which have appeared in the *Journal of Pathology and Bacteriology* during the past twenty years.

Mycobacterium tuberculosis, Human type

Isolation.—By Koch in 1882 from human tuberculous lesions.

Habitat.—Strict parasite, causing tuberculosis in man, pigs, monkeys, dogs, and parrots.

Morphology.—Rod-shaped organisms, 1–4 μ long and 0·2–0·8 μ broad, straight or slightly curved, with parallel or irregular sides, and rounded ends ; arranged singly or in small clumps ; non-motile, non-sporing, and non-capsulated. Fail to stain with simple dyes except after prolonged exposure. Stain best with hot carbol-fuchsin ; resist decolorization with 25 per cent. H_2SO_4 and with absolute alcohol for 10 minutes. Gram-positive ; staining may be even or granular ; beaded forms are common. In the animal body the bacilli are larger than in culture. Non-acid-fast and clubbed forms are not uncommon in culture.

Coagulated Ox serum.—4 *weeks*, 37° *C.* Thin, effuse, confluent, greyish-yellow growth, with a finely granular surface, looking like ground glass ; colour may be golden yellow ; consistency friable ; emulsifies with great difficulty.

5 per cent. Glycerine Ox serum.—4 *weeks*, 37° *C.* More luxuriant, thicker, raised, confluent, yellow or golden-yellow growth, with a coarsely granular surface ; irregularly heaped-up in places ; often a granular film over the water of condensation. Consistency friable, emulsifies with great difficulty.

Dorset Egg.—4 *weeks*, 37° *C.* Rather poor, discrete or confluent, slightly raised, greyish-yellow growth, with a finely granular surface.

5 per cent. Glycerine Egg.—4 *weeks*, 37° *C.* More luxuriant, raised, confluent, greyish-yellow growth, with a coarsely granular surface ; growth irregularly nodular and heaped-up in places.

5 per cent. Glycerine Agar.—4 *weeks*, 37° *C.* Thick, raised, confluent, cream-coloured growth with a nodular or wrinkled surface.

5 per cent. Glycerine Potato.—4 *weeks*, 37° *C.* Thick, raised, confluent growth, creamy or yellow in colour, with a wrinkled, nodular, or warty surface.

5 per cent. Glycerine Broth.—4 *weeks*, 37° *C.* Greyish-white surface pellicle, often irregularly thickened in places. On further incubation the pellicle increases in thickness, develops a deeply wrinkled surface, and spreads for about ½ inch up the sides of the flask. No turbidity, but often a slight granular deposit.

Plain Agar or Broth.—No growth, as a rule.

Resistance.—Cultures live for 4 to 8 weeks as a rule, but may remain viable for a year. Bacilli are killed by moist heat at 60° C. in 15 to 20 minutes. In excised tissues, kept at 37° C., they die in about a week. In dried sputum most of the bacilli die in a few days. Are fairly susceptible to sunlight and ultra-violet light. Moderately resistant to chemical disinfectants ; in sputum may survive exposure to 5 per cent. phenol or antiformin for 24 hours.

Metabolism.—Growth occurs between pH 4·5 and 8·0 ; optimum pH is 7·0–7·6. Optimum temperature 37° C. ; very little growth, if any, below 30° C. Growth occurs best in an atmosphere of 40–50 per cent. O_2 ; no growth under strictly anaerobic conditions. Growth is improved by addition of glycerine and of dead acid-fast bacilli to the medium ; and is said to be improved by substances rich in Vitamin B, and by very small quantities of iron salts. Golden-yellow pigment produced on glycerinated ox serum.

Biochemical.—Very little known about biochemical properties. Evidence that the bacilli can produce acid from glucose, maltose, lactose, sucrose, glycerol and trehalose.

Antigenic Structure.—By agglutination, absorption of agglutinins, and complement fixation the human bacilli are shown to form a homogeneous group indistinguishable from bovine tubercle bacilli, but easily distinguishable from avian, cold-blooded, and saprophytic acid-fast bacilli.

Pathogenicity.—Produces tuberculosis in man, pigs, monkeys, dogs, and parrots. Experimentally, it is highly pathogenic for the guinea-pig, but not for the rabbit, cat, goat, or ox. A minute quantity injected subcutaneously into a guinea-pig's thigh causes death in 6 to 12 weeks. P.M. local caseous abscess ; enlargement and caseation of the inguinal, sublumbar, portal, axillary, and bronchial glands ; enlargement of the spleen with production of irregular yellowish areas of necrosis ; enlargement of the liver with production of smaller, irregular, greenish-yellow areas of necrosis ; few rounded tubercles in the lungs. Tubercle bacilli are numerous in the local lesion and the inguinal glands ; more scanty elsewhere.

The characters of the different types of tubercle bacilli, including the saprophytic acid-fast bacilli, are summarized in the table on pp. 317–19 (Table XXIX).

The Leprosy Bacillus

The causative organism of leprosy was described by Hansen in 1874. He observed it in the tissues of lepers, where it occurs in large numbers in the granulation tissue cells. The bacilli vary in size and shape ; they may be straight or slightly curved, 1–8 μ in length, with parallel sides and rounded ends, arranged chiefly in clumps or bundles, and staining evenly ; or they may resemble diphtheroids and show granular staining, confined to the poles or distributed throughout their length. They are not easily stained without a mordant ; they are Gram-positive and strongly acid-fast. They are non-motile and non-sporing.

Though the leprosy bacillus was one of the first of the pathogenic organisms to be described, very little more is known about it now than at the time of its original discovery. Numerous attempts have been made to cultivate it, and many different organisms have actually been isolated from the tissues of lepers, but it is by no means certain that the real causative organism of the disease has yet been grown in pure culture.

In 1901 Kedrowski cultivated, apparently from 4 cases of leprosy, a non-acid-fast diphtheroid bacillus showing true branching. In very young cultures, 10 to 14 hours old, most of the bacilli withstood decolorization with 5 per cent. H_2SO_4, but in older cultures the organisms were non-acid-fast except for the metachromatic granules. He stated that

TABLE XXIX

	Human.	Bovine.	Avian.	Cold-blooded.	Saprophytic Acid-fast.
Nutrient agar. *4 weeks at* *37° C.*	No growth	No growth	Poor, partly confluent, effuse, translucent, ground-glass growth, with finely granular surface	7 *d*. 22° *C.* Moderate, semi-confluent, raised, irregularly heaped-up growth with smooth or granular surface	7 *d*. 22° *C.* or 37° *C.* Abundant, confluent, raised, irregularly heaped-up, pigmented growth with smooth, granular, or worm-cast surface.
Broth. *4 weeks at* *37° C.*	No growth	No growth	No turbidity, or surface growth; but a moderate viscous membrano-granular deposit, partly disintegrating on shaking	7 *d*. 22° *C.* Similar to avian type	7 *d*. 22° *C.* or 37° *C.* No turbidity; dull, dry, scaly or granular, often pigmented, surface pellicle, and a viscous membrano-granular deposit, partly disintegrating on shaking.
Coagulated Ox serum. *4 weeks at* *37° C.*	Thin, effuse, confluent, greyish-yellow growth with finely granular surface like ground glass	Similar to the human type, but often poorer	Similar to the human type	7 *d*. 22° *C.* Moderate, confluent, slightly raised growth with finely nodular surface	7 *d*. 22° *C.* or 37° *C.* Abundant, raised, confluent, often pigmented growth, irregularly heaped up in places, and with smooth or nodular surface.
Glycerine Ox serum. *4 weeks at* *37° C.*	More luxuriant, thicker, raised, confluent, yellow or golden-yellow growth, with coarsely granular surface; irregularly heaped up in places	Similar to growth on plain ox serum	Luxuriant, raised, confluent, yellow or golden-yellow growth with a smooth creamy surface	Similar to growth on plain serum, but often more abundant	Similar to growth on plain serum, but often more abundant.

TABLE XXIX (*continued*).

	Human.	Bovine.	Avian.	Cold-blooded.	Saprophytic Acid-fast.
Dorset egg. **4 weeks at** 37° C.	Rather poor, discrete or confluent, slightly raised, greyish-yellow growth, with a finely granular surface	Similar to human type, but often poorer	Similar to human type, but surface is more smooth and less granular	7 *d.* 22° C. Moderate, slightly raised, confluent growth with moist, glistening, finely granular surface	7 *d.* 22° C. or 37° C. Abundant, confluent, often pigmented, raised growth with dull, dry, finely granular surface ; growth may be irregularly heaped up.
5% Glycerine egg. **4 weeks at** 37° C.	More luxuriant, raised, confluent, greyish-yellow growth, with coarsely granular surface ; growth irregularly nodular and heaped up in places	Similar to growth on Dorset egg	Sometimes similar to human type, but usually more luxuriant, of a creamy-yellow or slightly pinkish colour, with a smoother surface ; growth often resembles butter-cream	7 *d.* 22° C. Good, raised, confluent growth, with relatively smooth surface ; often resembles butter-cream	7 *d.* 22° C. or 37° C. Luxuriant growth, raised, dry ; yellow, pink, or brick-red in colour, with a coarsely granular surface resembling dry bread-crumbs.
5% Glycerine agar. **4 weeks at** 37° C.	Good, sometimes luxuriant, generally confluent, raised, creamy-white growth with a finely granular, scaly, or wrinkled surface	Poor growth of small, discrete, granular colonies ; sometimes a thin, effuse, confluent film	Sometimes similar to human type ; but usually more luxuriant, creamy-white, with a paint-like surface	Luxuriant growth in 7 days at 22° C. ; creamy-white and paint-like	Similar to growth on glycerine egg.
5% Glycerine potato. **4 weeks at** 37° C.	Luxuriant, raised, confluent, cream-coloured growth, with a nodular, warty, or worm-cast surface	Poor, discrete or confluent, thin, effuse, greyish growth	Sometimes similar to human type, but usually profuse, confluent, paint-like growth, with slightly nodular surface	7 *d.* 22° C. Profuse, raised, confluent, cream-coloured growth, with a coarsely granular or worm-cast surface	7 *d.* 22° C. or 37° C. Abundant, raised, confluent, often pigmented growth, with coarsely granular surface, looking like dry bread-crumbs.

TABLE XXIX *(continued)*.

	Human.	Bovine.	Avian.	Cold-blooded.	Saprophytic Acid-fast.
5% *Glycerine broth.* *8 weeks at 37° C.*	Thick, white or cream-coloured, dull, wrinkled pellicle, extending up the sides of the flask ; no turbidity; slight granular or scaly deposit	Thin, greyish-white film over part of surface, slightly nodular in places. No turbidity ; slight finely granular deposit	Sometimes only a granular deposit at the bottom ; sometimes a thick veil over the bottom of the flask and part-way up the sides, made up of branching, interlacing columns, like tripe. No turbidity ; no surface growth	*4 weeks 22° C.* No turbidity, but thick veil over the bottom of the flask and part-way up the sides, made up of coarse inter-lacing columns ; no surface growth	*14 days 22° C. or 37° C.* Thick, coarsely granular sur-face pellicle, looking as if composed of dry bread-crumbs. May be yellowish-white or pink ; spreads up sides of flask. No turbidity. Deposit of coarse granules.
Antigenic structure	By aggluti-nation, absorption of agglu-tinins, and complement fixation, form a homogene-ous group	Indistin-guishable from the human group	Form a separate group	Form a separate group	Form a separate group— probably divided into sub-groups.
Pathogeni-city	Natural disease in man, pigs, monkeys, dogs and parrots. Experiment-ally, patho-genic for guinea-pig and for mice	Natural disease in bovines, pigs, cats, monkeys and man. Ex-perimentally, pathogenic for guinea-pig, rabbit, cat, mice, goat, and calf	Natural disease in birds and pigs. Experiment-ally, patho-genic for birds ; moderately pathogenic for rabbits, rats, and mice	Natural disease in cold-blooded animals and fish. Ex-perimentally, pathogenic for turtles, frogs, snails, lizards, and fish	Non-patho-genic.

when injected into rabbits, the organisms became acid-fast after a residence of several weeks in the tissues. He thought that the bacillus belonged to the *Actinomyces* group, and that the acid-fast rods seen in human leprosy represented only one stage in the developmental cycle of a single pleomorphic species. In 1905 Émile-Weil obtained a growth of Gram-positive, acid-fast bacilli on a medium consisting of a mixture of glycerine glucose peptone agar and egg-yolk. Single colonies appeared about the 5th day, and increased in size till the 15th or 20th day. Cultures were likewise successful in hens' eggs, the leprous juice being inoculated directly into the yolk of the whole egg. Subcultures were never obtained. In 1909 Clegg cultivated from 8 out of 10 lepers a weakly acid-fast chromogenic bacillus. The primary cultures were obtained in symbiosis with amœbæ and cholera vibrios ; by heating these cultures to 60° C. for 30 minutes, he obtained a pure culture of the acid-fast bacillus. The organisms, both morphologically and culturally, resembled the ordinary saprophytic acid-fast bacilli ; they resisted decolorization with alcohol for 3 minutes, but were largely decolorized by 5 per cent. HCl in 2 minutes. Cultures on agar were of a bright orange colour. Local lesions resulted from injection of the bacilli into guinea-pigs, similar apparently to those following injection of such organisms as *Myco. phlei* and the smegma bacillus.

In 1910 Duval cultivated from 4 cases of leprosy a non-chromogenic acid-fast bacillus ; cultures were made on an agar or banana medium enriched with a 1 per cent. solution of cystein or tryptophan. Glistening white colonies 1–2 mm. in diameter appeared after 1 to 2 months at 32–33° C., but not at 37° C. The organisms were nearly as acid-fast as the tubercle bacillus, but were decolorized by 30 per cent. HNO_3 followed by 95 per cent. alcohol ; they failed to grow on ordinary media. When injected, even in small numbers, subcutaneously or intraperitoneally into Japanese dancing mice, they gave rise to glistening white nodules, resembling miliary tubercles ; these were disseminated through-out the body, but were especially numerous in the spleen and lymph nodes. These nodules resembled the human lesions very closely ; they contained acid-fast bacilli in enormous numbers, chiefly intracellular in position. Injection into guinea-pigs, rabbits, rats, and mice was without effect. In the same year, Twort (1910) isolated an acid-fast bacillus from the nasal discharge of a leper by growth on an egg medium containing a glycerine extract of dead tubercle bacilli. Growth was not visible for 6 weeks. In 1911 Rost cul-tivated an acid-fast, chromogenic, highly pleomorphic bacillus from 3 cases of nodular leprosy at Rangoon. Primary isolation was obtained on a milk broth medium containing volatile alkaloids from rotten fish. Growth occurred in 3 days, and was yellow, pink, or orange-red in colour. A monkey injected repeatedly by different routes developed small nodules under the skin containing acid-fast bacilli. Using a medium similar to Rost's, but in which the rotten fish distillate was replaced by distilled water, Williams in 1911 cultivated two organisms from 5 cases of leprosy in Persia and Bombay ; one was a non-acid-fast streptothrix, the other an acid-fast bacillus like Rost's. In old cultures of the latter organism in liquid media, a non-acid-fast diphtheroid appeared.

In 1912 Bayon (1911–12) isolated a non-acid-fast diphtheroid bacillus, sometimes showing branching, from a case of nodular leprosy in London ; it was morphologically identical with Kedrowski's bacillus. Intraperitoneal injection into a rat caused a lump at the site of inoculation ; 3 months later the lump was punctured, and the fluid that was withdrawn showed leucocytes filled with acid-fast bacilli arranged in ray fungus form. Cultivation from this lump yielded a white, slowly growing, wrinkled culture of an organism that was moderately acid-fast, resisting 20 per cent. HNO_3 for 3 minutes. From the same leper he also obtained a pleomorphic diphtheroid bacillus that resisted 2 per cent. H_2SO_4 for 3 seconds. Injection of this organism into a mouse produced lesions in the spleen, liver, and lungs ; these lesions contained clumps of acid-fast bacilli. Bayon concludes that the bacillus of human leprosy has a non-acid-fast, a weakly acid-fast, and a fully acid-fast stage. In 1912 Duval and Wellman reported on 29 cases of leprosy ; from 14 they isolated an acid-fast chromogenic bacillus like Clegg's ; from 8 an acid-fast non-chromogenic bacillus similar to Duval's ; and from 1 a non-acid-fast diphtheroid bacillus like Kedrowski's. Injection of the 2 acid-fast strains into a number of animals, including monkeys, caused small lesions, which, however, could not be differentiated from those produced by the saprophytic acid-fast bacilli. In 1912 Currie, Clegg and Hollmann stated that they had isolated by Clegg's method an acid-fast bacillus 16 times from 15 cases of leprosy. All strains were chromogenic, and were culturally similar to the saprophytic acid-fast bacilli ; they could be distinguished from these, however, by agglutination with a specific antiserum prepared by injection of the horse, though they were rarely agglutinated by the sera of lepers. A similar organism was isolated by McCoy in 1914 from 11 out of 83 specimens of leprous tissue ; cultures were obtained with about equal facility whether amœbæ were present or not. The organism was incapable of producing leprosy-like lesions in laboratory animals.

More recently a number of apparently successful attempts to cultivate the leprosy bacillus have been recorded. Shiga (1929) stated that by treating lepra nodules with 5 per cent. H_2SO_4 and inoculating them on to glycerol potato, he was able to obtain minute colony formation in about 2 months. Subcultures were carried on for four generations. Schlossmann (1930, 1933) claimed to have obtained growth in sealed tubes of Martin's broth in 4 months, and Sonnenschein (1930) in sealed tubes of glycerol egg in 2 months. The most hopeful results, however, have been recorded by Soule and McKinley (1932), and Soule (1934). These workers inoculated saline suspensions of excised lepra nodules on to several different media, and following Wherry's (1930) recommendation, incubated the cultures in varying partial pressures of oxygen and carbon dioxide. In a number of instances they succeeded in obtaining colony formation after 6 weeks at 37° C. Several media yielded growth, including glycerol potato, Dorset egg, Petroff egg, and hormone glycerol agar. The most favourable gaseous conditions were afforded by a mixture of 40 per cent. oxygen and 10 per cent. CO_2. Sixteen serial subcultures were made over a period of 18 months. The colonies themselves were about 1 mm. in diameter, heaped up, non-chromogenic, with a mucoid appearance and a loose filamentous border. Microscopically they consisted of acid-fast bacilli. Similar success is said to have attended the cultivation of the bacilli in a minced chicken embryo medium incubated under suitable partial pressures of O_2 and CO_2 (McKinley and Verder 1933). (For fuller review of bacteriology of leprosy see McKinley 1934.)

This résumé, which is by no means complete, illustrates the variety of organisms that have been cultivated from leprosy. It will be seen that they fall into three classes : (i) diphtheroid bacilli, which are either non-acid-fast or weakly acid-fast, (ii) chromogenic acid-fast bacilli, and (iii) non-chromogenic acid-fast bacilli. What relation, if any, these organisms bear to leprosy, it is at present impossible to say. We are faced with three possibilities : either (i) they are contaminating organisms that have nothing to do with the causation of leprosy ; or (ii) they are different stages in the life-history of the true leprosy bacillus ; or (iii) they are organisms whose presence is in some way associated with that of the true leprosy bacillus, which has not yet been cultivated. Agglutination tests carried out with the serum of lepers do not help in determining the ætiological significance of these organisms, for it has been found that tubercle bacilli and saprophytic acid-fast bacilli are agglutinated as well as the bacilli cultivated from leprosy (Duval and Wellman 1912). And since it is impossible to reproduce typical leprosy in laboratory animals by inoculation even with ground-up leprous material, it is clear that animal inoculation tests are likewise useless in deciding this question.

There is reason to believe that the non-chromogenic acid-fast bacilli cultivated by various workers were in fact the real leprosy bacillus. Examination, however, of the records reveals the fact that, though colonial development was obtainable in the first two or three subcultures, attempts to carry on the bacilli indefinitely in subculture almost invariably failed. Even in Soule and McKinley's work, which incidentally Schlossmann (1933), Duval and Holt (1934a), and Holt (1934a, b) have failed to confirm, more and more difficulty was experienced in obtaining growth with each successive subculture. Duval (1910) many years ago brought evidence to show that leprosy bacilli were able to grow in artificial media only so long as some of the original human lepromatous tissue persisted in the culture, and that the bacilli derived their nutriment almost entirely from the autolytic products of this human protein material (see also Duval 1934). These findings are supported by the more recent work of Schlossmann (1933). If they are correct, they seem to afford an explanation of many of the observed facts. Whether it will be possible, as Duval and Holt (1934b) anticipate, to replace the natural autolytic tissue products by protein-split substances derived from other sources, is still doubtful. We may

P.B.   M conclude tentatively that the leprosy bacillus has been grown in culture, but that its indefinite subcultivation in artificial media has never been unequivocally demonstrated.

In these circumstances it is regrettable that a number of stock cultures in various collections are labelled *Mycobacterium lepræ*, and that so much work has been expended in studying the various properties of these so-called leprosy bacilli. Many of the strains are undoubtedly ordinary saprophytic acid-fast bacilli, and their description under a false name can do nothing but cause confusion in the literature. (For attempts at experimental reproduction of leprosy see Chapter LVII.)

The Rat Leprosy Bacillus

This organism was first described by Stefansky (1903) in 1901 at Odessa, where it was giving rise to a leprosy-like disease in rats. The organisms, which have never yet been definitely cultivated, are 3–5 μ long, are often slightly curved, and have rounded ends. They are Gram-positive and strongly acid-fast, withstanding 5 per cent. H_2SO_4 and 95 per cent. alcohol for at least 5 minutes. Staining is often granular. From the fact that human leprosy cannot be conveyed to rats, it is probable that the leprosy and the rat leprosy bacilli are different. (For experimental reproduction of the disease see Chapter LVII.)

Johne's Bacillus

This organism was found by Johne and Frothingham (1895) in a chronic disease of cattle characterized by massive infiltration of the intestinal tract. It was believed at first to be an avian type of tubercle bacillus, but subsequent work has rendered it clear that it is a different species of organism.

Morphologically it is a short, thick rod, 1–2 μ long, generally straight, with rounded ends and parallel or slightly bulging sides; it is non-motile, Gram-positive, and strongly acid-fast. Staining is generally uniform, but may occasionally be granular. It was first isolated in pure *culture* by Twort in 1910, on a glycerine egg medium containing dead tubercle bacilli (Twort and Ingram 1912, 1913). Subsequently it was found that the saprophytic acid-fast bacilli could replace the tubercle bacilli, and that a glycerine extract of the organisms, or even liquid tuberculin, could be used (M'Fadyean *et al.* 1912). Twort and Ingram advise the following medium : Cultures of *Myco. phlei* are killed by steaming ; the growth is scraped off and dried ; the bacilli are then ground in a mortar, and added in 0·5–1·0 per cent. concentration to Dorset's egg medium containing 4 per cent. of glycerine. On this medium primary cultures of Johne's bacillus consist of tiny, dull-white colonies, rarely visible to the naked eye in less than 4 weeks ; they are more or less circular in shape, and may be discrete or confluent. As they grow older, they increase in size, become more elevated, and turn a dull yellowish-white colour ; the edges remain thin, and from them numerous irregular striations rise towards the central peak. In subcultures the growth is more copious, more confluent, and may be slightly wrinkled. If the saline in Dorset's egg medium is replaced by peptone beef broth, the growth is still better ; and if sheep's brain broth is used, the growth cannot be distinguished from a Dorset's egg culture of human tubercle bacilli. On glycerine agar containing *phlei* extract the growth is slower and less vigorous. In glycerine broth with *phlei* extract added growth occurs in the form of a thin surface film, which may later show irregular areas of thickening. After several subcultures growth is more profuse, and may even occur in plain glycerine broth without the addition of *phlei* extract. Growth occurs between 28° C. and 43° C., the optimum temperature being 39° C. In culture the bacilli are very short, often only about 1 μ in length ; there is no branching, but occasional club forms are seen. Primary cultures are best made by treating the washed intestinal mucosa with 20 per cent. antiformin for about 30 minutes, and seeding on to a glycerine egg medium containing dead *phlei* or tubercle bacilli. In what way the added organisms serve to promote the growth of Johne's bacillus is not known ; they probably provide some nutrient substance, or enzyme, necessary for its metabolism; but that this substance is not specific to acid-fast bacilli is shown by the fact that alcoholic extracts of such diverse substances as currant-grapes, figs, oats, linseed, and the fungus *Cantharellus aurantiacus,* are all able to replace the acid-fast bacilli (Twort and Ingram 1914).

Whether the bacilli giving rise to Johne's disease in sheep are identical with those in cattle is not clear. Apparently they are more difficult to grow, and in primary culture may take 6 or 7 months to develop (Dunkin and Balfour-Jones 1935).

Reproduction of the Disease in Animals.—The injection intravenously, intraperitoneally, or subcutaneously of pure cultures of Johne's bacillus into bovine animals frequently gives rise to the typical disease, from the lesions of which pure cultures of the bacillus can be recovered (Twort and Ingram 1913). Feeding may also be successful. Sometimes goats and sheep can be infected by inoculation of pure cultures. Reproduction of the disease in laboratory animals has not so far been successful. Johne and Frothingham (1895) and Twort and Ingram (1913) found that guinea-pigs, rats, and mice were refractory. Later Twort and Craig (1913) found that the intraperitoneal inoculation of 100–120 mgm. of bacilli into rabbits gave rise in the abdominal cavity to a few nodules which were slightly caseous ; the animals remained perfectly well, and showed no signs of toxic disturbances. The same lesions were produced by *Myco. phlei.* Boquet (1925) found that the intraperitoneal injection of 5–10 mgm. of culture into white rats gave rise to pin-head, greyish nodules on the surface of the peritoneum and omentum ; these nodules contained pus very rich in bacilli. The mesenteric glands were enlarged ; the tracheo-bronchial glands were enlarged, hard, and sclerotic, and contained enormous numbers of bacilli. Even more marked lesions were obtained when the injection was repeated in 15 to 20 days with a dose of 10–30 mgm. White mice developed similar but less chronic lesions. It is doubtful whether these changes can be considered specific for Johne's bacillus ; similar lesions can often be produced by the saprophytic acid-fast bacilli. It is certain that no one has yet reproduced in laboratory animals the typical enteritis of the natural disease.

REFERENCES

AKSIANZEW, M. I. (1933) *Z. Tuberk.,* **68,** 249.
ALBISTON, H. E. (1930) *Aust. vet. J.,* **6,** 123.
ALVAREZ and TAVEL. (1885) *Arch. Phys. norm. Path.,* **6,** 303.
ANDERSON, R. J. (1932) *Physiol. Rev.,* **12,** 166.
ANDERSON, R. J. and Colleagues. (1927 *et seq.*) 34 papers, mainly in *J. biol. Chem.,* 1927–33, and 3 papers in *Z. physiol. Chem.* (1930), **191,** 157, 166, 172.
ARLOING, F. and DUFOURT, A. (1925) *C. R. Soc. Biol.,* **93,** 165.

ARLOING, F., DUFOURT, A., and MALARTRE. (1926) *C. R. Soc. Biol.*, **94**, 46.
ARONSON, H. (1898) *Berl. klin. Wschr.*, **35**, 484.
ARONSON, J. D. (1926) *J. infect. Dis.*, **39**, 315.
BALL, E. G. (1934) *J. biol. Chem.*, **106**, 515.
BATAILLON, E., DUBARD, and TERRE, L. (1897) *C. R. Soc. Biol.*, **49**, 446.
BAYON, H. (1911–12) *Trans. R. Soc. trop. Med. Hyg.*, **5**, 158.
BEAVEN, P. W. and BAYNE-JONES, S. (1931) *J. infect. Dis.*, **49**, 399.
BECK, M. (1905) *TuberkArb.*, **3**, 145.
BEGBIE, R. S. (1930) *Edin. med. J.*, **37**, 187 ; (1931) *Ibid.*, **38**, 173.
BEITZKE, H. (1910) *Berl. klin. Wschr.*, **47**, 1451.
BERNARD, L. and NÉLIS. (1927) *Pres. Méd.*, **35**, 721.
BEZANÇON, F. and PHILIBERT, A. (1926) *Pres. Méd.*, **34**, 33.
BIRKHAUG, K. E. (1935) *Ann. Inst. Pasteur*, **54**, 19.
BLACKLOCK, J. W. S. (1932) *Spec. Rep. Ser. med. Res. Coun., Lond.*, No. 172.
BLUMENBERG, W. (1931) " Ergebnisse der gesamten Tuberkuloseforschung." G. Thieme, Leipzig.
BOQUET, A. (1925) *C. R. Soc. Biol.*, **93**, 219.
BOQUET, A., NÈGRE, L., and VALTIS, J. (1926) *C. R. Soc. Biol.*, **94**, 235.
BOZZELLI, R. (1914) *Ann. Staz. Mal. Best. Napoli*, **2**, 77.
BREM, W. V. (1909) *J. Amer. med. Ass.*, **53**, 909.
BRUYNOGHE, R. and ADANT, M. (1933) *C. R. Soc. Biol.*, **111**, 1051.
BULLOCH, W. and MACLEOD, J. J. R. (1904) *J. Hyg., Camb.*, **4**, 1.
CADIOT, P. J., GILBERT, A., and ROGER, H. (1890) *C. R. Soc. Biol.*, **42**, 92.
CALDWELL, M. E. (1925) *J. infect. Dis.*, **37**, 465.
CALMETTE, A. (1920) " L'infection bacillaire et la tuberculose chez l'homme et chez les animaux." Masson et Cie, Paris.
CALMETTE, A., VALTIS, J., and LACOMME, M. (1926) *C. R. Acad. Sci.*, **183**, 835.
CALMETTE, A., VALTIS, J., NÈGRE, L., and BOQUET, A. (1925) *C. R. Acad. Sci.*, **181**, 491.
CHARGAFF, E., PANGBORN, M. C., and ANDERSON, R. J. (1931) *J. biol. Chem.*, **90**, 45.
CLEGG, M. T. (1909) *Philipp. J. Sci., B*, **4**, 403.
COBBETT, L. (1917) " The Causes of Tuberculosis." Cambridge ; (1932) *J. Path. Bact.*, **35**, 681.
COOPER, F. B. and PETROFF, S. A. (1928) *J. infect. Dis.*, **43**, 200.
CUMMING, W. M. (1925) *Tubercle, Lond.*, **7**, 105.
CUMMINS, S. L. and WILLIAMS, E. M. (1933) *Tubercle, Lond.*, **15**, 49.
CURRIE, D. H., CLEGG, M. T., and HOLLMANN, H. T. (1912) *Publ. Hlth Bull., Wash.*, No. 47.
CZAPLEWSKI, E. (1897) *Münch. med. Wschr.*, **44**, 1192.
DARZINE, E. (1932) *Ann. Inst. Pasteur*, **49**, 743.
DENYS, P. (1935) " Contribution à l'étude de la variabilité du virus tuberculeux." Imprimerie Saint-Alphonse, Louvain.
DERNBY, K. G. and NÄSLUND, C. (1922) *Biochem. Z.*, **132**, 393.
DIECKMANN, H. and MENZEL, G. (1932) *Z. Hyg. InfektKr.*, **113**, 709.
DOERR, R. and GOLD, E. (1932) *Z. ImmunForsch.*, **74**, 7.
DOUGLAS, S. R. and HARTLEY, P. (1934) *Tubercle, Lond.*, **16**, 97.
DOWNIE, A. W. and MEISZNER, G. (1934) *Zbl. Bakt.*, **130**, 465.
DREYER, G. and VOLLUM, R. L. (1931) *Lancet*, i. 9.
DUNKIN, G. W. and BALFOUR-JONES, S. E. B. (1935) *J. comp. Path.*, **48**, 236.
DURAND, H. and CHARCHANSKI. (1925) *C. R. Soc. Biol.*, **93**, 499.
DUVAL, C. W. (1910) *J. exp. Med.*, **12**, 649 ; (1934) *Proc. Soc. exp. Biol., N.Y.*, **32**, 498.
DUVAL, C. W. and HOLT, R. A. (1934a) *Proc. Soc. exp. Biol., N.Y.*, **31**, 453 ; (1934b) *Ibid.*, **31**, 828.
DUVAL, C. W. and WELLMAN, C. (1912) *J. infect. Dis.*, **11**, 116.
EASTWOOD, A. and GRIFFITH, F. (1916) *J. Hyg., Camb.*, **15**, 257.
EHRLICH. (1882) *Dtsch. med. Wschr.*, **8**, 269.
EIDINOW, A. (1927) *Brit. med. J.*, ii. 160.
ÉMILE-WEIL, P. (1905) *Ann. Inst. Pasteur*, **19**, 793.
FIELDING, J. W. (1934) *Aust. J. exp. Biol.*, **12**, 1.
FONTÈS, A. (1910) *Mem. Inst. Osw. Cruz*, **2**, 141.
FRIEDMANN, F. F. (1903) *Zbl. Bakt.*, **34**, 647, 793.
FROUIN, A. and GUILLAUMIE. (1923a) *C. R. Soc. Biol.*, **88**, 1002 ; (1923b) *Ibid.*, **88**, 1095.
FURTH, J. (1926) *J. Immunol.*, **12**, 273.
GLOYNE, S. R. (1933) *Bull. Hyg., Lond.*, **8**, 39.
GLOYNE, S. R., GLOVER, R. E., and GRIFFITH, A. S. (1929) *J. Path. Bact.*, **32**, 775.
GORIS, A. (1920) *Ann. Inst. Pasteur*, **34**, 497.
GOUGH, G. A. C. (1932) *Biochem. J.*, **26**, 248 ; (1933) *Biochem. J.*, **27**, 1049.
GRASSBERGER, R. (1899) *Münch. med. Wschr.*, **46**, 341, 382.

GRIFFITH, A. S. (1916) *Lancet*, i. 721 ; (1916–17) *J. Path. Bact.*, **21**, 54 ; (1924) *Tubercle, Lond.*, **5**, 569 ; (1925) *Tubercle, Lond.*, **6**, 417 ; (1931) *J. comp. Path.*, **44**, 144.
GROLIER, A. DE. (1933) *C. R. Soc. Biol.*, **113**, 1506.
GRÜNBERG, B. (1935) *Z. Tuberk.*, **73**, 197.
GUNN, F. D., NUNGESTER, W. J., and HOUGEN, E. T. (1934) *Proc. Soc. exp. Biol., N.Y.*, **31**, 527.
HAAG, F. E. (1927) *Zbl. Bakt.*, IIte Abt., **71**, 1.
HAGAN, W. A. and LEVINE, P. (1932) *J. Amer. vet. med. Ass.*, **81**, 723.
HANSEN, G. H. A. (1874) *Norsk. Mag. Laegevidensk.*
HARDEN, A. (1913) *Rep. roy. Comm. Tuberc., Lond.*, **6**, part ii. Appendix.
HERMAN, M. (1908) *Ann. Inst. Pasteur*, **22**, 92.
HOLT, R. A. (1934*a*) *Proc. Soc. exp. Biol., N.Y.*, **31**, 567 ; (1934*b*) *Ibid.*, **31**, 643.
ISHIMORI, K. (1924) *Z. Hyg. InfektKr.*, **102**, 329.
JACOBITZ and KAYSER, H. (1910) *Münch. med. Wschr.*, **57**, 1175.
JENSEN, K. A. (1932) *Zbl. Bakt.*, **125**, 222.
JOHNE, H. A. and FROTHINGHAM, L. (1895) *Dtsch. Z. Tiermed.*, **21**, 438.
KAHN, M. C. (1930) *Tubercle, Lond.*, **11**, 202.
KARLINSKI, J. (1901) *Zbl. Bakt.*, **29**, 521.
KARWACKI, L. and BIERNACKI, S. (1925) *Ann. Inst. Pasteur*, **39**, 476.
KAUFFMANN, F. (1932) *Z. Hyg. InfektKr.*, **114**, 121.
KEDROWSKI, W. J. (1901) *Z. Hyg. InfektKr.*, **37**, 52.
KENDALL, A., DAY, A., and WALKER, A. (1920) *J. infect. Dis.*, **26**, 45.
KIEFFER, J. (1921) *Amer. Rev. Tuberc.*, **5**, 662.
KLOPSTOCK, F. (1931) *Klin. Wschr.*, **10**, 967.
KOCH, R. (1882) *Berl. klin. Wschr.*, **19**, 221 ; (1886) "Microparasites in Disease." New Sydenham Soc., London.
KORN, O. (1899) *Zbl. Bakt.*, **25**, 532 ; (1900) *Ibid.*, **27**, 481.
KOSSEL, H., WEBER, A., and HEUSS. (1904) *TuberkArb.*, **1**, 1 ; (1905) *Ibid.*, **3**, 1.
KRAUS, R. and GERLACH, F. (1929) *Z. ImmunForsch.*, **62**, 339.
KRAUS, R. and KOREF, O. (1933) *Z. Tuberk.*, **67**, 42.
KRETSCHMER, O. S. (1934) *J. Lab. clin. Med.*, **19**, 350.
KÜSTER, E. (1905) *Münch. med. Wschr.*, **52**, 57.
LAIDLAW, P. P. and DUDLEY, H. W. (1925) *Brit. J. exp. Path.*, **6**, 197.
LANGE, B. (1922) *Z. Hyg. InfektKr.*, **98**, 229.
LANGE, L. (1932) See Kolle, W. (1932) *Dtsch. med. Wschr.*, **58**, 304.
LARSON, W. P. (1926) *Lancet*, ii. 1231.
LASER, H. (1897) *Münch. med. Wschr.*, **44**, 1191.
LEDOUX-LEBARD. (1898) *C. R. Soc. Biol.*, **50**, 610 ; (1900) *Ann. Inst. Pasteur*, **14**, 535.
LONG, E. R. (1926) *Amer. Rev. Tuberc.*, **13**, 393.
LONG, E. R. and SEIBERT, F. B. (1926, 1928) See series of 10 papers in *Amer. Rev. Tuberc.*, **13**, **17**
McCOY, G. W. (1914) *Publ. Hlth Bull.*, *Wash.*, No. 61, p. 27.
M'FADYEAN, J., SHEATHER, A. L., and EDWARDS, J. T. (1912) *J. comp. Path.*, **25**, 217.
McKINLEY, E. B. (1934) *Medicine, Baltimore*, **13**, 377.
McKINLEY, E. B. and VERDER, E. (1933) *Proc. Soc. exp. Biol., N.Y.*, **30**, 659.
MADDOCK, E. C. G. (1933) *J. Hyg., Camb.*, **33**, 103.
MAFFUCCI, A. (1890) *Zbl. Allg. Path. path. Anat.*, **1**, 409 ; (1892) *Z. Hyg. InfektKr.*, **11**, 445.
MARCHOUX, E. and HALPHEN, E. (1912) *C. R. Soc. Biol.*, **73**, 249.
MARZINOWSKY, E. J. (1900) *Zbl. Bakt.*, **28**, 39.
MAYER, E. (1921) *Amer. Rev. Tuberc.*, **5**, 75.
MAYER, E. and DWORSKI, M. (1932) *Amer. Rev. Tuberc.*, **26**, 105.
MEANWELL, L. J. (1927) *J. Hyg., Camb.*, **26**, 392.
MEISZNER, I. and PRAUSNITZ, C. (1934) *Zbl. Bakt.*, **132**, 23.
MERRILL, M. H. (1930) *J. Bact.*, **20**, 235.
MILLER, J. (1905) *J. Path. Bact.*, **10**, 1.
MIRONESCU, T. (1901) *Z. Hyg. InfektKr.*, **37**, 497.
MOELLER, A. (1898) *Dtsch. med. Wschr.*, **24**, 376 ; (1899) *Zbl. Bakt.*, **25**, 369 ; (1901) *Ibid.*, **30**, 513.
MORI, N. (1911) *Ann. Staz. Mal. Best. Napoli*, **1**, 327.
MUCH, H. (1907) *Beitr. klin. Tuberk.*, **8**, 85.
MUELLER, J. H. (1926) *J. exp. Med.*, **43**, 9.
NÉLIS, P. (1927) *C. R. Soc. Biol.*, **97**, 475.
NOCARD and ROUX. (1887) *Ann. Inst. Pasteur*, **1**, 19.
NOVY, F. G. and SOULE, M. H. (1925) *J. infect. Dis.*, **36**, 168.
NUTT, M. M. (1927) *J. Hyg., Camb.*, **26**, 44.
OERSKOV, J. (1932) *Zbl. Bakt.*, **123**, 271.
OERSKOV, J.-L. (1925) *C. R. Soc. Biol.*, **92**, 400.

PARK, W. H. and KRUMWIEDE, C. (1910) *J. med. Res.*, **23**, 205.
PEDERSEN-BJERGAARD, K. (1934) *Z. ImmunForsch.*, **82**, 258.
PELLEGRINO, P. L. (1906) *Ann. Igiene.* (*sper.*), **16**, 163.
PETRI, R. J. (1898) *Arb. ReichsgesundhAmt.*, **14**, 1.
PETROFF, S. A. (1927) *Proc. Soc. exp. Biol., N.Y.*, **24**, 632, 956.
PETROFF, S. A., BRANCH, A., and STEENKEN, W. (1927a) *Proc. Soc. exp. Biol., N.Y.*, **25**, 14 ; (1927b) *Amer. Rev. Tuberc.*, **19**, 9.
PETROFF, S. A. and STEENKEN, W. (1930) *J. exp. Med.*, **51**, 831 ; (1935) *J. infect. Dis.*, **56**, 27.
PINNER, M. (1932) *Proc. Soc. exp. Biol., N.Y.*, **30**, 214.
PINNER, M. and VOLDRICH, M. (1931) *Amer. Rev. Tuberc.*, **24**, 73.
RABINOWITSCH, L. (1897) *Z. Hyg. InfektKr.*, **26**, 90 ; (1900) *Dtsch. med. Wschr.*, **26**, 257.
RAVENEL. (1901) *Trans. Brit. Congr. Tuberc.*, **3**, 553.
REED, G. B. and RICE, C. E. (1929) *J. Bact.*, **17**, 407 ; (1931a) *Canad. J. Res.*, **4**, 389 ; (1931b) *Ibid.*, **5**, 111.
REMY, E. (1932) *Z. ImmunForsch.*, **75**, 527.
Report. (1907) Royal Commission on Tuberculosis, 2nd interim Rep., H.M. Stat. Off., London ; (1909) *Ibid.*, 3rd interim Rep. ; (1911) *Ibid.*, Final Rep. ; (1913) *Ibid.*, Final Rep., Appendix.
RHINES, C. (1935) *Amer. Rev. Tuberc.*, **31**, 493.
RICE, C. E. (1931) *Canad. J. Res.*, **5**, 375.
RICE, C. E. and REED, G. B. (1931) *Canad. J. Res.*, **5**, 122.
RIVOLTA. (1889) *G. anat. Fisiol.*, **1**, 122.
ROCHAIX, A. and COLIN, G. (1911) *C. R. Acad. Sci.*, **153**, 1253.
ROCKWELL G. E. and HIGHBERGER, J. H. (1926) *J. infect. Dis.*, **38**, 92.
ROST, E. E. (1911) *Sci. Mem. med. Sanit. Dep., India*, No. 42, p. 7.
SABIN, F. R. (1932) *Physiol. Rev.*, **12**, 141.
SABIN, F. R., DOAN, C. A., and FORKNER, C. E. (1930) *J. exp. Med.*, **52**, Suppl. No. 3.
SABIN, F. R., MILLER, F. R., DOAN, C. A., and WISEMAN, B. K. (1931) *J. exp. Med.*, **53**, 51.
SCHAEFER, W. (1935) *C. R. Soc. Biol.*, **120**, 1185.
SCHLOSSMANN, K. (1930) *Zbl. Bakt.*, **115**, 474 ; (1933) *Ibid.*, **128**, 369.
SCHMIDT, C. W. (1931a) *Z. Hyg. InfektKr.*, **112**, 95 ; (1931b) *Ibid.*, **113**, 90.
SCHMIDT, F. (1925) *Zbl. Bakt.*, **94**, 94.
SCHULTE-TIGES, H. (1920) *Dtsch. med. Wschr.*, **46**, 1225.
SCHWABACHER, H. (1933a) *Spec. Rep. Ser. med. Res. Coun., Lond.*, No. 182, p. 104 ; (1933b) *Ibid.*, p. 124.
SÉDYEH, A. and SELIBER, G. (1927) *C. R. Soc. Biol.*, **97**, 57.
SEIBERT, F. B., LONG, E. R., and MORLEY, N. (1933) *J. infect. Dis.*, **53**, 175.
SEIFFERT, V. (1932) *Z. ImmunForsch.*, **74**, 116.
SHAFFER, M. F. (1935) *J. Path. Bact.*, **40**, 107.
SHEN, T. H. (1934) *J. Shanghai Sci. Inst.*, Sect. iv. **1**, 157.
SHIGA, K. (1929) *Zbl. Bakt.*, **114**, 511.
SHOUB, H. J. (1923) *J. Bact.*, **8**, 121.
SIBLEY, W. K. (1889) *Zbl. Bakt.*, **5**, 831 ; (1890) *Lancet*, i. 804.
SMITH, T. (1898) *J. exp. Med.*, **3**, 451 ; (1899) *Ibid.*, **4**, 217 ; (1904–5) *J. med. Res.*, **8**, 253.
SMITHBURN, K. C. (1935) *J. exp. Med.*, **62**, 645.
SONNENSCHEIN, C. (1930) *Zbl. Bakt.*, **117**, 284.
SORDELLI, A. and ARENA, A. (1934) *C. R. Soc. Biol.*, **117**, 63.
SOULE, M. I. (1928) *J. infect. Dis.*, **42**, 93 ; (1934) *Proc. Soc. exp. Biol., N.Y.*, **31**, 1197.
SOULE, M. E. and MCKINLEY, E. B. (1932) *Amer. J. trop. Med.*, **12**, 1, 441.
STABLEFORTH, A. W. (1929) *J. comp. Path.*, **42**, 91.
STEENKEN, W., OATWAY, W. H., and PETROFF, S. A. (1934) *J. exp. Med.*, **60**, 515.
STEFANSKY, W. K. (1903) *Zbl. Bakt.*, **33**, 481.
STRAUS, I. and GAMALÉIA, N. (1891) *Arch. Med. exp.*, **3**, 457.
SWEANY, H. C. (1928) *Amer. Rev. Tuberc.*, **17**, 53.
TAMURA, S. (1913) *Z. physiol. Chem.*, **87**, 85.
THOMSON, H. M. (1932) *Amer. Rev. Tuberc.*, **26**, 162.
TIEDEMANN, H. J. (1931) *Zbl. Bakt.*, **122**, 483.
TOBLER, M. (1901) *Z. Hyg. InfektKr.*, **36**, 120.
TODA, T. (1931) *Z. Hyg. InfektKr.*, **112**, 463.
TOGUONNOFF A. (1927a) *C. R. Soc. Biol.*, **97**, 349 ; (1927b) *Ibid.*, **97**, 625.
TULLOCH, W. J., MUNRO, W. T., ROSS, G. R., and CUMMING, W. M. (1924) *Tubercle, Lond.* **6**, 18, 57, 105.
TWORT, C. C and CRAIG, T. (1913) *Zbl. Bakt.*, **68**, 455.
TWORT, F. W. (1910) *Proc. roy. Soc.*, B, **83**, 156.

Twort, F. W. and Ingram, G. L. Y. (1912) *Proc. roy. Soc.*, B, **84**, 517 ; (1913) " A Monograph on Johne's Disease." London. (1914) *Zbl. Bakt.*, **73**, 277.

Uga, T. (1935) *Jap. J. exp. Med.*, **13**, 167.

Uhlenhuth, P. and Seiffert, W. (1930) *Z. ImmunForsch.*, **69**, 187.

Uyei, N. (1927) *J. infect. Dis.*, **40**, 433.

Vagedes, (1898) *Z. Hyg. InfektKr.*, **28**, 276.

Valtis, J. (1924a) *C. R. Soc. Biol.*, **90**, 74 ; (1924b) *Ann. Inst. Pasteur*, **38**, 453 ; (1926a) *C. R. Soc. Biol.*, **94**, 237 ; (1926b) *Ibid.*, **94**, 376 ; (1927) *Ibid.*, **97**, 477.

Veber, T. (1926) *C. R. Soc. Biol.*, **94**, 8.

Villemin, J. A. (1868) " Études sur la Tuberculose." Paris.

Wámoscher, L. and Stoecklin, H. (1927) *Zbl. Bakt.*, **104**, Beiheft, p. 86.

Wells, H. G. and Long, E. R. (1932) " The Chemistry of Tuberculosis." Baillière, Tindall & Cox, London.

Wherry, W. B. (1930) *J. infect. Dis.*, **46**, 263.

Williams, R. S. and Hoy, W. A. (1930) *J. Hyg., Camb.*, **30**, 413.

Williams, T. S. B. (1911) *Sci. Mem. med. Sanit. Dep., India*, No. 42, p. 15.

Wilson, G. S. (1925) *J. Path. Bact.*, **28**, 69 ; (1930) *J. Hyg., Camb.*, **30**, 40.

Wolbach, S. B. and Ernst, H. C. (1904) *J. med. Res.*, **12**, 295.

Wyckoff, R. W. G. (1934) *Amer. Rev. Tuberc.*, **29**, 389.

Wyckoff, R. W. G. and Smithburn, K. C. (1933) *J. infect. Dis.*, **53**, 201.

Yersin, M. A. (1888) *Ann. Inst. Pasteur*, **2**, 245.

Ziehl, F. (1882) *Dtsch. med. Wschr.*, **8**, 451.

CHAPTER XVI

CORYNEBACTERIUM

The generic name *Corynebacterium* was allotted by Lehmann and Neumann in 1896 to the group of bacteria containing the diphtheria bacillus and other species resembling it in morphology. By its derivation the name emphasizes the tendency to the formation of club-like forms that is characteristic of the type species and of several other species within the generic group. This name was accepted by the Committee appointed by the Society of American Bacteriologists (Winslow *et al.* 1920), and was adopted as the valid generic name in the monograph on diphtheria issued under the ægis of the Medical Research Council in 1923 (Andrewes *et al.*). It is gaining increasing currency in the literature and is very unlikely to be superseded. The summary of the generic characters, as recorded by the American Committee, was emended by the Bacteriological Committee of the Medical Research Council by the omission of aerobiosis as a generic character, the addition of a reference to the fermentative activities of the group, and the omission of any reference to toxin production. There appear to us to be advantages in calling attention to a striking biological character possessed by the type species and perhaps shared by some related species. With the restoration of this reference to toxigenicity we should adopt the summary of generic characters as given by the Committee of the Medical Research Council, which would then read as follows :

Corynebacterium.—Gram-positive rod-like forms, arranged usually in a palisade. Not acid-fast. Often with club-shaped swellings at the poles, generally with irregularly stained segments or granules. Non-motile, non-sporing. Growing aerobically or under micro-aerophilic conditions, but often capable of anaerobic cultivation. Never forming gas in carbohydrate media, in which they may or may not produce acidity. They may or may not liquefy gelatin or serum. Some species produce a powerful exotoxin.

Type species, *Corynebacterium diphtheriæ.*

Although *C. diphtheriæ* is universally accepted as the type species, it was not in fact the first to be described. Reymond and his colleagues in 1881, and again in 1883, described the isolation from the conjunctival sac of a bacillus which is now recognized, under the name of *C. xerosis*, as belonging to this genus. This organism was described more fully by Kuschbert and Neisser in the latter year, which also witnessed Klebs' description of the diphtheria bacillus in the diphtheritic false membrane. It was not until 1884, the year following, that Loeffler published his classical paper on diphtheria, and provided a description of the causative organism which afforded a standard of reference for all subsequent studies on this bacterial group. Any claims that might have accrued to *C. xerosis* on account of priority would in any case have been vitiated by the fact that it is quite impossible at the present time to be sure that Reymond, and Kuschbert and Neisser, were dealing with a single bacterial species. It is, moreover, equally impossible to identify with certainty any of the strains now labelled *C. xerosis* with those described in the early 'eighties. The stage of technical development that bacteriology had then reached did not permit each new organism that was isolated to be fully studied and described. The importance of *C. diphtheriæ* as a human pathogen focussed attention on the differentiation of the species from others with which it might be confused. Our picture of the type species thus became more and more complete as time went on ; but to the related diphtheroids little attention was paid beyond that necessary to determine their probable relation to the diphtheria bacillus itself. As Andrewes and his colleagues point out it is extremely difficult to determine which of the strains, to which specific names have from time to time been assigned, represent well-differentiated species. Some of those who have reviewed the group as a whole have been liberal in the distribution of titles (Graham-Smith 1908, Mellon 1917, Eberson 1918, Chalmers and Macdonald 1920). Here, as elsewhere, we propose to adopt a conservative view, and to list as species only those organisms which have been adequately described, and appear from this description to be reasonably well-differentiated. In discussing this question of classification and nomenclature in greater detail we may consider *C. diphtheriæ* as an entity, since it has in fact been so regarded in most of the observations to which we shall refer. Recent work has, however, shown that it is divisible into three well-differentiated types, and that this differentiation is of considerable importance from the medical point of view. The discussion of this particular problem may, however, conveniently be dealt with in a separate section.

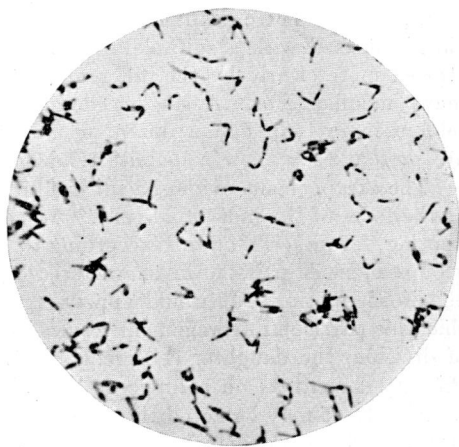

FIG. 64.—*C. diphtheriæ.*

From 24-hours' culture on Loeffler's serum (× 1000).

Habitat.

There is little evidence that any species of *Corynebacterium* exists as a free-living organism, apart from man and other animals. The genus, as a whole, appears to have developed the parasitic habit, living principally on the skin, or on the mucous surfaces, of some animal host. Many species are pathogenic, others form an important constituent of the normal bacterial flora of various hosts.

Morphology.

The club-form, from which the name is derived, is only one of many shapes which may be assumed by the individual cells of the type species, *C. diphtheriæ*. This organism is indeed characteristically pleomorphic. The most typical form (see Fig. 64), as seen in films prepared from a 24-hours' culture on Loeffler's serum, is that of a long, rather slender bacillus, often slightly curved, with rounded, somewhat swollen ends and sometimes with localized swellings elsewhere, and staining unevenly with such dyes as methylene blue : but in the same, or in other cultures, there will also

P.B. M*

be found much shorter forms, cells which stain solidly and evenly, cells in which the irregular staining takes the form of a series of transverse bars, and cells in which the combination of uneven staining and localized swellings gives to a single bacillus the appearance of a short chain of streptococci. This diversity of structure has led to attempts to classify the various forms of *C. diphtheriæ* into definite types, indicated by names, numbers or letters, and to a description of individual strains in accordance with the predominant morphological form. It is quite true that different strains of this organism differ very markedly in morphology and that a notable frequency of one particular type of cell may characterize a particular strain throughout repeated subcultures. It seems, however, very doubtful whether it is wise to assign labels to different strains of this organism on the basis of morphological characters alone.

Another feature that characterizes *C. diphtheriæ* as a species, and serves to differentiate it from some, but by no means all, of the related " diphtheroids," is the presence of the metachromatic granules described by Babes (1886) and by Ernst (1888, 1889). These granules are coloured a reddish purple when a film preparation is stained with a suitable sample of methylene blue. They may be demonstrated more clearly by the differential stain devised by Neisser, or by one of its many modifications. A single cell may contain one or more of these granules, seldom more than half a dozen, usually two or three. When only one or two are present they show a definite tendency to be situated at one or both poles.

The arrangement of the bacilli in film preparations is at least as characteristic as the form of the individual cells. Adjacent cells tend to lie at any angle to one another, forming a V or an L according to the degree of angular displacement ; and groups of such pairs form characteristic clusters, resembling Chinese letters, or cuneiform writing. It would appear, from the observations of Hill (1898–1902), that this particular arrangement results from incomplete separation at the moment of division, the daughter cells remaining attached at one point, and bending on this attachment as on a hinge as growth proceeds.

Finally, it may be noted that *C. diphtheriæ* provided the first instance in which true branching was demonstrated in a bacillary species. The observations of Hill showed that this appearance was not an artefact, but could be observed to take place during the growth of the living cell. This character, among others, decided the American Committee to separate this genus from the *Eubacteriales*, and include it with some others in a family of the order *Actinomycetales*. It has, however, been noted in a previous chapter that rudimentary branching has occasionally been noted in such typically bacillary forms as those of the genus *Bacterium*.

The morphology of other species of *Corynebacteria* departs, to a greater or less extent, from that of *C. diphtheriæ*. Sometimes, as with *C. ovis* and *C. murium*, the resemblance may be so close that an experienced observer would be unable to differentiate either of these species from the true diphtheria bacillus on morphological appearances alone. Sometimes, as with *C. hofmannii*, the differences are so clear-cut that little difficulty arises.

It is characteristic of many species of diphtheroids that their morphology, as displayed in films from young cultures, is far less variable than that of *C. diphtheriæ*. A film of *C. xerosis*, for example, may show a marked resemblance to some of the average long forms of *C. diphtheriæ*, but while pleomorphism will usually be minimal in the former it will be marked in the latter. Similarly the so-called *C. coryzæ segmentosum* may be very similar to the barred form which is sometimes assumed by *C. diphtheriæ* ; but again pleomorphism is slight or absent.

With regard to the staining reactions of this group the bare statement that the *Corynebacteria* are Gram-positive bacilli needs some qualification. The type species retains the stain to a sufficient degree to differentiate it quite clearly from the frankly Gram-negative bacteria ; but it is decolorized by alcohol more easily than are many Gram-positive species. The metachromatic granules, on the other hand, retain the stain tenaciously ; so that moderate overdecolorization, followed by the use of a red or brown counterstain, may give a picture very similar to that afforded by the use of Neisser's stain. Of the other species within this genus, *C. hofmannii* is very resistant to decolorization ; so that the application of Gram's stain, followed by a prolonged exposure to alcohol (15 mins. or so), affords a useful differential criterion between these two species. Of the rest, some species behave as *C. hofmannii*, others as *C. diphtheriæ*. Absence of flagella and lack of motility are characteristic of the genus, as also is the absence of capsulation.

The Growth Requirements of C. diphtheriæ.

One of the most striking characters of *C. diphtheriæ* is its ability to produce a powerful filtrable exotoxin with a specific pharmacological action (see below). Since this toxin is of great practical importance in the preparation of widely used prophylactic, therapeutic and diagnostic reagents, it is natural that toxin production, as well as growth *per se*, should have been studied by most of the workers who have investigated the nutritional requirements of this species.

So far as growth on synthetic media is concerned, our information is as yet relatively scanty, in spite of a considerable mass of experimental data (see Uschinsky 1893, 1897, Hadley 1907, Hadley and Gorham 1907, Koser and Rettger 1919, Davis and Ferry 1919, von Groer 1923, Hosoya and Kuroya 1923, Robertson 1924, Braun and Hofmeier 1927, Braun and Mündel 1927, 1929, Braun, Hofmeier and Mündel 1929, Maver 1930, Lindemann 1932, Ehrismann 1932–33, 1933, Hottinger and Hottinger 1933, Nitsch 1933, Schmidt 1933–34, Wadsworth and Wheeler 1934, Knight 1936). It may be summarized by noting (1) that *C. diphtheriæ* appears to be incapable of growth with ammonia as the sole source of nitrogen, carbon being supplied in an organic form ; (2) that growth, and toxin production, often occur when amino-acids are added to such a synthetic medium, and that, among these amino-acids, cystine, aspartic acid and perhaps tryptophan appear to be indispensable ; and (3) that it is only certain " non-exacting " strains that are capable of growing in such a medium, and even with these strains toxin production is usually much less abundant than with a more adequate food-supply. Knight (1936) emphasizes the difficulty of assessing the real significance of many of the recorded findings in view of the great difficulty of obtaining most amino-acids in a state of chemical purity.

· Attempts have been made (Bunker 1919, Hosoya *et al.* 1933, Mueller *et al.* 1933, Mueller 1935*a, b, c*) to identify the additional substances required for active growth and toxin production by fractionating peptone, meat extract and other types of complex protein extracts or hydrolysates in which *C. diphtheriæ* is known to grow abundantly. At the moment these studies have not proceeded further than the demonstration that the active substances are contained in certain fractions, but not in others.

So far as the large-scale production of diphtheria toxin is concerned, we have a mass of useful practical data, based on a large series of empirical observations ; and it is clear from these that optimal toxin production demands conditions that are not necessary for optimal growth. It was early recognized that the composition of the medium in which the organism is grown is of the first importance. Davis and Ferry (1919) tested the value of various media prepared from beef infusion, peptone and meat extract in various combinations with each other. The presence of beef infusion was found to be essential. Hartley and Hartley (1922) tested various specimens of peptone, and found that, while each brand of peptone gave a characteristic curve of toxin production, it was impossible to predict the value of any one brand by a preliminary chemical analysis. Hartley (1922) pointed out the superiority of a tryptic digest of horse muscle as a medium for the production of toxin, and his findings have been confirmed and extended by Watson and Langstaff (1927), who also confirm his observation that the value of such a medium is markedly influenced by the method of sterilization. In addition to growth-promoting substances, there are apparently toxin-inducing substances present, which are very labile to heat when the pH is at neutrality, or on its alkaline side. Autoclaving at pH 8·0 or over may completely destroy the value of a medium for toxin production. This may be avoided by filtration through a Seitz press, followed by a short steaming. The addition to the medium of maltose, or certain other energy sources, considerably increases the toxin yield, particularly if sodium acetate is also added (Pope 1932, Ramon and Berthelot 1932, Pope and Smith 1932, Pope and Healey 1933*a*). The initial reaction of the medium is of great importance, a fact which has been emphasized by many workers (Bunker 1919, Hartley 1922, Andrewes *et al.* 1923, Watson and Langstaff 1927). The most favourable starting reaction is at or just below pH 8·0, and it is important that, during the 7 to 10 days which elapse between sowing the culture and harvesting the toxin, the reaction should not swing far towards neutrality. The range over which growth of *C. diphtheriæ* takes place extends from about pH 5·7 to pH 8·7, but the zone over which toxin production occurs appears to be limited to pH 7·5–8·2. The growth of the organism during its initial stages is associated with a slight production of acid, probably derived in part from nitrogenous constituents of the medium. Later there is a reversion in the alkaline direction, due to the splitting-up of these organic acids with the formation of carbonates. The balance between these metabolic activities is in part determined by the oxygen pressure to which the culture is submitted. Partly for this reason, partly perhaps for others, the shape of the flask in which the medium is contained, the thickness of the layer of medium itself, and the type of plug used for closing the mouth of the flask, all exert an influence on the grade of toxin produced. It is also important to eliminate any movement which will prematurely break up the veil of growth which forms at the surface of the medium. In practice it is found that the best results are obtained by growing the organism in a shallow layer of broth in a cylindrical bottle which is kept lying on its side, and is plugged loosely with gauze or cotton-wool (Bunker 1919, Hartley and Hartley 1922, Andrewes *et al.* 1923, Watson and Langstaff 1927, Pope and Healey 1933*b*). The cultures are incubated at 37° C. for 7 to 10 days, at the end of which time phenol, or preferably toluol, is added in sufficient strength to ensure sterilization, the flasks are allowed to stand for 24 hours, and the contents are filtered. This filtrate constitutes the crude " toxin."

So far as ordinary growth on laboratory media is concerned we may note that the different species of *Corynebacteria* show certain preferences for particular media. *C. diphtheriæ*, for example, grows far more readily and abundantly on Loeffler's serum medium than on ordinary agar, while *C. hofmannii* grows freely on the latter.

The oxygen requirements of different species within this genus vary widely. Although all species are apparently able to grow in the absence of gaseous oxygen, some species, including *C. diphtheriæ* itself, grow far more freely under aerobic conditions, and display this preference for a free supply of oxygen by growing as a film or veil over the surface of a broth culture. Other species, such as *C. acnes* or *C. typhi*, are microaerophilic.

The temperature range over which *C. diphtheriæ* grows in artificial media extends from about 15° C. to 40° C., with an optimum at about 37° C.

Resistance.—This species is readily killed by heat, suspensions of the bacilli failing to survive 10 minutes' heating at 58° C. It is also easily destroyed by most of the usual antiseptics. It would appear to be relatively resistant to drying, though the evidence on this point is somewhat conflicting. Concerning the resistance of the various species of diphtheroid bacilli we have far less precise information ; such data as are available suggest that they behave, in this respect, in much the same way as the type species.

Biochemical Reactions.

The carbohydrates most frequently employed as test substrates for the differentiation of species within this genus are dextrose, maltose and saccharose. The type species, *C. diphtheriæ*, produces acid but no gas in dextrose and maltose, but does not attack saccharose. Other species, such as *C. xerosis* produce acid in all three sugars ; others again, such as *C. hofmannii*, attack none of them. No species produces gas. A more detailed and extended table of the fermentation reactions of eight named species within this genus, and of eleven unnamed diphtheroids examined by Barratt (see Andrewes *et al.* 1923) is appended to this chapter. The fermentation of certain other substrates by different varieties of the type species is considered below.

We may note here that certain species and types within this group, for instance *C. ovis*, *C. pyogenes* and certain unnamed diphtheroids liquefy gelatin, while *C. diphtheriæ* and most diphtheroid organisms do not.

Many strains of *C. diphtheriæ*, but not all, produce areas of hæmolysis on blood-agar plates, and lyse red cells when these are added to broth cultures (Schwoner 1904, Costa *et al.* 1918, Goldie 1933). The red cells of the guinea-pig are the most sensitive, then those of the rabbit, horse, man, pig, mouse and sheep in this order. There is a conflict of evidence in regard to the production of a soluble hæmolysin. The earlier observers stated that culture-filtrates did not cause hæmolysis ; but Goldie (1933) reports that cell-free filtrates are hæmolytic, and that their activity runs roughly parallel to their toxin content, though the hæmolysin is not neutralized by antitoxin. There is a similar conflict in regard to the heat-resistance of the hæmolytic agent, whether it be intracellular or extracellular. It was originally recorded as being inactivated by heating to 58° C. for half an hour. Goldie states that it is not inactivated by boiling.

Two species of diphtheroids that are pathogenic for animals, *C. ovis* and *C. pyogenes*, also exert a hæmolytic action on the red blood corpuscles of various species, including the rabbit and horse. The other species and types within this genus that have been examined from this point of view appear to be non-hæmolytic.

Antigenic Structure.

In considering the antigenic structure of *C. diphtheriæ* and of the other species and types within this genus, we may note that those workers who have attacked this problem have, in most instances, approached it with a view to the identification of the type species, and its differentiation from related species, types and variants. It is, therefore, only in regard to the type species that our knowledge is in any way detailed or systematized.

Almost all the studies on the antigenic structure of this group of organisms have been carried out by the method of agglutination ; and the application of this technique soon showed that *C. diphtheriæ* is an antigenically heterogeneous species. Langer (1916) demonstrated the existence of two serological types, Durand (1918, 1920) six, Havens (1920) two, Smith (1923) seven, Eagleton and Baxter (1923) ten, and Scott (1923) eight ; in all cases there remained strains that did not fall into any of the groups.

In regard to the serological relationships of normal toxigenic strains of *C. diphtheriæ* to the non-toxigenic variants derived from them, there is no evidence that loss of toxigenicity is necessarily associated with a change in the cell antigens that determine agglutination. For instance, while six of Scott's serological groups happened to contain only toxigenic strains, two contained both toxigenic and non-toxigenic strains, while Okell (1929) was able to demonstrate the serological identity of several pairs of toxigenic and non-toxigenic strains isolated under conditions which made it probable that the latter had been derived from the former. Although there is no necessary association between loss of toxigenicity and change in antigenic structure, it may, of course, often happen that a variant strain will have changed in one character as well as in the other ; and it would appear that any large random sample of non-toxigenic variants will usually differ from a random sample of toxigenic strains in their antigenic behaviour. Thus, Okell, using the ten antisera corresponding to the groups differentiated by Eagleton and Baxter, and another sixteen sera prepared by them, each of which agglutinated only the homologous toxigenic strain, examined one hundred non-toxigenic strains. Only two of these were found to be antigenically identical with any toxigenic strain ; and a study of the hundred non-toxigenic strains by antisera prepared against ten of them showed little cross-agglutination, and hence no possibility of serological grouping. Non-toxigenic strains of *C. diphtheriæ* would seem therefore to contain a very large number of different antigenic types, only some of which share the cell antigens of the normal toxigenic forms.

In this connection it may be noted that, among the toxigenic strains, there is no evidence that differences in the antigenic structure of the bacterial cell are associated with any difference in the nature of the toxin produced. The toxin produced by any one antigenic type is specifically neutralized by the antitoxin prepared against the toxin produced by that type or by any other (Paxson and Redowitz 1922, Hartley 1923).

It would seem, from the scanty evidence available, that there is little antigenic relationship, so far as agglutination reactions are concerned, between *C. diphtheriæ* and other species of *Corynebacteria*. Scott (1923) included in the series that he studied a number of strains of *C. xerosis* and *C. hofmannii*, but could detect no antigenic relationship between these species, or between either of them and any serological type of *C. diphtheriæ*. Similarly, Bailey (1925) studied two strains of toxigenic *C. diphtheriæ*, two of *C. hofmannii* and three of *C. xerosis*, together with seventeen non-toxigenic strains of *C. diphtheriæ*. He was unable to detect any significant antigenic relationship between these two species of diphtheroids and the diphtheria bacillus.

In regard to the antigenic structure of the various species of diphtheroids, apart from their relation to *C. diphtheriæ*, we have as yet very little information. Merchant (1935) has recorded some preliminary observations on the antigenic relationships of those species that are natural pathogens of animals, which suggest that this method may be of considerable value for identification ; but it is as yet far too early to assess their significance.

The fact that agglutination tests fail to reveal any antigenic relationship between *C. diphtheriæ* and the various diphtheroid organisms, does not, of course, mean that there is no sharing of antigenic components between them. It means only that, if such sharing exists, the shared antigens, either because of their position in the bacterium or for some other reason, are not concerned in the agglutination of the intact bacterial cells. It is not, therefore, surprising to find that certain antigenic components are distributed widely among the *Corynebacteria*, and even among related genera. Thus Krah and Witebsky (1930) record that alcoholic extracts of the diphtheria bacillus, of certain diphtheroids, and of the tubercle bacillus, all fix complement in the presence of an antiserum prepared against any one of these organisms. Again, a strain of *C. diphtheriæ* that has undergone antigenic variation, and lost its type-specific surface antigen, may agglutinate with antisera prepared against diphtheria bacilli of other serological types, or against various diphtheroids. Neill and his colleagues (1931) have described such a strain.

Pathogenicity and Toxin Production.

The type species, *C. diphtheriæ*, is an important human pathogen, giving rise to a characteristic and often fatal disease, the lesions of which are, in the main, produced by the action of a powerful exotoxin. This diffuses throughout the body from the primary focus of infection, which is most frequently situated in the tonsillar region. The pathogenesis of diphtheria in man, and its diagnosis, prevention and treatment so far as these depend on bacteriological methods, are dealt with in Chapter LVIII. The characters of the specific toxin, its effects on certain laboratory animals, and its immunological relationships with toxins produced by other species and types within this genus, are, however, so important as differential criteria, that it is necessary to discuss them here.

The production of diphtheria toxin in artificial culture has been dealt with above The product so obtained is, of course, extremely crude. In addition to the toxin itself, and the toxoid which is derived from it by some modification that destroys its toxicity without altering its immunological specificity, the crude filtrates contain substances derived from the bacterial cells, and others derived from the media in which they are grown.

Many attempts have been made to isolate diphtheria toxin, or toxoid, in a state of chemical purity ; but although a considerable degree of concentration, and with it the removal of much extraneous material, has been achieved, we have not yet been able to isolate the toxin as a chemical entity or to determine its constitution. This is in part due to the fact that the toxin itself is an extremely labile substance, easily inactivated or destroyed by heat or by strong chemical reagents. It is probable that the specific material of a toxic filtrate—toxin and toxoid—constitutes a very small fraction of the total constituents (about 1 per cent. according to Glenny, 1925*a*). A considerable concentration can be achieved by precipitation with weak acids, or ammonium sulphate, or acetone, or by dialysis, or by fractional filtration through graded collodion membranes, or by adsorption on to aluminium hydroxide followed by elution, or by a combination of these methods (see Glenny and Walpole 1915, Watson and Langstaff 1926, Locke and Main 1928, Leulier *et al.* 1931, Bunny *et al.* 1931, Schmidt 1931, Schmidt *et al.* 1931, Tasman and Pondman 1931, Brandwijk and Tasman 1932, 1933, Zajdel 1932, Tasman and van Waasbergen 1932, Wadsworth *et al.* 1932, Leonard and Holm 1933, Wadsworth and Quigley 1934, Eaton and Bayne-Jones 1934, Goldie 1934). The partially purified toxin would appear, from the results obtained by ultrafiltration and dialysis, to be in the form of, or intimately attached to, molecules of considerable size. It still contains nitrogen in significant amount, although the nitrogen content is greatly reduced in comparison with the crude filtrate. It is possible, therefore, that the toxin is either itself a protein, or is in intimate association with some protein complex.

We may note here certain other properties that characterize this toxin. Judged by the usual criterion (the amount of a potent filtrate that suffices to kill a sensitive animal) it ranks among the more active bacterial toxins ; 0·002 c.c. of such a filtrate often contains one minimum lethal dose (M.L.D.) for the guinea-pig. It is thermo-labile, being inactivated by exposure to a temperature of 58°–60° C. for 1 to 2 hours. It is actively antigenic, either in the unaltered or toxoided form, stimulating the production of a powerful antitoxin when injected into animals.

The classical paper in which Loeffler (1884) first described the isolation and characters of the diphtheria bacillus, and the report by Roux and Yersin (1888) of the separation of the filtrable toxin, contain descriptions of the lesions produced by the living organism, or by its separated toxin, in a variety of laboratory animals. These original observations have since been extended by a host of experimental studies. It will suffice to note here that, among laboratory animals, the guinea-pig and the rabbit are the most susceptible, while rats and mice are extremely resistant. Dogs, cats, pigeons, and other birds appear to occupy an intermediate position. (See Loeffler 1884, 1890, Roux and Yersin 1888, Wernicke 1893, Goodman 1907, Coca *et al.* 1921, Glenny and Allen 1922, Andrewes *et al.* 1923). It may be noted that the bacillus appears to have little power of tissue invasion ; whether the inoculum consists of a living culture, or of a toxic filtrate, death occurs as the result of a toxæmia in the strict sense. This general statement may require minor modification in regard to certain varieties of the diphtheria bacillus (see below). For our immediate purpose it will suffice to note the sequence of events that follow the injection of a living culture, or of a toxic filtrate, into the guinea-pig.

If a guinea-pig is inoculated subcutaneously into the flank with a dose of a virulent culture or of a toxic filtrate, of a size which will produce death within a few days, a soft œdematous swelling usually appears at the site of inoculation within 12 to 18 hours, and gradually extends. About the time the swelling appears, or shortly thereafter, the animal becomes obviously ill, developing a staring coat and sitting crouched in its cage. Death usually occurs between 18 and 96 hours, according to the size of the dose of culture or filtrate inoculated. With very large doses the time to death may be even shorter, but is never less than 10 to 14 hours (see Glenny 1925*b*). Animals that survive beyond the 4th day may develop cachexia and paralysis, and die at some later period ; but the pathogenesis of this condition appears to be essentially different from that of the acutely fatal toxæmia, and it is with the latter that we are here concerned. When a guinea-pig that has died within 4 days after a subcutaneous inoculation is examined post mortem, the typical findings are as follows :

At the site of inoculation is found an extensive area of gelatinous hæmorrhagic œdema, extending to the skin superficially, and deeply to the muscles or to the parietal peritoneal membrane. If the animal has survived for several days, the tissues in the more central parts of the œdematous area may be obviously necrotic. The regional lymph glands are usually swollen and congested. The peritoneum may contain a varying amount of fluid, which may be clear, cloudy or blood-stained. The abdominal viscera as a whole are congested ; but the most striking lesion is the marked swelling and congestion of the adrenal glands. On macroscopical section there are seen to be scattered hæmorrhages, situated in the medulla, in the cortex, or in both. Sometimes all naked-eye distinction between cortex and medulla is lost. On opening the thorax a serous exudate will often be found in the pleural cavities, usually clear, sometimes cloudy or blood-stained. A peri-cardial effusion may or may not be present. Films prepared from such effusions reveal a marked preponderance of mononuclear cells.

It is of some interest to note the relative frequency of the more important lesions associated with acute diphtheritic toxæmia in the guinea-pig. Wright (1894) records the findings in 160 necropsies : a local lesion was present in 90 per cent. of the animals ; con-gestion of the adrenals in 81·2 per cent. ; and a pleural effusion in 42·5 per cent. Barratt (1923) records the post-mortem findings in 50 guinea-pigs which died within 72 hours after the injection of 2 c.c. of a virulent culture ; œdema, of varying degree, was present at the site of inoculation in 94 per cent. of the animals ; the adrenals were abnormal in all and are noted as pink in 4 per cent., red in 22 per cent., and deep red in 74 per cent. ; a pleural exudate was present in 44 per cent.

For details of the histological changes associated with these lesions, reference may be made to the monograph published by the Medical Research Council. We may, however, note a few points which have a direct bearing on diphtheria as it occurs in man. Mollard and Regaud (1895) recorded the occurrence of degenerative changes in the myocardium in experimental diphtheria, and Flexner (1897) noted that fatty degeneration of the cardiac muscle was almost constantly present in animals which died within a short time after inoculation. There has been some discussion as to whether these changes are primary, or are a sequel to an initial reaction in the interstitial tissue, or to a primary lesion of afferent nerve fibres. The careful and detailed studies of Dudgeon (1906) gave a clear answer to this question, and afforded strong experimental support to the suggestion of Bolton (1905), that the direct action of diphtheria toxin on the cardiac muscle is the most important cause of acute cardiac failure in human diphtheria. Examining a large series of guinea-pigs, killed or dying in various stages of acute diphtheritic toxæmia, Dudgeon demonstrated the occurrence of fatty degeneration of the diaphragmatic muscle within 4 hours after inoculation, and of the cardiac muscle within 16 hours. Similar results have since been recorded by Jaffé (1920).

We may note also, since this method is now frequently employed in the identification of a toxigenic strain of C. diphtheriæ, that the intradermal injection of toxin, or of living bacilli, leads to a localized erythematous lesion, followed by necrosis (Römer 1909). This effect, as also the lethal action of the subcutaneous injection of larger doses, can, of course, be specifically neutralized by an antitoxic serum.

Although the production of this filtrable toxin, with its characteristic action in the guinea-pig and its property of being specifically neutralized by the homologous antitoxin, is one of the most important characters by which C. diphtheriæ is identified, there exist strains of bacilli that, while conforming in all other respects with the diphtheria bacillus, fail to form this filtrable toxin. These strains are commonly classed as non-toxigenic, or avirulent, diphtheria bacilli. Whether they should in all cases be assigned to this species is perhaps doubtful ; but there can be no reasonable doubt that many of them, at least, are actually non-toxigenic variants of C. diphtheriæ. We have noted above that certain avirulent strains can be shown to be antigenically related to typical toxigenic strains, and the actual emergence of an avirulent variant from a virulent organism, under laboratory conditions, has been recorded by several observers.

Thus Crowell (1926), starting from a single-cell culture of a fully virulent strain, derived from this parent culture a series of daughter strains, one of which was entirely avirulent. All attempts to raise the virulence of this variant were without result. Cowan (1927) records the derivation of avirulent variants from 2 strains of virulent C. diphtheriæ, one of them the classical " Park 8 " which has yielded toxin to most laboratories in the world. These variants were " rough," in the sense that they formed small, raised, dense and granular colonies, and gave increased deposit in broth, with an absence of pellicle formation.

The diphtheria bacillus is not the only species of Corynebacterium that is pathogenic under natural conditions. C. ovis, C. murium, C. pyogenes and C. renale, if the two latter can be regarded as well-established species, certainly fall into this category. So probably does C. acnes.

A great variety of diphtheroid organisms have, at one time or another, been isolated from various tissues in man and animals. Sometimes the tissue from which the diphtheroid bacillus was isolated has been the site of some obvious lesion ; sometimes it has been apparently healthy. It is exceedingly difficult, from the published reports, to determine whether these organisms have, or have not, played any pathogenic rôle ; and in most instances they have not been studied in sufficient detail to allow of any systematic identification or classification. We shall therefore confine ourselves here to a brief description of the lesions produced by the named species referred to above.

C. ovis, often referred to as the Preisz-Nocard bacillus, (see Nocard 1889, Preisz 1894) causes caseous lymphadenitis in sheep and ulcerative lymphangitis in horses. It differs sharply from *C. diphtheriæ* in that it is a pyogenic organism, and invades the tissues. It resembles *C. diphtheriæ* in producing a filtrable toxin.

Nicolle, Loiseau and Forgeot (1912) have carefully recorded the lesions met with in guinea-pigs, which have died as the result of inoculating either living cultures of *C. ovis* or bacteria-free filtrates subcutaneously. In the former case, and where the dose of living culture has been so adjusted that the animal dies about the 25th day, subcutaneous abscesses develop in various situations during life. At necropsy, in addition to these superficial lesions, small granulomatous masses are found in the liver, spleen and lungs, and beneath the parietal peritoneum. In the male guinea-pig similar lesions are found in the tunica of the testis and epididymis. Some of these lesions may have developed into large caseous or caseo-purulent masses.

When a guinea-pig is injected subcutaneously with a fatal dose of a toxic broth filtrate, death occurs within a few days, often in less than 24 hours, from an acute toxæmia. The necropsy findings in such cases are entirely different from those described above. There is a local, subcutaneous, inflammatory, gelatinous œdema at the site of inoculation, often hæmorrhagic in character. The abdominal viscera are congested, and often show small hæmorrhages, particularly in the stomach, large intestine, and kidneys. The latter may be almost black in colour. There is, however, no congestion of the adrenals, and no exudation into the pleura. Hall and Stone (1916) give a very similar picture.

Again (Petrie and McClean 1934) state that the effect produced by the injection of *C. ovis* toxin into the skin of a guinea-pig differs from that produced by the injection of diphtheria toxin. The former gives rise to a definitely papular lesion, and if the dose of toxin injected is large the lesions become pustular.

It has been shown by Bull and Dickinson (1935) that the pyogenic substance is largely contained in the bacterial cells, as is suggested by the observations of Nicolle and his colleagues, and that it is relatively thermostable. Suspensions of *C. ovis*, killed by heating at 60° C. for 1 hour, no longer produce toxic death in susceptible animals, but they give rise to sterile abscesses when injected in adequate dosage.

It may be noted that the exotoxin of *C. ovis* is different from that of *C. diphtheriæ*. Nicolle and his colleagues found that an antitoxin prepared against the former gave specific protection, while no protection against *C. ovis* toxin was afforded by diphtheria antitoxin. Dassonville (1907), Hall and Stone (1916), Minett (1922*a*, *b*), and Barratt (1933) recorded some degree of protection by diphtheria antitoxin against the toxin of *C. ovis* ; but the detailed study of Petrie and McClean (1934) leaves little doubt that these effects were due to the fact that the sera of normal horses may contain varying amounts of *C. ovis* antitoxin (*C. ovis* is a natural pathogen of the horse), and that the two toxins are immunologically quite distinct from one another.

Petrie and McClean have, however, found evidence of the existence of varieties of diphtheroid bacilli that are, in respect of certain characters, intermediate between *C. diphtheriæ* and *C. ovis*. These diphtheroids, all isolated by various observers from the human throat, were originally studied by Barratt (1933), who found them to have the power of liquefying gelatin, a property possessed by *C. ovis* but not by *C. diphtheriæ*. Petrie and McClean found that one of these strains produced both diphtheria toxin and a toxin that was immunologically related to that of *C. ovis*. The remaining strains produced only a toxin related to that of *C. ovis*.

C. pyogenes was first described by Lucet (1893), who isolated it from suppurative lesions in cattle. Similar organisms were isolated from similar lesions in cattle and swine by Grips (1898), Künnemann (1903) and Glage (1903). Since then they have been recorded by many workers (see Holth 1908, Poels 1912, Ward 1917). The conditions to which they most frequently give rise under natural conditions appear to be suppurative pneumonia, suppurative arthritis, and other suppurative lesions, including mastitis, the animals affected being swine, cattle and sometimes sheep (see Merchant 1935).

Among laboratory animals, the rabbit appears to be most susceptible, guinea-pigs less so, and mice relatively resistant (see Holth 1908, Ward 1917, Brown and Orcutt 1920).

The injection of living cultures of *C. pyogenes* into the rabbit is followed by the development of localized abscesses if the injections are given subcutaneously. If they are given intravenously, or if generalization occurs after a subcutaneous inoculation, abscesses develop in the bones and joints, less frequently in other organs.

Since both *C. ovis* and *C. pyogenes* produce suppurative lesions in animals, both liquefy gelatin, and both produce hæmolysis, the relation of these organisms, and their possible identity clearly arises. There is, however, a general consensus of opinion among those who have worked with them that they are different species. They tend to affect different animal hosts, and among laboratory animals, the guinea-pig is very susceptible to infection with *C. ovis*, but relatively resistant to *C. pyogenes*. There are also cultural differences. On a medium containing blood serum *C. pyogenes* gives small dewdrop colonies, which slowly enlarge and become granular in the centre. *C. ovis* gives colonies that are circular, umbonate and opaque, with a tendency to develop a yellowish pigment. It would clearly be of interest to know whether *C. pyogenes* produces a filtrable toxin, and, if so, what relation if any this bears to the toxin of *C. ovis*; but, so far as we are aware, there are no records of any studies of this kind.

Enderlen (1890–91) described a diphtheroid bacillus that he had isolated from the pus from a cow suffering from pyelitis. This organism has been named *C. renale*. A similar organism was isolated by Ernst (1905, 1906); and Jones and Little (1925) record an outbreak of infective cystitis and pyelitis in three dairy herds associated with the constant presence of a diphtheroid bacillus. In this last instance, at least, there would seem to be no reasonable doubt that the bacillus was ætiologically related to the disease; though the same organism may often be isolated from the genital tract of healthy calves (Jones and Little 1930). There are as far as we know no records of the lesions produced by this organism in laboratory animals, though Jones and Little have reproduced the disease in cattle. Ernst, indeed, states that the bacillus isolated by him produced no lesions in any animal, and he therefore regarded it as devoid of pathogenic significance. No attempt has apparently been made to ascertain whether it produces a filtrable toxin. Its claim to rank as a separate species must rest in part on its predilection for the urinary tract in cattle, but mainly on its behaviour in the laboratory. It is recorded as not producing a hæmolysin and not liquefying gelatin, in both of which characters it differs sharply from *C. pyogenes* (Merchant 1935).

C. murium, which was first described by Kutscher (1894), gives rise to a natural disease in mice, and its pathogenic activity is apparently confined to this small laboratory animal. It has been injected without effect into the guinea-pig, rabbit, cat, dog, pigeon, hen, rat, goat, calf, sheep, cow and horse (Kutscher 1894, Bongert 1901), but Gundel, György, and Pagel (1932) have recorded spontaneous infections in rats on a vitamin-deficient diet. We may give here a brief description of the natural disease as well as of the results of experimental inoculation.

The natural disease has been described by Kutscher and by Bongert, and has been observed on many occasions by the present authors during necropsies on mice, though it is certainly relatively infrequent. The most characteristic lesion in the naturally-occurring disease is the presence of large, firm, caseous areas in the lung. In sections or films from these lesions the bacilli are usually abundant. Caseous nodules may be found in the liver, though they are less frequent. When present they project from the surface, in contradistinction to the necrotic areas seen in mouse typhoid. The lymphatic glands of the axilla, neck, mediastinum and mesentery may be enlarged and caseous ; but the pulmonary lesions are frequently the only obvious sign of disease. Occasionally the bacillus may be isolated from a single caseous gland, found at necropsy without any other detectable lesion.

The disease may readily be reproduced by inoculating mice with pure cultures of *C. murium*, or by administration *per os*. The findings at necropsy depend largely on the route of administration. After feeding, lesions develop in the mesenteric glands and in the liver. After intraperitoneal inoculation, which usually leads to death within a week, the peritoneum is found to be studded with minute tubercles, and there is a spreading granulomatosis, of very varying extent, involving the regional lymphatic glands, the liver, and less frequently the spleen. In our experience pulmonary lesions are much less frequent in the experimental than in the natural disease, though they occasionally occur. Bongert (1901) has called attention to the trivial lesions which may sometimes be found post mortem after experimental infection. In animals dying after subcutaneous inoculation the only detectable lesion may be a small caseous abscess at the site of inoculation. Seeking an explanation for this fact, he inoculated mice with filtrates of broth cultures, or with cultures killed by heat, and found that death resulted in every case, after about 10–14 days. No obvious lesions of any kind were found at necropsy. Mice fed with filtrates died in about the same time, and with the same absence of lesions. We can in part confirm these findings as regards the inoculation of filtrates, or of killed cultures, though our own results were far less uniform than those recorded by Bongert. It would appear that this organism produces an exotoxin which is fatal for mice. According to Bongert this toxin is relatively heat-stable, since it withstands heating for 2 hours at 55° C., or for a few minutes at 74° C. ; but the particulars given are not sufficiently precise to allow of any definite conclusion with regard to the time or temperature required for inactivation.

The toxin of this organism has not, so far as we are aware, been compared with that of *C. diphtheriæ* or of *C. ovis*, but it seems exceedingly unlikely that there is any relationship, since the mouse is conspicuously resistant to diphtheria toxin, and the guinea-pig and rabbit, which are very susceptible to *C. ovis*, are resistant to *C. murium*.

There remains *C. acnes*, a diphtheroid organism described in the lesions of cutaneous acne by Unna (1896). It was first isolated by Sabouraud (1897), and has since then been studied by Gilchrist (1900, 1903), by Fleming (1909), and by Südmersen and Thompson (1909–10). Its claim to pathogenicity must rest in the main on its constant association with the disease in man. Südmersen and Thompson state that the two strains examined by them were pathogenic for the mouse but not for the guinea-pig ; but their description of the lesions in the latter animal is extremely scanty. *C. acnes* is clearly marked as a distinct species from those described above by its peculiar growth requirements (see p. 349) and particularly by the fact that it is microaerophilic.

C. typhi, another microaerophilic diphtheroid, was isolated by Plotz (1914) from the blood in typhus fever. It is now generally admitted to be an example of a parasitic diphtheroid with no established pathological rôle (Olitsky 1921).

The Gravis, Mitis and Intermediate Types of C. diphtheriæ.

Before summarizing the data set out above and attempting a classification of the genus so far as our present knowledge permits, we may consider the evidence that has accumulated during the last few years in regard to the existence of different types of *C. diphtheriæ*. These types were first distinguished by McLeod and his colleagues at Leeds (Anderson, Happold, McLeod and Thomson 1931). Using a heated blood-agar medium containing potassium tellurite, on which the diphtheria bacillus produces black or grey-black colonies, they noted the appearance on their plates of two distinct colony forms. Both of these, when subcultured and tested by the usual methods, gave all the reactions of typical toxigenic *C. diphtheriæ*. Examining these strains further they found that they were differentiated in other ways—by their power to ferment starch and glycogen, by their growth in broth, and by the production of hæmolysis. It happened that Leeds was, at that time, suffering from a severe epidemic of diphtheria, and one of the two types which was very prevalent in the district was isolated from many of the severe and fatal cases, while the other type was isolated only from mild cases of the disease. For this reason McLeod and his colleagues called one type *C. diphtheriæ gravis*, and the other *C. diphtheriæ mitis*. At the same time they noted the existence of a certain number of intermediate strains, which corresponded neither to the *gravis* nor to the *mitis* type. In a subsequent report (Anderson, Cooper, Happold and McLeod 1933a) they extended these observations, and noted that the " intermediate " strains formed a third type, with well-differentiated characters of its own. The illness to which this type gave rise appeared to be more severe than that caused by *mitis* strains, less severe than that caused by *gravis* strains ; but the number of cases due to this *intermediate* type was too small to permit a definite conclusion on this point.

Robinson and Marshall (1934) carried out a similar study in Manchester. They were able to confirm the occurrence of the three types described by McLeod and his colleagues ; but in the Manchester series the intermediate strains were more numerous than either the *gravis* or the *mitis*. Moreover, the disease to which they gave rise was at least as severe as that caused by the *gravis* strains. As at Leeds, the *mitis* strains were associated with the milder cases.

The characters of these three types of *C. diphtheriæ* may be summarized as follows (see references above and Robinson 1934) :

C. diphtheriæ gravis.—Gives a grey or grey-black " daisy head " colony on blood-tellurite medium, the degree of striation of the surface and crenation of the edge varying considerably. Ferments dextrin, starch and glycogen (in addition to dextrose and maltose, which are fermented by all types of *C. diphtheriæ*). Gives surface growth and granular deposit in broth, generally with an early (2–3 days) reversal of the pH to the alkaline side. Usually non-hæmolytic. Stained films from 18-hour cultures on Loeffler's medium (the morphology of *C. diphtheriæ* grown on the blood-tellurite medium is quite atypical) show bacillary forms with one or two darkly-staining areas, the rest of the cell staining very lightly. Metachromatic granules are rare, and when present are very small. Some 60 per cent. of *gravis* strains conform to this morphology, the others may show much the same appearance as *mitis* or *intermediate* strains.

C. diphtheriæ mitis.—Gives a convex, smooth, black, shining colony on blood-tellurite medium, with an entire edge. It does not ferment starch or glycogen. The fermentation of dextrin is variable. Gives diffuse turbidity in broth, with a non-granular deposit. Surface growth is infrequent ; when it occurs, it is soft. There is later a reversal of pH to the alkaline side (4–5 days). It is usually hæmolytic. The bacilli stain very irregularly, and metachromatic granules are very prominent.

C. diphtheriæ (intermediate).—Gives a small, flat colony on blood-tellurite medium, with a central, raised, black or grey-black portion, and a lighter, slightly crenated periphery. Does not ferment starch or glycogen. Fermentation of dextrin is variable. Gives a fine granular deposit in broth, with no surface growth. There is no reversal of pH. This type is consistently non-hæmolytic. The morphology is very characteristic, about 98 per cent. of the bacilli being barred.

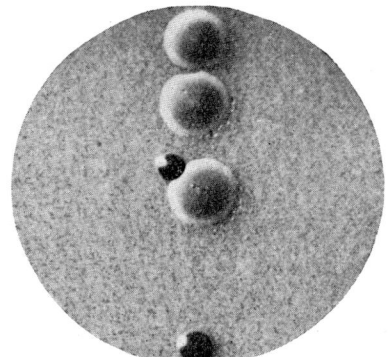

FIG. 65.—*C. diphtheriæ.*
Three colonies of *gravis* type and two of *mitis* type, on blood-tellurite-agar.

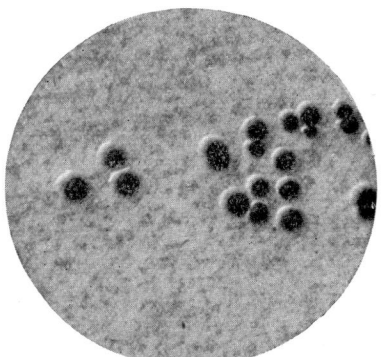

FIG. 66.—*C. diphtheriæ.*
Colonies of *intermediate* type on blood-tellurite-agar.

It will be noted that the type of colony formed on blood-tellurite medium (see Figs. 65 and 66), and the power to ferment starch and glycogen, afford the most reliable criteria for the differentiation of these three types ; though the other characters may often be helpful in arriving at a conclusion.

These important findings of McLeod and his colleagues have now been confirmed by many other workers. There was at first a failure to differentiate clearly between the *intermediate* and *mitis* types, and a tendency to rely on fermentative reactions alone, and this led to some apparently discrepant results (Parish *et al.* 1932*a, b,* Wright and Rankin 1932). But with the development of the necessary cultural methods, and a better knowledge of the essential differential criteria, the results obtained by workers in many different areas fell into line with those first recorded at Leeds, though it became clear that the frequency distribution of the three types varied widely from place to place, and from time to time (Anderson *et al.* 1933*b,* Carter 1933, Leete *et al.* 1933, Menton *et al.* 1933, Ali 1934, Christison 1934, Dudley *et al.* 1934, Schiff and Werber 1935, Gundel and Liebetruth 1935, Robinson and Marshall 1935, Whitley 1935).

Why the *gravis* and the *intermediate* strains produce more fatalities, in spite of treatment with antitoxin, than do the *mitis* strains, is a problem that is more conveniently considered when discussing diphtheria as a disease (Chapter LVIII). For the moment we may merely note that the *mitis* type appears to be at least as active in toxin production as either *gravis* or *intermediate* strains, and that the toxins produced by all three types are identical; while there is evidence suggesting that the *gravis* strains have a greater power of multiplication within the body.

The recognition of these three types naturally led to an examination of the antigenic relationships between them. Ewing (1933) examined 106 *gravis* (starch-fermenting) and 50 non-starch-fermenting strains. The *gravis* strains fell into five different serological types, and none of these were antigenically similar to any of the non-starch-fermenting strains. Thirty-five *mitis* strains yielded four different antigenic groups, and 15 *intermediate* strains yielded four groups. Murray (1935) examined 78 *gravis*, 70 *mitis* and 102 *intermediate* strains, and was able to differentiate three different antigenic types of *gravis*, four of *mitis* and four of *intermediate*. There was no antigenic relationship between the three different types.

It would seem, then, that the *gravis*, *mitis* and *intermediate* types of *C. diphtheriæ* are differentiated from one another in antigenic structure, as well as in the characters described above, and that each of them is separable into a number of different antigenic sub-types.

The Classification of Corynebacteria.

It will be obvious from the foregoing discussion that the time has not yet arrived to attempt any general systematic classification of the large number of different types of *corynebacteria* that have been described. Certain organisms have, however, been studied in sufficient detail to make it clear that they deserve specific rank. Among these the type species, *C. diphtheriæ*, is of course pre-eminent. Among the non-pathogenic species parasitic to man *C. hofmannii* is a well-recognized species, and *C. xerosis* would probably fall into the same category. We follow Andrewes and his colleagues (1923) in excluding the so-called *C. coryzæ segmentosum* from the list of identifiable species. Including the various species and types, of human or animal origin, that have been dealt with above, this leaves us with the following named species within the genus : *C. diphtheriæ* (types, *gravis*, *mitis* and *intermediate*), *C. hofmannii*, *C. xerosis*, *C. ovis*, *C. pyogenes*, *C. renale*, *C. murium*, *C. acnes* and *C. typhi*. For the rest, we are in entire agreement with Andrewes and his colleagues in believing that specific names should be withheld from the numerous diphtheroids that have been described until they have been examined in greater detail and their identity more fully established.

We append a summarized description of the named species, and a tabular description of the fermentation reactions of the eleven types of diphtheroid bacilli differentiated by the Committee of the Medical Research Council (see Andrewes *et al.* 1923).

C. diphtheriæ

Observed by Klebs (1883); isolated and described by Loeffler (1884).

The morphology and staining reactions of this species have been described above, and the absence of motility and capsulation, common to the genus, has been noted.

TYPE OF GROWTH.—*On Loeffler's serum*, the colonies, after 24 hours' incubation at 37° C., are about 1 mm. in diameter, circular, convex, with a slightly raised centre, a smooth or finely granular surface and an entire edge; granular in structure when viewed by transmitted light, butyrous in consistency, pale or deeper cream in colour, moderately opaque, and easily emulsifiable in water or saline. After 48 to 72 hours' incubation the colony shows a varying degree of enlargement, the centre becomes more raised, more opaque, and deepens in colour, while the periphery remains flat, extends outwards and appears more transparent than the centre, giving the so-called " poached-egg " appearance.

On agar, growth is much less abundant, and the individual colonies are, for the most part, smaller, often having a diameter of 0·25 mm. or less, after 24 hours' incubation at 37° C. These small colonies, which are greyish-white in colour, convex with a raised central portion, and usually with an entire margin, are frequently mingled with a few larger, whiter colonies.

On gelatin, the growth is very similar to that on agar, but develops much more slowly owing to the lower temperature of incubation. In stab culture growth develops along the whole length of the needle-track without lateral outgrowths, and with a slight surface growth consisting of a raised central portion and a flatter periphery, sometimes showing an irregular margin. The medium is never liquefied.

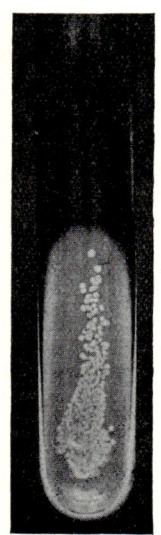

On potato, growth is usually very scanty and often invisible to the naked eye.

On tellurite-blood-agar plates, the colonial differences that characterize the *gravis*, *mitis* and *intermediate* types (see above) can most readily be observed. These colonial differences are, however, also observable on certain other media, such as trypsin-serum-agar (Dudley *et al.* 1934).

In broth, the *gravis* type gives surface growth and a granular deposit, the *mitis* type gives diffuse growth, a non-granular deposit, and infrequent, soft surface growth, the *intermediate* type gives a fine granular deposit and no surface growth.

C. diphtheriæ is aerobic and facultatively anaerobic.

The optimum temperature for growth is in the near neighbourhood of 37° C. ; with a range from about 15° C. to 40° C. over which growth occurs.

Heat resistance is slight, a temperature of 58° C. for 10 minutes sufficing to kill a suspension, or broth culture.

Fig. 67.—*C. diph-theriæ*.

24-hours' culture on Loeffler's serum.

BIOCHEMICAL REACTIONS.—*C. diphtheriæ* ferments glucose, galactose, and maltose, with the production of acid but no gas. It has no action on saccharose, lactose or mannitol. Litmus milk is unchanged. Indole is not formed ; but, according to the results obtained by Frieber (1921), *C. diphtheriæ* gives a colour reaction with sulphuric acid and potassium nitrite as a result of the formation of indole-acetic acid from tryptophan. This substance does not, however, give the colour reaction with paradimethylamidobenzaldehyde which is characteristic of indole itself. Nitrates are reduced. Gelatin is not liquefied.

The *gravis* type, in addition to the carbohydrate substrates referred to above, ferments dextrin, starch and glycogen. The *mitis* and *intermediate* types give irregular results with dextrin and do not ferment starch or glycogen.

The *mitis* type is usually hæmolytic, the *gravis* type is usually non-hæmolytic, and the *intermediate* type is consistently non-hæmolytic.

ANTIGENIC STRUCTURE.—*C. diphtheriæ* is divisible into a number of different antigenic types. The *gravis*, *mitis* and *intermediate* types differ antigenically from each other, and each is divisible into a number of antigenic sub-types.

TOXIN PRODUCTION AND PATHOGENICITY.—*C. diphtheriæ* is pathogenic for man and for certain laboratory animals. It produces a powerful exotoxin with a characteristic action on the animal tissues (see above).

C. hofmannii

Von Hofmann, in 1888, isolated from the throats of normal persons a diphtheroid bacillus which was probably identical with the species which now bears his name. The incompleteness of the earlier descriptions does not allow us to identify with any certainty the various strains which were, about this time, described under the general head of "pseudodiphtheria bacilli." The description which follows refers to a particular type of diphtheroid bacillus to which the name of *C. hofmannii* has been allotted by common consent. There are other forms of non-fermenting diphtheroid bacilli which possess quite a different morphology. These must, for the moment, be left unnamed, finding a temporary home in the appropriate groups of the fermentative types differentiated by the Committee of the Medical Research Council.

MORPHOLOGY.—Short rods, 1·5 to 2 μ in length, with parallel sides, rounded or slightly pointed ends, with a straight axis, and a single unstained central septum. Metachromatic granules are usually absent; if present they are few in number, small and inconspicuous. There is little or no tendency to pleomorphism. The bacilli are arranged in parallel rows, or in irregular groups, with the usual angular displacement of adjacent cells (see Fig. 68). The bacilli are more tenacious of the Gram stain than *C. diphtheriæ*, or than many other diphtheroids.

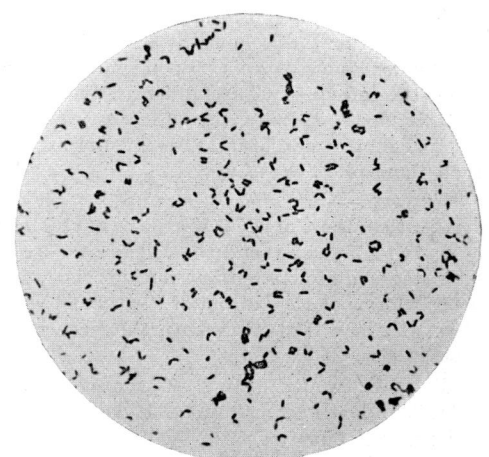

FIG. 68.—*C. hofmannii.*
From 24-hours' culture on Loeffler's serum (× 1000).

GROWTH.—*On Loeffler's serum*, after 24 hours at 37° C., *C. hofmannii* produces colonies which are larger than those of *C. diphtheriæ*, and whiter in colour. They vary in diameter from 1 to 1·5 mm., and are circular, convex, smooth, and opaque, with an entire edge. They are homogeneous in structure, butyrous in consistency, and emulsify readily. After 48 hours they increase in size to a diameter of 2 mm. or so, and the edge may become slightly erose. On *agar* this species, unlike *C. diphtheriæ*, grows readily and abundantly, forming colonies very similar to those produced on serum. In contrast to *C. diphtheriæ*, a confluent growth often occurs in primary culture, or in early subculture. In *broth* a moderate turbidity is produced, the growth gradually settling to the bottom as a powdery deposit. No pellicle is formed. In *agar* or in *gelatin stab C. hofmannii* produces little growth along the needle track, but a profuse surface growth. *C. hofmannii* is aerobic and facultatively anaerobic; the optimal temperature for growth is in the neighbourhood of 37° C. The resistance of this species to heat, or to antiseptics, has not been systematically examined, but there is no evidence that it differs in these respects from the type species.

BIOCHEMICAL REACTIONS.—*C. hofmannii* ferments none of the carbohydrates against which it has been tested, and these include all those referred to in the case of *C. diphtheriæ*. It produces no change in litmus milk, does not liquefy gelatin, and does not produce indole. Nitrates are reduced. It does not produce hæmolysis.

ANTIGENIC STRUCTURE.—All that is known on this point is that the antigenic make-up of such strains of *C. hofmannii* as have been examined differs entirely from that of *C. diphtheriæ* on the one hand, and from *C. xerosis* on the other.

Toxin Production and Pathogenicity.—*C. hofmannii* produces no toxin and is not pathogenic.

C. xerosis

An organism which possessed certain of the characters which we ascribe to *C. xerosis* was isolated from the conjunctiva by Reymond in 1881, and described somewhat more fully in 1883. The first detailed description of this organism was provided by Kuschbert and Neisser in 1883, if we may assume that these three records in fact refer to the same bacterial species. The original view, that *C. xerosis* was ætiologically related to a particular conjunctival lesion, has been generally abandoned. Griffith (1901) states that this organism is the commonest bacterial inhabitant of the normal conjunctival sac. Andrewes and his colleagues record their doubt as to whether *C. xerosis* is even now sufficiently well characterized to deserve specific rank; and their scepticism appears fully justified. The description which follows must be regarded as summarizing the characters of those strains to which most observers would allot this particular name.

Morphology.—The form assumed by *C. xerosis*, in films from a culture grown on Loeffler's serum for 24 hours at 37° C., is not unlike the bacillary form of *C. diphtheriæ*; the differences consist in a preponderance of barred or segmented forms over the granular form, the infrequency of club forms, the relative infrequency and inconspicuousness of metachromatic granules, though these are often present in small numbers, and the relatively slight pleomorphism. The cells of this species retain the Gram stain more tenaciously than those of *C. diphtheriæ*.

Growth.—On *Loeffler's medium*, or on *agar*, *C. xerosis* forms colonies which are smaller than those of *C. diphtheriæ* or of *C. hofmannii*; the margins may become irregular after 48 to 72 hours, and the colonies tend to adhere firmly to the medium during the later stages of growth. *Broth* remains clear, or shows a slight turbidity, while a granular deposit forms at the bottom of the tube. No pellicle is formed. The general conditions of growth, as regards temperature, oxygen pressure, etc., do not differ from those of the type species.

Biochemical Reactions.—*C. xerosis* produces acid in glucose, maltose and saccharose, but not in dextrin or mannitol. It does not acidify litmus milk, does not produce indole, and does not liquefy gelatin. Nitrates are reduced. It apparently forms no hæmolysin.

Antigenic Structure.—The antigenic constituents of those strains of *C. xerosis* which have been examined differ from those of *C. diphtheriæ* on the one hand, and from *C. hofmannii* on the other.

Pathogenicity.—There is no adequate evidence that *C. xerosis* is pathogenic.

C. ovis

(Synonym. *C. pseudotuberculosis ovis.*)

The Preisz-Nocard bacillus (see Nocard 1889, Preisz 1894) was originally isolated from pseudotuberculous lesions in sheep. Similar organisms have been isolated from ulcerative lymphangitis of horses by many workers. It resembles the type species very closely in its general morphology and behaviour.

Morphology.—Films from young cultures on Loeffler's medium show slender, clubbed bacillary forms, granular or segmented, often with numerous metachromatic granules, and exhibit a considerable degree of pleomorphism. The appearances are, in fact, indistinguishable from those presented by certain strains or cultures of *C. diphtheriæ*.

Growth.—The organism grows well on *Loeffler's medium*, giving colonies which are circular, umbonate, and opaque, with a tendency towards the development of a distinct yellowish pigment. As they enlarge they often develop a series of concentric rings round the raised centre. The growth is described as peculiarly friable, the colony breaking apart when touched by the needle (Hall and Stone 1916). The growth on *agar* is recorded as poor.   Growth in *broth* is scanty, but there is definite pellicle formation.   A slowly developing moderate granular growth is given on *gelatin*, which is liquefied.   *C. ovis* is an aerobe and a facultative anaerobe, with an optimal growth temperature in the neighbourhood of 37° C.

BIOCHEMICAL REACTIONS.—This species forms acid from dextrose and maltose, but not from saccharose, lactose, or mannitol (Hall and Stone 1916, Minett 1922*a* and *b*, Andrewes *et al.* 1923).   As regards its action on dextrin, galactose and glycerol the records are conflicting.   Hall and Stone report fermentation of dextrose and maltose alone, Minett records the fermentation of glucose, maltose, galactose, dextrin and glycerol by the 10 strains studied by him.   The Committee of the Medical Research Council studied 3 strains of *C. ovis*, and noted the fermentation of dextrose and maltose by all 3 strains, though the hydrolysis was less active than with *C. diphtheriæ*.   In two cases they noted slight acid production from galactose, and in all three transitory acidity in dextrin.   It is clear, therefore, that the fermentative capacities of this organism are almost identical with those of the type species.   *C. ovis* produces a hæmolysin, active against rabbit or horse corpuscles.   Indole is not produced, gelatin is liquefied ; nitrates are reduced.

ANTIGENIC STRUCTURE.—At present uninvestigated.

PATHOGENICITY.—*C. ovis* is a natural pathogen of horses, sheep and perhaps cattle, and is pathogenic for rabbits and guinea-pigs, but not for pigeons or fowls.   It produces a soluble toxin which differs from that of *C. diphtheriæ* (see above).

C. pyogenes

First described by Lucet in 1893.

MORPHOLOGY.—The organism is a small, Gram-positive, pleomorphic, diphtheroid bacillus, frequently assuming an almost coccal form, staining irregularly with methylene blue, but apparently without metachromatic granules.

GROWTH.—On *solidified serum C. pyogenes* forms minute colonies in 24 hours at 37° C., which slowly enlarge, if growth is prolonged, until they may attain a diameter of 3 mm. As they enlarge they develop a granular centre, and the medium is slowly liquefied, the liquefaction commencing as a small pit beneath each colony.   On *agar*, or in *broth*, the growth is said to be scanty, though Brown and Orcutt (1920) report moderately good growth in broth culture with strains which have been subcultured in the laboratory for several months.   On *gelatin* the growth is slight, but the medium is slowly liquefied.

BIOCHEMICAL REACTIONS.—*C. pyogenes* produces acid from dextrose, galactose, maltose and lactose, but not from mannitol.   Brown and Orcutt state that saccharose is fermented, but Holth reports that no acid is produced from this sugar.   Milk is acidified and clotted within 3 days, and the clot is later digested.   Gelatin, coagulated serum, and coagulated egg albumin are gradually liquefied.   There is no production of indole.   Nitrates are reduced.

C. pyogenes produces a hæmolysin, and the deep colonies in agar plates containing 5 to 10 per cent. of horse blood are surrounded by rings of true β-hæmolysis (Brown and Orcutt 1920).

This organism is very sensitive to heat, being rapidly killed at 57° C.   It is also very sensitive to the action of disinfectants (Brown and Orcutt 1920).

ANTIGENIC STRUCTURE.—A small series of experiments by Brown and Orcutt revealed no sharp difference in antigenic behaviour between 12 strains of *C. pyogenes*, tested against two antisera, or between 4 strains which were investigated by a complete series of cross-precipitation tests.   One of the 4 strains showed minor differences of behaviour as compared with the other 3 ; but these were not clear-cut.   Agglutination tests were not employed, owing to the frequency of auto-agglutination.   It is clear that the antigenic analysis of this species is as yet an unsettled problem.

PATHOGENICITY.—*C. pyogenes* gives rise to suppurative lesions in cattle and swine under normal conditions, and is pathogenic for the rabbit, producing suppurative lesions, including suppurative arthritis. It is less pathogenic for the guinea-pig and mouse.

C. renale

This organism was first described by Enderlen (1890), but it is very doubtful whether all the strains of diphtheroid bacilli that have since been isolated from pyelitis in cattle were identical with the bacillus isolated by him ; and it is by no means certain that the organism described by more recent workers is entitled to specific rank. It seems quite clear, however, that this organism differs in several ways from *C. pyogenes*, with which it has often been confused. The incomplete description that follows is taken mainly from the papers of Jones and Little (1925, 1930) and Merchant (1935) and is given with considerable reserve.

MORPHOLOGY.—*C. renale* is a typical Gram-positive barred diphtheroid, showing numerous metachromatic granules, and considerable pleomorphism.

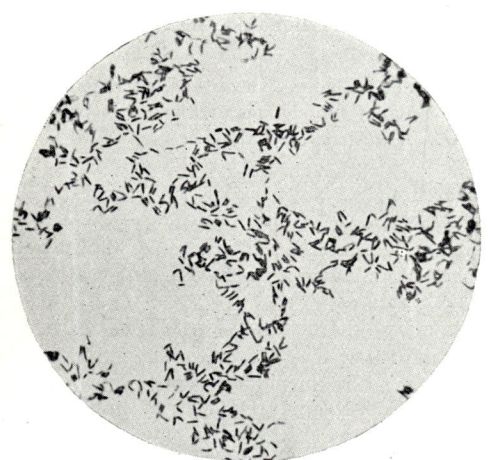

FIG. 69.—*C. murium.*

From 24-hours' culture on Loeffler's serum (× 1000).

GROWTH. — On *serum agar* gives moist, raised colonies showing a pigmentation that varies from cream to yellow. Later the growth becomes drier.

BIOCHEMICAL REACTIONS. — Most strains that have been examined have fermented dextrose alone, with the production of acid. According to Merchant (1935), lævulose and mannose may also be fermented. Gelatin is not liquefied. No hæmolysin is produced.

ANTIGENIC STRUCTURE.—The few data available (see Merchant 1935) are insufficient to allow any adequate description.

PATHOGENICITY. — The organism has been isolated by several observers from cattle suffering from pyelitis ; and Jones and Little (1925, 1930) have reproduced the disease experimentally in these animals by the injection of pure cultures. No data are available with regard to its pathogenicity for laboratory animals.

C. murium

(Synonym. *C. pseudotuberculosis murium.*)

Isolated from a mouse by Kutscher in 1894 and by Bongert in 1901. It has since been isolated by several observers (Andrewes *et al.* 1923).

MORPHOLOGY.—In films from cultures on Loeffler's medium the appearances are very similar to those presented by *C. ovis*, or by some strains of *C. diphtheriæ* (see Fig. 69).

GROWTH.—The type of growth on serum, agar, and gelatin appears to be very like that of *C. diphtheriæ*. Pellicle formation in broth has not been recorded, but suitable conditions have perhaps never been secured.

BIOCHEMICAL REACTIONS.—Acid is produced from dextrose, maltose, and saccharose ; galactose, dextrin, lactose, and mannitol are unchanged. Litmus milk is unchanged, or shows a slight and transitory acidity. Indole is not formed. Gelatin is not liquefied. Nitrates are reduced.

ANTIGENIC STRUCTURE.—At present uninvestigated.

TOXIN PRODUCTION AND PATHOGENICITY.—*C. murium* is a natural pathogen of mice, and appears to be pathogenic for no other species, with the possible exception of rats. There is evidence that some of its effects are due to the action of a soluble toxin (see above).

C. acnes

A diphtheroid organism was described in the ordinary lesions of cutaneous acne by Unna in 1896, and was isolated in culture by Sabouraud (1897).

MORPHOLOGY.—This has been generally reported as very variable, according to the medium employed, degree of acidity, oxygen pressure, etc. It is probable that, if any other diphtheroid species were submitted to the same fluctuations in environmental conditions, it would show an equally variable morphology. Often weakly Gram-positive.

GROWTH.—*C. acnes* will grow aerobically if the medium contains serum or blood, and is acidified by the addition of lactic, or of hydrochloric acid, so as to fall within the pH range 6·2–6·8. Growth occurs better under anaerobic conditions, and is favoured by glucose, glycerol, blood, boiled blood, Fildes' extract of blood, and serum. On *plain agar* growth is poor or absent. On a *glucose agar plate* anaerobically after 4 days at 37° C. the colonies are circular, 0·2–0·4 mm. in diameter, convex, amorphous, greyish-white, with a smooth glistening surface and an entire edge ; they are butyrous in consistency, and emulsify easily. The growth has a sour smell. After 6 weeks, colonies may be coloured pink. In a *glucose agar shake* medium no growth occurs for about 12 mm. below the surface ; there is then often a band growth for 10–20 mm. below the surface, with discrete colonies to the bottom of the tube ; the medium becomes milky and opaque. *Loeffler's serum*, no liquefaction. In *glucose broth* there is a slight turbidity after 3 days anaerobically, and a slight, finely granular sediment ; after a week or so there is a heavy loose floccular deposit, which occupies the lower centimetre of the tube and disintegrates on shaking to give a moderate turbidity. Slight to moderate turbidity in *cooked meat medium*. No growth in *gelatin stab* culture at 22° C.

BIOCHEMICAL REACTIONS.—According to Südmersen and Thompson (1909–10) *C. acnes* produces acid from glucose, galactose, maltose, glycerol, and mannitol, but does not ferment lactose. Of 2 strains examined by Südmersen and Thompson, one actively fermented saccharose, the other gave a late and slight acidity. In our experience acid is generally formed in glucose, maltose, and sucrose, sometimes in lactose, but not in mannitol. Slight acid in litmus milk. Indole negative. Nitrates reduced. Gelatin not liquefied.

ANTIGENIC STRUCTURE.—Not yet investigated.

PATHOGENICITY AND TOXIN PRODUCTION.—It is generally believed that *C. acnes* is ætiologically related to the lesions from which it has been isolated. Experimentally it shows some degree of pathogenicity for the mouse.

C. typhi

Isolated by Plotz (1914) from the blood of patients suffering from typhus fever. Originally regarded by Plotz and his colleagues as ætiologically related to the disease (Plotz, Olitsky and Baehr 1915), but now generally admitted to be an example of a parasitic, microaerophilic diphtheroid, without any established pathological significance (Olitsky 1921).

MORPHOLOGY is that of a small pleomorphic diphtheroid, with few elongated cells but numerous coccal forms. The rod-forms which occur may be straight or curved, with rounded or pointed ends. Metachromatic granules are present.

GROWTH.—*C. typhi* appears to demand more strictly anaerobic conditions for growth than *C. acnes* ; but there appears to be no record of the result of acidification of the medium. It is recorded as giving a creamy-white growth on Loeffler's serum, glucose serum agar, or potato ; the growth takes on a light brown colour in its later stages on the latter medium.

BIOCHEMICAL REACTIONS.—Tested on ascitic agar containing 2 per cent. of the test carbohydrate, and incubated in Buchner tubes, *C. typhi* is stated to produce acid from glucose, maltose, and galactose, but not from mannitol, dextrin, lactose or saccharose.

ANTIGENIC STRUCTURE unknown.

PATHOGENICITY.—Probably slight or absent.

We append, in tabular form (Table XXX), the chief differential character- istics of the nine named species described above, and the fermentation reactions of the eleven groups of diphtheroid bacilli differentiated by the Committee of the Medical Research Council (Table XXXI). In both tables the + sign signifies the formation of acid. Since the fermentation reactions of this group are habitually tested in Hiss's serum-water medium, the formation of acid will usually be followed by the formation of a clot, after a longer or shorter period, though some strains which produce definite acidity in the presence of a particular carbohydrate fail to clot the medium.

With regard to the eleven groups of unnamed diphtheroids, the Committee note that there is no correlation between the source from which any strain was derived and its biochemical reactions. Thus, of the 15 strains which fall into Group I, ten came from the nose, one from the ear, two from the eye, one from an infected wound, and one from a specimen of pus. As already noted, there was no consistent relation between pigment production and fermentative activity. Thus one strain

TABLE XXX

Species.	Production of Acid from :						Liquefaction of Gelatin.	Production of Hæmolysin.	Oxygen Requirements.	Pathogenicity.	Toxin Production.
	Dextrose.	Maltose.	Saccharose.	Dextrin.	Lactose.	Mannitol.					
C. diphtheriæ * .	+	+	—	+	—	—	—	+ or —	A. & F. An.	+	+
C. diphtheriæ (avirulent) .	+	+	—	+	—	—	—	+ ?	,,	—	—
C. hofmannii .	—	—	—	—	—	—	—	—	,,	—	—
C. xerosis . .	+	+	+	—	—	—	—	—	,,	—	—
C. pyogenes . .	+	+	+ ?	— ?	+	—	+	+	,,	+	— ?
C. renale . .	+	—	—	—	—	—	—	—	,,	+	— ?
C. ovis . . .	+	+	—	±	—	—	+	+	,,	+	+·
C. murium . .	+	+	+	—	—	—	—	— ?	,,	+	+ ?
C. acnes . .	+	+	±	— ?	—	+	—	— ?	micro- aero- philic	+ ?	— ?
C. typhi . . .	+	+	—	—	—	—	—	— ?	,,	— ?	— ?

* See above for differentiation between *gravis*, *mitis* and *intermediate*.

TABLE XXXI

FERMENTATION REACTIONS OF 79 UNSELECTED STRAINS OF DIPHTHEROIDS, EXAMINED FOR COMMITTEE OF MEDICAL RESEARCH COUNCIL (see Andrewes *et al.* 1923).

Group.	Dextrose.	Maltose.	Galac-tose.	Sac-charose.	Lactose.	Dextrin.	Mannitol.	No. of Strains in Group.
I	+	−	+	+	−	−	−	15
II	+	−	−	+	−	−	−	11
III	+	+	−	−	−	−	−	11
IV	+	±	−	−	−	−	−	6
V	+	+	±	−	−	−	−	4
VI	+	+	+	+	+	−	−	4
VII	+	+	−	+	−	−	−	5
VIII	+	+	+	+	−	−	−	3
IX	+	+	+	+	+	+	−	1
X	+	−	+	+	−	−	+	1
XI	−	−	−	−	−	−	−	18

of Groups IV, VII and XI produced pigment, as did the single representative of Group IX. The four strains of Group VI, on the other hand, and the three strains of Group VIII all formed pigment ; so that these two groups would appear to be characterized by a marked tendency to pigment production. It may be noted that none of the strains examined produced the pink or red pigments which have been so frequently noted by some observers, and especially by those who have examined numerous strains from lymphatic glands and other tissues (Hoag 1907, Harris and Wade 1915). The Committee note that the strains selected have been tested on many occasions, and at long intervals, with scarcely varying results.

REFERENCES

ALI, M. (1934) *J. Egypt. med. Ass.*, **17**, 77.
ANDERSON, J. S., COOPER, K. E., HAPPOLD, F. C., and McLEOD, J. W. (1933a) *J. Path. Bact.*, **36**, 169 ; (1933b) *Lancet*, i. 293.
ANDERSON, J. S., HAPPOLD, F. C., McLEOD, J. W., and THOMSON, J. G. (1931) *J. Path. Bact.*, **34**, 667.
ANDREWES, F. W. *et al.* (1923) Med. Res. Coun., " Monograph on Diphtheria." London.
BABES, V. (1886) *Bull. Soc. Anat., Paris*, **61**, 72.
BAILEY, G. H. (1925) *J. Immunol.*, **10**, 791.
BARRATT, M. M. (1923) see Andrewes *et al.*, p. 174 ; (1933) *J. Path. Bact.*, **36**, 369.
BOLTON, C. (1905) *Lancet*, i. 278.
BONGERT. (1901) *Z. Hyg. InfektKr.*, **37**, 449.
BRANDWIJK, A. C. and TASMAN, A. (1932) *Z. ImmunForsch.*, **77**, 390 ; (1933) *Ibid.*, **78**, 540.
BRAUN, H. and HOFMEIER, K. (1927) *Klin. Wschr.*, **6**, 690.
BRAUN, H., HOFMEIER, K., and MÜNDEL, F. (1929) *Zbl. Bakt.*, **113**, 530.
BRAUN, H. and MÜNDEL, F. (1927) *Zbl. Bakt.*, **103**, 182 ; (1929) *Ibid.*, **112**, 347.
BROWN, J. H. and ORCUTT, M. L. (1920) *J. exp. Med.*, **32**, 219.
BULL, L. B. and DICKINSON, C. G. (1935) *Aust. vet. J.*, **11**, 126.
BUNKER, J. W. (1919) *J. Bact.*, **4**, 217.
BUNNY, W. E., CIANIARULO, J., and KIAMIL, M. (1931) *J. Immunol.*, **20**, 417.
CARTER, H. S. (1933) *J. Hyg., Camb.*, **33**, 542.
CHALMERS, A. J. and MACDONALD, N. (1920) *J. trop. Med. Hyg.*, **23**, 85.
CHRISTISON, M. H. (1934) *J. Path. Bact.*, **37**, 243.
COCA, A. E., RUSSELL, E. F., and BAUGHMAN, W. H. (1921) *J. Immunol.*, **6**, 887.
COSTA, S., TROISIER, J., and DAUVERGNE, J. (1918) *C. R. Soc. Biol.*, **81**, 89.
COWAN, M. L. (1927) *Brit. J. exp. Path.*, **8**, 6.
CROWELL, M. J. (1926) *J. Bact.*, **11**, 65.
DASSONVILLE. (1907) *Bull. Soc. cent. Méd. vét.*, **61**, 576.
DAVIS, L. and FERRY, N. S. (1919) *J. Bact.*, **4**, 217.

DUDGEON, L. S. (1906) *Brain*, **29**, 227.
DUDLEY, S. F., MAY, P. M., and O'FLYNN, J. A. (1934) *Spec. Rep. Ser. med. Res. Coun., Lond.*, No. 195.
DURAND, P. (1918) *C. R. Soc. Biol.*, **81**, 1011 ; (1920) *Ibid.*, **83**, 613.
EAGLETON, A. J. and BAXTER, E. M. (1923) *J. Hyg., Camb.*, **22**, 107.
EATON, M. D. and BAYNE-JONES, S. (1934) *J. Bact.*, **29**, 56.
EBERSON, F. (1918) *J. infect. Dis.*, **23**, 1.
EHRISMANN, O. (1932–33) *Zbl. Bakt.*, **127**, 111 ; (1933) *Z. Hyg. InfektKr.*, **115**, 273.
ENDERLEN, E. (1890–91). *Dtsch. Z. Thierheilk.*, **17**, 325.
ERNST, W. (1888) *Z. Hyg. InfektKr.*, **4**, 25 ; (1889) *Ibid.*, **5**, 428 ; (1905) *Zbl. Bakt.*, **39**, 549, 660 ; (1906) *Ibid.*, **40**, 79.
EWING, J. O. (1933) *J. Path. Bact.*, **37**, 345.
FLEMING, A. (1909) *Lancet*, i. 1035.
FLEXNER, S. (1897) *Rep. Johns Hopk. Hosp.*, **6**, 259.
FRIEBER, W. (1921) *Zbl. Bakt.*, **87**, 254.
GILCHRIST, T. C. (1900) *Bull. Johns Hopk. Hosp.*, **9**, 409 ; (1903) *J. cutan. Dis.*, **21**, 107.
GLAGE, F. (1903) *Z. Fleisch-u. Milchhyg.*, **13**, 166.
GLENNY, A. T. (1925a) *J. Hyg., Camb.*, **24**, 301 ; (1925b) *J. Path. Bact.*, **28**, 251.
GLENNY, A. T. and ALLEN, K. (1922) *J. Path. Bact.*, **24**, 61.
GLENNY, A. T. and WALPOLE, G. S. (1915) *Biochem. J.*, **9**, 298.
GOLDIE, H. (1933) *C. R. Soc. Biol.*, **112**, 1210 ; (1934) *Ibid.*, **116**, 17.
GOODMAN, H. M. (1907) *J. infect. Dis.*, **4**, 509.
GRAHAM–SMITH, G. S. (1908) "Diphtheria." Nuttall and Graham-Smith, Cambridge.
GRIFFITH, A. S. (1901). *Rep. Thomps. Yates Lab. Univ. L'pool.*, **4**, 99.
GRIPS. (1898) *Z. Fleisch-u. Milchhyg.*, **8**, 166.
GROER, F. VON. (1923) *Biochem. Z.*, **138**, 13.
GUNDEL, M., GYÖRGY, P., and PAGEL, W. (1932) *Z. Hyg. InfektKr.*, **113**, 629.
GUNDEL, M. and LIEBETRUTH, E. (1935) *Z. Hyg. InfektKr.*, **117**, 66.
HADLEY, P. B. (1907) *J. infect. Dis.*, **3**, Suppl. No. 3., 95.
HADLEY, P. B. and GORHAM, F. P. (1907) *Zbl. Bakt., Ref.*, **40**, 392.
HALL, I. C. and STONE, R. V. (1916) *J. infect. Dis.*, **18**, 195.
HARRIS, W. H. and WADE, H. W. (1915) *J. exp. Med.*, **21**, 493.
HARTLEY, P. (1922) *J. Path. Bact.*, **25**, 479 ; (1923) *Lancet*, i. 17.
HARTLEY, P. and HARTLEY, O. (1922) *J. Path. Bact.*, **25**, 458.
HAVENS, L. C. (1920) *J. infect. Dis.*, **26**, 388.
HILL, H. W. (1898) *J. Boston. Soc. med. Sci.*, **3**, 86 ; (1899) *Ibid.*, **4**, 78 ; (1902a) *J. med. Res.*, **7**, 115 ; (1902b) *Ibid.*, **7**, 202.
HOAG, L. (1907) *Boston med. surg. J.*, **157**, 10.
HOFMANN, G. VON. (1888) *Wien. med. Wschr.*, **38**, 65, 108.
HOLTH, H. (1908) *Z. InfektKr. Haustiere*, **3**, 155.
HOSOYA, S. and KUROYA, M. (1923) *Sci. Rep. Inst. infect. Dis., Tokyo Univ.*, **2**, 233.
HOSOYA, S., OZAWA, E., and TANAKA, T. (1933) *Jap. J. exp. Med.*, **11**, 463.
HOTTINGER, A. and HOTTINGER, C. (1933) *Z. Kinderheilk.*, **54**, 440.
JAFFÉ, R. (1920) *Arb. Inst. exp. Ther. Georg Speyer Hause, Frank. am. M.*, **11**, 5.
JONES, F. S. and LITTLE, R. B. (1925) *J. exp. Med.*, **42**, 593 ; (1930) *Ibid.*, **51**, 909.
KLEBS, E. (1883) *Verh. Cong. inn. Med., Wiesbaden*, 139.
KNIGHT, B. C. J. G. (1936) *Spec. Rep. Ser. med. Res. Coun., Lond.*, No. 210.
KOSER, S. A. and RETTGER, L. F. (1919) *J. infect. Dis.*, **24**, 301.
KRAH, E. and WITEBSKY, E. (1930) *Z. ImmunForsch.*, **66**, 59.
KÜNNEMANN, O. (1903) *Arch. wiss. prakt. Tierheilk.*, **29**, 128.
KUSCHBERT and NEISSER. (1883) *Jber. schles. Ges. vaterl. Kult.*, **60**, 50.
KUTSCHER. (1894) *Z. Hyg. InfektKr.*, **18**, 327.
LANGER, H. (1916) *Zbl. Bakt.*, **78**, 117.
LEETE, H. M., McLEOD, J. W., and MORRISON, A. C. (1933) *Lancet*, ii. 1141.
LEHMANN, K. B. and NEUMANN, R. O. (1896) "Atlas u. Grundriss. d. Bakt. u. Lehrb. d. spez. bakt. Diagnostik." 6th Ed., Munich.
LEONARD, G. F. and HOLM, A. (1933) *J. infect. Dis.*, **53**, 376.
LEULIER, A., SÉDALLIAN, P., and CLAVEL. (1931) *C. R. Soc. Biol.*, **107**, 1136.
LINDEMANN, H. (1932) *Z. Hyg. InfektKr.*, **113**, 288.
LOCKE, A. and MAIN, E. R. (1928) *J. infect. Dis.*, **43**, 41.
LOEFFLER, F. (1884) *Mitt. ReichsgesundhAmt.*, **2**, 421 ; (1890) *Zbl. Bakt.*, **7**, 528.
LUCET, A. (1893) *Ann. Inst. Pasteur*, **7**, 325.
MAVER, M. E. (1930) *J. infect. Dis.*, **47**, 384.
MELLON, R. R. (1917) *J. Bact.*, **2**, 269.
MENTON, J., COOPER, T. V., DUKE, F. W., and FUSSELL, W. H. (1933) *J. Hyg., Camb.*, **33**, 414.
MERCHANT, I. H. (1935) *J. Bact.*, **30**, 95.

MINETT, F. C. (1922*a*) *J. comp. Path.*, **35**, 71 ; (1922*b*) *Ibid.*, **35**, 291.

MOLLARD, J. and REGAUD, C. (1895) *C. R. Soc. Biol.*, **2**, 828.

MUELLER, J. H. (1935*a*) *Science*, **81**, 50 ; (1935*b*) *J. Bact.*, **29**, 383 ; (1935*c*) *Ibid.*, **29**, 515.

MUELLER, J. H., KLISE, K. S., PORTER, E. F., and GRAYBIEL, A. (1933) *J. Bact.*, **25**, 509.

MURRAY, J. F. (1935) *J. Path. Bact.*, **41**, 439.

NEILL, J. M., RICHARDSON, L. V., FLEMING, W. L., SUGG, J. Y., and GASPARI, E. L. (1931) *Amer. J. Hyg.*, **13**, 499.

NICOLLE, M., LOISEAU, G., and FORGEOT, P. (1912) *Ann. Inst. Pasteur*, **26**, 83.

NITSCH, J. (1933) *Z. Kinderheilk.*, **54**, 470.

NOCARD, E. (1889) *C. R. Soc. Biol.*, **1**, 608.

OKELL, C. C. (1929) *J. Hyg., Camb.*, **29**, 309.

OLITSKY, P. K. (1921) *J. exp. Med.*, **34**, 525.

PARISH, H. J., WHATLEY, E. E., and O'BRIEN, R. (1932*a*) *J. Path. Bact.*, **35**, 653 ; (1932*b*) *Brit. med. J.*, ii. 915.

PAXSON, W. H. and REDOWITZ, E. (1922) *J. Immunol.*, **7**, 69.

PETRIE, C. F. and MCCLEAN, D. (1934) *J. Path. Bact.*, **39**, 635.

PLOTZ, H. (1914) *J. Amer. med. Ass.*, **62**, 1556.

PLOTZ, H., OLITSKY, P. K., and BAEHR, G. (1915) *J. infect. Dis.*, **17**, 1.

POELS. (1912) *Tijdschr. Veeartsenijk.*, **39**, 905.

POPE, C. G. (1932) *Brit. J. exp. Path.*, **13**, 207.

POPE, C. G. and HEALEY, M. (1933*a*) *Brit. J. exp. Path.*, **14**, 77 ; (1933*b*) *Ibid.*, **14**, 87.

POPE, C. G. and SMITH, M. L. (1932) *J. Path. Bact.*, **35**, 573.

PREISZ, H. (1894) *Ann. Inst. Pasteur*, **8**, 231.

RAMON, G. and BERTHELOT, A. (1932) *C. R. Soc. Biol.*, **110**, 530.

REYMOND, COLOMIATTI, and PERRONCITO. (1881) *Cong. period. int. ophthalm. C. R.* 1880, Milano, Annexes, 48 ; (1883) *G. Accad. Med.*, Torino, **31**, 519.

ROBERTSON, R. C. (1924) *J. infect. Dis.*, **35**, 311.

ROBINSON, D. T. (1934) *J. Path. Bact.*, **38**, 551.

ROBINSON, D. T. and MARSHALL, F. N. (1934) *J. Path. Bact.*, **38**, 73 ; (1935) *Lancet*, ii. 441.

RÖMER, P. H. (1909) *Z. ImmunForsch.*, **3**, 208.

ROUX, E. and YERSIN, A. (1888) *Ann. Inst. Pasteur*, **2**, 629.

SABOURAUD, R. (1897) *Ann. Inst. Pasteur*, **11**, 134.

SCHIFF, F. and WERBER, M. (1935) *Dtsch. med. Wschr.*, **61**, 259.

SCHMIDT, H. (1933–34) *Zbl. Bakt.*, **130**, 391.

SCHMIDT, S. (1931) *Z. ImmunForsch.*, **71**, 101.

SCHMIDT, S., HANSEN, A., and KHAER, K. A. (1931) *Ann. Inst. Pasteur*, **46**, 202.

SCHWONER, J. (1904) *Zbl. Bakt.*, **35**, 608.

SCOTT, W. M. (1923) *Rep. publ. Hlth med. Subj.*, Lond., No. 22.

SMITH, J. (1923) *J. Hyg., Camb.*, **22**, 1.

SÜDMERSEN, H. J. and THOMPSON, E. T. (1909–10) *J. Path. Bact.*, **14**, 224.

TASMAN, A. and PONDMAN, A. B. F. A. (1931) *Z. ImmunForsch.*, **72**, 245.

TASMAN, A. and WAASBERGEN, J. P. VAN. (1932) *Z. ImmunForsch.*, **75**, 164.

UNNA, P. G. (1896) "The Histopathology of Diseases of the Skin." Eng. Transl. by N. Walker, Edin.

USCHINSKY, N. (1893) *Zbl. Bakt.*, **14**, 316 ; (1897) *Ibid.*, **21**, 146.

WADSWORTH, A. and QUIGLEY, J. J. (1934) *Amer. J. Hyg.*, **20**, 225.

WADSWORTH, A., QUIGLEY, J. J., and SICKLES, G. R. (1932) *J. exp. Med.*, **55**, 815.

WADSWORTH, A. and WHEELER, M. W. (1934) *J. infect. Dis.*, **55**, 123.

WARD, A. R. (1917) *J. Bact.*, **2**, 619.

WATSON, A. F. and LANGSTAFF, E. (1926) *Biochem. J.*, **20**, 763 ; (1927) *J. Path. Bact.*, **30**, 383.

WERNICKE. (1893) *Arch. Hyg.*, **18**, 192.

WHITLEY, O. R. (1935) *J. Lab. clin. Med.*, **20**, 1024.

WINSLOW, C.-E. A., BROADHURST, J., BUCHANAN, R. E., KRUMWIEDE, C., ROGERS, L. A. and SMITH, G. H. (1920) *J. Bact.*, **5**, 191.

WRIGHT, H. A. and RANKIN, A. L. K. (1932) *Lancet*, ii. 884.

WRIGHT, J. H. (1894) *Boston med. surg. J.*, **131**, 329.

ZAJDEL, R. (1932) *C. R. Soc. Biol.*, **111**, 1029.

CHAPTER XVII

FUSIFORMIS

DEFINITION. *Fusiformis.*

> Obligate parasites. Anaerobic or microaerophilic. Cells frequently elongated and fusiform, staining somewhat unevenly. Filaments sometimes formed ; non-branching. Non-motile. No spores. Reaction to Gram variable. Growth in laboratory media feeble.

A number of organisms, anaerobic or microaerophilic in their oxygen requirements, have been isolated by different workers from necrotic lesions in man and animals. The first of these was the so-called *B. necrophorus*, which was observed by Loeffler (1884) in calf diphtheria. In 1896 Vincent described a fusiform bacillus, frequently associated with a spirochæte, *Trep. vincenti* (see Chapter XXXV) in necrotic and ulcerative lesions of the throat and other tissues in human beings. Veillon and Zuber (1898), studying the bacterial flora of appendicitis and other suppurative lesions, described a number of non-sporing anaerobic bacilli, to which they gave the names of *B. ramosus, B. serpens, B. fragilis, B. furcosus,* and *B. fusiformis* ; this last organism was apparently identical with the fusiform bacillus described by Vincent. Later work has revealed the frequent presence of organisms of this group in the mouth and on the teeth of man and certain animals (Tunnicliff 1906, Ellermann 1907, Varney 1927, Pratt 1927, Slanetz and Rettger 1933).

Relatively little attention has been paid to the systematic study of these organisms, and their classification presents considerable difficulties. The American Committee of Bacteriologists (see Report 1920) have described a genus *Fusiformis*, for the inclusion of organisms with certain characteristics resembling in some respects those possessed by the *Corynebacterium* and the *Pfeifferella* groups. As the definition of this genus (see above) seems to cover the main characteristics of the organisms we have mentioned, it seems permissible, at least for the moment, to include these organisms within it.

Group Characteristics.—The organisms of this group are typically rod-shaped ; but their size is subject to considerable variation. They may be very short, or they may grow out into long filaments which are generally curved. Their width is also variable ; not infrequently it is greater near the middle of the bacillus than at the end, giving the organism a fusiform appearance ; occasionally the greatest diameter is at one end, so that the organism appears clubbed. Pleomorphism is a marked characteristic of some species. The organisms are arranged singly, in pairs end-to-end, or in chains ; pseudo-filaments, showing evidence of subdivision are common. Some species show false branching, with the result that V- or Y-forms are seen, but true branching does not occur. Some species are said to be motile, but the

354

observations of recent workers render this doubtful. Spores are never formed. The organisms stain with the usual aniline dyes, but staining is often irregular. The reaction to Gram varies with different species. None of the organisms are acid-fast.

Culturally, growth occurs under anaerobic or microaerophilic conditions and is said to be favoured by the presence of 2 per cent. CO_2. Little is known of their respiratory mechanism, but it seems probable that in fluid media they do not produce such low oxidation-reduction potentials as do many of the spore-bearing anaerobes (Dack and Burrows 1935). Some species grow readily in ordinary media, while others require the addition of natural animal protein. According to Slanetz and Rettger (1933), growth is stimulated by aqueous extracts of various vegetables, and a potato extract gelatin medium is recommended for the preservation of stock cultures. The optimum temperature for growth is about 37° C. ; some species will develop at 23°, others not below 30° C. In solid media, colonies frequently do not become visible for 3 or 4 days, and usually remain small.

The organisms are not particularly resistant ; they are destroyed by exposure to moist heat at 55° C. within an hour. The fermentation reactions have been incompletely studied, but some species appear capable of producing acid and gas in certain carbohydrate media.

The organisms of this group appear to be obligatory parasites, and may be cultivated from certain inflammatory processes, particularly those accompanied by necrosis and ulceration, as well as from the normal mouth and teeth. There seems to be little doubt that some species are primarily responsible for the conditions from which they are isolated ; but the pathogenic rôle of others is probably more of a secondary nature. Many of the species are pathogenic to laboratory animals, producing necrotic lesions and death. Whether a true exotoxin is formed is not yet known.

Antigenically, little exact information is yet available about these organisms, but there is evidence that differences in antigenic structure do exist between different types.

We append descriptions of some of the named species. Whether all of these are true species, and what relation they bear to the four types established by Varney (1927) on the basis of morphological and serological characteristics, or the four possibly different types established by Slanetz and Rettger (1933) on the basis of morphological, cultural, and biochemical characteristics, is not clear.

F. necrophorus.—Synonyms : Schmorl's bacillus, *B. diphtheriæ vitulorum, Streptothrix cuniculi, Actinomyces necrophorus,* Bang's necrosis bacillus. First observed by Loeffler in 1884 in calf diphtheria. He succeeded in producing necrotic lesions in mice by subcutaneous inoculation of the diphtheritic membrane, and in obtaining a primary culture of the organism from mice on calf serum ; but he failed to subculture it. Schmorl in 1891 encountered apparently the same bacillus in a spontaneous epidemic amongst his laboratory rabbits, characterized by spreading necrosis of the lower lip. He inoculated mice with material from the rabbits, and obtained cultures of the organism from the mice. He classed it with the *Streptothrix* group under the *Leptothrix* or *Cladothrix* genera, and called it *Streptothrix cuniculi.* The organism has been described by a few other workers. (For a detailed description of it, see Orcutt 1930, Beveridge 1934.)

MORPHOLOGY.—In the diphtheritic membrane of calves, the bacilli appear as long threads—5 to 6 times as long as they are broad—arranged either in thick heaps or in long wavy rows. In the pleural or pericardial exudate of rabbits dying of labial necrosis they usually appear as Gram-negative, highly pleomorphic bacilli, varying in shape from cocci to bacilli and long threads. In the thread forms there are often oval unstained portions arranged at regular intervals, looking like spores ; but as they do not give the differential spore stain and are not particularly resistant to heat, they cannot be regarded as spores. The filaments may reach 80–100 μ in length ; they are 0·75–1·5 μ thick ; one end is often narrow and pointed, the other thicker or almost fusiform. They may be surrounded by a capsular material. Branching does not occur. In culture the organisms appear as straight or curved rods, or as filaments. The ends are rounded, and the sides are generally parallel, though fusiform enlargements are not uncommon. Except in young cultures, staining is irregular, and beaded forms are common.

CULTIVATION.—Schmorl cultivated the organism in deep inspissated sheep serum. It grows only under anaerobic conditions. Deep colonies in serum agar plates are round, pinhead in size, matt-white, with an entire edge ; under a low power they have a thicker centre and an irregularly radiate periphery ; under a high power the centre consists of a mesh-work of threads, and the periphery of streaming threads, which pass often for some distance into the surrounding medium. According to Shaw (1933), deep colonies in a semi-solid glucose serum agar medium have a grey, cotton-like, fluffy appearance, while in stiffer agar they are brown, circular or biconvex, with an entire edge. Surface colonies, after 2 days on a special serum agar medium (V.F.), made up with a peptic digest of ox muscle and liver, are circular, convex, about 1 mm. in diameter, almost water-clear, and glistening ; after 7 days they are differentiated into a convex centre and a narrow flat periphery with a slightly dentate edge ; they are butyrous in consistency and easily emulsified (Beveridge 1934). In V.F. broth there is a dense turbidity, with a small dirty-white deposit, which increases as the medium clears on further incubation. Stab growth in serum begins in 24 to 40 hours near the bottom of the tube, and spreads upwards to within $\frac{1}{2}$–1 cm. of the surface ; the growth is filiform with radiate branches ; the serum is partly clouded, but not liquefied. There is no growth on potato. In glucose agar, Schmorl obtained growth only in the presence of a coccus. He quotes this as an example of *metabiosis*— or the ability of one organism to grow in a particular medium only when another organism has prepared the medium for it, and rendered it suitable. V.F. gelatin (see above) is not liquefied. Turbidity and vigorous gas production occur in cooked heart medium and brain medium. A zone of hæmolysis, about 0·5 mm. wide, is said to surround deep colonies in blood agar plates. Cultures, especially in liquid media, have a foul odour. Growth occurs between 30° and 40° C., with an optimum at 37° C.

BIOCHEMICAL AND METABOLIC.—Gas, and a variable amount of acid, are produced in glucose, maltose, sucrose, and glycerol. A soft clot is formed in 4–14 days in litmus milk. Indole +. H_2S +. Nitrate reduction −. M.R. −. V.P. −. Methylene blue reduction +. Catalase weakly positive.

ANTIGENIC STRUCTURE.—Little exact knowledge. Said to be two groups distinguishable by direct agglutination, but Orcutt's (1930) results suggest a greater degree of antigenic heterogeneity.

PATHOGENICITY.—*F. necrophorus* appears to be responsible for several necrotic and gangrenous lesions in animals, such as calf diphtheria, labial necrosis of rabbits, and foot-rot of sheep, and occasionally for necrotic lesions in man. Organisms identical with or closely simulating *F. necrophorus* have been described by Harris and Brown (1927) in puerperal fever, and by Dack, Dragstedt and Heinz (1936) in chronic ulcerative colitis. (See Necrobacillosis, Chapter LXXVI).

Experimentally, the organism is pathogenic for rabbits and mice, and non-pathogenic for guinea-pigs, dogs, cats, pigeons, and hens. Inoculated subcutaneously into the lower lip of rabbits, it gives rise to the typical necrotic disease (see p. 1415), and causes death in 4–12 days. Injected intraperitoneally into rabbits, it proves fatal in about the same time ; p.m. the peritoneum is covered with large white masses, sticking the two layers of serosa together ; similar masses of caseous material occur between the intestinal loops.

Cultures can be obtained from the peritoneum. Intravenous inoculation into rabbits is fatal in about 8 days ; post mortem, there is a fibrino-purulent pleurisy, a caseous bronchitis, and disseminated lobular pneumonia ; the bacilli can be cultured from the affected organs. Histologically, the organisms give rise to intense inflammation, followed by a rapid necrosis not only of the fixed tissue cells but also of the cells of the exudate ; no liquefaction of the necrotic material occurs.

Mice inoculated subcutaneously at the root of the tail die after about 12 days in an emaciated condition. Two days after the inoculation, the local site is covered with a dry brownish crust ; later a yellowish-grey discoloration of the borders of the inoculation wound becomes visible, and gradually spreads till at the time of death the whole of the lower third of the back is involved. A purulent conjunctivitis develops, and the lids are stuck together. Post mortem, the subcutaneous tissue around the wound and over the lower part of the back is converted into a tough, dryish, yellowish-white necrotic mass ; the caseation involves the back muscles as well. The whole area is surrounded by œdema. Numerous organisms are found in the caseous material. The internal organs are normal.

In both rabbits and mice the organism is said to be found only in the affected parts, never in the blood or in those internal organs that are free from lesions, but on this question there is some doubt. The ability of the organism to produce lesions seems to be largely due to its production of a necrotizing endotoxin (Beveridge 1934).

F. fusiformis.—This organism was first described by Vincent in 1896, who found it frequently associated with *Trep. vincenti* (see Chapter XXXV) in necrotic and ulcerative lesions of the throat and other tissues. A similar, and possibly identical, organism was observed by Veillon and Zuber (1898) in appendicitis and other necrotic lesions of man, and named by them *B. fusiformis*. Smith (1933) has recorded its presence in tropical ulcer. In necrotic tissue the organisms appear as long rods, 5–12 μ in length, thickened in the middle, and with tapering or pointed ends. The axis is

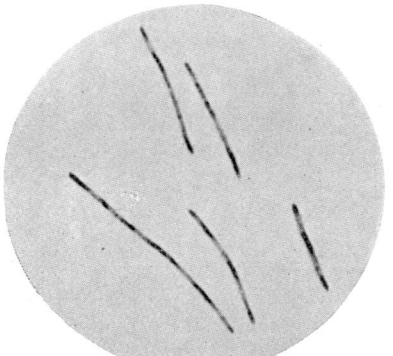

Fig. 70.—*Fusiformis fusiformis.*
From a surface culture on serum agar, anaerobically 2 days, 37° C. ($\times$ 1000).

straight or curved. They are arranged singly or in pairs end-to-end, and are non-motile. They stain readily with the usual aniline dyes, and are Gram-positive, but are decolorized if the treatment with alcohol is prolonged. In cultures the bacilli are pleomorphic (Leukowicz 1906) ; they vary greatly in size, and do not always show the typical fusiform shape. Long filamentous forms are common.

The organism can be cultivated under anaerobic conditions at 37° C., but not at room temperature, in serum agar or serum broth. The deep colonies appear in 2 days, and are 1–1½ mm. in diameter. The smallest colonies have a felt-like, branched appearance ; the larger ones are round ; and the largest of all are prismatic with angled projections, and are of a yellowish colour. On the surface of serum agar, the colonies are small and resemble those of streptococci, but on further incubation they may show a considerable peripheral extension, and come to resemble colonies of *Cl. sporogenes* (see p. 685). In serum broth, large white flocculi form in 24 hours, and later sink to the bottom (Ellermann 1904) (see Fig. 71). On plain agar there may be no growth at all, or a thin, very delicate whitish layer limited to the line of inoculation may develop after 48 hours (Weaver and Tunnicliff 1905). Loeffler's serum and Dorset's egg medium are both suitable. Neither is liquefied. Growth does not occur in media containing sugar, unless blood or ascitic fluid is added. Peters (1911) found that, in the presence of rabbit blood, acid was produced in glucose, maltose, mannitol, and lactose, but not in sucrose. There is no indole formation. The organisms do not form spores. They are killed in 15 minutes by moist heat at 55° C., but resist 1 per cent. antiformin for 5 minutes. In cultures they may remain alive for 6 to 8 weeks. Injections subcutaneously or intramuscularly into rabbits and guinea-pigs may have little or no effect; at most an abscess is produced (Ellermann 1905).

F. ramosus.—Said by Veillon and Zuber (1898) to be one of the commonest organisms in

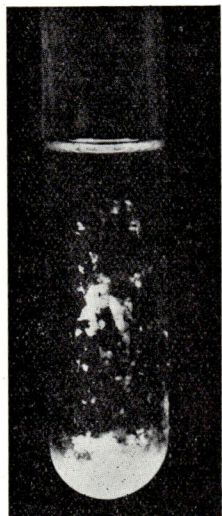

Fig. 71.—*Fusiformis fusiformis.*

Blood broth culture anaerobically, 3 days, 37° C. showing floccular growth.

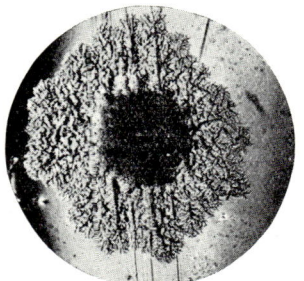

Fig. 72.—*Fusiformis fusiformis.*

Surface colony on serum agar, anaerobically, 7 days, 37° C. (× 8). Resembles Slanetz and Rettger's Type IV.

appendicitis. Gram-positive, non-motile, non-sporing rod, slightly larger than *Erysipelothrix muriseptica*; arranged in pairs or short chains; in pus it is rather short but in culture it may form pseudo-filaments, which are really made up of numerous short rods. V-forms and Y-forms are common. No growth occurs at room temperature; and at 37° C. colonies do not become visible for 3 or 4 days. Surface colonies on agar are very fine, effuse, greyish-white, and translucent; later, they become granular and slightly cloudy. Deep colonies in agar are very small greyish points, which under low magnification are seen to be ovoid and granular with hatched borders; as the colony grows, it becomes greyish-yellow, and the edges become more defined. In broth it produces a uniform turbidity in 3 or 4 days with a greyish-white muddy deposit. Cultures have a characteristic fœtid odour, but very little gas is formed. Strict anaerobe. Cultures live for over a month. Inoculated intravenously into rabbits, it causes death in some days by intoxication and cachexia. Subcutaneous inoculation into rabbits causes abscess formation with death in 8 to 10 days.

F. serpens.—Isolated by Veillon and Zuber (1898) from the pus of a mastoiditis in a child who died of pulmonary gangrene. Large, slightly motile, Gram-negative rod with rounded ends, arranged in pairs end-to-end, or in pseudo-filaments. Strict anaerobe. Grows best at 37° C., but develops at 20° C. Surface colonies on agar after 48 hours are only just visible; later they form small cloudy translucent masses of greyish colour. Deep colonies in agar after 24 hours at 37° C. are small, clear, rounded, greyish, granular masses with hatched edges, and sometimes a bouquet of filaments at one point on the periphery; later they increase in opacity and the edges become better defined. In gelatin stab there is a filiform growth; liquefaction occurs down the whole length of the stab; the liquefied gelatin remains clear, and flocculi of growth fall slowly to the bottom forming a white deposit. Deep colonies in gelatin are round, greyish, and liquefy the gelatin slowly.

In broth there is a rapid turbidity, followed by a clearing of the medium with the formation of a white deposit. Cultures have a fœtid odour, but only a small amount of gas is evolved. Cultures remain viable for about 20 to 25 days. Pathogenic for mice, guinea-pigs, and especially rabbits, but not so pathogenic as *F. ramosus*.

F. fragilis.—Said by Veillon and Zuber (1898) to be the commonest organism in appendicitis. Non-motile, Gram-negative, rod with rounded ends, slightly smaller than the diphtheria bacillus; axis straight or slightly curved; arranged singly or in pairs end-to-end. Strict anaerobe. Difficult to isolate. Surface colonies on agar are extremely fine, greyish, and translucent, and tend to undergo autolysis in a few days. Deep colonies in agar do not become visible for 3 or 4 days; they are very small, round, irregularly round, or ovoid, brownish-yellow, opaque, with an entire edge. Deep colonies in gelatin appear in 8 to 10 days; they are punctiform, yellow, granular, with an entire edge; no liquefaction. Uniform turbidity in broth with a whitish deposit. Cultures have a fœtid odour, but evolve little gas. Cultures in agar remain viable for less than a week. Sub-cutaneous inoculation into guinea-pigs produces abscess formation. The organism is more pathogenic for the rabbit, producing on subcutaneous inoculation an extensive phlegmon with sloughing of the skin, and death in 6 to 7 days. Intravenous inoculation of the rabbit is followed by death, but no organisms can be found in the tissues at necropsy; probably death is due to toxæmia, for the same result is brought about by killed cultures.

F. furcosus.—Not so common in appendicitis as *F. fragilis* and *F. ramosus*. In pus it is a very small rod, with one of its ends forming two little branches like a Y. In culture it forms rods; many of these increase in length, and divide at one of their extremities into two branches, each terminated by a swelling; others form branches, which themselves divide. The bacilli and their branches are never very long; the swellings are rounded or pyriform, and are numerous. The whole organism is slightly larger than the tubercle bacillus. Non-motile and Gram-negative. Strict anaerobe. No growth at room temperature; at 37° C. growth is not visible for 3 or 4 days. Surface colonies on agar are very fine grey points, scarcely raised at all from the medium; under low magnification they appear yellowish, very finely granular, and have transparent borders. Deep colonies in agar are so small and transparent that they are difficult to see; when magnified, they are round and yellowish, with delicate regular borders. A fine precipitate is formed in broth. Cultures have a slightly fœtid, sour odour, but evolve very little gas. Cultures remain viable for 15 to 20 days. Subcutaneous inoculation into a guinea-pig produces an abscess, which generally heals; sometimes death occurs after several weeks from cachexia.

REFERENCES

BEVERIDGE, W. I. B. (1934) *J. Path. Bact.*, **38**, 467.
DACK, G. M. and BURROWS, W. (1935) *Proc. Soc. exp. Biol., N.Y.*, **32**, 1441.
DACK, G. M., DRAGSTEDT, L. R., and HEINZ, T. E. (1936) *J. Amer. med. Ass.*, **106**, 7.
ELLERMANN, V. (1904) *Zbl. Bakt.*, **37**, 729 ; (1905) *Ibid.*, **38**, 383 ; (1907) *Z. Hyg. InfektKr.*, **56**, 453.
HARRIS, J. W. and BROWN, J. H. (1927) *Bull. Johns Hopk. Hosp.*, **40**, 203.
LEUKOWICZ, X. (1906) *Zbl. Bakt.*, **41**, 153.
LOEFFLER, F. (1884) *Mitt. ReichsgesundhAmt.*, **2**, 421.
ORCUTT, M. L. (1930) *J. Bact.*, **20**, 343.
PETERS, W. H. (1911) *J. infect. Dis.*, **8**, 455.
PRATT, J. S. (1927) *J. infect. Dis.*, **41**, 461.
Report. (1920) *J. Bact.*, **5**, 191.
SCHMORL, G. (1891) *Dtsch. Z. Thiermed.*, **17**, 375.
SHAW, F. W. (1933) *Zbl. Bakt.*, **129**, 132.
SLANETZ, L. W. and RETTGER, L. F. (1933) *J. Bact.*, **26**, 599.
SMITH, E. C. (1933) *J. Hyg., Camb.*, **33**, 95.
TUNNICLIFF, R. (1906) *J. infect. Dis.*, **3**, 148.
VARNEY, P. L. (1927) *J. Bact.*, **13**, 275.
VEILLON, A. and ZUBER, A. (1898) *Arch. Méd. exp.*, **10**, 517.
VINCENT, H. (1896) *Ann. Inst. Pasteur*, **10**, 488.
WEAVER, G. H. and TUNNICLIFF, R. (1905) *J. infect. Dis.*, **2**, 446.

CHAPTER XVIII

PFEIFFERELLA, AND CERTAIN ALLIED ORGANISMS

DEFINITION (emended from the American Committee's Report).

Small, slender, non-motile, Gram-negative rods, often staining irregularly, and sometimes forming threads or showing a tendency towards branching. Growth on all media is rather slow ; gelatin may be slowly liquefied ; fermentation of carbohydrates is very weak ; characteristic brown honey-like growth on potato. Type species is *Pfeifferella mallei*.

HISTORY.—The glanders bacillus was isolated by Loeffler and Schütz in 1882 (see Loeffler 1886) from a horse dying of acute glanders. An organism in many respects resembling *Pf. mallei* was isolated by Whitmore and Krishnaswami (1912) from a glanders-like disease of human beings in Rangoon. It was identified as *B. pseudomallei* by Whitmore (1913). Subsequently Stanton and Fletcher (1921, 1925) gave the name of Melioidosis to this disease and *Bacillus whitmori* to the causative organism.

The genus *Pfeifferella* was tentatively created by the American Committee as one of the genera intermediate in position between *Actinomyces* on the one hand and *Mycobacterium* on the other. The type species, and the only listed member of the group, is the glanders bacillus or *Pf. mallei*. The classification of this organism presents many difficulties, and it is by no means certain that the genus *Pfeifferella* will gain permanent recognition.

As regards the fermentative powers of *Pf. mallei*, the American Committee's definition states that carbohydrates are not fermented. According to our observations, and those of Stanton and Fletcher (1932), acid is formed in glucose in 2 to 3 weeks ; a small amount of acid, sufficient however to give a pink colour with Andrade's indicator, is produced in salicin. Moreover, there is a slow formation of acid in litmus milk, becoming apparent in about 5 days, and followed in 2 to 3 weeks by definite clotting.

In certain respects Whitmore's bacillus resembles *Pf. mallei*, but it differs from it in many others. For the moment we assign it to the *Pfeifferella* group, entering a caveat that, should that genus attain a permanent place in systematic bacteriology, it is by no means certain that Whitmore's bacillus will be placed within it. We are, however, faced with the same difficulty here as in so many other cases. If any agreed terminology is adopted in the near future, it seems certain that the generic name *Bacillus* will be reserved for the spore-bearing aerobes. We must, therefore, either leave this organism unnamed, or place it tentatively in the group with which it has most affinities.

Group Characteristics.

Morphologically the two organisms are fairly similar ; *Pf. whitmori*, however, is rather smaller, frequently shows bipolar staining, and is motile. In films of the smooth form, the organisms are arranged in long parallel bundles embedded in an interstitial substance, presenting a very characteristic appearance ; with Loeffler's methylene blue, the interstitial substance stains blue, the bacilli bluish-red ; films of the rough forms show no interstitial substance, and re-semble *Pf. mallei* more closely.

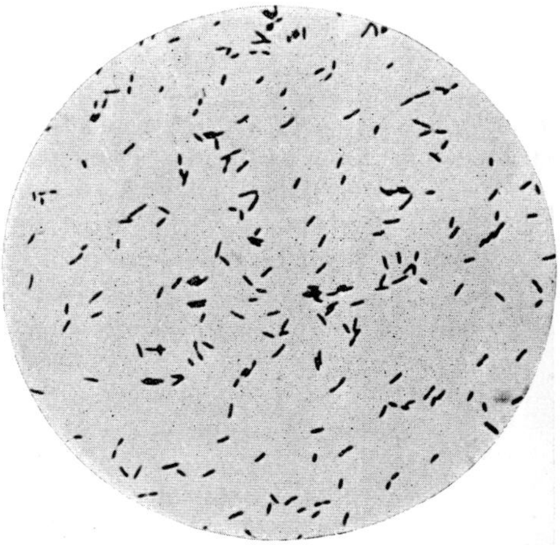

Culturally, the growth of *Pf. whitmori* is more rapid and more profuse than that of *Pf. mallei*. On glycerol agar it may give a smooth mucoid or a corrugated and wrinkled growth. Stanton and Fletcher (1927) have also described an ultra-rugose variant, with an extremely corrugated surface, and a consistency so tenacious that if the colony is touched with a needle, it adheres to it and peels bodily off the medium. Growth in gelatin at 20° C. is abundant, and liquefaction of the stratiform type is apparent in 4 or 5 days ; *Pf. mallei*, on the other hand, grows

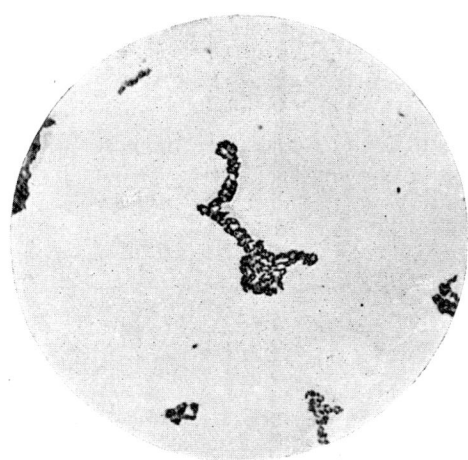

FIG. 73.—*Pfeifferella mallei.*
From an agar culture, 48 hours, 37° C. (× 1000).

very poorly in gelatin at 20° C. and never liquefies the medium, though accord-ing to Stanton and Fletcher (1925), if it is incubated at 37° C., permanent liquefaction occurs in 4 to 6 weeks. In broth the growth of the smooth form of

Pf. whitmori resembles that of *Pf. mallei* ; the rough form, however, gives rise to a wrinkled surface pellicle. On potato the smooth form gives a café-au-lait growth resembling that of *Pf. mallei*, whereas the rough form gives a much lighter growth of creamy or creamy-yellow colour. On Mac-Conkey's agar, *Pf. whitmori* grows freely, forming red colonies, while *Pf. mallei* entirely fails to grow.

Biochemically, Pf. whitmori is an active fermenter on first isola-tion, producing acid in glucose, mannitol, lactose, sucrose and dul-citol, and decolorizing Andrade's indicator ; but after long sub-cultivation in the laboratory it loses its power of fermenting any

FIG. 74.—*Pfeifferella whitmori.*
From an agar culture, 24 hours, 37° C. (× 1000).

sugars except glucose. In litmus milk acid is produced in 3 days ; later the casein is precipitated, and may be digested ; the litmus is partly decolorized. *Pf. mallei*, on the other hand, though it may produce acid and clot, never

P.B.   N* peptonizes the medium. Freshly isolated strains of *Pf. whitmori* liquefy blood serum, but this property is often lost during cultivation in the laboratory. *Pf. mallei* has no digestive action on serum. Both organisms may produce a small amount of H_2S, when tested by Huddleson's method on liver agar. (For the preparation of *mallein* see Chapter LIX.)

Antigenically, the two organisms appear to resemble each other closely. Stanton and Fletcher (1925), who examined 5 strains of *Pf. mallei* and 14 strains of *Pf. whitmori* by agglutination, absorption, and complement fixation, found that the strains of *Pf. whitmori* formed a homogeneous group, but that the 5 strains of *Pf.*

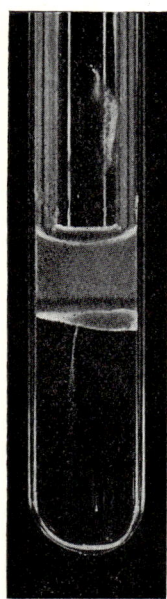

Fig. 75.—
Pfeifferella whitmori.

Gelatin stab culture, 10 days, 20° C., showing stratiform liquefaction.

mallei fell into two groups. One of these groups was very closely related to, if not identical with, the *Pf. whitmori* strains. It is important to note that the 2 strains of *Pf. mallei* which resembled *Pf. whitmori* were isolated from ponies in Java and India respectively; since they differed in certain respects from the other strains of *Pf. mallei*, which were isolated in England and Egypt, it is just possible that they were variant strains of *Pf. whitmori*. According to de Moor and his colleagues (1932), strains of *mallei* and *whitmori* show cross-agglutination to titre, and complete cross-absorption, with specific sera. Cross-allergic reactions are also said to be obtainable in infected animals with mallein and the corresponding product prepared from cultures of *Pf. whitmori*. Verge and Pairemaure (1928) have reported a positive complement-fixation reaction with the serum of a glandered horse in the presence of a *whitmori* antigen. Further work, however, is obviously desirable on the antigenic structure and relationship of these two organisms.

Pathogenically, *Pf. mallei* gives rise to disease in equines, while *Pf. whitmori* is a natural parasite of rodents. Both organisms can cause disease in man; both are infective for laboratory animals; and both are able to call forth the Straus reaction on intraperitoneal inoculation of male guinea-pigs.

Experimental Reproduction of Glanders in Animals.—Experimentally glanders may be reproduced in horses, asses, and mules by feeding with cultures of *Pf. mallei*, and by subcutaneous inoculation. Sheep and goats are easily infected, but cows and pigs are absolutely resistant. Of laboratory animals the guinea-pig and the field mouse (*Arvicola arvalis*) are the most susceptible to experimental inoculation; rabbits and dogs are less so; rats, birds, and perhaps white mice, are comparatively resistant.

Guinea-pigs.—Loeffler (1886) made 85 experiments on guinea-pigs, and every animal developed the disease. Not all observers, however, are agreed on the uniform susceptibility of the guinea-pig; young animals seem to be more resistant than older ones.

After *subcutaneous* inoculation of a small amount of a pure culture, an abscess develops, which ulcerates in 5 days; the regional glands break down and discharge pus. At this stage the disease may become stationary or retrogress, but usually it advances. In the second week hard nodular foci are palpable in the testicles and epididymis; inflammation of the tunica vaginalis occurs, and the testicle becomes fixed to the overlying skin; finally ulceration takes place with the discharge of purulent material. In female guinea-pigs the mammæ and labia may be inflamed. Swelling and inflammation of one or more joints is very common, sometimes leading to abscess formation and ulceration. Nodules often appear in the muscles, face, back, or beneath the periosteum of the bones. In about a third of the animals nodules appear on the nasal mucosa, and crusts collect around the external nares. Death follows in 1 to 8 weeks, generally in the 3rd or 4th week. At post mortem there is a local ulcer or scar ; the regional glands are swollen, and contain greyish-white purulent masses. Abscesses are found in the skin, subcutaneous tissues and around the joints. The lungs contain nodules, greyish-yellow and easily emulsifiable, particularly under the pleura. In the spleen there are numerous submiliary nodules of a greyish-yellow colour, projecting slightly above the surface. There are fewer nodules in the liver ; these are more greyish-white in colour. The kidneys are free, but nodules may be seen in the suprarenals. Small, greyish-yellow nodules are found in the testicles, or larger foci, relatively firm with a caseous centre. The nasal mucosa is red and swollen, and may be covered with friable caseous masses. In recent lesions the bacilli can always be found, but in the older ones they are scanty.

After *intraperitoneal* injection the testicles swell in 2 to 3 days ; by the 10th day they are greatly enlarged ; death occurs in a fortnight as a rule. The testicular lesion—*Straus' reaction* (Straus 1889a)—commences in the tunica vaginalis. The two layers of the serosa are covered with confluent yellowish-white granules of pinhead size. On the 3rd or 4th day the layers are united by a thick, purulent exudate rich in bacilli. The scrotal skin becomes inflamed and adherent to the underlying tissues ; later ulceration occurs (see Panisset 1910).

Guinea-pigs have been infected by insufflation with powdered cultures (Babes 1891).

FIELD MICE.—After *subcutaneous* inoculation these animals die in 3 to 4 days. Post mortem, there is a greyish-green infiltration at the site of injection. The lymph vessels leading to the enlarged glands are studded with little greyish-white nodules. The spleen is greatly enlarged, and contains numerous yellowish-white nodules projecting slightly above the surface. There are several tiny nodules in the liver.

WOOD MICE.—The wood mouse—*Mus sylvaticus*—is less susceptible than the field mouse—*Arvicola arvalis*. After subcutaneous inoculation it develops a chronic disease not proving fatal for 3 to 6 weeks. Post mortem, the spleen is enlarged, and contains numerous pin-head, greyish spots or nodules ; sometimes there is a fibrino-purulent exudate in the pleura, and enlargement of the lymphatic glands (Kitt 1887).

RABBITS.—*Subcutaneous* inoculation causes a local ulcerating lesion and swelling of the neighbouring lymphatic glands. If the animal is killed after a month, as well as the glandular swelling there may be a few greyish nodules in the lungs, and ulcers on the nasal mucosa. After *intravenous* inoculation, numerous nodules develop in the spleen and liver, but death may be delayed for some weeks.

WHITE MICE AND WHITE RATS.—These animals react to subcutaneous injection with a rapidly retrogressive local abscess. Occasionally an animal dies after about 7 weeks, and at post mortem shows caseous nodules in the spleen. Leo (1889) states that white mice can be rendered susceptible to glanders by being fed on a diet containing phloridzin. According to Sabolotny (1926), white mice are more susceptible than has generally been believed. In his experiments, after subcutaneous inoculations with a pure culture, the mice often died of an acute infection in 30 to 72 hours ; no macroscopic lesions were present at post mortem, but the bacillus could be recovered from the organs. After subcutaneous injection with glanders pus, they all died in 5 to 6 weeks of a chronic infection. Post mortem, the spleen was much enlarged and was riddled with nodules of varying sizes ; there were also a few nodules in the liver and lungs.

DOGS AND CATS.—After *subcutaneous* inoculation in dogs a local abscess occurs, followed by ulceration ; the disease apparently remains localized (Galtier 1881). Acute fatal glanders may follow intravenous injection of large doses of bacilli ; numerous small subcutaneous nodules develop, and at post mortem lesions are found in the liver and spleen (Straus 1889b).

Cats are more susceptible ; after subcutaneous inoculation a local lesion occurs followed by death in 15 to 30 days ; at post mortem nodules are found in the internal organs.

Classification.—There are many points of resemblance between *Pf. mallei* and the organisms of the *Brucella* group. Both this organism and *Br. melitensis* are small, non-motile, Gram-negative bacilli, developing slowly in culture media ; both give rise to a café-au-lait or chocolate-coloured growth on potato ; both have very weak fermentative powers in the sugars ; both give rise under natural conditions to acute or chronic disease in man and animals ; both are pathogenic to guinea-pigs, setting up necrotic changes in the viscera ; both may give the Straus reaction in male guinea-pigs ; and both are characterized by their extraordinary infectivity for man in artificial cultures in the laboratory. There are, however, certain differences between them, the importance of which from the point of view of classification it is difficult to assess. Thus *Br. melitensis* is a definite cocco-bacillus ; *Pf. mallei*, though often occurring in very short forms, is generally described as a slender rod, capable at times, especially in the animal body, of giving rise to long, and even branching, thread-like forms (Mayer 1900, Galli-Valerio 1900). In culture, however, it is not unusual for *Pf. mallei* to form short and almost ovoid bacilli, not unlike *Br. abortus*. Antigenically, there is, in our experience, no apparent relationship between *Pf. mallei* and organisms of the *Brucella group* (Wilson 1934).

It may be pointed out that *Pf. whitmori* bears certain points of resemblance to Friedländer's bacillus. Both these organisms are Gram-negative bacilli, and are surrounded by a capsule or an interstitial substance, which is not infrequently lost after artificial culture for some time. Both exhibit more or less similar appearances in culture, and both give rise to an extremely viscous deposit in broth. Both organisms give a café-au-lait growth on potato. Both are active fermenters of sugars on first isolation, and both may tend to lose this property after prolonged subculture in the laboratory. On the other hand, *Pf. whitmori* differs from Friedländer's bacillus in being motile, in liquefying gelatin, in failing to produce gas from carbohydrates, and in its capability of giving rise to the Straus reaction in the guinea-pig.

Thompson (1933) draws attention to certain morphological and cultural similarities between *Pf. mallei* and *Pf. whitmori* on the one hand and *Actinobacillus lignieresi* on the other, and states that the organisms are antigenically related. His protocols, however, furnish no evidence of specific cross-agglutination. The slight degree of agglutination that was observed may quite well have been due to normal agglutinins. *Pf. mallei* is frequently agglutinated by normal sera to a titre of 1/640 or over, and the actinobacillus is often affected by normal sera, though usually to a lower titre. Thomson's suggestion that all three organisms should be classified together in the *Mycobacterium* group cannot be accepted until further evidence in support of it is forthcoming.

Some workers (Legroux and Djemil 1931, Legroux and Genevray 1933) regard *Pf. whitmori* as being more nearly related to *Ps. pyocyanea* than to *Pf. mallei*, but the absence of pigment production by *Pf. whitmori*, and its demonstrated antigenic affinity to *Pf. mallei*, render this doubtful.

Pfeifferella mallei

Isolation.—By Loeffler and Schütz in 1882 (Loeffler 1886) from a horse dying of acute glanders.

Habitat.—Strict parasite ; found chiefly in equines and man.

Morphology.—Slender rod-shaped organism, about 1·5–3 μ × 0·3–0·6 μ broad. Straight or slightly curved, ends rounded, sides irregularly parallel or wavy; arranged singly, in pairs end-to-end, in parallel bundles, and in Chinese letter forms. In cultures there may be great variation in length and to a less extent in thickness; long filaments showing true or false branching, club, pear, flask, and other irregular forms have been described. Staining is usually uneven, deeply stained alternating with poorly stained or unstained areas; bipolar staining is common. Non-motile; non-capsulated; non-sporing; Gram-negative; non-acid-fast.

Agar Plate.—2 *days at* 37° *C.* Round, convex, amorphous, translucent, greyish-yellow colonies, 0·5–1·0 mm. in diameter, with smooth glistening surface and entire edge; butyrous in consistency and easily emulsifiable. 9 *days*, colonies are 1–2 mm. in diameter, more opaque, and may have a very finely granular surface; sometimes the centre is coloured slightly brown.

Agar Slope.—2 *days at* 37° *C.* Moderate, confluent, raised, greyish-yellow, translucent growth with beaten-copper surface and edge undulate or formed of single colonies. Medium unchanged. Not so profuse as growth of *Bact. coli.*

Gelatin Stab.—7 *days at* 20° *C.* Poor to moderate, filiform growth, extending nearly to the bottom of the tube, and consisting of small discrete colonies; raised surface growth about 3 mm. in diameter. No liquefaction. After 6 weeks the growth is often brownish in colour. If incubated at 37° C., gelatin is said to be permanently liquefied in 4 to 6 weeks.

Broth.—2 *days at* 37° *C.* Moderate growth with moderate uniform turbidity and a slight powdery sediment disintegrating completely. No surface growth. 14 *days*, ring growth is present, and there is a moderate, viscous deposit, very difficult to disintegrate.

Horse Blood Agar Plate.—3 *days at* 37° *C.* Good growth of round, low convex, greyish-green, opaque colonies, 1 mm. in diameter. No hæmolysis, but plate is browned.

Loeffler's Serum.—3 *days at* 37° *C.* Scanty growth, barely visible, of flat, discrete colonies, 0·3 mm. in diameter. No liquefaction.

Potato.—2 *days at* 37° *C.* Moderate, raised, greyish-yellow growth. After 4 days the colour deepens to café-au-lait, and in 10 days to chocolate.

MacConkey's Agar.—9 *days at* 37° *C.* No growth.

Resistance.—Killed by moist heat in 10 minutes at 55° C. Cultures dried on threads may live for 3 or 4 weeks; but infected pus or discharge, when dried, usually becomes sterile in a few days. Killed by 2 per cent. phenol in 1 hour, by 1/1000 $HgCl_2$ in 15 minutes, and by calcium hypochlorite with 2 parts of free chlorine per million in 30 minutes. In culture the organism rarely survives longer than a month or 6 weeks.

Metabolism.—Aerobe; either no growth at all, or only very slight growth after 14 days, under strict anaerobic conditions. Optimum temperature 37°; little or no growth below 20° C. On culture media it grows slowly; growth is often not apparent for 2 days. Tendency to formation of brownish pigment in cultures, especially on potato. No hæmolysis is produced.

Biochemical.—Acid, no gas in glucose, and sometimes very slight acid in salicin; no other sugars fermented. L.M. slight acid; after 2 to 3 weeks a clot forms, and the litmus is partly decolorized at the bottom. Indole —; M.R. —; V.P. —; nitrates reduced; H_2S slight +; NH_3 +; M.B. reduction —; catalase slight +.

Antigenic Structure.—By agglutination, absorption, and complement fixation there appear to be at least two types of *Pf. mallei*, of which one is related to *Pf. whitmori*. Sakamoto (1930) has isolated from culture filtrates of *Pf. mallei* a relatively non-specific nucleo-protein substance, and a soluble specific polysaccharide which gives a precipitation reaction with immune sera.

Pathogenicity.—Causes glanders or farcy in horses, mules, asses, and man. Experimentally the disease can be reproduced in equines, goats, cats, and guinea-pigs;

sheep, rabbits, dogs, rats and mice are less susceptible ; pigs and cattle are resistant. Intraperitoneal injection of the male guinea-pig is followed in 2 days by swelling of the testicles ; after 3 or 4 days the two layers of the tunica vaginalis are gummed together by a thick, purulent, yellowish exudate. The scrotal skin becomes adherent, and ulcerates. Death in 14 days. P.M., besides the testicular lesions, there may be submiliary nodules in the spleen projecting above the surface, greyish-white nodules in the lungs and liver, and subcutaneous or periarticular abscesses. Bacilli are present in the fresh lesions.

Pfeifferella whitmori

Isolation.—Isolated by Whitmore and Krishnaswami (1912) from human patients with melioidosis.

Synonyms.—*B. pseudomallei, B. whitmori.*

Habitat.—Parasite of rodents and man.

Morphology.—Small, slender rods, 1–2 μ long and 0·4–0·5 μ broad ; sides parallel, ends rounded, axis straight ; arranged singly, in pairs end-to-end, or sometimes in long parallel bundles, the bacilli being embedded in an interstitial substance. Variations occur in depth of staining ; bipolar staining common, especially in films from infected tissues. Motile ; Gram-negative ; non-acid-fast. The short, oval, bipolar-stained rods are characteristic of the rough form ; the longer, narrower rods, arranged in palisades, with irregular staining and shadow forms, are characteristic of the smooth variant.

Agar Plate.—24 *hours at* 37° *C.* Round, amorphous, low convex, translucent, greyish-yellow colonies, 1–2 mm. in diameter ; smooth, glistening surface and entire edge ; consistency mucoid ; emulsifiability easy. 14 *days,* colonies are opaque, often coloured yellow, brown, or pinkish, and may have a wrinkled centre.

Agar Slope.—24 *hours at* 37° *C.* Abundant, confluent, raised, greyish-yellow, mucoid, spreading growth, with glistening, beaten-copper surface, and edge undulate or made up of single colonies. Growth more profuse than that of *Bact. coli.* Cultures have a mouldy, earthy smell.

Gelatin Stab.—10 *days at* 20° *C.* Abundant, filiform growth, mostly of discrete colonies extending to bottom of tube. Stratiform liquefaction ; between the liquefied and unliquefied portions of the gelatin there is a thick nodular pellicle of growth.

Broth.—24 *hours at* 37° *C.* Good growth with moderate turbidity, and slight powdery deposit disintegrating completely ; may be slight pellicle formation. 10 *days,* luxuriant growth with dense turbidity and a heavy viscous deposit disintegrating with difficulty. The rough form gives rise to a slight turbidity and a wrinkled surface pellicle. According to Nicholls (1930), the rough form produces about 0·2 per cent. oxalate (calculated as calcium oxalate) in 4 days ; the smooth form produces not more than about 0·01 per cent., but renders the medium alkaline—pH 8·4.

Glycerol Agar.—3 *days at* 37° *C.* May be (1) profuse mucoid growth with smooth glistening surface, or (2) profuse growth with dull, wrinkled, corrugated, or honeycombed surface.

Horse Blood Agar Plates.—3 *days at* 37° *C.* Abundant growth of round, low convex, greyish-green colonies, 1–2 mm. in diameter. No hæmolysis, except, perhaps, with freshly isolated strains.

Loeffler's Serum.—3 *days at* 37° *C.* Good, confluent, slightly raised, creamy growth with smooth surface and undulate edge. Liquefaction by freshly isolated strains after a variable number of days. Sometimes the growth itself appears to become liquefied, and runs down the slope.

Potato.—24 *hours at* 37° *C.* S. type : good growth of a creamy or lemon-yellow colour, not very easy to see ; later the colour deepens to café-au-lait or chocolate. R. type : forms dry, dull, dirty-white growth.

MacConkey's Agar.—*3 days at* 37° *C.* Abundant growth of red, opaque, low convex or umbonate colonies, 2–3 mm. in diameter.

Resistance.—Destroyed by moist heat at 56° C. within 10 minutes. Killed within about 10 minutes by 1 per cent. phenol and 0·5 per cent. formol. Organisms may survive for a month or more in water, fæces, and dried soil, and for a week in putrefying carcasses.

Metabolism.—Aerobe ; very slight growth on agar and in broth after 14 days under strict anaerobic conditions. Optimum temperature for growth 37° C. In culture it grows more rapidly and more abundantly than *Pf. mallei.* No hæmolysis of sheep or horse blood, except perhaps with freshly isolated strains. Tendency to formation of brownish pigment in cultures, especially on potato. Oxalates formed in broth by rough form.

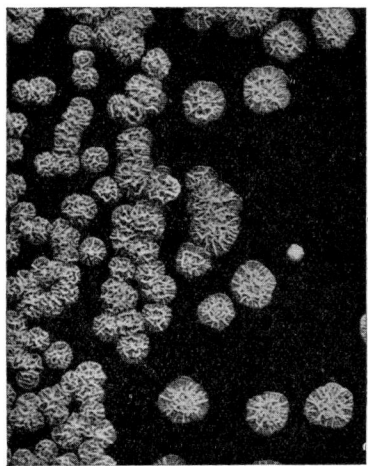

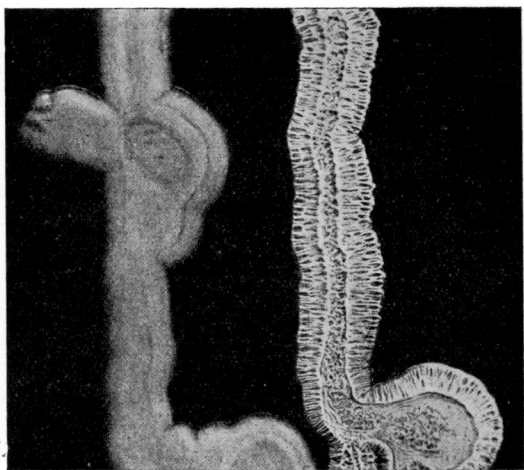

Fig. 76.—*Pf. whitmori.*
Surface colonies on glycerol agar plate.
Rough form.
(After Stanton and Fletcher.)

Fig. 77.—*Pf. whitmori.*
Growth on glycerol agar. Left : smooth form. Right :
rough form.
(After Stanton and Fletcher.)

Biochemical.—On first isolation it forms acid, no gas, in glucose, maltose, mannitol, lactose, dulcitol, dextrin, and sucrose ; after long cultivation in the laboratory it may attack glucose only ; Andrade indicator decolorized in 4–10 days. L.M. may be slightly acid in 3 days ; casein is precipitated and may be digested ; partial decolorization of litmus. Indole —; M.R. — ; V.P. — ; nitrates reduced ; $NH_3 +$; $H_2S \pm$ when tested by Huddleson's method on liver agar ; M.B. reduction $+$; catalase $+$.

Antigenic Structure.—By agglutination, absorption, and complement fixation cultures of *Pf. whitmori* form a homogeneous group, which is said to be closely allied to one group of *Pf. mallei.*

Pathogenicity.—Causes melioidosis in man, rats, cats, dogs, guinea-pigs, rabbits, and occasionally horses. Experimentally, rodents can be infected by feeding, injection into the tissues, or by rubbing on the scarified skin. Produces abscess at site of inoculation, generalized adenitis, and nodular abscesses of the spleen and lungs. After ip. injection of a small quantity of culture into a male guinea-pig, swelling of the testicles occurs in 2 days with caseous exudate between the two layers of the tunica vaginalis. If a large dose is used, death may occur in 24 hours from septicæmia, before there is time for the Straus reaction to develop or for nodular lesions to appear in the viscera. Small doses prove fatal in about a week. Guinea-pigs are so susceptible that even minute numbers of bacilli brought into contact with the scarified skin may give rise to a fatal infection. Rabbits are as susceptible as guinea-pigs, but rats are more resistant. The subcutaneous inoculation of 0·1 c.c. of a 24-hour broth culture into a rabbit usually causes death in 3 weeks. Post mortem, there is local necrosis, and necrotic or purulent lesions are found in the lungs, spleen, liver, joints, bones, or testicles ; purulent arthritis is common in the second week. Cats, monkeys, and goats can all be infected experimentally. The disease in the monkey is usually chronic, lasting 2 to 4 months, and is accompanied by severe emaciation. Horses are resistant (see Stanton and Fletcher 1932, de Moor *et al.* 1932, Nicholls 1934). According to Nicholls (1934), the rough type is the normal virulent form, while the smooth type is relatively avirulent if obtained completely free from rough organisms.

Perez's Bacillus, or Cocco-bacillus fœtidus ozænæ.

In 1899 Perez described, under the name of *Cocco-bacillus fœtidus ozænæ,* a small organism that he had isolated from the nose of patients suffering from ozæna. His work was confirmed by numerous observers (Hofer 1913*a, b,* Ward 1916, 1917, Busson 1923, Olinescu and Atineu 1925*a, b*), but there is insufficient evidence to show that this organism is causally related to ozæna. Perez (1901, 1913) found his bacillus also in the saliva and nasal mucus of apparently healthy dogs.

To avoid confusion, it may be stated here that Perez's bacillus is different from the ozæna bacillus described by Loewenberg (1894) and by Abel (1896), which undoubtedly belongs to the Friedländer group (see Chapter XXVII).

The classification of Perez's bacillus is very doubtful ; it is impossible to say to what group this organism will ultimately be assigned. Our reasons for including it in this chapter are to draw attention to certain points of resemblance that it shows to *Pf. whitmori* and *Br. bronchiseptica.*

Morphologically, Perez's bacillus is a small, Gram-negative cocco-bacillus, which was originally described as being non-motile, but which is said by Ferry and Noble (1918) to be sluggishly motile, and by Ward (1917) occasionally to acquire motility in culture. In fluid media, and in old cultures on solid media, long, irregular, deeply staining, filamentous forms may appear. In broth, and on agar if the tubes are sealed, cultures have a heavy, sweet, unpleasant, or even nauseating odour, which is said by Ward to be due to volatile sulphur compounds. According to our own observations, agar cultures tend to wither after a few days, suggesting the occurrence of autolysis. In gelatin stab cultures of Perez's bacillus, fine lateral filaments often appear in 2 or 3 weeks, radiating from the central stab. On potato a creamy-white growth is formed. Biochemically, the organism produces acid and gas in glucose only ; in litmus milk there may be a slight acidity ; indole is produced. Antigenically, all strains are said by Ward (1917) to be homogeneous ; but according to Olinescu and Atineu (1925*a*), this is doubtful. An antiserum to *Br. bronchiseptica* is without action on Perez's bacillus, and *vice versa* (Ferry and Noble 1918). Both Perez's bacillus and *Br. bronchiseptica* are parasites of the respiratory tract, and both seem to be secondary rather than primary agents in the causation of disease. It is probable that in the past they have been confused with each other. The following table (Table XXXII), modified from Ferry and Noble, enumerates the main differences between them.

An organism similar to Perez's bacillus has been isolated by Shiga (1922) from the nose of ozæna patients. The chief differences between the two are that Shiga's organism often ferments maltose and sucrose, as well as glucose ; it sometimes peptonizes milk ;

TABLE XXXII

Differentiation of Br. bronchiseptica from Perez's Bacillus.

	Br. bronchiseptica.	Perez's bacillus.
Morphology	Small narrow bacillus	Small coccoid bacillus.
Gelatin Stab	No lateral filaments	Lateral filaments after 2 to 3 weeks.
Potato	Yellowish-brown growth	Creamy-white growth.
Litmus Milk	Alkaline	Slightly acid.
Biochemical	No fermentation	Acid and gas in glucose.
Indole	—	+

it liquefies gelatin ; and it is not agglutinated by a serum prepared against Perez's bacillus. Blanc and Pangalos (1925) have isolated from the nose of ozæna patients a short, actively motile, Gram-negative bacillus, which they call *B. ozogenes*. It coagulates milk, ferments glucose, maltose, mannitol, lactose, and sucrose with the production of acid and gas, gives a variable indole reaction, and forms H_2S.

Cocco-bacillus fœtidus-ozænæ Perez

Synonym.—Perez's bacillus.

Isolation.—By Perez in 1899 from nose of ozæna patients.

Habitat.—Nose of ozæna patients ; saliva and nasal mucus of normal dogs. Probably strict parasite.

Morphology.—Small cocco-bacillus, 1–2 μ long by 0·5 μ broad ; some strains are coccoid, some are bacillary. Parallel or bulging sides, rounded ends ; axis straight ; arranged singly, in bundles of two or three members, and occasionally in pairs end-to-end. Long sinuous filaments and long straight or curved bacilli may be seen, especially in old cultures. Staining is fairly even. Non-motile or sluggishly motile. Non-capsulated. Gram-negative.

Agar Plate.—24 *hours at* 37° *C.* Round, amorphous, low convex, greyish-white, translucent colonies, up to 1 mm. in diameter ; smooth glistening surface and entire edge ; consistency butyrous or viscous ; emulsifiability easy. 7 *days,* colonies are larger, 1–2 mm. in diameter, but owing to autolysis are flattened, almost colourless, transparent, and adherent to the medium ; surface is dull and very finely granular.

Agar Slope.—24 *hours at* 37° *C.* Moderate, confluent, slightly raised, greyish-yellow, slightly translucent growth, with glistening beaten-copper surface and entire edge ; condensation water consists of greyish-white mucoid material. 7 *days,* whole growth is flattened, and withered ; surface dry and covered with secondary colonies.

Gelatin Stab.—7 *days at* 22° *C.* Moderate, mostly confluent, filiform growth, greyish-white in colour, extending to bottom of tube. Surface growth 2–4 mm. in diameter, slightly raised or flattened. No liquefaction, even after 3 weeks. After 2 to 3 weeks delicate feathery outgrowths from the stab appear in the upper half of the medium.

Broth.—24 *hours at* 37° *C.* Moderate growth with moderate, uniform turbidity and a slight powdery deposit, disintegrating completely ; heavy, unpleasant, sweetish odour. No surface growth.

Horse Blood Agar Plate.—24 *hours at* 37° *C.* Abundant greyish-white growth No hæmolysis, but plate is browned.

Potato.—7 *days at* 37° *C.* Poor, confluent, slightly raised, creamy white growth with smooth surface ; potato browned.

MacConkey's Agar.—24 *hours at* 37° *C.*   Good growth of small, round, low convex, yellow-ish colonies, not unlike those of *Bact. typhosum.*

Resistance.—Not known.

Metabolism.—Aerobe, facultative anaerobe.   Optimum temperature for growth 37° C., but growth occurs slowly at 20° C.   No hæmolysis of sheep's or horse's red cor-puscles.   Old cultures have a tendency to become brownish in colour.   Fœtid odour, especially noticeable in broth or serum broth cultures, and in corked agar cultures.

Biochemical.—Acid and gas in glucose only.   L.M. slight acid.   Indole $+$;   M.R. $-$; V.P. $-$;   nitrates reduced ; H_2S+ ; NH_3++ ;   M.B. reduced ;   catalase $++$.

Antigenic Structure.—Appears to be antigenically homogeneous, as tested by agglutina-tion and complement fixation, but not many strains have been tested.

Pathogenicity.—Pathogenic for guinea-pigs, rabbits, and mice.   After intravenous injection of rabbits a mucopurulent, sometimes hæmorrhagic, nasal discharge develops, containing large numbers of the bacilli.   Chronic rhinitis may develop, with atrophy of the turbinate bones.   Death occurs in from 24 hours to several weeks, according to the dose injected.   Intraperitoneal injection of 0·25 c.c. of a saline suspension off agar into guinea-pigs is fatal in 12 hours ; post mortem, there is peritonitis with abundant hæmorrhagic exudate.   A similar dose injected subcutaneously into mice is fatal in 48 hours ; post mortem, there is gelatinous œdema at local site, and enlargement of the spleen.   Neither in guinea-pigs nor in mice can the bacillus be recovered from the blood.

REFERENCES

ABEL, R.   (1896) *Z. Hyg. InfektKr.,* **21,** 89.
BABES, V.   (1891) *Arch. Méd. exp.,* **3,** 619.
BLANC, G. and PANGALOS, G.   (1925) *C. R. Soc. Biol.,* **93,** 1267, 1268.
BUSSON, B.   (1923) *Münch. med. Wschr.,* **70,** 426.
FERRY, N. S. and NOBLE, A.   (1918) *J. Bact.,* **3,** 499.
GALLI-VALERIO, B.   (1900) *Zbl. Bakt.,* **28,** 353.
GALTIER, V.   (1881) *C. R. Acad. Sci.,* **92,** 303.
HOFER, G.   (1913a) *Berl. klin. Wschr.,* **50,** 2413 ; (1913b) *Wien. klin. Wschr.,* **26,** 1011.
KITT, T.   (1887) *Zbl. Bakt.,* **2,** 241.
LEGROUX, R. and DJEMIL, K.   (1931) *C. R. Acad. Sci.,* **193,** 1117.
LEGROUX, R. and GENEVRAY, J.   (1933) *Ann. Inst. Pasteur,* **51,** 249.
LEO, H.   (1889) *Z. Hyg. InfektKr.,* **7,** 505.
LOEFFLER.   (1886) *Arb. ReichsgesundhAmt.,* **1,** 141.
LOEWENBERG.   (1894) *Ann. Inst. Pasteur,* **8,** 292.
MAYER, G.   (1900) *Zbl. Bakt.,* **28,** 673.
MOOR, C. E. DE, SOEKARNEN, and WALLE, N. V. D.   (1932) *Geneesk. Tijdsch. Ned.-Ind.,* **24,** 1618.
NICHOLLS, L.   (1930) *Brit. J. exp. Path.,* **11,** 393 ; (1934) *Ceylon J. Sci., Sect. D. med. Sci.,* **3,** 183.
OLINESCU, R. and ATINEU, A.   (1925a) *C. R. Soc. Biol.,* **93,** 740 ; (1925b) *Ibid.,* **93,** 741.
PANISSET, L.   (1910) *Rev. gén. Méd. vét.,* **15,** 561.
PEREZ, F.   (1899) *Ann. Inst. Pasteur,* **13,** 937 ; (1901) *Ibid.,* **15,** 409 ; (1913) *Berl. klin. Wschr.,* **50,** 2411.
SABOLOTNY, S. S.   (1926) *Zbl. Bakt.,* **98,** 37.
SAKAMOTO, K.   (1930) *J. Immunol.,* **18,** 331.
SHIGA, M.   (1922) *Zbl. Bakt.,* **88,** 521.
STANTON, A. T. and FLETCHER, W.   (1921) *Proc. 4th. Congr. Far Eastern Ass. trop. Med. Hyg.,* **2,** 196 ; (1925) *J. Hyg., Camb.,* **23,** 347 ; (1927) *Ibid.,* **26,** 31 ; (1932) *Studies Inst. med. Res., F.M.S.,* No. 21.
STRAUS, I.   (1889a) *Arch. Méd. exp.,* **1,** 460 ; (1889b) *Ibid.,* **1,** 489.
THOMPSON, L.   (1933) *J. Bact.,* **26,** 221.
VERGE, J. and PAIREMAURE, O.   (1928) *C. R. Soc. Biol.,* **99,** 182.
WARD, H. C.   (1916) *J. infect. Dis.,* **19,** 153 ; (1917) *Ibid.,* **21,** 338.
WHITMORE, A.   (1913) *J. Hyg., Camb.,* **13,** 1.
WHITMORE, A. and KRISHNASWAMI, C. S.   (1912) *Indian med. Gaz.,* **47,** 262.
WILSON, G. S.   (1934) *J. Hyg., Camb.,* **34,** 361.

CHAPTER XIX

AZOTOBACTER, RHIZOBIUM, NITROSOMONAS, NITROBACTER, HYDROGENOMONAS, METHANOMONAS, CARBOXYDOMONAS, AND ACETOBACTER

In this chapter we group together a number of organisms playing an important part in the nitrogen metabolism of the soil.

THE AZOTIFYING OR NITROGEN-FIXING BACTERIA

DEFINITION.—*Azotobacter.*

Relatively large rods, or even cocci, sometimes almost yeast-like in appearance, dependent primarily for growth energy upon the oxidation of carbohydrates. Motile or non-motile ; motile forms possess a tuft of polar flagella. Obligate aerobes, usually growing in a film upon the surface of the culture medium. Capable of fixing atmospheric nitrogen when grown in solutions containing carbohydrates and deficient in combined nitrogen.

Type species. *Azotobacter chroococcum*, Beijerinck.

Isolated by Beijerinck in 1901. He described two species, *Az. chroococcum*, so called from the brown pigment to which it gives rise, and *Az. agilis.* The former is widespread in garden earth and in fruitful soil of all kinds ; the latter was found in canal water in Holland. Since then four other species have been described—*Az. vinelandii, Az. beijerincki, Az. woodstowni,* and *Az. vitreus* ; all of them inhabit the soil.

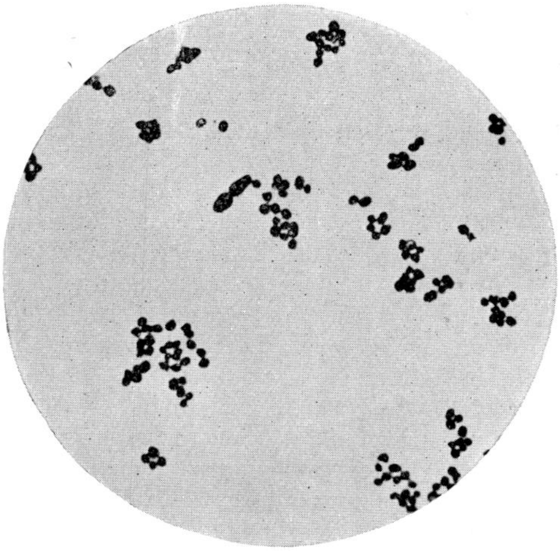

All species of *Azotobacter* are highly pleomorphic ; the cells may be short, thick and rod-like, ellipsoidal, pyriform, or spindle-shaped ; when occurring in pairs they often look like giant diplococci. Their size varies from 4–7 μ in length and 1·5-4 μ in breadth. Giant involution forms, looking like amœbæ or yeasts, are not uncommon. They are motile by one or more polar flagella, and are Gram-negative.

FIG. 78.—*Azotobacter chroococcum.*
From an agar culture, 3 days, 30° C. ($\times$ 1000).

The organism is strictly aerobic. It grows best in tap water containing 2 per cent. mannitol and 0·02 per cent. K_2HPO_4. If the medium is spread out in a thin layer in a wide-bottomed flask, *Azotobacter chroococcum* forms a surface pellicle in 2 or 3 days, which gradually becomes brown, and may later even turn black. Potassium, calcium, or sodium propionate in 0·5 per cent. solution may be substituted for the mannitol.

Of solid media, one of the best has the following composition :

Mannitol	.	.	.	.	.	.	.	2 gm.
K_2HPO_4	.	.	.	.	.	.	.	0·02 ,,
Washed Agar	.	.	.	.	.	.	.	2 ,,
Aq. Dist.	.	.	.	.	.	.	.	100 ,,

Azotobacter grows best in solutions containing little or no combined nitrogen ; according to Beijerinck (1901) ammonium salts are not easily assimilated, and peptone can be used only to a slight extent.

The peculiar property of this group of organisms is to fix atmospheric nitrogen and to convert it into ammonia, nitrites and nitrates (Beijerinck and van Delden 1902). To do this they must be supplied with a source of energy in the form of a suitable carbohydrate, such as mannitol. The energy gained from the oxidation of this substance is utilized in the fixation of nitrogen. Gainey (1918) found that in a synthetic mannitol medium inoculated with soil, about 8 mgm. of nitrogen were fixed for 50 c.c. of medium. Not all strains of *Azotobacter* are capable of utilizing mannitol (Smith 1935). *Azotobacter* is more susceptible to acid than most soil organisms. Its growth limits are about pH 6·5–8·6 in pure culture (Fred and Davenport 1918), but in soil it is probable that growth can occur down to about pH 6·0. Pigment formation is variable in *Az. chroococcum* ; some variants form a brown pigment, others are achromogenic ; intermediate forms occur (Omeliansky and Ssewerowa 1911). Pigment is formed only in the presence of a free supply of oxygen. We give a description of the type species *Az. chroococcum*, followed by notes on the lesser known species.

Azotobacter chroococcum

Isolation.—By Beijerinck in 1901.

Ecology.—Soil.

Morphology.—Short, thick rods with rounded ends ; large ovoid forms ; forms like giant diplococci ; pear-shaped rods, and other forms. 4–$5 \mu \times 1·5$–2μ. Slowly motile by polar flagella. Arranged singly, in pairs end-to-end, and in old cultures in packets. Cells often vacuolated ; when grown on mannitol, cells may contain fat droplets. In surface membranes on liquid media cells are surrounded by a thick mucoid capsule. Large involution forms not uncommon. Non-sporing. Gram-negative. Non-acid-fast.

Agar Plate.—*3 days at* 30° *C.* Round colonies, 1 mm. in diameter, convex, with smooth, moist, glistening surface ; edge entire ; structure amorphous ; consistency butyrous, easily emulsifiable ; often differentiated into an opaque brown centre and a translucent lighter periphery. After 6 days the colonies measure up to 3 mm. in diameter ; some remain homogeneous, undifferentiated and opaque ; others show an opaque brownish centre, and a clear, slightly radiate periphery.

Agar Slope.—*2 days at* 30° *C.* Moderate, confluent or partly confluent, slightly raised, translucent, greyish-yellow growth, with glistening, beaten-copper surface ; edge formed of single colonies.

Gelatin Stab.—*6 days at* 20° *C.* Poor to moderate, greyish-white, filiform growth, consisting chiefly of discrete colonies ; extends $\frac{2}{3}$ way down tube ; surface growth, 3–4 mm. in diameter, with a lobate edge and irregular surface. No liquefaction.

Broth.—2 *days at* 30° *C.* Moderate growth, with moderate, finely granular turbidity, and slight, finely granular sediment, not disintegrating on shaking. After 6 days, surface ring growth.

Loeffler's Blood Serum.—6 *days at* 30° *C.* Moderate, confluent, creamy growth, with slight yellowish colour ; smooth, mirror-like surface ; no liquefaction.

Potato.—10 *days at* 30° *C.* Abundant, raised, opaque brown growth, with wrinkled honeycombed surface. During first few days, growth is yellowish, but later it becomes brown. Potato unchanged.

Resistance.—Killed by 55° C. in 30 minutes.

Metabolism.—Aerobic. No growth anaerobically. Opt. temp. 28–30° C. Limits of pH 6·5–8·6 in pure culture. Pigment ; grown in mannitol and other suitable media, a surface scum is formed, which becomes brown, and later black. Pigment is insoluble in water, alcohol, $CHCl_3$, ether, CS_2, but slightly soluble in alkalies, which destroy it.

Nutritional. Grows best in 2–10 per cent. mannitol solutions, and in 0·5 per cent. solutions of K, Ca, or Na propionate. Growth on agar improved by 1 per cent. mannitol.

Biochemical.—Fixes atmospheric nitrogen, converting it into NH_3, nitrite and nitrate. Capable of growing in media free from combined nitrogen but containing carbohydrates. Can utilize nitrates for its nitrogen supply ; NH_3 and peptone can be used only slightly.

Utilizes dextrose, maltose, mannitol, lactose, dextrin, starch, glycerol, alcohol, propionate, acetate, butyrate, citrate, lactate, malate, and succinate ; gives off CO_2. Indole —. M.R. —. V.P. —. Nitrates —. M.B. reduction —. Catalase +. NH_3 very slight. L.M. partly decolorized, and rendered clearer and more fluid.

Pathogenicity.—Nil.

Az. agilis is a large, oval organism containing granules and vacuoles, and provided with a bundle of polar flagella. The other four species of *Azotobacter* that have been described differ in minor respects from the type species *Az. chroococcum.*

Numerous non-sporing rod-shaped organisms, capable of fixing nitrogen, have been found in horse and cow dung by Fulmer and Fred (1917). The chief of these, which they call *B. azophile*, is a rod-shaped organism, 1·6 × 0·8 μ, motile and Gram-positive. It gives a light-orange, wrinkled growth on agar, a heavy membranous surface growth in broth, and a brownish growth on potato. Gelatin is liquefied ; milk is peptonized. Nitrates are reduced to nitrites and to gaseous nitrogen. Indole +. Strict aerobe. Grows well in mannitol solution, in which it fixes nitrogen in considerable quantities.

RHIZOBIUM

DEFINITION.—*Rhizobium.*

Minute rods, motile when young. Specialized forms abundant and characteristic when grown under suitable conditions. Obligate aerobes,[1] capable of fixing atmospheric nitrogen when grown in the presence of carbohydrates and in the absence of compounds of nitrogen. Produce nodules on the roots of leguminous plants.

Type species. *Rhizobium leguminosarum*, Frank.

The first member of this group was isolated by Beijerinck in 1888, who named it *Bacillus radicicola.* He found this organism in the root-nodules of leguminous plants, and in numerous specimens of soil and water of different origin ; he noted its variable morphology ; he described its cultural and biochemical reactions ; and he showed how the bacilli in the " swarmer " stage penetrated

---

[1] This is not absolutely certain ; we have observed growth of one strain in broth, though not on agar, under strictly anaerobic conditions.

the pore-spaces in the roots of certain plants. Though suspecting it of being capable of fixing atmospheric nitrogen, he was unable to demonstrate this conclusively. Numerous strains of *Rhizobium* have since been described, but as it is doubtful whether they are separate species, we shall confine ourselves to a description of *Rhiz. leguminosarum.*

In pure cultures on nutrient agar this organism occurs in the form of rods, 1·5–3 μ × 0·5 μ, but by varying the constituents of the medium it can be made to pass through a cycle of changes, described by Bewley and Hutchinson (1920) as follows : (1) Pre-swarmer stage, non-motile. When a pure culture is inoculated into a neutral soil solution, the organisms assume this form in 4 to 5 days. Diameter about 0·4 μ. (2) Pre-swarmer stage ; larger, non-motile, cocci, 0·8 μ in diameter. Appear in mannitol agar. (3) Swarmer stage ; very actively motile. Cells are ellipsoidal ; 0·9 μ × 0·18 μ (Beijerinck). They are so small as to be

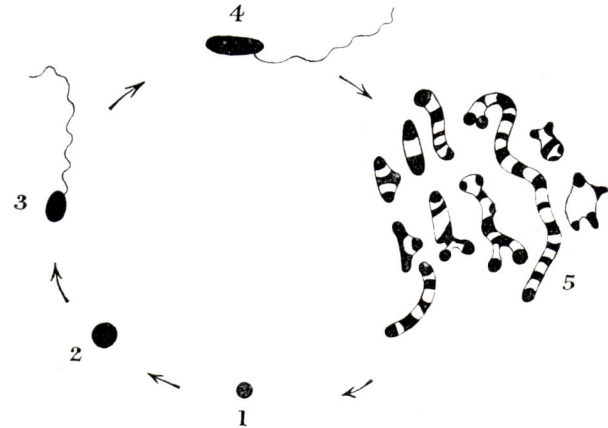

FIG. 79.—*Rhizobium leguminosarum.*
1. Pre-swarmer, first stage. 2. Pre-swarmer, second stage. 3. Swarmer. 4. Motile rod.
5. Highly vacuolated rods.
(After Bewley and Hutchinson.)

able to pass through a Chamberland filter. Appear in carbohydrate media. (4) Rod stage ; motile. Appearance favoured by carbohydrates ; as long as these are abundant, the organism remains in this stage. Dimensions 3·4 μ × 1 μ. (5) Stage of high vacuolation. In a neutral soil extract, or in a medium in which the carbohydrate has been exhausted, the organisms become highly vacuolated ; the chromatin divides into a number of bands. Later these bands become rounded off and escape from the rod as the coccoid pre-swarmers (Fig. 79). The formation of the pre-swarmers may also be induced by the addition of calcium and magnesium carbonate to the medium, or by incubating the culture anaerobically.

Calcium phosphate causes a change from pre-swarmers to rods. Acid soils favour the production of highly vacuolated cells, and eventually kill the organisms. Slightly alkaline soils support vigorous growth without altering the morphology. Relatively high temperatures, 30–37° C., prevent or postpone the change into the pre-swarming stage.

Inside the root nodules the organisms assume curious Y-shaped, pyriform, and racket-like forms, known as bacteroids. Filaments may likewise be formed. In culture the bacteroids develop into rods (Fremlin 1898).

The properties of *Rhiz. leguminosarum* vary in accordance with the species of plant from which they are derived. Fred and Davenport (1918), who studied 21 strains from different *Leguminosæ*, found a variation in their resistance to acids. Thus the strains from alfalfa and sweet clover had a limiting pH for growth of 4·9 ; for the garden pea and vetch of 4·7 ; for red clover and common beans of 4·2 ; for soya beans and velvet beans of 3·3 ; and for lupins of 3·15. All strains had much the same resistance to alkali. Incidentally their alkali tolerance was much greater than their acid tolerance.

Whether the strains from different plants should be regarded as varieties of one species is doubtful. Klimmer and Krüger (1914), who examined a number of strains from eighteen different species of *Leguminosæ* by means of the agglutination, complement-fixation, and precipitation tests, were able to classify them into 9 different groups (see also Fremlin 1898).

Rhiz. leguminosarum is an obligate aerobe, capable of fixing atmospheric nitrogen when grown in a medium free from combined nitrogen, but containing a fermentable carbohydrate. Such a medium is composed of :

Mannitol .	10·0	gm.
K_2HPO_4 .	0·2	,,
NaCl .	0·2	,,
$MgSO_4 \cdot 7H_2O$.	0·2	,,
$CaSO_4 \cdot 2H_2O$.	0·1	,,
Distilled Water .	1000	,,

Inoculated into the root of a leguminous plant it gives rise to a nodule, from which it can be recovered in pure culture. Each variety is apparently specialized to attack its own or closely related species of plants ; thus a strain isolated from a nodule on a pea (*Pisum sativum*) will produce nodules also on *vicia*, *Lathyrus* and *Lens*, but not on other legumes (Russell 1923).

We append a detailed description of *Rhiz. leguminosarum*.

Rhizobium leguminosarum Frank

Synonyms.—*Bacillus radicicola* ; *Ps. radicicola* ; nodule organism.

Isolation.—By Beijerinck in 1888 from root-nodules of leguminous plants.

Ecology.—Soil ; found also in water.

Morphology.—Has a life-cycle with gross changes in morphology. Shows non-motile coccoid forms ; very small, highly motile, ellipsoidal form (swarmer), $0.9 \mu \times 0.2 \mu$; motile rods, $2–3 \mu \times 0.5 \mu$; large vacuolated rod and Y-forms. In root nodules shows filamentous forms, and Y-forms (bacteroids). Swarmer forms motile by single, long, polar flagellum. Vacuolated forms show bands of chromatin. Nonsporing ; may be capsulated (see below). Gram-negative. Non-acid-fast.

Agar Plate.—*2 days at 25° C.* Round, 1 mm. in diameter, low convex, greyish-yellow, transparent colonies with smooth, glistening surface and lobate edge ; structure amorphous ; consistency butyrous ; easily emulsifiable. Differentiated into a smooth, raised, darker centre, and a thin, effuse, radiate periphery. Some strains are said to form mucoid colonies, consisting of bacilli embedded in a mucinous material which appears to consist of a carbohydrate material, yielding glucose on inversion (Kramár 1921).

Agar Slope.—2 *days at* 25° *C.* Moderate, partly confluent, slightly raised, greyish-yellow, translucent growth, with glistening, beaten-copper surface, and finely lobate edge.

Gelatin Stab.—5 *days at* 20° *C.* Moderate, filiform growth extending to bottom of tube; slight surface growth 1 mm. in diameter; no liquefaction except in very old cultures.

Broth.—2 *days at* 25° *C.* Poor growth with slight turbidity, and slight powdery deposit disintegrating on shaking. 5 *days*; moderate turbidity, slight surface ring growth, and moderate viscous deposit giving rise on shaking to dense turbidity.

Loeffler's Blood Serum.—6 *days at* 25° *C.* Abundant, mostly confluent, raised, chrome-yellow growth, slightly tinged with pink; smooth glistening surface. Medium not coloured; no digestion.

Potato.—6 *days at* 25° *C.* Poor, effuse, confluent, whitish-pink growth, with smooth, moist, glistening surface; medium not coloured, or coloured slightly grey.

Resistance.—Killed at 60° C. in 1 hour. Resists drying and freezing.

Metabolic.—Aerobic. No growth anaerobically on agar, but moderate growth in broth. Opt. temp. 25° C. Pigment yellowish-pink, not marked, on certain media only.

Biochemical.—No acid or gas in glucose, maltose, mannitol, lactose, sucrose or salicin. Indole —. M.R. —. V.P. —. Nitrate reduction —. Catalase +. M.B. reduction +. NH$_3$ +. H$_2$S slight +. L.M. acid and clot in 21 days. Capable of fixing atmospheric nitrogen in the presence of carbohydrates and in the absence of combined nitrogen.

Antigenic Structure.—Can be divided by agglutination into nine different groups.

Pathogenicity.—Nil to man or animals. Produces nodules upon the roots of the *Leguminosæ*.

NITROSOMONAS

Definition.—*Nitrosomonas.*

Cells rod-shaped or spherical, motile or non-motile; motile forms possess polar flagella. Capable of securing growth energy by the oxidation of ammonia to nitrites. Growth on media containing organic substances is scanty or absent. Type species. *Nitrosomonas europæa*, Winogradsky.

Winogradsky (1890*a*, *b*, *c*), finding that nitrification did not occur in a medium containing organic matter, seeded with soil, prepared the following solution:

Ammonium sulphate	1	gm.
Potassium phosphate	1	,,
Pure water	1000	,,

To each 100 c.c. was added 0·5–1·0 gm. of basic magnesium carbonate; when this medium was inoculated with soil, nitrification occurred satisfactorily, the ammonia being oxidized to nitrite. Five different types of organisms were found; one of them, which grew around the particles of carbonate at the bottom of the flask, failed to grow in gelatin on transplantation, but could be cultivated in a purely inorganic medium. This organism was obtained in pure culture, and was found to be responsible for nitrification. Morphologically it consists of ellipsoidal cells, intermediate between cocci and bacilli; its dimensions are 1·1–1·8 μ × 0·9–1·0 μ. It is motile by a single long flagellum. It is arranged singly, or aggregated into a zoogloeal mass by some slightly viscous substance; chains even of 3 or 4 members are rare.

Winogradsky found that this organism could grow in a medium devoid of all traces of organic matter. It must therefore obtain its carbon from the magnesium carbonate added to the medium; that is to say, it can assimilate the carbon of carbonic acid. It obtains its nitrogen from the ammonium sulphate, and oxidizes it to nitrite. From purely inorganic substances it can therefore synthesize organic matter—a process rarely accomplished independently of chlorophyll and sunlight.

Experiments showed that the amount of ammonia oxidized and the amount of carbon assimilated ran strictly parallel. For every 96 mgm. of nitrous acid formed it assimilated only 1 mgm. of carbon. This disproportion between the rapid oxidizing and the slow assimilating action of the organism explains why its growth is so slow.

Winogradsky and Omeliansky (1899) showed that *Nitrosomonas europœa* was very susceptible to the presence in the medium of organic nitrogenous substances such as peptone or asparagin. In fact the more nutritious a medium was for ordinary bacteria, the less suitable was it for the nitrite organism. It is possible, however, for it to grow in the presence of organic matter (Boullanger and Massol 1904, Fremlin 1914, Bonazzi 1919), but in artificial culture the results are not satisfactory. On the ordinary laboratory media, for example, growth is scanty or entirely absent. In the soil it is probable that its susceptibility to the presence of organic matter is less.

For the study of single colonies the best medium is a silicic acid gel poured into plates (Winogradsky 1891). After 3 or 4 weeks' incubation small, compact, sharply-defined colonies appear, of a brownish colour. Growth can be hastened by pouring a solution of ammonia over the plate.

Nitrosomonas europœa is most active at a temperature of 25–30° C., in a well-aerated medium contained in large flat-bottomed flasks, which are slowly agitated. The presence of scoria (cellular lava) in the medium is beneficial, apparently by increasing the surface exposed to the air (Boullanger and Massol 1903). Under such conditions in an inorganic solution it may oxidize as much as 169 mgm. of ammonia nitrogen to nitrite per litre of medium in 14 days (Bonazzi 1919). The accumulation of nitrite arrests the reaction. The type species is known as *Nitrosomonas europœa*, Winogradsky. Another similar organism, but of spherical shape, is called *Nitrosococcus americanus*; it is found in the New World.

Nitrosomonas is not by any means the only organism capable of forming nitrite from ammonia. Cutler and Mukerji (1931) isolated a number of organisms from soil that were able to perform this oxidation, though not so actively as *Nitrosomonas*. A full description of these organisms has not yet been published, but most of them were Gram-positive, non-sporing, non-motile rods, 1·4–1·9 μ long and 0·70–0·85 μ broad, which grew on ordinary agar, which oxidized various ammonium salts to nitrite, both in culture medium and in soil, which were unable to oxidize nitrite to nitrate, and which failed to grow in the absence of oxygen. Some strains liquefied gelatin and some did not. Nitrite formation was stimulated by the presence of 0·1 per cent. sucrose, but no growth occurred in pure sugar solutions. Unlike *Nitrosomonas*, which requires a distinctly alkaline medium, these organisms were able to form nitrite within a range of pH 4·8–7·3. Similar organisms have been described by Cutler and Crump (1933), who found that no fewer than 104 out of 229 strains of bacteria isolated from beet sugar effluent were able to produce nitrite from ammonium salts. Fremlin (1903, 1914, 1929–30) has worked for a long time on a very active nitroso-bacterium that grows in association with other organisms. S. Winogradsky and H. Winogradsky (1933) have described two further genera of nitrifying organisms—*Nitrosocystis* and *Nitrosospira*. Their article should be consulted not only for an account of these organisms, but also for much useful information on nitrifying bacteria in general.

NITROBACTER

DEFINITION.—*Nitrobacter*.

Cells rod-shaped, non-motile, not growing readily on organic media or in the presence of ammonia. Cells capable of securing growth energy by the oxidation of nitrites to nitrates.

Type species. *Nitrobacter winogradskyi*.

Nitrobacter winogradskyi was isolated by Winogradsky in 1891—the year after his discovery of *Nitrosomonas europœa*.

It is a small rod-shaped or pyriform organism, sometimes with one end drawn out or recurved. Size $0.5 \mu \times 0.25$–0.3μ. Non-motile. Arranged in more or less dense masses.

Winogradsky (1896) cultivated it in a medium of the following composition :

NaNO₂	1·0 gm.
Pot. phosphate	0·5 ,,
MgSO₄	0·3 ,,
Na₂CO₃ (anhydrous)	0·5 ,,
NaClO₃	0·5 ,,
Re-distilled water	1000 ,,

The medium is placed in a shallow layer in wide-bottomed flasks. Growth occurs in the form of a just perceptible gelatinous film at the bottom of the flask ; no turbidity appears. The nitrite is oxidized to nitrate. No organic nitrogen nor carbon is required. Indeed the presence of organic matter hinders its development, though not so markedly as that of the nitrite organism. On a washed-agar medium made up with sodium nitrite, sodium carbonate, and potassium phosphate (Omeliansky 1899) single colonies are formed, light brown in colour and of irregular shape. Similar colonies, but smaller and more compact, appear on silicic acid gel plates. No growth occurs in broth.

In artificial culture the nitrate bacillus is very susceptible to the presence of ammonia ; in soil it is less so. The accumulation of nitrate to the extent of 25 gm. per litre arrests the reaction (Boullanger and Massol 1903).

As well as the genera that we have described, there are numerous other organisms playing an important part in soil metabolism. We shall confine ourselves here to giving a definition of the genera *Hydrogenomonas*, *Methanomonas*, and *Carboxydomonas*, referring the reader to Chapter LXXXVII, for an account of the activity of some of these organisms, together with those organisms which play an important part in the processes of ammonification and denitrification.

DEFINITION.—*Hydrogenomonas*.

Monotrichate short rods, capable of growing in the absence of organic matter, and securing growth energy by the oxidation of hydrogen (forming water). Kaserer (1906), who first described the organism, states that his species will also grow well on a variety of organic substances.

Type species is *Hydrogenomonas pantotropha*. Niklewski (1908) described two additional species, *Hyd. vitrea* and *Hyd. flava*.

DEFINITION.—*Methanomonas.*

Monotrichate short rods, capable of growing in the absence of organic matter, and securing growth energy by the oxidation of methane (forming carbon dioxide and water).

Type species is *Methanomonas methanica* (Söhngen 1906).

DEFINITION.—*Carboxydomonas.*

Rod-shaped cells capable of securing growth energy by the oxidation of carbon monoxide (forming carbon dioxide).

The type species, *Carboxydomonas oligocarbophila* (Beijerinck and van Delden 1903), is described as non-motile.

DEFINITION.—*Acetobacter.*

Cells rod-shaped, frequently in chains, non-motile. Cells grow usually on the surface of alcoholic solutions as obligate aerobes, securing growth energy by the oxidation of alcohol to acetic acid. Also capable of utilizing certain other carbonaceous compounds, as sugar and acetic acid. Elongated, filamentous, club-shaped, swollen, and even branched cells may occur as involution forms.

Type species is *Acetobacter aceti* (Thomson 1852).

REFERENCES

BEIJERINCK, M. W. (1888) *Bot. Ztg.*, **46**, 724, 740, 756, 780, 796 ; (1901) *Zbl. Bakt.*, IIte Abt., **7**, 561.

BEIJERINCK, M. W. and DELDEN, A. VAN. (1902) *Zbl. Bakt.*, **9**, 3 ; (1903) *Ibid.*, **10**, 33.

BEWLEY, W. F. and HUTCHINSON, H. B. (1920) *J. agric. Sci.*, **10**, 144.

BONAZZI, A. (1919) *J. Bact.*, **4**, 43.

BOULLANGER, E. and MASSOL, L. (1903) *Ann. Inst. Pasteur*, **17**, 492 ; (1904) *Ibid.*, **18**, 181.

CUTLER, D. W. and CRUMP, L. M. (1933) *Ann. appl. Biol.*, **20**, 291.

CUTLER, D. W. and MUKERJI, B. K. (1931) *Proc. roy. Soc.*, *B*, **108**, 384.

FRED, E. B. and DAVENPORT, A. (1918) *J. agric. Res.*, **14**, 317.

FREMLIN, H. S. (1898) *J. Path. Bact.*, **5**, 389 ; (1903) *J. Hyg., Camb.*, **3**, 364 ; (1914) *Ibid.*, **14**, 149 ; (1929–30) *Ibid.*, **29**, 236.

FULMER, H. L. and FRED, E. B. (1917) *J. Bact.*, **2**, 423.

GAINEY, P. L. (1918) *J. agric. Res.*, **14**, 265.

KASERER, H. (1906) *Zbl. Bakt.*, IIte Abt., **16**, 681.

KLIMMER, M. and KRÜGER, R. (1914) *Zbl. Bakt.*, IIte Abt., **40**, 256.

KRAMÁR, E. (1921) *Zbl. Bakt.*, **87**, 401.

NIKLEWSKI, B. (1908) *Zbl. Bakt.*, IIte Abt., **20**, 469.

OMELIANSKY, V. (1899) *Zbl. Bakt.*, IIte Abt., **5**, 537.

OMELIANSKY, W. L. and SSEWEROWA, O. P. (1911) *Zbl. Bakt.*, IIte Abt., **29**, 643.

RUSSELL, E. J. (1923) "The Micro-organisms of the Soil." London.

SMITH, N. R. (1935) *J. Bact.*, **30**, 323.

SÖHNGEN, N. L. (1906) *Zbl. Bakt.*, IIte Abt., **15**, 513.

THOMSON, R. D. (1852) *Liebigs Ann.*, **83**, 89.

WINOGRADSKY, S. (1890a) *Ann. Inst. Pasteur*, **4**, 213 ; (1890b) *Ibid.*, **4**, 257 ; (1890c) *Ibid.*, **4**, 760 ; (1891) *Ibid.*, **5**, 92, 577 ; (1896) *Zbl. Bakt.*, IIte Abt., **2**, 329, 377, 429.

WINOGRADSKY, S. and OMELIANSKY, W. (1899) *Zbl. Bakt.*, IIte Abt., **5**, 329, 377, 429.

WINOGRADSKY, S. and WINOGRADSKY, H. (1933) *Ann. Inst. Pasteur*, **50**, 350.

CHAPTER XX

PSEUDOMONAS

DEFINITION.—*Pseudomonas.*

Rod-shaped organisms, usually motile, by means of polar flagella. Generally Gram-negative. Non-sporing. Aerobic ; some species are facultative anaerobes. Frequently produce a water-soluble pigment, which is yellow, green, blue, purple, or brown in colour, and which diffuses through the medium. Some species form a non-diffusible yellow pigment, and some species are photogenic. Fermentation of carbohydrates as a rule not active. Frequently gelatin-liquefiers, and active ammonifiers. Common in soil and water. Many yellow species are plant parasites.

Type species. *Pseudomonas pyocyanea.* (On grounds of priority the American Committee recommend that this organism should be called *Ps. æruginosa.*)

Ps. pyocyanea was first isolated by Gessard in 1882 from " blue pus." *Ps. fluorescens* was described originally by Flügge (1896) under the name of *Bacillus fluorescens liquefaciens.* This organism appears to be closely related to *Ps. pyocyanea* ; the possible differences between them will be discussed later.

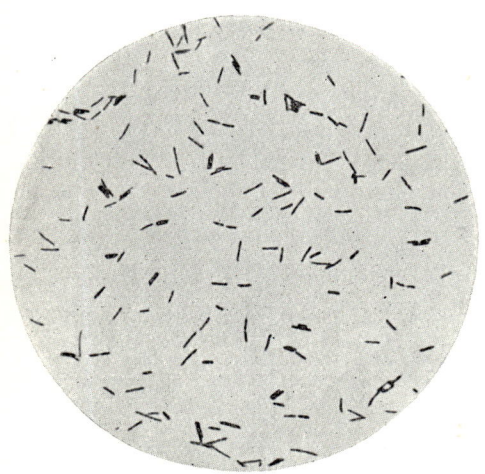

FIG. 80 —*Pseudomonas fluorescens.*
From an agar culture, 24 hours, 37° C. (× 1000).

Morphology.—The organisms of this group are rod-shaped and rather slender. Their length is subject to considerable variation ; even in a single strain some organisms may be very short, while others are long, or actually filamentous. The sides are parallel and the ends rounded. They are arranged singly, in small bundles, or in short chains. They are motile by one or more polar flagella ; they are non-sporing ; they stain readily with the ordinary aniline dyes, and are usually Gram-negative. They are non-acid-fast.

Cultural Appearances.—Growth occurs readily on the usual media. Many species form a water-soluble pigment, which diffuses through the medium. On potato *Ps. pyocyanea* and *Ps. fluorescens* give a pigmented growth, which frequently assumes a café-au-lait colour, not unlike that given by organisms of the *Brucella* and *Pfeifferella* groups, and *V. choleræ.*

380

Resistance.—None of the members of the group form spores, and none are particularly resistant to heat or chemical disinfectants. They all succumb on exposure in a water-bath to a temperature of 55° C. in 1 hour. The greenish-yellow fluorescent bacilli—*Ps. fluorescens* and *Ps. pyocyanea*—are said to be more resistant than other vegetative organisms to ultra-violet light (Burge and Neill 1915). It is suggested that they are able to convert the short wave lengths into longer waves, and hence dispose of the energy of the absorbed waves, which would otherwise be spent in coagulating them (see Chapter V).

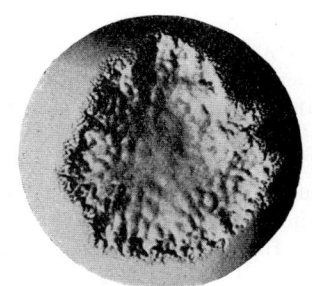

FIG. 81.—*Pseudomonas pyocyanea.*
Surface colony on agar, 24 hours, 37° C. (× 8).

Metabolic and Biochemical Characters.—Many of the organisms are obligatory aerobes ; others may give a very slight growth under anaerobic conditions. Growth of *Ps. pyocyanea* in broth is accompanied by a fall in oxidation-reduction potential, which reaches a limiting value of between Eh − 0·100 and − 0·200 volt. The pigment pyocyanin constitutes a reversible oxidation-reduction system, and acts as a respiratory catalyst, but according to Reed and Boyd (1933) the changes of potential in culture are not dependent on the presence of this substance. The optimum temperature for growth varies somewhat, but is usually about 25–30° C. Growth usually occurs as low as 0° C. The fermentative power is usually weak ; acid, but no gas, is formed by some species in certain sugars. According to Moltke (1927), 4 strains of *Ps. pyocyanea* which he examined failed to ferment any of the usual sugars. In our experience acid is generally formed from glucose, but from no other sugar. At least one member of the group, *Ps. denitrificans*, is able to reduce nitrates, with the evolution of free nitrogen.

FIG. 82.—*Pseudomonas fluorescens.*

Agar slope culture, 48 hours, 22° C.

Pathogenicity.—With the exception of *Ps. pyocyanea*, members of the group are non-pathogenic to man. *Ps. pyocyanea* itself gives rise occasionally to suppurative processes and less often to generalized infection. Among the commonest manifestations are middle-ear suppuration in children, destructive lesions of the skin, sometimes described as ecthyma gangrenosum, in children and adults, and necrotic and ulcerative lesions of the alimentary mucosa. The respiratory tract, the eye, the joints, and the kidneys are sometimes affected. There is also reason to believe that the organism plays a part in some cases of infantile diarrhœa. Infection may be primary or secondary, and is often acute and rapidly fatal. (For review of human infections see Waite 1908, Fraenkel 1917, and Lode 1929.)

Animals are rarely infected unless given large doses intravenously, when they may die of intoxication. *Ps. pyocyanea*, however, often produces fever and a local abscess after subcutaneous injection into rabbits ; and, if highly virulent, it may prove fatal in 24 hours.

Group forming Bluish-green Pigment.—*Ps. pyocyanea*, first isolated in pure culture by Gessard (1882), is widely distributed in nature, being found in water, sewage, and sometimes on the normal skin, particularly of the axilla and perineum (Růžička 1898). It is not infrequently found in wounds, where it gives rise to blue pus. It may invade the nasal fossæ, the middle ear, the meninges, the bronchi and other organs, and set up suppuration. In infants and young children it causes intestinal disturbances and diarrhœa ; sometimes it enters the blood stream, and gives rise to a general infection (Williams and Cameron 1896). According to Pons (1927), *Ps. pyocyanea* is especially pathogenic in the tropics, where it is not infrequently responsible for typhoid-like infections and abscess of the liver.

Injected subcutaneously or intravenously into guinea-pigs or rabbits in a dose of 0·5–1·0 c.c. of a 24 hours' broth culture, it may cause death in 24 to 48 hours ; post mortem there is a hæmorrhagic œdema at the site of injection (after subcutaneous inoculation), small punctate hæmorrhages are seen in the stomach and intestine, and sometimes nephritis. The bacilli can be recovered from the blood, viscera, and urine. As much the same appearances result from the injection of dead cultures, it is probable that an endotoxin is secreted. Different strains vary in virulence ; some do not kill for weeks, others not at all.

In culture, *Ps. pyocyanea* forms a bluish-green pigment. Gessard (1890, 1891, 1892) found that this pigment consists of two different substances. One, pyocyanin, is green in colour, non-fluorescent, is formed in peptone media, and is soluble both in chloroform and in water. The other, fluorescin, is yellowish in colour, fluorescent, is formed only in the presence of a phosphate, and is insoluble in chloroform, but soluble in water. By cultivation in different media he was able to obtain varieties that produced pyocyanin or fluorescin only, and some that were completely achromogenic. Fordos (1860) obtained pyocyanin in long blue crystals from a solution in chloroform. Wasserzug (1887) showed that its formation was prevented by several substances, such as 5 per cent. KNO_3, 8 per cent. $KClO_3$, 0·5 per cent. ammonium tartrate, 5 per cent. NaCl, and by many disinfectants not strong enough to inhibit the growth of the organism. Jordan (1899) studied 7 strains of *Ps. pyocyanea* ; 1 strain produced pyocyanin only, 5 both pyocyanin and fluorescin, and 1 fluorescin only. He found that the fluorescent pigment required for its formation both phosphate and sulphate, while neither of these substances was necessary for the production of pyocyanin. Both pigments are formed in suitable synthetic media. In old cultures a black pigment sometimes appears ; this appears to be an oxidation product of pyocyanin. A yellowish-brown pigment, which may also be found in cultures, appears to be an oxidation product of the fluorescent substance.

Jordan divided his species into four varieties : (*α*) pyocyanin +, fluorescin +, (*β*) pyocyanin +, fluorescin −, (*γ*) fluorescin +, pyocyanin −, (*δ*) non-chromogenic. These varieties could not readily be converted into one another.

Boland (1899), who worked with a solution of pyocyanin in chloroform, found that it became yellow if exposed to sunlight. Apparently the chloroform was broken up, and chlorine set free, which oxidized the pyocyanin to pyoxanthose. He showed that pyocyanin was largely dissolved by HCl, which turned it red, and pyoxanthose by 3 per cent. H_2SO_4, which turned it reddish-yellow. Both pigments were soluble in chloroform. In some cultures he found that a reddish-brown pigment was formed, soluble in 1 per cent. alkali and in water, but not in chloroform. In such cultures the pyocyanin reached its maximum development in a fortnight and then decreased in quantity ; the reddish-brown pigment did not make its appearance till the second week, and then increased as the pyocyanin diminished. He concluded therefore that this pigment was formed from pyocyanin.

More recently Wrede (1930) has been successful in determining the chemical constitution of pyocyanin, and in synthesizing it from lactic acid and salts. Chemically it appears to be an entirely new type of dye, containing two pentavalent nitrogen atoms. It affords, moreover, the first instance in which phenazine derivatives have been found in nature. Its empirical formula is $C_{26}H_{20}N_4O_2$, and its constitution probably

Wrede states that it dissolves poorly in cold, but readily in warm, water, as well as in chloroform, nitrobenzol, pyridine, and phenol. It is fairly resistant to acids and forms with them red-coloured salts. To alkali, on the other hand, in the presence of oxygen, it is much less resistant, and is rapidly broken down under its action.

Summarizing, we may say that *Ps. pyocyanea* forms two pigments : (1) Pyocyanin ; a green pigment, soluble both in chloroform and in water, from which it can be obtained in long blue crystals. For its production neither phosphate nor sulphate is required. It appears during the early stages of growth, and may later be oxidized to a reddish-brown or black pigment. (2) Fluorescin ; a yellowish-green fluorescent pigment, soluble in water but not in chloroform. For its production both phosphate and sulphate are required. In old cultures it may be oxidized to a yellowish-brown pigment. (For a very careful study of the factors controlling the production of pyocyanin and other pigments, see Sullivan 1905–06.)

Pyocyanin is formed only by *Ps. pyocyanea* ; the fluorescent pigment is formed by several other organisms. Both pigments are themselves oxidation products of colourless substances.

From Hadley's observations (1927) it appears fairly certain that the power of forming pyocyanin is subject to discontinuous variation. Under artificial conditions of cultivation, many strains of *Ps. pyocyanea* tend to lose their ability to produce a bluish-green coloured growth on agar. If such strains are inoculated into broth, and plated out, it will be found that only a proportion of the colonies are coloured bluish-green ; the remainder have merely the yellowish colour due to the presence of the fluorescent pigment. With many strains prolonged subcultivation is followed by the complete disappearance of the bluish-green variants, and their replacement by the yellowish variants. Once a strain has lost its power of producing pyocyanin, it is unable to recover it. According to Cataliotti (1935), cultivation in broth containing 2 per cent. zinc oxide or 1 per cent. zinc sulphate results after a few passages in suppression of pigment formation. The organisms, however, do not undergo dissociation, and when transferred back to normal media again give rise to pigment.

An interesting point about *Ps. pyocyanea* is that both in culture and in the animal body it appears to give rise to the production of hydrocyanic acid (Patty 1921).

We append a detailed description of this organism.

Pseudomonas pyocyanea

Synonyms.—*Bacterium aeruginosum* (Schröter) Migula. *B. pyocyaneus*, Gessard.

Ecology.—Intestinal canal, water, sewage, pus, sinuses, human skin; sometimes pathogenic to man.

Morphology.—Rods, 1·5–3·0 μ × 0·5 μ; axis straight, ends rounded, sides parallel, arranged singly, or in pairs and short chains; motile by 1–3 flagella at one pole. Nonsporing, non-capsulated. Gram-negative. Non-acid-fast.

Agar Plate.—*2 days at 25° C.* Round colonies, 1–2 mm. in diameter, low convex, with smooth, moist, glistening surface; edge entire or undulate; structure amorphous; butyrous consistency, easily emulsifiable; fluorescent yellowish-green colour, translucent. After 5 days it is differentiated into a smooth, convex, translucent centre and a radially striated, effuse, transparent periphery, with an undulate, lobate, or villous edge. Medium coloured green.

Agar Slope.—*2 days at 25° C.* Good growth, raised slightly, with beaten-copper surface, irregular edge, and sometimes clear phage-like areas; greenish-yellow, translucent. Medium green. 5 *days*: growth becomes effuse and scarcely visible.

Gelatin Stab.—Moderate filiform growth to bottom of stab; slow crateriform liquefaction. After 14 days the upper 1–2 cm. are digested in stratiform manner, and the fluid is turbid, yellowish-green, and sometimes granular; there may be saccate liquefaction around the filiform growth as well.

Broth.—*2 days at 25° C.* Abundant growth, with dense turbidity; yellowish-green colour; thick white ring growth and thin surface pellicle; slight powdery sediment, disintegrating on shaking. After 5 days there is an abundant, visco-floccular deposit, only partly disintegrating. Mawkish odour, like trimethylamine.

Blood Serum.—*7 days at 25° C.* Good, confluent, slightly raised growth, of greenish-yellow colour; medium is slightly green; medium is partly digested in 14 days.

Potato.—*6 days at 25° C.* Abundant, slightly raised, confluent, greenish-brown growth with moist, glistening, contoured surface. Potato coloured green. Later, both the growth and the potato take on a brownish colour.

Resistance.—Destroyed by 55° C. in 1 hour.

Metabolic.—Aerobic; no growth anaerobically. Opt. temp. 30–37° C. Forms a green pigment soluble in chloroform and in water, called pyocyanin; forms a yellowish-green fluorescent pigment, soluble in water but not in chloroform. Nutritional: grows well on ordinary media; in synthetic media, both phosphate and sulphate are essential for production of fluorescent pigment.

Biochemical.—Acid, no gas, in glucose. Indole —, as a rule, occasionally +. M.R. —, V.P.—, Nitrate reduction —. H_2S +. NH_3 production +. Catalase +. M.B. reduced. Starch diastase —. L.M. peptonization and decolorization complete in 5 days at 30° C., may be slight preliminary clot; milk often turned green.

Pathogenicity.—Low pathogenicity to man, giving rise to diarrhœa and general infections in infants, and to suppuration. Cause of "blue pus." Gives rise to fever and local abscess after subcutaneous injection into rabbits.

Ps. fluorescens.—This organism is found in water, hail (Belli 1902), sewage, and has been isolated from lemonade (Thöni 1911). It is motile by one or more polar flagella. Many authors consider it a variety of *Ps. pyocyanea*, which has become adapted to a purely saprophytic existence (Tanner 1918, Růžička 1898). The differential characters may be given as follows :

Ps. pyocyanea.	*Ps. fluorescens.*
(1) Opt. temp. 37° C.	Opt. temp. 25° C.
(2) Pyocyanin and fluorescent pigment formed.	Fluorescent pigment only formed.
(3) Liquefaction in gelatin stratiform and saccate.	Liquefaction in gelatin not always present : when present stratiform only.
(4) Pathogenic to rabbits and guinea-pigs.	Non-pathogenic to rabbits and guinea-pigs.

These differences are by no means constant. Further, since varieties of *Ps. pyocyanea* may occur that fail to produce pyocyanin, and since achromogenic varieties of both organisms are not uncommon, differentiation of the two organisms is often impossible.

Jordan (1899) studied 58 strains of *Ps. fluorescens* from water. He found that 33 of them liquefied gelatin, and produced acid, clot, and peptonization in milk ; 25 did not liquefy gelatin, and produced alkali in milk without coagulation. The variations in reaction that may occur can be judged from the fact that Tanner divided 42 strains, which he studied, into no fewer than 27 different groups.

Ps. fluorescens is generally non-pathogenic to animals, but it may give rise to a local abscess in rabbits and guinea-pigs. On the other hand, it is stated to be frequently pathogenic to plants, especially cultivated vegetables, such as carrots, cauliflowers and tomatoes, in which it causes areas of moist necrosis (Griffon 1909).

Ps. cyanogena is a motile bacillus possessing polar flagella. It forms two pigments : one fluorescent, the other varying in colour from blue to brown or black. In milk with an acid reaction it gives rise to a bright blue colour. It is the cause of epidemics of " blue milk."

Pseudomonas denitrificans.—We shall mention only one more organism of this group, *Ps. denitrificans*. This organism was originally described by Christensen (1903–04) under the name of *Bacillus denitrificans fluorescens*. Two varieties were recognized, A and B : variety A was isolated from garden earth, and was able to reduce nitrates to gaseous nitrogen ; variety B was isolated from horse dung, and was able to reduce nitrites, but not nitrates, to gaseous nitrogen.

Variety A is a small bacillus, 0.5–1.25 $\mu \times 0.5$–0.7 μ. It is surrounded by a large capsule, measuring 2–5 μ in diameter. Appears to be slightly motile. Often shows bipolar staining. Is Gram-negative. Grows freely at 25° C. Colonies on agar are 2–3 mm. in diameter after 3 days, and are circular, with an entire edge ; they have an opalescent sheen. In an agar stroke culture a whitish glistening growth is formed and the agar is coloured bright green. In gelatin stab there is a filiform growth, and a whitish surface growth with a lobate edge ; the gelatin is not liquefied. In a gelatin stroke culture there is a dirty-white layer of growth, which fluoresces brilliantly in transmitted light ; the gelatin is coloured bright-green. In broth there is a dense turbidity, and a very thick wrinkled surface pellicle, which climbs up the walls of the tube. In 0·2 per cent. nitrate broth a dense turbidity is produced, and a foam, due to the liberation of gaseous nitrogen, is seen, reaching its maximum in 40 hours ; the nitrate is not completely destroyed, even in 3 weeks.

Variety B is a larger bacillus, 1–3 μ long by 0.5–1.25 μ broad, and is surrounded by a capsule. Motility doubtful. Gram-negative. It is unable to reduce nitrates to nitrites, but is able to reduce nitrites to gaseous nitrogen. Colonies on agar are 2·5–3·5 mm. in diameter after 2 to 3 days, and are flat, whitish, and so fluid that they may flow over the agar if the plate is stood on edge. In agar stroke culture there is a thinnish filiform grey growth, having an effuse iridescent peripheral extension; after 10 days the agar is slightly coffee-coloured. In gelatin stroke culture there is a greyish or slightly brownish layer of growth, which fluoresces strongly in transmitted light; the gelatin is coloured brown. In broth there is a dense turbidity, and a thin, iridescent surface pellicle.

REFERENCES

BELLI, C. M. (1902) *Zbl. Bakt.*, IIte Abt., **8**, 445.
BOLAND, G. W. (1899) *Zbl. Bakt.*, **25**, 897.
BURGE, W. E. and NEILL, A. J. (1915) *Amer. J. Physiol.*, **38**, 399.
CATALIOTTI, F. (1935) *G. Batt. Immun.*, **15**, 161.
CHRISTENSEN, H. R. (1903–4) *Zbl. Bakt.*, IIte Abt., **11**, 190.
FLÜGGE, C. G. F. W. (1896) " Die Mikro-organismen," 3te Auflage, 2te Theil, p. 292. Leipzig.
FORDOS, M. J. (1860) *C. R. Acad. Sci.*, **51**, 215, 326.
FRAENKEL, E. (1917) *Z. Hyg. InfektKr.*, **84**, 369.
GESSARD, C. (1882) *C. R. Acad. Sci.*, **94**, 563 ; (1890) *Ann. Inst. Pasteur*, **4**, 88 ; (1891) *Ibid.*, **5**, 65 ; (1892) *Ibid.*, **6**, 801.
GRIFFON, E. (1909) *C. R. Acad. Sci.*, **149**, 50.
HADLEY, P. (1927) *J. infect. Dis.*, **40**, 74.
JORDAN, E. O. (1899) *J. exp. Med.*, **4**, 627.
LODE, A. (1929) Kolle & Wassermann Handb. path. Mikroorg., **6**, 149. Gustav Fischer. Jena.
MOLTKE, O. (1927) " B. proteus Vulgaris." Copenhagen.
PATTY, F. A. (1921) *J. infect. Dis.*, **29**, 73.
PONS, R. (1927) *Ann. Inst. Pasteur*, **41**, 1338.
REED, E. M. and BOYD, G. B. (1933) *Canad. J. Res.*, **8**, 173.
RŮŽIČKA, S. (1898) *Zbl. Bakt.*, **24**, 11.
SULLIVAN, M. X. (1905–6) *J. med. Res.*, **14**, 109.
TANNER, F. W. (1918) *J. Bact.*, **3**, 63.
THÖNI, J. (1911) *Zbl. Bakt.*, IIte Abt., **29**, 616.
WAITE, H. H. (1908) *J. infect. Dis.*, **5**, 542.
WASSERZUG, E. (1887) *Ann. Inst. Pasteur*, **1**, 581.
WILLIAMS, E. P. and CAMERON, K. (1896) *J. Path. Bact.*, **3**, 344.
WREDE, F. (1930) *Z. Hyg. InfektKr.*, **111**, 90.

CHAPTER XXI

VIBRIO AND SPIRILLUM

VIBRIO

Definition.—*Vibrio.*

> Short, curved, rigid rods, arranged singly or united into s-forms or spirals. Motile by a single polar flagellum, which is usually relatively short. (Some species may have two or three polar flagella.) Non-sporing. Usually Gram-negative. Aerobic and facultatively anaerobic. Many species liquefy gelatin and are active ammonifiers. Commonly found in water. Most species are saprophytic ; a few are pathogenic to man.
>
> Type species. *Vibrio choleræ.*

The first member of this group to be described was *V. choleræ*, which was found by Koch (1886) in the dejecta of cholera patients. In 1888 Gamaléia (1888a) isolated a vibrio from the blood and intestinal contents of chickens dying from a cholera-like disease at Odessa ; to this organism he gave the name of *V. metchnikovi.* During the next 10 years a large number of other vibrios, more or less resembling the cholera vibrio, were isolated from different sources, such as well, river, and sea water, the fæces of man and animals, cheese, and intestinal abscesses of pigs (Dunbar 1893, Smith 1894, Dieudonné 1894, Kutscher 1895, Gotschlich 1895, 1906, Ruffer 1907, Crendiropoulo 1912, Craster 1913). The differentiation of many of these organisms from *V. choleræ* proved impossible, until the introduction of the Pfeiffer test in 1894 (see Chapter LX). Even with the help of this test, it was not always possible to decide whether they were different species, or were merely variants of the main species. Since the chief interest of the vibrios—at least to the medical bacteriologist—has been their relationship to *V. choleræ*, it follows that a careful systematic study of the saprophytic species has not yet been made. For this reason it is premature to attempt a classification of the members of this group.

Morphology and Staining.—The *Vibrios* are short, curved rods, looking like commas. In size they vary considerably, from about 1 to 5 μ in length and about 0·3 to 0·6 μ in breadth ; the commas may appear long, thin, and delicate, or short, stunted and thick. They are arranged singly, in s-shaped or occasionally semicircular pairs, or in short chains. In fluid media spirals are often formed, and in old cultures a variety of forms may be seen ; most of these are very small, looking like granules and staining poorly ; but there are larger, swollen, shadow forms resembling bottles or clubs. When freshly isolated the resemblance to a comma is most striking ; but after long subculture in the laboratory the vibrios frequently lose their curved shape, and are then not unlike coliform bacilli. The organisms are very actively motile by a single polar flagellum. They stain best with dilute carbol-fuchsin. They are Gram-negative.

Growth Requirements.—Growth occurs readily on the usual media. One of the most characteristic properties is the rapidity of growth in peptone water (1 per cent. peptone, 0·5 per cent. NaCl). Multiplication occurs chiefly at the surface, where, after 6 to 9 hours, a delicate membrane is formed. There is very little turbidity as a rule ; the deposit that forms appears to be derived from the surface pellicle.

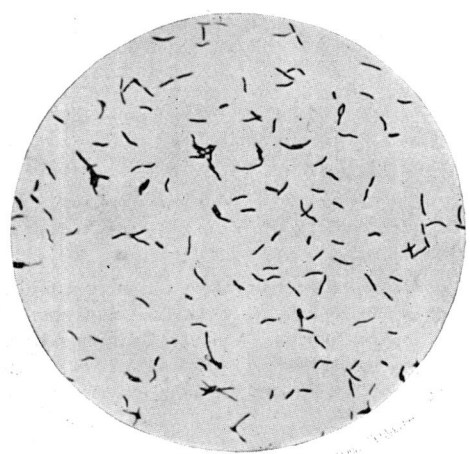

FIG. 83.—*Vibrio choleræ*.
From an agar culture, 24 hours, 37° C. (× 1000).

The vibrios are markedly aerobic ; they grow best in the presence of abundant oxygen. Under strictly anaerobic conditions some of the members fail to grow altogether ; the majority give rise to a very slight growth on agar or in broth in about a week. The optimum temperature is 30–40° C. ; no growth occurs macroscopically under 16° C.

For growth and survival a H-ion concentration of pH 7·6–8·0 is most suitable. The organisms have a high alkali, but a very low acid tolerance. Cultures containing a fermentable sugar are sterile in a day or two (Nobechi 1925).

A number of selective media have been devised for facilitating the isolation of *V. choleræ* from the fæces. One of the best known of these—Dieudonné's medium (1909)—is prepared by adding normal KOH solution to an equal quantity of defibrinated ox blood, and heating to 100° C. for half an hour. Thirty parts of this mixture are added to 70 parts of nutrient agar rendered neutral to litmus. According to Vedder and van Dam (1932), the medium should be allowed a day or two to " ripen." During this time CO_2 is taken up from the air and NH_3 is given off. The medium, when ready for use, should have a pH of 9·0–9·6. At a lower pH coliform and other organisms grow and the medium is no longer selective ; at a higher pH the growth of the cholera vibrio itself is inhibited. Ottolenghi's medium (see Bocchia 1911) consists of ox bile to which

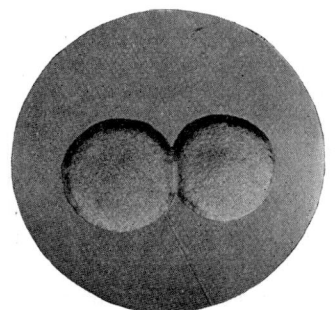

FIG. 84.—*Vibrio choleræ*.
Surface colonies on agar, 24 hours, 37° C. (× 8).

3 per cent. of a 10 per cent. solution of crystalline sodium carbonate has been added ; sterilization is effected in the autoclave. Bandi's medium, suitable for cultivation of the cholera vibrio from water, is a peptone water solution containing dilute anticholera agglutinating serum ; the vibrios multiply and fall to the bottom in clumps. Yen (1932–33) recommends a phenolphthalein starch medium for the

isolation of the cholera vibrio. It depends on the unusual property possessed by this organism of rapidly fermenting starch in an alkaline solution (see Gordon 1906).

Cultural Characters.—On agar the colonies are not distinctive ; they may be either clear and amorphous, or finely granular. Small, knob-like secondary colonies sometimes form in about a week on the surface of the parent colony. An effuse, transparent peripheral extension is not unusual. Crystals may form in the agar. Balteanu (1926) has described three colonial variants in cultures of cholera and cholera-like vibrios. Variant (1) was rugose ; (2) had a more opaque centre and a transparent periphery ; and (3) was opaque. Variants 1 and 2 reverted to type when subcultured on agar ; variant 3 reverted slowly in broth, but remained constant for a long time on agar. Variant 3 consisted of non-motile bacilli which had a mucoid envelope ; the organisms contained a heat-stable antigen only and were apparently of the pure O form (see antigenic structure).

In gelatin stab many species produce liquefaction. On potato some of the members—including *V. cholerœ* —give a raised growth of café-au-lait colour, resembling that of the *Brucella* group, *Pfeiff. mallei*, and *Ps. pyocyanea*. On MacConkey's medium growth is often poor ; *V. cholerœ* flourishes well on it, but the non-pathogenic members grow poorly. The colonies are colourless when young, but soon assume a pinkish-red appearance ; the medium changes simultaneously to a darker red. The rate at which the colour alters depends on the organism observed ; the colonies of *V. cholerœ* may remain yellow for a week ; those of the Nasik vibrio are bright red in 3 days.

On Loeffler's serum growth is plentiful, and is sometimes accompanied by slow liquefaction.

Resistance.—None of the vibrios form spores. Their resistance to heat and disinfectants is low, and they are easily destroyed by drying (see Chapter LX). They are killed by heat at 55° C. in 15 minutes or less (Kitasato 1889), and by 0·5 per cent. phenol in a few minutes. Dried on cover slips they perish in about 3 hours.

Biochemical Characteristics.—Acid, without gas, is generally formed within a day or two in glucose, maltose, mannitol and sucrose. Lactose is sometimes fermented

Fig. 85.—*Vibrio cholerœ.*

Gelatin stab culture, 5 days, 22° C., showing infundibuliform liquefaction.

after 10 or 14 days, and occasionally salicin. The Nasik vibrio ferments glucose only—at least in liquid media. Litmus milk may be unchanged ; more often it is acidified ; and sometimes it is clotted. Many species form indole, reduce nitrates to nitrites, and give the cholera-red reaction. This reaction is performed by adding pure sulphuric acid to a 24-hour peptone water culture of the organism ; if positive, a red coloration appears almost immediately. It depends on the ability of the organism to produce indole and reduce nitrates, so that on the addition of sulphuric acid the nitroso-indole reaction occurs. Many organisms not belonging to the *Vibrio* group are able to form indole and reduce nitrates, but most of them break down the nitrite to NH_3 (Maassen 1902). The reaction is given not only by *V. cholerœ*, but by a number of other vibrios, so that it no longer has the diagnostic significance with which it was at first accredited.   For its production it is essential to use a brand of peptone that contains a small amount of nitrate ; not all peptones are suitable.   Paladino-Blandini (1906) states that the indole and the nitrite must be formed in certain proportions ; if either is in excess, the reaction fails : but if the culture is heated to 60–70° C. for 15 minutes, the colour appears.

All the members appear to form catalase and ammonia.   Some reduce methylene blue, and some form H_2S—though not for several days.   Nobechi (1925), who studied a large number of cholera and cholera-like vibrios, concluded that it was impossible to distinguish them by their biochemical reactions.

Hæmolysin Formation.—Many members of this group form a hæmolysin acting on sheep, horse, or rabbit cells.   This can be demonstrated either on plates or in a broth culture.   In general, the cholera vibrio does not produce a soluble hæmolysin, while the El Tor and many non-cholera vibrios are able to do so.   For diagnostic purposes a standard technique is essential.   Much confusion has in the past been due to differences in method of studying hæmolysis.   Zimmermann (1932, 1933), working with 5 per cent. defibrinated sheep blood broth cultures, obtained conflicting results, but when he used a medium made up with peptone, asparagin, and ammonium lactate containing 4 per cent. sheep blood, and read his results after 48 hours' incubation at 37° C., a clear differentiation between the non-hæmolytic cholera and the hæmolytic El Tor and non-cholera vibrios was apparent.   Van Loghem (1932) states that sheep or goat's blood should be used ; guinea-pig and rabbit red cells are too sensitive.   He further points out that the cholera vibrio, though not forming a true soluble hæmolysin, does digest blood pigment.   It is this property that is responsible for the greenish zone around colonies on blood agar. The El Tor vibrio likewise digests blood, but it produces a soluble hæmolysin in addition.

The common routine method for testing hæmolytic activity is to grow the organism in broth for 3 days at 37° C., to add 1 c.c. of the culture to 1 c.c. of a 5 per cent. suspension of washed goat or sheep red cells, to incubate for 2 hours at 37° C., and to read the results after the tubes have been left in the cold overnight.

Doorenbos (1936) finds that hæmolysis is very much more active in 8-hour than in 24-hour cultures.   Many strains of true cholera vibrios that were non-hæmolytic after 24 hours produced hæmolysis of sheep or goat cells after 8 hours. With so many factors influencing hæmolysin production, it would clearly be dangerous to place too much weight on this characteristic as a means of differentiating between the vibrios.

Toxin Production.—Nicati and Rietsch (1884) injected dogs intravenously with the filtrate of a broth culture of *V. choleræ* a week or more old.   In their first series of experiments there were vomiting, defæcation, and general depression, with recovery in an hour. In their second series there were dyspnœa, vomiting, and paresis of the extremities, followed by recovery, or death in 12 hours.   At necropsy in the fatal cases, ecchymoses were found in the duodenum and larger hæmorrhages in the stomach.   Filtrates of young cultures were innocuous.

Pfeiffer (1892) likewise experimented with filtrates.   He found that even 4 c.c. of a 20-days' glycerine broth filtrate, injected intraperitoneally into guinea-pigs, had no more than a slight toxic effect.   Dead vibrios, however, are very toxic.   Pfeiffer (1892, 1895*b*) found that the lethal dose of living vibrios on intraperitoneal injection into guinea-pigs was 1·5 mgm. of an 18-hours' agar slope culture.   When the vibrios were killed by chloroform or thymol the lethal dose was 3–4·5 mgm.; when they were killed by drying, it was 6 mgm.; and when they were killed by heat at 55° C. for an hour it was 10–20 mgm. While immune serum was able to protect a guinea-pig against several fatal doses of living vibrios, it possessed no more protective power than normal serum against dead vibrios. From these experiments he concluded that in young cultures of *V. choleræ* there was a specific toxic substance bound to the bacterial bodies; and that the immune substances in the antiserum were not antitoxic but bactericidal in their action.

Von Dungern (1895) working with one highly virulent strain of cholera and another of very low virulence found that the lethal dose of heat-killed organisms was the same in each instance. The toxicity of the cultures therefore bore no relation to their virulence.

Manwaring, Boyd, and Okami (1923) perfused the mammalian heart with 2–7 days' culture filtrates of *V. choleræ*, added in 5–10 per cent. concentration to Locke's solution. Though non-toxic for the conducting and contractile tissues, the filtrates had a destructive effect on the capillary endothelium, as was evident from the œdema of the muscle and the hæmorrhages that occurred beneath the endocardium and pericardium.

We may conclude that the cholera vibrio does not secrete a true soluble exotoxin, but that it contains endotoxins which are liberated on the autolysis of the bacilli in culture or on the active disintegration of the bacilli by the cells of the animal body. The analogy that it presents with the meningococcus—another organism that readily undergoes autolysis—is very close, though the cholera vibrio is far more toxic.

Hahn and Hirsch (1929), working with El Tor and other hæmolytic vibrios, found that a soluble toxin was produced in peptone water cultures to which small quantities of glucose were added during growth, the reaction of the medium being kept alkaline by similar additions of NaOH. The toxin, which passed through a Seitz filter, became demonstrable in 6–10 hours, and reached its maximum in 1–4 days. Bacterial counts indicated that the increase in toxicity of the culture coincided with the death of the organisms. The heat resistance of the toxin seemed to vary with different batches; sometimes it was destroyed in 2 minutes, at others not for 30 minutes, when exposed to a temperature of 100° C. Injected intraperitoneally into guinea-pigs in a dose of 0·25 c.c., the toxin had a marked effect on the temperature, which often fell to 30° C. within 2–3 hours. The animals became progressively weaker, paralysis developed in their hind legs, and they died in 6–10 hours. Post mortem, the findings consisted of a large exudate in the peritoneal cavity, fibrino-purulent deposits on the liver, and sometimes hyperæmia of the intestine. Injection of horses with increasing doses of toxin led to the appearance in the serum of antibodies capable of neutralizing, to some extent, the lethal action of the toxin for guinea-pigs. It is to be noted that true, non-hæmolytic, cholera vibrios were almost completely devoid of toxin-producing power under the cultural conditions described (see also Andu and van Niekerk 1929).

Antigenic Structure.—The antigenic structure of the Vibrios has of late years received considerable attention. Kabéshima (1918), working with *V. choleræ*, discovered the occurrence of serological variants. Balteanu (1926) found a heat-labile H and a heat-stable O receptor in the cholera vibrio; immune serum prepared against organisms heated to 100° C. for 2 hours contained only O agglutinins. This finding was confirmed and extended by Shousha (1931), Abdoosh (1932), and Gohar (1932). These observations and a particularly careful study by Gardner and Venkatraman (1935) have done much to clarify the confusion resulting from the work carried out before the importance of flagellar and somatic antigens had been appreciated. The analysis is, however, by no means complete, and the scheme reproduced here must be regarded only as a working hypothesis, certain in the future to require considerable modification.

Attention has been concentrated mainly on the cholera and cholera-like vibrios, which we refer to for convenience as Group 'A. This group comprises organisms, most of which produce acid without gas in glucose, maltose, mannitol, and sucrose, but not in dulcitol, and which give the cholera-red reaction. All organisms of Group A possess a common H antigen. The major O antigens, on the other hand, of which six have already been differentiated, are much more specific and are used as a basis for the differentiation of Group A into sub-groups. The true cholera vibrios all appear to fall into sub-group I, which also contains most of the El Tor strains. Sub-groups II to VI contain organisms, referred to as paracholera and cholera-like, that have been isolated from cases of choleraic diarrhœa or from water. Thus, according to Gardner and Venkatraman, the true cholera vibrio is a non-hæmolytic organism containing the specific O antigen of sub-group I; except by hæmolysin production it is indistinguishable from El Tor vibrios containing the same O antigen. A non-specific O antigen, shared to a variable extent by all the members of Group A, has also been described by these workers.

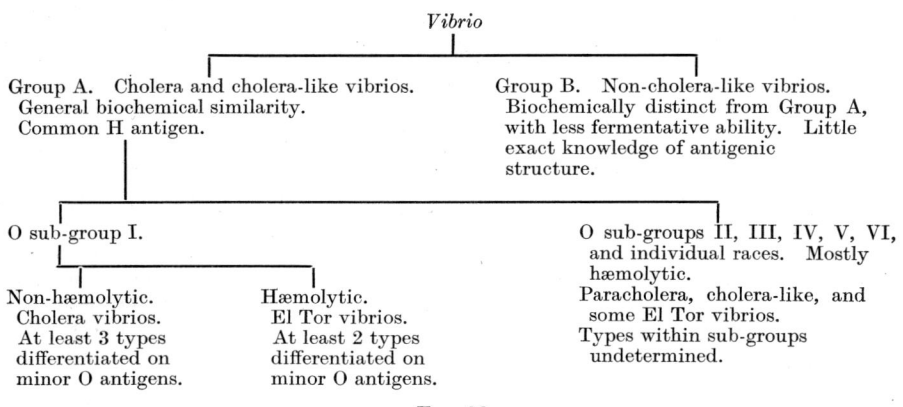

FIG. 86.

The classification just given refers to the antigenic structure of vibrios in the smooth state. White (1935a), however, has proposed another classification based on a study of vibrios in the rough state. Just as with the Salmonella group, he finds that the transformation of the smooth to the rough phase is accompanied by a loss of specific O antigens and the unmasking of a common rough antigen. In consequence, many organisms that are antigenically diverse in the smooth state show a close similarity in the rough. White has established four rough serological groupings. Rough group A contains strains derived from Gardner and Venkatraman's smooth O sub-group I; rough group B from smooth O sub-group II; rough group C from smooth O sub-groups III and IV; and rough group D from unclassified smooth O sub-groups.

Variants in a further stage of degradation, known as ρ variants, have been described by White (1934b, 1935a). Organisms of this type have lost their dominant rough O antigen, and appear serologically similar owing to the unmasking of a still deeper common ρ antigen.

The chemical analysis of the various antigens present in the *Vibrio* group is still in its infancy. The early work of Landsteiner and Levine (1927) has been followed up by Linton and Mitra (for references see Linton, Shrivastava, and Mitra 1935) who find that specific protein and specific carbohydrate substances are arranged in different combinations in different vibrios. Among the hydrolytic products of the polysaccharides, galactose and arabinose have been identified. These workers have suggested a classification of the *Vibrios* into 6 groups, but since the relationship between these groups and those based on pure serological study is not yet clear it seems advisable to await further work before attempting a classification along chemical lines. White (1934*a*, 1935*b*) has described the occurrence of alcohol-soluble protein antigens, which he refers to as Q antigens. There is reason to believe that these substances play a part in the non-specific O agglutination of boiled vibrios described by Gardner and Venkatraman. White (1936), moreover, has established, in smooth vibrios of Group A, the presence of three polysaccharides. In rough strains one, and in ρ strains two, of the polysaccharides are missing.

In an immune serum, prepared by injecting rabbits or goats with dead or living cholera vibrios, bacteriolysins are present, which can be demonstrated by Pfeiffer's test. This reaction is of some importance in identification, and is described fully in the chapter on Cholera. Specific bacteriolysins also appear in sera prepared by injection of other members of the group.

Pathogenicity.—The cholera vibrio causes Asiatic cholera in man. Metchnikoff's vibrio apparently is responsible for a choleraic disease in chickens (Gamaléia 1888*a*) —not for true chicken cholera, which is due to a member of the *Pasteurella* group. It is possible that *V. phosphorescens* may cause acute gastro-enteritis in man, but this has not been proved conclusively (Jermoljewa 1926).

A disease simulating cholera may be reproduced in guinea-pigs and new-born rabbits by certain experimental procedures (see Chapter LX). The cholera vibrio when given by mouth, or injected *per rectum*, is harmless to mice, rabbits, guinea-pigs, and monkeys. Intraperitoneal injection into guinea-pigs is fatal within 24 hours. If a small dose of vibrios—¼ loopful of an 18-hours' agar culture—is given, the animal dies of toxæmia, and at necropsy the peritoneal cavity is sterile. If a larger dose is given, ½ loopful, cultures from the peritoneal cavity may be positive ; and if a still larger dose is given, 1 or more loopfuls, the vibrios may be recovered also from the heart blood. Intraperitoneal injection of mice is fatal in 24 to 48 hours. Intravenous injection of young rabbits is fatal in 1 to 5 days.

Metchnikoff's vibrio is more invasive than the cholera vibrio. Even after a small dose given intraperitoneally to guinea-pigs, the vibrios can be recovered from the heart's blood. It is fatal to guinea-pigs even when given subcutaneously ; under these conditions the cholera vibrio gives rise merely to a local abscess. Both guinea-pigs and chickens can be infected by feeding with *V. metchnikovi*. Moreover this organism is pathogenic to pigeons, on intramuscular injection, while the cholera vibrio is not, except occasionally in large doses (Wherry 1905). Pigeons injected intramuscularly with ⅓ agar culture of *V. metchnikovi* die in about 8 hours with general septicæmia (Metchnikoff 1893). Intratracheal injection appears to be even more fatal, since not only guinea-pigs, pigeons, and fowls, but also rabbits may be infected by this route (Gamaléia 1888*b*). Deneke's *Vibrio tyrogenus* is pathogenic for the guinea-pig and the pigeon. Half an agar culture injected intraperitoneally into a guinea-pig was fatal in 6 hours, and a whole agar culture injected intramuscularly into a pigeon was fatal in 7 hours (Metchnikoff 1893). Finkler-Prior's *Vibrio proteus* resembles *V. tyrogenus*, but is slightly less virulent.

P.B.   O*

V. phosphorescens is pathogenic for guinea-pigs, rabbits, and pigeons. About 500 million organisms injected intraperitoneally into guinea-pigs, intravenously into rabbits, or intramuscularly into pigeons proved fatal in 24 hours ; vibrios were isolated post mortem from the heart's blood of the pigeons (Jermoljewa 1926). If a guinea-pig that has died after intraperitoneal injection is opened up and placed in the dark, the viscera are seen to exhibit a marked phosphorescence (Kutscher 1893).

Most other members of the group are non-pathogenic. The virulence of *V. choleræ* is variable. Freshly isolated strains are more virulent than those kept in the laboratory. Moreover, even on isolation, the virulence of different strains to laboratory animals appears to vary. Haffkine (1892) stated that it was possible to raise the virulence by passing the organisms through the peritoneal cavity of guinea-pigs ; between each injection the peritoneal exudate was exposed to the air for some time at room temperature. By growing the vibrio in broth in a constantly aerated atmosphere and subculturing every 2 or 3 days, the virulence was said to diminish. Gotschlich and Weigang (1895) also stated that the virulence might be raised by intraperitoneal passage through guinea-pigs.

We append a summarized description of *V. choleræ*, and brief notes on the characters of other species which have been described and named. (For general classification of members of this group, see Heiberg 1935.)

Vibrio choleræ

Synonym.—Comma bacillus.

Isolation.—Koch in 1884 (1886).

Ecology.—Intestinal contents of cholera patients and carriers.

Morphology.—Slightly curved bacillus, often resembling a comma. Varies considerably in size, 1·5–4 μ × 0·2–0·4 μ. One end often blunter than the other ; ends rounded ; axis generally curved ; sides converging or parallel. Arranged singly, or in s-shaped pairs ; sometimes short chains are found, and sometimes spirals. In the intestinal contents, arranged like fish in a stream. In old cultures the bacilli are very small, resembling granules, and stain poorly. Involution forms numerous. Actively motile by a single polar flagellum. Gram-negative. Non-sporing. Non-acid-fast.

Agar Plate.—24 *hours at* 37° C. Round, 1–2 mm. in diameter, low convex, translucent, greyish-yellow colonies with smooth, or finely granular, glistening surface and entire edge, and of amorphous or finely granular structure ; consistency butyrous ; easily emulsifiable. 7 *days* ; slightly larger ; edge entire or undulate ; surface sometimes studded with small, knob-like secondary colonies ; colony is sometimes surrounded by a narrow, effuse, transparent peripheral extension. Crystals often formed in the medium.

Agar Stroke.—24 *hours at* 37° C. Good, raised, translucent, greyish-yellow layer of growth, with smooth, glistening surface, and edge formed of single colonies. 7 *days* ; surface sometimes studded with small, knob-like secondary colonies. Crystals often formed in the medium.

Gelatin Plate.—2 *days at* 23° C. Round, 0·5 mm. in diameter, amorphous, raised or low convex, greyish-white, opaque colonies, with smooth or slightly granular surface and entire or crenated edge. Zone of liquefaction around colony ; small flocculi of growth in liquefied gelatin.

Gelatin Stab.—3 *days at* 22° C. Good filiform growth, confluent at top, discrete below, extending to bottom of tube. Infundibuliform or napiform liquefaction ; thick, yellowish-brown pellicle on surface of liquid gelatin, and coarsely granular turbidity.

Broth.—24 *hours at* 37° *C.* Abundant growth with moderate turbidity, a slight powdery deposit, and a thick surface pellicle, breaking up on shaking into coarse membranous and granular pieces.

Loeffler's Serum.—10 *days at* 37° *C.* Good growth with partial liquefaction.

Horse Blood Agar Plates.—24 *hours at* 37° *C.* Abundant growth ; colonies are surrounded for 2 mm. by a zone of α- or β-hæmolysis.

Potato.—7 *days at* 37° *C.* Good, confluent, café-au-lait growth with smooth glistening surface.

MacConkey Plate.—24 *hours at* 37° *C.* Good growth of clear, colourless colonies smaller than those on agar. After 7 to 9 days the colonies take on a reddish colour.

Resistance.—Not specially resistant. Easily killed by drying. Destroyed by heat at 55° C. in 15 minutes. Dried on linen or threads they survive 1 to 3 days. Killed by 0·5 per cent. phenol in a few minutes. Survive in clean tap water up to 30 days, but perish in 24 hours in cesspool water.

Metabolism.—Strongly aerobic ; very slight growth noticeable on agar and in broth after a week under strictly anaerobic conditions. Optimum temperature 37° C. ; limits 16–42° C. Optimum pH 7·0–8·0. Limits for growth pH 6·4–9·6. Growth favoured slightly by blood. Grows well and rapidly in peptone water. No soluble hæmolysin formed for sheep or goat cells. Proteolytic and diastatic ferments secreted.

Biochemical.—Acid, no gas, in glucose, maltose, mannitol, and sucrose in 1 to 3 days ; after 14 days there may be slight acid in lactose. L.M. acid, or acid and clot in 14 days. Indole $+$. Cholera-red reaction $+$. M.R.$-$. V.P. $-$. Nitrates reduced. $NH_3 +$. $H_2S +$ in 14 days. Catalase $+$. M.B. reduction $+$.

Antigenic Structure.—All strains have a common O antigen, but 3 sub-types are distinguishable. Immune sera prepared by injection of rabbits, goats, or horses with living vibrios contain specific bacteriolysins, demonstrable by Pfeiffer's test.

Pathogenicity.—Causes Asiatic cholera in human beings. A similar disease may be reproduced experimentally in new-born rabbits by feeding, and in young guinea-pigs by Koch's procedure. Pathogenic on *ip.* or *iv.* inoculation into guinea-pigs, rabbits, and mice, but not as a rule into pigeons. One loopful of an 18-hours' agar culture of a virulent strain injected *ip.* into a young guinea-pig is fatal within 24 hours. P.M. congestion of peritoneal and pleural cavities with some sero-sanguineous fluid. Small gut congested ; may be fibrin over the abdominal viscera. Vibrios may or may not be cultivated from the peritoneal cavity. If a large dose is given the vibrios can be recovered from the peritoneal fluid and the heart blood. *Iv.* injection of five loopfuls of an 18-hour agar culture of a virulent strain into rabbits is fatal in 48 hours or less. P.M. small gut congested and contains thin fluid. Vibrios generally recoverable from the blood. No true exotoxin formed, but disintegrated bodies of bacilli are very toxic to animals. Virulence rapidly falls on artificial cultivation.

Finkler-Prior's Vibrio proteus.—Isolated by Finkler and Prior (1884) from the old putrid excreta of a patient suffering from gastro-enteritis. Morphologically and culturally it resembles the cholera vibrio, but it can be differentiated by serological reactions, and by its failure to give the cholera-red reaction. Has frequently been found in water.

Deneke's Vibrio tyrogenus.—Found by Deneke (1885) in cheese. Resembles the cholera vibrio, but liquefies gelatin more rapidly, grows poorly or not at all on potato, and does not give the cholera-red reaction.

Vibrio metchnikovi.—Isolated by Gamaléia (1888a) from the blood and intestinal contents of chickens dying from a cholera-like disease at Odessa. Resembles the cholera vibrio very closely ; gelatin is liquefied more rapidly ; growth on MacConkey is poorer. Cholera-red and other biochemical reactions are identical with those of *V. choleræ*. It is much more invasive when injected into animals, killing guinea-pigs injected subcutaneously, and pigeons injected intramuscularly (see Pathogenicity). Can be separated from *V. choleræ* by agglutination and Pfeiffer's reactions. Has been isolated from water.

Vibrio phosphorescens.—Isolated by Dunbar (1893) from the Elbe in 1893. Shown by Kutscher (1893) to exhibit phosphorescence in the dark. This occurs on ordinary media at 22° C., reaching its maximum in 24 to 48 hours in gelatin, broth, or peptone water, and disappearing rapidly. It is a function of the living bacilli. Phosphorescence is not visible in cultures incubated anaerobically. *V. phosphorescens* grows in, and liquefies gelatin, more rapidly than V. *choleræ*. Grows very poorly or not at all on potato. Hæmolytic and diastatic ; produces indole ; gives acid in glucose, mannitol, lactose, and later maltose (Jermoljewa 1926). It has been isolated from human fæces (Jermoljewa 1926).

El Tor Vibrio.—Isolated by Gotschlich (1906) in 1905 from six pilgrims who had died of dysentery or gangrene of the colon at the Tor quarantine station on the Sinai Peninsula. Forms soluble hæmolysin for sheep and goat cells. Gives atypical Pfeiffer reaction (Neufeld and Haendel 1907). Relation to *V. choleræ* still doubtful (see Fig. 86).

Vibrio berolinensis.—Isolated by Neisser (1893) from water to which cholera vibrios had intentionally been added. Resembles the cholera vibrio closely ; gelatin colonies are smaller and animal pathogenicity is low. But probably it is merely a variant of the true cholera vibrio. Similarly the " **Vibrio ivanoff** " (Ivanoff 1893), which was cultured from the fæces of a typhoid patient to which cholera vibrios had been added, and which differed in unimportant particulars from the cholera vibrio, is also a variant of the true cholera vibrio (Dieudonné 1894).

Vibrio danubicus.—Isolated by Heider (1893) from the Danube canal. Resembles the cholera vibrio closely, but can be differentiated by serological reactions.

Vibrio helcogenes.—Isolated by Fischer (1893) from the diarrhœal fæces of a woman. Some of the mice inoculated subcutaneously developed ulcers of the skin ; hence the name.

The Massauah vibrio was isolated by Pasquale (1891) from the fæces of a patient who was probably not suffering from cholera. Resembles the cholera vibrio closely, but has four peritrichate flagella ; it is therefore not a true *Vibrio*. The **Ghinda vibrio** was isolated by Pasquale from water ; it was regarded as a true cholera vibrio, but has since been shown to be distinguished from it by its immunity reactions.

The Nasik vibrio differs in several respects from *V. choleræ*. It is less like a comma and is short and rather fat : arranged singly, and with great regularity ; filamentous forms are common. The colonies on agar are more opaque than those of cholera. Infundibuliform liquefaction occurs in gelatin, later stratiform ; the liquefied gelatin is uniformly turbid and contains no flocculi. No growth under anaerobic conditions. Acid in glucose only ; L.M. purple and clotted ; indole — ; nitrate reduction — ; $NH_3 +$; H_2S — ; Catalase $++$; M.B. reduction — ; cholera-red reaction — ; β-hæmolysis in horse blood agar plates in 4 days. Café-au-lait growth on potato. Broth cultures are very toxic to rabbits on intravenous injection (Kolle and Schürmann 1912).

Vibrio fetus.—This organism, on account of its special characteristics, must be considered separately. It was first isolated and described by Macfadyen and Stockman in 1913 (see Report 1913), who found it in the uterine exudate of aborting sheep. Smith (1918) cultivated the same organism in America from the fœtuses of aborting cows (see Chapter LXII) ; he named it *V. fetus* (Smith and Taylor 1919). In young cultures it is generally shaped like a comma, but later it assumes a spirillar appearance. It is questionable whether this organism should be classified as a *Vibrio* or as a *Spirillum* ; its characters partake of both groups. But since Smith has placed it with the *Vibrios*, since it has a single polar flagellum, and since it is Gram-negative, it is perhaps best to regard it as belonging to the *Vibrio* group.

Morphologically, the smallest forms appear as minute, slender, s-shaped lines ; the longest forms may stretch nearly across the field of the microscope. In length it is 1·5 to 5 μ or more, and in breadth about 0·2 to 0·3 μ. A single organism shows one or two spirals , the length of each spiral is about 2 μ, and the amplitude about 0·5 μ. In the long forms the spirals are drawn out, so that their length is far greater than their breadth. The short forms are sharply curved ; the spirals often show an obtuse-angled curve. In young cultures the vibrios are actively motile by a single polar flagellum ; in cultures a week old very few are motile. The organism is best stained with alkaline methylene blue, the staining being prolonged over-night. It is Gram-negative. In old cultures many of the organisms show granular degeneration.

For growth in artificial media, a reduced oxygen pressure is required. When first isolated, it will not grow on agar without the addition of blood or some other animal fluid. The growth is very delicate, and occurs at the edges of the slope between the agar and the glass ; subsequently it spreads round the convexity of the agar. After some months of cultivation in the laboratory, a thin surface growth may be obtained. Growth in fluid media, even in blood broth, does not occur till the strain has become thoroughly accustomed to saprophytic conditions. There is no growth in gelatin, milk or potato. Sugars are not fermented, and there is no production of indole. In cultures, it lives for 2 to 20 weeks at room temperature, but dies rapidly in the ice-chest. Dried on threads, it lives for less than 3 hours. It is killed by 56° C. in 5 minutes. The optimum temperature for growth is 37° C. Antigenically it appears by agglutination to be homogeneous (Smith and Taylor 1919). It is non-pathogenic to laboratory animals. Under natural conditions it gives rise apparently to abortion in cattle and sheep. Experimental inoculation of pure cultures into pregnant cows may be followed by disease of the fœtal membranes (Smith 1919).

A closely related organism, named *Vibrio jejuni*, has been described by Jones and Little (1931), and Jones, Orcutt, and Little (1931). It appears to be responsible for a disease of calves and older cattle, which may occur in epidemic form during the autumn and winter months, and is known as *winter dysentery* or *black scours*. The organisms are most abundant in the jejunum.

SPIRILLUM

DEFINITION.—*Spirillum.*

Rigid rods of spiral form, varying considerably in the number, length, and breadth of the spirals. Usually motile by means of a tuft of polar flagella (5 to 20), which are mostly semicircular in shape. The flagella occur at one or both poles ; their number varies greatly, and is difficult to determine, since in stained preparations several are often united into a common strand. Generally Gram-positive. Some species form a reddish-yellow, or greenish-yellow pigment. Found in water or putrid infusions.

Type species. *Spirillum undula.*

Not many organisms in this group have been described. One of the best known is *Spirillum rubrum*, which was isolated by Esmarch (1887) from a mouse that had been decomposing for 3 months under water.

Morphologically the *Spirilla* show considerable variation. Their length may vary from 1 to 50 μ, and the number of spirals from 1 to about 50. The length of the individual spiral varies according to the species of organism ; in some *Spirilla* the spirals are close set, each one being not more than about 1 μ in length ; in others they are looser, and may be 10 μ or so in length. The width of the organisms varies from about 0·3 to 1·0 μ, and the amplitude of the spirals from about 0·8 to 2·0 μ. Even amongst different organisms of the same strain, there is often considerable variation in the number and size of the spirals ; together with organisms showing regularly disposed spirals, there may be seen others of two or three times the length, with only one or two irregular undulations. In shape the whole organism may be straight, or it may be bent in one or more places, generally acutely. Filamentous forms are not uncommon. On agar or gelatin the spiral shape may be almost lost, and the organisms closely resemble vibrios. As a rule the curvature is very marked, and there is a tendency for the organisms to be arranged in pairs end-to-end with the concavities facing in the same direction, so as to present a scalloped appearance ; s-shaped forms too are common. In young cultures the *Spirilla* are motile—generally by tufts of flagella at the poles. Unlike the *Spiro-chætæ*, the *Spirilla* stain readily with the ordinary aniline dyes, and are usually Gram-positive. Growth is fairly free, though not abundant, on the ordinary media. Most of the water *Spirilla* form a pigment of red, yellow, or greenish-yellow colour. The pigment, at least of *Sp. rubrum*, is formed most readily at a low oxygen pressure ; it is well marked in the depths of gelatin stab cultures, and hardly noticeable on surface growths. The optimum temperature for growth is

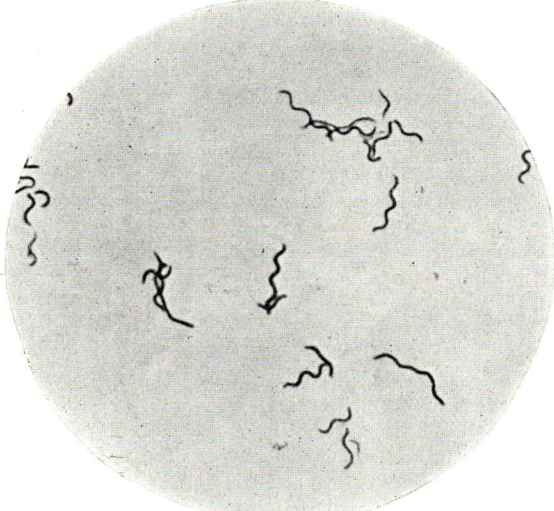

Fig. 87.—*Spirillum rubrum*.
From a broth culture, 2 days, 30° C. (× 1000).

25–30° C. as a rule. Aerobic conditions are preferred ; growth under strict anaerobiosis is very slight. None of the species form spores, and none are particularly resistant to heat or disinfectants. The biochemical characteristics have not been fully studied. None of the members are pathogenic for man or animals. We append a description, based largely on personal observations, of *Spirillum rubrum*.

Spirillum rubrum

Isolation.—Esmarch 1887, from a mouse decomposing under water.
Ecology.—Water.
Morphology.—On solid media the organisms are sharply curved rods, 2–3 μ × 0·4 μ. arranged singly and in s-shaped or semicircular pairs. In fluid media long spirals are formed, 3–10 μ or more in length. The axis of the spiral is straight, or bent sharply at a right-angle ; the number of spirals varies from about 1 to 8. Ends

are sharp, drawn out, or sometimes blunt. Long thread-like forms also seen. Motile by bundles of flagella at both poles. Gram-positive.

Agar Plate.—2 *days at* 28° C. Round, 0·4 mm. in diameter, convex, amorphous, almost colourless and transparent colonies with smooth glistening surface and entire edge ; consistency butyrous ; easily emulsifiable. 7 *days* ; rather larger and of a pinkish colour.

Agar Stroke.—2 *days at* 28° C. Poor, slightly raised, and almost transparent, partly confluent growth, with irregular surface, and edge formed of single colonies. 7 *days* ; slight pinkish coloration.

Gelatin Plate.—4 *days at* 23° C. Small, 0·3 mm. in diameter, water-clear, convex colonies, with smooth surface and entire edge. No liquefaction. Deep colonies are pink.

Gelatin Stab.—5 *days at* 23° C. Poor to moderate, filiform growth of very tiny discrete red colonies, extending nearly to bottom of tube. No surface growth ; no liquefaction.

Broth.—2 *days at* 28° C. Moderate growth with slight turbidity, and a pale pink flocculogranular deposit, not disintegrating completely on shaking ; no surface growth.

MacConkey.—7 *days at* 28° C. No growth.

Potato.—7 *days at* 28° C. Poor growth of discrete or partly confluent red colonies.

Horse Blood Agar Plate.—2 *days at* 28° C. Very small, low convex colonies ; no hæmolysis.

Resistance.—Not specially resistant. Dried on silk threads, the organisms do not survive longer than 6 to 8 days.

Metabolism. Aerobic ; grows very poorly under anaerobic conditions. Optimum temperature 25–30° C., often little growth at 37° C. Grows very poorly in peptone water. No hæmolysin formed. Red pigment formed, best under a low oxygen pressure.

Biochemical—No sugars fermented. L.M. unchanged. Indole —. Cholera-red reaction —. M.R. —. V.P. —. Nitrates not reduced. NH_3+. H_2S —. Catalase +. M.B. reduction—.

Pathogenicity.—Non-pathogenic to man or animals.

Other members of this group that have been described are *Spirillum undula*, *Spirillum serpens*, *Spirillum volutans*, and *Spirillum minus* (see Chapter LXXIX).

REFERENCES

ABDOOSH, Y. B. (1932) *Brit. J. exp. Path.*, **13**, 42.
ANDU, A. B. and NIEKERK, J. VAN. (1929) *Zbl. Bakt.*, **112**, 519.
BALTEANU, I. (1926) *J. Path. Bact.*, **29**, 251.
BOCCHIA, I. (1911) *Zbl. Bakt.*, **60**, 434.
CRASTER, C. V. (1913) *J. infect. Dis.*, **12**, 472.
CRENDIROPOULO. (1912) *Conseil san. maritime quarant. d'Égypte.*
DENEKE, T. (1885) *Dtsch. med. Wschr.*, **11**, 33.
DIEUDONNÉ. (1894) *Zbl. Bakt.*, **16**, 363 ; (1909) *Ibid.*, **50**, 107.
DOORENBOS, W. (1936) *C. R. Soc. Biol.*, **121**, 128, 130.
DUNBAR. (1893) *Dtsch. med. Wschr.*, **19**, 799.
DUNGERN, VON. (1895) *Z. Hyg. InfektKr.*, **20**, 147.
ESMARCH, E. (1887) *Zbl. Bakt.*, **1**, 225.
FINKLER and PRIOR. (1884) *Dtsch. med. Wschr.*, **10**, 579, 632.
FISCHER. (1893) *Dtsch. med. Wschr.*, **19**, 541, 575, 598, 627.
GAMALÉIA, M. N. (1888a) *Ann. Inst. Pasteur*, **2**, 482 ; (1888b) *Ibid.*, **2**, 552.
GARDNER, A. D. and VENKATRAMAN, K. V. (1935) *J. Hyg., Camb.*, **35**, 262.
GOHAR, M. A. (1932) *Brit. J. exp. Path.*, **13**, 371.
GORDON, M. H. (1906) *Brit. med. J.*, ii. 197.
GOTSCHLICH, E. (1895) *Z. Hyg. InfektKr.*, **20**, 489 ; (1906) *Ibid.*, **53**, 281.

GOTSCHLICH, E. and WEIGANG, J. (1895) *Z. Hyg., InfektKr.*, **20**, 376.
HAHN, M. and HIRSCH, J. (1929) *Z. Hyg. InfektKr.*, **110**, 355.
HAFFKINE, W. M. W. (1892) *C. R. Soc. Biol.*, **44**, 635, 671.
HEIBERG, B. (1935) " On the Classification of the *V. cholerae* and the cholera-like Vibrios."
  Arnold Busck, Copenhagen.
HEIDER, A. (1893) *Zbl. Bakt.*, **14**, 341.
IVANOFF, M. (1893) *Z. Hyg. InfektKr.*, **15**, 434.
JERMOLJEWA, S. (1926) *Zbl. Bakt.*, **100**, 170.
JONES, F. S. and LITTLE, R. B. (1931) *J. exp. Med.*, **53**, 835, 845.
JONES, F. S., ORCUTT, M., and LITTLE, R. B. (1931) *J. exp. Med.*, **53**, 853.
KABÉSHIMA, T. (1918) *C. R. Soc. Biol.*, **81**, 618.
KITASATO, S. (1889) *Z. Hyg. InfektKr.*, **5**, 134.
KOCH, R. (1886) " The Etiology of Cholera," New Sydenham. Soc., **115**, 327.
KOLLE, W. and SCHÜRMANN, W. (1912) See Kolle and Wassermann Handb. path. Mikroorg.
  (1912–13) **4**, 1.
KUTSCHER. (1893) *Dtsch. med. Wschr.*, **19**, 1301; (1895) *Z. Hyg. InfektKr.*, **19**, 461.
LANDSTEINER, K. and LEVINE, P. (1927) *J. exp. Med.*, **46**, 213.
LINTON, R. W., SHRIVASTAVA, D. L., and MITRA, B. N. (1935) *Indian J. med. Res.*, **22**, 633.
LOGHEM, J. J. VAN. (1932) *Ned. Tijdschr. Geneesk.*, **76**, 1939.
MAASSEN, A. (1902) *Arb. ReichsgesundhAmt.*, **18**, 21.
MANWARING, W. H., BOYD, W. H., and OKAMI, S. (1923) *J. infect. Dis.*, **32**, 307.
METCHNIKOFF, E. (1893) *Ann. Inst. Pasteur*, **7**, 562.
NEISSER, M. (1893) *Arch. Hyg.*, **19**, 194.
NEUFELD and HAENDEL. (1907) *Arb. ReichsgesundhAmt.*, **26**, 536.
NICATI, W. and RIETSCH, M. (1884) *C. R. Acad. Sci.*, **99**, 928.
NOBECHI, K. (1925) *J. Bact.*, **10**, 197.
PASQUALE, A. (1891) *G. med. Eserc.*, **39**, 1009.
PALADINO-BLANDINI, A. (1906) *Ann. Igiene (sper.)*, **15**, 301.
PFEIFFER, R. (1892) *Z. Hyg. InfektKr.*, **11**, 393; (1894) *Ibid.*, **18**, 1; (1895a) *Ibid.*, **19**, 75;
  (1895b) *Ibid.*, **20**, 198.
Report. (1913) Rep. Dep. Comm. Epizootic Abortion, Part III. London.
RUFFER, M. A. (1907) *Conseil san. mar. et Quarant. d'Égypte.*
SHOUSHA, A. T. (1931) *Bull. Off. int. Hyg. publ.*, **23**, 1022.
SMITH, T. (1894) *Zbl. Bakt.*, **16**, 324; (1918) *J. exp. Med.*, **28**, 701; (1919) *Ibid.*, **30**, 313.
SMITH, T. and TAYLOR, M. S. (1919) *J. exp. Med.*, **30**, 299.
VEDDER, A. and DAM, W. VAN. (1932) *Zbl. Bakt.*, **126**, 145.
WHERRY, W. B. (1905) *J. infect. Dis.*, **2**, 309.
WHITE, P. B. (1934a) *J. Path. Bact.*, **39**, 529; (1934b) *Ibid.*, **39**, 530; (1935a) *J. Hyg.*,
  Camb., **35**, 347; (1935b) *Ibid.*, **35**, 498; (1936) *Pers. comm.*
YEN, A. C. H. (1932–3) *Proc. Soc. exp. Biol., N.Y.*, **30**, 884.
ZIMMERMANN, E. (1932) *Zbl. Bakt.*, **127**, 146; (1933) *Z. ImmunForsch.*, **79**, 219.

CHAPTER XXII

NEISSERIA

DEFINITION.—*Neisseria.*

Gram-negative cocci, usually arranged in pairs. Strict parasites, often growing poorly on ordinary media, but growing well on serum media. Frequently pathogenic.

Type species is *N. gonorrhœœ.*

The first member of this group to be described was the gonococcus; it was observed by Neisser in 1879 in the pus cells of patients with gonorrhœa, and was successfully cultivated by Bumm (1885*a, b*) and by Leistikow and Loeffler (Leistikow 1882) in 1882. Weichselbaum isolated the meningococcus from the cerebrospinal fluid of patients with cerebrospinal meningitis in the year 1887. In 1895 Jaeger described a similar organism, which he regarded as identical with the meningococcus, but which was almost certainly not this organism; it is now known as the *Diplococcus crassus.* R. Pfeiffer (see Flügge 1896) described the *Micrococcus catarrhalis* in 1896; he found it in the bronchioles and alveoli of children with broncho-pneumonia; it was carefully studied in 1902 by Ghon and H. Pfeiffer. In 1906 von Lingelsheim described a number of Gram-negative cocci in the nasopharynx of healthy and diseased persons; these included the *Micrococcus pharyngis siccus,* the *Micrococcus pharyngis cinereus,* the *Diplococcus mucosus,* and the *Micrococcus pharyngis flavus i, ii, and iii.* More recently Branham (1930) has added another member to the group, *N. flavescens.* This organism was isolated from the spinal fluid of patients with epidemic cerebrospinal meningitis.

Habitat.—With the exception of the gonococcus, which is the causative organism of gonorrhœa, those species of Gram-negative cocci which have been adequately described are found almost exclusively in the naso-pharynx of healthy and diseased persons, or, in the case of the meningococcus, in the meninges and cerebrospinal fluid of patients with cerebrospinal fever.

Morphology.—The members of the group are all Gram-negative cocci, but they differ considerably in their morphology and arrangement, and in the ease with which they are decolorized by alcohol. Not only do they differ from one another, but the same organism may vary considerably according to environmental conditions; thus, in the body, the meningococcus and the gonococcus present an almost typical arrangement in the form of diplococci with flattened or slightly concave adjacent sides, but in culture they appear as oval or spherical cocci without the typical diplococcal arrangement. Most of the members of the group are arranged in pairs, tetrads, or small groups; but some members, such as *N. pharyngis.*

401

appear frequently in the form of dense clumps with occasional isolated organisms. One difference in arrangement that serves to distinguish Gram-negative from Gram-positive diplococci is the way in which the main axis of the oval is directed ; with the Gram-negative cocci this axis is always at right angles to the axis joining the two cocci ; with the Gram-positive cocci it is often coincident with it. In other words, pairs of Gram-negative cocci are usually compressed laterally, Gram-positive cocci often longitudinally. As a rule the Gram-negative cocci are decolorized without difficulty, but some members tend to retain the gentian violet, and so take on an indeterminate colour, which is most confusing. The most notable example of this is Jaeger's coccus or the *Diplococcus crassus* ; in a single film Gram-positive and Gram-negative, and numerous other cocci with an indeterminate colour, are found lying side by side. One reason for the indeterminate staining of some of the Gram-negative cocci is the tendency they have to be arranged in groups or dense clumps ; once these have been stained with gentian violet, they are not easily decolorized. Hence it is important always to make films as thin and as uniform as possible. In young cultures the cocci stain fairly evenly, but after about 24 hours autolytic changes set in, with the result that so-called involution forms appear ; these are generally large, swollen cocci, which stain poorly. Both the meningococcus and the gonococcus are characterized, as compared with most other *Neisseriæ*, by the frequency with which such forms appear ; and it may be noted that many of the large swollen forms, in cultures of these species, stain deeply and uniformly.

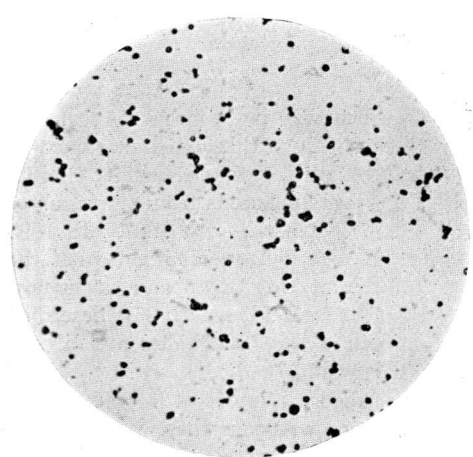

FIG. 88.—*Neisseria meningitidis.*
From a serum agar slope culture, 4 days, 37° C.
(× 1000).

J. E. Gordon (1921) described a variety of *N. catarrhalis* in which the degenerative forms began to appear after the 4th hour, but this is unusually early. Some workers have described the presence of Babes-Ernst bodies or metachromatic granules in members of this group. Elser and Huntoon (1909) state that the meningococcus, when stained with Loeffler's methylene blue, often shows a brightly stained central spot, whilst the remainder of the cell is scarcely coloured ; with Neisser's stain the granules stain bluish-black, the cell body brown. Marx and Woithe (1900) found these granules in gonococci, but only in organisms taken from the florid stage of gonorrhœa ; they state that the whole cell may appear filled with granules.

Growth Requirements.—Culturally many of the Gram-negative cocci are characterized by a reluctance to grow on ordinary media, especially fluid media. Most of the nasopharyngeal cocci will grow—though often poorly—on nutrient agar, but the meningococcus will not do so ; the addition, however, of a small quantity of blood or serum is sufficient to enable growth to occur. The most fastidious is the gonococcus ; to cultivate this organism a great variety of media have been devised, the majority depending on the addition of some natural protein such as blood, serum, ascitic fluid, or hydrocele fluid to a basis of nutrient agar. The meningococcus and the gonococcus are not always easy to maintain in culture ; even though transplants are made every 2 or 3 days, the organisms not infrequently die out, and the strains are lost.

All the members of the group are aerobic ; little or no growth occurs under strictly anaerobic conditions. Many workers have stated that the meningococcus and the gonococcus grow best under a lowered oxygen pressure, and that their growth is improved by 10 per cent. CO_2 (Wherry and Oliver 1916, Chapin 1918, Kohman 1919, Ruediger 1919, Rockwell and McKhann 1921) ; but numerous other workers have failed to substantiate this (Cook and Stafford 1921, Erickson and Albert 1922, Torrey and Buckell 1922a). When making experiments on the effect of altering the gaseous constitution of the atmosphere, it is very difficult

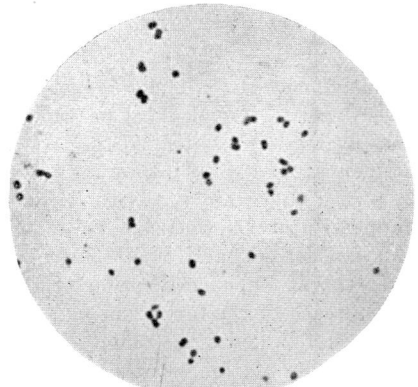

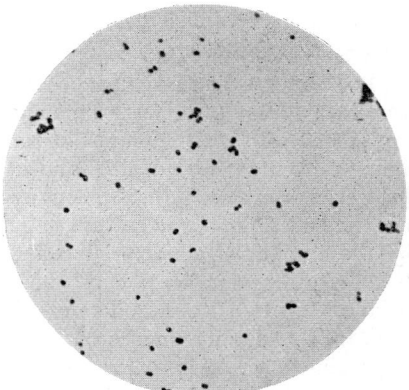

FIG. 89.—*Neisseria gonorrhœæ.*
From a blood agar slope culture, 24 hours, 37° C. (× 1000).

FIG. 90.—*Neisseria pharyngis.*
From a blood agar slope culture, 24 hours, 37° C. (× 1000).

to control all the factors involved ; the technique used may, for instance, change the moisture content of the atmosphere and the rate of evaporation from the medium. The presence of 10 per cent. CO_2 alters the H-ion concentration, and will interfere with the change in the reaction of the medium that normally occurs during growth ; thus CO_2 may be beneficial if the medium has been made too alkaline, and it may by its buffering action prevent the accumulation of acid. The failure to standardize these secondary factors is probably sufficient to explain the diverse results obtained by different workers. The work of McLeod and his colleagues (1934), however, does suggest that growth is improved by the addition of 10 per cent. CO_2, particularly that of freshly isolated strains. Glucose and glycerine have little or no beneficial effect ; peptone in a 1–3 per cent. concentration seems to be favourable. The optimum H-ion concentration for growth is about pH 7·4–7·6 ; the limits within which growth will occur are comparatively narrow, but they depend largely on the constitution of the medium. The optimum temperature for all the members is 37° C. ; some of them, including the meningococcus and the gonococcus, will not grow at all below 30° C. ; many of the nasopharyngeal cocci will grow at 22° C., but not always on first isolation. The meningococcus forms a weak hæmolysin, reaching its maximum in trypagar cultures in about 4 days.

Some of the members—the *pharyngis flava* group—produce a greenish-yellow pigment on solid media, and occasionally a Gram-negative coccus is met with that forms a bright yellow pigment. Some of the Gram-negative cocci, particularly the gonococcus and the meningococcus, contain an active autolysin, which is destroyed by heating to 65° C. for half an hour.

Cultural Characteristics.—The colonial appearances of all the Gram-negative cocci appear to be subject to considerable variation. Two different types of colony of both the meningococcus and the gonococcus have been described (Wassermann 1898, Lipschütz 1904, Atkin 1923, 1925, Cohn 1923) ; and S. P. Wilson (1928) and G. S. Wilson and Smith (1928) have observed and studied rough and smooth types of numerous nasopharyngeal cocci. In fluid media—broth and serum broth —growth is generally poor, and takes the form of a slight turbidity and a finely granular deposit, which disintegrates hardly at all on shaking ; occasionally growth occurs on the surface.

Resistance.—The resistance of the Gram-negative cocci to inimical agencies is very low. In culture most of them die out in a few days ; though if the organisms are seeded into ascitic agar stab tubes—preferably made up with 0·75 per cent. agar—prevented from drying, and kept in the incubator at 37° C., they may live for weeks or even months. Though it is not known with certainty why the Gram-negative cocci die out in culture so quickly, it appears probable that they are killed by the amount of alkali produced ; the production of NH_3 and of alkaline carbonates of organic acids may apparently lower the H-ion concentration of the medium to pH 8·6–9·0, and thus bring about the death of the organisms (Phelon *et al.* 1927). The meningococcus and the gonococcus are killed by heating to 55° C. in 5 minutes or less ; they are very susceptible to desiccation, death occurring usually within an hour or two. Weak disinfectants, such as 1 per cent. phenol or 0·1 per cent. $HgCl_2$, prove fatal in 1 or 2 minutes.

Biochemical Reactions.—Biochemically the members of the group are not very active ; the production of acid in glucose, maltose, and sucrose is used as a means of classification. Other sugars, such as galactose, lævulose, and dextrin, are used by some workers, but those who have had most experience agree that they are unsatisfactory. Since many species of *Neisseria* will not grow on the ordinary peptone water sugar medium, it is necessary in testing their sugar reactions to add a small amount of serum, or to grow them on ascitic fluid agar containing litmus and 1 per cent. of the sugar. Litmus milk is unaltered, except by the *Diplococcus crassus*, which turns it acid. Indole is not produced. The methyl-red test is weakly positive or frankly negative, according to whether or not the organism tested produces acid from glucose ; as the increase in H-ion concentration is rarely greater than to pH 6·0, the red colour developed with methyl red is usually faint. The Voges-Proskauer reaction is negative. Nitrates are not reduced. Catalase is produced, and all the members that have been tested give the oxydase reaction described by Gordon and M'Leod (1928).

Antigenic Structure.—Most attention has been concentrated on the meningococcus and the gonococcus. The meningococcus has been divided into four antigenic types—Types I, II, III and IV (see pp. 408–410) ; but the results obtained depend largely on the source from which the strains are obtained. In epidemic times most of the cocci isolated can be readily typed, but strains isolated from sporadic cases in non-epidemic times are frequently inagglutinable with any of the type sera. The gonococcus is even more irregular ; clear types are difficult to establish. The majority of the strains appear to be related anti-genically, and to fall more or less into one or other of two groups (Atkin 1925) (see pp. 416–418). Little work has been done on the other Gram-negative cocci ; one of the chief reasons for this is that most of them are auto-agglutinable, and homogeneous suspensions cannot be obtained. The complement-fixation test, however, seems to show that there is a group relationship between *N. catarrhalis*, *N. pharyngis*, the gonococcus and the meningococcus (see Oliver 1929, Price 1933).

Studies on the *chemical fractionation* of these organisms are still in their infancy. Boor and Miller (1934) and Miller and Boor (1934), amplifying the work of Zozaya (1931) and Zozaya and Wood (1932) (see p. 410), have extracted " nucleoproteins " and polysaccharides from various members of the group. By the precipitation reaction it was found that the nucleoproteins from the meningococcus, the gonococcus, and *N. catarrhalis* not only resembled each other closely, but also had an affinity with nucleoproteins extracted from pneumococci. Polysaccharides prepared from the meningococcus and the gonococcus reacted in high dilution with Type III antipneumococcal serum, as well as with antimeningococcal and anti-gonococcal serum. The polysaccharide extracted from *N. catarrhalis* reacted with antigonococcal but not with antimeningococcal serum (see also p. 418).

Pathogenicity.—The meningococcus gives rise to rhinopharyngitis, to epidemic cerebrospinal meningitis, and to post-basic meningitis in children ; by intraspinal injection of monkeys it is possible to produce a meningitis with pure cultures of the organism. The gonococcus gives rise in human beings to gonorrhœa, with all its complications, but it is impossible to reproduce this disease in animals.

Towards laboratory animals all the Gram-negative cocci behave in much the same way. Injected intraperitoneally in large doses into mice or guinea-pigs, they cause death in 1 to 3 days. Post mortem, there is a small amount of peritoneal exudate, and sometimes a little fibrin deposit on the organs ; the spleen is slightly enlarged, and there is hyperæmia and degeneration of the viscera. The organisms can be cultivated from the peritoneal exudate, but rarely from the heart's blood. There is little multiplication of organisms inside the body ; no true infection is set up, and death occurs from toxæmia. A similar result follows the injection of heat-killed organisms, though generally a rather larger dose is needed than of living cocci. It seems probable that the toxicity is due to some constituent of the nucleoprotein, since " nucleoprotein " extracted from meningo-cocci and gonococci is almost as toxic to mice as are the dead organisms themselves (Boor and Miller 1934).

Classification

The Gram-negative cocci, as a group, have been studied so little that it is impossible to lay down any satisfactory basis for classification. Apart from the meningococcus and the gonococcus, the definition of the different species is far from clear. This is due largely to the fact that the colonial appearances are sub-ject to such great variation that the descriptions given of apparently the same species by different workers are often quite contradictory. The cultural descrip-tions, for example, of *N. catarrhalis* are most varied (Ghon and Pfeiffer 1902,

Dunn and Gordon, M. H., 1905, von Lingelsheim 1906, Arkwright 1907, Gurd 1908, Elser and Huntoon 1909, Martin 1911, Netter and Debré 1911, Dopter 1921, Gordon, J. E., 1921), and the only sound basis for identification of this organism appears to be its failure to ferment any sugars. Again, in Germany and America, several chromogenic species have been described, forming a greenish-yellow pigment, producing acid in glucose, maltose, and sometimes sucrose, and generally giving a smooth type of colony. In this country a large number of Gram-negative cocci have been isolated from the nasopharynx, giving the same sugar reactions, but quite devoid of pigment. Further it has been found that the colonies formed are sometimes smooth and sometimes rough, and that an organism which gives a smooth colony on isolation may subsequently give a rough type of colony. The differentiation of those organisms giving rough colonies from *N. pharyngis sicca* is in our experience frankly impossible (Wilson, S. P., 1928, Wilson, G. S. and Smith 1928).

At the moment, therefore, it must be confessed that our ignorance is too great to allow of any satisfactory classification. For provisional purposes the classification on sugar reactions may be used, but this is subject to severe

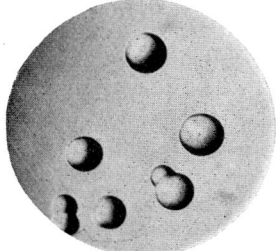

Fig. 91a.—*Neisseria meningitidis.*
Surface colonies on serum agar, 24 hours, 37° C. (× 8).

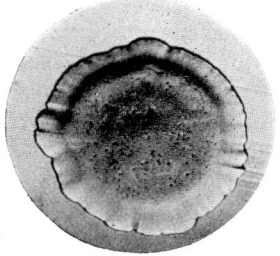

Fig. 91b.—*Neisseria meningitidis.*
Surface colony on serum agar, 7 days, 37° C. (× 8).

limitations. Briefly, it can be said that *N. catarrhalis* ferments no sugars, the gonococcus ferments glucose, and the meningococcus glucose and maltose; the other nasopharyngeal cocci give varied reactions, some being like the meningococcus, and others also fermenting sucrose. The *Diplococcus crassus* can be differentiated by its fermentation of lactose. When first isolated from the body the fermentative reactions of the Gram-negative cocci may be irregular. Nabarro (1917), for example, found that quite a number of meningococci from the cerebrospinal fluid of children with meningitis failed on first isolation to ferment either glucose or maltose. We ourselves have isolated organisms from the nasopharynx which fermented maltose, but not glucose. Other workers have observed similar irregularities in the behaviour of this group.

We append a detailed description of *N. meningitidis* and *N. gonorrhœœ*, together with some further notes on their differentiation; descriptions of those Gram-negative cocci which have received specific names; and a Table giving particulars of the main differential criteria that have been relied upon by different workers in subdividing this group. We would add our personal opinion that there is, at present, little justification for the recognition of separate species among the

Gram-negative cocci of the normal nasopharynx, with the possible exception of *N. catarrhalis*. We should, ourselves, combine the remaining types into a single species, with some appropriate name such as *N. pharyngis*, which we might define as follows :

Neisseria pharyngis.—Non-motile, Gram-negative diplococcus, arranged sometimes in tetrads and often in dense clumps. Grows on agar, giving rise to either rough or smooth colonies, which are generally coherent, tenacious, membranous, and friable, are difficult to emulsify, and are auto-agglutinable when suspended in saline. Grows in serum broth with the production of little or no turbidity, as a rule, and a coarsely granular sediment not disintegrating completely on shaking ; a surface ring growth is not infrequently formed, particularly by the rough variants. A yellow, golden-yellow, or greenish-yellow pigment may be produced, but is variable in its appearance. The sugar reactions are subject to variation ; glucose, maltose, or sucrose may be fermented with the production of acid. Aerobic ; will not grow under strictly anaerobic conditions. Growth is best at 37° C., but will generally occur at 23° C. Non-pathogenic on subcutaneous injection into mice ; large doses intraperitoneally may cause death from toxæmia. The species is subject to great variation in colonial appearance, and, apart from the smooth and rough types, a smooth variant may occur that is of butyrous consistency and easy to emulsify, and also a mucoid variant containing capsulated diplococci (Wilson, G. S. and Smith 1928).

The Meningococcus

Cultural Characters—The meningococcus generally gives rise to a smooth typically lenticular colony. Atkin (1923), however, has demonstrated the existence of colonial variants ; the particular type of colony formed depends partly on the medium and partly on the serological type of coccus. Grown on thick layers (8 mm. deep) of Gordon's trypagar, Type I formed large, irregularly round, raised, whitish colonies with a rough surface and crenated or dentate edge ; secondary papillæ frequently appeared on the surface after the colony had reached its maximum size, and a halo developed in the medium around it, due apparently to precipitation of a salt of legumin by the alkali formed. Type III gave a similar colony, but its colour tended to be pinkish, and the surface to be lumpy ; papillæ did not usually develop, and no halo was formed. Type II gave a smaller, round, convex, yellowish colony with a smooth surface and an entire edge ; there was no development of a halo or of papillæ. Type IV resembled Type II. It is interesting to note that the rough colonies belonged to Types I and III, and the smooth colonies to Types II and IV ; because serologically Types I and III are closely allied, as are also Types II and IV. It was found that Type I could be differentiated from the other types by its shorter life on trypagar plates ; as a rule Type I strains died out in 10 or 12 days, whereas strains of the other types lived for about 3 weeks. On thick glucose trypsin broth agar, the colonial appearances were rather different ; this medium was found to be very useful for developing the colours of the different colonial types ; colonies of Type I were pure white ; Type II had a deep yellow or even reddish-brown tint ; Type III a pinkish or purplish tint, and Type IV a yellow tint.

The meningococcus, on primary isolation, must be provided with such accessory growth factors as are present in blood, serum, milk, and other animal fluids, and in certain vegetable extracts (Lloyd 1916–17). After a few generations on such an enriched medium, it may sometimes be brought to grow on what are described as ordinary culture media, but its vitality under these conditions is very uncertain (Murray 1929). For preservation, the meningococcus should be maintained in ascitic fluid agar stabs or on Dorset egg slopes ; the tubes should be corked to prevent evaporation, and should be kept in the incubator.

The meningococcus forms a very active autolysin ; this is responsible for the swelling and loss of staining properties in cultures more than a few hours old. This autolysin is destroyed by heating to 65° C. for 30 minutes. If the organisms are suspended in saline, covered with toluol to prevent contamination, and incubated at 37° C., autolysis is said to be nearly complete in 4 hours (Flexner 1907*a*). For this reason all suspensions intended for agglutination should have their autolysin inactivated by heat.

Antigenic Structure.—Soon after the agglutination test was introduced for the identification of meningococci, it was noticed that different strains possessed varying degrees of agglutinability. Kutscher (1906), who employed the absorption test, observed that there was a marked difference between strains isolated from different sources, but he was unable to classify them by this method. In 1909 Elser and Huntoon found that 40 per cent. of meningococci were inagglutinable by a monovalent serum, and that these inagglutinable strains, which they term pseudo-meningococci, exhibited a reduced absorption capacity ; they further divided the pseudo-meningococci by absorption into two sub-groups. In the same year Dopter (1909) noticed the presence in nasopharyngeal mucus of cocci resembling the meningococcus in morphology, cultural and fermentation reactions, but differing from it in their complete absence of agglutination with a meningococcal serum ; these organisms he termed parameningococci. Arkwright, also in 1909, studied 25 strains of meningococci from cases occurring in epidemic areas, and 20 strains from sporadic cases ; he noticed not only that by agglutination and absorption the organisms could be roughly divided into groups, but that, serologically, the sporadic strains tended to deviate more from the type to which most strains conformed than did the epidemic strains. In 1914 Dopter and Pauron divided the parameningococci into 3 types, α, β, and γ. Soon after the commencement of the War, Ellis (1915) examined 46 strains from 6 epidemic foci, and found that they fell by agglutination into 2 types, I and II, of which Type II was probably identical with Dopter's parameningococcus. Simultaneously Arkwright (1915) was able to classify 30 out of 35 strains from epidemic cases into 2 main groups, Types I and II, of which Type II, like Ellis's Type II, corresponded to Dopter's parameningococcus ; of the remaining 5 strains, 3 were difficult to classify by agglutination, and 2 were intermediate between the two types. Gordon and Murray (1915) by using the absorption test found that 32 strains from the cerebrospinal fluid of epidemic cases fell sharply into 4 groups, which they called Groups I, II, III, and IV ; none of these groups however showed any relation to Dopter's parameningococcus. In 1917 Nicolle, Debains and Jouan (1918), using the agglutination test alone, were able to classify the meningococci into 4 types, called A, B, C and D. The following correspondence was demonstrated :

> Gordon's I and III strains corresponded to N., D. and J.'s Type A.
>   ,,   II and IV strains   ,,   ,,   ,,   ,, B.
> Dopter's meningococcus   ,,   ,,   ,,   ,, A.
>   ,,   parameningococcus α   ,,   ,,   ,,   ,, B.
>   ,,   ,,   β   ,,   ,,   ,, Type B or C.
>   ,,   ,,   γ   ,,   ,,   ,, Type D.

Finally, F. Griffith (1917), working at the Local Government Board Laboratories, found that meningococci could be divided into two main groups by simple agglutination, Groups I and II ; his Group I corresponded roughly with Gordon and Murray's Groups I and III, and his Group II with Gordon and Murray's Groups II and IV.

Amidst this apparent confusion it will be noticed that the main issue between the different workers is not whether the meningococci can be classified serologically, but whether they are to be classified into 2 or into 4 groups. Before discussing this question, we may remark that Gordon and Murray's work was conducted solely on strains isolated from epidemic cases in adults, whereas Griffith's work included also a number of strains isolated from sporadic cases in children. The differences observed by different workers in the serological behaviour of the meningococcus may perhaps be explained by assuming that the antigenic structure of this organism is complex, and that different strains contain the various antigenic components in different proportions. Such differences may be figured diagrammatically as follows (Fig. 92):

In Type I, A antigen is in excess, and in Type II B antigen. Type III consists mostly of C with a certain amount of A; Type IV consists mostly of D with a certain amount of B. A serum prepared against Type I will agglutinate Type I and, to a less extent, Type III strains, but it will have practically no effect on Type II or Type IV strains. Similarly a serum prepared against Type II will agglutinate Type II and, to a less extent, Type IV strains, while being without action on Type I or Type III strains. A serum prepared against Type III will

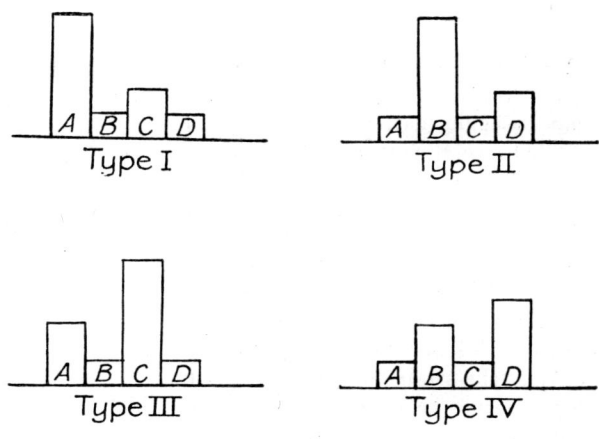

Fig. 92.

agglutinate not only Type III, but probably also some Type I strains; a serum prepared against Type IV will agglutinate not only Type IV, but probably also some Type II strains. These diagrams correspond to Gordon's 4 types. It must be realized that, within any one type, the proportions of the different antigens vary to some extent; the greater the excess of the type antigen over the others, the greater will be the specificity of that particular strain. Gordon noticed this difference in type-specificity, and therefore took care to choose the most specific strains of each of his four types for the preparation of his agglutinating sera. In this way he succeeded in drawing a fairly sharp line of demarcation between them.

Griffith, who did not confine his attention to epidemic strains, obtained a picture of the antigenic relationships of the meningococci which differed in certain respects from that described by Gordon. He found that strains which were agglutinated by Group II sera absorbed the homologous agglutinins from these sera with equal readiness. On the other hand, the strains which were agglutinated by

Group I sera varied in their ability to absorb the agglutinins from those sera. This difference he attributed to variations in complexity of the structure of Group I antigen. Griffith was led by his observations, therefore, to recognize two main groups, the individual strains of which, particularly in the case of Group I, might show varying degrees of complexity. Scott (1917) similarly found that his strains fell into 2 groups.

The more recent, and very thorough, work of Branham, Taft and Carlin (1931) and Branham (1932), based on a study of 221 strains of meningococci isolated during a time of epidemic prevalence in the U.S.A., has merely served to demonstrate the impossibility of laying down hard-and-fast lines for the serological classification of these organisms. Though it is true that these workers ultimately succeeded in assigning every strain to one or other of Gordon and Murray's 4 types, they were able to do so only after prolonged study, involving examination of their agglutinability, their power to absorb agglutinins, and their agglutinogenic capacity. They ascribe the difficulty of classifying meningococci to two main factors—the lack of type specificity and the lack of antigenic stability. These conclusions, which have been reached independently by other workers, and which explain so many of the discrepancies between different reports, render it clear that no rigid system of classification by serological methods can at present be justified.

As well as agglutination, *complement fixation* has been used for classifying the meningococci. Nicolle, Debains and Jouan (1918) found this reaction less specific than that of agglutination, serving to demonstrate the affinities of the different types. Bell (see Report 1920), on the other hand, found that by complement fixation the type-specificity was rendered clearer than by agglutination. Butterfield and Neill (1920) obtained much the same results. The titre of rabbit's serum is often higher in complement-fixing bodies than in agglutinins. Evans (1920) studied the *opsonin* reactions of antimeningococcal serum. By this means she found that 63 strains of meningococci fell sharply into 4 groups ; 4 atypical strains were found. A 5th group could also be demonstrated, which was closely related to the other 4 ; its members were able to effect a partial absorption of the sera prepared against the strains of the other groups.

Too little work has yet been carried out on *chemical fractionation* to enable a satisfactory picture of the antigenic structure of the meningococci to be obtained. Zozaya (1931) and Zozaya and Wood (1932) have reported the presence of polysaccharide and nucleoprotein substances common to the *Neisseria* group. A group-specific polysaccharide and a group-specific protein have been isolated from meningococci by Rake and Scherp (1933b), which are probably similar to those described by Zozaya. In addition, Rake and Scherp (1933a) have isolated from autolysates of the meningococcus a polysaccharide that appears to be common to Types I and III, and another that is specific to Type II strains. Analysis of the type-specific polysaccharide extracted from the closely allied Types I and III showed it to be a sodium salt of a polysaccharide acid composed of a nitrogen-containing sugar and phosphoric acid units (Scherp and Rake 1935). It seems probable that the serological reactions of the meningococci are determined by the amount of type-specific and group- or species-specific substances present. There is evidence that the type-specific polysaccharide is more abundant in freshly isolated strains, and that continued cultivation in the laboratory is accompanied by a regression towards the group phase.

The presence of the polysaccharide is generally demonstrated by the precipitation reaction, using as antigen a specially prepared extract of the organisms. Petrie (1932), however, has described a simple alternative method. It consists in growing the organisms on agar plates containing the homologous immune serum. Characteristic haloes develop around the colonies. These are found to consist of a precipitate that is formed by the interaction of the specific polysaccharide, which has diffused out into the medium, with the homologous antibody. The method has obvious possibilities of extension to other organisms.

Pathogenicity.—MICE.—In his original communication Weichselbaum (1887) observes that *subcutaneous* injection into mice is without effect. Injected *intrapleurally* with 0·5 c.c. of a thick suspension from a 24-hours' agar culture, the mouse becomes ill, develops paralysis of the hind limbs, and dies in 1 to 2 days. Post mortem, there is a viscid, often hæmor-rhagic, fluid in both pleural cavities ; the lungs are hyperæmic in places and may be covered with a false membrane ; the spleen is generally enlarged and congested. The organisms are present in enormous numbers in the pus cells of the pleural exudate, and often, but not always, in the blood and the spleen, in both of which situations they remain mostly extra-cellular.

Intraperitoneal injection with the same dose kills the mouse in 18 to 24 hours. Post mortem, there is a small amount of sticky fluid in the peritoneal cavity, containing pus cells ; the spleen is generally swollen and congested ; cocci are found in varying numbers in the exudate, and in small numbers in the spleen and heart's blood.

GUINEA-PIGS.—Weight for weight these animals are said to be somewhat more sus-ceptible than mice (Rist and Paris 1904), but here again subcutaneous injection, even of massive doses, fails to give rise to a general infection ; at most a small abscess is produced.

Intrapleural injection of 1 c.c. of a thick suspension of a young agar culture causes death in 1 to 3 days. Post mortem, there is a thick exudate, poor in fibrin, in both pleural cavities ; the lungs are thickened and dark red ; the spleen is not enlarged. Cocci are found in the exudate, but are generally absent from the spleen and heart's blood.

Intraperitoneal injection causes death in 1 to 3 days. Post mortem, there is an exudate, clear or turbid, in the peritoneal cavity ; on the rolled-up omentum and on the anterior surface of the liver there is a deposit of fibrin and pus ; there are hæmorrhages into the mesentery, and into the visceral and parietal peritoneum ; the adrenals are vividly con-gested and may be hæmorrhagic ; the pancreas and surrounding tissues are œdematous. In the pleural cavities there is often an exudate of clear fluid ; the lymphatic glands are swollen and congested. Cocci are found in moderate numbers in the peritoneal exudation, but are absent from the blood and viscera.

Sub-dural injection causes death in 20 to 24 hours ; post mortem, there is œdema and congestion of the meninges, with pus at the site of injection ; there is a large amount of clear fluid in the peritoneum, free from cocci (Albrecht and Ghon 1901). There is no multi-plication of organisms in the spinal fluid itself.

RABBITS.—Subcutaneous, intrapleural, and intraperitoneal injections are generally without effect.

Intravenous injection with 1–4 c.c. of a thick suspension of a young agar culture kills the animals in 1 to 4 days. Post mortem, apart sometimes from a few areas of congestion in the lungs, there is nothing abnormal to be found. No cocci are present in the blood stream.

Sub-dural injection into the skull occasionally causes death. Post mortem, there is congestion of the meninges ; the cocci may be recovered in culture (Weichselbaum 1887).

Intracisternal injection by the sub-occipital route is stated to give rise to cerebrospinal meningitis (Branham and Lillie 1932, Zdrodowski and Voronine 1932). To achieve success virulent cultures and young rabbits (1,300–1,500 gm.) are desirable. The disease may be acute and prove fatal in 24 hours, or sub-acute and cause death between the 2nd and 7th days. Clinically, rigidity of the neck, retraction of the head, spasticity, and sensitiveness to touch, or progressive paralysis may be noted. At necropsy the brain and cord are markedly hyperæmic and are covered with a thin layer of purulent exudate. The cerebrospinal fluid may be almost clear, turbid, or frankly purulent. Meningococci can be recovered from the spinal fluid and usually also from the blood.

Dogs.—Weichselbaum (1887) stated that he had succeeded, by sub-dural injection, in producing a pachy- and lepto-meningitis with acute encephalitis ; death occurred from a few hours to the 12th day after inoculation.

Monkeys.—Von Lingelsheim (1905) was apparently the first to reproduce the disease in monkeys. After intraspinal injection one monkey became ill in 6 hours ; there was retraction of the head and opisthotonos, and death took place in 30 hours. At necropsy the pia mater was turbid along the vessels, with here and there small collections of pus. Meningococci were found in the pus and in the blood.

Flexner (1907*b*) made a number of experiments on monkeys, mostly *Macacus rhesus.* After intraspinal injection of $\frac{1}{2}$ to 1 agar slope he found that the monkeys became generally weak and apathetic ; the head drooped so as to touch the floor of the cage ; occasionally, however, it was retraced ; death occurred in 18 hours to 4 days as a rule, and was not infrequently preceded by general convulsions. Post mortem, the chief lesions were lepto-meningitis, particularly at the base of the brain, encephalitis and abscesses, hæmorrhages into the pia, inflammation of the dorsal root ganglia, and acute endarteritis of the vessels. The inflammation of the meninges extended into the membranes covering the olfactory lobes and along the dura mater into the ethmoid plate and nasal mucosa, which was often inflamed and beset with hæmorrhages. Diplococci were found in the meningeal exudate and in the nasal mucosa, but were not cultivated from the latter situation. They were also present in the sero-purulent fluid in the ventricles.

By giving small repeated doses Flexner succeeded in setting up a chronic meningitis lasting for several weeks. Post mortem, there was abundant exudate, rich in meningococci ; the foramen of Magendie was closed, and hydrocephalus and pyocephalus with ependymitis and dilatation of the ventricles were found. Neither in acute nor chronic cases did the internal organs, apart from the central nervous system, show any marked changes. Occasionally the organism is found in the blood stream.

Flexner found that not all the monkeys developed the disease. Those that did so generally died within 2 days, or else recovered after a severe illness. From his experiments it is clear that the disease is more acute in monkeys than in man.

M'Donald (1908) confirmed Flexner's results in monkeys. Though unable to infect *rhesus* monkeys, he obtained successes with *Callithrix* by sub-dural inoculation of cerebro-spinal fluid from human cases of disease.

The experimental lesions which we have discussed are not produced with the regularity which one might expect, partly because the meningococci themselves vary considerably in virulence, and partly because the susceptibility of different animals—even of the same species—varies within a wide range.

The variations in virulence of the meningococcus depend on the source of origin of the strain, the length of time it has been isolated, the age of the subculture, the nature of the medium (Murray and Ayrton 1924), and doubtless on other factors. By passage through mice some observers state that they have been able to raise its virulence (Ruppel 1906, Gordon 1918, Murray 1924), but others have not been successful (Bettencourt and França 1904, Neill and Taft 1920).

Toxin Production.—Flexner (1907*a*) pointed out that one of the earliest results of intraperitoneal inoculation into guinea-pigs was a marked fall of temperature. This is not the normal course in an acute infection, and he was led to conclude that the animals died from the effects of a poison liberated from the bodies of the organisms. Albrecht and Ghon (1901) found that filtered cultures were without effect on mice, but that 24-hour cultures heated to 65° C. for 1 hour, when injected intraperitoneally into mice, produced death with the same picture as that found after injection of living cocci. Subsequent observers have found that the dose of dead and of living organisms necessary to kill mice is practically identical. Thus Neill and Taft (1920) found that 4,000 million living organisms injected intraperitoneally killed 6 out of 10 mice, whereas the same dose of dead cocci killed 5 out of 10. Gordon (see Report 1920) showed that, when freshly isolated, the living cocci were fatal in smaller doses than the dead cocci, but after subculture for some time in the laboratory, the lethal doses tended to approximate.

From these results, and from the fact that in animals dying from injection of living cocci the blood and viscera are frequently sterile, it would appear that the main cause of death is a toxæmia. Flexner (1907a) found that meningococci undergo very rapid autolysis in culture ; as a result of this the endotoxins are liberated from the bodies of the organisms, and it is these which are responsible for the pathogenic effects in animals. This view is substantiated by the frequent occurrence of hæmorrhages on the serous membranes, of sterile transudates in the cavities of the body, and of the adrenal hæmorrhages which are found both in animals and in human beings dying from the disease (Maclagan and Cooke 1917).

The endotoxin can be extracted from the bodies of the meningococci. One of the simplest methods (Gordon, see Report 1920) is to grind 0·05 gm. of dried cocci in an agate mortar with 1·25 c.c. of distilled water, to which after a few minutes 1·25 c.c. of N/20 NaOH are added ; the grinding is continued for about a minute. The cocci pass into solution on the addition of the alkali. The M.L.D. of the fluid thus obtained is generally 0·1 to 0·15 c.c.—that is, an amount corresponding to about 2 mgm. of the dried cocci.

Though most workers have regarded the toxin of the meningococcus as essentially an endotoxin there seems to be little doubt that under certain conditions it can readily diffuse out into the medium. According to Ferry, Norton, and Steele (1931), hormone broth cultures of pH 6·6 incubated for 4–6 days contain a filtrable toxin, specific for each of the serological types of meningococci, as well as a group-specific toxin common to all four types. Ferry and Schornack (1934) and Maegraith (1935) have shown that these toxins, when inoculated by the intracisternal route into guinea-pigs, give rise to convulsions and death within 24 hours. It would serve no useful purpose to discuss how much of the toxic activity of these filtrates is due to substances secreted by the living organisms and how much to substances liberated from the dead organisms. There is evidence that the polysaccharide found in Types I and III is soluble in suitable media (Petrie 1932, Kirkbride and Cohen 1934), and it may be that the nucleoprotein to which Boor and Miller (1934) ascribe the toxicity of the meningococci is likewise soluble to a greater or less degree. The main conclusion is that for laboratory animals dead cocci are almost as fatal as living cocci, and that the tissue reactions are determined by toxic substances liberated from the organisms either before or after their death.

Neisseria meningitidis

Synonyms.—Meningococcus ; *Diplococcus intracellularis meningitidis* of Weichselbaum.
Isolation.—From cerebrospinal fluid of patients with meningitis by Weichselbaum in 1887.
Habitat.—Strict parasite ; found in nasopharynx of man.
Morphology.—Oval or spherical cocci, 0·8 × 0·6 μ, often arranged in pairs, with adjacent sides flattened ; long axis of oval lies at right angles to axis joining the two cocci. In cultures great variation in size and in depth of staining occurs, due to

autolysis ; in the body the cocci are more regular and are generally intracellular. Non-motile ; non-capsulated ; Gram-negative.

Serum Agar Plate.—24 *hours,* 37° *C.* Round, convex, bluish-grey, translucent, amorphous colonies, 1 mm. in diameter, with smooth, moist, glistening surface and entire edge ; consistency butyrous ; easily emulsifiable. Colony is typically lenticular. Later, colonies increase in size, become more yellow and opaque, and may show a granular centre, and a radiate periphery.

Serum Agar Slope.—24 *hours,* 37° *C.* Moderate, partly confluent, raised, greyish-yellow growth with smooth or irregular surface due to imperfect fusion of colonies ; edge is undulate or made up of single colonies.

Gelatin Stab.—No growth.

Serum Broth.—24 *hours,* 37° *C.* Poor to moderate turbidity with slight granular or viscous deposit. No surface growth.

Resistance.—Highly susceptible to inimical agencies. When dried, and kept at room temperature, cocci die in under 3 hours. Killed by moist heat at 55° C. in less than 5 minutes. Killed by 1 per cent. phenol in 1 minute, and by 0·1 per cent. $HgCl_2$ almost instantaneously. Sealed cultures kept at 37° C. often live for 4 or 5 weeks, and occasionally for 2 or 3 months, but when kept at room temperature they generally die in a few days.

Metabolism.—Optimum H-ion concentration is pH 7·4–7·6. Optimum temperature for growth is 37° C. ; little or no growth below 30° C. Fails to grow on plain nutrient agar, but grows on trypagar, glucose agar, and agar to which blood, serum, or ascitic fluid has been added. Some strains show a slight formation of yellow pigment. Aerobe ; no growth under strictly anaerobic conditions. Produces a weak hæmolysin.

Biochemical—Produces acid, no gas, in glucose and maltose. No change in litmus milk. Catalase + ; methylene blue reduction +. M.R. — or weak + ; V.P. — ; indole — ; H_2S —.

Antigenic Structure.—Divided by agglutination and absorption of agglutinins into four serological types, I, II, III, and IV. Types II and IV are very closely allied, and are sometimes grouped together. By some workers only two types are recognized (see pp. 408–410).

Pathogenicity.—Responsible for sporadic and epidemic cerebrospinal meningitis in man. Experimentally, it is pathogenic to mice, guinea-pigs, and rabbits, if injected intraperitoneally in fairly large doses ; causes death by toxæmia in 1 to 4 days ; there is little or no multiplication of the organisms in the body.

The Gonococcus

Cultural Characters.—In culture the isolated cocci are round. According to Neisser (1882), as the spherical coccus grows, it becomes oval ; division occurs, and two cocci are formed, which cling closely together. These then separate a little, and each one grows and divides again, but in a plane at right angles to that of the first division, so that tetrads result. Each member of the tetrad divides in the same plane as that of the first division. The result is that four pairs of cocci are formed.

The gonococcus is the most difficult member of the group to cultivate. It was first grown by Leistikow and Loeffler (Leistikow 1882) on blood serum gelatin at 37° C., and by Bumm (1885*a*) first on coagulated bovine or sheep serum at 30°–34° C., and later (Bumm 1885*b*) with more success on coagulated human serum. Since then a host of other media have been introduced ; reference may be made to a few (Wertheim 1891, Kiefer 1895, Wassermann 1897, Thalmann 1900, Lipschütz 1904, Martin 1911, Vedder 1915, Hall 1916, Cole and Lloyd 1917, Thomson 1917, Clark

1920, Swartz and Davis 1920, Buschke and Langer 1921, Cook and Stafford 1921, Jenkins 1921, 1922, Costa and Boyer 1922, Erickson and Albert 1922, Kandiba 1922, Lorentz 1922, Torrey and Buckell 1922a, Torrey *et al.* 1922, Macnaughton 1923, Lebœuf 1924, Gordon, J. E., 1926). According to Sordelli, Miravent, and Negroni (1926), an excellent medium results from adding to nutrient agar 17 per cent. of liver extract. This extract is prepared by macerating ox liver in 5 per cent. NaCl solution for 2–4 hours at 45° C., raising the temperature gently to 60° C., keeping it at 60° C. for 10 minutes, and filtering first through paper, then through a Berkefeld candle. The liver extract, if kept in the ice-chest, remains potent for months. As the result of long experience in routine cultivation, McLeod and his colleagues (1934) recommend the use of 10 per cent. heated blood agar of pH 7·4, prepared from broth in which the extraction of the meat has been carried out by Wright's (1933) method. The minimum amount of agar consistent with stability is used. The cultures are incubated in air containing 8 per cent. CO_2. For ordinary purposes a satisfactory medium is provided by nutrient agar containing 10 per cent. ascitic or hydrocele fluid, and having a pH of 7·6 ; the slopes or

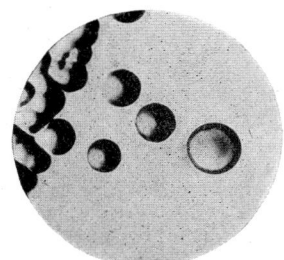

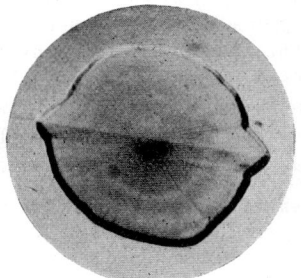

FIG. 93.—*Neisseria gonorrhœæ.*
Surface colonies on serum agar, 24 hours,
37° C. (× 8).

FIG. 94.—*Neisseria gonorrhœæ.*
Surface colony on serum agar, 7 days,
37° C. (× 8).

plates should be moist, and the air in the incubator should be saturated with water vapour. Stock cultures are best kept in a similar medium containing 0·75 per cent. agar, and put up in the form of stabs ; these tubes should be corked and kept in the incubator. Media with a high amino-acid concentration are not usually satisfactory (Torrey and Buckell 1922a, Gordon, J., and M'Leod 1926). Glucose is not beneficial.

Numerous workers (de Christmas 1897, Wassermann 1898, Lipschütz 1904, Gurd 1908, Martin 1911, Cohn 1923) have noticed that the cultural characters of the gonococcus are subject to variation. Recently Atkin (1925) has studied this phenomenon, and has found that, as with the meningococcus, there is a definite correlation between the serological type of the organism and its colonial appearance. By growing gonococci on thick trypagar plates of pH 7·8 he observed two different types of colony : Type I gave a large, irregularly round, flattened, translucent colony with an undulate edge, and a surface that in 5 days or so became covered with papillæ ; Type II gave a smaller, round, low convex or raised, yellowish-white, opaque colony, with a slightly uneven surface, and an entire or faintly lobate edge ; no papillæ were formed. Serologically, colonies of Type I could be differentiated from those of Type II. Atkin found that the organisms in the papillæ of Type I colonies lived about twice as long as did those in the flat part ; he therefore concludes that the papillæ arise as a reaction to an un-favourable environment, and represent the first step in the change over to Type II. In some colonies the papillæ actually fuse together, so that they constitute the entire colony ; the papillated appearance is thus lost. During the course of subculture in the laboratory, there will be a constant selection of the longer-living organisms in the papillæ, so that eventually the strain will consist entirely of these organisms ; when this process is complete, the strain will belong culturally, and probably serologically, to Type II. Type I colonies are usually observed when pus from acute gonorrhœa is plated out ; Type II colonies are usually found in old laboratory cultures, or occasionally in chronic gonorrhœal lesions.

Atkin would regard Type I as being highly parasitic, and Type II as a more saprophytic form of the gonococcus. Though he obtained evidence that, in the laboratory, Type I strains gradually acquired the properties of Type II strains, he was never able to follow the complete transition ; probably this is a matter of months or years. It must not be supposed that gonococci can in practice be divided sharply into two colonial types ; between the two main types there are probably numerous sub-types, each representing one stage in the process of trans-ition. This accounts for the numerous arbitrary subdivisions that have been made on serological grounds by different workers (see below). But, broadly speak-ing, there appear to be two main centres around which the different strains may be grouped ; the type strains can be differentiated both by colonial form and serological behaviour. In these respects the gonococcus closely resembles the meningococcus.

Antigenic Structure.—Agglutination.—The serological study of the gonococci may be said to have commenced with Bruckner and Cristéanu's work in 1906 (1906a). Using immune horse serum prepared by the injection of pure cultures of different strains, they found that the gonococci were agglutinated to a titre of about 1–750. A close relationship was established between the gonococcus and the meningococcus, both of which were agglutinated to nearly equal titre by a gonococcal serum (Bruckner and Cristéanu 1906b). Vannod in the same year (1906) found that immune gonococcal rabbit serum contained agglutinins for the gonococcus and to a less extent for the meningococcus. Torrey (1907) was the first to use the agglutination test for the serological differentiation of the gonococci. Working with 10 different strains and 8 immune sera, he found that there was a difference in the agglutinability of the gonococci ; and in conjunction with the absorption of agglu-tinins test he was able to divide the 10 strains into 3 groups. Such a differentiation was obviously of interest, but many subsequent workers failed to confirm this (Wollstein 1907, Vannod 1907, Thomsen and Vollmond 1921, Cook and Stafford 1921, Warren 1921). More recent work has, however, tended to show the essential correctness of Torrey's findings. Thus Pearce (1915) drew a distinction on the basis of direct agglutination between strains of gonococci isolated from infants—vulvovaginitis and ophthalmia—and those isolated from adults—acute urethritis. Hermanies (1921a) studied 85 strains, and using the absorption of agglutinins test he was able to classify them into 6 types, of which Types I and II contained the greatest numbers. Later (1921b) he subdivided his Type II strains into 4 races, a, b, c, and d. He found a considerable amount of lability in the antigenic structure of these races ; some were simple, while others were more complex. Jötten (1921), by direct agglutination, classified 20 out of 27 strains into 4 groups, A, B, C, and D ; 7 remained ungrouped. The strains falling into Groups A and B were mostly from severe cases of disease with complications ; those falling into Groups C and D were mostly from simple cases with no complications. He therefore established a correlation between the agglutinability and the toxicity of his strains. Torrey, who together with Buckell (1922b) again studied the problem of agglutination, was able to a large extent to confirm his original conclusions. They used 77 strains of widely separated origin. By simple agglutination they were unable to obtain any definite grouping, but on the basis of absorption they found that their strains could be divided into 3 groups, which they called regular, intermediate, and irregular. The regular strains were most generalized as regards antigenic properties ; the intermediate strains were closely related to the regular types ; the irregular strains exhibited marked individual variations. The regular strains were the most complex antigenically, and appeared on the whole to be more virulent for man ; the irregular strains were less complex, and appeared to be less virulent. These findings are analogous to those of Griffith with the meningococcus. Torrey and Buckell, however, point out that the antigenic structure of the gonococci is variable, and so prone to individualistic expression that grouping of the organisms into sharply defined types is not warranted.

Tulloch (1923*a*, *b*) studied 100 strains of gonococci. By simple agglutination he obtained no direct evidence of grouping, but by absorption he was able to classify them as follows :

Type I 72	main sub-group
„ I 7	lesser „
„ I 3	„ „
„ I 5	„ „
„ I 5	„ „
Unplaced 8	

It will be seen that he classifies 92 per cent. in one group, of which 72 strains fall into one sub-group. Tulloch states that Gordon found 25 out of 30 strains by absorption of agglutinins to belong to a well-defined sub-group.

Atkin (1925) was able to classify gonococci into two serological types. Most strains isolated from cases of acute urethritis could be classified in Type I, whereas strains isolated from chronic infection, such as cervicitis or arthritis, generally belonged to Type II. Many strains agglutinated to a greater or less extent with serum of each type. Atkin suggests that in the body, during the process of a chronic infection, or in the laboratory during long periods of subcultivation, Type I may gradually change into Type II. The evidence for this, however, is admittedly inconclusive. Atkin's work does seem to reconcile to some extent the varying results of different workers, and to agree in particular with the findings of Torrey and Buckell.

Summarizing, we may say that the serological classification of the gonococcus is beset with difficulties ; that there are probably two main types, of different degrees of antigenic complexity ; that between these two main types there are a number of intermediate types, containing one or more antigens common to both main types ; and that recently isolated strains from acute forms of the disease appear to belong chiefly to Type I, while old laboratory strains, or strains isolated from chronic disease, tend to belong to Type II.

Precipitins.—Torrey (1907) prepared a precipitinogen by filtering a 5-weeks' broth culture through a layer of sterile talc on filter paper. With this he obtained a precipitin reaction with immune gonococcal rabbit serum. Bruckner and Cristéanu macerated a culture in 0·15 per cent. NaOH, which dissolved the gonococci in a few minutes ; the solution was filtered through porcelain. They found a close relation between the gonococcus and the meningococcus ; thus anti-gonococcal horse serum contained precipitins for both organisms ; similarly with anti-meningococcal goat serum.

Complement Fixation.—Bruck (1906) was the first to study the presence of immune bodies in artificially prepared gonococcal serum. He showed that the injection of watery extracts of gonococci into rabbits called forth the production of specific antibodies, which were detectable by the complement-fixation test.

Vannod (1906) found the complement-fixation test to be more suitable than agglutination for distinguishing between the gonococcus and the meningococcus, since no group reaction was apparent. Watabiki (1910) was likewise able to distinguish between these two organisms by the complement-fixation test. Teague and Torrey (1907) showed that the serum of an animal immunized to one strain of gonococcus might not cause fixation of complement when tested against another strain ; they concluded that the gonococci formed a heterogeneous family. Martin (1911) found both specific and group antibodies for the gonococcus and the meningococcus in their corresponding sera. The work of Oliver (1929) and Price (1933) indicates the existence of a group relationship between the gonococcus and certain other members of the *Neisseria* group. Pearce (1915) divided her strains into 2 groups.

Jötten (1921) found that the results of the complement-fixation test ran parallel with the agglutination test ; by both he was able to place 20 out of 27 strains in 4 separate groups, A, B, C and D. Cook and Stafford (1921), on the other hand, were unable by the complement-fixation test to obtain any evidence of grouping amongst the gonococci. Thomsen and Vollmond (1921), though unable to classify their strains by direct agglutination, succeeded by employing the complement-fixation test, with previous absorption of the sera, in dividing 26 strains into 4 different groups, *a*, *b*, *c* and *d*. Of these, the group *b* strains were most toxic for rabbits.

Bactericidins, Opsonins.—Torrey (1908), who studied the bactericidins present in normal and immune rabbit serum, found that gonococci varied in their susceptibility to these bodies. His experiments indicated too that there was a parallelism in the specificity of the results obtained by the complement-fixation and the bactericidin tests, both of which demonstrated the heterogeneity of the gonococcus group. The bactericidal action of the sera did not run parallel with the agglutination results. Martin (1910) found that the normal serum of the guinea-pig, rabbit, cat and man, was bactericidal to both gonococci and meningococci, though the action of guinea-pig and of human serum was more marked with meningococci than with gonococci. In immune sera the bactericidins were found to be relatively specific ; an immune serum prepared against the meningococcus had but little effect on the gonococcus, and vice versa. Jötten (1921), who divided the gonococci by agglutination and complement fixation into 4 groups, A, B, C and D, found that the strains of A and B groups were more resistant to the opsonins, tropins, and bactericidins present in normal serum than were the strains of C and D groups. This was correlated with the greater toxicity of the A and B groups to human beings.

The serological study of the gonococci therefore shows that the group is not absolutely homogeneous ; that there are certain sub-groups in it ; that these sub-groups are not very clearly defined ; and that there is a close relation between the gonococcus and the meningococcus.

Recent work on the *chemical fractionation* of the gonococcus by Boor and Miller (1934) and Miller and Boor (1934) suggests that the gonococci contain polysaccharide and nucleoprotein substances shared in part by other members of the *Neisseria* group. It may be anticipated that further work will reveal the presence of type-specific soluble substances similar to those found in meningococci, and responsible, according to the amount in which they are present, for the serological reactions of different strains.

Pathogenicity.—The gonococcus is not only a strict parasite, but it is a specifically human parasite. Of the numerous attempts which have been made to reproduce gonorrhœa in animals other than man, not one has been successful (Leistikow 1882, Neisser 1882, Bumm 1885*a*, Nicolaysen 1897). Neither inoculation of pus nor of pure cultures on to the mucosa of the urethra or conjunctiva gives rise to disease, even in the anthropoid apes. Experiments on the lower animals, however, have shown that the injection of gonococci directly into the peritoneum or the blood stream frequently proves fatal.

MICE.—*Subcutaneous* injection of pure cultures is without effect. *Intraperitoneal* injection of a saline suspension of a young serum agar culture is often fatal in 24 hours. Post mortem, there is slight congestion of the peritoneum, and sometimes a small amount of viscous exudate, containing pus cells. Gonococci are found in varying numbers, both intra- and extra-cellular in position. They may frequently be cultivated from the peritoneum, and occasionally from the heart's blood. With smaller doses, many of the mice do not succumb for 2 to 3 days; at necropsy in these mice it is rare to find gonococci microscopically, and cultures are uniformly sterile. Some mice survive without showing signs of illness. Almost exactly the same results follow the injection of cultures which have been killed by heating to 70° C. for 1 hour (Wassermann 1898). There is no increase of virulence by passage.

GUINEA-PIGS.—*Intraperitoneal* injection of 5 c.c. of a 6-days' serum broth culture (Nicolaysen 1897), or of a 24-hours' growth on a Blake bottle of serum glucose agar (Wollstein 1907), kills the animals in 24 hours as a rule. Post mortem, there is congestion of the serosa, with small hæmorrhages; a little clear or turbid fluid in the peritoneal cavity; œdema of the pancreas and surrounding tissues; congestion or hæmorrhage into the adrenals; a layer of fibrin and pus over the liver, spleen and omentum; sometimes clear fluid in the pleural cavities. Films from the peritoneum and omentum show varying numbers of polymorphonuclears, and diplococci situated intra- and extra-cellularly. Cultures from the peritoneum are generally positive. It will be seen that the post-mortem findings are similar to those following injection of guinea-pigs with meningococci; as a rule, however, larger doses of gonococci are required to produce the same effect. After some generations *in vitro* the gonococci lose their virulence, and become innocuous to guinea-pigs.

RABBITS.—*Subcutaneous* injection of 10 c.c. of a 4 to 5-days' serum broth culture (Maslovski 1900) gives rise to slight inflammatory swelling after 24 hours; later suppuration occurs, so that in 10 days a small abscess is formed, containing thick, sterile pus. The temperature rises somewhat, and the animal loses weight. The same result follows the injection of heat-killed cultures. Smaller doses are without effect.

Intraperitoneal injection of large doses of gonococci, washed off young serum agar cultures, kills the animal in 24 hours. Post mortem, there is some peritoneal reaction, and the organisms may be cultivated from the peritoneum, and occasionally from the heart's blood. Bruckner and Cristéanu (1906c) claimed to have raised the virulence to such an extent that a rabbit injected intraperitoneally with 1/20 of a serum agar slant died in 2–10 hours. These results have not been confirmed.

Intravenous injection produces fatal results with smaller doses. The gonococci may be recovered from the blood after 24, sometimes after 48 hours. The results of different workers are, however, at variance. Vannod (1907), for example, injected living cocci in a dose of 5 c.c. of an ascitic peptone broth culture intravenously into rabbits, and obtained practically no reaction.

Maslovski (1900) injected a few drops of a 3-day's serum broth culture into the anterior chamber of the eye of rabbits. The following day there was diffuse turbidity of the cornea, accompanied by hypopyon; in the pus cells gonococci could not be detected microscopically, but could be cultured for the first two days.

Nicolaysen (1897) injected an aqueous suspension of gonococci into the knee joint of a rabbit. Arthritis followed with abundant purulent exudate, which persisted for a week; no organisms could be demonstrated in it, however. The same result occurred when a culture killed by heat at 70° C. for 1 hour was injected.

From these results it is seen that the gonococcus does not live for long in the animal body ; cultures are rarely positive after 2 days, and then only when the injections are made directly into serous cavities or the blood stream. In fact it is doubtful whether true proliferation occurs at all. De Christmas (1897), for instance, found that if the cocci were introduced, enclosed in collodion sacs, into the peritoneal cavity of laboratory animals, they failed to grow. The reaction following the injection of gonococci is due therefore, not to a true infection, but to a toxic action of the organisms. That this is true is abundantly clear from the numerous experiments on gonotoxin.

Toxin Production.—De Christmas (1897, 1900) recorded experiments from which he concluded that the gonococcus forms a true exotoxin. His results have not, however, been confirmed by other workers. Wassermann (1898), for instance, found that heat-killed cultures were as fatal to mice, injected intraperitoneally, as living cultures ; on the other hand, filtered cultures, unless a filtrate of a 2 to 3 weeks' culture was used, proved innocuous ; even then, the filtrate was never as toxic as the whole culture. He grew the gonococci in 33 per cent. ascitic broth in a thin layer of fluid in flat-bottomed flasks. After a week, the cocci were collected, dried, and ground in an agate mortar ; weighed quantities of the powder were suspended in water, and sterilized by steaming or in the autoclave. Injected intraperitoneally into mice this powder was fatal in a dose of 0·01 gm., death occurring in 24 hours or later. Injected into rabbits or guinea-pigs subcutaneously, it caused wide-spread doughy infiltration, often passing on to necrosis. Injected into the anterior chamber of the eye of rabbits, it caused corneal turbidity, hypopyon, and sometimes complete destruction of the eye. He was unable to extract the toxin by heat, by distilled water, or by N/10 NaOH ; the cocci still remained toxic. The toxin was not destroyed in the bacterial bodies by drying or by heat at 120° C. ; it was not destroyed by absolute alcohol, or by prolonged boiling ; nor was he able to immunize rabbits or mice against it. These results point strongly to the conclusion that the toxin is an endotoxin—a body contained in the cell substance, and adhering strongly to it.

Schäffer (1897) found that filtered ascitic broth cultures, 2 to 6 days old, were without effect when injected in large doses—3–10 c.c.—into guinea-pigs and rabbits. Maslovski (1900) likewise found that the filtrate of a 9–days' serum broth culture, injected subcutaneously into rabbits, gave rise to nothing but a slight rise of temperature and loss of weight. He concluded too that the toxic substance was an endotoxin. Scholtz (1900) came to the same conclusion. On the other hand, Vannod (1907) working with filtrates of 17–20-days' cultures in de Christmas's medium—concentrated veal broth containing 75 per cent. of ascitic fluid—found that they were fatal to rabbits injected intraperitoneally. Post mortem, there was a purulent effusion into the peritoneal cavity ; the serosa was congested and covered with purulent deposits ; the suprarenals were enlarged and hyperæmic. Vannod, however, used large and repeated doses—a total of 18 to 24 c.c. in 10 days to 3 weeks.

We may conclude that the gonococcus contains a toxin which can be extracted by grinding the dried organisms and suspending the resultant powder in water. In cultures in fluid media the toxin may be liberated from the cocci by autolysis ; after 2 or 3 weeks' incubation, the organisms may have autolysed to such an extent that a certain amount of toxin may be present in filtrates of the cultures. The available evidence leaves little doubt that the toxin belongs to the class of so-called endotoxins.

Neisseria gonorrhœæ

Synonym.—Gonococcus.

Isolation.—First described by Neisser in 1879 ; first cultivated by Bumm (1885a, b), and Leistikow and Loeffler (Leistikow 1882).

Habitat.—Strict parasite of man. Found in genito-urinary system of patients suffering from gonorrhœa.

Morphology.—Oval or spherical coccus ; $0.8 \mu \times 0.6 \mu$, frequently arranged in pairs, with adjacent sides flattened or slightly concave, resembling a pair of kidney beans ; long axis of oval lies at right angles to axis joining the two cocci. In cultures great variation in size and in depth of staining occurs, due to autolysis ; in the body the cocci are more regular, and are generally intracellular. Non-motile, non-capsulated, Gram-negative.

Serum Agar Plate.—*24 hours, 37° C.* Round, convex, or slightly umbonate, greyish-white, translucent, amorphous colonies, 0.5–1 mm. in diameter, with smooth, glistening surface and entire edge ; consistency butyrous or slightly viscid ; fairly easily emulsifiable. Later, colonies increase in size, and may develop a roughened surface and a crenated edge.

Serum Agar Slope.—*24 hours, 37° C.* Rather poor, partly confluent, raised, greyish-yellow growth with smooth surface ; edge entire or formed of single colonies. Consistency often viscid.

Gelatin Stab.—No growth.

Serum Broth.—*24 hours, 37° C.* Very poor growth with little or no turbidity, and a slight granular deposit, partly disintegrating on shaking.

Resistance.—Highly susceptible to inimical agencies. When dried, the cocci succumb in an hour or two. Killed by moist heat at 55° C. in less than 5 minutes, and at 42° C. in 5–15 hours (Carpenter *et al.* 1933). In serum cultures they are killed by 1/4000 $AgNO_3$ in $7\frac{1}{2}$ minutes, and in pus in 2 minutes. Sealed cultures kept at 37° C. may live for 4 or 5 weeks ; when kept at room temperature, they die in a day or two.

Metabolism.—Optimum H-ion concentration for growth is pH 7.5. Optimum temperature for growth is 37° C. ; no growth under 30° C. or over 38.5° C. Fails to grow on plain agar as a rule ; requires the presence of serum, blood, ascitic fluid, or hydrocele fluid ; glucose is not beneficial. Aerobic, but growth is said to be improved by a lowered oxygen pressure, and by 10 per cent. of CO_2 in the atmosphere. Little or no growth under strictly anaerobic conditions.

Biochemical.—Produces acid, no gas, in glucose. No change in litmus milk. Catalase $+$. M.B. reduction $-$. M.R. $-$; V.P. $-$; indole $-$; H_2S $-$.

Antigenic Structure.—No clear definition into separate serological types ; most strains appear by agglutination and absorption of agglutinins to belong to one or other of two main groups ; numerous other less important groups.

Pathogenicity.—Responsible for gonorrhœa and ophthalmia neonatorum in man. Experimentally, it proves fatal to mice, guinea-pigs, and rabbits, if injected in large doses intraperitoneally ; there is little or no multiplication of the organisms in the body.

Differentiation of the Gonococcus from the Meningococcus.—Morphologically the two organisms are very similar. In the body, both occur chiefly in pairs situated intracellularly. It is sometimes stated that the adjacent sides of the meningococci are flattened, whereas those of the gonococci are concave, thus leaving an oval space between the two organisms. Possibly the meningococcus is slightly larger than the gonococcus in the body, though smaller in a 24-hours' culture in the laboratory (Wollstein 1907). Culturally the gonococcus is more dysgonic ; it grows more slowly, forms smaller colonies, and grows on a smaller range of media than the meningococcus ; the colonies are slightly viscous and do not emulsify so readily ; colonies of the meningococcus, on the other hand, are butyrous and emulsify with the greatest of ease. Biochemically, the meningococcus produces acid in glucose and maltose, the gonococcus in glucose only.[1] The agglutination test is only of limited value, since there exists a group relationship between the two organisms (Bruckner and Cristéanu 1906*b*, Wollstein 1907,

---

[1] Horse serum should not be used in testing the fermentation reactions, since many strains of gonococcus produce acid from maltose in its presence (Rosher 1936).

Elser and Huntoon 1909, Gordon, M. H., 1925). The meningococcus is more toxic to animals; tested by intraperitoneal injection on mice or guinea-pigs a smaller dose of meningococci is required, whether alive or dead, to cause death than of gonococci.

N. catarrhalis.—This organism has been variously described by different workers. Ghon and Pfeiffer (1902), who first studied it fully, stated that in sputum it occurred in pairs, tetrads, or occasionally small groups; the organisms were shaped like coffee-beans, and were both intra- and extra-cellular. In culture they appeared larger, were generally in tetrads, and stained evenly. On agar after 24 hours, the colonies resembled in size those of *Streptococcus pyogenes*; they were convex, whitish-grey, with a glistening surface and an eaten edge. After 3 or 4 days they were 3 to 4 mm. in diameter, and were differentiated into a prominent, more elevated, opaque, slightly brownish centre, and a thinner, grey, transparent, wave-like periphery with a crenated edge; the consistency was friable, and in saline they auto-agglutinated. A more or less similar description was given by von Lingelsheim (1906); he stated that the colony was smaller than that of a meningococcus colony, and that even on ascitic agar the diameter never exceeded 1–2 mm. Elser and Huntoon (1909) described two types of colony, one resembling Ghon and Pfeiffer's description, the other like a small meningococcus colony. Gordon described four types of colony: (1) like Ghon and Pfeiffer's description; (2) similar to the first, but coloured pale yellow; (3) small, flat, grey, translucent, amorphous colonies with a smooth glistening surface and entire edge; (4) almost pin-point, transparent glistening colonies with a smoothly rounded edge; morphologically, these consisted of giant cocci showing metachromatic staining. It seems clear that the colonial appearance of *N. catarrhalis* is subject to variation; in all probability both smooth and rough types are formed, similar to those of the meningococcus and the gonococcus. In gelatin stab culture there is a poor growth confined to the upper part of the tube; there is no liquefaction. There is no turbidity in broth, but a granular deposit is formed; if the tube is kept still, a surface membrane may appear. Growth occurs within a range of 18° to 42° C., the optimum being at 37° C. There is no development under anaerobic conditions. Growth is favoured by blood, serum, and ascitic fluid, but not by glycerine. The organism appears to be more resistant than the meningococcus or gonococcus; cultures are said to live for 4 or 5 months at 21° C., if prevented from drying; the organisms may live in dried sputum for 27 days; they are killed by heating to 65° C. for 30 minutes. No sugars are fermented. The virulence of this organism to laboratory animals is low. The rabbit is resistant, but guinea-pigs injected intraperitoneally with large doses—half to one agar slope—die of toxæmia in about 24 hours. At post mortem there is a mild degree of peritonitis, slight enlargement of the spleen, and hyperæmia and degeneration of the viscera; the organisms may be recovered from the peritoneal exudate, but rarely from the heart's blood. Heat-killed cultures are almost as fatal as living ones.

N. pharyngis flava, i, ii and iii.—A number of Gram-negative cocci have been described whose characteristic feature is the formation of greenish-yellow colonies on agar or ascitic agar. von Lingelsheim (1906) and some other workers have called them *Micrococcus* or *Diplococcus pharyngis flavus*, and have differentiated them on the basis of colonial appearance and sugar reactions into three groups, i, ii and iii (Martin 1911, Report 1916, Dopter 1921). Elser and Huntoon (1909) have called them chromogenic cocci, and have divided them similarly into three groups i, ii and iii; J. E. Gordon (1921) has likewise called them chromogenic cocci, and has divided them into six groups, i to vi. Elser and Huntoon's chromogenic iii and Gordon's chromogenic iii agree with von Lingelsheim's *flava* iii in fermenting glucose and maltose only; Elser and Huntoon's chromogenic ii and Gordon's iv agree with von Lingelsheim's i and ii in fermenting glucose, maltose and lævulose; Elser and Huntoon's chromogenic i agrees with Gordon's chromogenic v in fermenting glucose, maltose, lævulose, and sucrose; but has no counterpart in von Lingelsheim's classification. Over and above these are Gordon's chromogenic i, which ferments glucose only, his chromogenic ii, which ferments glucose and lævulose, and his chromogenic vi, which ferments glucose, maltose, lævulose, sucrose, and lactose. Undoubtedly one of the reasons for the discrepancies in the sugar reactions is due to the fact that von Lingelsheim, who described the *flava* group, read all his reactions after 24 hours; this probably explains why he never observed the fermentation of sucrose. In colonial appearance von Lingelsheim's *flava* i and iii resemble the meningococcus, and *flava*

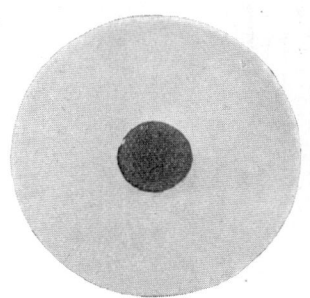

Fig. 95.—*Neisseria pharyngis.*
Surface colony on agar, 24 hours, 37° C. (× 8). Smooth type.

ii *N. catarrhalis*; Elser and Huntoon's chromogenic ii agrees with von Lingelsheim's *flava* i and iii. Gordon describes his organisms as giving colonies either like the meningococcus or like *N. catarrhalis*; his group vi gives pale yellow colonies, larger and more opaque than the others. In the face of these divergencies in cultural and biochemical reactions, it is clear that no fixed types can be described. Our own work has shown that the cultural appearances of the Gram-negative

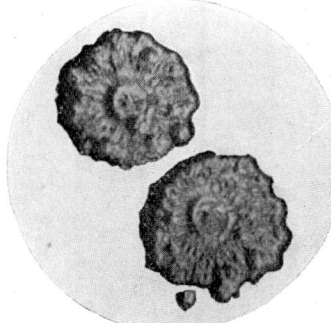

Fig. 96.—*Neisseria pharyngis.*
Surface colonies on agar, 5 days, 37° C., showing differentiation. Secondary rough type (× 8).

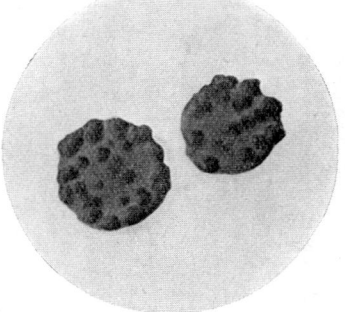

Fig. 97.—*Neisseria pharyngis.*
Surface colonies on agar, 5 days, 37° C., showing formation of secondary papillæ (× 8).

cocci from the nasopharynx are subject to great variation, and most workers agree now that lævulose is an unreliable sugar. Division therefore of these organisms either on colonial appearance or on the basis of lævulose fermentation is most unsatisfactory. We must await further work before a classification can be attempted.

N. pharyngis sicca.—According to von Lingelsheim (1906) this organism consists of fine Gram-negative diplococci. On agar it gives rise to an irregularly round, raised, opaque, slightly yellowish colony, up to 3 mm. in diameter, with a dull, dry, deeply

TABLE XXXIII

Organism.	Morphology.	24–48 hour Colony on Ascitic Agar.	Serum Broth.	Growth on Agar.	Growth at 22° C.	Dextrose.	Maltose.	Sucrose.	Remarks.
Neisseria meningitidis	Oval or spherical coccus, often in pairs, with adjacent sides flattened	Round, convex, bluish-grey, translucent, amorphous, 1–2 mm. in diameter, with smooth glistening surface and entire edge; butyrous and easily emulsifiable	Moderate turbidity, and slight granular deposit	±	−	A	A	−	Two or four main antigenic types.
Neisseria gonorrhœæ	Oval or spherical coccus, often in pairs, with adjacent sides concave	Round, convex, or slightly umbonate, greyish-white, translucent, amorphous, 1 mm. in diameter, with smooth glistening surface and entire edge; slightly viscid and fairly easily emulsifiable	Little or no turbidity; slight granular deposit	−	−	A	−	−	Growth is slower and poorer than meningococcus. Probably 2 main antigenic types.
Neisseria catarrhalis	Spherical or oval coccus arranged singly, in pairs, in tetrads, or in clumps	*Smooth Type.* Round, low convex, greyish-white, translucent, and amorphous, with smooth, glistening surface and entire edge *Rough Type.* Larger, raised, whitish-grey, with slightly uneven surface and eaten edge; later differentiated into a raised, brownish, more opaque centre, and a thinner greyish translucent periphery with a crenated edge; friable and difficult to emulsify	No turbidity; coarse, granular, sandy deposit; sometimes a surface pellicle and ring growth	+	+	−	−	−	Auto-agglutinable.
N. pharyngis sicca	Small diplococci, uniform in size, and arranged in dense clumps	Irregularly round, raised, greyish-white, opaque, 2–3 mm. in diameter; with dry, deeply wrinkled surface and an undulate edge; very tough and brittle consistency; adherent to medium; impossible to emulsify		+	+	A	A	A	

Organism	Microscopy	Colony	Broth					Remarks
N. flava i	Similar to the meningococcus	Round, low convex, greenish-yellow, translucent, amorphous, 0·5–2 mm. in diameter, with smooth, glistening surface and entire edge. Consistency butyrous; emulsifies fairly well	No turbidity; granular deposit; often a surface pellicle	+	+	A	—	
N. flava ii	Similar to *N. catarrhalis*	Round, low convex, opaque, yellow, 0·5–1·0 mm. in diameter, with smooth surface and entire edge. Brittle, and difficult to emulsify	Like *N. flava* i	—	—	A	A	
N. flava iii	Similar to the meningococcus	Resembles colony of meningococcus, but slightly yellow in colour; butyrous, and fairly easily emulsifiable	Like *N. flava* i	±	±	A	—	
Diplococcus mucosus	Cocci arranged in pairs and tetrads, surrounded by capsules	Luxuriant, round, convex, greyish, translucent, and mucoid, 3–4 mm. in diameter, with smooth glistening surface and entire edge; viscous consistency		+	+	?	?	
Diplococcus crassus	Plump cocci in pairs, tetrads, or chains. Gram staining indeterminate	Round, convex, greyish-white, granular, and translucent, 0·5–1·5 mm. in diameter, with entire edge		+	+	A	A	Acid in lactose.
N. flavescens	Similar to the meningococcus	Like those of the meningococcus, but less moist and characterized by a golden-yellow pigmentation		+ on semi-solid agar	?	—	—	Very poor growth on dextrose agar. Antigenically homogeneous, and different from *N. meningitidis* and *N. catarrhalis*.

P.B.

P*

furrowed surface, and a crenated edge ; the colony is very firm, often adherent to the medium, difficult to disintegrate, and impossible to emulsify ; it is so coherent that it can be picked up bodily. von Lingelsheim says that it produces acid in glucose, maltose, and lævulose, but other workers have found that it also ferments sucrose (Elser and Huntoon 1909, Gordon, J. E., 1921). It seems doubtful whether this organism should be regarded as a distinct species. Our own work suggests that it is merely a rough variant of one of the other nasopharyngeal cocci which ferments glucose, maltose, and sucrose. We have observed the formation by cocci giving these sugar reactions of smooth colonies when first isolated from the nose, and the appearance in later cultures of typically rough colonies indistinguishable from those described as being characteristic of *N. pharyngis sicca.*

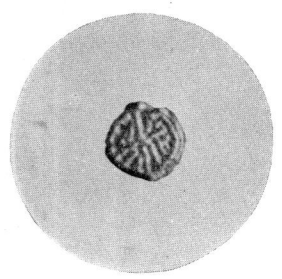

Fig. 98.—*Neisseria pharyngis.*
Surface colony on agar, 24 hours, 37° C. × 8, showing primary rough type of colonial variant.

N. pharyngis cinerea.—von Lingelsheim (1906) described this organism as consisting of plump cocci, arranged in pairs or more usually loose heaps. On agar it forms small, round, grey or greyish-white colonies, 1–1·5 mm. diameter, with an entire edge ; under a low magnification their colour is brownish, and they appear coarsely granular. Some authors state that the colonies are dry, brittle, and opaque (Netter and Debré 1911). It ferments no sugars. This organism closely resembles *N. catarrhalis* and is probably merely a variety of it ; it corresponds closely in description to Gordon's *N. catarrhalis* sub-group III (Gordon, J. E., 1921).

Diplococcus mucosus.—On ascitic agar this organism is said to form luxuriant, round, convex, grey, translucent, mucoid colonies, 3–4 mm. in diameter, of a juicy viscous consistency. Microscopically it consists of fine diplo- and tetracocci surrounded by capsules. It grows well on agar and gelatin. No sugar reactions are reported. Possibly this organism is merely a mucoid variant of one of the common nasopharyngeal cocci. It is said to be the only Gram-negative coccus that is pathogenic for white mice—presumably on subcutaneous injection (von Lingelsheim 1908).

Diplococcus crassus.—This organism is not easy to define. It was first described by Jaeger (1895) as a meningococcus, but as it was said to form long chains in culture, to be Gram-positive in the cerebrospinal fluid and in pure cultures, to be able to grow on gelatin at room temperature, and to be highly resistant to drying, it is certain that it was not the meningococcus (Jaeger 1903*a*). On agar it forms rather small, greyish-white, granular colonies, 1–1·5 mm. in diameter, with an entire edge. Growth occurs at 20° C. Microscopically it consists of plump diplo- and tetracocci, some of which are Gram-positive and some Gram-negative ; it appears in reality to be a Gram-positive organism that is very easily decolorized. Its sugar reactions differentiate it from all the other members of the group, since in addition to fermenting glucose, maltose, lævulose, and sucrose, it ferments lactose. It is said to be sometimes agglutinated by antimeningococcal serum (Jaeger 1903*b, c*, Netter and Debré 1911, Dopter 1921). According to von Lingelsheim (1906) an antimeningococcal serum agglutinates *Dip. crassus* almost or quite to titre, whereas an anti-crassus serum agglutinates the meningococcus to only $\frac{1}{32}$–$\frac{1}{16}$ titre. According to Jaeger (1899) dried cultures remain alive for 3 or 4 months.

N. flavescens.—This organism was isolated by Branham (1930) from the spinal fluid of a number of patients suffering from epidemic cerebrospinal meningitis. It differs from the meningococcus chiefly in its production of pigment, its lack of fermentative action, and its antigenic constitution. In the spinal fluid it appears in the form of Gram-negative biscuit-shaped cocci arranged in flattened pairs ;

individual cells vary in size and depth of staining ; giant forms are common. The organisms grow well on blood agar and semi-solid agar, but poorly on dextrose agar. They produce a golden-yellow pigment. They are without fermentative action on any of the usual carbohydrates. They are not agglutinated by type antimeningococcal sera, but constitute among themselves a serologically homogeneous group. Their ability to give rise under favourable conditions to meningitis appears to be unquestioned.

REFERENCES

ALBRECHT, H. and GHON, A. (1901) *Wien. klin. Wschr.*, **14**, 984.
ARKWRIGHT, J. A. (1907) *J. Hyg., Camb.*, **7**, 145 ; (1909) *J. Hyg., Camb.*, **9**, 104 ; (1915) *Brit. med. J.*, ii, 885.
ATKIN, E. E. (1923) *Brit. J. exp. Path.*, **4**, 325 ; (1925) *Ibid.*, **6**, 235.
BETTENCOURT, A. and FRANÇA, C. (1904) *Z. Hyg. InfektKr.*, **66**, 463.
BOOR, A. K. and MILLER, C. P. (1934) *J. exp. Med.*, **59**, 63.
BRANHAM, S. E. (1930) *Publ. Hlth Rep., Wash.*, **45**, 845 ; (1932) *J. Immunol.*, **23**, 49.
BRANHAM, S. E. and LILLIE, R. D. (1932) *Publ. Hlth Rep., Wash.*, **47**, 2137.
BRANHAM, S. E., TAFT, C. E., and CARLIN, S. A. (1931) *Publ. Hlth Rep., Wash.*, **46**, 897.
BRUCK, C. (1906) *Dtsch. med. Wschr.*, **32**, 1368.
BRUCKNER, J. and CRISTÉANU, C. (1906a) *C. R. Soc. Biol.*, **60**, 846 ; (1906b) *Ibid.*, **60**, 907 ; (1906c) *Ibid.*, **60**, 942.
BUMM, E. (1885a) *Dtsch. med. Wschr.*, **11**, 508 ; (1885b) *Ibid.*, **11**, 910.
BUSCHKE, A. and LANGER, E. (1921) *Dtsch. med. Wschr.*, **47**, 65.
BUTTERFIELD, C. T. and NEILL, M. H. (1920) *Bull. U.S. hyg. Lab.*, No. 124, p. 11.
CARPENTER, C. M., BOAK, R. A., MUCCI, L. A., and WARREN, S. L. (1933) *J. Lab. clin. Med.*, **18**, 981.
CHAPIN, C. W. (1918) *J. infect. Dis.*, **23**, 342.
CHRISTMAS, J. DE. (1897) *Ann. Inst. Pasteur*, **11**, 609 ; (1900) *Ibid.*, **14**, 331.
CLARK, G. W. (1920) *J. Bact.*, **5**, 99.
COHN, A. (1923) *Klin. Wschr.*, **2**, 873.
COLE, S. W. and LLOYD, D. J. (1917) *J. Path. Bact.*, **21**, 267.
COOK, M. W. and STAFFORD, D. D. (1921) *J. infect. Dis.*, **29**, 561.
COSTA, S. and BOYER, L. (1922) *C. R. Soc. Biol.*, **87**, 856.
DOPTER, C. (1909) *C. R. Soc. Biol.*, **67**, 74 ; (1921) " L'Infection Méningococcique." Paris.
DOPTER and PAURON. (1914) *C. R. Soc. Biol.*, **77**, 231. 292.
DUNN, R. A. and GORDON, M. H. (1905) *Brit. med. J.*, ii, 421.
ELLIS, A. W. M. (1915) *Brit. med. J.*, ii, 880.
ELSER, W. J. and HUNTOON, F. M. (1909) *J. med. Res.*, **20**, 371.
ERICKSON, M. J. and ALBERT, H. (1922) *J. infect. Dis.*, **30**, 268.
EVANS, A. C. (1920) *Bull. U.S. hyg. Lab.*, No. 124, p. 45.
FERRY, N. S., NORTON, J. F., and STEELE, A. H. (1931) *J. Immunol.*, **21**, 293.
FERRY, N. S. and SCHORNACK, P. J. (1934) *J. Immunol.*, **26**, 143.
FLEXNER, S. (1907a) *J. exp. Med.*, **9**, 105 ; (1907b) *Ibid.*, **9**, 142.
FLÜGGE, C. (1896) " Die Mikroorganismen." Leipzig.
GHON, A. and PFEIFFER, H. (1902) *Z. klin. Med.*, **44**, 262.
GORDON, J. E. (1918) *Brit. med. J.*, i. 110 ; (1921) *J. infect. Dis.*, **29**, 462 ; (1926) *J. Path. Bact.*, **29**, 319.
GORDON, J. and M'LEOD, J. W. (1926) *J. Path. Bact.*, **29**, 13 ; (1928) *Ibid.*, **31**, 185.
GORDON, M. H. (1925) *Spec. Rep. Ser. med. Res. Coun., Lond.*, No. 98, p. 105.
GORDON, M. H. and MURRAY, E. G. (1915) *J. R. Army med. Cps.*, **25**, 411.
GRIFFITH, F. (1917) *Rep. loc. Govt Bd publ. Hlth*, New Ser., No. 111, p. 52.
GURD, F. B. (1908) *J. med. Res.*, **18**, 291.
HALL, I. C. (1916) *J. Bact.*, **1**, 343.
HERMANIES, J. (1921a) *J. infect. Dis.*, **28**, 132 ; (1921b) *Ibid.*, **29**, 11.
JAEGER, H. (1895) *Z. Hyg. InfektKr.*, **19**, 351 ; (1899) *Dtsch. med. Wschr.*, **25**, 472 ; (1903a) *Zbl. Bakt.*, **33**, 23 ; (1903b) *Ibid.*, **33**, 681 ; (1903c) *Z. Hyg. InfektKr.*, **44**, 225.
JENKINS, C. E. (1921) *J. Path. Bact.*, **24**, 160 ; (1922) *Ibid.*, **25**, 105.
JÖTTEN, K. W. (1921) *Z. Hyg. InfektKr.*, **92**, 9.
KANDIBA, L. (1922) *Z. Hyg. InfektKr.*, **96**, 347.
KIEFER. (1895) *Berl. klin. Wschr.*, **32**, 332.
KIRKBRIDE, M. B. and COHEN, S. M. (1934) *Amer. J. Hyg.*, **20**, 444.
KOHMAN, E. F. (1919) *J. Bact.*, **4**, 571.
KUTSCHER, K. (1906) *Dtsch. med. Wschr.*, **22**, 1071.
LEBŒUF, F. (1924) *C. R. Soc. Biol.*, **90** 768.

LEISTIKOW. (1882) Berl. klin. Wschr., **19**, 500.
LINGELSHEIM, W. VON. (1905) Dtsch. med. Wschr., **31**, 1217 ; (1906) Klin. Jahrb., **15**, 373 ; (1908) Z. Hyg. InfektKr., **59**, 457.
LIPSCHÜTZ, B. (1904) Zbl. Bakt., **36**, 743.
LLOYD, D. J. (1916–17) J. Path. Bact., **21**, 113.
LORENTZ, F. H. (1922) Münch. med. Wschr., **69**, 1695.
MAEGRAITH, B. (1935) Brit. J. exp. Path., **16**, 109.
MACLAGAN, P. W. and COOKE, W. E. (1917) J. R. Army med. Cps, **29**, 228.
MACNAUGHTON, F. G. (1923) J. Path. Bact., **26**, 297.
McLEOD, J. W., COATES, J. C., HAPPOLD, F. C., PRIESTLEY, D. P., and WHEATLEY, B. (1934) J. Path. Bact., **39**, 221.
M'DONALD, S. (1908) J. Path. Bact., **12**, 442.
MARTIN, W. B. M. (1910) J. Path. Bact., **14**, 136 ; (1911) Ibid., **15**, 76.
MARX, H. and WOITHE, F. (1900) Zbl. Bakt., **28**, 1, 33, 65, 97.
MASLOVSKI. (1900) Zbl. Bakt., **27**, 541.
MILLER, C. P. and BOOR, A. K. (1934) J. exp. Med., **59**, 75.
MURRAY, E. G. D. (1924) J. Hyg., Camb., **22**, 175 ; (1929) Spec. Rep. Ser. med. Res. Coun., Lond., No. 124, p. 15.
MURRAY, E. G. D. and AYRTON, R. (1924) J. Hyg., Camb., **23**, 23.
NABARRO, D. (1917) Rep. loc. Govt Bd. publ. Hlth, New Ser., No. 114, p. 207.
NEILL, M. H. and TAFT, C. E. (1920) Bull. U.S. hyg. Lab., No. 124, p. 93.
NEISSER, A. (1879) Zbl. med. Wiss., **17**, 497 ; (1882) Dtsch. med. Wschr., **8**, 279.
NETTER, A. and DEBRÉ, R. (1911) " La Méningite Cérébro-spinale." Paris.
NICOLAYSEN, L. (1897) Zbl. Bakt., **22**, 305.
NICOLLE, N., DEBAINS, E., and JOUAN, C. (1918) Ann. Inst. Pasteur, **32**, 150.
OLIVER, J. O. (1929) J. Hyg., Camb., **29**, 259.
PEARCE, L. (1915) J. exp. Med., **21**, 289.
PETRIE, G. F. (1932) Brit. J. exp. Path., **13**, 380.
PHELON, H. V., DUTHIE, G. M., and M'LEOD, J. W. (1927) J. Path. Bact., **30**, 133.
PRICE, I. N. O. (1933) " The Complement Fixation Test for Gonorrhœa." London County Council.
RAKE, G. and SCHERP, H. W. (1933a) J. exp. Med., **58**, 341 ; (1933b) Ibid., **58**, 361.
Report. (1916) Spec. Rep. Ser. med. Res. Coun., Lond., No. 2 ; (1920) Ibid., No. 50.
RIST, E. and PARIS, A. (1904) Bull. Inst. Pasteur, **2**, 338.
ROCKWELL, G. E. and McKHANN, C. F. (1921) J. infect. Dis., **28**, 249.
ROSHER, A. B. (1936) Pers. comm.
RUEDIGER, E. H. (1919) J. infect. Dis., **24**, 376.
RUPPEL, W. G. (1906) Dtsch. med. Wschr., **32**, 1366.
SCHÄFFER, J. (1897) Fortschr. Med., **15**, 813.
SCHERP, H. W. and RAKE, G. (1935) J. exp. Med., **61**, 753.
SCHOLTZ, W. (1900) Zbl. Bakt., **27**, 162.
SCOTT, W. M. (1917) Rep. loc. Govt Bd Publ. Hlth, New Ser., No. 114, p. 111.
SORDELLI, A., MIRAVENT, J. M., and NEGRONI, P. (1926) Rev. Inst. bact., B. Aires, **4**, 636.
SWARTZ, E. O. and DAVIS, D. M. (1920) J. Amer. med. Ass., **75**, 1124.
TEAGUE, O. and TORREY, J. C. (1907) J. med. Res., **17**, 223.
THALMANN. (1900) Zbl. Bakt., **27**, 828.
THOMSEN, O. and VOLLMOND, E. (1921) C. R. Soc. Biol., **84**, 326.
THOMSON, D. (1917) Brit. med. J., i. 869.
TORREY, J. C. (1907) J. med. Res., **16**, 329 ; (1908) Ibid., **19**, 471.
TORREY, J. C. and BUCKELL, G. T. (1922a) J. infect. Dis., **31**, 125 ; (1922b) J. Immunol., **7**, 305.
TORREY, J. C., WILSON, M. A., and BUCKELL, G. T. (1922) J. infect. Dis., **31**, 148.
TULLOCH, W. J. (1923a) J. State Med., **31**, 501 ; (1923b) J. R. Army med. Cps, **40**, 12, 98.
VANNOD, T. (1906) Dtsch. med. Wschr., **32**, 1984 ; (1907) Zbl. Bakt., **44**, 10, 110.
VEDDER, E. B. (1915) J. infect. Dis., **16**, 385.
WARREN, S. H. (1921) J. Path. Bact., **24**, 424.
WASSERMANN, A. (1897) Berl. klin. Wschr., **34**, 685 ; (1898) Z. Hyg. InfektKr., **27**, 298.
WATABIKI, T. (1910) J. infect. Dis., **7**, 159.
WEICHSELBAUM, A. (1887) Fortschr. Med., **5**, 573, 620.
WERTHEIM, E. (1891) Dtsch. med. Wschr., **17**, 1351.
WHERRY, W. B. and OLIVER, W. W. (1916) J. infect. Dis., **19**, 288.
WILSON, G. S. and SMITH, M. M. (1928) J. Path. Bact., **31**, 597.
WILSON, S. P. (1928) J. Path. Bact., **31**, 477.
WOLLSTEIN, M. (1907) J. exp. Med., **9**, 588.
WRIGHT, H. D. (1933) J. Path. Bact., **37**, 257.
ZDRODOWSKI, P. and VORONINE, E. (1932) Ann. Inst. Pasteur, **48**, 617.
ZOZAYA, J. (1931) J. exp. Med., **54**, 725.
ZOZAYA, J. and WOOD, J. E. (1932) J. infect. Dis., **50**, 177.

CHAPTER XXIII

STREPTOCOCCUS

THE term *Streptococcus* was first used by Rosenbach in 1884, when describing a coccus, growing in chains, that had been isolated from suppurative lesions in man. To this organism he gave the name *Streptococcus pyogenes*. A chain-forming coccus had, however, been described by Fehleisen in the previous year as the causative organism of erysipelas (Fehleisen 1883) ; and Pasteur, Chamberland and Roux, in 1881, had described a septicæmic infection in rabbits, resulting from the inoculation of these animals with human saliva, which probably affords the earliest recorded reference to the pneumococcus, although no clearly identifiable description of this species was published prior to the independent studies of Fraenkel and of Weichselbaum in 1886. In 1887 Nocard and Mollereau reported the experimental production of mastitis in the cow and goat, by the inoculation into the udder of a streptococcus isolated from the milk of a cow suffering from that disease. In 1888 Schütz described a streptococcus that he had isolated from the lesions of strangles in the horse. In more recent years, chain-forming cocci have been isolated from a variety of pathological conditions in man and animals, from the mouth or from the fæces of healthy subjects, from milk and various milk products, and from other sources.

The tendency to grow in chains of varying length gives to the members of this group a very characteristic morphology, and they possess in common other characters that appear to justify their inclusion in a single bacterial genus. The Committee of the Society of American Bacteriologists (Winslow *et al.* 1920) separated the pneumococcus from the main streptococcal group, by forming a genus *Diplococcus*, with *Diplococcus pneumoniæ* as the type species. It appears to the authors, for reasons which will become apparent, that this separation is undesirable, and the summary of generic characters as set out by the American Committee has been modified in the required sense. As so modified, and with other minor emendations, including the substitution of *Str. pyogenes* for *Str. hæmolyticus* as the name of the type species, the description of these generic characters would read as follows :

DEFINITION.—*Streptococcus.*

Spherical or ovoid cells, arranged in short or long chains, or in pairs. Usually non-motile. Non-sporing. Most species Gram-positive. Some species form capsules. Growth tends to be relatively slight on artificial media, and some species grow poorly in the absence of added native protein. Several species produce characteristic changes in media containing blood. Various carbohydrates are fermented, with the production of acid. Most species fail to liquefy gelatin. Most species are aerobic and facultatively anaerobic ; some are anaerobic. Many species are normally parasitic on man or animals ; some species are highly pathogenic, and some produce soluble toxins.

Type species. *Streptococcus pyogenes.*

The many attempts that have been made to evolve a satisfactory classification of the *Streptococci* provide an admirable example of the difficulties with which the systematic bacteriologist is faced. As will be seen, there is no single criterion on which reliance can be placed, even in making a primary division into sub-groups that are themselves to be further divided by the application of other tests. It happens that, in this particular genus, one of the most useful differential criteria is provided by the changes induced by the growing organisms in media containing blood ; but we shall note that this test, valuable as it is, cannot be too rigidly applied. Here, as elsewhere, we have to apply a variety of criteria selected, on the usual basis of statistical empiricism, as differentiating between groups each of which possesses several highly correlated characters. Here, as elsewhere, we find that the method of antigenic analysis is playing an increasingly important part in the differentiation and identification of those ultimate types, or varieties, for which we need distinguishing names or labels.

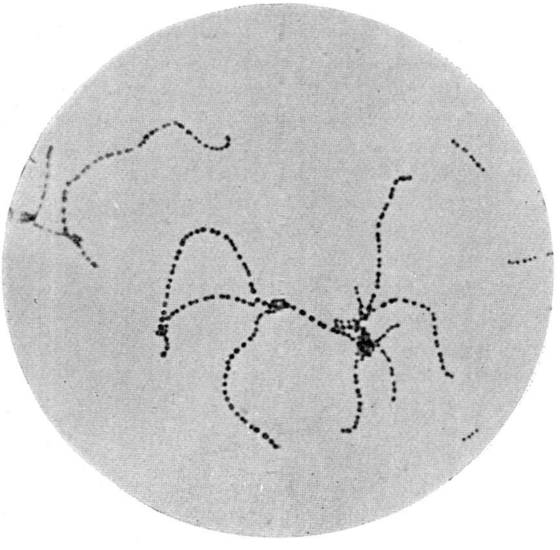

FIG. 99.—*Str. pyogenes.*
From 24-hours' culture on agar, showing long chains
($\times$ 1000).

The most convenient method of discussing this problem will be to take various characters in turn, and see how far they enable us to differentiate between one species, or type, and another.

Morphology.—Taking the genus as a whole, the characters that might be regarded as supplying possible differential criteria are (1) the length of the chains formed, (2) the shape of the individual cells forming them, (3) the presence or absence of capsules, and (4) in the light of certain recent observations, the very occasional presence of flagella.

In the earlier days of bacteriology much attention was paid to chain formation as a differential criterion, and such names as *Streptococcus brevis, Streptococcus longus, Streptococcus longissimus,* and *Streptococcus conglomeratus* were coined to denote strains with the corresponding tendencies to grow in short chains, long chains, or chains which were very long or tangled. It has, however, come to be generally recognized (Thamann 1912, Brown 1919) that these characters are often variable within a single strain ; so that, while the modal chain length of any species may be sufficiently characteristic to deserve inclusion in a description of the specific characters, it is quite useless for purposes of classification, and misleading when employed for purposes of nomenclature. Some species or groups, such as *Str. pneumoniæ* and the enterococcus, usually occur in pairs or very short chains and never form chains of any considerable length. Others, such as *Str. pyogenes,* usually occur in chains of eight or more cocci and often form long chains. Others again, such as the strains of the viridans type, are markedly variable in this respect, occurring both as very short chains, or pairs, and as chains of enormous length.

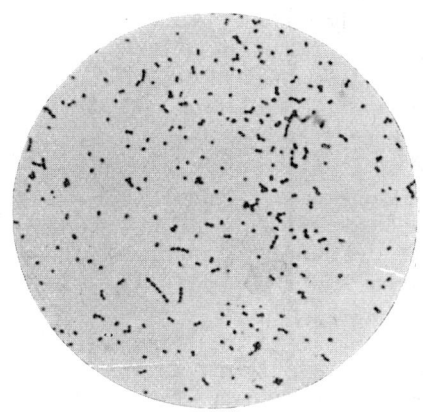

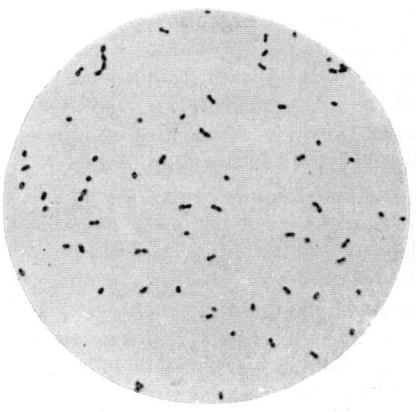

FIG. 100.—Viridans streptococci.

From 24-hours' culture in broth, showing short chains (× 1000).

FIG. 101.—*Str. pneumoniæ.*

From 24-hours' culture on agar, showing diplococci and short chains (× 1000).

The shape of the individual cocci forming the chain also varies, and there is a tendency for the cells of short-chained streptococci to be ovoid, with the long axis in the axis of the chain. When, as in the pneumococcus, a majority of the cocci occur in pairs, each cell of a pair may be definitely lanceolate, the blunt ends being adjacent. The individual cells of long-chained streptococci tend to approach more closely to the spherical form; or they may sometimes be compressed in such a way that the longer axis of the cell lies at right angles to the axis of the chain as a whole. Cell shape, like modal chain length, may vary from one species of streptococcus to another, but it forms no better criterion for systematic purposes.

Capsule formation, when it occurs, is of greater value for classification. It is almost constantly shown by *Str. pneumoniæ* when growing within the tissues (see Fig. 102) and is absent in most other species, though not in all.

Seastone (1934), for instance, has shown that *Str. pyogenes* may show well-marked capsulation during the first 2–2½

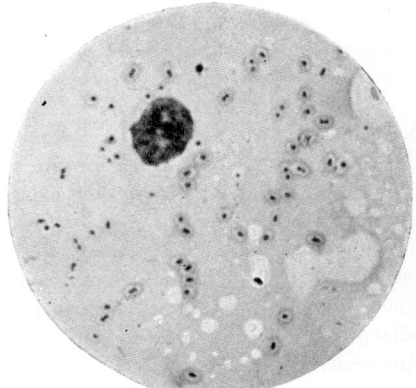

FIG. 102.—*Str. pneumoniæ.*

In peritoneal exudate of mouse, showing capsulation (× 1000).

hours of growth in serum broth, though the capsules have usually disappeared by the 3rd or 4th hour.

From time to time, accounts have appeared in the literature of motile streptococci, but many of these have been based on somewhat inadequate observations, and the genus *Streptococcus* has, until recently, been regarded by most bacteriologists as composed exclusively of non-flagellated species. It is certain that flagellated forms are very rare; but two observers (Koblmüller 1935, Pownall 1935) have recently given careful and detailed descriptions of motile strains of streptococci. In each case the organism described was apparently a motile variant of the species, or group, that is generally known by the name of "enterococcus."

Streptococci stain readily with the ordinary dyes; none of them are acid-fast; and the great majority are frankly Gram-positive. Some strains tend to lose the Gram stain if decolorization is prolonged; a few species, or varieties, have been described as frankly Gram-negative.

Cultural Requirements.—Some species of streptococci, such as *Str. pneumoniæ* and to a less extent *Str. pyogenes*, grow poorly on the simpler media of the laboratory when first isolated; though they can usually be trained to grow on these media after a limited number of subcultures. The growth of these species is markedly improved by the addition to the medium of such materials as blood or serum. A few species, or types, such as the enterococci, grow well in the presence of bile or bile salts, while most do not.

The optimal temperature for growth is, with most parasitic species, in the near neighbourhood of 37° C. Some species found in milk have an optimum about 30° C. The range over which growth occurs is, for the more sensitive species, somewhat restricted; 42° C. or thereabouts marks the upper limit; growth is usually slow at temperatures below 30° C. and often ceases below 20° C. Some species, on the other hand, including certain streptococci found in milk, grow actively at temperatures of 45° C. or over (see Sherman and Stark 1931). Such thermophilic types are of considerable economic importance in relation to pasteurization (see Chapter LXXXIX).

Most species are aerobic and facultatively anaerobic. Some are strict anaerobes, or microaerophilic. It will be more convenient to discuss the other characters of these anaerobic streptococci, which have not yet been studied in any detail, in a separate section of this chapter (p. 463).

These cultural requirements, while supplying useful ancillary evidence in identification, do not, except in the case of the anaerobic species and the markedly thermophilic streptococci, afford an adequate basis for any primary classification.

Growth Characters.—*On solid media* the streptococci tend to form small, discrete, slightly raised colonies, 1 mm. or less in diameter. The modal colonial form varies in different species; and it may in some cases be sufficiently characteristic to assist in identification, particularly in recently isolated strains. Many strains of pneumococci, for instance, give characteristic "draughtsman" colonies, with an entire, sharply raised edge and a central depressed area. A Type III pneumococcus frequently gives a characteristic watery, or mucoid, colony. One type of hæmolytic streptococcus gives easily recognizable minute, clear colonies, and so on.

Many species grow poorly in gelatin; and in a gelatin stab such growth as occurs is mainly confined to the track of the needle. The only streptococci, apart from some of the anaerobic species, that are known to liquefy gelatin are certain strains of enterococci. When liquefaction occurs it is usually infundibuliform in type.

In broth or other liquid media many species of streptococci give a granular growth, the medium remaining clear and the granular masses collecting as a powdery deposit, or adhering to the sides of the tube. Although this type of growth shows a characteristically high frequency among certain species of streptococci, especially when first isolated, it is by no means constant ; and the degree of granularity may vary over a wide range.   In some cases a granular deposit may be associated with a varying degree of turbidity of the medium ; in others the growth, as a whole, may be distinctly though finely granular, the granules remaining dispersed throughout the medium.   Any one strain may undergo marked changes in this respect on subculture ; if a strain which, on first isolation, gives a markedly granular growth, is subjected to repeated subculturing at short intervals, it is often possible to produce a diffuse growth within a limited number of generations.   In all cases the type of growth in a fluid medium is closely associated with the character of chain formation.   A strain which is forming long chains will give a typically granular growth ; if the growth becomes diffuse it will be found that the average chain length has diminished.   Those species in which the diplococcal form predominates, as for instance *Str. pneumoniæ* or enterococci, usually give diffuse, non-granular growths in fluid media.

Metabolic Activities.—Most of the early attempts to classify the streptococci were based on their fermentation reactions in an empirically selected series of

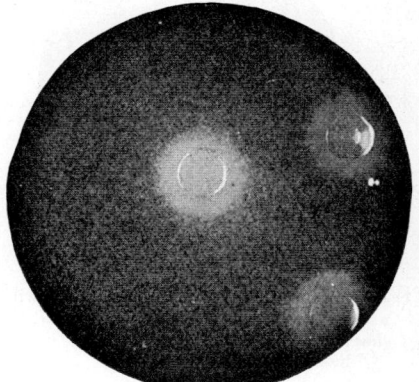

FIG. 103.—*Str. pyogenes.*

Surface colony on blood agar plate, showing
zone of hæmolysis round colony ($\times$ 8).

FIG. 104.—*Str. pneumoniæ.*

Surface colonies on blood agar plate, showing
zones of discoloration and partial hæmolysis round colonies ($\times$ 8).

substrates.   The behaviour of the different members of this genus in blood-containing media has, however, come to occupy so important a place as a criterion for primary classification, that it will be convenient to deal with it first.

Classification Based on Changes Produced in Blood.—Marmorek (1895) first noted the ability of certain strains of streptococci to lyse red blood corpuscles *in vivo* and *in vitro*, but it was Schottmüller (1903) who proposed that the ability to produce hæmolysis *in vitro* should be adopted as a differential criterion for purposes of classification.   He noted that certain strains of streptococci produced clear zones of lysis when grown on blood agar plates, while others gave colonies which were surrounded by zones of greenish discoloration.   For the former type Schott-müller proposed the name *Str. hæmolyticus*, for the latter *Str. viridans*.   These observations formed the basis of a system of classification and nomenclature which has been developed by many subsequent investigators.   It has, indeed, been shown that the green-producing streptococci are not devoid of hæmolytic activity, though the zones which they produce on blood agar plates are different in kind, as well as in extent, from those formed round the colonies of the frankly hæmolytic strains. Mandelbaum (1907) emphasized the importance of microscopical examination of the colonies formed on blood agar plates, and noted that, while the colonies of the long pathogenic streptococci were surrounded by clear colourless zones, those of the viridans type, and also those of the pneumococcus, were surrounded by a zone of discoloured, non-hæmolysed corpuscles lying immediately next the colony, and an outer narrow hæmolysed zone containing only corpuscular shadows.

These phenomena were studied in much greater detail by Smith and Brown (1915), and by Brown (1919). The monograph by Brown, in which the appearances met with and the factors which determine or modify them are fully discussed, contains an admirable review of the literature dealing with the classification of streptococci up to 1919. In this monograph great emphasis is laid on the importance

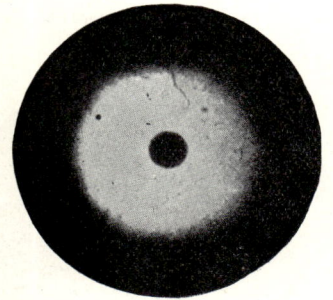

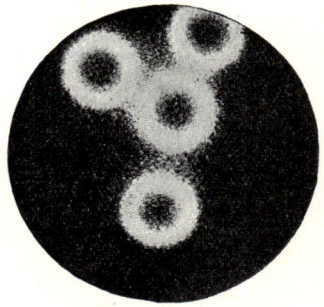

Fig. 105.—*Str. pyogenes.*

Deep colony in blood agar plate, showing wide zone of complete hæmolysis, and the sharply differentiated margin of the colony —β-hæmolysis (× 8).

Fig. 106.—Viridans streptococci.

Deep colonies in blood agar plate, showing zone of discoloured cells round colony, obscuring margin, and zone of incomplete lysis beyond—α-hæmolysis (× 8).

of employing a uniform and standardized technique, and, in particular, on the superiority of poured plates, and the observation of deep colonies, over plates which have been inoculated by surface spreading only. The medium recommended by Brown consists of veal peptone agar containing 5 per cent. of horse blood. The agar is stored in tubes in 12 c.c. amounts ; when required for use a tube is melted and cooled to 45° C. ; 0·66 c.c. of horse blood is added and evenly mixed with the agar, the medium is inoculated with a loop or two of a 24-hours' broth culture that has been so diluted as to give about 100 colonies ; and is then poured into a Petri dish 9 cm. in diameter, thus giving a layer about 2 mm. thick. The plates, after preliminary drying in the inverted position with the plate tilted on the lid, are incubated at 37° C. for 24 hours. They are then examined and the appearances noted. They are re-examined after another 24 hours' incubation at 37° C., and finally after a further 24 hours in the ice-chest. For the recognition of hæmolytic and non-hæmolytic strains in primary mixed cultures the use of blood agar plates with a surface inoculation usually suffices, and has certain advantages ; but for the critical determination of the type of hæmolysis given by any strain, once it has been isolated in pure culture, the technique recommended by Brown should be strictly adhered to, at least in regard to the medium used and the examination of deep colonies. The use of horse blood is particularly important. It is well known that the red corpuscles of different animal species vary widely in their resistance to different hæmolytic agents. In spite of this fact, many workers have used the blood of the rabbit or ox or some other animal, in testing the hæmolytic activity of various species, or strains, of streptococci ; and it is probable that some at least of the discrepancies met with in the literature are due to this variable factor. It may, at times, be desirable to use the blood or red cells of some particular species in a given series of observations on streptococcal hæmolysin ; but, if the results are to be used for purposes of identification or classification, they should always be controlled by parallel tests made with horse blood.

Brown records four different types of reaction in blood agar plates, which he designates as follows :

α. A somewhat greenish discoloration and partial hæmolysis of the blood corpuscles immediately surrounding the colony, forming a rather indefinitely bounded zone 1–2 mm. in diameter, outside of which is a second, narrow, clearer, not discoloured zone. Under the microscope many corpuscles are seen in the inner zone, and these are obviously discoloured, the discoloration varying in degree with different strains of streptococci. Very few corpuscles remain in the outer, clearer zone ; and these are never discoloured. These typical appearances may fail to appear after 24 hours', or even after 48 hours' incubation, at the end of which time the narrow outer zone of hæmolysis may not have developed. In such cases this zone makes its appearance during the subsequent 24 hours in the ice-chest. If a plate, which has developed the typical appearances, is reincubated for 24 to 48 hours, and then placed in the ice-chest for a further 24 hours, a double series of rings will frequently develop, so that the colony is surrounded by a hazy discoloured ring, a clear hæmolysed ring, a second hazy ring, and a second clear ring. By repeating the whole process it is sometimes possible to develop three or more series of such rings.

β. The colonies are surrounded by sharply defined, clear, colourless zones of hæmolysis, 2–4 mm. in diameter. Under the microscope no corpuscles can be seen within this zone. The zones of β-hæmolysis develop more rapidly than those of the α type. They are often well developed after 18 hours' incubation. They extend slightly between the 24th and 48th hour, but show no qualitative changes. They undergo no alteration or extension during the subsequent 24 hours in the ice-chest.

α′ (α prime). The colonies are surrounded by a zone of hæmolysis, which is slightly hazy, and less sharply limited than in the case of true β-hæmolysis. The colony itself is not sharply defined, and examination with the microscope shows that the hæmolysed zone contains, throughout, a moderate number of unaltered corpuscles, which are most numerous in the immediate neighbourhood of the colony. There is no discoloration. Unlike the zones of β-hæmolysis, a considerable extension of the zones may occur during the 24 hours in the ice-box. It is noted that some strains which produce α′-hæmolysis on horse blood agar may produce typical α-hæmolysis on rabbit blood agar.

γ. The colonies develop in the blood agar without any change in the surrounding medium.

The β-hæmolytic strains of Smith and Brown correspond to Schottmüller's *Str. hæmolyticus.* The α-hæmolytic strains may be regarded as equivalent to his *Str. viridans* ; though it may be noted that strains are encountered that produce the characteristic green coloration without the formation of a detectable zone of hæmolysis. The significance of the α′ type of hæmolysis is not clear. It seems to be of infrequent occurrence. There seems no good reason for attaching the label γ to those streptococci that cause no change in blood media. Strains of this type have sometimes been referred to as " indifferent streptococci."

The terms α- and β-hæmolysis have attained general usage in bacteriological literature and serve a useful purpose. No effort has been made, however, to reconcile this usage with that of the terms " hæmolytic " and " non-hæmolytic " as applied to streptococci. By a " hæmolytic " streptococcus " is meant almost always a strain that causes β-hæmolysis on blood agar. By a " non-hæmolytic streptococcus " is meant a strain that either produces α-hæmolysis, or gives rise to no change at all. Some workers would confine the term " hæmolytic streptococcus," or at least the specific name *Str. hæmolyticus* if that be used, to strains that, in addition to causing β-hæmolysis in blood agar, can be shown to produce a soluble hæmolysin, and this is an aspect of the problem that must be discussed in more detail.

Marmorek (1895) showed that cultures of certain strains of streptococci in a fluid medium had the power of lysing added blood corpuscles, and Besredka (1901) obtained hæmolytic filtrates from cultures of streptococci in heated rabbit's serum. Braun (1912) reported that all strains of streptococci which produced hæmolysis on rabbit blood agar plates gave rise to a filtrable hæmolysin when grown in rabbit serum broth. The factors which determine this hæmolysin production have been studied by McLeod (1912), Meader and Robinson (1920) and de Kruif and Ireland (1920). All these observers noted that hæmolysin production was absent or minimal in cultures grown in plain broth without the addition of serum. More recently Todd (1932a) and Todd and Hewitt (1932) have shown that potent hæmolytic filtrates may be obtained by growing hæmolytic streptococci in a medium containing yeast extract, or in a special broth medium, sterilized by filtration instead of by autoclaving, and containing dextrose, sodium bicarbonate and sodium phosphate.

De Kruif and Ireland have carried out careful quantitative studies of the rate of hæmolysin production, and of its inactivation in the culture medium. They found that the hæmolytic titre of the supernatant fluid from their cultures after centrifugalization reached its maximum after 8 hours' incubation at 37° C., and then rapidly declined. In many cases no hæmolysin could be detected after 14 hours ; though, when the whole culture was tested instead of the supernatant fluid, some lytic action might persist up to the 24th hour. A hæmolytic filtrate is completely inactivated by heating at 55° C. for 30 minutes, and may lose most of its activity when incubated at 37° C. for 2 hours or more (see McLeod 1912).

It has been shown by Neill and Mallory (1926) that streptolysin, when exposed to air at relatively low temperatures, undergoes an oxidation that is readily reversible by suitable chemical reagents. The hæmolysin is active in the reduced form, inactive in the oxidized. At higher temperatures (55° C.) an irreversible inactivation occurs.

It would seem (Todd 1934) that certain strains of hæmolytic streptococci, including most of those pathogenic for man, produce two kinds of hæmolysin, one of which is oxygen-sensitive, and undergoes a reversible oxidation, while the other is not oxygen-sensitive, but is very sensitive to heat or to acid. Other types of hæmolytic streptococci appear to produce only an oxygen-stable type of hæmolysin, the heat or acid resistance of which varies from one species or type to another.

Meanwhile we may note that the extreme sensitivity of streptococcal hæmolysin to oxidation, to heat and to acid (see Todd 1934) makes it extremely difficult to assert with confidence that any particular strain that gives β-hæmolysis on blood agar plates is incapable of producing a filtrable hæmolysin in a fluid medium ; all we can safely say is that it does not do so when tested by the ordinary methods.

In this connection it may be noted that it is not only in regard to the production of a filtrable hæmolysin that the oxygen-sensitivity of the active substance must be taken into account. Fry (1933) has noted that certain strains of streptococci that give characteristic α-hæmolysis on aerobic blood agar plates give typical β-hæmolysis when incubated anaerobically. Such strains may yield an active filtrable hæmolysin. Dr. Edith Straker (unpublished), working in the authors' laboratory, has encountered similar strains ; but they seem to be relatively infrequent, at least in cultures isolated from the normal human throat. Anaerobic incubation of surface-spread plates from primary cultures showed the presence of hæmolytic streptococci in a significantly higher proportion of cases than did aerobic plates ; but most of the hæmolytic strains that appeared in primary mixed culture only on the anaerobic plates gave β-hæmolysis aerobically and anaerobically when retested in pure culture. It would seem that, apart from the occasional occurrence of the oxygen-sensitive strains referred to above, anaerobic conditions afford better opportunities for hæmolytic streptococci to grow and exert their hæmolytic activity when they are mixed with other organisms ; and it is therefore desirable that primary plate cultures should be incubated anaerobically rather than aerobically, or preferably in duplicate.

When we turn to those streptococci that produce α-hæmolysis on blood agar plates, we have two mechanisms to consider : the reaction that causes the lysis of the red cells, and the reaction that causes the green coloration.

Cole (1914) described the presence in pneumococci of a labile intracellular hæmolysin which was liberated from the cells on autolysis. It was commonly stated by subsequent workers that the pneumococcus produced no filtrable hæmolysin in fluid media ; and the agent causing α-hæmolysis was supposed to be of some quite different nature. It has, however, been quite clearly demonstrated within recent years (see Neill 1926, Sickles and Coffey 1928, Cowan 1934, Todd 1934) that the pneumococcus, when grown under suitable conditions, produces a soluble hæmolysin of the oxygen-sensitive, heat-sensitive type, which undergoes reversible oxidation at low temperatures. Whether other streptococci that produce α-hæmolysis would also elaborate a filtrable hæmolysin under suitable conditions is at present unknown.

Until recently the most widely accepted view in regard to the green coloration associated with α-hæmolysis was that it was due to the formation of methæmoglobin or of some closely allied substance (Schnabel 1921, McLeod and Gordon 1922, Rother 1925). It was shown by McLeod and Gordon that the pneumococcus produces hydrogen peroxide and that hydrogen peroxide will discolour heated blood agar, in which the blood catalase has been inactivated. The mechanisms involved in the production of hydrogen peroxide by the pneumococcus, or by pneumococcal extracts, have been studied in considerable detail by Avery, Morgan and Neill (Avery and Morgan 1924, Morgan and Avery 1924, Avery and Neill 1924a, b, c, Neill and Avery 1924a, b, 1925, Morgan and Neill 1924, Neill 1925). The systems involved appear to include the catalysed oxidation-reduction and peroxidase mechanisms discussed in Chapter III, and the actual course of the reaction seems to be determined in the main by the oxygen pressure to which the reacting system is exposed. It is, however, clear that the formation of methæmoglobin is not itself the cause of the green pigmentation, unless the apparent greenness is due to an optical delusion resulting from a colour contrast ; and, in view of the amount of catalase present in unheated blood, it is difficult to believe that hydrogen peroxide is the active agent in cultures on unheated blood agar plates.

This problem has been brought nearer solution by the studies of Hart and Anderson (1933) (see also Anderson and Hart 1934a). Working with the pneumococcus, they found that when small quantities of laked blood were added to broth cultures in the presence of an alkaline buffer solution, an olive-green precipitate was formed. This could be separated, washed, and dissolved in dilute alkali to give a green solution. Crystalline hæmoglobin, or methæmoglobin, gave the same green pigment when incubated under suitable conditions with pneumococcal cultures. The spectroscopic and chemical analysis of this pigment suggest that it is an iron-containing derivative of hæmoglobin. It is rapidly bleached by hydrogen peroxide, but it is not affected by reducing agents. An identical, or very similar, green pigment can be obtained by incubating laked blood, hæmoglobin, or methæmoglobin with various chemical reducing systems, such as ascorbic acid, cysteine-glucose, etc. From the results obtained with autolysed bacterial cells, washed bacteria, bacterial extracts, etc., it would seem that the green pigment results from the activity of a bacterial oxidation-reduction system, one component of which is intracellular. This system is not peculiar to the pneumococcus; it is shared, not only by those streptococci that produce the green pigment on blood agar plates, but by *Str. pyogenes* which gives β-hæmolysis, and by the enterococci which normally produce no change on unheated blood media. It is also possessed by unrelated bacteria, such as *Staph. aureus* and *Bact. coli*. The production of green pigmentation by some species and not by others would seem to be due, not so much to the presence or absence of the necessary enzyme system as to secondary factors, themselves determined by the metabolic activities of the bacteria concerned, which sometimes permit this system to function, and sometimes suppress it. We have already noted that some strains of hæmolytic streptococci may produce β-hæmolysis under anaerobic conditions, while giving typical α-hæmolysis with green coloration when cultivated aerobically.

Summarizing the observations recorded above we may say that a study of the appearance of the colonies on blood agar plates, together with a test for the production of a filtrable hæmolysin, enables us to divide streptococci into three, or possibly four, different categories.

(1) *Hæmolytic streptococci*.—These produce β-hæmolysis on blood agar plates. They may be differentiated into two sub-groups.

(*a*) Those that produce a filtrable hæmolysin.

(*b*) Those that do not produce a filtrable hæmolysin.

(2) *Streptococci giving α-hæmolysis*.

(3) *Streptococci that have no action on blood media under the usual conditions of testing*.

Classification Based on Fermentation Reactions.—The capacity of different species or types of streptococci to ferment different substrates played a very large part in the earlier attempts to separate this group of bacteria into its natural elements. The classification of Andrewes and Horder (1906), based largely on the earlier studies of Gordon (1902–03, 1903–04, 1905), and the more extensive and detailed classification proposed by Holman (1916) (see also Floyd and Wolbach 1914, Lyall 1914, Broadhurst 1915), depended almost wholly on a selected series of fermentation tests. It is hardly necessary to-day to set out these classifications in their original form; since few would now accept them as affording an adequate basis for the differentiation of named species or types. This does not of course mean that these fermentation tests are of no value in classifying the streptococci. The reverse is the case. In more recent years, however, the tendency has been to employ fermentation reactions as ancillary, rather than as primary differential criteria. When a particular substrate has been found to be of value in differentiating between certain related species or types, it has been used for this purpose, but has not necessarily been employed in the differentiation of other species within the genus. It will therefore be more convenient to consider the exact systematic significance of these fermentation tests after we have discussed certain other differential criteria, and, in particular, the results obtained by antigenic analysis: but it will be useful to summarize here the observations that have been made on the correlation between enzymic activities and natural habitat.

The early observations that streptococci isolated from pathogenic lesions in man usually ferment lactose and salicin, seldom, if ever, mannitol, raffinose or inulin, and give acid without clot in milk has been amply confirmed. The value of inulin fermentation as a differential test for the identification of the pneumococcus has also been firmly established. It is clear that this species almost always ferments this glucoside, while most other streptococci fail to do so. There has been a tendency to exclude from the species *Str. pneumoniæ* any strain that fails to ferment inulin ; but it is doubtful, as Berger and Silberstein (1926) point out, whether this test can be applied with such complete rigidity. As regards other substrates, the pneumococcus ferments lactose and usually raffinose, but not salicin or mannitol. Milk is acidified and frequently clotted.

There is general agreement that the streptococcus commonly found in the human mouth, which is of the α-hæmolytic type, frequently ferments raffinose, usually fails to ferment salicin, inulin and mannitol, and usually forms a clot in milk.

There is also agreement that the fermentation of mannitol is characteristic of the streptococci that normally inhabit the human intestine (see Winslow and Palmer 1910, Fuller and Armstrong 1913, Hopkins and Lang 1914, Dible 1921, Bagger 1926, Meyer 1926, Meyer and Schönfeld 1926, Downie and Cruickshank 1928). These streptococci usually ferment salicin and lactose, seldom inulin or raffinose, and usually clot and decolorize litmus milk. A few of them are peculiar in liquefying gelatin. In relation to this group of streptococci an additional fermentation test was introduced by Rochaix (1924)—the fermentation of æsculin in a bile-containing medium. This reaction has been studied by Meyer and Schönfeld (1926) and by Weatherall and Dible (1929). It has been found by many workers to be of considerable differential value ; but, as Weatherall and Dible point out, the inclusion of bile salts in the medium removes it from the ordinary category of fermentation tests, since bile salts inhibit the growth of many species of streptococci (see below) and in their absence æsculin is attacked, though often slowly, by many non-fæcal species or types.

Comparing the streptococci of man with those from other animals, several points of interest have emerged.

Winslow and Palmer (1910), while confirming the frequency of mannitol-fermenting streptococci in human fæces, noted their rarity in fæces from the cow or horse. They found also that raffinose-fermenting strains, while relatively uncommon in human fæces, were very common in the fæces of cattle. Fuller and Armstrong (1913) examined 349 strains of streptococci isolated from fæces—123 from man, 129 from the horse and 97 from cattle. They found that 65 per cent. of the fæcal streptococci from man fermented mannitol, as compared with 2–3 per cent. of the bovine or equine fæcal strains. Raffinose-fermenting streptococci, on the other hand, were not found among the human fæcal strains, while 12 per cent. of the equine fæcal strains, and 73 per cent. of the bovine fæcal strains fermented this sugar. The equine fæcal strains were characterized by a frequent failure to ferment lactose.

The fact that streptococci isolated from horses, whether from suppurative lesions or from the mouths or intestines of normal animals, frequently fail to ferment lactose has been noted by many observers (see Jones 1919).

The importance of milk as a human food, and of the cow as a stock animal, has led to a careful and detailed study of the streptococci that occur in normal milk, or in the milk from diseased animals, or that have been isolated from the udder in acute or chronic mastitis.

A type of streptococcus that is almost constantly present in milk, and has been given the name *Str. lactis*, resembles in many ways the streptococcus commonly found in human fæces ; and it will therefore be more convenient to deal with its fermentation reactions when considering its probable relation to that organism in a later section.

In regard to those streptococci that are associated with mastitis in the cow, acute or chronic, certain additional criteria, based on fermentation reactions, have been introduced within recent years in an attempt to differentiate the characteristically bovine strains from those of human origin. Among these are (1) the final pH produced in glucose broth (Avery, R. C., and Cullen 1919, Ayers and Mudge 1922, Frost *et al.* 1927, Minett *et al.* 1929, Avery, R. C. 1929*a, b*, Minett and Stableforth 1931, 1934, Lancefield 1933, Hare and Colebrook 1934) ; and (2) the capacity to hydrolyse sodium hippurate (Ayers and Rupp 1922 and other references above). It has been found that mastitis strains of human origin produce a final pH of 5·0–5·6 in glucose broth, and fail to hydrolyse sodium hippurate. Bovine strains, on the other hand, produce a final pH of 4·2–4·8 in glucose broth, and hydrolyse sodium hippurate. It has also been found that the fermentation of trehalose and sorbitol afford a valuable criterion in the examination of a particular group of hæmolytic streptococci that are found both in men and cattle. The human strains in the group usually ferment trehalose but not sorbitol ; the bovine strains ferment sorbitol but not trehalose (Ogura 1929, Edwards, P. R. 1932, 1933, Minett 1935*a*, *b*).

Certain Other Biological Tests Employed in Classification.—Before discussing the important problem of the antigenic structure of the *Streptococci*, we may deal briefly with certain other biological tests that have been found useful in identification and classification within this group.

It was shown by Neufeld (1900) that pneumococci are soluble in bile, while other species of streptococci are not.

The mechanism of the *bile-solubility test* has been studied in some detail by many subsequent observers. The pneumococcus is an organism that readily undergoes autolysis in culture ; and Avery and Cullen (1923) have shown that extracts of washed pneumococci contain an enzyme that lyses the bacterial cells. This enzyme is inactivated by heating at 60° C. for half an hour ; but in its active state it is able to act on heat-killed pneumococci, though not on hæmolytic streptococci or other organisms. There seems little doubt (see Mair 1929) that the effect of bile is simply to accelerate this natural autolytic process. In regard to the active substance in the bile, many samples of ordinary commercial sodium taurocholate induce lysis, but the action is very variable, and Mair (1917) has shown that the most actively lytic bile constituent is sodium deoxycholate, a pure solution of which forms the most satisfactory test reagent (see also White 1929, Downie, Stent and White 1931). Other factors, besides the presence of bile-acids, are concerned in this test. It is usually stated (see Avery, R. C., and Cullen 1923, Mair 1929) that the optimum pH for autolysis lies between pH 6 and pH 8, and that the range for bile solubility is about the same, with the limitation that, since the bile-acids are thrown out of solution at pH 6·5, the test must be carried out in a solution more alkaline than this. It is, however, customary to employ a reaction of pH 7·6, or thereabouts ; and it is also customary if a negative bile-solubility test is obtained, to add a drop of dilute alkali before regarding the test as negative. It seems doubtful whether this solubility in alkaline solutions is entirely dependent on the presence of bile-acids. Dr. Edith Straker (unpublished), working in the authors' laboratory, has found that simple addition of alkali to a suspension of pneumococci lyses the great majority of recently isolated strains, though old laboratory strains are often more resistant.

The salt content, apart from acidity or alkalinity, also exerts a pronounced effect. Nicolle and Adil-Bey (1907) reported that the addition of magnesium sulphate favoured the lysis of pneumococci by bile salts, while Falk and Yang (1926) state that chlorides of monovalent cations inhibit lysis in low concentrations (0·004–1 per cent.), but may accelerate it in high concentrations (2·0–4·0). Anderson and Hart (1934*b*) studied this phenomenon in more detail. They found that there was a reciprocal relation between the concentration of sodium deoxycholate required to induce lysis and the concentration of sodium chloride in the suspending fluid. There was no evidence of any inhibition by the salt. Lysis occurred in the absence of sodium chloride, but as the concentration increased up to about 5 per cent., less and less deoxycholate was required to produce lysis.

Bile salts are not the only reagents that cause, or accelerate, the lysis of pneumococci ; Downie, Stent and White (1931) noted that saponin had a similar effect. Klein and Stone (1931) noted the same fact and Klein (1933, 1935) has extended the study of this reaction. He has found that, in order to induce the lysis of pneumococci by saponin it is essential that there should be added to the medium in which the organism is grown either a sterol (cholesterol) or an animal fluid such as blood or serum. Under these conditions he has found all pneumococci to be saponin-soluble. Eight cultures of *Str. hæmolyticus* or *Str. viridans* were found to be saponin-insoluble.

The question arises as to whether the " bile-solubility " test is to be regarded as a completely reliable criterion, bile-insoluble strains being excluded from the species *Str. pneumoniæ*. Neufeld originally regarded bile solubility as being characteristic only of recently isolated pneumococcal strains ; but when the test is made with sodium deoxycholate and with due precautions as to the reaction of the medium, etc., the consensus of opinion is that all, or almost all, strains of normal, smooth pneumococci undergo lysis. The behaviour of rough variants appears to be inconstant. Many, probably most, rough strains are bile-soluble (Griffith 1923, Reimann 1927, Downie *et al.* 1931) ; but some are less readily lysed than normal, smooth strains, and a few are apparently quite insoluble. It seems clear that this test, properly performed, is one of the most reliable at our disposal. A smooth strain that proves insoluble in sodium deoxycholate should not be given the title *Str. pneumoniæ* without a clear statement that, because of this important divergence from the specific characters, the diagnosis must be regarded as uncertain.

The use of bile has provided another differential test within this group. Weissenbach (1918) noted that enterococci grew well in a medium containing 10 per cent. of bile, while *Str. pyogenes* and other streptococci tested by him failed to grow in this medium. The observation that enterococci grow freely in high concentrations of bile has been confirmed by many subsequent observers ; but it would appear that this character is not peculiar to this species, or group. The ability of other species and types to grow in bile-containing media (10 per cent. and 40 per cent.) has been studied by several workers (see Belenky and Popowa 1929, Minett and Stableforth 1931, Lancefield 1933, Hare and Colebrook 1934, Hare 1935, Hare and Maxted 1935, Colebrook, Maxted and Johns 1935). The possible significance of this character in the classification of streptococci other than the enterococci will be more conveniently discussed in relation to the results obtained by antigenic analysis.

Another test that has been applied in the classification of this group is the ability to *reduce, and thus decolorize, methylene blue* added to milk, usually in a concentration of 1 : 5,000 (Avery, R. C. 1929*a, b*). This test would appear to depend in part on the ability of the organism to multiply in the presence of methylene blue, in part on the Eh that the growing organism induces. Many of the strains that reduce methylene blue have been isolated from animal sources or from milk. There is general agreement that strains of hæmolytic streptococci isolated from severe human infections fail to do so. Enterococci, however, reduce methylene blue actively (Kleckner 1935). Here again, the significance of this test must be considered in relation to the antigenic structure of the various species or types.

A fourth test that is of considerable value from the point of view of classification is that of *heat resistance*. It has long been known that heat-resistant streptococci occur in milk (see Ayers and Johnson 1910, 1913, Ayers, Johnson and Davis 1918) ; and Logan (1914) recorded the presence of heat-resistant streptococci in the human faeces. Houston and McCloy (1916) noted that heat resistance was characteristic of enterococci, and this observation has been amply confirmed by Dible (1921) and by many subsequent observers. It is usual to employ exposure to a temperature of 60° C. for 20 to 30 minutes as an arbitrary test of heat resistance. The problem that arises in this connection is the identity or non-identity of the milk and faecal strains of heat-resistant streptococci ; and this will be considered in a later section.

Antigenic Structure.—Before we consider in detail the antigenic analysis of the various species, or types, of streptococci, and the interrelations that this method of study reveals, it will be well to review briefly the evidence that has been set out in the preceding pages. With the proviso that there are many species, or types, of which no mention has yet been made, we may note that we have been able to recognize certain broad groups.

There is a group associated with pyogenic infections in man and animals. This is characterized in the laboratory by the production of β-hæmolysis on blood agar plates, and by the production of a filtrable hæmolysin.

There is a group that is characterized in the laboratory by the production of α-hæmolysis on blood agar plates. The strains that fall into this group have been derived from many different sources. Some have been isolated from cases of pneumonia, and from various other pyogenic lesions in man. These strains are characterized by a tendency to capsule formation, by the capacity to ferment inulin, and by bile solubility. They form a well-differentiated sub-group to which the specific name *Str. pneumoniæ* has been given.

Other α-hæmolytic strains have been derived from the mouths and throats of normal persons, from subacute lesions in man, from the mouths or intestines of healthy animals, from the udders of cattle suffering from mastitis, and from a variety of other sources. These clearly form a heterogeneous sub-group.

There is another group that is characterized in the laboratory by the ability to grow in the presence of bile, by resisting a temperature of 60° C. for 20 minutes or more, and by the reduction of methylene blue in milk. It contains many of the strains that have been isolated from human fæces, and many that have been isolated from milk. It is in other respects a somewhat heterogeneous group, and its claim to specific rank needs further consideration.

Apart from the pneumococcus, indeed, none of these groups are sufficiently homogeneous, or separated with sufficient sharpness from each other, to justify the definition of species on these criteria alone.

The β-hæmolytic group, for instance, is certainly divisible into different fermentative types. We have noted that the strains isolated from pyogenic lesions in man fail to hydrolyse sodium hippurate, while the strains isolated from mastitis in cattle do so. Strains from the horse frequently fail to ferment lactose, while most other hæmolytic strains attack this sugar, and so on. But the complications do not end here. Strains of this group isolated from severe infections in man almost always cause β-hæmolysis in blood agar plates, and produce a filtrable hæmolysin; but among the sodium-hippurate-splitting strains isolated from mastitis in cattle there are many that, while conforming in all their biochemical reactions with the typically hæmolytic strains, produce α-hæmolysis, or no change, on blood agar plates, and produce no filtrable hæmolysin. Are we, in this instance, to accord to the reaction produced in a blood-containing medium its customary pre-eminence as a systematic criterion, regarding the mastitis β-hæmolytic strains as a variety of the species *Str. pyogenes*, and relegating the α-hæmolytic mastitis strains to another species, or placing them in a separate sub-group; or should we accept the source of origin and the correlated biochemical reactions as differentiating a separate species, pathogenic for cattle, that happens to contain both hæmolytic and non-hæmolytic strains?

Again, the group of streptococci that grow in the presence of bile, and are heat resistant, are for the most part without action on blood-containing media; but a few of them give rise to frank hæmolysis on blood agar plates. Are we to retain them within our hæmolytic group, in spite of their obvious affinities with the non-hæmolytic strains isolated from human fæces, or from milk; or should we, in this case, let their broader affinities take precedence of their hæmolytic activity, and class them as hæmolytic varieties of enterococci?

It is questions such as these that we should have in mind when considering the results that have been obtained by the antigenic analysis of this important group of organisms.

It will be convenient to begin our discussion of antigenic structure with the pneumococcus, in part, because this is a well-defined species in which the complications referred to above do not arise, in part, because it was in fact one of the first species in which a division into immunologically different races, or types, was clearly demonstrated, and, in part, because the chemical study of antigenic structure was initiated with this organism, and we still know far more about the chemical differences that determine the antigenic specificity of the various types of pneumococci than we do about similar differences in any other bacterial species.

The Antigenic Structure of the Pneumococci.—Neufeld and Händel (1909) first demonstrated the existence of antigenically different types of pneumococci. They studied the protective effect of different antipneumococcal sera in mice, and found that a given serum would protect against the homologous strain of pneumococcus, but not against heterologous strains. Dochez, Avery and their colleagues (Dochez and Gillespie 1913, Dochez and Avery 1915, Avery 1915, Avery *et al.* 1917) later studied the antigenic relationships of a large collection of pneumococci, using the methods of direct agglutination and agglutinin absorption. They confined their attention, for the most part, to strains isolated from cases of lobar pneumonia in man, and among these they were able to recognize three well-differentiated types, Types I, II and III, leaving a large heterogeneous group unclassified. Lister (1916) carried out a similar study on strains isolated from cases of pneumonia among the mine-workers in South Africa. He was able to differentiate several antigenic types, which he labelled with letters instead of numbers. These observations have since been confirmed and extended by workers in many parts of the world, the three classical American types being generally accepted as the standard of reference ; and it was not long before we obtained a reasonably adequate picture of the distribution of these three types in cases of lobar pneumonia, in other pneumococcal infections, in healthy contacts and in the population at large. For many years, however, no serious attempt was made to analyse the unclassified heterologous group, which formed a considerable proportion (25–50 per cent.) of the strains isolated from cases of lobar pneumonia, and the majority of those isolated from the upper respiratory tract of normal persons. It was the custom to refer. to such strains as belonging to Group IV, an unfortunate nomenclature that became frankly misleading when the label was changed to " Type IV " which not infrequently happened.

Within recent years, Cooper and her colleagues (Cooper, Edwards and Rosenstein 1929, Cooper *et al.* 1932, Cooper and Walter 1935) have made a detailed study of this previously unclassified group. Among strains isolated from lobar and bronchopneumonia, from various other pneumococcal infections, and from normal persons, they have identified 29 new antigenic types, making 32 in all, including the classical Types I, II and III. Most of these types are, it should be noted, sharply differentiated from each other, so that they may be identified by direct agglutination. The main exceptions are as follows : Type VI is divisible into two antigenically related sub-types (Types VI*a* and VI*b*), and there is a significant degree of cross-agglutination between Types II and V, Types III and VIII, Types VII and XVIII, and Types XV and XXX. The species *Str. pneumoniæ* is, therefore, now divisible into 32 different types, which are labelled by the Roman numerals I to XXXII, Type VI being divided into Type VI*a* and Type VI*b*. We may be quite sure that there are still new types of pneumococci to be identified, and new labels to be given ; but it seems likely that our present 32 types include most of those that are parasitic in man. Gundel and Schwarz (1932), for instance, report that, of 364 strains of pneumococci, isolated from sick or healthy children or adults, and containing no examples of the classical Types I, II and III, only 3 per cent. were unassignable to one or other of Cooper's new Types IV–XXXII.

It has long been recognized that the antigenic behaviour of intact pneumococci, in the normal smooth state, is probably determined by the nature of the capsules surrounding the bacterial cells. Neufeld (1902), for instance, noted that the capsules of pneumococci, when acted upon by a specific antiserum, become greatly swollen ; and, within recent years, it has been shown that this phenomenon can be utilized in the identification of pneumococcal types (Neufeld and Etinger-Tulczynska 1931, Etinger-Tulczynska 1932, Armstrong 1932, Logan and Smeall 1932, Sabin 1933, Beckler and MacLeod 1934, Cooper and Walter 1935).

A great advance was made in the study of the antigenic structure of the pneumococci, and, indeed, of bacteria in general, when Avery, Heidelberger and their colleagues attacked the problem from the chemical side (Heidelberger and Avery 1923, 1924, Avery and Heidelberger 1923, 1925, Avery *et al.* 1925, Heidelberger *et al.* 1925, Avery and Morgan 1925, Heidelberger 1927, Heidelberger and Goebel 1927). By suitable methods of extraction, followed by fractional precipitation, it was found possible to separate the capsular components that determine type-specificity in a state of chemical purity. These components were found to be complex polysaccharides ; and some of the main chemical and physical characters of the capsular polysaccharides of the three classical types have been determined (see Table XXXIV). Solutions of these polysaccharides, it will be noted, give specific precipitation, in high dilution, when mixed with the corresponding antisera.

TABLE XXXIV

CHARACTERS OF THE TYPE-SPECIFIC ANTIGENS OF PNEUMOCOCCI, AFTER AVERY AND
HEIDELBERGER.

Type.	Optical Rotation.	Per cent. Nitrogen.	Substances obtained on Hydrolysis.	Dilution giving Specific Precipitation.
I	$+ 300°$	5	Galacturonic acid, and amino-sugar derivative	1 : 6,000,000
II	$+ 74°$	0	Glucose	1 : 5,000,000
III	$- 33°$	0	Glucose and Glucuronic acid	1 : 6,000,000

The chemical constitution of the capsular antigens of the new types of pneumococci differentiated by Cooper and her colleagues has yet to be determined, though a start has been made with this work (see Heidelberger and Kendall 1931). We may, however, safely assume that each pneumococcal type is characterized by a specific capsular polysaccharide that determines its antigenic behaviour. We may identify these types either by agglutination, or by the capsule-swelling reaction, or by precipitin tests carried out with an autolysate, or extract, of the pneumococcal cells.

Some, at least, of these pneumococcal polysaccharides may exist in immunologically different forms, or may be altered during the process of chemical extraction and purification. Thus, the studies of Enders (1930), and of Wadsworth and Brown (1931), showed the presence in Type I pneumococci of a specific antigenic component that differed in its immunological reactions from the specific capsular polysaccharide as ordinarily prepared. Avery and Goebel (1933) were able to show that this component is an acetylated form of the Type I capsular polysaccharide, and that it is apparently in this form that the polysaccharide exists in the normal bacterial cell. The acetyl groups are removed by the methods of extraction and purification that had been commonly employed, leaving a deacetylated polysaccharide that is still specific for the Type I pneumococcus, but has lost certain antigenic activities possessed by the normal acetylated form. It is important to note that the type-specificity of the capsular antigen is not destroyed by this particular chemical change ; and it seems quite likely that similar minor alterations in chemical structure may be induced during the extraction and purification of many other antigenic components.

This polysaccharide capsular component is not, of course, the only antigenic constituent of the pneumococcal cell. Tillett, Goebel and Avery (1930) have isolated another component that gives all the usual reactions of a polysaccharide, is not inactivated by peptic or tryptic digestion, and yields about 30 per cent. of reducing sugar on hydrolysis. It contains about 6·1 per cent. of nitrogen, and differs from the capsular polysaccharides in containing phosphoric acid. It is not type-specific, but appears to characterize the pneumococcus as a species.

There is also (Avery and Heidelberger 1923) a nucleo-protein antigenic component, precipitable from extracts by acetic acid. It is probably situated deeply within the intact bacterial cell. It is shared by all pneumococci and by many other bacteria, including all those species of streptococci that have been examined.

The picture of the antigenic structure of the species *Str. pneumoniæ* that emerges from these studies may be tentatively outlined as follows : There is a central protoplasmic portion of the cell which, in its antigenic relationships, is neither species- nor type-specific. Situated probably at the cell surface, there is another component, mainly carbohydrate in nature, but containing nitrogen and phosphorus, that is specific for *Str. pneumoniæ* as a species. External to this, in the normal smooth forms, there is a capsule, composed wholly or in part of a polysaccharide that is specific for each pneumococcal type. There are, we must suppose, at least thirty-two of these capsular polysaccharides within the pneumococcal species ; probably there are many more. The virulence, and the antigenic behaviour, of the intact pneumococcal cells are, it should be noted, determined by these capsular antigenic components, so that they are of particular importance to the medical bacteriologist.

The Antigenic Structure of the Hæmolytic Streptococci.—When we come to study the antigenic structure of the hæmolytic streptococci we are on much more difficult and debatable ground ; in part because, as we have already indicated, it is by no means easy to define exactly what we mean by a hæmolytic streptococcus ; in part because, if we accept the usual definition—the occurrence of β-hæmolysis on a blood agar plate—we shall include in our hæmolytic group, not one species, but several ; in part because the technical difficulties of antigenic analysis are far greater than in the case of the pneumococcus. In spite of all these difficulties a great advance in our knowledge has been made during recent years ; and, though we cannot as yet present any clear and detailed picture, we can provide a sketch-plan which, with the necessary modifications, will certainly provide the basis for any future, and more complete, classification.

To obtain a clear picture of the present position, it is necessary to follow, if only in outline, the sequence in which our present knowledge has been obtained. All the earlier, and the majority of the more recent attempts to define the antigenic relationships of hæmolytic streptococci have been carried out by medical bacterio-logists, mainly with the object of determining what differences, if any, distinguish the strains causing such human infections as erysipelas, cellulitis, tonsillitis, scarlet fever, puerperal septicæmia, and so on. It happened, therefore, that all these studies were carried out, not on hæmolytic streptococci as a group, but on collections of strains isolated from particular types of infection in a particular host species. The method mainly employed has been that of agglutination and agglutinin absorp-tion. It is not, in this case, at all an easy method. Many strains of hæmolytic streptococci give a granular growth in broth and are auto-agglutinable in saline, so that it may be very difficult to obtain a satisfactory suspension for agglutination tests. Moreover, there is much more cross-agglutination between different types of hæmolytic streptococci than between different types of pneumococci, so that the absorption method has to be freely employed. The earlier attempts (Moser and Pirquet 1902, Meyer 1902, Neufeld 1903, Aronson 1903, Hasenknopf and Salge 1903, Rossiwall and Schick 1905), although they gave definite indications of antigenic differentiation, left a confusing picture ; and it was not until certain observations on the ætiology of scarlet fever (see Chapter LXIII) stimulated a renewed interest in the immunological relationships within this group that further progress was made ; but when it came it was rapid. The findings recorded by Dochez, Avery and Lancefield (1919), Bliss (1920, 1922), Gordon (1921), Eagles (1924), and Stevens and Dochez (1926*a, b*) made it clear that it was possible to differentiate and identify many different antigenic types among hæmolytic streptococci isolated from various infections in man ; and the more detailed and extensive studies of Griffith (1926, 1927, 1928, 1934, 1935), Smith (1926, 1927), James (1926), McLachlan and Mackie (1928), Gunn and Griffith (1928) and Dora Colebrook (1935) have served to establish many of these types on a satisfactory serological basis, so that they can be identified and labelled. Griffith, who has been the main contributor to this particular problem, has differentiated and numbered 27 types of pathogenic hæmolytic streptococci isolated from various lesions in man (see Griffith 1935) ; and it is probable that, with a few possible exceptions, these strains will in future be known by the numbers that he has assigned to them.

Lancefield (1928, 1933) has attacked the same problem from another angle. Instead of employing the agglutination test, she prepared extracts from different strains of streptococci and tested them against homologous and heterologous antisera by means of the precipitin reaction. She has been able to differentiate at least three different antigenic components in her extracts, and to determine their distribution among hæmolytic streptococci derived from different sources. One of these antigens is an acid-soluble protein. The nature of this component varies among the different strains of hæmolytic streptococci derived from human infections, and serves to differentiate them into antigenic types, just as pneumococci are divided by their capsular polysaccharides. Lancefield names this the " M substance." It seems clear that it is this component that determines the specificity of the antigenic types differentiated by Griffith and others on the results of agglutination tests. Another component is a complex carbohydrate. It is widely distributed among hæmolytic streptococci ; and in Lancefield's earlier observations, in which she was studying only hæmolytic streptococci of human origin, the same polysaccharide was shared by all her strains, though not by such strains of non-hæmolytic streptococci as were examined. It was, therefore, considered to be species-specific for hæmolytic streptococci, and, in this sense, analogous to the non-capsular carbohydrate component that characterizes the species *Str. pneumoniæ*. Later investigations, in which strains from a variety of human and animal sources were included showed, however, that this component was not shared by hæmolytic streptococci as a class, but served to differentiate them into several well-defined groups, with a definite correlation between antigenic type and natural habitat. Thus 21 of 23 strains possessing the polysaccharide antigen characterizing Lancefield's Group A —her original group—were derived from human sources, mainly from cases of acute infection ; 18 of 21 strains falling into a second group (B) were derived from cattle, mainly from cases of mastitis ; 49 strains falling into a third group (C) were derived from various animals (guinea-pig, cow, rabbit, horse, fox, pig and fowl) almost all of which were suffering from a definite infection ; 8 strains falling into a fourth group (D) were all derived from cheese ; and 3 strains falling into a fifth group (E) were all isolated from Certified milk. These " group-specific " components were named by Lancefield the " C substances."

It has already been noted that Group A is further differentiated into a number of different types by the type-specific, acid-soluble, protein components. Group B is also divisible into several antigenic types, of which three have so far been identified (Stableforth 1932, Lancefield 1934). It would seem, however, that the type-specific antigens of Group B differ from those of Group A in that they, like the group-specific C substances, are carbohydrates, not proteins. To distinguish them from the group-specific carbohydrates, Lancefield named them " S substances." There can be little doubt that the other antigenic groups of hæmolytic streptococci will be found to resemble Groups A and B in being divisible into a number of different types ; but as to the chemical nature of the antigens concerned we as yet know nothing.

In addition to these type-specific and group-specific antigens, hæmolytic streptococci possess a non-specific nucleo-protein antigen (called " P " by Lancefield) which is shared by hæmolytic streptococci, by the pneumococcus, by viridans streptococci, and by certain more distantly related organisms, such as *Staph. aureus*. There is also at least one other non-type-specific protein (" Y ") about which little is as yet known.

We may note that, as a result of the studies next described, the number of antigenic groups into which hæmolytic streptococci can be divided on the basis of the precipitin reaction have been increased. Groups F, G, H and K have been added to Groups A–E.

The studies that have brought this addition to our knowledge, and have served to define the significance and limitations of the antigenic grouping that has been revealed, have been concerned with the identification and differentiation, by any available means, of strains of streptococci of importance in the problems of human and veterinary medicine, rather than with the antigenic analysis of streptococci as a systematic problem. Many of the relevant observations have not, indeed, been concerned directly with antigenic relationships in any form, and their significance must largely be assessed on a basis of inference and analogy.

Two main streams have, within recent years, contributed to our knowledge of this subject. One has been derived from an intensive study of the hæmolytic streptococci concerned in the causation of puerperal fever, in an attempt to differentiate strains of pathogenic importance from those that can be neglected from this particular point of view (Hare and Colebrook 1934, Lancefield and Hare 1935, Hare 1935, Hare and Maxted 1935, Colebrook, Maxted and Johns 1935). In these studies, it may noted, the method of antigenic analysis has been largely employed. The second stream derives from a study, along rather different lines, of the streptococci, hæmolytic or non-hæmolytic, associated with bovine mastitis. Here the object has been, in the main, to differentiate the pathogenic from the non-pathogenic forms among the wide variety of strains that may be isolated from milk, or from the cow's udder, and, to a less extent to distinguish if possible between strains of human and bovine origin (Jones 1918, Jones and Little 1928, Diernhofer 1928, 1930, 1932*a*, *b*, Klimmer, Haupt and Roots 1928, Proscholdt 1928, 1933, Minett, Stableforth and Edwards 1929, 1932, Klimmer and Haupt 1930, Seelemann and Hadenfeldt 1930, 1932, 1933*a*, *b*, Minett and Stableforth 1931, Rosell 1931, Haupt 1931, 1933, Stableforth 1932, Edwards, S. J. 1932, Edwards, P. R. 1932, Seelemann 1932, 1933*a*, *b*, Plastridge and Anderson 1933, Hansen, Hucker and Snyder 1933, Seelemann and Siemonsen 1933, Plastridge *et al.* 1934, Minett 1935*a*, *b*). Of these observers only Stableforth (1932) was concerned directly with the application of agglutination and precipitation tests to the problem at issue. Much of the work recorded in the other papers referred to is concerned with the characters and definition of the species that is responsible for a large proportion of all cases of bovine mastitis, and is now generally known as *Str. agalactiæ*.

It is impossible, in the space at our disposal, to give any detailed account of the observations referred to above ; but we may summarize them in their relation to each of the antigenic groups of hæmolytic streptococci, and try to assess their significance from the point of view of classification and nomenclature. In doing so we must again remember that the workers who defined these antigenic groups were not studying random samples of streptococci, but strains specifically selected because they produced β-hæmolysis on blood agar plates. It will, therefore, be one of our main problems to determine, where we can, whether a given antigenic group falls wholly within the category of hæmolytic streptococci, or whether it includes non-hæmolytic as well as hæmolytic strains. In the latter case we shall have to arrive at some conclusion as to whether hæmolysin production or antigenic structure should be given more weight in classification ; and here we shall clearly be guided to a considerable extent by any correlated characters, including natural habitat.

Group A.

Streptococci belonging to this group share in common the Group A carbohydrate component described by Lancefield. They are divisible into a number of different serological types, either by agglutination reactions with absorbed sera, or by precipitin reactions carried out with type-specific antisera and suitably prepared bacterial extracts. The type-specific antigens concerned are protein in nature, and soluble in dilute acids. Of the 27 types described by Griffith (1935), it would appear that four (Types 7, 20, 21 and 16) do not possess the group-specific carbohydrate, and should therefore be excluded from this group. Types 7, 20 and 21 belong, antigenically, to Group C ; Type 16 to Group G (Hare 1935).

Group A streptococci, in addition to producing β-hæmolysis in blood agar plates, appear, without exception, to form a soluble hæmolysin.

In regard to their other biological and biochemical characters, Group A streptococci produce a final pH of 5·0–5·6 in dextrose broth ; they do not hydrolyse sodium hippurate ; they do not reduce methylene blue in milk ; they ferment trehalose but not sorbitol ; they may or may not grow in 10 per cent. bile agar, and seldom grow in 40 per cent. bile agar. These are the main differential group characters. In addition, Group A strains almost always ferment salicin, and lactose, seldom mannitol, and very seldom raffinose or inulin.

The strains that have been adequately identified as belonging to this group have, in the main, been derived from infections in man—tonsillitis, scarlet fever, cellulitis, erysipelas, puerperal fever, other types of septicæmia, acute broncho-pneumonia, otitis media and so on. They have also been isolated from the throat, nasopharynx, or nose, in normal persons. They have occasionally been isolated from cases of mastitis in cattle ; but in such instances there have usually been grounds for suspecting a human source of infection.

It is clear that streptococci falling into Group A possess all the characters that have been attributed to the classical *Str. pyogenes* ; and the group itself is so well differentiated that it clearly requires a distinctive label. Should it be given specific rank ? It is certain that we cannot include in a single species all the antigenic groups of hæmolytic streptococci (A–K). The only question is, into how many different species they should be divided. The balance of the evidence at present available appears to us to be in favour of recognizing the Group A strains as constituting a species in the generally accepted bacteriological sense. Its relation to the strains falling into other antigenic groups will be discussed in succeeding sections. There remains the question of the correct specific name. The name *Str. hæmolyticus* has obtained wide currency. It was used by the Committee of the Society of

American Bacteriologists to denote the type species (Winslow *et al.* 1920), and we adopted it in the first edition of this book.

But the knowledge that has accumulated during recent years seems to us to render the name inconvenient and misleading. If we adhered to it, we should no longer mean by *Str. hæmolyticus* a "hæmolytic streptococcus," or even a "streptococcus giving β-hæmolysis," but only a particular group of streptococci falling into that category. It therefore seems to us wiser to revert to the name *Str. pyogenes*, defining that name as equivalent to " a streptococcus of Group A," with the proviso that this definition may well have to be modified in the future.

Before leaving this group and turning to others we may note briefly the existence of certain strains that have been isolated from milk and from the throats of infected persons during milk-borne epidemics of tonsillitis (Davis and Rosenow 1912, Davis 1912, 1929, Stokes and Hachtel 1912, Capps and Davis 1914). These streptococci differ only from the classical *Str. pyogenes* in giving mucoid or semi-mucoid colonies on blood agar plates and in showing well-defined capsules. Because of this difference Davis allotted to them a separate specific name, *Str. epidemicus*. It seems very doubtful, however, whether this procedure is justified. Although *Str. pyogenes* is not a capsulated species in the same sense as *Str. pneumoniæ*, it not infrequently forms recognizable capsules when growing in the tissues, or during the first few hours of its growth in serum broth. Seelemann and Hadenfeldt (1932) compared a large number of strains bearing the label *Str. epidemicus* with typical strains of *Str. pyogenes*, and were unable to differentiate between them. On the basis of the available evidence we think that the name *Str. epidemicus* should be provisionally discarded, and that the strains bearing that label should be included in the species *Str. pyogenes*. It may be noted that there is some tendency for other organisms to produce capsules when growing in milk.

Similarly, there seems to us no adequate reason for allotting different specific names to strains that, while possessing all the essential characters of *Str. pyogenes*, differ from one another in regard to certain fermentation reactions. We should not, therefore, recognize a *Str. infrequens*, fermenting mannitol as well as salicin, or a *Str. anginosus* fermenting neither of these sugars. It is, indeed, by no means certain that all the strains to which these names have been attached are true hæmolytic streptococci of the *pyogenes* type.

Group B.

The streptococci of this group share in common a group-specific antigen that is carbohydrate in nature and differs from the group-specific antigen of Group A, or of any of the groups subsequently described. Group B streptococci are further divisible into a number of antigenic types, of which three have so far been identified, either by precipitation or agglutination tests against type-specific antisera. The type-specific antigens within this group are apparently not acid-soluble proteins, but complex carbohydrates of a different chemical structure from the carbohydrate that determines group-specificity.

Streptococci falling within this group may or may not produce β-hæmolysis in blood agar plates. It would appear (see Stableforth 1932) that something over half of these strains are β-hæmolytic ; but the exact proportion is still a subject of controversy. Although many hæmolytic Group B strains yield a soluble hæmolysin, it would seem that this character is much less constant than with Group A strains ; and the titres of the filtrates obtained are usually much lower.

In regard to their other biological and biochemical characters, Group B strains differ from Group A strains in that they produce a lower final pH in glucose broth ($4\cdot2$–$4\cdot8$), hydrolyse sodium hippurate, and usually grow both on 10 per cent. and 40 per cent. bile agar. They resemble Group A strains in failing to reduce methylene blue in milk, and in fermenting trehalose but not sorbitol. As regards their other fermentation reactions, Group B strains would appear to resemble Group A strains in fermenting lactose, but not usually mannitol, raffinose or inulin. Nearly all the non-hæmolytic strains ferment salicin, but a proportion of the hæmolytic strains fail to do so.

The great majority of Group B strains that have been adequately identified have been isolated from cases of mastitis in cattle, in many cases under conditions which have made it almost certain that they were the primary cause of the disease. They have occasionally been isolated from the normal human throat and vagina. There is no evidence that they are pathogenic for man.

Group B, like Group A, clearly demands a label ; and we feel that it may provisionally be accorded specific rank. We follow Klimmer and Haupt, and Minett and his colleagues, in giving it the name *Str. agalactiæ* (Kitt 1893) (see Klimmer and Haupt 1930, Minett 1935*b*), in preference to the name *Str. mastitidis contagiosæ*, assigned by Nocard and Mollereau (1887) to streptococci isolated from a similar source. There can, we think, be no doubt that, in defining this species, antigenic structure should take precedence over hæmolysin production as a systematic criterion, and that the specific name should be applied to the non-hæmolytic as well as to the hæmolytic strains. We should, therefore, describe hæmolysin production as being a constant character within the species *Str. pyogenes*, but a variable character within the species *Str. agalactiæ* ; whether the non-hæmolytic strains of *Str. agalactiæ* should be classed as a distinct variety, the future must decide.

Group C.

The strains that fall within this antigenic group are characterized by sharing in common a group-specific antigen that serves to differentiate them from the other groups with which we are here concerned. The chemical nature of this group-specific antigen has not yet been determined, nor have we yet any definite information in regard to the separation of this group into different antigenic types ; though we can hardly doubt that such types exist.

Group C strains appear to behave consistently in producing β-hæmolysis on blood agar plates, and in forming a filtrable hæmolysin.

In regard to their other biological and biochemical characters Group C strains display certain significant differences among themselves. They produce in glucose broth a final pH intermediate between that produced by Group A strains on the one hand and by Group B strains on the other ; the range covered by the group as a whole appears to vary between pH 4·5 and pH 5·4. No Group C strains hydrolyse sodium hippurate. Many of them grow on 10 per cent. bile agar, but few on 40 per cent. bile agar. On the basis of their action on trehalose and sorbitol Group C streptococci can be differentiated into three sub-groups (Edwards, P. R. 1934). One of these sub-groups ferments neither trehalose nor sorbitol, another ferments sorbitol but not trehalose, a third ferments trehalose but not sorbitol.

There is a correlation between fermentation reactions and habitat that gives to these sub-groups an importance that they would not otherwise possess. Most of the strains belonging to the trehalose-negative, sorbitol-negative sub-group have been isolated from horses, particularly from cases of strangles, though they have also been obtained from infections in other animals. They are further differentiated from the groups of streptococci that have been described above by their failure to ferment lactose. They share with these other groups the ability to ferment salicin, and the inability to reduce methylene blue in milk. This sub-group clearly corresponds in its biochemical characters to the *Str. equi* of many authors.

The second sub-group ferments sorbitol but not trehalose. It also ferments both lactose and salicin. It fails to reduce methylene blue in milk. Strains of this sub-group have been isolated from infective conditions in a variety of animals—horses, cattle suffering from mastitis, guinea-pigs, rabbits and so on. There is as yet no evidence that streptococci belonging to this, or to the preceding, sub-group are pathogenic for man.

The third sub-group is characterized by the fermentation of trehalose but not of sorbitol. The strains belonging to this sub-group have been derived both from animal and human sources, and it seems clear that some strains at least are pathogenic for man. Three of Griffith's 27 types of human-pathogenic, hæmolytic streptococci belong to this C sub-group, not to Group A. All strains of this sub-group are recorded as fermenting salicin, but the action on lactose appears to vary. The results recorded by P. R. Edwards (1934) and by Hare (1935) suggest that many of the animal strains fail to ferment lactose, while almost all the human strains act on this sugar. It is, however, impossible at the moment to determine whether this particular difference in enzymic activity has any systematic significance. The strains of this trehalose-positive, sorbitol-negative C sub-group are stated by P. R. Edwards (1934) to differ from the preceding sub-groups in possessing some ability to reduce methylene blue in milk. This difference does not, however, appear to be so reliable a test as trehalose and sorbitol fermentation for separating the C sub-groups. It serves to distinguish, at least to some extent, between the trehalose-positive, sorbitol-negative Group C strains, and the Group A strains to which we have allotted the name *Str. pyogenes*; but this distinction is far more readily and certainly made by determining the antigenic structure.

The labelling of Group C hæmolytic streptococci presents a problem of peculiar difficulty. There is no specific name that can be applied to the group as a whole. If we are to retain the name *Str. equi* it is clear that we must take failure to ferment lactose as our crucial test, and include in this species the trehalose-negative, sorbitol-negative, lactose-negative sub-group, together, perhaps, with those strains of the trehalose-positive, sorbitol-negative strains that happen to be lactose-negative. But it comports ill with modern bacteriological practice to employ different specific names for strains that, so far as we know at present, are antigenically identical or very similar, and resemble each other closely in many other ways, on the basis of a single fermentation test.

The trehalose-positive, sorbitol-negative strains raise another difficulty. Apart from their antigenic structure, they differ from the Group A (*Str. pyogenes*) only in the production of a somewhat lower final pH in glucose broth, a greater tendency to reduce methylene blue in milk, and, apparently, in their failure to produce the oxygen-sensitive type of hæmolysin. Some of these strains are certainly pathogenic, though perhaps not highly pathogenic, for man; and on the basis of the older criteria would certainly have been labelled *Str. pyogenes*. If, however, we are to give due weight to antigenic structure they cannot, in view of our knowledge as it stands to-day, be included in this species.

At the moment, we feel that no useful purpose would be served by any attempt to allot specific names within this group. The non-committal label of " Group C hæmolytic streptococci " will serve our purpose; and the thorny questions of systematic relationships can well await an increase in our knowledge.

Group G.

It will be convenient at this point to ignore the alphabet and proceed to a consideration of Group G (Lancefield and Hare 1935, Plummer 1935, Hare 1935). The strains of this group share in common a group-specific antigen that distinguishes them from any of the other named groups. Hare (1935) notes that some sera produced by the injection of Group C strains tend to give cross-precipitation with extracts from Group G strains; and it seems possible that these two groups may be less sharply differentiated, from the antigenic point of view, than the others here described. We have as yet no information with regard to the chemical nature of the group-specific antigen, or the possible separation of this group into different antigenic types.   Very few strains falling within it have yet been described.

As regards their other biological and biochemical properties, there appears to be a conflict of evidence in regard to the final pH attained in glucose broth.   Plummer (1935) gives this as pH 4·4–4·6, which would place these strains in the " high-acid " group ; but Lancefield and Hare (1935) and Hare (1935) give figures of pH 4·6–5·2.   Group G strains do not hydrolyse sodium hippurate.   The majority are able to multiply on 10 per cent. bile agar, but few on 40 per cent. bile agar.   They do not reduce methylene blue in milk. They ferment trehalose, but not sorbitol.   All strains tested have fermented lactose, but the fermentation of salicin appears to be less constant than with Groups A, B and C.

Most of the strains that have been identified as belonging to this group have been isolated from man, a few from the monkey or the dog.   Several of the human strains have been derived from normal persons, but it seems clear that some, at least, are pathogenic for man, though there is a suggestion that they seldom cause very severe infections.   One of Griffith's 27 types of human-pathogenic hæmolytic streptococci falls into this group.

The labelling of this group should clearly be provisional.   It shows obvious relationships to Group C, and, apart from its antigenic structure, to Group A. There seems no reason, at the moment, to allot to it any specific name.   " Group G hæmolytic streptococci " will serve our immediate purpose.

Group F.

This group has been differentiated by Lancefield and Hare (1935) and by Hare (1935). It possesses a characteristic group-specific antigen, by means of which it may be identified. We know nothing as yet with regard to the chemical nature of this antigen, or the possible existence of separate antigenic types.

Group F strains grow slowly on blood agar plates, forming minute pin-point transparent colonies surrounded by a narrow zone (1·5–1·8 mm. in diameter) of β-hæmolysis.   They are identical with the strains described by Long and Bliss (1934) as " minute hæmolytic streptococci."   They do not, when tested by the usual methods, form a filtrable hæmolysin.

Group F strains produce a final acidity in glucose broth of pH 4·8–5·2.   They do not hydrolyse sodium hippurate.   They do not reduce methylene blue in milk.   They do not grow either on 10 per cent. or on 40 per cent. bile agar.   Some, but not all, strains ferment trehalose, none ferment sorbitol.   All that have been tested ferment lactose and salicin.

The strains that have been identified as belonging to this group have been derived mainly from the human throat.   There is some evidence that they may be responsible for some cases of tonsillitis, and perhaps for other infections of the respiratory tract.

The provisional label for this group is clearly " Group F hæmolytic streptococci," with a proviso that we are not insisting on the demonstration of the formation of a filtrable hæmolysin before admitting a streptococcus to the hæmolytic class.

Groups H and K.

These two additional antigenic groups have been differentiated by Hare (1935).   They appear to differ from each other, and from the other groups of hæmolytic streptococci that have been described, in regard to their group-specific antigens.   Those strains that have been examined have shown other cultural or biochemical characters that may have differential significance ; but so few strains belonging to these two groups have yet been studied that it would be premature to describe their characters in any detail.   They have all been isolated from the nose or throat of normal persons, and there is as yet no evidence that they are pathogenic.

Group E.

The few strains belonging to this antigenic group were isolated from cow's milk by Lancefield (1933). Here again, in view of the very small number of strains examined, it is too soon to give any generalized description of the other group characters.

Group D.

This group of hæmolytic streptococci, which was differentiated by Lancefield (1933), raises a very difficult problem from the point of view of classification. The strains belonging to it possess a common group-specific antigen, the chemical nature of which has not yet been determined. Whether the hæmolytic Group D strains are separable into different antigenic types is as yet unknown.

Group D hæmolytic streptococci give β-hæmolysis on blood agar. They have usually been reported as failing to produce a filtrable hæmolysin; but Todd (1934) has recorded the preparation of lytic filtrates by growth in a very highly buffered medium containing sodium bicarbonate. The hæmolysin produced is oxygen-stable, and relatively stable to heat, but is very sensitive to acid.

Group D strains show certain striking biochemical differences from most of the groups described above. They produce a low final pH in glucose broth (4·2–4·8). They grow freely on 10 per cent. and 40 per cent. bile agar. They reduce methylene blue in milk. They are heat resistant, most strains withstanding a temperature of 60° C. for 30 minutes. For the rest, Group D strains fail to hydrolyse sodium hippurate, usually but not always ferment trehalose and sorbitol, always ferment lactose and salicin, and usually but not always mannitol. It may also be noted that they commonly tend to assume the diplococcal as opposed to the streptococcal grouping.

The strains that have been identified as belonging to this group have, in the main, been derived from cheese, and from human fæces.

It will at once be noted that Group D strains possess almost all the characters that belong to enterococci. There can indeed be little doubt that they represent hæmolytic strains belonging to this species or group. We cannot assign to them a specific name, because we do not know whether the non-hæmolytic types of enterococci share the same group-specific antigen. We know (Takeda 1935) that enterococci as a group are divisible into numerous different antigenic types, showing a group relationship to one another; but the method used was that of agglutination and agglutinin absorption, and it is impossible to determine, from the data available, the relation of these antigenic differences to the groups and types that are revealed by precipitin reactions carried out by Lancefield's method.

For the moment we may refer to the strains belonging to this group as " Group D hæmolytic streptococci." Their relation to the enterococci is considered more fully in the following section, in which we discuss the classification of that group as a whole.

In concluding this summary of our present knowledge of the antigenic structure of hæmolytic streptococci, we may, perhaps, enter a plea for the use, by workers in this field, of an agreed terminology. The literature, as it stands, is rendered very confusing to the student by the use of different terms, letters and numbers. The " Type " of one worker is the " Group " of another. " Type I " in one paper may be equivalent to " Group B " in another, and so on. The " Groups " of Lancefield, in so far as they are confirmed and established by future work, would seem to have a good claim to precedence, and it will be noted that Hare has followed her alphabetical sequence in labelling his strains. Within Group A the numbered types of Griffith should, we think, be accorded similar precedence, with the transference to the appropriate groups of those strains that do not possess the group-specific A antigen.

The Antigenic Structure of the Non-Hæmolytic Streptococci.—In regard to the antigenic structure of the many species, types or varieties of non-hæmolytic, or α-hæmolytic streptococci of the viridans type, we know too little as yet to attempt any classification on this basis. There have, indeed, been sporadic observations on collections of strains of this type, mainly by the methods of agglutination and agglutinin absorption ; but they have in the main been related to some particular infection in which the streptococci concerned might be acting as causal agents, rather than to the study of systematic relationships.

We may now turn to a consideration of the systematic relationships of those species, groups or types that the preceding discussion has left undefined.

The Classification of Enterococci and Related Organisms.—We have already noted certain characters of the streptococci isolated from human fæces, such as their tendency to ferment mannitol, to produce a high acidity in dextrose, and to grow in a bile-containing medium. Many bacteriologists, and especially French observers, have long recognized the occurrence in the human intestine of a characteristic streptococcus, usually occurring in pairs of ovoid cocci, sometimes in short chains. The characteristic morphology of this organism was described by Thiercelin in 1899, who called it the *Enterococcus* ; and under that name it has made frequent appearances in later literature.

The interrelation of the streptococci of the human intestine has been studied by Dible (1921), whose paper on this subject affords an admirable example of the methods which should be employed in differentiating bacterial groups. He tested 134 strains of streptococci from human fæces as regards their behaviour in a large number of biological tests, including heat resistance (see Houston and McCloy 1916) and chain formation as well as various biochemical reactions ; and measured the association between different pairs of reactions by calculating a statistical coefficient of association. Using one such coefficient, which gives the value of $+ 1$ where the association between two characters is absolute, 0 where there is no association, and $- 1$ where the characters are mutually exclusive, he obtained the following values for the association between a particular series of characters among his 134 strains :

Heat resistance and mannitol fermentation	$+ 0 \cdot 93$
,, ,, ,, raffinose fermentation	$- 0 \cdot 85$
,, ,, ,, chain formation	$- 0 \cdot 96$
Mannitol fermentation and chain formation	$- 0 \cdot 93$

Heat resistance, as here designated, was tested by the ability of the various strains to survive heating at 60° C. for 30 minutes. Those organisms were classed as chain-formers which showed any wide departure from the diplococcal form. Dible thus succeeded in demonstrating the existence in human fæces of a characteristic group of organisms which possessed a predominantly diplococcal morphology, were unusually resistant to heat, almost always fermented mannitol, and very seldom fermented raffinose. It may be added that the streptococci belonging to this group constantly fermented salicin, very seldom fermented inulin, and gave good growth on gelatin at 22° C. About 10 per cent. of them liquefied gelatin. None of them caused hæmolysis in blood agar, or produced a green pigment. In a later communication (Weatherall and Dible 1929), it was noted that some strains of enterococci, having all the characters referred to above, produced areas of hæmolysis when grown on blood agar plates ; but no filtrable hæmolysin could be obtained by the usual methods of cultivation. It seems clear that these hæmolytic strains correspond to the " Group D " hæmolytic streptococci referred to above.

It has already been noted that streptococci from the human fæces grow freely in the presence of bile (Weissenbach 1918), ferment æsculin in a bile-containing medium (Rochaix 1924, Meyer and Schönfeld 1926, Weatherall and Dible 1929), and reduce methylene blue in milk. They have also been shown to produce a low final pH (in the neighbourhood of 4·2) when grown in glucose broth (Sherman and Stark 1931).

We may then safely recognize the existence of a group of streptococci, forming a characteristic constituent of the human intestinal flora and usually possessing the following biological characters : growth in pairs, or very short chains ; the ability to grow in the presence of bile ; the ability to ferment mannitol and usually salicin, but not raffinose or inulin ; the ability to ferment æsculin in a bile-containing medium ; the ability to reduce methylene blue in milk ; the production of a low final pH in glucose broth ; and an unusual degree of heat resistance.

Most strains belonging to this group produce no change on a blood-agar medium. A few produce hæmolysis.

Are we justified in allotting to members of this group the specific name *Str. fœcalis* ? It seems very probable that such a species will ultimately be defined ; but its definition at the moment would be no easy matter. Many of those who have recently studied this group (see, for instance, Koch 1935, Ehrismann *et al.* 1935) note that the correlation between the various differential criteria referred to above, though it undoubtedly exists, is far from perfect ; and that no single character can be regarded as constant. Some strains, for instance, that would on all other grounds be regarded as typical enterococci fail to show the characteristic heat resistance. Unless we can define a species rigidly enough to make it possible to determine, in the great majority of cases, whether a given strain belongs to that species or not, the use of a specific name tends to be misleading rather than helpful ; and since *Str. fœcalis* cannot at the moment be so defined it would, we think, be wiser to discard it or hold it in abeyance, until agreement has been reached as to its real significance.

There is another reason that leads us to this conclusion—the extreme difficulty of determining the relation of enterococci to the high-acid-producing streptococci that are almost constantly found in milk.

Günther and Thierfelder (1895) described the occurrence in milk of an organism which was responsible for spontaneous souring and clotting. They described the organism as a short bacillus ; but Heinemann (1906), when investigating the bacterial flora of milk some ten years later, pointed out that a particular streptococcus, which was almost constantly present in fresh milk, was probably identical with the organism of Günther and Thierfelder. Baehr (1910) confirmed the frequent presence of this streptococcus and noted that it produced a large amount of acid, and rapid clotting. Ruediger (1912) noted the absence of hæmolysis on blood agar plates. Sherman and Albus (1918), in a careful comparative study of strains of this organism, and of other strains referred to as *Str. pyogenes*, noted the following points of difference. The lactic-acid streptococcus grew predominantly as diplococci or short chains, it clotted milk within 24 hours, it produced high acidity in milk (0·75 per cent. or more measured as lactic acid), it grew well at 10° C., but very poorly at 43° C., and it rapidly reduced methylene blue, litmus, indigo carmine and neutral red. In each of these characters it differed sharply from *Str. pyogenes*. Ayers, Johnson and Mudge (1924) report that the lactic-acid streptococcus produces high acidity, rapidly clots and decolorizes litmus milk, and reduces methylene blue, or Janus green. This particular streptococcus has for long enjoyed specific rank, under the title *Str. lactis* ; but it will be noted that many of its most striking characteristics are shared by enterococci. Ayers and Johnson (1924) carried out a careful comparative study of these two types, testing them as regards their reaction on blood agar, their morphology, their ability to withstand heating at 60° C., their reaction in litmus milk and Janus green medium, their fermentation reactions, and the final pH attained. They were unable to detect any difference in behaviour, except that enterococci appeared to form acid somewhat less vigorously than *Str. lactis*. Kleckner (1935) also concludes that it is not possible to differentiate with certainty between lactic-acid streptococci and enterococci, though there are minor points of difference. Many strains of lactic-acid streptococci, for instance, fail to ferment mannitol. Sherman and Stark (1934), on the other hand, consider that differentiation is possible. They state that enterococci grow vigorously at 45° C., their maximum temperature for growth being 48–52° C., while lactic-acid streptococci have a maximum growth temperature of 41–43° C. ; that enterococci will resist a temperature of 65° C. for 30 minutes, while lactic-acid streptococci will not ; that enterococci will grow in a lactose-agar medium at pH 9·6 while lactic-acid streptococci will not ; and that enterococci are more resistant to high concentrations of NaCl (6·5 per cent.).

It seems clear that enterococci and lactic-acid streptococci are very closely related. Perhaps the wisest course at the present moment would be to use an inclusive group label—" the enterococcus-lactis group " or " the fæcalis-lactis group "—noting that certain characters, such as heat resistance and mannitol fermentation, are more constantly present in strains isolated from the fæces than in strains isolated from milk.

The origin of these streptococci in milk is an unsolved problem. It seems clear that they are not normal inhabitants of the cow's udder, but find their way into the milk from some outside source (Sherman and Albus 1918, Ayers, Johnson and Mudge 1924). Stark and Sherman (1935) have recently recorded their common occurrence on certain plants.

The Classification of the α-hæmolytic Streptococci.—It has been noted in preceding sections that streptococci giving α-hæmolysis with a characteristic green coloration on blood agar plates, failing to produce a soluble hæmolysin, usually fermenting raffinose but not mannitol, and possessing certain other characters in common, can constantly be isolated from the human mouth and throat and from the fæces of cattle. The problem that confronts us is whether these streptococci form a group or a species, and, if a group, whether the species of which that group is formed are sufficiently well differentiated to be allotted specific names.

Ayers and Mudge (1923) express the view that the α-hæmolytic streptococci of the bovine intestine differ in certain minor characters from the α-hæmolytic streptococci of the human mouth and throat ; and reference to several of the papers quoted above will reveal a tendency to accord the bovine strains specific rank, under the name *Str. bovis*. It is, however, by no means clear that this procedure is justified, or on what differential characters the proposed nomenclature is to be based.

There is another streptococcus falling into this group that seems to merit separate consideration. Freudenreich (1897) isolated a streptococcus from Kefir, a form of fermented milk. This streptococcus has the usual characters of the viridans type (Sherman 1921, Ayers *et al.* 1921, Ayers and Rupp 1922). When tested in the ordinary way, with a Durham fermentation tube, this organism, like other streptococci, produces acid, but no gas, from various substrates. If, however, it is tested in the Eldridge fermentation tube in which it is grown in a shallow layer of fluid medium, freely exposed to the air, and the CO_2 evolved is taken up by a standard solution of barium hydroxide, exposed in a connected tube of the same kind, as large an amount of CO_2 is evolved from lactose as is given off when that sugar is fermented by *Bact. coli*. It would seem that the almost anaerobic conditions existing in the closed Durham fermentation tube inhibit the production of CO_2 by the Kefir streptococcus. It is difficult to assess the real significance of this observation, since we have no knowledge of the way in which most species of non-gas-producing bacteria would behave if tested in the Eldridge tube, instead of in the closed Durham, or Smith, tubes in which they have in fact been tested ; but no CO_2 was formed in the Eldridge tube by such other strains of streptococci as were tested by Ayers and his colleagues, including strains isolated from the bovine faeces, and the lactic acid streptococcus.

There can, we think, be little doubt that the α-hæmolytic streptococci of the viridans type will ultimately be separated into a number of distinct species or types ; but we doubt very greatly whether it is yet possible to define with any exactitude either an inclusive species *Str. viridans*, or any of the fermentative types that have in the past been given specific names ; such as—

Str. salivarius, fermenting lactose and raffinose, but not salicin ;

Str. mitis, fermenting lactose and salicin, but not raffinose ;

Str. equinus, fermenting raffinose and usually salicin, but not lactose ; and

Str. bovis referred to above.

It is therefore our personal view that it would be wiser to use the non-committal group term " viridans streptococci " rather than the specific name *Str. viridans*. The present position in regard to this group of streptococci is, indeed, closely analogous to that existing in regard to the fæcalis-lactis group.

The Named Species, Groups and Types of Streptococci.—Summarizing the observations described in the preceding paragraphs, and the conclusions based upon them, we should recognize the following species, groups and types within the genus *Streptococcus*.

(1) **Str. pyogenes**—the type species, regarded as equivalent to Group A hæmolytic streptococci. This species is divisible into a number of antigenic types, in accordance with the numbers given by Griffith.

(2) **Str. agalactiæ**—regarded as antigenically equivalent to Group B streptococci, but comprising the non-hæmolytic as well as the hæmolytic strains that fall within this group. This group is divisible into a number of serological types, three of which have been identified by Stableforth and Lancefield.

(3) **Str. pneumoniæ**—divisible into a number of antigenic types in accordance with the American clasification introduced by Avery and his colleagues and extended by Cooper.

(4) **The Fæcalis-Lactis (Enterococcus-Lactis) Group**—including the Group D hæmolytic strains. This group probably consists of several different species, which await adequate differentiation.

(5) **The Viridans Group**—including all the α-hæmolytic streptococci that have been isolated from the human mouth and throat, bovine fæces and other sources. This group probably consists of several different species, which await adequate differentiation.

(6) **Hæmolytic Streptococci of Group C.**

(7) **Hæmolytic Streptococci of Group E.**

(8) **Hæmolytic Streptococci of Group F.**

(9) **Hæmolytic Streptococci of Group G.**

(10) **Hæmolytic Streptococci of Group H.**

(11) **Hæmolytic Streptococci of Group K.**

In regard to these last six groups it is possible that each of them represents either a distinct species of streptococcus, or an antigenic type that will in time be regarded as belonging to a named species. It is improbable that any of them will be further subdivided into different species. We do not yet know whether there are non-hæmolytic strains having an antigenic structure identical with that of any of these groups ; and it would at the moment be premature to allot to any of them a specific name. Groups C and G appear to be closely related, in many of their characters, to *Str. pyogenes*.

Pathogenicity and Toxin Production.

The various species of streptococci described above include some of the most important pathogens of man, and are responsible for many infections of economic importance among animals.

Str. pyogenes gives rise to numerous pyogenic and septicæmic infections in man (see Chapter LXIV), as well as being the cause of scarlet fever (see Chapter LXIII).

It is pathogenic for a number of laboratory animals, including the rabbit, the mouse and the guinea-pig ; but the virulence of different strains for these animals is by no means uniform, and the guinea-pig is often relatively resistant. To obtain a highly virulent strain for the mouse, or for the rabbit, it is often necessary to test a large number of strains of human origin, or to adapt a strain to the new host by repeated passage. When a highly virulent strain has been obtained, its intravenous injection leads to a fatal septicæmia, frequently associated in the rabbit with suppurative lesions in the joints, and sometimes with an ulcerative endocarditis. Intraperitoneal injection is followed by a suppurative peritonitis leading to a septicæmic infection ; while subcutaneous injection is followed by a localized abscess, with or without a subsequent generalization. With some strains, so far at least as the rabbit is concerned, intradermal injection is followed by a spreading erysipelatous infection of the skin, or by a more severe dermal infection leading to necrosis ; and an infection of the latter type not infrequently terminates as a septicæmia.

Str. pyogenes is of particular interest to the pathologist in that it combines the capacity for tissue invasion with the production of filtrable exotoxins.

One of these toxins, streptococcal hæmolysin, has already been considered. That this substance is toxic in the animal body, as well as being lytic for red blood corpuscles *in vitro*, there can be no doubt. Its minimal lethal dose is large (5–10 c.c. for the rabbit), but when administered intravenously in this amount it kills the animal within 24–36 hours with an associated hæmoglobinuria, and with evidence of intravascular hæmolysis at necropsy (McLeod and McNee 1913, Channon and McLeod 1929). Weld (1934, 1935) has recently described preparations of streptolysin, obtained by extracting the cocci with serum, that are fatal for mice in a dose of 0·1 c.c. Streptococcal hæmolysin is, as we have seen, thermolabile, being inactivated at 58° C. in 30 mins. As already noted, Todd (1934) has demonstrated the presence in lytic filtrates of two hæmolysins, one oxygen-sensitive, but reactivable by reduction, and another which is oxygen-stable but is very sensitive to heat and to acid. The oxygen-labile hæmolysin is antigenic, and gives rise to a specific antitoxin when injected into animals (Todd 1932a, 1934), though special precautions are required for its demonstration. It has been shown by Todd that the oxygen-labile hæmolysins produced by antigenically different types of *Str. pyogenes* (hæmolytic streptococci of group A) are identical, in that they are neutralized by a single antihæmolysin. The oxygen-stable hæmolysin appears not to be antigenic ; what part, if any, it plays in the toxicity of unheated streptococcal filtrates we do not know.

In addition to their action on red blood corpuscles, filtrates of broth cultures of *Str. pyogenes* have a destructive action on polymorphonuclear leucocytes. This was first demonstrated by Van der Velde (1894) in his studies on experimental infections with streptococci ; and he named the active principle *leucocidin*. It was subsequently shown by Neisser and Wechsberg (1900, 1901) that this action could be demonstrated *in vitro*, since the streptococcal filtrates, in killing the leucocytes, deprive them of their power of reducing methylene blue. It was early noted that streptococcal leucocidin is relatively thermolabile, and most authors (see Nakayama 1920, Channon and McLeod 1929) have concluded that its thermolability is of the same order as that of streptococcal hæmolysin. Channon and McLeod conclude, from this and other observations, that streptococcal hæmolysin and leucocidin are identical ; but Nakayama regards them as different, a view that is put forward more strongly by Evans (1931) and by Gay and Oram (1933), who dispute the previous findings in regard to the thermolability of streptococcal leucocidin, and state that it withstands heating at 70° C. for 30 minutes. This problem must be regarded as awaiting final solution.

The studies of Dick and Dick (1924a, b, 1925a, b) on the ætiology of scarlet fever, and the observations of subsequent workers, have shown that Str. pyogenes produces another filtrable toxin, which is quite distinct from the hæmolysin and leucocidin. The properties of this toxin are described in some detail in Chapter LXIII. For our immediate purpose a brief summary will suffice.

The injection of this toxin in small amounts into the skin of persons susceptible to its action gives rise to a characteristic localized erythema. Its injection in larger amounts in particularly susceptible persons may result in a generalized erythematous rash, associated with fever and malaise (" miniature scarlet fever "). Because of this action in man this component of streptococcal filtrates is known as the erythrogenic toxin, or scarlatinal toxin. It is toxic for the rabbit when injected intravenously, but its minimal lethal dose is very large (5–10 c.c. of an unconcentrated filtrate). It can be concentrated and partially purified by various methods (Hartley 1928, Pulvertaft 1928), but the M.L.D. remains relatively large (0·1–1 c.c.), and the purification is certainly very incomplete. A skin reaction has been induced in certain laboratory animals, but none of them are as sensitive as man, and many are quite resistant.

The erythrogenic toxin differs sharply from streptococcal hæmolysin in being relatively heat resistant. It requires a temperature of 96° C. for 45 minutes for complete inactivation. It is antigenic, producing an antitoxin that gives specific neutralization, and is immunologically distinct from antistreptolysin (Todd, Laurent and Hill 1933).

This does not exhaust the toxic armoury of Str. pyogenes. It has been shown (Tillett and Garner 1933) that pathogenic strains of hæmolytic streptococci produce a substance that dissolves human fibrin (see also Tillett, Edwards and Garner 1934, Tillett 1935). This fibrinolysin seems to be almost constantly present in strains of Group A hæmolytic streptococci (Lancefield and Hare 1935, Hare 1935, Hare and Maxted 1935, Colebrook, Maxted and Johns 1935). The action appears to be relatively specific for the fibrin of certain animal species. Thus the fibrinolysin produced by many strains of Str. pyogenes dissolves human, but not rabbit fibrin. The fibrinolysin also acts on human fibrinogen, so altering it that it is no longer able to form fibrin. Garner and Tillett (1934) have been able to obtain partially purified streptococcal fibrinolysin from filtrates by alcohol precipitation, followed by adsorption and elution. The product obtained is remarkably heat resistant ; its activity may be maintained after heating at 100° C. for 50 minutes. It exerts no hydrolytic action on casein, gelatin or peptone. Its lytic action on human fibrin appears to be associated with a slight increase in the amino-nitrogen content of the reacting mixture.

Finally, Duran-Reynals (1933) has described the presence in lysates and filtrates of invasive streptococci of a " spreading factor," which markedly increases the permeability of the rabbit's skin to suspensions of Indian ink, or to bacterial cells.

In summary, Str. pyogenes produces the following toxins, or aggressive substances (see Chapter XLV) which, in one way or another, determine its pathogenic activity— (1) streptococcal hæmolysin, (2) streptococcal leucocidin, (3) an erythrogenic toxin, (4) a fibrinolysin, and (5) a substance that increases skin permeability.

Str. agalactiæ.—Our knowledge of the pathogenicity and toxigenicity of this species is, as yet, very incomplete. It produces mastitis in cattle, but, so far as our present knowledge goes, is not pathogenic for man. Its pathogenicity for the mouse, or the rabbit, is low (Minett and Stableforth 1931, Minett 1935b). Some, but not all, strains, produce a filtrable hæmolysin, which Todd (1934) has found to be of the oxygen-stable, non-antigenic type. Whether Str. agalactiæ produces a leucocidin is not known. It has been shown by Smith (1929) that strains of hæmolytic streptococci isolated from cattle may produce an erythrogenic toxin that is neutralized by scarlatinal antitoxin ; but there is no evidence that these strains were *Str. agalactiæ*. No erythrogenic toxin was produced by the mastitis strains examined by Minett and Stableforth (1931). *Str. agalactiæ* does not produce a fibrinolysin active against human fibrin (Lancefield and Hare 1935, Hare 1935). Whether it produces a fibrinolysin that acts on cattle fibrin is unknown. There is as yet no evidence as to whether *Str. agalactiæ* produces a substance that increases skin permeability.

Str. pneumoniæ.—The pneumococcus is an important pathogen of man, giving rise to pneumonia, particularly the lobar form, sinusitis, otitis media, less frequently meningitis, suppurative arthritis, or peritonitis, and occasionally other infections.

It is highly pathogenic for the mouse and rabbit, rather less so for the guinea-pig. The cat, dog and chicken are relatively resistant. It is a characteristically invasive organism, causing a fatal bacteræmic infection when injected intravenously, an acute peritonitis followed by bacteræmia when injected intraperitoneally, localized suppuration followed by generalization when injected subcutaneously, and a spreading inflammatory lesion followed by generalization when injected intradermally in the rabbit. Different serological types of pneumococci may show differences in their virulence for different laboratory animals ; for instance, many strains of Type III pneumococcus are relatively avirulent for the rabbit (Tillett 1927). Again, different strains belonging to the same type may show wide variations in virulence as judged by their minimal lethal dose. With a strain of maximal virulence the injection of 1–10 pneumococci into the peritoneum of a mouse will cause an infection that leads to death within 18–48 hours.

In contrast to *Str. pyogenes*, the pneumococcus is not an actively toxigenic organism, in the sense of producing filtrable toxins. Some observers have, indeed, regarded it as being devoid of this capacity, and as affording a typical example of a bacterium the pathogenicity of which is determined entirely by its powers of invasion, associated, of course, with the effects of those nebulous " endotoxins " (see Chapter XLI) that must always be concerned in invasive bacterial infections. There is little doubt that this contrast is a true one, in the sense that filtrable toxins play a much more prominent part in *Str. pyogenes* infections than in those due to pneumococci ; but the difference is not so absolute as it has been supposed to be.

We have seen that *Str. pneumoniæ* produces a filtrable hæmolysin when grown under optimal conditions. This is of the oxygen-sensitive type, and is antigenic. There is evidence (Todd 1934) that it bears some antigenic relationship to the oxygen-sensitive hæmolysin of *Str. pyogenes*, but is certainly not identical with it. Oram (1934) has described the presence in pneumococcal filtrates of a leucocidin, active for rabbit leucocytes. Like the streptococcal leucocidin described by Gay and Oram (1933), this substance is relatively thermostable. It is not inactivated in one hour at 70° C., but is completely inactivated at 85° C. for a similar period.

Several observers (Julianelle and Reimann 1926, Reimann and Julianelle 1926, Mair 1928, Pittman and Falk 1930, Goodner 1931) have noted purpuric lesions following the injection of pneumococcal extracts and autolysates. The active agent would appear to be an " endotoxin," *i.e.* some constituent of the bacterial cell, rather than a soluble toxin. It may be noted that Avery and Goebel (1933) report that mice may develop purpura after injections of the acetylated form of the Type I pneumococcal polysaccharide, while this effect is not produced by the deacetylated form.

Whether pneumococci produce a fibrinolysin active against human fibrin, or a spreading factor similar to that described by Duran-Reynals (1933) in invasive streptococci and staphylococci is not certainly known. The formation of the characteristic fibrin network in the alveoli in lobar pneumonia in man would seem to make it unlikely that the pneumococci concerned act vigorously on human fibrin ; but it would appear that they are able to attack rabbit fibrin or fibrinogen. Goodner (1931, 1933) has recorded that the œdema fluid, withdrawn from the spreading œdematous lesions caused by the injection of virulent pneumococci into the rabbit's skin, not only fails to clot, but retards the coagulation of normal rabbit's blood, and that a similar anticoagulant property is possessed by pneumococcal extracts and autolysates. The active substance is relatively thermostable, since it withstands heating to 70° C. for 15 minutes. Such autolysates, when injected into the skin together with a slightly virulent strain of pneumococcus, greatly extend the area of the lesion produced.

None of the other groups, species, or types of pneumococci that we have described above have been studied, in regard to their pathogenicity for laboratory animals, in the same detail as *Str. pyogenes* and *Str. pneumoniæ*. A few brief notes will give most of the information that we possess.

Streptococci of the Fæcalis-Lactis Group.—The organisms of this group are far less pathogenic than *Str. pyogenes* or *Str. pneumoniæ*. They have, however, occasionally been isolated from the blood stream in man, usually in cases of subacute endocarditis (see Chapter LXV), rarely in other conditions. They are normal inhabitants of the intestinal tract, and are not infrequently present in suppurative abdominal lesions, though their pathogenic rôle is often doubtful. They are also not uncommonly present in infections of the urinary tract. Their virulence for laboratory animals is usually low. Dible (1921) tested 83 fæcal strains by injection into mice, and 6 of these showed some degree of pathogenicity. It is very probable that such pathogenicity as this group possesses is confined to particular species, or strains; and that many strains, such for example as most of those isolated from milk or cheese, are altogether non-pathogenic. It may, perhaps, be noted that the hæmolytic strains belonging to this group (Group D hæmolytic streptococci) do not produce a fibrinolysin active against human fibrin.

Streptococci of the Viridans Group.—The position of this group, in regard to pathogenicity, is very similar to that of the fæcalis-lactis group. Streptococci of the viridans type are of low virulence, both for man and for animals. In man they are frequently isolated from localized septic lesions in connection with the teeth and gums, and they are the most frequent cause of subacute bacterial endocarditis. Here again, it is probable that different species or types within the group vary considerably in their pathogenicity for different animal species. Many of them are probably quite avirulent. In none of them is the virulence high.

Very brief notes must suffice for the remaining labelled groups of hæmolytic streptococci, since our knowledge of their pathogenic potentialities is as yet in its earliest infancy. The data available are contained in the recent papers by Lancefield, Hare, and others, to which frequent reference has already been made.

Hæmolytic Streptococci of Group C are certainly pathogenic. They have been frequently isolated from suppurative and acute inflammatory lesions in horses, cattle, guinea-pigs and other animals. They have also been isolated from human infections; but their pathogenicity for man appears to be lower than that of *Str. pyogenes*. The human pathogenic strains that have been examined produce a fibrinolysin active against human fibrin; the strains derived from animals do not.

Hæmolytic Streptococci of Group F.—The strains that have been identified as belonging to this group have been derived from minor infections of the respiratory tract in man, and from the normal human throat. Their possible pathogenic rôle must be regarded as *sub judice*; but their virulence would seem, in any case, to be of a low order. They do not produce a fibrinolysin action on human fibrin.

Hæmolytic Streptococci of Group G.—The streptococci of this group are certainly pathogenic. They have been isolated from tonsillitis in man, from pneumonia in the monkey, and from otitis in the dog. They have also been isolated from the normal human throat. Such evidence as is available suggests that Group G, like Group C strains, have a definitely lower virulence for man than has *Str. pyogenes*. Group G strains produce a fibrinolysin acting on human fibrin.

Hæmolytic Streptococci of Groups E, H and K.—There is as yet no evidence that the streptococci belonging to these groups are pathogenic.

Variation in the Characters of Streptococci.

It is not always possible from the records to identify the strain in which particular variations have been observed with one or other of the groups, species or types that have been defined in this chapter. It is, for instance, sometimes impossible to tell whether the term " hæmolytic streptococci " or *Str. hæmolyticus*, is equivalent to *Str. pyogenes*, in the sense in which we have used that term. In almost all the instances given below, however, the identity of the strain or strains concerned is not in doubt, and the reservation that it is necessary to make is little more than formal.

Variations in Str. pyogenes.—There are many reports in the literature of the appearance of non-hæmolytic, or α-hæmolytic, variants in cultures derived from an originally hæmolytic strain. These reports have at times been regarded as invalidating hæmolysin production as a differential test ; but in view of our more detailed knowledge of the factors that determine the action of streptococci on red blood corpuscles, it is clearly unnecessary to assume that the appearance, in a culture of a β-hæmolytic streptococcus, of a variant that gives typical α-hæmolysis, or no hæmolysis at all, on the surface of an aerobic blood agar plate affords an instance of the mutation of *Str. pyogenes* into a streptococcus of the viridans type, or into a completely non-hæmolytic form.

An illuminating example is given by Todd (1928*b*). By repeated mouse passage he was able to obtain, from a typical β-hæmolytic strain of streptococcus, a variant that produced no hæmolysis at all on the surface of aerobic blood agar plates. When grown anaerobically, this variant maintained full hæmolytic activity. Moreover, the aerobically non-hæmolytic variant not only inactivated its own hæmolysin when exposed to a free supply of oxygen, but, under the same conditions, inactivated the hæmolysin produced by the original hæmolytic strain, if the latter was grown in symbiosis with it. The appearance of non-hæmolytic variants in an originally hæmolytic strain has, it may be noted, been recorded by many other workers.

We have already noted in Chapter VIII the types of antigenic variation that occur in this species, and the associated changes in virulence. The loss of the type-specific, acid-soluble, protein antigen, that characterizes the surface of *Str. pyogenes* in its normal form, is apparently associated with a loss of virulence (Todd 1928*a*, Todd and Lancefield 1928, Lancefield and Todd 1928). This change clearly corresponds to the S $\longrightarrow$ R variation that occurs in many bacterial species ; but it happens that the associated change that has been observed in colony form is not from smooth to rough, but from " matt " to " glossy." The influence of oxygen pressure on this change has been studied by Todd (1930). He finds that repeated subculture on solid media under aerobic conditions favours the appearance of glossy avirulent variants, while cultivation under anaerobic conditions prevents it. The effect of free aerobiosis is apparently due to the formation of bacterial peroxide, the glossy variants being more resistant to this agent than the original matt virulent form. In broth cultures the effects of increasing the oxygen pressure by aeration is somewhat different, matt avirulent variants tending to appear under anaerobic conditions, while the virulence of the original matt strain is maintained when the culture is freely aerated, though glossy variants make their appearance.

It should perhaps be noted that the change from matt to glossy is not associated with a loss of the power to produce hæmolysin.

Variations in Str. pneumoniæ.—The more important types of variation that are encountered in the pneumococcus have already been noted in Chapter VIII. The S $\longrightarrow$ R variation is here associated with the loss of the characteristic capsule, and with it the polysaccharide antigen that confers type-specificity. Here, as elsewhere, the rough variants of pneumococci usually retain the characteristic bile solubility. They also retain the power of producing a hæmolysin and a leucodicin (Oram 1934).

We have also referred in Chapter VIII to the important observations of Griffith (1928) on the conversion of a smooth strain of pneumococcus, belonging to a particular antigenic type, through the corresponding rough variant to a smooth strain belonging to a different antigenic type ; and we have noted that these observations have been confirmed by several subsequent workers. Up to the present time this remains the only instance in which a transmutation of one normal bacterial type into another has been demonstrated under experimental conditions ; and it affords no grounds for the assumption that such types are unstable under natural conditions.

In regard to the other groups or species, referred to in the present chapter, we know too little as yet of the variations to which they are subject to attempt any systematic description of them. The description of variants that fit into no general scheme tends to confusion rather than to the clarification of knowledge. We must not, of course, ignore the fact that such variations occur ; but to assess their true significance we must wait until we can allot them their proper place in the picture of bacterial structure, which is being slowly but surely pieced together by modern methods of study.

A note should, perhaps, be added in regard to fermentation reactions. There is general agreement that the enzymic activities that have been accorded differential value in the preceding sections of this chapter are relatively stable, though there is no doubt that variants may from time to time appear that have lost the power of attacking one or other of the test substrates. There is no evidence that the change from the matt to the glossy form in *Str. pyogenes*, or the change from smooth to rough in *Str. pneumoniæ*, is associated with any change in the characteristic fermentation reactions.

The Anaerobic Streptococci.

All the species, or groups, of streptococci described above are aerobic and facultatively anaerobic. Cocci growing in short or long chains have, however, been isolated, which are either strictly anaerobic, or grow only under micro-aerophilic conditions.

These anaerobic streptococci are of considerable importance to the medical bacteriologist, since some, at least, are certainly pathogenic for man ; and the studies of recent years have shown that organisms of this type are a frequent source of severe puerperal infection (see Chapter LXIII). Apart from puerperal sepsis, and puerperal septicæmia, most of the strains of anaerobic streptococci that have been isolated have been derived from suppurative or gangrenous lesions, which have often been noted as producing a foul or fœtid odour (see Veillon 1893, Krönig 1895, Sternberg 1900, Rist 1901, Lowkewicz 1901, Silberschmidt 1902, Marwedel and Wehrsig 1915, Kissling 1924, 1929, Prévot 1924, 1925, 1933). The importance of these organisms in relation to puerperal septicæmia was first insisted on by Schottmüller (1910, 1928), though their presence in the genital tract during the puerperium had been noted by several earlier workers. Schottmüller's observations have since been extended and confirmed by many subsequent observers (Bingold 1921, 1932, Lehmann 1926, Harris and Brown 1929, Colebrook 1930, Colebrook and Hare 1933). It would seem (Natvig 1905, Wegelius 1909, Rosowsky 1912, Soule and Brown 1932, White, E. 1933) that these anaerobic streptococci form part of the normal flora of the female genital tract ; and it seems possible (White, E. 1933) that this is their principal normal habitat. Such attempts as have been made to isolate them from the normal human throat or intestine have been unsuccessful.

It is certain that the anaerobic streptococci comprise many different groups, species or types ; but the data available are as yet far too scanty to permit of any systematic classification or nomenclature. Reference to the papers by Prévot, and by Colebrook and Hare, will afford descriptions of several of the strains that have been isolated, and of certain differential criteria on which a future classification may in part be based.

It may be noted that many of these cocci are very small (0·3–0·4 μ) ; but the size tends to vary considerably in subculture (Colebrook and Hare 1933). Many but not all strains form abundant gas in fluid cultures, differing sharply in this way from the aerobic and facultatively anaerobic species that we have described above. Many, but not all strains produce an extremely foul odour.

Colebrook and Hare (1933) have studied the growth of 60 strains of anaerobic strepto-cocci on blood agar, and have thus been able to distinguish four different types on the basis of rate of growth, colony form, and changes produced in the medium. Only two of the 60 strains produced hæmolysis ; three others gave characteristic coal-black colonies. The remaining 55 strains produced no change in the medium. About half the strains tested failed to ferment any test substrate ; with the remainder it was not found possible to cor-relate the fermentation reactions with the colonial characters. A preliminary attempt at antigenic analysis, using antisera to eight of the strains, showed considerable diversity of antigenic structure, but many group reactions. The two main types differentiated on colonial appearances were shown to be antigenically distinct. Finally, those strains that were tested for heat resistance were found to be killed by heating to 58–60° C. for 30 minutes.

It may be noted that the pathogenicity of anaerobic streptococci for laboratory animals appears to vary widely. Wegelius (1909) produced small abscesses in the peritoneal cavity of mice. Marwedel and Wehrsig (1915), with one strain examined, produced an acutely fatal infection in a guinea-pig. Prévot (1925) records pathogenic lesions of a suppurative gangrenous or œdematous type, sometimes fatal, with most of his strains. Harris and Brown (1929) found that three of 57 strains derived from cases of puerperal fever killed mice within 24 hours. Colebrook and Hare (1933) tested seven puerperal strains by sub-cutaneous injections into mice. Two of them gave rise to small caseous foci at the site of inoculation, but none of the mice died.

We append a summarized description of the more important species, or groups, to which names, or labels, can at the moment be attached.

SPECIES, GROUPS AND TYPES

Str. pyogenes

MORPHOLOGY.—Cocci, usually spheroidal, about 0·5–0·75 μ in diameter, arranged in chains of varying length, but usually including ten or more cocci. With few exceptions, not capsulated in culture. Capsules usually absent or poorly developed in tissues. Non-motile. No spores. Gram-positive ; not acid-fast.

GROWTH REQUIREMENTS.—When first isolated may grow poorly on ordinary nutrient agar. Growth is markedly improved by the addition of blood or serum. Optimal tem-perature 37° C. Grows at temperature slightly over 40° C. Poor growth below 20° C., and usually fails to grow at 10° C. Aerobic and facultatively anaerobic.

TYPE OF GROWTH.—*On solid media* after 24 hours' incubation, the colonies are small, about 0·5–0·75 mm. in diameter, opaque, slightly raised, circular, with an entire margin, a slightly granular surface, and a granular structure, when viewed by transmitted light, showing some differentiation into a more opaque central portion, and a more translucent periphery. After further incubation (48 to 72 hours) the colony may extend in diameter, and become differentiated into a raised central portion, smooth or contoured, and a flatter peripheral zone. The colonial forms presented by different strains are subject to considerable variation ; and a plate from a single strain may show colonies of very varying appearance ; particularly with regard to the smoothness, contouring, or granularity of the surface, and the degree of differentiation between the central and peripheral zones.

Streaked cultures on solid media give a relatively scanty growth, with a tendency for a majority of the colonies to remain discrete. The growth emulsifies easily, but usually gives a granular suspension.

In blood agar plates.—The colonies are surrounded by a zone of β-hæmolysis (see above), best seen in the deep colonies. A filtrable hæmolysin is formed in fluid cultures, which is oxygen-labile. An oxygen-stable hæmolysin is also produced.

In broth, or serum broth.—When first isolated, the growth may be finely granular, or may form a powdery deposit at the bottom of the tube, or cling to its sides. Turbidity of the medium may be moderate, or slight. After subculture, and particularly when repeatedly subcultured at short intervals, the turbidity may increase markedly, and the granular deposit decrease, or disappear ; but the turbidity almost always remains of a finely granular type, and the growth seldom or never becomes evenly diffuse. There is no pellicle formation.

On gelatin the growth is slight, and the colonies are minute and punctiform.

In gelatin stab there is a slight growth along the track, with minimal growth on the surface. The gelatin is not liquefied.

On potato growth is very slight, and often not detectable by the naked eye.

HEAT RESISTANCE, AND VIABILITY.—*Str. pyogenes* is killed by heating to 55° C. for 30 minutes. It tends to die out in subculture unless preserved under particularly favourable conditions, but it remains viable for long periods in the dry state.

BIOCHEMICAL REACTIONS.—*Str. pyogenes* does not hydrolyse sodium hippurate ; does not reduce methylene blue in milk ; produces a final pH of 5·0–5·6 in glucose broth ; ferments trehalose, lactose, saccharose, salicin and occasionally mannitol, with the formation of acid but no gas ; does not ferment sorbitol, inulin or raffinose. Produces acid in litmus milk, but no coherent clot. Does not liquefy gelatin. Does not reduce nitrates. Does not form indole. Is not soluble in bile. Its growth is inhibited by bile.

ANTIGENIC STRUCTURE.—*Str. pyogenes* possesses the group-specific polysaccharide antigen of Lancefield's Group A hæmolytic streptococci. It is differentiated into a large number of antigenic types by type-specific protein antigens ; 23 of these types have so far been identified by Griffith by agglutination and absorption tests.

PATHOGENICITY AND TOXIN PRODUCTION.—*Str. pyogenes* produces a variety of infections in man, and more rarely in domestic animals. Some strains are highly pathogenic for the mouse or the rabbit, less so for the guinea-pig. It produces a soluble hæmolysin, a leucocidin, an erythrogenic toxin and a fibrinolysin acting on human fibrin.

Str. agalactiæ

MORPHOLOGY, GROWTH REQUIREMENTS AND TYPE OF GROWTH.—In these characters *Str. agalactiæ* does not differ significantly from *Str. pyogenes*.

ACTION ON BLOOD.—Between one-third and one-half of the strains of *Str. agalactiæ* that have been examined produce β-hæmolysis in blood agar plates. These strains produce a filtrable hæmolysin of the oxygen-stable type.

HEAT RESISTANCE.—*Str. agalactiæ* is killed by heating to 60° C for 30 minutes.

BIOCHEMICAL REACTIONS.—*Str. agalactiæ* hydrolyses sodium hippurate ; it does not reduce methylene blue in milk ; it produces a final pH of 4·2–4·8 in glucose broth ; it produces acid in trehalose, lactose, saccharose and usually salicin, but not in sorbitol, mannitol or inulin ; it forms acid and clot in milk ; it does not liquefy gelatin. It is not soluble in bile. Its growth is not inhibited by 10 per cent. bile, and usually not by 40 per cent.

ANTIGENIC STRUCTURE.—*Str. agalactiæ* possesses the group-specific polysaccharide antigen of Lancefield's Group B streptococci. It is separable into different antigenic types, three of which have so far been identified, by type-specific antigens which appear to be carbohydrate, not protein in nature.

PATHOGENICITY AND TOXIN PRODUCTION.—*Str. agalactiæ* is an important cause of mastitis in cattle. Its pathogenicity for laboratory animals is low. Some, if not all, strains produce a filtrable hæmolysin. It does not produce a fibrinolysin acting on human fibrin. Whether it produces a leucocidin is unknown. There is no evidence that it produces an erythrogenic toxin.

Str. pneumoniæ

MORPHOLOGY.—Ovoid or lanceolate cocci, arranged in pairs or short chains ; when in pairs, the adjacent ends of the cocci are usually bluntly rounded, the opposite ends more acutely pointed. Some strains (particularly Type III) tend to form longer chains. As seen in films from the tissues, the pneumococcus shows a well-marked capsule ; and this capsule is frequently retained in cultures on suitable media. Non-motile. No spores. Gram-positive. Not acid-fast.

GROWTH REQUIREMENTS.—Grows poorly on ordinary media, especially when first isolated ; the addition of blood or serum to the medium greatly improves growth. Optimal temperature 37° C., range of growth more restricted than with other species of *Streptococcus*. Usually no growth on gelatin at 20° C. Aerobic and facultatively anaerobic.

TYPE OF GROWTH.—*On solid media.* Small, raised, circular colonies, 0·5–1 mm. in diameter, with a smooth surface, an entire edge, and very little differentiation. On a favourable medium, such as blood agar, the colonies are often characteristic ; the surface is flat and smooth, and the edges are sharply and steeply raised from the surface of the medium. In some cases the edge may be raised above the surface of the colony, forming a raised circumferential ring. Several adjacent colonies may become confluent, forming a raised area of growth with a flat, even surface and a sharply delimited edge. With longer periods of growth (48–72 hours) the central portion of the colony often undergoes autolysis. Some strains (particularly Type III) give characteristic mucoid colonies. Old laboratory strains of pneumococci, particularly when grown on a relatively unfavourable medium such as ordinary nutrient agar, often give smaller colonies which lack the characteristic appearance of a recently isolated strain grown on a favourable medium. The consistency of the colonies is butyrous, and the growth emulsifies easily. In blood agar plates, the colonies are surrounded by a zone of α-hæmolysis showing the characteristic green coloration. In a suitable fluid medium, a filtrable hæmolysin is formed, which is of the oxygen-labile type.

In broth, or serum broth, Str. pneumoniæ gives a diffuse turbid growth, with a slight deposit, increasing on prolonged incubation. No pellicle is formed.

On gelatin very slight growth, usually none at or below 20° C.

Gelatin stab—very slight growth along track, with minimal surface growth. No liquefaction.

Potato—growth slight, or absent.

HEAT RESISTANCE AND VIABILITY.—*Str. pneumoniæ* is sensitive to heat, being killed at a temperature of 55° C. in 20 minutes or less. It is a relatively delicate organism, and dies out rapidly in artificial cultures unless maintained under particularly favourable conditions, as, for instance, in semi-solid agar to which blood has been added.

BIOCHEMICAL ACTIVITIES.—The pneumococcus produces acid, but no gas, from lactose, saccharose, and inulin, and usually from raffinose. Salicin is rarely fermented ; when fermented, acid is not usually produced for some days. Mannitol is not fermented. Milk is acidified, and frequently clotted. Nitrates are not reduced. Indole is not formed. Gelatin is not liquefied. The pneumococcus is soluble in bile.

ANTIGENIC STRUCTURE.—The pneumococcus possesses a species-specific carbohydrate antigen, the presence of which is not detected by agglutination reactions carried out with normal smooth forms. The species is divided into a number of antigenic types by type-specific polysaccharide antigens contained in the capsules. Thirty-two of these types have so far been identified.

PATHOGENICITY AND TOXIN PRODUCTION.—The pneumococcus causes pneumonia and certain other infections in man. It is highly pathogenic for mice and slightly less so for rabbits. Guinea-pigs are rather more resistant, and cats, dogs, fowls and pigeons much more resistant.

The pneumococcus produces a soluble hæmolysin, and a leucocidin. It also produces a substance acting on rabbit fibrin or fibrinogen, and preventing the formation of a clot.

Streptococci of the Viridans Group

MORPHOLOGY.—Cocci in short or long chains, spheroidal or ovoid ; when ovoid, long axis in axis of chain. Non-capsulated. No spores. Non-motile. Gram-positive. Not acid-fast.

GROWTH REQUIREMENTS.—Most strains grow more readily on ordinary media than does *Str. pyogenes* or *Str. pneumoniæ*, but growth is usually improved by addition of blood or serum. Some strains, on the other hand, grow very poorly. Optimal temperature for most strains 37° C.—the range of temperature for growth extends further than that of *Str. pyogenes* or *Str. pneumoniæ* in the downward direction. Aerobic and facultatively anaerobic.

TYPE OF GROWTH.—*On solid media* the colonies do not differ in any distinctive way from those of *Str. pyogenes* (see above). With streak cultures, the growth may be slightly more profuse, and more confluent.

In blood agar plates.—The colonies are surrounded by a zone of α-hæmolysis, showing the characteristic green coloration.

In broth.—The type of growth varies with chain length. Many strains or varieties grow in short chains and produce a uniform, but slightly granular, turbidity in broth, with little or no deposit ; but some strains grow in long chains and give growths which are indistinguishable from those of *Str. pyogenes*.

On gelatin, or in gelatin stab, the growth does not differ from that of *Str. pyogenes*, except that it may be slightly more profuse.

On potato, growth is slight, and often not detectable by the naked eye.

HEAT RESISTANCE.—Most strains are killed by heating at 55–58° C. for 30 minutes. The general vitality is greater than that of *Str. pyogenes*.

BIOCHEMICAL REACTIONS.—Milk is acidified, and often clotted. Most strains produce acid from lactose and saccharose, often from raffinose and/or salicin, rarely from inulin or mannitol. Nitrates are not reduced. Indole is not formed. Gelatin is not liquefied. Not soluble in bile.

PATHOGENICITY AND TOXIN FORMATION.—Viridans streptococci form no soluble toxin, nor hæmolysin. Usually non-pathogenic for laboratory animals other than the rabbit, in which some strains give rise to arthritis and valvular lesions. They are a common cause of subacute ulcerative endocarditis in man.

DIFFERENTIATION WITHIN THE GROUP.—It is certain that the viridans group of strep-tococci contains more than a single species. It is possible that the common streptococcus of bovine fæces deserves specific rank with the title *Str. bovis*, and that a streptococcus isolated from Kefir, which produces CO_2 from lactose when grown in Eldridge tubes should be known as *Str. kefir*. Our knowledge is, however, not yet sufficient to allow us to define species or to assign specific names with any degree of certainty.

The Fæcalis-Lactis Group of Streptococci

MORPHOLOGY.—Ovoid cocci, growing in pairs or short chains. Some strains resemble the pneumococcus in morphology, but possess no capsule. More rarely, the appearance may be almost bacillary. The streptococci of this group, as of others, are characteristically non-motile, but a few motile strains have recently been described. No spores are formed. Gram-positive and not acid-fast.

GROWTH REQUIREMENTS.—Grow well on the ordinary laboratory media. Optimal temperature about 37° C., but grow up to 42° C. ; grow well on gelatin at 20° C. Aerobic, and facultatively anaerobic.

TYPE OF GROWTH. *On solid media*, the colonies are somewhat larger than those of the species referred to above. After 24 hours the colonies are usually 0·75 mm. in average diameter, and, on longer incubation, increase to a diameter of 1–2 mm. The colonies are smooth, circular, low convex in elevation, with an entire edge ; they have a homogeneous, or slightly granular structure, and show little differentiation. In streaked cultures the colonies tend to be confluent, and growth may appear as a uniform film. The growth is easily emulsified.

In blood agar—some strains belonging to this group give β-hæmolysis. These strains correspond to Lancefield's Group D hæmolytic streptococci. They form no filtrable hæmolysin when tested by the ordinary methods, but a hæmolysin of the oxygen-stable type may be demonstrated by special cultural methods. Most strains are non-hæmolytic.

In broth there is an abundant, diffuse growth, with a very slight deposit. No pellicle formation occurs.

On gelatin, these streptococci give a good growth, with colonies very similar to those produced on agar. Growth occurs at 20° C., or at rather lower temperatures. Most strains fail to liquefy the gelatin, but a few do so.

In gelatin stab, there is good growth along the track, with little surface growth. Some strains produce liquefaction, which is usually infundibuliform.

HEAT RESISTANCE AND VIABILITY.—Streptococci of the fæcalis-lactis group are characteristically resistant to heat. Most strains, including the great majority of those isolated from the human fæces, will withstand a temperature of 60° C. for 30 minutes or more. Other strains, including a proportion of those isolated from milk, are rather less resistant, though more resistant than *Str. pyogenes*, *Str. pneumoniæ*, or the streptococci of the viridans group. Streptococci of this group usually have great vitality, and can easily be maintained in culture over prolonged periods.

BIOCHEMICAL ACTIVITIES.—Streptococci of the fæcalis-lactis group fail to hydrolyse sodium hippurate. They produce a final pH of 4·2–4·7 in glucose broth. They reduce methylene blue in milk. They produce acid in trehalose, sorbitol, lactose, saccharose, usually mannitol, frequently salicin, but not in raffinose or inulin. They also produce acid from æsculin in a bile-containing medium. They clot, acidify and decolorize litmus milk. They reduce nitrates. A few strains liquefy gelatin ; most do not. Some strains produce H_2S. Streptococci of this group are not bile-soluble. They grow freely on agar containing 10 per cent. or 40 per cent. of bile.

ANTIGENIC STRUCTURE.—Those members of the fæcalis-lactis group of streptococci that cause β-hæmolysis on blood agar possess the group-specific antigen of Lancefield's Group D. Whether some or all of the non-hæmolytic strains possess the same antigen we do not know. The group has been shown to contain a large number of different serological types, showing group relationships. But no attempt has yet been made to give a systematic description of the antigenic structure of the group as a whole.

PATHOGENICITY AND TOXIN PRODUCTION.—Most strains of the fæcalis-lactis group appear to be non-pathogenic, or to possess a pathogenicity of a low order. Streptococci of this group occasionally cause urinary infections in man, or infections in relation to the intestinal tract. They have occasionally been isolated from the blood stream, and are the cause of some cases of subacute endocarditis. Most strains are non-pathogenic for laboratory animals. A few show some degree of pathogenicity. There is no evidence that any of the streptococci form a filtrable toxin. Such strains as have been examined do not form a fibrinolysin acting on human fibrin.

DIFFERENTIATION WITHIN THE GROUP.—There is no doubt that the fæcalis-lactis group of streptococci contains several different species or types. It is possible that the strains that are normal inhabitants of the human intestine are of a different species from those found normally in milk. It would appear, for instance, that many of the milk strains fail to ferment mannitol and are less resistant to heat than the intestinal strains. On the basis of various combinations of the reactions referred to above it is possible to divide the intestinal strains into a number of " biochemical " types, and this has been done by some workers. There is as yet, however, no adequate evidence on which species or types can be clearly, or certainly, defined.

The characters of the other labelled groups or types of streptococci, as far as we yet know them, have been summarized in the body of this chapter.

REFERENCES

ANDERSON, A. B. and HART, P. D'A. (1934a) *J. Path. Bact.*, **39**, 465 ; (1934b) *Lancet*, ii. 359.
ANDREWES, F. and HORDER, T. (1906) *Lancet*, ii. 708, 775, 852.
ARMSTRONG, R. R. (1932) *Brit. med. J.*, i. 187.
ARONSON, H. (1903) *Dtsch. med. Wschr.*, **29**, 439.
AVERY, O. T. (1915) *J. exp. Med.*, **22**, 804.
AVERY, O. T., CHICKERING, H. T., COLE, R., and DOCHEZ, A. R. (1917) *Monogr. Rocke-feller Inst. med. Res.*, No. 7.
AVERY, O. T. and GOEBEL, W. F. (1933) *J. exp. Med.*, **58**, 731.
AVERY, O. T. and HEIDELBERGER, M. (1923) *J. exp. Med.*, **38**, 81 ; (1925) *Ibid.*, **52**, 367.
AVERY, O. T., HEIDELBERGER, M., and GOEBEL, W. F. (1925) *J. exp. Med.*, **42**, 709.
AVERY, O. T. and MORGAN, H. J. (1924) *J. exp. Med.*, **39**, 275, 289 ; (1925) *Ibid.*, **42**, 347.
AVERY, O. T. and NEILL, J. M. (1924a) *J. exp. Med.*, **39**, 347 ; (1924b) *Ibid.*, **39**, 357 ; (1924c) *Ibid.*, **39**, 543.
AVERY, R. C. (1929a) *J. exp. Med.*, **50**, 463 ; (1929b) *Ibid.*, **50**, 787.
AVERY, R. C. and CULLEN, G. E. (1919) *J. exp. Med.*, **29**, 215 ; (1923) *Ibid.*, **38**, 199.
AYERS, S. H. and JOHNSON, W. T. (1910) *Bull. U.S. Dep. Agric.*, B.A.I., 126 ; (1913) *Ibid.*, 161 ; (1924) *J. infect. Dis.*, **34**, 49.
AYERS, S. H., JOHNSON, W. T., and DAVIS, B. J. (1918) *J. infect. Dis.*, **23**, 290.
AYERS, S. H., JOHNSON, W. T., and MUDGE, C. S. (1924) *J. infect. Dis.*, **34**, 29.
AYERS, S. H. and MUDGE, C. S. (1922) *J. infect. Dis.*, **31**, 40 ; (1923) *Ibid.*, **33**, 155.
AYERS, S. H. and RUPP, P. (1922) *J. infect. Dis.*, **30**, 388.
AYERS, S. H., RUPP, P., and MUDGE, C. S. (1921) *J. infect. Dis.*, **29**, 235.
BAGGER, S. V. (1926) *J. Path. Bact.*, **29**, 225.
BAEHR, J. (1910) *Arch. Hyg.*, **72**, 91.
BECKLER, E. and MACLEOD, P. (1934) *J. clin. Invest.*, **13**, 901.
BELENKY, D. E. and POPOWA, N. N. (1929) *Zbl. Bakt.*, **113**, 22.
BERGER, E. and SILBERSTEIN, W. (1926) *Klin. Wschr.*, **5**, 2307.
BESREDKA, A. (1901) *Ann. Inst. Pasteur*, **15**, 880.
BINGOLD, K. (1921) *Virchows Arch.*, **232**, 22 ; (1932) *Dtsch. med. Wschr.*, **57**, 443.
BLISS, W. P. (1920) *Bull. Johns Hopk. Hosp.*, **31**, 173 ; (1922) *J. exp. Med.*, **36**, 575.
BRAUN, H. (1912) *Zbl. Bakt.*, **62**, 383.
BROADHURST, J. (1915) *J. infect. Dis.*, **17**, 277.
BROWN, J. H. (1919) *Monogr. Rockefeller Inst. med. Res.*, No. 9.
CAPPS, J. A. and DAVIS, D. J. (1914) *Arch. intern. Med.*, **14**, 650.
CHANNON, H. A. and McLEOD, J. W. (1929) *J. Path. Bact.*, **32**, 283.
COLE, R. (1914) *J. exp. Med.*, **20**, 346.
COLEBROOK, DORA C. (1935) *Spec. Rep. Ser. med. Res. Coun., Lond.*, No. 205.
COLEBROOK, L. (1930) *Brit. med. J.*, ii. 134.
COLEBROOK, L. and HARE, R. (1933) *J. Obstet. Gynaec.*, **40**, 609.
COLEBROOK, L., MAXTED, W. R., and JOHNS, A. M. (1935) *J. Path. Bact.*, **41**, 521.
COOPER, G., EDWARDS, M., and ROSENSTEIN, C. (1929) *J. exp. Med.*, **49**, 461.
COOPER, G., ROSENSTEIN, C., WALTER, A., and PEIZER, L. (1932) *J. exp. Med.*, **55**, 531.
COOPER, G. and WALTER, A. W. (1935) *Amer. J. publ. Hlth*, **25**, 469.

COWAN, S. T. (1934) *J. Path. Bact.*, **38**, 61.
DAVIS, D. J. (1912) *J. Amer. med. Ass.*, **58**, 1852 ; (1929) *Ibid.*, **93**, 978.
DAVIS, D. J. and ROSENOW, E. C. (1912) *J. Amer. med. Ass.*, **58**, 773.
DIBLE, J. H. (1921) *J. Path. Bact.*, **24**, 3.
DICK, G. F. and DICK, G. H. (1924a) *J. Amer. med. Ass.*, **82**, 265 ; (1924b) *Ibid.*, **83**, 84 ; (1925a) *Ibid.*, **84**, 802 ; (1925b) *Ibid.*, **84**, 1477.
DIERNHOFER, K. (1928) *Zbl. Bakt.*, **108**, 280 ; (1930) *Arch. Tierheilk.*, **61**, 181 ; (1932a) *Milchw. Forsch.*, **13**, 368 ; (1932b) *Z. InfektKr. Haustiere*, **42**, 17.
DOCHEZ, A. R. and AVERY, O. T. (1915) *J. exp. Med.*, **21**, 114.
DOCHEZ, A. R., AVERY, O. T., and LANCEFIELD, R. C. (1919) *J. exp. Med.*, **30**, 159.
DOCHEZ, A. R. and GILLESPIE, L. P. (1913) *J. Amer. med. Ass.*, **61**, 727.
DOWNIE, A. W. and CRUICKSHANK, R. (1928) *Brit. J. exp. Path.*, **9**, 171.
DOWNIE, A. W., STENT, L., and WHITE, S. M. (1931) *Brit. J. exp. Path.*, **12**, 1.
DURAN-REYNALS, F. (1933) *J. exp. Med.*, **58**, 161.
EAGLES, G. H. (1924) *Brit. J. exp. Path.*, **5**, 199.
EDWARDS, P. R. (1932) *J. Bact.*, **23**, 259 ; (1933) *Ibid.*, **25**, 527 ; (1934) *Ibid.*, **27**, 527.
EDWARDS, S. J. (1932) *J. comp. Path.*, **45**, 43.
EHRISMANN, O., HARTMANN, P., SEEFRIED, J., and WIECHERT, F. (1935) *Z. Hyg. InfektKr.*, **117**, 307.
ENDERS, J. F. (1930) *J. exp. Med.*, **52**, 235.
ETINGER-TULCZYNSKA, R. (1932) *Z. Hyg. InfektKr.*, **114**, 769.
EVANS, A. C. (1931) *Publ. Hlth Rep., Wash.*, **46**, 2539.
FALK, I. S. and YANG, S. Y. (1926) *J. infect. Dis.*, **38**, 1.
FEHLEISEN. (1883) "Aetiologie des Erysipels." Berlin.
FLOYD, C. and WOLBACH, S. B. (1914) *J. med. Res.*, **29**, 493.
FRAENKEL, A. (1886) *Z. klin. Med.*, **10**, 401 ; (1886) *Ibid.*, **11**, 437.
FREUDENREICH, E. VON. (1897) *Zbl. Bakt.*, IIte Abt., **3**, 47.
FROST, W. D., GUMM, M., and THOMAS, R. C. (1927) *J. infect. Dis.*, **40**, 698.
FRY, R. M. (1933) *J. Path. Bact.*, **37**, 337.
FULLER, C. A. and ARMSTRONG, V. A. (1913) *J. infect. Dis.*, **13**, 442.
GARNER, R. L. and TILLETT, W. S. (1934) *J. exp. Med.*, **60**, 239.
GAY, F. P. and ORAM, F. (1933) *J. Immunol.*, **25**, 501.
GOODNER, K. (1931) *J. exp. med.*, **54**, 847 ; (1933) *Ibid.*, **58**, 153.
GORDON, M. H. (1902–3) *Rep. loc. Govt Bd publ. Hlth*, **32**, 421 ; (1903–4) *Ibid.*, **33**, 388, 422 ; (1905) *Lancet*, ii. 1400 ; (1921) *Brit. med. J.*, i. 632.
GRIFFITH, F. (1923) *Rep. publ. Hlth med. Subj., Lond.*, No. 18 ; (1926) *J. Hyg., Camb.*, **25**, 385 ; (1927) *Ibid.*, **26**, 363 ; (1928) *Ibid.*, **27**, 113 ; (1934) *Ibid.*, **34**, 542 ; (1935) *Ibid.*, **35**, 532.
GUNDEL, M. and SCHWARZ, F. K. T. (1932) *Z. Hyg. InfektKr.*, **113**, 498.
GUNN, W. and GRIFFITH, F. (1928) *J. Hyg., Camb.*, **28**, 250.
GÜNTHER, C. and THIERFELDER, H. (1895) *Arch. Hyg.*, **25**, 164.
HANSEN, P. A., HUCKER, G. J., and SNYDER, M. A. (1933) *Amer. J. publ. Hlth*, **23**, 1262.
HARE, R. (1935) *J. Path. Bact.*, **41**, 499.
HARE, R. and COLEBROOK, L. (1934) *J. Path. Bact.*, **39**, 429.
HARE, R. and MAXTED, W. R. (1935) *J. Path. Bact.*, **41**, 513.
HARRIS, J. W. and BROWN, J. H. (1929) *Bull. Johns Hopk. Hosp.*, **44**, 1.
HART, P. D'A. and ANDERSON, A. B. (1933) *J. Path. Bact.*, **37**, 91.
HARTLEY, P. (1928) *Brit. J. exp. Path.*, **9**, 259.
HASENKNOPF and SALGE. (1903) *Jb. Kinderheilk.*, **58**, 218.
HAUPT, H. (1931) *Zbl. Bakt.*, **120**, 291 ; (1933) *Ibid.*, **130**, 53.
HEIDELBERGER, M. (1927) *Physiol. Rev.*, **7**, 107.
HEIDELBERGER, M. and AVERY, O. T. (1923) *J. exp. Med.*, **38**, 73 ; (1924) *Ibid.*, **40**, 301.
HEIDELBERGER, M. and GOEBEL, W. F. (1927) *J. biol. Chem.*, **74**, 613.
HEIDELBERGER, M., GOEBEL, W. F., and AVERY, O. T. (1925) *J. exp. Med.*, **42**, 727.
HEIDELBERGER, M. and KENDALL, F. E. (1931) *J. exp. Med.*, **53**, 625.
HEINEMANN, P. G. (1906) *J. infect. Dis.*, **3**, 173.
HOLMAN, W. L. (1916) *J. med. Res.*, **34**, 377.
HOPKINS, J. G. and LANG, A. (1914) *J. infect. Dis.*, **15**, 63.
HOUSTON, T. and McCLOY, J. M. (1916) *Lancet*, ii. 632.
JAMES, G. R. (1926) *J. Hyg., Camb.*, **25**, 415.
JONES, F. S. (1918) *J. exp. Med.*, **28**, 149, 243 ; (1919) *Ibid.*, **30**, 159.
JONES, F. S. and LITTLE, R. B. (1928) *J. exp. Med.*, **47**, 945, 957.
JULIANELLE, L. A. and REIMANN, H. A. (1926) *J. exp. Med.*, **43**, 87.
KISSLING, K. (1924) *Münch. med. Wschr.*, **71**, 1457 ; (1929) *Ibid.*, **76**, 1163.
KITT. (1893) see Minett (1935b).
KLECKNER, A. L. (1935) *J. Lab. clin. Med.*, **21**, 111.
KLEIN, S. J. (1933) *J. Bact.*, **26**, 215 ; (1935) *Ibid.*, **30**, 43.

KLEIN, S. J. and STONE, F. M. (1931) *J. Bact.*, **22**, 387.
KLIMMER, M. and HAUPT, H. (1930) *Ergebn. Hyg.*, **11**, 354.
KLIMMER, M., HAUPT, H., and ROOTS, E. (1928) *Zbl. Bakt.*, **107**, 206.
KOBLMÜLLER, L. O. (1935) *Zbl. Bakt.*, **133**, 310.
KOCH, F. E. (1935) *Zbl. Bakt.*, **134**, 348.
KRÖNIG. (1895) *Zbl. Gynäk.*, **19**, 409.
KRUIF, P. H. DE and IRELAND, P. M. (1920) *J. infect. Dis.*, **26**, 285.
LANCEFIELD, R. C. (1928) *J. exp. Med.*, **47**, 91, 469, 481, 843, 857 ; (1933) *Ibid.*, **57**, 571 ; (1934) *Ibid.*, **59**, 441.
LANCEFIELD, R. C. and HARE, R. (1935) *J. exp. Med.*, **61**, 335.
LANCEFIELD, R. C. and TODD, E. W. (1928) *J. exp. Med.*, **48**, 769.
LEHMANN, W. (1926) *Münch. med. Wschr.*, **73**, 233.
LISTER, F. S. (1916) *Publ. S. Afr. Inst. med. Res.*, No. 8.
LOGAN, W. R. (1914) *J. Path. Bact.*, **18**, 527.
LOGAN, W. R. and SMEALL, J. T. (1932) *Brit. med. J.*, i. 189.
LONG, P. H. and BLISS, E. A. (1934) *J. exp. Med.*, **60**, 619.
LOWKEWICZ, X. (1901) *Arch. med. Exp.*, **13**, 633.
LYALL, H. W. (1914) *J. med. Res.*, **30**, 487.
McLACHLAN, D. G. S. and MACKIE, T. J. (1928) *J. Hyg., Camb.*, **27**, 225.
McLEOD, J. W. (1912) *J. Path. Bact.*, **16**, 321.
McLEOD, J. W. and GORDON, J. (1922) *Biochem. J.*, **16**, 499.
McLEOD, J. W. and McNEE, J. W. (1913) *J. Path. Bact.*, **17**, 524.
MAIR, W. (1917) *J. Path. Bact.*, **21**, 305 ; (1928) *Ibid.*, **31**, 215 ; (1929) " A System of Bacteriology," *Med. Res. Coun.*, London, **2**, 168.
MANDELBAUM, M. (1907) *Z. Hyg. InfektKr.*, **58**, 26.
MARMOREK, A. (1895) *Ann. Inst. Pasteur*, **9**, 593.
MARWEDEL and WEHRSIG. (1915) *Münch. med. Wschr.*, **62**, 1023.
MEADER, P. D. and ROBINSON, G. H. (1920) *J. exp. Med.*, **32**, 639.
MEYER. (1902) *Dtsch. med. Wschr.*, **28**, 751.
MEYER, K. (1926) *Zbl. Bakt.*, **99**, 416.
MEYER, K. and SCHÖNFELD, H. (1926) *Zbl. Bakt.*, **99**, 402.
MINETT, F. C. (1935a) *J. Path. Bact.*, **40**, 357 ; (1935b) *Proc. Twelfth Int. Vet. Cong.*, p. 511.
MINETT, F. C. and STABLEFORTH, A. W. (1931) *J. comp. Path.*, **44**, 114 ; (1934) *J. Dairy Res.*, **5**, 223.
MINETT, F. C., STABLEFORTH, A. W., and EDWARDS, S. J. (1929) *J. comp. Path.*, **42**, 213 ; (1932) *Ibid.*, **45**, 1.
MORGAN, H. J. and AVERY, O. T. (1924) *J. exp. Med.*, **39**, 335.
MORGAN, H. J. and NEILL, J. M. (1924) *J. exp. Med.*, **40**, 269.
MOSER and PIRQUET. (1902) *Wien. klin. Wschr.*, **15**, 1086.
NAKAYAMA, Y. (1920) *J. infect. Dis.*, **27**, 86.
NATVIG, H. (1905) *Arch. Gynäk.*, **76**, 701.
NEILL, J. M. (1925) *J. exp. Med.*, **41**, 299, 535 ; (1926) *Ibid.*, **44**, 199.
NEILL, J. M. and AVERY, O. T. (1924a) *J. exp. Med.*, **39**, 757 ; (1924b) *Ibid.*, **40**, 405, 423 ; (1925) *Ibid.*, **41**, 285.
NEILL, J. M. and MALLORY, T. B. (1926) *J. exp. Med.*, **44**, 241.
NEISSER, M. and WECHSBERG, F. (1900) *Münch. med. Wschr.*, **47**, 1261 ; (1901) *Z. Hyg. InfektKr.*, **36**, 299.
NEUFELD, F. (1900) *Z. Hyg. InfektKr.*, **34**, 454 ; (1902) *Ibid.*, **40**, 54 ; (1903) *Ibid.*, **44**, 161.
NEUFELD, F. and ETINGER-TULCZYNSKA, R. (1931) *Z. Hyg. InfektKr.*, **112**, 492.
NEUFELD, F. and HÄNDEL, L. (1909) *Arb. ReichsgesundhAmt.*, **34**, 293.
NICOLLE, M. and ADIL-BEY. (1907) *Ann. Inst. Pasteur*, **21**, 20.
NOCARD and MOLLEREAU. (1887) *Ann. Inst. Pasteur*, **1**, 109.
OGURA, K. (1929) *J. Jap. Soc. vet. Sci.*, **8**, 174.
ORAM, F. (1934) *J. Immunol.*, **26**, 233.
PASTEUR, L., CHAMBERLAND, C., and ROUX, E. (1881) *C. R. Acad. Sci.*, **92**, 159.
PITTMAN, M. and FALK, I. S. (1930) *J. Bact.*, **19**, 327.
PLASTRIDGE, W. N. and ANDERSON, E. O. (1933) *Storrs agric. Exp. Sta. Bull.*, No. 184.
PLASTRIDGE, W. N., ANDERSON, E. O., BRIGHAM, G. D., and SPAULDING. E. H. (1934) *Storrs agric. Exp. Sta. Bull.*, No. 195.
PLUMMER, H. (1935) *J. Bact.*, **30**, 5.
POWNALL, M. (1935) *Brit. J. exp. Path.*, **16**, 155.
PRÉVOT, A. (1924) " Les Streptocoques Anaerobes," Paris ; (1925) *Ann. Inst. Pasteur*, **39**, 417 ; (1933) *Ann. Sci. Nat. (Séries Botaniques)*, **15**, 163.
PROSCHOLDT, O. (1928) *Arch. Tierheilk.*, **58**, 485 ; (1933) *Landw. Jb.*, **78**, 389.
PULVERTAFT, R. J. V. (1928) *Brit. J. exp. Path.*, **9**, 276.
REIMANN, H. A. (1927) *J. exp. Med.*, **45**, 807.
REIMANN, H. A. and JULIANELLE, L. A. (1926) *J. exp. Med.*, **43**, 97.

Rist, E. (1901) *Zbl. Bakt.*, **30**, 287.

Rochaix, A. (1924) *C. R. Soc. Biol.*, **90**, 771.

Rosell, J. M. (1931) *Cornell Vet.*, **21**, 317.

Rosenbach, F. J. (1884) "Mikroorganismen bei den Wundinfektionskrankheiten." Wiesbaden.

Rosowsky, A. (1912) *Zbl. Gynäk.*, **36**, 4.

Rossiwall, E. and Schick, B. (1905) *Wien. klin. Wschr.*, **18**, 3.

Rother, W. (1925) *Dtsch. med. Wschr.*, **51**, 1031.

Ruediger, G. F. (1912) *Science*, **35**, 223.

Sabin, A. B. (1933) *J. Amer. med. Ass.*, **100**, 1584.

Schnabel, A. (1921) *Z. Hyg. InfektKr.*, **93**, 175.

Schottmüller, H. (1903) *Münch. med. Wschr.*, **50**, 849, 909 ; (1910) *Mitt. Grenzgeb. med. Chir.*, **21**, 450 ; (1928) *Münch. med. Wschr.*, **75**, 1580, 1634.

Schütz, W. (1888) *Arch. wiss. prakt. Tierheilk.*, **14**, 456.

Seastone, C. V. (1934) *J. Bact.*, **28**, 481.

Seelemann, M. (1932) "Die Streptokokkeninfektionen des Euters." M. & H. Schaper, Hanover ; (1933a) *Dtsch. tierärztl. Wschr.*, **41**, 337 ; (1933b) *Arch. Tierheilk.*, **66**, 168.

Seelemann, M. and Hadenfeldt, A. (1930) *Zbl. Bakt.*, **118**, 331 ; (1932) *Ibid.*, **126**, 231 ; (1933a) *Dtsch. tierärztl. Wschr.*, **41**, 533 ; (1933b) *Z. Fleisch- u. Milchhyg.*, **44**, 25.

Seelemann, M. and Siemonsen. (1933) *Arch. Tierheilk.*, **67**, 10.

Sherman, J. M. (1921) *J. Bact.*, **6**, 127.

Sherman, J. M. and Albus, W. R. (1918) *J. Bact.*, **3**, 153.

Sherman, J. M. and Stark, P. (1931) *J. Bact.*, **22**, 275 ; (1934) *J. Dairy Sci.*, **17**, 525.

Sickles, G. M. and Coffey, J. M. (1928) *J. infect. Dis.*, **43**, 490.

Silberschmidt, W. (1902) *Z. Hyg. InfektKr.*, **41**, 427.

Smith, J. (1926) *J. Hyg., Camb.*, **25**, 165 ; (1927) *Ibid.*, **26**, 420 ; (1929) *J. Path. Bact.*, **32**, 401.

Smith, T. and Brown, J. H. (1915) *J. med. Res.*, **31**, 455.

Soule, S. D. and Brown, T. K. (1932) *Amer. J. Obstet. Gynaec.*, **23**, 532.

Stableforth, A. W. (1932) *J. comp. Path.*, **45**, 185.

Stark, P. and Sherman, J. M. (1935) *J. Bact.*, **30**, 639.

Sternberg. (1900) *Wien. klin. Wschr.*, **13**, 551.

Stevens, F. A. and Dochez, A. R. (1926a) *J. exp. Med.*, **43**, 379 ; (1926b) *Ibid.*, **44**, 439.

Stokes, W. R. and Hachtel, F. W. (1912) *Publ. Hlth Rep., Wash.*, Nov. 22.

Takeda, K. (1935) *Z. ImmunForsch.*, **86**, 341.

Thalmann. (1912) *Zbl. Bakt.*, **66**, 240.

Thiercelin. (1899) *C. R. Soc. Biol.*, **5**, 269.

Tillett, W. S. (1927) *J. exp. Med.*, **45**, 1093 ; (1935) *J. Bact.*, **29**, 111.

Tillett, W. S., Edwards, L. B., and Garner, R. L. (1934) *J. clin. Invest.*, **13**, 47.

Tillett, W. S. and Garner, R. L. (1933) *J. exp. Med.*, **58**, 485.

Tillett, W. S., Goebel, W. F., and Avery, O. T. (1930) *J. exp. Med.*, **52**, 95.

Todd, E. W. (1928a) *Brit. J. exp. Path.*, **9**, 1 ; (1928b) *J. exp. Med.*, **48**, 493 ; (1930) *Brit. J. exp. Path.*, **11**, 368, 469, 480 ; (1932a) *J. exp. Med.*, **55**, 267 ; (1932b) *Brit. J. exp. Path.*, **13**, 248 ; (1934) *J. Path. Bact.*, **39**, 299.

Todd, E. W. and Hewitt, L. F. (1932) *J. Path. Bact.*, **35**, 973.

Todd, E. W. and Lancefield, R. C. (1928) *J. exp. Med.*, **48**, 751.

Todd, E. W., Laurent, L. J. M., and Hill, N. G. (1933) *J. Path. Bact.*, **36**, 201.

Veillon, M. A. (1893) *C. R. Soc. Biol.*, **40**, 807.

Van der Velde, H. (1894) *La Cellule*, **10**, 401.

Wadsworth, A. and Brown, R. (1931) *J. Immunol.*, **21**, 245.

Weatherall, C. and Dible, J. H. (1929) *J. Path. Bact.*, **32**, 413.

Wegelius, W. (1909) *Arch. Gynaek.*, **88**, 249.

Weichselbaum, A. (1886) *Med. Jb.*, i. 483.

Weissenbach, R. J. (1918) *C. R. Soc. Biol.*, **81**, 559, 819.

Weld, J. T. (1934) *J. exp. med.*, **59**, 83 ; (1935) *Ibid.*, **61**, 473.

White, E. (1933) *J. Obstet. Gynaec.*, **40**, 630.

White, S. M. (1929) *Biochem. J.*, **23**, 1165.

Winslow, C.-E. A., Broadhurst, J., Buchanan, R. E., Krumwiede, C., Rogers, L. A., and Smith, G. H. (1920) *J. Bact.*, **5**, 191.

Winslow, C.-E. A. and Palmer, G. T. (1910) *J. infect. Dis.*, **7**, 1.

CHAPTER XXIV

STAPHYLOCOCCUS, MICROCOCCUS, SARCINA, RHODOCOCCUS, AND LEUCONOSTOC

STAPHYLOCOCCUS

DEFINITION.—*Staphylococcus*.

Spherical or ovoid, non-motile, Gram-positive cells, arranged in grape-like clusters on solid media, and in pairs, small groups, or short chains in liquid media. On agar the growth is of a golden, white, or yellow colour. Great variation in biochemical activities, hæmolytic power, and pathogenicity. Actual or potential parasites.

Type species is *Staphylococcus aureus* Rosenbach.

HISTORY.—The presence of micrococci in pus was noted by Koch in 1878 ; they were cultivated in a liquid medium by Pasteur in 1880 ; they were shown by Ogston in 1881 to be constantly present in acute and chronic abscesses ; they were cultivated by him in eggs, and were found to be pathogenic to mice and guinea-pigs ; but it was left to Rosenbach in 1884 to make a thorough study of the *Staphylococci*, to obtain pure cultures on solid media, and to divide them into two species—*Staphylococcus pyogenes aureus* and *Staphylococcus pyogenes albus*. In the following year Passet (1885) added another species—*Staphylococcus pyogenes citreus*. In 1887 Biondi isolated two types from saliva, both pathogenic for laboratory animals ; one of these was apparently identical with an organism described as *M. tetragenus* by Koch and Gaffky (Gaffky 1883), who had found it in the sputum of patients suffering from pulmonary tuberculosis ; the other was distinguished from *Staphylococcus aureus* by its diminutive size—0·3–0·5 μ in diameter—and the slowness with which it liquefied gelatin ; to this he gave the name of *Staphylococcus salivarius pyogenes*. Welch (1891) noticed a white staphylococcus in stitch abscesses following the suturing of operation wounds ; this he called the *Staphylococcus epidermidis albus*. Andrewes and Gordon (1905–6), who investigated a large number of cocci from different sources, found a special type commonly present in saliva which they named the *Staphylococcus salivarius* ; this differed in many respects from the *Staphylococcus salivarius pyogenes* of Biondi ; they also found a coccus of peculiar characteristics present in scurf, but did not identify it by a special name. Winslow and Rogers (1906), in an attempt to arrive at a classification on a statistical basis, conducted a painstaking investigation into the *Coccaceæ*, and proposed a division into six genera, from which the original genus *Staphylococcus* was omitted. Later, however, Winslow, Rothberg and Parsons (1920) modified this classification, and reinstated the *Staphylococcus* in its old place, dividing the genus into six species.

Ecology.—There are but few situations from which staphylococci may not be isolated. In the animal body they are normally found on the skin, in saliva, in the intestinal contents, and in fæces ; they are frequently isolated from suppurative processes (see Pathogenicity) ; and they are present in varying numbers in air, water, milk, sewage, and on all articles liable to come in contact with these substances. Ubiquitous as they are, however, it would appear that their natural habitat is the animal body, and that it is the animal body which furnishes the main supply to the outside world.

Morphology.—The *Staphylococci* consist of round or somewhat oval cells, having an average diameter of 0·8–1·0 μ. The size is variable, not only from one species to another, but in members of the same species ; it depends partly on the age of the culture and the nature of the medium on which it is grown. Some species are generally smaller than others ; thus the average diameter of *Staphylococcus aureus* is 0·7–0·9 μ, whereas the salivary staphylococci are said to be larger, 1·0–1·2 μ. All the members of the group are non-motile, non-flagellated, non-capsulated, and non-sporing.

The true staphylococci are arranged in grape-like clusters, that is to say they form groups, the members of which are disposed in three planes of space without regard to any definite configuration. This distribution is best appreciated when a hanging drop preparation is examined—especially if a stereoscopic microscope is employed. The characteristic grouping into clusters is more evident on solid than in liquid media. Indeed in broth it is common to find the cocci occurring, not only in groups, but in pairs and in short chains ; they are then liable to be mistaken for streptococci. This confusion may be accentuated owing to the fact that streptococci on solid media tend to lose their capacity for forming chains, and may develop in small clusters. The differentiation between these two types morphologically, therefore, is not always easy ; on a single medium alone it may be impossible, but if the appearance of the coccus is studied in both liquid and solid media, not much difficulty will be experienced. The differential points are (1) that the chains formed by staphylococci rarely contain more than four members and (2) that the clusters formed by streptococci generally consist of aggregations of chains ; the chain is the fundamental unit of the streptococcus.

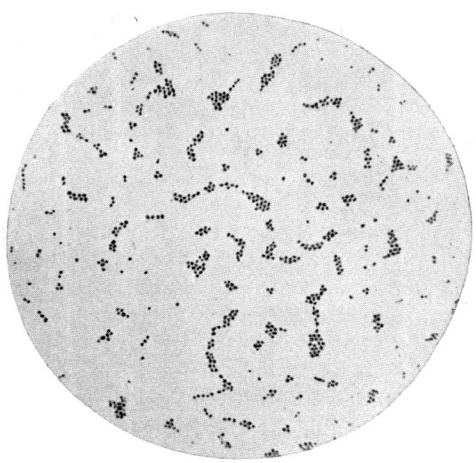

Fig. 107.—*Staphylococcus aureus.*
From an agar culture, 24 hours, 37° C. ($\times$ 1000).

Staining Reactions.—The *Staphylococci* stain well with most of the aniline dyes, and are uniformly Gram-positive. It is not uncommon, however, to see them described as being sometimes negative. Winslow, Rothberg and Parsons (1920), in a study of 180 strains, encountered 5 Gram-negative strains, and the same authors make the generalization that, whereas the orange and white cocci are

Gram-positive, the yellow and red ones, including the *Sarcinæ*, are Gram-negative. This discrepancy can be explained by the facts, firstly that different types of staphylococci do vary in their resistance to decolorization, and secondly that many strains which are Gram-positive in an 18 or 24 hours' culture become Gram-negative as they grow older. To obtain uniformity, therefore, it is essential to use a young culture—never more than a day old—and not to prolong unduly the process of decolorization. If these precautions are taken, it will be found that almost without exception the staphylococci, at any rate on first isolation, as also the sarcinæ, react positively to Gram's stain.

Cultural Reactions.—The *Staphylococci* are among the easiest of micro-organisms to cultivate *in vitro*. Though some develop more slowly than others, particularly *Staphylococcus citreus*, they all give abundant growths.

In *nutrient broth* after 24 hours at 37° C. there is a moderate to dense turbidity, with a moderate deposit of a powdery nature, which, on shaking, swirls up and disappears completely, increasing the turbidity. This is the usual picture. But some types, the salivary staphylococci, for example, form a thick, weedy, glutinous deposit, leaving the supernatant fluid clear. After 2 days' incubation, a surface ring growth is generally present. In no case is there any distinctive pigment formation in fluid media.

On *nutrient agar*, there is produced within 1 to 2 days a moderately thick, raised, confluent growth, with a moist, glistening, smooth, or somewhat honey-combed surface—due to the imperfect fusion of individual colonies; in most cases it is of butyrous consistency and easy to emulsify, but in the case of the salivary staphylococci, it is glutinous, adherent to the medium, and more difficult to emulsify. Pigment production is most obvious on agar at 22° C.

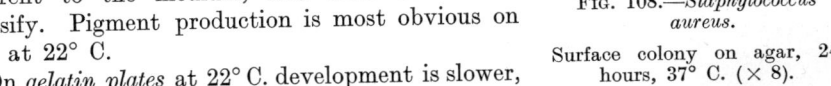

FIG. 108.—*Staphylococcus aureus.*

Surface colony on agar, 24 hours, 37° C. (× 8).

On *gelatin plates* at 22° C. development is slower, there being often no visible growth for 2 to 3 days; the colonies which are then formed are small and relatively unpigmented; later a zone of liquefaction may appear around them.

In *gelatin stab* cultures there is a filiform growth reaching to the bottom of the tube, and a surface growth of variable degree. Liquefaction may or may not occur; when it does, the usual type given by the white and golden cocci is infundibuliform or saccate, by the yellow cocci crateriform. The time of its appearance is likewise subject to a considerable amount of variation; it may be noticeable after 2 days, or it may be a fortnight or even longer before it becomes apparent. Speaking broadly, it may be said that the pyogenic staphylococci liquefy gelatin early, the saprophytic ones late.

On *potato* there is a moderate confluent growth. *Loeffler's serum* is a good nutritive medium, on which pigment is well developed. On *MacConkey's* neutral red lactose bile salt agar, the colonies are very small, pale pink after 24 hours, and deep pink after 48 hours.

Chapman and Berens (1935) state that, on proteose lactose agar containing a final concentration of 1–300,000 crystal violet, white colonies, violet colonies, or orange colonies with a violet fringe may be formed. As a rule, the strains giving rise to either of the latter two types of colony are hæmolytic, produce coagulase, and are toxic to rabbits on intravenous inoculation, while strains forming white colonies are negative in all these respects. If their results are confirmed, this medium may serve as a useful preliminary means of differentiating pathogenic from non-pathogenic strains of staphylococci.

Variant colonial types—including rough and G forms—have been described by Hoffstadt and Youmans (1932), Bigger, Boland, and O'Meara (1927), and Swingle (1935).

Metabolism.—The *Staphylococci* are facultative anaerobes, growing best in the presence of oxygen. On agar plates incubated anaerobically, the growth tends to spread out on the surface of the medium, so that the colonies instead of being convex, are flat and effuse. Lubinski (1894) was the first to point out that no pigment is produced under anaerobic conditions, though, if a culture which has been incubated anaerobically is exposed to the air, it soon develops its characteristic

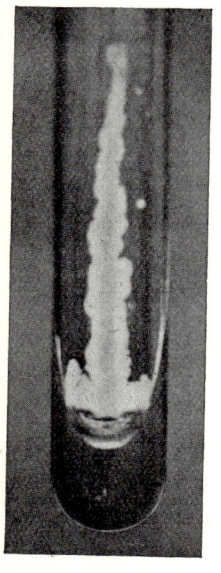

colour. He found, however, that continuous anaerobic cultivation generally caused a strain to lose its power of producing pigment—a power which was not regained by subsequent cultivation in the presence of oxygen.

The limits of temperature between which growth is possible are wide, varying from about 12° to 45° C., but as a rule development is most rapid at 37° C. A slightly alkaline medium of pH 7·4–7·6 is preferable for the initiation of growth, but some growth will occur even at pH 4·0–5·0. Growth is slightly increased by the addition of blood and glucose to the medium ; serum has no beneficial effect. According to Hucker (1924a), the staphylococci are unable to use ammonium salts as their sole source of nitrogen. Hughes (1932), and later Knight (1935), both of whom have studied the nutritive requirements of *Staph. aureus*, describe the existence of an essential growth factor. This substance (see Knight 1935) can be prepared in a concentrated form from marmite, and is a weak base yielding relatively soluble compounds with most base precipitants. Typical strains of *Staph. aureus* can grow aerobically on a medium composed of acid-hydrolysed gelatin plus tryptophan, tyrosine, cystine, and glucose, with the further addition of the essential growth substance. Later work has suggested that the substance separated from marmite is complex, consisting of two factors, one of which is a weak acid and the other a

FIG. 109. — *Staphylococcus aureus*.
Agar stroke culture, 24 hours, 37° C.

weak base. The second factor appears to be necessary for the proper growth of *B. anthracis*. As with many other organisms, no growth occurs in the complete absence of CO_2 (Gladstone *et al.* 1935).

Hewitt (1930) has shown that *Staph. aureus*, when grown in ordinary infusion broth, brings about a rapid fall in electrode potential to between Eh − 0·1 and − 0·2 volt. Owing to lack of peroxide formation the potential remains at a low level for a long time, showing no tendency to rise as it does with streptococci. In glucose broth the potential does not fall as low as in ordinary broth.

Pigment Production.—As already mentioned, the *Staphylococci* are active pigment producers. *Staphylococcus aureus* forms a golden, *Staphylococcus citreus* a lemon-yellow pigment, while cultures of *Staph. albus* are of a porcelain-white colour. The development of the pigment and its actual tint depend, however, on several factors. As in the case of many other organisms, the optimum temperature for pigment production does not coincide with the optimum temperature for growth ; more pigment is produced at 22° C. than at 37° C. ; if cultures that have been incubated at 37° C. are subsequently left at room temperature, the colour is seen to deepen. Gelatin and broth are unsuitable. Oxygen is requisite for its development ; under anaerobic conditions the growth is colourless. Carbon dioxide is said to favour its production, provided oxygen is also present (Lubinski 1894).

A very important point to remember is that a given strain of staphylococcus under conditions of artificial cultivation, may lose its power of producing pigment. The cause of this loss is unknown. It is most noticeable in the case of *Staphylococcus aureus*, which, when freshly isolated from the animal body, gives a rich golden pigment, but often loses this character on prolonged cultivation. This variation adds greatly to the difficulty of classification, and it must be emphasized that in the study of a particular strain, the property of pigment formation should be noted as soon after isolation as possible (Dudgeon 1908).

Gelatin Liquefaction.—There is a considerable amount of discrepancy in the reports of various authors as to the power of staphylococci to liquefy gelatin. Of 41 white strains examined by Gordon (1903–4), 24 liquefied gelatin. Kutscher and Konrich (1904) reported upon 57 strains of staphylococci, and found that all liquefied gelatin. Similarly with Klopstock and Bockenheimer (1904) who examined 30 strains, and with Fraenkel and Baumann (1905) who examined 36 strains. Dudgeon (1908) found that 44 out of 46 *aureus* strains and 35 out of 56 *albus* strains liquefied gelatin, while Winslow, Rothberg and Parsons (1920), in examining 180 strains, found that 67 per cent. of the *aureus* and 47 per cent. of the *albus* strains liquefied gelatin.

These discrepancies are to be explained partly by possible differences in the cocci examined and partly by the length of time during which growth was observed. There is general agreement that staphylococci isolated from pathological sources liquefy gelatin more frequently than those isolated from water, air, skin, etc.

There is likewise general agreement that the orange cocci are more rapid liquefiers than the white, and the white cocci more rapid than the yellow.

Summing up, it may be said that *Staphylococcus aureus* liquefies gelatin almost always, *Staphylococcus albus* frequently, and *Staphylococcus citreus* sometimes.

Resistance to Heat and Disinfectants.—The *Staphylococci* are among the more resistant of the non-sporing organisms. In broth or agar tubes sealed with paraffin and kept in the ice-chest, cultures may remain alive for months. Dried on threads they retain their vitality for 3 to 6 months, and from dried pus they have been cultivated after 2 to 3 months. Many of them are heat-resistant, in that they will withstand a temperature of 60° C. for half an hour. In pure culture they resist a concentration of 1 per cent. phenol for 15 minutes, but are killed by a concentration of 2 per cent. Mercuric chloride is a poor disinfectant for staphylococci ; to kill them in 10 minutes a 1 per cent. solution is required. Many of the aniline dyes exert a strongly bactericidal action on the staphylococci—as indeed they do on most Gram-positive organisms. This selective action is made use of in certain technical procedures, such as the isolation of *Br. abortus* from milk, where it is endeavoured by the incorporation of a dye—gentian violet or crystal violet—to inhibit the growth of Gram-positive organisms. Use is also made of the great susceptibility of staphylococci to the violet dyes in the isolation of streptococci, whose susceptibility to these dyes is very much less (see p. 115). Other dyes, of which malachite green appears to be the strongest and acid fuchsin the weakest, are also employed, usually in a concentration of about 1/10,000 (Oesterlin 1925).

Biochemical Reactions.—The ability of the *Staphylococci* to ferment sugars varies greatly according to the strain employed. For this reason it is not possible to classify them on this basis with anything like the same precision as, for example, the coliform group of bacilli. As a rule the golden cocci have the greatest fermentative power, the white are less active. There is a wealth of literature on the fermentative capacities of the staphylococci, with a corresponding difference of opinion amongst the various authors as to the importance of the different sugars. Thus, Andrewes and Gordon (1905–6) lay stress on the reactions in maltose, lactose, glycerol and mannitol. Winslow, Rothberg and Parsons (1920), on the other hand, come to the conclusion that the only sugar of differential value is lactose. Working with *Staphylococcus aureus* and *albus*, these authors found that 68 per cent. of the strains formed acid from glucose, 63 per cent. from maltose, 61 per cent. from sucrose, and 49 per cent. from lactose ; salicin, inulin and raffinose were rarely fermented, mannitol and dulcitol never. With these findings most authors disagree, particularly with regard to mannitol, which is generally held to be attacked by *Staphylococcus aureus*, and frequently by *Staphylococcus albus* (Dudgeon and Simpson 1928). It is quite clear, however, that it is impossible to dogmatize on the reactions of any one strain. Dudgeon (1908), who examined 121 *aureus* and *albus* strains on a large number of sugars, found that very few agreed in giving identical results.

Similarly with *litmus milk* the reactions are variable. Studying 180 *aureus* and *albus* strains, Winslow, Rothberg and Parsons (1920) found that 75 produced acid, clot and peptonization, 60 acid, generally clot, and no peptonization, 22 alkali and peptonization 16 alkali but no peptonization, while 7 produced no change. These findings are in agreement with those of other authors, except with regard to peptonization, which is less commonly reported.

The *methyl-red* test is generally positive with the *aureus* and *albus* strains, negative with the *citreus* strains. The *Voges-Proskauer* reaction is given by most strains of *Staphylococcus aureus*. According to Winslow, Rothberg, and Parsons (1920), most strains of staphylococci reduce nitrates to nitrites. Hucker (1924a), on the contrary, found that, though 49 out of 50 *aureus* strains reduced nitrates, only 23 out of 152 *albus* strains were able to do so. *Hydrogen sulphide* is stated by Andrewes and Gordon (1905–6) to be formed in small quantity by the pyogenic staphylococci, in greater quantity by *Staphylococcus albus*. We have been unable to confirm this. *Ammonia* is produced by 89 per cent. of the golden and white strains (Winslow et al. 1920). *Indole* is apparently never produced (Hucker 1924a).

Antigenic Structure.—Studying agglutination of *Staphylococci* by immune rabbits' sera, the early workers (Kolle and Otto 1902, Otto 1903, Pröscher 1903, Kutscher and Konrich 1904, Veiel 1904, Klopstock and Bockenheimer 1904, and Koch 1908) reported that they could be sharply divided into two types—the pathogenic and the saprophytic types. The great majority of strains isolated from purulent lesions in the human body were agglutinated by a serum prepared against one such strain, whereas the strains isolated from saprophytic sources were not agglutinated. The difference in titre to which agglutination occurred rather suggested that there might be one or more sub-groups within the main types. This suggestion was confirmed by later workers, who employed the more delicate test of absorption of agglutinins. Thus Julianelle (1922) found that the staphylococci could be divided into three types with two sub-groups, whereas Hine (1922), working with 81 strains, was able to classify them into two main types, each of which had at least three sub-groups. There was evidence to suggest that the pathogenic strains form a more homogeneous serological group than the saprophytic.

More recently Julianelle and Wieghard (1934, 1935), and Wieghard and Julianelle (1935), as the result of *chemical fractionation* of staphylococci, have isolated two polysaccharides each containing about 4 per cent. nitrogen, and differentiated from each other by optical rotation and by the type of sugar produced on hydrolysis. The first polysaccharide was extracted from pathogenic (A), the second from non-pathogenic (B), strains. The sera of rabbits that had been inoculated intraven-ously with whole cocci reacted specifically to a high titre with the polysac-charides when tested by the precipitation reaction. The polysaccharides were non-antigenic and non-toxic for rabbits and mice, but type A gave rise on intra-dermal inoculation of patients with staphylococcal infections to an immediate skin reaction of the " wheal and erythema " type. Besides the carbohydrates, a complex protein substance was isolated from both pathogenic and non-pathogenic strains of staphylococci. This protein, though non-toxic to rabbits and mice, was antigenic, giving rise to precipitins that reacted, however, only with the protein and not with the polysaccharide substances. On intradermal inoculation into susceptible patients the protein evoked a skin reaction of the delayed inflammatory type. Serological observations showed that the protein was responsible for the species-specificity of staphylococci, while the type-specificity was determined by the soluble specific carbohydrate substances. For the differentiation of pathogenic from non-pathogenic strains it was essential to employ the precipitation reaction, using as an antigen either the extracted polysaccharide, the supernatant fluid of centrifuged young broth cultures, or an acid extract of the sedimented organisms. The aggluti-nation reaction was affected by the group protein, and was unfitted for type differentiation.

Toxin Production.—When grown under suitable conditions, certain strains of staphylococci give rise to a filtrable toxin having a series of effects which, though described a long time ago by such workers as van de Velde (1894), Denys and Havet (1898), von Lingelsheim (1899), Kraus and Clairmont (1900), and Neisser and Wechsberg (1901), have received intensive study during recent years. This activity followed largely on the reinvestigation of the problem by Parker in 1924. A toxic filtrate is hæmolytic, especially towards rabbit cells; it has a destructive action on leucocytes; when injected intradermally into the skin of the rabbit or the guinea-pig it gives rise to necrosis; and when injected intravenously into the rabbit it causes acute and fatal toxæmia.

Toxin formation is a property of pathogenic strains and is therefore limited mainly to the *aureus* type. Considerable variation exists between different strains, and if toxin is required on a large scale for immunological or other purposes it is important to select a strain with a high toxigenic capacity. Various methods are used in the production of the toxin. In a fluid medium it develops rather slowly. Thus Neisser and Wechsberg (1901), by testing broth cultures filtered at intervals, found that the toxin, as judged by the hæmolytic titre, was first demonstrable on the 4th day of incubation at 37° C., and that it rose to a maximum between the 10th and 14th days, after which it gradually diminished. Burnet's (1930) technique of growing the organisms on 0·8 per cent. nutrient agar for 24 hours in air containing 10–20 per cent. CO_2, and extracting the toxin from the agar with saline, is very satisfactory, and is widely used, either in its original or a slightly modified form (Parish and Clark 1932, Dolman 1932a). The medium used should have a re-action of between pH 6·0 and 7·0 (Walbum 1922). Though the toxin can traverse a Seitz filter, some of its activity is lost in passage, and it is therefore advisable to separate the organisms from the toxin by centrifugation. A good toxin should hæmolyse a 1 per cent. suspension of rabbit cells in a dose of 0·0005–0·002 c.c. ; 0·001–0·005 c.c. should cause necrosis on intradermal inoculation, and 0·25–0·8 c.c. per kilo injected intravenously should kill a rabbit within a few minutes (Burnet 1929, Grosz 1931c, Parish and Clark 1932).

Whether the various activities of a toxic filtrate are due to one and the same toxin, or to a number of different toxins, is a question still under dispute. The fact that (1) in different batches of toxin there appears to be a fairly constant relationship between the hæmolytic, the necrotic, and the lethal powers of the toxin, (2) all manifestations of toxicity are abolished by exposure to a temperature of 56° C. for half an hour, and (3) an antiserum prepared against any given toxin seems to have a specific neutralizing effect against all manifestations of the toxin, has led many workers to conclude that only one toxin is produced (Burnet 1929, Grosz 1931c, Gengou 1932). On the other hand there are a number of more recent findings that point in the opposite direction. The work of Bigger (1933) and Glenny and Stevens (1935) suggests that there are at least two hæmolysins : one, an α-lysin acting on both sheep and rabbit cells and causing lysis rapidly at 37° C. ; the other a β-lysin acting on sheep but not on rabbit cells, and causing lysis only after the tubes have stood at room temperature overnight—the so-called " hot-cold " lysis. Dolman (1932b) has failed to find any parallelism between the hæmolytic titres of a series of different filtrates against red cell suspensions of different laboratory animals, and therefore postulates the existence of a multiplicity of hæmolysins. Panton and Valentine (1932) find a close relation in different toxic filtrates between the hæmo-lysin and the necrotoxin, but no relation between these and the leucocidin. Their findings in this respect, however, differ from the earlier observations of von Lingel-sheim (1899). According to Burky (1933), the lethal toxin is formed anaerobically or in a synthetic medium, while hæmolysin production is markedly inhibited under these conditions. The probability is that the toxin is complex, but that the α-hæmolysin, the necrotoxin, and the lethal toxin are all closely associated.[1]

Immunologically, the toxin gives rise on inoculation into rabbits to an antitoxin that combines with it according to the law of multiple proportions. This anti-toxin can be titrated by determining its antihæmolytic power (see Chapter LXIV). A typical toxin-antitoxin flocculation reaction may be observed (Burnet 1931). Treatment of the toxin with 0·2–0·5 per cent. formol at 37° C. leads in the course of a few days to a disappearance of the hæmolytic and toxic properties, but has little effect on its flocculating capacity. Toxoid so prepared is antigenic, and is now being used extensively as a vaccine (see Chapter LXIV).

Besides the toxic manifestations that have just been considered, certain strains of staphylococci, when grown under suitable conditions, give rise to a so-called enterotoxin. This substance has an intensely irritating effect on the gastro-

---

[1] According to Wright (1936) the leucocidin tested by the Neisser-Wechsberg technique (see p. 458) is different from that tested by the microscopic method of Panton and Valentine. The former appears to be identical with the α-hæmolysin.

intestinal mucosa of human beings, and to a less extent of monkeys, and has been responsible for a number of outbreaks of food poisoning (see Chap. LXIX). The enterotoxin is filtrable and is heat resistant, not being completely destroyed even after exposure to 100° C. for 30 minutes. There seems little doubt that the enterotoxin is distinct from the hæmolytic, necrotizing, and lethal toxins. The factors governing its formation are imperfectly understood, though the nature of the nutrient medium appears to be of prime importance (Jordan and Burrows 1935).

Staphylocoagulase.—The ability of certain staphylococci to coagulate citrated or oxalated rabbit plasma was first described by Much (1908), and has since been studied by a number of other workers (Darányi v. 1926, Gross 1931*a,b*, Stephan 1934, Vanbreuseghem 1934, Chapman *et al.* 1934, Walston 1935). For its demonstration a loopful of a 24-hour culture on a solid medium is mixed with 0·5 c.c. of citrated plasma and incubated for 3 hours at 37° C. The coagulase seems to be formed mainly by pathogenic strains, especially those of the *aureus* type. Most strains producing coagulase are also hæmolytic, but it is doubtful whether the coagulating and the hæmolytic activities are due to the same substance. According to Vanbreuseghem (1934), the hæmolysin is destroyed in half an hour by exposure to a temperature of 56° C., while the coagulase withstands heating to 100° C. ; Chamberland candles allow the hæmolysin to pass through, but not the coagulase ; the hæmolysin is adsorbed by red corpuscles, the coagulase is not. Gross (1931*a*) failed to obtain an antiserum in rabbits capable of neutralizing the coagulase. Birch-Hirschfeld (1934) maintains that the ability of staphylococci to coagulate plasma runs strictly parallel to the ability of plasma to agglutinate staphylococci.

It may be noted here that extracts prepared from certain strains of staphylococci contain a substance which increases the permeability of the skin to invasion by staphylococci and other organisms. This so-called *spreading factor*, which has been described by Duran-Reynals (1933, 1935), is similar in its effect to the substance contained in testicular extracts.

Pathogenicity.—The *Staphylococci* can be fairly sharply divided into pathogenic and non-pathogenic types. Thus the great majority of strains isolated from suppurative lesions in the animal body are found to be pathogenic for rabbits, and to a less extent for mice and guinea-pigs. On the other hand, the great majority of strains isolated from normal skin, air, water, dust, etc., are harmless to these animals. Sometimes the virulence of the pathogenic strains diminishes on prolonged cultivation, but this is not always so ; even after years of subculture in the laboratory the virulence may remain intact. Moreover, by passage through rabbits, it is generally possible to raise the virulence of a strain which has become temporarily avirulent ; with the saprophytic strains this is impossible. According to Lubinski (1894) the virulence of *Staph. aureus* for rabbits can be increased by growth under anaerobic conditions ; growth in pure oxygen was said to have the reverse effect.

Man.—The *Staphylococci* which are responsible for disease in the human body generally belong to the *aureus* or *albus* varieties ; only occasionally can *Staphylococcus citreus* be incriminated. *Staphylococcus aureus* is more pathogenic to man than *Staphylococcus albus* ; it gives rise to the severer lesions, such as osteomyelitis, pyæmia, sometimes associated with an infective endocarditis, mastitis, boils and abscesses in various parts of the body ; whereas *Staphylococcus albus* is responsible for the milder inflammatory lesions, such as acne pustules, stitch abscesses, and other minor suppurative conditions of the skin. Staphylococci are frequently found in conjunction with other organisms, particularly in the chronic stages of gonorrhœa, in bronchitis, in post-influenzal pneumonia, and in catarrhal conditions of the nose and respiratory passages. Their exact significance in these cases is difficult to assess, but it is probable that they assist these other organisms in giving rise to suppuration.

Several observers have made personal experiments on themselves to test the pathogenicity of the staphylococci in pure culture. Thus Garré (see Neisser 1912) found that by rubbing staphylococci into the skin of his arm he was able to produce boils, which took a considerable time to heal. (For further information on Pathogenicity to man, see Chapter LXIV.)

Experimental Inoculation.—The numerous experiments which have been conducted on the pathogenicity of the *Staphylococci* suffice to show that the only laboratory animals that can be artificially infected with ease are the rabbit, the mouse, and the guinea-pig. Of these undoubtedly the most susceptible is the rabbit.

Not all strains are equally pathogenic. As a rule the cocci which are isolated directly from suppurative processes in the body prove virulent, whereas those isolated from skin, air, water, etc., are avirulent. The most pathogenic are the golden strains ; many of the white strains are pathogenic, though to a less degree ; the yellow cocci are generally non-pathogenic.

RABBITS.—The subcutaneous injection of 1 c.c. of a 24-hours' broth culture of *Staph. aureus* gives rise to a local abscess, from which the organisms can be recovered.

Intravenous injection of 0·1 to 0·5 c.c. of a strain of *Staph. aureus* recently isolated from a suppurative focus generally proves fatal in 24 to 48 hours. Post mortem, there are hæmorrhages and bloody exudations on the serous membranes, and parenchymatous degeneration of the glandular organs ; the cocci can be recovered from the blood stream.

Intravenous injection of a smaller dose—about 0·01 to 0·05 c.c.—gives rise to a pyæmic condition, accompanied by loss of weight and general weakness, and proving fatal in 1 to 6 weeks. Post mortem, multiple small or large circumscribed abscesses are found particularly in the kidneys, and less frequently in the myocardium, lungs, spleen, bone marrow, and costal cartilages. Sometimes vegetations develop on the mitral and tricuspid valves and the chordæ tendineæ, without any artificial wounding of these structures. Acute osteomyelitis of the long bones not infrequently develops. The cocci can be recovered from the suppurative lesions. In animals that recover, reparative processes occur.

Staphylococcus albus is usually much less pathogenic. Strains recently isolated from suppurative foci may cause death on intravenous injection of 1–2 c.c. of a 24-hours' broth culture. Strains isolated from saprophytic sources are non-pathogenic unless given in large doses, when death occurs apparently from toxæmia.

Staphylococci which have been killed by heat at 60° C. for 2 hours, if given in large doses—2–4 agar slopes—at repeated intervals of 10 days, may give rise to progressive cachexia with death in 2 or 3 weeks. Post mortem much the same changes are found as those following acute death from a living culture, namely a hæmorrhagic exudate in the peritoneal cavity, serous hæmorrhages, and parenchymatous degeneration of the glandular organs (Koch 1908).

MICE AND GUINEA-PIGS are much less susceptible than rabbits, and though death may follow the intraperitoneal injection of virulent cultures, there is frequently no more than a local abscess formation from which the animal recovers.

Protection Experiments.—Pröscher (1903), who attempted to prepare an immune serum suitable for prophylactic and therapeutic use, obtained some hopeful results by the injection of living, virulent staphylococci into goats and horses. 1·5 c.c. of immune goat serum given subcutaneously protected rabbits against 0·5 c.c. of a virulent broth culture injected intravenously 24 hours later. But if given at the same time as, or subsequently to, the injection of the cocci, it had but little or no effect. There is no evidence to suggest that the serum has any directly bactericidal action; its main value lies in stimulating phagocytosis and in neutralizing the toxin secreted by the organisms. For this reason attention is at present concentrated on the production of sera with a high antitoxic titre prepared by the injection of horses with, at first, toxoid, and later with toxin. The value of such a serum in neutralizing the various effects of staphylococcal toxin can be readily demonstrated on laboratory animals, and its use is now being extended to the treatment of pyogenic infections in man.

CLASSIFICATION

As will have been gathered from the preceding pages, the *Staphylococci* form a somewhat heterogeneous collection of organisms, differing from each other in many characteristics. The early attempts at classification of the group depended chiefly upon the character of the pigment produced. Thus the staphylococci were separated into the golden and the white varieties by Rosenbach (1884); to these Passet (1885) added the yellow variety. But pigment formation cannot be considered a satisfactory criterion for purposes of differentiation, as it is determined by several factors, such as oxygen pressure, temperature, light, nature of medium, and length of cultivation. Nevertheless, pigment production has a certain taxonomic value, and provided not too much weight is placed upon it, it can be used for subsidiary classification.

Following the division of the group on the basis of pigment production, there came a classification which paid no attention whatever to this property—a classification depending on the joint determination of hæmolysin formation, and of agglutinability by an immune serum prepared against a strain isolated from a purulent lesion in man. The results of several workers were unanimous in showing that only those strains which are pathogenic to man are capable of producing a hæmolysin. Likewise it was found that a serum prepared against a strain isolated from a pathological source would agglutinate all strains isolated from pathological sources, but not—with a few exceptions—any of the saprophytic strains. By the use of the hæmolysin and agglutination tests it was therefore proposed to divide the staphylococci into two groups: (1) strains reacting positively to both these tests; these corresponded in general to the pathogenic staphylococci; (2) strains reacting negatively to both these tests; these corresponded in general to the saprophytic staphylococci.

The next attempt at classification was made by Winslow and Rogers (1906). By the combined study of pigment formation and biochemical activity, and by the correlation of different properties on a statistical basis, they were able to divide the *Coccaceæ* into six genera—*Streptococcus, Aurococcus, Albococcus, Micrococcus, Sarcina* and *Rhodococcus*. This grouping was supported by Kligler (1913), but was withdrawn by Winslow, Rothberg and Parsons (1920), who after an extensive re-investigation came to the conclusion that the golden and white staphylococci—at any rate—form a single group. They found that there is a gradual passage from the actively fermentative, gelatin-liquefying, pathogenic group, of which the type is *Staphylococcus aureus*, down to the weakly fermentative, gelatin-non-liquefying, saprophytic group, of which Gordon's scurf staphylococcus is a typical representative. This contention is supported by the work of Dudgeon (1908), who, in an examination of 121 *aureus* and *albus* strains, showed that, provided they were tested on a sufficiently wide range of sugars, it was uncommon to obtain two strains giving identical results.

Dudgeon (Dudgeon and Simpson 1928), who has again investigated the classification of the staphylococci, comes to essentially the same conclusions as those reached by Winslow, Rothberg and Parsons (1920). He regards all the pyogenic Gram-positive staphylococci as members of one common group. This is represented at one end of the scale by the strongly pigmented *Staph. aureus*, pathogenic to man and rabbits, hæmolytic, liquefying gelatin, fermenting lactose and mannitol, and forming active precipitinogens ; at the other end of the scale is the non-pigmented *Staph. albus*, feebly pathogenic to man, non-pathogenic to rabbits, often non-hæmolytic, failing to liquefy gelatin, failing to ferment mannitol, and without the power of forming precipitinogens in peptone broth, or of producing active precipitating antisera in rabbits. Hucker (1924*a*), who made a very careful study of the *Staphylococcus-Micrococcus* group, failed to find any natural lines of cleavage. For purposes of classification, however, he concluded that most attention should be paid to chromogenesis, nitrate reduction, ability to utilize ammonium salts as the sole source of nitrogen, gelatin liquefaction, and action on milk.

In the light of our present knowledge it is impossible to suggest any classification of the staphylococci which is other than tentative. If we confine our attention to pigment formation and fermentation reactions no subdivision of the group is possible, since one type shades by imperceptible degrees into another, save perhaps in the case of those staphylococci which produce the true lemon-yellow pigment. If, however, we include pathogenicity, toxin formation, and antigenic structure in our differential criteria, there appears to be some justification for the recognition of three sub-groups, to which we may tentatively assign specific names.

The first of these, *Staphylococcus aureus*, is a pathogenic species, producing suppurative lesions of varying severity in man, and in experimental animals ; it usually produces a golden-yellow pigment, but often loses this character on subculture ; it produces a soluble toxin with hæmolytic, leucocytolytic, necrotizing, and lethal properties for the rabbit, and sometimes with irritating properties for the gastro-intestinal tract of man ; it almost always liquefies gelatin, and ferments lactose and mannitol ; it contains a specific polysaccharide not possessed by non-pathogenic staphylococci ; its antigenic structure differs from that of the following species.

The second of these, *Staphylococcus albus*, is feebly pathogenic, or non-pathogenic ; it is normally present on the skin, in the hair, and apparently in air, water and dust. It gives porcelain-white or indifferently coloured colonies, but never produces a yellow or golden pigment. It forms no toxin, or does so less frequently than *Staph. aureus* ; though white variants of *Staph. aureus* are often highly toxigenic. It frequently liquefies gelatin, but less constantly than *Staph. aureus*. It often ferments lactose, but not mannitol ; it appears to contain, as a rule, a polysaccharide different from that in virulent *Staph. aureus* strains.

The third species, *Staphylococcus citreus*, is a non-pathogenic saprophyte. It produces a distinctive lemon-yellow pigment ; it is doubtful whether it ever forms a toxin ; it liquefies gelatin less frequently and less rapidly than the preceding species. It has little or no fermentative ability.

We append, for purposes of reference, a detailed description of *Staph. aureus*, together with some of the characters ascribed to those types of staphylococci which have, at various times, received specific names.

Staphylococcus aureus Rosenbach

Isolation.—First described fully by Rosenbach (1884).

Habitat.—Actual or potential parasite found in suppurative lesions of man, on the normal skin, and in cow's milk.

Morphology.—Spherical cells, 0·8–1·0 μ in diameter ; in cultures on solid media the cocci are arranged in grape-like clusters ; in broth they occur as small groups, pairs, and short chains of not more than four members. Stain well with the usual aniline dyes. Non-motile, Gram-positive, non-acid-fast.

Agar Plate.—24 *hours*, 37° *C.* Circular colonies, 1–2 mm. in diameter, low convex, amorphous, opaque, and of a golden colour, having a smooth glistening surface and an entire edge ; butyrous in consistency and easily emulsifiable. No differentiation visible.

Agar Stroke.—24 *hours*, 37° *C.* Abundant, confluent, raised, golden-yellow, opaque growth, with a glistening, smooth or slightly contoured surface, and an entire or slightly undulate edge.

Gelatin Stab.—5 *days*, 22° *C.* Abundant filiform growth reaching to bottom of stab ; surface growth about 5 mm. in diameter ; liquefaction of infundibuliform or saccate type.

Broth.—24 *hours*, 37° *C.* Moderate uniform turbidity with a moderate, powdery deposit, disintegrating readily on shaking ; slight ring growth at surface.

Horse Blood Agar Plate.—48 *hours*, 37° *C.* Good growth. Blood is partly or completely hæmolysed around colonies.

MacConkey's Agar.—24 *hours*, 37° *C.* Tiny, convex, pinkish colonies about 0·5 mm. in diameter. Later they increase somewhat in size, and take on a deep red colour.

Potato.—24 *hours*, 37° *C.* Poor, yellowish, effuse growth. 5 *days* ; moderate, confluent, slightly raised, golden-yellow growth.

Loeffler's Serum.—24 *hours*, 37° *C.* Good, raised, confluent, golden-yellow growth.

Resistance.—May withstand moist heat at 60° C. for 30 minutes ; generally killed in one hour. Destroyed by 2 per cent. phenol in 15 minutes.

Metabolism.—Aerobic, facultatively anaerobic. Growth occurs best at 37° C., limits 12° to 45° C. Optimum pH for growth is 7·4–7·6. Pigment formed most readily at 22° C. ; is not formed in cultures grown anaerobically. Filtrable hæmolysin produced, most active on rabbit's red cells.

Biochemical Reactions.—Acid, no gas, in glucose, maltose, mannitol, lactose, and sucrose. L.M. acid, clot, and sometimes peptonization. Indole —. M.R. +. V.P. +. Nitrates reduced to nitrites. M.B. reduction +. H_2S ?. NH_3 +.

Antigenic Structure.—The pathogenic species appear to be fairly homogeneous, when tested by agglutination (see p. 478).

Pathogenicity.—Forms exotoxin with hæmolytic, leucocytolytic, skin-necrosing, and lethal properties for the rabbit. Some strains also form an enterotoxin acting on man. *Staph. aureus* is frequently responsible for suppurative lesions in the human body, such as boils and abscesses, acute osteomyelitis, infective endocarditis, pyæmia, etc. Experimentally, it is pathogenic for rabbits, less so for mice and guineapigs. 0·1–0·5 c.c. of a 24-hours' broth culture injected intravenously into a rabbit is generally fatal in 24 to 48 hours ; post mortem, hæmorrhages on the serous membranes ; the cocci can be recovered from the blood stream. A smaller dose may not prove fatal for 1 to 6 weeks ; post mortem, multiple abscesses are frequently seen, especially in the kidneys, less frequently in the myocardium, lungs, spleen, bone marrow, and costal cartilages.

Staphylococcus albus.—Resembles *Staph. aureus* in many respects.   For chief differences, see p. 484.

Staphylococcus citreus.—Resembles *Staph. aureus* in many respects.   For chief differences, see p. 484.

TABLE XXXV

	Pigment.	Glucose.	Maltose.	Mannitol.	Lactose.	Sucrose.	Gel. liq.	Path. to Man.
Staph. aureus Rosenbach .	Golden	A	A	A	A	A	+	High
Staph. aurantiacus Schroeter	Golden	A	A	—	—	A	—	High
Staph. epidermidis Gordon .	White	A	A	—	A	A	+	Feeble
Staph. candidus Cohn . .	White	A	A	?	A	A	—	Feeble
[1]*Staph. salivarius* Gordon .	White	A	A	—	—	A	—	
Staph. candicans Flügge . .	White	A	A	?	—	A	—	Feeble
Scurf staphylococcus Gordon	White	A	—	A	—	—	—	—
Staph. citreus	Lemon yellow	—	—	—	—	—	∓	—

[1] Viscid growth in broth.

MICROCOCCUS, SARCINA, RHODOCOCCUS AND LEUCONOSTOC

In their monograph on the *Systematic Relationships of the Coccaceæ*, C.-E. A. Winslow and Anne R. Winslow (1908) emphasize that the white and golden cocci belong to a series of cocci, including the streptococci, which are essentially parasitic in nature and active in fermentative power, whereas the yellow and red forms, including the sarcinæ, are generally saprophytic in nature and possess a restricted fermentative power.

Micrococcus

DEFINITION.—*Micrococcus.*

> Spherical or ovoid cells, non-motile, arranged in pairs, tetrads, or groups, but not in grape-like clusters or chains. Generally Gram-positive. Grow freely on ordinary media. Sometimes produce a yellowish pigment. Gelatin liquefaction is not constant, and is usually slow. Fermentative activities weak. Usually non-pathogenic to man or animals.
>
> Type species is *Micrococcus luteus* Cohn.

The term *Micrococcus* was first used in a generic sense by Cohn (1875), who applied it to small spherical or oval non-motile organisms which occurred in chains or groups. This, it will be observed, was a comprehensive description ; it was not long in fact before certain members, such as the *Streptococci* and the *Staphylococci*, were removed from it, and awarded generic names of their own. The term *Micrococcus*, as now used, is defined above.

As with most saprophytic organisms, the *Micrococci* have not been studied so fully as the pathogenic cocci—the *Streptococci* and the *Staphylococci*. It must therefore be made clear that, in the following account, we record the characters of certain micrococci which have been from time to time described by different workers, without committing ourselves to any judgment as to their claims to be accorded specific rank. In general, we have been guided in our selection by Hucker (1924*b*, 1928), who uses pigment production, gelatin liquefaction, nitrate reduction, and ability to use ammonium salts as the sole source of nitrogen, as his main differential criteria. To his reports we would refer the reader who is anxious for more detailed information.

(1) **Micrococcus luteus** (Schroeter) Cohn.—Isolated by Schroeter (1875) from a potato on which a yellow growth was found ; is a non-motile, Gram-positive coccus, $1 \cdot 0$–$1 \cdot 2$ μ in diameter, occurring in pairs, tetrads or small groups. It grows well on ordinary media, giving a smooth, lemon-yellow layer. Gelatin is not liquefied, though on this point various workers disagree. Nitrates are not reduced. The optimum temperature of growth is 25° C. Its fermentative powers are weak, acid being formed in glucose, not in lactose. It is commonly found in air, water, milk and milk products. The pigment is insoluble in water.

(2) **Micrococcus varians** (Dyar) Migula (1900) is similar to *M. luteus*, but is differentiated from it by its ability to reduce nitrates.

(3) **Micrococcus conglomeratus** Flügge (Migula 1900). Forms large clumps of organisms, often in pairs. Generally Gram-positive. Liquefies gelatin and reduces nitrates. Forms an abundant light yellow growth on agar. Can utilize ammonium salts as the sole source of nitrogen.

(4) **Micrococcus flavus.**—Isolated by Prove (1884–87) from human urine. About $0 \cdot 8$ μ in diameter, occurring singly, in pairs or short chains. On gelatin gives colonies 5 mm. in diameter by the 3rd day. Liquefies gelatin about the 12th day. Does not reduce nitrates. Forms a considerable amount of slimy matter. Is said to ferment certain carbohydrates. Grows between 6° C. and 36° C. ; optimum temperature 22° C. Is distinguished by the fact that it forms a yellow pigment only when it is exposed to light —sunlight or diffused daylight ; when kept in the dark the growth is colourless.

(5) **Micrococcus coronatus** Flügge.—Described by Flügge (1896). A coccus 1 μ in diameter, occurring in groups or short chains, Gram-positive. On gelatin plates in two days it forms whitish points ; around these there appears a fresh growth, which later becomes separated from the colony by a clear ring of liquefaction. The central part assumes a dark brown, the peripheral a yellowish-brown colour. It is the halo around the colony which gives the organism its name. Found in air.

(6) **Micrococcus caseolyticus** Evans (1916). This organism is similar in many respects to *M. coronatus*. It occurs in large clumps, is generally Gram-positive, and is found in milk, milk products, and in the udder of the cow. It produces a luxuriant white growth on agar slants. It liquefies gelatin, and reduces nitrates. It produces an acid curd in milk and peptonizes it rapidly. It generally utilizes ammonium salts as the sole source of nitrogen, and usually produces acid in glucose and lactose.

(7) **Micrococcus radiatus** Flügge.—Described by Flügge (1896). Small coccus, less than 1 μ in diameter, occurring in small groups, or sometimes short chains. On gelatin plates the colonies after 2 days are about 1 mm. in diameter, whitish in colour, with a slightly irregular edge. During the next two days outgrowths occur radiating from the centre in an orderly manner, so that the colony assumes an appearance not unlike that of a starfish ; meanwhile liquefaction sets in, and the centre sinks gently into the medium. The ends of the outgrowths are joined together by a ring of growth, from which after another two days fresh radiations may arise, and from these yet a third set. When fully grown, the colony has a diameter of $1 \cdot 0$–$1 \cdot 5$ cm. In a gelatin stab, the colonies down the stab send out horizontal shoots, giving the growth a feathery appearance ; on the surface there is a slow liquefaction of infundibuliform type.

(8) **Micrococcus ureæ** Cohn (1875) is a spherical organism, occurring singly, in pairs, or in short chains. Diameter $0 \cdot 8$–$1 \cdot 0$ μ. Gram-positive, though often weakly so. On agar it forms whitish, low convex, opaque colonies. Gelatin is not liquefied as a rule. Nitrates not reduced. Can utilize urea and ammonium salts as sole source of nitrogen. Found in stale urine.

(9) **Micrococcus freudenreichii** is closely related to *M. ureæ*. It is a facultative parasite,

Cells occur singly or in clumps. Generally Gram-positive. Liquefies gelatin, but does not reduce nitrates. Does not usually produce sufficient acid to curdle milk. Can utilize ammonium salts, but not urea, as the sole source of nitrogen. Is one of the commonest non-pigment-producing micrococci in milk and dairy utensils.

(10) **Micrococcus tetragenus** Gaffky.—First described by Gaffky in 1883. It was isolated by Koch from lung cavities in patients with pulmonary tuberculosis. Gram-positive, spherical organism, dividing in two planes at right angles to each other, so that tetrad forms are produced. In the human and animal body a capsule is formed. Grows freely on ordinary media. Optimum temperature for growth is 37° C. The growth on agar is of a glutinous consistency, often adherent to the medium, and difficult to emulsify. Colonies are whitish in colour. In broth a thick, weedy, glutinous deposit is formed, the supernatant fluid being comparatively clear. Gelatin is not liquefied. Nitrates are not reduced. Acid is said to be produced in glucose, maltose, lactose, and sucrose. The organism is occasionally pathogenic to man, and may even give rise to septicæmia. One of its most notable characteristics, differentiating it from other micrococci, is its high pathogenicity for the mouse. Subcutaneous or intraperitoneal inoculation leads to the production of a septicæmia, which proves fatal, according to circumstances, in 1 to 8 days. At post mortem there may be small abscesses in the spleen. The cocci are found in large numbers in the blood and tissues. Guinea-pigs are susceptible, though less so than mice. Non-capsulated avirulent and other variants have been described by Wreschner (1921) and Reimann (1936).

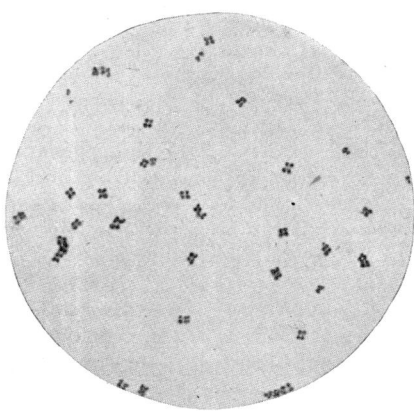

Fig. 110.—*Micrococcus tetragenus.*

From an agar culture, 24 hours, 37° C.
(× 1000).

(11) **Micrococcus buccalis** is a small, non-motile, Gram-positive coccus, about 0·5 μ in diameter, isolated by Ozaki (1915) from the mouth. It is peculiar in being an obligate anaerobe. In stab glucose agar it gives a filiform growth with gas formation. There is turbidity in dextrose broth and a greyish sediment. It ferments glucose, maltose, lactose, and sucrose, but not mannitol, with the production of acid and gas. There is no liquefaction of gelatin ; H₂S positive ; indole negative. Its optimum temperature is 37° C. ; there is no growth under 20° C. It is non-pathogenic to laboratory animals. This coccus differs in several important points—notably its active fermentative powers and its anaerobic nature—from most other micrococci, but as no special group is available for it as yet, we choose to place it here.

Other anaerobic micrococci have been described at various times, notably the *Micrococcus gingivalis* Ozaki (1912), the *Micrococcus minimus* Gioelli (1907), and the somewhat paradoxically named *Micrococcus aerogenes* Schottmüller (1912). (For the last three references, see Ozaki 1915.)

Sarcina

DEFINITION.—*Sarcina.*

Same definition as *Micrococcus*, except that cell division occurs, under favourable conditions, in three planes, so that cubical packets are formed.

The type species is *Sarcina ventriculi* Goodsir.

The first description of the *Sarcinæ* was by Goodsir (1842), who found an organism arranged in cubical packets in the stomach of a patient suffering from gastric disease; to this he gave the name *Sarcina ventriculi.* Schroeter (1875) was the next to describe a sarcina—the *Sarcina aurantiaca*—and since then several others have been isolated, some from suppurative processes, but the majority from non-pathological sources.

The following is a description of certain of the sarcinæ that have been described as separate species :

Sarcina ventriculi, Goodsir.—This, the first sarcina described, was not cultured till long after Goodsir (1842) had noticed it microscopically in the stomach contents.

Morphology.—Spherical coccus, 0·8–1·0 μ in diameter, arranged in cubical packets and groups. In liquid media it occurs in pairs, small groups, and packets. Nonmotile. Gram-positive, but decolorizes easily. Non-acid-fast.

Agar Plate.—48 *hours*, 37° *C.* Circular colonies, 1 mm. in diameter, convex, amorphous, opaque, pale-yellow, with a smooth surface and entire edge ; rather viscous in consistency, and easily emulsifiable.

Agar Slope.—48 *hours*, 37° *C.* Moderate, confluent, raised, opaque, creamy-yellow growth with a smooth or contoured surface and an undulate edge.

Gelatin Stab.—Moderate filiform growth ; no liquefaction.

Broth.—48 *hours*, 37° *C.* Moderate uniform turbidity with a viscous deposit, disintegrating on shaking. No surface growth.

Metabolic and Biochemical Activities.—Aerobic, facultatively anaerobic. Optimum temperature for growth 22–30° C. Pigment formed most readily at 22° C. No hæmolysin formed. Ferments no sugars. L.M. unchanged. M.R. —. V.P. —. M.B. reduction —.

Pathogenicity.—Non-pathogenic.

Sarcina lutea Schroeter.—This organism, which was described by Schroeter (1875) as the *Bacteridium aurantiacum*, is a Gram-positive sarcina, giving a chrome-yellow growth on culture media. On agar the colonies are raised, yellow, coarsely granular, with an entire margin and a moist glistening surface. On potato they are dry, dull and granular. In broth there is an abundant yellow sediment with no turbidity. The optimum temperature of growth is 25° C. It is found in air, soil and water.

Sarcina aurantiaca Flügge.—Described by Flügge (1896). Gram-positive spheres developing in packets. On gelatin plates forms slowly-growing orange-yellow colonies gradually liquefying gelatin. On agar slope, gives a thick reddish-yellow growth composed of single colonies ; similarly on potato. In broth gives a turbidity with abundant sediment. Grows best at room temperature. Found in air and water.

Sarcina ureæ Beijerinck (1901) is a spherical organism, 0·7–1·2 μ in diameter, occurring singly, in pairs, and in packets. Said to be motile by peritrichate flagella and to form spores. Gram-positive. Resists heating to 100° C. for 5 minutes. Gelatin not liquefied. Found in stale urine (see Gibson 1935).

Sarcina conjunctivæ Verderame.—Isolated by Verderame (1911) from the conjunctival sac of a girl suffering from acute conjunctivitis. Named by him *Sarcina conjunctivæ citrea.* Is stated to be Gram-negative. On agar after 24 hours the colonies are pinhead in size, round, bright-yellow, opaque, with an entire edge, and of butyrous consistency ; after 48 hours they are 4 mm. in diameter and lemon-yellow in colour. On an agar slope there is a thick creamy layer of growth after 2 days. Similar growth, but more abundant on ascitic agar. In gelatin stab there is a surface growth of 2–3 mm. in diameter after 24 hours, and a filiform growth of fine, light, greyish-yellow, opaque colonies ; no liquefaction. On potato an abundant, creamy, lemon-yellow growth of rather dry appearance. In broth after 24 hours there is a very light turbidity, with a suspension in the liquid of fine flocculi which are easily broken up on shaking, and a cloudy viscous deposit of light yellow colour. Optimum temperature 37° C., but grows well at 14–18° C. Facultative anaerobe. Forms acid in glucose, lævulose, maltose, lactose, sucrose and inulin, not in mannitol or galactose. H_2S positive. Indole negative. Nitrates not reduced. Non-pathogenic to mice or guinea-pigs.

Numerous other sarcinæ have been described, such as *Sarcina citrea* Menge in 1892, and an unnamed Gram-negative *Sarcina* isolated by Nagano (1902) from the pus of an ovarian abscess. Ørskov (1930) draws attention to a sarcina found in the mouth and throat which, though non-motile itself, gives rise to motile cocci, each provided with a flagellum. The cocci themselves are not reproducible. For this remarkable organism the name *Sarcina mirabilis* is suggested.

Rhodococcus

DEFINITION.—*Rhodococcus.*

Spherical or ovoid cells occurring in groups or regular packets. Usually Gram-positive, but are easily decolorized. Growth on agar abundant with formation of red pigment. Weak fermentative powers. Gelatin rarely liquefied. Nitrates generally reduced. Saprophytes.

Type species is *Rhodococcus rhodochrous* Zopf. The term *Rhodococcus* was first introduced by Zopf in 1891 (see Buchanan 1925).

Rhodococcus rhodochrous Zopf.—Found in water. Spherical organism, about 0·8–1·0 μ in diameter, occurring singly, in pairs and in small groups. Gram-positive. Gives a confluent, raised growth of a carmine hue on agar. Thick, rose-red pellicle in broth, with a red flocculent sediment (Bergey 1923). L.M. slightly alkaline. Carmine-red streak on potato. Does not liquefy gelatin, but generally reduces nitrates. Aerobic. Optimum temperature 25° C. Non-pathogenic.

Rhodococcus cinnabareus Flügge.—Described by Flügge as a large, spherical, Gram-positive coccus, occurring in twos, threes, and fours; grows very slowly. On gelatin after 4 days the colonies are 0·5–1·0 mm. in diameter; at first they are brick-red, later cinnabar-red in colour. In gelatin stab small white colonies are formed down the stab in 4 to 5 days; on the surface there is a large red knob of growth; no liquefaction. On potato the growth is even slower. Optimum temperature 25° C. Does not reduce nitrates, and cannot utilize ammonium salts as the sole source of nitrogen. Found in air and water.

Rhodococcus roseofulvus Flügge.—Described by Babes as the cause of red sweat (see Flügge 1896). The cocci are oval in shape, 1 μ long by 0·6–0·8 μ broad, and are bound by gelatinous material into a reddish zoogloeal mass. In the body they surround the hairs, particularly of the axilla, and impart a red coloration to the sweat. Gram-positive. Grows on egg white at 37° C., forming a red pigment. Does not liquefy gelatin. Generally curdles milk and causes slight peptonization. Produces acid in glycerol and mannitol.

Rhodococcus agilis Ali-Cohen.—Isolated by Ali-Cohen (1889) from drinking water and named *Micrococcus agilis*. Peculiar in being motile, possessing one or two flagella. Occurs mostly in pairs, sometimes in short chains or in tetrads. Gram-positive; 1 μ in diameter. Grows in all media at room temperature, forming a rose-coloured pigment. Liquefies gelatin slowly. Optimum temperature 25° C. Found in water.

Leuconostoc

DEFINITION.—*Leuconostoc.*

Spherical or ovoid cells, arranged in pairs and chains; the cocci are surrounded by a gelatinous envelope, which unites them into zoogloeal masses. Usually Gram-positive, but decolorize easily. Saprophytes, usually growing in cane sugar solutions.

Type species is *Leuconostoc mesenterioides* van Tieghem.

The first organism of this group was described by Cienkowski in 1878 as the *Ascococcus mesenterioides.* This name was amended by van Tieghem in 1878 to *Leuconostoc mesenterioides* (see Flügge 1896).   According to Hucker and Pederson (1930), to whom reference should be made for more detailed information, organisms of the genus *Leuconostoc* are found in slimy sugar solutions, in fermenting vegetables, and in milk and milk products.   Morphologically, they are intermediate between the *Streptococci* and the *Lactobacilli*.   They all produce about 45 per cent. lævo-lactic acid from glucose, 20 per cent. CO_2, and 25 per cent. volatile products, includ-ing acetic acid and ethyl alcohol.   They form mannitol from fructose and sucrose, and a levulan or dextran from sucrose.

Leuconostoc mesenterioides (Cienkowski) van Tieghem.—A spherical coccus, 0·9–1·2 μ in diameter, occurring in pairs and in chains.   Usually Gram-positive.   The chains are surrounded by a thick, tough, gelatinous coating, which is stated by von Scheibler to consist of dextrin ; the aggregation of several chains within their envelopes gives rise to large, compact, gelatinous, zoogloeal masses.   Develops on the surface of parsnip-root and beetroot solutions in the form of thick cakes of cartilaginous consistency (Flügge 1896).   It likewise thrives on grape-sugar and cane-sugar solutions, provided nitrate and phosphate are added.   Cultivated in peptone water, or in gelatin to which lactose or maltose has been added, it is morphologically similar to a streptococcus, no gelatinous envelope being formed ; but if glucose or cane sugar is incorporated in the gelatin, then the characteristic zoogloeal masses appear.   On either of these media there appears in 10 to 14 days a thick whitish mass of confluent colonies, having a glassy surface, looking rather like a layer of crystals.   During the first week the growth is dry and of cartilaginous consistency, but later it becomes softer and moister, and assumes an almost pulp-like consistency.   Ferments glucose, maltose, lactose, sucrose, mannitol and either arabinose or xylose, with the formation of acid and gas.   Facultative anaerobe.   Optimum tempera-ture 25° C.   Is found in fermenting vegetable material and in sugar solutions.

Hucker and Pederson (1930) recognize two other species.   *Leuconostoc dextranicus* ferments sucrose, but not pentoses, produces a moderate amount of slime from sucrose, and may be associated with either vegetable or dairy products.

Leuconostoc citrovorus does not ferment sucrose or pentoses, produces no slime from sucrose, and is generally associated with milk or milk products.

REFERENCES

ALI-COHEN, CH. H. (1889) *Zbl. Bakt.*, **6**, 33.
ANDREWES, F. W. and GORDON, M. H. (1905–6) *Rep. loc. Govt Bd publ. Hlth Suppl.*, p. 543.
BEIJERINCK, M. W. (1901) *Zbl. Bakt.*, IIte Abt., **7**, 33.
BERGEY, D. H. (1923) " Manual of Determinative Bacteriology."   Baltimore.
BIGGER, J. W. (1933) *J. Path. Bact.*, **36**, 87.
BIGGER, J. W., BOLAND, C. R., and O'MEARA, R. A. Q. (1927) *J. Path. Bact.*, **30**, 261.
BIONDI, D. (1887) *Z. Hyg. InfektKr.*, **2**, 194.
BIRCH-HIRSCHFELD, L. (1934) *Klin. Wschr.*, **13**, 331.
BUCHANAN, R. E. (1925) " General Systematic Bacteriology."   Baltimore.
BURKY, E. L. (1933) *J. Immunol.*, **24**, 93.
BURNET, F. M. (1929) *J. Path. Bact.*, **32**, 717 ; (1930) *Ibid.*, **33**, 1 ; (1931) *J. Path. Bact.*, **34**, 759.
CHAPMAN, G. H. and BERENS, C. (1935) *J. Bact.*, **29**, 437.
CHAPMAN, G. H., BERENS, C., PETERS, A., and CURCIO, L. (1934) *J. Bact.*, **28**, 343.
COHN, F. (1875) *Cohns Beitr. Biol. Pflanz.*, **1**, Hft. 2, 127.
DARÁNYI, J. v. (1926) *Zbl. Bakt.*, **99**, 74.
DENYS, J. and HAVET, J. (1898) *La Cellule*, **10**, 7.
DOLMAN, C. E. (1932a) *Can. publ. Hlth J.*, **23**, 125 ; (1932b) *Trans. roy. Soc. Can.*, Section V, 3rd Series, **26**, 309.
DUDGEON, L. S. (1908) *J. Path. Bact.*, **12**, 242.
DUDGEON, L. S. and SIMPSON, J. W. H. (1928) *J. Hyg., Camb.*, **27**, 160.
DURAN-REYNALS, F. (1933) *J. exp. Med.*, **58**, 161 ; (1935) *Ibid.*, **61**, 617.
EVANS, A. C. (1916) *J. infect. Dis.*, **18**, 437.

FLÜGGE, C. (1896) "Die Mikroorganismen," Part II, p. 96, 3rd edit. Leipzig.
FRAENKEL, C. and BAUMANN. (1905) *Münch. med. Wschr.*, **52**, 937.
GAFFKY. (1883) *Arch. klin. Chir.*, **28**, 495.
GENGOU, O. (1932) *Ann. Inst. Pasteur*, **48**, 135.
GIBSON, T. (1935) *Arch. Mikrobiol.*, **6**, 73.
GLADSTONE, G. P., FILDES, P., and RICHARDSON, G. M. (1935) *Brit. J. exp. Path.*, **16**, 335.
GLENNY, A. T. and STEVENS, M. F. (1935) *J. Path. Bact.*, **40**, 201.
GOODSIR, J. (1842) *Edin. med. surg. J.*, **57**, 430.
GORDON, M. H. (1903–4) *33rd ann. Rep. loc. Govt Bd publ. Hlth Suppl.*, p. 388.
GROSS, H. (1931a) *Zbl. Bakt.*, **122**, 354 ; (1931b) *Ibid.*, **123**, 212 ; (1931c) *Z. ImmunForsch.*, **73**, 14.
HINE, T. G. M. (1922) *Lancet*, ii. 1380.
HEWITT, L. F. (1930) *Biochem. J.*, **24**, 676.
HOFFSTADT, R. E. and YOUMANS, G. P. (1932) *J. infect. Dis.*, **51**, 216.
HUCKER, G. J. (1924a) *N.Y. St. agric. Exp. Sta., Tec. Bull.*, No. 100 ; (1924b) *Ibid.*, No. 102 ; (1928) *N.Y. St. agric. exp. Sta., Tec. Bull.*, No. 135.
HUCKER, G. J. and PEDERSON, C. S. (1930) *N.Y. St. agric. Exp. Sta., Tec. Bull.*, No. 167.
HUGHES, T. P. (1932) *J. Bact.*, **23**, 437.
JORDAN, E. O. and BURROWS, W. (1935) *J. infect. Dis.*, **57**, 121.
JULIANELLE, L. A. (1922) *J. infect. Dis.*, **31**, 256.
JULIANELLE, L. A. and WIEGHARD, C. W. (1934) *Proc. Soc. exp. Biol. N.Y.*, **31**, 947 ; (1935) *J. exp. Med.*, **62**, 11, 31.
KLIGLER, I. J. (1913) *J. infect. Dis.*, **12**, 432.
KLOPSTOCK and BOCKENHEIMER. (1904) *Arch. klin. Chir.*, **72**, 325.
KNIGHT, B. C. J. G. (1935) *Brit. J. exp. Path.*, **16**, 315.
KOCH, J. (1908) *Z. Hyg. InfektKr.*, **58**, 287.
KOLLE, W. and OTTO, R. (1902) *Z. Hyg. InfektKr.*, **41**, 369.
KRAUS, R. and CLAIRMONT, P. (1900) *Wien. klin. Wschr.*, **13**, 49.
KUTSCHER and KONRICH, F. (1904) *Z. Hyg. InfektKr.*, **48**, 249.
LINGELSHEIM, W. VON (1899) *Beitr. exp. Ther.*, Heft. 1, 49.
LUBINSKI, W. (1894) *Zbl. Bakt.*, **16**, 769.
MIGULA, W. (1900) "System der Bakterien," IIte Band, p. 1. Gustav Fischer, Jena.
MUCH, H. (1908) *Biochem. Z.*, **14**, 143.
NAGANO, J. (1902) *Zbl. Bakt.*, **32**, 327.
NEISSER, M. (1912) See Kolle and Wassermann, "Hdb. der path. Mikroorg.," IIte Abt. (1912–13), **4**, 356.
NEISSER, M. and WECHSBERG, F. (1901) *Z. Hyg. InfektKr.*, **36**, 299.
OGSTON, A. (1881) *Brit. med. J.*, i, 369.
OESTERLIN, E. (1925) *Zbl. Bakt.*, **94**, 313.
ØRSKOV, J. (1930) *Acta path. Microbiol. scand. Suppl.*, **3**, 519.
OTTO, R. (1903) *Zbl. Bakt.*, **34**, 44.
OZAKI, Y. (1915) *Zbl. Bakt.*, **76**, 118.
PANTON, P. N. and VALENTINE, F. C. O. (1932) *Lancet*, i. 506.
PARISH, H. J. and CLARK, W. H. M. (1932) *J. Path. Bact.*, **35**, 251.
PARKER, J. T. (1924) *J. exp. Med.*, **40**, 761.
PASSET. (1885) *Fort. Med.*, **3**, 33.
PRÖSCHER. (1903) *Zbl. Bakt.*, **34**, 437.
PROVE, O. (1884–7) *Cohns Beitr. Biol. Pflanz.*, **4**, 409.
REIMANN, H. A. (1936) *J. Bact.*, **31**, 385, 407.
ROSENBACH, F. J. (1884) "Mikroorganismen bei den Wundinfektionskrankheiten des Menschen." Wiesbaden.
SCHROETER, J. (1875) *Cohns Beitr. Biol. Pflanz.*, **1**, Heft. 2, 109.
STEPHAN, F. (1934) *Z. Hyg. InfektKr.*, **116**, 550.
SWINGLE, E. L. (1935) *J. Bact.*, **29**, 467.
VANBREUSEGHEM, R. (1934) *C. R. Soc. Biol.*, **116**, 650.
VEIEL, F. (1904) *Münch. med. Wschr.*, **51**, 13.
VELDE, H. VAN DE (1894) *La Cellule*, **10**, ii. 401.
VERDERAME, P. (1911) *Zbl. Bakt.*, **59**, 377.
WALBUM, L. E. (1922) *Biochem. Z.*, **129**, 367.
WALSTON, H. D. (1935) *J. Hyg., Camb.*, **35**, 549.
WELCH, W. H. (1891) *Int. J. med. Sci.*, **102**, 439.
WIEGHARD, C. W. and JULIANELLE, L. A. (1935) *J. exp. Med.*, **62**, 23.
WINSLOW, C.-E. A. and ROGERS, A. F. (1906) *J. infect. Dis.*, **3**, 485.
WINSLOW, C.-E. A., ROTHBERG, W., and PARSONS, E. I. (1920) *J. Bact.*, **5**, 145.
WINSLOW, C.-E. A. and WINSLOW, A. R. (1908) "The Systematic Relationship of the Coccaceæ." New York.
WRESCHNER, H. (1921) *Z. Hyg. InfektKr.*, **93**, 74.
WRIGHT, J. (1936) *Lancet*, i, 1002.

CHAPTER XXV

CHROMOBACTERIUM AND ACHROMOBACTERIUM

CHROMOBACTERIUM

DEFINITION.—*Chromobacterium.*

Small, non-sporing, aerobic rods, usually motile and usually Gram-negative, producing a yellow, red, or violet pigment, which is generally insoluble in water. Saprophytic ; commonly found in water or soil.

Type species. *Chromobacterium violaceum.*

Numerous organisms of this group have been isolated at various times from water, soil, sewage, and occasionally from contaminated food-stuffs. *Chr. violaceum* was described by Bergonzoni in 1881 (see Report 1920). *Chr. prodigiosum* was first observed by Bizio in 1823 (see Breed and Breed 1924), who found it in " bleeding polenta ". *Chr. aquatilis* was isolated from water by Frankland and Frankland in 1889.

The classification of these organisms presents considerable difficulties. The American Committee of Bacteriologists has created a genus, which they call *Erythrobacillus*, for the inclusion of those bacilli which produce a red or pink pigment. The genus *Chromobacterium* they reserve for those bacilli which produce a violet pigment. As these organisms have received relatively little attention from bacteriologists, and as in consequence their properties have been incompletely studied, it would seem advisable for the moment to group all the aerobic non-sporing pigment-forming rods into the single genus *Chromobacterium*. With regard to the naming of the individual species within the genus, there is considerable confusion. One and the same organism has frequently been described under two names, and specific names have been given to organisms which appear to be merely varieties of existing species. We shall therefore describe in some detail those organisms which undoubtedly deserve specific rank, and shall refer briefly to others whose claim to this distinction is more doubtful.

Morphology.—The organisms of this group are small rods, varying in length from about 1·0 to 3·0 μ, and in breadth from about 0·5 to 0·7 μ. *Chr. prodigiosum* may be regarded as an exception, since it is usually described as a small cocco-bacillus. It is necessary to point out, however, that the size of this organism is subject to considerable variation, and that even on the same type of medium a single strain may at one time give rise to cocco-bacilli, and at another to rod-forms indistinguishable from those formed by other members of the *Chromobacteria* (Fig. 111). Motility is a frequent characteristic, and is dependent on the possession of peritrichate, or sometimes polar flagella. Most members of this group are Gram-negative.

Cultural Reactions.—Growth occurs readily on the ordinary media ; a particularly heavy growth is generally observed in broth.

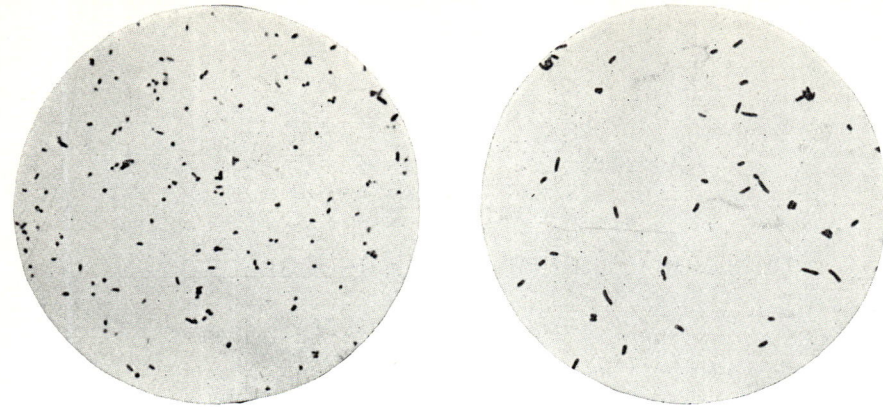

Fig. 111.—*Chromobacterium prodigiosum.*
From an agar culture, 24 hours, 37° C. (× 1000).
Left.—Strain showing cocco-bacillary forms.
Right.—Same strain from a different culture showing definite rods.

The colonies on agar are usually homogeneous for the first day or two, and then become differentiated into a convex, pigmented, and relatively opaque centre, and an effuse, colourless, almost transparent periphery with an irregularly crenated edge. This differentiation results from the secondary outgrowth around the original colony of a film, which may be so thin as to escape observation unless a careful search is made for it.

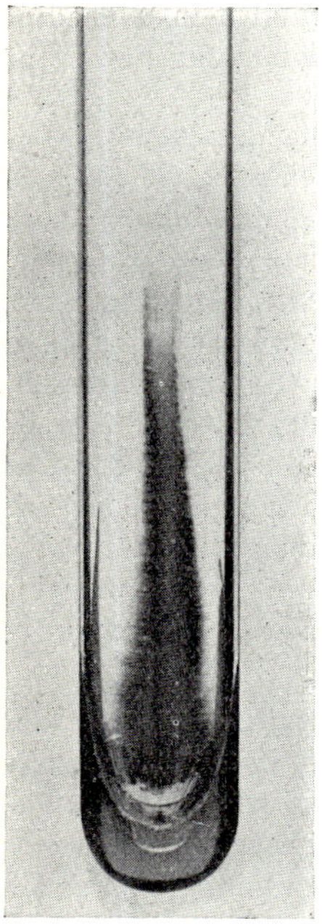

In agar stroke cultures there is a raised, confluent, pigmented growth, with a smooth or beaten-copper surface, and an undulate or lobate edge.

In gelatin stab culture there is a moderate, filiform growth extending to the bottom of the tube, usually succeeded by liquefaction, which may occur rapidly or slowly. In general, the liquid is turbid and granular, and in the upper centimetre or so is pigmented; below this, out of contact with the air, the growth is colourless. A surface pellicle or ring growth, strongly pigmented, and a slightly pigmented deposit at the bottom of the liquefied gelatin, are not uncommon.

In broth there is a dense turbidity, generally with a pigmented ring growth or surface pellicle, and a slightly pigmented deposit, which frequently becomes viscous and is difficult to disintegrate on shaking. The broth itself often remains colourless. Multiplication of the bacilli seems to occur chiefly near the surface; a membrane forms in contact with the air, sinks to the bottom, and is replaced by a fresh membrane. This accounts for the heavy deposit that is generally present after a week.

Fig. 112.—*Chromobacterium prodigiosum.*
Agar stroke culture, 24 hours, 37° C.

Blood serum is frequently liquefied.

Resistance.—The organisms of this group are non-sporing, and show no particular resistance to heat or disinfectants. They appear to be killed by a temperature of 55° C. in 1 hour.

Metabolism and Biochemical Characters.—All the members are markedly aerobic, growing best in the presence of an ample supply of oxygen. Growth under anaerobic conditions is poor, and is not accompanied by pigment formation.

Proteins are broken down readily as a rule ; gelatin, casein, and often blood serum are digested. Carbohydrates are attacked freely by some, sparingly by others, generally with the production of acid only.

Growth can be obtained on synthetic media devoid of protein. The optimum temperature of growth is between 25° and 37° C., but some strains will grow as low as 0° C.

All form catalase and reduce methylene blue. Indole is rarely produced ; the M.R. and V.P. reactions are generally negative. Nitrates are often reduced to nitrites ; and ammonia is generally formed from peptone. Formation of H_2S is slight or absent.

Pigment is produced only in the presence of oxygen, and at a suitable temperature. The optimum temperature for pigment formation does not necessarily correspond with that for growth. Thus many organisms grow best at 30–37° C., but form little or no pigment, whereas at a lower temperature growth is poorer, but pigment formation is abundant. Pigment is developed best on the surface of solid media ; in broth and in the depths of stab cultures there is little or none formed. Potato is a medium that may be specially recommended for the study of pigment production. As a rule pigment is formed most abundantly on primary isolation ; after subculture in the laboratory for some time, the power to form it may diminish seriously, or be altogether lost. Not all bacilli in a given culture produce the same amount of pigment ; some colonies are deeply coloured, others are faintly or partly coloured, while still others are completely colourless.

Sullivan (1905–6) states that the formation of pigment is dependent on the reaction of the medium, the temperature, the free access of oxygen, and the presence of certain salts. In synthetic media, asparagin, succinic, lactic and citric acids, when combined with an ammonium base, allow of growth and pigment formation. Malic, tartaric, and oxalic acids, combined with ammonia, allow of growth but not of pigment production. Acetic, uric, and formic acids, combined with ammonia, are unfavourable for both growth and pigment production. (This refers to solutions of 0·4 per cent. or under.) The salts favouring the production of pigment serve either to provide nutrient material, or to fix the acid produced, or to afford material for chemical syntheses.

Pathogenicity.—The organisms of this group are essentially saprophytic. A few doubtful cases of suppuration in man have been described (see Schütz and Laun 1933), but generally speaking these organisms do not give rise to natural disease in man or in animals. On experimental inoculation into laboratory animals they prove harmless except in very large doses.

Variation.—It is convenient to mention here that the characters of a single strain are liable to considerable variation. Its cultural appearances are by no means uniform ; colonies may vary in their size, shape, opacity, surface, and consistency.

In their ability to produce pigment there is likewise great variation. From 7 different strains of *Chr. prodigiosum* and *Chr. kielense*, Eisenberg (1914) isolated no fewer than 22 variants, differing in colour from dark red to red, orange-red, pink, pale-pink, pinkish-white, and colourless ; most of these remained stable on subculture. From *Chr. violaceum* 5 variants were obtained. Eisenberg found that variants appeared most readily in ageing cultures, and more rapidly in fluid than in solid media.

Group Producing a Violet Pigment.—*Chr. violaceum*, the chief member of the group, is a common inhabitant of water. The violet pigment is soluble in alcohol, but insoluble in water, chloroform, or benzol. For its formation in synthetic media both magnesium sulphate and a phosphate are required. On subculture the organism frequently loses its pigment-forming power. We append a detailed description of this organism, together with brief accounts of some of the other violet-pigment-producing members.

Chromobacterium violaceum

Synonym.—*B. violaceus.*

Isolation.—Described by Bergonzoni in 1881 (see Text).

Habitat.—Water.

Morphology.—Rods ; 1·5–3·0 $\mu \times$ 0·6 μ ; axis straight, sides parallel, ends rounded ; arranged singly. Motile by peritrichate flagella. Non-sporing ; non-capsulated. Gram-negative, non-acid-fast. May show bipolar staining.

Agar Plate.—2 *days at* 37° *C.* Round colonies, $\frac{1}{2}$–1 mm. in diameter, low convex, violet coloured, translucent, with a smooth glistening surface and an entire edge ; butyrous consistency and easily emulsifiable ; structure appears floccular. After 5 days colonies are larger, 1–2 mm. in diameter, have a finely lobate edge, and are differentiated into a dark convex centre, and a paler, flattened, radiate periphery.

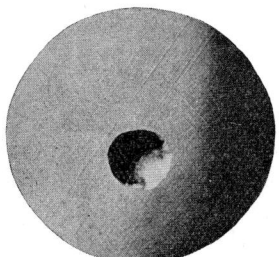

Fig. 113.—*Chromobacterium violaceum.*

Surface colony on agar, 48 hours, 22° C. ($\times$ 8).

Agar Slope.—2 *days,* 25° *C.* Moderate growth, raised, violet, opaque, with glistening, smooth or beaten-copper surface and an undulate edge. Medium unchanged.

Gelatin Stab.—5 *days,* 20° *C.* Moderate, filiform growth to bottom of stab ; violet surface growth ; slow infundibuliform or saccate liquefaction ; liquefied portion is granular and violet.

Broth.—2 *days,* 25° *C.* Abundant growth, with dense, colourless turbidity ; a violet ring growth, and a moderate viscous deposit, disintegrating on shaking. Mawkish odour.

Blood Serum.—9 *days,* 25° *C.* Moderate, confluent growth, colourless, with an uneven surface. Digestion is very slow, or may be absent.

Potato.—6 *days at* 25° *C.* Abundant, raised, confluent, creamy growth of violet colour, with smooth or contoured glistening surface.

Resistance.—Killed by 55° C. in 1 hour.

Metabolism.—Aerobic ; slight colourless growth anaerobically. Opt. temp. 25° C. Pigment formation best at 25–30° C. Pigment : soluble in alcohol, insoluble in chloroform or water.

Nutritional.—Grows well on ordinary media. In synthetic media, pigment is formed only in the presence of $MgSO_4$ and a phosphate.

Biochemical.—Sometimes acid in glucose and maltose. Indole — or slight +. M.R. —. V.P. —. Nitrate reduction +. NH_3 +. Catalase +. M.B. reduction +. H₂S slight +. L.M. 6 days 25° C. alkaline, violet ring growth ; later may be coagulated, and slowly peptonized.

Pathogenicity.—Non-pathogenic to man and animals.

Chr. janthinum, found in water and soil ; is said to be motile by one or two polar flagella. Colonies on agar are at first milky white, but later become violet. Liquefaction of gelatin is slow. On broth it forms a violet surface pellicle. Optimum temperature 30° C. It is doubtful whether this organism is a distinct species.

Chr. amethystium is a non-motile bacillus found in water. On agar the growth is first non-pigmented, later it assumes a dark violet colour with a wrinkled surface of metallic lustre. Gelatin is liquefied ; a violet surface pellicle forms on the liquid. In broth a surface pellicle appears ; the fluid itself is coloured brown. Optimum temperature 30° C.

Chr. cœruleum is said to be motile by polar flagella. Colonies are spreading and of a bluish-grey colour. Slow liquefaction of gelatin. Greyish surface pellicle on broth. Milk is rendered sky-blue at the surface, and is digested with an alkaline reaction. The pigment is soluble in water and alcohol, but not in ether or chloroform. Optimum temperature 30° C.

Group Forming a Pink or Red Pigment.—The most important member of this group is *Chr. prodigiosum.* It was first demonstrated by Bartolomeo Bizio in 1823 as a cause of " bleeding polenta " (Breed and Breed 1924). Infections of meat, fish, bread and other articles of food with this organism from time to time give rise to alarm. Klein (1894) describes an instance where the food in a large mercantile establishment in London became contaminated with it. In spite of the fact that the residents consumed pink meat for some days, they suffered from no apparent ill-effects. The pigment is soluble in absolute alcohol, ether, chloroform, benzol, and carbon disulphide, but is insoluble in water. An alcoholic solution when acted on by mineral acids is turned first carmine-red, then reddish-violet. Alkalies turn it brownish-yellow, and chlorine water, after turning it reddish-brown, then golden-yellow, finally decolorizes it. In the spectrum, blue and violet are completely absorbed, and an absorption band is seen in the green. Wrede (1930) gives its empirical formula as $C_{20}H_{25}N_3O$, and says that only one of the nitrogen atoms is combinable with acids. The pigment is destroyed in a few days by sunlight. It is very resistant to reduction, but is fairly easily oxidized. In synthetic media it is formed only in the presence of magnesium sulphate and a phosphate, preferably potassium phosphate (Kuntze 1900, and Sullivan 1905–06). Its formation is said to be inhibited by the presence of calcium salts (Bordet 1930). It is produced most readily at 22° C., and according to Amako (1930) there is a close parallelism in cultures between the catalase content and the amount of pigment formed.

Hefferan (1904), whose detailed study is one of the most valuable on this group of bacteria, proposed the following classification.

Pigment insoluble in water :

    Group I. *Chr. prodigiosum, Chr. indicum, Chr. kielense,* etc. Pigment red at first, later becomes darker—carmine or violet-red.

    Group II. *Chr. rubricum, Chr. ruber,* etc. Develop more slowly. Pigment is orange-red or yellow-red, never becoming darker.

    Group III. *Chr. mycoides roseum,* etc. Pigment is salmon-pink, coral-pink, rose, or flesh-coloured.

Pigment soluble in water :

    Group IV. *Chr. lactis erythrogenes, Chr. rubefaciens,* etc. Rose-red pigment.

We append a detailed description of *Chr. prodigiosum* and *Chr. indicum*. For a description of other members of this group, see Hefferan (1904).

Chromobacterium prodigiosum

Synonyms.—*Serratia marcescens* Bizio. *Micrococcus prodigiosus* Cohn.

Isolation.—First described by Bizio in 1823 (see Text).

Ecology.—Water and air ; found on bread, meat, milk, potatoes and other food stuffs.

Morphology.—Tiny rods, often oval or cocco-bacillary ; 0·7–1·0 $\mu \times$ 0·7 μ ; sides convex, ends rounded, arranged singly and in groups ; irregularity in shape frequent, there being generally some definitely bacillary forms present. Motile by 2–4 peritrichate flagella. Non-sporing, non-capsulated. Gram-negative, non-acid-fast ; bipolar staining not uncommon.

Agar Plate.—*2 days*, 25° C. Round colonies, 1–2 mm. in diameter, low convex, smooth, glistening, paint-like surface, entire edge, amorphous structure ; butyrous consistency, easily emulsifiable. Individual colonies vary from colourless to bright red in colour ; all are translucent. *5 days.* Colonies are larger, 2–4 mm. in diameter, surface radially striated, edge finely lobate ; differentiated into a low convex, red, opaque centre, and an effuse, transparent, colourless periphery.

FIG. 114.—*Chromobacterium prodigiosum.*

Surface colony on agar, 24 hours, 37° C. ($\times$ 8).

Agar Slope.—Abundant, raised, opaque, scarlet growth, with smooth, paint-like surface and lobate edge. Medium unchanged.

Gelatin Stab.—Abundant, filiform growth to bottom of tube. Liquefaction infundibuliform reaching to bottom of tube in 5 days at 20° C. ; liquid is pink at upper part and turbid ; red ring growth at surface ; pink floccular deposit ; rest of growth uncoloured.

Broth.—*2 days*, 25° C. Luxuriant, pink growth, with dense turbidity, a red ring growth, and a moderate, reddish, powdery or finely granular deposit, mostly disintegrating on shaking. After 5 days there is a red surface pellicle and a heavy flocculo-granular deposit. Mawkish odour, like trimethylamine.

Blood Serum.—*7 days*, 25° C. Profuse growth ; medium mostly liquefied ; fluid is red and turbid.

Potato.—*6 days at 25° C.* Abundant, thick, raised, confluent growth of dark maroon colour ; surface papillate and slightly glistening. Potato not coloured.

MacConkey Plate.—*24 hours at 37° C.* Circular, low convex, opaque, amorphous, pink colonies, 1 mm. in diameter, with smooth glistening surface and entire edge.

Resistance.—Destroyed by 55° C. for 1 hour.

Metabolic.—Aerobe ; slight colourless growth anaerobically. Opt. temp. 25–30° C. Grows at 37° C., but no pigment produced. Pigment : blood-red, soluble in chloroform, not in water.

Nutritional.—Grows well on ordinary media. In synthetic media pigment is formed only in the presence of $MgSO_4$ and a phosphate.

Biochemical.—Acid or acid and gas in glucose, maltose, mannitol, sucrose and salicin, occasionally in lactose. Indole —. M.R. —. V.P. +. Nitrates reduced. NH_3 production +. Catalase +. M.B. reduction ++. Starch diastase —. H_2S +. L.M. clotted in 2 days, peptonized in 5 days ; fluid pinkish.

Pathogenicity.—Non-pathogenic to man ; and to animals except in enormous doses.

Chromobacterium indicum

Isolation.—By Koch from the stomach of an ape.

Morphology.—Slender, often curved, bacillus, 2–4 μ long by 0·6 μ broad ; motile by peritrichate flagella. Gram-negative. Non-acid-fast.

Cultural Characters.—Grows readily on ordinary media.

> *Agar plate.*—*2 days at* 25° *C.* Colonies are circular, 1 mm. in diameter, amorphous, low convex, translucent, and pink, with a smooth surface and entire edge ; butyrous in consistency and easily emulsifiable. After 5 days, there is usually a thin, transparent, colourless peripheral fringe with a finely lobate edge.

> *Gelatin.*—*5 days at* 20° *C.* Abundant growth ; complete liquefaction of gelatin ; upper $\frac{1}{2}$ cm. of the liquefied gelatin is densely turbid and bright red in colour; pinkish deposit at bottom of tube.

> *Broth.*—*2 days,* 25° *C.* Luxuriant growth, with dense turbidity, a pink surface pellicle and ring growth, and an abundant, moderately granular, pink deposit, which disintegrates partly on shaking.

> *Potato.*—*6 days,* 25° *C.* Moderate, slightly raised, confluent growth of café-au-lait colour, having a smooth or finely granular, contoured, moist, glistening surface.

> *Loeffler's serum.*—*5 days,* 25° *C.* Abundant, confluent, raised, pinkish growth, with a glistening contoured surface ; slight digestion, increasing with further incubation.

Biochemical Reactions.—Same as *Chr. prodigiosum.*

Pathogenicity.—Nil.

Chromobacterium kielense.—This organism, which was isolated from water, resembles *Chr. prodigiosum* very closely ; it is not clear, in fact, that it is a separate species. It is said uniformly to produce both acid and gas in carbohydrate media ; but as many strains of *Chr. prodigiosum* also produce gas, this distinction is an imperfect one.

Group Forming a Yellow or Orange Pigment.—*Chr. aquatile,* an organism isolated by the Franklands (1889) from deep wells in the Kent chalk, is a typical example of this group. The yellow pigment is insoluble in water but dissolves in alcohol, ether and chloroform. In non-albuminous media it is developed slowly ; but it appears rapidly in a peptone solution containing magnesium sulphate and dipotassium hydrogen phosphate.

We append a detailed description of *Chr. aquatile* and *Chr. typhi-flavum,* together with brief notes on a few of the other members of this group. The identity of *Chr. aquatile* is not very certain, since the original description was incomplete. The present description is founded on a study of the strain of *Chr. aquatile* obtained from the National Collection of Type Cultures, London. *Chr. typhi-flavum* is the name we suggest for the organism commonly known as *Bact. typhi flavum.* Though suspected by certain German workers of being a pigmented variant of the true typhoid bacillus, the evidence, which has been critically reviewed by Cruickshank (1935), is quite insufficient to establish any such relationship.

Chromobacterium aquatile

Synonym.—*Bacillus aquatilis* Frankland.

Habitat.—Water.

Morphology.—Slender rod-shaped organism, 2·5 μ × 0·6 μ ; axis straight, sides parallel, ends rounded ; arranged in bundles ; length irregular. Motile by peritrichate flagella. Non-sporing ; non-capsulated. Gram-negative ; non-acid-fast.

Agar Plate.—*2 days at* 25° *C.*   Round colonies, 1–2 mm. in diameter, low convex, opaque, yellowish-grey colour, with a dull, dry, granular or rugose surface, and an entire edge ; consistency slightly membranous but emulsification fairly easy.   After 5 days, colony shows differentiation into finely granular, yellowish-brown, convex centre, and a clear almost transparent, effuse, and sometimes radiate periphery, which has an erose or villous edge.

Agar Slope.—Abundant, confluent, opaque, yellowish, raised growth, with smooth glistening surface and a lobate or villous edge.

Broth.—*2 days at* 25° *C.*   Slight turbidity, with slight powdery deposit.   After 5 days the growth is more abundant ; there is a very slightly granular turbidity, and sometimes a surface pellicle and ring growth ; moderate membranous deposit, disintegrating incompletely on shaking.

Gelatin Stab.—*5 days at* 20° *C.*   Good growth, extending to bottom of tube ; gelatin shows commencing infundibuliform liquefaction ; the liquefied gelatin shows a floccular turbidity, and is covered with a granular pellicle.

Potato.—*6 days at* 25° *C.*   Abundant, slightly raised, confluent, greyish-brown growth, with a dry, dull, worm-cast surface.

Loeffler's Serum.—*5 days at* 25° *C.*   Good, confluent, raised, yellowish-white growth, with wrinkled surface.   14 *days*, partial digestion.

Metabolism.—Strict aerobe ; no growth under anaerobic conditions.   Yellow pigment formed on agar, soluble in alcohol, ether, and chloroform, but insoluble in water. Optimum temperature for growth 25–30° C.

Biochemical Characters.—Acid in glucose, maltose, mannitol, and sucrose.   L.M. clot, peptonization, and partial decolorization in 3 days.   Indole —.   M.R. —.   V.P. +. Nitrates reduced to nitrites. NH_3 sl. +. H_2S +.   M.B. reduction +.   Catalase +.

Pathogenicity.—Nil.

Chromobacterium typhi-flavum

Synonym.—*Bacterium typhi flavum* (Dresel and Stickl 1928).

Habitat.—Air, grass, plants.   Has been found in normal human fæces and urine.

Morphology.—Slender, rod-shaped organism, 1–3 $\mu \times$ 0·5–0·7 μ : axis straight, sides parallel, ends rounded ; sometimes filaments up to 15–20 μ in length ; arranged singly, in pairs end-to-end or in groups ; in fluid media sausage-like aggregations may occur.   Briskly motile when grown at 22° C., but poorly or not at all at 37° C.   Flagella peritrichate.   Non-sporing. Non-capsulated.   Gram-negative ; occasional bipolar staining.   Non-acid-fast.

Agar Plate.—*24 hours at* 37° *C.*   Ready growth of colonies 1–2 mm. in diameter, round, low convex, amorphous, smooth, glistening, opaque, with entire edge ; consistency butyrous, emulsifiability easy.   Ochre or rusty yellow pigment, not diffusing into the medium.

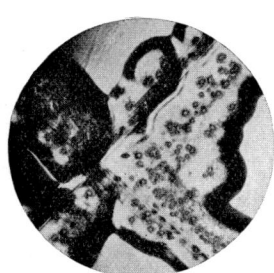

Fig. 115.—*Chromobacterium typhi-flavum.*

Surface growth on agar plate, showing the peculiar appearance caused by aggregations of the bacteria.   One biconvex body is clearly visible. 24 hours, 37° C.

5 *days.*—Colonies are larger, 2–4 mm., differentiated frequently into a central plateau, often with a granular surface, and a smooth bevelled periphery ; edge sometimes crenated.

In the centre of the colonies aggregated masses with radiating extensions of a granular nature, or biconvex bodies with a clear-cut margin, may often be seen with the lens by transmitted light.   The granular structures are aggregations of organisms, known to the German workers as *Bakterien-verbänden* or *symplasmata* (Fig. 115).   The biconvex bodies represent downgrowths of the colony into the medium.

Agar Slope.—24 *hours at* 37° *C.* Abundant, confluent, smooth, glistening, yellow, opaque growth, with entire or slightly undulate edge.

5 *per cent. Glycerine Agar Slope.*—Growth similar to that on agar slope but very mucoid in character.

Agar Shake.—Yellow surface growth with a few small colonies throughout the medium.

Agar Pour-Plate.—Deep colonies are biconvex, sometimes with lateral knobs or projections.

Broth.—24 *hours at* 37° *C.* Uniform turbidity with a powdery white or yellowish deposit easily dispersed on shaking. After 5 days, increased turbidity with a fine surface scum or ring.

Horse-blood Agar Plate.—No hæmolysis. Colonies as on agar plate.

MacConkey's Agar.—24 *hours at* 37° *C.* Growth hardly perceptible. 5 *days.*—Irregularly round colourless colonies with a rough surface and crenated edge.

Loeffler's Serum Slope.—24 *hours at* 37° *C.* Good, confluent, glistening, yellow growth with smooth or slightly contoured surface and undulate edge. No liquefaction.

Potato.—3 *days at* 37° *C.* Abundant, confluent, yellow, glistening, mucoid growth.

Gelatin Stab.—Filiform growth along line of inoculation. After 6–10 days liquefaction begins and progresses till the medium is entirely liquefied in the next 10–15 days. Liquefaction is infundibuliform ; a yellow surface pellicle forms, and later sinks to the bottom.

Resistance.—Destroyed by 56° C. in 10 minutes.

Metabolism.—Aerobic. Poor unpigmented growth anaerobically. Grows freely at 20–37° C., with optimum nearer to 37° C. Pigment ochre or rusty-yellow, insoluble in water and chloroform, partly soluble in alcohol and ether.

Biochemical Reactions.—Acid in glucose, mannitol, sucrose, salicin, rhamnose, arabinose, xylose ; maltose usually later. Lactose, inositol and dulcitol not fermented. Litmus milk neutral or transient acidity, becoming alkaline after 3–7 days ; occasional soft clot. Indole —. M.R. +. V.P. —. Nitrates reduced. Very slight H_2S production at 22° C. Catalase +

Antigenic Structure.—The organisms are antigenically heterogeneous. Both as regards flagellar and somatic antigens, sera prepared against any one strain will agglutinate the homologous strain, and usually several other strains. There is a tendency for the organisms to fall roughly into antigenically similar groups, the " H " antigens being more cosmopolitan than the " O."

Pathogenicity.—It has been suggested that the organism is a variant of *Bact. typhosum*, of potential pathogenicity to man, but this has not been substantiated. Pathogenic to mice only on injection of enormous doses.

There are several organisms in water and in soil belonging to this group, amongst which may be mentioned :

Chr. ochraceum.—Motile by polar flagella. Infundibuliform liquefaction in gelatin with a pale yellow, later ochre-coloured, deposit. On agar and potato a thin, ochre-yellow streak.

Chr. fuscum.—Non-motile ; liquefies gelatin slowly or not at all. On agar and potato gives a thick, wrinkled, chrome-yellow growth.

Chr. aurantiacum.—Motile by peritrichate flagella. No liquefaction of gelatin. On agar and potato forms a light orange growth.

Chr. denitrificans.—Described by Burri and Stutzer (1895), who isolated it from horse fæces ; called by them *B. denitrificans* I. Appears to be common in the soil. Rods with rounded ends, 1·5–2·5 μ × 0·75 μ. Actively motile. Gram-negative. Grows freely on ordinary media, more quickly at 37° C. than at room temperature, and is aerobic. Colonies on agar are very thin and membranous, having a thicker centre ; generally circular, but may have a lobate or irregularly erose edge. In broth there is a dense turbidity in 24 hours, with a reddish-white deposit disintegrating on shaking ; surface ring growth. Produces large amount of gas in nitrate broth, reducing the nitrate to free nitrogen. Non-pathogenic. This organism is not to be confused with *Ps. denitrificans* (*q.v.* Chapter XX).

ACHROMOBACTERIUM

DEFINITION.—*Achromobacterium*.

> Motile or non-motile, Gram-negative rods, usually small to medium in size, forming no pigment on agar, and varying in their fermentative ability. Optimum temperature for growth about 25° C. ; little or no growth at 37° C. Saprophytic ; commonly found in water, soil, and milk.

Organisms of this group are widespread in nature, but have so far received little systematic study. The public health bacteriologist meets them mainly in the analysis of water, milk, and soil, where they attract attention by their frequency on agar and gelatin plates incubated at 22° C. They are differentiated from the *Chromobacterium* group mainly by their failure to form pigment. Discussion of their classification would at present serve no useful purpose, and all that we need do here is to give a brief account of their more common characteristics.

Morphologically they are Gram-negative, motile or non-motile rods, often of the size of coliform bacilli, but varying considerably in thickness ; rather fat rods, and fat cocco-bacilli are quite common.

Growth occurs best at about 25° C. ; there is little or no growth at 37° C., but growth often takes place at 0° C. (Coyne 1933). The colonial appearances vary. After 24 hours at 22° C. colonies on agar are about 0·5 mm. in diameter, circular, smooth, convex, greyish white, and translucent with an entire edge ; after 5 days they are 3–5 mm. in diameter, raised or low convex, greyish, opaque, with a smooth surface and entire edge, or sometimes with a beaten-copper surface and an irregular edge. Mucoid colonies are not uncommon, and seem to be formed most frequently by the short fat cocco-bacillary type. Colonies with central crateriform depressions, draughtsman-like colonies, colonies with a roughish surface, and colonies showing radial striation are sometimes met with. An aromatic odour may be noticeable.

In broth there is a uniform turbidity of varying degree with a powdery, granular, or viscous deposit. On potato a layer of growth is formed, which is sometimes mucoid or creamy, and which often takes on a café-au-lait appearance after a week or two.

Most, but not all, strains seem to grow in MacConkey's bile-salt medium. In liquid MacConkey they give rise to turbidity, but not usually to acid production ; on solid MacConkey they form small yellowish colonies, which after 5 days at 22° C. may reach a diameter of 1–2 mm.

Litmus milk may be unchanged. More often it is turned alkaline, or peptonized. Some strains produce acid and curdle the milk. The litmus is often reduced to within a few millimetres of the surface.

Sugar reactions are variable. Most strains have little or no fermentative ability, but some produce acid in glucose, or in glucose, maltose, mannitol, sucrose, and salicin, less often in lactose. Gelatin may or may not be liquefied. Some strains give a positive M.R. or V.P. reaction, or both. Nitrates are not uncommonly reduced to nitrites, but indole is rarely formed.

Little or nothing is known of their antigenic characteristics. It is probable that they are all non-pathogenic.

REFERENCES

AMAKO, T. H. (1930) *Zbl. Bakt.*, **116,** 494, 499.

BORDET, P. (1930) *Ann. Inst. Pasteur*, **45,** 26.

BREED, R. S. and BREED, M. E. (1924) *J. Bact.*, **9,** 545.

BURRI, R. and STUTZER, A. (1895) *Zbl. Bakt.*, IIte Abt., **1,** 257, 350.

COYNE, F. P. (1933) *Proc. roy. Soc.*, B, **113,** 196.

CRUICKSHANK, J. C. (1935) *J. Hyg., Camb.*, **35,** 354.

DRESEL, E. G. and STICKL, O. (1928) *Dtsch. med. Wschr.*, **54,** 517.

EISENBERG, P. (1914) *Zbl. Bakt.*, **73,** 466.

FRANKLAND, G. C. and FRANKLAND, P. F. (1889) *Z. Hyg. InfektKr.*, **6,** 373.

HEFFERAN, M. (1904) *Zbl. Bakt.*, IIte Abt., **6,** 311, 397, 456, 520.

KLEIN, E. (1894) *J. Path. Bact.*, **2,** 217.

KUNTZE, W. (1900) *Z. Hyg. InfektKr.*, **34,** 169.

Report. (1920) *Rep. Comm. Amer. Bacteriologists, J. Bact.*, **5,** 191.

SCHÜTZ, F. and LAUN, H. (1933) *Zbl. Bakt.*, **129,** 124.

SULLIVAN, M. X. (1905–6) *J. med. Res.*, **14,** 109.

WREDE, F. (1930) *Z. Hyg. InfektKr.*, **111,** 531.

CHAPTER XXVI

PROTEUS AND ZOPFIUS

PROTEUS

DEFINITION.—*Proteus.*

Highly pleomorphic rods, filaments and curved cells being common in young cultures. Gram-negative. Actively motile. Characteristic spreading growth on moist media. Often liquefy gelatin and often produce vigorous decomposition of proteins. Ferment glucose and usually sucrose, but not mannitol or lactose, with fermentation of acid and gas.

Type species. *P. vulgaris* Hauser.

Habitat.—Organisms of the *Proteus* group have been known since the earliest days of bacteriology. They are widely distributed in nature, and constitute an important part of the flora of decomposing organic matter of animal origin. They are constantly present in rotten meat and in sewage, and very frequently in manure. Though often demonstrable in the fæces of man and animals, they are rarely found in large numbers except when the normal intestinal mechanism is deranged. They are not uncommon in garden soil and on certain vegetables, such as melons and celery (Cantu 1911), but it seems probable that their access to these materials results largely from contamination with sewage or manure.

Besides their wide saprophytic existence, *Proteus* bacilli are able under certain conditions to grow in the animal body and even to give rise to pathological disturbances. The rôle they play in summer diarrhœa is not yet entirely clear, but there is no doubt that in some outbreaks of this disease they multiply enormously in the intestinal canal, particularly of infants. This holds particularly true of Morgan's bacillus which, in the light of Rauss's (1936) recent work, must be regarded as belonging to the *Proteus* group. They are primarily responsible for some cases of cystitis, and they are to be met with as secondary invaders in infections of the bladder and in wounds. Many strains, referred to as *Proteus X* strains, have been isolated from the urine, fæces, or blood of patients suffering from typhus fever, though their exact relationship to the ætiological agent of this disease is still obscure (see Chapter LXXX).

Morphology.—The organisms are rod-shaped, but are subject to great variation in size. In agar cultures after 24–48 hours, the majority are of the coliform type, 1–3 μ long by 0·4–0·6 μ wide, though short fat cocco-bacillary forms are not uncommon (Figs. 118, 119). In young rapidly growing cultures, however, in which swarming (see p. 505) is apparent, many of the organisms are long, curved, and filamentous, reaching 10, 20, or even 30 μ in length (Fig. 117). There is no very characteristic arrangement; the bacilli are distributed singly, in pairs, in short chains, in small bundles, or in larger bundles in which the members tend to be arranged concentrically, more or less simulating the isobars in a diagram of a cyclone. There is some variation in depth of staining. Except for non-flagellated O variants, all members are actively motile by peritrichate flagella in young cultures. Neither spores nor capsules are formed. The reaction to Gram's stain is uniformly negative.

Cultural Characters.—Growth occurs freely on the usual media. One of the most characteristic properties of *Proteus* strains is their ability to "swarm" on solid media. Cantu (1911), who made a study of this feature, found that if an organism of the *Proteus* group was inoculated into the water of condensation of an agar slope, a rapid growth occurred, which spread over the whole surface, producing a uniform layer hardly distinguishable from the medium. This process has been more fully described by Moltke (1927, 1929). "Swarming" may be defined as a "progressive surface spreading by the microbes from the edge of the parent colony." It is best studied by touching the centre of an agar plate with a needle dipped in a *Proteus* culture. First of all a colony develops, and then after about 6 hours

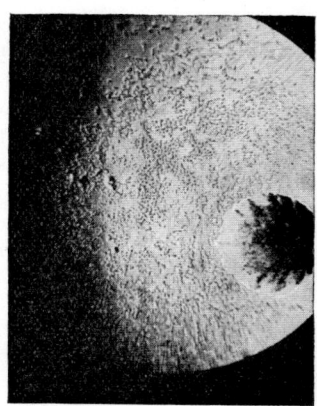

Fig. 116.—*Proteus vulgaris,* showing swarming on agar, 6 hours, 37° C. (× 8).

at 37° C. a thin, effuse, ground-glass type of growth appears round the edge of the colony, and rapidly spreads over the whole plate (Fig. 116). If it is examined under the microscope, it is seen that, when swarming commences, long slender rods in continuous motion break away from the periphery of the colony, and, after travelling some distance from the parent colony, join neighbouring lateral offshoots, to form arches, which are rapidly filled with other rods from within. Whole rafts of rods tear loose from the peninsula so formed, and work across the agar, so that in a short time the colony is surrounded by an archipelago of islands and solitary organisms, all constantly in motion. The very long rod forms are the predominant feature in the picture ; they form arches, islands, spirals, and question-mark forms (Fig. 117). Once the plate is completely covered with "swarmers", the long rods are replaced by quite short forms

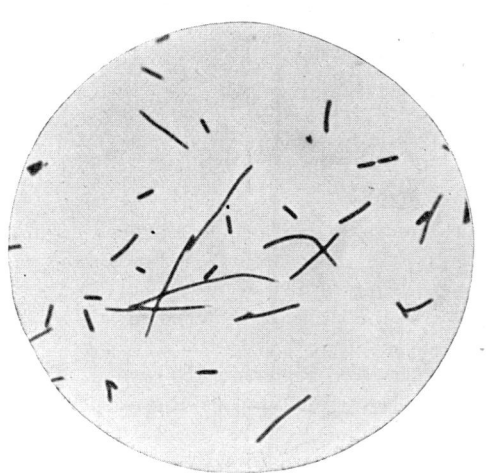

Fig. 117.—*Proteus vulgaris.* From an agar culture, 6 hours, 37° C., showing long filaments (× 1000).

(Figs. 118 and 119). This property of swarming is observed only on the surface of solid media. In the depths of an agar shake or pour plate culture the colonies are compact. This circumstance may be made use of in the isolation of organisms mixed with *Proteus* bacilli (Fry 1932). According to Lode and Howard (1932), swarming can also be inhibited by certain narcotic drugs, such as chloral hydrate, morphine, and sodium phenylethylbarbiturate. For this purpose chloral hydrate should be used in a final concentration of 1/500–1/1000, or phenol in about 1/1000. Swarming is due essentially to the active motility of the bacilli. Non-motile O variants give rise to compact colonies which, according to Felix (1922), may be of three types: (1) smooth, translucent, homogeneous, with an entire edge ; (2) granular and opaque with an irregular edge ; (3) tiny colonies, barely visible to the naked eye after 24 hours.

Russ-Münzer (1935) finds that swarming on an agar plate is a discontinuous phenomenon. On a plate inoculated centrally and incubated at 37° C., a thin layer of bacteria is present at the site of inoculation after about 4 hours. Swarming then begins, and in 6 hours the breadth of the growth is 1–1·5 cm. Further progress

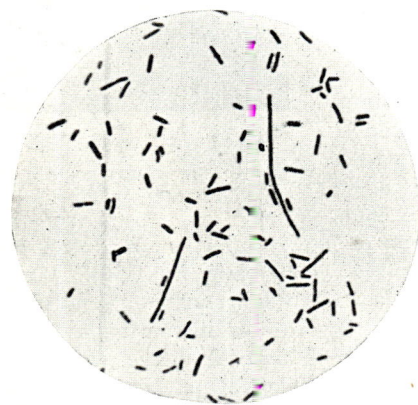

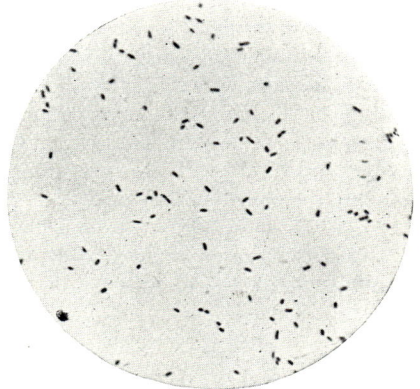

FIG. 118.—*Proteus vulgaris.*
From an agar culture, 2¼ hours, 37° C., showing chiefly rod forms (× 1000).

FIG. 119.—*Proteus vulgaris.*
From an agar culture, 48 hours, 37° C., showing short rods only (× 1000).

outwards ceases, but the layer of growth becomes thicker. After 8 hours swarming again starts, and a fresh ring of growth appears. The alternation of swarming and rest occurs regularly, a fresh ring of growth being formed about every 4 hours till the plate is covered. It is due to this periodic extension that the surface of the growth appears rippled.

Though the property of swarming is generally considered to be peculiar among aerobic bacteria to the *Proteus* group, it has been pointed out by Rauss (1936) that strains of Morgan's (1905) bacillus, which have not hitherto been included in this group, also exhibit the ability to swarm under appropriate conditions. On ordinary agar at 37° C. this organism forms circumscribed colonies, but on solid media containing only 1 per cent. agar incubated at 20°–28° C., characteristic swarming occurs. Variant forms are described having a less marked power to spread, and these give rise to colonies distinguished by varying degrees of peripheral spread as well as by their structural appearance.

In broth *Proteus* gives rise to a uniform turbidity accompanied by a slight to moderate powdery deposit and a faint ammoniacal smell. Cantu (1911) states that a surface pellicle is never formed, while Wenner and Rettger (1919) and Yacob (1932) say that a thin fragile pellicle may develop in older cultures. Gelatin plate colonies are very characteristic (Cantu 1911).

Resistance.—Few observations appear to have been made on the resistance of *Proteus* bacilli. Our own limited experience has shown that they are readily destroyed by heat and disinfectants. Exposure to moist heat at 60° C. for 1 hour is sufficient to sterilize a broth culture. A 1 per cent. phenol solution, inoculated with one million organisms per c.c., is found to be sterile within 30 minutes.

Metabolism.—The members of this group are aerobes and facultative anaerobes. Growth under strict anaerobic conditions is very poor, and certain enzymic activities may be suppressed. The optimum temperature for growth is about 34°–37° C., though rapid multiplication occurs above 20° C. The limits of growth are between about 10° C. and 43° C.

Reports on the hæmolytic activity of *Proteus* are discrepant. Wenner and Rettger (1919) obtained uniformly negative, and Norton, Verder, and Ridgway (1928) uniformly positive results. In neither of these reports is the type of blood mentioned. Taylor (1928), using human blood, observed hæmolysis regularly within 24 hours in 1 per cent. blood broth, but not on 10 per cent. blood agar plates. Yacob (1932) used 5 per cent. rabbit blood agar plates, and found that all strains produced β-hæmolysis in 24–48 hours. As with many other organisms, it seems probable that the nature of the blood is an important factor in determining the result.

The main features that distinguish *Proteus* bacilli from other Gram-negative gelatin-liquefying rods are the production of H_2S and the decomposition of urea (Moltke 1927). According to Wolf (1918–19), urea is broken down very actively, as much as 45 per cent. of the total nitrogen of urine being transformed into ammonia. The production of indole and the digestion of serum proteins varies with different strains ; as a rule these two properties are negatively correlated. The power to digest serum proteins is often lost during cultivation in the laboratory. Catalase is formed, but the oxidase reaction described by Gordon and McLeod (1928) is negative.

Since the *Proteus* bacilli are found most constantly in decomposing animal matter, they are generally regarded as putrefactive organisms. Rettger and Newell (1912–13) dispute this. They define putrefaction as a " particular process of protein decomposition which is brought about through the agency of bacteria with the evolution of foul-smelling products which are characteristic of ordinary cadaveric decomposition." Amongst these decomposition products they consider mercaptan and the oxy-acids to be of particular significance ; indole, skatole, and H_2S are less characteristic. According to this definition the *Proteus* group would be classed amongst the non-putrefactive bacteria. The connotation that Rettger and Newell attach to the term putrefaction is that it is essentially an anaerobic process ; it is dependent therefore on the anaerobic growth of bacteria. *Proteus* bacilli, when grown under anaerobic conditions, do not digest proteins, and therefore cannot be regarded as capable of causing true putrefaction. They are, however, frequently associated with the anaerobes in putrefying organic material, and no doubt assist these greatly by using up oxygen and rendering the conditions suitable for their growth. It may be noted that this definition would not meet with universal acceptance.

Biochemical Reactions.—Acid and gas are formed from glucose, sucrose, glycerol, xylose, and almost always from salicin. Mannitol, lactose, dulcitol, starch, dextrin, sorbitol, and raffinose are never fermented. The action on maltose is variable and is of value in classification. Moltke (1927), who examined 194 strains, found that 37 fermented maltose, and 157 did not. The maltose-positive strains fermented sucrose and salicin within 24 hours, while the maltose-negative strains took 3–15 days to ferment sucrose and 10–21 days to ferment salicin. All but one of the maltose-positive strains produced indole, while the maltose-negative strains uniformly failed to do so. A negative correlation was observed between the fermentation of maltose and the ability to digest coagulated horse serum. In the definition of the group by Winslow and his colleagues (1920) it is stated that the gas produced from glucose and sucrose consists entirely of CO_2. Mendel (1911), however, gives the gas ratio as $H_2 : CO_2 = 6\text{–}8 : 1$, while Yacob (1932) gives it as $3\text{–}4 : 1$. These latter figures agree with our own findings. The fermentative activity of *Proteus* is fairly constant, but some strains lose their power to attack certain sugars on prolonged cultivation, while other strains, such as *Proteus morgani*, are restricted in their fermentative power from the start. The action on litmus milk is subject to slight variation. Usually a true rennet-like clot is produced, which retracts and squeezes out whey. Digestion of the clot sets in and is accompanied by progressive alkalinization of the medium. The litmus is reduced. The clot is often digested completely within a week, and the reaction is strongly alkaline. Slight initial acidity is sometimes observed, and not infrequently proteolysis may overshadow coagulation, so that there is not time for a definite clot to form. The methyl-red reaction is positive and the Voges-Proskauer negative. Nitrates are reduced to nitrites. Methylene blue is decolorized slowly in broth cultures.

Antigenic Structure.—Our knowledge is both deficient and conflicting. Most workers (Cantu 1911, Wenner and Rettger 1919, Taylor 1928) who have prepared immune sera against different strains have found that a given serum may agglutinate either the homologous strain only or a number of heterologous strains as well. Any simple subdivision by agglutination or absorption of agglutinins has proved impossible. Moltke (1927), who paid special attention to the H and O antigens, found that by direct agglutination the swarming strains could be divided into 3 main groups, and that by absorption these main groups could be divided into a number of sub-groups. The non-swarming strains differed from the swarming strains in their absence of an H antigen, and differed among themselves in the type of their O antigen. The relation of the *vulgaris* to the *X* strains is still somewhat doubtful. The O antigens of the *X* strains differ from those of the *vulgaris* strains, but there appears to be a certain group relationship between the H antigens (Yacob 1932). Among the O antigens of the *X* strains there are at present three fairly well-defined groups, represented by the strains *OX* 2, *OX* 19, and *OX* K (see Chapter LXXX). White (1933) has brought evidence to show that the O antigen of *OX* 19 contains two receptors, one of which is alkali-labile and is mainly responsible for agglutination of this organism by an antiserum prepared against it, the other of which is alkali-stable, and is responsible for the reaction of the bacillus with the sera of patients suffering from typhus fever—the Weil-Felix reaction. Meisel and Mikulaszek (1933) and Castaneda (1934, 1935) have reported the extraction of soluble specific polysaccharide substances from *Proteus X* strains. Castaneda's results agree closely with those obtained by White. They show that the alkali-stable polysaccharide, referred to as X, is common to both *Proteus X* 19 and *Rickettsia prowazeki* (see Chapter XXXVI), while the alkali-labile polysaccharide, referred to as P, is specific to *Proteus X* 19.

With regard to *Proteus morgani*, Rauss states that the H antigen tends to be group-specific, and the O antigen type-specific. In an examination of 48 strains, 7 types of H antigen were differentiated, but as many as 17 types of O antigen. A relationship was found between the H receptor of one group of *morgani* and a strain of *Proteus vulgaris*.

Pathogenicity.—*Proteus* bacilli are frequently found in, and appear to be responsible for, a number of inflammatory and suppurative conditions in man. They are a very common cause of cystitis and may be isolated in pure culture from the urine of infected patients. They are not uncommonly found in abscesses, either alone or in combination with other organisms. Metchnikoff and his co-workers (see Chapter LXVIII) found them almost constantly in the fæces of infants with summer diarrhœa. They are frequently present, apparently as secondary invaders, in gunshot wounds, where they probably favour the development of the pathogenic anaerobes. And they have been isolated from a variety of conditions, such as volvulus, peritonitis, croupous pneumonia, acute gastro-enteritis of the food-poisoning type (Wichels and Barner 1925), empyema, gangrene of the lung, and septicæmia. Jensen (1913) considers them responsible for one form of epidemic calf dysentery ; and Wyss (1898) has encountered them in an epidemic disease of fish in Lake Zürich.

The relation of *Proteus X* 19 to typhus fever is discussed in Chapter LXXX.

Their pathogenicity to laboratory animals is variable ; virulent strains on introduction into the tissues are able to proliferate and invade the blood stream. Strains of lower virulence cause chronic inflammatory processes, either of the suppurative or of the infective granuloma type (Larson and Bell 1913, Wenner and Rettger 1919) ; the latter are best seen after intraperitoneal injection.

The inoculation intraperitoneally of 0·5–1·0 c.c. of a 24-hour broth culture of a virulent strain generally proves fatal to rats and mice in 18–48 hours, and to guinea-pigs and rabbits in 1–7 days. Severe infections in rabbits are said to be characterized by extreme emaciation (Larson and Bell 1913). Though invasion of the tissues may occur on parenteral inoculation, Jensen (1913) states that in naturally infected calves, even when the organisms are seething in the gut, the blood and tissues remain sterile.

Classification.—Hauser (1885) divided the *Proteus* group into three species : (1) *Proteus vulgaris* ; Gram-negative, liquefies gelatin, peptonizes fibrin, produces indole, and has a variable action on glucose and sucrose. (2) *Proteus mirabilis* ; Gram-negative, more highly pleomorphic, and liquefies gelatin more slowly. (3) *Proteus zenkeri* ; Gram-positive, does not liquefy gelatin, does not form indole, and fails to attack sugars. *Proteus zenkeri* was found to be very similar to an organism described two years previously by Kurth (1883) under the name of *B. zopfii* ; as both of these organisms are Gram-positive, they had to be transferred to a separate genus, which is known as *Zopfius*.

Hauser's subdivision of the *Proteus* group on the basis of morphology, rate of liquefaction of gelatin, and indole production, has been found impracticable. The morphology is variable, depending especially on the medium and the age of the culture. The rate of liquefaction of gelatin is likewise variable ; it is rapid with newly isolated strains, and is often much slower, or even absent, with strains that have been long under artificial cultivation. Indole production used to be tested by the nitroso-indole reaction ; but as Berthelot (1914) has shown, this reaction is untrustworthy, and is given by indolacetic acid as well as by indole ; when tested by Ehrlich's reagent, using the ether extraction method, it is found that the results are different, and that indole production is not nearly so constant a feature of *Proteus* as it was originally considered to be.

The most striking characteristics of the members of this group are their ability to swarm on solid media, their production of H_2S, their decomposition of urea, their liquefaction of gelatin, and their failure to ferment lactose or any of the polyhydric alcohols. It should however be added that O variants occur which have lost their power of swarming, and that old strains may no longer liquefy gelatin.

The recent observations of Rauss (1936) suggest very strongly that Morgan's bacillus, which has hitherto occupied an invidious position in the Salmonella group, is closely related to *Proteus*. Its ability to swarm under suitable conditions, its frequent fermentation of xylose and its occasional fermentation of sucrose, its production of indole and H_2S, its formation of alkali in litmus milk, the greater group specificity of its H and the greater type specificity of its O antigens, the group relationship of at least one of its H antigens to *Proteus*, its multiplication under favourable conditions in the intestine of human beings, and its general pathogenicity for experimental animals—all bring it closely into line with organisms of the *Proteus* group. Its failure to liquefy gelatin or constantly to ferment sucrose must be considered in relation to the negative reactions obtained in these two respects with known *Proteus* strains, particularly those that have been long cultivated in the laboratory. Intermediate types that peptonize milk, and the organisms described by Magath (1928), which were isolated from cystitis and which liquefied gelatin but did not ferment sucrose, seem to show that too much stress should not be laid on any single biochemical characteristic.

Until a more thorough study has been made, we consider that the most convenient method of classifying the *Proteus* group is on the basis of maltose fermentation and gelatin liquefaction, though we hesitate to ascribe specific names to the members of the sub-groups. The X strains belong mostly to the maltose-positive sub-group, but the Kingsbury strain differs in this respect, as well as in its failure to liquefy gelatin.

(For review of the *Proteus* group, see Cantu 1911, Berthelot 1914, Wenner and Rettger 1919, Besson and Ehringer 1923, Moltke 1927, Taylor 1928, Yacob 1932.)

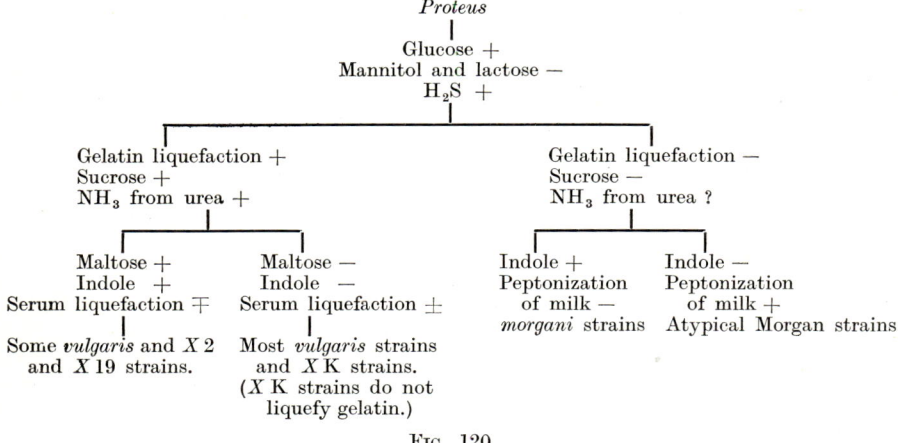

FIG. 120.

This diagram must be regarded as merely tentative, and subject to both exceptions and alterations.

Proteus vulgaris

Synonym.—B. *proteus vulgaris.*

Isolation.—By Hauser in 1885 from putrefying material.

Habitat.—Putrefying animal and vegetable matter; often in fæces, soil and gun-shot wounds.

Morphology.—Straight or slightly curved rods, 1·0–2·5 μ × 0·4–0·6 μ, with parallel sides and rounded ends; arranged singly, in pairs end-to-end, and in short chains. In young swarming cultures, long curved filamentous forms are common. Considerable variation in length; ovoid forms in pairs may be seen, and in old cultures large bloated forms. Staining is fairly uniform, though variations in depth occur. Actively motile by numerous peritrichate flagella, though slightly motile forms with 4 flagella, two at each end, and non-motile forms devoid of flagella may occur. Gram-negative.

Agar Plates.—24 *hours*, 37° *C.* The whole plate is covered with a slightly raised layer of growth, which, but for a faint rippling or contouring of the surface and a marked odour, is easily overlooked. Sometimes indefinite primary colonies are seen, of variable diameter, having a smooth or slightly ringed draughtsman-like surface and an entire edge. The whole growth is translucent, of the same colour as the medium, butyrous, and easily emulsifiable. The complete layer of growth over the whole plate is due to swarming of the bacilli (see text). Non-flagellated O forms give rise to compact colonies.

Agar Slope.—If the organisms are inoculated into the condensation water, they swarm rapidly, and in about 8 hours at 37° C. form a uniform, slightly raised, translucent growth with a glistening, faintly contoured surface over the whole slope. There is a thick turbid growth in the water of condensation itself.

Gelatin Stab.—24 *hours*, 22° *C.* Good filiform growth, consisting of discrete and confluent colonies, extending to the bottom of the tube; smooth raised surface growth 2 or 3 mm. in diameter. Crateriform liquefaction is generally visible after 24 hours in newly isolated strains; liquefaction later becomes stratiform and is complete in 2 to 4 days. With old laboratory strains liquefaction is slower and may not be complete for 3 weeks; sometimes the power to liquefy gelatin is lost altogether. Occasionally very fine tangled branches grow out from the filiform stab. Sometimes the liquefaction is infundibuliform or saccate.

Broth.—24 *hours*, 37° *C.* Moderate growth with a slight to moderate uniform turbidity, and a moderate powdery deposit, disintegrating completely on shaking. No surface growth. The growth increases only slightly on further incubation.

Glucose Agar Shake.—24 *hours*, 37° *C.* Profuse growth of tiny colonies throughout medium, and layer of growth over whole surface. Numerous bubbles of gas throughout medium, sometimes blowing the agar up to the plug.

Horse Blood Agar Plates.—24 *hours*, 37° *C.* Uniform growth over whole surface with indefinite single colonies. The blood is cleared, translucent, and of a slightly brownish colour. β-hæmolysis on 5 per cent. rabbit blood agar plates.

MacConkey Plates.—24 *hours*, 37° *C.* Good growth of colourless, discrete or partly confluent colonies. The colonies may be smooth, but more often have a slightly roughish surface with an irregularly crenated, radially striated edge.

Loeffler's Serum.—Spreading growth over whole surface. On further incubation the serum is liquefied partly or completely, but this power of liquefaction is confined chiefly to maltose-negative strains. Newly isolated strains are more active liquefiers than old laboratory strains.

Dorset Egg.—24 *hours*, 37° *C.* Spreading growth over whole surface. On further incubation digestion occurs, but does not usually proceed to completion.

Cooked Meat Medium.—5 *days*, 37° *C.* Good growth with some bubbles of gas. No blackening or visible digestion occurs.

Potato.—5 *days*, 37° C. Raised, confluent, glistening, greyish-brown growth. The potato itself takes on a café-au-lait colour.

Resistance.—Not specially resistant. Killed by moist heat at 55° C. in 1 hour.

Metabolism.—Aerobe and facultative anaerobe. Growth under anaerobic conditions is poor ; only a very thin, effuse, barely visible growth is formed on agar in 4 days at 37° C. No digestion of protein media occurs under anaerobic conditions. Optimum temperature for growth 34°–37° C. Good growth occurs at 20° C. A hæmolysin is formed, acting on rabbit blood. No pigment formed, except the café-au-lait pigment on potato. Growth is improved by the addition of glucose and of nitrates. No soluble toxin formed.

Biochemical.—All strains produce acid and gas in glucose, galactose, glycerol, and sucrose. Nearly all strains ferment salicin, and some ferment maltose. Lactose, mannitol, and mannose are never attacked. Old laboratory strains may lose their power of fermenting sucrose. *Litmus milk.* Alkaline ; some strains coagulate the casein and then digest it ; others digest it without preliminary coagulation ; the litmus is reduced. Indole is produced by the maltose-fermenting, but not by the maltose-negative strains. $H_2S ++$. $NH_3 ++$. Catalase $++$. Methylene blue reduction $+$. Nitrates reduced to nitrites. M.R. $+$. V.P. $—$. Urea is decomposed with the formation of NH_3.

Antigenic Structure.—Incompletely worked out. By direct agglutination the swarming strains can be divided into 3 main groups, but several smaller groups are present ; by absorption the main groups can be divided into sub-groups. No apparent relationship between the serological and the biochemical grouping. The O antigens tend to be type-specific. Among the *X* strains the *OX* 2, *OX* 19, and *OX* K strains are distinct.

Pathogenicity.—Produces no specific infection under natural conditions, but is frequently found in cystitis, infantile diarrhœa, and suppurative lesions generally. Is probably responsible for one form of calf dysentery. Virulence to laboratory animals is variable. Highly virulent cultures inoculated intraperitoneally into rabbits, rats, or guinea-pigs cause death in a few hours, presumably from toxæmia. Less virulent cultures cause emaciation with death in a week or more after intraperitoneal inoculation, and abscesses and inflammatory conditions lasting for months after subcutaneous inoculation. In fatal cases the organisms can generally be recovered from the blood and viscera.

Proteus morgani was isolated by Morgan (1906) from the stools of patients with summer diarrhœa. It is motile by 25–30 peritrichate flagella. Motility is sometimes lost after long cultivation, but it may sometimes be restored by passage through broth at 20° C. Though not swarming at 37° C. on ordinary agar, it swarms readily at 20°–28° C. on 1 per cent. agar. Variant types, however, occur which are less actively motile, and which give rise to characteristic streaming colonies. The general cultural characters resemble those of the coliform group. Acid and a small amount of gas are produced in glucose peptone water within 24 hours. Xylose is often fermented with the production of acid only, while occasional strains are said to produce acid and a small amount of gas in sucrose after 10 days. Gelatin is not liquefied, but both indole and H_2S are formed abundantly. Litmus milk is turned alkaline. About 30 per cent. of strains give rise to a hæmolysin for sheep red cells. Antigenically, most workers (Lewis 1911–12, Kligler 1919, Thjøtta 1920, Jordan, Crawford, and McBroom 1935), including ourselves, have noted the extraordinary heterogeneity of members of this species. Rauss (1936), who has made a careful study of this question, finds that the H antigen tends to be group-specific and the O antigen type-specific. Seven H receptors and 17 O receptors were differentiated in 48 strains. One of the H antigens in *P. morgani* is similar to one of the H antigens in *P. vulgaris*. The organism seems to be mainly parasitic and potentially pathogenic, assuming a considerable rôle in some outbreaks of infantile diarrhœa. It has been isolated from paratyphoid-like fevers (Havens and Mayfield 1930). Infections in birds, mammals, and reptiles are not uncommon (Lovell 1929), while in mice it may give rise to spontaneous epidemics of enteritis (Wilson 1927), especially in the late summer and autumn months. Experimentally, it produces a rapidly fatal infection in mice on intraperitoneal inoculation. It does not produce a soluble toxin.

Other types of bacilli were isolated by Morgan (1906, 1907), which are sometimes called after him, and which differ from his No. 1 bacillus in their motility, their action on milk, or some other characteristic ; but the term Morgan's bacillus is generally used to indicate the organism we have just described.

ZOPFIUS

Definition.—*Zopfius*.

Long rods, occurring in evenly curved chains. Gram-positive. Motile. Spider-web growth on solid media. Facultative anaerobes. Carbohydrates and gelatin not attacked ; hydrogen sulphide not formed.

Type species, *Zopfius zopfii* (Kurth) Wenner and Rettger ; isolated originally from the intestinal tract of hens.

Organisms of this group are differentiated in several ways from those of the *Proteus* group. Apart from being Gram-positive, they ferment no carbohydrates, they form no H_2S, they do not liquefy gelatin, and they do not exhibit the phenomenon of swarming.

Morphologically, rods are formed, about 3.5μ long by 0.8μ broad, having rounded ends and parallel sides, and occurring in long evenly curved chains ; filamentous forms are common. The organisms are motile by peritrichate flagella (Fig. 6, p. 24).

On agar they form small indistinct colonies having, on magnification, a spider-web appearance ; sometimes the colonies are thinnest at the centre and are surrounded by arborescent tufts. In gelatin stab arborescent lateral branches, interlacing freely, grow out from the stab. There is a slow, moderate growth in broth, with occasionally a thin fragile pellicle. Optimum temperature for growth is 25° C. ; growth occurs freely between 20° and 30° C., but is very poor at 37° C. No sugars are fermented, and there is only a scanty growth in litmus milk with no visible change in the medium. On potato there is a moderate growth ; the medium is darkened. Gelatin, serum, and egg are not digested. No indole or H_2S are formed, but there is some production of NH_3.

REFERENCES

Berthelot, A. (1914) *Ann. Inst. Pasteur*, **28**, 839, 913.
Besson, A. and Ehringer, G. (1923) *Paris méd.*, i. 225.
Cantu, C. (1911) *Ann. Inst. Pasteur*, **25**, 852.
Castaneda, M. R. (1934) *J. exp. Med.*, **60**, 119 ; (1935) *J. exp. Med.*, **62**, 289.
Felix, A. (1922) *Z. ImmunForsch.*, **35**, 57.
Fry, R. M. (1932) *Brit. J. exp. Path.*, **13**, 456.
Gordon, J. and McLeod, J. W. (1928) *J. Path. Bact.*, **31**, 185.
Hauser, G. (1885) " Ueber Fäulnisbakterien." Leipzig.
Havens, L. C. and Mayfield, C. R. (1930) *J. prev. Med.*, **4**, 179.
Jensen, C. O. (1913) " Handbuch der pathogenen Mikroorganismen." Kolle and Wassermann, 2te Aufl., **6**, 121.
Jordan, E. O., Crawford, R. R., and McBroom, J. (1935) *J. Bact.*, **29**, 130.
Kligler, I. J. (1919) *J. exp. Med.*, **29**, 531.
Kurth, H. (1883) *Bot. Ztg.*, **41**, 369, 393, 409, 425.
Larson, W. P. and Bell, E. T. (1913) *J. infect. Dis.*, **13**, 510.

Lewis, G. J.   (1911–12) 41*st Ann. Rep. loc. Govt Bd*, M.O's Suppl. 265.

Lode, A. and Howard, A.   (1932) *Zbl. Bakt.*, **124**, 538.

Lovell, R. D.   (1929) *J. Path. Bact.*, **32**, 79.

Magath, T. B.   (1928) *J. infect. Dis.*, **43**, 181.

Meisel, H. and Mikulaszek, E.   (1933) *C. R. Soc. Biol.*, **114**, 364.

Mendel, J.   (1911) *Zbl. Bakt.*, IIte Abt., **29**, 290.

Moltke, O.   (1927) " Contributions to the characterization and systematic classification of Bac. proteus vulgaris (Hauser)." Levin and Munksgaard, Copenhagen ;   (1929) *Zbl. Bakt.*, **111**, 399.

Morgan, H. de R.   (1906) *Brit. med. J.*, i. 908 ; (1907) *Ibid.*, ii. 16.

Norton, J. F., Verder, E., and Ridgway, C.   (1928) *J. infect. Dis.*, **43**, 458.

Rauss, K. F.   (1936) *J. Path. Bact.*, **42**, 183.

Rettger, L. F. and Newell, C. R.   (1912–13) *J. biol. Chem.*, **13**, 341.

Russ-Münzer, A.   (1935) *Zbl. Bakt.*, **133**, 214.

Taylor, J. F.   (1928) *J. Path. Bact.*, **31**, 897.

Thjøtta, T.   (1920) *J. Bact.*, **5**, 67.

Wenner, J. J. and Rettger, L. F.   (1919) *J. Bact.*, **4**, 331.

White, P. B.   (1933) *Brit. J. exp. Path.*, **14**, 145.

Wichels, P. and Barner, W.   (1925) *Med. Klin.*, **21**, 1880.

Wilson, G. S.   (1927) *J. Hyg., Camb.*, **26**, 170.

Winslow, C.-E. A., Broadhurst, J., Buchanan, R. E., Krumwiede, C., Rogers, L. A., and Smith, G. H.   (1920) *J. Bact.*, **5**, 191.

Wolf, C. G. L.   (1918–19) *J. Path. Bact.*, **22**, 289.

Wyss, O.   (1898) *Z. Hyg. InfektKr.*, **27**, 143.

Yacob, M.   (1932) *Indian J. med. Res.*, **19**, 787.

CHAPTER XXVII

BACTERIUM

THE group of bacteria that comprises the colon bacillus, the typhoid bacillus, and a host of related species and varieties, is differentiated from most other bacterial genera by well-defined morphological and physiological characters, and clearly merits a generic name. In accordance with the reports of the American Committee (Winslow *et al.* 1917, 1920) we shall adopt the generic name of *Bacterium*. The exact content of this genus is, however, not easy to define. Certain groups of organisms that were originally included within it have, by common consent, been given separate generic rank. This is, for instance, the case with the genus *Brucella* (see Chapter XXXI). Some authorities (see Bergey *et al.* 1934) have carried the process of division much further, and have recognized such generic names as *Escherichia* or *Bact. coli* and certain allied organisms, *Eberthella* for the typhoid bacillus, and so on. It is very probable that it will eventually be found desirable to divide this large and important group into several different genera ; but international agreement is essential if the new genera are to receive general recognition, and without it they will merely add to the existing confusion. At the moment, therefore, it seems best to retain the genus more or less in its present form, noting that it is to-day in a state of flux, and that any species within it will be found in the current literature under several different names. One particular convention—that of according to the organisms of the typhoid-paratyphoid group the generic name of *Salmonella*—has become so general that it merits further discussion. The question at issue in this particular case turns largely on the way in which differences in antigenic structure should be reflected in nomenclature, and it will therefore be more convenient to deal with it in a later section of this chapter.

With these reservations, and with certain emendations necessitated by the exclusion of the genus *Brucella* and by other minor changes in content, we should adopt the generic description given by the American Committee.

Bacterium.

> Gram-negative, non-sporing rods : often motile, with peritrichate flagella. Some species capsulated. Easily cultivable on ordinary laboratory media. Aerobic and facultatively anaerobic. All species ferment dextrose with the formation of acid, or acid and gas. Many species are active fermenters of a wide range of carbohydrates and allied substrates. Typically intestinal parasites of man and animals, though some species may occur in other parts of the body, on plants, or in the soil. Many species are pathogenic.
>
> Type species. *Bacterium coli.*

Classification and Nomenclature within the Genus.

In this, as in other bacterial groups, species have been differentiated from one another by the application of a variety of tests, devised as need arose and applied as opportunity offered itself.

The description of *Bact. typhosum*, as seen in stained preparations, by Eberth in 1880, and its cultivation by Gaffky in 1884, was followed by the isolation of the colon bacillus by Escherich in 1885. The differentiation of these two bacteria, one the causative organism of an important infective disease, the other a normal inhabitant of the intestinal tract, offered a problem of immediate practical importance ; and the literature of this subject during the immediately succeeding years consists largely of the description of differential tests, and particularly of various differential media, whereby these species could be easily and with certainty distinguished from one another.

Following the discoveries of Eberth, Gaffky and Escherich came numerous reports of the isolation of coli-like or typhoid-like bacteria from various diseases of man or animals. In 1886 Salmon and Smith described *Bact. choleræ-suis*, as an organism associated with swine plague. In 1888 Gaertner described *Bact. enteritidis* as a cause of food poisoning. In 1889 Klein recorded the isolation of *Bact. gallinarum* from cases of fowl typhoid. In 1892 Loeffler isolated a bacillus of this group from mouse typhoid, and gave it the name of *B. typhi-murium*. Kilbourne (1893) described *Bact. abortus equi*, as a cause of abortion in mares. In 1894 Basenau described *Bact. bovis-morbificans* as a cause of disease in cattle. Achard and Bensaude in 1896, and Gwyn in 1898, isolated from cases of enteric fever in man organisms that differed from the typhoid bacillus in certain of their fermentation reactions, notably in their ability to produce gas as well as acid from dextrose and other substrates. They were first clearly differentiated by Schottmüller (1900) under the names of paratyphoid bacillus A, corresponding to the organism described by Gwyn, and paratyphoid bacillus B, corresponding to the bacillus of Achard and Bensaude. In 1898 Shiga described the type of dysentery bacillus which bears his name ; and in 1900 Flexner recorded the isolation of the other main type of dysentery bacillus, which we now know as *Bact. flexneri*. Since the beginning of the century many other members of this group have been isolated and described, and it has been shown that certain of the organisms referred to above have been described by other workers under different names. These more recent observations will be considered later in this chapter.

Morphology.—Neither the shape, size, structure or arrangement of the bacterial cells, nor the appearances presented by cultures on the ordinary solid or liquid media, afford any adequate criteria for the differentiation of species within this group.

The modal form of the individual cell is that of a bacillus, 2 to 3 μ in length and 0·6 μ in breadth, with parallel sides and rounded ends (see Fig. 121). By the usual methods of examination the cell appears to be almost devoid of internal structure. It stains evenly ; it forms no spores ; and it shows no granules. It is Gram-negative, and non-acid-fast. This modal form is, however, widely departed from as regards the shape and size of the individual cells. Some strains are almost coccal in form, others show long, sometimes filamentous bacilli. There is a tendency for the cocco-bacillary, or the elongated, form to predominate in any single strain, but some cultures show a wide diversity in this respect. Cell length is, indeed, a highly variable character in this group ; and it is possible, as Barber (1907) has shown, to obtain long-celled strains of *Bact. coli* by simple selection of individual cells for successive subculture.

Rudimentary branching, with the formation of Y forms, followed by division at each of the three points of the Y, has been described by Hort (1920), and by Gardner (1925), as an occasional happening in some species of *Bacteria*.

Many species are motile, and show numerous peritrichate flagella ; others are non-motile and have no flagella. This particular difference in structure possesses a definite though limited value as a differential criterion. Motility is characteristic of some species, such as *Bact. typhosum*, while its absence is characteristic of others such as the various species of dysentery bacilli. But this character is not absolutely constant, so far as the normally motile species are concerned. A normal strain of *Bact. typhosum*, for instance, may give rise to non-motile variants. Those species which are normally non-motile, on the other hand, appear never to give rise to motile variants. The presence or absence of motility is rightly regarded as a valuable criterion in the differentiation of *Bact. typhosum* from the various types of dysentery bacilli ; because it is correlated with other important characters, and particularly with a striking difference in pathogenic action. In other cases, in which it forms the only detectable difference between two otherwise identical types, its significance from the point of view of classification is extremely doubtful. Thus, in the case of certain varieties of *Bact. coli*, there are groups of strains which show identical fermentation reactions over a wide range of test substrates, but can be separated into motile and non-motile sub-groups. This single difference has, in the past, been recognized in nomenclature ; but it is very doubtful whether this is justifiable.

Some species, such as *Bact. friedländeri*, are normally capsulated, and this character, or rather the frequency of its occurrence, has some differential value ; but those bacilli which are normally capsulated, and form mucoid colonies when first isolated from the

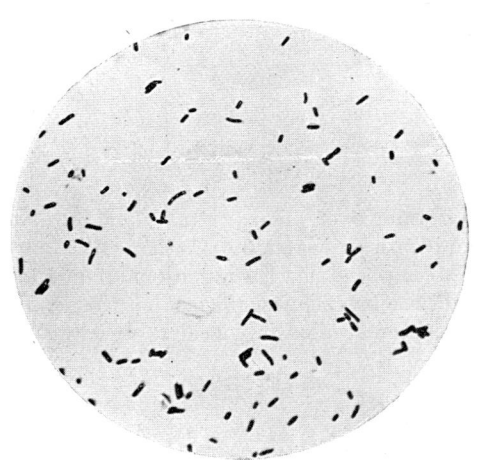

Fig. 121.—*Bact. coli.*
From 24-hours' culture on agar (× 1000).

tissues, frequently lose the property of capsule formation during subculture on artificial media, while such normally non-capsulated species as *Bact. typhosum* may acquire a capsule under particular conditions (Kühnemann 1911, Carpano 1913, Marrassini 1913, Shimidsu 1913, Gay and Claypole 1913). It may be noted that many coliform strains isolated from milk are normally capsulated. Most of these strains belong to the intermediate-aerogenes-cloacæ group, but some undoubted strains of *Bact. coli* form a capsule, and give rise to a mucoid growth on solid media. It may further be noted that the presence of a capsule is not incompatible with active motility.

Conditions of Growth.—The members of this group grow readily on the ordinary nutrient media of the laboratory, without the addition of any accessory substances. They are aerobic, and facultatively anaerobic, though the growth is usually far less copious under the latter conditions. The optimum temperature is, for most species, in the neighbourhood of 37° C., and the range over which growth occurs is fairly wide, extending for most species from about 42° C. as an upper limit to 18° C. or lower.

There are, however, certain differences in behaviour that are of significance from the systematic point of view. Thus, *Bact. aerogenes* grows very poorly, or not at all, at a temperature of 44° C., and differs in this respect from the closely related *Bact.*

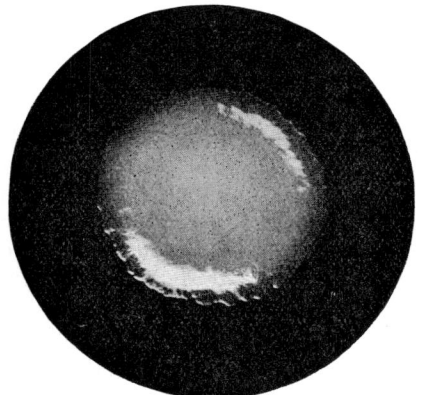

Fig. 122.—*Bact. coli.*
Colonies on agar plate after 24 hours
(× 8).

Fig. 123.—*Bact. coli.*
Larger and flatter type of colony on agar
plate after 24 hours (× 8).

coli. Moreover, many strains of *Bact. aerogenes* have their optimum growth temperatures nearer 30° C. than 37° C.

It happens that the nutritional requirements of several species within this genus, and the enzymic mechanisms that they employ in their attack on various substrates, have been studied in considerable detail by the methods that have recently been introduced in the investigation of the biochemical activities of bacteria. Many of the results obtained in these studies have been described and discussed in Chapter III. In the present chapter we may therefore confine our attention to such reactions as are of value in identifying the different species within the genus, or in distinguishing between them.

Type of Growth.—The type of growth given by the various species within this genus is very similar. When normal smooth strains are grown in broth a uniform turbidity develops, increasing rapidly during the first 12 to 18 hours of growth, and then more slowly up to 48 to 72 hours. Pellicle formation is rare and when present is very slight. A slight deposit forms as growth increases, and this is easily dispersed on shaking the tube.

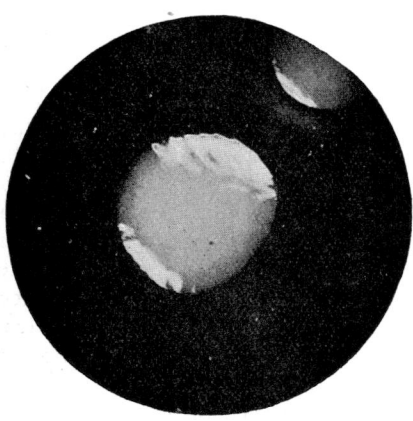

Fig. 124.—*Bact. enteritidis.*
Colony on agar plate after 24 hours (× 8).

On agar, the colonies are relatively large, with an average diameter of 2–3 mm., but vary considerably in size. They may be circular, raised and low convex, with an entire edge and smooth surface; they may be flatter with a more irregular surface, and a more effuse and irregular edge, or they may assume the typical vine-leaf form which is commonly described as characteristic of *Bact. typhosum*. With

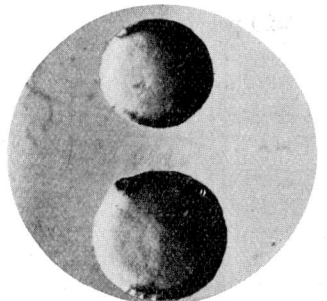

FIG. 125.—*Bact. typhosum.*

Surface colonies on agar, 24 hours, at 37° C. (× 8).

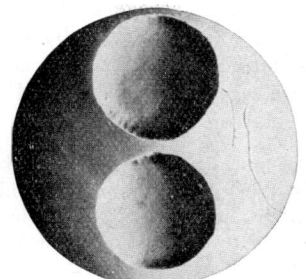

FIG. 126.—*Bact. typhi-murium.*

Surface colonies on agar, 24 hours, at 37° C. (× 8).

freshly isolated strains it is perfectly true that the colonial form usually assumed by *Bact. typhosum*, and some of the paratyphoids, does differ in the way described from the modal circular, low convex colony of *Bact. coli*; but even with freshly isolated strains the range of variation is wide; and when old laboratory strains are in question no reliance can be placed on colonial appearances. Apart altogether from the possible appearance of the characteristic rough variants, a single strain may show wide divergence in this respect, if successive subcultures in broth are interspersed with platings and subculture of individual colonies. In the figures illustrating this chapter, we have attempted to give some idea of the colonial forms that are commonly encountered.

As an exception to this general rule we may note that members of the Friedländer group, when freshly isolated, give rise to typically mucoid colonies. The differential value of this characteristic is diminished by the fact that certain other members, particularly those belonging to the intermediate-aerogenes-cloacæ group, may similarly give rise to this type of growth. It is very common in strains isolated from milk, and is often lost on subculture in the laboratory.

There are a few other growth characters which possess some differential value. Thus, we may note the classical difference between the growth of *Bact. typhosum* and *Bact. coli* on potato, the former being colourless and barely visible, the latter displaying a characteristic yellowish tint (Fremlin 1893). Again there is the so-called "nail-head" growth of Friedländer's bacillus when grown in stab culture in gelatin, due to the raised, circular, convex growth which sometimes develops on the surface above the inoculation-track; but this phenomenon is inconstant.

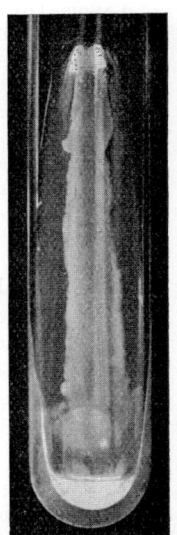

FIG. 127.—*Bact. typhosum.*

24-hours' culture on agar slope.

Resistance to Heat, and to various chemical Substances.—Most members of this group are killed by exposure to a temperature of 55° C. for about 1 hour, or of

60° C. for 15–20 minutes. So far as they have at present been studied, the various species within the genus, do not, with one exception, differ from one another in any significant way. The exception concerns the typical fæcal *coli* strains, which have, on the whole, a rather higher resistance to heat than the closely related members of the intermediate-aerogenes-cloacæ group. About 20 per cent. of these strains are not completely destroyed by exposure to 60° C. for 30 minutes in broth, or by pasteurization at 62·8° C. for the same time in milk.

There are certain chemical substances which exert a definitely selective bactericidal or inhibitory action.

The typhoid bacillus is less resistant to the lethal action of mineral acids than is the colon bacillus. Winslow and Lochridge (1906) showed that the bactericidal effect was due to the action of the dissociated hydrogen ions ; and found that the concentration required to bring about a 99 per cent. reduction in the viable organisms in a bacterial suspension was 2·94 per million in the case of *Bact. typhosum*, and 7·49 per million in the case of *Bact. coli*.

Malachite green, in suitable concentration, kills *Bact. coli* or inhibits its growth without exerting the same effect on *Bact. typhosum* (Loeffler 1903, 1906, Lentz and Tietz 1903, 1905). There are other green dyes that have a similar selective action ; and more recent studies (see Browning, Gilmour and Mackie 1913, Krumwiede and Pratt 1914) have shown that brilliant green gives the best differential results. To this dye the bacilli of the para-typhoid group are most resistant, the typhoid bacillus is somewhat less resistant, while the dysentery bacilli, and still more the members of the *Bact. coli* group, are very susceptible.

Caffeine (Roth 1903, Hoffman and Ficker 1904) and lithium chloride (Gray 1931, Havens and Mayfield 1933) are other substances that inhibit the growth of *Bact. coli* in concentra-tions that have no effect on the typhoid bacillus ; while cholesterin (see Manfredi 1917) appears to inhibit the growth of typhoid or paratyphoid bacilli in concentrations that permit the growth of *Bact. coli*.

Differences of this kind have not, however, been employed for the purposes of identi-fication or classification. They have, on the other hand, been extensively exploited in devising selective, or "enrichment," media for the isolation of the pathogenic species from fæces or water. They are considered from this point of view in Chapters LXVI, LXXXVIII.

Biochemical Activities.—From the first isolation of *Bact. coli* by Escherich, fermentation tests were found to provide the readiest method of distinguishing one species of *Bacterium* from another. It was soon found, for instance, that *Bact. coli* actively fermented lactose, while *Bact. typhosum* did not (Chantemesse and Widal 1887, Smith 1890) ; and the production of acid and gas from glucose by *Bact. coli*, but of acid alone by *Bact. typhosum*, was pointed out by Chantemesse and Widal in 1891. The addition of a suitable indicator to the test media, to register acidity (Wurtz 1892), and the introduction of the simple fermentation tube as a test for gas production (Smith 1890, 1893, Durham 1898) greatly increased the facility with which a large series of comparative qualitative tests could be carried out. To dextrose and lactose other test substances have, from time to time, been added, such as the hexoses, fructose, lævulose and galactose ; the disaccharides, maltose and saccharose ; the trisaccharide, raffinose ; polysaccharides, such as dextrin, starch and inulin ; the pentoses, arabinose and xylose ; the methyl-pentose, rhamnose ; the hexahydric alcohols, dulcitol and mannitol ; the glucoside, salicin ; and the cyclohexanhexol, inositol. The reaction in litmus milk, the presence or absence of indole production in peptone water, and the production of hydrogen sulphide have served as additional differential criteria ; and other tests, such as the final pH attained in a dextrose-containing medium, the nature and amount of the gases evolved, or the production of some particular fermentation product, have been employed as aids to differentiation within particular sub-groups.

It soon became clear that the presence or absence of the power to ferment lactose, originally noted as differentiating *Bact. coli* from *Bact. typhosum*, corresponded to a fundamental line of cleavage within this group. The lactose fermenters were, for the most part, found to be normal inhabitants of the intestinal tract of man or the higher animals or to exist on various plants or in the soil. They were active fermenters of many carbohydrates, including polysaccharides ; they tended to clot milk, as well as acidify it ; they frequently formed indole ; and they tended to reduce various dyes (Dunbar 1892, Rothberger 1898). The non-lactose-fermenters tended, as a class, to comprise the pathogenic species, producing intestinal infections in man and animals ; and the range of their fermentative activity tended to be less extensive than that of the lactose fermenters, though most species attack a considerable number of substrates.

This early division of the genus into two broad sub-groups on the basis of the lactose fermentation has stood the test of time, although there are a few species or types for which some intermediate position must be found. It will therefore be convenient to discuss the further subdivision of the lactose-fermenting and non-lactose-fermenting species under separate headings.

THE LACTOSE-FERMENTING BACTERIA

The Coli-Aerogenes Group

Biochemical Differentiation.—In his original description of *Bact. coli*, Escherich noted the occurrence of two types, one of which, *Bact. coli*, formed relatively long rods, was motile and clotted milk slowly, while the other, *Bact. lactis aerogenes*, formed shorter, plumper rods, was non-motile, and clotted milk more actively. Kruse (1894) emphasized the heterogeneity of the group covered by the term " B. coli " as usually employed, pointing out that it included a variety of related species, widely distributed as intestinal parasites and in water and soil. The use of a relatively small series of fermentation tests, including especially dextrose, lactose, sucrose, starch, inulin, action on litmus milk, and indole formation, resulted in the recognition of certain primary divisions within this group (Refik 1896, Grimbert and Legros 1900, Durham 1901, Jordan 1903). One of the groups so defined fermented polysaccharides, such as starch and inulin, and usually failed to form indole ; this corresponded with the *Bact. lactis aerogenes* type of Escherich and became established as a separate species, the *lactis* being usually omitted from the name. The second and third groups differed from *Bact. aerogenes* in failing to ferment starch and inulin, and in forming indole in peptone water. They differed from each other in regard to their action on saccharose. One, corresponding to the existing strains of Escherich's *Bact. coli commune*, failed to ferment this sugar ; the other fermented it, and Durham (1901), who found it to occur more frequently than the saccharose-negative type, named it *Bact. coli communius*. The application of a more extended series of tests resulted in further subdivision of this group, and elaborate classifications were suggested by various observers on the basis of the results obtained (Bergey and Deehan 1908, MacConkey 1905, 1909, Jackson 1911). It may be noted that one important correlation between biochemical activity and natural habitat had already been detected. The *Bact. aerogenes* type was found to be a relatively infrequent inhabitant of the intestine, but was frequently isolated from certain grasses and from the soil, while *Bact. coli commune* and *Bact. coli communius*, were noted to be typically intestinal parasites (Winslow and Walker 1907). This correlation was of practical as well as of theoretical importance. The presence or absence of " B'. coli " in water supplies, and the relative number of this organism if present, soon came to be recognized as a very valuable indication of the presence and degree of fæcal pollution (see Chapter LXXXVIII), and it became very desirable, apart from any question of systematic classification, to differentiate between those types which were of intestinal origin, and those which might occur in unpolluted waters. The investigations of those who have been primarily concerned with the practical aspects of the bacteriological analysis of water supplies have added materially to our knowledge of this group.

Apart from the merely positive or negative results, as regards acid or gas production in the various sugars, certain observations made in the earlier days had indicated a difference in kind between the fermentation of one and the same carbohydrate by different strains of bacilli of the colon type. Thus Smith (1895), using the method of the fermentation tube, noted that gas was produced more rapidly and in greater amount by *Bact. aerogenes* than by *Bact. coli* ; and a rough estimation of the ratio of CO_2 to H_2 in the gas evolved showed that this was higher with the former organism than with the latter. He noted also that the degree of final acidity was lower with *Bact. aerogenes* than with *Bact. coli*. In both respects *Bact. cloacæ*, a coliform organism isolated from sewage by Jordan (1890) and differentiated from all other types of coliform bacilli by its power of liquefying gelatin, corresponded with *Bact. aerogenes*. Russell and Bassett (1899) confirmed the differential value of a high or low $CO_2 : H_2$ ratio, and noted that the high-ratio strains appeared to be normal soil forms, rather than intestinal parasites. This question was placed on an entirely new footing by the careful quantitative studies of Harden and his colleagues (Harden 1901, 1905, Harden and Walpole 1906), who showed that strains of coliform bacilli were divisible into two well-defined classes. In one, typified by *Bact. coli*, the $CO_2 : H_2$ ratio of the gas evolved gave a value closely approximating unity. In the other, typified by *Bact. aerogenes*, the $CO_2 : H_2$ ratio gave a value of $2 : 1$, or thereabouts. These observations have been amply confirmed by later observers.

Voges and Proskauer (1898) had described a colour reaction given by certain bacteria, but not by *Bact. coli*. It is obtained by adding a few drops of a strong solution of potassium hydrate to a culture grown in a dextrose medium. In a positive reaction a red, fluorescent coloration appears, which may develop relatively slowly. The nature of this reaction was elucidated by Harden and his colleagues (Harden 1906, Harden and Norris 1911), who showed that it depends on the production of acetyl-methyl-carbinol ($CH_3 \cdot CHOH \cdot CO \cdot CH_3$) which, in the presence of alkali and of atmospheric oxygen, is oxidized to diacetyl ($CH_3 \cdot CO \cdot CO \cdot CH_3$) which reacts with the peptone of the broth to give the red colour.

This reaction had been applied to the examination of the colon group by some of the observers referred to above, and it had been noted that *Bact. aerogenes*, as opposed to *Bact. coli*, gave a positive reaction (Durham 1901). MacConkey (1909) observed the great preponderance of Voges-Proskauer negative types among strains isolated from the fæces ; positive reactions were given by 11 of 178 strains isolated from human fæces ; 8 of 67 strains from the fæces of the horse, and none of 87 strains from fæces of the calf, goat, pig or goose.

The fundamental importance of the Voges-Proskauer reaction, and of the $CO_2 : H_2$ ratio, as compared with the presence or absence of fermentation in particular carbohydrates other than lactose, was not however realized by the earlier investigators, so that the reaction was simply assigned a place among some selected series of tests, and V.P. positive and V.P. negative strains were often allocated to the same sub-group ; though it was noted by Howe (1904) during the examination of strains of lactose-fermenting bacilli derived from water, that there was almost perfect correlation between a positive V.P. reaction and the ability to produce large amounts of gas from dextrose.

Petruschky (1889, 1890) made the first attempt to measure, by titration, the degree of acidity produced by various members of the coli-typhoid group ; while Smith (1895), as noted above, called attention to the low acid production of *Bact. aerogenes* as compared with *Bact. coli*. A great advance in the investigation of this aspect of bacterial metabolism was marked by the introduction of indicators, which rendered possible the ready determination of the hydrogen-ion concentration attained during the bacterial fermentation of any test substance. Clark and Lubs (1915), on this basis, devised the methyl-red test for the differentiation of members of the coli-typhoid group. The addition of this indicator to five-day cultures in dextrose phosphate peptone water differentiates between those strains which produce and maintain a high concentration of hydrogen-ions, and those which produce an initial lower concentration of hydrogen-ions and then cause reversion towards neutrality by the further decomposition of the organic acids to carbonates, and perhaps by the formation of ammonium compounds from proteins. The former type, such as *Bact. coli*, give a red coloration and are referred to as methyl-red positive ; the latter, such as *Bact. aerogenes*, give a yellowish colour and are referred to as methyl-red negative. It soon became clear that there was a very high negative correlation between the methyl-red test and the Voges-Proskauer reaction (Levine 1916*a*, *b*), and a series of intensive studies soon placed on a firm foundation the conclusion, already propounded as a tentative hypothesis, that the lactose-fermenting coliform bacilli could be divided into two primary divisions on the basis of the $CO_2 : H_2$ ratio, the Voges-Proskauer reaction, and the methyl-red test. The first of these, containing strains giving a $CO_2 : H_2$ ratio of about 2 : 1, V.P. positive and M.R. negative, comprised the great majority of the strains isolated from plants, grain, and unpolluted soil or water. Such strains were relatively infrequent in material obtained from the intestines of man or animals. This group could be further subdivided, on the basis of gelatin liquefaction, into the non-liquefying form *Bact. aerogenes*, and the much less common liquefying form *Bact. cloacæ*. The second group, containing strains giving a $CO_2 : H_2$ ratio of approximately 1 : 1, V.P. negative and M.R. positive, contained the great majority of those strains isolated from the intestines of man or animals, as exemplified by *Bact. coli commune* or *Bact. coli communius*. This group was found to be further divisible, on the basis of the ordinary fermentation tests, along lines which will be considered later (Keyes 1909, Rogers *et al.* 1914, 1915, 1918, Johnson 1916, Hulton 1916, Levine 1916*c*, *d*, 1917, Burton and Rettger 1917, Chen and Rettger 1920, Winslow *et al.* 1919, Bardsley 1926, 1934, Pawan 1931).

Besides the division rendered possible by the tests we have just outlined into a *coli* group on the one hand and an *aerogenes-cloacæ* group on the other, further work revealed the occurrence of a third group of strains possessing properties intermediate between those of the two main groups. This group is, as yet, not completely defined, and is therefore most conveniently referred to as the "intermediate" group. Brown (1921) drew attention to the usefulness of a medium containing citrate for the differentiation of *Bact. coli* from *Bact. aerogenes*. Koser (1923, 1924, 1926*a*, *b*) devised a synthetic medium in which citrate was provided as the sole source of carbon. He found it possible to differentiate coliform bacilli into a M.R. +, V.P. —, citrate — *coli* type, a M.R. —, V.P. +, citrate + *aerogenes* type, and a M.R. +, V.P. —, citrate + intermediate type. Examination of 104 soil strains from fields subjected to only chance pollution showed that 23·1 per cent. were of the *coli*, 67·3 per cent. of the *aerogenes*, and 7·7 per cent. of the intermediate type. Further work in numerous countries soon revealed the value of this test in differentiating the intermediate from the *coli* group (see Bardsley 1926, 1934, Pawan 1931).

In Table XXXVI we have summarized the results recorded by various observers (see Bardsley) with regard to the percentage of strains isolated from different sources, which give the particular reactions to which we have referred. We have included the indole reaction, because recent work suggests that it is particularly significant in relation to habitat. It will be noted that figures are available for all tests only in the case of the strains derived from animal fæces ; but it may safely be assumed that the strains with a high gas ratio would have given positive V.P. and negative M.R. reactions, and *vice versa*.

TABLE XXXVI

SHOWING THE PERCENTAGE OF LACTOSE-FERMENTING, COLIFORM BACILLI, FROM VARIOUS SOURCES, WHICH GIVE THE REACTIONS INDICATED (VARIOUS AUTHORS).

Source.	Percentage.					
	$CO_2 : H_2$		M.R. +.	V.P. +.	Indole +.	Citrate +.
	2 : 1	1 : 1				
Fæces (human and animal) .	14·37%	85·62%	90·40%	7·87%	93·03%	6·71%
Sewage (and similar material)	—	—	82·74%	17·26%	—	—
Soil	—	—	14·70%	80·24%	33·40%	89·6%
Grasses and grains . . .	95·18%	4·82%	—	—	—	—

Though both intermediate and *aerogenes* types are citrate +, they differ in their ability to utilize uric acid as the sole source of nitrogen. Koser (1918), Chen and Rettger (1920), and numerous subsequent workers (see Bardsley 1926, 1934) found that, whereas *aerogenes* strains were uric acid positive, strains of *coli* and intermediate type were uric acid negative.

A further test, of which limited use has been made, is the fermentation of cellobiose, a glucoside derived from cellulose (see Jones 1924, Jones and Wise 1926). *Bact. aerogenes* and intermediate strains ferment this substance, while *Bact. coli* fails to do so (see Koser 1926*c*).

Considerable help is afforded by a test introduced as long ago as 1904 by Eijkman (1904, 1914), who found that *coli*, but not *aerogenes*, strains were able to form gas in a glucose broth medium incubated at 46° C. This test has had a chequered career, having been reported on favourably by some workers, and utterly condemned by others. Recent work (see Levine *et al.* 1934, Wilson *et al.* 1935) has rendered it clear that the success of the test depends on exact standardization of the incubating temperature, which must be adjusted to 43°–45° C. in the *medium* itself. The only satisfactory means of doing this is to incubate the tubes in a constant-temperature water-bath. The differential value of the test is greatly enhanced by the replacement of glucose by lactose. Our own experience suggests that MacConkey's lactose bile salt broth is the medium of choice. Using this medium in the way described, it was found that of 193 M.R. +, V.P. —, citrate —, indole + *coli* strains, 180 gave a positive Eijkman reaction, while of 303 other strains, 40 of which belonged to the indole — *coli* group, only 10 did so. As a method, therefore, of picking out typical fæcal *coli* strains, it is of probably greater value than any other single test.

There can, we think, be no doubt that the primary division of the lactose fermenters must be made on the basis of the gas ratio, methyl red, Voges-Proskauer, and citrate tests. By this means we obtain a primary classification into *coli*, intermediate, and *aerogenes* groups. The secondary division is more difficult. From an ecological standpoint, we believe that the indole, modified Eijkman, and gelatin liquefaction tests afford the most satisfactory grouping, but from a systematist's point of view there is much to be said in favour of classification on sugar reactions. Taking the first method of grouping, we may note that about 93 per cent. of strains from human and animal fæces produce indole, and that about 95 per cent. give a positive Eijkman reaction. On the other hand, indole-negative and Eijkman-negative fæcal strains are uncommon. A positive indole test given by a citrate-negative strain, or a positive Eijkman test given by any strain, is therefore strongly suggestive of its fæcal origin. The evidence suggests that intermediate strains, at any rate in this country, are derived mainly from soil, while *aerogenes* and *cloacæ* strains are distributed chiefly on grains, grasses, and in food-stuffs, though it should be noted that these organisms are often present in mammalian fæces in small numbers (Cruickshank and Cruickshank 1931). The classification reached by this method is of special value in the interpretation of water analysis tests and is depicted in Chapter LXXXVIII.

With regard to the second method of grouping, the test substances that have been accorded special prominence are saccharose, dulcitol and salicin, the value of the last being emphasized by Kligler (1914*a, b*) and by Levine (1917). Winslow, Kligler and Rothberg (1919), in their excellent review of the classification of the whole coli-typhoid group, conclude that the types set out in Table XXXVII under their appropriate names are the only ones which are sufficiently well established to merit separate consideration.

TABLE XXXVII

FERMENTATIVE TYPES OF *Bact. coli* (Winslow *et al*).

	Saccharose.	Salicin.	Dulcitol.	Adonitol.	Motility.
Bact. neapolitanum	A.G.	A.G.	—	—	—
Bact. coli communius	A.G.	—	A.G.	—	+
Bact. coscoroba	A.G.	—	A.G.	—	—
Bact. coli commune	—	A.G.	A.G.	—	+
Bact. immobile	—	A.G.	A.G.	—	—
Bact. acidi lactici	—	—	—	A.G.	—
Bact. grünthal	—	—	—	A.G.	+

It will be noted that, although the reactions in dulcitol and adonitol are included in the table, the species are adequately defined by the reactions in saccharose and salicin, together with the presence or absence of motility. It will also be noted that *Bact. coscoroba* differs from *Bact. coli communius* in being non-motile, *Bact. immobile* from *Bact. coli commune* in the same way, and *Bact. grünthal* from *Bact. acidi lactici* only in being motile. Winslow and his colleagues express the view that the presence or absence of motility, taken alone, does not justify specific differentiation ; and they suggest the recognition of four species, *Bact. neapolitanum*, *Bact. coli communius*, *Bact. coli commune*, and *Bact. acidi lactici*, regarding the *coscoroba*, *immobile*, and *grünthal* types as varieties of the corresponding species. This appears to us a wise and conservative view. We should, ourselves, prefer to narrow the limits still further, regarding *Bact. coli* as a single species, and placing the *neapolitanum, communius, commune* and *acidi lactici* types as varieties.

Serological Differentiation.—Several attempts have been made to study the antigenic structure of various strains of *Bact. coli* by the method of agglutination. The results display an extreme heterogeneity of antigenic factors (Mackie 1913). In some cases, as in the hæmolytic strains of *Bact. coli* isolated by Dudgeon from cases of acute urinary infection, there is evidence that antigenically homogeneous groups may be related to particular infective conditions (Dudgeon *et al.* 1921, 1922). The detailed antigenic analysis of the group remains for future study.

Pathogenicity.—The majority of the lactose-fermenting coliform bacilli appear to be non-pathogenic, under ordinary conditions. The M.R. −, V.P. + group have their normal habitat on plants ; the M.R. +, V.P. −, citrate + group appear to live in the soil ; while the M.R. +, V.P. −, citrate − forms are normal intestinal parasites. Under abnormal conditions these bacilli may cause acute or chronic infective lesions in the urinary tract, or elsewhere (see Chapter LXIV). It seems probable also that they may sometimes play a part in the causation of enteritis, in man or in animals, though their rôle is almost always a secondary one.

The pathogenicity of most strains for laboratory animals is low. Very large doses administered intraperitoneally to the mouse, or intravenously to the rabbit, may prove fatal ; but it seems likely that death results in these cases from a toxæmia rather than from a true infection. Occasionally strains of greater virulence are found.

Several observers have described the presence of soluble toxic substances in young broth cultures of *Bact. coli* (see, for instance, Steinberg and Ecker 1926). But most of these " toxins " have proved to be heat-stable, and there is no reason to believe that they differ from the toxic components that can be extracted, in larger quantity, from the bacterial cells. Since there is at the moment no clear evidence that the toxic substances that can be extracted from the colon bacillus differ in their action from those of other species within this genus, a discussion as to their probable nature may be deferred to a later section.

The Friedländer Group

There are certain species of lactose-fermenting coliform bacilli which cannot readily be placed in any of the groups which we have differentiated above. There are, for instance, the so-called capsulated bacilli, including Friedländer's pneumo-bacillus, Abel's bacillus of ozæna, the bacillus of rhinoscleroma, and others. There appears to be a preponderance of opinion that the organisms of this group are in some way related to *Bact. aerogenes*, principally because that organism is sometimes capsulated ; but the fermentation reactions, as described by those who have isolated and studied these capsulated coliform bacilli, appear to be extremely variable, and several observers have recorded the fermentation of saccharose, but not of lactose.

The balance of evidence suggests that these strains should be included in the genus *Bacterium*, but it is convenient in the meantime to consider them in a separate sub-section of this group.

GROUP CHARACTERISTICS.

> Short, non-motile, non-sporing, capsulated Gram-negative rods, giving a profuse mucoid growth on solid media, and usually fermenting carbohydrates with the production of acid and gas. Usual habitat, respiratory tract of man and certain animals.

Under the general term *B. mucosus capsulatus* a large number of organisms have been described with the characteristics enumerated above. V. Frisch in 1882 isolated a capsulated bacillus from patients with rhinoscleroma. In 1883 Friedländer cultivated a similar organism—generally known as Friedländer's bacillus or *Bact. friedländeri*—from the lungs of patients who had died of pneumonia. Loewenberg in 1894 and Abel in 1896 cultivated a similar organism from the nasal

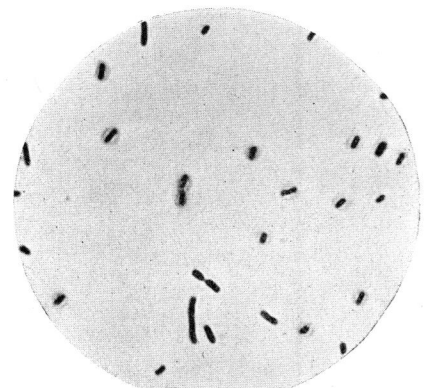
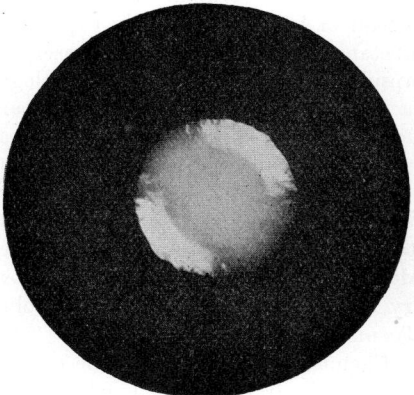

FIG. 128.—*Friedländer's Bacillus.*
From an agar culture, 24 hours, 37° C., showing capsules (× 1000).

FIG. 129.—*Friedländer's Bacillus.*
Surface colony of mucoid type on agar, 24 hours, 37° C. (× 8).

secretion of patients with ozæna. Besides these, several organisms have been described by other workers, such as *B. pseudopneumonicus* Passet, *B. canalis capsulatus* Mori, *Proteus hominis capsulatus* Bordoni-Uffreduzzi, *B. capsulatus* Pfeiffer (Pfeiffer 1889), *B. mucosus capsulatus* Paulsen, *B. crassus sputigenus* Kreibohm, *B. buccalis muciferens* Miller, the bacillus of sputum septicæmia Miller, the granuloma bacillus (Small and Julianelle 1923), *Bacterium mucogenum* (Edwards, R. T. 1905), *B. capsulatus* (Wright and Mallory 1895), and *Klebsiella paralytica*, an organism isolated by Wallace, Cahn, and Thomas (1933) from a paralytic tick-borne disease of moose. (For references see Fricke 1896, Bamforth 1928.) The ozæna bacillus described by Abel must not be confused with the non-capsulated coccobacillus described by Perez (1899). (See Chapter XVIII.)

Ecology.—Friedländer's bacillus appears to lead a parasitic existence. The commonest situation in which it is found is the respiratory tract of man. It is an occasional inhabitant of the nasopharynx; it is found in diseased conditions of the nose, such as ozæna and rhinoscleroma; and it is sometimes present in the lungs in pneumonia, influenza, bronchitis, bronchiectasis, tuberculosis, and other diseases. It has been isolated from a large number of suppurative conditions in different parts of the body, such as pleurisy, appendicitis, cystitis, pyelonephritis, ulcerative endocarditis, endometritis, brain abscess, and general septicæmia (Perkins 1904), and was found by Dudgeon (1926) in 5·5 per cent. of fæces examined from normal and abnormal conditions.

Morphology.—In the body the organism generally takes the form of short, ovoid, diplobacilli, surrounded by large capsules, looking not unlike pneumococci. In culture it is pleomorphic. The usual form is a short, straight, thick rod, about 1–2 μ long and 0·8 μ wide, with parallel or bulging sides, and rounded or slightly pointed ends. The bacilli are usually in pairs end-to-end, or arranged singly. Besides this form there are several others of most varied appearance—thick curved sausage forms, clubbed forms, long sinuous filamentous forms, long straight rods— staining regularly or irregularly. In most strains the organisms are surrounded by a capsule, apparent in cultures, which can be demonstrated by Gram's stain, or by any of the ordinary capsule stains. In some strains however the organisms, instead of being individually capsulated, are embedded in an interstitial mucoid substance, which stains less intensely than the bacilli. There are, moreover, non-capsulated variants, which morphologically and culturally resemble the coliform bacilli ; these often become predominant in old cultures. The organisms are non-motile and non-sporing. They stain easily, sometimes show bipolar staining, and are Gram-negative.

The capsule of these organisms is formed not only in the animal body but in culture. To demonstrate it in body fluids, it is sufficient to fix it by heat, and stain with carbol-fuchsin or methylene blue. To demonstrate it in culture, it is advisable to suspend the bacilli in a low dilution—not higher than 1/5—of serum, dry in air, and fix in a saturated solution of corrosive sublimate before staining (Toenniessen 1912).

Chemical examination of the capsule has revealed the presence of a nitrogen-free carbohydrate material, which according to Toenniessen (1921) and Kramár (1921) is a polysaccharide of galactose ; but Heidelberger, Goebel and Avery (1925) regard it as a polysaccharide containing glucose. The capsule therefore consists of gum. This substance may be separated from the bacilli in the following manner (Toenniessen 1921) : The organisms are dried, suspended in water, to which 1 per cent. KOH is added, and heated until the gum covering passes into solution. On cooling, the undissolved bacilli form a sediment, and the opalescent supernatant fluid is pipetted off. This is acidified with acetic acid, and 3 volumes of 91 per cent. alcohol are added, when a heavy precipitate of the gummy substance occurs ; this precipitate is purified by dissolving it in distilled water, and re-precipitating it with acid and alcohol. In the pure state it is a loose, snow-white powder, giving an opalescent solution in distilled water, acids, or alkalies ; it is free from nitrogen, and does not reduce Fehling's solution. It has special antigenic properties, which will be referred to later.

Cultural Reactions.—One of the characteristic features of this group is the luxuriant, greyish-white, mucoid, almost diffluent, growth on agar. This results no doubt from the presence of the gummy envelope around the bacilli, containing a high proportion of water—92 per cent. (Toenniessen 1921). The condensation water on an agar slope is converted into a greyish-white mucoid mass. In broth the organisms grow freely, giving rise after a few days to a marked viscosity, so that the medium takes on the consistency of melted gelatin. Great stress used to be laid on the nail-headed growth in stab gelatin cultures ; a circular, convex growth may occur on the surface, with a filiform growth in the stab, the whole resembling a round-headed nail. This appearance is not constant, and is given only by some strains ; it depends too on the amount of gelatin in the culture ; with small amounts, about 4 per cent., the surface growth is flat (Friedländer 1883). There is no liquefaction of the gelatin, but often a large napiform bubble of gas accumulates just beneath the surface, giving on first sight the appearance of lique- faction. On potato there is a moderate creamy-yellow mucoid growth, later turning to a buff or light café-au-lait colour.

The cultural appearances of the Friedländer group are subject to considerable variation. This is due to the production of variants which have different forms of growth from the parent strain. Toenniessen (1913) found that when the usual mucoid type was kept in the incubator and subcultured every few days, non- mucoid variants rapidly appeared. As the original colonies grew older, white, more or less translucent peripheral sectors developed, which on microscopical examination were found to consist largely of non-capsulated bacilli ; these could be subcultured, and obtained pure. The growth of these non-capsulated bacilli was no longer mucoid, but resembled the growth of *Bact. coli*. Regression to the mucoid type might occur—often suddenly. As well as this non-mucoid type, Toenniessen (1914) later observed three other variants. The mucoid, capsulated type may be regarded as the smooth form, and the non-mucoid, non-capsulated type as the rough form of Friedländer's bacillus (Julianelle 1926*b*). Dissociation may take other forms. Thus, according to our own observations, secondary colonies may appear in the substance or on the surface of the original colonies ; or there may develop a jelly-like, translucent peripheral fringe showing slight radial striation ; or sometimes the whole colony may dry up and wither away, leaving an effuse, transparent layer looking like ground glass. Hadley (1927) and Beham (1912) have recorded similar observations.

Resistance and Metabolism.—The organisms are killed by moist heat at 55° C. in half an hour. They may survive drying for months (Loewenberg 1894). If kept at room temperature, cultures remain viable as a rule for weeks or months. They are aerobic ; growth under strictly anaerobic conditions is very poor. There is no hæmolysis of horse's or sheep's red cells. The optimum temperature for growth is 37° C., the limits are 12° and 43° C. Some strains form a slightly brownish pigment, most easily produced by growth on potato.

Biochemical Reactions.—The fermentation of sugars by members of this group is subject to considerable variation (Clairmont 1902, Perkins 1904, 1907, Edwards 1905, Page 1912, Fitzgerald 1914, Coulter 1917, Small and Julianelle 1923, Bamforth 1928, Edwards 1928, 1929*a*, Julianelle 1930, 1935, Elbert and Guerkess 1930, Hay 1932, Wallace, Cahn and Thomas 1933, Morris and Julianelle 1934, Kliewe and Hsü 1935, Wilson *et al.* 1935). Many strains produce acid and gas in glucose, maltose, mannitol, lactose, sucrose, and salicin. Several, however, do not attack lactose, and others either do not ferment sucrose, or ferment it late. Gas may be formed rapidly or not for several days; some strains do not form gas. Occasionally no sugars are fermented, but this lack of fermentative ability seems to be observed only in strains that have been subcultured for a long time in the laboratory. In litmus milk also the reaction of different strains varies. Generally acid and clot are formed, but many strains do not produce sufficient acid to precipitate the caseinogen, while some strains produce no change at all. The litmus is occasionally decolorized.

There is fairly general agreement that biochemical reactions do not afford an adequate basis for classification, since most workers have been unable to discover any constant relationship between the biochemical activities of a given strain and its source of origin or antigenic structure. Generally speaking, however, it may be said that strains of the Friedländer and ozæna types, at any rate on first isolation, have the following reactions. Acid and gas are produced in glucose, usually in sucrose, and often in lactose ; acid is formed in milk and not infrequently clot ; the methyl red reaction is generally positive and the Voges-Proskauer reaction generally negative ; the indole test is generally negative, certainly with respiratory strains ; nitrates are reduced to nitrites ; ammonia is formed from peptone ; methylene blue is reduced in broth ; growth occurs in Koser's citrate medium ; gelatin is not liquefied ; and there is usually an abundant production of catalase. In our experience H_2S is not formed, though Lieb (1932) states that it is formed by strains of the ozæna group. Rhinoscleroma type strains seem to be less active. Lactose is rarely fermented ; sucrose is not fermented, or is fermented late ; and gas production, even in glucose, is often lacking ; milk is not clotted ; and the methyl red reaction is often negative. According to Hay (1932), one of the most characteristic features of the *mucosus capsulatus* group is their ability to ferment inositol.

Antigenic Structure.—Till quite recently no satisfactory division of the Friedländer group had been made on the basis of antigenic structure. The main difficulty was due to the fact that, though injection of the capsulated bacilli into rabbits is able to give rise to an agglutinating serum, this serum has little action except on non-capsulated organisms ; several attempts were therefore made to rid the bacilli of their capsules. Porges' method (1905) was one of the most successful. He suspended an agar culture in 10 c.c. of saline, filtered through paper, mixed it with a quarter of its volume of N/4 HCl solution, and heated for 15 minutes ; it was cooled rapidly, and neutralized with N/4 NaOH solution. The resultant suspension was homogeneous and non-viscous, and agglutinated with a specific immune serum. Though this method undoubtedly removes the capsules, it often renders the bacilli spontaneously agglutinable or agglutinable by normal serum. Streit (1906) found that if the bacilli were grown on potato or potato agar, they gradually lost their capsules, and became more agglutinable. Small and Julianelle (1923) obtained the same result by growing them on agar for 24 hours, storing the cultures in the ice-chest, and subculturing monthly ; after 1 to 2 years many of the strains had lost their capsules. Agglutination tests made with non-capsulated bacilli obtained in these ways gave, however, very inconstant results ; nor could a method of analysis in which the natural capsular antigens were disregarded be accepted as satisfactory. (Streit 1906, Beham 1912, Fitzgerald 1914, Coulter 1917, Small and Julianelle 1923).

Recent work in America (Avery *et al.* 1925, Heidelberger *et al.* 1925, Julianelle 1926*a, b, c*) has largely cleared up the confusion. It would appear that the immunological reactions of the Friedländer group are similar to those of the pneumococci, depending on the presence in the cell of two entirely different factors— a polysaccharide in the capsule responsible for the type-specificity, and a nucleoprotein in the soma responsible for the species-specificity. According to Julianelle (1926*a*) there are three serological types, distinguishable by agglutination, absorption, precipitin, and protection tests, and a heterogeneous group (X) of strains that have not yet been antigenically differentiated. If a serum is prepared against Type A by injection of heat-killed encapsulated organisms, it will agglutinate encapsulated bacilli of its own type, but not those of any other type ; similarly with Types B and C. The serum contains an antibody that reacts specifically with the polysaccharide fraction in the capsule ; and as the polysaccharide varies in the different types, the serum against each type is specific. The polysaccharide of Types A and B has been isolated, and has been found to flocculate in the presence of a specific serum. If the bacilli are deprived of their capsules, they lose their specificity, and agglutinate equally, though only to a low titre, with sera prepared against any type.

The nucleo-protein can be separated from the dissolved bacilli by precipitation with acetic acid in the cold. It gives rise to a species antibody, which does not react with the capsulated bacilli or with the polysaccharide, but which agglutinates capsule-free cells of any type, and reacts with the nucleo-protein of any type.

A serum prepared by injection of smooth, capsulated bacilli contains antibodies to the polysaccharide and the nucleo-protein ; a serum prepared by injection of rough, non-capsulated bacilli contains only one antibody—active against the nucleo-protein. For the classification of the Friedländer group into types it is essential to use smooth bacilli both for the preparation of sera and for agglutinating antigens. Unless this rule is strictly observed, the results will be unsatisfactory. Failure to realize this principle probably accounts for the discrepant results of the earlier workers.

The capsulated bacilli stimulate the production not only of type-specific agglutinins and precipitins, but also of type-specific protective bodies. Thus a serum prepared by injection of capsulated bacilli of Type A will protect mice against intraperitoneal injection of Type A, but not against injection of bacilli of Types B or C. The nucleo-protein does not stimulate the production of protective bodies ; a serum, therefore, prepared by injection of capsule-free bacilli of any type is unable to protect mice against infection with capsulated bacilli of any type. It is important to note that the polysaccharide in the pure state, though precipitable by immune anti-S serum of the homologous type, is unable to stimulate the production of immune bodies ; it must be present in combination with the proteins of the cell. The nucleo-protein, on the other hand, is able by itself to stimulate the production of non-specific antibodies. The polysaccharide is present in quite young cultures of Friedländer's bacillus ; so that filtrates of these cultures may be used as antigens in the precipitin test. Incidentally precipitation occurs up to a much higher titre—1/1000 or more—than agglutination—about 1/10.

A few tabular results may make these relations clear.

TABLE XXXVIII

Anti-smooth Serum acting on Smooth Capsulated Bacilli and on Rough Non-capsulated Bacilli, or on Smooth Bacilli that have been artificially deprived of their Capsules.

	Anti-S Serum.		
	Type A.	Type B.	Type C.
Type A S	+++	—	—
Type B S	—	+++	—
Type C S	—	—	+++
Type A R	±	±	±
Type B R	±	±	±
Type C R	±	±	±

TABLE XXXIX

Anti-rough Serum, or an Anti-protein Serum, acting on Smooth Capsulated and Rough Non-capsulated Bacilli.

		Anti-R or Anti-P Serum.		
		Type A.	Type B.	Type C.
Type A	S	—	—	—
Type B	S	—	—	—
Type C	S	—	—	—
Type A	R	+++	+++	+++
Type B	R	+++	+++	+++
Type C	R	+++	+++	+++

There is one further point of interest. The B type of Friedländer's bacillus is similar immunologically to Type II pneumococcus. The specific polysaccharide in the B type, in conjunction with the protein fraction, stimulates the formation of an immune serum that will agglutinate pneumococcus Type II, and will protect mice against infection with it; similarly pneumococcus Type II serum will agglutinate Friedländer Type B and protect mice against infection with it. The polysaccharides in the two organisms appear to be closely alike, though not absolutely identical (Avery *et al.* 1925). A Friedländer Type B organism will not, however, absorb the agglutinins from pneumococcus Type II serum, nor a pneumococcus Type II organism from a Friedländer Type B serum. This probably indicates that though the polysaccharides are alike, the protein fractions of the organisms are different.

Edwards (1929*a*), studying capsulated bacilli of diverse origin, was able to divide them into 3 groups by agglutination ; (1) strains, chiefly from human pneumonia and pleuritis, identical with Julianelle's Type A ; (2) strains from metritis of mares, together with some strains of *Bact. aerogenes* isolated from soil, water or milk, and an occasional strain of human origin, identical with Type B ; (3) some soil strains of *Bact. aerogenes* and an inguinal granuloma strain.

Edwards confirmed these results by agglutinin-absorption and precipitation tests, and like Julianelle, obtained evidence that the type-specificity of the capsulated bacilli depended on their capsule formation. Julianelle (1930) in a study of 80 strains of human and animal origin, found that 42 belonged to Type A, 12 to Type B, 7 to Type C, and 19 to Group X. Most of the Type A strains were of human, and most of the Type B strains of animal, origin.

According to Tomášek (1925), Quast (1926), Prica (1930), and Neuber (1934) the rhinoscleroma bacillus can be distinguished by agglutination and complement fixation from Friedländer's and the ozæna bacillus. Morris and Julianelle (1934), however, who examined 10 strains of the rhinoscleroma bacillus, were unable to distinguish this organism antigenically from strains of Friedländer's Type C. These results are not entirely incompatible, since it is possible that the former group of workers were using a Type A or B strain of Friedländer's bacillus for serum production, and had no serum against Type C.

According to Julianelle (1935), the ozæna bacillus can be distinguished by agglutination and absorption of agglutinins from Friedländer and rhinoscleroma bacilli. Of 19 ozæna strains studied, 12 fell into one group, 2 into another, while the remaining 5 were antigenically heterogeneous.

Prášek and Prica (1933) state that they have been successful in extracting a soluble specific carbohydrate-containing substance, which is probably a galactan, from the capsules of the ozæna and the rhinoscleroma bacillus. The substances from the two organisms were quite distinct, and showed no cross-precipitation when tested against the heterologous immune sera. They were likewise distinct from the polysaccharide extracted from a Friedländer's bacillus. It seems clear that the relationship of these various organisms to each other will not be understood until a sufficient number of fully representative strains of each group are examined.

Pathogenicity.—Organisms of this group are frequently encountered in diseases of the respiratory tract in man. As a rule they appear to act chiefly as secondary invaders, but it is possible that they are sometimes responsible for the primary disease (see Bhatnagar and Singh 1935). They are not uncommonly isolated from suppurative processes of various kinds throughout the body ; occasionally they invade the blood stream, and give rise to septicæmia. Jampolis and his colleagues (1932) record a hospital outbreak of infectious diarrhœa in infants, accompanied by severe constitutional disturbance and a high case mortality. Friedländer's bacillus was isolated from the nasal secretions, stomach contents, and stools of most of the patients, and appeared to be the primary cause of the condition. Webster (1928, 1930) has described a spontaneous respiratory epidemic in mice caused by Friedländer's bacillus ; Edwards (1928) has isolated this organism from metritis of mares ; while Wallace, Cahn, and Thomas (1933) have found it in a paralytic disease of moose.

Experimentally the virulence of Friedländer bacilli is subject to considerable variation. The smooth type is pathogenic, the rough type non-pathogenic for laboratory animals (Toenniessen 1914, Julianelle 1926*b*, Webster 1928). Other variants have differing grades of pathogenicity. Many observers have drawn attention to the differences in pathogenicity between Friedländer's bacillus, the ozæna bacillus, the rhinoscleroma bacillus, and other members of this group, and have endeavoured to make use of these differences in classification. Unfortunately the protocols in the literature are not sufficiently definite to enable one to assert that there is any constant difference between these organisms. It is therefore possible that the actual virulence of any strain depends upon the proportion of smooth bacilli in the culture. When this consists entirely of the smooth type, it is usually virulent ; in proportion as the rough type appears, the virulence falls ; and when the smooth has been replaced completely by the rough type, the culture proves avirulent. On the whole it would appear that Friedländer Types A and B bacilli are highly pathogenic to mice when injected intraperitoneally, while Friedländer Type C, ozæna, and rhinoscleroma strains are usually non-virulent.

The smooth type is capsulated ; the rough type is not. It might therefore be thought that virulence depends on capsule formation. Toenniessen (1914) discusses this possibility, but concludes that the association between capsule formation and virulence is fortuitous. He isolated, for example, one variant which, though non-capsulated, was highly virulent. He states that old cultures of the smooth type, in which the capsules have largely become autolysed, have just the same virulence for mice as fresh young capsulated cultures. Moreover, Julianelle's Friedländer Type C strains, though capsulated, were non-virulent. It would appear, therefore, that capsule formation is often associated with, but is not essential to virulence.

After subcutaneous injection of a very small dose—about 0·0000001 c.c. of a 24-hours' broth culture of a virulent strain—into mice, the animals die in 12 to 72 hours. Post mortem, there is a local exudate, the focal glands are swollen, and the spleen is enlarged. Capsulated bacilli are found in the blood and viscera (Pfeiffer 1889, Fricke 1896, Toenniessen 1914).

Guinea-pigs are refractory to subcutaneous, but succumb to intraperitoneal injection, death occurring in 12 to 72 hours. The fatal dose is about 0·01 c.c. of a 24-hours' broth culture. Post mortem, there is a viscous exudate in the peritoneum ; the spleen may be enlarged, and the suprarenals hæmorrhagic. The bacilli are found in large numbers in the blood and viscera.

Rabbits appear to be more resistant, but they succumb after intravenous or intra-peritoneal injection with a dose of about 0·1 c.c. of a broth culture. Intraperitoneal inoculation is likewise fatal to pigeons.

Classification.—The demarcation of this group from other groups of capsulated bacilli, and the subdivision of the group itself, are both in a very unsatisfactory state. In the first place it is doubtful what relation capsulated organisms of the *aerogenes* and intermediate type have to Friedländer's bacillus. It is usual to regard *Bact. aerogenes* as a saprophyte of grains, the intermediate types of coliform bacilli as saprophytes of soil, and the Friedländer-ozæna-rhinoscleroma group as parasites of man and animals. But the fact that most Friedländer strains of respiratory origin are indistinguishable from strains of intermediate I type, see Chapter LXXXVIII, and that many strains found in cystitis appear to be identical with *Bact. aerogenes*, renders dangerous any attempt to separate these organisms on the basis of habitat alone. It is difficult to avoid the conclusion that all these organisms should be classified in a single group, but whether that group should be called *Aerobacter, Encapsulatus,* or *Klebsiella* is very doubtful. For the moment we prefer to keep them within the wide *Bacterium* genus.

Attempts to make subdivisions within the group must necessarily await the definition of the group itself. At the moment a study of antigenic structure seems to hold out the only promise of throwing any light on this problem. A careful comparison of adequate numbers of freshly isolated strains from different sources is urgently called for. Until this is done, it will be impossible to decide whether ozæna and rhinoscleroma strains are specifically distinct from strains of Friedländer, or whether they are merely types of the same species differing in the polysaccharide constituents of their capsule. Any such attempt should include a thorough study of intermediate and *aerogenes* strains.

Mention should perhaps be made here of an organism that appears to be responsible for joint ill of foals, and that is referred to by a variety of names, such as *B. nephritidis equi, B. equirulis, Bact. viscosum equi,* and *B. pyosepticus equi.* Morphologically, this organism is a pleomorphic Gram-negative bacillus occurring singly, in streptococcus-like chains, and as filaments. Some authors describe it as capsulated, others as non-capsulated. It forms tenacious colonies on agar, gives rise to a very viscous sediment in broth, gives a nail-head growth in gelatin stab without liquefaction, ferments glucose, maltose, mannitol, lactose, and sucrose with the production of acid but not gas, is M.R. —, V.P. —, citrate —, indole —, reduces nitrates to nitrites, produces acid, and sometimes clot, in litmus milk, is antigenic-ally heterogeneous, and is non-pathogenic to laboratory animals. The normal form on isolation is said to be mucoid, but a non-mucoid variant is sometimes cultivated directly from foals, though more often it is seen only as the result of *in vitro* variation. (For refer-ences see Edwards 1931, 1932.) The exact relationship of this organism to the members of the Friedländer group is doubtful.

A detailed description of Friedländer's bacillus is given on p. 571.

The Paracolon Bacilli

There remain a number of lactose-fermenting species or types that, for one reason or another, cannot be included in any of the groups described above. A few of these ferment lactose regularly. Many ferment it late, or irregularly. Some constantly give rise to lactose-fermenting variants. Certain of these species are definitely pathogenic for man. Others are under suspicion in this respect. Others again are almost certainly non-pathogenic. A few have been isolated from persons suffering from dysentery, and it will be convenient to deal with these in association with the dysentery sub-group of the non-lactose-fermenting *Bacteria*.

The species, or types, that are described in the present section are sometimes grouped together under the name of " Paracolon bacilli." They have frequently been isolated from the fæces of persons suffering from enteric-like infections, or from acute enteritis. Occasionally an organism belonging to this group has been isolated from the blood stream. In very many instances, however, they have been cultivated from the fæces of normal persons (see Sandiford 1935) ; and it seems doubtful whether they have any real significance as primary infecting agents in epidemic infections of the enteric or dysenteric type, though there can be no doubt that some species at least possess pathogenic potentialities when they invade the tissues from the intestinal tract. The great majority of the organisms included in this group have, it may be noted, been isolated in the tropics ; and there seems no doubt (Sandiford 1935) that they form a more important constituent of the normal intestinal flora under tropical than under temperate conditions.

The classification of these strains raises problems of considerable difficulty. Various schemes have been suggested (Chalmers and Macdonald 1916, Castellani and Chalmers 1920), but these are not in accordance with the general lines which we have discussed above, and, in the authors' opinion, lay too much stress on minor differences in fermentative ability. It is probable that these strains will finally find a place in relation to the M.R. +, V.P. — group of the lactose-fermenting coliform bacilli, but until they have been submitted, in sufficient number, to the detailed and extensive study which has been devoted to other members of the coli-typhoid group, it is impossible to do more than note their existence, and some of their characters. A few of these are set out in Table XL. (For more detailed information, see Castellani 1902–1914, 1907, 1912, Castellani and Chalmers 1920, Archibald 1911, Chalmers and Macdonald 1916.) The strains which have from time to time been described as *B. coli anaerogenes*, on account of the failure to produce gas from certain carbohydrates, probably possess affinities with some members of this group, or with the lactose-fermenting types of dysentery bacilli described in the following section.

It is of interest to note that Dudgeon has recorded a considerable series of cases of acute urinary infection, associated with a pyrexial reaction simulating enteric fever, and caused by a late-lactose-fermenting coliform bacillus which appears to have affinities with some of the atypical strains referred to above. Lactose is fermented slowly, saccharose is unchanged, mannitol and dulcitol are fermented with the production of acid and gas, and litmus milk is rendered acid and usually clotted (Dudgeon 1924, Dudgeon and Pulvertaft 1927).

It may be noted that this organism is hæmolytic for human red cells, and that Dudgeon and his colleagues (Dudgeon *et al.* 1921, 1922) have shown that strains of *Bact. coli* from the fæces, or from the urine in cases of cystitis, may be divided into hæmolytic and non-hæmolytic types. The hæmolytic strains are particularly frequent in certain types of acute urinary infection. It may clearly be necessary to elaborate our classification, when these, or other tests, have been applied to the group as a whole.

The curious organism described by Massini (1907) as *Bact. coli mutabile* is itself a non-lactose-fermenting strain, but is characterized by the property of giving rise to lactose-fermenting mutants, which show no tendency to revert to the parent form. This species

TABLE XL

THE FERMENTATION REACTIONS OF CERTAIN ATYPICAL, LACTOSE-FERMENTING, COLIFORM BACILLI.

	Lactose.	Saccharose.	Dextrose.	Maltose.	Dulcitol.	Mannitol.	Dextrin.	Salicin.	Litmus Milk.	Indole.	V.P.	Gelatin.	Motility.
Bact. columbense . .	O or S	O	A.G.	A.G.	A.G.	A.G.	A.G. (S)	A.G.	A (S) or alk. or D	+	—	—	+
Bact. giumai . . .	A (G.v.s.)	O	A.G.	A.G.	O	O	A.G. (S)	A.G.	A alk.(S)	+	—	—	—
Bact. khartoumense .	A.G. (Slow)	O	A.G.	A.G.	A.G.	A.G.	O	A.G.	A	+	—	—	—
Bact. wesenbergi . .	A	A.G.	A.G.		A	A			A	+	—	—	+

Notes.—O or S = no fermentation, or very slight.
A.G. (S). = slight acid and gas.
A (G.v.s.) = acid, very little gas.
A(S), or alk., or D = slight acid, or alkalinity, or decolorized.
A alk. (S) = acid, reverting to slight alkalinity.

has been discussed in some detail in Chapter VIII. It may be noted that Dulaney and Michelson (1935) have recently described a severe epidemic of diarrhœa in infants, apparently caused by this organism. It is clearly allied to the paracolon group of *Bacteria* ; though the exact relationship remains obscure.

It will be convenient to describe at this point an organism originally isolated by Castellani (1912), and studied in more detail by Khaled (1923). This species, *Bact. asiaticum,* is a non-lactose-fermenter, and on this criterion would be excluded from the " paracolon group." In saccharose, however, it forms both acid and gas ; and in its ability to attack this sugar it differs sharply from the gas-forming, non-lactose-fermenting bacilli of the paratyphoid group that will be considered in a later section. It differs from them also in its ability to form indole. *Bact. asiaticum* is a motile bacillus having the usual characters of the genus. It ferments dextrose, mannitol and saccharose with the formation of acid and gas, but produces no change in lactose or dulcitol. It acidifies, but does not clot milk. It usually forms indole. It does not liquefy gelatin. It appears to be a cause of enteric-like infections in man, particularly in the tropics.

THE NON-LACTOSE-FERMENTING BACTERIA

It will have been noted from the preceding sections that the ability, or inability, of different species of *Bacteria* to attack an empirically selected series of test substrates has played a large part, not only in the division of the genus into two primary groups (lactose-fermenting and non-lactose-fermenting) but also in the separation of the lactose-fermenting group into its constituent sub-groups and species. It will also have been noted, however, that there has within recent years been a wide departure from the older plan of rigid adherence to a particular series of fermentation tests as a basis for classification. In this genus as in others the modern method is to study the reactions of a bacterial group to a wide variety of biological tests, and to pay far more attention to the correlation of several different characters than to any isolated biochemical or biological reaction. Our confident separation of

Bact. aerogenes from *Bact. coli*, for instance, is not based on the fermentation of one or more glucosides or polysaccharides by the former, but not by the latter. It rests on the far firmer foundation of the correlation in the former species of the characters described, in laboratory shorthand, as V.P. +, M.R. −, citrate +, high gas ratio, and in the latter of the characters V.P. −, M.R. +, citrate −, low gas ratio. Schemes of classification drawn up on the basis of exclusive categories and sub-categories, each separated from the other on the basis of ability, or inability, to ferment one or other test substrate would not now be regarded as valid.

In common with other bacterial groups, however, the non-lactose-fermenting bacilli of the coli-typhoid group were, in fact, first subdivided on this basis, due care of course being taken that the test substrates selected should be such as to divide the group, as far as possible, in accord with its other known characters. The tests that were found most useful for the primary subdivisions were the production of acid only, or of acid and gas, from the substrates fermented, and the ability or inability to attack substrates other than dextrose. Mannitol was empirically selected as a convenient test-substrate for the latter purpose, since it was found that any strain that attacked substrates other than dextrose included mannitol in its range of activity (see Smith, J. H. 1915, Winslow *et al.* 1919).

By these tests the non-lactose-fermenting *Bacteria* were divided into two primary subgroups, one of which was further divided into two secondary sub-groups as follows :

(1) Non-lactose-fermenting *Bacteria* producing acid without gas from dextrose alone, or from dextrose and other substrates.

(*a*) Fermenting dextrose alone.

(*b*) Fermenting dextrose and mannitol, and usually other substrates in addition.

(2) Non-lactose-fermenting *Bacteria* producing acid and gas from dextrose, and usually from other substrates.

The categories so defined corresponded in a general way with some, at least, of the divisions indicated by the natural habitats, and the pathogenic action, of the species included in them. The sub-group (*a*) included, among pathological species, only Shiga's dysentery bacillus. The sub-group (*b*) included the Flexner group of dysentery bacilli and the typhoid bacillus. It was customary to separate these from each other on the grounds that the typhoid bacillus is motile, the dysentery bacillus non-motile. The sub-group (2) included an increasing host of organisms associated with enteric infections, or acute gastro-enteritis, in man, and with various infections in animals. The organisms in this group were commonly classed together as the human and animal paratyphoids, and were further distinguished from one another, in part by an increasing range of fermentation tests, in part by agglutination reactions and absorption tests.

In the light of our present knowledge, however, it is clear that this grouping is entirely unnatural, and should therefore be abandoned. The test of gas production places the typhoid bacillus in the same category as the dysentery bacillus, and the paratyphoids in another. This corresponds neither with the natural history of the species, nor with the decisive facts that have been revealed by antigenic analysis. There can be no doubt at all that, whatever system of grouping is finally employed, *Bact. typhosum* must be placed with the paratyphoids in a well-defined category, for which the name " Salmonella Group " is now commonly employed. The classification of this group is now based, by general consent, on the antigenic structure of its constituent species or types. The subdivision of the Flexner group of dysentery bacilli is also based mainly on antigenic structure, though here the differences are not so clear-cut. It will be most convenient therefore to discuss the classification of the non-lactose-fermenting bacteria under the following headings.

(1) The Dysentery Sub-group, including *Bact. shigœ*, the Flexner dysentery bacilli, and certain species or types that show an affinity with the paracolon group by fermenting lactose irregularly or slowly.

(2) The Salmonella, or typhoid-paratyphoid sub-group.

The Dysentery Sub-Group

The definition of this group presents considerable difficulties. Besides comprising certain organisms that ferment lactose, it seems necessary to include at least one type that forms small quantities of gas from glucose.

The organisms that we propose to discuss are (1) *Bact. shigœ*, described by Shiga (1898*a*, *b*, 1901) in Japan, and Kruse (1900, 1901) in Germany : (2) *Bact. flexneri*, described by Flexner (1900*a*, *b*) in the Philippines, and Strong and Musgrave (1900) in Manila : (3) Schmitz's bacillus, isolated by Schmitz (1917) in Roumania, and called *B. ambiguus* by Andrewes (1918)—now *Bact. ambiguum* ; (4) *Bact.* *sonnei*, a late-lactose-fermenting organism defined by Sonne (1915) in Denmark, though almost certainly described by previous workers in the United States and Germany (see Koser *et al.* 1930, Bojlén 1934) : (5) *Bact. dispar*, a name given by Andrewes (1918) to lactose-fermenting dysentery bacilli, but now applied only to a sub-group of the lactose fermenters which can be differentiated from Sonne's bacillus : (6) *Bact. alkalescens*, described by Andrewes (1918) : (7) The Newcastle bacillus, described by Clayton and Warren (1929*a*, *b*), and characterized by the formation of small quantities of gas from certain sugars. A few other organisms of less importance will be mentioned occasionally.

Morphological and cultural Characteristics.—With the possible exception of the Newcastle bacillus, which may show evidence of motility on isolation, the members of this group are non-motile, Gram-negative, coliform bacilli indistinguishable morphologically from the other members of the *Bacterium* group. Their cultural characteristics are likewise insufficiently distinctive to require separate description. It may be noted, however, that the colonies of Sonne's bacillus tend to be larger and more opaque than those of the Shiga-Flexner types, and to have raised, thickened centres, and irregularly crenated edges (Thjøtta 1919, Patterson and Williams 1922). On MacConkey's medium after 24 hours smooth colonies of this organism are circular, low convex, 2 mm. in diameter, slightly granular, with an entire edge and a creamy, faint pink appearance. Rough colonies are raised, rather larger, and have a translucent peripheral extension with a crenated or undulate edge (see Johnston and Kaake 1932) ; a central umbonation is not uncommon. Both types of Sonne colony become red on further incubation.

Morphological and cultural variants of the dysentery bacilli have been described by several workers. Differences have often been noted in the antigenic structure, saline and acid agglutinability, and pathogenicity for laboratory animals of the rough and smooth variants. Indeed, as with many other members of the *Bacterium* group, the antigenic structure is of far more importance in defining smooth and rough types than the colonial appearance. (For references to variation see Krumwiede *et al.* 1916, Arkwright 1921, Carver 1921, Isabolinsky 1926, Koser and Styron 1930, Braun and Baake 1930, Kobayashi *et al.* 1931, Johnston and Kaake 1932, Wyckoff 1933, Waaler 1935.)

Resistance and Metabolism.—The members of this group are not specially resistant. They are killed by a temperature of 55° C. in 1 hour, by 0·5 per cent.

phenol in 6 hours, and by 1 per cent. phenol in about 15–30 minutes. They resist drying for 20 to 25 days (Vaillard and Dopter 1903).

They are aerobes and facultative anaerobes. Their optimum temperature is about 37° C. Shiga's bacillus is characterized by its inability to form catalase.

With the exception of certain strains of *Bact. alkalescens,* none of the members appear capable of producing a hæmolysin active against sheep cells.

Biochemical Reactions.—*Bact. shigæ* and Schmitz's bacillus produce acid from glucose ; the remaining members, with the exception of some strains of the Newcastle bacillus, also ferment mannitol. Hence the primary classification of the group is into mannitol and non-mannitol fermenters. *Bact. sonnei* and *Bact. dispar* produce acid from lactose ; the fermentation, however, is slow, and is not usually apparent for 2–10 days. The same two organisms are often late sucrose fermenters. This sugar is sometimes attacked by certain of the Flexner strains (Strong type). Dulcitol is fermented slowly by *Bact. alkalescens,* by the Newcastle bacillus, and by occasional strains of *Bact. dispar.* The Newcastle bacillus is distinguished from all the other members by its ability to form gas in glucose and dulcitol. The amount of gas is very small, often amounting to not more than a bubble in a Durham fermentation tube. Most workers report that *Bact. dispar* differs from *Bact. sonnei* in fermenting xylose and sorbitol, but Bojlén (1934), who divides the Sonne group into six fermentative types, states that three of these types are able to ferment xylose. In litmus milk there is generally a slight acidity for a few days. The reaction may remain permanently acid as with Sonne's bacillus and *Bact. dispar,* or it may revert to neutral as with *Bact. shigæ,* Schmitz's bacillus, and *Bact. flexneri.* Many strains of *flexneri,* after a preliminary acidity, turn milk alkaline. *Bact. alkalescens* produces an initial and lasting alkalinity. Both *Bact. sonnei* and *Bact. dispar* not infrequently clot the milk after a week or two.

Indole is of some differential importance, serving to distinguish Schmitz's bacillus from *Bact. shigæ,* and *Bact. dispar* from *Bact. sonnei.* The Newcastle bacillus does not form indole, but *Bact. alkalescens* does. As regards the Flexner group, Gettings (1919) found that of 285 strains tested, 158 produced indole, while 127 did not. The methyl red test is of limited value, but it may help to differentiate the positive *Bact. dispar* from the negative *Bact. sonnei.* All strains reduce nitrates to nitrites ; none forms H_2S ; none grows in Koser's citrate ; and none gives a positive Voges-Proskauer reaction. A list of biochemical reactions is given on p. 547. (For references to the more recent studies on these reactions, see Lester 1926, Smith and Fraser 1928, Kerrin 1928*a,* Nelson 1930, Bojlén 1930, Johnston and Brown 1930, Buchanan and Roux 1930, Koser *et al.* 1930, Cann and de Navasquez 1931, Welch and Mickle 1932, 1934, Downie *et al.* 1933, Forsyth 1933, Bamforth 1934, Whitehead and Scott 1934, Mandry 1935.)

Antigenic Structure.—The serological behaviour of the dysentery bacilli is complicated. Of the non-mannitol fermenters the Shiga group is homogeneous ; all strains of *Bact. shigæ* are agglutinated by a specific serum prepared against any one strain. An anti-shigæ serum has some agglutinating action on Schmitz's bacillus and on some strains of the Flexner group. A serum prepared against Schmitz's bacillus will agglutinate a Shiga bacillus to $\frac{1}{4}$ or $\frac{1}{2}$ titre ; but antigenically Schmitz's bacillus and Shiga's bacillus are easily distinguishable ; a Shiga bacillus cannot absorb the agglutinins from a serum prepared against Schmitz's bacillus, nor a Schmitz bacillus from an anti-shigæ serum.

The mannitol-fermenting group, on the other hand, is heterogeneous. The work of Gettings (1919), Murray (1918), and Andrewes and Inman (1919) has made it clear that the Flexner bacilli contain at least four antigenic components. These are now known as the V, W, X, and Z antigens. Each of these is represented to some extent in every strain, but in any given strain there is usually a preponderance of one antigen over the rest. In certain races, V, W, and Z, there is so great a preponderance of a single antigenic component, different in each instance, over the rest, as to make them behave like distinct serological types ; each race requires its own antiserum for adequate agglutination. The X race is peculiar in that it will not agglutinate with any sera but its own ; yet it is able to give rise to a serum that will agglutinate not only X races, but also Z, and, to a certain extent, V races. The agglutinins corresponding to each of these four types cannot be more than partially absorbed by the others. Andrewes and Inman found at least two sub-races, VZ and WZ ; these were members of the V and W races respectively, but contained so large a proportion of a second antigenic constituent as to modify their serological behaviour. One race, which is called Y, and which corresponds to the original Y-strain of Hiss and Russell (1903), contains a more evenly balanced mixture of V, W, and Z components, with a small amount of X. For this reason a serum prepared against a Y strain is more cosmopolitan than the rest, having a wide range of agglutination (Fig. 130).

Flexner V.   Flexner W.   Flexner X.   Flexner Z.   Flexner Y.

Fig. 130.—Diagram representing the Variation in Antigenic Structure of *Bact. flexneri*.
(After Andrewes.)

The antigenic constitution of the Flexner and allied dysentery bacilli has been studied by numerous other workers, particularly Kruse and his colleagues (1907) and Lentz and Prigge (1931) in Germany, and Aoki (1921, 1923) in Japan. Sartorius and Reploh (1931, 1932), Clauberg (1932), and Kemper (1933) have endeavoured to relate the different types established by these workers to each other, but with only partial success. It seems clear that, though the Andrewes and Inman classification comprises the majority of the *flexneri* strains, there are occasional types, such as those described by Boyd (1932, 1936) in India, which appear to be antigenically distinct.

Sonne's bacillus is antigenically homogeneous (Kerrin 1928a, Nelson 1930, Koser *et al.* 1930). It is true that Johnston and Brown (1930) described two distinct serological types, but they were probably dealing with smooth and rough variants. *Bact. dispar*, on the other hand, appears to be antigenically heterogeneous (see Forsyth 1933, Watanabe 1935). It has no relation to Sonne's bacillus, but may be agglutinated to part titre with certain Flexner sera (Welch and Mickle 1932, 1934). *Bact. alkalescens* and the Newcastle bacillus both have distinctive antigenic constitutions.

It may be noted that the agglutination of dysentery bacilli occurs rather slowly, and that it is advisable to incubate all tests for 4–6 hours at 50–55° C., and to delay the final reading till the tubes have been left at room temperature overnight. This holds particularly for the Newcastle, *alkalescens*, *sonnei*, and *dispar* types.

Chemical studies on the antigens of the dysentery bacilli are still in their infancy. Specific polysaccharides have been isolated from *Bact. shigæ* by Kurauchi (1929), Meyer (1930, 1931*a*) and Morgan (1931), and from *Bact. flexneri* and *Bact. sonnei* by Kurauchi (1929). According to Meyer and Morgan (1935), the specific bacterial polysaccharide hapten obtained from the smooth form of *Bact. shigæ* is a weakly acidic polysaccharide, containing about 1·6 per cent. nitrogen and 92 per cent. reducing sugar ; it precipitates with $1/12 \times 10^6$ dilution of antiserum, and neutralizes specifically the hæmolytic action of *shigæ* heterophile antibody (see Chapter VII) on sheep red cells in the presence of complement. The fact that a chemically homogeneous polysaccharide hapten can enter into specific combination with two entirely different types of antibody is of considerable interest, and suggests that it may contain in each of its molecules two kinds of receptors differing in their specificity. According to Kurauchi, the polysaccharides for *Bact. flexneri* and *Bact. sonnei* are specifically distinct.

Apart from the serological differentiation of the dysentery bacilli, certain indirect tests may be used to distinguish between the types, such as Michaelis's (1917) acid agglutination test, and susceptibility to action of the bacteriophage. The acid agglutination test depends on the different H-ion concentrations necessary for flocculation. Using the particular range employed by Michaelis, Andrewes and Inman (1919) found that Schmitz's bacillus, *Bact. alkalescens*, and *Bact. dispar* were agglutinated, whereas *Bact. shigæ* and *Bact. flexneri* were not. The test is only a rough one, and it is doubtful whether the information it furnishes justifies its use under ordinary conditions. On the other hand, the susceptibility of different types of dysentery bacilli to the action of certain phages appears to be very much more specific. According to Burnet and McKie (1930), whose article should be consulted for further details, bacteriophages that are active against Flexner bacilli can be divided into four main groups. One of these groups is capable of lysing bacilli only in the smooth phase, while the other three may or may not lyse smooth strains but generally lyse rough strains of all types. Characteristic differences in their sensitivity to a series of phages are presented by the V, W, X, Y, and Z types of *Bact. flexneri*.

Toxin Formation by Dysentery Bacilli.—In 1903 Conradi prepared an autolysate of dysentery bacilli—probably Shiga's bacillus—which he found to be toxic for rabbits and guinea-pigs. An 18-hours' culture was suspended in saline, and incubated for 24 to 48 hours at 37·5° C. ; after centrifugalization the yellowish supernatant fluid was removed, diluted with 5 times its volume of saline, and filtered through a Berkefeld candle ; the filtrate was tested for sterility, and then concentrated to 1/10–1/50 of its bulk at 35° C. This product, when injected intravenously into rabbits or intraperitoneally into guinea-pigs in a dose of 0·1 c.c., proved fatal in about 48 hours. In rabbits death was preceded by diarrhœa, collapse, and paralysis of the legs ; in guinea-pigs by a rapid fall of temperature and collapse. At necropsy Conradi found in both animals congestion of the intestine, mucus and blood adhering to the mucosa, and frequently small hæmorrhages of the mucous and the serous coats. When a smaller dose was injected into rabbits, the animals lived for 4 to 6 days ; and he found that post mortem the mucosa of the last third of the large intestine was swollen, blackish-red in colour, and ulcerated in several places.

Neisser and Shiga (1903) confirmed Conradi's results, and noted in addition that the toxic substances were precipitated by alcohol and ether, and largely destroyed by heat at 75° C. Todd (1904) in this country was able to show that 4 to 6 weeks' cultures of Shiga's bacillus contained a soluble toxin, which was highly active on rabbits and horses, but to a much less extent on guinea-pigs, rats, and mice. Flexner's bacillus proved incapable of giving rise to a soluble toxin. Dopter (1905), studying the histological appearances of rabbits dying of paralysis subsequent to injection with 24-hours' broth cultures of *Bact. shigæ*, observed definite lesions in the spinal cord, consisting chiefly of chromatolysis of the anterior horn cells, sometimes with small interstitial hæmorrhages and focal necroses of the grey matter. The lesions occurred as frequently after the injection of toxin as of bacilli. Further work by Kraus and Dörr (1905) led to the conclusion that Shiga's bacillus gave rise to two toxins : (1) a soluble toxin, present in 8–10-days' broth cultures and in filtered saline suspensions of 24-hours' agar cultures ; this was fatal to rabbits but not to guinea-pigs, and gave rise to the production of a specific neutralizing antitoxin ; (2) an insoluble toxin present in the bacterial bodies, which was fatal both to rabbits and to guinea-pigs. No soluble toxins were found in cultures of Flexner's bacillus.

Flexner and Sweet (1906), using a modification of Conradi's method, obtained a toxin from 24-hours' agar cultures of Shiga's bacillus, which, injected intravenously into rabbits, gave rise to diarrhœa, paralysis, convulsions, and death. The paralysis began in the upper limbs and extended at times to the lower limbs. Sometimes the animals survived for 10 days after the extremities were paralysed ; they lay on one side in a position of opisthotonos. Post mortem, small hæmorrhages were seen in the brain, and softening of the grey matter in the spinal cord. In the intestine there was congestion of the serosa ; the walls of the gut, especially of the cæcum and appendix, were thickened and œdematous, the mucosa was yellowish-white and thrown into deep folds, which were sometimes covered by a pseudo-membrane or stippled with hæmorrhages. The mesenteric glands were swollen, œdematous, and congested. Heat at 81° C. for 1 hour destroyed the toxin. These observations were largely confirmed by Bessau (1911), who concluded that there were two different toxins—one a paretic or neuro-toxin causing paralysis of the muscles, the other a marasmic or intestinal toxin causing a fall in temperature, diarrhœa, and chronic marasmus. The paretic toxin was neutralized by antitoxin, the marasmic toxin was not. Further, rabbits were affected by both toxins, whereas in guinea-pigs the paretic toxin was without effect.

There has been considerable discussion on the dual nature of the toxin. At the risk of some repetition we may summarize the evidence for and against this hypothesis. Many workers, notably Flexner and Sweet (1906), and Olitsky and Kligler (1920), have concluded that two separate toxins are produced by *Bact. shigæ* : one a neuro-toxin acting on the central nervous system of the rabbit, and identified by Olitsky and Kligler as an exotoxin ; the other having a specific affinity for the intestine, and regarded by Olitsky and Kligler as an endotoxin. Kraus and Dörr (1905), as noted above, consider the exotoxin to be pathogenic for rabbits, and the endotoxin to be pathogenic for both rabbits and guinea-pigs. It seems doubtful whether these conclusions are justifiable. The development of paralysis in rabbits and not in guinea-pigs can be equally well ascribed to a difference in the reaction of the animals as to a difference in the nature of the toxins (see Barg 1932). The fact that the same lesions are produced in experimental animals by the dried bacillary bodies as by broth culture filtrates seems to indicate the unity of the toxin produced. This view is strongly supported by the work of Okell and Blake (1930), who made comparative observations on the pH, viable count, and toxicity of broth cultures of Shiga's bacillus. Though the maximum viable count was reached in 12 hours, a filtrate of the culture at this time proved non-toxic to mice injected intravenously, even in a dose of 1 c.c. Toxin was first demonstrable after 24 hours, but did not reach its height till the pH rose to its maximum of 8·6–8·8 after about 3 weeks. The M.L.D. of the filtrate was then about 0·005 c.c. These observations suggested that the toxin was formed within the cell in the early period of growth, and was liberated into the medium as the result of gradual bacterial autolysis. Support of this explanation was afforded by the fact that the dried bacillary bodies, prepared from 30-hour agar cultures, were highly toxic to mice, though, when they were suspended in saline and shaken at intervals, no toxin diffused out during an observation period of 7 days at room temperature. In other words, toxin was not liberated from the cells when the conditions were unfavourable for autolysis.

Summarizing our present knowledge, we may say that *Bact. shigæ* gives rise to a soluble toxin, which is present in broth cultures about a week old, in filtered autolysates of 24-hours' agar cultures, and in the dried bacterial bodies. It is destroyed by a temperature of 75–80° C. maintained for 1 hour. In a dose of about 0·02 mgm. of the dried bacillary bodies it proves fatal to mice inoculated intravenously. It is fatal to the rabbit, causing paralysis of the limbs, diarrhœa, and collapse, and has less action on the guinea-pig, in which diarrhœa and collapse alone are produced. It may be partly precipitated from a 14-days' broth culture filtrate by the addition of 40 per cent. of solid ammonium sulphate (Blake and Okell 1929). It gives rise to, and is neutralized by, a specific antitoxin, the union of toxin and antitoxin taking place in accordance with the law of multiple proportions. It is probably best regarded as an endotoxin in that it is formed intracellularly. It differs, however, from many other endotoxins in the specificity of its receptor grouping, and in its power of giving rise to a potent antitoxin.

None of the other members of the dysentery group is toxigenic to anything like the same extent as Shiga's bacillus. The ground-up bacterial bodies of *Bact. flexneri*, *Bact. sonnei*, and *Bact. dispar* prove fatal on intravenous inoculation of rabbits, but only in a dose that is about 20 times greater than the corresponding fatal dose of dried Shiga cells. Schmitz's bacillus is variable in its toxicity. *Bact. alkalescens* appears to be non-toxic.

Pathogenicity.—*Bact. shigæ*, Schmitz's bacillus, *Bact. flexneri*, the Newcastle bacillus, and *Bact. sonnei* undoubtedly give rise to dysentery in man. The rôle played by *Bact. alkalescens* is more doubtful, while *Bact. dispar* appears to be non-pathogenic. (For further information see Chapter LXVII.)

So far as we know animals do not suffer naturally from dysentery caused by *Bact. shigæ* or *Bact. flexneri*, though the latter organism has occasionally been isolated from monkeys in captivity (see Lovell 1929). It is not possible to reproduce the typical disease, as it occurs in man, by experimental inoculation or feeding of the ordinary laboratory animals. Nevertheless both organisms, especially *Bact. shigæ*, are toxic to rabbits, horses, and mice, and to a less extent to guinea-pigs. After subcutaneous inoculation into rabbits, dogs, and young pigs the living bacilli may become localized in the intestine and give rise to catarrhal and necrotic lesions, which often prove fatal (Vaillard and Dopter 1903).

RABBITS.—A small dose—0·01 mgm. of a 24-hours' agar culture of *Bact. shigæ*—injected intravenously proves fatal in 1 to 4 days. Death is preceded by diarrhœa, paresis or total paralysis of the extremities, and collapse. Post mortem, there may be hæmorrhages into the subcutaneous tissue and peritoneum ; the intestine, especially the cæcum and colon, is congested and may show submucous hæmorrhages. The mucosa itself is congested, œdematous, and sometimes studded with petechiæ (Vaillard and Dopter 1903, Amako 1908). In the lumen of the gut there is often mucoid or bloody fluid. A similar picture is seen after injection of dead bacilli in larger quantity, or of toxin. If a smaller dose of bacilli is given, there may be time for necrosis and actual ulceration of the intestine to occur. The living bacilli can be recovered from the mucosa and from the corresponding mesenteric glands. Subcutaneous injection has much the same effect as intravenous, but the animals survive longer. The lesions following injection of Flexner's and Sonne's bacillus are not unlike those produced by *Bact. shigæ*, if a sufficient dose is given, but they are rarely so severe.

MICE.—0·1 mgm. of a 24-hours' culture of *Bact. shigæ* injected intraperitoneally or subcutaneously kills the animal in 1 to 4 days. At necropsy there may be no evident change, or there may be catarrhal inflammation of the intestine with watery mucus in the gut. *Bact. flexneri* and *Bact. sonnei* often prove fatal on intraperitoneal inoculation of large doses.

GUINEA-PIGS.—These animals are less susceptible, weight for weight, to *Bact. shigæ* than are rabbits and mice. The lesions produced by subcutaneous or intraperitoneal injection of living bacilli vary. After a fatal dose there may be no marked macroscopic changes, or there may be intestinal lesions similar to those found in rabbits. Death may be produced by large intraperitoneal doses of Flexner's or Sonne's bacillus.

OTHER ANIMALS.—By giving a cat ½ drop of croton oil, and injecting a whole agar slope of Shiga's bacillus directly into the stomach, Shiga (1898) succeeded in setting up diarrhœa for a week ; the animal passed grey, slimy stools, from which the bacilli could always be cultivated. It died 4 weeks later ; at necropsy there was congestion of the rectal mucosa, and a covering of mucus over the whole of the large gut. The bacillus was recovered from the cæcum and large intestine. Most workers have failed completely to reproduce true dysenteric lesions in cats, dogs, rabbits, or monkeys either by injection *per os* or *per rectum*, though the feeding of monkeys with large doses of Flexner's bacillus may give rise to severe dysenteric symptoms (see Dack and Petran 1934).

Classification.—One of the first to suggest a working classification of the dysentery bacilli was Hiss (1904). On the basis of fermentation reactions in glucose, maltose, mannitol, sucrose, and dextrin he divided them into four groups. The fault of this classification lies in the fact that the reactions of the mannitol fermenters in maltose, sucrose, and dextrin are inconstant ; moreover, the divisions made on this basis do not accord with those reached on serological grounds. Though the majority of workers have abandoned the classification of the Flexner group on the basis of biochemical reactions, it may be noted that an attempt has recently been made to resuscitate this method by Bojlén (1934), who divides the bacilli of this group into ten biochemical types. It is stated that an antigenic difference was found corresponding to the sucrose-positive and sucrose-negative sub-groups.

In 1907 Kruse and his colleagues in Germany carried out a thorough examination of the serological reactions of the group. The Shiga-Kruse bacillus he regarded as the true dysentery bacillus ; the remainder—the mannitol fermenters—he called pseudo-dysentery bacilli. These, on the basis of agglutination and absorption of agglutinins, he divided into a number of types A to H, of which the first five were fully described. It is impossible to say to which of our present types Kruse's bacilli corresponded. It is probable that his type A or D was identical with the Hiss-Y bacillus, and his type E with Sonne's bacillus. Though his classification has now been abandoned, to Kruse must be ascribed the merit of being the first to point out the serological complexity of the mannitol-fermenting group.

The following year, Shiga (1908) and Amako (1908) in Japan proposed a classification on the basis of fermentation reactions, asserting that the five resulting types were also separable by agglutination.

The war gave a great impetus to the further study of the dysentery bacilli. It was soon realized that the sugar reactions were incapable of affording any but a rough classification, and workers therefore devoted their attention to the finer study of the serology of the bacilli using the agglutination, often combined with the absorption test. Gettings (1919), Murray (1918), and Andrewes and Inman (1919) arrived independently at results agreeing closely with each other. The Shiga group was antigenically distinct and homogeneous. The Flexner group was heterogeneous and divisible into four types, according to the preponderance of one or other of the antigenic components V, W, X, and Z.

Work during the post-war years has been characterized mainly by concentration on types of dysentery bacilli other than *Bact. shigæ* and *Bact. flexneri*. In the classification of these organisms both antigenic structure and biochemical reactions have proved of value. It has become clear that certain late-lactose fermenters, like *Bact. sonnei* and *Bact. dispar*, must be included in the dysentery group, and that an even further extension must be made to include a gas-producing organism, the Newcastle bacillus.

The main lines of cleavage are (1) between the mannitol and the non-mannitol fermenters, and (2) in the mannitol-fermenting group, between the non-lactose and the late-lactose fermenters.

In the non-mannitol-fermenting group, *Bact. ambiguum* (Schmitz's bacillus) is distinguished from *Bact. shigæ* by fermenting rhamnose, producing indole, and being antigenically distinct. The Newcastle bacillus often fails to ferment mannitol, but it can be readily distinguished from *shigæ* and *ambiguum* by its production of a bubble or two of gas in tubes of glucose and dulcitol, and by its different serological behaviour.

In the non-lactose-fermenting subdivision of the mannitol-fermenting group, *Bact. alkalescens* differs from most strains of *Bact. flexneri* in fermenting dulcitol, xylose, and sorbitol, but not dextrin. It is M.R. + and produces indole, whereas many strains of *flexneri* are M.R. − and indole negative. It is, moreover, susceptible to acid agglutination. The *flexneri* strains themselves are differentiated by antigenic structure into at least four types, V, W, X, and Z. Certain other types must also be included in this group, such as Gettings' bacillus—an indole + strain susceptible to acid agglutination and serologically distinct from *flexneri*—and some of the strains described by Boyd (1936) and other workers in different parts of the world which appear to have a fairly definite antigenic constitution of their own.

In the lactose-fermenting subdivision of the mannitol-fermenting group, *Bact. dispar* ferments xylose and sorbitol, produces indole, and is generally M.R. +, while *Bact. sonnei* is negative in all these respects. Sonne's bacillus appears to be antigenically homogeneous, and to differ from *Bact. dispar*, which is antigenically heterogeneous. In contrast to most other workers, Bojlén (1934), who has made a study of Sonne dysentery in Denmark, maintains that many strains ferment xylose. He divides the Sonne group into six sub-groups on the basis of maltose and xylose fermentation. Maltose fermentation is admitted to be irregular, except with freshly isolated strains, and two of the sub-groups are differentiated from two of the others merely by their slightly delayed fermentation of certain sugars. The justification advanced for such a procedure is that in any given closed epidemic the strains isolated belonged to one sub-group. It is very doubtful whether, in the absence of other correlated properties, attention should be paid by systematists to minor fermentative activities that may be characteristic of strain rather than of type differences. The fact, moreover, that xylose-positive strains of Sonne appear to be uncommon outside of Denmark suggests that Bojlén's classification should be accepted with reserve until it has received confirmation from other countries.

There is in the lactose-fermenting sub-group an undefined series of strains usually referred to by the term *Bact. coli anaerogenes*. Some of these strains are undoubtedly of the Sonne or *dispar* type (see Nabarro 1923, 1927 ; Koser *et al.* 1930). Others are distinguished from these organisms by the fact that they produce small quantities of gas, often late, in glucose, maltose, mannitol, sucrose, or salicin, maltose being one of the commonest. Organisms of this type are not infrequently found in milk (Wilson *et al.* 1935), and appear to be related more nearly to the coli-ærogenes than to the dysentery group. Some *anærogenes* strains are motile, and some liquefy gelatin.

We give in Figure 131 a tentative classification of the dysentery group, and in Table XLI some of their more important properties.

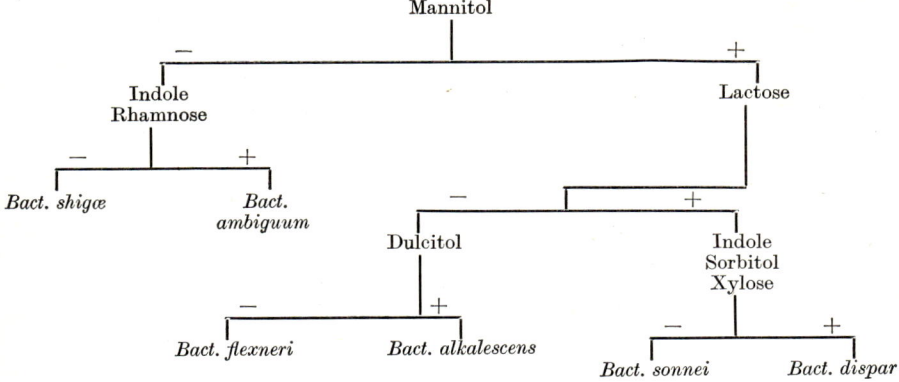

FIG. 131.—TENTATIVE CLASSIFICATION OF THE DYSENTERY BACILLI.

Note.—The Newcastle bacillus may or may not ferment mannitol, and has been omitted from the figure.

The Salmonella (Typhoid-paratyphoid) Sub-group

As has already been noted, the classification of the Salmonella Group is now firmly based on the antigenic structure of the species, or types, of which it is comprised. The arrangement of the various antigenic components in the cells and flagella of the Salmonella bacilli has already been described in Chapter VII in relation to the general problem of antigenic structure, and in Chapter VIII in relation to the study of bacterial variation. Before considering the different species and types that have been differentiated by this method of analysis, we may however recall the relevant facts and consider some of them in greater detail.

In the Salmonella Group of bacilli we are dealing, in the main, with flagellated organisms. We therefore have to consider both the H (flagellar) and O (somatic) antigens. By appropriate methods we can test for these components separately. A formolized broth culture of a flagellated species readily agglutinates in the presence of the homologous H agglutinins, but responds very poorly, if at all, to the homologous O agglutinins. The reason for this behaviour is, perhaps, that the formalin fixes the flagella over the bacterial surface in such a way that the somatic antigens are no longer exposed to the action of the O agglutinins. To test for the O antigens we can employ a bacterial suspension that has been extracted with hot alcohol, thus removing or inactivating the flagellar antigens.

In respect to their flagellar antigens many of the species, or types, with which we are concerned are diphasic. That is to say, their flagella may assume two alternative antigenic forms. One of these is known as the *specific phase*. The antigenic components associated with it are either peculiar to the particular species, or type, concerned, or are shared by only a few other species, or types. The other is known as the *group phase*. The antigenic components associated with it are shared by many other species, or types. Any given culture of a particular diphasic strain may consist entirely of bacilli in the

TABLE XLI

REACTIONS OF DYSENTERY BACILLI

All strains are non-motile with the possible exception of the Newcastle bacillus, reduce nitrates, are V.P. —, reduce methylene blue in broth cultures, form NH_3, and fail to form H_2S or to grow in Koser's citrate.

Organism.	Glucose.	Mannitol.	Lactose.	Sucrose.	Dulcitol.	Rhamnose.	Xylose.	Sorbitol.	Litmus Milk.	Indole.	M.R.	Catalase.	Acid Agglutination.	Shiga.	Ambiguum.	Newcastle.	Flexneri.	Alkalescens.	Sonnei.	Dispar.	Toxicity for Rabbit.
Bact. shigæ	A	—	—	—	—	—	—	—	Sl. A	—	—	—	—	+	—	—	—	—	—	—	+++
Bact. ambiguum, Schmitz bacillus	A	—	—	—	—	A	—	A ⊦	Sl. A	+	—	+	+	—	+	—	—	—	—	—	V
Newcastle bacillus	A g	A ⊦	—	—	A g late	?	Sl. A V	—	Sl.A → Sl. alk.	—	+	+	?	—	—	+	—	—	—	—	+⊦
Bact. flexneri	A	A	—	A ⊦	—	A ⊦	—	A ⊦	Sl.A. → Sl. alk.	⊦	⊦	+	—	—	—	—	+	—	—	—	+
Bact. alkalescens	A	A	—	—	A	A	A	A	alk.	+	+	+	+	—	—	—	—	+	—	—	—
Bact. sonnei	A	A	A late	A late	—	A	—	—	A late clot	—	—	+	+	—	—	—	—	—	+	—	+
Bact. dispar	A	A	A late	A late	—	A	A	A	A late clot	+	+	+	+	—	—	—	—	—	—	H	+

Sl. = slight. A = acid. g = small amount of gas. alk. = alkaline. V = variable. H = heterogeneous.

specific phase, or entirely of bacilli in the group phase, or may contain representatives of both phases. A bacillus in one phase, although always capable of giving rise to descendants in the alternative phase, usually maintains a constant phase over a number of generations. If therefore we prepare plate cultures of a diphasic organism and make numerous sub-cultures, each from a single colony, we should usually obtain some suspensions in the specific phase, others in the group phase. If these are killed by the addition of formalin after 18–24 hours' growth, there will usually not have been time for any change in phase to occur.

In any given species, or type, however, there may be more than one H antigen in the specific phase, and there are generally several different H antigens in the group phase. The number of H antigens in the specific phase of the known species, or types, actually varies from one to four, the number of antigens in the group phase from two to four. It is possible that some species may have a single O (somatic) antigen, though this now seems doubtful. Most species have two. Some have three. There may also be additional minor factors. The determination of the antigenic structure of a particular species of Salmonella organism may involve the identification of eight different antigenic components. The method adopted is, in the main, that of direct agglutination of H and O suspensions with antisera which, by previous absorption with appropriate antigenic types, have been rendered specific for one or other antigenic component, or a small group of such components. Up to the present time some thirteen different somatic antigens, twenty-eight specific flagellar antigens, and six group flagellar antigens have been identified. The identification and labelling of these was initiated by White (1926, 1929a, b) and continued and extended by Kauffmann (1929a, b, 1930b, 1931, 1934c). In their earlier studies the two investigators used a different system of labelling, so that the descriptions given in the English and German papers during the period can be correlated only by the aid of an appropriate key, giving the equivalent numbers and letters in the two systems (see Lovell 1932a). Recently, however, the terminology introduced by Kauffmann has been adopted for general use by a special subcommittee of the International Society for Microbiology (see Salmonella Subcommittee 1934); and each member of the Salmonella group is now allotted an antigenic formula based on this system of labelling.

The somatic (O) antigens are accorded Roman numerals; these at present run from I to XIII. The specific flagellar (H) antigens are accorded small letters; these antigens have already illustrated the limitations of an alphabetical notation by exceeding twenty-six in number. By convention, those discovered later than the antigen that received the label y have been accorded an additional distinguishing numeral, z_1, z_2 and so on. The group flagellar (H) antigens are accorded arabic numerals; these at present run from 1 to 6.

In terms of this notation, the antigenic formula for *Bact. paratyphosum A*, which is a monophasic flagellated bacillus, existing only in the specific phase is I, II : a : —, the final : — being inserted to emphasize the absence of group flagellar antigens. The formula for *Bact. paratyphosum C* which is a diphasic flagellated bacillus is VI, VII : c : 1, 4, 5. This formula means that, in the specific phase, the organism possesses the O antigens VI and VII and the H antigen c; while, in the group phase, it possesses the same O antigens, VI and VII, and the H antigens 1, 4 and 5. A few monophasic species, or types, exist only in the group phase. Thus the antigenic formula of *Bact. choleræ-suis* var. *kunzendorf* is VI, VII : 1, 3, 4, 5. Again there are at least two Salmonella bacilli that are non-flagellated, and hence possess no H antigens. *Bact. gallinarum*, for instance, has the antigenic formula IX : — : —.

One of the most interesting features of the Salmonella group is the way in which the same antigenic components recur in different combinations. Thus, different O antigens are found in combination with the same H antigens. The same set of group H antigens are replaced by different specific H antigens, when different diphasic species, or types, change from the group to the specific phase. The same set of antigenic components recurs, in different combinations, in the group phase of different species and so on. The implications of these facts, in relation to the evolution of the Salmonella group are discussed by White (1926).

It is clear that the observed distribution of these antigenic components forms a basis for a natural scheme of classification, and this has been adopted in the Kauffmann-White scheme, proposed for international adoption by the Salmonella Subcommittee (1934). It seems reasonable to regard the antigenic structure of the bacterial cell as more fundamental than the antigenic structure of the appended flagella. The Salmonella group, as a whole, has therefore been divided into sub-groups, each of which shares a common somatic antigen. Where more than one somatic antigen is present, one of these antigens is regarded as determining the sub-group to which the species, or type, concerned shall be allocated. Thus, Group B consists of those organisms that possess the O antigen IV, or the antigens IV or V. Group D consists of those organisms that possess the O antigen IX, and so on. The group letter, it should be noted, forms no essential part of the name of any species, or type, or of its antigenic formula. The groups display the natural relations of the different Salmonella bacilli, but the antigenic components that determine those relationships are labelled according to the Kauffmann convention. It should, perhaps, be recalled that there is an essential difference between this scheme of classification and that adopted in describing the antigenic structure of other bacterial groups. A " Group B hæmolytic streptococcus," for instance, means a hæmolytic streptococcus that possesses the Group B antigen, and that antigen has no other label.

There is a further difference in regard to nomenclature. In most bacterial species the ultimate entities that can be differentiated by means of antigenic analysis have been labelled with numbers, or letters, but have not been given separate specific names. We speak, for instance, of *Str. pneumoniæ* Type VIII, or more commonly of a Type VIII pneumococcus. In the Salmonella group, on the other hand, the practice has arisen of giving each new antigenic type a separate specific name. We have followed this convention here, since there is no obvious alternative ; but we doubt whether it can be justified. While in full agreement with the Salmonella Subcommittee in regard to the fundamental importance of antigenic structure and the necessity for labelling each new antigenic type, it appears to us that the accordance of specific rank to each of the ultimate types that can be differentiated by these means is a questionable procedure. It will clearly increase the present chaos of bacteriological nomenclature if we attach one meaning to the term " species " in the genus *Bacterium*, and another meaning in the genus *Streptococcus*. When international agreement is reached we shall be forced either to diminish the number of named species within the Salmonella group, differentiating each species into a number of labelled types, or to recognize and invent names for at least thirty-two species of pneumococci, and at least twenty-four species of *Str. pyogenes* in place of our present numbered types. There seems to us no doubt that the former is the better method.

Similarly, we feel unable to adopt the generic name *Salmonella*, which the Subcommittee upholds. The organisms of this group clearly fall within the genus *Bacterium*, as that genus is here defined. It may be that similarities of antigenic structure will one day be accepted as the basis on which both species and genera are determined ; but, pending some agreed ruling on this and similar systematic usages, it seems wise to adopt a conservative attitude.

We have, in most instances, followed the Salmonella Subcommittee in regard to the names that they have attached to the " species " defined in their report. In regard to those recently described no difficulty arises. The convention that has been universally followed is to give to the new organism the name of the place in which it was first isolated. In regard to the older species or types, many of which have in the past received several different specific names as the result of inadequate identification and differentiation, we have followed the rulings of the subcommittee in regard to priority. This involves the disappearance of certain familiar names, such as *Bact. aertrycke*. In a few instances we have retained the more familiar form of a specific name—for instance, *Bact. typhosum* and *Bact. paratyphosum A* instead of *Bact. typhi* and *Bact. paratyphi A*.

The classification of the organisms belonging to the Salmonella group, as set out by the Salmonella Subcommittee on the basis of the Kauffmann-White notation, is given in Table XLII, with certain additions. We have added to the table *Bact. aberdeen*, recently described by Smith (1934), which, since it possesses a new O antigen must be placed in a new group (F), and *Bact. poona*, still more recently described by Bridges and Scott (1935), which, since it possesses a hitherto undescribed O antigen, must be placed in a separate group (G). We have also included certain fermentation types of *Bact. enteritidis* and one new antigenic type (*Bact. enteritidis* var. *blegdam*) recently described by Kauffmann (1935b). We have added in brackets an additional antigenic component of certain previously described species (XII) that has recently been described and labelled by Kauffmann (1935a). We have omitted certain additional H components that Kauffmann (1935b) has described in certain species of Group D, since the label attached to one of these (z_1) would cause confusion with the newly described specific H antigen of *Bact. poona*. They are, however, included in the notes on pp. 554–562.

Although antigenic structure has attained a position of unquestioned priority in the classification of this group—as it probably will in the classification of all other bacterial species—the enzymic reactions of the different types or species cannot be neglected. They afford an important aid in identification ; and, in a few instances, they serve to differentiate between named types, or varieties, that are antigenically identical. The more important fermentation reactions of the different Salmonella bacilli are set out in Table XLIII, taken mainly from Kauffmann (1934a).

In this table we have included, in addition to the fermentation tests employed by most of the observers who have studied this group (see references below), three additional reactions that have been extensively used within recent years, particularly by Kauffmann and other German workers. One of these, first described by Stern (1916), consists in growing the organism under test in a fuchsin-sulphite-glycerol meat-extract medium. Certain organisms, known as " Stern positive," produce in this medium a deep lilac colour after varying periods of incubation. The reaction is apparently due to the formation of an aldehyde. It is certainly not due solely to acid formation. The second reaction was described by Bitter, Weigmann and Habs (1926). It consists in growing the organism under test in a special synthetic medium containing a small amount of peptone (0·05 per cent.) and 1 per cent. of the sugar under test. The sugar that has been the most frequently used in differential tests with Bitter's medium is rhamnose ; but many other substrates have also been employed under these conditions. The inoculated medium is incubated for 15–20 hours at 37° C., and methyl red is then added to determine whether or not the pH has been lowered to the point at which this indicator gives its characteristic red colour.

The third additional test included in the table is the ability to ferment *d*-tartrate. Brown, Duncan and Henry (1924) first drew attention to the value of salts of various organic acids as test substrates for bacteria of the Salmonella group. Their results have been confirmed by subsequent workers, who have employed a slightly different technique for demonstrating the hydrolysis of the substrate (Kristensen and Bojlén 1929, Silberstein 1931, Kauffmann 1934a). Of these substrates *d*-tartrate has shown itself to possess the greatest differential value within this group. The action of the various Salmonella bacilli on the salts of other organic acids is described in the papers referred to above.

TABLE XLII

Group.	Species.	O Antigen.	H Antigen. Specific.	Non-specific.
A	Bact. paratyphosum A	I, II	a	—
	Bact. senftenberg	I, III	gs	—
	Bact. senftenberg var. newcastle		gs	—
B	Bact. paratyphosum B	IV, V, (XII)	b	1, 2
	Bact. typhi-murium		i	1, 2, 3
	Bact. typhi-murium var. binns		—	1, 2, 3
	Bact. stanley		d	1, 2
	Bact. heidelberg		r	1, 2, 3
	Bact. reading		eh	1, 4, 5
	Bact. derby	IV, (XII)	fg	—
	Bact. abortus-equi		enx	—
	Bact. abortus-ovis		c	1, 4, 6
	Bact. brandenburg		enlv	—
C	Bact. paratyphosum C		c	1, 4, 5
	Bact. cholerœ-suis		c	1, 3, 4, 5
	Bact. cholerœ-suis var. kunzendorf		—	1, 3, 4, 5
	Bact. typhi-suis		c	1, 3, 4, 5
	Bact. typhi-suis var. voldagsen		—	1, 3, 4, 5
	Bact. thompson	VI, VII	k	1, 3, 4, 5
	Bact. thompson var. berlin		—	1, 3, 4, 5
	Bact. virchow		r	1, 2, 3
	Bact. oranienburg		mt	—
	Bact. potsdam		enlv	—
	Bact. bareilly		y	1, 3, 4, 5
	Bact. newport		eh	1, 2, 3
	Bact. newport var. puerto-rico		—	1, 2, 3
	Bact. newport var. kottbus	VI, VIII	eh	1, 3, 4, 5
	Bact. bovis-morbificans		r	1, 3, 4, 5
	Bact. muenchen		d	1, 2
D	Bact. typhosum		d	—
	Bact. enteritidis		gom	—
	Bact. enteritidis var. danysz		gom	—
	Bact. enteritidis var. chaco		gom	—
	Bact. enteritidis var. essen		gom	—
	Bact. enteritidis var. dublin		gp	—
	Bact. enteritidis var. rostock		gpu	—
	Bact. enteritidis var. moscow		goq	—
	Bact. enteritidis var. blegdam	IX, (XII)	gomq	—
	Bact. sendai		a	1, 4, 5
	Bact. dar-es-salaam		enlw	—
	Bact. eastbourne		eh	1, 3, 4, 5
	Bact. panama		lv	1, 3, 4, 5
	Bact. gallinarum		—	—
	Bact. gallinarum var. duisburg		—	—
	Bact. pullorum		—	—
E	Bact. london		lv	1, 4, 6
	Bact. anatum	X, III	eh	1, 4, 6
	Bact. anatum var. muenster		eh	1, 4, 5
F	Bact. aberdeen	XI	i	1, 2, 3
G	Bact. poona	XIII	z_1	1, 4, 6

TABLE XLIII

	Production of Gas.	Mannitol.	Dulcitol.	Sorbitol.	Inositol.	Maltose.	Arabinose.	Rhamnose.	Xylose.	Trehalose.	Dextrin.	Litmus Milk.	H₂S Production.	Bitter Rhamnose.	Stern Glycerol.	d-tartrate.
Bact. paratyphosum A .	+	+	#	+	−	+	+	+	−	+	+	Ac. or Neut.	#	−	−	−
Bact. senftenberg .	+	+	+	+	−	+	+	+	+	+	+	Alk.	+	+	+	+
Bact. senftenberg var. *newcastle* .	+	+	+	+	−	+	+	+	+	+	+	Alk.	−	+	+	+
Bact. paratyphosum B .	+	+	#	+	#	+	+	+	#	+	+	Alk.	+	#	#	#
Bact. typhi-murium .	+	+	+	+	#	+	+	+	+	+	+	Alk.	+	#	#	#
Bact. typhi-murium var. *binns* .	+	+	+	+	#	+	+	+	+	+	+	Alk.	+	+	+	+
Bact. stanley .	+	+	+	+	−	+	+	+	+	+	+	Alk.	+	+	+	+
Bact. heidelberg .	+	+	+	+	+	+	+	+	+	+	+	Alk.	+	+	+	+
Bact. reading .	+	+	+	+	+	+	+	#	+	+	+	Alk.	+	+	#	+
Bact. derby .	+	+	+	+	+	+	+	+	+	+	+	Alk.	+	+	+	+
Bact. abortus-equi .	+	+	+	+	−	+	+	+	+	+	+	Alk.	#	#	−	#
Bact. abortus-ovis .	+	+	#	+	−	+	#	−	+	−	#	Ac. or Neut.	#	−	−	#
Bact. brandenburg .	+	+	+	+	−	+	+	+	+	+	+	Alk.	+	#	+	+
Bact. paratyphosum C .	+	+	+	+	−	+	+	#	+	#	+	Alk.	+	−	−	+
Bact. cholerae-suis .	+	+	#	+	−	+	−	+	+	−	+	Alk.	−	−	−	+
Bact. cholerae-suis var. *kunzendorf*	#	+	#	+	−	+	+	−	+	−	+	Alk.	+	−	−	+
Bact. typhi-suis .	#	+	#	+	−	#	+	#	+	+	+	Ac. or Neut.	−	−	−	−
Bact. typhi-suis var. *voldagsen* .	#	#	#	#	−	#	+	#	+	+	+	Ac. or Neut.	−	−	−	−
Bact. thompson .	+	+	+	+	−	+	+	+	+	+	+	Alk.	+	+	+	+
Bact. thompson var. *berlin* .	+	+	+	+	+	+	+	+	+	+	+	Alk.	+	+	+	+

The following table gives the fermentation reactions. The organisms are listed below, and each band of symbols across the table records one reaction for the four groups of organisms.

Organisms (in order):

Bact. virchow
Bact. oranienburg
Bact. potsdam
Bact. bareilly
Bact. newport var. *puerto-rico*
Bact. newport var. *kottbus*
Bact. bovis-morbificans
Bact. muenchen
Bact. typhosum

Bact. enteritidis
Bact. enteritidis var. *danysz*
Bact. enteritidis var. *dublin*
Bact. enteritidis var. *rostock*
Bact. enteritidis var. *moscow*
Bact. sendai

Bact. dar-es-salaam
Bact. eastbourne
Bact. panama
Bact. gallinarum
Bact. pullorum

Bact. london
Bact. anatum
Bact. anatum var. *muenster*
Bact. aberdeen
Bact. poona

Reaction bands (each cell group corresponds to the four organism-groups above):

Group 1	Group 2	Group 3	Group 4
+ + + + + + + + + #	+ +	# +			+ + #		+ + + ? ?
+ + + + + + + + +		+	#	#		+ + +			+ + + ? ?
# + + + + + + + # +		+ #		+		+	+			+ + + ? ?
+ + + + + + + + + +	+ + + + +		+ + + # +	+ + + + +
Alk. Alk. Alk. Alk. Alk. Alk. Alk. Alk. Ac. or Neut.	Alk. Alk. Alk. Alk. Ac. or Neut.	Alk. Alk. Alk. Alk. Ac. or Neut.	Alk. Alk. Alk. Alk.
+ + + + + + + + + +	+ + + + + +	+ + + +		+ + + ? ?
+ + + + + + + + + +	+ + + + + +	+ + + # #	+ + + ? +
+ + + + + + + + + #	+ + + + + #	+ + + # #	+ + + + +
+ + + + + + + # +		+ + +	+ +	+ + + # +	+ + + + +
+ + + + + + + + + #	+ + # + + +	+ + + # +	+ + + + +
+ + + + + + + + + +	+ + + + + +	+ + + +		+ + + ? +
+	+ +		+ + +													+	+		
+ + + + + + + + + +	+ + + + + +	+ + + # #	+ + + ? +
+ + + + + + + + + #	+ + + + # #	+ + # #		+ + + + +
+ + + + + + + + + +	+ + + + + +	+ + + + +	+ + + + +
+ + + + + + + + +		+ + + + +		+ + +	+	+ + + + +

+ = positive. | = negative. # = variable or delayed fermentation. ? = not yet recorded.

Certain fermentation reactions that, in Kauffmann's view, serve to differentiate different types, or sub-types, within the *Bact. enteritidis* and certain other groups, are not included since they depend on additional tests, the inclusion of which would render the table unduly cumbersome.

Those who desire to know more of the historical development of the identification and classification of the salmonella group, particularly in relation to the enzymic activities of its different constituent species, should consult the following papers : Schottmüller 1901, Kayser 1904, Sacquépée and Chevrel 1905, Boycott 1906, Springer 1911, Harding and Ostenberg 1912, Ditthorn 1913, Krumwiede *et al.* 1916, 1916–17*a*, *b*, 1919, Jordan 1917, 1918*a*, *b*, 1920, Jordan and Victorson 1917, Weiss and Rice 1917, Tenbroeck 1918*a*, *b*, Winslow *et al.* 1919.

We give below further details of each of the species, or types, of Salmonella bacilli. In compiling these notes we have made free use of the Report of the Salmonella Subcommittee (1934), and of Kauffmann's (1934*a*) review. We have added such information as is available with regard to the normal habitat of the various types and the diseases to which they give rise under natural conditions. In regard to the animal infections to which these organisms give rise a useful summary will be found in a paper by Lovell (1932*b*).

We have not in these notes included in the antigenic formulæ the somatic component XII that Kauffmann (1935*a*) has recently added to certain of the named species or types listed by the Salmonella Subcommittee. It is not yet possible to describe the distribution of this antigen in any detail, and it will be more conveniently considered in the summary at the end of this section.

GROUP A.

Bact. paratyphosum A (Antigens I, II : a : —).

Isolated from enteric fever in man (Gwyn 1898, Schottmüller 1900, 1901, Brion and Kayser 1902). Causes enteric fever, but not acute gastro-enteritis, in man. Has once been isolated from a pig (Broudin 1927), but is not a natural pathogen of animals. *Bact. paratyphosum A* shares its H antigen with the specific phase of *Bact. sendai* (see below).

Bact. senftenberg (Antigens I, III : g, s : —).

Isolated by Kauffmann from cases of acute gastro-enteritis (food poisoning) in man (Kauffmann and Mitsui 1930) ; see also Boecker and Silberstein (1932), Kauffmann (1934*a*). *Bact. senftenberg* shares an H antigen (g) with *Bact. derby* and *Bact. enteritidis* (see below). It is not known to be a natural pathogen of animals.

Bact. senftenberg var. newcastle (Antigens I, III : g, s : —).

Isolated from human fæces (Warren and Scott 1930). The circumstances of its isolation precluded any opinion as to its pathogenic rôle. It will be noted that it has the same antigenic structure as *Bact. senftenberg*, but differs from it in failing to produce H_2S.

GROUP B.

Bact. paratyphosum B (Antigens IV, V : b : 1, 2).

Isolated from cases of enteric infection in man (Achard and Bensaude 1896, Schottmüller 1900, 1901). A common cause of enteric fever in man. It occasionally gives rise to an acute gastro-enteritis during the early stages of the disease ; but seldom, if ever, to a sharply limited gastro-enteritis of the "food poisoning" type. It does not appear to be a natural pathogen of animals.

Bact. typhi-murium (Antigens IV, V : i : 1, 2, 3).

A natural pathogen of rodents, particularly mice, in which it causes a typhoid-like disease (Loeffler 1892). This organism is identical with *Bact. aertrycke*, which was originally isolated from a case of acute gastro-enteritis (food poisoning) in man (de Nobele 1898). It is under the name of *Bact. aertrycke* that it appears in almost all the recent and current literature ; so that this synonym is an important one to remember. It is also identical with *B. pestis caviæ*, described by Wherry (1908) as the cause of an epidemic disease in guinea-pigs, and with the bacillus that Nocard (1893) isolated from a parrot suffering from psittacosis, and named *Bact. psittacosis* under the mistaken impression that it was the cause of that disease. The same organism is frequently referred to in German literature as the " Breslau bacillus." *Bact. typhi-murium* is pathogenic for man as well as for animals and is the most frequent cause of outbreaks of Salmonella food poisoning. It commonly gives rise in man to an acute gastro-enteritis, not infrequently fatal, but it occasionally causes a prolonged fever of the enteric type. Although it has most often been recorded as causing epidemic disease in mice and rats (see, for instance, Meyer and Matsumura 1927), it is naturally pathogenic for many other animal species. In addition to causing infections in guinea-pigs and parrots, it has been isolated from epidemics in sheep (Bruns and Gasters 1920, White 1929*b*, Lovell 1932*b*), chicks (Doyle 1927, Edwards 1929*b*), pigeons (Beaudette 1926, Lesbouvries and Verge 1932, Cernaianu and Popovici 1933), turkeys (Rettger *et al.* 1933), and canaries (Beaudette 1926). It also causes infections in ducks, and has been isolated from ducks' eggs (Scott 1932, 1933, Dalling and Warrack 1932, Lovell 1932*b*). It has occasionally been isolated from pigs that have died of swine fever (see Lovell 1932*b*). It shares its H antigens with *Bact. aberdeen.*

Bact. typhi-murium var. **binns** (Antigens IV, V : — : 1, 2, 3).

Isolated from a case of food poisoning, and examined by Schütze (1920) and by Kauff-mann (1931). It will be noted that this is a variety of *Bact. typhi-murium* which exists only in the group phase. It is not known to be a natural pathogen of animals.

Bact. stanley (Antigens IV, V : d : 1, 2).

Isolated from cases of food poisoning, and examined by Schütze (1920), Savage and White (1925), White (1926), and Kauffmann (1931). (See also Boecker and Silberstein 1932, Kauffmann 1930*a*, 1934*a*.) It will be noted that the H antigen of this type, in its specific phase, is identical with the H antigen of *Bact. typhosum* (see below). *Bact. stanley* is not known to be a natural pathogen of animals.

Bact. heidelberg (Antigens IV, V : r : 1, 2, 3).

Isolated from a case of food poisoning by Habs (1933). (See also Kauffmann 1934*a* and Kauffmann and Silberstein 1934.) It will be noted that this type has the same specific H antigen as *Bact. virchow* and *Bact. bovis-morbificans* (see below). *Bact. heidelberg* is not known to be a natural pathogen of animals.

Bact. reading (Antigens IV : e, h : 1, 4, 5).

Isolated from a water supply (Schütze 1920). Has since been isolated from fæces of cases or carriers in relation to outbreaks of gastro-enteritis (Kauffmann 1930*a*, 1931, 1934*a*, Boecker and Silberstein 1932). The specific H antigens of *Bact. reading* are identical with the specific H antigens of *Bact. newport*, *Bact. eastbourne* and *Bact. anatum* (see below), and the component " e " is also shared by *Bact. abortus-equi*, *Bact. brandenburg*, *Bact. potsdam* and *Bact. dar-es-salaam*, which exist only in the specific phase. *Bact. reading* has been isolated from an epidemic among laboratory guinea-pigs (see Lovell 1932*b*) but is not known to be a natural pathogen of animals.

Bact. derby (Antigens IV : f, g : —).

Isolated from cases of food poisoning by Peckham (1923). (See also Savage and White 1925, White 1926, Kauffmann 1931, 1934*a*.) This organism shares an H antigen (g) with *Bact. senftenberg* (see above) and with *Bact. enteritidis* (see below), both of which, as *Bact. derby* itself, exist only in the specific phase. *Bact. derby* was originally isolated from pork and has occasionally been cultivated from pigs that have died of swine fever (see Lovell 1932*b*).

Bact. abortus-equi (Antigens IV : e, n, x : —).

Isolated by Kilbourne (1893) from a case of abortion in a mare. Has since been isolated, or studied, by Smith (1893), de Jong (1913), Meyer and Boerner (1913), Good and Corbett (1913), van Heelsbergen (1914), Murray (1919), and Fitch and Billings (1920). For antigenic structure see White (1926) and Kauffmann (1931, 1934a). This organism shares two H antigens (e, n) with *Bact. brandenburg, Bact. potsdam* and *Bact. dar-es-salaam,* and one (e) with *Bact. reading, Bact. newport, Bact. eastbourne* and *Bact. anatum. Bact. abortus-equi* is a natural pathogen of the horse, causing abortion in mares. It is not known to be a pathogen of other animals. It is not known to have caused infection in man.

Bact. abortus-ovis (Antigens IV : c : 1, 4, 6).

Isolated by Schermer and Ehrlich (1921) from cases of abortion in sheep. For antigenic structure see Lovell (1931), and Kauffmann (1931, 1934a). The H antigen of this organism, in the specific phase, is identical with the specific H antigen of *Bact. paratyphosum C, Bact. choleræ-suis* and *Bact. typhi-suis* (see below). *Bact. abortus-ovis* is not known to infect man or any animal other than the sheep.

Bact. brandenburg (Antigens IV : e, n, l, v : —).

Isolated from a case of acute gastro-enteritis by Kauffmann and Mitsui (1930). It will be noted that this organism differs in its antigenic structure from *Bact. abortus-equi* only in that the specific H components (l, v) replace the specific H component (x). It differs also in that it ferments glycerol in the medium devised by Stern, while *Bact. abortus-equi* does not (Kauffmann 1934a). For its antigenic relations with other types see *Bact. abortus-equi* above. *Bact. brandenburg* is not known to be a natural pathogen of animals.

(Bact. essen 173.)

Very recently Hohn and Herrmann (1936) have described a new Salmonella type isolated from a fatal pyrexial infection in an infant, the antigenic structure of which is recorded as IV, XII : g, o, m : —. This would place the organism in Group B, although it possesses the flagellar antigens characteristic of *Bact. enteritidis* and its varieties. This new type is not included in Table XLII, mainly because it seems very unlikely that the name " essen 173 " will stand. Its O antigens separate it widely from the *essen* variety of *Bact. enteritidis,* and the 173, which is simply the serial laboratory number of the culture, does not accord with any system of nomenclature.

Bact. paratyphosum C (Antigens VI, VII : c : 1, 4, 5).

Isolated from cases of enteric fever in man, mainly in Eastern Europe, also recently in British Guiana. It has received many other names and, in particular, is often referred to as " Hirschfeld's Bacillus," or the " Eastern European type of *Bact. paratyphosum C* " (see Weil 1917, Neukirch 1918, MacAdam 1919, Mackie and Bowen 1919, Hirschfeld 1919, Schütze 1920, Dudgeon and Urquart 1920, Andrewes and Neave 1921, Weigmann 1925a, b, Iwaschenzoff 1926, White 1926, Kauffmann 1931, 1934a, Giglioli, 1930). This type is very closely related antigenically to *Bact. choleræ-suis* and to *Bact. typhi-suis.* It also shares its specific H antigen with *Bact. abortus-ovis.* This type is an important pathogen of man, giving rise to enteric fever that is often associated with septic lesions. It is not known to be a natural pathogen of animals.

Bact. choleræ-suis (Antigens VI, VII : c : 1, 3, 4, 5).

The American hog-cholera organism, isolated by Salmon and Smith (1885, 1886). It is from the co-discoverer of this organism that the group receives its name of " Salmonella." For antigenic structure see White (1926) and Kauffmann (1931, 1934a). It will be noted that, in regard to its antigenic structure, *Bact. choleræ-suis* differs from *Bact. paratyphosum C* only in possessing an additional H component (3) in the group phase. These organisms also show certain differences in their fermentation reactions. *Bact. paratyphosum C* ferments arabinose, and forms H_2S, *Bact. choleræ-suis* does neither. Since its original isolation *Bact. choleræ-suis* has been isolated by numerous workers from pigs suffering from hog cholera. It is now known that this disease is due to a filtrable virus (see pp. 1529). *Bact. choleræ-suis* is, however, an important secondary invader, and plays a large part in the disease as it occurs in nature. It is not known to be a natural pathogen of any other animal, though it has once been isolated by Dalling from the blood and liver of a foxhound (see Lovell 1932*b*). It would seem that it occasionally gives rise to acute gastro-enteritis in man (Clauberg 1931, Boecker and Silberstein 1932, Kauffmann 1934*a*). *Bact. choleræ-suis* is commonly referred to in the literature under the synonym, *Bact. suipestifer* (American Type).

Bact. choleræ-suis var. kunzendorf (Antigens VI, VII : — : 1, 3, 4, 5).

This organism has been isolated by numerous observers from cases of acute gastro-enteritis and of enteric fever in man, sometimes associated with suppurative lesions. The description given by most of the earlier observers does not enable the strain or strains isolated to be identified with certainty (see, for instance, Heimann 1912, Weil and Saxl 1917, Pfeiler 1920, Dudgeon and Urquart 1920, Andrewes and Neave 1921, Wordley 1923), but certain of these strains have been re-examined by subsequent workers and found to belong to this type (see Schütze 1920, White 1926, Kauffmann 1929*b*, 1931, 1934*a*, Kauffmann and Mitsui 1930). It will be noted that in regard to its antigenic structure, this type differs from *Bact. choleræ-suis* in that it is monophasic, occurring only in the group phase. In regard to its known fermentation reactions it differs from that organism only in that it forms H_2S, in this respect resembling *Bact. paratyphosum C*. It resembles *Bact. choleræ-suis* in failing to ferment arabinose. In addition to causing enteric infections and gastro-enteritis in man (see Clauberg 1931, Seligmann and Clauberg 1932, Kauffmann 1934*a*) the *kunzendorf* variety of *Bact. choleræ-suis* has been isolated from pigs suffering with swine fever and in one instance from a monkey in captivity (see Lovell 1932*b*).

Bact. typhi-suis (Antigens VI, VII : c : 1, 3, 4, 5).

This organism was isolated from young pigs suffering from a typhoid-like disease by Glässer (1909, 1910). It is the " Ferkeltyphus " bacillus of German literature (see also Neukirch 1918, Andrewes and Neave 1921, White 1926, Kauffmann 1931, 1934*a*). It will be noted that this organism, although it has been accorded a separate specific name, is antigenically identical with *Bact. choleræ-suis*. It differs from that organism, however, in its fermentation reactions, which are, when taken as a whole, unlike those of any organisms of this group, except that next to be described. It forms gas very slowly, and very sparsely, from any substrate ; it usually fails to ferment mannitol or does so very slowly ; it does not form H_2S ; and it produces a slight permanent acidity in litmus milk. It also ferments trehalose, while *Bact. choleræ-suis* does not. So far as is known this organism does not naturally infect animals other than the pig, nor does it give rise to disease in man.

Bact. typhi-suis var. voldagsen (Antigens VI, VII : — : 1, 3, 4, 5).

Isolated from a typhoid-like disease in young pigs by Dammann and Stedefeder (1910). This type, like the last, is included in the " Ferkeltyphus " bacilli of German literature (see also Neukirch 1918, Andrewes and Neave 1921, White 1926, Kauffmann 1931, 1934*a*). It will be noted that this type is monophasic, occurring only in the group phase, and that it is antigenically identical with *Bact. choleræ-suis* var. *kunzendorf*. In regard to its fermentation reactions, however, it is practically identical with *Bact. typhi-suis*. So far as is known it does not infect man or animals other than the pig.

Bact. thompson (Antigens VI, VII : k : 1, 3, 4, 5).

Isolated from cases of food poisoning in man by Scott (1926), and since by other workers (see Kauffmann 1931, 1934*a*, Clauberg 1931, Seligmann and Clauberg 1932, Boecker and Silberstein 1932). Antigenically this organism differs from *Bact. choleræ-suis* in possessing a different H antigen in the specific phase. It is not known to be a natural pathogen of animals.

Bact. thompson var. **berlin** (Antigens VI, VII : — : 1, 3, 4, 5).

Isolated from cases of food poisoning (Kauffmann 1929*a*, *b*. (See also Kauffmann 1931, 1934*a*, Boecker and Kauffmann 1930, Kauffmann and Mitsui 1930, Clauberg 1931, Seligmann and Clauberg 193 , Boecker and Silberstein 1932). Antigenically this organism, which exists only in the group phase, is identical with *Bact. choleræ-suis* var. *kunzendorf* and with *Bact. typhi-su* var. *voldagsen*. In its fermentation reactions it differs from the former only in fermenting rhamnose in Bitter's medium and glycerol in Stern's medium, in both of which reactions it resembles *Bact. thompson*. It differs from *Bact. typhi-suis* var. *voldagsen* in showing none of the enzymic peculiarities of that type. Two strains of animal origin have been reported by Kauffmann (1929*b*) to belong to this type ; but it is not known to be a natural pathogen of animals.

Bact. virchow (Antigens VI, VII : r : 1, 2, 3).

Isolated by Kauffmann from a case of food poisoning (see Kauffmann 1930*b*, 1931, 1934*a*). This organism shares the specific H antigen of *Bact. heidelberg* (see above) and *Bact. bovis-morbificans* (see below). It is not known to be a natural pathogen of animals.

Bact. oranienburg (Antigens VI, VII : m, t : —).

Isolated by Kauffmann from cases of food poisoning (see Kauffmann 1930*b*, 1931, 1934*a*, Clauberg 1932, Seligmann and Clauberg 1932, Boecker and Silberstein 1932). This organism, which is monophasic in the specific phase, shares one of its H antigens (m) with *Bact. enteritidis* (see below). It is not known to be a natural pathogen of animals.

Bact. potsdam (Antigens VI, VII : e, n, l, v : —).

Isolated from cases of food poisoning. Examined by Kauffmann and Mitsui (1930). (See also Kauffmann 193 , 1934*a*, Clauberg 1931, Seligmann and Clauberg 1932.) This organism, which exists only in the specific phase, has the same H antigens as *Bact. brandenburg* (see above). It shares three antigenic components (e, n, l) with *Bact. dar-es-salaam*, two (e, n) with *Bact. abortus-equi*, and one (e) with *Bact. reading*, *Bact. newport*, *Bact. eastbourne* and *Bact. anatum*. It is not known to be a natural pathogen of animals.

Bact. bareilly (Antigens VI, VII : y : 1, 3, 4, 5).

Isolated in India from mild enteric infections (Bridges and Scott 1931). This organism possesses a characteristic specific H antigen. It is not known to be a natural pathogen of animals.

Bact. newport (Antigens VI, VIII : e, h : 1, 2, 3).

Isolated from cases of food poisoning in man (Schütze 1920). Corresponds to Paratyphus *β*2 of Weil and Saxl (1917). (See also White 1926, Kauffmann 1929*a*, 1931, 1934*a*, Schütze 1930, Clauberg 1931, Seligmann and Clauberg 1932, Boecker and Silberstein 1932.) Has the same specific H antigen as *Bact. reading*, *Bact. eastbourne*, and *Bact. anatum*. The still wider range of the " e " factor among specific H antigens has been referred to above (see *Bact. potsdam*). *Bact. newport* has been isolated from the fæces of a dog (White 1926), but is not known to be a natural pathogen of animals.

Bact. newport var. **puerto-rico** (Antigens VI, VIII : — : 1, 2, 3).

Isolated in Puerto Rico from cases of acute enteritis (Jordan 1934). Antigenic structure determined by Kauffmann (1934*a*). This organism is monophasic, existing only in the group phase, and showing the same antigenic structure as the group phase of *Bact. newport*. It is not known to be a natural pathogen of animals.

Bact. newport var. **kottbus** (Antigens VI, VIII : e, h : 1, 3, 4, 5).

Isolated from cases of acute gastro-enteritis, Kauffmann (1934*a*). Differs antigenically from *Bact. newport* in regard to the components of its group H antigen. It is not known to be a natural pathogen of animals.

Bact. bovis-morbificans (Antigens VI, VIII : r : 1, 3, **4, 5**).

Was isolated from an infected cow by Basenau (1894). It has also been isolated from gastro-enteritis in man (see White 1926, Sladden and Scott 1927, Kauffmann and Mitsui 1930, Kauffmann 1931, 1934*a*, Clauberg 1931, Seligmann and Clauberg 1932, Boecker and Silberstein 1932). This organism, in the type phase, has the same specific H antigen as *Bact. heidelberg* and *Bact. virchow*.

Bact. muenchen (Antigens VI, VIII : d : 1, 2).

Isolated by Mandelbaum (1932) from a fatal case of gastro-enteritis (see also Silberstein 1932, Kauffmann 1934*a*). This organism, in the specific phase, has the same H antigen as *Bact. stanley* and *Bact. typhosum*. It is not known to be a natural pathogen of animals.

Group D.

Bact. typhosum (Antigens IX : d : —).

The cause of typhoid fever in man. Its general characters have been referred to in earlier sections. It differs from all other Salmonella organisms except *Bact. sendai* and *Bact. gallinarum* in failing to produce gas from dextrose, or the various other substrates on which it acts. It is monophasic. It has the same specific antigen as *Bact. stanley* and *Bact. muenchen*. It has never been isolated from natural infections in animals.

Bact. enteritidis (Antigens IX : g, o, m : —) [Kauffmann g, o, m, z_1, z_2].

Isolated from a case of food poisoning (Gaertner 1888), and since then by many others from similar cases (see White 1926, 1930, Kauffmann 1930*b*, 1931, 1934*a*, Warren and Scott 1930, Boecker and Silberstein 1932, Boecker 1936). The organism is monophasic. The " g " component of the specific H antigen is shared by *Bact. senftenberg* and *Bact. derby*. The " m " component is shared by *Bact. oranienburg*. *Bact. enteritidis* has several times been reported as having been isolated from cattle ; but these reports should perhaps be accepted with reserve in view of the possibility of confusion with the *dublin* variety (see below). Is probably a natural pathogen of rodents, especially rats (see below).

Bact. enteritidis var. danysz (Antigens IX : g, o, m : —) [Kauffmann g, o, m, z_1, z_2].

Isolated by Danysz (1900) from an epidemic of enteric infection in field mice. The Ratin strain of this type was isolated from the urine of a sick child by Neumann in 1902 (see Salmonella Subcommittee 1934, and also Kauffmann, 1934*a*). This organism is antigenically identical with *Bact. enteritidis*. It differs from this type in that it fails to ferment glycerol in Stern's medium while *Bact. enteritidis* does so. Although *Bact. enteritidis* var. *danysz* was originally isolated from an epidemic in field mice there is little doubt, from numerous subsequent observations, that *Bact. enteritidis* or the *danysz* variety— the two have not always been differentiated—is a common pathogen of the rat (see, for instance, Savage and White 1923, Meyer and Matsumura 1927, Kerrin 1928*b*), but infects mice more rarely. This type has also been isolated from infections in man (Ströman and Örn 1932, Kauffmann 1935*b*).

Bact. enteritidis var. chaco (Antigens IX : g, o, m : —) [Kauffmann g, o, m, z_1, z_2].

Isolated by Savino and Menéndez (1934) from cases of continued fever in the Chaco war. Examined by Kauffmann (1935*b*). Antigenically identical with *Bact. enteritidis* and *Bact. enteritidis* var. *danysz*. It differs in certain of its fermentation reactions, particularly when tested by the method of Bitter, Weigmann and Habs. Using this medium with glucose, arabinose, dulcitol and rhamnose, Kauffmann (1935*b*) finds that there are two different fermentative types of *Bact. enteritidis* itself, one of which gives a positive methyl-red reaction after 20 hours' incubation at 37° C. with all these substrates, the other with none. The *danysz* variety behaves as the second fermentative type, but, as we have seen, gives a negative Stern reaction. The *chaco* variety gives a positive Bitter reaction with glucose, arabinose, and rhamnose, but not with dulcitol. The *chaco* variety has not yet been isolated from any other source.

Bact. enteritidis var. **essen** (Antigens IX : g, o, m : —) [Kauffmann g, o, m, z_1, z_2].

Isolated by Hohn and Herrmann (1935*a*, *b*) from cases of gastro-enteritis in man, from ducks and from ducks' eggs. Examined by Kauffmann (1935*b*). Antigenically identical with *Bact. enteritidis* and the *danysz* and *chaco* varieties. Differs in its fermentation reactions. When cultivated in Bitter's medium gives a positive methyl-red reaction with glucose and rhamnose, but not with arabinose or dulcitol.

Bact. enteritidis var. **dublin** (Antigens IX : g, p : —).

Isolated on several occasions from calf diarrhœa, but not adequately differentiated till examined by White (1930). (See also Warren and Scott 1930, Smith and Scott 1930, Ströman and Örn 1932, Kauffmann 1930*b*, 1931, 1934*a*, Bosworth and Lovell 1931, Boecker and Silberstein 1932, Hohn and Herrmann 1935*a*). It will be noted that this type differs from *Bact. enteritidis* in the components of its specific H antigen. There can be no doubt that *Bact. enteritidis* var. *dublin* is an important pathogen of cattle, causing epidemic diarrhœa in calves (Bosworth and Lovell 1931), and infecting adult animals. It seems very probable that many of the strains from cattle that have in the past been described as *Bact. enteritidis* belonged in reality to the *dublin* type. This type has also been isolated, though rarely, from pigs and foals (Ströman and Örn 1932, Hohn and Herrmann 1935*a*). In man it may give rise to a continued fever of the enteric type (Smith and Scott 1930), and, here again, it seems very probable that the earlier reports of continued fever in man caused by *Bact. enteritidis* were due to the fact that the *dublin* type had not been differentiated.

Bact. enteritidis var. **rostock** (Antigens IX : g, p, u : —).

Isolated from cattle. First differentiated from other *enteritidis* types on the basis of fermentation reactions (Bahr 1930*a*, *b*). Its antigenic structure, which differs from that of other *enteritidis* types in the H components, was determined by Kauffmann (1930*b*, 1931, 1934*a*, 1935*b*). (See also Ströman and Örn 1932, Hohn and Herrmann 1935*a*). It has not yet been isolated from infections in man.

Bact. enteritidis var. **moscow** (Antigens IX : g, o, q : —) [Kauffmann g, o, m, z_3].

This organism has been isolated from febrile infections in man, occurring mostly in Russia (Weigmann 1925*a*, *b*, Iwaschenzoff 1926). It is perhaps doubtful whether it is to be regarded as one of the Salmonella types causing true enteric fever ; since many of the patients from whom these strains were isolated were diagnosed as cases of relapsing fever. It has since been isolated from cases of gastro-enteritis in man (Hohn and Herrmann 1935*a*, Kauffmann 1935*b*) and from a cow and a horse (Kauffmann 1935*b*). Its structure was first determined by Hicks (1930). (See also Kauffmann 1930*b*, 1931, 1934*a*, 1935*b*.)

Bact. enteritidis var. **blegdam** (Antigens IX : g, o, m, q : —) [Kauffmann g, o, m, q, z_1].

Isolated from the blood of a patient suffering from pneumonia (Kauffmann 1935*b*). This is the only instance in which the type has yet been isolated. It differs from the other varieties of *Bact. enteritidis* in the combination of components present in the H antigens.

Bact. sendai (Antigens IX : a : 1, 4, 5).

Isolated from cases of enteric fever in Japan (Aoki and Sakai 1925). Antigenic structure determined by White (1926) and Kauffmann (1931, 1934*a*). It will be noted that this is a diphasic organism and that its specific H antigen is identical with that of *Bact. paratyphosum A*. *Bact. sendai* resembles *Bact. typhosum* and *Bact. gallinarum*, and differs from all other Salmonella organisms in that it fails to form gas from dextrose or the other substrates on which it acts. It is not known to be a natural pathogen of animals.

Bact. dar-es-salaam (Antigens IX : e, n, l, w : —).

Isolated from a case of pyrexia in man. Antigenic structure determined by White (1926). (See also Kauffmann and Mitsui 1930, Kauffmann 1931, 1934*a*.) It is a monophasic organism. It shares the H components (e), (n) and (l) with several other types. It is not known to be a natural pathogen of animals. It differs from all other Salmonella types in liquefying gelatin, liquefaction being slow (Jordan 1936).

Bact. eastbourne (Antigens IX : e, h : 1, 3, 4, 5).

Isolated from a case of enteric fever (Leslie and Shera 1931). (See also Kauffmann 1934*a*.) It is a diphasic organism and the H antigens in the specific phase are identical with those of *Bact. reading* and *Bact. newport* (see above). It is not known to be a natural pathogen of animals.

Bact. panama (Antigens IX : 1, v : 1, 3, 4, 5).

Isolated by Jordan (1934) from a food-poisoning outbreak. Typed and named by Kauffmann (1934*a*). It is a diphasic organism, and the H antigens of the specific phase are identical with those of *Bact. london* (see below). They are also present, together with other components, in *Bact. brandenburg* and *Bact. potsdam* (see above). The (1) component is also present in *Bact. dar-es-salaam*. *Bact. panama* is not known to be a natural pathogen of animals.

Bact. gallinarum (Antigens IX : — : —).

Isolated from fowls suffering from fowl typhoid (Klein 1889). (See also Moore 1895, Pfeiler and Rehse 1913, Pfeiler and Roepke 1917, White 1926, Kauffmann 1934*a*, *b* and references under *Bact. pullorum* below). *Bact. gallinarum* differs sharply from all the Salmonella organisms described above in that it is non-flagellated. It therefore possesses only an O antigen ; but as this is identical with the O antigens of *Bact. typhosum, Bact. enteritidis* and the other types belonging to the Salmonella sub-group D, there can be no doubt that it should be classed with them. It resembles *Bact. typhosum* and *Bact. sendai*, and differs from all other members of the Salmonella group, in that it forms no gas from dextrose or from the other substrates on which it acts. It is also characterized by its relatively slow and feeble fermentation of several substrates. It is not known to infect man.

Bact. gallinarum var. duisburg (Antigens IX : — : —).

Isolated from cases of acute gastro-enteritis in man (see Müller 1933) and studied by Kauffmann (1934*b*). Antigenically identical with *Bact. gallinarum*. Kauffmann classes it as a separate variety because of certain minor differences in its fermentation reactions. It fails to ferment *d*-tartrate, while *Bact. gallinarum* constantly produces H_2S and ferments *d*-tartrate, though sometimes slowly. The *duisburg* variant is also stated to act more slowly than *Bact. gallinarum* on maltose and dextrose.

Bact. pullorum (Antigen IX : — : —).

Isolated from chicks suffering from bacillary white diarrhœa by Rettger (1900). (For further references particularly in relation to the differentiation of this organism from *Bact. gallinarum* see Rettger and Harvey 1908, Rettger 1909, Smith and Tenbroeck 1915, Gage and Martin 1916, Krumwiede and Kohn 1917, Rettger and Koser 1917, Hadley *et al.* 1917, Muslow 1919, Winslow *et al.* 1919, Brooks and Rhodes 1923, White 1926, Kauffmann 1931, 1934*a*, *b*.) *Bact. pullorum*, like *Bact. gallinarum*, is a non-flagellated organism, and the two types are antigenically identical. They differ, however, in certain important fermentation reactions. *Bact. pullorum* produces gas in dextrose, and in other substrates, though the amount may be small. It fails to ferment maltose, dulcitol or dextrin, all of which substrates are attacked by *Bact. gallinarum*. Although *Bact. pullorum* is characteristically a pathogen of young chicks it is apparently able to infect other birds, since Dalling, Mason and Gordon (1928) have isolated it from sparrows. It is not known to infect man.

Group E.

Bact. london (Antigens X, III : 1, v : 1, 4, 6).

Isolated from human fæces (White 1926). See also Kauffmann (1930*b*, 1931, 1934*a*). Previously known as L. This type shares its specific H components with *Bact. panama*. It is not known to be a natural pathogen of animals.

Bact. anatum (Antigens X, III : e, h : 1, 4, 6).

Isolated from an epidemic intestinal infection in ducklings (Rettger and Scoville 1919, 1920). (See also Edwards and Rettger 1927, Lovell 1932*b*, Kauffmann 1934*a*, Kauffmann and Silberstein 1934.) This organism shares its specific H antigens with *Bact. reading*, *Bact. newport* and *Bact. eastbourne* (see above). Edwards (1935) has described a second antigenic type of *Bact. anatum*, isolated from ducklings by Rettger in 1918, which possesses a somatic antigen peculiar to itself in place of the component X. He gives this type the formula III, XII : e, h : 1, 4, 6. The label " XII " has also been used by Kauffmann for the somatic antigen that he records as being present in various species of Groups B and D (see Table XLII and below). If Edwards's new type obtains general recognition one or other of these factors will require relabelling.

Bact. anatum var. **muenster** (Antigens X, III : e, h : 1, 4, 5).

Isolated from cases of food poisoning in man (Kauffmann and Silberstein 1934). Differs antigenically from *Bact. anatum* only in one of its three group H components. The only fermentative difference between these types is that the *muenster* variety ferments inositol while *Bact. anatum* does not (Kauffmann 1934*a*).

GROUP F.

Bact. aberdeen (Antigens XI : i : 1, 2, 3).

Isolated from a case of acute gastro-enteritis (Smith 1934). This type is diphasic, and its antigens in both the specific and group phase are identical with those of *Bact. typhimurium*.

GROUP G.

Bact. poona (Antigens XIII : z_1 : 1, 4, 6).

Isolated from a case of acute gastro-enteritis in a child (Bridges and Scott 1935). Possesses a hitherto undescribed O antigen, and also a new specific H antigen. The label given to the new H antigen is the same as that used, almost synchronously, by Kauffmann for one of the new components that he has described in the specific H antigens of certain varieties of *Bact. enteritidis*. Here again relabelling will be required.

The summarized descriptions given above present a picture of the Salmonella group as it is known to us to-day ; and, in its main outlines, it seems likely that our picture will stand the test of time. But some parts of it are much clearer and more definite than others ; and it is wise to note where its present weaknesses lie. Taking first the question of antigenic structure, we can be reasonably certain that the species and types differentiated on this basis represent distinct entities that deserve separate labels ; though we cannot exclude the possibility that some of the named organisms that show minor antigenic differences, such as those varieties of *Bact. enteritidis* that differ from one another only in respect of a single component of a complex H antigen, may turn out to be variants rather than stable types. A more serious criticism of the antigenic formulæ set out in Table XLII, and in the notes that follow it, is that they are certainly over-simplified, so far at least as the somatic antigens are concerned. The table, as drawn up by the Salmonella Subcommittee and without the introduction of Kauffmann's Antigen XII, shows no overlapping between the somatic antigens of Groups A, B, C and D. With Kauffmann's antigen it shows only an overlap between Groups B and D. Reference to Chapter LXVI will show that, when we use alcoholized suspensions of *Bact. typhosum*, *Bact. paratyphosum A* and *Bact. paratyphosum B* in diagnostic tests on cases of enteric fever in man, there is gross overlapping of the O agglutinins acting on *Bact. typhosum* and *Bact. paratyphosum B*, and considerable overlapping between either of these organisms and *Bact. paratyphosum A*. The tests on which the scheme presented in the table have been based have been carried out with high-titre agglutinating sera prepared in the rabbit ; and it is quite true that such sera show much less overlapping of O agglutinins than sera obtained from infected human beings. They may indeed, under optimal conditions, behave exactly as would be expected from the antigenic formulæ shown in Table XLII ; but this is by no means always the case. There is no doubt that there is a far greater degree of sharing of O antigens than the table indicates, and this has, in fact, been generally recognized. White, in his original (1926) report, indicated the existence in several of his named species of minor O antigens, with a wider distribution than the major components. It is, we think, a pity that the Salmonella Committee omitted these minor components from their antigenic formulæ ; and we should regard Kauffmann's labelling of the component that is certainly shared by at least *Bact. typhosum*, *Bact. paratyphosum B*, *Bact. typhi-murium* and *Bact. enteritidis* as a very desirable modification. Some of the published records, and still more perhaps the un-published experience of many who have worked with these bacterial groups, suggest that the somatic antigenic components of the various types and their relations to one another need further investigation. It is not likely that the results will in-validate the position of any of the types that are now recognized, but they may well display and define relationships that our present formulæ leave unacknowledged. In regard to the flagellar antigens this position does not seem to arise. There is general agreement that the formulæ set out in Table XLII account satisfactorily for the experimental results obtained. It may well be necessary, from time to time, to make minor adjustments, to recognize for instance that a particular antigenic formula is incomplete, or that an antigen that has hitherto behaved as a single entity is, in reality, composed of two or more components. But there is not, with the flagellar antigens, the overlapping in practice that is not accounted for by theory, which at present exists in the case of the somatic components.

Another point that perhaps needs some comment is the recognition of fermenta-tive varieties that are antigenically identical. As a systematic procedure this is a reversal of the common practice, in which we recognize different antigenic types within a species that is homogeneous as regards its enzymic activities. It will, moreover, have been noted that many of the fermentative differences that have been accepted as defining separable varieties are very slight. Sometimes they are only revealed by the use of a special medium, or a special reaction. The definition and labelling of these fermentative types has been carried out by a few observers, particularly by Kauffmann, who would extend the process even further than has been indicated above (see Kauffmann and Burón 1935). The significance of these types must, we think, remain very doubtful until we have far more extensive data than are at present available. At the same time the existence of the differences in enzymic activity can clearly not be ignored, if only because the evidence that exists to-day, scanty as it is, suggests that they are correlated with natural habitat and natural pathogenicity.

To take, as an example, the fermentative varieties of *Bact. enteritidis*. Kauffmann (1935*b*) records the origin of small samples of these strains. Of 8 strains of *Bact. enteritidis* examined by him, 7 were isolated from man, one from a guinea-pig. Of 22 strains of *Bact. enteritidis* var. *danysz*, 13 strains came from human infections, 9 from rats, or from the Ratin virus used for the extermination of these vermin. The 8 strains of *Bact. enteri-*

tidis var. *chaco* all came from infected soldiers in the Chaco war. Of 7 strains of *Bact. enteritidis* var. *essen,* some came from human infections, some from infections in ducks.

Such numbers as these are of course far too small to allow of any conclusions. But if the fermentative abilities described are found to be constant for any particular strain, and if the varieties differentiated by them are found to show significant differences in their natural distribution, there will clearly be a good case for providing them with separate labels. At the moment it is wisest to regard these labels as provisional.

We have not, in the description given above of the antigenic components of the Salmonella Group, made any reference to the Vi antigen of *Bact. typhosum* described by Felix and Pitt (1934*a, b*) and since extensively studied and reported on by Felix and his colleagues. The main interest of this component lies, for the moment, in its relation to virulence and immunity ; and in this relation it is considered in some detail in Chapter LXVI. Kauffmann (1935*a*) has made some preliminary observations from the systematic viewpoint, but it is yet far too early to say how many of the other Salmonella types possess antigens of the Vi type, or, if they are found to possess them, how they will affect the classification based on the antigenic components previously described.

We may add a brief note on our knowledge, such as it is, of the chemical constitution of the antigens on which the present classification of the Salmonella Group is based. Of the nature of the flagellar antigens we as yet know nothing beyond the hints conveyed by heat lability and sensitiveness to extraction with alcohol.

Of the somatic antigens we know rather more. Furth and Landsteiner (1928, 1929) isolated several different chemical components from bacilli of the Salmonella Group. Some of these were polysaccharides. The studies of White (1929*a, b,* 1931) make it clear that the somatic antigens—those labelled I, II, III and so on in our antigenic formulæ— are polysaccharides, or have a polysaccharide component ; and further evidence on similar lines has been recorded by subsequent observers (Casper 1928–29, Combiesco *et al.* 1930, Meyer 1931*b,* Basilewsky and Remgild 1935). More recent studies which give an indication of the form in which these antigens exist in the bacterial cell are considered in the following section.

Pathogenicity and Toxin Production.

The natural pathogenicity of the various species of Salmonella bacilli has been briefly described in the summarized descriptions given above. Clearly we cannot deal *seriatim* with the lesions produced by each of these species in laboratory animals ; many of them have in fact never been studied from this point of view. The typhoid bacillus, because it is an important human pathogen, has been the subject of very extensive and detailed investigation along these lines ; and numerous experiments on laboratory animals have been carried out with *Bact. typhi-murium,* and *Bact. enteritidis,* which are natural pathogens of rodents, and with *Bact. choleræ-suis,* which was once regarded as the cause of hog-cholera. The other members of the Salmonella Group, and particularly those numerous species and types that have been isolated during the last few years, have received less attention. It will be sufficient in this chapter to give a brief description of the effects produced in experimental animals by the injection of the typhoid bacillus and of a few other species, and a short discussion of the nature of the toxic substances that these organisms produce.

Bact. typhosum.

If massive doses of living typhoid bacilli are administered by the mouth to chimpanzees, it is possible to produce a disease that is very similar to typhoid fever in man (Metchnikoff and Besredka 1911).

Administration of typhoid bacilli by the mouth to ordinary laboratory animals (rabbit, guinea-pig, rat or mouse) does not give rise to an infection of this type, or usually to any harmful result at all.

The intraperitoneal or intravenous injection of living typhoid bacilli in adequate doses induces a fatal infection, and the bacilli can be recovered from the blood and tissues post mortem. The effect of such injections would seem to be in part toxæmic, in part dependent on the multiplication of the bacteria in the body. With some strains of typhoid bacilli it may be necessary to inject 1,000 million living bacilli or more into the peritoneum of a mouse to produce a fatal result. A low multiple of this dose (5,000–10,000 million bacilli) will usually cause a purely toxæmic death when the bacilli have been killed by heat before inoculation. A highly virulent strain will induce a fatal infection following the intraperitoneal injection of 50 million bacilli, or even a little less. But there is no evidence that the typhoid bacillus possesses an ability to multiply freely in the blood or tissues of small laboratory rodents when injected in small doses, such as would certainly prove fatal in the case of a frankly invasive organism.

There is nothing characteristic in the findings at necropsy in a mouse, or guinea-pig, that has died as the result of an intraperitoneal injection of living typhoid bacilli. There is, of course, the usual inflammatory reaction in the peritoneum, sometimes associated with subserous hæmorrhages ; and the organism which has become generalized throughout the body may be recovered from the blood or from any of the tissues. Following the intravenous injection into the rabbit of doses of living typhoid bacilli too small to produce a rapidly fatal infection, the bacilli tend to localize themselves in certain situations, particularly in the gall-bladder. But experiments of this type will be more conveniently considered in Chapter LXVI, in relation to the pathogenesis of enteric infections in man.

Bact. typhi-murium.

The effects produced by the administration of living cultures of this organism to the small rodents of the laboratory are entirely different from those produced by the typhoid bacillus. We are dealing with a natural pathogen of these animals, which gives rise in them to a characteristic disease, usually known as mouse typhoid. This disease is produced when living cultures of *Bact. typhi-murium* are given by the mouth as well as when they are administered by subcutaneous or intraperitoneal injection, though the time to death is longer in the former case than in the latter. The organism has a very definite invasive power for the tissues of mice and of other laboratory rodents. A virulent strain will kill 50 per cent. or more of mice injected intraperitoneally with a dose of 100 bacilli, as compared with the 50–100 million that are required in the case of a virulent typhoid bacillus. Mice dying within 2 to 3 days after the injection of a moderate dose of a virulent strain will be found to have succumbed to an acute septicæmia with few obvious lesions ; but mice dying after the more usual period of 5 to 10 days often show characteristic lesions, including a varying degree of splenic enlargement, often associated with the presence of small necrotic foci, larger and very characteristic necrotic lesions in the liver, and sometimes scattered pneumonic patches in the lungs, associated with a scanty pleural exudate. These lesions have been described in some detail by many observers (see, for instance, Seiffert, Jahncke and Arnold 1928). The spread of infection from the intestine, and the subsequent involvement of the various tissues, have been studied and described by Müller (1912) and by Ørskov and his colleagues (Ørskov, Jensen and Kobayashi 1928, Ørskov and Moltke 1928, Ørskov and Lassen 1930). These experiments will be considered in some detail in Chapter XLI.

One other point should be emphasized. The disease produced in the mouse by *Bact. typhosum* shows no tendency to spread by contact from mouse to mouse. The disease produced by *Bact. typhi-murium* is highly contagious, and there are few laboratories that have not experienced serious epidemics of this infection among their normal stock of mice or guinea-pigs.

Bact. enteritidis.

It need only be said that this species, particularly the *danysz* variety, behaves in much the same way as *Bact. typhi-murium*. Whether all varieties of *Bact. enteritidis* are equally pathogenic for small rodents, as judged by experimental infection in the laboratory, we do not know.

Bact. paratyphosum B.

The main interest of this species, from our present point of view, is that it occupies a position in some ways intermediate between that of *Bact. typhosum* and *Bact. typhi-murium*. It is a natural pathogen of man but not of rodents, but antigenically it is very closely related to the mouse-typhoid bacillus. When injected into mice it kills them in far smaller doses than does *Bact. typhosum*, though it is less virulent than *Bact. typhi-murium*. When administered by the mouth, as Ørskov and his colleagues have shown, it has a limited ability to invade the tissues and multiply in them ; but it rarely gives rise to fatal infections.

It is probable that many other species of Salmonella bacilli will be found to possess high or moderate virulence for laboratory animals, and in some instances we already know this to be the case. *Bact. choleræ-suis*, for instance, is highly virulent for the rabbit. But the mapping-out of the relative virulence, or pathogenicity, of all the 46 species or varieties of Salmonella bacilli that have so far been described, and of the new arrivals that may well be imminent, will clearly be a laborious undertaking, and one that is perhaps not very likely to be embarked on in the near future.

The Toxins of the Salmonella Group.

As we have noted above, the injection of killed typhoid bacilli, in adequate dosage, will produce toxæmic death in the usual laboratory animals ; and the " toxins " of the typhoid bacillus were studied by several of the earlier bacteriological workers (Pfeiffer 1894, Sanarelli 1894, Chantemesse 1897, Brieger 1902).

Macfadyen and Rowland (1901, 1903), by grinding typhoid bacilli in the frozen state and subsequently extracting them with 0·1 per cent. KOH, prepared a solution which was highly toxic for rabbits but only slightly toxic for guinea-pigs. Meyer and Bergell (1907) obtained an extract of typhoid bacilli that was toxic for rabbits by suspending the bacilli from agar cultures in slightly alkaline distilled water, and filtering the extracts through Chamberland candles after they had stood for 48 hours at room temperature. Conradi (1906) found that a filtrate from an autolysed saline suspension of *Bact. typhosum*, after evaporation at 35° C. to one-tenth of its original volume, was toxic for guinea-pigs in a dose of 0·2 c.c. Yamanouchi (1909) reported that filtrates of cultures of *Bact. typhosum* in 5 per cent. peptone water were toxic for rabbits in a dose of 0·5–1 c.c. per kilo body-weight. Arima (1912) grew *Bact. typhosum* on weakly alkaline agar, suspended the growth in saline and later separated the bacillary bodies by centrifugation. The supernatant fluid was pipetted off and examined separately. The bacillary bodies were washed three times, ground up, and extracted with saline. Both solutions were toxic for rabbits, less so for guinea-pigs and mice. Douglas (1921) showed that tryptic digests of acetone-extracted typhoid bacilli were highly toxic. The statements with regard to the thermo-stability of these toxic extracts or filtrates are somewhat conflicting. But most workers report them as heat-resistant. Taken as a whole these observations indicate that typhoid bacilli elaborate toxic substances which are, in the main, retained within the bacterial cell, though they are liberated into the surrounding medium when autolysis occurs. There is, at the moment, no evidence that the typhoid bacillus produces an exotoxin in the ordinary sense of that term.

Most other Salmonella bacilli that have been examined behave, in this respect, in the same way as *Bact. typhosum*, though the toxicity of killed cultures or extracts of the different species may show significant differences in toxicity for laboratory animals, particularly the rabbit (White 1926, 1929*b*).

The two natural pathogens of rodents, *Bact. typhi-murium* and *Bact. enteritidis*, may be considered in rather more detail from this point of view, since it happens that we have recently obtained some knowledge of the constitution of one, at least, of their toxic products.

Ecker (1917), Ecker and Richardson (1925), Branham (1925), Ecker and Rimington (1928) and Menten and King (1930) noted the toxicity for rabbits or mice of broth filtrates of *Bact. typhi-murium* and of certain other Salmonella organisms ; and Casper (1928–29) prepared a toxic extract of the bacterial bodies by extraction with antiformin. Ecker and Rimington (1928), Menten and King (1930) and Casper (1928–29) were able, by various methods of adsorption or precipitation, to obtain a partially purified toxic fraction from these crude filtrates or extracts. The fractions so obtained were thermostable. The purification was very incomplete, and though qualitative tests indicated the presence of polysaccharide constituents, no serious attempt was made to determine the chemical constitution of the toxic components. Martin (1934) showed that the greater part of the toxic material present in a broth culture of *Bact. typhi-murium* was contained in the bacterial cells ; and that these constituted the most favourable starting material for obtaining a purified toxin. His method of purification is considered below.

Independent studies on the immunological properties of chemical fractions isolated from *Bact. typhi-murium* and *Bact. enteritidis* by Boivin and his colleagues (1933, 1934, 1935) and by Raistrick and Topley (1934), Delafield (1934) and Martin (1934) have thrown further light on this problem. These studies were undertaken, in the main, with the object of obtaining a chemically pure immunizing substance from these organisms. The point that concerns us here is that fractions obtained by both groups of workers were found to be highly toxic.

Boivin and his colleagues obtained their fractions by extraction with trichloracetic acid, followed by alcohol precipitation. Raistrick and Topley extracted the bacilli with acetone, digested them with trypsin, and submitted the tryptic digest to fractional precipitation with alcohol.

The final product obtained by both groups of workers was free from protein, as judged by the ordinary chemical tests, but contained a polysaccharide component that gave rise to reducing sugars on hydrolysis. Nitrogen and phosphorus were also present, and the results of micro-combustion analysis, taken with various qualitative tests, suggested that the active fraction consisted of a complex polysaccharide combined with a phosphatide. The polysaccharide can be separated from the phosphatide residue by heating with weak acetic acid. When this is done, the polysaccharide is entirely, and the phosphatide almost, non-toxic. The unhydrolysed toxic material, as prepared and tested by Martin (1934), had an average lethal dose for the mouse of 0·5 mgm. The substance obtained by Boivin and his colleagues is reported as being slightly more toxic.

A point of considerable interest in regard to these findings is that there seems little doubt that the toxic substance is itself the somatic antigen of the bacterial cell. Rabbits immunized with the purified fractions produce characteristic somatic agglutinins. The polysaccharides isolated from Salmonella organisms by previous workers, and identified with the somatic antigens, or with their hapten constituents, were in most cases found to be non-toxic. But this was probably because the method of preparation had resulted in the splitting of the polysaccharide from the phosphatide component.

The same series of experiments have given an indication of one of the ways in which these toxic substances produce their effects. It had already been shown by several workers (see Chapter XLI) that natural infections in man, and experimental infections in animals, might be associated with an increase in the concentration of sugar in the blood ; and Menten and King (1930) had found that rabbits injected with the fraction isolated by them from *Bact. typhi-murium* developed hyperglycæmia.

Delafield (1934), who had already made a detached study of the chemical changes occurring in the blood of the rabbit following the injection of killed suspensions of various bacteria (see Chapter XLI), was able to show that the purified fractions prepared by Raistrick and Topley induced a marked hyperglycæmia, followed in many cases by a fall in blood sugar far below the normal level. These findings were confirmed by Boivin and Mesrobeanu (1934*b*).

These observations suggest that the toxic substances isolated from *Bact. typhi-murium* and *Bact. enteritidis* are representatives of a group of antigenic components, possessing very similar toxic properties but differing widely in the chemical structure that determines their antigenic specificity, and that bacterial components of this type are very widely distributed among different bacterial groups. Delafield (1931, 1932) found that a wide variety of Gram-negative bacteria, including *Bact. coli*, *Bact. aerogenes*, *Bact. shigœ*, *Bact. typhosum*, *Bact. typhi-murium*, *H. influenzœ*, *Br. bronchiseptica*, *Past. muriseptica*, *Proteus vulgaris* and the meningococcus, induced hyperglycæmia in rabbits, while the Gram-positive species studied did not ; and Boivin and Mesrobeanu (1935*b*) have isolated fractions of the same type as those obtained from *Bact. typhi-murium* from a variety of bacilli of the coli-typhoid group, though the toxicity of most of these fractions has not yet been determined.

There is, of course, no reason to suppose that these particular substances are the only toxic constituents of the bacteria in which they occur. It is possible that there are many others. They do, however, afford examples of " endotoxins " that are definable chemical substances, and not merely crude extracts containing all the multitudinous components of the bacterial cells from which they were derived.

Variation in the Salmonella Group.

The variations that occur within this group have been studied by many observers ; and these studies have been particularly fruitful in adding to our knowledge of the mechanisms of bacterial variation as a general phenomenon. For this reason they have been discussed in some detail in Chapters VII and VIII ; and there is no need to repeat that discussion here.

A few notes, however, may be added. The H ⟶ O variation—the change from the flagellated to the non-flagellated form—although it undoubtedly occurs, appears to be an infrequent event in nature. Nor can this variation be readily induced in the laboratory. The production of " O forms " of a flagellated species by growth on phenolized agar is not an impressed variation, since there is a rapid reversion to the normal flagellated form when the organisms are re-inoculated on to non-phenolized media.

The S ⟶ R variation, on the other hand, seems to occur rather more frequently in nature, is a common occurrence in strains maintained through many generations on any of the ordinary laboratory media, and can readily be induced by several different procedures—the prolonged incubation of a broth culture, growth in the presence of antibodies acting on the smooth somatic antigens, subjection to the action of an anti-smooth phage, and so on.

In connection with this particular type of variation it is of interest to note that the distribution of the rough polysaccharide antigen appears to be limited to members of the Salmonella group. It is possessed by all those strains that have been examined, but not by other species of bacteria, such as colon or dysentery bacilli (White 1929*a*).

Many of the observations recorded by workers in this field indicate quite clearly that the S ⟶ R variation is not an " all-or-none " process. It is gradual, or step-like. A smooth strain may lose some of its normal somatic antigen and uncover some of its rough antigen, or develop it to replace the smooth, so that it will respond both to an anti-smooth and to an anti-rough serum. As has already been noted (see Chapters VII and VIII) variation by loss may proceed further than the R form, giving rise to the ρ form of White (1932), in which the R polysaccharide is lost.

There are, in addition, other antigenic variations of which no mention has yet been made. Kauffmann (1934*b*) and Zahn (1935), for instance, record the isolation from human cases and carriers of strains of *Bact. paratyphosum B* and of *Bact. typhi-murium* that differ from the normal forms in possessing only the somatic antigen IV, instead of the two antigens IV and V. Whether these forms are " variants " or " varieties " seems a little doubtful. But a fact that points to the former conclusion is that Kauffmann, on a few occasions, isolated both the " IV " form and the normal " IV, V " form from the same patient.

In regard to variations in virulence, we have seen that the S $\longrightarrow$ R variation is always accompanied by a change from the virulent to the avirulent state. But smooth forms may lose their virulence without becoming rough (see, for instance, Wilson 1928, 1930). In the particular case of *Bact. typhosum* we have also to consider the loss of the Vi antigen described by Felix which is discussed more fully in Chapter LXVI.

In regard to variations in fermentative capacity, reference may be made to the instances described in Chapter VIII.

There are many other variations within this group that will be found recorded in the literature, but of which no mention has here been made. Among them are many of the forms that appear when Salmonella strains are submitted to bacteriophage action (see Chapter X). Here, as elsewhere, we have confined our attention to those variants of which sufficient is known to allow us to fit them into some significant place in our general picture of the group.

Other Species or Types of Bacteria.

There remain a few other organisms that must be mentioned in this chapter.

Bahr (1922) described a bacillus isolated from an outbreak of infective dysentery among hive bees in Denmark. It has many of the characters of a Salmonella bacillus, and was at first regarded as a member of that group ; but it bears no antigenic relationship to it (White 1926, Kauffmann 1934*a*) and should therefore be excluded.

The bacillus described by Morgan (1906, 1907) as a cause of summer diarrhœa in children has long been regarded as a member of the genus *Bacterium*, but recent studies by Rauss (1936) have shown that it has a closer affinity to the *Proteus* group. It is therefore described in Chapter XXVI.

Petruschky (1896) described a Gram-negative bacillus, isolated from human fæces. This organism, which is commonly known as *Bact. alkaligenes*, differs from all other species of *Bacteria* in failing to ferment dextrose. It has for long been included in this genus ; but, here again, recent studies have raised serious doubts as to its true systematic position. It is therefore described, with other unclassified organisms, in Chapter XXXIV.

We append to this chapter a summarized description of some of the more important species within this genus.

Bact. coli

Isolation.—Isolated from fæces by Escherich (1885).

Habitat.—The intestinal tract of man and animals.

Morphology.—Bacilli with parallel sides and rounded ends, varying in length from almost coccal forms to long rods. The predominating form is a short rod about 2–3 μ long and 0·6 μ in breadth. The bacilli stain evenly, form no spores, and are not usually capsulated. They are Gram-negative and not acid-fast. Some strains are actively motile, with peritrichate flagella. Some are non-flagellated and non-motile.

Agar Plates.—24 *hours at* 37° *C.   Bact. coli* forms circular, low convex, smooth, colourless colonies, about 1–3 mm. in diameter, with a finely granular structure, and an entire edge. The consistency is butyrous, and the growth emulsifies readily. The typical form is often departed from. The surface may be more contoured, and the edge less regular and more effuse.

Broth.—There is abundant growth with a uniform turbidity, increasing up to 24–72 hours, with a slight, powdery deposit that disperses readily on shaking, and sometimes with a minimal degree of surface growth.

Gelatin Stab.—There is good growth along the track, and moderate growth on the surface. The medium is not liquefied.

Blood Agar Plate.—The medium in the neighbourhood of the colonies is discoloured, and there may be hæmolysis. Different strains may vary widely in their action on blood-containing media.

MacConkey's Lactose Agar.—*Bact. coli* gives rise to circular, smooth, convex colonies, similar to those formed on ordinary agar, but coloured red as a result of the action of the acid formed from the lactose on the neutral red that diffuses into the colony from the medium.

Potato.—There is slight but obvious growth, with a cream or faintly yellow colour.

Resistance.—*Bact. coli* is usually killed by exposure to a temperature of 60° C. for 15 minutes, or of 55° C. for 1 hour, but some strains are more resistant. It is less resistant than many other species of this genus to the action of certain green dyes, particularly brilliant green.

Growth Requirements.—*Bact. coli* grows readily on all ordinary laboratory media. The optimum temperature for growth is in the neighbourhood of 37° C., but growth occurs over an extended range, from about 15 to 45° C.

Enzymic Activities.—*Bact. coli* produces acid and gas from dextrose, maltose, mannitol, lactose, xylose, rhamnose and arabinose. It acidifies and clots milk, usually forms indole, and reduces nitrates. Saccharose, salicin, raffinose and ducitol are attacked by some strains but not by others. Inositol and dextrin are not attacked. Some strains form H_2S.

The methyl-red reaction is positive. The Voges-Proskauer reaction is negative. The $CO_2 : H_2$ ratio is 1 : 1. The organism does not grow with citrate as the only source of carbon.

Antigenic Structure.—*Bact. coli* is an antigenically heterogeneous species, the antigenic structure of which has not yet been studied in any detail.

Pathogenicity.—*Bact. coli* is a normal inhabitant of the intestine of man and other animals. In certain circumstances it may play a pathogenic rôle, sometimes in the intestine itself, more commonly in organs or tissues anatomically related to it, such as the gall-bladder. It is a frequent cause of infection of the urinary tract in man.

Varieties.—On the basis of the fermentation reactions, *Bact. coli* may be divided into the following varieties :—

> *var. commune* ferments salicin but not saccharose.
> *var. communius* ferments saccharose but not salicin.
> *var. neapolitanum* ferments both saccharose and salicin.
> *var. acidi lactici* ferments neither saccharose nor salicin.

Some authorities recognize further varieties which are differentiated by being non-motile.

Bact. aerogenes

Bact. aerogenes differs from *Bact. coli* in the following points. Morphologically the rods are often shorter and plumper and they are occasionally capsulated. They may be motile or non-motile. The colonies on agar are more convex, smoother and often mucoid. The deposit in broth is often more viscous. Growth is rather more abundant at lower temperatures, less abundant at temperatures over 37° C., and usually very slight, or absent, at temperatures of 42–44° C. Inositol, dextrin and starch are frequently fermented. Most strains fail to form indole. There is a more abundant formation of gas, but a lower acidity. The CO_2 : H_2 ratio is high, approximately 2 : 1. The Voges-Proskauer reaction is positive. The methyl-red reaction is negative. Growth occurs with citrate as the only source of carbon. The normal habitat of this species is on grains and plants, but it can frequently be isolated from the intestine of man or animals, if careful search is made for it.

Bact. cloacæ

Bact. cloacæ resembles *Bact. aerogenes*, except that it is usually motile, is seldom capsulated, and liquefies gelatin. Its distribution in nature appears to be the same.

Intermediate Forms

The existence of strains that are intermediate between *Bact. coli* and *Bact. aerogenes* has been noted in the text, and their characters have been described (see p. 524). They are differentiated (1) from *Bact. coli* mainly in being citrate-positive, in generally failing to form indole, and by their inability to produce gas in MacConkey's medium incubated at 44° C. ; (2) from *Bact. aerogenes* in being M.R. +, V.P. —, and in failing to utilize uric acid as their sole source of nitrogen. In this country they appear to be distributed chiefly in the soil.

Friedländer's bacillus

Synonyms.—Pneumobacillus, *Bact. friedländeri*, *Bact. pneumoniæ*, *B. pneumoniæ*, *B. mucosus capsulatus*, *Encapsulatus pneumoniæ*, *Klebsiella pneumoniæ*.

Isolation.—Isolated by Friedländer in 1883 from the lungs of patients dying of pneumonia.

Habitat.—Chiefly a parasite. Found in the nose, mouth, and intestine of normal persons ; in the lungs of patients with pneumonia, influenza, and tuberculosis, and other respiratory diseases ; and in suppurative conditions of other parts of the body.

Morphology.—Short, thick, oval rod, about 1–2 μ long and 0·5–0·8 μ broad. Axis straight, sides parallel or bulging, ends rounded, arranged singly and in pairs end-to-end. Some strains are highly pleomorphic, curved rods, sausage forms, and long wavy filaments being found in culture ; in the body diplobacilli, very like pneumococci, are commonest. Considerable variation in staining, particularly of pleomorphic forms. Non-motile. A capsule is present even in cultures ; it contains a nitrogen-free polysaccharide of glucose. Gram-negative.

Agar Plate.—24 *hours at* 37° C. Round, amorphous, convex, greyish-white, faintly translucent, mucoid colonies, 1–2 mm. in diameter, with smooth, glistening surface and entire edge ; consistency mucoid, emulsifiability easy. 7 *days*, larger, from 3–10 mm. in diameter, raised, with flattened surface, sometimes studded with secondary colonies, and slightly undulate edge ; sometimes differentiated into an opaque porcelain-white centre and a less opaque, jelly-coloured periphery showing more translucent radial sectors. A non-mucoid variant occurs.

Agar Slope.—24 *hours at* 37° C. Abundant, raised, faintly translucent, greyish-yellow, mucoid, almost diffluent growth, with glistening, smooth or beaten-copper surface, and entire or undulate edge.

Gelatin Stab.—7 *days at* 20° C. Moderate, filiform, greyish-white growth, confluent in the upper part, extending to bottom of tube. Convex, mucoid surface growth about 3 mm. in diameter—nail-headed appearance. No liquefaction, even after 4 weeks, but a large napiform gas bubble often appears near the surface. Sometimes numerous lateral outgrowths occur from the stab after 3 or 4 weeks.

Broth.—24 *hours at* 37° C. Moderate growth with moderate uniform turbidity, and a slight, powdery deposit disintegrating easily. Ring growth at surface. 7 *days*, heavy turbidity with abundant, viscous deposit ; marked ring growth. The culture is viscous in consistency.

Glucose Agar Shake.—24 *hours at* 37° *C.* Multiple tiny colonies throughout medium, more numerous near the top. Medium is torn into rifts with gas.

Horse Blood Agar Plate.—24 *hours at* 37° *C.* Convex, milky-white colonies, 1 mm. in diameter, with smooth surface and entire edge. No hæmolysis, but plate is browned.

MacConkey's Agar.—24 *hours at* 37° *C.* Reddish colonies, 1–3 mm. in diameter. 7 *days,* round, convex or umbonate, red colonies with smooth surface and entire or lobate edge.

MacConkey's Fluid Medium.—7 *days at* 37° *C.* Moderate turbidity ; magenta colour ; sometimes gas formation.

Potato.—24 *hours at* 37° *C.* Yellowish, confluent, mucoid growth. 7 *days,* abundant, raised, mucoid, creamy, buff-yellow, or café-au-lait growth, with smooth, slightly pitted, or nodular surface.

Resistance.—Killed by moist heat at 55° C. in half an hour. Cultures at room temperature live for months.

Metabolism.—Aerobe. Very slight growth in 10 days under strict anaerobic conditions. Grows luxuriantly in culture. No hæmolysis of sheep's or horse's red cells. Tendency to form brownish pigment on potato.

Biochemical.—Highly variable. Acid, and generally gas, in glucose, maltose, mannitol, lactose, sucrose, and salicin. Inositol is said to be fermented. L.M. acid, or acid and clot. Indole $\mp$; M.R. $+$; V.P. $-$; nitrates reduced ; $NH_3 ++$; $H_2S -$; M.B. reduced ; catalase $++$; Koser's citrate $+$; modified Eijkman $-$.

Antigenic Structure.—By agglutination, absorption, and precipitin tests there are three types, A, B, and C of Friedländer's bacillus, and a heterogeneous group X. The specificity of the types is determined by the carbohydrate fraction in the capsule. The B type is similar immunologically to Type II pneumococcus.

Pathogenicity.—Is found in lesions of the respiratory tract and in suppurative conditions generally in the human body. Experimentally, it is highly pathogenic to mice on intraperitoneal or intravenous injection. Rabbits are less susceptible, but often succumb to intravenous or intraperitoneal injection. Types A and B are highly virulent for mice ; Type C is avirulent. After intraperitoneal injection of a very small quantity of broth culture mice die in 18 to 24 hours ; P.M. viscous exudate in peritoneum ; capsulated bacilli numerous in blood, lungs and spleen.

The Paracolon Group

The organisms of this group, many of which differ from *Bact. coli.* in fermenting lactose slowly, or irregularly, have been described on pp. 535, 536.

The Dysentery Group

These organisms have been described on pp. 538–546.

The Typhoid-Paratyphoid (Salmonella) Group

The more important characters of this large and important group have been described on pp. 546–569.

REFERENCES

ABEL, R. (1896) *Z. Hyg. InfektKr.,* **21,** 89.
ACHARD and BENSAUDE. (1896) *Bull. Mém. Soc. méd. Hop.,* **13,** 820.
AMAKO, T. (1908) *Z. Hyg. InfektKr.,* **60,** 93.
ANDREWES, F. W. (1918) *Lancet,* i. 560.
ANDREWES, F. W. and INMAN, A. C. (1919) *Spec. Rep. Ser. med. Res. Coun., Lond.,* No. 42.
ANDREWES, F. W. and NEAVE, S. (1921) *Brit. J. exp. Path.,* **2,** 157.
AOKI, K. (1921) *Tokohu J. exp. Med.,* **2,** 142 ; (1923) *Ibid.,* **4,** 12.
AOKI, K. and SAKAI, K. (1925) *Zbl. Bakt.,* **95,** 152.
ARCHIBALD, R. G. (1911) *4th Rep. Wellcome trop. Res. Lab.*
ARIMA, R. (1912) *Zbl. Bakt.,* **63,** 424.

ARKWRIGHT, J. A. (1921) *J. Path. Bact.*, **24**, 36.
AVERY, O. T., HEIDELBERGER, M., and GOEBEL, W. F. (1925) *J. exp. Med.*, **42**, 709.
BAHR. (1922) " Paratyphus der Honigbiene." Freiburg.
BAHR, L. (1930a) *Dtsch. tierarztl. Wschr.*, **38**, 145 ; (1930b) *Ibid.*, **38**, 165.
BAMFORTH, J. (1928) *J. Hyg., Camb.*, **27**, 343 ; (1934) *J. Hyg. Camb.*, **34**, 69.
BARBER, M. A. (1907) *Kansas Univ. Sci. Bull.*, **4**, 1.
BARDSLEY, D. A. (1926) *J. Hyg., Camb.*, **25**, 11 ; (1934) *Ibid.*, **34**, 38.
BARG, G. S. (1932) *Z. ImmunForsch.*, **74**, 372.
BASENAU, F. (1894) *Arch. Hyg.*, **20**, 242.
BASILEWSKY, B. G. and REMGILD, W. I. (1935) *Z. ImmunForsch.*, **85**, 10.
BEAUDETTE, F. R. (1926) *J. Amer. vet. med. Ass.*, **68**, 642.
BEHAM, L. M. (1912) *Zbl. Bakt.*, **66**, 110.
BERGEY, D. H. *et al.* (1934) " Manual of Determinative Bacteriology." 4th Edit. Baltimore & London.
BERGEY, D. H. and DEEHAN, S. J. (1908) *J. med. Res.*, **19**, 175.
BESSAU, G. (1911) *Zbl. Bakt.*, **57**, 27.
BHATNAGAR, S. S. and SINGH, K. (1935) *Indian J. med. Res.*, **23**, 337.
BITTER, L., WEIGMANN, F., and HABS, H. (1926) *Münch. med. Wschr.*, **73**, 940.
BLAKE, A. V. and OKELL, C. C. (1929) *J. Path. Bact.*, **32**, 120.
BOECKER, E. (1936) *Zbl. Bakt.*, **135**, 501.
BOECKER, E. and KAUFFMANN, F. (1930) *Zbl. Bakt.*, **116**, 458.
BOECKER, E. and SILBERSTEIN, W. (1932) *Zbl. Bakt.*, **125**, 257.
BOIVIN, A. and MESROBEANU, L. (1933) *C. R. Soc. Biol.*, **112**, 76 ; (1934a) *Ibid.*, **115**, 304, 309 ; (1934b) *Ibid.*, **117**, 273 ; (1934c) *C. R. Acad. Sci.*, **198**, 2211 ; (1935a) *C. R. Soc. Biol.*, **118**, 612 ; (1935b) *C. R. Acad. Sci.*, **201**, 168.
BOIVIN, A., MESROBEANU, I., and MESROBEANU, L. (1933a) *C. R. Soc. Biol.*, **113**, 490 ; (1933b) *Ibid.*, **114**, 307 ; (1934a) *Ibid.*, **115**, 306 ; (1934b) *Ibid.*, **117**, 271 ; (1935) *Arch. roum. Path. exp. Microbiol.*, **8**, 45.
BOJLÉN, K. (1930) *C. R. Soc. Biol.*, **103**, 613 ; (1934) " Dysentery in Denmark." Bianco Lunos Bogtrykkeri A/s, Copenhagen.
BOSWORTH, T. J. and LOVELL, R. (1931) *Univ. Camb. Inst. Animal Path.*, 2nd Ann. Rep., p. 21.
BOYCOTT, A. E. (1906) *J. Hyg., Camb.*, **6**, 33.
BOYD, J. S. K. (1932) *J. R. Army med. Cps*, **59**, 241, 331 ; (1936) *Ibid.*, **66**, 1.
BRANHAM, S. E. (1925) *J. infect. Dis.*, **37**, 291.
BRAUN, H. and BAAKE, F. (1930) *Zbl. Bakt.*, **116**, 462.
BRIDGES, R. F. and SCOTT, W. M. (1931) *J. R. Army med. Cps.*, **56**, 241 ; (1935) *Ibid.*, **65**, 221.
BRIEGER, L. (1902) *Dtsch. med. Wschr.*, **28**, 477.
BRION, A. and KAYSER, H. (1902) *Münch. med. Wschr.*, **49**, 611.
BROOKS, R. ST. JOHN and RHODES, M. (1923) *J. Path. Bact.*, **26**, 433.
BROUDIN, L. (1927) *C. R. Soc. Biol.*, **97**, 1589.
BROWN, H. C. (1921) *Lancet*, i, 22.
BROWN, H. C., DUNCAN, J. T., and HENRY, T. A. (1924) *J. Hyg., Camb.*, **23**, 1.
BROWNING, C. H., GILMOUR, W., and MACKIE, T. J. (1913) *J. Hyg., Camb.*, **13**, 335.
BRUNS, H. and GASTERS. (1920) *Z. Hyg. InfektKr.*, **90**, 263.
BUCHANAN, G. and ROUX, P. (1930) *J. med. Ass. S. Africa*, **4**, 685.
BURNET, F. M. and McKIE, M. (1930) *J. Path. Bact.*, **33**, 637.
BURTON, L. V. and RETTGER, L. F. (1917) *J. infect. Dis.*, **21**, 162.
CANN, L. W. and NAVASQUEZ, S. DE. (1931) *J. Hyg., Camb.*, **31**, 361.
CARPANO, M. (1913) *Zbl. Bakt.*, **70**, 42.
CARVER, J. R. (1921) *Lancet*, i. 687.
CASPER, W. (1928–29) *Z. Hyg. InfektKr.*, **109**, 170.
CASTELLANI, A. (1902–14) *Ceylon med. Rep. Colombo* ; (1907) *J. Hyg., Camb.*, **7**, 1 ; (1912) *J. trop. Med. Hyg.*, **15**, 161.
CASTELLANI, A. and CHALMERS, A. J. (1920) *Ann. Inst. Pasteur*, **34**, 600.
CERNAIANU, C. and POPOVICI, I. (1933) *C. R. Soc. Biol.*, **112**, 829.
CHALMERS, A. J. and MACDONALD, N. (1916) *Lancet*, ii. 139.
CHANTEMESSE, A. (1897) *C. R. Soc. Biol.*, **49**, 96, 101.
CHANTEMESSE, A. and WIDAL, F. (1887) *Arch. Physiol. norm. path.*, **9**, 217 ; (1891) *Bull. Méd.*, **5**, 935.
CHEN, C. C. and RETTGER, L. F. (1920) *J. Bact.*, **5**, 253.
CLAIRMONT, P. (1902) *Z. Hyg. InfektKr.*, **39**, 1.
CLARK, W. M. and LUBS, H. A. (1915) *J. infect. Dis.*, **17**, 160.
CLAUBERG, K. W. (1931) *Klin. Wschr.*, **10**, 540 ; (1932) *Zbl. Bakt.*, **124**, 23.
CLAYTON, F. H. A. and WARREN, S. H. (1929a) *J. Hyg., Camb.*, **28**, 355 ; (1929b) *Ibid.*, **29**, 191.

COMBIESCO, D., STAMATESCO, S., and SARU, E.   (1930) *Arch. roum. Path. exp. Microbiol.*, **3**, 189.
CONRADI, H.   (1903) *Dtsch. med. Wschr.*, **29**, 26 ; (1906) *Dtsch. med. Wschr.*, **32**, 58.
COULTER, C. B.   (1917) *J. exp. Med.*, **26**, 763.
CRUICKSHANK, J. and CRUICKSHANK, R.   (1931) " A System of Bacteriology," Med. Res. Coun., London.   Vol. **8**, p. 353.
DACK, G. M. and PETRAN, E.   (1934) *J. infect. Dis.*, **55**, 1.
DALLING, T., MASON, J. H., and GORDON, W. S.   (1928) *Vet. Rec.*, **8**, 329.
DALLING, T. and WARRACK, G. K.   (1932) *J. Path. Bact.*, **35**, 655.
DAMMANN and STEDEFEDER.   (1910) *Arch. wiss. prakt. Tierheilk.*, **36**, 432.
DANYSZ, J.   (1900) *Ann. Inst. Pasteur*, **14**, 193.
DELAFIELD, M. E.   (1931) *J. Path. Bact.*, **34**, 177 ; (1932) *Ibid.*, **35**, 53 ; (1934) *Brit. J. exp. Path.*, **15**, 130.
DITTHORN, E.   (1913) *Zbl. Bakt.*, **67**, 497.
DOPTER, C.   (1905) *Ann. Inst. Pasteur*, **19**, 353.
DOUGLAS, S. R.   (1921) *Brit. J. exp. Path.*, **2**, 175.
DOWNIE, A. W., WADE, E., and YOUNG, J. A.   (1933) *J. Hyg., Camb.*, **33**, 196.
DOYLE, T. M.   (1927) *J. comp. Path.*, **40**, 71.
DUDGEON, L. S.   (1924) *J. Hyg., Camb.*, **22**, 348 ; (1926) *Ibid.*, **25**, 119.
DUDGEON, L. S. and PULVERTAFT, R. J. V.   (1927) *J. Hyg., Camb.*, **26**, 285.
DUDGEON, L. S. and URQUART, A. L.   (1920) *Lancet*, ii. 15.
DUDGEON, L. S., WORDLEY, E., and BAWTREE, F.   (1921) *J. Hyg., Camb.*, **20**, 137 ; (1922) *Ibid.*, **21**, 168.
DULANEY, A. D. and MICHELSON, I. D.   (1935) *Amer. J. publ. Hlth*, **25**, 1241.
DUNBAR, W.   (1892) *Z. Hyg. InfektKr.*, **12**, 485.
DURHAM, H. E.   (1898) *Brit. med. J.*, i. 1387 ; (1901) *J. exp. Med.*, **5**, 353.
EBERTH, C. J.   (1880) *Virchows Arch.*, **81**, 58.
ECKER, E. E.   (1917) *J. infect. Dis.*, **21**, 541.
ECKER, E. E. and RICHARDSON, M. L.   (1925) *J. infect. Dis.*, **37**, 538.
ECKER, E. E. and RIMINGTON, C.   (1928) *J. Hyg., Camb.*, **27**, 44.
EDWARDS, P. R.   (1928) *J. Bact.*, **15**, 245 ; (1929*a*) *Ibid.*, **17**, 339 ; (1929*b*) *J. infect. Dis.*, **45**, 191 ; (1931) *Kentucky agric. Exp. Sta. Bull.*, No. 320 ; (1932) *J. infect. Dis.*, **51**, 268 ; (1935) *J. Bact.*, **30**, 269.
EDWARDS, P. R. and RETTGER, L. F.   (1927) *J. Bact.*, **13**, 73.
EDWARDS, R. T.   (1905) *J. infect. Dis.*, **2**, 431.
EIJKMAN, C.   (1904) *Zbl. Bakt.*, **37**, 436, 742 ; (1914) *Ibid.*, IIte Abt., **39**, 75.
ELBERT, B. J. and GUERKESS, W. M.   (1930) *Ann. Inst. Pasteur*, **44**, 548.
ESCHERICH, T.   (1885) *Fortschr. Med.*, **3**, 515, 547.
FELIX, A. and PITT, R. M.   (1934*a*) *J. Path. Bact.*, **38**, 409 ; (1934*b*) *Lancet*, ii. 186.
FITCH, C. P. and BILLINGS, W. A.   (1920) *J. Bact.*, **5**, 469.
FITZGERALD, J. G.   (1914) *J. infect. Dis.*, **15**, 268.
FLEXNER, S.   (1900*a*) *Zbl. Bakt.*, **28**, 625 ; (1900*b*) *Bull. Johns Hopk. Hosp.*, **11**, 231.
FLEXNER, S. and SWEET, J. E.   (1906) *J. exp. Med.*, **8**, 514.
FORSYTH, W. L.   (1933) *J. trop. Med. Hyg.*, **36**, 65.
FREMLIN, H.   (1893) *Arch. Hyg.*, **19**, 295.
FRICKE, C.   (1896) *Z. Hyg. InfektKr.*, **23**, 380.
FRIEDLÄNDER, C.   (1883) *Fortschr., Med.*, **1**, 715.
FURTH, J. and LANDSTEINER, K.   (1928) *J. exp. Med.*, **47**, 171 ; (1929) *Ibid.*, **49**, 727.
GAERTNER.   (1888) *KorrespBl. ärztl. Ver. Thüringen*, **17**, 573.
GAFFKY.   (1884) *Mitt. ReichsgesundhAmt.*, **2**, 372.
GAGE, G. E. and MARTIN, J. F.   (1916) *J. med. Res.*, **34**, 149.
GARDNER, A. D.   (1925) *J. Path. Bact.*, **28**, 189.
GAY, F. P. and CLAYPOLE, E. J.   (1913) *Arch. intern. Med.*, **12**, 621.
GETTINGS, H. S.   (1919) *Spec. Rep. Ser. med. Res. Coun., Lond.*, No. 30.
GIGLIOLI, G.   (1930) *J. Hyg., Camb.*, **29**, 273.
GLÄSSER, C.   (1909) *Dtsch. tierärztl. Wschr.*, **16**, 513 ; (1910) *Zbl. Bakt. Ref.*, **45**, 612.
GOOD, E. S. and CORBETT, L. S.   (1913) *J. infect. Dis.*, **13**, 53.
GRAY, J. D. A.   (1931) *J. Path. Bact.*, **34**, 335.
GRIMBERT, L. and LEGROS, G.   (1900) *C. R. Soc. Biol.*, **52**, 491.
GWYN, N. B.   (1898) *Johns Hopk. Hosp. Bull.*, **9**, 54.
HABS, H.   (1933) *Zbl. Bakt.*, **130**, 367.
HADLEY, P.   (1927) *J. infect. Dis.*, **40**, 1.
HADLEY, P. B., CALDWELL, D. W., ELKINS, M. W., and LAMBERT, D. J.   (1917) *R. I. agric. Exp. Sta. Bull.*, No. 172.
HARDEN, A.   (1901) *J. chem. Soc.*, **79**, 610 ; (1905) *J. Hyg., Camb.*, **5**, 488 ; (1906) *Proc. roy. Soc.*, B, **77**, 424.
HARDEN, A. and NORRIS, D.   (1911) *Proc. roy. Soc.*, B, **84**, 492.

HARDEN, A. and WALPOLE, G. S.   (1906) *Proc. roy. Soc., B,* **77,** 399.
HARDING, E. R. and OSTENBERG, Z.   (1912) *J. infect. Dis.,* **11,** 109.
HAVENS, L. C. and MAYFIELD, C. R.   (1933) *J. infect. Dis.,* **52,** 157.
HAY, H. R.   (1932) *J. Hyg., Camb.,* **32,** 240.
HEELSBERGEN, T. VAN.   (1914) *Zbl. Bakt.,* **72,** 38.
HEIDELBERGER, M., GOEBEL, W. F., and AVERY, O. T.   (1925) *J. exp. Med.,* **42,** 701.
HEIMANN, W.   (1912) *Zbl. Bakt.,* **66,** 211.
HICKS, E. P.   (1930) *J. Hyg., Camb.,* **29,** 446.
HIRSCHFELD, L.   (1919) *Lancet,* i. 296.
HISS, P. H.   (1904) *J. med. Res.,* **13,** 1.
HISS, P. H. and RUSSELL, F. F.   (1903) *Med. News,* **82,** 289.
HOFFMAN, W. and FICKER, M.   (1904) *Hyg. Rundsch.,* **14,** 1.
HOHN, J. and HERRMANN, W.   (1935a) *Zbl. Bakt.,* **133,** 183 ; (1935b) *Ibid.,* **134,** 277 ; (1936) *Ibid.,* **135,** 505.
HORT, E. C.   (1920) *J. Hyg., Camb.,* **18,** 369.
HOWE, F.   (1904) *Zbl. Bakt.,* **36,** 484.
HULTON, F.   (1916) *J. infect. Dis.,* **19,** 606.
ISABOLINSKY, M.   (1926) *Zbl. Bakt.,* **97,** 148.
IWASCHENZOFF, G.   (1926) *Arch. Schiffs- u. Tropenhyg.,* **30,** 1.
JACKSON, D. D.   (1911) *J. infect. Dis.,* **8,** 241.
JAMPOLIS, M., HOWELL, K. M., CALVIN, J. K., and LEVENTHAL, M. L.   (1932) *Amer. J. Dis. Child.,* **43,** 70.
JOHNSON, B. R.   (1916) *J. Bact.,* **1,** 96.
JOHNSTON, M. M. and BROWN, A.   (1930) *Canad. publ. Hlth J.,* **21,** 394.
JOHNSTON, M. M. and KAAKE, M. J.   (1932) *Canad. publ. Hlth J.,* **23,** 159.
JONES, H. N.   (1924) *Science,* **60,** 455.
JONES, H. N. and WISE, L. E.   (1926) *J. Bact.,* **11,** 359.
JONG, A. DE.   (1913) *Zbl. Bakt.,* **67,** 148.
JORDAN, E. O.   (1890) *Rep. Mass. Bd. Hlth,* **11,** 836 ; (1903) *Science,* **3,** 1 ; (1917) *J. infect. Dis.,* **20,** 457 ; (1918a) *J. infect. Dis.,* **22,** 252 ; (1918b) *Ibid.,* **22,** 511 ; (1920) *Ibid.,* **26,** 427 ; (1934) *Amer. J. trop. Med.,* **14,** 27 ; (1936) *J. infect. Dis.,* **58,** 128.
JORDAN, E. O. and VICTORSON, R.   (1917) *J. infect. Dis.,* **21,** 554.
JULIANELLE, L. A.   (1926a) *J. exp. Med.,* **44,** 113 ; (1926b) *Ibid.,* **44,** 683 ; (1926c) *Ibid.,* **44,** 735 ; (1930) *J. exp. Med.,* **52,** 539 ; (1935) *J. Bact.,* **30,** 535.
KAUFFMANN, F.   (1929a) *Zbl. Bakt., Ref.,* 94, 282 ; (1929b) *Z. Hyg. InfektKr.,* **110,** 537 ; (1930a) *Ibid.,* **111,** 210 ; (1930b) *Ibid.,* **111,** 221 ; (1931) *Zbl. ges. Hyg.,* **25,** 273 ; (1934a) *Ergebn. Hyg.,* **15,** 219 ; (1934b) *Zbl. Bakt.,* **132,** 337 ; (1935a) *Z. Hyg. InfektKr.,* **116,** 617 ; (1935b) *Ibid.,* **117,** 401.
KAUFFMANN, F. and BURÓN, F. A.   (1935) *Z. Hyg. InfektKr.,* **117,** 650.
KAUFFMANN, F. and MITSUI, C.   (1930) *Z. Hyg. InfektKr.,* **111,** 749.
KAUFFMANN, F. and SILBERSTEIN, W.   (1934) *Zbl. Bakt.,* **132,** 431.
KAYSER, H.   (1904) *Zbl. Bakt.,* **35,** 154.
KEMPER, F.   (1933) *Zbl. Bakt.,* **130,** 265.
KERRIN, J. C.   (1928a) *J. Hyg., Camb.,* **28,** 4.
KERRIN, J. C.   (1928b) *J. Path. Bact.,* **31,** 588.
KEYES, F. G.   (1909) *J. med. Res.,* **21,** 69.
KHALED, Z.   (1923) *J. Hyg., Camb.,* **21,** 362.
KILBOURNE, F. L.   (1893) *Misc. Invest. infect. parasit. Dis.,* 8° Washington, 49.
KLEIN, E.   (1889) *Zbl. Bakt.,* **5,** 689.
KLIEWE, H. and HSÜ, M.   (1935) *Z. ImmunForsch.,* **86,** 481.
KLIGLER, I. J.   (1914a) *J. infect. Dis.,* **14,** 81 ; (1914b) *Ibid.,* **15,** 187.
KOBAYASHI, R., OHKUBO, H., OHNO, J., IDE, M., NAKAMURA, B., MACHIDA, S., KOBAYASHI, E., MATSUMOTO, I., and MATSUYAMA, S.   (1931) *Kitasato Arch. exp. Med.,* **8,** 99.
KOSER, S. A.   (1918) *J. infect. Dis.,* **23,** 377 ; (1923) *J. Bact.,* **8,** 493 ; (1924) *Ibid.,* **9,** 59 ; (1926a) *J. Amer. Wat. Wks Ass.,* **15,** 641 ; (1926b) *J. Bact.,* **11,** 409 ; (1926c) *J. infect. Dis.,* **38,** 506.
KOSER, S. A., REITER, D. O., BORTNIKER, E., and SWINGLE, E. L.   (1930) *J. prev. Med.,* **4,** 477.
KOSER, S. A. and STYRON, N. C.   (1930) *J. infect. Dis.,* **47,** 443.
KRAMÁR, L.   (1921) *Zbl. Bakt.,* **87,** 401.
KRAUS, R. and DÖRR, R.   (1905) *Wien. klin. Wschr.,* **18,** 1077.
KRISTENSEN, M. and BOJLÉN, K.   (1929) *Zbl. Bakt.,* **114,** 86.
KRUMWIEDE, C. and KOHN, L. A.   (1917) *J. med. Res.,* **36,** 509.
KRUMWIEDE, C. and PRATT, J. S.   (1914) *J. exp. Med.,* **19,** 501.
KRUMWIEDE, C., PRATT, J. S., and KOHN, L. A.   (1916) *J. med. Res.,* **34,** 355 ; (1916–17a) *Ibid.,* **35,** 55 ; (1916–17b) *Ibid.,* **35,** 357.
KRUMWIEDE, C., PRATT, J., and McWILLIAMS, H.   (1916) *J. infect. Dis.,* **18,** 1.

KRUMWIEDE, C., VALENTINE, E., and KOHN, L. A. (1919) *J. infect. Dis.*, **39**, 449.
KRUSE, W. (1894) *Z. Hyg. InfektKr.*, **17**, 1 ; (1900) *Dtsch. med. Wschr.*, **26**, 637 ; (1901) *Ibid.*, **27**, 370, 386.
KRUSE, RITTERSHAUS, KEMP, and METZ. (1907) *Z. Hyg. InfektKr.*, **57**, 417.
KÜHNEMANN, G. (1911) *Zbl. Bakt.*, **57**, 497.
KURAUCHI, K. (1929) See Ando, K. (1929) *J. Immunol.*, **17**, 555.
LENTZ, O. and PRIGGE, R. (1931) Kolle, Kraus, and Uhlenhuth's " Handbuch der pathogenen Mikroorganismen." Gustav Fischer, Jena. 3te Aufl., **3**, 1377.
LENTZ, O. and TIETZ, J. (1903) *Münch. med. Wsch.*, **50**, 2139 ; (1905) *Klin. Jb.*, **14**, 495.
LESBOUVRIES and VERGE. (1932) *Bull. Acad. Vét. France*, **5**, 294.
LESLIE, P. H. and SHERA, A. G. (1931) *J. Path. Bact.*, **34**, 533.
LESTER, V. (1926) *Act. path. Microbiol. scand.*, **3**, 696.
LEVINE, M. (1916a) *J. Bact.*, **1**, 87 ; (1916b) *Ibid.*, **1**, 153 ; (1916c) *J. infect. Dis.*, **18**, 358 ; (1916d) *Ibid.*, **19**, 773 ; (1917) *Amer. J. publ. Hlth*, **7**, 784.
LEVINE, M., EPSTEIN, S. S., and VAUGHN, R. H. (1934) *Amer. J. publ. Hlth*, **24**, 505.
LIEB, F. (1932) *Zbl. Bakt.*, **124**, 546.
LOEFFLER, F. (1892) *Zbl. Bakt.*, **11**, 129 ; (1903) *Dtsch. med. Wschr.*, **29**, 36 ; (1906) *Ibid.*, **32**, 289.
LOEWENBERG. (1894) *Ann. Inst. Pasteur*, **8**, 292.
LOVELL, R. (1929) *Proc. roy. Soc. Med.*, **22**, 820 ; (1931) *J. Path. Bact.*, **34**, 13 ; (1932a) *Bull. Hyg.*, **7**, 405 ; (1932b) *Vet. Rec.*, **12**, 1052.
MACADAM, W. (1919) *Lancet*, ii. 189.
MACCONKEY, A. (1905) *J. Hyg., Camb.*, **5**, 333 ; (1909) *Ibid.*, **9**, 86.
MACFADYEN, A. and ROWLAND, S. (1901) *Zbl. Bakt.*, **30**, 753 ; (1903) *Proc. roy. Soc.*, **71**, 77.
MACKIE, F. P. and BOWEN, G. J. (1919) *J. R. Army med. Cps*, **33**, 154.
MACKIE, T. J. (1913) *J. Path. Bact.*, **18**, 137.
MANDELBAUM. (1932) *Münch. med. Wschr.*, **79**, 1566.
MANDRY, O. C. (1935) *Puerto Rico J. publ. Hlth*, **10**, 308.
MANFREDI, L. (1917) *Rif. med.*, **33**, No. 35, 849.
MARRASSINI, A. (1913) *Zbl. Bakt.*, **71**, 113.
MARTIN, A. R. (1934) *Brit. J. exp. Path.*, **15**, 137.
MASSINI, R. (1907) *Arch. Hyg.*, **61**, 250.
MENTEN, M. L. and KING, C. G. (1930) *J. infect. Dis.*, **46**, 275.
METCHNIKOFF, E. and BESREDKA, A. (1911) *Ann. Inst. Pasteur*, **25**, 193.
MEYER, K. (1930) *Z. ImmunForsch.*, **68**, 98 ; (1931a) *Ibid.*, **69**, 134, 499 ; (1931b) *Ibid.*, **71**, 331.
MEYER, K. and BERGELL. (1907) *Berl. klin. Wschr.*, **54**, 568.
MEYER, K. F. and BOERNER, F. (1913) *J. med. Res.*, **29**, 325.
MEYER, K. F. and MATSUMURA, K. (1927) *J. infect. Dis.*, **41**, 395.
MEYER, K. and MORGAN, W. T. J. (1935) *Brit. J. exp. Path.*, **16**, 476.
MICHAELIS, L. (1917) *Dtsch. med. Wschr.*, **43**, 1506.
MOORE, V. A. (1895) *U.S. Dept. Agric. Bur. Animal Ind.*, **8**, 71.
MORGAN, H. DE R. (1906) *Brit. med. J.*, i. 908 ; (1907) *Ibid.*, ii. 16.
MORGAN, W. T. J. (1931) *Brit. J. exp. Path.*, **12**, 62.
MORRIS, M. C. and JULIANELLE, L. A. (1934) *J. infect. Dis.*, **55**, 150.
MÜLLER, M. (1912) *Zbl. Bakt.*, **62**, 335.
MÜLLER, R. (1933) *Münch. med. Wschr.*, **80**, 1771.
MURRAY, C. (1919) *J. infect. Dis.*, **25**, 341.
MURRAY, E. G. D. (1918) *J. R. Army med. Cps*, **31**, 257, 353.
MUSLOW, F. W. (1919) *J. infect. Dis.*, **25**, 135.
NABARRO, D. (1923) *J. Path. Bact.*, **26**, 429 ; (1927) *Ibid.*, **30**, 176.
NEISSER, M. and SHIGA, K. (1903) *Dtsch. med. Wschr.*, **29**, 61.
NELSON, R. L. (1930) *J. Bact.*, **20**, 183.
NEUBER, E. (1934) *Arch. Derm. Syph., Berlin*, **170**, 154.
NEUKIRCH, P. (1918) *Z. Hyg. InfektKr.*, **85**, 103.
NOBELE, DE. (1898) *Ann. Soc. Méd. Gand.*, **72**, 281.
NOCARD. (1893) *Cons. Hyg. Publ. Sal. Dept. Seine.* Séance. Mar. 24.
OKELL, C. C. and BLAKE, A. V. (1930) *J. Path. Bact.*, **33**, 57.
OLITSKY, P. K. and KLIGLER, I. J. (1920) *J. exp. Med.*, **31**, 19.
ØRSKOV, J., JENSEN, K., and KOBAYASHI, K. (1928) *Z. ImmunForsch.*, **55**, 34.
ØRSKOV, J. and LASSEN, H. C. A. (1930) *Z. ImmunForsch.*, **67**, 137.
ØRSKOV, J. and MOLTKE, O. (1928) *Z. ImmunForsch.*, **59**, 357.
PAGE, C. G. (1912) *J. med. Res.*, **26**, 489.
PATTERSON, S. W. and WILLIAMS, F. E. (1922) *J. Path. Bact.*, **25**, 393.
PAWAN, J. L. (1931) *J. trop. Med. Hyg.*, **34**, 229, 267, 288, 310, 317, 345, 360, 380, 391, 413.
PECKHAM, C. F. (1923) *J. Hyg., Camb.*, **22**, 69.
PEREZ, F. (1899) *Ann. Inst. Pasteur*, **13**, 937.

PERKINS, R. G. (1904) *J. infect. Dis.*, **1**, 241 ; (1907) *Ibid.*, **4**, 51.
PETRUSCHKY, J. (1889) *Zbl. Bakt.*, **6**, 625, 657 ; (1890) *Ibid.*, **7**, 49 ; (1896) *Ibid.*, **19**, 187.
PFEIFFER, R. (1894) *Dtsch. med. Wschr.*, **20**, 898.
PFEIFFER. (1889) *Z. Hyg. InfektKr.*, **6**, 145.
PFEILER, W. (1920) *Z. InfektKr. Haustiere*, **20**, 218.
PFEILER, W. and REHSE, A. (1913) *Zbl. Bakt.*, **68**, 174.
PFEILER, W. and ROEPKE, E. (1917) *Zbl. Bakt.*, **79**, 125.
PORGES, O. (1905) *Wien. klin. Wschr.*, **18**, 691.
PRÁŠEK, E. and PRICA, M. (1933) *Zbl. Bakt.*, **128**, 381.
PRICA, M. (1930) *Zbl. Bakt.*, **115**, 334.
QUAST, G. (1926) *Zbl. Bakt.*, **97**, 174.
RAISTRICK, H. and TOPLEY, W. W. C. (1934) *Brit. J. exp. Path.*, **15**, 113.
RAUSS, K. F. (1936) *J. Path. Bact.*, **42**, 183.
REFIK, E. (1896) *Ann. Inst. Pasteur*, **10**, 242.
RETTGER, L. F. (1900) *N. Y. med. J.*, **71**, 803 ; (1909) *J. med. Res.*, **21**, 115.
RETTGER, L. F. and HARVEY, S. C. (1908) *J. med. Res.*, **18**, 277.
RETTGER, L. F. and KOSER, S. A. (1917) *J. med. Res.*, **35**, 443.
RETTGER, L. F., PLASTRIDGE, W. N., and CAMERON, R. (1933) *J. infect. Dis.*, **53**, 272.
RETTGER, L. F. and SCOVILLE, M. M. (1919) *Abst. Bact.*, **3**, 8 ; (1920) *J. infect. Dis.*, **26**, 217.
ROGERS, L. A., CLARK, W. M., and DAVIS, B. J. (1914) *J. infect. Dis.*, **14**, 411.
ROGERS, L. A., CLARK, W. M., and EVANS, A. C. (1914) *J. infect. Dis.*, **15**, 99 ; (1915) *Ibid.*, **17**, 137.
ROGERS, L. A., CLARK, W. M., and LUBS, H. A. (1918) *J. Bact.*, **3**, 231.
ROTH, E. (1903) *Hyg. Rundsch.*, **13**, 489.
ROTHBERGER, C. J. (1898) *Zbl. Bakt.*, **24**, 513.
RUSSELL, H. L. and BASSETT, V. H. (1899) *Proc. Amer. publ. Hlth. Ass.*, **25**, 570.
SACQUÉPÉE, E. and CHEVREL, F. (1905) *C. R. Soc. Biol.*, **57**, 535.
SALMON, D. and SMITH, T. (1885) *Ann. Rep. Bureau Animal Industry* ; (1886) *Amer. mon. micr. J.*, **7**, 204.
Salmonella Subcommittee (Nomenclature Co. Int. Soc. Microbiol.). (1934) *J. Hyg., Camb.*, **34**, 333.
SANARELLI, J. (1894) *Ann. Inst. Pasteur*, **8**, 193, 353.
SANDIFORD, B. R. (1935) *J. Path. Bact.*, **41**, 77.
SARTORIUS, F. and REPLOH, H. (1931) *Klin. Wschr.*, **10**, 2216 ; (1932) *Zbl. Bakt.*, **126**, 10.
SAVAGE, W. G. and WHITE, P. B. (1923) *J. Hyg., Camb.*, **21**, 258 ; (1925) *Spec. Rep. Ser. med. Res. Coun., Lond.*, No. 91.
SAVINO, E. and MENÉNDEZ, P. E. (1934) *Rev. Inst. Bact.*, **6**, 347.
SCHERMER and EHRLICH. (1921) *Berl. tierärztl. Wschr.*, **37**, 469.
SCHMITZ, K. E. F. (1917) *Z. Hyg. InfektKr.*, **84**, 449.
SCHOTTMÜLLER, H. (1900) *Dtsch. med. Wschr.*, **26**, 511 ; (1901) *Z. Hyg. InfektKr.*, **36**, 368.
SCHÜTZE, H. (1920) *Lancet*, i. 93 ; (1930) *Brit. J. exp. Path.*, **11**, 34.
SCOTT, W. M. (1926) *J. Hyg., Camb.*, **25**, 398 ; (1932) *J. Path. Bact.*, **35**, 655 ; (1933) *Bull. Office int. Hyg.*, **25**, fasc. 5.
SEIFFERT, G., JAHNCKE, A., and ARNOLD, A. (1928) *Zbl. Bakt.*, **109**, 193.
SELIGMANN, E. and CLAUBERG, K. W. (1932) *Zbl. Bakt.*, **125**, 266.
SHIGA, K. (1898a) *Zbl. Bakt.*, **23**, 599 ; (1898b) *Zbl. Bakt.*, **24**, 817, 870, 913 ; (1901) *Dtsch. med. Wschr.*, **27**, 741, 765, 783 ; (1908) *Z. Hyg. InfektKr.*, **60**, 75.
SHIMIDSU, K. (1913) *Zbl. Bakt.*, **71**, 338.
SILBERSTEIN, W. (1931) *Zbl. Bakt.*, **122**, Beiheft 131 ; (1932) *Z. Hyg. InfektKr.*, **114**, 124.
SLADDEN, A. F. and SCOTT, W. M. (1927) *J. Hyg., Camb.*, **26**, 111.
SMALL, J. C. and JULIANELLE, L. A. (1923) *J. infect. Dis.*, **32**, 456.
SMITH, J. (1934) *J. Hyg., Camb.*, **34**, 351.
SMITH, J. and FRASER, A. M. (1928) *J. Path. Bact.*, **31**, 511.
SMITH, J. and SCOTT, W. M. (1930) *J. Hyg., Camb.*, **30**, 32.
SMITH, J. H. (1915) *Brit. med. J.*, ii. 1.
SMITH, T. (1890) *Zbl. Bakt.*, **7**, 502 ; (1893) *Misc. Invest. infect. parasit. Dis. Dom. Animals*, 8° Washington, 53 ; (1895) *Amer. J. med. Sci.*, **110**, 283.
SMITH, T. and TENBROECK, C. (1915) *J. med. Res.*, **31**, 503.
SONNE, C. (1915) *Zbl. Bakt.*, **75**, 408.
SPRINGER. (1911) *Zbl. Bakt.*, **60**, 2.
STEINBERG, B. and ECKER, E. E. (1926) *J. exp. Med.*, **43**, 443.
STERN, W. (1916) *Zbl. Bakt.*, **78**, 481.
STREIT, H. (1906) *Zbl. Bakt.*, **40**, 709.
STRÖMAN, R. and ÖRN, C. (1932) *Zbl. Bakt.*, **126**, 340.
STRONG, R. P. and MUSGRAVE, W. E. (1900) *J. Amer. med. Ass.*, **35**, 498.
TENBROECK, C. (1918a) *J. exp. Med.*, **28**, 749 ; (1918b) *Ibid.*, **28**, 759.
THJØTTA, T. (1919) *J. Bact.*, **4**, 355.

U

TODD, C. (1904) *J. Hyg., Camb.*, **4**, 480.

TOENNIESSEN, L. (1912) *Zbl. Bakt.*, **65**, 23 ; (1913) *Ibid.*, **69**, 391 ; (1914) *Ibid.*, **74**, 241 ; (1921) *Ibid.*, **85**, 225.

TOMÁŠEK, V. (1925) *Zbl. Bakt., Ref.*, **79**, 564.

VAILLARD, L. and DOPTER, C. (1903) *Ann. Inst. Pasteur*, **17**, 463.

VOGES, O. and PROSKAUER, B. (1898) *Z. Hyg. InfektKr.*, **28**, 20.

WAALER, E. (1935) " Studies on the Dissociation of the Dysentery Bacilli." I Kommisjon Hos Jacob Dybwad, Oslo.

WALLACE, G. I., CAHN, A. R., and THOMAS, L. J. (1933) *J. infect. Dis.*, **53**, 386.

WARREN, S. H. and SCOTT, W. M. (1930) *J. Hyg., Camb.*, **29**, 415.

WATANABE, K. (1935) *Z. ImmunForsch.*, **84**, 156.

WEBSTER, L. T. (1928) *J. exp. Med.*, **47**, 685 ; (1930) *Ibid.*, **52**, 909.

WEIGMANN, F. (1925a) *Zbl. Bakt.*, **95**, 396 ; (1925b) *Ibid.*, **97**, Beiheft 299.

WEIL, E. (1917) *Wien. klin. Wschr.*, **30**, 1061.

WEIL, E. and SAXL, P. (1917) *Wien. klin. Wschr.*, **30**, 519.

WEISS, H. and RICE, J. L. (1917) *J. med. Res.*, **35**, 403.

WELCH, H. and MICKLE, F. L. (1932) *Amer. J. publ. Hlth*, **22**, 263 ; (1934) *Ibid.*, **24**, 219.

WHERRY, W. B. (1908) *J. infect. Dis.*, **5**, 519.

WHITE, P. B. (1926) *Spec. Rep. Ser. med. Res. Coun., Lond.*, No. 103 ; (1929a) *J. Path. Bact.*, **32**, 85 ; (1929b) *Med. Res. Coun.*, " System of Bacteriology," **4**, 86 ; (1930) *J. Hyg., Camb.*, **29**, 443 ; (1931) *J. Path. Bact.*, **34**, 325 ; (1932) *Ibid.*, **35**, 77.

WHITEHEAD, H. and SCOTT, W. M. (1934) *Lancet*, ii. 248.

WILSON, G. S. (1928) *J. Hyg., Camb.*, **28**, 295 ; (1930) *Ibid.*, **30**, 40.

WILSON, G. S., TWIGG, R. S., WRIGHT, R. C., HENDRY, C. B., COWELL, M. P., and MAIER, I. (1935) *Spec. Rep. Ser. med. Res. Coun., Lond.*, No. 206.

WINSLOW, C.-E. A., BROADHURST, J., BUCHANAN, R. E., KRUMWIEDE, C., ROGERS, L. A., and SMITH, G. H. (1917) *J. Bact.*, **2**, 505 ; (1920) *Ibid.*, **5**, 191.

WINSLOW, C.-E. A., KLIGLER, I. J., and ROTHBERG, W. (1919) *J. Bact.*, **4**, 429.

WINSLOW, C.-E. A. and LOCHRIDGE, E. E. (1906) *J. infect. Dis.*, **3**, 547.

WINSLOW, C.-E. A. and WALKER, L. T. (1907) *Science New Ser.*, **26**, 797.

WORDLEY, E. (1923) *Lancet*, ii. 105.

WRIGHT, J. H. and MALLORY, F. B. (1895) *Z. Hyg. InfektKr.*, **20**, 220.

WURTZ, R. (1892) *Arch. Méd. exp.*, **4**, 85.

WYCKOFF, R. W. G. (1933) *J. exp. Med.*, **57**, 165.

YAMANOUCHI, T. (1909) *C. R. Soc. Biol.*, **66**, 1050.

ZAHN, E. (1935) *Z. ImmunForsch.*, **86**, 162.

CHAPTER XXVIII

LACTOBACILLUS

DEFINITION.—*Lactobacillus.*

Rods, often long and slender. Gram-positive; non-motile; without endo-spores. Usually produce acid from carbohydrates, as a rule lactic. Some species grow best at 40–44° C., and some species are microaerophilic. Surface growth on media poor.

Type species is *Lactobacillus caucasicus* Beijerinck.

HISTORY.—The first organism of this group was isolated by Kern in 1881 from the fermented milk of the Caucasus, known as *Kefir*. The name he gave it was *Dispora Kaukasica*, but later it was called *Bacillus Kaukasicus*, and is now known as *Lactobacillus caucasicus*. As Kern did not give a complete description of the organism, and as it is impossible to be certain of its identity, it is somewhat unfortunate that it has been adopted as the type species. A similar bacillus was observed by Döderlein in 1892 in the acid vaginal secretion of preg-nant women; this is usually known as Döderlein's bacillus, but is also known as *B. vaginalis* and *B. crassus*. Slender Gram-positive bacilli were observed microscopically in the stomach contents of patients with gastric carcinoma by Oppler in 1895, working in the clinic of Dr. Boas at Berlin; this organism, which was not cultivated, is generally known as the Boas-Oppler bacillus. In 1900 Moro (1900*a*, *b*) cultivated a similar bacillus from the fæces of breast-fed infants; this organism he called *B. acidophilus*; his findings were confirmed in the same year by Finkelstein (1900). Tissier, also in 1900, isolated two new organisms of the same group from the fæces of infants, to which he gave the names *B. bifidus* and *B. exilis*. In 1905 Grigoroff, working in Massol's laboratory, isolated from *Kissélo-mléko*, better known as *Yoghurt*, the fermented milk of Bulgaria, three organisms to which he gave the names A, B, and C; the first of these is now known as *Lactobacillus bulgaricus* or Massol's bacillus. Similar bacilli have been found by other workers in a number of fermented milks, chiefly the Armenian *Mazun*, the Sardinian *Gioddu*, and the Egyptian *Leben raib* (Cohendy 1906, White and Avery 1910); they have also been isolated from ordinary market milk and from human milk (Moro 1900*a*, Heinemann and Hefferan 1909, Sherman and Stark 1927). Bacilli of this group have been cultivated by Mereshkowsky and his pupils (Mereshkowsky 1905, 1906, Petrow 1907) from the fæces of a large series of inverte-brates, fishes, and mammals; by Heinemann and Hefferan (1909) from human saliva and gastric juice, from soil, and from a number of different foods, such as bran, silage, cornmeal, and olive-juice; by McIntosh, James and Lazarus-Barlow (1922, 1924) from carious teeth; and by Kendall (1910) from sewage.

Morphology.—The members of this group are in general fairly large, non-motile, non-sporing, Gram-positive bacilli. They are arranged singly, in pairs end-to-end, in chains, and sometimes in palisades (Fig. 132). Some members are markedly pleomorphic, especially in old cultures, forming clubbed, knobbed, curled, spiral, candle-flame, vacuolated, whorled, and filamentous forms, and frequently showing irregular, granular, or beaded staining. In some species the bacilli tend to be arranged at angles to each other, giving rise to Y-forms, which may simulate true branching. Another characteristic of some members is the formation of lateral offshoots or buds, either directly adherent to the parent cell, or connected with it by a short stem ; these buds may themselves be bifid.

Cultivation.—These bacteria do not as a rule grow well on the usual laboratory media ; their growth is much improved by the addition of whey or glucose. Surface colonies show a good deal of variation, but on the whole conform to one or other of the two types described by Mereshkowsky (1905, 1906) : (1) round or navicular, pinhead in size, opaque, whitish, and surrounded by an areola of turbid agar ; (2) round or irregularly round, less than pinhead in size, greyish, translucent colonies with a finely erose edge, and with no areola around them ; microscopically these colonies are of typically rhizoid structure. Deep colonies in glucose agar likewise tend to be either compact, with an entire edge or sometimes a single lateral knob (Rettger and Horton's (1914) Y type), or curled, rhizoid, and feathery, looking like a tuft of hair or moss (Rettger and Horton's X type). Intermediate types of colony are not uncommon. The compact and feathery types of colony are referred to by some writers as " smooth " and " rough "

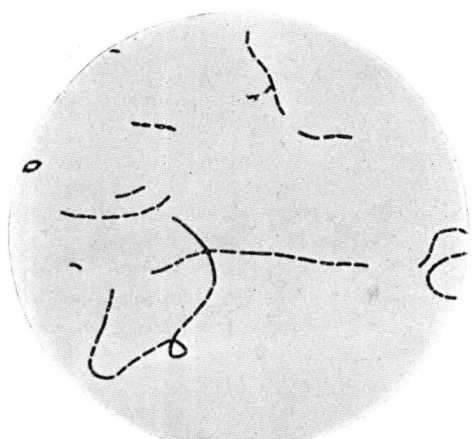

Fig. 132.—Döderlein's bacillus.
From an agar culture, 48 hours, 37° C. (× 1000).

respectively, but since the particular type of colony formed seems to depend largely on environmental conditions, and since there seems to be little relationship between the colonial type and any other important characteristic of the organisms, it is probably wiser to refrain from the use of terms that have now come to possess a wider connotation. A very characteristic appearance is the turbidity or milkiness of the agar produced in shake plates or tubes ; it is a variable characteristic however, and has little or no differentiating value amongst the members of the group. Growth in gelatin is either poor or absent ; liquefaction never occurs.

Resistance and Methods of Isolation from Natural Sources.—The organisms are not particularly resistant to heat, and are generally destroyed by an exposure to 60° C. for half an hour. One of their most striking features, which gives to them the names acidophilic, acid-resisting, or aciduric, is their ability to survive in concentrations of acid that usually prove fatal to other non-sporing bacteria. It is this characteristic that is generally made use of in their isolation. One of the most successful methods is to incubate the material for 1 to 3 days in 0·5 per cent.

acetic acid broth, and subsequently to plate on 2 per cent. glucose agar. McIntosh and his co-workers (1922) recommend incubating the material in broth of pH 3·5 for 24 hours, then subculturing into a series of broth tubes varying in pH from 3·0 to 4·5, and plating after a further 24 hours. Kendall (1910) made three consecutive subcultures in acid broth, and plated the last on dextrose agar containing 0·2 per cent. sodium oleate, which is said to improve the growth. The acid may be added to the tubes directly, or the organisms may be seeded into a medium containing a fermentable carbohydrate; the acid produced in this medium is usually sufficient to kill off most other organisms. Thus Cruickshank (1925) recommends, for the isolation of *L. bifidus*, inoculating the fæces into a deep tube containing 20 c.c. of 1 per cent. glucose or lactose broth together with a small piece of fresh sterile rabbit kidney; the kidney is added to promote anaerobiosis, but does not appear to be essential; the medium is covered with a vaseline seal. The culture is incubated for about a week at 37° C. and then plated on to 1 per cent. glucose agar or Loeffler's serum, which is incubated aerobically and anaerobically. After 48 hours on the anaerobic plates, greyish pinhead colonies appear. The only other organism that is likely to develop under these conditions is the enterococcus, which forms larger whitish colonies. Another method that may be employed for the isolation of the acid-resistant bacteria is the use of Veillon tubes (Veillon and Zuber 1898, Rettger and Cheplin 1921), containing 2 per cent. glucose agar or whey agar; the different organisms adapt themselves to the varying oxygen pressure in the medium, and form characteristic colonies, which may be picked off with ease. The tomato broth medium described by Kulp (1927) has given very favourable results; if the primary cultures are plated on tomato agar, single colony isolations are frequently successful. The presence of added CO_2 seems to be beneficial for growth (Kulp 1926, Cruickshank 1934).

Metabolism.—Most of the members are microaerophilic or facultative anaerobes. For their isolation fairly strict anaerobic conditions are often, though not always, necessary; but after one or two subcultures they can almost invariably be brought to grow aerobically. Peroxide is produced without, or with only very small quantities, of catalase. This probably accounts for the poor viability of the organisms in media not maintaining a low oxidation-reduction potential. According to Curran, Rogers, and Whittier (1933), the optimum growth temperature is 37°–40° C.; the range of growth with most strains is 25°–46° C., but certain strains, particularly those of the *casei* type, may grow even at 10° C. Though some of the earlier workers (Rodella 1901) stated that an alkaline was preferable to an acid medium, later workers (Morishita 1929, Weiss and Rettger 1934, Longsworth and MacInnes 1935) have found that both growth and acid production occur best in the neighbourhood of pH 6·0, the optimal range being about pH 5·4–6·8. No pigment is produced, but deep colonies in glucose agar often develop a brownish centre, and the agar itself is frequently clouded. Hæmolysin production is variable and has not been studied fully. No toxins are formed. The organisms have very little effect on proteins, and growth on protein media without carbohydrates is very poor. Peterson, Pruess and Fred (1928) have found that they do possess some proteolytic action, as judged by the quantitative estimation of non-protein and amino-acid nitrogen, but according to Kendall and Haner (1924*a*, *b*) this is very slight; no indole, scatole, or histamine is formed.

On the other hand they are very active in fermenting carbohydrates. The acid produced from lactose is partly fixed, consisting of lævo- or dextro-rotatory or inactive lactic acid, and partly volatile, consisting of formic, acetic, and butyric acids in the ratio of 6 : 3 : 1 (Curran, Rogers and Whittier 1933). The proportion of volatile to fixed acids varies with different strains from about 4–20 per cent. Malic acid is said to be produced by *L. odontolyticus* in greater quantity than lactic acid (McIntosh *et al.* 1924). Gas production is not detectable by the ordinary Durham fermentation tube, except with *L. acidophil-aerogenes* (Torrey and Rahe 1915), which produces 4–6 volumes of H_2 to 1 of CO_2. Curran, Rogers, and Whittier (1933), however, have shown that most strains produce small quantities of gas from fermentable carbohydrates. The formation of lactic acid from glucose does not require the presence of oxygen or lead to the production of CO_2. Consequently CO_2 is not a major product of fermentation with most strains. An exception to this rule is furnished by *L. pentoaceticus*, which is able to oxidize lactic to acetic acid (Hunt 1933). In this process one molecule of O_2 is used and one molecule of CO_2 produced. Hence CO_2 constitutes a more important product of fermentation with this organism than with the other members of the group. The usual products of fermentation, such as alcohol, acetone, acetyl methyl carbinol, and butylene glycol, are not formed (Bertrand and Duchacek 1909). For all practical purposes the organisms may be considered as of the obligatory saccharolytic type.

Biochemical.—There is considerable variation in the sugars fermented. Glucose and lactose are fermented by practically all strains, maltose and sucrose by a high proportion, mannitol, salicin, and raffinose by a small proportion, while dextrin, inulin, dulcitol, and starch are rarely fermented. Strains of *L. bifidus* are said, however, to ferment inulin (Weiss and Rettger 1934), and strains isolated from soil and grain are said not to ferment lactose (Hunt and Rettger 1930). Both these statements await confirmation. *L. pentoaceticus*, the organism described by Fred, Peterson, and Davenport (1919) from silage, sauerkraut, and manure, is peculiar in its ability to ferment xylose. According to Weinstein and Rettger (1932), it is further distinguished from most of the other members of the group by its failure to ferment lactose or to curdle milk. Cruickshank (1934) says that Döderlein's bacillus ferments glycogen with the production of lactic acid in a few days, while strains of *acidophilus*, *odontolyticus*, and *bifidus* take 7–10 days to ferment it ; *bulgaricus* does not ferment it at all. It is very doubtful whether the reactions of individual species and strains are constant ; according to some authors they are not (McIntosh *et al.* 1924, Day and Gibbs 1928). Most, but not all, the members produce acid in milk, often in sufficient quantity to precipitate the casein in the form of a loose clot, which does not contract and express whey ; the litmus is frequently decolorized, especially in the lower part of the tube. The rate at which clotting is produced is of some slight differential significance. White and Avery (1910) divided the acid-resistant organisms obtained from milk into two types ; their Type A produced a large quantity of lactic acid in milk—2·7 to 3·7 per cent. ; their Type B produced a smaller quantity—1·2 to 1·6 per cent. The most active acid producer is *L. bulgaricus* ; the least active *L. bifidus* ; *L. acidophilus* occupies an intermediate position.

Antigenic Structure.—The serological reactions of these organisms have been incompletely studied, and so far no satisfactory classification of the group has been possible by agglutination or absorption. Generally speaking, the members of a single species show a considerable amount of heterogeneity (Kendall and Haner 1924*b*, Lash and Kaplan 1926, Thomas 1928, Howitt 1930). McIntosh and his co-workers (McIntosh *et al.* 1924), however, observed a marked group reaction between members of the *acidophilus* and *acidophilus-odontolyticus* types ; and Cruickshank (1925) and Weiss and Rettger (1934) found a close relationship between *L. bifidus* and *L. acidophilus.* Thomas (1928) found that Döderlein's bacillus had some relation to *L. acidophilus,* but none to *L. bulgaricus.*

Pathogenicity.—None of the members appear to be pathogenic to man or animals. It is true that in fermentative diarrhœa acid-resisting bacteria may be present in large numbers in the stools, but whether they are responsible for initiating the diarrhœa, or whether they merely take advantage of the abnormal conditions prevailing in the intestine to multiply abundantly, is not clear. Their numbers increase in the intestine when lactose or dextrin are given in considerable quantities in the diet (Rettger and Cheplin 1921, Cannon and McNease 1923) ; and because, under these conditions, they tend to replace the proteolytic flora, their administration along with these sugars has been advocated for therapeutic purposes. McIntosh, James, and Lazarus-Barlow (1922, 1924) have brought evidence to suggest that they may be responsible for dental caries ; two varieties, known as *L. odontolyticus* I and II, were isolated from carious teeth. In glucose broth cultures these organisms produced a final pH of 2·2 to 3·4 ; and it was found that teeth left in these cultures gradually became decalcified, the change being evident in 7 weeks. The repeated inoculation intravenously of very large doses of lactobacilli into rabbits is said to be followed by the development of joint lesions. A mucopurulent exudate is found in the joints, and cultures can be obtained for a week after the last inoculation (Howitt and van Meter 1930). It is doubtful, however, whether the organisms actually multiply within the tissues under these conditions.

CLASSIFICATION

At the present stage of inquiry no satisfactory classification of these organisms is possible. Classification on morphological and colonial appearances is unsatisfactory, because both of these characters are subject to considerable variation. Rahe (1914, 1915) utilizes the fermentation reactions for classification, but it is extremely doubtful whether these are sufficiently constant to serve this purpose. Albus (1928) considers that a classification may be based on the surface tension requirements of the different members, but Day and Gibbs (1928) and Curran, Rogers, and Whittier (1933) deny that this method is of any value.

The most serious attempt to classify the *Lactobacilli* is undoubtedly that made by Curran, Rogers, and Whittier (1933). As the result of a very careful study, particularly of their metabolic characteristics, these workers were able to divide 103 strains of varied origin into three groups. Group A strains produced inactive lactic acid, *i.e.,* equal quantities of dextro- and lævo-acid, from whey, failed to grow above 43°–46° C. or as low as 20° C., fermented raffinose but not mannitol, and on agar plates formed either the fuzzy (X) type of colony, or a mixture of fuzzy and compact (Y) types. As a rule they gave rise to more CO_2 and a larger proportion of volatile to fixed acids, and grew in higher concentrations of phenol and indole (see Kulp 1929), than the members of the second group. Group B strains produced an excess of dextro-lactic acid, grew as high as 43°–50° C. and as low as 10°–15° C., fermented mannitol but not raffinose, and formed either the compact (Y) type of colony, or a mixture of compact and fuzzy (X) types. They were less active than Group A strains in the production of volatile acids and CO_2, and were inhibited by relatively dilute solutions of phenol and indole. Group C strains differed from Group A in growing at 20° C. and in a number of minor particulars. Of the 103 strains, Group A comprised 58, Group B 30, and Group C 15. With regard to their source of origin, about three-quarters of the intestinal strains belonged to Group A, while over half of the dental strains belonged to Group B. Group A probably represented the typical *L. acidophilus*; Group B probably included *L. bulgaricus* and *L. casei*; while Group C comprised a heterogeneous collection of strains whose identity was doubtful, and whose classification into one group was largely a matter of temporary convenience.

As has frequently happened with other groups, several members have been accredited with specific names without an adequate description being given of them. Moreover it seems probable that some species that have been called by different names are in reality identical. It seems likely that Döderlein's bacillus, for example, is the same as *L. acidophilus* (Heinemann and Ecker 1916, Thomas 1928), and for that reason we have not given a separate description of it. Similarly, according to Schlirf (1926), Goadby's *B. necrodentalis* is identical with *L. acidophilus*. It is doubtful whether the Boas-Oppler bacillus is a separate species ; it may quite well be identical with, or a variety of, *L. acidophilus* (Heinemann and Ecker 1916). *L. bulgaricus* is quite possibly the same as the type species *L. caucasicus*, of which no adequate description has ever been given (White and Avery 1910). Cruickshank (1925) suggests that *L. exilis* is the aerobic phase of *L. bifidus* ; but from Tissier's (1900) original description this seems doubtful. Weiss and Rettger (1934) were unable to detect any greater difference between strains of *L. bifidus* and *L. acidophilus* than existed between the individual strains themselves, and they would therefore regard *L. bifidus* as a variant of the species of which *L. acidophilus* is the central type. The organisms described by McIntosh and his colleagues as *L. odontolyticus* I and II have received considerable study. Morishita (1929), Rosebury, Linton, and Buchbinder (1929), Howitt (1930), and Hadley, Bunting, and Delves (1930) have failed to find any clear distinction between oral and intestinal strains of *L. acidophilus*, while Curran, Rogers, and Whittier (1933), on the other hand, as the result of a very careful study conclude that the lactobacilli in carious teeth are not of one species and are not usually of the *acidophilus* type. For this reason we shall describe the *odontolyticus* strains separately from *L. acidophilus*.

A number of lactic-acid-forming bacilli were isolated from cheese by von Freudenreich and Thöni (1903), and named *Bacillus casei* by Orla-Jensen (1904). These organisms have not been fully described, and we do not propose to deal with them further here. They are frequently found in milk (Sherman and Stark 1927).

With regard to the nomenclature of this group, the term " acid-resisting " is frequently employed, and, though correct, it is open to the objection that it may cause confusion with the acid-fast bacilli. The term " acidophilic " is justifiable, but is unfortunately a hybrid. Probably Kendall's (1910) term " aciduric " (able to endure acid), which has the advantages of not being a hybrid, of not being hyphenated, and of being technically correct, is the best one to employ.

Workers studying this group may consult the annotated bibliography on *L. acidophilus* drawn up by Frost and Hankinson (1931). Those interested in the chemical constitution of this organism are referred to a series of papers by Crowder and Anderson (1932, 1934*a*, *b*).

TABLE XLIV

| | Morphology in Culture. | Surface Colonies on Tomato Agar. | Growth at 20° C. | Acid production in | | Type of Lactic Acid produced. | Clotting of Milk at 37° C. | Growth in presence of 1/250–1/400 Phenol and 1/1100–1/1900 Indole. |
				Mannitol.	Raffinose.			
L. acidophilus Group A	Large stumpy bacillus, often in chains and palisades; pleomorphic	Fuzzy, or fuzzy and compact	−	−	+	Inactive	1–3 days with firm curd. Litmus reduced.	+
L. acidophilus Group B probably includes *L. bulgaricus* and *L. casei*	Variable size, often stout; frequently in chains; pleomorphic	Compact, or compact and fuzzy	+[1]	+	−	Inactive and dextro-rotatory	1–3 days with firm curd. Litmus reduced.	−
L. bifidus	More delicate bacillus with slightly pointed ends; rarely in chains; pleomorphic	Compact or intermediate	⧺	−	+	?	Usually several days. Loose or irregular curd.	?
L. acidophil-aerogenes .	Rather long bacillus, slenderer than *L. bulgaricus*; often arranged in long, curved chains	Compact or fuzzy	?	−	+	?	Little or no growth; some strains produce late clotting.	?

[1] *L. bulgaricus* is generally stated not to grow at 20° C, but it is nevertheless included by Curran, Rogers, and Whittier (1933) in their Group B.

While emphasizing again the impossibility of classifying these organisms satisfactorily at present, we give a differential table of some of the main species, pointing out, however, that it is to be used only as a very rough indication of the characteristics of these organisms, Table XLIV, p. 585.

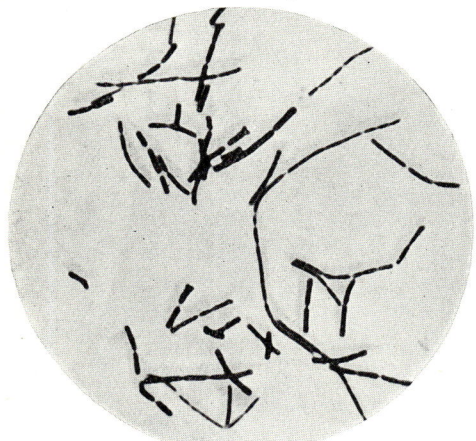

FIG. 133.—*Lactobacillus acidophilus.*
From an agar culture, 48 hours, 37° C. (× 1000).

Lactobacillus acidophilus

Synonyms.—Probably identical with Döderlein's bacillus, which is sometimes called *B. vaginalis* or *B. crassus.*

Isolation.—Isolated by Moro (1900*b*) in 1900 from the fæces of breast-fed infants.

Habitat.—Found in milk; the fæces of bottle-fed infants, and often of adults; the fæces of nearly all mammalia, and of many fish and invertebrates; in saliva and carious teeth.

Morphology.—In fæces it is a large stumpy bacillus of variable length and fairly constant breadth, generally straight, with parallel sides and rounded ends. On agar plate cultures, after 48 hours at 37° C., it forms fairly thick rods, 1–3 μ long by 1·0 μ broad, straight or slightly curved, with parallel sides and rounded or slightly truncated ends; arranged singly, in pairs end-to-end, in short chains, and in palisades. On glucose agar longer chains and filamentous forms are common. In broth and

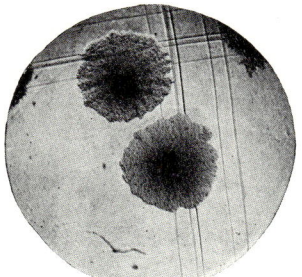

FIG. 134.—*Lactobacillus acidophilus.*

Surface colony on agar, 4 days, 37° C., showing differentiation (× 8).

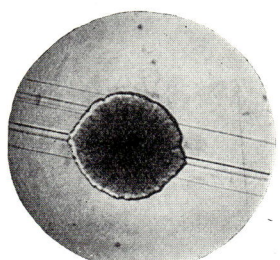

FIG. 135.—*Lactobacillus acidophilus.*

Surface colony on agar, 4 days, 37° C. (× 8).

litmus milk cultures the bacilli are thinner, 0·6–0·8 μ broad. Considerable variation in morphology on artificial media; forms with markedly curved extremities, curled forms, forms with bulbous extremities, clubbed forms, filamentous forms, and large swollen oval forms in pairs are not uncommon. Under anaerobic conditions long curved filamentous forms, often with pointed, swollen, or spatulate ends are seen. Non-motile. Gram-positive. Staining is uniform in young cultures, but irregularly stained, bipolar-stained, and beaded forms are met with in old cultures. Non-acid-fast.

Agar Plates.—Great variability in colonial appearance. After 48 hours at 37° C. one of the commonest is a small, irregularly round, raised, colourless, transparent colony, about 0·5 mm. in diameter, of coarsely frosted-glass structure, with a dull uneven relief-map-like surface and a fimbriate or curled edge ; later, differentiation occurs into a thicker darker centre, and a thinner periphery consisting of delicately curled and branched hair-like streamers—not unlike a colony of *Cl. tetani.* Other forms are feathery colonies, rosette-like colonies, smooth colonies with entire or slightly fimbriate edges, and opaque striated colonies.

Agar Slope.—24 *hours*, 37° C. Poor filiform growth of small transparent granular colonies, 0·25 to 0·5 mm. in diameter. Sometimes after a few days a thick greyish-yellow secondary growth occurs, having a contoured surface, and an edge from which thin translucent branching tufts, looking like sea-anemones, project.

2 per cent. Glucose Agar Shake.—48 *hours*, 37° C. Good growth throughout tube of small, spherical, lenticular, or lobulated colonies, 0·25 mm. in diameter, having an entire edge (Y type), or of small irregular spherical colonies with a fuzzy, filamentous border (X type). The agar is clouded and has an almost milky look. After a week the colonies are 0·5 mm. in diameter, are porcelain-white in colour, and look like colonies of moulds.

Gelatin Stab.—7 *days*, 22° C. Very poor greyish-white filiform growth ; no surface growth ; no liquefaction.

Broth.—48 *hours*, 37° C. Poor to moderate growth with a very slight, only just perceptible turbidity, and a moderate flocculo-granular deposit disintegrating to some extent on shaking ; sometimes the deposit sticks to the walls of the tube.

2 per cent. Glucose Broth.—Growth is better than in plain broth. Sometimes after a week an enormous loose flocculent deposit forms, filling the lowest 1 cm. of the tube ; it disintegrates partly on shaking, producing a dense turbidity.

Potato.—No growth.

Horse Blood Agar Plates.—48 *hours*, 37° C. Small discrete colonies, similar to those on agar. No hæmolysis.

Glucose Blood Liver Agar Plates.—48 *hours*, 37° C. Flat, dingy colonies with a serrated edge.

MacConkey Plate.—Results discrepant. Cruickshank (1931) says that all strains grow on this medium, but this has not been our own experience.

Resistance.—Not particularly resistant. Killed by moist heat at 56° C. in 30 minutes. Very resistant to acids, living for 1 to 3 days in broth containing 0·5–1·0 per cent. acetic or lactic acid. Glucose broth cultures at 37° C. remain viable for about a fortnight.

Metabolism.—Often microaerophilic on first isolation. Grows better under aerobic than anaerobic conditions. Grows slightly or not at all at 20° C. ; optimum temperature for growth 37° C. Forms no pigment and no toxin. Does not lyse horse blood. Growth is improved by glucose and by whey, but not by blood serum. Grows best at pH 6·0, but will grow even at pH 5·0.

Biochemical.—Sugar reactions variable. Produces acid in glucose and in lactose ; often in maltose and sucrose ; sometimes in mannitol, salicin, and raffinose ; less frequently in other sugars. L.M. acid and clot in 24 to 48 hours ; the clot is really an acid precipitate, and does not contract ; on shaking it breaks up into flocculent masses ; the litmus is at first reduced at the bottom of the tube only, but later the decolorization spreads upwards. Indole negative. M.R. positive. V.P. negative. Nitrates reduced slightly or not at all. Catalase very weak positive. H_2S negative. NH_3 negative.

Antigenic Structure.—Not studied fully. By agglutination numerous groups can be made out, having little affinity with each other. Some group relationship to *L. bifidus.*

Pathogenicity.—Non-pathogenic to man or to laboratory animals.

Lactobacillus odontolyticus I

Isolation.—Isolated by McIntosh, James, and Lazarus-Barlow in 1922 from carious teeth and from saliva, and called *B. acidophilus odontolyticus* I.

Morphology.—Thin bacillus, 2–3 μ long by 0·75 μ broad, occurring singly, in pairs, or chains, and in palisades. Non-motile. Gram-positive.

Agar Plates.—48 *hours*, 37° C. Small, round, greyish, opaque colonies, 0·6–1·0 mm. in diameter, with a finely granular appearance and an entire edge. On serum agar the colonies are larger—up to 2 mm. in diameter.

Gelatin Stab.—Grows to the bottom. No liquefaction.

Gelatin Agar Shake.—Deep colonies are roughly biconvex or tam-o'-shanter-shaped.

Broth.—Uniform turbidity ; sometimes the growth settles to the bottom.

Resistance.—Not particularly resistant. Killed by 56° C. in 25 minutes, and by 2 per cent. phenol in 7½ minutes. Highly resistant to acids ; will withstand incubation for 24 hours at 37° C. in broth of pH 3·5. No growth above pH 9·1–9·6.

Metabolism.—Aerobe and facultative anaerobe.

Biochemical.—Sugar reactions variable. Usually produces acid in glucose, maltose, salicin and lactose, but not in sucrose, dextrin, dulcitol, or raffinose. L.M. acid and clot in 2 to 3 days ; lower ⅔ of tube decolorized. Indole negative. Final pH in glucose broth cultures is about pH 2·75. Chief acid formed is malic acid ; lactic acid is formed in only a very small amount. Methyl-red positive. Voges-Proskauer negative. Nitrates not reduced. Catalase, very slight positive. NH₃ negative.

Antigenic Structure.—Appears to be fairly homogeneous, and to be closely related to *L. odontolyticus* II, and to *L. acidophilus*.

Pathogenicity.—Suspected of being responsible for production of dental caries. Non-pathogenic to laboratory animals.

Lactobacillus odontolyticus II

Isolation.—Isolated by McIntosh, James, and Lazarus-Barlow in 1922 from carious teeth and from saliva, and called *B. acidophilus odontolyticus* II.

Morphology.—Rather short bacillus, 1–2 μ long by 0·5 μ broad, usually arranged in short chains. Often very pleomorphic, coccal forms being mixed with bacillary forms in the same chain ; may closely resemble a streptococcus. Non-motile. Gram-positive.

Cultural Reactions.—Similar to *odontolyticus* I.

Resistance and Metabolism.—Similar to *odontolyticus* I.

Biochemical.—Variable sugar reactions. 7 out of 18 strains produced acid in glucose, lactose, and sucrose. L.M. Some strains produce acid and clot, others have no action on it. Indole negative.

Antigenic Structure.—Closely allied to *odontolyticus* I and to *L. acidophilus*.

Pathogenicity.—Like *odontolyticus* I.

Lactobacillus acidophil-aerogenes

Isolation.—By Torrey and Rahe in 1915 from the fæces of human beings, sheep, and hens.

Morphology.—Variable morphology. Fairly large bacilli, 1·5–11·5 μ long by 0·8 μ broad, but generally slenderer than *L. bulgaricus* ; often arranged in long, curved strings. Non-motile. Gram-positive. Stain uniformly with Loeffler's methylene blue.

Cultural Reactions.—On glucose oleate agar it forms either (1) small, round or navicular, opaque, whitish colonies surrounded by an areola of turbid agar : or (2) tiny, round, translucent, greyish colonies with a finely erose edge ; on microscopic examination these appear typically rhizoid. In glucose broth a growth forms adherent to the bottom and sides of the tube ; on shaking this gives rise to a dense turbidity.

Resistance.—Highly resistant to acids ; will remain alive in a glucose broth culture at 37° C. for 1 week.

Biochemical.—Produces acid and gas in glucose, maltose, lactose, sucrose, and raffinose. The gas ratio is $4H_2/1CO_2$ or $6H_2/1CO_2$. L.M. grows poorly or not at all ; some strains produce partial clotting in 2 to 3 weeks.

Antigenic Structure.—Appears to be more homogeneous than the non-gas-forming group.

Lactobacillus bifidus

Isolation.—Isolated by Tissier in 1900 from the fæces of breast-fed infants.

Habitat.—Common in the fæces of breast-fed, and much less common in those of bottle-fed infants. Sometimes present in the fæces of adults and of animals. In breast-fed infants during the first few weeks of life it may form 99 per cent. of the fæcal flora.

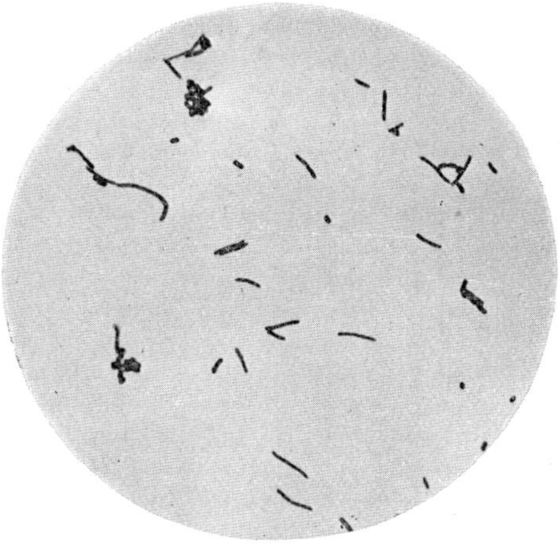

Morphology.—In fæces it is a delicate bacillus, about 4 μ long and 0·7 μ broad, with tapering pointed ends ; arranged in pairs end-to-end, with the distal ends pointed and the proximal ends swollen ; they generally lie parallel to one another, rarely intertwined.

FIG. 136.—*Lactobacillus bifidus.*
From a glucose agar culture, 7 days, 37° C. ($\times$ 1000).

Two or three bacilli often radiate from a single point, forming a Y-shaped structure, simulating branching ; clubbed forms and forms ending in knobs are not uncommon. Often arranged in palisades or Chinese letters. General appearance is not unlike a diphtheroid bacillus. In young cultures bacilli with slightly pointed ends of varying length, arranged singly or in pairs end-to-end, are usual. In older cultures longer clubbed forms, geniculate forms, bifid forms showing false branching, forms ending in knobs, forms with lateral buds, bladder forms, candle-flame forms, and filamentous forms may appear. Both in fæces and in culture there is a striking pleomorphism. The absence of chain formation is noteworthy. Non-motile. In young cultures staining is fairly uniform, but in older cultures and in fæces irregular, granular, and beaded staining are common. Gram-positive in young cultures ; later Gram-negative forms appear. Non-acid-fast.

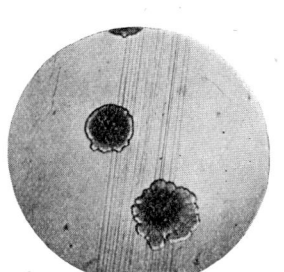

FIG. 137.—*Lactobacillus bifidus.*

Surface colonies on glucose agar, 6 days, 37° C. ($\times$ 8).

Agar Plate.—No growth.

Glucose Agar Plate.—48 *hours*, 37° C. Small round low convex colonies, 0·5 mm. in diameter, showing under the microscope a delicately granular structure, a brownish opaque centre, a thinner translucent periphery, and a finely crenated edge (Fig. 137).

Glucose Agar Shake Tubes.—3 *days*, 37° C. Small, greyish-brown, lenticular or ovoid colonies, 1–2 mm. in diameter, extending up to within about 3 cm. of the surface, where they may form a ring. At first the edge of the colony is entire, but after 4 or 5 days a lateral projection or bud often develops from one of the faces.

Gelatin Shake.—If incubated at 37° C. for 24 hours, and then left at room temperature for some days, fine discrete colonies appear ; no liquefaction.

Broth.—24 *hours,* 37° *C.* Granular turbidity.

Glucose Broth.—24 *hours,* 37° *C.* More abundant growth ; in 3 or 4 days the organisms fall to the bottom of the tube, producing an abundant loose flocculo-granular deposit, easily disintegrated on shaking.

Blood Agar.—White colonies surrounded by a greenish halo of α-hæmolysis.

Glucose Blood Liver Agar Plates.—48 *hours,* 37° *C.* Raised, globular, opaque colonies, 1–3 mm. in diameter, buff to reddish-brown in colour.

Resistance.—Cultures live for about a month at room temperature. Broth cultures are killed by heat at 55° C. in half an hour, and at 70° C. in 5 minutes. Is resistant to acids ; will withstand 0·5–1·0 per cent. acetic or lactic acid in broth for 2 to 3 days.

Metabolism.—Strict anaerobe on first isolation ; later it may be grown in air. Very slight or no growth at 20° C. ; optimum temperature 37° C. No pigment or toxin formed. α-hæmolysis on blood agar. Growth improved by glucose, serum, and blood.

Biochemical.—Sugar reactions variable. Produces acid in glucose, maltose, inulin, and generally in lactose, sucrose, salicin, and raffinose ; sometimes in mannitol and dextrin ; occasionally in dulcitol. Produces mainly lactic acid. L.M. grows well and produces an acid clot. Indole negative. Methyl-red positive. Voges-Proskauer negative. Nitrates very slight reduction, or none at all. Catalase very slight positive. NH_3 slight production or none at all.

Antigenic Structure.—Not fully worked out. By agglutination they appear to fall into more than one group. Some relationship to *L. acidophilus.*

Pathogenicity.—Non-pathogenic to man and laboratory animals.

Lactobacillus bulgaricus

Synonyms.—Massol's bacillus. Probably identical with *L. caucasicus.*

Isolation.—Isolated by Grigoroff in 1905 from kissélo-mléko, the fermented milk of Bulgaria ; described originally as " Bacillus A."

Habitat.—Found in milk, particularly the fermented milks of Bulgaria, Turkey, Egypt, and Sardinia.

Morphology.—Large rods, 2–20 μ long and about 1 μ broad, with parallel sides and slightly rounded ends ; arranged singly or in short chains. Non-motile. Gram-positive. Two morphological types are described by White and Avery (1910) in whey. Type A consists of chains of short bacilli with oval or reniform nodules extruding from the cell substance ; the bacilli stain uniformly ; Type B forms long bacilli arranged singly, having spherical bodies attached to the cell wall, not stemmed nodules as in A ; the bacilli show intense granular staining with Loeffler's methylene blue or Neisser's stain.

Agar Plate.—No growth.

Whey Agar Plate.—Usual type of colony is irregularly round, greyish-white, 0·5–1·5 mm. in diameter, of loose curled structure with a streaming filamentous edge ; microscopically these colonies are typically rhizoid. Sometimes, especially in old laboratory cultures, a rounder, more regular colony is formed, with a smooth or slightly fissured surface and an entire edge.

Whey Agar Shake Tubes.—Deep colonies are lenticular or umbilicated, whitish in colour, and 1 mm. in diameter.

Whey Agar Stab.—Filiform growth, beaded, later with horizontal ramifications ; no surface growth ; medium is clouded.

Gelatin.—Not liquefied.

2 per cent. Glucose Broth.—Heavy uniform turbidity.

Potato.—No growth.

Resistance.—Killed by moist heat at 60° C. in 1 hour. Is very resistant to acids ; glucose broth cultures at 37° C. remain viable for about 6 days.

Metabolism.—Facultative anaerobe ; is said by some authors to prefer anaerobic conditions. No growth at 15° C. ; grows very slightly at 25° C. ; growth is poor under 35° C. ; optimum temperature for growth is 44–45° C. No pigment, toxin, or hæmolysin formed. Is resistant to acids, but grows best in a neutral or slightly alkaline medium. Difficult to cultivate ; growth in most media is feeble, and when freshly isolated it will grow only on media containing whey or malt, or in milk.

Biochemical.—Sugar reactions described differently by different authors. Is generally considered to produce acid in glucose, lactose, and sometimes lævulose, but not in maltose, sucrose, mannitol, or raffinose. Lactic acid is the chief acid formed from fermentable carbohydrates. L.M. acid and coagulation in 18 hours at 37° C. ; the clot does not contract. Indole negative. White and Avery's Type A in milk produces 2·7–3·7 per cent. of lactic acid of the inactive variety ; Type B produces only 1·2–1·6 per cent. of lactic acid, of the lævo-rotatory variety.

Antigenic Structure.—Nothing known.

Pathogenicity.—Non-pathogenic to man and animals.

Grigoroff's Bacillus C.—Isolated from kissélo-mléko, the fermented milk of Bulgaria, by Grigoroff in 1905. Is a streptobacillus forming short rods arranged in chains of four to twenty members. Gram-positive. Culturally it resembles *L. bulgaricus*, but is more heat resistant, requiring an exposure of 1 hour at 70° C. to kill it. Produces acid in glucose, lævulose, lactose, sucrose, and glycerol, but not in maltose, mannitol, or dulcitol. Produces acid and clot in milk, the acid being inactive lactic acid.

Lactobacillus exilis.—Isolated by Tissier in 1900 from the fæces of children on milk or mixed diets. It is a thin, straight, slender bacillus, arranged singly, in pairs, or in chains of four or five elements ; non-pleomorphic. Non-motile. Gram-positive. On agar plates it forms very tiny bluish colonies with entire edges in 48 hours, no bigger than the point of a needle. On glucose agar they may reach 0·5 mm. in diameter. In broth there is a slight filamentous deposit without turbidity. No growth in gelatin. In deep glucose agar small, oval, regular colonies with entire edges are formed throughout the tube. Cultures die out in 10 to 15 days. Grows at 20° C., but better at 37° C. Grows both aerobically and anaerobically. Milk is coagulated in 8 to 10 days ; there is no retraction of the clot. Non-pathogenic for mice. Differs from *L. acidophilus* in being slender and constant in morphology, in forming small regular colonies in agar shake cultures, and in being less resistant to acid. Cruickshank (1925) regards *L. exilis* as probably the aerobic phase of *L. bifidus*.

The Boas-Oppler Bacillus.—Observed microscopically in the stomach contents of patients with gastric carcinoma by Oppler in 1895, working in Boas' clinic in Berlin. He did not succeed in cultivating it. In stomach contents it occurs as a rather slender bacillus, arranged in long threads and zigzags ; the bacilli may be so numerous as to fill every space between the other elements in the field. Has since been isolated by Heinemann and Ecker (1916) from the stomach contents of patients with gastritis, gastric ulcer, carcinoma, and pernicious anæmia. It probably occurs in moderate numbers in normal gastric juice. In culture the organism is a large, rather slender bacillus, showing granular staining. Gram-positive. Forms compact colonies as a rule, but colonies with woolly edges have been described. Does not ferment maltose. Produces acid in milk. Is of the low acid-producing type—White and Avery's Type B.

REFERENCES

ALBUS, W. R. (1928) *J. Bact.*, **16**, 197.
BERTRAND, G. and DUCHACEK, F. (1909) *Ann. Inst. Pasteur*, **23**, 402.
CANNON, P. R. and McNEASE, B. W. (1923) *J. infect. Dis.*, **32**, 175.
COHENDY, M. (1906) *C. R. Soc. Biol.*, **58**, 558.
CROWDER, J. A. and ANDERSON, R. J. (1932) *J. biol. Chem.*, **97**, 393 ; (1934*a*) *Ibid.*, **104**, 399 ; (1934*b*) *Ibid.*, **104**, 487.

CRUICKSHANK, R. (1925) *J. Hyg., Camb.*, **24,** 241 ; (1931) *J. Hyg., Camb.*, **31,** 375 ; (1934) *J. Path. Bact.*, **39,** 213.
CURRAN, H. R., ROGERS, L. A., and WHITTIER, E. O. (1933) *J. Bact.*, **25,** 595.
DAY, A. A. and GIBBS, W. M. (1928) *J. infect. Dis.*, **43,** 97.
DÖDERLEIN. (1892) " Das Scheidensekret und seine Bedeutung für das Puerperalfieber." Leipzig.
FINKELSTEIN, H. (1900) *Dtsch. med. Wschr.*, **26,** 263.
FRED, E. B., PETERSON, W. H., and DAVENPORT, A. (1919) *J. biol. Chem.*, **39,** 347.
FREUDENREICH, E. VON and THÖNI, J. (1903) *Zbl. Bakt.*, IIte Abt., **10,** 305, 340.
FROST, W. D. and HANKINSON, H. (1931) " Lactobacillus acidophilus." Davis-Greene Corp., Milton, Wis.
GRIGOROFF, S. (1905) *Rev. med. Suisse rom.*, **25,** 714.
HADLEY, F. P., BUNTING, R. W., and DELVES, E. A. (1930) *J. Amer. dent. Ass.*, **17,** 2041.
HEINEMANN, P. G. and ECKER, E. E. (1916) *J. Bact.*, **1,** 435.
HEINEMANN, P. G. and HEFFERAN, M. (1909) *J. infect. Dis.*, **6,** 304.
HOWITT, B. (1930) *J. infect. Dis.*, **46,** 351.
HOWITT, B. and METER, M. VAN. (1930) *J. infect. Dis.*, **46,** 368.
HUNT, G. A. (1933) *J. Bact.*, **26,** 341.
HUNT, G. A. and RETTGER, L. F. (1930) *J. Bact.*, **20,** 61.
KENDALL, A. I. (1910) *J. med. Res.*, **22,** 153.
KENDALL, A. I. and HANER, R. C. (1924a) *J. infect. Dis.*, **35,** 77 ; (1924b) *Ibid.*, **35,** 89.
KERN. (1881) *Bull. Soc. Nat. Moscou.* No. 3.
KULP, W. L. (1926) *Science*, **64,** 304 ; (1927) *Ibid.*, **66,** 512 ; (1929) *J. Bact.*, **17,** 355.
LASH, A. F. and KAPLAN, B. (1926) *J. infect. Dis.*, **38,** 333.
LONGSWORTH, L. G. and MACINNES, D. A. (1935) *J. Bact.*, **29,** 595.
MCINTOSH, J., JAMES, W. W., and LAZARUS-BARLOW, P. (1922) *Brit. J. exp. Path.*, **3,** 138 ; (1924) *Ibid.*, **5,** 175.
MERESHKOWSKY, S. S. (1905) *Zbl. Bakt.*, **39,** 380, 584, 696 ; (1906) *Ibid.*, **40,** 118.
MORISHITA, T. (1929) *J. Bact.*, **18,** 181.
MORO, E. (1900a) *Jb. Kinderheilk.*, **52,** 38 ; (1900b) *Wien. klin. Wschr.*, **13,** 114.
OPPLER, B. (1895) *Dtsch. med. Wschr.*, **21,** 73.
ORLA-JENSEN. (1904) *Zbl. Bakt.*, IIte Abt., **13,** 161, 291, 428, 514, 604, 687, 753.
PETERSON, W. H., PRUESS, L. M., and FRED, E. B. (1928) *J. Bact.*, **15,** 165.
PETROW, N. P. (1907) *Zbl. Bakt.*, **43,** 349.
RAHE, A. H. (1914) *J. infect. Dis.*, **15,** 141 ; (1915) *Ibid.*, **16,** 210.
RETTGER, L. F. and CHEPLIN, H. A. (1921) " A Treatise on the Transformation of the Intestinal Flora with Special Reference to the Implantation of Acidophilus." New Haven.
RETTGER, L. F. and HORTON, G. D. (1914) *Zbl. Bakt.*, **73,** 362.
RODELLA, A. (1901) *Zbl. Bakt.*, **29,** 717.
ROSEBURY, T., LINTON, R. W., and BUCHBINDER, L. (1929) *J. Bact.*, **18,** 395.
SCHLIRF, K. (1926) *Zbl. Bakt.*, **97,** 104.
SHERMAN, J. M. and STARK, C. N. (1927) *J. Bact.*, **13,** 60.
THOMAS, S. (1928) *J. infect. Dis.*, **43,** 218.
TISSIER, H. (1900) " Recherches sur la flore intestinale des nourrissons." Paris.
TORREY, J. C. and RAHE, A. H. (1915) *J. infect. Dis.*, **17,** 437.
VEILLON, A. and ZUBER, A. (1898) *Arch. Méd. exp.*, **10,** 517.
WEINSTEIN, L. and RETTGER, L. F. (1932) *J. Bact.*, **24,** 1.
WEISS, J. E. and RETTGER, L. F. (1934) *J. Bact.*, **28,** 501.
WHITE, B. and AVERY, O. T. (1910) *Zbl. Bakt.*, IIte Abt., **25,** 161.

CHAPTER XXIX

PASTEURELLA

DEFINITION.—*Pasteurella.*

Small, Gram-negative, ovoid bacilli, showing bipolar staining. Aerobic and facultatively anaerobic. Powers of carbohydrate fermentation relatively slight; no gas produced. Gelatin not liquefied. Parasites in man and animals, producing characteristic infections.

The type species is *Pasteurella aviseptica.*

Isolation.—The first member of this group was isolated by Kitt in 1878 from an epidemic disease affecting wild hogs and deer. Similar organisms have been isolated from several species of animals and birds suffering from a disease known as hæmorrhagic septicæmia. It has become customary to give a specific name to each organism, corresponding to the animal from which it was derived; thus we have *Past. aviseptica* from fowls, *Past. lepiseptica* from rabbits, *Past. suiseptica* from pigs, *Past. vituliseptica* from calves, *Past. oviseptica* from sheep, *Past. boviseptica* from cattle, and *Past. muriseptica* from mice (not to be confused with *Erysipelothrix muriseptica*). Such a nomenclature is purely arbitrary, and is clearly unjustifiable from the sytematic point of view. The differentiation of species within this group, as in all others, must depend on the detailed study of an adequate sample of strains. Such data as are available do not suggest that the strains from the various animal species, which are liable to natural pasteurellosis, are themselves specifically distinct. In the description which follows we have taken *Past. aviseptica* as a type of the hæmorrhagic septicæmia group; but, as we point out in a later section, it is doubtful whether this name will survive as a designation for a distinct species.

Malassez and Vignal (1883) were apparently the first to describe pseudotuberculosis in the guinea-pig. Several workers recorded the finding of a bacillus in this disease (see Chapter LXX), chief amongst whom was Pfeiffer (1890), who named it *B. pseudotuberculosis.* It is not to be confused with *Corynebacterium pseudotuberculosis ovis*, described by Preisz and Nocard as the cause of pseudotuberculosis in sheep (see Chapter XVI), or with *Corynebacterium pseudotuberculosis murium*, described by Kutscher (1894) and Bongert (1901) as the cause of pseudotuberculosis in mice (see Chapter XVI).

The plague bacillus, *Past. pestis*, was isolated almost simultaneously by Kitasato (1894) and by Yersin (1894), from human patients suffering from plague.

These three organisms resemble each other in so many characters, and appear to be so closely related, that they may well be considered as falling within a single genus.

Morphology and Staining.—All the members of the group are small, ovoid bacilli, with convex sides and rounded ends; there is no characteristic arrange-

593

ment ; they are generally disposed singly, in pairs, in short chains, or in small groups. The most striking feature is their pleomorphism, which is most noticeable with *Past. pestis*, least with the hæmorrhagic septicæmia bacilli. Though well marked on ordinary media, it is best brought out by cultivation on nutrient agar containing 3 per cent. sodium chloride. The growth on this medium is poor ; microscopically, as well as the usual ovoid or short bacillary forms, there will be found shadow forms, filamentous snake-like forms, club forms, large yeast-like globules, and other irregular forms. *Past. pestis and Past. pseudotuberculosis* are larger and more ovoid than *Past. aviseptica*, but their shape varies considerably with the medium on which they are grown. Generally speaking, the bacilli of all three species tend to be ovoid and to show bipolar staining when taken from smooth colonies, and to be more bacillary, filamentous, or pleomorphic, without bipolar staining, when taken from rough colonies, but many exceptions occur.

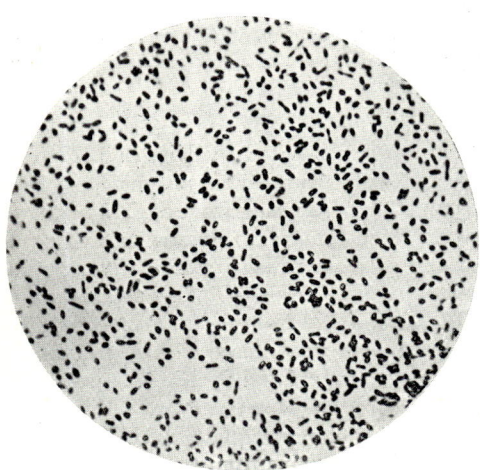

FIG. 138.—*Pasteurella pestis.*
From an agar culture, 3 days, 37° C. (× 1000).

Past. pestis and Past. aviseptica are non-motile. *Past. pseudotuberculosis*, on the other hand, though usually non-motile in cultures incubated at 37° C., is often motile in broth cultures grown for 18 hours at 20–22° C. The possession of motility by this organism is of considerable value in differentiating it from *Past. pestis*, with which it may easily be confused (Arkwright 1927). The value of this test, however, is limited. Weitzenberg (1935), for example, made observations on 25 strains of *pseudotuberculosis*, and found that, though all were motile at room temperature, some were very poorly so, and had to be examined repeatedly before their motility could be definitely established. A negative result, therefore, on a single examination cannot be regarded as conclusive. Both Levinthal (1930) and Weitzenberg (1935) have demonstrated the presence of flagella on *Past. pseudotuberculosis*. The usual number appears to be 1–2, arranged at one or both poles.

In the animal body *Past. pestis* may form a true capsule with a definite edge (Kitasato 1894). More often it is surrounded by a gelatinous envelope of ill-defined capsular material, which is soluble in weak alkalies (Rowland 1914a). The same envelope may be formed in artificial media, especially in 10 per cent. inactivated horse serum broth incubated at 36° C. According to Schütze (1932a), it develops best at 37° C. and not at all at 20° C. By serological methods it can be shown to contain a special antigen distinct from that present in the body of the organism. *Past. aviseptica* may show an indefinite capsule in the animal body. From this capsule Hoffenreich (1928) has extracted a polysaccharide, which, though unable to give rise to precipitins on injection into rabbits, yet reacts to a high titre with a specific precipitating serum.

Bipolar staining is very common and gives to the ovoid bacilli a characteristic appearance. The rod forms often stain irregularly, appearing as granular or barred forms. The reaction to Gram's stain is uniformly negative.

Cultural Characteristics.—Moderate growth occurs on the ordinary media. *Past. pseudotuberculosis* and *Past. aviseptica* grow fairly rapidly, giving a confluent growth on agar after 24 hours ; *Past. pestis*, on the other hand, develops more slowly, and gives a less abundant growth, often barely noticeable after this time. The agar colonies of *Past. pestis* and *Past. pseudotuberculosis* resemble each other in many respects, and are characterized by the effuse, clear or slightly granular, peripheral extension that occurs after 2 to 4 days' growth (Figs. 139, 140) ; the colonies of *Past. pseudotuberculosis*, however, develop more rapidly, and are larger and more granular. With further incubation the central raised part of the colony may assume a ringed or draughtsman-like appearance. On moist agar the colonies, especially of *Past. pestis*, are of viscous consistency, and tend to adhere to the medium (Eastwood and Griffith 1914).

Colonial variants have been described for each member. From *Past. pestis* Gotschlich (1912) obtained round, slimy, undifferentiated colonies, which were

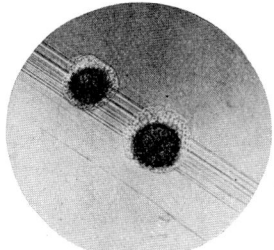

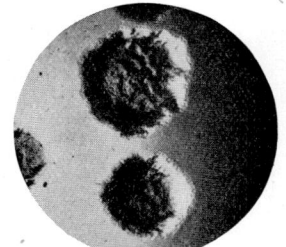

Fig. 139.—*Pasteurella pestis.*

Surface colonies on agar, 3 days, 37° C., showing differentiation, and effuse edge (× 8).

Fig. 140.—*Pasteurella pseudotuberculosis.*

Surface colonies on agar, 24 hours, 37° C., showing irregular granular surface and effuse edge (× 8).

poorly agglutinable and proved avirulent for rats ; they subsequently reverted to the normal virulent type. Variant types, including smooth compact, small-fringed, large irregular, and " sunflower " types, have been described by a number of other workers (see Bessonowa, Sémikoz, and Kotelnikow 1927, Pirie 1929, Burgess 1930, Bessonowa and Lenskaja 1931), but the exact form produced seems to be so influenced by environmental factors that it is probably better not to refer to these types by the terms rough and smooth. Kakehi (1915–16) described two variants of *Past. pseudotuberculosis* ; A was almost transparent and had a bluish, glimmering appearance ; B was greyish-white and opaque. A rendered broth turbid, B did not. Zlatogoroff and Moghilewskaja (1928*a*, *b*) have similarly encountered two variants. On first isolation from the animal body, the organisms formed smooth colonies, consisting of short bacilli, which often showed well-marked bipolar staining ; on plates seeded from old broth cultures, rough colonies developed, with a dull wrinkled surface and a lobate or crenated edge ; morphologically these colonies consisted of larger, often longer, bacilli, which did not exhibit bipolar staining. These two variants likewise differed in their biochemical and serological characters (see below). In cultures of *Past. lepiseptica* De Kruif (1921, 1922*a*, *b*, 1923) found two different types ; Type D grew diffusely in broth, formed rather opaque, fluorescent colonies on serum agar, and was highly virulent for rabbits ; Type G gave a granular deposit in broth, formed translucent bluish colonies with little fluorescence, and was completely avirulent. The D type gave rise to G variants, but the G type did not revert to D. A mucoid variant of intermediate virulence has been described for *Past. lepiseptica* by Webster and Burn (1926), while colonies similar in many respects to the D and G types have been recorded for *Past. aviseptica* by Anderson, Coombes, and Mallick (1929), Mørch and Krogh-Lund (1930), and Hughes (1930).

In broth *Past. pestis* causes little or no turbidity, but gives rise to a deposit of fine flocculi ; with *Past. pseudotuberculosis* there is no turbidity but a deposit of coarse flocculi ; with *Past. aviseptica* there is a uniform turbidity with a powdery deposit (Zlatogoroff 1904). These differences are not constant. A noteworthy feature is that while growth of all three organisms on an agar slope reaches its maximum in 2 to 4 days, in broth growth continues for 7 to 10 days, or, at room temperature, for several weeks. An old broth culture is almost clear ; there is a heavy deposit which is difficult or impossible to disintegrate, and there may be a surface pellicle and ring ; in the case of *Past. aviseptica* the deposit is viscous ; in the case of the other two it is usually floccular or membranous.

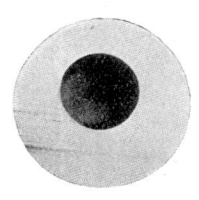

Fig. 141.—
*Pasteurella
muriseptica.*

Surface colony of smooth type on agar, 24 hours, 37° C. (× 8).

If *Past. pestis* is seeded into broth covered with melted butter or oil, and the flask is allowed to remain undisturbed in the incubator, growth occurs in the form of stalactites depending from the under-surface of the droplets. This property is not peculiar to the plague bacillus, nor is it possessed by all strains of that species. *Past. pseudotuberculosis* may likewise give a stalactite growth in broth.

None of the members liquefy gelatin ; in a stab culture there is a surface layer, and a filiform growth extending to the bottom of the tube. In the case of *Past. pestis* little feathery projections sometimes occur from the stab into the surrounding gelatin.

Potato is not a suitable medium. *Past. pestis* and *Past. aviseptica* give little or no growth (Kitasato 1894, Magnusson 1914, Tanaka 1926). *Past. pseudotuberculosis* either gives no growth at all or else forms a thin, yellowish layer, which may later turn brown (Preisz 1894).

In bile salt media—MacConkey's liquid or solid medium—*Past. pestis* and *Past. pseudotuberculosis* give a slight but definite growth, which disappears in the course of 2 or 3 days, owing presumably to autolysis of the bacilli ; *Past. aviseptica* entirely fails to grow.

Resistance.—None of the members is highly resistant to inimical agencies. Broth cultures are killed by heat at 55° C., and by 0·5 per cent. phenol, within 15 minutes. Agar plate cultures exposed to sunlight are sterilized in 3 or 4 hours (Ogata 1897). Dried on threads and kept at room temperature in a desiccator the bacilli survive for not more than a few days. In bubo juice, dried on a cover slip, *Past. pestis* dies in under 4 days (Kitasato 1894). The blood of animals dying from hæmorrhagic septicæmia remains virulent in the dried state for about 3 weeks ; blood which is allowed to putrefy in a glass tube may remain virulent for 100 days (Ostertag 1908). Bacilli in cultures or infected organs, kept in the ice-chest, may survive for months. According to Francis (1932), *Past. pestis*, in an infected guinea-pig's spleen kept in pure neutral glycerol at $-15°$ C., may retain its virulence for years.

Metabolism.—The bacilli have a wide range of growth. *Past. pestis* and *Past. pseudotuberculosis* can grow to some extent at very low temperatures—according to Tumansky and his colleagues (1935) even at $0°$ C. Their upper limit of growth is about $43°$ C. Different observers disagree about their optimum temperature for growth, but $30°$ C. is generally considered to be the most favourable. Growth, however, at both $24°$ C. and $37°$ C. is often nearly as good as at $30°$ C. *Pasteurella septica* has a rather narrower range of growth, and develops best at $37°$ C.

All the members are aerobes and facultative anaerobes. Working with *Past. lepiseptica*, Webster (1924*a*, 1925) and Webster and Baudisch (1925) found that the D or smooth variant would not grow in plain broth unless large numbers of organisms were introduced—about 100,000 per c.c. ; whereas the G or rough variant grew if only a few organisms were introduced. But if a trace of rabbit blood, or an iron compound with strongly catalytic properties, was added to the medium, or the partial pressure of oxygen was lowered mechanically, growth of the D variant occurred with the smallest inoculum. Schütze and Hassanein (1929) made similar observations on *Past. pestis*. They found that the difficulty of obtaining growth from small inocula on agar plates could be overcome by the addition of a small amount of blood or of 0·025 per cent. sodium sulphite to the medium, or by incubation under anaerobic conditions. Their conclusion that the organisms were sensitive to oxygen was confirmed by Wright (1934), who found that plague bacilli were destroyed fairly rapidly on the surface of agar plates if exposed at $37°$ C. to a partial pressure of oxygen exceeding 1 per cent. Aerobic surface cultivation was, however, successful if 0·1 per cent. of blood, 10 per cent. of serum, or 0·05 per cent. of sodium sulphite was added to the agar. Under these conditions growth was more profuse aerobically than anaerobically.

On horse blood agar plates there is no hæmolysis, but the whole plate is slightly cleared and browned. When a suspension of bacilli is incubated with sheep's red cells there is again no hæmolysis, but the oxyhæmoglobin is reduced to hæmoglobin. In this respect all members behave alike.

No true exotoxin is formed (Hadley 1918). Old broth cultures are, however, very toxic to animals, suggesting that endotoxins are liberated by the autolysis of the bacilli.

Biochemical Reactions.—(MacConkey 1908, Vourloud 1908, Magnusson 1914, Kakehi 1915–16, Besemer 1917, Brooks and Rhodes 1923, Pons 1925, Colas-Belcour 1926, Csontos 1926, Tanaka 1926, Mørch and Krogh-Lund 1931.)

Past. pestis and *Past. pseudotuberculosis* produce acid, without gas, in glucose, maltose, mannitol, and salicin within 14 days ; salicin is not usually fermented for about 10 days. Some strains of *Past. pestis* fail to attack maltose, and some strains of *Past. pseudotuberculosis* ferment sucrose. *Past. pseudotuberculosis* is stated (Colas-Belcour 1926, Zlatogoroff and Moghilewskaja 1928*a*) to form acid from glycerol, but so also do some strains of *Past. pestis* (Bessonowa 1928). Bessonowa (1930) says that *Past. pseudotuberculosis* ferments rhamnose, while *Past. pestis* does not ; Kauffmann (1932), however, says that *Past. pestis* may ferment rhamnose, though its reaction in this sugar is inconstant. *Past. aviseptica* produces acid in glucose, mannitol and sucrose ; some types also produce acid in maltose. Tanaka

(1926) found that *Past. bubaliseptica* (from buffaloes) formed acid in lactose and clotted milk ; the same observation was made by Magnusson (1914) for a reindeer strain, and by Besemer (1917) for a calf strain of *Pasteurella*. We have encountered a strain of *Past. lepiseptica* that fermented lactose, and to a less extent salicin. In practice great care is required in determining the fermentation reactions, since growth in sugar peptone water media is very poor.

In plain broth *Past. pestis* produces alkali ; the maximum production is not reached for 6 to 8 weeks (Bannerman 1908) in a litre flask of medium. In peptone water containing 0·5 per cent. glucose the hydrogen-ion concentration reached in 7 days is pH 4·6–4·9 for *Past. pestis*, pH 4·6–4·8 for *Past. pseudotuberculosis*, and pH 5·6–6·1 for *Past. aviseptica* (Otten 1926). That is to say the first two give a positive, the last a negative methyl-red reaction. But in peptone water containing 0·05 per cent. glucose the final hydrogen-ion concentration is pH 5·1–5·5 for *Past. pestis*, 7·0–7·3 for *Past. pseudotuberculosis*, and pH 5·8–6·1 for *Past. aviseptica*. After exhausting the sugar *Past. pseudotuberculosis* would therefore appear to produce alkali more rapidly than the other two. According to Zlatogoroff and Moghilewskaja (1928a), cultures of the rough variant form of *Past. pseudotuberculosis* return to neutral more rapidly than those of the smooth variant form. It is not yet certain whether the different end-reactions in glucose broth can be used for differentiating between *Past. pestis* and *Past. pseudotuberculosis*; according to d'Aunoy (1923) the results obtained depend to some extent on the initial H-ion concentration of the medium.

Past. aviseptica forms indole and gives a negative M.R. reaction ; *Past. pestis* and *Past. pseudotuberculosis* form no indole, and give a positive M.R. reaction. *Past. pestis* and *Past. aviseptica* have no action on litmus milk ; *Past. pseudotuberculosis* turns it slightly alkaline. All members reduce nitrates, form ammonia and a small amount of H_2S, and give a positive catalase test. According to our observations *Past. pestis* does not reduce methylene blue, whereas *Past. aviseptica* and *Past. pseudotuberculosis* are able to do so. In confirmation of this Iwanowsky and Sassykina (1930) have found that saline suspensions of *Past. pseudotuberculosis* reduce Schardinger's reagent (formolized M.B. solution) much more rapidly than those of *Past. pestis*. *Past. aviseptica* is stated to form phenol in peptone water (Bunzl-Federn 1891).

Antigenic Structure.—Antigenically all the members of the group are closely related. An agglutinating serum prepared against any one of them is said to act not only on its homologous strain but to a less extent on the heterologous strains. It is stated that the relationship between *Past. pestis* and *Past. pseudotuberculosis* is very close, and that it is often impossible to distinguish between them by direct agglutination. *Past. aviseptica* is not so closely allied, but nevertheless it may give a definite group reaction with sera prepared against either of the other members. This, however, has not been our experience ; using low titre sera we have had no difficulty in distinguishing between the three species by direct agglutination.

According to Schütze (1932a), there are only two antigens in the plague bacillus, one corresponding to the envelope and the other to the somatic substance. The envelope antigen is developed best in cultures grown at 37° C. and is heat-labile ; the somatic antigen is formed as well at 20° C. as at 37° C. and is heat-stable. The antigenic structure of the flagellated *Past. pseudotuberculosis* is more complex. Arkwright (1927) has shown that agar cultures incubated for 24 hours at 18 to

22° C. contain a heat-labile H, and a heat-stable O antigen. The H antigen is apparently associated with the flagella, and is destroyed by boiling for half an hour, though not by exposure to 56° C. for a similar length of time ; it agglutinates in the form of loose flocculi ; the O antigen is apparently associated with the bacterial bodies, is not destroyed by boiling for 1 hour, and agglutinates in the form of granules. Schütze (1928, 1932b), in confirming this work, has obtained evidence of the existence of 3 antigens : (I) a flagellar antigen which is formed only in cultures grown at 26° C. or lower, which is heat-labile, and which is common to all strains within the species ; (II) a smooth somatic antigen, of which according to Schütze there are at least 3, and according to Kauffmann (1932) at least 5 types, and which is specific for each type ; (III) a rough somatic antigen which, like the flagellar antigen, is common to all strains. The rough somatic antigen is apparently identical with the somatic antigen of the plague bacillus, and it is to this antigen that the two organisms owe their affinity. The smooth somatic antigen of *Past. pseudotuberculosis* corresponding to Schütze's Group 2 and to Kauffmann's groups iiA and iiB is closely related to the O antigen present in *Bact. paratyphosum B* and related organisms of the Salmonella group. Schütze's conception of the antigenic structure of the plague bacillus involves the assumption that this organism is permanently in the rough phase, and that it possesses no smooth somatic antigen. Certain considerations, such as the findings of Otten (1935a, b), render it doubtful whether this is altogether a true picture, and further observations, particularly on freshly isolated strains, are desirable. According to Zlatogoroff and Moghilewskaja (1928a), the smooth and the rough variants of *Past. pseudotuberculosis* are antigenically dissimilar. Since both *Past. pestis* and *Past. aviseptica* are non-motile, they do not exhibit the floccular type of agglutination characteristic of the flagellated species ; they agglutinate, rather, in the form of very small clumps.

As to the antigenic identity of the members of the *Pasteurella septica* group of organisms, the observations of a number of workers show that a serum prepared against any one member will agglutinate the others to titre. Direct agglutination, that is to say, fails to identify the animal source of the strain. With regard to *Past. muriseptica*, we have found two distinct types, distinguishable either by direct agglutination or by absorption of agglutinins. The two types were further distinguished by the fact that one type fermented maltose and the other did not. Using the complement-fixation reaction, Lal (1927) found that there was a cross-reaction between different members of the hæmorrhagic septicæmia group, but that differences in the degree of fixation were usually sufficient to enable strains coming from one animal source to be separated from those from another. Cornelius (1929), by means of the agglutinin-absorption test, classified 17 out of 26 strains of *Pasteurella* of diverse origin into 4 groups ; the remaining 9 strains defied classification. Very similar results have been recorded by Yusef (1935) using the precipitation test. The antigenic study of the group is rendered difficult by the extraordinary irregularity of results obtained from day to day under apparently similar conditions. Clearly there are factors operative, particularly in the method of preparing suspensions, which will have to be controlled before further progress is likely to be made. It is interesting to note that Hoffenreich (1928) reported the isolation of a polysaccharide substance from *Past. aviseptica* which, though incapable of giving rise to antibodies, reacted to a high titre with a specific precipitating serum. Further work on the chemical fractionation of this group is urgently called for.

Immune sera can be prepared for all the members by injection of rabbits or horses with living or dead organisms (Haffkine 1905). If living organisms are used, a weakly virulent culture should be chosen for the first few injections. The sera have prophylactic, and to a less extent curative, properties for laboratory animals (Yersin *et al.* 1895, Chamberland and Jouan 1906). Schütze's (1932c, 1934) observations suggest that the protective power of a plague vaccine is largely dependent on the presence of the envelope antigen. Working with rats he found that a plague culture grown at 37° C.—a temperature at which the envelope antigen is well developed—was considerably more potent for purposes of immunization than one grown at 26° C.—a temperature which is less favourable for the formation of the capsular material. Moreover, heating of a culture to 100° C. for 15 minutes destroyed the envelope substance and rendered the vaccine useless, while exposure to a temperature of 56° C. for 30 minutes had no such deleterious effect. Sokhey and Maurice (1935), however, working with mice, found that cultures grown at 25° C. were as effective as those grown at 37° C. The explanation of this discrepancy is not possible at the moment. It may be that both the envelope and the somatic antigens are involved in the stimulation of protective substances, but that their relative importance varies according to the type of animal under experimentation.

It has been stated that it is possible, by the use of a *pseudotuberculosis* vaccine, to immunize rats and guinea-pigs against infection with virulent plague bacilli (MacConkey 1908, McCoy 1911, Report 1915). Zlatogoroff (1904), on the other hand, was unable to immunize animals against plague with a *pseudotuberculosis* antigen, or against pseudotuberculosis with a *pestis* antigen. He also found that a specific anti-plague serum would protect guinea-pigs against plague, but not against pseudotuberculosis.

As regards the hæmorrhagic septicæmic group, most workers agree that a strain from one animal can be used to vaccinate against infection with strains from other animals (Chamberland and Jouan 1906, Magnusson 1914). A fowl-cholera strain, *Past. aviseptica*, for example, will protect mice against infection with a strain from swine plague or pleuropneumonia of calves. Likewise an immune serum prepared against one strain is said to protect against all other strains. Schirop (1908), however, obtained evidence of racial differences in the species; according to him protection can be realized with certainty only by the use of monovalent sera.

Pathogenicity.—*Past. pestis* and *Past. pseudotuberculosis* cause disease in rodents; *Past. pestis* is also pathogenic for man. The hæmorrhagic septicæmia group is pathogenic for a large number of animals and birds, but not for man (see Chapter LXX).

The virulence of all three organisms is subject to considerable variation, and appears to be determined, at least in part, by the particular variant that has gained the ascendancy. The D variant of *Past. lepiseptica* is highly virulent, the G variant comparatively avirulent. There is evidence that the smooth type of *Past. pseudotuberculosis* is more virulent for guinea-pigs than the rough type (Zlatogoroff and Moghilewskaja 1928a). There are several reports on variations in virulence of the plague bacillus occurring under natural and experimental conditions. (See Yersin, Calmette, and Borrel 1895, Report 1906, McCoy 1911, Rowland 1914b, Eberson 1917, Pirie 1929, Burgess 1930.) Many of the statements are conflicting, rendering it impossible at the moment to draw any definite conclusions on the relation of virulence to colonial appearance or antigenic structure. Further study of this problem by careful quantitative methods is required.

Experimental Reproduction of Plague in Animals.

Bubonic plague can be reproduced in rodents and monkeys by experimental inoculation. Dogs, cats, pigs, cattle, sheep, goats, and horses are difficult to infect ; birds, with the exception of sparrows, are completely resistant. The disease is said to occur naturally in camels ; but these animals are refractory to experimental inoculation (Zabolotny 1923). Even the rodents show great variation in susceptibility to infection. The less resistant members succumb rapidly, whereas the more resistant ones either fail to develop the disease, or else develop a sub-acute or chronic type. Spencer (1921) found in America that about 30 per cent. of the rats from a plague-free district were resistant to subcutaneous inoculation of *Past. pestis*.

Pneumonic plague has been produced in rats and also in marmots (*Spermophilus citellus*) by causing them to inhale cultures of *Past. pestis* (Eberson and Wu Lien Teh 1917, Wu Lien Teh and Eberson 1917).

RATS.—*Subcutaneous injection* of a very small number of virulent plague bacilli leads to death in 2 to 8 days. Post mortem, there is necrosis and œdema at the site of inoculation ; the regional lymph glands are swollen and surrounded by a hæmorrhagic infiltration of the subcutaneous tissue. Glands in other parts of the body are often congested and swollen ; the spleen may be enlarged and dark red ; the liver and lungs are hyperæmic, and sometimes a pleural exudate is seen. Bacilli are found in large numbers in the local lesion and the nearest glands ; they are usually irregular in size and shape, exhibit bipolar staining, and may show involution forms. They are often present in the spleen and in the blood. If the animal lives for a week, small, irregular, necrotic foci may be observed in the spleen and liver.

The German Plague Commission (Report 1899) had apparently no difficulty in infecting rats by the mouth, but other workers have not been so successful. They fed the animals with a drop of plague culture or with the cadaver of a rat that had died of plague. Death followed uniformly in 2 to 3 days. Post mortem, three types of lesion were found. (*a*) Most commonly enlargement and congestion of the submaxillary and suprahyoid glands, with the general picture of septicæmia. (*b*) Less often primary infection of the stomach and intestine, numerous punctiform hæmorrhages round the pylorus, swelling and hæmorrhagic infiltration of the lymph follicles and mesenteric glands, which were often quite large, and contained innumerable plague bacilli. (*c*) Quite frequently an aspiration pneumonia ; the lungs showed inflammatory foci of varying size, containing large numbers of plague bacilli ; the spleen was enlarged, and the liver hyperæmic.

The English Plague Commission had less success with feeding. Of the wild rats of Bombay only 38 per cent. were found to be susceptible when fed on the carcasses of dead plague rats. In the Punjab the proportion was nearly 70 per cent. The lesions found in rats infected by feeding were of a similar type to those in rats infected naturally. Two striking differences, however, were present. (*a*) In naturally infected plague rats the bubo is in the neck ; a mesenteric bubo was not encountered in 5,000 examinations : in the case of fed rats the bubo is generally in the mesentery. (*b*) In naturally infected rats the stomach and intestines show no marked pathological changes : in rats infected by feeding well-marked lesions are found in the intestines—hæmorrhages in the stomach wall 3 per cent., congestion of intestines 27 per cent., enlargement of Peyer's patches 31 per cent.

The *nasal mucosa* and *conjunctiva* are favourable spots for inoculation in rats (Report 1899). A trace of infective material smeared over the conjunctiva proves fatal in 3 to 4 days. Post mortem, there is swelling of the cervical lymph glands, enlargement of the spleen, and frequently numerous hæmorrhages in the stomach and jejunum. The appearances are in fact similar to those of an animal dying after oral infection. Contamination of the nasal mucosa is frequently followed by an inhalation pneumonia.

The English Plague Commission (Report 1912, p. 287) were able to reproduce the lesions of chronic or—as they prefer to call it—of resolving plague in rats by inoculating large numbers of animals with small doses, and retaining the survivors for 3 weeks after inoculation. The chief lesions found were chronic buboes, necrotic areas in the spleen, and chronic abscesses in the spleen or more rarely the liver.

MICE.—The mouse reacts to inoculation in much the same way as the rat. After subcutaneous inoculation the septicæmia is very marked ; the blood and internal organs swarm with bacilli. Infection can be accomplished by feeding, if a sufficiently large dose of a virulent culture is used.

GUINEA-PIGS.—Guinea-pigs are highly susceptible to plague, dying in 2 to 5 days after *subcutaneous* injection of a pure culture. Post mortem, there is a necrotic focus at the site of injection surrounded by intense congestion and œdema ; the regional lymph glands are swollen and embedded in a bloody œdema ; their interior is soft and necrotic. There is enlargement and congestion of the spleen, which is often studded with miliary, soft, grey nodules up to 1 mm. in diameter, containing large numbers of bacilli. The suprarenals may be congested (Yersin 1894). Small areas of necrosis are seen in the liver and lungs. Sometimes there is a pleural effusion. Guinea-pigs can be infected by the *cutaneous* route. If the plague material is rubbed on the shaven skin of the abdomen, an inflammatory reaction appears in the neighbourhood, marked by a slight reddening and the formation of umbilicated pustules in which plague bacilli are present (Dieudonné and Otto 1912). After a few days the regional glands swell and death occurs in 4 to 5 days. The post-mortem signs are similar to those after subcutaneous inoculation.

Intraperitoneal injection is fatal in 24 to 36 hours. Post mortem, there is a rich fibrinous exudate, containing enormous quantities of plague bacilli. Infection by the mouth, nasal mucosa, and conjunctiva is not constant.

The animals are very sensitive to *conjunctival* infection. By *inhalation* or *intratracheal* inoculation it is possible to set up an acute primary pneumonia. Symptoms appear in 48 hours, and death occurs in about 72 hours. At necropsy there is a confluent broncho-pneumonia with œdema or commencing necrosis of the lung tissue (Bessonowa, Kotelnikow, and Sémikoz 1927, Bablet and Girard 1933). However infection occurs, the organisms sooner or later gain access to the blood stream. At post mortem they can be isolated from the blood, spleen, liver, lung, and bone marrow. After bacteræmia has developed, the organisms may often be found in the bile, urine, and less frequently in other excretions (Sémikoz, Bessonowa, and Kotelnikow 1927).

RABBITS are less susceptible to plague than rats and guinea-pigs, but they can generally be infected by subcutaneous inoculation (Dieudonné and Otto 1912).

MONKEYS vary in susceptibility. The German Commission (Report 1899) infected *Macacus radiatus* by subcutaneous and intraperitoneal inoculation, and by feeding. This species was not nearly so susceptible, however, as *Presbytes entellus* (*Semnopithecus entellus*) which succumbed after minute quantities of plague culture subcutaneously.

Experimental Reproduction of Pasteurellosis in Animals.

Most animals are susceptible to experimental infection with *Pasteurella*. On primary isolation, a strain from one species of animal may prove of low infectivity for other species (Karlinski 1890), but this is by no means always true. Magnusson, for example, found that his reindeer organism was pathogenic to mice, guinea-pigs, rabbits, sheep, dogs, and pigeons. The most suitable animals for inoculation are the mouse, rabbit and pigeon.

MICE.—Subcutaneous inoculation of a small quantity of a 24-hours' broth culture proves fatal in 24 to 48 hours. Post mortem, there may be local œdema and congestion, with practically no other signs. Microscopically the bacilli are found in large numbers in the blood and viscera. If very few organisms are injected, or a culture of relatively low virulence is used, the mouse does not die for 2 to 8 days, or even longer ; at necropsy there is a fibrino-purulent pericarditis, a layer of fibrin over the pleura, partial consolidation of the lungs, and not infrequently a purulent exudate in the peritoneum. Bacilli are plentiful in the blood and organs. Intraperitoneal inoculation is more rapidly fatal.

RABBITS can be infected by subcutaneous, intraperitoneal, intravenous, intratracheal, or intranasal inoculation. Death occurs in 2 to 5 days as a rule after intraperitoneal injection, with lesions similar to those in mice. In addition there may be a hæmorrhagic tracheitis (Magnusson 1914), and hyperæmia of the kidneys and intestine (Poels 1886). Intranasal insufflation of the bacilli is often followed by snuffles or pleuro-pneumonia (Beck 1893, Webster 1924b, 1926), and sometimes by purulent otitis media (Smith and Webster 1925).

PIGEONS are very susceptible to intravenous or intraperitoneal, less so to intramuscular, injection. Death occurs in 24 to 48 hours. Bacilli are abundant in the blood.

Experimental Reproduction of Pseudotuberculosis in Animals.

The term pseudotuberculosis is used to refer to a number of diseases that are caused by different organisms (see Chapter LXX). We shall restrict ourselves here to the lesions due to *Past. pseudotuberculosis*. The experimental disease can be produced in guinea-pigs, rabbits, rats, mice, and according to Pallaske (1933), to whom reference should be made for a detailed account of the lesions produced, in cats, pigeons, canaries, and turkeys. For laboratory purposes the guinea-pig is the most suitable animal to study.

Subcutaneous or *intramuscular* inoculation of the guinea-pig is followed by a disease which, depending on the dose and the virulence of the strain, may be acute, subacute, or chronic. The acute disease resembles plague and is fatal in a few days. The differential diagnosis can be made only by cultivation and a thorough study of the organism responsible. Macroscopically, the focal lymphatic glands tend to be more affected in plague than in pseudotuberculosis. The subacute disease proves fatal in about 2 weeks, and the chronic in 3 weeks or longer. Post mortem there is a caseous local swelling, the regional lymphatic glands are enlarged, and there are nodules varying in number, size, and degree of caseation, in the spleen, liver, and lungs. If the animal lives for 3 weeks or so, the nodules are usually very conspicuous. They are more or less spherical, greyish-white in colour, and 0·2 to 3·0 mm. in diameter ; they project above the surface of the organ, and in the liver they show no particular localization for the free border, as do the necrotic areas in rodent typhoid infection. Microscopically the bacilli are generally present in considerable numbers at the site of inoculation and in the regional glands, and they can be readily cultivated from all the lesions. The disease can also be reproduced by *feeding*, which is the natural method of infection. Death occurs in 1 to 3 weeks. Nodules of varying size are found in the intestinal wall, the mesenteric glands are enlarged and often caseous, and nodules may be present in the spleen, liver, and lungs.

Classification and Identification.—The members of this group resemble each other very closely ; between *Past. pestis* and *Past. pseudotuberculosis* the similarity is so great that the identification of a given strain is not always easy. MacConkey laid stress on the inability of *Past. pseudotuberculosis* to grow in bile salt media : but this characteristic is by no means constant ; using generous inocula we have had no difficulty in obtaining growth. Agglutination and precipitation may be

of assistance, especially if supplemented by the absorption test.   The production
of alkali in litmus milk by *Past. pseudotuberculosis*, and its comparative harmlessness
for white rats (Report 1912, p. 350), are two differential tests that are sometimes recommended.   *Past. pseudotuberculosis* is often motile in broth cultures
incubated for 18 hours at 20–22° C. whereas *Past. pestis* is uniformly non-motile.
The greater rapidity and luxuriance of growth of *Past. pseudotuberculosis* is usually
very striking, particularly if studied on nutrient agar plates incubated aerobically for
24 hours.   Under these conditions *Past. pestis* shows very slight confluent growth
restricted to the first line of inoculation.   Single colonies are rarely seen unless a
strong reducing substance is present in the inoculum.   On the other hand colonies
of *Past. pseudotuberculosis* reaching 0·5 or 1 mm. in diameter are usually evident over
the whole plate.   The hæmorrhagic septicæmia bacilli can be differentiated from
Past. pestis and *Past. pseudotuberculosis* by their fermentation of sucrose, their
production of indole, and their negative methyl-red reaction ; it must be noted,
however, that sucrose is fermented by certain strains of *Past. pseudotuberculosis*.
According to Brigham and Rettger (1935), *Past. pestis* and *Past. pseudotuberculosis*
grow on potato at 20° C., while *Past. septica* does not.   Between the hæmorrhagic
septicæmia strains of different animal origin, there appears to be no constant characteristic of diagnostic value.   Most workers therefore agree that these bacilli form
a single group, though it appears possible, using a careful technique, to make out
serological differences between them.   At present each member is given a specific
name ; probably it would be better to call them all by one specific name, such as
Pasteurella septica, and to indicate the animal origin where necessary.
     We may note here that Dungal (1931) in Iceland, studying acute contagious
pneumonia in sheep, cultivated an organism which resembled the hæmorrhagic
septicæmia group, but differed from it in the following respects.   It was Gram-
positive in young broth cultures, and tended to be definitely rod-shaped, $1-3\,\mu$

TABLE XLV

	Past. pestis.	Past. pseudotuber-culosis.	Past. aviseptica.
Motility in 18-hour cultures at 22° C.	—	+	—
Litmus Milk	— or slight acid	Alkaline	—
Sugars	Acid in glucose, maltose, mannitol and salicin	Acid in glucose, maltose, mannitol and salicin, some-times in sucrose	Acid in glucose, mannitol and su-crose, sometimes in maltose
Indole	—	—	+
M.R.	+	+	—
[1] Methylene Blue Reduction.	—	+	+
Growth on MacConkey . .	+	+	—
Pathogenicity to white rats .	+	—	+

[1] Personal observations on a relatively few strains.

in length ; it failed to grow at 22° C., in gelatin or broth ; it grew on MacConkey agar ; it fermented maltose ; it did not produce indole ; it died out in 2 to 5 days in culture at room temperature ; and it was non-pathogenic to rabbits.

Fedorova and Lalazarow (1935) described a Pasteurella-like organism, which they isolated from a spontaneous epidemic among mice in the outskirts of Astrakhan. The organisms were 1–2 μ long by 0·5 μ wide, Gram-negative, non-motile, and capsulated. Acid was formed in lactose, mannitol, and dextrin, and acid plus gas in glucose. Sucrose was unchanged. No indole was formed. The organism was highly pathogenic for mice, but had no effect on rabbits, pigeons, or rats injected by various routes.

It is doubtful whether these two organisms should be placed in the *Pasteurella* group.

Pasteurella pestis

Isolation.—Independently by Kitasato (1894) and by Yersin (1894).

Ecology.—Parasite of rodents and man.

Morphology.—Small, straight, ovoid bacillus, 1·5 $\mu \times$ 0·7 μ, with rounded ends and convex sides ; arranged singly, in short chains, or in small groups. Shows high degree of pleomorphism, especially in buboes and on 3 per cent. salt agar ; there is every degree of variation in depth of staining, and clubs, shadow forms, snake-like filaments, coccoid forms, yeast-like forms, and numerous others may be seen. Non-motile. Non-sporing. In the animal body a true capsule may be formed ; in culture media there is often a slimy envelope around each bacillus. Shows bipolar staining, is Gram-negative, and non-acid-fast.

Agar Plate.—24 *hours at* 37° *C.* Very small, 0·1–0·2 mm. in diameter, round, glistening, transparent, colourless, finely granular, umbonate colonies, with smooth or finely granular surface and an entire or delicately notched edge ; differentiated into a raised centre and a flat periphery.

5 *days at* 37° *C.* Larger, up to 4 mm. in diameter, with a raised, sometimes ringed, nearly opaque, greyish-yellow centre and a flat or shelving, finely granular, translucent, greyish-white periphery ; consistency is butyrous or viscous, emulsifiability easy ; sometimes a secondary ring of growth is seen. Variant colonies occur.

Deep Agar Shake.—5 *days at* 37° *C.* Maximum growth at the surface ; numerous round, transparent, colourless, punctiform colonies, visible with a hand lens, scattered throughout the medium.

Agar Stroke.—24 *hours at* 37° *C.* Poor, slightly raised, translucent, greyish-yellow, glistening growth, with a wavy or frosted-glass surface, and an irregularly lobate edge. Growth increases very little with subsequent incubation.

Gelatin Stab.—7 *days at* 22° *C.* Good, filiform growth, confluent at top, discrete below, extending to bottom of tube, and sometimes sending out little feathery projections into medium. Surface growth is raised, 5 mm. in diameter, with a slightly lobate edge. No liquefaction.

Broth.—24 *hours at* 37° *C.* Moderate growth ; little or no turbidity ; a floccular or powdery deposit, not disintegrating completely on shaking. Later the flaky deposit increases and may crawl up the sides of the tube ; a delicate surface pellicle often forms. If butter or oil is floated on the medium, stalactites grow down from the under-surface of the droplets.

Loeffler's Serum.—24 *hours at* 37° *C.* Fairly good, confluent growth, better than that on agar.

Horse Blood Agar Plate.—2 *days at* 37° *C.* Colonies are similar to those on agar but show less tendency to differentiation and peripheral spread. No hæmolysis ; whole plate is slightly cleared and browned.

Potato.—7 *days at* 22° *C.* Usually a thin layer of growth.

MacConkey Plate.—24 *hours at* 37° *C.* Very slight, effuse, confluent growth, just visible to the naked eye. Colonies disappear after 2 or 3 days, owing presumably to autolysis.

Resistance.—Fairly susceptible to inimical agencies. Killed by drying in a day or two, by heat at 55° C. in 5 minutes, by 5 per cent. phenol immediately, and by 0·5 per cent. phenol in 15 minutes. Agar plate cultures exposed to sun are sterilized in 1 to 5 hours. Cultures in the ice-chest may survive for months.

Metabolism.—Aerobic, facultative anaerobe. Requires low O-R potential for initiation of growth. Opt. temp. 30° C.; limits 5–43° C. Opt. pH 6·2–7·0; limits pH 5·0–8·2. Forms alkali in broth. Growth favoured slightly by serum, uninfluenced by glucose; partly inhibited by glycerol. No hæmolysis.

Biochemical.—Acid, no gas, in glucose, maltose, mannitol, salicin, arabinose, xylose, and sometimes rhamnose and glycerol within 14 days. L.M. unaltered or turned slightly acid; Indole —; M.R. +; V.P. —; Nitrates +; NH_3 +; Methylene blue reduction —; H_2S very slight +; Catalase + +·

Antigenic Structure.—Appears to possess a heat-labile envelope antigen and a heat-stable somatic antigen. The somatic antigen is similar to the rough somatic antigen in *Past. pseudotuberculosis.* Immune sera with protective and curative properties for animals can be prepared by injection of horses with living or dead bacilli.

Pathogenicity.—No true exotoxin formed. Virulence subject to considerable variation. Causes plague in man and rodents. Experimental inoculation reproduces disease in mice, rats, guinea-pigs, rabbits, marmots, ground squirrels, and other rodents; also in monkeys. Dogs, cats, pigs, cattle, sheep, goats, and horses are difficult to infect. Birds, with exception of sparrows, are completely resistant.

Subcutaneous inoculation of a 24-hours' broth culture into a mouse or guinea-pig is fatal in 2 to 5 days. P.M. necrotic local lesion surrounded by congestion and œdema. Regional glands enlarged and embedded in bloody œdema; they are soft and necrotic on section. Spleen firm, slightly enlarged and congested; may contain miliary, soft, grey nodules; liver peppered with tiny necrotic foci. Microscopically, bacilli found in abundance in local lesion and bubo; smaller numbers in spleen and heart's blood.

Pasteurella aviseptica

Isolation.—First member of the *Pasteurella* group isolated by Kitt in 1878. *Past. aviseptica* isolated by Pasteur in 1880.

Ecology.—Parasites of domestic and wild animals and birds.

Morphology.—Very small, 0·7–2 μ × 0·3–0·6 μ, ovoid bacilli, with straight axis, slightly convex sides, and rounded ends; arranged singly, in pairs, or in small bundles. In smears from the animal body the organisms are regular, ovoid, and evenly distributed; on agar cultures they are more rod-shaped and often show pleomorphism. Non-motile, non-sporing. May form a capsule in animal body, not in artificial media. Shows bipolar staining. Gram-negative and non-acid-fast.

Agar Plate.—24 *hours at* 37° *C.* Round, 0·5–1·0 mm. in diameter, low convex, amorphous, greyish-yellow, translucent colonies, with smooth, glistening surface and entire edge; consistency butyrous; emulsifiability easy.

5 *days at* 37° *C.* Up to 6 mm. in diameter, differentiated into a brownish, finely granular, sometimes ringed or striated, nearly opaque centre and a clearer, smooth, homogeneous, greyish-yellow translucent periphery.

Deep Agar Shake.—5 *days at* 37° *C.* Thick surface growth; numerous, punctiform, undifferentiated colonies scattered throughout medium.

Agar Stroke.—24 *hours at* 37° *C.* Moderate, confluent, raised, greyish-yellow, translucent growth, with glistening, wavy or beaten-copper surface and finely lobate edge.

Gelatin Stab.—7 *days at* 22° *C.* Good, filiform growth, confluent at top, discrete below, extending to bottom ; raised surface growth, 5 mm. in diameter, with crenated edge, no liquefaction.

Broth.—24 *hours at* 37° *C.* Moderate growth with slight turbidity, and a slight powdery or viscous deposit. Later the turbidity increases, and a heavy, viscous deposit forms, disintegrating partly on shaking but leaving irregularly-sized wisp-like masses of growth in suspension. An incomplete surface pellicle forms with an inconspicuous ring growth.

Loeffler's Serum.—24 *hours at* 37° *C.* Good confluent growth, similar to that on agar.

Horse Blood Agar Plate.—2 *days at* 37° *C.* Good growth similar to that on agar ; no hæmolysis, but blood plate is slightly cleared and browned.

Potato.—7 *days at* 22° *C.* No visible growth.

MacConkey Plate.—5 *days at* 37° *C.* No visible growth.

Resistance.—Very susceptible to inimical agencies ; killed by heat at 60° C. in a few minutes ; by 0·5 per cent. phenol in 15 minutes.

Metabolism.—Aerobe, facultative anaerobe. May require low O-R potential on first isolation. Opt. temp. 37° C., limits 12°–43° C. Growth improved slightly by serum, uninfluenced by glucose, slightly inhibited by glycerol. No hæmolysis.

Biochemical.—Acid, no gas, in glucose, mannitol, sucrose, and sorbitol within 14 days ; one type forms acid in maltose. Some strains produce acid in arabinose, xylose, and glycerol. L.M. unchanged ; Indole $+$; M.R. $-$; V.P. $-$; Nitrates reduced ; NH_3 very slightly $+$; M.B. reduction $++$; H_2S $+$; Catalase $++$.

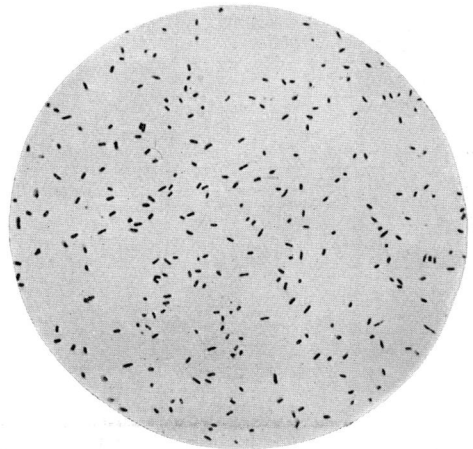

Fig. 142.—*Pasteurella muriseptica.*
From an agar culture, 24 hours, 37° C. ($\times$ 1000).

Antigenic Structure.—At least two types distinguishable by agglutination. Specific sera agglutinate *Past. pestis* and *Past. pseudotuberculosis* to a certain extent. Immune sera with protective and curative properties for animals can be prepared by injection of horses with living or dead bacilli.

Pathogenicity.—No true exotoxin produced. Virulence subject to alteration. Causes fowl cholera in birds. Other members of this group produce hæmorrhagic septicæmia in pigs, cattle, sheep, rabbits, mice, rats, reindeer, buffaloes, and other animals. Experimental inoculation reproduces the disease in these animals. *Subcutaneous* inoculation of a 24-hours' broth culture into a mouse proves fatal in 18 to 72 hours. P.M. local œdema and congestion ; often no other signs ; microscopically bacilli present in enormous numbers in blood and viscera. If a small dose is given and the animal does not die for 4 to 7 days, there is often a fibrino-purulent pericarditis, a layer of fibrin over the pleura, and partial consolidation of the lungs. Bacilli are numerous in blood and organs.

Pasteurella pseudotuberculosis

Synonym.—*B. pseudotuberculosis rodentium.*

Isolation.—First observed by Malassez and Vignal in 1883, named *B. pseudotuberculosis rodentium* by Pfeiffer (1890) in 1889.

Ecology.—Parasite of rodents, particularly guinea-pigs.

Morphology.—Small, pleomorphic cocco-bacillus varying greatly in length and shape. Some strains consist of regular ovoid or coccoid organisms, $0.8-2.0 \mu \times 0.8 \mu$, with convex sides, rounded ends, and straight axis ; arranged singly. Other strains consist of rod-shaped organisms, $1.5-5.0 \mu \times 0.6 \mu$, with parallel sides, rounded ends, and straight or curved axis ; arranged singly, in groups, or in short chains. Long curved filaments are not uncommon (Fig. 143). Motile in broth cultures at 22° C. Non-sporing. Non-capsulated. Ovoid forms show bipolar staining ; rod forms show great irregularity of staining ; the barred and granular type of staining is very common. Gram-negative, and non-acid-fast.

Agar Plate.—24 *hours at* 37° C. Round, $0.5-1.0$ mm. in diameter, umbonate, granular, translucent, greyish-yellow colonies, with dull, finely granular or beaten-copper surface and entire edge ; butyrous consistency ; easily emulsifiable ; differentiated into a raised, more opaque centre and a flat, clearer periphery with radial striation. A rough variant with an irregular surface and a crenated edge also occurs.

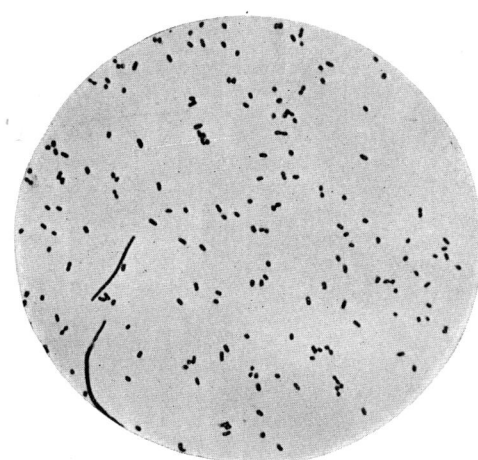

Fig. 143.—*Pasteurella pseudotuberculosis.*
From an agar culture, 24 hours, 37° C. ($\times$ 1000).

Deep Agar Shake.—5 *days at* 37° C. Heavy surface growth. No colonies beneath surface.

Agar Stroke.—24 *hours at* 37° C. Moderate, confluent, raised, greyish - yellow, translucent growth, with glistening, wavy or beaten-copper surface and an irregularly lobate edge.

Gelatin Stab.—7 *days at* 22° C. Good filiform growth, confluent at top, discrete below, extending to bottom of tube. Raised surface growth, 5 mm. in diameter, with finely lobate edge. No liquefaction.

Broth.—24 *hours at* 37° C. Moderate growth with moderate turbidity and a viscous deposit disintegrating on shaking. Later the broth clears and a heavy, flocculo-membranous deposit forms, partly disintegrating on shaking. Incomplete surface and ring growth.

Loeffler's Serum.—24 *hours at* 37° C. Confluent growth, not so good as on agar.

Horse Blood Agar Plate.—2 *days at* 37° C. Good growth, but colonies are more compact and less differentiated than on agar. No hæmolysis ; whole plate is slightly cleared and browned.

Potato.—7 *days at* 22° C. A thin yellowish membrane, which subsequently turns brown.

MacConkey Plate.—24 *hours at* 37° C. Very slight effuse confluent growth. Colonies disappear after a few days, owing presumably to autolysis.

Resistance.—Fairly susceptible to inimical agencies. Killed by moist heat at 60° C., in 10 minutes.

Metabolism.—Aerobe, facultative anaerobe. Opt. temp. 30° C., limits 5–43° C. Growth uninfluenced by serum and glucose, slightly inhibited by glycerol. No hæmolysis.

Biochemical.—Acid, no gas, in glucose, maltose, mannitol, salicin, arabinose, xylose, rhamnose, and glycerol within 14 days, sometimes in sucrose. L.M. usually slight alkali formation ; Indole — ; M.R. + ; V.P. — ; Nitrates + ; NH_3 + ; M.B. reduction + + ; H_2S + ; Catalase + +.

Antigenic Structure.—Apparently contains (1) a heat-labile flagellar antigen, which is formed only in cultures grown below about 25° C. ; (2) a heat-stable smooth somatic antigen of which there are 3 to 5 specific types, and of which one type is related to the O antigen of *Bact. paratyphosum B* ; and (3) a heat-stable rough somatic antigen which is similar to the somatic antigen of the plague bacillus. A plague serum does not protect animals against infection with *Past. pseudotuberculosis.*

Pathogenicity.—No true exotoxin formed. Virulence subject to alteration. Causes pseudotuberculosis in rodents, especially guinea-pigs. Experimental inoculation reproduces the disease in rodents. Subcutaneous injection of a 24-hour broth culture into a guinea-pig proves fatal in 1 to 3 weeks. P.M. caseous local swelling, enlargement of regional glands, and nodules in spleen, liver, and lungs. Microscopically the bacilli are numerous in the local lesion and glands.

REFERENCES

ANDERSON, L. A. P., COOMBES, M. G., and MALLICK, S. M. K. (1929) *Indian J. med. Res.* **17,** 611.

ARKWRIGHT, J. A. (1927) *Lancet*, i. 13.

D'AUNOY, R. (1923) *J. infect. Dis.,* **33,** 391.

BABLET, J. and GIRARD, G. (1933) *C. R. Soc. Biol.,* **114,** 471.

BANNERMAN, W. B. (1908) *Sci. Mem. med. sanit. Dep. India,* New Ser., No. 33.

BECK, M. (1893) *Z. Hyg. InfektKr.,* **15,** 363.

BESEMER, A. M. (1917) *J. Bact.,* **2,** 177.

BESSONOWA, A. (1928) *Rev. Microbiol. Saratov,* **7,** 336 ; (1930) *Zbl. Bakt.,* **119,** 32.

BESSONOWA, A., KOTELNIKOW, G., and SÉMIKOZ, F. (1927) *C. R. Ist. Congr. antipest. U.R.S.S.,* p. 485.

BESSONOWA, A. and LENSKAJA, G. (1931) *Zbl. Bakt.,* **119,** 430.

BESSONOWA, A., SÉMIKOZ, T., and KOTELNIKOW, G. (1927) *Rev. Microbiol. Saratov,* **6,** 472.

BONGERT. (1901) *Z. Hyg. InfektKr.,* **37,** 449.

BRIGHAM, G. D. and RETTGER, L. F. (1935) *J. infect. Dis.,* **56,** 225.

BROOKS, R. ST. J. and RHODES, M. (1923) *J. Path. Bact.,* **26,** 433.

BUNZL-FEDERN, E. (1891) *Zbl. Bakt.,* **9,** 787.

BURGESS, A. S. (1930) *J. Hyg., Camb.,* **30,** 165.

CHAMBERLAND and JOUAN. (1906) *Ann. Inst. Pasteur,* **20,** 81.

COLAS-BELCOUR, J. (1926) *C. R. Soc. Biol.,* **94,** 238.

CORNELIUS, J. T. (1929) *J. Path. Bact.,* **32,** 355.

CSONTOS, J. (1926) *Zbl. Bakt.,* **97,** 178.

DIEUDONNÉ, A. and OTTO, R. (1912) See Kolle and Wassermann's " Hdb. path. Mikroorg," IIte Abt., 1912–13, **4,** 155.

DUNGAL, N. (1931) *J. comp. Path.,* **44,** 126.

EASTWOOD, A. and GRIFFITH, F. (1914) *J. Hyg., Camb.,* **14,** 285.

EBERSON, F. (1917) *J. infect. Dis.,* **20,** 180.

EBERSON, F. and WU LIEN TEH. (1917) *J. infect. Dis.,* **20,** 170.

FEDOROVA, T. and LALAZAROW, G. (1935) *Rev. Microbiol. Saratov,* **14,** 55.

FRANCIS, E. (1932) *Publ. Hlth Rep., Wash.,* **47,** 1287.

GOTSCHLICH, E. (1912) See Kolle and Wassermann, " Hdb. path. Mikroorg.," IIte Abt., 1912–13, **1,** 167.

HADLEY, P. (1918) *J. Bact.,* **3,** 277.

HAFFKINE, W. M. (1905) *Sci. Mem. med. sanit. Dep. India,* New Ser., No. 20.

HOFFENREICH, F. (1928) *Zbl. Bakt.,* **108,** 87.

HUGHES, T. P. (1930) *J. exp. Med.,* **51,** 225.

IWANOWSKY, N. and SASSYKINA, T. (1930) *Zbl. Bakt.,* **117,** 535.

KAKEHI, S. (1915–16) *J. Path. Bact.,* **20,** 269.

KARLINSKI, J. (1890) *Zbl. Bakt.,* **7,** 335.

KAUFFMANN, F. (1932) *Z. Hyg. InfektKr.,* **114,** 97.

KITASATO, S. (1894) *Lancet*, ii. 428.

KRUIF, P. H. DE (1921) *J. exp. Med.,* **33,** 773 ; (1922a) *Ibid.,* **35,** 561 ; (1922b) *Ibid.,* **36,** 309 ; (1923) *Ibid.,* **37,** 647.

KUTSCHER. (1894) *Z. Hyg. InfektKr.,* **18,** 327.

LAL, R. B. (1927) *Amer. J. Hyg.,* **7,** 561.

LEVINTHAL, W. (1930) *Z. Hyg. InfektKr.,* **111,** 140.

MACCONKEY, A. T. (1908) *J. Hyg., Camb.,* **8,** 335.

McCOY, G. W. (1911) *Publ. Hlth Bull., Wash.,* No. 43.

MAGNUSSON, H. (1914) *Z. InfektKr. Haustiere*, **15**, 61.
MALASSEZ, L. C. and VIGNAL, W. (1883) *Arch. Physiol. norm. path.*, 3rd Series, **2**, 369.
MØRCH, J. R. and KROGH-LUND, G. (1930) *C. R. Soc. Biol.*, **105**, 319 ; (1931) *Z. Hyg. InfektKr.*, **112**, 471.
OGATA, M. (1897) *Zbl. Bakt.*, **21**, 769.
OSTERTAG, R. (1908) *Z. InfektKr. Haustiere*, **4**, 1.
OTTEN, L. (1926) *Zbl. Bakt.*, **98**, 484 ; (1935a) *P. V. Séances Comité permanent Off. int. Hyg. publ.*, *Session d'Octobre*, 1934, p. 93 ; (1935b) *Bull. Off. int. Hyg. publ.*, **29**, 1542.
PALLASKE, G. (1933) *Z. InfektKr. Haustiere*, **44**, 43.
PFEIFFER, A. (1890) *Zbl. Bakt.*, **7**, 219.
PIRIE, J. H. H. (1929) *Publ. S. Afr. Inst. med. Res.*, **4**, 203.
POELS, J. (1886) *Fortschr. Med.*, **4**, 388.
PONS, R. (1925) *Ann. Inst. Pasteur*, **39**, 884.
PREISZ, H. (1894) *Ann. Inst. Pasteur*, **8**, 231.
Reports. (1899) Germ. Plague Comm., *Arb. ReichsgesundhAmt*, **16**, 1 ; (1906) Engl. Plague Comm., *J. Hyg.*, *Camb.*, **6**, 421 ; (1912) Engl. Plague Comm., *J. Hyg.*, *Camb.*, **12**, Suppl., p. 287 ; (1915) *Ibid.*, **14**, Suppl., p. 754.
ROWLAND, S. (1914a) *J. Hyg.*, *Camb.*, Engl. Plague Comm., **13**, Suppl., 418 ; (1914b) *Ibid.*, 440.
SCHIROP, H. (1908) *Zbl. Bakt.*, **47**, 307.
SCHÜTZE, H. (1928) *Arch. Hyg.*, **100**, 181 ; (1932a) *Brit. J. exp. Path.*, **13**, 284 ; (1932b) *Ibid.*, **13**, 289 ; (1932c) *Ibid.*, **13**, 293 ; (1934) *Ibid.*, **15**, 200.
SCHÜTZE, H. and HASSANEIN, M. A. (1929) *Brit. J. exp. Path.*, **10**, 204.
SÉMIKOZ, F., BESSONOWA, A., and KOTELNIKOW, G. (1927) *C. R. 1st. Congr. antipest. U.R.S.S.*, p. 488.
SMITH, D. T. and WEBSTER, L. T. (1925) *J. exp. Med.*, **41**, 275.
SOKHEY, S. S. and MAURICE, H. (1935) *Bull. Off. int. Hyg. publ.*, **27**, 1534.
SPENCER, R. R. (1921) *Publ. Hlth Rep.*, *Wash.*, No. 36, p. 2836.
TANAKA, A. (1926) *J. infect. Dis.*, **38**, 421.
TUMANSKY, W., MÜLLER, M., BOKALO, A., WEDISTSCHEW, S., and SABININ, A. (1935) *Rev. Microbiol. Saratov*, **14**, 128.
VOURLOUD. (1908) *Zbl. Bakt.*, **45**, 97, 193.
WEBSTER, L. T. (1924a) *Proc. Soc. exp. Biol.*, **22**, 139 ; (1924b) *J. exp. Med.*, **49**, 109, 117 ; (1925) *Ibid.*, **41**, 571 ; (1926) *Ibid.*, **43**, 555.
WEBSTER, L. T. and BAUDISCH, O. (1925) *J. exp. Med.*, **42**, 473.
WEBSTER, L. T. and BURN, C. G. (1926) *J. exp. Med.*, **44**, 343, 359.
WEITZENBERG, R. (1935) *Zbl. Bakt.*, **133**, 343.
WRIGHT, H. D. (1934) *J. Path. Bact.*, **39**, 381.
WU LIEN TEH, and EBERSON, F. (1917) *J. Hyg.*, *Camb.*, **16**, 1.
YERSIN. (1894) *Ann. Inst. Pasteur*, **8**, 662.
YERSIN, CALMETTE, and BORREL. (1895) *Ann. Inst. Pasteur*, **9**, 589.
YUSEF, H. S. (1935) *J. Path. Bact.*, **41**, 203.
ZABOLOTNY, D. (1923) *Ann. Inst. Pasteur*, **37**, 618.
ZLATOGOROFF, S. J. (1904) *Zbl. Bakt.*, **37**, 345, 513, 654.
ZLATOGOROFF, S. I. and MOGHILEWSKAJA, B. I. (1928a) *Ann. Inst. Pasteur*, **42**, 1615 ; (1928b) *C. R. Soc. Biol.*, **99**, 506.

CHAPTER XXX

HÆMOPHILUS

SINCE the isolation and description by Pfeiffer (1892, 1893) of the bacillus which, though not the primary causal organism of influenza, is closely associated with that disease, several other small, Gram-negative bacilli have been described, which share with it certain characteristic growth requirements. In their final report on classification and nomenclature, the American Committee (see Winslow *et al.* 1920) grouped these species together under the generic name of *Hæmophilus*. The generic definition suggested in the Committee's report opens the door more widely than insistence on a close similarity in behaviour to the type species would allow ; and such species as the Bordet-Gengou bacillus of whooping cough, the Morax-Axenfeld bacillus of angular conjunctivitis, and Ducrey's bacillus of soft sore, have been included, by certain writers, within this generic group. Such an extension of the term " hæmophilic bacilli," whether in the form of a generic name or as a convenient appellation for a characteristic bacterial group, has been opposed by Kristensen (1922) and by Fildes (1923). It seems clear that their objection is valid if the character from which the name is derived is to retain a decisive differential significance.

To include all the species referred to, it would be necessary to define the genus on some other basis, with a sub-group characterized by the particular growth requirements that *H. influenzæ* displays. It is very doubtful, however, whether the Morax-Axenfeld bacillus, or Ducrey's bacillus, would be included in this genus by any such redefinition, and we have therefore described these organisms in Chapter XXXIV, together with others that cannot at present be assigned to any named bacterial genus. The Bordet-Gengou bacillus cannot, we think, be dealt with in the same way. It resembles *H. influenzæ* so closely in morphology, in habitat, and in many other ways, that it would certainly be placed in close association with it by any systematic definition that did not rely exclusively on a narrow nutritional criterion. We have therefore provisionally included this organism in the genus, and have emended the generic definition accordingly.

DEFINITION.—*Hæmophilus.*

Minute rods, sometimes almost coccal, sometimes thread-like ; may be highly pleomorphic. Non-motile, non-sporing, Gram-negative, non-acid-fast. On first isolation dependent for growth on some factor, or factors, contained in blood, or in plant tissues. Some species retain this dependence after prolonged cultivation on laboratory media. Some species are obligatory aerobes, or grow very poorly under anaerobic conditions. All known species appear to be obligatory parasites, inhabiting particularly the upper respiratory tract ; and most of the described species or types are pathogenic.

Type species. *H. influenzæ.*

611

Morphology.—*H. influenzæ*, as originally described by Pfeiffer (1893), and as most commonly seen in strains recently isolated from cases of influenza, is a short rod, so short as to be almost coccal. It is very small, 1–1·5 μ by 0·3–0·4 μ, with rounded, sometimes rather pointed ends. In some cultures these cocco-bacillary forms are the only forms seen. More usually, among these predominating short forms, are found a proportion of longer bacilli, and a few long thread forms. In other cultures, the cocco-bacilli may be relatively scanty, or altogether absent; and longer and somewhat stouter rods may predominate. Other strains, again, may present an entirely different picture, the bacilli being thin, long, wavy or curved and sometimes lying together in tangled masses. In films prepared from strains showing any of these diverse morphological types, but especially those which show some proportion of thread forms, it is not unusual to encounter large, spherical swollen bodies, often attaining a diameter of 2–3 μ, or even more. These are sometimes attached to the end of a thread, sometimes laterally, and sometimes appar-

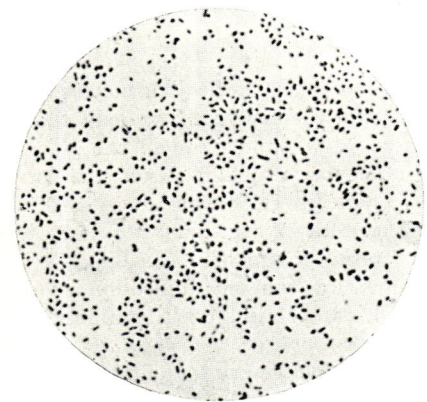

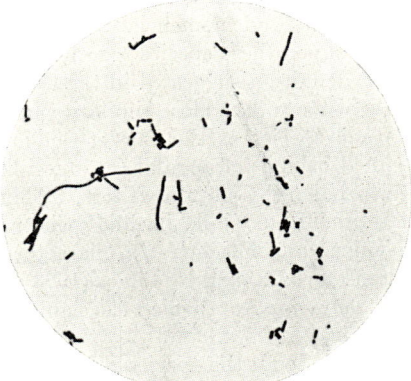

Fig. 144.—*H. influenzæ.*

From 24-hours' culture on Fildes' agar, showing typical cocco-bacillary forms (× 1000).

Fig. 145.—*H. influenzæ.*

From 24-hours' culture on Fildes' agar, showing short and long bacillary forms (× 1000).

ently at the end of a short lateral stalk (Wade and Manalang 1920, Kristensen 1922). Another form which is occasionally met with consists of a long thread with an enormous fusiform swelling, situated centrally or towards one end.

This morphological diversity raises a problem of considerable difficulty from the point of view of classification. Any one of the types we have referred to may predominate in a single strain; and two strains may yield a microscopical picture so different that it is difficult to believe that we are dealing with a single bacterial species. The only test of the real significance of such morphological differences is their constancy; and this test is not so easy to apply as might at first sight appear. It is quite certain that many strains maintain their morphological individuality over long periods of artificial cultivation, involving numerous successive sub-cultures; and Dible (1924) regards these morphological characters as sufficiently well differentiated, and sufficiently stable, to justify the recognition of several different varieties, or types. Many of those who have studied this group, on the other hand, have rejected morphological criteria as a basis of classification within the group, on the following grounds. If a large series of strains is carefully examined the variation in form is not found to be discontinuous. In a small sample of strains it is easy to obtain an appearance of discontinuity ; but, unless one classes all strains which depart from the typical cocco-bacillary form in a single heterogeneous group, it is not possible to define a limited number of morphological categories, to which all strains can be definitely assigned. Between the minute, short bacilli, and the long tangled threads, there exists a long range of intermediate forms. Moreover, while some strains are morphologically homogeneous, others display, in the same culture, a heterogeneous mixture of cocco-bacilli, rods, and long threads. Finally, though many strains retain their morphological characters unchanged for weeks, months, or longer periods, others show quite definite changes in form after a few cultures. Wollstein (1915) has noted the frequency with which the cocco-bacillary type acquires the power of forming threads in artificial culture ; and there has been a very general tendency to discard the old conception of a para-influenza bacillus, differentiated on purely morphological grounds (Pfeiffer 1893), in favour of

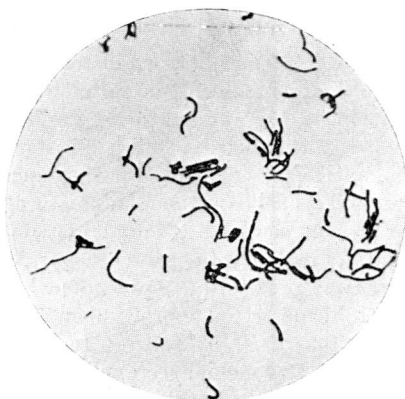

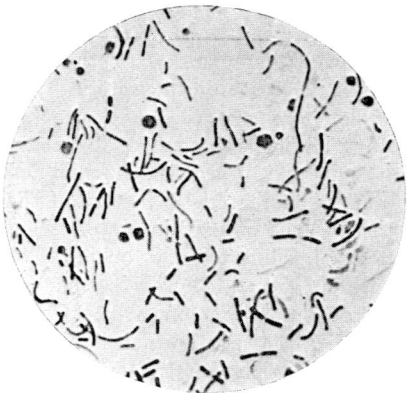

Fig. 146.—*H. influenzœ.*

From 24-hours' culture on Fildes' agar, atypical form, showing long, curved bacillary forms (× 1000).

Fig. 147.—*H. influenzœ.*

From 24-hours' culture on Fildes' agar, showing thread forms, and large spherical bodies (× 1000).

the tentative view that such differences, unless associated with other well-marked characters, must be disregarded by the systematist (Kristensen 1922). Smith (1931) records a careful study of a series of strains isolated from the human nasopharynx. In almost every instance morphological variation occurred after a varying period of cultivation in artificial media, the most usual change being from the short cocco-bacillary form to longer bacilli, or to curved or jointed filaments. This change was in general associated with a change in colony form (see below). There is general agreement that it is possible to make a rough classification of strains into two groups, " typical " and " atypical " on the basis of morphology alone ; and there are indications that, apart from certain strains isolated from cases of meningitis (see Cohen 1909, Ritchie 1910, Henry 1912, Wollstein 1915), the typical morphology predominates among strains isolated from pathological conditions. Recent studies by Pittman (1931), which will be discussed more fully in relation to the problem of antigenic structure, have emphasized the possible importance of this distinction. But the evidence at present available suggests that typical and atypical morphology are associated with a change presenting many analogies to the smooth → rough type of variation, rather than permanent characters, serving to differentiate stable varieties or types.

The organisms of this genus are, as has been noted, non-flagellated, and form no spores. They are usually described as non-capsulated ; but Pittman (1931) describes the " smooth " form of *H. influenzæ* isolated by her as displaying a capsule when stained by appropriate methods.

H. influenzæ stains with some difficulty, and many of the ordinary bacteriological dyes are unsuitable for this purpose. Dilute carbol-fuchsin applied for 5 to 15 minutes usually gives satisfactory results. All species within this genus are frankly Gram-negative and non-acid-fast.

It may be added that it is impossible to differentiate any given strain of *H. pertussis* from *H. influenzæ* on grounds of morphology alone. If, however, large samples of strains are compared, certain modal differences may be observed. *H. pertussis* displays a more constant morphology than *H. influenzæ*, and there is a marked tendency towards the predominance of the short oval form of cell. Longer bacillary or thread forms may occur, but they are relatively uncommon.

Cultural Characters. Growth Requirements.—Since peculiarities in nutritional requirements provide the criteria by which this genus is defined, and also the basis on which many of the species included within it are differentiated from one another, it will be convenient to discuss this aspect of their behaviour before dealing with their type of growth, enzymic activities, antigenic structure or pathogenicity. The most characteristic feature of the hæmophilic bacilli is their failure to grow in the absence of certain factors which are present in blood. The ability of the influenza bacillus to grow on blood agar, and its inability to grow on agar, with or without the addition of serum, or other native protein, has been noted by all workers from Pfeiffer onwards. Grassberger (1897) described another phenomenon —that of satellitism—which is highly characteristic of *H. influenzæ*. In cultures on blood agar plates, streaked with sputum or with bronchial secretion, he noted the appearance of relatively large colonies of the influenza bacillus, with a slightly granular central portion. These large colonies (1 mm. or more in diameter) always developed in the immediate vicinity of a colony of *Staphylococcus*. Studying this phenomenon in greater detail, Grassberger streaked agar plates with a suspension of *H. influenzæ* mixed with a small quantity of blood, and then inoculated the central portion of the plate with a trace of a pure culture of *Staph. aureus*. After 24 hours' incubation such plates showed a well-defined zone of colonies of *H. influenzæ*, surrounding each colony of *Staphylococcus*. A similar result was obtained with *Staph. albus*, *Staph. citreus*, and certain other chromogenic micrococci. These observations have been repeatedly confirmed (see Davis 1921, Kristensen 1922).

The inability of *H. influenzæ* to grow on serum agar indicates that some constituent of the red cells is essential for growth ; and it was at first assumed that this constituent was hæmoglobin itself. More detailed study, however, showed that the addition to an agar medium, prepared with water or with peptone solution, of pure crystallized hæmoglobin does not suffice to ensure growth (Ghon and von Preyss 1904, Thalimer 1914, Davis 1917, Olsen 1920, Fildes 1921). It would appear (Fildes 1921) that the growth-promoting substance derived from the blood pigment is methæmoglobin, or hæmatin, rather than hæmoglobin itself. Hæmatin is more active in this respect than the other derivatives which have been tested ; while hæmatoporphyrin is inactive (Fildes 1921). There is, however, another factor which comes into play, besides the presence of some suitable iron-containing pigment. Davis (1917) showed that *H. influenzæ* required for its growth the presence of two distinct substances : one contained in, or derived from, hæmoglobin ; the other present in the tissues of various plants and animals, and synthesized by most bacterial species other than *H. influenzæ*. This second factor he likened to a vitamin. These observations clearly provide an explanation of the satellitism described by Grassberger. The staphylococci synthesize the vitamin-like substance, which diffuses into the medium and stimulates the growth of the influenza bacillus. This substance, as compared with the factor provided by blood pigment, is relatively thermolabile ; it is inactivated by heating to 120° C. for 30 minutes. Both substances are present in blood. The label " X factor " is generally applied to the substance present in blood pigments, the label " V factor " to the relatively thermolabile substance provided by animal or vegetable tissues or by most bacterial cells (see also Thjøtta 1921, Thjøtta and Avery 1921, Davis 1921, Fildes 1922, 1923, 1924, Kristensen 1922, Valentine and Rivers 1927).

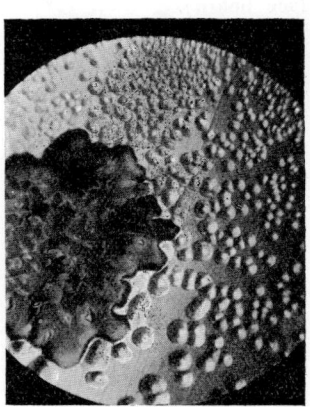

Among the species included within this genus, besides *H. influenzæ* itself, are (1) the bacillus associated with conjunctivitis, described by Koch (1887) and Weeks (1887), and commonly known as the " Koch-Weeks bacillus " ; (2) the bacillus isolated by Friedberger (1903) from the prepuce of dogs, named by him *B. hæmoglobinophilus canis* and now known as *H. canis* ; (3) the organism isolated by Shope (1931) (see also Lewis and Shope 1931) from swine influenza and named by him *H. influenzæ suis* ; and (4) the causative organism of whooping-cough, described by Bordet and Gengou (1906) and named by them *B. pertussis*, now known as *H. pertussis*. The nutritional requirements of most of these species have been studied in some detail by various observers, with results that may be summarized as follows :

Fig. 148.

Showing satellite growth of *H. influenzæ* in the neighbourhood of a composite colony of *Staph. aureus* on blood agar (× 8).

With regard to the Koch-Weeks bacillus, the statements in the literature are somewhat contradictory (see Kristensen 1922) ; thus, some authors have stated that this organism grows on ascitic agar and hydrocele-fluid agar. Recent studies by Fildes (1923) and by Knorr (1924), however, show quite clearly that the strains, isolated by them from cases of muco-purulent conjunctivitis, behave in exactly the same way as *H. influenzæ*, and requires both the X and the V factor.

H. canis is unable to synthesize the X factor, and is therefore dependent on hæmatin, or some similarly-acting substance. It can, however, synthesize the V factor, and hence it does not show the phenomenon of satellitism, but can itself induce the formation of satellite colonies of *H. influenzæ* (see Friedberger 1903, Krage 1910, Odaira 1911, Rivers 1922, Kristensen 1922, Fildes 1923, Valentine and Rivers 1927).

H. influenzæ suis requires both the X and V factors for its growth, resembling in this as in almost all other respects the human influenza bacillus (Lewis and Shope 1931).

H. pertussis differs from the other species within this genus in being capable of growth in the absence of both the X and V factors. For primary isolation Bordet and Gengou (1906) employed an agar medium containing blood, glycerine and potato extract ; and this medium, with various minor modifications, is still used for this purpose. Even on first isolation *H. pertussis* and *H. influenzæ* show differences in their nutritional requirements. The former grows well on media containing large amounts of blood and vegetable extract, poorly on media containing the X and V factors in the absence of other blood or tissue constituents ; the latter grows better on Fildes' or Levinthal's medium than on media of the Bordet-Gengou type (see Gundel and Schlüter 1933). On subculture in the laboratory these differences become more marked. *H. pertussis* can readily be trained to grow on serum agar, and, with slightly more difficulty, on ordinary agar. There is, however, general agreement that on such media the organism rapidly loses its natural virulence (see below).

These relations are clearly shown in the observations recorded by Fildes (1923), who examined 8 strains of *H. influenzæ*, 23 strains of the Koch-Weeks bacillus, and one strain of *H. canis*, by testing their growth in (a) peptone water, (b) peptone water + hæmatin, (c) peptone water + yeast extract, and (d) peptone water + hæmatin + yeast extract. The results he obtained with these strains, and with the Bordet-Gengou bacillus, are recorded in Table XLVI.

TABLE XLVI

Showing Growth of certain Bacterial Species in Peptone Water, with and without Hæmatin and Yeast Extract (after Fildes).

	H. influenzæ.	Koch-Weeks.	H. canis.	Bordet-Gengou.
Peptone water	0	0	0	+
,, ,, + hæmatin . . .	0	0	+ +	+ +
,, ,, + yeast	0	0	0	+ +
,, ,, + hæmatin + yeast	+ +	+ +	+ +	+ +

As will be noted below, certain strains of *H. influenzæ*, which differ from the normal form in being hæmolytic, can grow in the presence of V factor alone, synthesizing the X factor for themselves.

Our knowledge as to how the X and V factors produce their effects is, at the moment, far from complete. So far as it goes it may be summarized as follows :

The X Factor.—We have noted that this factor is contained in blood pigments, and that it is more active when supplied in the form of an iron-containing derivative of hæmoglobin—methæmoglobin, hæmatin, or hæmin—than as unaltered hæmoglobin. Pure, crystallized hæmoglobin is, indeed, almost inactive in this respect. An obvious suggestion is that the X factor is functioning as a respiratory catalyst, and early observations (Olsen 1920, Fildes 1921) suggested that its growth-promoting activity was correlated with its ability to catalyse the oxidation of guaiacum or benzidine by peroxides. More recent studies have not, however, supported this view. Certain organic substances, or simple iron compounds, have been shown to possess *peroxidase* activity without promoting the growth of *H. influenzæ*, while other compounds and particularly certain compounds of Fe_2O_3 studied by Baudisch (1932) have been shown to function as X factor although devoid of peroxidase activity. All iron compounds that promote the growth of *H. influenzæ*, and have been tested in this respect, have, however, shown *catalase* activity (see Davis 1921, Webster and Baudisch 1925, Bourn 1927, Baudisch 1932, Knight 1936).

An interesting sidelight has been thrown on this problem by recent studies on the anaerobic growth of *H. influenzæ*. This organism has usually been regarded as an obligate aerobe, or, at least, as growing very poorly under anaerobic conditions (see below), but Kopp (1927–28), Eirund (1929), and Anderson (1931) have recorded the anaerobic growth of certain strains. Moreover, under these conditions, the organism was found to grow in the absence of the X factor. This clearly suggests the possibility that, under aerobic conditions, the X factor may be acting as a protective catalyst, shielding the growing organism against the injurious action of peroxide (see p. 61). Further evidence on this point is clearly needed.

The V Factor.—This factor, unlike the X factor, is inactivated at 120° C. It also shows some sensitiveness to oxidation and it was regarded by some of the earlier workers as a vitamin. It had indeed been suggested that it was identical with Vitamin C (ascorbic acid) ; but this was disproved by Meyer (1934). Of its mode of action we as yet know almost nothing. Pittman (1935) describes a relation between the V requirements of certain strains of influenza bacilli and the concentration of molecular oxygen. These strains, which showed no growth in a fluid medium containing traces of V factor, grew well if the medium was freely aerated without any addition of V factor, or if V factor was added without any aeration of the medium. It seems possible, therefore, that the V factor is also concerned in some way with the oxidation-reduction processes of the growing cell ; but the solution of this problem will remain very difficult until we can isolate the active substance in a form less crude than any that is at present available.

It may be convenient at this point to indicate the various media that are, at the present time, employed in the study of the hæmophilic bacilli.

Ordinary blood agar is by no means a satisfactory medium from this point of view ; far better results are obtained with media in which the red cells have been broken up, and their modified contents distributed throughout the medium. The well-known " chocolate " agar, prepared by adding blood to melted agar, raising the mixture to the boiling-point for 3 minutes, and then preparing slopes or plates from the chocolate-coloured mass, is a considerable improvement on the ordinary blood agar plate, but it shares the disadvantage that the medium is opaque.

The medium devised by Levinthal (1918) has the great advantage of being colourless and transparent. It is prepared by adding 5 per cent. of defibrinated rabbit or human blood to melted agar in a flask, and raising it to the boiling-point over a flame, with several shakings. The precipitate of coagulated blood and serum protein is allowed to settle, and the clear supernatant fluid is carefully decanted, or may be filtered through sterile glass-wool. The medium may be, for safety, sterilized by a further short heating, but must not be subjected to prolonged sterilization in the steamer.

Fildes (1920) has introduced a peptic digest of blood, which is preserved with chloroform and may be added to broth, or melted agar, as required. This medium, which is transparent and has the colour of ordinary broth or agar, gives copious growths of *H. influenzæ*, and inhibits the growth of many other organisms. It is admirably suited for the primary isolation of the influenza bacillus.

For primary culture from such a source as the nasopharynx advantage may be taken of the selective action of a mould-product, penicillin, described by Fleming (see Fleming 1929, Fleming and Maclean 1930). This inhibits the growth of Gram-positive cocci and of diphtheroid bacilli but has almost no action on *H. influenzæ*.

With regard to other conditions of growth, the optimum temperature for *H. influenzæ* is in the neighbourhood of 37° C. The minimal temperature for growth lies between 20° and 25° C. The same conditions hold for other hæmophilic bacilli.

P.B.   X*

There is general agreement that *H. influenzæ* grows far better under aerobic than under anaerobic conditions. Statements with regard to its ability to develop under strictly anaerobic conditions are somewhat contradictory (see Kristensen 1922). Fildes (1921) states that *H. influenzæ* gives good initial anaerobic growth on a suitable medium, but quickly dies out.

Cultural Reactions. Type of Growth.—The type of colony given by *H. influenzæ* on solid media varies widely with the kind of medium employed. On blood agar it forms tiny transparent, pin-point colonies, sometimes flat, and tending to become confluent, sometimes more convex, and with less tendency to confluence. On a more favourable medium, such as Levinthal's agar, and especially Fildes' agar, the colonies are far larger. After 24 hours' incubation they attain a diameter of 0·5–0·8 mm. They are circular in outline, raised and dome-shaped, with a slightly splayed-out, entire edge. The surface is usually smooth ; the colony is translucent ; there is little differentiation ; and the growth emulsifies easily (Fig. 149)

On further incubation, and in many cases during the first 24 hours of growth,

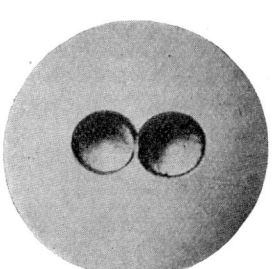

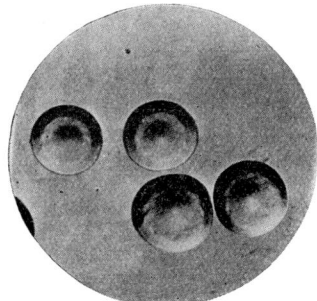

FIG. 149.—*H. influenzæ.*
Colonies on Fildes' agar after 24 hours (× 8).

FIG. 150.—*H. influenzæ.*
Colonies on Fildes' agar after 48 hours (× 8).

the colony becomes differentiated into a central portion with a granular or contoured surface, an intermediate flattened portion, and a sharply bevelled periphery with a narrow splayed-out edge. Between the 24th and 48th hours there is usually a considerable enlargement of the colonies, which may attain a diameter of 1–1·5 mm. This increase in size results in the formation of a flatter colony, retaining a raised central boss, sometimes smooth, sometimes granular or contoured (Fig. 150). Some colonies may be, from the start, flatter and more granular ; others may remain raised, conical and smooth, with little central differentiation. Kristensen (1922) lays considerable stress on such colonial differences, especially those which develop on blood agar, and apparently regards them as more important than cellular differences in morphology, in distinguishing " typical " from " atypical " strains. Smith (1931), in the study referred to above, noted a definite but not absolute correlation between morphology and colony form. The morphologically typical strains tended to give, on Fildes' agar, smooth colonies with little differentiation. The morphologically atypical strains, or variants, tended to produce a more granular colony, with earlier and more considerable differentiation.

The " smooth " strains described by Pittman (1931) have distinctive colonial characters. Levinthal's agar gives rather better differentiation than Fildes'. Smooth strains give relatively large colonies, sometimes attaining 3 mm. in diameter. They are slightly opaque, and viewed by obliquely transmitted light they are iridescent. This iridescence is, perhaps, their most characteristic property. The surface is smooth and slightly mucoid in appearance. The edge is entire.

These " smooth " strains are described by Pittman as readily giving rise to " rough " variants producing colonies of varying granularity and differentiation, the organisms composing them being in the form either of short bacilli, or of longer rods or threads. The rough variants were never capsulated.

The relation of Pittman's " smooth " strains to the strains isolated by other workers from infective conditions, or from the normal respiratory tract, raises a problem in terminology which is at the moment difficult to solve. Her observations have been confirmed, in whole or in part, by several subsequent workers, and there can be little doubt that the strains she has differentiated correspond to a form of *H. influenzæ* that is frequently associated with acute infections in man. If, however, we accept Pittman's colonial differentiation as a criterion separating " smooth " from " rough " strains, we must include among our " roughs " many, probably the majority, of those strains that give, on Fildes' or Levinthal's agar, colonies of the type that earlier observers had generally regarded as " smooth," and that consist of morphologically typical cocco-bacillary organisms. The balance of evidence is, we think, in favour of accepting Pittman's nomenclature, but this question will be discussed more fully in relation to antigenic structure.

H. canis forms colonies that are at first indistinguishable from those of *H. influenzæ*, but as they grow older they become larger and distinctly more opaque.

H. pertussis, when grown on Bordet-Gengou medium, also forms colonies that, during the early stages of growth, may resemble those of *H. influenzæ*. But when incubation is prolonged beyond 24 hours the colonies become larger, more opaque, and greyish in colour, a form that is never assumed by *H. influenzæ*. They are also smoother, more shining and more distinctly dome-shaped. The combination of slight opacity, greyness of hue, and shining surface, gives them an appearance that has not inaptly been compared to that of a bisected pearl. They have also been compared to drops of mercury ; but this overstates their metallic appearance. A confluent row of colonies has been compared to an " aluminium streak," and this simile again is not inapt.

In liquid media, such as Fildes' broth, the majority of strains of *H. influenzæ* give rise to a uniform turbidity, with or without a slight powdery deposit. Some, on the other hand, give a flocculent deposit, with a varying degree of turbidity of the supernatant fluid. There is, as would be expected, a correlation between morphology and type of growth in a fluid medium. Cocco-bacillary strains give a uniform turbidity. Many of those showing long bacilli, or twisted and convoluted threads, give flocculent growths.

H. canis gives a diffuse growth with a slight deposit. So does *H. pertussis*.

Resistance.—*H. influenzæ* is killed by exposure to a temperature of 50–55° C. for 30 minutes. *H. canis* and *H. pertussis* behave similarly.

Hæmolysin Production.—Before considering the fermentation of carbohydrates, or other substrates, it will be convenient to discuss the hæmolytic activity of the influenza bacillus, since this character serves to divide the species into two distinct types.

Pritchett and Stillman (1919) noted the occurrence, among a large sample of cultures of hæmophilic bacilli isolated from cases of influenza and from normal persons, of a small proportion of strains which produced a well-defined zone of hæmolysis on blood agar. These strains were morphologically of the bacillary or thread type. They were studied in greater detail by Stillman and Bourn (1920) ; and their occurrence has been noted by many subsequent workers. Kristensen (1922) studied several strains of these hæmolytic bacilli, and noted that some of them seemed less dependent on the presence of hæmoglobin than *H. influenzæ.* On the other hand, the majority of his strains showed well-marked satellitism ; thus demonstrating their dependence on the V factor. Fildes (1924) found that 13 of 14 hæmolytic strains grew in the presence of the V factor alone. In morphology these strains are, for the most part, definitely atypical, showing numerous threads, and coarser bacillary forms than are commonly encountered in *H. influenzæ* itself. The colonies produced by these strains tend to assume the characters which Kristensen regards as atypical, being more opaque and more friable than the typical form. Another striking characteristic of these hæmolytic strains is their tendency to die out in subculture, a character which has been noted by subsequent observers (Dible 1924). Kristensen notes that the power to cause hæmolysis is maintained unaltered by those strains which survive artificial cultivation for considerable periods ; and that there is no tendency for other strains to acquire this property. Dible (1924) studied 67 strains of hæmophilic bacilli isolated from the nasopharynx of normal persons, and found 14 of them to be hæmolytic. Five of these strains resembled the cocco-bacillary form of *H. influenzæ,* with the single exception that the bacilli were a little larger, and rather more definitely bacillary : the other 9 were atypical, in forming larger colonies, giving a flocculent growth in broth, or departing widely from the cocco-bacillary form. Valentine and Rivers (1927) report that the majority of these hæmolytic strains require the V factor only for their growth, while a minority require both the X and V factors. They state, however, that a proportion of non-hæmolytic strains of hæmophilic bacilli require the V factor only. Strains of this latter type are sometimes spoken of as " para-influenza bacilli."

Biochemical Activities.—The study of the fermentation reactions of *H. influenzæ,* and of other hæmophilic bacilli, has been retarded by the difficulty experienced in preparing a medium which allows of copious growth, and has, at the same time, the transparency and absence of colour which are essential, if changes in hydrogen-ion concentration are to be detected by the usual methods. Some of the media which have been devised within recent years are, however, well adapted for this purpose.

Levinthal (1918) added various carbohydrates to the agar medium which he devised, tinted it with litmus, and tested the fermentative ability of several strains of *H. influenzæ.* He noted acid production from glucose, but not from lævulose, lactose, mannitol or maltose. Messerschmidt, Hundeshagen and Scheer (1919), using a similar technique, noted slight acid production in glucose, but not in mannitol, lactose, or saccharose.

Stillman and Bourn (1920) employed a liquid medium prepared by adding an extract of boiled rabbit blood to peptone water, and carried out a careful series of tests on 119 strains of *H. influenzæ* and 29 hæmolytic strains. More than 90 per cent. of the 119 non-hæmolytic strains produced acid from dextrose and galactose, and reduced nitrates ; 73 per cent. produced acid from lævulose, and about 25 per cent. from maltose, saccharose and dextrin ; no strain fermented mannitol or lactose ; 53 per cent. produced indole. Of the 29 hæmolytic strains, all fermented dextrose and reduced nitrates, the majority fermented maltose and saccharose, 3 fermented galactose, 10 lævulose, and 15 dextrin ; none fermented mannitol or lactose ; 3 produced indole ; and 4 formed gas. It would appear that the hæmolytic, as compared with the non-hæmolytic strains, ferment maltose and saccharose more frequently, galactose and lævulose less frequently, and seldom produce indole ; but the number of hæmolytic strains examined was small. Stillman and Bourn specifically note that they obtained irregular results when they carried out repeated tests on the same strains. Fildes (1924) notes that the hæmolytic strains studied by him fermented glucose, saccharose, and maltose ; but not lactose, dulcitol, or mannitol. The non-hæmolytic strains of *H. influenzæ* which he examined did not ferment any of these sugars.

Kristensen (1922) carried out a considerable number of fermentation tests, but obtained almost entirely negative results. It seems probable that these were due to an unsatisfactory technique.

Dible (1924), using a technique which did not differ essentially from that employed by Stillman and Bourn, obtained results which he regarded as sufficiently sharp and constant to afford a basis for a tentative grouping of his strains ; though he notes that, of 25 strains which were retested after 8 months, 9 showed changes in their fermentation reactions. In 8 cases this change involved a loss of the power to ferment one or more carbohydrates ; in the remaining instance a strain, previously inactive, was found to ferment glucose. It may be noted that, of 14 hæmolytic strains, 9 fermented glucose and lævulose, none galactose, 8 saccharose, and 6 maltose, while none formed indole. Of 6 non-hæmolytic strains, which Dible excludes from the species *H. influenzæ* on account of their bacillary or thread-like morphology, 4 fermented glucose, 4 lævulose, 5 galactose, 4 saccharose and none maltose, while none produced indole. Of 45 strains which showed the typical minute bacilli and cocco-bacilli, 38 fermented glucose, lævulose and galactose, none fermented saccharose or maltose, while 16 produced indole. Dible's results thus tend to confirm those of Stillman and Bourn with regard to the frequency of saccharose fermentation, and infrequency of indole formation, among the hæmolytic as compared with the non-hæmolytic strains.

In regard to the relation between morphology and fermentation reactions among the non-hæmolytic strains, Smith (1931) records observations on 143 strains isolated from the nasopharynx of normal persons. There was no clear-cut fermentative separation between morphologically typical and atypical strains, but, in conformity with the results recorded by other workers, it was found that the typical strains showed a more restricted enzymic activity than the atypical. Thus, 22·6 per cent. of the atypicals fermented saccharose, as compared with 4·3 per cent. of the typicals. The correlation between typical morphology and ability to form indole was further confirmed ; 63·9 per cent. of the cocco-bacillary strains were indole-producers, as against 18·0 per cent. of the morphically atypical strains.

On the basis of hæmolysin production, indole production and other fermentative reactions, taken in conjunction with morphology and dependence on the X and V factors, we may, then, recognize several different types of *H. influenzæ.*

(1) Typical *H. influenzæ*—requiring both X and V factors, showing a predominantly cocco-bacillary morphology, not producing hæmolysis, usually showing a restricted range of enzymic activities, particularly in failing to ferment saccharose, and usually producing indole.

(2) Atypical *H. influenzæ*—requiring both X and V factors and not producing hæmolysis, but differing from typical strains in showing a predominantly bacillary or filamentous morphology, fermenting saccharose and some other substrates more frequently, and less frequently producing indole.

(3) Hæmolytic *H. influenzæ*—these require only the V factor, and this, taken with the ability to produce hæmolysis, differentiates this type rather sharply from types (1) and (2). The significance of this differentiation is, however, rendered somewhat uncertain by the existence of types (4) and (5), below. In their other characters the hæmolytic influenza bacilli resemble the strains of type (2). They are morphologically atypical, usually ferment saccharose, and seldom produce indole.

(4) A small group that resemble types (1) and (2) except that they require only factor V for growth. These are sometimes referred to as " para-influenza " bacilli ; but this term is sometimes used to include hæmolytic as well as non-hæmolytic strains.

(5) A small group of hæmolytic influenza bacilli that require both the X and V factor for growth.

We have not, it will be noted, made any reference in the classification given above to Pittman's " smooth " strains. These will be further considered in relation to antigenic structure.

The fermentation reactions of *H. canis* were studied by Rivers (1922), who records the formation of acid in dextrose, lævulose, galactose, mannitol, saccharose, and xylose, but not in maltose, lactose, dextrin, arabinose or glycerol. Indole was produced by all strains examined and nitrates were reduced. Fildes (1924) states that *H. canis* ferments glucose, saccharose and mannitol; but not lactose, dulcitol or maltose.

The strains of *H. influenzæ suis* tested by Lewis and Shope (1931) are recorded as producing no change in dextrose, lactose, saccharose, mannitol, dulcitol, glycerol, inulin or arabinose. They produced no indole. They reduced nitrates. It has been noted that some observers have recorded similar negative results with strains of *H. influenzæ*, and it is doubtful whether this apparent absence of enzymic activity should be taken as differentiating the swine influenza bacillus from the human type in the absence of further evidence. Kirchenbauer (1934), who has studied several strains of this organism, confirms the reduction of nitrates and the absence of indole production.

H. pertussis, which is sharply differentiated from *H. influenzæ* in other ways, has been recorded by Stillman and Bourn (1920) as failing to ferment dextrose, lævulose, galactose, maltose, saccharose, dextrin, mannitol, lactose or inulin, as producing no indole and as failing to reduce nitrates. It produces a hazy zone of hæmolysis.

It may be added that *H. influenzæ suis* and *H. canis* are non-hæmolytic.

Many of the fermentative reactions within this group appear to be so irregular that they have little value in classification, or in the identification of particular strains. We may, however, tabulate for purposes of reference the reactions that have actually been observed, using + and — signs as rough indicators of the frequency with which the various substrates are attacked (Table XLVII).

TABLE XLVII

SHOWING THE FERMENTATION REACTIONS OF VARIOUS SPECIES, OR GROUPS, OF HÆMOPHILIC BACILLI, AND OF THE PERTUSSIS BACILLUS OF BORDET AND GENGOU.

	Dextrose.	Lævulose.	Galactose.	Maltose.	Lactose.	Saccharose.	Mannitol.	Dextrin.	Indole formed.	Nitrates reduced.
H. influenzæ . .	+	+	+	—+	—	—+	—	—+	+—	+
Hæmolytic Group.	+	+—	—+	+	—	+	—	+—	—+	+
H. canis . . .	+	+	+	—	—	+	+	—	+	+
H. pertussis . .	—	—	—	—	—	—	—	—	—	—

The Antigenic Relationships of the Hæmophilic Bacilli.

Taking first *H. influenzæ*, as a species, the peculiarity that has emerged from most of the recorded attempts at serological analysis is its extreme antigenic heterogeneity.

By direct agglutination with 20 antisera, followed by absorption tests where necessary, Park, Williams and Cooper (1918) could find only four identical pairs among 160 strains. Valentine and Cooper (1919) record a similar experience. Among 10 strains isolated at autopsy, tested against the 10 homologous antisera, no two were identical. Among 73 miscellaneous strains tested against 18 antisera no two were identical. Among 54 strains isolated from a group of marines, and tested against 18 antisera, 2 strains from different individuals were identical. It was noted in this group that strains isolated from the same individual on different days were usually, but not always, identical. Among 28 strains isolated from the inmates of an orphan asylum, there was one pair of identical strains. Of 6 strains isolated from the members of a single family, all of whom had contracted influenza at about the same time, no two strains were identical.

This extreme heterogeneity, as judged by agglutination tests, has been amply confirmed by numerous workers (Rivers and Kohn 1921, Yabe 1921, Anderson and Schultz 1921, Cooper *et al.* 1921, Povitsky and Denny 1921, Kristensen 1922, Knorr 1924, and others).

The actual significance of these earlier observations has been rendered very doubtful by the recent observations of Pittman (1931).

Among 97 strains of influenza bacilli isolated from various sources, she noted 15 that produced colonies of a characteristic " smooth " type (see above). All these 15 strains were isolated from sources, or under conditions, which indicated that they were playing a pathogenic rôle. In addition to forming a characteristic colony, the bacilli of these " smooth " strains were found to be capsulated. When tested by agglutination at 37° C. these 15 strains were found to fall into two antigenic types A and B, one containing 12 strains, the other 3. This specificity was not apparent if the reactions were carried out at a higher temperature, a possible reason being the loss of the bacterial capsules. It was also found possible to separate from these 15 strains a soluble specific substance, apparently carbohydrate in nature, and presumably associated with the capsule. Precipitin tests carried out with this material gave the same antigenic grouping as the agglutination tests carried out at 37° C. These smooth strains, in artificial culture, readily gave rise to non-capsulated rough variants, usually with a bacillary or filamentous morphology. The rough variants no longer produced the soluble specific substance, nor did they conform to the antigenic grouping of the smooth parent strains. These findings have been confirmed, in their essential points at least, by several subsequent workers (see Dochez *et al.* 1932, Wright and Ward 1932, Platt 1936). It may be noted also that several earlier workers had found that complement-fixation tests gave evidence of the presence of an antigenic relationship that was not revealed by agglutination (Wollstein 1919, Bieling and Weichbrodt 1920, Kristensen 1922).

It is clear that the change that Pittman describes as occurring in her smooth strains falls within the definition that we adopted for the S $\rightarrow$ R variation in Chapter VII, the loss of the surface antigen which determines type-specificity in the normal, virulent form of a bacillus. Her designation of this small minority of strains of *H. influenzæ* as smooth, with its implication that most of the strains isolated from the nose and throat of normal persons are rough, or in an intermediate phase, must therefore, we think, be accepted. We must also, it would appear, accept the view that the antigens that dominate the rough forms in this bacterial species are more heterogeneous than those present in the normal smooth phase, a finding that differs from that recorded for most other groups.

It will be noted that, under this definition, all the strains referred to in preceding sections as " atypical " and many, probably the great majority, of those referred to as " typical," would be classed as rough variants. The antigenic structure of the hæmolytic influenza bacilli has not yet been submitted to any special study ; but it seems very unlikely that any of them would fall into Pittman's " smooth " category. Whether they are in any way antigenically different from the non-hæmolytic rough forms we do not know.

The Koch-Weeks bacillus, in its serological relationships as in all its other characters, appears to be indistinguishable from *H. influenzæ*. Knorr (1924) has found that different strains of this organism show marked antigenic heterogeneity, while some strains are identical with certain strains of the influenza bacillus.

A small sample of strains of *H. influenzæ suis* examined by Lewis and Shope (1931) showed the same type of antigenic heterogeneity that is encountered among the ordinary strains of human influenza bacilli. Comparison with a few strains of *H. influenzæ* of human origin did not reveal any example of antigenic identity, though there was some overlapping in cross-agglutination tests. Similar findings are recorded by Kirchenbauer (1934). These observations were made before the publication of Pittman's findings, so that there was no differentiation between smooth and rough strains.

We have as yet no information in regard to the antigenic relationships of *H. canis*.

H. pertussis differs from *H. influenzæ* in that all recently isolated smooth strains appear to belong to a single antigenic type. Moreover, it would seem that all strains, when first isolated from the body on an optimal medium, are in the smooth state. The behaviour of these strains on artificial culture raises points of considerable interest.

Bordet and Sleeswyk (1910) noted that recently isolated strains of *H. pertussis*, grown on the Bordet-Gengou medium, all agglutinated with a serum prepared against any one of them. Strains that had been trained to grow on agar, however, failed to agglutinate with the sera prepared against the recently isolated strains, and sera prepared against the agar strains failed to agglutinate the strains grown on the Bordet-Gengou medium. These observations were confirmed and extended by Bordet (1912). The change in antigenic structure was ascribed to the medium, but it was noted that a similar change might occur on a blood-containing medium after repeated subculture. Most observers have confirmed Bordet's findings that all recently isolated strains belong to a single sero- logical type (see Kristensen 1922, 1927). A few have recorded the existence of two different types among strains maintained permanently on a blood-containing medium (Krumwiede *et al.* 1923) ; but there is little doubt that such findings have been due to the slow occurrence of an antigenic variation that takes place more rapidly when smooth strains are grown on an unsuitable medium. Leslie and Gardner (1931) made a careful study of 32 strains of *H. pertussis*, none of which had been regarded as rough variants. They found that these strains fell into four different antigenic groups, to which they refer as Phases I, II, III and IV. Of 20 recently isolated strains 18 fell into Phase I, and 2 were intermediate between Phase I and Phase II. Of 7 laboratory strains that had been maintained on an egg medium, 3 were in Phase III and 4 in Phase IV. Of 5 other laboratory strains, one was intermediate between Phases II and III, 3 were in Phase III and 1 in Phase IV. Studies by later workers (Shibley and Hoelscher 1934, Toomey *et al.* 1935) have been in general agreement with Leslie and Gardner's findings, though there has not been unanimity in regard to the existence of four clearly differentiated phases. Taking these studies as a whole it seems safe to conclude that *H. pertussis*, in the form in which it exists in the tissues or in recent cultures on Bordet-Gengou medium, belongs to a single, homogeneous antigenic type ; but that an S $\longrightarrow$ R variation occurs somewhat readily, even in cultures kept on a blood-containing medium, and very readily on less favourable media. This variation is apparently step-like, so that intermediate stages exist between the normal smooth form, which corresponds to Leslie and Gardner's Phase I, and the fully developed rough form which corresponds to their Phase IV. The practical importance of this obser- vation lies in the fact that the antigenic state is here, as elsewhere, intimately related to virulence and to immunizing potency, and that many of the existing laboratory strains are in fact in the rough phase. It is noted by Leslie and Gardner that there is no very obvious and striking colonial difference between the rough and the smooth forms, nor any constant and measurable difference in salt sensitiveness, though strains in their Phase III and Phase IV are, on the average, rougher in colonial appearance and less stable in saline sus- pensions than strains in Phase I or II.

Finally, we may note that such comparative tests as have been performed show little if any antigenic relationship between *H. pertussis* and H. *influenzæ* (Odaira 1911, Shiga *et al.* 1913, Winholt 1915, Olmstead and Povitsky 1916, Kristensen 1922).

Pathogenicity and Toxin Production.

The probable rôle of *H. influenzæ* in human influenza, which is now known to be a virus disease, is considered in Chapter LXXI. It is a common cause of sinusitis, alone or in association with the pneumococcus, an occasional cause of meningitis, almost always in children, and a rare cause of ulcerative endocarditis. The Koch-Weeks bacillus has been isolated from epidemics of conjunctivis in many parts of the world, children being mainly infected. As, however, there is no known method by which this organism can be distinguished from *H. influenzæ*, it seems unnecessary to regard it as a different species.

H. pertussis is the cause of whooping cough, and as such is one of the more important human pathogens. Unlike *H. influenzæ* it seems seldom to play a harmless parasitic rôle.

H. influenzæ suis plays an important part in swine influenza (see Chapter LXXI). *H. canis* was isolated by Friedberger (1903) from 19 of 20 dogs suffering from a suppurative inflammation of the prepuce, but he was unable to reproduce the disease with it, and concluded that it was a harmless parasite of the preputial sac. It has also been isolated from normal dogs by Krage (1910), Kristensen (1922), Rivers (1922), and Kirchenbauer (1934).

Experimental Infections.

H. influenzæ.—Attempts to produce an infection resembling influenza in man by experiments on human volunteers or on the higher apes are considered in Chapter LXXI.

As regards the usual laboratory animals, the injection of large doses of living culture (the growth from $\frac{1}{2}$ to 1 blood-agar slope suspended in saline) into the peritoneum of rabbits, guinea-pigs, or mice, often results in death within 24–48 hours. At autopsy petechial hæmorrhages may be found, scattered over the peritoneum, and sometimes over the pleura. The suprarenals may be congested or hæmorrhagic. The organisms can be recovered from the peritoneal cavity, but not often from the heart's blood. The cause of death seems to be a toxæmia, rather than an invasive infection (see Pfeiffer 1893, Delius and Kolle 1897, McIntosh 1922). Similar results may be obtained with filtrates of cultures in liquid media, and these may produce death on intravenous injection into rabbits or guinea-pigs, though relatively large doses (0·5–5 c.c.) are usually required (see Parker 1919, Ferry and Houghton 1919, Wollstein 1919, McIntosh 1922). There is no evidence that these filtrates contain an exotoxin in the usually accepted sense. In view of Pittman's observations and of her reports that her smooth strains are more virulent than the usual rough strains, it is of interest to note that many observers have recorded wide variations in virulence when a number of strains are tested by the intraperitoneal injection of living cultures. McIntosh (1922), for instance, found that only a small minority of recently isolated strains proved to be of high virulence when tested in this way. It would seem also that strains of *H. influenzæ* isolated from cases of meningitis are usually far more virulent for laboratory animals than strains isolated from the respiratory tract, and that some of these meningeal strains have definite invasive powers (Cohen 1909, Henry 1912, Wollstein 1915).

H. pertussis.—The effect of the intraperitoneal injection of this organism into rabbits or guinea-pigs is very similar to that of *H. influenzæ*. Here again large doses are required to produce death, and the infection seems to be toxæmic rather than invasive (Bordet and Gengou 1907, 1909, Wollstein 1909). Leslie and Gardner (1931) carried out a careful series of experiments in which they determined the relative toxicity of suspensions of strains of

H. pertussis, antigenically in Phase I, II, III or IV, by intraperitoneal injections in guinea-pigs. They found that the minimal lethal dose of strains in Phase III or IV (rough strains) was twenty to thirty times greater than the minimal lethal dose of strains in Phase I or II (smooth, or relatively smooth strains). Here again, the evidence suggests that we are concerned with one of the so-called endotoxins.

H. influenzæ suis.—In association with a filtrable virus (see Chapter LXXI) this organism is an important natural pathogen of swine, and the disease can be experimentally produced in these animals. In relation to the small animals of the laboratory this organism appears to behave much in the same way as *H. influenzæ.* Large intravenous injections may be fatal for rabbits, and large intraperitoneal injections for guinea-pigs or mice ; but the results are very irregular, and there appear to be great differences in the virulence, or toxicity, of different strains (see Lewis and Shope 1931, Kirchenbauer 1934).

H. canis.—The data with regard to the pathogenicity of this species for laboratory animals are extremely scanty. Rivers (1922) notes that the intraperitoneal injection of 1 c.c. of a 24-hours' culture in blood broth failed to kill a mouse ; 2 c.c. intraperitoneally did not kill a small guinea-pig ; 1 c.c. intravenously did not kill a small rabbit.

Variation.

The available data with regard to variation in the genus *Hæmophilus* have already been referred to in the discussion of antigenic structure and of pathogenicity.

Both *H. influenzæ* and *H. pertussis* give rise in artificial culture to variants that are essentially of the rough type. It would, indeed, seem that these species are peculiarly liable to undergo this change. The evidence suggests that rough strains of *H. influenzæ* occur very commonly in the normal nasopharynx, so that the smooth $\rightarrow$ rough variation must be supposed in this case to be of frequent occurrence when the organism is living in its normal habitat. In the case of *H. pertussis* we have, at present, no evidence that rough variations occur among recently isolated parasitic strains ; but there is much evidence to suggest that the production of rough variants is readily induced by growing the organism on a relatively unfavourable medium.

We have, as yet, no evidence with regard to variation in the other species of this group.

H. influenzæ

Isolation.—Isolated by Pfeiffer (1892) from cases of influenza in man.

Habitat.—Strict parasite, living particularly in the upper respiratory tract of man.

Morphology.—In its typical form *H. influenzæ* is a tiny cocco-bacillus (1–1·5 by 0·3–0·4 μ).
According to Pittman (1931), the bacillus in its virulent smooth form is capsulated. Most strains, even when first isolated from the tissues are non-capsulated, but it is possible that these should be regarded as rough variants. Among any large sample of strains, or in any one strain during prolonged subculture in the laboratory, wide departures from the typical morphology will usually be found. Longer bacillary forms and definitely filamentous forms often occur, and the latter may show angular bendings or sinuous curves. In the filamentous forms globular or ovoid swellings are not uncommon. The organism is non-flagellated, and forms no spores. It stains feebly with many of the ordinary bacteriological dyes, more readily with dilute carbol-fuchsin. It is Gram-negative and not acid-fast.

Growth requirements.—*H. influenzæ* requires both the X factor and V factor for its growth. It grows far more readily under aerobic than under anaerobic conditions, and it would appear that some strains are incapable of prolonged anaerobic growth. The optimal temperature for growth is in the neighbourhood of 37° C.

Growth on Solid Media.—On Fildes' or Levinthal's medium the usual type of colony produced by *H. influenzæ* is transparent, or slightly opaque, circular and dome-shaped, or slightly conical, with a slightly splayed-out entire edge. At the end of 24 hours' growth at 37° C. these colonies usually attain a diameter of 0·5–0·8 mm. On further incubation, and in some cases during the first 24 hours, the colony becomes differentiated into a central portion with a granular or contoured surface, an intermediate flattened portion, and a sharply bevelled periphery with a narrow splayed-out edge. During the second 24 hours of growth the colony usually enlarges to a diameter of 1–1·5 mm. There is a tendency, which is not absolute, for differentiation to occur earlier, and to be more pronounced, in strains that have an atypical morphology. The growth is butyrous and emulsifies easily.

Some strains, described by Pittman (1931), give colonies that differ from those described above in having a smooth, undifferentiated, slightly mucoid surface. They have an entire edge. They tend to attain a larger size (1–3 mm. in diameter). They are slightly opaque ; and, when viewed by obliquely transmitted light, they are iridescent. Strains that give this type of colony show antigenic characters, and differences in pathogenicity, which are in accord with the view that they represent the " smooth " phase of the organism, while the more frequently encountered strains, giving the colonial appearances previously described, are in the rough, or partially rough state.

Growth in Liquid Media.—In a suitable liquid medium most strains of *H. influenzæ* give rise to a uniform turbidity, with or without a slight powdery deposit. Some give a more flocculent deposit. The latter usually show an atypical morphology, and the colonial appearances associated with the more advanced stage of rough variation.

Resistance.—*H. influenzæ* is killed by an exposure to a temperature of 50–55° C. for 30 minutes.

Biochemical Activities.—*H. influenzæ* usually ferments dextrose, though not vigorously, producing acid without gas. Lactose and mannitol are never fermented. The action on maltose, saccharose and dextrin varies. Smooth, and morphologically typical strains tend not to attack these substrates. The rougher, morphologically atypical strains ferment them rather more frequently. The production of indole shows a high correlation with other characters that differentiate between relatively smooth and relatively rough strains ; a high proportion of the former, including both Pittman's smooth strains and the more " typical " strains isolated from the normal nasopharynx, produce indole, only a small proportion of the latter. All strains reduce nitrates.

H. influenzæ, as that species is here defined, does not produce hæmolysis.

Antigenic Structure.—Smooth strains, as defined by Pittman (1931), fall into a few well-differentiated antigenic types which appear to be characterized by specific polysaccharide surface antigens, sometimes occurring in a capsular form. The more common rough, or partially rough, strains are antigenically heterogeneous.

Pathogenicity.—Pathogenic for man, particularly in association with virus infections, or with other bacterial diseases. Produces toxic death when injected in large doses into laboratory animals.

Hæmolytic Influenza Bacilli

These differ from the typical form of *H. influenzæ*, (*a*) in producing hæmolysis in solid or fluid media containing blood corpuscles, (*b*) in requiring the V factor, but not the X factor, for their growth, (*c*) in fermenting maltose and saccharose and often dextrin. In this last respect they resemble the rougher strains of *H. influenzæ*, except that their action on maltose and saccharose is far more consistent. They also resemble these strains in presenting an atypical morphology, and in usually failing to produce indole. It seems possible that they deserve a separate specific name, or at least recognition as a named variety.

Para-influenza Bacilli

These strains, though not often encountered, have been isolated from cases of ulcerative endocarditis in man (Stuart-Harris *et al.* 1935). They resemble the hæmolytic strains in requiring the V factor, but not the X factor for their growth, and in most other ways; but they do not produce hæmolysis.

The Koch-Weeks Bacillus

There is no known way in which this organism can be distinguished from *H. influenzæ*. The fact that strains so labelled have been isolated from the conjunctiva does not seem to warrant the allotment of a separate specific name.

H. influenzæ suis

Isolated from cases of swine influenza in which it is associated with a filtrable virus. The characters of this species as recorded by Lewis and Shope (1931) differ from the human strains of *H. influenzæ* only in that no carbohydrates are fermented, and no indole is produced. The number of strains as yet examined does not, however, justify any definite generalized statement on this point. (See also Kirchenbauer 1934.)

H. canis

Isolated by Friedberger (1903) from the prepuce of dogs. It is apparently parasitic, but not pathogenic. It differs from *H. influenzæ* in the following ways: It requires the X factor, but not the V factor, for its growth. On solid media it forms colonies that are at first indistinguishable from those of *H. influenzæ*, but later become larger and more opaque. As regards its fermentation reactions it ferments dextrose, saccharose and mannitol, produces indole and reduces nitrates. In its fermentation of mannitol it differs from both typical and atypical strains of *H. influenzæ*.

H. pertussis

Isolation.—Isolated by Bordet and Gengou (1906) from cases of whooping cough, and now recognized as the causal organism of that disease.

Morphology.—*H. pertussis* bears a general resemblance to *H. influenzæ* in its morphology. The cell-form is more constant, being usually of the short bacillary type. Longer bacillary or thread forms may occur, but they are relatively uncommon.

Growth Requirements.—*H. pertussis* is not dependent on either the V factor or the X factor for growth. On first isolation it requires a complex medium, the most suitable being that devised by Bordet and Gengou, containing blood, potato extract and glycerol. It can, however, be trained to grow on agar. The optimal temperature for growth is in the near neighbourhood of 37° C.

Growth on Solid Media.—On the Bordet-Gengou medium *H. pertussis* gives smooth, dome-shaped, glistening colonies, with an entire edge. They are more opaque than those of *H. influenzæ*, and are greyish as well as glistening. They have been likened not inappropriately to a bisected pearl, less appropriately to a small drop of mercury. When fully developed they tend to be rather larger than the colonies of *H. influenzæ*; but they develop more slowly and the characteristic appearances described above are often not obvious in less than 48–72 hours' incubation.

Growth in Liquid Media.—In serum *H. pertussis* gives a uniform turbidity with a slight deposit, which is sometimes slightly flocculent.

Resistance.—*H. pertussis* is killed by exposure to a temperature of 55° C. for 30 minutes.

Biochemical Activities.—*H. pertussis* does not ferment any sugar. It does not form indole, or reduce nitrates. It produces a hazy zone of hæmolysis.

Antigenic Structure.—H. pertussis in the normal smooth phase constitutes a single antigenic type. In artificial culture, particularly on a relatively unfavourable medium, it gives rise to rough, or partially rough, variants, with a different antigenic structure.

Pathogenicity.—H. pertussis is the cause of whooping cough in man. Injected in large doses into laboratory animals it gives rise to a fatal toxæmic infection very similar to that produced by *H. influenzæ.*

REFERENCES

ANDERSON, L. R. (1931) *Amer. J. Hyg.*, **13**, 164.
ANDERSON, R. A. and SCHULTZ, O. T. (1921) *J. exp. Med.*, **33**, 653.
BAUDISCH, O. (1932) *Biochem. Z.*, **245**, 265.
BIELING, R. and WEICHBRODT, R. (1920) *Dtsch. med. Wschr.*, **46**, 1183.
BORDET, J. (1912) *Zbl. Bakt.*, **66**, 276.
BORDET, J. and GENGOU, O. (1906) *Ann. Inst. Pasteur*, **20**, 731 ; (1907) *Ibid.*, **21**, 720 ; (1909) *Ibid.*, **23**, 415.
BORDET, J. and SLEESWYK. (1910) *Ann. Inst. Pasteur*, **24**, 476.
BOURN, J. M. (1927) *J. infect. Dis.*, **41**, 294.
COHEN, C. (1909) *Ann. Inst. Pasteur*, **23**, 273.
COOPER, G. M., MISHULOW, L., and BLANC, N. E. (1921) *J. Immunol.*, **6**, 25.
DAVIS, J. D. (1917) *J. infect. Dis.*, **21**, 392 ; (1921) *Ibid.*, **29**, 178, 187.
DELIUS, W. and KOLLE, W. (1897) *Z. Hyg. InfektKr.*, **24**, 327.
DIBLE, J. H. (1924) *J. Path. Bact.*, **27**, 151.
DOCHEZ, A. R., MILLS, K. C., and KNEELAND, Y. JR. (1932) *Proc. Soc. exp. Biol., N.Y.*, **30**, 314.
EIRUND, A. (1929) *Zbl. Bakt.*, **111**, 195.
FERRY, N. S. and HOUGHTON, E. M. (1919) *J. Immunol.*, **4**, 233.
FILDES, P. (1920) *Brit. J. exp. Path.*, **1**, 129 ; (1921) *Ibid.*, **2**, 16 ; (1922) *Ibid.*, **3**, 210; (1923) *Ibid.*, **4**, 265 ; (1924) *Ibid.*, **5**, 69.
FLEMING, A. (1929) *Brit. J. exp. Path.*, **10**, 226.
FLEMING, A. and MACLEAN, I. H. (1930) *Brit. J. exp. Path.*, **11**, 127.
FRIEDBERGER, E. (1903) *Zbl. Bakt.*, **33**, 401.
GHON, A. and PREYSS, W. VON. (1904) *Zbl. Bakt.*, **35**, 531.
GRASSBERGER, R. (1897) *Z. Hyg. InfektKr.*, **25**, 453.
GUNDEL, M. and SCHLÜTER, W. (1933) *Zbl. Bakt.*, **129**, 461.
HENRY, H. (1912) *J. Path. Bact.*, **17**, 174.
KIRCHENBAUER, H. (1934) *Z. InfektKr. Haustiere*, **45**, 273.
KNIGHT, B. C. J. G. (1936) *Spec. Rep. Ser. med. Res. Coun., Lond.*, No. 210.
KNORR, M. (1924) *Zbl. Bakt.*, **92**, 371, 385.
KOCH, R. (1887) *Arb. ReichsgesundhAmt.*, **3**, 62.
KOPP, H. (1927–8) *Zbl. Bakt.*, **105**, 54.
KRAGE, P. (1910) *Z. InfektKr. Haustiere*, **7**, 380.
KRISTENSEN, M. (1922) " Hæmoglobinophilic Bacteria." Copenhagen ; (1927) *C. R. Soc. Biol.*, **96**, 355.
KRUMWIEDE, C., MISHULOW, L., and OLDENBUSCH, C. (1923) *J. infect. Dis.*, **32**, 22.
LESLIE, P. H. and GARDNER, A. D. (1931) *J. Hyg., Camb.*, **31**, 423.
LEVINTHAL, W. (1918) *Z. Hyg. InfektKr.*, **86**, 1.
LEWIS, P. A. and SHOPE, R. E. (1931) *J. exp. Med.*, **54**, 361.
McINTOSH, J. (1922) *Spec. Rep. Ser. med. Res. Coun., Lond.*, No. 63.
MESSERSCHMIDT, T., HUNDESHAGEN, K., and SCHEER, K. (1919) *Z. Hyg. InfektKr.*, **88**, 552.
MEYER, K. (1934) *Zbl. Bakt.*, **131**, 289.
ODAIRA. (1911) *Zbl. Bakt.*, **61**, 289.
OLMSTEAD, M. and POVITZKY, O. R. (1916) *J. med. Res.*, **33**, 379.
OLSEN, O. (1920) *Zbl. Bakt.*, **85**, 12.
PARK, W. H., WILLIAMS, A. W., and COOPER, G. (1918) *Proc. Soc. exp. Biol., N.Y.*, **16**, 120.
PARKER, J. T. (1919) *J. Amer. med. Ass.*, **72**, 476.
PFEIFFER, R. (1892) *Dtsch. med. Wschr.*, **18**, 28 ; (1893) *Z. Hyg. InfektKr.*, **13**, 357.
PITTMAN, M. (1931) *J. exp. Med.*, **53**, 471 ; (1935) *J. Bact.*, **30**, 149.
PLATT, A. E. (1936) (In Press).
POVITZKY, O. R. and DENNY, H. T. (1921) *J. Immunol.*, **6**, 65.
PRITCHETT, I. W. and STILLMAN, E. G. (1919) *J. exp. Med.*, **29**, 259.
RITCHIE, J. (1910) *J. Path. Bact.*, **14**, 615.
RIVERS, T. M. (1922) *J. Bact.*, **7**, 579.

RIVERS, T. M. and KOHN, L. A.   (1921) *J. exp. Med.*, **34**, 477.
SHIBLEY, G. S. and HOELSCHER, H.   (1934) *J. exp. Med.*, **60**, 403.
SHIGA, K., IMAI, N., and EGUCHI, C.   (1913) *Zbl. Bakt.*, **69**, 104.
SHOPE, R. E.   (1931) *J. exp. Med.*, **54**, 349.
SMITH, M. M.   (1931) *J. Hyg., Camb.*, **31**, 321.
STILLMAN, E. G. and BOURN, J. M.   (1920) *J. exp. Med.*, **32**, 665.
STUART-HARRIS, C. H., WELLS, A. Q., ROSHER, A. B., MACKIE, F. P., and WILSON, G. S.
       (1935) *J. Path. Bact.*, **41**, 407.
THALIMER, W.   (1914) *Zbl. Bakt.*, **74**, 189.
THJØTTA, T.   (1921) *J. exp. Med.*, **33**, 763.
THJØTTA, T. and AVERY, O. T.   (1921) *J. exp. Med.*, **34**, 97, 455.
TOOMEY, J. A., RANTA, K., ROBEY, L., and McCLELLAND, J. E.   (1935) *J. infect. Dis.*,
       57, 49.
VALENTINE, E. and COOPER, G. M.   (1919) *J. Immunol.*, **4**, 359.
VALENTINE, F. C. O. and RIVERS, T. M.   (1927) *J. exp. Med.*, **45**, 993.
WADE, H. W. and MANALANG, C.   (1920) *J. exp. Med.*, **31**, 95.
WEBSTER, L. T. and BAUDISCH, O.   (1925) *J. exp. Med.*, **42**, 473.
WEEKS, J. E.   (1887) *Arch. Augenheilk.*, **17**, 318.
WINHOLT, W.   (1915) *J. infect. Dis.*, **16**, 389.
WINSLOW, C.-E. A., BROADHURST, J., BUCHANAN, R. E., KRUMWIEDE, C., ROGERS, L. A.,
       and SMITH, G. H.   (1920) *J. Bact.*, **5**, 191.
WOLLSTEIN, M.   (1909) *J. exp. Med.*, **11**, 41 ; (1915) *Ibid.*, **22**, 445 ; (1919) *Ibid.*, **30**, 555.
WRIGHT, J. and WARD, H. K.   (1932) *J. exp. Med.*, **55**, 235.
YABE, S.   (1921) *Brit. J. exp. Path.*, **2**, 197.

CHAPTER XXXI

BRUCELLA

DEFINITION.—*Brucella.*

Small, non-sporing, Gram-negative cocco-bacilli, usually non-motile. Grow rather poorly on ordinary media, or may require special media. Aerobic; no growth under strict anaerobic conditions. Growth often improved by CO_2. Fail to ferment carbohydrates. Usually tend to produce alkali in litmus milk, and a brown pigmentation on potato. Strict parasites, occurring in man and animals, and producing characteristic infections.

Type species. *Brucella melitensis.*

HISTORY.—The first member of the group, *Br. melitensis*, was isolated in 1887 by Bruce from the spleen of patients who had died of Malta fever. At that time, and for a long time afterwards, the bacillary nature of the organism was not recognized; in all the older textbooks it is therefore described as a micrococcus. The organism finds its natural habitat in the goat and the sheep. It may, however, infect other animals. In man it gives rise to undulant fever. It is fairly widely distributed throughout the world.

The discovery of the second member, *Br. abortus*, was made by Bang of Copenhagen in 1897. Working in conjunction with Stribolt, he isolated the organism from cows suffering from infectious abortion, and by a series of experiments demonstrated its specific rôle in this disease. The organism is parasitic in cattle. To a less extent it infects certain other animals. In man it gives rise to undulant fever. It is perhaps even more widespread than *Br. melitensis*, having been found in practically every country of the world.

In 1911, Ferry in the United States described a short bacillus that he had isolated from the respiratory tract of dogs in the early stage of distemper; to this organism he gave the name of *Bacillus bronchicanis*. A similar organism had been described as early as 1896 by Galli-Valerio, by Tartakowsky (1897–98) in 1898, by Strada and Traina in 1900 as *B. pneumoniæ caviarum*, by Martini in 1900 as *B. pulmonum glutinosus*, and by Selter in 1906 as *B. cavisepticus mobilis*; Ferry, however, was the first to study it fully. Later Ferry (1912, 1912–13) found the same bacillus in a guinea-pig epizootic, and in monkeys and rabbits; he therefore changed its name to *B. bronchisepticus*.

Working at about the same time in Edinburgh, M'Gowan (1911) isolated a similar organism from dogs suffering from distemper, and from a number of other animals, and came to much the same conclusions as Ferry with regard to the pathogenicity of this organism. *Br. bronchiseptica*, like the other members of the group, is essentially parasitic, giving rise to lesions in the respiratory tract of dogs, monkeys, guinea-pigs, and other laboratory animals; it is occasionally

631

found in the nasopharynx of man. In distemper it appears to be a secondary invader, being frequently responsible for the pulmonary complications of the disease (Laidlaw and Dunkin 1926).

The fourth member of the group, *Brucella tularensis*, was isolated by McCoy and Chapin in 1912 from a plague-like disease among rodents in California, and was called by them *Bacterium tularense*. It infects ground-squirrels, jack-rabbits, and other rodents, and occasionally gives rise to a disease in man called tularæmia.

The fifth member, *Br. suis*, was isolated by Traum (1914) from the fœtus of a sow. It is a natural parasite of pigs, in which it gives rise to a disease frequently character-ized by inflammatory lesions in the reproductive organs. It may occasionally infect other animals. In man it shares with *Br. melitensis* and *Br. abortus* the ability to produce undulant fever. It appears to be very much less widespread than these two organisms, its chief home being in the large hog-raising districts of the middle western states of North America. In Denmark, *Br. suis* strains have been isolated by Thomsen (1931, 1934), which differ in certain respects from those found in the United States ; they will be referred to as the Danish porcine type. The American type has been found occasionally in Europe (see Thomsen 1934), and has been reported from Brazil (Neiva, 1934), the Argentine, and Australia (King 1934).

Nomenclature.—We have no space to discuss the early confusion of terminology that existed over members of this group. The whole position was altered when Evans in 1918 drew attention to the essential similarity of the organisms which at that time were described as *Micrococcus melitensis* and *Bacillus abortus*. Nor do we propose to discuss the validity of the generic name *Brucella* suggested for them by Meyer and Shaw (1920) and by Feusier and Meyer (1920) in honour of Sir David Bruce. This is so appropriate and has met with such universal approval that no other term seems likely to enter into serious competition with it. There are, however, certain points that require discussion. The three organisms isolated from goats, cattle, and pigs respectively are so closely allied that their differentiation can be accomplished only with difficulty. The question is, therefore, whether they should be regarded as varieties of one species, or should be ranked as separate species. Both proposals have their advocates. On the whole we favour the latter course, mainly for the sake of convenience. We shall therefore refer to these three organisms as *Br. melitensis*, *Br. abortus* and *Br. suis*. It must be pointed out, however, that the differences between the American and Danish porcine types are almost as great as those between the porcine and bovine types, and the decision to treat them as varieties of *Br. suis* is purely arbitrary.

The names *paramelitensis*, *para-abortus*, and *parasuis* are frequently used to refer to inagglutinable strains of *Brucella*, corresponding most closely to the *meli-tensis*, *abortus*, and *suis* types. So long as the so-called para-strains were regarded as distinct species, no objection could be raised to this terminology ; but now that they are known to be merely rough variants of the original smooth forms, this practice is no longer justifiable and merely serves to confuse the nomenclature. We shall refer to these, therefore, as rough *melitensis*, *abortus*, or *suis* strains, as the case may be.

Br. bronchiseptica falls into a different category. Its exact relationship to the other members of the group is doubtful, mainly because it has not yet been subjected to a comprehensive systematic study. Smith (1913) emphasizes its relationship to *Ps. pyocyanea*, and Ferry and Noble (1918) to *H. pertussis*. It differs from the former in being neither monotrichate, saprophytic, nor chromogenic, and from the latter in being motile and in having different growth requirements. We ourselves have pointed out many resemblances to Perez's bacillus (p. 368). It differs from *Br. melitensis*, *Br. abortus* and *Br. suis* in being motile, but since in several other respects it closely resembles these organisms, we consider it advisable to place it temporarily at least in the *Brucella* group.

The inclusion of *Br. tularensis* in this group is largely tentative. Reimann (1932), along with several other workers, would assign it to the *Pasteurella* group on account of its bipolar staining, its solubility in 1/800 sodium ricinoleate, and its transmission by insect vectors. On the other hand its general morphology, the beneficial effect of CO_2 on its growth, its failure to develop anaerobically, its production of H_2S, its very weak fermentative ability, its antigenic affinity to *Br. melitensis* and *Br. abortus*, and its high pathogenicity for man in the laboratory qualify it perhaps even better for inclusion in the *Brucella* group. Since, however, it has not been studied with the same thoroughness as the other members, we shall exclude it from the

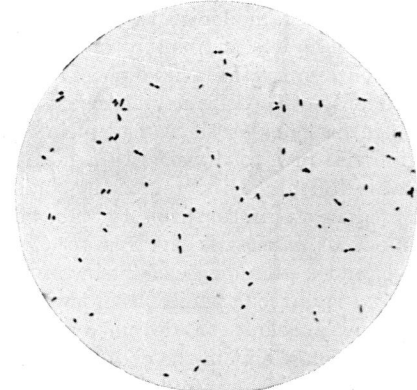

Fig. 151.—*Brucella abortus*.
From an agar culture, 24 hours, 37° C., showing very short bacillary forms ($\times$ 1000).

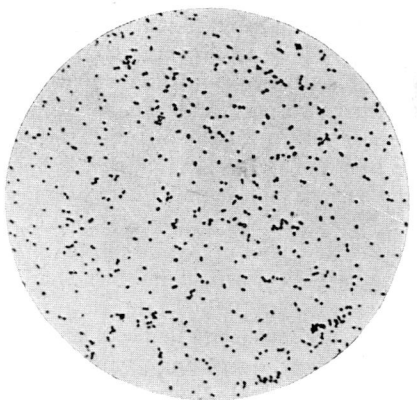

Fig. 152.—*Brucella melitensis*.
From an agar culture, 2 days, 37° C., showing mainly coccal forms ($\times$ 1000).

following description of the group characteristics, and describe it separately at the end of the chapter.

Morphology and Staining.—With the exception of *Br. bronchiseptica*, which is motile by means of 4–6 peritrichate flagella, all four organisms resemble each other fairly closely. The bacilli are short and slender; the axis is straight; the ends are rounded; the sides may be parallel or convex outwards. In length they vary from about 0·6 to 1·5 μ, and in breadth from 0·5 to 0·7 μ. The short forms may appear as oval cocci, or, if they are about to divide, as diplococci. As a rule they are arranged singly, in pairs end-to-end, or in small groups; sometimes short chains of 4–6 members may be seen, especially in liquid media. Owing to the frequent coccoid appearance, their bacillary nature may be in doubt, but it may be noted that in size they are smaller than any of the Gram-negative cocci. Moreover, when arranged in pairs, their long diameter is in the same axis as that in which they are lying, in distinction to the Gram-negative diplococci, whose long axis is generally at right angles to that in which they are lying.

Br. melitensis is generally considered to be more coccal in form than *Br. abortus*, and for this there is some justification. The difference in size and shape, however, is so slight as to render it impossible to distinguish with certainty between individual strains. Duncan (1928) has pointed out that these organisms, when grown on agar or glucose agar, show no marked morphological differences ; but if they are cultivated on a relatively rich medium, such as Fildes' peptic digest blood agar, the *Br. abortus* strains frequently develop long bacillary forms, reaching 2·0 or 3·0 μ in length, whereas *Br. melitensis* strains usually retain their coccal shape and rarely exceed 1·0 μ in length.

The organisms stain fairly well with the ordinary dyes. Bipolar staining is not uncommon, and occasionally irregularity in the depth of colour is seen. In old cultures irregular forms may be seen. They are Gram-negative, non-acid-fast, and form neither capsules nor spores.

Cultural Reactions.—Apart from their different CO_2 requirements, the members of this group resemble each other closely in their cultural characteristics. None of them are difficult to grow ; none grow profusely. On agar the colonies are small, translucent and undifferentiated. In broth there is a moderate turbidity with a slight powdery or viscous sediment, which disintegrates completely on shaking ; after about 2 weeks in the incubator or at room temperature the deposit becomes extremely viscous, and can be disintegrated only with difficulty. According to Thomsen (1933), if the organisms are grown in flasks of broth instead of in tubes the *suis* and CO_2-sensitive *abortus* types give rise in 1 to 3 weeks to a mealy or scaly surface pellicle and a heavy deposit that is difficult to disintegrate by shaking. Aerobic *abortus* strains form no pellicle, but produce a uniform turbidity and a slight deposit that is easily disintegrated. Strains of *Br. melitensis* give rise to a fairly dense turbidity, a moderately heavy deposit, and a granular, usually incomplete, surface growth. Growth in gelatin is poor, and is unaccompanied by liquefaction. Perhaps the most striking peculiarity is the yellowish colour that develops on potato in 2 to 3 days, deepening to a café-au-lait or chocolate tint in the course of a fortnight. Individual strains vary in the depth of colour they produce, some giving a darker brown than others. The pigment is not confined to the layer of growth ; it spreads throughout the potato. It will be recalled that a brown growth on potato is also given by *Pf. mallei*, *Pf. whitmori*, *V. choleræ*, and *Ps. pyocyanea*, and certain other organisms. A similar but less intense brownish colour is sometimes noticeable in old agar slope cultures, particularly of *Br. melitensis* (Kristensen 1931) ; it is not sufficiently constant, however, to be of differential value.

Huddleson, Hasley, and Torrey (1927) and Huddleson and Winter (1927) have observed the development of crystals of ammonium magnesium phosphate in cultures of *Brucella* on liver agar incubated aerobically, but not in 5–10 per cent. CO_2. They regard their formation as being due to the production of ammonia by the growing organisms, and to its combination with the magnesium phosphate in the medium. In their experience crystals are formed much more rapidly by *melitensis* and *paramelitensis* than by *abortus* strains. Our own experience (Wilson 1933) bears out their observations to some extent, but does not suggest that the differences between different types are sufficient to be of value in the identification of individual strains. Incidentally American *suis* strains appear to be most active in the production of ammonia.

Attention has been drawn by de Santis (1933) to the different appearances presented on Petragnani's egg medium. Strains of *Br. melitensis* are said to grow on this medium, and usually to change the colour from light yellowish-green to dark green. *Br. abortus* strains, on the other hand, generally fail to develop. The behaviour of *Br. suis* strains is doubtful, but in our limited experience growth is not infrequent. The reliability of this test for differential purposes is still under discussion (see Menzani 1934, Tosatti 1934, Messieri 1935, Vittone 1935, Pagnini 1935, Foresti 1935). The general opinion seems to be that it is less satisfactory than the H_2S and dye tests (see later). The mode of preparation of the medium appears to be of importance. If it is heated to a temperature above 80° C. for too long the normal inhibitory action of the egg albumin on the bovine and porcine strains is destroyed, thus allowing some development of these organisms to occur (de Santis 1935). According to Martini (1935), the inhibitory effect of the egg albumin on *abortus* strains can be removed by the addition of sufficient HCl to lower the reaction of the finished medium from pH 8·4 to pH 6·8. If this is true, it suggests that the effect may be related to the greater necessity of *abortus* strains for CO_2. *Br. bronchiseptica* behaves on this medium like *Br. melitensis*.

With the exception of *Br. bronchiseptica*, growth is rather slow, and unless a fairly heavy inoculum is made, colonies are not usually visible for 2 days or even longer. In broth the maximum turbidity is not reached for a week or more. On the whole the American porcine strains probably give the best, and the Danish porcine strains the poorest growth, the *melitensis* and *abortus* strains occupying an intermediate position. The behaviour, however, of different strains of the same type is subject to so much variation that no reliance can be placed on this character for differential purposes.

Growth Requirements.—Growth is generally improved by the addition of natural animal protein to the medium. The most satisfactory media, particularly for the growth of *Br. abortus* and *Br. melitensis*, are liver extract agar—first described by Holth (1911), subsequently by Stafseth (1920), and frequently referred to as Huddleson's medium—2 per cent. glycerol agar (Zeller and Stockmayer 1933), Fleming's (1919) chocolate agar (Henry *et al.* 1932), and 5 per cent. serum agar. Zobell and Meyer (1932) have described a synthetic medium in which the metabolism of *Brucella* strains may be studied.

The range of temperature consistent with growth is 20°–40° C. ; the optimum being about 37° C. At 20° C. growth is very slow. The effect of H-ion concentration is rather difficult to dissociate from that of CO_2. Many strains of *Br. abortus* require for their optimum development a concentration of 5–10 per cent. CO_2 in the atmosphere. This has the effect of turning an alkaline medium acid. For the growth of these organisms an initial H-ion concentration of pH 6·6 is desirable. The other members of the group usually grow as well on an alkaline as on a slightly acid medium ; but since, as will be pointed out directly, even *melitensis* strains are often benefited by a small amount of extra CO_2, it is advisable for practical purposes to adjust media to pH 6·6–6·8.

CO_2 Requirements.—One of the most interesting features of the *Brucella* group is their peculiar respiratory behaviour. Ever since its original isolation by Bang (1897), *Br. abortus* has presented certain difficulties in cultivation. No growth occurs on a solid medium under aerobic conditions. If, however, the tube is suitably sealed (Preisz 1903) (see Fig. 153), or if it is attached by rubber tubing to another tube inoculated with an organism such as *B. subtilis* (Nowak 1908), growth occurs after a delay of a few days. These observations were generally interpreted as showing that *Br. abortus* was microaerophilic, and could not grow till the partial pressure of oxygen over the culture had been lowered to a suitable extent. A similar interpretation was also placed on the fact that, when inoculated into a serum agar gelatin shake medium, it grew in the form of a band situated about $\frac{1}{2}$ cm. below the surface (Fig. 154).

Credit is due to Huddleson (1921) for showing that this organism requires for its development a partial pressure of CO_2 higher than that normally present in the atmosphere (0·03–0·0≤ per cent.). He found that if slopes of *Br. abortus* were incubated in a glass jar containing 10 per cent. CO_2, good growth occurred in 24 hours, while under aerobic conditions there was no growth at all. Analysis of the gas over a culture of *B. subtilis* revealed the presence of CO_2, and it was therefore concluded that the success of Nowak's method depended on the evolution of this gas rather than on a decrease in the partial pressure of oxygen. Further work by Smith (1924) and McAlpine and Slanetz (1928*b*) confirmed the importance of CO_2. Smith showed that development was much better in an atmosphere of 10 per cent. CO_2 than in sealed tubes, and that in agar shake cultures, either sealed or incubated in an atmosphere of 10 per cent. CO_2, growth occurred, not in a band below the surface as Bang (1897) and his co-worker Stribolt had found, but on the surface itself.

In spite of these observations, it was not easy to understand why growth should occur in sealed tubes, or why, in the absence of added CO_2, growth in shake tubes should occur in a band below the surface. A fuller study of the gaseous requirements of *Br. abortus* (Wilson 1931*a*) showed (1) that the organism would not grow anaerobically even in the presence of added CO_2, nor aerobically in its absence ; (2) that growth would occur in partial pressures of oxygen varying from 0·5–99·0 per cent., provided a minimum of 0·5 per cent. CO_2 was added, and in partial pressures of CO_2 varying from 0·5–98·0 per cent., provided a minimum of 0·5 per cent. oxygen was added ; (3) that the optimum partial pressure of oxygen for development was about 21 per cent., i.e., that normally present in the atmosphere, and of CO_2 about 10 per cent. No evidence was obtained to suggest that a partial pressure of oxygen lower than that normally present in the atmosphere was beneficial to growth. It seemed clear, therefore, that neither growth in sealed tubes nor the band phenomenon in shake tubes could be due to a preference of the organism for microaerophilic conditions. Further observations (Wilson 1930) showed that CO_2 was given off by burning cotton-wool plugs, and to a less extent by heated paraffin wax, rubber stoppers, and sealing wax. Analysis of the gas inside sterile sealed tubes revealed the presence of CO_2 in amounts varying from about 1–3 per cent. —a proportion ample to initiate growth in inoculated tubes. The larger the number of organisms inoculated, the less need was there for additional CO_2, since the organisms themselves produced a certain amount of this gas. But with inocula of any size, growth was always most rapid and luxuriant when the partial pressures of oxygen and CO_2 most nearly approached the optima.

Similarly, evidence was brought (Wilson 1931*b*) to suggest that the band phenomenon in shake tubes was due to the necessity of an adequate concentration of

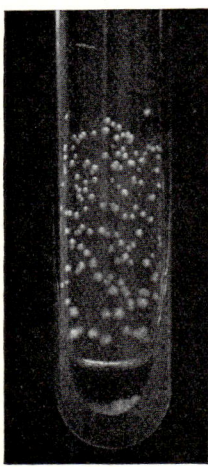

Fig. 153.—*Brucella abortus.*

Glycerine agar slope culture, 3 days, 37° C., in corked tube, showing character of growth on direct isolation from the tissues.

CO_2 (Fig. 154). It was found that this gas was given off to a certain extent by the organisms themselves, and to a still greater extent by certain media, particularly those containing serum. Growth could not occur at the surface, because the CO_2 was given off into the atmosphere ; nor could it occur in the depths of the medium, because the conditions were anaerobic. It therefore commenced in a zone as near the surface as was consistent with the maintenance of an adequate partial pressure of CO_2. If the tube was sealed, or was incubated in an atmosphere of 10 per cent. CO_2, then growth occurred at the surface, where the optimum partial pressure of oxygen existed. This explanation, when slightly amplified, was found to fit the numerous observations on variation in the distance of the band from the surface, and on the so-called double zone phenomenon, in which two bands of growth, separated from each other by apparently unaltered medium, are visible.

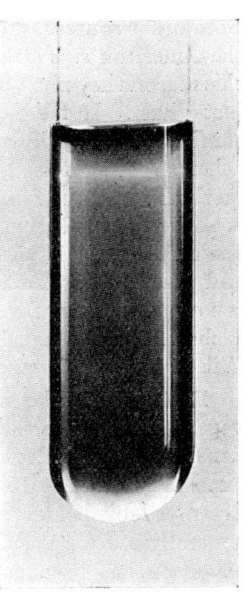

The demand for an increased partial pressure of CO_2 is particularly characteristic of *abortus* strains. Not all strains, however, of this organism require it (see Smith 1924, 1926*b*). The Southern Rhodesian strains (Bevan 1930), for example, grow quite well under ordinary aerobic conditions. Moreover, even strains that need extra CO_2 on isolation frequently become adapted, after a variable time in the laboratory, to do without it. The growth of many strains of *Br. melitensis* is greatly benefited by incubation in an atmosphere of 5–10 per cent. CO_2, though some growth always occurs in ordinary air. The porcine strains, both American and Danish, appear to be least dependent upon CO_2. The addition of this gas to the air never improves their growth and sometimes actually inhibits it. How the CO_2 acts is not definitely known. Alteration in the H-ion concentration of the medium does not seem to be the explanation. It has been suggested that the gas passes through the cell wall and brings about a change in the intracellular H-ion concentration or oxidation-reduction potential, which is necessary for the initiation of growth. As Gladstone, Fildes, and Richardson (1935) have shown, CO_2 seems to be required in a greater or less degree by practically all bacteria, and presumably plays an important part in their metabolism.

Fig. 154.—*Br. abortus.* Growth in form of band situated 6–8 mm. below the surface. Bang's gelatin agar serum medium, pH 7·0, incubated aerobically.

Cultivation in the Presence of Dyes.—To Huddleson and Abell (1928) and Huddleson (1929, 1931) we owe a valuable method of distinguishing between the *melitensis*, *abortus*, and *suis* types, depending on their ability to grow in the presence of certain aniline dyes. Without entering into the detailed technique of the method, we may say that the general procedure is to prepare plates of liver agar, pH 6·6, containing 1/30,000 and 1/60,000 thionin, 1/25,000 and 1/50,000 basic fuchsin, 1/50,000 and 1/100,000 methyl violet, and 1/100,000 and 1/200,000 pyronin. The dyes used must be obtained from the National Aniline Chemical Company of New York, or standardized against these dyes. The organisms are inoculated rather heavily on to the plates, which are then incubated for 3 days aerobically, or in 10 per cent. CO_2, according to the probable nature of the strains under examination. Strains of *Br. melitensis* usually grow to some extent in the presence of all four dyes ; *Br. abortus* strains are inhibited by thionin, but grow freely in the presence of the other three ; *Br. suis* strains grow well in the presence of thionin, but are inhibited by basic fuchsin, methyl violet, and pyronin. Though this is the general behaviour of the three types, there is considerable variation between different strains of the same type, especially those coming from different localities (Meyer and Zobell 1932, Wilson 1933). Some strains of *melitensis*, for example, may grow very poorly on the thionin, methyl violet, or pyronin plates. Southern Rhodesian strains of *Br. abortus* often have a rather greater resistance to thionin than *abortus* strains from other sources. The Danish *suis* strains are more susceptible to all dyes than the American *suis* strains, though their differential susceptibility is the same ; for this reason they must be tested on plates containing only half the dye concentrations just given. If reliance is placed exclusively on this method of differentiation, confusion will not infrequently result between strains of different types. If on the other hand, it is used, as we believe it should be used, in conjunction with other methods, it will be found of considerable value. No other method, it may be noted, is so useful in distinguishing between bovine and porcine strains. The method has been subjected to some criticism (Saitta 1929, Meyer and Eddie 1930, Marshall and Jared 1930, Cerruti 1932, Maggiora-Vergano 1932), but most workers have reported on it very favourably (Kristensen and Holm 1929, Kristensen 1931, Taylor, Lisbonne and Roman 1932, Grumbach and Grillichess 1932, Meyer and Zobell 1932, Wilson 1933, Olin and Lindström 1934, Pagnini 1934, di Mino 1935).

Resistance.—The members of this group exhibit the usual susceptibility of vegetative bacteria to heat and disinfectants. In aqueous suspensions of moderate density they are destroyed by heating for about 10 minutes at 60° C., and by exposure for about 15 minutes to 1·0 per cent. phenol. In milk they are readily destroyed by holder pasteurization. In agar cultures kept sealed at 0° C. they generally live for at least 1 month, and often for considerably longer. Considerable attention has been paid to their resistance under natural conditions, and much information on this subject will be found in the Report of the Mediterranean Fever Commission (1905–07). So many factors determine the exact outcome of any given observation under natural conditions that it is dangerous to draw general conclusions from the data so collected. In favourable circumstances, however, *Br. melitensis* may remain alive for 6 days in urine, 6 weeks in dust, and 10 weeks in water or soil. *Br. abortus* may survive for 7 months in infected uterine exudate kept at about freezing-point (Bang 1897). In raw milk at room temperature it seems to die out fairly rapidly with the production of acid. Acid production also seems to be the cause of its rapid death in butter and cheese ; the organisms can rarely be found in these articles for more than a few days (Smith 1934, Pullinger 1935). It may live for a month in ice-cream (Thompson 1933). *Br. suis* may live on sacking for 4 weeks and in sterile fæces for 100 days in the dark (Cameron 1932, 1933).

Metabolism and Biochemical Properties.—The effect of temperature and H-ion conditions on growth has already been considered. With the possible exception of *Br. bronchiseptica*, which according to Torrey and Rahe (1913) may grow slightly under anaerobic conditions, all the members require the presence of oxygen, while most strains of *Br. abortus* require in addition a partial pressure of CO_2 considerably higher than that found in atmospheric air. Under ordinary aerobic conditions of incubation broth cultures become markedly alkaline, owing to the production of ammonia. Litmus milk is turned definitely alkaline by *Br. bronchiseptica*, but only weakly so by the other three members of the group. *Br. bronchiseptica* is credited with the production of a hæmolysin acting on rabbit red cells. Occasional hæmolytic strains of *Br. melitensis* have been described (Forni 1927), but usually neither the *melitensis, abortus,* nor *suis* strains have any lytic action on blood. The effect of bile-salt on growth has not been studied fully ; on MacConkey's medium *Br. bronchiseptica* usually grows quite well, while strains of *Br. abortus, Br. melitensis,* and *Br. suis* generally give rise to small non-lactose-fermenting colonies after 3 or 4 days.

In ordinary sugar media no fermentation is observable. Unlike most pathogenic organisms, the members of this group are unable to produce obvious acid even from glucose. However, quantitative observations have shown that some *melitensis* and American *suis* strains, if grown in 1 per cent. glucose peptone water, may utilize 5–20 per cent. of the glucose within a week, while *abortus* strains are unable to use more than 2 per cent. The acid produced is more than neutralized by the alkali formed as the result of protein breakdown, so that it is not detected by the usual indicators. McAlpine and Slanetz (1928*a*) have recommended the glucose utilization test as a means of differentiating between the *abortus, melitensis,* and *suis* types, but most workers have found it unreliable, and it has now been generally discarded. There is evidence that arabinose and xylose are fermented by members of the *Brucella* group (Mallardo 1930, Coleman *et al.* 1930, McNutt and Purwin 1931, Silberstein 1932), but the reaction is of no differential significance.

The methyl red and Voges-Proskauer tests are negative. No indole is formed. According to Zobell and Meyer (1932), all types reduce nitrates to nitrites. Nitrites are also rapidly reduced, so that the Griess-Ilosvay test on nitrate broth cultures may be negative. American *suis* strains are more active than the other types in reducing nitrites. Ammonia is produced to a variable extent from peptone, urea, and asparagin. The catalase test is positive, especially with *Br. bronchiseptica*. The reducing action of these organisms is comparatively weak (Habs 1930), and in broth cultures methylene blue is often not decolorized. Tuttle and Huddleson (1934) found that liver extract broth cultures showed a negative drift to a limiting potential after 8 days of $+ 0.15$ to $+ 0.09$ volt. *Br. suis* appeared to be slightly more active than the *abortus* or *melitensis* types, but the difference was insufficient to be of value in species identification (see also Bau and Wang 1935). It may be noted that some strains of *Br. abortus* reduce basic fuchsin. Huddleson (1931) thought that this was a property of non-pathogenic strains, but our observations do not bear this out.

H₂S Production.—One of the most important differential criteria, to which attention was first drawn by Huddleson and Abell (1927), and Huddleson (1929), is the production of H₂S. This test should be carried out on liver agar using lead acetate papers (see p. 259). Freshly isolated strains of *Br. abortus* and *Br. suis* (American variety) give off H₂S for at least the first 4 days, while strains of *melitensis* produce either none at all, or only during the first 24 hours of incubation. The Danish variety of *Br. suis* forms no H₂S. In the laboratory, *abortus* and American *suis* strains sometimes lose their ability to produce H₂S ; the test should therefore be made as soon after isolation as possible. The interpretation of this test can be summed up by saying that, while failure of a given strain to produce H₂S beyond the first day does not exclude its being of *abortus* or American *suis* type, the continued production of H₂S after the first day affords a strong presumption that it is not of *melitensis* or Danish *suis* type. This test has now been widely used, and to those who have realized its limitations it has given satisfaction (Favilli 1930, Kristensen 1931, Taylor, Lisbonne, and Roman 1932, Zobell and Meyer 1932, Zeller and Stockmayer 1933, Wilson 1933, Olin and Lindström 1934, Pagnini 1934, di Mino 1935).

Antigenic Structure.—It would be idle to recapitulate here the confusion that reigned for so long over the antigenic relationship of members of this group. Previous to 1918, when Evans demonstrated an antigenic affinity between *Br. melitensis* and *Br. abortus*, most workers had concerned themselves with comparison of *melitensis* and so-called *paramelitensis* strains, while for many years subsequently progress was hindered by a failure to realize the difference in antigenic structure between strains in the smooth and rough phases.

The early work of Sergent, Gillot, and Lemaire (1908), and Nègre and Raynaud (1912*a*, *b*), demonstrated the existence of strains morphologically and culturally resembling *Br. melitensis* but failing to agglutinate to more than a fraction of the titre with an anti-melitensis serum. These irregular strains were given the name of *paramelitensis*. Later on, so-called *para-abortus* strains were encountered, and these were believed to represent merely a special antigenic type of *Br. abortus*. Further study, however, by such workers as Favilli (1926*a*, *b*), Ross (1927*a*), Valenti (1927), Vidal and Abella (1928), de Antoni (1929), Zdrodowski *et al.* (1930), Pampana (1931) and Pandit and Wilson (1932), showed that *paramelitensis* and *para-abortus* strains were agglutinable by non-specific agents, particularly acid, salt, peptone, and certain aniline dyes, whereas freshly isolated strains of *Br. melitensis* and *Br. abortus* were unaffected by these agents under similar conditions. Moreover, it was found that continued cultivation in broth, or better still in broth containing immune serum, led to a transition of *melitensis* and *abortus* strains into *paramelitensis* and *para-abortus* respectively. The transition, it may be noted, occurs much more readily with *melitensis* than with *abortus* strains, and evidence of its commencement is often noticeable within a very short time of isolation, even when the organisms are kept on solid media. There seems to be little doubt that this change, which may be accompanied by alterations in colonial appearance and by a decrease in virulence for laboratory animals, is essentially a manifestation of the S $\rightarrow$ R variation. The antigenic change involved is not yet clearly understood, but there is evidence that it involves a loss of the specific smooth antigen. Strains of different degrees of roughness are encountered, varying from those that agglutinate to titre with a smooth serum but are slightly susceptible to non-specific agglutination to those that are unaffected by a smooth serum and are incapable of remaining homogeneously distributed even in cold saline. In practice the degree of roughness is best estimated by boiling in saline for 2 hours (thermoagglutination test), by incubation at 37° C. with 1/500 or 1/1000 trypaflavine (Alessandrini and Sabatucci 1931, Pampana 1931), or by testing with an antiserum prepared against a completely rough strain of the corresponding type. Little work has so far been done on the antigenic structure of the rough types. Our own incomplete observations suggest that, though there may be a common antigen to *paramelitensis*, *para-abortus*, and *parasuis* types, there are certain differences between them. One important practical point is that partly rough strains are liable to be agglutinated non-specifically by the sera of normal persons, and particularly of those suffering from certain febrile diseases (see Mohr 1935), and are therefore liable to lead to an erroneous diagnosis of undulant fever in routine serological work.

Turning now to the differentiation of *Br. melitensis*, *Br. abortus*, and *Br. suis* on the basis of antigenic structure, we are faced with a mass of conflicting reports most of which may be summarized by saying, either that no difference was found between the three organisms, or that they fell serologically into a number of different types (see Feusier and Meyer 1920, Burnet 1925, Evans 1925*a, b*, Ross 1927*b*, Cerruti 1927, Kristensen and Holme 1929, Bieling 1930, Kristensen 1931, Francis 1931, Plastridge and McAlpine 1932). The reason for this confusion is probably due to the failure of most of these workers to realize the disturbance caused by antigenic variation of the S $\rightarrow$ R type. If, as Wilson and Miles (1932) showed, care is taken to exclude all but absolutely smooth strains, then it is possible by means of quantitative agglutinin-absorption tests to differentiate between *Br. melitensis* on the one hand and *Br. abortus* and *Br. suis* on the other. The antigenic picture so obtained is represented in Fig. 155. It will be seen that all three types contain the same two antigens, but with a different quantitative distribution, the M antigen being in excess in the *melitensis*, the A antigen in the *abortus* and *suis* types. By carefully adjusting the absorbing dose to the titre of the serum, it is generally possible to absorb out all the minor agglutinins without removing more than a fraction of the major agglutinins. The resulting serum is therefore monospecific,

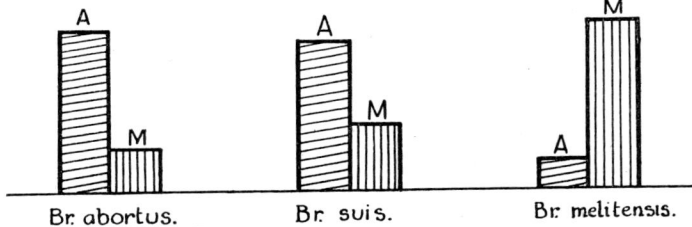

FIG. 155.—SCHEMATIC REPRESENTATION OF ANTIGENIC STRUCTURE OF *Brucella* STRAINS.

and will agglutinate only those strains in which the corresponding antigen is predominant. Usually an absorbing dose standardized by opacity to match $3,000 \times 10^6$ *coli* per c.c. is satisfactory for absorbing a serum diluted to $1/32$–$1/64$ of its titre, but preliminary adjustment may be necessary before a monospecific serum can be obtained. With such a serum direct agglutination tests can be put up against strains of unknown type, and their antigenic identity established.

Why it is that a serum, from which the whole of the minor and part of the major agglutinins have been absorbed, will agglutinate only those organisms in which the corresponding antigen predominates, is rather puzzling. Why is it, for example, that a *melitensis* serum, from which the minor A agglutinin has been absorbed by an *abortus* or *suis* strain, will agglutinate only *melitensis* strains? On general grounds, *abortus* and *suis* strains, each of which contains a certain amount of M antigen, might be expected to agglutinate with such a serum to at least a quarter or half titre, since there must be ample M agglutinins in the serum to satisfy the limited number of M receptors on the organisms. The fact that no agglutination does occur suggests that the quantitative and spatial distribution of the satisfied M receptors is such that any considerable degree of adhesion between adjacent organisms is improbable.

The conclusions reached on the antigenic structure of these organisms have received confirmation from the work of Miles (1933), who has shown that the

P.B.   Y *melitensis* may be separated from the *abortus-suis* types by the optimal proportion agglutination method, and from that of Habs (1933), Habs and Sievert (1935), Olin and Lindström (1934), and Olin (1935), using the method of quantitative absorption.

As a means of typing unknown strains, direct agglutination with monospecific serum is one of the simplest and most rapid methods. Like other tests, however, for differentiation of this group, it cannot be relied upon entirely, because, as Wilson (1933) has shown, certain strains, particularly from the South-East of France, may possess the antigenic structure of *abortus*, while having the biochemical and pathogenic characteristics of *melitensis*.

Several workers claim to have established an antigenic affinity between members of the *Brucella* group and those of the *Pasteurella*, *Proteus*, or *Pfeifferella* groups. Most of these conclusions have been based on the observation that a given serum agglutinated strains both of *Brucella* and some other group. By itself this is, of course, quite insufficient evidence on which to base any such conclusion, since it takes no account of non-specific agglutination or of the presence of specific agglutinins to two different organisms co-existing in the same serum. Absorption and other experiments have entirely failed to confirm the conclusions of these workers (for references see Priestley 1933, Wilson 1934). The relationship of *Br. bronchiseptica* to other members of the *Brucella* group still awaits definition.

Chemical Fractionation.—Few reports are yet available on the results of chemical fractionation of *Brucella* strains, and those that are available are in some ways conflicting. Favilli and Biancalani (1932, 1934) separated from *Br. abortus* and *Br. melitensis* substances of polysaccharide nature which were precipitated in high titre by sera prepared against either organism. No difference could be detected between the two polysaccharides. Topping (1934), who likewise failed to distinguish between the polysaccharides extracted from *Br. abortus* and *Br. melitensis*, isolated substances of nucleo-protein nature which behaved alike, irrespective of the type of organism from which they were derived. Huston, Huddleson, and Hershey (1934) examined two strains each of *melitensis*, *abortus*, and *suis* types, and isolated polysaccharides which, when nearly free from nitrogen, were biologically inactive. The nucleo-proteins, however, were precipitable with *Brucella* sera, were slightly antigenic, and gave rise to severe reactions on intradermal inoculation into sensitive persons. Lipoid substances were also extracted. The three species were differentiated from each other by the relative proportions, rather than kinds, of two polysaccharide and two lipoid constituents which they contained. *Br. melitensis* was further differentiated from the other two members by the possession of a non-protein, non-polysaccharide, precipitating antigen (S) of a type hitherto undescribed. Later work, however (Hershey, Huddleson, and Pennell 1935) suggested that this S substance was present in all types of *Brucella*, but that in the *abortus* and *suis* types it was more closely bound to protein-like substances than in *Br. melitensis*. Incidentally the same authors showed that the precipitating substance described by Favilli and Biancalani (1932, 1934) in extracts obtained by heat was not a polysaccharide, but was closely allied to the S substance. On the whole the results of chemical fractionation experiments support those obtained by quantitative agglutinin absorption in indicating that the antigens in the three main species show a qualitative similarity but a quantitative difference in distribution.

Pathogenicity.—*Br. bronchiseptica*, like the other three members of the group, is a parasite of animals, but unlike them it appears to be non-infective for man.

It is a frequent cause of infectious pneumonia in the lower animals, particularly guinea-pigs (Smith 1913), and is often found as a secondary invader in distemper of dogs.

Br. melitensis, *Br. abortus*, and *Br. suis* are all infective for man. Though undulant fever is the most characteristic result of infection, numerous other clinical manifestations occur. Frequently the infection remains latent, giving rise to no recognizable symptoms of disease. Since we cannot carry out large-scale experiments on man under similar conditions, it is impossible to make any definite statement on the comparative virulence of these three organisms, but the limited observations on human volunteers of Morales-Otero (1929, 1930, 1933), a careful study of the available epidemiological data, and the frequency with which laboratory infections occur, suggest that *Br. melitensis* is the most pathogenic and *Br. abortus* the least pathogenic of the three types. The American *suis* type appears to occupy an intermediate position. The Danish *suis* type, on the other hand, is probably even less pathogenic than *Br. abortus*, since there is no record of its ever having been responsible for disease in man.

Under natural conditions *Br. melitensis* is pathogenic for goats and sheep, giving rise to an infection which may be acute and accompanied by abortion, but is more frequently chronic and detectable only by bacteriological examination of the milk, blood, or urine, or by allergic skin tests. In areas where infected goats or sheep are numerous, cows may also become infected (Taylor, Vidal, and Roman 1934). No symptoms of disease are manifest, the animals do not abort when pregnant, but the organisms are often excreted in the milk.

Both varieties of *Br. suis* are pathogenic for pigs, in which they give rise to a disease sometimes accompanied by abortion. Like *Br. melitensis*, the American type of *Br. suis* may infect cows and be excreted in the milk (Huddleson 1934, Beattie and Rice 1934). Horses, dogs, and fowls are occasionally infected.

Br. abortus probably has the widest range of pathogenicity. Besides being responsible for the almost universal and economically important disease of contagious abortion in cattle, it infects other animals, especially horses and dogs. It is sometimes found in sheep and goats. In the United States it is said to give rise to fairly extensive infection of fowls and other birds (Emmel and Huddleson 1929, 1930, Emmel 1930), though the evidence for this is not wholly satisfactory. Guinea-pigs have also been found infected under natural conditions (Manzullo 1935).

All three species are infective to a variable extent for laboratory animals. On the whole the guinea-pig appears to be the most susceptible, but rabbits, rats, and mice can often be infected. In the guinea-pig the disease produced by parenteral inoculation with moderate doses is usually chronic and retrogressive. The brunt of the infection is borne by the reticulo-endothelial system. The resulting lesions are relatively inconspicuous, and consist mainly of a non-hyperæmic enlargement of the lymphatic glands, some degree of enlargement of the spleen, and the presence of a variable number of circular necrotic foci in the spleen and liver. In male guinea-pigs abscess formation is not uncommon in the testicle or epididymis, and intraperitoneal inoculation is sometimes followed by a Straus reaction. Occasionally the bones, joints, or other organs may be affected. The lesions are extremely variable in size and number, and may be completely absent on naked-eye inspection. In infections with *Br. suis* (American variety) the necrotic lesions tend to be few in number, large in size, and purulent in consistency The lesions in *melitensis* and *abortus* infections, on the other hand, are smaller, more numerous, and generally non-purulent, except in the testicle. Numerous statements have been made about the relative virulence of the three main types for guinea-pigs, but workers who have had the widest experience are the most cautious in drawing conclusions. At the moment it is probably safe to conclude that there is no satisfactory method of distinguishing between them on the basis of pathogenicity to laboratory animals. Kristensen (1931) and Bang (1931) regard the Danish *suis* type as probably the least virulent, while Thomsen (1934) regards it as slightly more virulent than *Br. abortus*. Its differentiation from the other members is not practicable by guinea-pig inoculation. The rough, so-called *paramelitensis*, *para-abortus*, and *parasuis* varieties are comparatively avirulent to guinea-pigs. Kritschewski and Halperin (1934) state that a suspension of *Br. abortus* has a powerful stimulating effect on the uterine muscle of the virgin guinea-pig. According to Jadassohn, Riedmüller, and Schaaf (1934), the Schultz-Dale technique may be used to differentiate between the different types of *Brucella*, the reaction in sensitized guinea-pigs being type specific.

Little work has been done on monkeys, but the observations of Huddleson and Hallman (1929), Weigmann (1931), and Zeller, Beller, and Stockmayer (1934) suggest that *melitensis* and American *suis* strains are more virulent than *abortus* strains. (For reproduction of disease in the larger animals see Chapter LXXII.)

Pathogenicity of Br. melitensis for Small Animals.

GUINEA-PIGS.—Though death within a few days may follow intracerebral inoculation (Durham 1898, Eyre 1905), or intraperitoneal inoculation with large doses, the disease set up by *intramuscular* or cutaneous inoculation is chronic, retrogressive, and rarely proves fatal. Small numbers of organisms cannot be relied on to cause infection. Most of the animals continue to gain weight. If they are killed 6 weeks after inoculation, the following lesions may be found. Occasionally there is a local abscess containing creamy pus. The regional and the more distal lymphatic glands often show a certain amount of hyperplasia of the pale bloodless variety. The spleen may show a variable degree of enlargement, and may contain a number of circular, greyish-yellow necrotic foci, 0·1–0·5 mm. in diameter, rarely projecting above the surface. Similar foci, usually few in number, may be present in the liver. Sometimes abscesses are found in connection with the joints or bones. The organisms can be cultivated most readily from the glands, spleen, and bone-marrow. The blood usually contains agglutinins in fairly high titre. The lesions are very variable, and may not be detectable by naked-eye examination. The diagnosis must always be made by testing the blood serum for agglutinins and by cultivation of the causative organism from the tissues. A titre of 1/25 or over is strongly suggestive of infection. The intradermal test with a nucleo-protein extract may be used during life for diagnostic purposes, but reliance must never be placed on it alone. After 6 weeks the diagnosis becomes less easy, because the infection tends to retrogress. Guinea-pigs may also be infected by feeding, by conjunctival or nasal instillation, and by inoculation of the scarified skin. Sometimes they contract the disease naturally from their fellows.

RABBITS appear to be rather less susceptible, but otherwise the infection runs much the same course as in guinea-pigs. The lymphatic system is less affected, and the organisms can rarely be demonstrated in the blood stream. Agglutinin formation is common, but the intradermal reaction is negative.

RATS AND MICE.—There is little information about the effect of inoculation of *rats* or *mice* with *Br. melitensis*, but there is reason to believe that these animals are slightly susceptible to infection.

MONKEYS may be infected either by feeding or by subcutaneous inoculation. Frequently an intermittent fever is set up, simulating in many respects undulant fever. If the animals are killed after some weeks, there may be some enlargement of the lymph glands and spleen ; occasionally necrotic lesions are found in the lungs or liver. Agglutinins are demonstrable in the serum, and the organisms can often be recovered from the tissues (see Bruce 1893, Hughes 1893, Horrocks and Kennedy 1906, Huddleson and Hallman 1929, Weigmann 1931, Zeller, Beller, and Stockmayer 1934).

(References to pathogenicity of *Br. melitensis* for small animals : Durham 1898, Eyre 1905, 1908–09, Nicolle and Conseil 1909, Burnet 1922, Zdrodowski *et al.* 1930, Rainsford 1933.) For reproduction of disease in larger animals see Chapter LXXII.

Pathogenicity of Br. abortus for Small Animals.

In GUINEA-PIGS a disease is set up closely resembling that caused by *Br. melitensis*. After intramuscular inoculation a local suppurating lesion is rare, but abscess formation in the testis or epididymis is not uncommon. A mild infection can be produced in RABBITS, RATS and MICE. In MICE inoculated subcutaneously with 10–1000 million organisms a retrogressive disease is set up. The organisms can be demonstrated in the regional lymphatic glands and the spleen for a month or so, and agglutinins are present in the blood serum. Mice may also be infected by feeding with large doses. According to Emmel and Huddleson (1929, 1930), FOWLS can be infected by feeding or parenteral inoculation. The birds stop laying and develop severe diarrhœa. There is a gradually increasing pallor of the head, comb, and wattles, emaciation, and often paralysis and death. The course of the disease ranges from about 2 to 14 weeks. Post mortem, the main lesions consist of a necrotic enteritis and degenerative changes in the liver and kidneys. The majority of other workers, however, who have studied this question, have found that, on the whole, fowls are resistant to infection except with large doses administered parenterally (McNutt and Purwin 1930, 1932, van Roekel *et al.* 1932, Beller and Stockmayer 1933). With smaller doses the organisms can rarely be recovered from the tissues. In the absence of direct cultural experiments, a rise in the agglutinin titre cannot be interpreted as necessarily indicative of infection. The conclusions of Emmel and Huddleson require confirmation before being accepted.

MONKEYS may be infected with *Br. abortus*, but they are less susceptible to it than to infection with *Br. melitensis*. (References to pathogenicity of *Br. abortus* for small animals : Schroeder and Cotton 1911, Smith and Fabyan 1912, Emmel and Huddleson 1929, 1930, Morales-Otero 1930, McNutt and Purwin 1930, 1932, Bang 1931, Pagnini 1932, Henry, Traum, and Haring 1932, Henricsson 1932, Helms, Holm, and Ørskov 1932, Rainsford 1933, Ber 1933, Olin and Lindström 1934, Huddleson 1934, Thomsen 1934, Feldman and Olson 1935.) For reproduction of disease in larger animals, see Chapter LXXII.

Pathogenicity of Br. suis for Small Animals.

Experimentally, this organism gives rise in GUINEA-PIGS to a disease closely resembling that caused by *Br. melitensis*. Local abscess formation is rare, but in infections by the American type large suppurating lesions, few in number, are not uncommon in the spleen, liver, lymph glands, testicles, and joints. The Danish type appears to be less virulent than the American type. *Br. suis* appears to resemble *Br. abortus* in its infectivity for MICE, RABBITS, and FOWLS, but there is little exact information available. For MONKEYS it appears to be perhaps even more virulent than *Br. melitensis*. (References to pathogenicity of *Br. suis* for small animals : Smith 1926a, Hardy *et al.* 1930, Cotton 1932, Thomsen 1934, Huddleson 1934, Feldman and Olson 1935.) For reproduction of disease in larger animals, see Chapter LXXII.

Variation.—It has already been mentioned that under artificial conditions of cultivation *Brucella* strains, particularly of the *melitensis* type, tend to undergo a change which is characterized by a gradual loss of specific, and gradual increase of non-specific, agglutinability, together with a decrease in virulence to animals. This change appears to be an example of the smooth → rough variation. Whether the change is accompanied by any corresponding alteration in the morphological and colonial appearances of the organisms is still a little doubtful, though there is reason to believe that some change does occur. The descriptions of various workers, however, many of whom have used different media, are so difficult to summarize, that we shall content ourselves with giving references to some of the more important papers on this subject (Henry 1928, 1929, Plastridge and McAlpine 1930, Marshall and Jared 1930, 1931, Morales-Otero 1931, Grumbach and Grillichess 1932). The growth of smooth and rough forms in the presence of dyes appears to be very much the same, but there is some evidence that the S $\longrightarrow$ R variation may be accompanied by a decrease in biochemical activity, particularly in the production of H_2S. Though it is true that some rough *abortus* and American *suis* strains still produce H_2S, it is equally true that many do not. Since practically all freshly isolated smooth strains produce H_2S, it seems not improbable that the loss of this property on continued subcultivation is a manifestation of the S $\longrightarrow$ R variation.

Classification and Identification.—As has already been pointed out, the inclusion of *Br. bronchiseptica* and *Br. tularensis* in the *Brucella* group is largely tentative. Both of these organisms may be distinguished from the other three members on the basis of morphological, cultural, biochemical, antigenic, and pathogenic properties.

The main difficulty lies in distinguishing between *Br. melitensis*, *Br. abortus*, and *Br. suis*. This difficulty is accentuated by the fact that within each species there are a number of sub-types differing from one another in minor respects and approaching closely to the sub-types of adjacent species (see Meyer and Zobell 1932, Wilson 1933). These sub-types are often associated with some special topographical distribution. *Melitensis* strains, for example, from Malta, may differ from those from Palestine or from the South of France. Southern Rhodesian *abortus* strains differ from European or American strains. The American *suis* strains differ from the Danish strains, and so on. For purposes of identification, therefore, the fullest possible examination is required, and no strain should be definitely allocated to a particular species without a careful study by all available bacteriological methods, including CO_2-sensitivity, growth in the presence of dyes, H_2S formation, antigenic analysis, and if possible virulence. Once the infecting type has been firmly established, help is often afforded by a knowledge of the animal source and country of origin. For instance, in this country neither the *suis* nor the *melitensis* type has ever been definitely found as the primary infecting agent in man or animals, so that any strain of *Brucella* isolated, certainly from man, horses, dogs, or cattle, is probably of the *abortus* type. In any country, strains isolated from sheep or goats are usually of the *melitensis* type, from pigs of the *suis* type, from cattle, horses, and dogs of the *abortus* type, while strains isolated from man usually belong to that type which is most prevalent in the neighbouring animal population. Exceptions, however, are not uncommon, so that too much reliance should not be placed on this particular aid to identification.

Though there are numerous sub-types of *Brucella* with particular geographical locations, indicating that the members of the group are relatively labile and responsive to environmental changes, no one has yet succeeded in converting one type into another. Even prolonged residence of the *melitensis* and *suis* types in cows, and of the *abortus* type in sheep, seems to have no effect on the type of organism introduced. For practical purposes, therefore, the main types can be regarded as constant. Table XLVIII summarizes the main differential features of members of this group. (Useful reviews of the *Brucella* group will be found in papers by Kristensen 1931,

Taylor, Lisbonne, and Roman 1932, Zeller 1933, Habs 1933, Wilson 1933, Huddleson 1934, Thomsen 1934, Olin and Lindström 1934.)

TABLE XLVIII

CLASSIFICATION OF *Brucella* GROUP

Type.	Usual Habitat.	Growth in absence of extra CO_2.	Growth in presence of				H_2S Formation.	Antigenically.
			Thionin.	Basic Fuchsin.	Methyl Violet.	Pyronin.		
melitensis .	Goats, sheep	+	+	+	+	+	−	*melitensis*
abortus . .	Cows, horses, dogs	−	−	+	+	+	+	*abortus*
American suis	Pigs	+	+	−	−	−	+	*abortus*
Danish suis .	Pigs	+	+	−	−	−	−	*abortus*

Brucella melitensis

Synonyms.—*M. melitensis, Alkaligenes melitensis.*

Isolation.—Isolated by Bruce (1887) from the spleen of patients dying of Malta fever.

Ecology.—Strict parasite living in goats, sheep and man.

Morphology.—Small bacilli, 0·6–1·2 μ long × 0·5–0·7 μ broad, coccoid forms abundant. Axis straight, ends rounded, sides bulging or parallel. Arranged singly, in pairs end-to-end, in small groups, or—especially in liquid media—in short chains of four to six members. Non-motile. Bipolar staining not uncommon. Gram-negative.

Agar Plate.—48 *hours at* 37° *C.* Small, round, convex, amorphous colonies about 0·5 mm. in diameter. Smooth, glistening surface, entire edge, translucent, greyish-white by reflected light, almost colourless by transmitted light ; consistency butyrous ; emulsification easy. 6-day colonies slightly larger, and greyish-yellow. No differentiation.

Agar Stroke.—48 *hours at* 37° *C.* Poor to moderate, partly confluent slightly raised, translucent growth, with pitted surface, and edge formed of single colonies. After a week the agar is turned brownish and crystals may appear.

Gelatin Stab.—10 *days at* 22° *C.* Poor to moderate, filiform, greyish-white growth, consisting of very small colonies closely packed ; extends to bottom of tube. No surface growth and no liquefaction.

Broth.—24 *hours at* 37° *C.* Poor growth with slight turbidity ; no surface growth and no deposit. After 10 days there is an abundant growth with moderate turbidity, and a moderate powdery deposit disintegrating completely on shaking. Later the deposit becomes very viscous, and almost impossible to disintegrate.

Loeffler's Serum.—48 *hours at* 37° *C.* Moderate, slightly raised, chiefly confluent growth of yellowish colour. No liquefaction.

Potato.—6 *days at* 37° *C.* Thin, mostly confluent growth of greyish-brown colour. After 14 days the growth has a café-au-lait or chocolate colour.

Shake Agar.—4 *days at* 37° *C.* Growth of tiny, discrete colonies, situated at the surface, or some distance below the surface ; exact position depends on the CO_2-sensitivity of the strain.

Liver Agar Plates containing Dyes.—3 *days at* 37° *C.* Usually some growth in presence of thionin, basic fuchsin, methyl violet, and pyronin, but reaction varies considerably according to source of origin of strain.

MacConkey Agar Plate.—7 *days at* 37° *C.* Small, circular, convex, amorphous, yellowish colonies, 0·1–1·0 mm. in diameter, with smooth surface and entire edge. May appear slightly mucoid.

Resistance.—Not specially resistant. Killed by moist heat at 60° C. in 10 minutes, and by 1·0 per cent. phenol in about 15 minutes. In the dried, powdered condition they may survive for 3 months. Sealed agar slope cultures at room temperature may remain alive for 1–6 months.

Metabolism.—Aerobic ; no growth under strictly anaerobic conditions. Growth is often improved by 10 per cent. CO_2. Opt. temp. 37° C. ; limits 20–40° C. Opt. H-ion concentration pH 6·6–7·4. Growth slightly improved by glucose, glycerine, liver extract, blood and serum. Brown pigment formed on potato and sometimes in old agar cultures. Broth turned alkaline—to pH 8·0 or even higher. Growth in all media is relatively slow. Some growth on MacConkey's medium. Does not hæmolyse blood.

Biochemical.—No carbohydrates fermented. L.M. turned slightly alkaline. Indole — ; M.R. — ; V.P. — ; Nitrates and nitrites reduced. NH_3 sometimes + ; H_2S — ; M.B. reduced ; catalase +.

Antigenic Structure.—Only one serological type known. Appears to contain the same antigens as *Br. abortus* and *Br. suis,* but in different quantitative proportions. Provided absolutely smooth strains are used, it may be differentiated from *Br. abortus* and *Br. suis* by quantitative absorption of agglutinins. The rough variant, incorrectly called *Br. paramelitensis,* is agglutinable by non-specific agents, but not by a serum prepared against the smooth form.

Pathogenicity.—Causes undulant fever in man, and a septicæmic infection of goats and sheep, sometimes accompanied by abortion. May infect cows and be excreted in the milk. Experimentally, it is pathogenic to a variable degree for man, goats, sheep, monkeys, and the small laboratory animals. The rough variant is avirulent.

Brucella abortus

Isolation.—By Bang (1897) from cows with infectious abortion.

Ecology.—Strict parasite, occurring in cattle, horses, dogs, and man.

Morphology.—Similar to that of type species, but usually more bacillary ; rods reach 1·5 μ in length, or on special media even 3·0 μ.

Cultural Characters.—Similar to those of type species, except that growth of the bovine type, whether isolated from cattle or from man, usually occurs only in the presence of added CO_2, preferably 5–10 per cent. In shake agar cultures growth occurs 1–2 mm. or more below the surface, and extends downwards for $\frac{1}{2}$–1 cm. Old laboratory cultures grow freely under aerobic conditions ; no growth under strictly anaerobic conditions.

Resistance.—Similar to type species. In uterine exudate kept in the ice-chest it survives for 9 months. May live in sterile water for 3 or 4 months. Readily killed in milk by holder pasteurization. May survive in ice-cream for a month.

Metabolism.—Similar to type species, but as most strains on isolation require CO_2, the optimum H-ion concentration of media is about pH 6·6. Brown coloration in old agar cultures less common than with *Br. melitensis.*

Biochemical.—Similar to type species, but nearly all strains on isolation produce H_2S in liver agar for at least 4 days.

Antigenic Structure.—Appears to possess the same antigens as *Br. melitensis,* but distributed in different quantitative proportions. Provided absolutely smooth strains are used, it may be differentiated from *Br. melitensis* by quantitative absorption of agglutinins. The rough variant, incorrectly referred to as *Br. para-abortus,* is agglutinable by non-specific agents.

Pathogenicity.—Causes epizootic abortion in cattle, fistulous withers in horses, and a mild septicæmic infection in dogs. Is said to infect rats. Gives rise to undulant fever in man. Experimentally, it is pathogenic to a variable degree for man, cattle, horses, dogs, fowls, monkeys, and the small laboratory animals. The rough variant is avirulent.

Brucella suis

Isolation.—American type by Traum (1914) from the fœtus of a sow, and Danish type by Thomsen (1931).

Ecology.—Strict parasite, occurring in pigs and man.

Morphology.—Similar to *Br. abortus.*

Cultural Characters.—Similar to those of type species, except that growth is never improved by addition of CO_2. In shake agar cultures growth occurs on the surface. No growth under strictly anaerobic conditions. The American type grows rather more freely than the Danish type. On liver agar plates both types grow in the presence of thionin, but are inhibited by basic fuchsin, methyl violet, and pyronin. The Danish type has the same differential susceptibility as the American type, but is rather more susceptible to all dyes ; consequently half the usual concentrations of dye should be employed when testing it.

Resistance.—Similar to that of type species and *Br. abortus.*

Metabolism.—Similar to type species, but growth is not improved by CO_2. Brown coloration in old agar cultures less common than with *Br. melitensis.*

Biochemical.—Similar to type species, but American type produces H_2S in liver agar for at least 4 days ; Danish type produces no H_2S.

Antigenic Structure.—Appears to possess the same antigens as *Br. melitensis*, but distributed in quantitative proportions nearer those of *Br. abortus* than *Br. melitensis.* Provided absolutely smooth strains are used, it may be differentiated from *Br. melitensis*, but not from *Br. abortus*, by quantitative absorption of agglutinins. The rough variant, incorrectly referred to as *Br. parasuis*, is agglutinable by non-specific agents.

Pathogenicity.—Gives rise to a disease of pigs, which may be accompanied by abortion, and to undulant fever in man. May infect cows and be excreted in the milk. Experimentally, it is pathogenic to a variable degree for man, pigs, cows, monkeys, and the small laboratory animals. Possibly pathogenic to some degree for horses and dogs. The rough variant is avirulent.

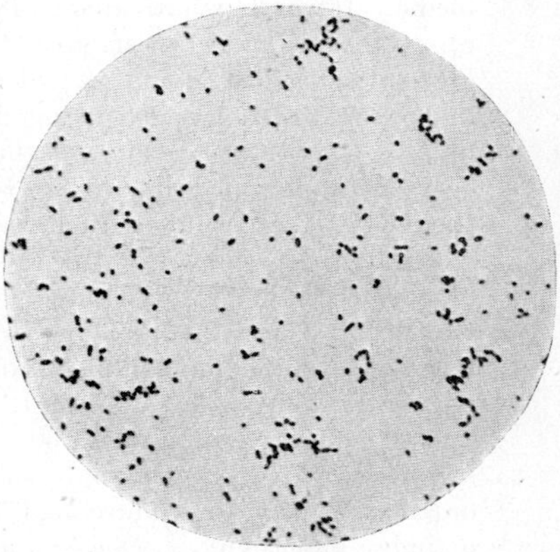

Fig. 156.—*Brucella bronchiseptica.*
From an agar culture, 24 hours, 37° C.
($\times$ 1000).

Brucella bronchiseptica

Isolation.—By Ferry (1911) in the United States, and by M'Gowan (1911) in Edinburgh from dogs affected with distemper.

Ecology.—Strict parasite, occurring in several different species of animals, and sometimes in man.

Morphology.—Similar to *Br. abortus*, but is motile by peritrichate flagella.

Cultural Characters.—Similar to type species, but grows rather more freely. Grows best under aerobic conditions ; no growth under strictly anaerobic conditions. In agar shake culture growth is almost entirely on the surface.

Resistance.—Similar to type species.

P.B.   Y*

Metabolism.—Similar to type species, but growth is rather more rapid. Hæmolysin produced, active on red corpuscles of rabbit, dog, and guinea-pig. Grows freely on MacConkey.

Biochemical.—Similar to type species. Produces marked alkalinity in litmus milk. Nitrates often reduced. H_2S — ; NH_3 very slight production, or none at all. Catalase $+++$. Grows in Koser's citrate.

Antigenic Structure.—Shows some affinity to *Br. melitensis* and *Br. abortus*, but detailed study has not yet been made.

Pathogenicity.—Frequent cause of broncho-pneumonia in rodents, and of broncho-pneumonia complicating distemper in dogs. Experimentally, intraperitoneal inoculation of guinea-pigs with 0·5 c.c. of a 24-hours' broth culture causes death in 24 to 48 hours. Post mortem, there are small hæmorrhages on the peritoneum, and a viscid translucent exudate forming pseudo-membranes on the liver, spleen, and the less mobile parts of the intestine. The bacilli are easily recovered from the peritoneal cavity, but with difficulty from the blood, liver, and lungs. Subcutaneous inoculation produces only a local lesion. Feeding and inhalation are without effect. The organism is non-pathogenic to mice. It rapidly loses its virulence in culture.

Brucella tularensis

This organism is a tiny, non-motile, Gram-negative bacillus, which was isolated by McCoy and Chapin in 1912 from rodents suffering from tularæmia (see Chapter LXXII). In the animal body, it occurs as a coccoid or rod-shaped organism surrounded by a clear area, which probably represents a capsule. The diameter of the organism is 0·3–0·7 μ long by 0·2 μ wide ; the diameter with the capsule is 0·4–1·0 μ by 0·3–0·5 μ. The organisms stain best with carbol-fuchsin or aniline gentian violet ; with methylene blue they stain very poorly and show no capsule. In culture, coccoid forms alone are seen (Wherry and Lamb 1914) ; a capsule is visible if the organisms are mixed with serum. No growth occurs in the usual media. It was first cultivated on Dorset's egg, but later it was found that coagulated egg yolk was more satisfactory (McCoy 1912). On this medium the maximum growth is reached in 2 days ; it is pale, translucent, slightly mucoid, and pearly in appearance, not easily distinguishable from the medium ; it is readily emulsifiable. Growth occurs also on glucose blood agar, glucose serum agar, and blood agar slopes, provided that a piece of rabbit's spleen is rubbed over the surface and then left in the condensation water (Francis and Lake 1922) ; and on agar to which 0·02 per cent. of cystine is added (Francis 1922, 1923). On these media the organism should be subcultured every other day, but on egg yolk it may remain viable for 3 months (Wherry and Lamb 1914). Shaw and Hunnicutt (1930) recommend a medium composed of brain veal infusion agar, pH 7·6, containing 5 per cent. rabbit serum, 1 per cent. dextrose, and 0·05 per cent. cystine, while Kudo (1934) prepares a mixture of 60 per cent. egg yolk and 40 per cent. rabbit serum sterilized at 70°–75° C. on 3 successive days. Under suitable conditions the organism is said to produce acid in glucose and glycerol, and usually in maltose, mannose and lævulose (Downs and Bond 1935) ; but the acid produced seems to be very slight, and may possibly be of the order of that formed by *melitensis* and American *suis* stains.

Moist heat at 55–60° C. is fatal in 10 minutes. Serologically *Br. tularensis* is allied to the other members of the *Brucella* group. Francis and Evans (1926) found that a serum prepared against *Br. tularensis* agglutinated *Br. melitensis* and *Br. abortus* to about $\frac{1}{4}$ or $\frac{1}{6}$ of the titre. Neither organism was able, however, to absorb the homologous agglutinins from a *tularensis* serum. *Br. tularensis* was agglutinated to a low titre by anti-melitensis and anti-abortus sera, but was unable to absorb the homologous agglutinins from these sera. The 3 strains of *Br. tularensis* examined appeared to be antigenically homogeneous.

Under natural conditions it gives rise to tularæmia in rodents—especially ground-squirrels and jack-rabbits—and occasionally in man. Sheep are sometimes affected (Parker and Dade 1929). Experimentally the disease can be reproduced in ground-squirrels, gophers, guinea-pigs, rabbits, mice, and monkeys ; rats are more resistant (Dieter and Rhodes 1926) ; cats, dogs, and pigeons appear to be immune. Feeding, nasal instillation, cutaneous, subcutaneous, intraperitoneal, and conjunctival infection are all successful. After subcutaneous infection of the guinea-pig, death occurs in 5 to 8 days. Post mortem there is a whitish membrane-like area at the site of inoculation ; the regional lymphatic glands may be enlarged and caseous ; the spleen is enlarged, very dark in colour, and contains discrete, yellowish-white, caseous granules up to 1 mm. in diameter, projecting slightly above the surface ; there are numerous granules in the liver ; focal necrotic areas are sometimes present in the bone marrow (Lillie and Francis 1933) ; the lungs are rarely involved. The bacilli are present in large numbers in the blood and organs ; as little as 0·000,000,1 c.c. of the heart's blood may prove infective for fresh animals. The virulence of the organism may decline in culture, so that instead of causing an acute or subacute disease in guinea-pigs, it gives rise to a chronic disease from which the animal often recovers (McCoy 1912, Foshay 1932). Strains of lowered virulence have also been isolated directly from ticks (Davis *et al.* 1934). The organism is extremely dangerous to handle in the laboratory, and large numbers of workers have contracted infection.

REFERENCES

ALESSANDRINI, A. and SABATUCCI, M. (1931) *Ann. Igiene (Sper.)*, **41**, 29, 852.
ANTONI, V. DE. (1929) *Boll. Ist. sieroter. Milano*, **8**, 651.
BANG, B. (1897) *Z. Thiermed.*, **1**, 241.
BANG, O. (1931) *2me Congr. int. Path. comp.*, i. 95.
BAU, K. H. and WANG, K. (1936) *Z. Hyg. InfektKr.*, **117**, 399.
BEATTIE, C. P. and RICE, R. M. (1934) *J. Amer. med. Ass.*, **102**, 1670.
BELLER, K. and STOCKMAYER, W. (1933) *Dtsch. tierärztl. Wschr.*, **41**, 551.
BER, A. (1933) *Z. InfektKr. Haustiere*, **44**, 129.
BEVAN, L. E. W. (1930) *Brit. med. J.*, ii. 267.
BIELING, R. (1930) *Z. Hyg. InfektKr.*, **111**, 728.
BRUCE, D. (1887) *Practitioner*, **39**, 161 ; (1893) *Ann. Inst. Pasteur*, **7**, 289.
BURNET, E. (1922) *Arch. Inst. Pasteur Afrique nord*, **2**, 165 ; (1925) *Arch. Inst. Pasteur, Tunis*, **14**, 247.
CAMERON, H. S. (1932) *Cornell Veterinarian*, **22**, 212 ; (1933) *Rep. N.Y. St. vet. Coll.* 1931–32, No. 18.
CERRUTI, C. F. (1927) *Boll. Ist. sieroter. Milano*, **6**, 425 ; (1932) *Ibid.*, **11**, 400.
COLEMAN, M. B., OWEN, H. H., and DACEY, H. G. (1930) *J. lab. clin. Med.*, **15**, 641.
COTTON, W. E. (1932) *J. agric. Res.*, **45**, 705.
DAVIS, G. E., PHILIP, C. B., and PARKER, R. R. (1934) *Amer. J. Hyg.*, **19**, 449.
DIETER, L. V. and RHODES, B. (1926) *J. infect. Dis.*, **38**, 541.
DOWNS, C. M. and BOND, G. C. (1935) *J. Bact.*, **30**, 485.
DUNCAN, J. T. (1928) *Trans. roy. Soc. trop. Med. Hyg.*, **22**, 269.
DURHAM, H. E. (1898) *J. Path. Bact.*, **5**, 377.
EMMEL, M. W. (1930) *J. Amer. vet. med. Ass.*, **76**, 452, 564.
EMMEL, M. W. and HUDDLESON, I. F. (1929) *J. Amer. vet. med. Ass.*, **75**, 578 ; (1930) *Ibid.*, **76**, 449.
EVANS, A. C. (1918) *J. infect. Dis.*, **22**, 580 ; (1925a) *Amer. J. trop. Med.*, **5**, 419 ; (1925b) *Bull. U.S. hyg. Lab.*, No. 143.
EYRE, J. W. H. (1905) *Rep. Comm. Medit. Fev., Lond.*, Part II, p. 67 ; (1908–9) *Proc. roy. Soc. Edin.*, **29**, 537.
FAVILLI, G. (1926a) *Sperimentale*, **80**, 41 ; (1926b) *Ibid.*, **80**, 396 ; (1930) *Ibid.*, **84**, 287.
FAVILLI, G. and BIANCALANI, G. (1932) *Sperimentale*, **86**, 357 ; (1934) *Ibid.*, **88**, 337.
FELDMAN, W. H. and OLSON, C. (1935) *J. infect. Dis.*, **57**, 212
FERRY, N. S. (1911) *J. infect. Dis.*, **8**, 399 ; (1912) *Vet. J.*, **68**, 376 ; (1912–13) *Amer. vet. Rev.*, **41**, 77.
FERRY, N. S. and NOBLE, A. (1918) *J. Bact.*, **3**, 193.
FEUSIER, M. L. and MEYER, K. F. (1920) *J. infect. Dis.*, **27**, 185.
FLEMING, A. (1919) *Lancet*, i. 138.
FORESTI, C. (1935) *Nuova Vet.*, **13**, 11.

FORNI, G. (1927). *G. Batt. Immun.*, **2**, 823.

FOSHAY, L. (1932) *J. infect. Dis.*, **51**, 280.

FRANCIS, E. (1922) *Publ. Hlth Rep., Wash.*, No. 17, **37**, 987 ; (1923) *Ibid.*, No. 25, **38**, 1391 ; (1931) *Publ. Hlth Rep., Wash.*, **46**, 2416.

FRANCIS, E. and EVANS, A. C. (1926) *Publ. Hlth Rep., Wash.*, No. 26, **41**, 1273.

FRANCIS, E. and LAKE, G. C. (1922) *Publ. Hlth Rep., Wash.*, No. 3, **37**, 83.

GALLI-VALERIO, B. (1893) *Zbl. Bakt.*, **19**, 694.

GLADSTONE, G. P., FILDES, P., and RICHARDSON, G. M. (1935) *Brit. J. exp. Path.*, **16**, 335.

GRUMBACH, A. and GRILLICHESS, R. K. (1932) *Zbl. Bakt.*, **126**, 321.

HABS, H. (1930) *Zbl. Bakt.*, **116**, 89 ; (1933) *Zbl. ges. Hyg.*, **28**, 481.

HABS, H. and SIEVERT, L. (1935) *Dtsch. med. Wschr.*, **61**, 1398.

HARDY, A. V., JORDAN, C. F., BORTS, I. H., and HARDY, G. C. (1930) *Nat. Inst. Hlth. Bull.*, No. 158.

HELMS, T., HOLM, P., and ØRSKOV, J. (1932) *Z. ImmunForsch.*, **75**, 55.

HENRICSSON, E. (1932) "Epizootischer Abortus und Undulantfieber." Isaac Marcus Boktryckeri-Aktiebolag, Stockholm.

HENRY, B. S. (1928) *Proc. Soc. exp. Biol., N.Y.*, **26**, 101 ; (1929) *Ibid.*, **27**, 8.

HENRY, B. S., TRAUM, J., and HARING, C. M. (1932) *Hilgardia*, **6**, 355.

HERSHEY, A. D., HUDDLESON, I. F., and PENNELL, R. B. (1935) *J. infect. Dis.*, **57**, 183.

HOLTH, H. (1911) *Z. InfektKr. Haustiere*, **10**, 207.

HORROCKS, W. H. and KENNEDY, J. C. (1906) *Rep. Comm. Medit. Fev., Lond.*, Part IV, p. 37.

HUDDLESON, I. F. (1924) *Cornell veterinarian*, **11**, 210 ; (1929) *Mich. State College, agric. Exp. Sta., Tec. Bull.*, No. 100 ; (1931) *Amer. J. publ. Hlth*, **21**, 491 ; (1934) "Brucella Infections in Animals and Man." Commonwealth Fund, New York.

HUDDLESON, I. F. and ABELL, E. (1927) *J. Bact.*, **13**, 13 ; (1928) *J. infect. Dis.*, **43**, 81.

HUDDLESON, I. F. and HALLMAN, E. T. (1929) *J. infect. Dis.*, **45**, 293.

HUDDLESON, I. F., HASLEY, D. E., and TORREY, J. P. (1927) *J. infect. Dis.*, **40**, 352.

HUDDLESON, I. F. and WINTER, O. B. (1927) *J. infect. Dis.*, **40**, 476.

HUGHES, M. L. (1893) *Ann. Inst. Pasteur*, **7**, 628.

HUSTON, R. C., HUDDLESON, I. F., and HERSHEY, A. D. (1934) *Mich. agric. Exp. Sta., Tec. Bull.*, No. 137.

JADASSOHN, W., RIEDMÜLLER, L., and SCHAAF, F. (1934) *Klin. Wschr.*, **13**, 879.

KING, R. O. C. (1934) *Aust. vet. J.*, **10**, 93.

KRISTENSEN, M. (1931) *Zbl. Bakt.*, **120**, 179.

KRISTENSEN, M. and HOLM, P. (1929) *Zbl. Bakt.*, **112**, 281.

KRITSCHEWSKI, I. L. and HALPERIN, E. P. (1934) *Z. ImmunForsch.*, **82**, 421.

KUDO, M. (1934) *Jap. J. exp. Med.*, **12**, 371.

LAIDLAW, P. P. and DUNKIN, G. W. (1926) *J. comp. Path.*, **39**, 222.

LILLIE, R. D. and FRANCIS, E. (1933) *Publ. Hlth Rep., Wash*, **48**, 1127.

McALPINE, J. G. and SLANETZ, C. A. (1928a) *J. infect. Dis.*, **42**, 66, 73 ; (1928b) *Ibid.*, **43**, 232.

McCoy, G. W. (1912) *Publ. Hlth Bull., Wash.*, No. 53, p. 17.

McCoy, G. W. and CHAPIN, C. W. (1912) *J. infect. Dis.*, **10**, 61.

M'GOWAN, J. P. (1911) *J. Path. Bact.*, **15**, 372.

McNUTT, S. H. and PURWIN P. (1930) *J. Amer. vet. med. Ass.*, **30**, 350 ; (1931) *J. infect. Dis.*, **48**, 292 ; (1932) *J. Amer. vet. med. Ass.*, **81**, 641.

MAGGIORA-VERGANO, L. (1932) *Boll. Ist. sieroter. Milano*, **11**, 400.

MALLARDO, C. A. (1930) *J. trop. Med. Hyg.*, **33**, 125.

MANZULLO, A. (1935) *Fol. biol.*, No. 47, 211.

MARSHALL, M. S. and JARED, D. (1930) *Proc. Soc. exp. Biol., N.Y.*, **27**, 525 ; (1931) *J. infect. Dis.*, **49**, 318.

MARTINI, E. (1900) *Arch. Hyg., Berl.*, **38**, 114.

MARTINI, G. (1935) *Boll. Ist. sieroter. Milano*, **14**, 431.

MENZANI, C. (1934) *Nuova Vet.*, **12**, 83.

MESSIERI, A. (1935) *Nuova Vet.*, **13**, 1, 13.

MEYER, K. F. and EDDIE, B. (1930) *J. lab. clin. Med.*, **15**, 447.

MEYER, K. F. and SHAW, E. B. (1920) *J. infect. Dis.*, **27**, 173.

MEYER, K. F. and ZOBELL, C. E. (1932) *J. infect. Dis.*, **51**, 72.

MILES, A. A. (1933) *Brit. J. exp. Path.*, **14**, 43.

MINO, G. DI. (1935) *Boll. Ist. sieroter. Milanese*, **14**, 123.

MOHR, W. (1935) *Z. ImmunForsch.*, **86**, 235.

MORALES-OTERO, P. (1929) *Porto Rico J. publ. Hlth. trop. Med.*, **5**, 144 ; (1930) *Ibid.*, **6**, 3; (1931) *Porto Rico J. publ. Hlth trop. Med.*, **7**, 233 ; (1933) *J. infect. Dis.*, **52**, 54.

NÈGRE, L. and RAYNAUD, M. (1912a) *C. R. Soc. Biol.*, **72**, 791 ; (1912b) *Ibid.*, **72**, 1052.

NEIVA, C. (1934) *Brasil-Medico*, **48**, 421.

NICOLLE, C. and CONSEIL, E. (1909) *C. R. Soc. Biol.*, **67**, 267.

Nowak, J. (1908) *Ann. Inst. Pasteur*, **22**, 541.

Olin, G. (1935) " Studien über das Undulantfieber in Schweden." Isaac Marcus Boktryckeri-Aktiebolag, Stockholm.

Olin, G. and Lindström, B. (1934) *Zbl. Bakt.*, **131**, 257.

Pagnini, U. (1932) *G. Batt. Immun.*, **9**, 1004 ; (1934) *Boll. Ist. sieroter. Milano*, **13**, 145 ; (1935) *G. Batt. Immun.*, **15**, 847.

Pampana, E. J. (1931) *Ann. Igiene (Sper.)*, **41**, 537.

Pandit, S. R. and Wilson, G. S. (1932) *J. Hyg., Camb.*, **32**, 45.

Parker, R. R. and Dade, J. S. (1929) *Publ. Hlth Rep., Wash.*, **44**, 126.

Plastridge, W. N. and McAlpine, J. G. (1930) *J. infect. Dis.*, **46**, 315 ; (1932) *J. infect. Dis.*, **50**, 555.

Preisz, H. (1903) *Zbl. Bakt.*, **33**, 190.

Priestley, F. W. (1933) *J. comp. Path.*, **46**, 38.

Pullinger, E. J. (1935) *Lancet*, i. 1342.

Rainsford, S. G. (1933) *Irish J. med. Sci.*, April, p. 150.

Reimann, H. A. (1932) *Amer. J. Hyg.*, **16**, 206.

Report. (1905–7) *Comm. Mediterranean Fever*, Parts I, III, IV. Harrison and Sons, London.

Roekel, H. van, Bullis, K. L., Flint, O. S., and Clarke, M. K. (1932) *J. Amer. vet. med. Ass.*, **80**, 641.

Ross, G. R. (1927a) *J. Hyg., Camb.*, **26**, 279 ; (1927b) *Ibid.*, **26**, 403.

Saitta, S. (1929) *G. Batt. Immun.*, **4**, 307.

Santis, M. de. (1933) *Boll. Ist. sieroter. Milano*, **12**, 846 ; (1935) *Ibid.*, **14**, 113.

Schroeder, E. C. and Cotton, W. E. (1911) *Bur. Animal Ind., 28th Ann. Rep.*, p. 139.

Selter, H. (1906) *Z. Hyg. InfektKr.*, **54**, 347.

Sergent, E., Gillot, V., and Lemaire, G. (1908) *Ann. Inst. Pasteur*, **22**, 209.

Shaw, F. W. and Hunnicutt, T. (1930) *J. Lab. clin. Med.*, **16**, 46.

Silberstein, W. (1932) *Z. Hyg. InfektKr.*, **114**, 177.

Smith, J. (1934) *J. Hyg., Camb.*, **34**, 242.

Smith, T. (1913) *J. med. Res.*, **29**, 291 ; (1924) *J. exp. Med.*, **40**, 219 ; (1926a) *Ibid.*, **43**, 207 ; (1926b) *Ibid.*, **43**, 317.

Smith, T. and Fabyan, M. (1912) *Zbl. Bakt.*, **61**, 549.

Stafseth, H. J. (1920) *Mich. agric. exp. Sta., Tec. Bull.*, No. 49.

Strada, F. and Traina, R. (1900) *Zbl. Bakt.*, **28**, 635.

Tartakowsky, M. G. (1897–8) *Arch. Sci. biol., St. Pétersb.*, **6**, 263.

Taylor, R. M., Lisbonne, M., and Roman, G. (1932) *Ann. Inst. Pasteur*, **49**, 284.

Taylor, R. M., Vidal, L. F., and Roman, G. (1934) *C. R. Soc. Biol.*, **116**, 132.

Thomsen, A. (1931) *Rev. gén. Méd. vét.*, **40**, 457 ; (1933) *Zbl. Bakt.*, **130**, 257 ; (1934) " Brucella Infection in Swine." *Acta path. microbiol. Scand., Suppl.* No. 21.

Thompson, R. (1933) *Canad. med. Ass. J.*, **29**, 9.

Topping, L. E. (1934) *J. Path. Bact.*, **39**, 665.

Torrey, J. C. and Rahe, A. H. (1913) *J. med. Res.*, **27**, 291.

Tosatti, E. (1934) *Pathologica*, **26**, 247.

Traum, J. E. (1914) *Rep. Chief Bur. Anim. Industry*, p. 30.

Tuttle, C. D. and Huddleson, I. F. (1934) *J. infect. Dis.*, **54**, 259.

Valenti, E. (1927) *Biochim. Terap. sper*, **14**, 77.

Vidal, J. and Abella, R. (1928) *C. R. Soc. Biol.*, **99**, 1271.

Vittone, R. (1935) *Boll. Sez. ital., Soc. int. Microbiol.*, **7**, 277.

Weigmann, F. (1931) *Zbl. Bakt.*, **121**, 318.

Wherry, W. B. and Lamb, B. H. (1914) *J. infect. Dis.*, **15**, 331.

Wilson, G. S. (1930) *Brit. J. exp. Path.*, **11**, 157 ; (1131a) *Ibid.*, **12**, 88 ; (1931b) *Ibid.*, **12**, 152 ; (1933) *J. Hyg., Camb.*, **33**, 516 ; (1934) *Ibid.*, **34**, 361.

Wilson, G. S. and Miles, A. A. (1932) *Brit. J. exp. Path.*, **13**, 1.

Zdrodowski, P., Brenn, H., and Voskressenski, B. (1930) *Ann. Inst. Pasteur*, **45**, 768.

Zeller, H. (1933) *Münch. tierärztl. Wschr.*, **84**, 337, 349, 361, 373, 389.

Zeller, H., Beller, K., and Stockmayer, W. (1934) *Münch. tierärztl. Wschr.*, **85**, 143.

Zeller, H. and Stockmayer, W. (1933) *Z. InfektKr. Haustiere*, **44**, 67.

Zobell, C. E. and Meyer, K. F. (1932) *J. infect. Dis.*, **51**, 91, 99, 109, 344, 361.

CHAPTER XXXII

BACILLUS

AEROBIC SPORE-BEARING BACILLI

Definition.—*Bacillus.*

> Aerobic, spore-bearing rods, usually Gram-positive. Often occur in long threads, and form rhizoid colonies. Form of rod not greatly changed at sporulation. Liquefy gelatin. Mostly saprophytes.
>
> Type species. *Bacillus subtilis.*

Introductory

The aerobic spore-bearing *Bacilli* form one division of the family *Bacillaceæ*, while the anaerobic spore-bearing *Clostridia* form the other. As many of the organisms in the former division are widely distributed, being found in air, soil, water, milk, dust, fish-meal, wool, fæces, and other situations, it is not unnatural that they were among the first micro-organisms to be studied; but as there are large numbers of different species, almost all of which are devoid of pathogenic action, it follows from the way in which bacteriological investigation has been directed mainly along medical, veterinary, or agricultural lines, that our knowledge of these organisms is far from complete.

Some authors have separated the group into two divisions, the one containing *B. anthracis* and the closely allied pseudoanthrax bacillus, the other containing *B. subtilis* and other saprophytic forms. As, however, *B. subtilis* may itself be confused with *B. anthracis*, this division is of no real value. We shall treat all the members as belonging to one single group—the group of *Bacilli*—reserving the term "pseudoanthrax bacillus" as an inexact but convenient designation for any organism of the aerobic spore-bearing group that is liable to be confused with the true *B. anthracis*.

There is a large group of thermophilic bacilli found in milk, manure, and other situations which grow best at temperatures round about 60° C. We do not propose to describe these organisms, but references to them will be found in a paper by Wilson and his colleagues (1935). Not all of them belong to the *Bacillus* group; many species appear to be streptococci or non-sporing rods.

Group Characteristics

Morphology and Staining.—The *Bacilli* are large rod-shaped organisms varying in size from about $3 \mu \times 0.4 \mu$ to $9 \mu \times 2 \mu$. The sides are parallel, the axis straight or slightly curved, the ends either truncated, as in *B. anthracis*, or more usually convex. Their arrangement varies considerably; though single and diplobacillary forms predominate, they may be arranged in chains, often of considerable length, or in groups. Long, unjointed filaments are characteristic of some species, notably of the anthrax bacillus. Irregular forms, consisting mainly of poorly-stained thin bacilli, or of club- or bottle-shaped bacilli, are not uncommon. With a few exceptions, of which *B. anthracis* is the most important, all the members are motile by about 4–12 peritrichous flagella. Spores are present in all ; and are formed only in the presence of oxygen ; they vary in shape from spherical to ellipsoidal, and may appear at the equator, subterminally, or at the very end of the bacillus. Capsules are met with in only one member, *B. anthracis*, and then only when it is growing in the animal body, or in media rich in animal protein. The *Bacilli* are usually Gram-positive, but considerable variation may be shown ; some are strongly positive, others weakly positive, and a few frankly negative. When stained with various dyes, it is generally possible to distinguish areas of uneven staining ; in large bacilli a number of small particles are seen, quite distinct from spores. Some of these particles appear to consist of fat, others of volutin or glycogen. By a few authors the volutin granules have been regarded as nuclear material scattered diffusely through the cell ; the evidence against this contention has already been given in Chapter II. None of the vegetative bacilli are acid-fast, though, in the sporing condition, they resist decolorization for a short time with weak acids and alcohol.

Cultural Reactions.—Growth is free on all the ordinary media. Single colonies on agar are generally large, varying from 2 to several millimetres in diameter. Some have a finely granular, mealy appearance, others are membranous and thrown into wrinkles. In broth there is a tendency towards the formation of a surface scum, with or without turbidity, or of a heavy flocculent or membranous deposit. Gelatin is

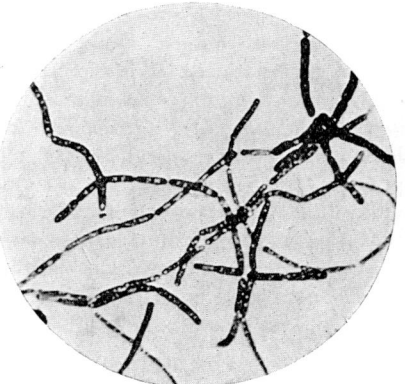

Fig. 157.—*B. megatherium.*
From an agar slope culture (× 1000).

usually liquefied rapidly. In a stroke agar culture the growth is raised and confluent, and generally of membranous consistency, rendering emulsification difficult. Growth is not improved by the addition of blood, serum, or glucose. Variant colonial types have been described for several members of the group.

Resistance.—In the vegetative condition the bacilli are killed by moist heat at a temperature of 55° C. in 1 hour. The spores vary greatly in resistance ; some, like those of *B. anthracis*, are destroyed by boiling for about 10 minutes ; others, like those of *B. subtilis*, may withstand boiling for hours. All are killed by steam under pressure at 120° C. in 40 minutes. Similarly with disinfectants the resistance varies ; $HgCl_2$ even in a 1/1000 solution may fail to kill anthrax spores in less than 70 hours (Poppe 1922). Potassium permanganate, on the other hand, in a 4 per cent. solution kills them in 15 minutes, and a 3 per cent. solution of hydrogen peroxide in 1 hour. Generally speaking, the spores are extremely resistant to chemical disinfectants, with the exception of those substances which act by oxidation.

Metabolic and Biochemical Reactions.—Some members form a pigment, generally brownish-yellow in colour, occasionally pink. On the whole, pigment formation is not a striking characteristic, and tends to appear late. The optimum temperature for growth varies from 25° C. to 37° C. ; few grow below 12° C., and excluding the thermophilic bacilli, none grows above 45° C. As regards oxygen pressure, they are aerobic or facultatively anaerobic.

On carbohydrate media they form acid only, no gas ; most of the members ferment glucose, maltose and sucrose ; some are able to attack mannitol and salicin. Lactose is rarely fermented. A diastatic ferment capable of inverting starch is secreted by some. A proteolytic ferment for gelatin is produced by nearly all, and by a few for blood serum. A true rennet-like clot is often formed in litmus milk, and is subsequently digested ; the litmus is reduced. Some strains peptonize milk without actually clotting it. The reaction becomes alkaline. Both the catalase test and the oxidase reaction described by Gordon and McLeod (1928) are usually positive. Methylene blue is reduced in broth. Some members are able to produce H_2S, and some to reduce nitrates to nitrites. A powerful filtrable hæmolysin is formed by one member of the group—*B. megatherium*—but many species are said to be hæmolytic (Poppe 1922).

Antigenic Structure.—Most of the serological work has been carried out with a view to separating *B. anthracis* from the other members of the group. A precipitating serum prepared against the anthrax bacillus will react not only with its homologous antigen, but also with the pseudoanthrax bacilli, though in a lower titre ; conversely the anthrax bacillus will react in a low titre with a serum prepared against some of the pseudoanthrax bacilli. A similar group reaction is noticeable in the complement-fixation test (Poppe 1922). From this we gather that the aerobic spore-bearing bacilli form a group, the members of which are closely related serologically ; the differentiation of *B. anthracis*, at least, can be carried out on a quantitative basis ; how far the other members may be distinguished is at present doubtful.

Pathogenicity.—Speaking generally, we may say that the anthrax bacillus is highly pathogenic for most animals ; and that most other *Bacilli* are non-pathogenic for all animals. This statement, however, must be modified. Under natural conditions the anthrax bacillus gives rise to disease in man, cattle, sheep, and certain others of the domesticated animals ; under experimental conditions it is pathogenic for the laboratory animals. Under natural conditions other species of *Bacilli* rarely give rise to disease, but an exception must be made for *B. subtilis*, which may cause severe eye lesions, notably iridocyclitis and panophthalmitis (Axenfeld 1908), and which may occasionally invade the blood stream of patients whose powers of resistance are lowered by the attack of some fatal disease (Sweany and Pinner 1925). Occasionally too, infections such as meningitis and pneumonia may be due to pseudoanthrax bacilli (Senge 1913, Wilamowski 1912). Under experimental conditions, the pseudoanthrax bacilli are non-pathogenic for all laboratory animals except mice, and for these animals only when injected intraperitoneally in a large dose—1–3 loopfuls of an agar culture. *B. megatherium* is, however, definitely toxic, and is able to kill guinea-pigs injected intraperitoneally in less than 24 hours. This is due to the formation of a hæmolysin. The fact that some pseudoanthrax bacilli may on occasion prove pathogenic to man and animals, and that after long subculture *B. anthracis* may lose its virulence for laboratory animals, suggests that there may be a gradual transition from the non-pathogenic to the pathogenic state (but see p. 660).

Classification.—This is very difficult, and any classification adopted is bound to be arbitrary. Some authors divide the group on the basis of motility, others on the character and situation of the spore, others on cultural characteristics, and others on several properties taken together. To each of these methods there are objections, and taking into consideration the fact that bacteriologists are not yet agreed on the identification of some of the commonest members of the group, it appears to us that no useful purpose would be served by discussing the criteria of classification. The main point of importance to the medical and veterinary student is the differentiation of *B. anthracis* from the other members of the group ; this will be considered under the description of *B. anthracis*.

In addition to *B. anthracis* there are several species to which specific names have been allotted, and some of these are described below.

Bacillus anthracis.

Named *B. anthracis* by Cohn (1875*b*) and Bacteridium by Davaine (1864). This bacillus is non-motile, forms capsules in the animal body and sometimes on artificial media, and grows on agar in characteristic long, segmented, parallel or interwoven chains. The spores are ellipsoidal or oval in shape, are found equatorially, and germinate by polar rupture. It is interesting to note that the anthrax bacillus was the first micro-organism in which the presence of resistant spores was demonstrated. Spores are never found in the animal body during life, and in culture appear more slowly than those of the other members of the group. They seem to be formed under conditions unfavourable to continued growth of the vegetative bacilli. Their appearance can be hastened by the addition of distilled water, 2 per cent. sodium chloride, and other salts (Bongert 1903). According to Bordet and Renaux (1930), sporulation is inhibited by the presence of calcium chloride and favoured by its absence. Cultures grown on oxalated agar often come to consist mainly of spores, while those grown on agar to which $CaCl_2$ has been added may lose their spore-forming power completely.

The curled hair-lock appearance of single colonies on agar or gelatin is characteristic, but may be closely simulated by *B. subtilis*. Microscopically this is seen to be due to the growth of the bacilli in long interwoven chains. Growth, particularly in broth, at a temperature of 42·5° C. for some days, causes the appearance of several different *variants* ; some have tough, well-defined capsules, give rise on agar to the typical curled colonies, and are highly virulent ; some have soft poorly-defined capsules, form thin, shining colonies on agar, and are slightly virulent ; others are non-capsulated, give rise to smooth, round, convex, glistening, mucoid colonies on agar, and are entirely avirulent (Preisz 1911, Nungester 1929*a, b*, Bordet and Renaux 1930). Some variants are asporogenous ; it was these which attracted Pasteur's attention, and which he considered to be avirulent. Preisz (1911) has, however, shown that, though there is a definite correlation between capsule formation and virulence, there is none between spore formation and virulence. Virulent strains may be either sporogenous or asporogenous ; similarly with avirulent strains. Asporogenous varieties may appear spontaneously in cultures incubated at the usual temperature (Behring 1889), or in cultures containing weak antiseptics, such as 1/2,000 potassium dichromate, or 1/1,000 phenol (Roux 1890). Such varieties, when arising from a virulent strain, are themselves fully virulent, though prolonged contact with weak antiseptics may eventually lower their virulence. The normal highly virulent bacillus forms a large, rough colony of frosted glass appearance with a curled edge ; morphologically it consists of bacilli arranged in chains (Figs. 159, 161). The avirulent bacillus forms a smaller, smoother

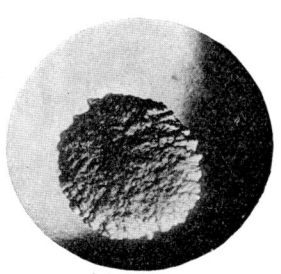

FIG. 158.—*B. anthracis.*

Smooth type of colony. Agar, 24 hours, 37° C. (× 8).

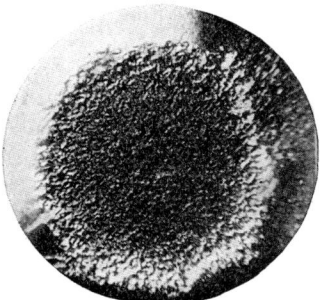

FIG. 159.—*B. anthracis.*

Rough type of colony. Agar, 24 hours, 37° C. (× 8).

type of colony, with a slightly crenated edge ; morphologically it consists of bacilli arranged singly, in pairs end-to-end, or in small bundles (Figs. 158, 160).

In the dry state the spores may remain alive for 12 years or more (Pasteur 1881*a*). According to Murray (1931), a saline suspension containing 1,000,000 spores per c.c. is sterilized by moist heat at 90° C. in 15 to 45 minutes, at 95° C. in 10 to 25 minutes, and at 100° C. in 5 to 10 minutes.

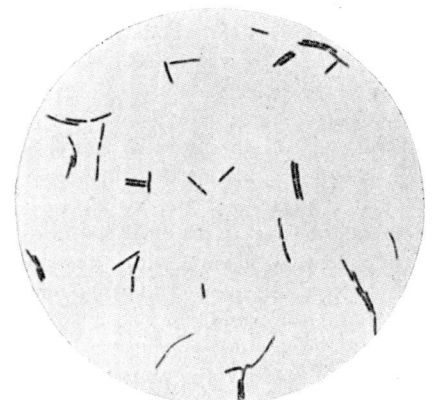

FIG. 160.—*B. anthracis.*

From smooth colony on agar, 24 hours, 37° C. (× 1000).

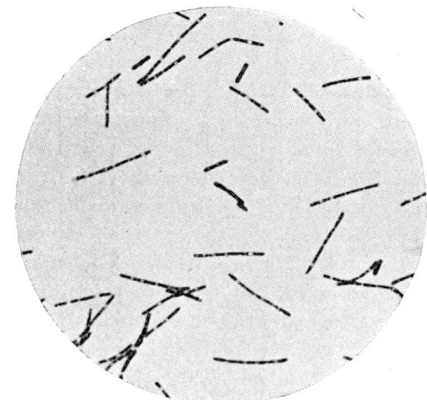

FIG. 161.—*B. anthracis.*

From rough colony on agar, 24 hours, 37° C. (× 1000).

The *antigenic structure* of the anthrax bacillus has received considerable attention. As early as 1921 Kramár obtained evidence that the capsule contained a glycoprotein probably belonging to the class of pseudomucins. A soluble specific carbohydrate, incapable of giving rise to antibodies on injection into animals, but reacting to a high titre with anti-anthrax serum, was extracted from anthrax bacilli by Combiesco, Soru, and Stamatesco (1929). A similar substance was prepared by Schockaert (1929). It is, however, mainly to the work of Tomcsik (1930), Tomcsik and Szongott (1932, 1933), Tomcsik and Bodon (1934, 1935), Bodon and Tomcsik (1934), Sordelli and Deulofeu (1930, 1933) and Sordelli, Deulofeu, and Ferrari (1932) that our knowledge of the antigenic structure of this organism is due. There appear to be two main antigens ; one a protein-like substance present in the capsule, the other a polysaccharide substance present in the body of the organism. The protein is fully antigenic, while the polysaccharide, though reacting with a precipitating serum, cannot itself stimulate the production of antibodies. Specific precipitins for both the protein and the polysaccharide constituents are found in serum prepared by the injection of animals with capsulated bacilli, and each can be differentially absorbed in the usual way. In animals infected with anthrax both antigens can be demonstrated in the tissues by the use of precipitating sera. There is reason to believe that the polysaccharide antigen is not strictly specific, but has a group affinity to the somatic antigens of certain anthrax-like bacilli.

The anthrax bacillus is naturally *pathogenic* mainly to the herbivora and to man, but occasionally it attacks other animals. Experimentally it proves fatal to the mouse, guinea-pig, and rabbit, less often to the rat. The dose is of considerable importance ; the larger it is, the shorter is the time to death. Subcutaneous injection of 1 loopful of an 18 hours' agar culture kills mice, guinea-pigs, and rabbits in about 12 to 30 hours ; a smaller dose, 1/100 of a loopful, kills them in 30 to 40 hours ; a still smaller dose, 1/2,000,000 of a loopful kills mice in 96 hours, guinea-pigs in 56 hours, and rabbits in 104 hours (Sobernheim 1897). Other *Bacilli* never kill in such small doses.

Post mortem, there is a gelatinous hæmorrhagic local œdema ; the viscera are congested, the blood is dark red and coagulates less firmly than usual ; the spleen is enlarged, dark red, and very friable. Microscopically, the bacilli are found in large numbers in the local lesion, in the blood, and in the thoracic and abdominal viscera ; they are confined almost entirely to the interior of the capillaries, where their numbers may be so great as to cause obstruction to the blood flow ; the tissues themselves are rarely penetrated. Though the disease terminates in a septicæmia, it is not till 4 or 5 hours before death, as a rule, that the bacilli actually gain access to the blood stream.

Infection may also be successfully achieved by cutaneous, intracutaneous, intramuscular, intraperitoneal or intravenous injection, or by feeding. The most certain route is the intramuscular, the least certain the oral (Sobernheim and Murata 1924). In general it requires a large dose to produce a fatal infection by the mouth (Giovanardi 1931). Post mortem in cases of oral infection, in addition to the enlargement of the spleen and the occurrence of septicæmia, the intestinal mucosa is seen to be covered with small furuncular swellings, through which the bacilli have gained access to the blood. Of the three animals the mouse is the most susceptible and the rabbit the least, the guinea-pig occupying an intermediate position. This difference in susceptibility is scarcely noticeable, except with a strain of weakened virulence (see Chapter LXIII). Rats are more difficult to infect than other rodents, but are said to succumb easily if fatigued by continuous exercise on a revolving drum (Charrin and Roger 1890). They may develop a chronic disease after subcutaneous injection, which does not prove fatal for 4 or 5 weeks. Dogs may be infected by subcutaneous injection, though not uniformly. Birds, with the exception of sparrows and young doves, and cold-blooded animals are resistant, likewise Algerian sheep (Chauveau 1880*a*, *b*). (See Davaine 1863*a*, *b*, 1864, Koch 1877, Frank and Lubarsch 1892, Sobernheim 1897, Oppermann 1906, Balteano 1922, Poppe 1922, Basset 1925, Katzu 1925, Muller 1925, Sanarelli 1925.) The experimental reproduction of the disease in larger animals is considered on p. 1374.

Pasteur (1881*b*, *c*) found that by growing the anthrax bacillus at 42·5° C. for about a month, he was able to lower its virulence to such an extent that it proved harmless to all animals except new-born guinea-pigs. By successive passage through these animals, the bacillus gradually regained its virulence till it was able to kill 2, 3, and 4-day, and later fully grown guinea-pigs ; eventually its virulence was entirely restored. From the work of Preisz (1911) it would appear that this resumption of virulence is due not to a gradually increasing virulence of the individual organisms, but to an alteration in the proportions of virulent and avirulent bacilli in the culture. He found that the effect of incubating a virulent culture at 42·5° C. was to cause the appearance of variants that were no longer virulent to animals, so that in one and the same culture both virulent and avirulent bacilli were found side by side. The longer the incubation, the higher was the proportion of avirulent bacilli. After a month or more the culture consisted almost entirely of avirulent variants, and on injection into mice proved to be harmless ; the virulent bacilli that were still present were too few to cause death. But if such a culture is injected into a new-born guinea-pig, these few virulent bacilli may be just sufficient to overcome the very low resistance of the animal ; in consequence they proliferate, and during the course of successive passages increase in proportion relatively to the avirulent variants, till eventually the culture consists almost entirely of the virulent type. The modern conception of the essential heterogeneity of single strains, *i.e.* the presence in one and the same strain of organisms showing sharp discontinuous variations in virulence, not only has more evidence in its favour than the older conception of the simultaneous and equal raising or lowering of all the bacilli in the strain, but explains more easily the variations in virulence that are noted consequent on altered environmental conditions.

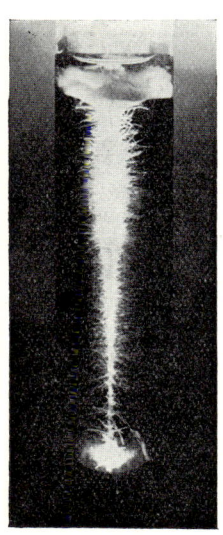

FIG. 162.—*B. anthra-
cis.*

In gelatin stab culture, 3 days, 22° C., showing inverted fir-tree growth, with commencing liquefaction.

Several observers (Hankin 1889, Martin 1890, Marmier 1895, Standfusz and Schnauder 1925) have shown that when *B. anthracis* is grown in a broth culture toxic albumoses are formed, which prove fatal on injection into animals ; Martin also found a toxic alkaloid. There is no evidence that a true exotoxin is formed ; the toxic substances appear to be formed largely by the disintegration of the proteins in the medium. The formation of a hæmolysin has been asserted by some authors, and denied by others ; it is possible that different strains may vary in this respect. There is certainly no hæmolysin produced for cattle or horse blood, but there is evidence to suggest that one may be formed for sheep, goat and rabbit blood (Poppe 1922).

The main criteria of value in the differentiation of *B. anthracis* from those bacilli which may be confused with it may be given in tabular form :

B. anthracis.	*Anthrax-like or so-called pseudoanthrax bacilli.*
1. Non-motile.	Generally motile.
2. Capsulated.	Non-capsulated.
3. Grows in long chains.	Grow in short chains.
4. No turbidity in broth.	Frequent turbidity in broth.
5. Inverted fir-tree growth in gelatin.	Fir-tree growth absent or atypical.
6. Precipitin reaction strongly positive.	Precipitin reaction weakly positive.
7. Pathogenic to laboratory animals.	Non-pathogenic to laboratory animals.
8. Liquefaction of gelatin slow.	Liquefaction of gelatin rapid.

An inverted fir-tree growth in gelatin is given by some strains of pseudoanthrax bacilli, but the branches are thick and interlaced, quite different from the regular, delicate, lateral outgrowths of *B. anthracis*. It is sometimes stated that the anthrax bacillus does not show hæmolysis on blood agar plates, whereas the pseudoanthrax bacilli form colonies surrounded by a zone of hæmolysis. This depends on the type of blood used, and is at best an uncertain criterion for differentiation.

When freshly isolated from the animal body, the anthrax bacillus rarely causes difficulty in identification, but after prolonged subculture in the laboratory it may lose several of its important characteristics, such as capsule formation, the inverted fir-tree growth in stab gelatin, and its pathogenicity for laboratory animals, and may then be very difficult to classify. Nevertheless bacilli have been described which have given rise to an anthrax-like disease in man and other animals, yet which have not conformed to the usual criteria of *B. anthracis* (Schulz 1901, Wilamowski 1912, Senge 1913). Such bacilli have usually been classed as pseudoanthrax bacilli, but it is probable that some at least have been variants of the real *B. anthracis*, similar to those described by Preisz (1911).

The characters of certain species of *Bacilli* are summarized below.

Bacillus anthracis

Synonyms.—Bactéridie du charbon, Milzbrandbacillus.

Ecology.—Parasitic in man, cattle, sheep and other animals.

Morphology.—Rods, 3–8 $\mu \times$ 1–1·2 μ. Straight or slightly curved, ends truncate ; on agar plates arranged characteristically in very long, segmented, parallel, or interwoven chains. Unjointed filaments not infrequent in cultures. In blood of animals mostly in pairs or chains of 3 or 4. Spores equatorial, ellipsoidal, not bulging ; polar germination ; not formed in animal body. Non-motile. Capsule found in animal body, and on serum media ; lost on agar ; surrounds entire chain of bacilli. Gram-positive. Non-acid-fast.

Agar Plate.—Irregularly round, 2–3 mm. in diameter, raised, dull, opaque, greyish-white, plumose colonies, with a tessellated or reticular structure, an uneven surface and a curled edge. Membranous consistency, emulsifiability difficult ; colony consists of parallel interlacing chains of bacilli, and is characteristic. After about a week irregular round scales appear on the surface of the colony. Several colonial variants have been described.

Agar Slope.—Thick, raised, spreading, greyish-yellow growth, with an uneven surface and an undulate edge showing little curled projections ; moist and slightly glistening. Looks as if there were innumerable tiny air bubbles beneath the surface. After about a week irregular round scales appear on the surface of the growth.

Gelatin Stab.—Poor filiform growth followed by outgrowth of delicate lateral extensions, longest at the upper part of the culture, giving an inverted fir-tree or lamp-brush effect. Liquefaction crateriform ; occurs very slowly.

Broth.—No turbidity, or very fine floccular turbidity ; moderate floccular deposit, consisting of interwoven threads, and disintegrating partly on shaking. No surface growth.

Blood Serum.—Abundant, creamy-yellow, confluent, curled growth with uneven surface. No liquefaction.

Potato.—Raised, dry, greyish-white, slightly spreading growth, with undulate or serrated edge.

Resistance.—Spores killed by boiling in 10 minutes. In dry state remain alive for years.

Metabolic.—Aerobic ; facultative anaerobe. Opt. temp. 37° C. Limits 12° to 44° C. Pigment none. Hæmolysis : some strains are stated to hæmolyse sheep's red cells. Nutritional ; grows well on ordinary media ; growth not improved by blood, serum or glucose.

Biochemical.—Acid, no gas, in glucose, maltose, sucrose, and later in salicin ; final pH 5·5–5·9. Indole — ; M.R. ± ; V.P. ± ; nitrates reduced to nitrites. H_2S — ; NH_3 ++ ; methylene blue reduced ; catalase +. Litmus milk coagulated and decolorized ; later peptonized.

Antigenic Structure.—There is a capsular protein-containing antigen and a somatic polysaccharide-containing antigen ; the latter has some group relationship to somatic antigens found in certain anthrax-like bacilli. Both antigens react specifically with precipitating sera.

Pathogenicity.—Naturally pathogenic to man, cattle, sheep (not Algerian), goats, pigs, and camels ; rarely to carnivores. Experimentally mice, guinea-pigs, and rabbits, injected *sc.* or *im.*, die in 12 to 40 hours ; p.m., hæmorrhagic local exudate, enlarged spleen, and bacilli in blood. Rats less susceptible. Birds, except sparrows and young pigeons, cold-blooded animals, and fish are resistant.

" Bacillus anthracoides," or " Bacillus pseudoanthracis."

Bacilli more or less closely resembling the anthrax bacillus have been isolated by numerous workers from such substances as soil, water, meat-, fish- and bone-meal, wool, dust, oil-cake, and less frequently from animals and man. These organisms have frequently been termed *B. pseudoanthracis* or *B. anthracoides.* Reference to the available papers renders it evident that more than one species has been described. We do not propose to consider these organisms in more detail, since their differential diagnosis from the anthrax bacillus has already been dealt with. It is sufficient to point out that most of them are motile, non-capsulated, form spores abundantly within 24 hours on agar, produce an even turbidity or a surface pellicle in broth, give rise to colonies on agar which are less curled and have fewer and less regular outgrowths at the edges, are more resistant to heat, form alkali in litmus milk, and are generally non-pathogenic, though sometimes they may be fatal to mice and even guinea-pigs on intraperitoneal inoculation in fairly large doses. The classification of these organisms is at present impossible ; they seem to range from avirulent variants of *B. anthracis*, on the one hand, to virulent variants of *B. subtilis* on the other. For some of the strains which have been described, see Hueppe and Wood (1889), Hartleb and Stutzer (1897), Schulz (1901), Bainbridge (1903), Wilamowski (1912), and Grierson (1928) ; and for two useful reviews see Pokschischewsky (1914) and Poppe (1922).

B. subtilis.

Great confusion has prevailed, and in fact still prevails, over this organism. It was described by Ehrenberg in 1838, who found it in hay infusion, as *Vibrio subtilis*, and by Cohn (1875a) as *Bacillus subtilis*. Neither of the descriptions was sufficiently full to enable the organism to be differentiated from others that simulate it closely, and in consequence organisms that are almost certainly different from Cohn's original bacillus have been identified with this organism. In an extensive investigation of the *Bacilli*, Lawrence and Ford (Ford 1916) in America have given this name to an organism that differs in several important particulars from that given by Cohn. The bacillus described by the German workers is fairly large, 3–4 μ long by 1 μ thick, may form threads, is actively motile, forms anthrax-like colonies on agar, gives rise to a thick, wrinkled surface membrane in broth, liquefies blood serum, and gives a thick, yellowish-white, creamy growth on potato, later appearing as if strewn with dry, white granules. The bacillus described by the American bacteriologists is one of the smallest of the aerobic spore-bearing bacilli, is 2 μ long by 0·4 μ broad, does not usually form threads, is sluggishly motile, forms dry, hard, glassy colonies on agar, adherent to the medium, gives rise to a thin branching scum in broth, later becoming more dense, fails to liquefy blood serum, and on potato gives a luxuriant, warty, pink growth.

According to Conn (1930), there are two different types of bacilli commonly called *B. subtilis*, one forming small spores which germinate equatorially (Marburg type), the other forming larger spores showing polar germination (Michigan type). Conn advances reasons to prove that the Marburg type is the original and genuine type, while Soule (1932) maintains that the classical *B. subtilis* is represented by the Michigan type. (See also Breed and Brooks 1935.)

In the following summary of the properties of this organism we have adhered to the description given by most of the German bacteriologists, with certain additions derived from a personal study of strains obtained from the National Collection of Type Cultures.

Variant colonies with different bacillary morphology have been described by a number of workers. According to Soule (1928), there is a rough and a smooth type closely simulating the corresponding type of *B. anthracis* (see p. 658). Graham (1930), who, like Soule, probably worked mainly with strains of the Michigan type, described four variants, two of which were motile and two usually non-motile. Variants I and III formed smooth, circular, shiny colonies with regular margins; II formed "medusa-head" colonies; while IV formed slightly irregular colonies with an uneven surface and a rather granular texture. All four variants had the same heat-stable somatic antigen. Variants I and II had in addition a common heat-labile flagellar antigen.

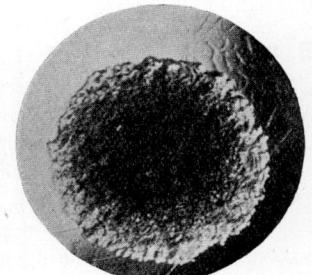

FIG. 163.—*B. subtilis.*

Smooth type of colony. Agar 24 hours, 37° C. (× 8).

Bacillus subtilis (Ehrenberg) Cohn

Synonyms.—Hay bacillus.

Habitat.—Hay, dust, milk, soil, water.

Morphology.—Rods, 3–4 μ × 1 μ, straight or curved, rounded ends, occurring singly or in short chains. Actively motile by 8–12 peritrichate flagella. Non-capsulated. Spores are oval, 1·2 μ × 0·6 μ, formed equatorially or subterminally, and germinate laterally; appear on agar in 18 hours. Gram-positive. Non-acid-fast.

Agar Plate.—Irregularly circular colonies, 4–6 mm. in diameter, slightly raised, greyish-yellow, and having a darker crumbly centre surrounded by a lighter periphery with a curled edge. Surface is finely granular; membranous or friable consistency; emulsification rather difficult. Resemble anthrax colonies.

Agar Slope.—Abundant, confluent, greyish-white, raised, opaque, sometimes wrinkled growth, with an undulate and finely serrated edge and a mealy surface. Membranous consistency, emulsifying fairly easily.

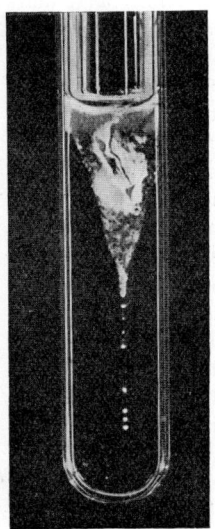

FIG. 164.—*B. subtilis.*

In gelatin stab culture, 4 days, 20°C., showing infundibuliform liquefaction.

Gelatin Stab.—Filiform growth with rapid infundibuliform or saccate liquefaction ; thick white membrane on surface adhering to the sides of the tube.

Broth.—Moderate turbidity, slight deposit, with formation of a thick wrinkled surface membrane adhering to the walls of the tube ; pellicle often sinks to the bottom.

Blood Serum.—Thick folded membrane ; liquefaction.

Potato—Thick, yellowish-white, raised, dull, creamy growth, later sprinkled with dry white granules, giving a mealy appearance.

Biochemical.—Acid, no gas, in glucose, maltose and sucrose. Indole —. M.R. — ; V.P. — ; nitrates reduced to nitrites. H_2S — ; NH_3 + ; methylene blue reduced ; catalase +. Litmus milk partially clotted, peptonized, and decolorized from above downwards.

Metabolic.—Aerobe, facultative anaerobe. Opt. temp. 37° C. Limits 12–44° C.

Pigment.—None.

Nutritional.—Grows freely on ordinary media ; growth not improved by blood, serum, or glucose.

Hæmolysis.—β-type on horse blood agar plates given by some strains.

Resistance.—Spores withstand boiling for hours.

Antigenic Structure.—Little exact knowledge available. Motile strains appear to have a heat-labile flagellar and a heat-stable somatic antigen.

Pathogenicity.—May give rise to conjunctivitis, iridochoroiditis, and panophthalmitis in man. Occasionally invades the blood stream in cachectic diseases. 1 c.c. 24-hours' broth culture sometimes proves fatal to mice injected intraperitoneally ; subcutaneous inoculation into rats occasionally gives rise to a local infiltration, and to submiliary abscesses in the lungs. Most strains are non-pathogenic.

B. mesentericus vulgatus.

First described by Flügge (1886), and generally known as the potato bacillus. Very common in soil. Some authors regard *B. mesentericus* and *B. vulgatus* as distinct organisms. Several variant types have, however, been described, and it seems not improbable that the two organisms belong essentially to the same species (Flynn and Rettger, 1934).

A variety, by some regarded as a distinct species, of this organism is *B. mesentericus fuscus* (Flügge) or the brown potato bacillus. It resembles *B. mesentericus vulgatus*, but differs in being slightly smaller, in having less tendency to thread formation, and in forming on agar and potato a thinner, greyish-brown layer of growth. A red potato bacillus was described by Globig (1888) as *B. mesentericus ruber*. It is sometimes known as *B. globigii* Migula. On potato it forms a reddish wrinkled growth of a tough viscous consistency. There is also a black potato bacillus, first described as *B. mesentericus niger*, and sometimes known as *B. aterrimus* Lehman and Neumann ; on solid media, especially on potato, it gives a characteristic thick, wrinkled, black growth. A bacillus, *B.*

mesentericus panis viscosi, sometimes known as *B. panis*, is responsible for ropy bread.

Bacillus mesentericus vulgatus (Flügge) Trevisan

Synonyms.—*B. vulgatus* ; potato bacillus.
Habitat.—Found in dust, soil, water, milk.
Morphology.—Rather slender, about 2–4

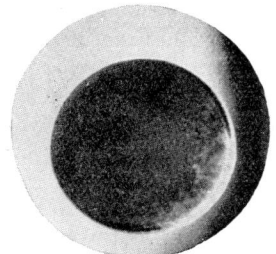

FIG. 165.—*B. mesentericus vulgatus.*
Smooth type of colony. Agar, 24 hours, 37° C. (× 8).

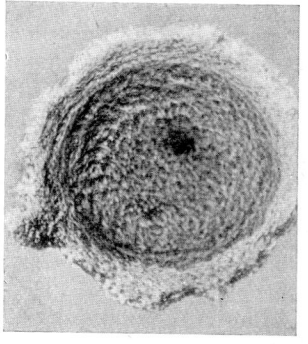

FIG. 166.—*B. mesentericus vulgatus.*
Same colony as in Fig. 145, after 48 hours' incubation, showing marked irregularity of surface and edge, and raised peripheral ring (× 8).

$\mu \times 0{\cdot}75\ \mu$; slightly rounded ends, occurring singly and in small groups. Motile by peritrichate flagella. Spores ellipsoidal, bulging, large in relation to cell, appear subterminally. Non-capsulated. Gram-positive. Non-acid-fast.

Agar Plate.—Round or oval, 4 mm. in diameter, raised greyish-yellow, opaque colonies with heaped-up edge, which is entire or finely serrated. Surface is finely granular and often wrinkled. Consistency membranous or friable ; emulsification difficult.

Agar Slope.—Profuse, confluent, raised, greyish-yellow, dull, opaque, wrinkled growth, with finely granular surface, and undulate or curled edge; membranous and difficult to emulsify. Membrane on water of condensation.

Gelatin Stab.—Filiform growth ; rapid liquefaction, infundibulo-saccate, with heavy surface membrane and deposit.

Broth.—Forms thick surface scum, which falls to the bottom, but re-forms ; turbidity moderate at first, later clears, with heavy tough membranous deposit.

Blood Serum.—Moderate, confluent, greyish-yellow growth, with uneven or nodular surface ; slight liquefaction.

Potato.—Thick, white, coarsely wrinkled, viscous growth, surface mealy and yellowish.

Biochemical.—Acid in glucose, mannitol, sucrose, salicin, sometimes maltose, but not lactose. Indole — ; M.R. — ; V.P. — ; nitrates reduced to nitrites. H_2S — ; $NH_3 +$; methylene blue not reduced ; catalase $+$. Litmus milk decolorized, and peptonized from above downwards.

Metabolism.—Aerobe, facultative anaerobe. Opt. temp. 37° C. Limits 12–44° C.

Pigment.—Slight yellowish or none.

Hæmolysis.—β-hæmolysis on horse blood agar plate by some strains.

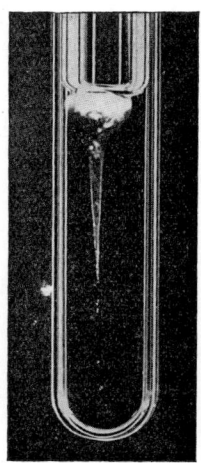

FIG. 167.—*B. mesentericus vulgatus.* In stab gelatin, 4 days, 20° C., showing napiform liquefaction.

Nutritional.—Grows freely on ordinary media. Growth not improved by blood, serum, or glucose.

Pathogenicity.—1 c.c. 24-hours' broth culture may kill mice injected intraperitoneally. Otherwise non-pathogenic.

B. megatherium de Bary.

First described by de Bary in 1884, who found it on cooked cabbage leaves. It is one of the largest of the *Bacilli*, and is found freely in dust, soil, air, milk, and water. Morphological and colonial variants have been described by Knaysi (1933). According to Rettger and Gillespie (1935), the well-known morphological pleomorphism of this organism is governed largely by environmental conditions, particularly oxygen starvation. It forms a powerful hæmolysin (Todd 1901, 1902, Warden *et al.* 1921), most active towards the red corpuscles of man, monkey, and the guinea-pig ; it appears in broth cultures at 37° C. on the 2nd or 3rd day, increases to a maximum on the 6th or 7th day, and then diminishes slowly. Oxygen is essential for its production. The hæmolysin, which can be filtered through a Pasteur-Chamberland candle, deteriorates rapidly on keeping, and like many other true toxins is destroyed by heating at 56° C. for half an hour. Subcutaneous injection into guinea-pigs gives rise to a large local swelling with subsequent necrosis. On intravenous injection into guinea-pigs it gives rise to hæmoglobinuria, but is not fatal except in large doses—about 10 c.c. Antihæmolysin can be prepared by injection of the hæmolysin into goats. Warden, Connell and Holly (1921) found that when 2 c.c. of centrifuged broth culture were injected intraperitoneally into guinea-pigs, the animals died in less than 12 hours. Post mortem the abdomen was distended, the peritoneum congested, there was hæmolysed blood in the peritoneal cavity, and bloody fluid in the lumen of the gut, in the pleural cavities and over the thighs. They bring evidence to suggest that the toxin and the hæmolysin are one and the same body.

Bacillus megatherium de Bary

Synonyms.—Probably represents some strains known as *B. anthracoides* or *B. pseudo-anthracis.*

Habitat.—Found in dust, soil, water, milk.

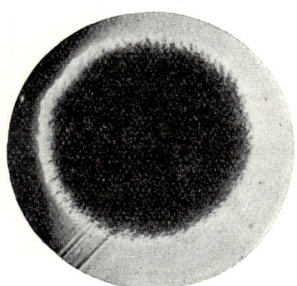

FIG. 168.—*B. megatherium.*

Surface colony on agar, 36 hours, 37° C. (× 8).

Morphology.—Large, rod-shaped, 3–9 μ × 1·2 μ. Long unsegmented forms are common, and shadow forms appear early. Ends slightly rounded, axis curved ; occurs singly, in pairs and in chains. Cells contain fat globules. Motile by 4–8 peritrichate flagella. Spores equatorial, oval, or ellipsoidal, not bulging ; formed freely in 24 hours. Non-capsulated. Gram-positive. Non-acid-fast.

Agar Plate.—Round, 3–5 mm. in diameter, raised, dull, greyish-white, opaque colonies with entire edge and finely granular surface, sometimes radially striated ; may show differentiation into raised opaque centre and thin translucent periphery ; membranous consistency ; emulsifiability fairly easy. After about a week irregular round scales appear on the surface of the colony, similar to those on anthrax colonies.

Agar Slope.—Profuse, moist, raised, glistening, greyish-yellow, creamy growth with smooth surface and entire edge ; butyrous consistency ; sometimes may show parallel raised ridges like contour lines ; emulsifies easily. After about a week irregular round scales appear on the surface of the growth, similar to those of anthrax.

Gelatin Stab.—Abundant filiform growth with infundibuliform or saccate liquefaction ; no surface membrane.

Broth.—Moderate, finely floccular, turbidity, with slight ring growth and a powdery deposit, later becoming heavy and viscous.

Blood Serum.—Abundant, moist, creamy, yellowish growth, with granular structure and finely contoured surface. No liquefaction.

Potato.—Thick, greyish-yellow, mealy growth.

Resistance.—Spores are said to withstand 18 lbs. steam pressure for 1 hour ; killed by 19 lbs. for 1 hour.

Metabolism.—Aerobe, facultative anaerobe. Opt. temp. 35° C. Limits 12–45° C.

Pigment.—None.

Hæmolysis.—Powerful hæmolysin produced, acting especially on the red cells of man, monkeys, and guinea-pigs.

Toxin.—The hæmolysin is fatal to laboratory animals.

Nutritional.—Grows well on ordinary media ; not improved by blood, serum, or glucose.

Biochemical.—Acid, no gas, in glucose, maltose, and sucrose. Indole — ; M.R. — ; V.P. —. Nitrates reduced to nitrites, slight ; $NH_3 +$; H_2S — ; methylene blue reduced ; catalase +. Litmus milk sometimes clot, followed by peptonization and decolorization.

Pathogenicity.—Non-pathogenic under natural conditions. The hæmolysin is fatal in 1–2 c.c. doses to mice and guinea-pigs injected intraperitoneally. P.M. hæmorrhagic exudate in peritoneum and pleura.

B. mycoides Flügge.

First described by Flügge (1886) ; common in milk, water, soil, and dust. Is easily distinguishable from other members by its typical rhizoid growth on agar. It is a highly proteolytic organism, which is said to convert half the protein nitrogen of the medium into ammonia ; when growing in the soil it therefore plays an important part in the process of denitrification. Some strains are said to secrete a highly active proteolytic ferment capable of lysing cultures of certain bacteria (Schubert 1928). Variant morphological and colonial types have been described by Lewis (1932, 1933) and den Dooren de Jong (1933).

Bacillus mycoides

Synonyms.—*B. ramosus* Eisenberg. Root bacillus.

Habitat.—Found in milk, water, soil and dust.

Morphology.—Rod-shaped, 3–5 μ × 1·0 μ ; truncated or slightly rounded ends, occurring singly, in pairs, small groups, and chains ; long unjointed threads not uncommon. Motile by peritrichate flagella. Spores are large, equatorial and ellipsoidal, measuring 1·8 μ × 0·8 μ ; appear within 24 to 48 hours. Non-capsulated. Cells store fat as reserve material. Gram-positive. Non-acid-fast.

Agar Plate.—Large, spreading, raised, greyish-white, dull, opaque and rhizoid colonies, with finely granular surface ; denser nuclei, dark in colour, are visible from which the peripheral shoots arise ; membranous consistency ; emulsification fairly easy.

Agar Slope.—Abundant, confluent, spreading, rhizoid, opaque growth, greyish-white and slightly glistening ; surface honeycombed, due to the presence of arborescent ridges forming a raised network. Growth penetrates the medium, and is hence firmly adherent to it.

Gelatin Stab.—Arborescent, filamentous growth ; saccate liquefaction ; clearing of gelatin with formation of a deposit and a surface membrane.

Broth.—No turbidity ; firm, sometimes wrinkled, surface membrane, depositing later.
Blood Serum.—Luxuriant, rhizoid growth ; no digestion.

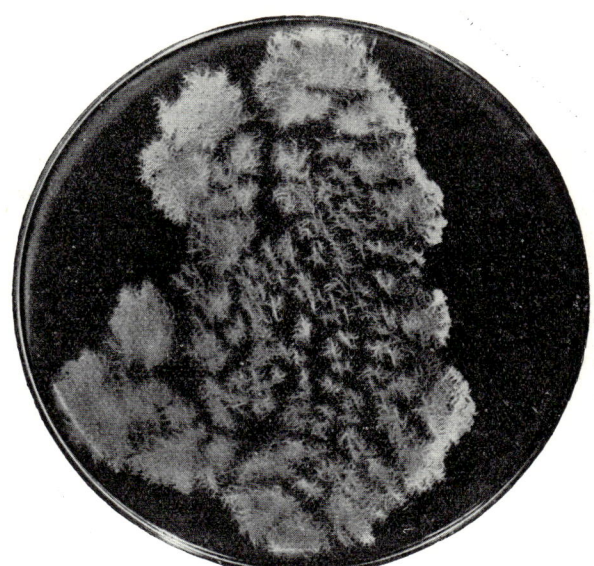

FIG. 169.—*B. mycoides.*
Surface growth of rhizoid type on agar, 3 days, 30° C.   (⅘ths natural size.)

Potato.—Abundant, mealy, greyish-brown, growth of viscous consistency ; surface
granular.
Resistance.—Spores are said to withstand 15 lbs. steam pressure for 1 hour.   Killed by
20 lbs. in half an hour.

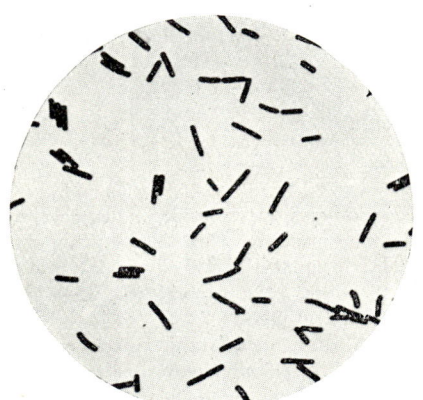

FIG. 170.—*B. mycoides.*
From an agar slope culture, 2 days, 30° C.
(× 1000).

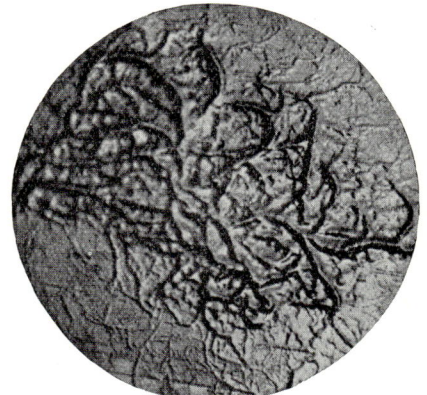

FIG. 171.—*B. mycoides.*
Central part of a surface colony on agar, 3
days, 30° C., showing rhizoid structure (× 8).

Metabolism.—Aerobe ; facultative anaerobe.   Opt. temp. 30° C.   Pigment none.   Some
strains secrete a lysin capable of dissolving certain bacteria.

Hæmolysis.—None on horse blood agar plates.

Nutritional.—Grows fairly well on ordinary media ; growth not improved by blood, serum, or glucose, but augmented by nitrates.

Biochemical.—Acid, no gas, in glucose, maltose and sucrose. Indole — ; M.R. — ; V.P. + ; nitrates + ; NH_3 + ; H_2S slight + ; methylene blue reduced ; catalase +. Litmus milk, slow peptonization and decolorization.

Pathogenicity.—Non-pathogenic to man and animals.

As well as the more common representatives, there are large numbers of other organisms that have been described, such as *B. cereus* Frankland, *B. albolactus* Migula, *B. fusiformis* Gottheil, *B. cohærens* Gottheil, *B. terminalis* Migula, *B. petasites* Gottheil, *B. tumescens* Zopf, and *B. graveolens* Gottheil. For their description the reader is referred to the publications of Loeffler 1887, Globig 1888, Hueppe and Wood 1889, Flügge 1896, Lehmann and Neumann 1896, Hartleb and Stutzer 1897, Chester 1901, Gottheil 1901, Schulz 1901, Bainbridge 1903, Neide 1904, Neufeld 1913, Poppe 1913, 1922, Senge 1913, Pokschischewsky 1914, Ford 1916, Laubach 1916, Bergey 1923, and to the monograph of de Soriano, 1935.

A bacillus described as *Urobacillus pasteurii* Miquel (see Beijerinck 1901) may be mentioned here, since it seems to be of some importance in soil metabolism. It is a motile rod, 4–5 μ long by 1·5 μ broad, forming subterminal spherical spores. It fails to grow on ordinary media, but grows well in meat-extract gelatin containing 0·3 per cent. ammonium carbonate and 2 per cent. urea. Though its optimum growth temperature is 32° C., its power of breaking down urea is stated to be most manifest at 50° C. Gibson (1934, 1935), who has subjected this organism to a careful study, regards it as being represented by three different species, which he calls *B. pasteuri*, *B. loehnisii*, and *B. freudenreichii*. These organisms are not to be confused with *Urobacillus miquelii*, described by Beijerinck as a motile, non-sporing rod, not unlike *Zopfius zopfii*. Beijerinck described a similar bacillus forming oval spores, and capable of decomposing urea, under the name of *Urobacillus leubei*.

REFERENCES

AXENFELD, T. (1908) " The Bacteriology of the Eye." London.

BAINBRIDGE, F. A. (1903) *J. Path. Bact.*, **8**, 117.

BALTEANO, L. (1922) *Ann. Inst. Pasteur*, **36**, 805.

BARY, H. A. DE. (1884) " Vergleichende Morphologie und Biologie der Pilze, Mycetozoen, und Bakterien." Leipzig.

BASSET, J. (1925) *C. R. Soc. Biol.*, **93**, 1513, 1515, 1517.

BEHRING. (1889) *Z. Hyg. InfektKr.*, **7**, 171.

BEIJERINCK, M. W. (1901) *Zbl. Bakt.*, IIte Abt., **7**, 33.

BERGEY, D. H. (1923) " Manual of Determinative Bacteriology." Baltimore.

BODON, G. and TOMCSIK, J. (1934) *Proc. Soc. exp. Biol., N.Y.*, **32**, 122.

BONGERT, J. (1903) *Zbl. Bakt.*, **34**, 497, 623, 772.

BORDET, J. and RENAUX, E. (1930) *Ann. Inst. Pasteur*, **45**, 1.

BREED, R. S. and BROOKS, R. St. J. (1935) *Zbl. Bakt.*, IIte Abt., **92**, 481.

CHARRIN, A. and ROGER, G. H. (1890) *Arch. Physiol. norm. path.*, **22**, 273.

CHAUVEAU, A. (1880a) *C. R. Acad. Sci.*, **91**, 33 ; (1880b) *Ibid.*

CHESTER. (1901) " A Manual of Determinative Bacteriology." New York.

COHN, F. (1875a) *Cohn's Beitr. Biol. Pflanz.*, **1**, Heft 2, p. 175 ; (1875b) *Ibid.*, **2**, Heft 3, p. 141.

COMBIESCO, D., SORU, E., and STAMATESCO, S. (1929) *C. R. Soc. Biol.*, **102**, 124.

CONN, H. J. (1930) *J. infect. Dis.*, **46**, 341.

DAVAINE, C. (1863a) *C. R. Acad. Sci.*, **57**, 220 ; (1863b) *Ibid.*, **57**, 351 ; (1864) *Ibid.*, **59**, 393.

DOOREN DE JONG, L. E. DEN. (1933) *Arch. Mikrobiol.*, **4**, 36.

EHRENBERG. (1838) " Infusionsthierchen als vollkommene Organismen." Leipzig.

FLÜGGE, C. G. F. W. (1886) " Die Mikroorganismen." Leipzig. (1896) *Ibid.*, 3te Aufl., Vol. 2. Leipzig.

FLYNN, C. S. and RETTGER, L. F. (1934) *J. Bact.*, **28**, 1.

FORD, W. W. (1916) *J. Bact.*, **1**, 273.

FRANK, G. and LUBARSCH, O. (1892) *Z. Hyg. InfektKr.*, **11**, 259.
GIBSON, T. (1934) *J. Bact.*, **28**, 295, 313 ; (1935) *Ibid.*, 491.
GIOVANARDI, A. (1931) *Krankheitsforschung*, **9**, 13.
GLOBIG. (1888) *Z. Hyg. InfektKr.*, **3**, 322.
GORDON, J. and McLEOD, J. W. (1928) *J. Path. Bact.*, **31**, 185.
GOTTHEIL, O. (1901) *Zbl. Bakt.*, IIte Abt., **7**, 430, 449, 529, 627, 680, 717.
GRAHAM, N. C. (1930) *J. Path. Bact.*, **33**, 665.
GRIERSON, A. M. M. (1928) *J. Hyg., Camb.*, **27**, 306.
HANKIN, E. H. (1889) *Brit. med. J.*, ii, 810.
HARTLEB, R. and STUTZER, A. (1897) *Zbl. Bakt.*, IIte Abt., **3**, 81, 129, 179.
HUEPPE, F. and WOOD, G. C. (1889) *Berl. klin. Wschr.*, **26**, 347.
KATZU, S. (1925) *Zbl. Bakt.*, **94**, 165.
KNAYSI, G. (1933) *J. Bact.*, **26**, 623.
KOCH, R. (1877) *Cohn's Beitr. Biol. Pflanz.*, **2**, 277.
KRAMÁR, E. (1921) *Zbl. Bakt.*, **87**, 401.
LAUBACH, C. H. (1916) *J. Bact.*, **1**, 493.
LEHMANN, K. and NEUMANN, R. (1896) "Atlas und Grundriss der Bakteriologie, etc."
　　J. F. Lehmann, Munich.
LEWIS, I. M. (1932) *J. Bact.*, **24**, 381 ; (1933) *Ibid.*, **25**, 359.
LOEFFLER, F. (1887) *Berl. klin. Wschr.*, **24**, 607, 629.
MARMIER, L. (1895) *Ann. Inst. Pasteur*, **9**, 533.
MARTIN, S. (1890) *20th Rep. loc. Govt Bd publ. Hlth, Suppl.*, p. 255.
MULLER, L. (1925) *C. R. Soc. Biol.*, **93**, 1243.
MURRAY, T. J. (1931) *J. infect. Dis.*, **48**, 457.
NEIDE, E. (1904) *Zbl. Bakt.*, IIte Abt., **12**, 1, 161, 337, 539.
NEUFELD. (1913) *Zbl. Bakt., Ref. Beiheft.*, **57**, 279.
NUNGESTER, W. J. (1929a) *J. infect. Dis.*, **44**, 73 ; (1929b) *Ibid.*, **45**, 214.
OPPERMANN. (1906) *J. comp. Path.*, **19**, 264.
PASTEUR, L. (1881a) *C. R. Acad. Sci.*, **92**, 209 ; (1881b) *Ibid.*, **92**, 429 ; (1881c) *Ibid.*,
　　92, 666.
POKSCHISCHEWSKY, N. (1914) *Arb. ReichsgesundhAmt.*, **47**, 541.
POPPE, K. (1913) *Zbl. Bakt., Ref.* **57**, 277 ; (1922) *Ergebn. Hyg. Bakt.*, **5**, 597.
PREISZ, H. (1911) *Zbl. Bakt.* **58**, 510
RETTGER, L. F. and GILLESPIE, H. B. (1935) *J. Bact.*, **30**, 213.
ROUX, E. (1890) *Ann. Inst. Pasteur*, **4**, 25.
SANARELLI, G. (1925) *Ann. Inst. Pasteur*, **39**, 209.
SCHOCKAERT, J. (1929) *Arch. int. Méd. exp.*, **5**, 155.
SCHUBERT, J. (1928) *Zbl. Bakt.*, **108**, 151.
SCHULZ, R. (1901) *Zbl. Bakt.*, **30**, 582.
SENGE, J. (1913) *Zbl. Bakt.*, **70**, 353.
SOBERNHEIM, G. (1897) *Z. Hyg. InfektKr.*, **25**, 301.
SOBERNHEIM, G. and MURATA, H. (1924) *Z. Hyg. InfektKr.*, **103**, 691.
SORDELLI, A. and DEULOFEU, V. (1930) *C. R. Soc. Biol.*, **105**, 721 ; (1933) *Folia biol.*,
　　No. 26–27, p. 121.
SORDELLI, A., DEULOFEU, V., and FERRARI, J. (1932) *Folia biol.*, No. 11, p. 45 ; No. 20,
　　p. 93 and 94.
SORIANO, A. M. de. (1935) *Rev. Inst. bact., B. Aires*, **6**, 507.
SOULE, M. H. (1928) *J. infect. Dis.*, **42**, 93 ; (1932) *Ibid.*, **51**, 191.
STANDFUSZ, R. and SCHNAUDER, F. (1925) *Zbl. Bakt.*, **95**, 61.
SWEANY, H. C. and PINNER, M. (1925) *J. infect. Dis.*, **37**, 340
TODD, C. (1901) *Lancet*, ii. 1663 ; (1902) *Trans. path. Soc., Lond.*, **53**, 196.
TOMCSIK, J. (1930) *Z. Hyg. InfektKr.*, **111**, 119.
TOMCSIK, J. and BODON, G. (1934) *Z. ImmunForsch.*, **83**, 426 ; (1935) *Ibid.*, **84**, 308.
TOMCSIK, J. and SZONGOTT, H. (1932) *Z. ImmunForsch.*, **76**, 214 ; (1933) *Ibid.*, **78**, 86.
WARDEN, C. C., CONNELL, J. T., and HOLLY, L. E. (1921) *J. Bact.*, **6**, 103.
WILAMOWSKI, B. I. (1912) *Zbl. Bakt.*, **66**, 39.
WILSON, G. S., TWIGG, R. S., WRIGHT, R. C., HENDRY, C. B., COWELL, M. P., and MAIER, I.
　　(1935) *Spec. Rep. Ser. med. Res. Coun., Lond.*, No. 206, p. 376.

CHAPTER XXXIII

CLOSTRIDIUM

THE SPORE-BEARING ANAEROBES

DEFINITION.—*Clostridium.*

Anaerobic or microaerophilic rods, producing endospores, which are usually wider than the vegetative organisms in which they arise—so-called clostridium forms. Generally Gram-positive. Often decompose protein media through the agency of enzymes, and often ferment carbohydrates. Many species are pathogenic. Type species is *Clostridium butyricum* Prazmowski.

Previous to the War, the study of the spore-bearing anaerobes had been undertaken fitfully and by imperfect methods ; much attention had been paid to their pathogenicity, but little to their general biological characters. One and the same organism had received many different names, and many organisms with the same name undoubtedly belonged to different species. The only two organisms about which no doubt existed were the two that formed a highly potent toxin, recognizable by the specific effects they produced on injection into animals—namely *Cl. tetani* and *Cl. botulinum.* It was not till the pressure of the War rendered an intensive study of the anaerobes necessary, and till the introduction of McIntosh and Fildes' jar made it feasible to obtain pure cultures with relative ease, that the obscurity surrounding this group was dispersed.

Most of the older workers had failed to realize the difficulty inherent in obtaining pure cultures of the anaerobic bacilli. The new technique, especially by enabling plate cultures to be made, revealed at once the impurity of many of the classical strains, and provided a means for the preparation of single-colony cultures. For the first time a distinctive account was provided of the main species, which made possible their identification, and which disposed of many spurious characters that had been attributed to them. Incidentally fresh species were discovered. (For references on the production of anaerobiosis see Liborius 1886, Frankland 1889, Smith 1890, Tarozzi 1905, Smith *et al.* 1905–06, Laidlaw 1915, Report 1917, Holker 1918–19, Rockwell 1924, Varney 1926, Wilson 1928, Hall 1929*a*, Dickens 1934, McClung *et al.* 1935).

Ecology.—The anaerobes are widely distributed in nature, but their main habitat is undoubtedly the soil. Some of them appear to be common inhabitants of the intestinal canal of man and animals. *Cl. welchii,* for example, is uniformly present in human fæces ; *Cl. tetani* has been found in about 10–40 per cent. of fæcal specimens of domestic animals ; *Cl. sporogenes* is frequently, and *Cl. histolyticum* occasionally present. It has been held by some that the intestinal canal is the main habitat of certain of the anaerobes, particularly *Cl. tetani,* and that their presence in the soil can be explained by fæcal contamination. The fact that this

671

organism is found in virgin soil taken far from human or animal habitations renders this view improbable. It would seem more likely that the primary habitat of the majority of the anaerobes is the soil; that they are ingested frequently with vegetables and fruit; and that some of them are able to adapt themselves temporarily or permanently to a life in the intestinal canal.

Their presence in soil and fæces accounts for their frequent appearance in dust, milk and sewage. In spite of the fact that they lead a saprophytic existence, several of these species are causally related to well-recognized diseases in man and animals.

Morphology.—The anaerobes are endowed with a pleomorphism that renders their identification on a morphological basis very difficult, and often frankly impossible. Not only may an organism assume different shapes under changing environmental conditions, but under one and the same set of conditions it may present very different forms.

Like the aerobic spore-bearing bacilli they are large, rod-shaped organisms. In length they vary from about 3 μ to 7 or 8 μ, but long filamentous forms are quite common. Their breadth varies from about 0·4 to 1·2 μ. The vegetative bacilli are straight or curved, their sides are parallel, and their ends rounded or somewhat truncated. Most are arranged singly, but some occur in pairs or in chains, others in bundles the members of which are arranged parallel to each other. Irregular forms include navicular or boat-shaped organisms; citron forms shaped like a lemon with a small knob at each end; large, swollen, non-sporing rods or " orgonts "; snake-like filaments; deeply stained bulb-like types; and a great variety of so-called involution forms varying both in shape and in depth of staining. Autolysis frequently sets in with the commencement of sporulation so that shadow forms are numerous, particularly in certain species.

Sporulation is common to all members, but there is considerable variation in the readiness with which it occurs. *Cl. sporogenes*, for example, spores readily on all media; *Cl. welchii* only in media free from a fermentable carbohydrate, and then inconstantly. All the pathogenic members are able to form spores in the animal body.

It has been customary to classify the anaerobes according to the shape of the spore and the position in the rod at which it appears. Thus we have (1) those with an equatorial or subterminal spore; (2) those with an oval terminal spore; a. ' (3) those with a spherical terminal spore. This division is useful for certain purposes, but it must not be used too rigidly. It is common, for instance, to find organisms that usually form subterminal spores giving rise to spores that are strictly terminal. The differentiation between a spherical and an oval terminal spore may also be a matter of the utmost nicety.

The spores of most members are wider than the vegetative bacilli; they therefore confer on the organism a distinctive appearance according to the position in which they arise. If they are formed at the equator the clostridium is spindle-shaped; if subterminally club-shaped; with an oval terminal spore the organism may look like a tennis racket; with a spherical terminal spore like a drum-stick.

With the exception of *Cl. welchii*, *Cl. bifermentans*, and possibly *Cl. tertium*, all the members are motile, by peritrichate flagella. Motility, however, is often difficult to demonstrate, especially in artificial cultures and in strains that have been subcultured for some time. Young cultures in broth or cooked meat medium, not more than 6 to 24 hours old, are the most suitable for examination. If these are negative, the organisms should be examined in the tissue fluids of injected animals. The usual coverslip method is satisfactory in most instances, but if this fails, examination should be conducted in a closed capillary tube that has been inoculated with a young broth culture and kept at 37° C. for about half an hour. As is customary with large organisms, motility is rarely well marked, and is usually of the slow and stately variety, in contrast to the rapid, darting movements of smaller organisms such as *Bact. typhosum*.

Cl. butyricum and *Cl. welchii* are the only members possessing a capsule ; the capsule of *Cl. welchii* is noticeable in the animal body, and sometimes in cultures containing serum.

Staining Reactions.—All members stain readily with the usual dyes. Great irregularity is noticeable in the depth of staining, especially in cultures more than a day or two old. Sometimes metachromatic granules are noticeable, or points of more intense coloration. Provided young cultures are examined, the bacilli are all Gram-positive. Some species rapidly lose this property, and some can be decolorized if the alcohol is applied for too long. In the early stages of spore formation, the position of the spore is often marked by an area of intense staining ; as it matures, however, the spore presents a colourless centre surrounded by a peripherally stained ring.

Cultural Reactions.—On solid media growth is relatively slow, and takes the form of a thin, effuse, often spreading film, which may be difficult to distinguish from the underlying medium.

The tendency to film formation is promoted by moisture. *Cl. tetani* can spread rapidly over a moist surface ; if it is inoculated into the condensation water of an agar slope, it will in the course of a day spread over the whole medium ; the film is so thin that, were it not for the dentate edge presented at the upper end of the slope, where the medium is drier, it might easily escape detection. Advantage may be taken of this fact in the isolation of this organism (Fildes 1925*a*).

For obtaining single colonies of the anaerobes it is therefore advisable to use plates from which all surface moisture has evaporated. Even then the task is not always easy.

Agar Plates.—Single colonies are rounded, generally effuse, and present crenated, fimbriate, or rhizoid edges. *Cl. welchii*, which is one of the less strict anaerobes, forms low convex colonies with an entire edge ; *Cl. sporogenes* and *Cl. histolyticum* may form umbonate colonies with a raised centre and a flat periphery. The colonial appearances are often characteristic, but some species give rise to variants which not only are unlike the typical colony, but which strongly suggest the occurrence of contamination. Several different types of colony may be formed by *Cl. tetani*, for example.

Glucose Agar Shake Cultures.—These are commonly employed for studying the form of deep colonies, and by many workers for the preparation of pure cultures. Except near the surface, growth occurs throughout the medium ; this is frequently disrupted and blown upwards by the development of gas. Single colonies are rounded or biconvex in shape ; sometimes they are differentiated into an opaque centre and a translucent periphery ; their edge may be entire, but is more often woolly, erose, or presents that curious reticular filamentous appearance of a cigarette thrown into water.

Blood Agar Plates.—On these, not only is the colonial form characteristic, but the degree and type of hæmolysis affords a useful differentiating feature between the members of the group. Hæmolysis is well marked after 3-days' incubation at 37° C.; if the plates are then stored in a dark cupboard at room temperature it continues to increase. With a thick seeding the whole plate may be completely decolorized.

Many organisms give hæmolysis of the α-prime type after 3-days' incubation (see Chapter XXIII); after a further 3 days this passes into the fully developed β-variety.

COOKED MEAT MEDIUM.—Most of the members grow well in this medium. All render the fluid turbid to some extent, and most produce gas. The proteolytic members digest the meat and may turn it black; the saccharolytic members do not digest the meat, but frequently turn it pink. Varying reactions are recorded in this medium, depending on the strain used, the batch of medium, and the length of incubation. Both in this medium and in other media the proteolytic members form a characteristic pervasive odour, while cultures of the saccharolytic members are practically odourless.

COAGULATED SERUM AND COAGULATED EGG.—These media are used for testing the proteolytic powers. None of the saccharolytic organisms are able to liquefy them.

GELATIN.—At 23° C. most members grow poorly. In stab culture *Cl. tetani* gives a characteristic fir-tree growth, followed later by liquefaction. At 37° C. growth is improved, and is generally accompanied by permanent liquefaction.

Resistance.—In the sporing stage all the members present a marked but variable resistance to heat, drying, and disinfectants. Thus the spores of *Cl. botulinum* withstand boiling for 3 or 4 hours, and even at 105° C. are not killed completely in less than 100 minutes. On the other hand, spores of *Cl. welchii* are said to be destroyed by boiling in less than 5 minutes (Headlee 1931). *Cl. sporogenes* can survive exposure for 8 days to a 5 per cent. phenol solution. In dried earth or dust *Cl. tetani* may live for years. Stock cultures of most members in cooked meat medium remain viable for months; some, such as *Cl. fallax* and *Cl. cochlearium*, are more delicate and require transferring frequently.

Metabolism.—Up till within recent years it was generally believed that members of this group were unable to grow except when oxygen was rigidly excluded from the medium. Though free oxygen does inhibit their growth, and may actually destroy organisms in the non-sporing state, it is quite possible to obtain growth of anaerobic bacteria in the presence of air provided a sufficiently low oxidation-reduction potential is established in the medium. This can be done by including substances in the medium which will take up molecular oxygen and bring about a fall in the Eh below that necessary for the initiation of growth. Many such substances are available, some of which act mainly by absorbing oxygen, others of which are chiefly responsible for the establishment of a low Eh after the molecular oxygen has been nearly used up or removed by mechanical means. Sulphites, reduced iron compounds, unsaturated fatty acids, activated glucose, cysteine, and glutathione are examples of some of the substances commonly added to media to bring about the requisite anaerobic conditions. Cooked meat is an example of a medium that affords excellent conditions for anaerobic growth even when incubated aerobically. Its virtue lies in its containing (1) unsaturated fatty acids, which take up oxygen, the reaction being catalysed by the haematin of the muscle, and (2) glutathione, which brings about a negative O-R potential corresponding to an Eh of about − 0·2 volt (Lepper and Martin 1929, 1930). Fildes (1929) has shown that for the germination of tetanus spores an Eh in the medium approximating to $+ 0.01$ volt at pH 7·0 is required ; this corresponds to the zone of complete reduction of thionin. It is probable that similar conditions determine the growth of most other anaerobes. *Cl. histolyticum* and *Cl. tertium,* however, are exceptions. These organisms are microaerophilic rather than anaerobic, and can grow to a limited extent aerobically, though they are said to be incapable of forming spores under these conditions (Hall and Duffett 1935). Once growth has started, most anaerobic organisms appear to bring about a rapid fall in the O-R potential of the medium, probably owing to the production of a more active reducing system than that present in the medium itself. The Eh frequently falls to below $- 0.4$ volt. In the presence of such a powerful system growth may continue even though considerable quantities of oxygen are gaining access to the medium.

Little is yet known about the exact nutritive requirements of the *Clostridia,* but the work of Fildes and his colleagues (see Fildes 1935, Fildes and Knight 1933, Knight and Fildes 1933, Fildes and Richardson 1935, Pappenheimer 1935, Knight 1936), and of Stickland (1934, 1935) is rapidly throwing light on this subject. For the few organisms, such as *Cl. sporogenes* and *Cl. botulinum,* that have so far been studied, various amino-acids appear to be essential, especially tryptophan. A so-called *sporogenes* vitamin (see p. 39) is necessary for some organisms, while an adequate concentration of CO_2 seems to be as essential for the growth of the anaerobic as it is for so many of the aerobic bacteria (Gladstone, Fildes, and Richardson 1935).

On ordinary media growth of the anaerobes is poor compared with that of the aerobic spore-bearers. Some strains grow better than others—*Cl. welchii, Cl. sporogenes, Cl. botulinum* ; some give poorer growths—*Cl. chauvœi, Cl. cochlearium.*

Glucose favours the saccharolytic species ; blood or serum improves the growth of all. The optimum H-ion concentration for growth is about pH 7·0 to 7·4 (Reddish and Rettger 1924).

On media containing bile salts, such as MacConkey's medium, growth of *Cl. sporogenes, Cl. botulinum, Cl. histolyticum, Cl. welchii, Cl. tetani,* and *Cl. septique* is accompanied by a greenish fluorescence. In our experience, *Cl. chauvœi* and *Cl. œdematiens* have failed to grow on this medium.

Most of the members with which we are dealing here grow best at about 37° C., though many of them are capable of growing at temperatures of 20° C. and even lower. There is a group of thermophilic *Clostridia* which have an optimum temperature about 50°–60° C., and which sometimes do not grow at all below 30° C.

HÆMOLYSIN PRODUCTION.—Apart from their action on blood agar plates, many of the anaerobes, such as *Cl. tetani, Cl. welchii, Cl. septique, Cl. œdematiens,* and *Cl. chauvœi,* produce a filtrable hæmolysin capable of dissolving sheep's red blood corpuscles. Kerrin (1930) states that atoxic strains of *Cl. tetani* produce as powerful a hæmolysin as do toxic strains, and that normal rabbit, horse, and human serum have a very strong antihæmolytic effect. Leucocidins are formed by some species.

Biochemical Reactions.—The action on sugars is of some value in differentiating the anaerobes, and constitutes one basis of classification. Great care must be exercised in carrying out the tests, since even with known stock strains the results are often irregular and must be repeated two or three times before they can be relied on.

One of the striking features of the anaerobic bacteria is the large amount of gas that they are able to produce even in media free from fermentable carbohydrates.

Thus Wolf and Harris (1917) found that *Cl. welchii* in casein water produced 90 c.c. of gas per litre of medium, and in peptone water 186 c.c. *Cl. sporogenes* formed 1,044 c.c. of gas per litre of casein water in 157 hours, and in peptone water 360 c.c. in 24 hours. The gas consists of CO_2 and H_2 in different proportions according to the species of anaerobe. The addition of a fermentable carbohydrate to the medium increases the gas production. Acids are formed as the result of the fermentation ; with *Cl. welchii* rather more than 50 per cent. are volatile—mostly butyric acid. Ammonia appears to be formed in large quantities by the proteolytic, and in much smaller quantities by the saccharolytic anaerobes.

An attempt has been made (Anderson 1924) to classify the anaerobes on the basis of their gaseous metabolism. Growth in plain peptone water results in the production of CO_2 and H_2 in different proportions ; the CO_2/H_2 ratio is said to be high with the proteolytic and low with the saccharolytic members. Thus for *Cl. histolyticum* it is over 91, for *Cl. sporogenes* 36·9, for *Cl. botulinum* 18·3, for *Cl. tetani* 1·17, for *Cl. septique* 0·98, and for *Cl. welchii* 0·4.

Litmus milk is a useful medium for differentiation ; the reactions are given in the table at the end of the chapter (see Wolf and Harris 1917, Weinberg and Séguin 1918, Wolf 1918–19, 1919–20, Report 1919, Anderson 1924, Wagner *et al.* 1924).

It has been stated that none of the anaerobes are able to form catalase (Adamson 1919–20). This statement probably needs modification ; we have obtained evidence of its production by *Cl. sporogenes* and *Cl. histolyticum*, though only in small amounts.

Antigenic Structure.—Antisera have been prepared against a number of species, and agglutination and complement-fixation reactions have been carried out. Difficulty has often been experienced in the preparation of stable suspensions ; there is a great tendency for auto-agglutination to occur. The work of Felix and Robertson (1928) showed that the motile species of anaerobes contained thermolabile H and thermostable O antigens, similar to those described for so many of the aerobic bacteria. It was thought that type-specificity, as determined by agglutination, was dependent on the H antigen, and group-specificity on the O antigen. The more recent work of Henderson and others, however, seems to show that the position is rather more complex. With *Cl. septique,* for example, Henderson (1934) finds that the most convenient subdivision is made on the basis of the O antigen. Though there is considerable overlapping in different strains, there appear to be four specific O receptors. These four primary groups can be further subdivided according to the type of the H antigen. Henderson (1932) states that there is an O antigen common to the ovine and the bovine strains of *Cl. chauvœi*, but that the H antigen is complex, differing to some extent according to the animal source and the country of origin of the strain (see also McEwen 1926, Roberts 1931). The relation between *Cl. septique* and *Cl. chauvœi* is not very clear, but the work of Weinberg, Davesne, Mihailesco, and Sanchez (1929) suggests that the two organisms are closely related antigenically. *Cl. sporogenes* can be divided into at least two groups, *Cl. tetani* into at least seven groups, and *Cl. botulinum* into seven or eight groups. *Cl. welchii* has so far withstood classification, since there appears to be a wide distribution of group receptors (Howard 1928).

Toxin Formation.—It is remarkable that, with the exception of the diphtheria bacillus, the organisms forming powerful exotoxins belong almost entirely to the group of anaerobic spore-bearing bacilli. Two of them—*Cl. botulinum* and *Cl. tetani*—give rise to toxins more poisonous than any other substances with which we are acquainted. It has been calculated that the most powerful toxin of *Cl. tetani* would kill a man in a dose of 0·25 mgm., and of *Cl. botulinum* in a dose of 0·0084 mgm.

The formation of a powerful exotoxin does not appear to be associated with the proteolytic activity of the organism. It is doubtful whether the actively proteolytic species—*Cl. sporogenes, Cl. bifermentans,* and *Cl. aerofœtidum*—form exotoxins at all, but *Cl. histolyticum* is said to form a true exotoxin, capable of giving rise to antitoxin on injection into horses. Whether the toxins are formed intra- or extra-cellularly is still unknown. Stark, Sherman, and Stark (1928) have found that, if bacteria-free filtrates of *Cl. botulinum* are added to sterilized skim milk in suitable proportions and incubated for 4 days at 37° C., a considerable increase in toxicity occurs, suggesting that enzymes present in the filtrate have formed fresh toxin from some constituent of the milk. The preparation of these toxins requires attention to a number of factors with which we have no space to deal. But their properties are important, and must be considered briefly.

Tetanus Toxin.—This varies in potency ; a good filtrate will kill a mouse in a dose of 0·00001 c.c. It is destroyed by heat at 65° C. for 5 minutes, but if dried it will resist 120° C. for 1 hour. Exposure to 55° C. for 1 hour is said to destroy the greater part of its toxicity, while having little effect on its antitoxin-combining power (Tschertkow 1929). It is destroyed by direct sunlight in about 15 hours at 40° C. ; exposure to diffuse daylight results in a gradual weakening of the toxin. If precipitated with ammonium sulphate, dried over sulphuric acid, ground to powder, and preserved in the dark at 5° C. in vacuum tubes under pentaphosphoric acid, the toxin will remain unchanged for 2 years or more. 0·55 per cent. HCl, 0·3 per cent. NaOH, and 70 per cent. alcohol each destroy the toxin in 1 hour. The toxicity can be modified by iodine trichloride and by formol ; these reagents are used for weakening the toxin prior to injection of animals in serum institutes. Tetanus toxin is not absorbed from the intact alimentary canal ; there is evidence that it is destroyed by the digestive juices. It combines with and is neutralized by specific antitoxin.

The toxin of *Cl. botulinum* resembles tetanus toxin in many respects, but is more resistant to heat and to acids. Thus it requires for its destruction a temperature of 80° C. for half an hour. Normal hydrochloric acid fails to destroy it even in 24 hours, but normal soda destroys it rapidly. It is non-dialysable. The potency of the toxin varies ; it has been possible to obtain filtrates with a M.L.D. for a guinea-pig of 0·000001 c.c., but this is exceptionally strong. It is often said to be the only exotoxin that can be absorbed from the alimentary canal, but the recent work on entero-toxæmic diseases of sheep (see Chapter LXXV) suggests that the toxin of *Cl. welchii* may share this property to some extent.

The toxins of *Cl. welchii, Cl. septique,* and *Cl. œdematiens* may be considered together. They are all moderately thermolabile, being destroyed by heating to 70° C. for 30 to 60 minutes. They are likewise destroyed by weak concentrations of acids. When injected into guinea-pigs or mice they give rise to a gelatinous œdema and a varying amount of necrosis. According to Glenny and his colleagues (1933), the toxin formed by *Cl. welchii* is complex, there being at least four different toxins, each of which is neutralizable by a specific antitoxin. Not all strains of *welchii* form all four toxins. Weinberg and Combiesco (1930) state that *welchii* toxin lyses the red blood corpuscles, producing hæmoglobinuria, causes focal areas of necrosis in the kidney and liver, and leads to an increase in blood pressure, which may in its turn be responsible for hæmorrhages in various parts of the body. The toxin of *Cl. septique* produces very marked liquefactive necrosis of muscle. The toxin of *Cl. œdematiens* is the most potent ; the average M.L.D. for a mouse is about 0·0002 c.c. ; of *welchii* toxin the M.L.D. is about 0·25 c.c. ; and of *Cl. septique* toxin about 0·005 c.c. All three toxins give rise on injection into suitable animals to specific antitoxins.

Cl. chauvœi under suitable conditions forms a weak toxin that is very heat-labile, being destroyed in 5 minutes by exposure to a temperature of 52° C. Injected intravenously into mice in a dose of 0·025–0·5 c.c., it causes respiratory embarrassment and death within a few minutes. It is also toxic to guinea-pigs, though not rabbits, on intravenous inoculation. Subcutaneous inoculation into mice and guinea-pigs is not fatal, but produces a local blood-stained œdema (Kerrin 1934).

It is interesting to note that all the different groups of *Cl. tetani* give rise to identical toxins ; the antitoxin prepared against any one type will neutralize the toxins of all types. With *Cl. botulinum* it is otherwise. Type A toxin is different from Type B toxin. By agglutination Type A strains can be divided into 4, and Type B into 3 groups (Starin and Dack 1923), but the divisions do not appear to be clear-cut. Three further types have been described, C, D, and E, which appear to differ in the type of toxin produced.

Pathogenicity.—The pathogenicity of the anaerobes appears to depend almost entirely on their toxin production. *Cl. tetani*, for example, multiplies locally, and does not invade the body. *Cl. botulinum* is not even a parasite ; it is apparently unable to grow in the tissues, and its pathogenic effects are determined by the formation of toxin in food-substances prior to their ingestion. *Cl. œdematiens* remains almost confined to the site of inoculation. *Cl. welchii* and *Cl. septique* do invade the tissues in the final stages of an infection, but they multiply little before the death of the animal. Tetanus, botulism, and to a large extent gas gangrene are intoxications.

Pathogenicity of Cl. botulinum for Laboratory Animals.

MONKEYS.—Van Ermengem (1897) fed a *Macacus rhesus* with 5 c.c. of a preparation of macerated ham, which was known to be toxic. Symptoms developed in 12 hours, and consisted of restlessness, crying, coughing, and sneezing ; later there was a secretion of viscid mucus in the nose and mouth, leading to transient suffocation ; the pupils were dilated, reacting weakly to light. The animal became motionless, its head drooped, its eyes were fixed and half covered by the lids. Death occurred after 24 hours from the time of feeding. At necropsy the stomach, the bases of the lungs, and the meninges were congested, and petechial hæmorrhages were noticed on the arachnoid and throughout the brain and medulla.

CATS.—The typical toxæmia may be reproduced in cats by feeding, but more certainly by subcutaneous injection of cultures or of toxin. After a latent period of about 24 hours the animal becomes quiet, loses its interest in external objects, and may refuse food. In 2 or 3 days the characteristic paralyses appear, giving a peculiar facies to the animal. Its general aspect is stupid, the lids remain open, the eyes fixed in a glassy stare, the pupils dilated and sluggish in their reaction to light. The animal sits in a dark corner, moves little, and when disturbed takes a few uncoordinated steps across the cage and drops down as if exhausted. Its head droops and its tongue protrudes. Thick, viscous secretion fills the throat and nose, and causes severe paroxysmal attacks of suffocation relieved by a hoarse croup-like cough. The mew takes on a dull tone, and is succeeded by complete aphonia. For the first 2 or 3 days milk is accepted, but later owing to the dysphagia or complete aphagia it is left untouched ; when delivered by a pipette into the mouth it is not swallowed, but trickles down the trachea and causes choking. No urine or fæces are voided. The animal remains susceptible to sensory impressions till the end, but is unable to express its emotions in any way. Death occurs after a week or more, according to the dose, and is apparently due as much to starvation as to the lethal effect of the toxin. Occasionally life may be prolonged for 3 or 4 weeks, and recovery may eventually take place. At necropsy no local lesion is visible at the site of injection ; the mucosa of the small and large intestine is hyperæmic. The kidneys are congested, and the liver may show areas of degeneration. Clear urine distends the bladder. In the lungs, which are very congested, there may be infarcts or areas of hepatization. Sometimes œdema or hæmorrhages of the central nervous system may be observed, especially round the fourth ventricle. Cultures of the organs are usually sterile.

Dogs are very much less susceptible than cats, but they may succumb to the disease after subcutaneous injection of toxin, or occasionally after feeding with large doses. Mice and guinea-pigs are highly susceptible, and succumb in 1–4 days.

Pathogenicity of Cl. tetani for Laboratory Animals.

Tetanus can be reproduced by the inoculation of pure cultures, or of the toxin, into mice, rats, guinea-pigs, rabbits, goats, horses and monkeys. Cats and dogs are more resistant ; birds and cold-blooded animals are highly resistant. The most susceptible animal, calculated on the amount of toxin per gram of body weight necessary to prove fatal on injection, is the horse. This is about 12 times as susceptible as the mouse ; the guinea-pig is 6 times, and the monkey 4 times, as susceptible as the mouse (von Lingelsheim 1912, Sherrington 1917). On the other hand, the rabbit is twice, the dog 50 times, the cat 600, and the hen 30,000 times as resistant as the mouse (Kitasato 1891, von Lingelsheim 1912).

MICE.—After the *subcutaneous* injection of a small quantity of toxin or of pure culture into the mouse near the root of the tail, symptoms develop in about 12 to 24 hours. The spasms start near the site of injection, and spread to the rest of the body, till the animal dies in a state of general tonic contraction. The first symptom noticed is a stiffening of the tail, which becomes erect and is turned towards the side of inoculation ; the hinder extremity of that side becomes stiff, followed later by rigidity of the opposite leg. The contractions pass to the muscles of the trunk, and the mouse develops kyphosis or pleuro-thotonos. Next, the fore-legs become involved, and finally trismus and opisthotonos set in. The contractions occur spasmodically and are succeeded by intervals of rest, during which the animal lies exhausted ; in this phase they can be readily excited by the slightest touch or a breath of air. Death follows in about 24 hours. Post mortem there is little to be seen. There may be slight congestion and œdema round the site of inoculation, and the spleen may be somewhat enlarged. An exudate of fluid, sometimes blood-stained, may be seen in the pleura or peritoneum. After injection of a pure culture, the bacilli can generally be cultivated from the local site, but are difficult to find under the microscope. The heart's blood and viscera are sterile.

GUINEA-PIGS.—The experimental disease in guinea-pigs follows much the same course in about the same time as in mice.

RABBITS.—After subcutaneous or intramuscular injection the incubation period in rabbits is at least 24, and generally 36 hours ; death does not occur for 3 or 4 days. The general tetanic spasms are more marked than in mice or guinea-pigs (Rosenbach 1886).

Pathogenicity of Cl. welchii for Laboratory Animals.

Intramuscular injection of about 0·2 c.c. of an 18-hours' glucose broth culture into the thigh of a guinea-pig results in typical gas gangrene with death in 12–48 hours. Post mortem, there is a large, brawny, crepitant swelling at the site of inoculation, covered with a dark-red, tense layer of skin. The muscle is pale and is undergoing liquefactive necrosis. In the subcutaneous tissue around the local lesion and spreading up to the abdomen, reaching sometimes to the sternum and over to the opposite thigh, is a collection of slightly blood-stained fluid and gas smelling of hydrogen sulphide. The suprarenal glands are often congested, so that the normally sharp differentiation of cortex from medulla becomes obscured. Microscopically, the organisms are present in large numbers in the local effusion and in much smaller numbers in the blood stream. Sporing forms are absent. An even more typical picture of gas gangrene can be obtained by the injection of *Cl. welchii* intramuscularly into pigeons (Bull and Pritchett 1917*a*). Mice are also highly susceptible.

Pathogenicity of Cl. septique for Laboratory Animals.

Intramuscular injection of about 0·1 c.c. of a 36-hours' glucose broth culture into a guinea-pig causes death in 12 to 24 hours. Post mortem, there is a blood-stained gaseous œdema at the site of inoculation, spreading up over the abdominal wall, with collections of gas in the groins and axillæ. The thigh and abdominal muscles are soft and deep red in colour. In the pericardial and peritoneal cavities there may be some fluid ; the suprarenals are congested, but not so markedly as in animals infected with *Cl. welchii*. Microscopically the exudate shows large numbers of motile rods and usually the characteristic navicular or citron forms. Most characteristic are the long curved filaments found on the peritoneal surface of the liver. A similar picture can be reproduced by the inoculation of mice.

Pathogenicity of Cl. œdematiens for Laboratory Animals.

Intramuscular injection of about 1 c.c. of a 24-hours' glucose broth culture into a guinea-pig or mouse produces death in 1 to 2 days. Post mortem, the muscles at the site of inoculation are very congested, purplish-red in colour, and infiltrated with small bubbles of gas. There is a spreading, gelatinous œdema, sometimes slightly blood-tinged, extending over the thigh. The abdominal muscles are unaltered. Microscopically, bacilli are found in small numbers in the œdema fluid, and on the peritoneal surface of the liver ; cultures from the heart's blood may or may not be positive.

It will be seen that the action of these last three organisms varies in certain particulars. *Cl. welchii* gives rise to a large amount of gas, *Cl. œdematiens* to very little. The œdema fluid of *Cl. œdematiens* infections is practically clear, of *Cl. welchii* infections slightly blood-tinged, and of *Cl. septique* infections strongly blood-tinged. With *Cl. welchii* the muscles are pale pink, with *Cl. œdematiens* purplish-red, and with *Cl. septique* intensely and deeply red. Human cases of gas gangrene differ too in certain respects ; as a rule either œdema or gas production is dominant ; sometimes both are apparent. The particular form in any individual case is determined by the nature of the organisms present.

CLASSIFICATION

Although it is clear that the time is not yet ripe for any rigid classification of the anaerobic bacilli, we can recognize certain well-differentiated types, which should clearly be accorded specific rank. In Table XLIX we include such organisms as were considered by the Anaerobic Committee of the Medical Research Council (Report 1919) to be separate species. We may note, however, that the characters differentiating *Cl. parasporogenes* from *Cl. sporogenes* are hardly of sufficient importance to entitle it to classification as a separate species ; it may prove on further investigation to be merely a variant of the latter organism. Moreover the identity of *Cl. butyricum* with the organism originally described by Pasteur seems to be very doubtful ; it is unfortunate that this organism has been selected as the type species. Other organisms have as yet not been studied in sufficient detail to provide an adequate description of their biological characters, or to differentiate them clearly and unmistakably from other forms which have been described and named.

The grouping of the species within the genus presents even greater difficulties. Whether the primary division should be made on morphological grounds—mainly on the shape and position of the spore—or on physiological grounds—mainly on the relative activity of proteolytic and saccharolytic fermentation—must at the moment remain a matter of choice. We give in Table XLIX a provisional classification which has been suggested by the Anaerobic Committee of the Medical Research Council, and in Table L (pp. 683, 684) the more important characters of the recognized species. We also append a summarized description of each of the more important species, and a series of notes on some of the less important or less fully described strains, which are recorded in the literature.

We have made but brief reference in this chapter to the group of *thermophilic Clostridia*, which are apparently responsible for producing the type of spoilage of non-acid canned foods known in the United States as " hard swell." These organisms appear to be fastidious in their nutritive requirements, and to have an optimum temperature of growth between about 50° and 60° C. They manifest little or no proteolytic activity, but ferment a number of carbohydrates and glucosides with the production of acid and gas. They are non-pathogenic when fed to rats.

TABLE XLIX.

Giving a Classification of the *Clostridia*.

Spores.	Both Proteolytic and Saccharolytic Properties.		Slight Proteolytic but no Saccharolytic Properties.	Saccharolytic but no Proteolytic Properties.	Neither Proteolytic nor Saccharolytic Properties.
	Proteolytic Predominating.	Saccharolytic Predominating.			
Equatorial or Subterminal	*Cl. sporogenes* *Cl. parasporogenes* *Cl. histolyticum* *Cl. aerofœtidum* *Cl. bifermentans* *Cl. botulinum*	*Cl. welchii* *Cl. septique* *Cl. chauvœi* *Cl. œdematiens*	—	*Cl. fallax* *Cl. butyricum* *Cl. multifermentans*	—
Oval and Terminal	—	—	—	*Cl. tertium*	*Cl. cochlearium*
Spherical and Terminal	—	—	*Cl. tetani*	*Cl. tetanomorphum* *Cl. sphenoides*	—

(For classification see Weinberg and Séguin 1918, Report 1919, Heller 1921, and Hall 1922.)

TABLE L

Name.	Motility.	Spores.	Liquefaction of Gelatin.	Digestion of Serum.	Cooked Meat Medium.	Litmus Milk.	Glucose.	Maltose.	Mannitol.	Lactose.	Sucrose.	Salicin.	Exotoxin.	Pathogenicity to Guinea-pigs.	Remarks.
Cl. butyricum	+	Oval; sub-terminal. Readily	−	−	No digestion	Acid; clot	A G	A G	−	A G	A G	?	−	−	Fixes atmospheric nitrogen in soil. Possesses a capsule.
Cl. sporogenes and Cl. parasporogenes	+	Oval; sub-terminal. Readily	+	+	Gas; digested; blackened	Ppt.; digestion; alk.	A G	A G	−	−	−	−	−	−	At least 2 serological types. Non-specific toxic products found in culture media.
Cl. histolyticum	+	Oval; sub-terminal. Readily	+	+	Digested; sl. blackening; Tyrosin crystals	Ppt.; digestion	A	A	−	−	−	−	+ weak	Variable	Antigenically heterogeneous.
Cl. aerofœtidum	Slight	Oval; sub-terminal. Not readily	+	+	Gas; digestion; blackened	Gas; clot; digestion	A G	A G	−	A G	−	?	−	−	
Cl. bifermentans	−	Oval; equatorial. Readily	+	+	Gas; digested; blackened	Ppt.; digestion	A G	A G	−	−	−	−	−	−	
Cl. botulinum	+	Oval; sub-terminal. Not readily	+	Types A and B + C −	A and B, gas; digested; blackened C −	A and B. ppt.; digestion; alk. C −	A G	A G	−	±	−	A G A type	+ very strong	+	3 serological types, A, B, and C, each with a different toxin.

682

Cl. œdematiens	+ under strict anaerobiosis	Oval; sub-terminal. Readily	–	+	Gas; pink; later bleached	Acid; gas; later free clot	A G	A G	–	–	–	+ strong	+	Antigenically heterogeneous.
Cl. fallax	+	Oval; sub-terminal. Not readily	–	+	Gas; pink	Acid; clot; sometimes gas	A G	A G	–	?	?	+ weak	+ when freshly isolated	
Cl. chauvœi	+	Oval; sub-terminal. Readily	–	+	Gas; pink	Acid; clot; some gas	A G	A G	A G	A G	–	+ moderate	+	Antigenically homogeneous.
Cl. septique	+	Oval; sub-terminal. Readily	–	+	Gas; pink	Acid; clot; some gas	A G	A G	A G	–	A G	+ moderate	+	4 serological types.
Cl. welchii	–	Oval; sub-terminal; only in sugar-free media	–	+	Gas; pink	Acid, clot, gas; stormy fermentation	A G	A G	A G	A G	–	+ moderate	+	Possesses a capsule. Antigenically heterogeneous.
Cl. tertium	– or very slight +	Oval; terminal. Readily	–	–	Gas	Acid; clot	A G	A G	A G	A G	A G	–	–	
Cl. cochlearium	+	Oval; terminal. Not readily	–	–	Gas		–	–	–	–	!	–	–	
Cl. tetani	+	Spherical; terminal. Readily	–	+	Gas		–	–	–	–	–	+ very strong	+	At least 7 different serological types, but only one type of toxin.
Cl. tetanomorphum	+	Spherical; terminal. Readily	–	–	Gas		A G	A G	–	–	–	–	–	
Cl. sphenoides	+	Spherical; subterminal or terminal. Readily	–	–	Slight gas	Acid; sometimes clot	A G	A G	±	±	A G	–	–	Clostridia are wedge-shaped.

McClung (1935) studied 27 strains and found that they all belonged to a single species ; for this he suggested the name *Cl. thermosaccharolyticum*. This organism is a long, slender, motile, Gram-negative bacillus with granular staining and a spherical terminal spore. A similar, if not identical, organism was previously described by Paine (1931).

Clostridium butyricum

Synonyms.—*Clos. pasteurianum, B. amylobacter, Granulobacter saccharobutyricum*. Pasteur's *Vibrion butyrique*.

Isolation.—Apparently first described by Prazmowski (see Report 1919). Possibly identical with Pasteur's *Vibrion butyrique*, described fully by Winogradsky in 1902.

Habitat.—Soil.

Morphology.—Rods, 3–4 μ × 0·7 μ ; parallel sides, flattened ends, axis straight or slightly curved ; arranged singly or in pairs end-to-end ; considerable variation in length. Motile by peritrichate flagella. Spores oval, subterminal, measuring 1·6 μ × 1·3 μ ; rod becomes spindle-shaped. Germination polar. Capsule formed on agar. Cells store glycogen ; stain yellow with iodine. Gram-positive.

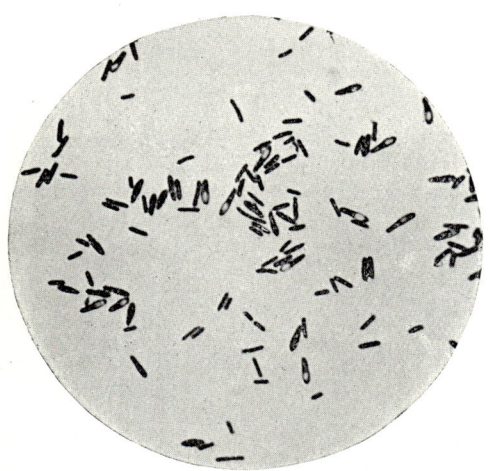

FIG. 172.—*Clostridium butyricum*.
From a surface agar culture, anaerobically, 5 days, 37° C. (× 1000).

Agar Plate.—2 *days*, 30° C. Circular colonies, 0·5–1·0 mm. in diameter, low convex, amorphous, faintly translucent or opaque, greyish-white, with smooth glistening surface and entire edge ; butyrous consistency and easily emulsifiable. After 6 days the colonies are slightly larger.

Agar Stroke.—4 *days at* 30° C. Very poor growth of discrete, irregular colonies, slightly raised, and water-clear. On 0·5 per cent. mannitol agar there is a moderate, raised, greyish-white, opaque growth, consisting chiefly of discrete colonies, with a moist, glistening, smooth surface.

Gelatin Stab.—No growth.

Glucose Agar Shake.—2 *days at* 30° C. Good growth ; the medium is disrupted by large bubbles of gas, and blown up the tube. Colonies are yellowish-grey, opaque, biconvex with clear-cut edges, and about 1 mm. in diameter.

Broth.—2 *days at* 30° C. Poor to moderate growth, with slight turbidity, and slight, very finely granular deposit ; after 6 days, moderate turbidity, and moderate powdery deposit, disintegrating completely on shaking.

Loeffler's Blood Serum.—2 *days at* 30° C. Moderate, raised, confluent, colourless growth with irregularly contoured surface. No digestion.

Cooked Meat Medium.—5 *days*, 37° C. Marked turbidity ; no digestion.

Potato.—14 *days at* 30° C. No definite growth visible on the potato itself, but there is a considerable evolution of gas from the liquid in which the potato is soaked ; the liquid is turbid.

Metabolic.—Obligate anaerobe. Opt. temp. 30–40° C. Pigment none. *Nutritional :* grows best in sugar solutions. Growth on agar improved by 1 per cent. mannitol. Non-proteolytic.

Biochemical.—Forms acid and gas in dextrose, lævulose, maltose, galactose, lactose, sucrose, inulin, dextrin and starch. Indole— ; M.R. + ; V.P. — ; nitrates reduced ; M.B. reduction — ; catalase — ; NH_3 slight + ; L.M. acid and clot. Can fix atmospheric nitrogen in presence of a fermentable sugar ; the sugar is broken down with the formation of butyric and acetic acids, CO_2, and H_2. Can utilize NH_3, peptone, and asparagin as its source of nitrogen.

Pathogenicity.—Nil.

Clostridium sporogenes

Isolation.—Described by Metchnikoff in 1908.

Ecology.—Found in soil, and in fæces of man and animals.

Morphology.—Rod-shaped, 3–6 $\mu \times$ 0·5 μ, parallel sides, rounded ends, axis straight or slightly curved, arranged singly, in pairs, and small groups ; long filaments occasionally formed. Spores

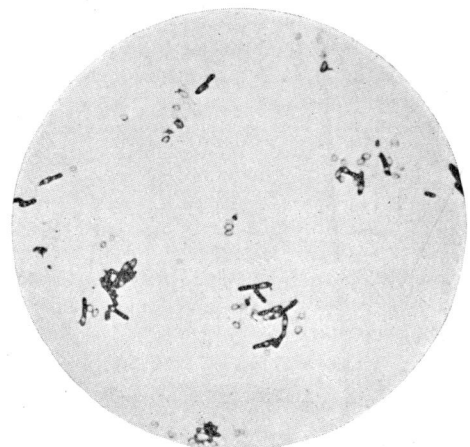

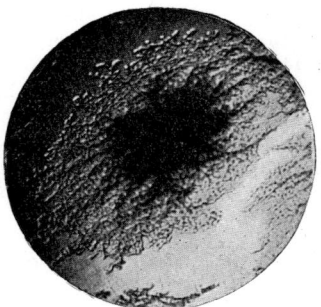

Fig. 173.—*Clostridium sporogenes.*
From a surface agar culture anaerobically, 2 days, 37° C. ($\times$ 1000).

Fig. 174.—*Clostridium sporogenes.*
Surface colony on agar anaerobically, 4 days, 37° C. ($\times$ 8).

freely ; spores are oval, subterminal, and wider than bacillus ; free spores numerous. Motile. No capsule. Strongly Gram-positive, except in old cultures.

Agar Plate.—4 days at 37° C. Irregularly round colonies, growing from a central focus like *B. mycoides* ; 2–6 mm. in diameter, effuse or slightly umbonate, and rhizoid ; surface covered by arborescent ridges, edge rhizoid ; rather dull, greyish-yellow by reflected, bluish-grey by transmitted light ; butyrous and easily emulsifiable ; differentiated into brownish opaque centre and bluish translucent periphery.

Deep Glucose Agar.—4 days at 37° C. Abundant gas formation ; medium driven to plug and disrupted. Colonies throughout medium ; rounded, 0·5–2 mm. in diameter, with opaque brown centre and a woolly translucent periphery.

Horse Blood Agar.—3 days at 37° C. Round dew-drop, or rhizoid colonies. β-hæmolysis for 2–4 mm. around colony.

Agar Slope.—4 days at 37° C. Moderate, confluent, effuse, glistening, greyish-yellow, translucent growth, with beaten-copper surface and cigarette-in-water edge.

Gelatin.—2 days at 37° C. Liquefied.

Broth.—4 days at 37° C. Good growth with moderate turbidity, and moderate powdery or irregularly granular sediment, not disintegrating completely ; strong putrid odour.

Loeffler's Serum.—15 *days at* 37° C. Serum partly digested and rendered turbid ; medium dark blue.

Coagulated Egg.—15 *days at* 37° C. Poor, effuse growth ; slight digestion. In alkaline egg broth the white coagulum is digested.

Cooked Meat Medium.—15 *days at* 37° C. Heavy growth with dense turbidity ; gas production ; meat digested and blackened ; putrid odour.

Resistance.—Withstands moist heat at 100° C. for 10 to 150 minutes, at 105° C. for 4 to 45 minutes, and at 110° C. for 1 to 12 minutes.

Metabolic.—Anaerobic, but not strictly so. Opt. temp. 37° C. Hæmolysis on horse blood agar plates. Hæmolyses human but not sheep's red cells. *Nutritional :* grows well on ordinary media, and in media containing very little nutrient material, such as tap water containing fragments of coagulated egg white. Certain amino-acids, such as tryptophan, leucine, phenylalanine, tyrosine, and arginine, as well as the *sporogenes* vitamin, are essential. Growth not improved by glucose. Green fluorescent colonies on MacConkey plate.

Biochemical.—Acid and gas in glucose and maltose. No action on mannitol, lactose, sucrose or salicin. Indole — ; M.R. — ; V.P. — ; nitrates not reduced ; $NH_3 \pm$; $H_2S +++$; M.B. reduction — ; catalase weak $+$. Litmus milk : casein precipitated and almost completely digested in 15 days ; reduction, and marked alkaline reaction ; acid in young cultures.

Antigenic Structure.—Can be divided by agglutination into at least two groups.

Pathogenicity.—Not naturally pathogenic. Experimentally is non-pathogenic to laboratory animals, but enhances the pathogenicity of other anaerobes, such as *Cl. welchii*, in mixed cultures. No exotoxin formed, but a broth filtrate is toxic to guinea-pigs in a dose of 1 c.c. ; this is due apparently to a volatile substance, possibly an ammonium base.

(See von Hibler 1908, Wolf and Harris 1917, Weinberg and Séguin 1918, Report 1919, Hall 1922, de Smidt 1924, Weinberg and Ginsbourg 1927, Knight and Fildes 1933, Fildes and Richardson 1935, Stickland 1934, 1935, Pappenheimer 1935.)

Clostridium histolyticum

Isolation.—Described by Weinberg and Séguin in 1916 (1916, 1918).

Ecology.—Soil ; possibly intestinal canal of man and animals.

Morphology.—Rod-shaped, 3–5 $\mu \times$ 0·5–0·8 μ ; parallel sides, rounded ends, axis generally straight ; occur singly and as diplobacilli. In cultures more than a day old irregular forms appear—long curved filaments, and irregularly stained forms. Spores are readily formed in all media ; they are oval, subterminal, and wider than the bacillus ; become free in old cultures. Motile by about 20 peritrichate flagella. Gram-positive in young cultures. No capsule.

Agar Plate.—4 *days at* 37° C. Variable. Colonies may be delicate and flat with crenated edges ; or may be cuttle-fish-like, umbonate, amorphous, and glistening, with very finely granular surface and a fimbriate edge ; greyish-white by reflected light, bluish-grey by transmitted light ; differentiated into opaque yellowish centre and greyish translucent periphery ; butyrous and easily emulsifiable.

Deep Glucose Agar Shake.—4 *days at* 37° C. No gas. Abundant growth throughout medium. Colonies are 1 mm. in diameter, irregularly round, opaque, brown, with blunt, coral-like projections with very fine woolly ends.

Horse Blood Agar Plate.—4 *days at* 37° C. Irregularly round colonies, slightly raised, 2–3 mm. in diameter, with irregularly lobate edge, and smooth or pitted surface. No hæmolysis.

Agar Slope.—4 *days at* 37° C. Moderate, partly confluent, effuse, glistening, translucent, greyish-yellow growth with beaten-copper surface and delicate fimbriate edge.

Gelatin.—Liquefied in 3 days at 37° C.

Broth.—4 *days at* 37° *C.* Moderate growth, with moderate turbidity, and a granulo-powdery deposit partly disintegrating ; slight fœtid odour.

Loeffler's Serum.—15 *days at* 37° *C.* Almost completely digested ; the fluid is almost clear.

Coagulated Egg.—15 *days at* 37° *C.* Partly digested ; butt turned bluish-green.

Cooked Meat Medium.—15 *days at* 37° *C.* Abundant growth ; meat digested and slightly blackened ; long column of slightly turbid fluid ; gas produced ; a deposit of white tyrosine crystals occurs, increasing with age. Slightly fœtid odour.

Resistance.—Killed in 6 minutes at 105° C. (moist heat).

Metabolism.—Strict anaerobe. Opt. temp. 37° C. No hæmolysis on horse blood agar plates. Hæmolyses human but not sheep's red cells. *Nutritional :* grows well in ordinary media ; growth not improved by glucose. Green fluorescent colonies on MacConkey plate.

Biochemical.—Acid, no gas, in glucose and maltose, not in mannitol, lactose, sucrose or salicin ; sometimes no acid produced at all. Indole — ; M.R. — ; V.P. — ; nitrates not reduced ; NH_3 — ; H_2S +++ ; M.B. reduction — ; catalase + weak. Litmus milk : casein precipitated and digested ; reduction ; after 8 to 10 days it is transformed into a clear, amber-coloured fluid.

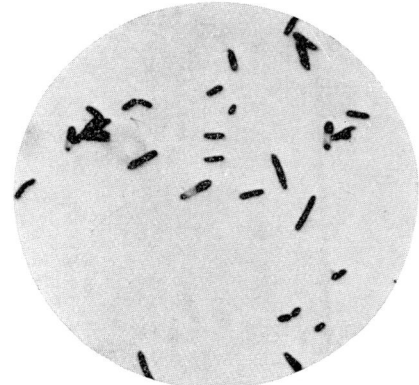

FIG. 175.—*Clostridium histolyticum.*
From a surface culture on agar anaerobically,
6 days, 37° C. ($\times$ 1000).

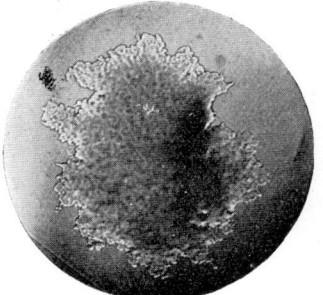

FIG. 176.—*Clostridium histolyti-cum.*
Surface colony on agar anaerobi-cally, 2 days, 37° C. ($\times$ 8).

Antigenic Structure.—Agglutinating sera seem to act chiefly on homologous strains. Anti-toxin can be prepared by injection of toxin into horses.

Pathogenicity.—Exotoxin is said to be formed in very young cultures. Natural patho-genicity doubtful ; appears often in gangrenous processes in man. Experimentally, strains vary in pathogenicity ; susceptible animals are guinea-pig, rabbit, and mouse. Bacillus is actively proteolytic and digests living tissue. 1 c.c. of a young broth culture injected intramuscularly into a guinea-pig causes digestion of skin and muscles, and a hæmorrhagic liquefaction of the softer parts of the limb. This digestion may spread over the abdomen, and death occur during the next 12 to 24 hours ; or recovery may follow with more or less complete necrosis of the limb. The fluid contains no gas and is not putrid.

(See Weinberg and Séguin 1918, Report 1919, Hall 1922, Torrey 1925, Weinberg *et al.* 1926.)

Clostridium botulinum

Isolation.—By van Ermengem from ham in 1896 (1896, 1897). Several other organisms have since been isolated from botulism-like diseases in animals. These are some-times referred to as *Cl. parabotulinum*, but it is probably better to give them letters, using A and B to refer to the two main toxigenic types. Type C_α was isolated by Bengtson (1922*a*, *b*, 1923) and by Graham and Boughton (1923*a*, *b*) in the United States from chickens and ducks; Type C_β by Seddon (1922) in Australia from cattle; Type D by Theiler and his colleagues (1926) in South Africa from cattle, and Type E by Theiler (1928) in South Africa from horses. The relation between Types C, D and E is not yet entirely clear, but they differ mainly in toxin production. Following description refers chiefly to Types A and B.

Ecology.—Widely distributed in soil, both virgin and cultivated. Not infrequently present in intestinal tract of domestic animals.

Morphology.—4-*day agar slope at* 37° *C*. Rather large, stout rods, 4–6 $\mu \times$ 0·9 μ; axis straight, parallel sides, and slightly rounded ends; arranged singly, or sometimes in pairs or chains. Variations in depth of staining. Spores are oval, wider than the bacillus, thick-walled, and situated at or near the end. Free spores are numerous. Some strains spore readily, others hardly at all. Spores formed best in sugar-free media. Sluggishly motile by 4–8 peritrichate flagella. No capsule. Gram-positive in young cultures.

Agar Plate.—4 *days at* 37° *C*. Irregularly round, 5–10 mm. in diameter, glistening, translucent, effuse, filamentous colonies, with an alternately smooth and granular surface (due to crossing of fila-

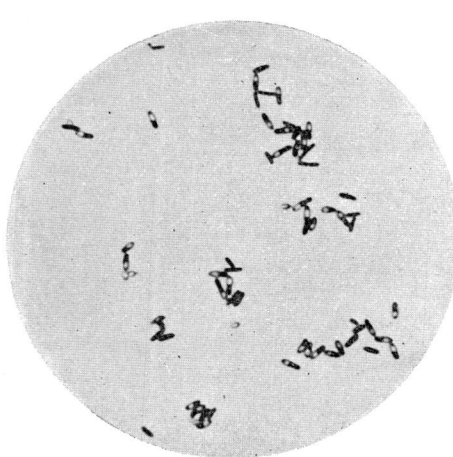

Fig. 177.—*Clostridium botulinum.*
From a surface agar culture anaerobically, 2 days, 37° C. (× 1000).

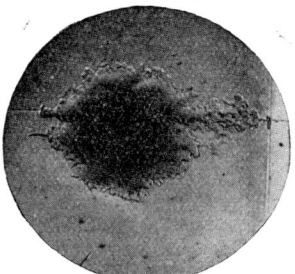

Fig. 178.—*Clostridium botulinum.*
Surface colony on agar, anaerobically, 2 days, 37° C. (× 8).

ments), and an indefinite, fimbriate, reticular edge. Greyish-yellow by reflected, bluish-grey by transmitted light. Butyrous consistency, easily emulsifiable. Differentiated into thicker, browner centre, and thinner, more translucent periphery. Single colonies often difficult to obtain owing to tendency to spread. Variant types have been described on blood agar (Schoenholz 1928).

Deep Glucose Agar Shake.—4 *days at* 37° *C*. Abundant gas formation; medium disrupted and driven up to plug. Colonies throughout medium, varying in size. Large colonies are 1–2 mm. in diameter, having an opaque, brown, spherical or biconvex centre and a large, clear, more translucent, cigarette-in-water edge. Another type consists of a thin, translucent disc with an eccentric opaque nucleus, the edge of the disc being indented at the point nearest the nucleus; the disc may contain gas bubbles. Types C, D and E form woolly colonies without a central nucleus.

Agar Slope.—4 *days at* 37° *C*. Moderate, confluent, effuse, greyish-yellow, translucent growth with a very finely granular surface, and an irregular villous edge.

Gelatin.—7 *days at* 37° *C.* Completely liquefied.

Broth.—4 *days at* 37° *C.* Abundant growth with dense turbidity and a moderate, powdery and granular deposit, mostly disintegrating. Rancid odour. Types C, D and E cause little turbidity, but form a flaky deposit, sticking to the sides of the tube.

Loeffler's Serum.—15 *days at* 37° *C.* Moderate growth of small, discrete colonies ; digestion by A and B, but not by C and D types.

Horse Blood Agar Plates.—3 *days at* 37° *C.* Irregularly round, 2–3 mm. in diameter, umbonate colonies, with smooth centre and curled or fimbriate periphery ; zone of α-prime hæmolysis, co-extensive with the colony ; around the colony blood is clear, transparent, and brown.

Coagulated Egg.—21 *days at* 37° *C.* Very poor growth. Butt turned bluish-green, and egg partly digested by A and B, but not by C and D types.

Cooked Meat Medium.—15 *days at* 37° *C.* Abundant growth ; gas produced ; long column of slightly turbid fluid with digested meat beneath ; blackening. Rancid odour. No digestion by C, D or E types.

Resistance.—Spores are destroyed by dry heat at 180° C. in 5 to 15 minutes. Moist heat at 100° C. destroys them in 5 hours, at 105° C. in 100 minutes, and at 120° C. in 5 minutes. Gelatin cultures remain viable for a year or more.

Metabolic.—Strict anaerobe. Opt. temp. 35° C. Grows well at 20° C. α-prime hæmolysis on horse blood agar plates. Hæmolysis of human, but not of sheep's red cells. Types A and B are generally proteolytic, digesting gelatin, serum, egg. and meat ; Types C and D digest gelatin only. *Nutritional :* grows fairly well on ordinary media ; growth not improved by glucose ; tryptophan and the *sporogenes* factor are both required. Green fluorescent colonies on MacConkey plates. Powerful exotoxin produced, specific to each type.

Biochemical.—Type A gives acid and gas in glucose, maltose and salicin ; Types B and C do not ferment salicin. Types A and B ferment glycerol ; Type C does not. Indole — ; M.R. — ; V.P. — ; nitrate reduction — ; $NH_3 +$; $H_2S + +$; methylene blue reduction — ; catalase —. Litmus milk : fine precipitate of casein, with almost complete digestion in a fortnight ; litmus reduced, reaction alkaline.

Antigenic Structure.—Two main types, A and B, distinguished by their toxin production. Antitoxin to A does not neutralize toxin of B, nor *vice versa*. By agglutination and complement fixation the two types can also be distinguished, and are found to contain 3 or 4 sub-types each. Three other types, C, D and E, have been described forming separate specific toxins.

Pathogenicity.—Types A and B cause botulism in man. Type C_α causes limberneck in chickens and ducks ; C_β causes one type of forage poisoning in horses in Australia and U.S.A. ; D causes lamziekte in cattle in South Africa ; E causes botulism in equines in South Africa. (For fuller description see Chapter LXIX.) The organism itself is a saprophyte and does not multiply in the body ; it acts entirely by its toxin. Injected subcutaneously, a broth culture of Type A or B is fatal to guinea-pigs, mice, rabbits, cats, monkeys, and often chickens in 1 to 4 days ; symptoms are muscular paralysis, dilatation of the pupils, shallow breathing, intense salivation, prostration and death. The toxin is the most powerful known, and may kill a mouse in a dose of 0·00001 c.c.

(See Kempner 1897, v. Hibler 1908, Leuchs 1910, Dickson 1918, Weinberg and Séguin 1918, Burke 1919*a*, *b*, Graham and Brueckner 1919, Report 1919, Shippen 1919, Edmonson *et al.* 1920, Orr 1920, 1922, Bengtson 1921, 1922*a*, *b*, 1923, 1924*a*, Nevin 1921, Weiss 1921, Coleman 1922, 1923, Coleman and Meyer 1922, Dubovsky and Meyer 1922*a*, *b*, Esty and Meyer 1922, Hall 1922, Meyer and Dubovsky 1922*a*, *b*, *c*, Schoenholz and Meyer 1922, 1924, Seddon 1922, Tanner and Dack 1922, Graham and Boughton 1923*a*, *b*, Hall and Davis 1923, Starin and Dack 1923, 1924, 1925, Dozier 1924, Easton and Meyer 1924, Pfenninger 1924, Starin 1924, Wagner 1924, Wheeler and Humphreys 1924, Dickson *et al.* 1925, Tanner and Twohey 1926, Theiler *et al.* 1926,

Weinberg and Ginsbourg 1927, Theiler 1928, Schoenholz 1928, Stark, Sherman, and Stark 1928, Robinson 1929, Graham and Thorp 1929, Lommel and Gunnison 1929, Kerrin 1930, Gunnison and Meyer 1930, Sommer and Sommer 1932, Gunnison and Coleman 1932, Fildes 1935).

Clostridium œdematiens

Isolation.—Described by Weinberg and Séguin in 1915.

Synonyms.—Probably identical with Novy's *B. œdematis maligni* II, or *Cl. novyi* I (Novy 1894), and Zeissler and Raszfeld's (1929) *B. gigas.*

Habitat.—Soil.

Morphology.—Rod-shaped, 3–10 $\mu \times$ 0·8–1·0 μ, not unlike *Cl. welchii,* but longer; sides parallel; ends rounded; axis straight or curved; arranged singly, in pairs or chains; jointed filaments not uncommon. Spores formed freely in all media; they are large, oval and subterminal, generally free. Motile by 20 or more peritrichate flagella; but motility is only observed under strictly anaerobic conditions. No capsule. Gram - positive in young cultures.

Agar Plate.—4 *days at* 37° *C.* Irregularly round colonies, 2–3 mm. in diam-

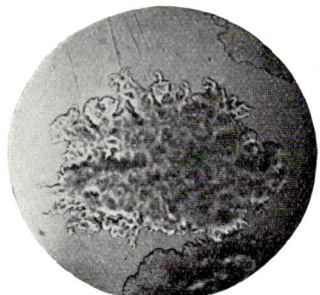

Fig. 179.—*Clostridium œdematiens.*

Surface colony on agar anaerobically, 2 days, 37° C. (× 8).

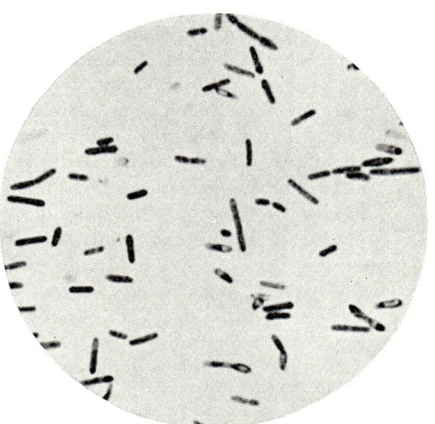

Fig. 180.—*Cl. œdematiens.*

From a surface agar culture anaerobically, 2 days, 37° C. (× 1000).

eter, effuse, filamentous or curled, glistening, translucent with finely sponge-like surface and irregularly lobate edge with very fine dentations; greyish-yellow by reflected, greyish-blue by transmitted light; butyrous and easily emulsifiable.

Deep Glucose Agar Shake.—4 *days at* 37° *C.* Good growth, gas produced, and agar disrupted. Colonies throughout medium, varying in appearance; some have an opaque, brownish centre with a finely filamentous or fluffy periphery; some resemble snowflakes; some have the appearance of a conventional bursting grenade.

Horse Blood Agar Plates.—3 *days at* 37° *C.* Round, slightly umbonate colonies, with entire or undulate edge and a finely granular surface; about 3 mm. in diameter. Zone of β-hæmolysis coincident with colony. Centre of colony is more opaque, periphery more translucent.

Agar Slope.—4 *days at* 37° *C.* Poor to moderate, partly confluent, slightly raised, glistening, greyish-yellow growth with finely granular surface, and an edge made up of single colonies.

Gelatin.—3 *days at* 37° *C.* Liquefaction.

Broth.—4 *days at* 37° *C.* Poor growth with no turbidity and a granulo-powdery deposit, partly disintegrating; slight rancid odour. In glucose broth there is an early turbidity, which clears after a day or two with the deposit of the organisms in a flocculent mass.

Loeffler's Serum.—15 *days at* 37° *C.* Moderate, confluent, slightly raised growth; no digestion.

Coagulated Egg.—15 *days at* 37° *C.* No digestion.

Cooked Meat Medium.—15 *days at* 37° *C.* Moderate growth; fluid turbid; gas produced, meat turned slightly pink or bleached; no digestion; rancid odour.

Resistance.—Destroyed by moist heat at 105° C. in 6 minutes.

Metabolic.—Strict anaerobe. Opt. temp. 37° C. β-hæmolysis on horse blood agar plates. Hæmolyses human and sheep's red cells. *Nutritional :* grows fairly well in ordinary media; growth improved by glucose. No growth in bile-salt media. Toxin produced.

Biochemical.—Acid and gas in glucose, and maltose, not in mannitol, lactose, sucrose, or salicin. Indole — ; M.R. — ; V.P. — ; Nitrates — ; NH_3 — ; H_2S + ; M.B. reduction — ; catalase —. Litmus milk: acid production in 1 to 5 days with gas formation; after 10 to 30 days a clot appears in the form of fine flocculi. No digestion.

Antigenic Structure.—Agglutinins act on homologous strains only; auto agglutination frequent. Antitoxin can be produced by injection of horses.

Pathogenicity.—Produces a potent exotoxin. One agent in causation of gas gangrene in man. Responsible for one type of braxy in Europe and for black disease in Australia. Experimentally it is pathogenic for guinea-pigs, mice and rabbits. 0·25–1 c.c. of a 24-hour broth culture injected intramuscularly into a guinea-pig causes death in 24 to 48 hours. P.M. muscles are red and softened; little gas production, but a spreading gelatinous œdema. Bacilli found at site of inoculation, and occasionally on surface of liver. Blood cultures may or may not be positive. (See p. 680.)

(See Weinberg and Séguin 1918, Report 1919, Wolf 1919–20, Hall 1922, Turner 1930, Mieszner, Meyn and Schoop 1931.)

Clostridium chauvœi

Isolation.—First distinctive description by Arloing, Cornevin and Thomas in 1879 (Arloing *et al.* 1887).

Habitat.—Lives in soil.

Morphology.—4-*day agar plate at* 37° *C.* Rod-shaped, 3–8 μ × 0·6 μ, with parallel sides and rounded ends. Short filaments are not uncommon. On serum or in meat medium navicular and swollen forms are seen. Axis straight or slightly curved; arranged singly, in small groups, or in short chains. Variation in depth of staining; some organisms show chromatic granules near the poles. Spores are elongated oval, subterminal, and wider than the bacillus. Clostridial forms are lemon- or pear-shaped. Motile. Gram-positive, but weakly so after 4 days. No capsule. On surface of liver of infected animals it is found singly or in pairs, not in chains or filaments like *Cl. septique.*

Agar Plate.—4 *days at* 37° *C.* Irregularly round, 4–8 mm. in diameter, granulo-fila-mentous, effuse, transparent colonies, difficult to see; surface is glistening and very finely granular; edge is fern-like and irregularly dentate; greyish by reflected, and bluish-grey by transmitted light; consistency butyrous, easily emulsifiable; no differentiation.

Deep Glucose Agar Shake.—4 *days at* 37° *C.* Abundant growth of discrete colonies throughout medium, except for 3 mm. below surface. Colonies are irregularly round, 0·5–1 mm. in diameter, with an opaque brownish centre and a lighter, translucent, plumose periphery, with an irregularly erose edge. Moderate gas formation; medium split slightly in 4 or 5 places.

Horse Blood Agar Plate.—3 *days at* 37° *C.* Colonies irregularly round, 3–6 mm. in diameter, effuse, transparent, with granulo-filamentous structure, and entire or rhizoid edge. No definite hæmolytic zone, but plate is cleared slightly.

Agar Slope.—4 *days at* 37° *C.* Poor, confluent, effuse, transparent growth, difficult to see. Surface smooth or very finely granular, edge fern-like and irregularly dentate.

Gelatin.—Liquefaction complete in 14 days at 37° C.

Broth.—4 *days at* 37° *C.* Poor growth, no turbidity, slight powdery deposit disintegrating on shaking; weakly rancid odour. In young cultures a turbidity is noticeable, but this clears as the bacilli sediment.

Loeffler's Serum.—15 *days at* 37° *C.* Effuse, confluent growth; no digestion.

Coagulated Egg.—15 *days at* 37° *C.* Poor, effuse, confluent growth; no digestion.

Cooked Meat Medium.—15 *days at* 37° *C.* Very slight or no turbidity; some gas production; meat turned pink. Rancid odour.

Resistance.—Dried on silk threads spores are destroyed by steam in 38 to 48 minutes.

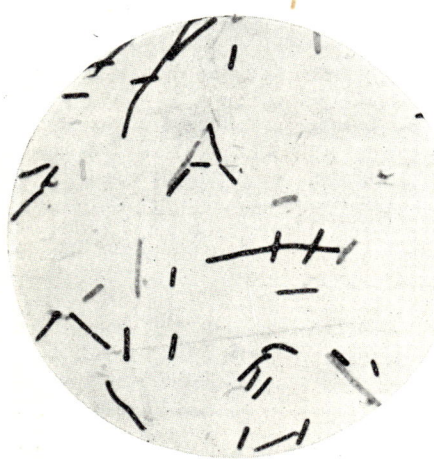

Metabolic.—Strict anaerobe. On the whole grows poorly. Opt. temp. 37° C. Very slight hæmolysis on horse blood agar plates. Hæmolyses human and sheep's red cells. *Nutritional :*

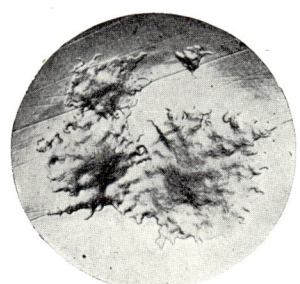

Fig. 181.—*Clostridium chauvœi.*
From a surface agar culture, anaerobically, 2 days, 37° C. (× 1000).

Fig. 182.—*Clostridium chauvœi.*
Surface colonies on agar anaerobically, 6 days, 37° C. (× 8).

grows poorly in ordinary media; growth improved by glucose, and by heart extract; very poor growth in casein digest broth. No growth in bile-salt media. Weak toxin produced.

Biochemical.—Acid and gas in glucose, maltose, lactose, and sucrose, not in mannitol or salicin. Indole — ; M.R. — ; V.P. — ; nitrate reduction — ; NH_3 — ; H_2S + ; M.B. reduction — ; catalase —. Litmus milk: variable; sometimes no change; sometimes slight acid production, and partial precipitation of casein.

Antigenic Structure.—Appears by agglutination to be serologically homogeneous. Agglutinating sera prepared against *Cl. chauvœi* agglutinate this organism, but do not agglutinate *Cl. septique* except to very low titre. By complement fixation *Cl. chauvœi* and *Cl. septique* appear to be closely related. Antitoxin is specific, protecting against *Cl. chauvœi* but not against *Cl. septique.*

Pathogenicity.—Exotoxin produced. Causes blackleg in cattle, and less often in sheep. Non-pathogenic to man. Experimentally it is fatal to guinea-pigs and less often to mice; rabbits and pigeons are fairly resistant. 0·25 c.c. of a 24-hour culture in Hibler's medium injected intramuscularly kills a guinea-pig in 24 to 48 hours; p.m. slightly blood-stained serous exudate at site of injection; abdominal muscles are deep red and contain numerous small gas bubbles. *Cl. chauvœi* can be recovered from local lesion, peritoneal cavity, and heart blood.

(See Kitt 1887, Nocard and Roux 1887, Roux 1888, Kitasato 1889*a*, 1890, Leclainche and Vallée 1900, Eisenberg 1907, Markoff 1911, Landau 1917, Weinberg and Séguin 1918, Haslam and Lumb 1919, Report 1919, Heller 1920, Goss *et al.* 1921, Gaiger 1922, 1924, Hall 1922, Weinberg and Ginsbourg 1927, Weinberg and Mihailesco 1929, Roberts 1931, Henderson 1932, Kerrin 1934.)

Clostridium septique

Isolation.—Described by Pasteur and Joubert in 1877.

Synonyms.—*B. œdematis maligni*, Koch (1881).   *Vibrion septique*, Pasteur.

Ecology.—Found chiefly in soil.

Morphology.—Rod-shaped, of variable length and thickness ; on agar cultures, 2–6 $\mu \times$ 0·4–0·6 μ ; sides parallel, ends rounded, axis straight or curved, arranged singly,

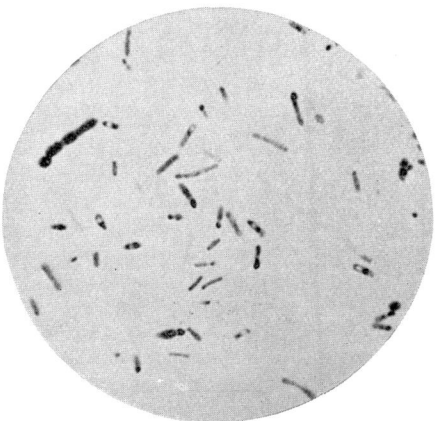

Fig. 183.—*Cl. septique.*
From a surface agar culture anaerobically,
2 days, 37° C. ($\times$ 1000).

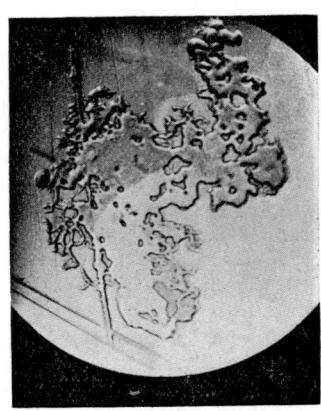

Fig. 184.—*Clostridium septique.*
Surface colony on agar anaerobically, 2 days, 37° C. ($\times$ 8).

in pairs, and in short chains.   On peritoneal surface of dead guinea-pig it forms long jointed filaments.   In tissue exudates and in fluid media containing fresh tissue there are navicular or citron forms with pale swollen bodies and deeper-staining pointed extremities.   In agar cultures there is marked pleomorphism ; organisms vary in size, shape, and depth of staining, large numbers of shadow forms are seen.   Spores readily formed, and are oval, subterminal, and slightly wider than bacilli ; often found free.   Motile by 4–16 peritrichate flagella.   No capsule.   Gram-positive in young cultures, but often frankly Gram-negative in 4 to 5 days.

Agar Plate.—*4 days at* 37° *C.*   Irregularly round, having a general cigarette-in-water appearance, 10 mm. in diameter, effuse, filamentous, translucent colonies, with finely honeycombed surface due to crossing of numerous filaments, and fimbriate edge ; greyish by reflected, bluish-grey by transmitted light ; butyrous and easily emulsifiable.   No definite differentiation but filaments are less dense at periphery.

Deep Glucose Agar Shake.—*4 days at* 37° *C.*   Abundant gas formation ; medium disrupted and driven up nearly to plug.   Numerous colonies throughout medium, varying in appearance ; most usual type is delicate, arborescent, and flocculent ;

sometimes opaque with an irregularly dentate, well-defined edge, from which later woolly filamentous outshoots appear.

Horse Blood Agar Plates.—3 *days at* 37° *C.* α-prime hæmolysis; after 6 days hæmolysis is of β-type.

Agar Slope.—4 *days at* 37° *C.* Scanty to moderate, effuse, translucent, glistening, greyish-yellow growth, forming little islands, each with a coarsely erose edge; surface smooth or very finely granular.

Gelatin.—7 *days at* 37° *C.* Liquefied.

Broth.—4 *days at* 37° *C.* Poor to moderate growth with slight turbidity and a moderate, powdery deposit disintegrating completely; slight rancid odour.

Loeffler's Serum.—15 *days at* 37° *C.* Fairly good confluent growth; no liquefaction.

Coagulated Egg.—15 *days at* 37° *C.* Fairly good, partly confluent growth, with a moderately granular surface; no digestion.

Cooked Meat Medium.—15 *days at* 37° *C.* Moderate growth with slight turbidity; gas production; meat turned pink; no digestion; rancid odour.

Resistance.—Not recorded.

Metabolic.—Strict anaerobe. Opt. temp. 37° C. α-prime, and later β-hæmolysis on horse blood agar plates. Hæmolyses human and sheep's red cells. *Nutritional*: grows fairly well on ordinary media; growth improved by glucose. Green fluorescent colonies on MacConkey plate. Toxin produced.

Biochemical.—Acid and gas in glucose, maltose, lactose and salicin, not in mannitol or sucrose. Indole — ; M.R. — ; V.P. — ; nitrates reduced; NH_3 slight + ; H_2S + ; M.B. reduction — ; catalase —. Litmus milk: acid and clot and some gas; the clot does not form for 3 to 6 days.

Antigenic Structure.—By agglutination four groups can be distinguished on basis of O antigen; further subdivision is possible on basis of H antigen. Some cross-agglutination and much cross-complement-fixation with *Cl. chauvœi* strains. Antitoxin appears to be specific.

Pathogenicity.—Exotoxin produced. One agent in production of gas gangrene in man. Causes blackleg and braxy in sheep, and sometimes blackleg in cattle. Experimentally, it is pathogenic to guinea-pigs, mice, rabbits, and pigeons. Pathogenicity is retained for years in subculture. 0·01–0·5 c.c. of a 24-hour glucose broth culture injected intramuscularly into guinea-pigs causes death in 12 to 24 hours. P.M. blood-stained œdema and gas production; muscles intense deep red in colour and softened; sometimes fluid in peritoneum and pericardium. Motile rods and navicular forms at site of injection, and long, jointed, snake-like filaments on peritoneal surface of liver. (See p. 680.)

(See von Hibler 1908, Meyer 1915, Weinberg and Séguin 1918, Wolf 1918–19, Report 1919, Heller 1920, Gaiger 1922, 1924, Hall 1922, Weinberg and Ginsbourg 1927, Henderson 1934.)

Clostridium welchii

Synonyms.—*B. aerogenes capsulatus, B. phlegmonis emphysematosœ, B. perfringens, B. saccharobutyricus immobilis, B. enteritidis sporogenes, Granulobacillus butyricus, B. cadaveris butyricus, B. vaginœ emphysematosœ,* Achalme's bacillus.

Isolation.—First complete description by Welch and Nuttall in 1892, who isolated it from a cadaver. Various organisms closely resembling *Cl. welchii,* but differing from it in type of toxin production, have been isolated from diseased sheep, and called the lamb dysentery bacillus (Dalling 1926), *Cl. paludis* (McEwen 1930), and *Cl. ovitoxicum* (Bennetts 1932). Exact relation of these organisms to *Cl. welchii* and to one another is doubtful, but Wilsdon's (1931) classification into A, B, C, and D types corresponding respectively to the *welchii,* lamb dysentery, *paludis,* and *ovitoxicum* types may be temporarily accepted.

Ecology.—Found in soil, water, milk, dust, sewage, and intestinal canal of man and animals.

Morphology.—Rather short rods, varying considerably in length ; 4–8 $\mu \times$ 0·8–1·0 μ ; sometimes shorter and more slender ; filaments not uncommon. Parallel sides, ends truncated or slightly rounded ; axis straight. Arranged singly, often side by side forming small bundles. Variation in depth of staining ; involution forms —clubs, filaments, tadpoles, granular forms—frequent in old cultures. Spores large, oval, and subterminal. Sporulation occurs more readily with some strains than with others, and is favoured by an alkaline reaction ; does not occur below pH 6·6, and hence is unusual in media containing a fermentable carbohydrate. Non-motile. Capsules formed in animal body.

Agar Plate.—4 *days at* 37° *C.* 2 types of colony formed. One round, 2–4 mm. in diameter, low convex, amorphous, greyish-yellow, opaque, with smooth surface and entire edge ; butyrous and easily emulsifiable. Other is umbonate, and is differentiated into an opaque brownish centre and a lighter, more translucent, radially striated periphery with a crenated edge (Fig. 186). Other variant forms

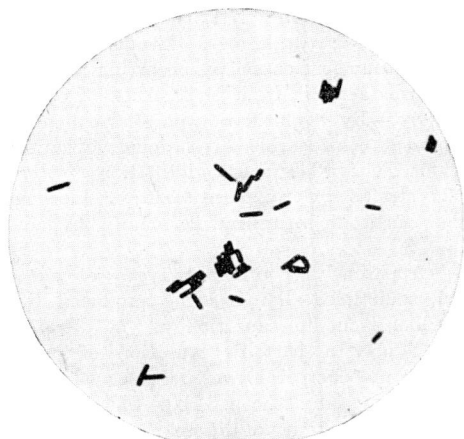

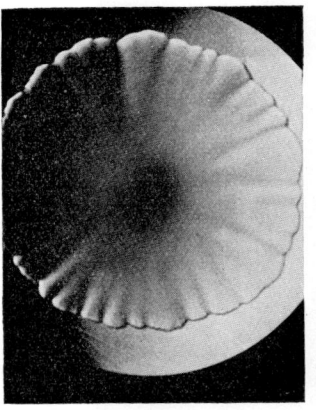

FIG. 185.—*Clostridium welchii.*
From a surface agar culture, anaerobically, 2 days, 37° C. ($\times$ 1000).

FIG. 186.—*Clostridium welchii.*
Surface colony on agar anaerobically, 5 days, 37° C. ($\times$ 8).

have been described, differing in morphology, colonial appearance, and sometimes toxicity (Sordelli, Prado, and Ferrari 1932, McGaughey 1933, Livesay 1933, Stevens 1935).

Deep Glucose Agar Shake.—4 *days at* 37° *C.* Abundant gas, medium ruptured and driven nearly to plug. Numerous colonies throughout medium ; they are biconvex, 1 mm. long, opaque, with an entire edge.

Horse Blood Agar.—3 *days at* 37° *C.* Round colonies, 2–5 mm. in diameter, umbonate, greyish-white, with opaque raised centre, and a translucent flattened periphery ; surface smooth ; entire edge. Zone of β-hæmolysis for 1 mm. around colony.

Agar Slope.—4 *days at* 37° *C.* Good growth consisting of discrete colonies.

Gelatin.—2 *days at* 37° *C.* Complete liquefaction.

Broth.—4 *days at* 37° *C.* Good growth with moderate turbidity, and moderate powdery deposit, disintegrating completely. Slight sour odour.

Loeffler's Serum.—15 *days at* 37° *C.* Good confluent, slightly raised growth with crenated edge ; no digestion.

Coagulated Egg.—15 *days at* 37° *C.* Fairly good, confluent, slightly raised growth ; no digestion.

Cooked Meat Medium.—15 *days at* 37° *C.* Good growth; fluid slightly turbid; gas evolved; meat turned pink; no digestion; acid reaction; sour odour.

Resistance.—Cultures in fermentable carbohydrate media die in a few days owing to the effect of the acid produced. In sugar-free protein media, in which spores have formed, the organisms may live for months. A suspension containing a million spores per c.c. is sterilized in 30 minutes at 90° C. and in 5 minutes or less at 100° C. (Headlee 1931).

Metabolic.—Fairly strict anaerobe. Opt. temp. 37° C. Hæmolysins and leucocidins are formed by some, but not by all strains. Gives β-hæmolysis on horse blood agar plates; hæmolyses human and sheep's red cells. *Nutritional*: grows fairly well on ordinary media; growth greatly improved by 1 per cent. glucose. Green fluorescence on MacConkey plate. Toxin produced.

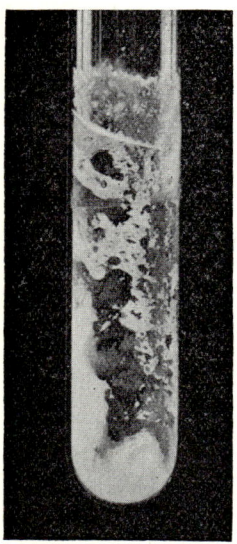

Fig. 187.—*Clostridium welchii.*

Culture in litmus milk anaerobically, 24 hours, 37° C., showing stormy fermentation.

Biochemical.—Acid and gas in glucose, maltose, lactose, and sucrose, not in mannitol or salicin; some strains ferment inulin, some glycerol. Indole — ; M.R. + ; V.P. — ; nitrates slight reduction; NH_3 slight + ; H_2S ++ ; M.B. reduction — ; catalase —. Litmus milk: acid, gas, clot—stormy fermentation—occurring in 12 to 48 hours. Forms acrolein from glycerol.

Antigenic Structure.—By agglutination no clear-cut grouping is apparent; considerable overlapping of antigens. No obvious relation between agglutination results and typing of strains by toxin-antitoxin or biochemical methods. Antitoxic serum can be readily prepared in horses.

Pathogenicity. — Apparently 4 different types of exotoxin produced, sometimes all four being produced by one strain. Chief agent in causation of gas gangrene in man. May play a part in causation of enteritis, appendicitis, and puerperal fever. Causes gas gangrene in animals, especially sheep. Experimentally, great variation in pathogenicity of different strains. Washed bacilli or spores are non-pathogenic. 0·1–1·0 c.c. broth culture injected intramuscularly into guinea-pig causes local tumefaction, spreading œdema, and death in 24 to 48 hours. P.M. suprarenal glands congested. Also pathogenic to mice, pigeons, and less so to rabbits (see p. 679). B type is responsible for lamb dysentery, C type for " struck "—an enteritis of sheep—and D type for an enterotoxæmic disease and for pulpy kidney disease of sheep (see Chapter LXXV).

(See Kamen 1904, Simonds 1915*a*, *b*, *c*, Robertson 1916, Bull 1917, Bull and Pritchett 1917*a*, *b*, De Kruif and Bollman 1917, De Kruif *et al.* 1917, Weinberg and Séguin 1918, Report 1919, Bengtson 1920, Caulfeild 1920, Hall 1922, Humphreys 1924, Dalling 1926, Weinberg and Ginsbourg 1927, Howard 1928, Weinberg 1929, Weinberg and Combiesco 1930, McEwen 1930, Torrey, Kahn and Salinger 1930, Headlee 1931, Mason, Ross and Dalling 1931, Wilsdon 1931, 1933, Bennetts 1932, Glenny *et al.* 1933, Walbum and Reymann 1933, McGaughey 1933, Livesay 1933, Weinberg and Guillaumie 1936.)

Clostridium tetani

Isolation.—Described by Nicolaier in 1884; isolated by Kitasato in 1889 (1889*b*).

Ecology.—Found in soil—especially cultivated soil—and in the intestine of man and animals.

Morphology.—*4-day agar slope at* 37° C. Rods, 2–5 $\mu \times$ 0·5 μ; considerable variation in length; long, curved, filamentous forms are not uncommon. Axis straight, sides parallel, ends rounded; arranged singly and occasionally in chains. Variation in depth of staining. Spores spherical, terminal, and wider

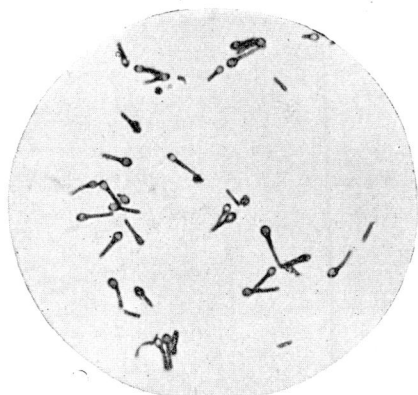

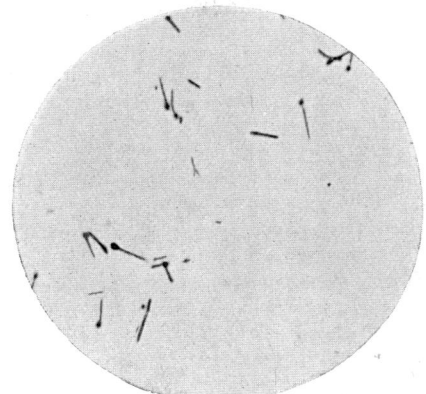

Fig. 188.—*Clostridium tetani.*

From a surface agar culture anaerobically, 7 days, 37° C., showing ring form of staining (× 1000).

Fig. 189.—*Clostridium tetani.*

From a broth culture anaerobically, 7 days, 37° C., showing the spores stained solidly (× 1000).

than the bacillus, giving characteristic drum-stick appearance. Sluggishly motile; peritrichate flagella. No capsule. Strongly Gram-positive in young cultures. In early stages, spores stain solidly; later, only the thin wall stains; spores rarely become free. Bizarre involution forms appear in old cultures.

Agar Plate.—*4 days at* 37° C. Irregularly round, 2–5 mm. in diameter, effuse, glistening, translucent, greyish-yellow colonies with irregularly granular surface, and ill-defined edge, showing filamentous, curled projections; structure very finely granular or filamentous; butyrous consistency, emulsifying easily. Differentiated into thicker, translucent, yellowish-brown centre, and thinner, transparent, almost colourless periphery. Whole colony has a fuzzy appearance. Isolated colonies of the normal motile type of *Cl. tetani* are extremely difficult to obtain, owing to the tendency of the organisms to spread in a proteus-like film over the surface of the agar; but it is stated that non-motile variants give rise to separate discrete colonies, even on moist media.

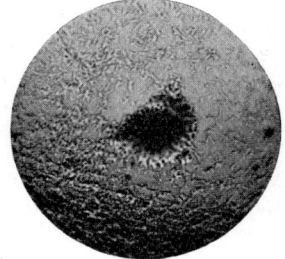

Fig. 190.—*Clostridium tetani.*

Surface colony on agar anaerobically, 2 days, 37° C., showing parent colony surrounded by an effuse outgrowth (× 8).

Deep Glucose Agar Shake.—*4 days at* 37° C. Slight gas formation; medium disrupted in 2 or 3 places. Colonies scattered throughout medium, except at surface; they are rounded, 1–2 mm. in diameter, opaque, with a brownish centre and a lighter more translucent periphery; fuzzy, filamentous, branching edge.

Agar Slope.—*4 days at* 37° C. Scanty to moderate, greyish-yellow, almost transparent, effuse growth, stretching to sides of tube, with very finely granular, glistening surface. If inoculated into condensation water, spreads rapidly over the whole surface of the agar, and presents a filamentous edge at the top.

Gelatin Stab.—10 *days at* 23° *C.*   Poor growth of fir-tree appearance.   At 37° C. liquefies gelatin in a week.

Broth.—4 *days at* 37° *C.*   Poor to moderate growth with slight turbidity, and a finely granular deposit, not disintegrating on shaking.   Odour of manure.

Loeffler's Serum.—4 *days at* 37° *C.*   Poor, effuse, mostly discrete growth ; serum may be softened after several days, but no true liquefaction occurs.

Horse Blood Agar Plates.—3 *days at* 37° *C.*   Rounded, 2–5 mm. in diameter, effuse, greyish, translucent colonies, with finely granular surface and lobate or fimbriate edge. Zone of α-prime hæmolysis for 1–5 mm. around colony, later passing into the β-type.

Coagulated Egg.—4 *days at* 37° *C.*   Poor, effuse, partly confluent growth ; no digestion.

Cooked Meat Medium.—4 *days at* 37° *C.*   Good growth ; fluid shows moderate turbidity ; some gas production ; no blackening, and no digestion of meat.   Slight blackening is said to occur after some weeks.

Resistance.—Spores resist boiling for 15 to 90 minutes.   Killed at 105° C. in 3 to 25 minutes ; killed by 5 per cent. phenol in 15 hours.

Metabolic.—Strict anaerobe.   Opt. temp. 37° C.   Grows poorly at 20° C.   α-prime or β-hæmolysis on blood agar plates.   Hæmolysin acts on R.B.C. of rabbit, goat, sheep, horse, and many other animals.   *Nutritional :* grows fairly well on ordinary media ; growth improved by blood and serum ; not by glucose.   Tulloch's exhausted medium is particularly suitable.   Produces green fluorescence on MacConkey's agar.   Possesses slight proteolytic properties.

Biochemical.—Ferments no sugars.   Indole + ;   M.R. — ;   V.P. — ;   nitrates not reduced ; NH_3 slight + ; H_2S — ;   M.B. reduction — ;   catalase —.   Litmus milk : reduction of litmus, may be slight precipitation of casein, but usually no change.   Said to form phenol.

Antigenic Structure.—Differentiated by agglutination into at least 7 types, of which Types I and III appear to be the commonest in this country.   Toxin formed by all types is identical and is neutralized by antitoxin prepared against any one type.   Antibacterial sera contain agglutinins and opsonins specific to each type.

Pathogenicity.—Potent exotoxin formed.   Naturally pathogenic to man and horses in particular.   Experimentally, mice, guinea-pigs, and rabbits are susceptible, dying of tetanus in 1 to 4 days after subcutaneous injection of a broth culture.   Washed spores or bacilli are innocuous.   The toxin is very potent, and will kill a mouse in a dose of 0·0001 c.c.   Birds are resistant.   (See Chapter LXXIV.)

(See Rosenbach 1886, Behring and Kitasato 1890, Kitasato and Weyl 1890, Kitasato 1891, Toledo and Veillon 1891, Behring 1892, Vaillard and Rouget 1892, Uschinsky 1893, Pizzini 1898, Madsen 1899, Ritchie 1901, Rosenau and Anderson 1908, von Hibler 1908, Metchnikoff 1908, Smith 1908, Noble 1915, Corbitt 1918, Weinberg and Séguin 1918, Report 1919, Tulloch 1919, Hall 1922, Heller 1922*a, b*, Anderson 1924, Bengtson 1924*b*, Descombey 1924, Fildes 1925*a, b*, Weinberg and Ginsbourg 1927, Tschertkow 1929, Fildes 1929, Knight and Fildes 1930, Kerrin 1930, 1934, Belin 1931, Mutermilch *et al.* 1933.)

Notes on Less Important Strains.

Cl. fallax was found by Weinberg and Séguin (1918) in infected wounds and gas gangrene.   It is a motile, Gram-positive bacillus, 1·2–5 μ × 0·6 μ in diameter, with rounded ends, straight axis, arranged singly.   Spores rarely formed ; may appear on coagulated serum.   Surface colonies are round and slightly granular, with crenated edge.   Deep colonies are biconvex, irregular, or bean-shaped.   Produces a soluble toxin.   When freshly isolated is pathogenic for mice and guinea-pigs.

Cl. parasporogenes.—Described by McIntosh (1917).   Resembles *Cl. sporogenes*, but deep colonies in agar shake cultures are biconvex or irregular in shape.   Also forms specific agglutinins, which do not act on *Cl. sporogenes*.   Non-pathogenic to guinea-pigs.

Cl. tertium.—Described by Henry (1917).   Resembles, but is probably different from, *Cl. paraputrificum* (see below).   Thin, slightly curved bacillus, 3–5 μ long, sluggishly motile,

Gram-positive, often showing granular staining. Spores freely, giving rise to large, oval, elongated terminal spores. Surface colonies are rounded, delicate, iridescent, and almost transparent, with entire or slightly crenated edge. Deep colonies are small, biconvex or irregular in shape. Ferments mannitol and xylose. Non-pathogenic to guinea-pigs. (See von Hibler 1908, Hall and Matsuma 1924.) According to Hall and Duffett (1935), both *Cl. tertium* and *Cl. histolyticum* are microaerophilic rather than strictly anaerobic, but spores are formed only under anaerobic conditions.

Cl. cochlearium.—Described by McIntosh (1917) as Type III C, and named *B. cochlearis* by Douglas, Fleming and Colebrook (1920) on account of its likeness to a spoon. Actively motile, slender rod of variable length, weakly Gram-positive; forms oval terminal spores. Surface colonies are delicate, transparent droplets, sometimes with faintly crenated edges; deep colonies are biconvex. Non-pathogenic to guinea-pigs.

Cl. tetanomorphum.—Described by McIntosh (1917) as Type IX. Morphologically resembles *Cl. tetani*, but differs in cultural and biochemical characteristics; fails to form a specific toxin. Surface colonies are small, flat, irregularly round, and almost transparent; deep colonies are small and irregular in shape, but are not woolly or branched. Non-pathogenic to guinea-pigs.

Cl. aerofœtidum.—Described by Weinberg and Séguin (1918). Small, slender bacillus, 3–5 μ long, slightly motile, and weakly Gram-positive. Spores are subterminal, and are not readily formed. Surface colonies are round and transparent; deep colonies are small and irregular. Non-pathogenic to guinea-pigs.

Cl. bifermentans.—Isolated in 1902 by Tissier and Martelly from putrefying meat, and named *B. bifermentans sporogenes*. So-called from its being the first anaerobe shown to decompose both sugars and proteins. Stout rod resembling *Cl. welchii*; Gram-positive. Usually described as non-motile, but Levenson (1936) states that in 3–4 hour glucose broth cultures the organisms are actively motile, if they are examined by the sealed capillary tube method; peritrichate flagella can be demonstrated in freshly isolated strains. Spores are oval and subterminal, and are formed readily. Surface colonies are round or crenated; deep colonies are biconvex or coral-like. Non-pathogenic to guinea-pigs.

Cl. putrificum.—Described by Bienstock (1884, 1899, 1901), who isolated it from fæces. Appears to have been a slender Gram-positive rod with spherical or oval terminal spores, which digested proteins but had no action on carbohydrates. Its identity is doubtful. Many workers regard it as probably identical with *Cl. cochlearium*, but this is disputed by Hartsell and Rettger (1934). (For critical discussion see Hall and Snyder 1934, Morgan and Wright 1934.)

Cl. paraputrificum.—According to Hall and Snyder (1934), this organism, which was described by Bienstock (1906), is probably identical with Escherich's " Köpfchenbakterien," von Hibler's ix bacillus, and Rodella's iii bacillus. It is found in the fæces, particularly of new-born infants, and is a slender, motile, Gram-variable bacillus with terminal oval spores. It is non-proteolytic; it ferments glucose, maltose, lactose, sucrose, and salicin, but not mannitol or xylose, with the production of acid and gas. It is non-pathogenic for guinea-pigs and rabbits.

Cl. sphenoides.—Isolated by Douglas, Fleming and Colebrook (1920) from wounds. So-called from the wedge-shape of the sporing bacillus. Small, motile, weakly Gram-positive; vegetative bacilli are fusiform in shape and arranged in pairs end-to-end. Spores are large and round, appear subterminally, but soon become strictly terminal. Surface colonies are round with entire edges. Pathogenicity not examined.

Cl. multifermentans tenalbus.—Described by Stoddard (1919*a*); isolated from a case of gas gangrene. Resembles *Cl. septique* morphologically, especially in its formation of citrons, but is non-pathogenic. Gram-positive, motile bacillus with subterminal spores. Surface colonies are large, round, with slightly irregular edges; after several days they become white and opaque, and rise up from the surface. Deep colonies are white and opaque, irregular or biconvex, with projecting outgrowths. Acid and gas in glucose, maltose, lactose, sucrose, and salicin; acid and clot in L.M. Non-proteolytic. Non-pathogenic to guinea-pigs.

Cl. bellonensis.—Described by Sacquépée in 1915. Found frequently in war wounds. Doubtful whether it was ever obtained in pure culture.

Cl. centrosporogenes.—Described by Hall (1922), probably identical with *Cl. bifermentans* (McCoy and McClung 1936). Large, Gram-positive, motile rod occurring singly, in pairs and short chains. Spores are small, oval, equatorial, and are formed readily, particularly in sugar-free media; often become free. Surface colonies on blood agar are hæmolytic and like transparent dew-drops; later become more opaque and yellowish. Deep colonies are large, globular with central nucleus and woolly periphery. Digests gelatin, egg, casein; meat is digested and blackened. Ferments glucose. Non-pathogenic to guinea-pigs.

Cl. egens.—Described by Stoddard (1919b). Closely resembles *Cl. welchii*; apparently does not form spores. Non-proteolytic. Does not ferment lactose or milk.

Cl. sordellii. Synonym *B. œdematis sporogenes*. Isolated by Sordelli (1922, 1923) in Buenos Aires from a human case of gas gangrene. Weinberg, Davesne, and Lefranc (1931) have isolated it in France from gas gangrene in a sheep and from a human case of appendicitis. Named *Cl. sordellii* by Hall and Scott (1927). Motile, Gram-positive rod, 3·6–6·0 μ × 1·2–1·5 μ, forming equatorial or subterminal spores, which are destroyed by heating to 100° C. for 75 minutes. Uniform turbidity in glucose broth with filament production and a viscous zoogloeal deposit, which is easily disintegrated by shaking; nauseous odour. Gelatin liquefied rapidly. Coagulated serum becomes transparent and is disintegrated in 2 to 4 weeks. Slight digestion of egg white. Milk is coagulated and peptonized. Ferments glucose and maltose; sucrose attacked feebly. 0·01 c.c. of a 48-hour glucose broth culture injected intramuscularly kills a guinea-pig in 2 days with lesions similar to those caused by *Cl. œdematiens*. Fairly powerful toxin formed; destroyed by 30° C. in 60 minutes. Doubtful whether it is a distinct species; may possibly be a virulent form of *Cl. bifermentans*. Appears to be morphologically, culturally, and antigenically more or less identical with *Cl. œdematoides*, an organism isolated from a wound infection by Meleney, Humphreys, and Carp (1926–27, 1927). (See Humphreys and Meleney 1927–28, Hall, Rymer, and Jungherr 1929, Hall and Scott, 1931.)

Cl. hæmolyticum.—Described by Vawter and Records (1926, 1931) as the cause of red-water disease or bacillary hæmoglobinuria of cattle in the United States, and by Sordelli, Ferrari, and Prado (1930) in South America. Named *B. hæmolyticus* by Hall (1929b). It is a fairly large bacillus, 3·0–5·6 μ × 1·0–1·3 μ, occurring individually, in pairs, and occasionally in short chains. Spores are oval terminal or subterminal. Sluggishly motile by 6–16 peritrichate flagella. Gram-positive in young cultures. Deep colonies in agar are at first lenticular, later fluffy. Gelatin is liquefied, but otherwise no proteolytic action. Acid and gas produced in glucose, acid and clot in litmus milk. Complete hæmolysis on blood agar plates in 24 hours. A toxin is produced. By agglutination most strains appear to be antigenically homogeneous. Intramuscular inoculation of guinea-pigs with a toxic culture gives rise to an extensive bloody œdema, sometimes accompanied by hæmoglobinuria. Rabbits also susceptible. A disease simulating in many respects the natural disease can be reproduced in cattle by injection of toxic cultures.

Cl. capitovale.—Isolated by Snyder and Hall (1935) from various situations including the pleural fluid of a sheep that had died of gas gangrene, the heart blood and peritoneal fluid at post mortem of cases of septic infection in human beings, and the fæces of normal infants. It is a slender, motile, Gram-positive rod with rounded ends, measuring 2·0–2·5 μ × 0·5–0·8 μ, and forming terminal oval spores. It gives rise on blood agar to minute, circular or irregularly circular, transparent, non-hæmolytic surface colonies. It produces acid and gas in glucose, but not in maltose, mannitol, lactose, sucrose, or salicin. It liquefies gelatin, is mildly proteolytic, clots milk irregularly but does not digest the clot, is non-pathogenic to guinea-pigs and rabbits inoculated subcutaneously, and appears to be antigenically homogeneous. For its differentiation from *Cl. paraputrificum*, *Cl. caloritolerans*, and *Cl. cochlearium*, see Snyder and Hall.

REFERENCES

ADAMSON, R. S. (1919–20) *J. Path. Bact.*, **23**, 241.

ANDERSON, B. G. (1924) *J. infect. Dis.*, **35**, 213, 244.

ARLOING, S., CORNEVIN, C. E., and THOMAS, O. (1887) " Le charbon symptomatique du bœuf," 2nd edition. Paris.

BEHRING. (1892) *Z. Hyg. InfektKr.*, **12**, 45.

BEHRING and KITASATO. (1890) *Dtsch. med. Wschr.*, **16**, 1113.

BELIN, M. (1931) *C. R. Soc. Biol.*, **105**, 840.

BENGTSON, I. A. (1920) *Bull. U.S. hyg. Lab.*, No. 122 ; (1921) *Publ. Hlth Rep., Wash.*, No. 29, p. 1665 ; (1922a) *Publ. Hlth Rep., Wash.*, **37**, 164 ; (1922b) *Ibid.*, **37**, 2252 ; (1923) *Ibid.*, **38**, 340 ; (1924a) *Bull. U.S. hyg. Lab.*, No. 136 ; (1924b) *Ibid.*, No. 139.

BENNETTS, H. W. (1932) *Aust. Counc. sci. industr. Res., Bull.* No. 57.

BIENSTOCK, B. (1884) *Z. klin. Med.*, **8**, 1 ; (1899) *Arch. Hyg.*, **36**, 335 ; (1901) *Ibid.*, **39**, 390 ; (1906) *Ann. Inst. Pasteur*, **20**, 407.

BULL, C. G. (1917) *J. exp. Med.*, **26**, 603.

BULL, C. G. and PRITCHETT, I. W. (1917a) *J. exp. Med.*, **26**, 119 ; (1917b) *Ibid.*, **26**, 867.

BURKE, G. S. (1919a) *J. Bact.*, **4**, 555 ; (1919b) *J. Amer. med. Ass.*, **72**, 88.

CAULFEILD, A. H. W. (1920) *J. infect. Dis.*, **27**, 151.

COLEMAN, G. E. (1922) *J. infect. Dis.*, **31**, 556 ; (1923) *Ibid.*, **33**, 384.

COLEMAN, G. E. and MEYER, K. F. (1922) *J. infect. Dis.*, **31**, 622.

CORBITT, H. B. (1918) *Bull. U.S. hyg. Lab.*, No. 112.

DALLING, T. (1926) *J. comp. Path.*, **39**, 148.

DESCOMBEY, P. (1924) *C. R. Soc. Biol.*, **91**, 239.

DICKENS, P. F. (1934) *U.S. nav. med. Bull.*, **32**, 267.

DICKSON, E. C. (1918) *Monogr. Rockefeller Inst. med. Res.*, No. 8.

DICKSON, E. C., BURKE, G. S., BECK, D., and JOHNSTON, J. (1925) *J. infect. Dis.*, **36**, 472.

DOUGLAS, S. R., FLEMING, A., and COLEBROOK, L. (1920) *Spec. Rep. Ser. med. Res. Coun., Lond.*, No. 57.

DOZIER, C. C. (1924) *J. infect. Dis.*, **35**, 105.

DUBOVSKY, B. J. and MEYER, K. F. (1922a) *J. infect. Dis.*, **31**, 501 ; (1922b) *Ibid.*, **31**, 595.

EASTON, L. J. and MEYER, K. F. (1924) *J. infect. Dis.*, **35**, 207.

EDMONDSON, R. B., GILTNER, L. T., and THOM, C. (1920) *Arch. intern. Med.*, **26**, 357.

EISENBERG, P. (1907) *C. R. Soc. Biol.*, **62**, 613.

ERMENGEM, E. VAN. (1896) *Zbl. Bakt.*, **19**, 442 ; (1897) *Z. Hyg. InfektKr.*, **26**, 1.

ESTY, J. R. and MEYER, K. F. (1922) *J. infect. Dis.*, **31**, 650.

FELIX, A. and ROBERTSON, M. (1928) *Brit. J. exp. Path.*, **9**, 6.

FILDES, P. (1925a) *Brit. J. exp. Path.*, **6**, 62 ; (1925b) *Ibid.*, **6**, 91 ; (1929) *Brit. J. exp. Path.*, **10**, 151 ; (1935) *Brit. J. exp. Path.*, **16**, 309.

FILDES, P. and KNIGHT, B. C. J. G. (1933) *Brit. J. exp. Path.*, **14**, 343.

FILDES, P. and RICHARDSON, G. M. (1935) *Brit. J. exp. Path.*, **16**, 326.

FRANKLAND, P. F. (1889) *Z. Hyg. InfektKr.*, **6**, 13.

GAIGER, S. H. (1922) *J. comp. Path.*, **35**, 191, 235 ; (1924) *Ibid.*, **37**, 163.

GLADSTONE, G. P., FILDES, P., and RICHARDSON, G. M. (1935) *Brit. J. exp. Path.*, **16**, 335.

GLENNY, A. T., BARR, M., LLEWELLYN-JONES, M., DALLING, T., and ROSS, H. E. (1933) *J. Path. Bact.*, **37**, 53.

GOSS, L. W., BARBARIN, R. E., and HAINES, A. W. (1921) *J. infect. Dis.*, **29**, 615.

GRAHAM, R. and BOUGHTON, T. B. (1923a) *Abstr. Bact.*, **1**, 29 ; (1923b) *Ibid.*, **7**, 30.

GRAHAM, R. and BRUECKNER, A. L. (1919) *J. Bact.*, **4**, 1.

GRAHAM, R. and THORP, F. (1929) *J. Immunol.*, **16**, 391.

GUNNISON, J. B. and COLEMAN, G. E. (1932) *J. infect. Dis.*, **51**, 542.

GUNNISON, J. B. and MEYER, K. F. (1930) *J. infect. Dis.*, **46**, 335.

HALL, I. C. (1922) *J. infect. Dis.*, **30**, 445 ; (1929a) *J. Bact.*, **17**, 255 ; (1929b) *J. infect. Dis.*, **45**, 156.

HALL, I. C. and DAVIS, N. C. (1923) *J. exp. Med.*, **37**, 585.

HALL, I. C. and DUFFETT, N. D. (1935) *J. Bact.*, **29**, 269.

HALL, I. C. and MATSUMA, K. (1924) *J. infect. Dis.*, **35**, 502.

HALL, I. C., RYMER, M. R., and JUNGHERR, E. (1929) *J. infect. Dis.*, **45**, 42.

HALL, I. C. and SCOTT, A. L. (1927) *J. infect. Dis.*, **41**, 329 ; (1931) *J. Bact.*, **22**, 375.

HALL, I. C. and SNYDER, M. L. (1934) *J. Bact.*, **28**, 181.

HARTSELL, S. E. and RETTGER, L. F. (1934) *J. Bact.*, **27**, 497.

HASLAM, T. P. and LUMB, J. W. (1919) *J. infect. Dis.*, **24**, 362.

HEADLEE, M. R. (1931) *J. infect. Dis.*, **48**, 468.

HELLER, H. H. (1920) *J. infect. Dis.*, **27**, 385 ; (1921) *J. Bact.*, **6**, 521 ; (1922a) *J. infect. Dis.*, **30**, 18 ; (1922b) *Ibid.*, **30**, 33.

HENDERSON, D. W. (1932) *Brit. J. exp. Path.*, **13**, 412 ; (1934) *Ibid.*, **15**, 166.

HENRY, H. (1917) *J. Path. Bact.*, **21**, 344.

HIBLER, E. VON. (1908) "Untersuchungen über die pathogenen Anaëroben." Jena.

HOLKER, J. (1918–19) *J. Path. Bact.*, **22**, 28.

HOWARD, A. (1928) *Ann. Inst. Pasteur*, **42**, 1403.

HUMPHREYS, F. and MELENEY, F. L. (1927–8) *Proc. Soc. exp. Biol., N.Y.*, **25**, 611.

HUMPHREYS, F. B. (1924) *J. infect. Dis.*, **35**, 282.

KAMEN, L. (1904) *Zbl. Bakt.*, **35**, 686.

KEMPNER, W. (1897) *Z. Hyg. InfektKr.*, **26**, 481.

KERRIN, J. C. (1930) *Brit. J. exp. Path.*, **11**, 153 ; (1934) *J. Path. Bact.*, **38**, 219.

KITASATO, S. (1889a) *Z. Hyg. InfektKr.*, **6**, 105 ; (1889b) *Ibid.*, **7**, 225 ; (1890) *Ibid.*, **8**, 55 ; (1891) *Ibid.*, **10**, 267.

KITASATO, S. and WEYL, TH. (1890) *Z. Hyg. InfektKr.*, **8**, 41, 404.

KITT, T. (1887) *Zbl. Bakt.*, **1**, 684, 716, 741.

KNIGHT, B. C. J. G. (1936) *Spec. Rep. Ser. med. Res. Coun., Lond.*, No. 210.

KNIGHT, B. C. J. G. and FILDES, P. (1930) *Biochem. J.*, **24**, 1496 ; (1933) *Brit. J. exp. Path.*, **14**, 112.

KOCH, R. (1881) *Mitt. ReichsgesundhAmt.*, **1**, 49.

KRUIF, P. H. DE, ADAMS, T. W., and IRELAND, P. M. (1917) *J. infect. Dis.*, **21**, 580.

KRUIF, P. H. DE and BOLLMAN, J. L. (1917) *J. infect. Dis.*, **21**, 588.

LAIDLAW, P. P. (1915) *Brit. med. J.*, i. 497.

LANDAU, H. (1917) *Zbl. Bakt.*, **79**, 417.

LECLAINCHE, E. and VALLÉE, H. (1900) *Ann. Inst. Pasteur*, **14**, 202.

LEPPER, E. and MARTIN, C. J. (1929) *Brit. J. exp. Path.*, **10**, 327 ; (1930) *Ibid.*, **11**, 137, 140.

LEUCHS, J. (1910) *Z. Hyg. InfektKr.*, **65**, 55.

LEVENSON, S. (1936) *C. R. Soc. Biol.*, **121**, 221.

LIBORIUS, P. (1886) *Z. Hyg. InfektKr.*, **1**, 115.

LINGELSHEIM, VON. (1912) See Kolle and Wassermann's "Hdb. path. Mikroorg." IIte Abt. (1912–13), **4**, 737.

LIVESAY, H. R. (1933) *J. infect. Dis.*, **53**, 125.

LOMMEL, J. and GUNNISON, J. B. (1929) *J. Immunol.*, **16**, 403.

McCLUNG, L. S. (1935) *J. Bact.*, **29**, 189.

McCLUNG, L. S., McCOY, E., and FRED, E. B. (1935) *Zbl. Bakt.*, IIte Abt., **91**, 225.

McCOY, E. and McCLUNG, L. S. (1936) *J. Bact.*, **31**, 557.

McEWEN, A. D. (1926) *J. comp. Path.*, **39**, 253 ; (1930) *Ibid.*, **43**, 1.

McGAUGHEY, C. A. (1933) *J. Path. Bact.*, **36**, 263.

McINTOSH, J. (1917) *Spec. Rep. Ser. med. Res. Coun., Lond.*, No. 12.

MADSEN, T. (1899) *Z. Hyg. InfektKr.*, **32**, 214.

MARKOFF, W. N. (1911) *Zbl. Bakt.*, **60**, 188.

MASON, J. H., ROSS, H. E., and DALLING, T. (1931) *J. comp. Path.*, **44**, 258.

MELENEY, F. L., HUMPHREYS, F. B., and CARP, L. (1926–7) *Proc. Soc. exp. Biol., N.Y.*, **24**, 675 ; (1927) *Surg. Gynec. Obstet.*, **45**, 775.

METCHNIKOFF, E. (1908) *Ann. Inst. Pasteur*, **22**, 929.

MEYER, K. F. (1915) *J. infect. Dis.*, **17**, 458.

MEYER, K. F. and DUBOVSKY, B. J. (1922a) *J. infect. Dis.*, **31**, 541 (1922b) *Ibid.*, **31**, 559 ; (1922c) *Ibid.*, **31**, 600.

MIESZNER, H., MEYN, A., and SCHOOP, G. (1931) *Zbl. Bakt.*, **120**, 258.

MORGAN, E. L. and WRIGHT, H. D. (1934) *J. Path. Bact.*, **39**, 457.

MUTERMILCH, S., BELIN, M., and SALAMON, E. (1933) *C. R. Soc. Biol.*, **114**, 1005.

NEVIN, M. (1921) *J. infect. Dis.*, **28**, 226.

NICOLAIER. (1884) *Dtsch. med. Wschr.*, **10**, 842.

NOBLE, W. (1915) *J. infect. Dis.*, **16**, 132.

NOCARD and ROUX. (1887) *Ann. Inst. Pasteur*, **1**, 257.

NOVY, F. G. (1894) *Z. Hyg. InfektKr.*, **17**, 209.

ORR, P. F. (1920) *Abstr. Bact.*, **4**, 10 ; (1922) *J. infect. Dis.*, **30**, 118.

PAINE, F. S. (1931) *Zbl. Bakt.*, IIte Abt., **85**, 122.

PAPPENHEIMER, A. M. (1935) *Biochem. J.*, **29**, 2057.

PASTEUR and JOUBERT. (1877) *Bull. Acad. Méd.*, **6**, 781.

PFENNINGER, W. (1924) *J. infect. Dis.*, **35**, 347.

PIZZINI, L. (1898) *Zbl. Bakt.*, **24**, 890.

REDDISH, G. F. and RETTGER, L. F. (1924) *J. Bact.*, **9**, 13.

Reports. (1917) *Spec. Rep. Ser. med. Res. Coun., Lond.*, No. 12 ; (1919) *Ibid.*, No. 39.

RITCHIE, J. (1901) *J. Hyg., Camb.*, **1**, 125.

ROBERTS, R. S. (1931) *J. comp. Path.*, **44**, 246.

ROBERTSON, M. (1916) *J. Path. Bact.*, **20**, 327.

ROBINSON, E. M. (1929) *15th Ann. Rep. Dir. vet. Serv. Union S. Afr.*, **1**, 111.

ROCKWELL, G. E. (1924) *J. infect. Dis.*, **35**, 581.

ROSENAU, M. J. and ANDERSON, J. F. (1908) *Bull. U.S. hyg. Lab.*, No. 43.
ROSENBACH. (1886) *Arch. klin. Chir.*, **34**, 306.
ROUX, E. (1888) *Ann. Inst. Pasteur*, **2**, 49.
SACQUÉPÉE, E. (1915) *Pr. méd.*, **23**, 183.
SCHOENHOLZ, P. (1928) *J. infect. Dis.*, **42**, 40.
SEDDON, H. R. (1922) *J. comp. Path.*, **35**, 147.
SHERRINGTON, C. S. (1917) *Lancet*, ii. 964.
SHIPPEN, L. P. (1919) *Arch. intern. Med.*, **23**, 346.
SIMONDS, J. P. (1915*a*) *J. infect. Dis.*, **16**, 31 ; (1915*b*) *Ibid.*, **16**, 35 ; (1915*c*) *Monogr. Rocke-*
    feller Inst., No. 5.
DE SMIDT, F. P. G. (1924) *J. Hyg.*, *Camb.*, **22**, 314.
SMITH, T. (1890) *Zbl. Bakt.*, **7**, 502 ; (1908) *Trans. Chicago path. Soc.*, **7**, 1.
SMITH, T., BROWN, T. H. R., and WALKER, E. L. (1905–6) *J. med. Res.*, **14**, 193.
SNYDER, M. L. and HALL, I. C. (1935) *Zbl. Bakt.*, **135**, 290.
SOMMER, H. and SOMMER, E. W. (1932) *J. infect. Dis.*, **51**, 243.
SORDELLI, A. (1922) *C. R. Soc. Biol.*, **87**, 838 ; (1923) *Ibid.*, **89**, 53.
SORDELLI, A., FERRARI, J., and PRADO, M. (1930) *Rev. Inst. bact.*, *B. Aires*, **5**, 797.
SORDELLI, A., PRADO, M., and FERRARI, J. (1932) *Folia biol.*, *B. Aires*, Nos. 14 and 15,
    pp. 58, 63.
STARIN, W. A. (1924) *J. infect. Dis.*, **34**, 148.
STARIN, W. A. and DACK, G. M. (1923) *J. infect. Dis.*, **33**, 169 ; (1924) *Ibid.*, **34**, 137 ; (1925)
    Ibid., **36**, 383.
STARK, C. N., SHERMAN, J. M., and STARK, P. (1928) *J. infect. Dis.*, **43**, 565.
STEVENS, F. A. (1935) *J. infect. Dis.*, **57**, 275.
STICKLAND, L. H. (1934) *Biochem. J.*, **28**, 1746 ; (1935) *Ibid.*, **29**, 288, 889.
STODDARD, J. L. (1919*a*) *Lancet*, i. 12 ; (1919*b*) *J. exp. Med.*, **29**, 187.
TANNER, F. W. and DACK, G. M. (1922) *J. infect. Dis.*, **31**, 92.
TANNER, F. W. and TWOHEY, H. B. (1926) *Zbl. Bakt.*, **98**, 136.
TAROZZI, G. (1905) *Zbl. Bakt.*, **37**, 619.
THEILER, A. (1928) *13th and 14th Rep.*, *Director vet. Educat. Res.*, *S. Africa*, p. 47.
THEILER, A., VILJOEN, P. R., GREEN, H. H., DU TOIT, P. J., MEIER, H., and ROBINSON,
    E. M. (1926) *11th and 12th Rep.*, *Director vet. Educat. Res.*, *S. Africa*, Part ii. p. 821.
TISSIER, H. and MARTELLY. (1902) *Ann. Inst. Pasteur*, **16**, 865.
TOLEDO, S. and VEILLON. (1891) *Zbl. Bakt.*, **9**, 18.
TORREY, J. C. (1925) *J. infect. Dis.*, **36**, 517.
TORREY, J. C., KAHN, M. C., and SALINGER, M. H. (1930) *J. Bact.*, **20**, 85.
TSCHERTKOW, L. (1929) *Z. ImmunForsch.*, **63**, 262.
TULLOCH, W. J. (1919) *J. Hyg.*, *Camb.*, **18**, 103.
TURNER, A. W. (1930) *Aust. Coun. sci. industr. Res.*, *Bull.*, No. 46.
USCHINSKY, N. (1893) *Zbl. Bakt.*, **14**, 316.
VAILLARD, L. and ROUGET, J. (1892) *Ann. Inst. Pasteur*, **6**, 385.
VARNEY, P. L. (1926) *J. Lab. clin. Med.*, **11**, 1.
VAWTER, L. R. and RECORDS, E. (1926) *J. Amer. vet. med. Ass.*, **68**, 494 ; (1931) *J. infect.*
    Dis., **48**, 581.
WAGNER, E. (1924) *J. infect. Dis.*, **35**, 353.
WAGNER, E., DOZIER, C. C., and MEYER, K. F. (1924) *J. infect. Dis.*, **34**, 63.
WALBUM, L. E. and REYMANN, C. G. (1933) *J. Path. Bact.*, **36**, 469.
WEINBERG, M. (1929) *Bull. Inst. Pasteur*, **27**, 529, 577.
WEINBERG, M. and COMBIESCO, N. (1930) *Ann. Inst. Pasteur*, **45**, 547.
WEINBERG, M., DAVESNE, J., and LEFRANC, M. (1931) *C. R. Soc. Biol.*, **107**, 506.
WEINBERG, M., DAVESNE, J., MIHAILESCO, M., and SANCHEZ, C. (1929) *C. R. Soc. Biol.*,
    101, 907.
WEINBERG, M. and GINSBOURG, B. (1927) " Données récentes sur les microbes anaérobies
    et leur rôle en pathologie." Masson et Cie., Paris.
WEINBERG, M. and GUILLAUMIE, M. (1936) *C. R. Soc. Biol.*, **121**, 1275.
WEINBERG, M. and MIHAILESCO, M. (1929) *Ann. Inst. Pasteur*, **43**, 1408.
WEINBERG, RENARD, C., and DAVESNE, J. (1926) *C. R. Soc. Biol.*, **94**, 813.
WEINBERG and SÉGUIN, P. (1915) *C. R. Soc. Biol.*, **78**, 274 ; (1916) *C. R. Acad. Sci.*, **163**,
    449 ; (1918) "·La gangrène gazeuse." Paris.
WEISS, H. (1921) *J. infect. Dis.*, **28**, 70.
WELCH, W. H. and NUTTALL, G. H. F. (1892) *Johns Hopk. Hosp. Bull.*, **3**, 81.
WHEELER, M. W. and HUMPHREYS, E. M. (1924) *Johns Hopk. Hosp. Bull.*, **35**, 305.
WILSDON, A. J. (1931) *2nd Rep. Director, Inst. Anim. Path.*, *Camb.*, p. 53 ; (1933) *Ibid.*,
    3rd Rep., p. 46.
WILSON, G. S. (1928) *J. Path. Bact.*, **31**, 113.
WINOGRADSKY, S. (1902) *Zbl. Bakt.*, IIte Abt., **9**, 43, 107.
WOLF, C. G. L. (1918–19) *J. Path. Bact.*, **22**, 115 ; (1919–20) *Ibid.*, **23**, 254.
WOLF, C. G. L. and HARRIS, J. E. (1917) *J. Path. Bact.*, **21**, 386.
ZEISSLER, J. and RASZFELD, L. (1929) *Arch. wiss. prakt. Tierheilk.*, **59**, 419.

CHAPTER XXXIV

MISCELLANEOUS BACTERIA

WE include in this chapter a number of organisms which, for one reason or another, cannot justifiably be allotted to any of the named groups.[1]

The Morax-Axenfeld Bacillus.

This organism, which is responsible for subacute or angular conjunctivitis in human beings, was described independently by Morax (1896) and Axenfeld (1897). The name *B. lacunatus* was suggested for it by Eyre (1900).

MORPHOLOGY.—In films of the conjunctival secretion it occurs in the form of rods, 2–3 μ long and 1 μ broad, with parallel or slightly convex sides and rounded ends. The bacilli occur in pairs, placed end-to-end, and sometimes in short chains. They are found free in the secretion, or within the polymorphonuclear and desquamated epithelial cells. They are non-motile, non-sporing, Gram-negative, and except for the absence of a capsule, they closely resemble Friedländer's pneumobacillus. In old cultures pleomorphic forms are numerous, ranging in size and shape from short stunted diplococcal forms to long, jointed or filamentous, sometimes fusiform threads (Eyre 1900).

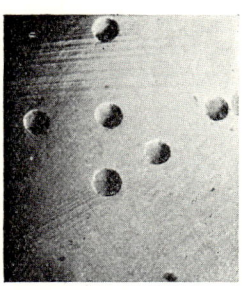

FIG. 191.—MORAX-AXEN-FELD BACILLUS.

Surface colonies on Fildes' agar plate, 24 hours, 37° C. (× 8).

CULTIVATION.—Growth occurs only in the presence of some natural animal protein, such as serum, blood, or ascitic fluid ; there is no development on ordinary nutrient agar or potato, nor in broth, milk, or gelatin. Development is best on Fildes' agar and on serum or egg medium ; it is poor on blood agar and very poor on chocolate agar. The organism is said to grow only between 30° and 40° C., and to be strictly aerobic. Our own limited experience suggests that some growth may occur below 30° C., and that under anaerobic conditions on favourable media slight but definite growth may be evident. On serum agar plates after 24 hours at 37° C. the colonies are round, up to 1 mm. in diameter, raised, greyish, and translucent ; during the next few days they increase in size, reaching 2–5 mm. in diameter, and become differentiated into a slightly raised opaque whitish centre, and a thin, translucent periphery with a lobate edge ; the medium becomes pitted owing to liquefaction of the serum. On Loeffler's serum no actual colonies are visible, but the whole surface is covered with pits of liquefaction—hence the term *lacunatus*. On Fildes' agar after 24 hours at 37° C. the colonies are water-clear, amorphous, low convex, 0·4 mm. or so in diameter, with a smooth glistening surface and entire edge ; after 4 days they are larger, and are differentiated into a smooth, raised, central papilla and a wide, effuse, granular, dull, transparent, peripheral extension with an irregularly undulate margin. The central papilla may be so small and the peripheral portion so transparent that the colonies are difficult to see. By transmitted light they have a frosted-glass appearance. On Dorset egg low

---

[1] The terms *Bact. pneumosintes*, *Bact. granulosis*, and *Bact. monocytogenes* are used for convenience, but it must be pointed out that none of these organisms belongs to the *Bacterium* group as defined on p. 515.

convex colonies are formed, which lead in a few days to slight pitting of the surface. There is no growth on MacConkey agar. In serum broth after 24 hours at 37° C., there is a uniform turbidity ; later a greyish-white deposit appears, and increases for 6 to 10 days, after which the medium clears, the whole of the growth sinking to the bottom of the tube.

RESISTANCE, BIOCHEMICAL REACTIONS, AND PATHOGENICITY.—Cultures in serum broth live for weeks at 35° C., but die in 48 hours if left at room temperature. The bacillus is killed by moist heat at 58° C. in 15 minutes, and is apparently very susceptible to zinc salts, which have an almost specific action in the treatment of angular conjunctivitis. In our experience no sugars are fermented, and litmus milk becomes very slowly alkaline. Nitrates are reduced. Catalase is negative. No indole is formed in serum broth cultures, even after 7 days. The organism is non-pathogenic to laboratory animals, whether inoculated into the conjunctival sac or directly into the tissues ; but a drop of culture instilled into the conjunctival sac of a healthy human volunteer gives rise in about 5 days to a typical attack of angular conjunctivitis.

A similar organism was described by Petit in 1900, who isolated it from cases of conjunctivitis associated with corneal ulceration. It differs from the Morax-Axenfeld bacillus mainly in its ability to grow on media without the addition of natural animal protein (though no growth may occur in ordinary broth), in its development at room temperature, in its liquefaction of gelatin, and in its more active digestion of Loeffler's serum, which it liquefies in 3 or 4 days. On ascitic agar it gives rise to convex, not umbonate, colonies, which are greyish in colour, viscous, and not so translucent as those of the Morax-Axenfeld bacillus.

Ducrey's Bacillus.

This organism is a small Gram-negative bacillus. It was first described by Ducrey, who recognized it as the probable cause of soft chancre (see Chapter LXXVI). *Morphologically* in the purulent discharge from the ulcerated surface of the lesion the organisms appear as small ovoid rods, arranged in pairs, in groups, or in chains lying parallel to one another. Several forms may, however, be assumed. Thus, it may appear as a short rod with parallel sides and rounded ends, staining evenly ; or it may be ovoid or navicular in shape with marked bipolar staining ; or it may occur in pairs end-to-end, having a dumb-bell appearance. In size the bacillus is about 1·1–1·5 μ long by 0·6 μ broad (Stein 1928). It may be intra- or extracellular in position. It does not form spores ; it is Gram-negative, and non-acid-fast. In cultures on solid media the organisms appear as isolated individuals, in groups, and in short chains ; in fluid media very long chains are frequently formed.

The organisms may be *cultivated* by inoculating scrapings from the floor of the ulcer on to a medium consisting of 3 per cent. agar containing 20–33 per cent. defibrinated rabbit's blood : the medium should be prepared on the day of inoculation, and should be distributed into wide tubes having a large surface exposed to the air (Nicolle 1923, Reenstierna 1923, Nicolle and Durand 1924). Several tubes should be inoculated, and incubated at 35° C. Colonies appear in 24 hours, and may be picked off for purification. On blood agar after 24 hours the colonies are circular, 0·5–1·0 mm. in diameter, low convex, greyish-white and glistening, with a smooth surface and entire edge ; after 2 to 3 days, they may reach a diameter of 2 mm., and the surface may show a crateriform depression. According to Hunt (1935), growth occurs best in sealed tubes, suggesting that it is favoured by an increased partial pressure of CO_2.

Another medium that is recommended for primary isolation consists of 1 part of 5 per cent. glycerine agar and 4 parts of Besredka's egg medium. On this medium the colonies are said to be round, transparent, and of a rose mother-of-pearl colour (Hababou-Sala 1925). After preliminary incubation at 35° C., cultures are said to remain viable at room temperature for about a month.

In Martin's broth, to which 20 per cent. of defibrinated rabbit's blood has been added, the organism develops rapidly, forming granules, which are suspended in the liquid or become attached to the walls of the tube. After a few days, an incomplete film may form on the surface. Cultures in this medium remain viable in the incubator for at least 10 days.

For preserving the organism, it should be inoculated into a medium consisting of 0·25 per cent. of nutrient agar, 1 per cent. starch, and 20 per cent. of defibrinated rabbit's blood. Cultures on this medium remain alive for a month at incubator temperature, and for a similar period at room temperature, provided they are previously incubated for 5 days.

The organism is not specially resistant : it is killed by moist heat at 55° C. within an hour, and by 0·5 per cent. phenol in a comparatively short time.

The fermentation reactions of this organism do not appear to have received much attention. Serologically, suspensions from blood-agar cultures are agglutinated by a specific antiserum ; this reaction may be used for identification.

There appears to be little doubt that Ducrey's bacillus is responsible for soft chancre, and for the buboes which are sometimes associated with the primary lesion. Tomasczewski (1903) was successful in reproducing the disease in human subjects with pure cultures. Ulcerative lesions have likewise followed the inoculation of monkeys and rabbits with cultures several generations removed from primary isolation (Reenstierna 1921, Nicolle 1923).

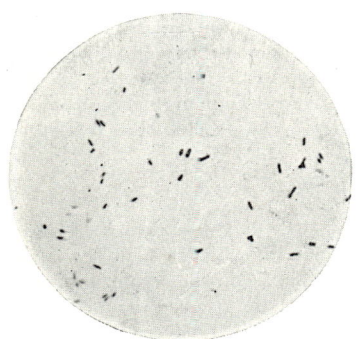

Fig. 192.—*Bacterium pneumo-sintes.*

From a surface growth on blood agar anaerobically, 12 days, 37° C. (× 1000).

Bacterium pneumosintes.

Isolated by Olitsky and Gates (1921a, b, c, 1922a, b) from the nasopharyngeal washings of patients in the early stage of influenza, and since observed by certain other workers (Hall 1926). It is a very small organism and is capable of passing through Berkefeld N and V candles.

MORPHOLOGY.—In Smith-Noguchi medium on first isolation, it is described as consisting of minute bodies, arranged singly, in pairs, or short chains ; its length is given as 0·15-0·3 μ, and its breadth as two or three times less. After subculture for some time in the laboratory, the organisms appear in dextrose peptone broth as plump rods with rather pointed ends, arranged in pairs end-to-end, and in fairly long chains. It may be 0·5-1·0 μ long ; it stains more deeply in the middle than at the ends. Our own observations on one of Olitsky and Gates's original strains, grown anaerobically for 12 days on blood agar, show that it is a very small straight rod-shaped organism, 0·5-1·0 μ long by 0·2-0·3 μ broad, with parallel sides and rounded ends ; it is arranged singly, in pairs end-to-end, and in small dense groups. No irregular forms are seen ; it stains regularly with the usual aniline dyes, is Gram-negative, and non-motile (Fig. 192).

CULTURALLY, the organism can be isolated only in Smith-Noguchi medium (human ascitic fluid containing a piece of sterile rabbit kidney, and covered with a vaseline seal) ; but after three or four subcultures in this medium it can be brought to grow anaerobically on blood agar, chocolate agar, Fildes' agar, Bordet's medium, and certain other media.

Smith-Noguchi Medium at 37° C.—A faint haze becomes visible around the kidney about the 5th day, and reaches a maximum about the 8th day, when it is 3 cm. deep. These appearances are not characteristic ; they often appear in uninoculated tubes.

Horse Blood Agar.—7 *days*, 37° C. Round, convex, milky-white opaque colonies, 0·5 mm. in diameter, of amorphous structure, and with a smooth glistening surface and an entire edge ; butyrous in consistency and easily emulsified ; no hæmolysis.

Horse Blood Agar or Chocolate Agar Slope.—12 *days*, 37° C. Slightly raised, partly confluent, glistening growth with an irregular surface, due to imperfect fusion, and an edge made up of very tiny discrete colonies.

Bordet's Medium.—12 *days*, 37° *C.* Slightly raised, confluent, glistening growth with a finely pitted surface.

Glycerol Egg.—7 *days*, 37° *C.* Good, slightly raised, glistening, viscous growth with a smooth surface and an entire edge.

Loeffler's Serum.—7 *days*, 37° *C.* Similar to growth on glycerol egg, but not so abundant.

Trypsinized Heart Agar Slope, and Glycerol Agar Slope.—7 *days*, 37° *C.* Rather poor, slightly raised, confluent, nearly colourless, translucent growth with an irregular surface due to imperfect fusion ; edge made up of single colonies.

Trypsinized Heart Broth.—7 *days*, 37° *C.* Poor to moderate, uniform turbidity, with a moderate, highly viscous deposit, which, on shaking, coheres in a ropy mass and is difficult to disintegrate. No surface growth ; slightly aromatic odour.

Fildes' Broth.—7 *days*, 37° *C.* No turbidity, but slight powdery deposit disintegrating on shaking. After 14 days the deposit is viscous, coherent, and difficult to disintegrate.

Nitrate Broth.—7 *days*, 37° *C.* Slight turbidity ; moderate, viscous deposit, disintegrating completely ; no surface growth.

Serum Broth.—Growth similar to that in heart broth.

Coli-Broth.—5 *days*, 37° *C.* (Prepared by growing a strain of *Bact. coli* in 1 per cent. dextrose broth till the first sign of turbidity appears ; the culture is then steamed for half an hour.) Moderate to dense turbidity ; moderate viscous deposit, very difficult to disintegrate.

RESISTANCE.—Cultures in Smith-Noguchi medium, after 5 to 7 days' incubation at 37° C., remain viable at room temperature for $2\frac{1}{2}$ years. Cultures in coli-broth become sterile in about a week. The organisms withstand freezing, and drying *in vacuo*, and appear to remain alive for a long time when dried. Infected lungs of rabbits, kept in 50 per cent. glycerol at 4° C., remain virulent for 9 months. The organism is destroyed by moist heat at 56° C. in 30 minutes, and by chloroform vapour in 1 to $1\frac{1}{2}$ hours.

METABOLISM.—Strict anaerobe. Grows best at 37° C. ; no growth at room temperature. When used to artificial conditions, it grows best on Fildes' agar and blood agar ; it also grows well in coli-broth. In our experience it does not grow on the V or X factors, either alone or in combination (see Chapter XXX). Does not hæmolyse horse blood. Optimum pH for growth 7·6 ; limits 7·0–8·0.

BIOCHEMICAL.—Acid is produced in dextrose. Indole negative. Nitrates not reduced. Catalase negative. Methylene blue reduction negative.

SEROLOGICAL.—Agglutinins are formed by injection of cultures into rabbits, but a serological study of different strains of the organism has not been made.

PATHOGENICITY.—Was originally suspected of being responsible for human influenza, but is now regarded as having no causal relationship to this disease. Is mildly pathogenic for rabbits, but loses its virulence after artificial culture for some time in the laboratory. Injection of mass cultures intratracheally into rabbits produces a rise of temperature in 24 hours ; usually a conjunctivitis, and a mononuclear leucopænia. The symptoms disappear in 2 to 3 days, and the rabbit recovers. If killed during the reaction, the rabbits are found to have voluminous lungs, affected with œdema and emphysema. Numerous hæmorrhages, discrete or diffuse, are seen on the surface of the lungs. The pleura is not involved. On section the lungs drip a frothy, blood-stained fluid, and hæmorrhages are seen scattered through the parenchyma. The trachea and bronchi contain a muco-purulent exudate, covering an exfoliated and hæmorrhagic epithelium. The organisms may be recovered from the lungs in pure culture, using Smith-Noguchi medium. Much the same reaction is produced by intratracheal inoculation of guinea-pigs. Nonpathogenic to monkeys, injected intratracheally or subconjunctivally.

Several other tiny anaerobic bacilli have been isolated from the nasopharynx of healthy and diseased persons, differing from *Bact. pneumosintes* in cultural reactions, pathogenicity, and certain other respects (Olitsky and Gates 1922*b*, Gates 1926). Olitsky and McCartney (1923) found them in the nasal washings of persons with colds and in normal persons. Mills, Shibley and Dochez (1928) found them in 75 per cent. of normal persons. This high percentage was observed only when buffered broth was used for the nasal irrigation ; Ringer's fluid gave much lower figures. The bacilli were of variable morphology, and appeared by agglutination tests to belong to several different types. In this country Garrod (1928) has demonstrated similar filter-passing, anaerobic, Gram-negative organisms in the upper respiratory tract of both healthy and diseased subjects. He states that morphologically they appear either as very tiny cocci, about ⅙ the diameter of a staphylococcus, or as very short, sometimes curved bacilli. These organisms can be cultivated anaerobically on rabbit blood agar.

Bacterium granulosis.

This organism was isolated by Noguchi (1927) from American Indians suffering from trachoma. It is a very small Gram-negative bacillus, with a tendency to pointed ends and a diploid arrangement. In young blood-agar cultures it measures 0·8–1·2 μ in length and 0·2–0·3 μ in breadth. In older cultures large irregular involution forms are common. In the condensation water of blood-agar slopes the organism is actively motile by a single polar flagellum. It has a superficial resemblance to *C. xerosis*, but it is smaller, Gram-negative, and motile. It was first cultivated on semi-solid leptospiral medium, in which it gives rise to a diffuse nebulous greyish-white growth in the uppermost centimetre, extending for some distance down the stab. No growth occurs on agar, but on horse blood agar incubated at 30° C. minute, shiny, almost transparent or slightly greyish, circular, convex colonies are evident in 48 hours, which later increase in size and acquire a greyish opalescence and a viscous consistency. Growth occurs best at 30° C., and hardly at all at 37° C. ; the lower limit appears to be about 15° C. The optimum H-ion concentration for growth is pH 7·8, and the range 6·8–8·8. No growth occurs under strict anaerobic conditions. When freshly isolated the organism is devoid of fermentative activity, but after cultivation in the laboratory for some months it is said to produce acid from a number of sugars. Indole is not formed ; nitrates are reduced to nitrites ; and gelatin is not liquefied. It is destroyed by heat at 57° C. in 10 minutes (Olitsky 1930). The organism is non-pathogenic for laboratory animals, but when inoculated subconjunctivally into *rhesus* monkeys it gives rise to a granular conjunctivitis simulating trachoma (see Chapter LXXVI). (For a fuller description of this organism see Noguchi 1928, Tilden and Tyler 1930.)

A Gram-negative bacillus simulating *Bact. granulosis* in many respects has been described under the name of *Bact. simiæ* by Olitsky, Syverton, and Tyler (1933), who isolated it from monkeys suffering from spontaneous conjunctival folliculosis. Like *Bact. granulosis*, which it resembles in size, it is motile by a single polar flagellum, produces a nebulous opacity in leptospiral medium, fails to grow anaerobically, has an optimum growth temperature of 30° C., and is non-pathogenic for laboratory animals. It differs, however, from this organism in having a capsule, in growing on plain nutrient agar, in fermenting different carbohydrates, in failing to reduce nitrates, and in showing no agglutination with *granulosis* antisera. What relation *Bact. granulosis* and *Bact. simiæ* bear to Ducrey's bacillus, and to the less exacting members of the *Hæmophilus* group, has still to be determined.

Bacterium monocytogenes and related Organisms

In 1926 Murray, Webb, and Swann at Cambridge described a disease of rabbits characterized by a large mononuclear leucocytosis, and caused by a small Gram-positive non-sporing bacillus which they termed *Bact. monocytogenes*. Similar organisms have since been isolated by Pirie (1927) from a plague-like disease of gerbilles in South Africa, by Gill (1933) from a disease of sheep in New Zealand known as " circling," by Jones and Little (1934) from cases of bovine encephalitis in New Jersey, by Tenbroeck (1932) from a sporadic disease of chickens in New

Jersey, and by Burn (1933–34, 1935) from meningeal infections in human beings in the United States. These organisms are characterized by their ability to give rise on injection into chickens, rabbits, and guinea-pigs to an increase in the circulating mononuclear cells, and by their tendency to localize in the myocardium and cause a massive necrosis (Seastone 1935). Pirie suggested for them the generic name *Listerella*, and this has been adopted by certain American workers. Until, however, these organisms have been studied more fully, and compared with members of the *Erysipelothrix* group, which they resemble in many respects, it is probably wiser not to label them prematurely. We give a description of the chief member of the group, *Bact. monocytogenes*.

Bact. monocytogenes

MORPHOLOGY.—In smears and sections of the tissues it is a small, Gram-positive rod, with rounded ends, and 1–2 μ in length. In cultures it is 1–4 μ in length, and about 0·5 μ broad ; axis is usually straight, but sometimes curved. Arranged in packets, and often in pairs lying at an angle to each other, like a V. Sluggishly motile, apparently by a single polar flagellum. Non-sporing ; non-capsulated. Stains fairly uniformly, but sometimes shows beading. Non-acid-fast. No clubbing or branching has been observed. Occasional short filaments, up to 10 or 12 μ in length, are seen in cultures.

CULTIVATION.—Growth is poor on the ordinary media, but is enhanced by liver extract, glucose and glycerol. Aerobe ; grows very poorly under strictly anaerobic conditions. Grows readily at 37° C., and quite well at 18–20° C. Cultures have a penetrating, rather unpleasant, acid smell.

Liver Extract Agar.—24 *hours*, 37° *C*. Colonies are very small, dew-drop-like, and almost transparent. After 2 or 4 days the colonies are round, 1·5–2·5 mm. in diameter, slightly flattened, with a smooth surface, appearing transparent by transmitted and milky white by reflected light ; rather viscous in consistency, but emulsify easily.

1 *per cent. Glucose Peptone Agar.*—Growth similar to that on liver extract agar.

1 *per cent. Peptone Agar.*—Growth is thinner and poorer.

Gelatin Stab.—Slow growth, filiform, not liquefying the gelatin ; no surface growth.

1 *per cent. Peptone Broth.*—Flocculent growth tending to deposit.

Inspissated Ox Serum.—Very thin transparent film.

Dorset's Egg.—An even thinner film than on ox serum.

Glycerol Potato.—No apparent growth.

RESISTANCE.—Killed by moist heat at 55° C. within an hour. Cultures remain viable for several months. Organisms, when dried under reduced pressure, may remain alive for at least 4 months.

BIOCHEMICAL.—Acid produced rapidly in glucose and salicin, and often, though more slowly and weakly, in maltose, sucrose, lactose, and glycerol. No action on mannitol. L.M. slight acid formation and decolorization of the litmus. Indole — ; Nitrates not reduced to nitrites ; H_2S — ; M.R. + ; V.P. — ; Catalase + ; M.B. not reduced in broth. Gelatin not liquefied.

ANTIGENIC STRUCTURE.—Most strains of different animal origin are similar antigenically (Seastone 1935).

PATHOGENICITY.—Produces a disease in rabbits, guinea-pigs, and probably certain other rodents characterized by a large mononuclear leucocytosis (see Chapter LXXVI). Intravenous inoculation of large doses into rabbits may produce death within a week with signs of involvement of the central nervous system. At post mortem there are multiple focal necroses in the liver, abscesses in the myocardium, and extensive inflammation of the meninges (see Burn 1935).

Bact. alkaligenes and Vibrio alkaligenes.

Petruschky (1896) isolated from human fæces an organism that produced an alkaline reaction in certain media, and was named by him *Bact. fæcalis alkaligenes*. It was described as a Gram-negative bacillus, and has long been included by most authorities in the genus *Bacterium* under the name of *Bact. alkaligenes*. Though it appears to be an almost constant inhabitant of the intestinal tract of man, this organism may give rise to infections of the enteric type (Petruschky 1896, Hirst 1917, Khaled 1923).

The characters usually ascribed to *Bact. alkaligenes* are as follows : The cells are very variable in size, but are usually larger and thinner than those of *Bact. coli* (5–7 μ × 0·4 μ), and the ends are less definitely rounded. The bacilli are motile, with peritrichate flagella. The colonies on agar are flatter than those of *Bact. coli*, and more contoured, with a raised central portion and a spreading undulate edge. Neither acid nor gas is produced in any of the usual test substrates. Litmus milk is rendered strongly alkaline. A characteristic brown colour is produced on potato.

Many of these characters are very unlike those of the genus *Bacterium*, and doubts have been frequently expressed as to its real systematic affinities. A recent study by Nyberg (1935) raises even stronger doubts as to whether the strains that have been described under this name can be regarded as forming a bacterial entity. Nyberg examined with great care 134 strains labelled *Bact. alkaligenes*, and was able to distinguish among them two quite distinct forms, and a number of less well-differentiated types. The form for which he would reserve the name *Bact. alkaligenes* is a short, thick bacillus, usually non-motile or very feebly motile, but possessing in most cases poorly formed peritrichate flagella. It fails to ferment dextrose, lævulose, lactose, maltose, saccharose, rhamnose, xylose, arabinose, mannitol, sorbitol, dulcitol, inositol or salicin. It does not form indole, and it produces no change in milk. Of the 134 strains examined, 71 were of this type. Nyberg notes that this description does not agree with that given of *Bact. alkaligenes* in many books and papers, and that it is impossible to be certain that his strains correspond to the organism originally isolated by Petruschky. He considers, however, that they probably belong to the same species, and that the name must certainly be given to them and not to the type to which his other strains belong.

This second type is a long, thin, slightly curved rod, actively motile by lophotrichate flagella. It is therefore not a bacillus, but a vibrio. Unlike the former type, it renders a dextrose medium slightly but definitely alkaline. Nyberg regards this organism as identical with the *Vibrio alkaligenes* of Lehmann and Neumann (1896) ; and there would seem no doubt that this is its proper name. It also seems very probable, as Nyberg emphasizes, that many of the strains that have been isolated by various workers, and have been given the description summarized earlier, were *Vibrio alkaligenes*, not *Bacterium alkaligenes*.

Bartonella, Eperythrozoon, and Grahamella

Various bodies have been described by different workers in close association with the red blood corpuscles of man and animals suffering usually, though not always, from certain types of anæmia. The evidence that *Bartonella* and *Eperythrozoon* are living reproducible micro-organisms capable of giving rise under favourable conditions to disease is now very strong, but considerably less is known about the *Grahamella*, and it would be unwise to assert at the moment that these bodies are definite bacteria. The interest that *Bartonella muris* particularly has stimulated of recent years is due to the remarkable part played by the spleen in the normal defence mechanism of the host (see Chapter LXXVI).

Bartonella bacilliformis.

This organism is a small bacillus, which invades the red blood cells, and is responsible for Peruvian **Oroya fever** and for **verruga peruviana** (see Chapter LXXVI). It was called *Bartonella bacilliformis* by Strong and his colleagues (1915) in honour of Barton, who was one of the first to observe the bacillus in the red cells. Noguchi and Battistini in 1926 cultivated the organism, and reproduced a disease in monkeys bearing a close resemblance to the natural disease in human beings. The organism was recovered in pure culture from the blood of the injected monkeys.

Morphologically, in culture, it is a small pleomorphic bacillus, varying in length from 0·3–2·5 μ and in breadth from less than 0·2 to as much as 0·5 μ. Dumb-bell forms predominate, and coccoid forms are common. It is arranged singly and in dense masses. It is motile, Gram-negative, and stains reddish-violet with Giemsa. Cultivation can be effected on the semi-solid serum hæmoglobin agar medium used for leptospiræ, and on horse blood agar slopes. It is aerobic, grows well at 25–37° C., prefers a pH of 7·8, and survives in cultures for 1 to 4 months. Injected intravenously into young *rhesus* monkeys it gives rise to a peculiar, irregularly remittent type of fever, sometimes accompanied by severe anæmia ; injected intradermally into the eyebrow, it gives rise to a nodule rich in cellular elements and capillary formation. (For further description see Noguchi 1926, Kikuth 1931.)

Bartonella muris.

This organism was first described by Mayer (1921), who found it in the blood cells of rats experimentally infected with trypanosomes. Morphologically it closely resembles *Bartonella bacilliformis*. It is actively motile in culture media, and flagella have been demonstrated. On blood agar minute colonies appear in 48 hours, and gradually increase in size till after a few days they coalesce to form a thin, filmy, tenacious growth on the surface of the medium. The blood is not hæmolysed.

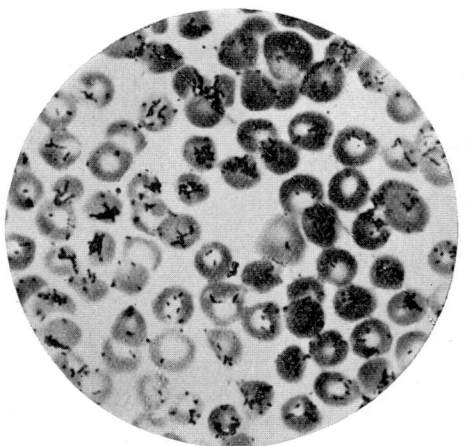

Fig. 193.—*Bartonella muris.*

Organisms in red blood cells of rat (× 1000). [From specimen kindly supplied by Professor J. G. Thomson.]

Cultures on solid media have a sweet odour resembling canned pineapple. The optimum temperature for growth is 25° C. In infected blood the organisms are destroyed by exposure to a temperature of 57° C. for 30 minutes (Ford and Eliot 1928). Pure cultures inoculated into splenectomized rats give rise to anæmia (see Chapter LXXVI). The organism is fairly common in rats, causing an infection which normally remains latent, but which can be activated by splenectomy, by poisons such as toluylendiamine, and by certain infections (for general description see Lauda and Marcus 1928, Marmorston-Gottesman and Perla 1932, Kikuth 1931, 1934).

Bartonella canis.

A similar organism has been described under this name by Kikuth (1928), which is responsible for infectious anæmia of dogs. In the red cells the organisms are very pleomorphic, large and small, coccoid and rod-shaped forms being seen. Kikuth was unsuccessful in cultivating them on artificial media. (See Kikuth 1929, Pérard 1929, Lwoff and Provost 1929, Regendanz and Reichenow 1932, and Chapter LXXVI.)

Eperythrozoon coccoides.

This is a parasite of mice which was discovered independently by Dinger (1928, 1929), and Schilling (1928). A considerable proportion of normal mice appear to be infected, but the organisms are rarely found unless the spleen is removed. Two to four days after splenectomy the organisms appear in the blood in the form of rings or discs stuck on to the external surface of the red blood corpuscles, and staining a bluish-purple colour with Giemsa. Unlike *Bartonella muris*, they have a preference for polychromatic red cells. They may persist in the blood for weeks or months, their numbers varying from time to time. Beyond producing a slight degree of anæmia, they seem to be without any very definite effect on the animal. Mice infected with *Eperythrozoon coccoides* are susceptible to *Bartonella muris*, showing that the two organisms are distinct (see also McCluskie and Niven 1934, Schwetz 1934, Marmorston 1935).

Grahamella.

This parasite was first described by Graham-Smith (1905) at Cambridge, who observed it in the red blood cells of 10 per cent. of moles that were being examined for *Piroplasma*. They appear as longer or shorter rods of irregular contour lying within the red corpuscles. Though resembling the *Bartonella*, they are much coarser, and more like ordinary bacteria. With Giemsa they take on a blue rather than a reddish tint. Only occasional red cells are affected. The organisms appear to be non-pathogenic and to have no influence on the health of the host. They are not influenced by splenectomy. They have not so far been cultivated, and though it is probable that they are living micro-organisms, the evidence in favour of this is not yet conclusive (see also Kikuth 1934).

REFERENCES

AXENFELD, T. (1897) *Zbl. Bakt.*, **21**, 340.
BURN, C. G. (1933–34) *Proc. Soc. exp. Biol., N.Y.*, **31**, 1095 ; (1935) *J. Bact.*, **30**, 573.
DINGER, J. E. (1928) *Ned. Tijdschr. Geneesk.*, No. 48, **72**, 5903 ; (1929) *Zbl. Bakt.*, **113**, 503.
EYRE, J. W. (1900) *J. Path. Bact.*, **6**, 1.
FORD, W. W. and ELIOT, C. P. (1928) *J. exp. Med.*, **48**, 475.
GARROD, L. P. (1928) *Brit. J. exp. Path.*, **9**, 155.
GATES, F. L. (1926) *J. exp. Med.*, **44**, 787.
GILL, D. A. (1933) *Vet. J.*, **89**, 258.
GRAHAM-SMITH, G. S. (1905) *J. Hyg., Camb.*, **5**, 453.
HABABOU-SALA, J. (1925) *C. R. Soc. Biol.*, **92**, 498.
HALL, M. W. (1926) *J. exp. Med.*, **44**, 539.
HIRST, L. F. (1917) *J. R. Army med. Cps*, **29**, 476.
HUNT, G. A. (1935) *Proc. Soc. exp. Biol., N.Y.*, **33**, 293.
JONES, F. S. and LITTLE, R. B. (1934) *Arch. Path.*, **18**, 580.
KHALED, Z. (1923) *J. Hyg., Camb.*, **21**, 362.
KIKUTH, W. (1928) *Klin. Wschr.*, **7**, 1729 ; (1929) *Zbl. Bakt.*, **113**, 1 ; (1931) *Z. ImmunForsch.*, **73**, 1 ; (1934) *Proc. roy. Soc. Med.*, **27**, 1241.
LAUDA, E. and MARCUS, H. (1928) *Zbl. Bakt.*, **107**, 104.
LEHMANN, K. and NEUMANN, R. (1896) " Atlas und Grundriss der Bakteriologie, etc." J. F. Lehmann, Munich.
LWOFF, A. and PROVOST, A. (1929) *C. R. Soc. Biol.*, **101**, 8.
McCLUSKIE, J. A. W. and NIVEN, J. S. F. (1934) *J. Path. Bact.*, **39**, 185.
MARMORSTON, J. (1935) *J. infect. Dis.*, **56**, 142.
MARMORSTON-GOTTESMAN, J. and PERLA, D. (1932) *J. exp. Med.*, **56**, 763.
MAYER, M. (1921) *Arch. Schiffs- u. Tropenhyg.*, **25**, 150.
MILLS, K. C., SHIBLEY, G. S., and DOCHEZ, A. R. (1928) *J. exp. Med.*, **47**, 193.
MORAX, V. (1896) *Ann. Inst. Pasteur*, **10**, 337.
MURRAY, E. G. D., WEBB, R. A., and SWANN, M. B. R. (1926) *J. Path. Bact.*, **29**, 407.
NICOLLE, C. (1923) *C. R. Soc. Biol.*, **88**, 871.
NICOLLE and DURAND. (1924) *Arch. Inst. Pasteur, Tunis*, **13**, 243.
NOGUCHI, H. (1926) *J. exp. Med.*, **44**, 533, 697, 715, 729 ; (1927) *J. Amer. med. Ass.*, **89**, 739 ; (1928) Monograph on Trachoma ; *J. exp. Med.*, **48**, No. 2, Suppl. No. 2.

NOGUCHI, H. and BATTISTINI, T. S. (1926) *J. exp. Med.*, **43**, 851.
NYBERG, C. (1935) *Zbl. Bakt.*, **133**, 443.
OLITSKY, P. K. (1930) *Trans. 35th ann. Meeting Amer. Acad. Ophthal. Oto-Laryngol.*, p. 225.
OLITSKY, P. K. and GATES, F. L. (1921*a*) *J. exp. Med.*, **33**, 125 ; (1921*b*) *Ibid.*, **33**, 361 ; (1921*c*) *Ibid.*, **33**, 713 ; (1922*a*) *J. exp. Med.*, **35**, 813 ; (1922*b*) *Ibid.*, **36**, 501.
OLITSKY, P. K. and McCARTNEY, J. E. (1923) *J. exp. Med.*, **38**, 427.
OLITSKY, P. K., SYVERTON, J. T., and TYLER, J. R. (1933) *J. exp. Med.*, **57**, 871.
PÉRARD, C. H. (1929) *C. R. Soc. Biol.*, **100**, 1111.
PETIT, P. (1900) " Recherches cliniques et bactériologiques sur les infections aiguës de la cornée." Thèse de la Faculté de Médecine de Paris. G. Steinheil, Paris.
PETRUSCHKY, J. (1896) *Zbl. Bakt.*, **19**, 187.
PIRIE, J. H. H. (1927) *Publ. S. Afr. Inst. med. Res.*, **3**, 163.
REGENDANZ, P. and REICHENOW, E. (1932) *Arch. Schiffs- u. Tropenhyg.*, **36**, 305.
REENSTIERNA, J. (1921) *Acta. derm-venereol., Stockh.*, **2**, 1 ; (1923) *Arch. Inst. Pasteur, Tunis*, **12**, 273.
SCHILLING, V. (1928) *Klin. Wschr.*, **7**, 1853.
SCHWETZ, J. (1934) *Zbl. Bakt.*, **132**, 211.
SEASTONE, C. V. (1935) *J. exp. Med.*, **62**, 203.
STEIN, R. O. (1928) See Kolle and Wassermann, " Hdb. path. Mikroorg.," IIte Aufl., 1928–9, **6**, 185.
STRONG, R. P., TYZZER, E. E., BRUES, C. T., SELLARDS, A. W., and GASTIABURU, J. C. (1915) *Rep. 1st Expedition S. America*, 1913. Harvard Univ. Press, Cambridge, Mass.
TENBROECK. (1932) See Seastone (1935).
TILDEN, E. B. and TYLER, J. R. (1930) *J. exp. Med.*, **52**, 617.
TOMASCZEWSKI, E. (1903) *Z. Hyg. InfektKr.*, **42**, 327.

CHAPTER XXXV

THE SPIROCHÆTES

The name Spirochæte was first given by Ehrenberg in 1833 to a large flexible motile organism occurring in water ; it is now used as a general term for all elongated, motile, flexible organisms that are twisted spirally around their long axis. Though the spirochætes vary greatly in size, they all possess certain features in common : thus they possess no flagella ; they exhibit no antero-posterior polarity (*i.e.* they can move either forwards or backwards) ; they contain no colouring matter and no cyanophycin granules ; they show no definite localized nucleus ; they divide transversely, division being either simple or multiple ; and they exhibit no sexual phenomena of reproduction. These properties bring them closely into line with the Bacteria, to which they are more nearly related than to the Protozoa. Indeed, as Dobell (1912) points out, while there are many features in which they differ from the Protozoa, there is only one feature that differentiates them from the bacteria, namely motility without flagella.

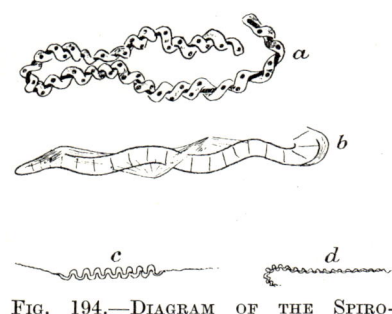

Fig. 194.—Diagram of the Spirochætes.

a. Spirochæta.   *b. Cristispira.*
c. Treponema.   *d. Leptospira.*
(After Noguchi.)

Without entering into the disputed question of their classification, it is convenient for descriptive purposes to divide the spirochætes into four groups—*Spirochæta, Cristispira, Treponema,* and *Leptospira.*

Spirochaeta.—The members of this group possess an axial fibre, around which the body is twisted in a spiral manner, in just the same way as a spiral staircase is built round the newel. The organism possesses a series of regular primary spirals ; during motion a series of secondary waves may be superimposed on these, but whatever form the organism as a whole may assume, the primary spirals remain intact. Metachromatic granules of volutin are distributed uniformly throughout the length of the organism. The type species, *Spirochæta plicatilis* Ehrenberg, is usually 200–500 μ in length and 0·5–0·7 μ in thickness (Wenyon 1926). The number of primary spirals is 100 to 250, the distance between successive turns being about 2 μ. So far no members of this group have been found to be capable of causing disease.

Cristispira.—The peculiar characteristic of members of this group is the possession of a band-like membrane or *crista*, which runs in a spiral manner along the organism.

714

This membrane is extremely thin; its width is much the same as that of the organism itself, except at the ends, where it narrows down to fuse with the surface pellicle. The body of the organism is divided into chambers by septa of thickened cytoplasm, and on either side of each septum, or sometimes distributed irregularly through the more fluid cytoplasm in the chambers, are a number of metachromatic granules. The type species, *Cristispira balbianii*, is found in the crystalline style of the oyster; it is about 45–100 μ long and 1–1·5 μ broad (Wenyon 1926). Other species have been found in a similar situation in other Mollusca.

Treponema.—Members of this group possess neither an axial fibre nor a crista. According to some observers the body is divided up into chambers like that of a *Cristispira*, but this is by no means certain. The presence of metachromatic granules is doubtful. The organism shows a number of primary spirals, which may be closely or loosely wound; during movement secondary turns may develop, but at rest these disappear so that the organism is straight. The ends may be rounded or pointed, and in some members it is possible to distinguish a thin drawn-out filament at the ends; this is probably not a true flagellum, but the remains of the thin connecting bridge of cytoplasm that is seen during transverse division. *Treponemata* are widely distributed; numerous species have been described in water, in the gut of certain insects such as white ants and cockroaches, and in the large gut of the toad; in human beings they are found in the mouth, sometimes in the alimentary tract and the bronchi, around the urethral orifice, in certain ulcerating conditions of the skin, in condylomata, in the blood of patients with relapsing fever, and in the manifold lesions of syphilis. They vary considerably in size; thus *Treponema termitidis* Leidy is 20–60 μ long and 0·5 μ broad; on the other hand, *Treponema parvum* may be only 3 μ in length and 0·2 μ in thickness (Dobell 1912).

Leptospira.—The members of this group possess neither axial filament nor crista; their cytoplasm is not obviously chambered. They show, however, a large number of closely wound, primary spirals; this differentiates them from the *Treponemata*, the spirals of which are fewer and less closely wound. Moreover, the *Leptospiræ* frequently have their ends turned round at a sharp angle to the rest of the body. When the organism is at rest the ends appear characteristically hooked; but when it is in motion, rotating round its long axis, the ends take on the appearance of button-holes, the narrow pointed end of the button-hole being attached to the body of the organism, the wider and rounded end being free. During motion secondary curves often appear and disappear in rapid succession, giving the organism a resemblance to a C, O, S, or other curved letter. The primary spirals are absolutely regular, and remain intact throughout all the various contortions executed by the organism as a whole. The *Leptospiræ* are widely distributed in water, and can be easily demonstrated in it by simple cultural methods (Hindle 1925). They are found in the tissues of patients with Weil's disease and seven-day fever. In length they vary from about 6–85 μ, but are generally about 9–12 μ; their thickness is only about 0·1 μ. The length of the middle portion is variable, but the hooked ends are always of about the same size, suggesting that growth may occur only in the middle portion (Zuelzer 1925).

The brief account that has been given of the different groups is necessarily dogmatic, and it may well be that further work will necessitate a revision of our present classification.

General Characteristics of the Spirochætes

Spirochætes have no flagella ; they are nevertheless motile.   Three kinds of movement are generally described : (1) Movements of flexion, in which the whole organism undergoes a change in shape.   As a rule the natural shape of a spirochæte at rest is straight ; but during movement all sorts of twists and turns may develop, one form following another in rapid succession, but each one tending to return to the normal straight form.   During these movements of flexion the primary spirals remain unaltered.   (2) Movements of rotation around the long axis ; these are difficult to see unless the ends of the organism are bent at an angle to the main axis, when the rotatory movement is especially apparent.   When the rotation is very rapid, and when as in *Leptospira* the ends are hooked, the spirochæte may take on the appearance of a spiral thread with a button-hole at each end.   (3) Movements of translation, by which the organism changes its position, moving from one place to another.   This change in place is probably dependent upon the rotatory movement, which acts like a propeller driving the organism forwards or backwards according to the direction of the rotation.

Different spirochætes vary greatly in their activity ; some, for example, exhibit very active movements of flexion, lashing furiously in various directions, but making very little progress from their original position ; others dart rapidly hither and thither, rendering their ocular pursuit almost impossible.

Multiplication occurs by transverse fission.

Generally speaking, the spirochætes are more difficult to stain than the bacteria. Methylene blue, which is usually a satisfactory bacterial stain, leaves many of the spirochætes unstained.   It has been suggested that the spirochætes are devoid of nucleo-protein, and to the absence of this substance has been ascribed the failure of the *Treponemata* and all the known *Leptospiræ* to stain with this dye.   On the other hand, the fact that an organism does stain with methylene blue is not definite proof that it contains nucleic acid (Zuelzer 1925).   The spirochætes that stain with methylene blue are generally coloured blue by Giemsa, whereas those that do not are generally coloured red.   But the exact tint that results from Giemsa's stain depends to some extent on the medium in which the organism is grown ; thus in the blood, *Trep. recurrentis* stains blue with occasional reddish granules, whereas in culture it stains red.   In the larger spirochætes it is possible by such stains as Giemsa's and iron hæmatoxylin to bring out the finer details of structure, but in the smaller ones this is practically impossible.   The reaction to Gram's stain is negative, though this stain is rarely used in practice.

For the demonstration of spirochætes in tissue-sections Levaditi's method is one of the most successful.   It depends on the ability of the organisms, when treated with silver nitrate followed by reduction with a formol-pyrogallic acid mixture, to become impregnated with metallic silver, and therefore to appear black.   By this means spirochætes can be easily distinguished from bacteria, protozoa, and artefacts.   For the demonstration of spirochætes in films the Fontana method of silver impregnation is most useful.

Many species, particularly the *Leptospiræ*, are able to pass through the usual bacterial filter candles.   This property they owe to their extreme tenuity.   Exact measurements by Hindle and Elford (1933), made with graded collodion membranes, show that the width of *Trep. pallidum* is about 0·2 μ and of *Lepto. biflexa* 0·1 μ. Use is often made of their filtrability to separate them from contaminating bacteria.

The cultivation of spirochætes *in vitro* is not so simple as that of most bacteria. Nearly all the methods that have proved successful involve the use of a medium containing native animal protein, such as blood, serum, or ascitic fluid. Whether this acts chemically as a nutrient material, or physically as a protective colloid preventing the organisms from being poisoned by the products of their own metabolism, is not clear. A further requirement for many spirochætes is a low oxygen pressure ; this is obtained by culturing them in narrow tubes containing a high column of medium ; or by adding a piece of sterile kidney, which produces an area of anaerobiosis in its neighbourhood (Theobald Smith's method). It is usual to cover the medium with a layer of paraffin oil ; this was at first believed to prevent the ingress of oxygen, but it appears now that this explanation is incorrect. The beneficial action of the oil probably depends partly on the prevention of evaporation of water from the medium, and partly on the prevention of the loss of CO_2 from the medium, which would otherwise become progressively more alkaline (Gates and Olitsky 1921, Kligler and Robertson 1922). Spirochætes have been cultivated mainly in liquid or in semi-solid media. Colony production on the surface of solid media under aerobic or anaerobic conditions has been reported by a few workers (Twort 1921, Gates 1923, Aksjanzew-Malkin 1933), but in general little success has been obtained with this method.

Multiplication occurs rather slowly, and may not be evident for a week or more. When a clear medium is used, growth may be evident from the appearance of a faint turbidity ; but generally microscopical examination is necessary, particularly for motility and signs of transverse division. Most spirochætes seem to prefer a slightly alkaline medium, about pH 7·2–7·6. Subculture has to be performed every few days as a rule, the exact time depending on the particular organism. In young cultures the organisms are actively motile and under dark-ground illumination appear uniformly refractile ; but in older cultures when degeneration sets in, they lose their motility, tend to agglutinate into clumps, and become granular ; the granules, some of which result from a change in the cytoplasm within the organism, and some of which are probably particles of the culture medium adhering to their exterior, are more highly refractile than the rest of the spirochæte, and show up as bright, glistening points. Some observers consider that these granules are not the result of degeneration, but are analogous to bacterial spores, affording a means of continuing life under unfavourable environmental conditions. The evidence in favour of this view is not convincing.

With some organisms, such as *Leptospira icterohæmorrhagiæ*, *in vitro* culture is remarkably successful ; but with organisms such as *Trep. pallidum* and *Trep. recurrentis* it is not so satisfactory. For this reason these organisms are generally preserved by *in vivo* culture ; that is to say, they are injected into a susceptible animal, which henceforth becomes a chronic carrier, and which can be drawn upon at will for a fresh supply of infective material.

The resistance of spirochætes to inimical agencies is no greater and generally less than that of the vegetative bacteria. Dry heat, moist heat, and desiccation prove quickly fatal, as do comparatively low concentrations of the chemical disinfectants. Some of the highly parasitic members, such as *Trep. pallidum*, are unable to survive outside the animal body for more than an hour or two. Indeed this particular organism is extremely susceptible to heat, being destroyed in an hour at 41·5° C. Advantage is now being taken of this property to sterilize the organisms in the tissues by exposure to fever-heat temperatures (see Chapter LXXVIII).

Practically nothing is known about the metabolism of spirochætes. Scheff (1935), who made observations on two strains of *Trep. pallidum*, one of *Trep. recurrentis*, and one of *Trep. anserinum*, stated that, when these organisms were grown in a medium containing glucose, they broke down the sugar to lactic acid and CO_2 without using up any of the oxygen.

Antigenically, spirochætes behave very much as bacteria. They can give rise on injection to agglutinins, spirochætocidins, spirochætolysins, and protective bodies. Agglutination tests are usually conducted by the microscopic method, and observations made on the loss of motility and the clumping of the organisms, which may occur in radiate fashion. Similarly the destruction and lysis of the organisms that frequently follows contact with a highly immune serum are generally watched under the microscope. Protective bodies in serum are tested for in the usual way by animal inoculation.

A valuable method of study is afforded by the test described by Rieckenberg (1917), known sometimes as the *thrombocytobarin reaction* or the *adhesion phenomenon*. It depends on the fact that if a suspension of blood platelets or bacteria is added to a mixture of a spirochæte and its specific antiserum, and the preparation is observed under dark-ground illumination after preliminary incubation at 30° C. for 20 minutes, the platelets or bacteria are seen to have become adherent to the spirochætes in the form of small clumps. In the presence of a non-specific serum no such clumping or adhesion occurs. By this reaction it is possible to distinguish rapidly between two such closely-allied forms as *Lepto. icterohæmorrhagiæ* and *Lepto. hebdomadis* (Brown and Davis 1927). Living motile spirochætes are required and fresh complement must be present. The specific antibody is destroyed by heating to 72° C. for 30 minutes (Inoue 1930). Pfeiffer's test and cross-immunity protection tests in animals are likewise of value in distinguishing between closely allied species, and even between variants of the same species.

The virulence of spirochætes appears to be subject to considerable variation. Many members are strictly parasitic and give rise to infections in man or animals, while others are saprophytic and appear to be devoid of any pathogenic effect. There is evidence, however, that the virulence of the parasitic members may undergo change as the result of residence in the body of the host. In relapsing fever, for example, the strains that appear in the blood at the second or third relapses may differ antigenically from the strain responsible for the original attack, and by virtue of this change are able to multiply in the tissues of a host that has become immunized to the original parent strain. Again, strains of certain spirochætes, such as *Trep. pallidum*, may be brought by passage to grow readily in an animal which at first resists their invasion. *Trep. pertenue*, the organism that is responsible for yaws, is regarded by many observers as merely a variant of *Trep. pallidum* which, by residence in the negro, has developed dermotropic affinities (Parham 1922). Residence outside the body of certain parasitic strains may apparently be accompanied by a fall in virulence, which renders them indistinguishable from naturally saprophytic strains. Thus *Lepto. icterohæmorrhagiæ*, if kept in water, may become indistinguishable from *Lepto. biflexa* (Zuelzer 1925). Whether the virulence of naturally saprophytic species ever becomes increased so as to render them pathogenic for man is doubtful. Baermann and Zuelzer (1927, 1928) have brought a considerable amount of evidence to show that *Lepto. biflexa* may be transformed by repeated animal passage into *Lepto. icterohæmorrhagiæ*. Their findings, however, are not in harmony with the experience of most other workers nor with the epidemiological picture of Weil's disease, and it seems probable that such instances are due to the recovery in virulence of a real *icterohæmorrhagiæ* strain.

Though the spirochætes may be classified into the free-living, the commensal, and the pathogenic types, it must be realized that there is no sharp line of demarcation between the three groups. An organism that is pathogenic in one animal may be purely commensal in another, and an organism that is highly pathogenic at one time to a particular host may at another give rise to no more than a latent infection.

We append a description of some of the members that are of most interest to the student of medical and veterinary bacteriology.

Treponema recurrentis

Isolation.—Observed by Obermeier (1873) in the blood of patients with European relapsing fever.

Morphology.—Actively motile spiral organisms, varying considerably in length but usually 10–20 μ long. Series of 5–10 fairly regular but loose primary waves; each spiral is 2–3 μ long and about 1 μ in amplitude (Fig. 195). The width is usually given as 0·2–0·3 μ (Wenyon 1926, Hindle 1931), but this is probably an under-estimate. Personal observations on the organisms in blood have suggested that 0·4 μ more nearly represents their true diameter [1]. After transverse fission the two new organisms may remain connected by a remnant of the periplast. Stains purplish-red with Giemsa. Organisms are said to be shorter and thinner in young culture, thicker and longer in old (Plotz 1917).

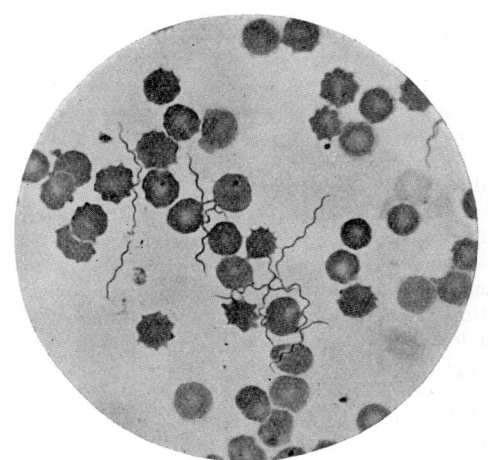

Fig. 195.—*Treponema duttoni.*

In film of blood. In one place the spirochætes show a tendency to agglutination in rosette form. Giemsa. (×1000). [From specimen kindly supplied by Prof. J. G. Thomson.]

Cultivation.—First successfully cultivated by Noguchi (1912e), who seeded a few drops of citrated blood from the heart of an infected mouse or rat into a tube containing 15 c.c. of unheated and unfiltered ascitic or hydrocele fluid and a small piece of sterile rabbit's kidney. The blood was taken from the animal 48 to 72 hours after inoculation. Multiplication of the spirochætes in the cultures was visible in 2 to 3 days, and reached its maximum about the 7th to the 9th day. No change was noticeable in the medium, but actively motile spirochætes could be found in every field, arranged either singly, in chains, or in masses. After about the 9th day a sudden decrease in their numbers occurred, and spherical bodies and irregular protoplasmic masses appeared, indicating that the organisms were undergoing degeneration. Subcultures were most successfully made on the 4th to the 9th days. In 1917 Plotz, using Noguchi's technique, cultivated the organisms from the blood of human patients with relapsing fever. More recently Sinton (1924) claims to have grown the organisms from human patients in a medium of hydrocele fluid or horse serum containing 0·75 per cent. glucose. Kligler and Robertson (1922) have used a medium consisting of horse or rabbit serum diluted with 1 or 2 parts of saline; 1 per cent. of peptone broth is added to the mixture. In initial cultures the animal's blood furnishes a loose

[1] Mr. J. E. Barnard, F.R.S., has kindly measured for us a strain of *Trep. duttoni*; he finds it to be 0·35 μ in diameter.

fibrin network, which seems to be beneficial for the growth of the organisms ; in sub-cultures a drop of fresh rabbit's blood is added. The whole is covered with a layer of liquid paraffin. In this medium the organisms multiply, and remain alive for 3 to 7 weeks, though it is advisable to make subcultures every 2 or 3 weeks. Lapidari and Sparrow (1928) recommend a medium consisting of 20 per cent. rabbit serum and 80 per cent. of Hartley's broth, distributed into narrow tubes, each of which contains 1 gm. of coagulated egg white ; the medium is covered with vaseline. Yuan-Po (1933) has obtained successful results with a medium prepared from coagulated egg white and diluted yolk solution ; a drop of blood is required for each tube. Scheff (1935) has described a synthetic medium in which growth may be obtained. Cultures are best incubated at 30° C. ; at 37° C. degeneration sets in early. Very irregular results are often obtained in culture ; the reasons for this are not clear (Moroder 1929).

Resistance and Metabolism.—Resistance is apparently similar to that of the more sus-ceptible vegetative bacteria. Little is known about metabolism. According to Scheff (1935), glucose is broken down with production of lactic acid and CO_2, but no oxygen is used up. A moderate partial pressure of oxygen, however, is required for growth ; there is no multiplication under strict anaerobic conditions.

Antigenic Structure.—Little exact information. Some evidence that " relapse " strains differ from the parent strain.

Pathogenicity.—Causes European relapsing fever in human beings. Infection can be transmitted to monkeys, rats, and mice, but not to rabbits or guinea-pigs. In monkeys the disease runs much the same course as in man. Two or three days after subcutaneous inoculation with the patient's blood a pyrexial attack occurs, lasting for 3 or 4 days ; two, three, or four relapses may occur at intervals of 2 to 8 days, each relapse lasting from 1 to 4 days (Norris *et al.* 1906). After intraperitoneal inoculation of mice the organisms appear in the blood within 24 hours, and persist for 3 to 4 days ; they then disappear for several days, after which a relapse may occur ; three or four relapses may follow each other, separated by an interval of about 7 days (Novy and Knapp 1906). As many as 10 to 50 organisms may be present per field during the first infection, but in the relapses only 1 or 2 organisms are seen as a rule. Intraperitoneal inoculation of white rats is followed by the appearance of spirochætes in the blood in about 40 hours ; they disappear about 2 days later. The spirochætes are found not only in the blood, but in all the organs of the body. Infection is never fatal. Novy and Knapp (1906) state that rats never relapse.

Numerous strains of relapsing fever spirochætes have been isolated in different parts of the world. As these exhibit certain antigenic differences from *Trep. recurrentis*, they have been regarded as different species and named accordingly. Thus we have *Trep. duttoni* of Central Africa, *Trep. novyi* of America, *Trep. kochi* of East Africa, *Trep. carteri* of India, and several others.

Treponema anserinum

Described by Sakharoff (1891), who observed it in the blood of infected geese. Mor-phologically it closely resembles *Trep. recurrentis*. In blood its mean length is about 14 μ, and the mean number of coils about five (Knowles *et al.* 1932). The organism was cultivated by Noguchi (1912*g*), using his ascitic-fluid rabbit kidney medium. Growth reaches its maximum about the 5th day, after which degeneration sets in ; death is usually complete in 3 weeks. Growth occurs best at 30° C. Subcultures should be made every 4 days. In culture the organism is said to be 8–16 μ long, 0·3 μ wide, and to show rounded spirals, each of which is about 1·8 μ long and 1 μ in amplitude. According to Landauer (1931) and to Knowles and his colleagues (1932), one of the best media for its cultivation is that devised by Galloway (1925) ; this consists of coagulated egg white to which dilute in-activated serum is added. In early cultures blood is advantageous. No growth occurs anaerobically. *Trep. anserinum* is pathogenic for birds, but not for rodents. Intramuscular inoculation of fowls with 0·5 c.c. of infected blood gives rise to acute spirochætosis in 24 hours. A high mortality occurs. Spirochætes are numerous in the blood (Knowles *et al.* 1932).

Treponema vincenti

Described by Vincent (1896, 1899), who observed it in the throat of patients suffering from Vincent's angina. This organism is very delicate, about 5–10 μ long, and has 3 to 8 irregular spirals. In cultures filamentous forms are common. It stains poorly but uniformly, is Gram-negative, and is actively motile. It can be cultivated under anaerobic conditions in serum agar or in serum broth. Growth occurs most readily at 37° C. ; there is no growth at room temperature. In serum agar, colonies appear in 3 days, and are very tiny and tenacious (Ellermann 1904). Injected subcutaneously into guinea-pigs, the organisms are generally without effect (Tunnicliff 1906). It is not clear whether *Trep. vincenti* is responsible for the necrotic lesions in human beings in which it is found, or whether it is a mere secondary invader. Since the organism may sometimes be demonstrated in the depths of the infected tissues, it is possible that it may possess actual invasive properties (Ellermann 1907). It is very frequently found in association with a characteristic fusiform bacillus, likewise described by Vincent (1896, see Chapter XVII). It has been suggested (Tunnicliff 1906) that *Trep. vincenti* and the fusiform bacillus represent two phases of the same organism ; but the balance of evidence is definitely against this view.

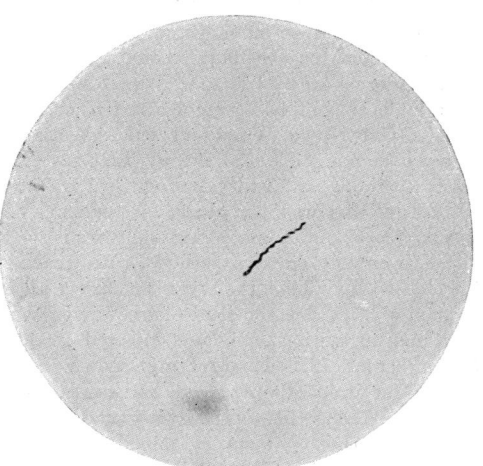

Treponema pallidum

Isolation.—Described by Schaudinn and Hoffmann (1905), who observed it in chancres and inguinal glands of syphilitic patients (see Schuberg and Schlossberger 1930).

Morphology.—Thin, delicate spirochæte with tapering ends. Its length varies from 4–14 μ, and its breadth

FIG. 196.—*Treponema pallidum.*
In material scraped from a hard chancre. Fontana.
(× 1000).

is about 0·2 μ. It contains a number of regular primary spirals, which appear rather sharp and angular, and each of which is a little over 1 μ in length. During motion secondary curves may appear and disappear in rapid succession, but the primary spirals remain undisturbed. The organism is actively motile ; the movements were originally described by Schaudinn and Hoffmann (1905) as being of 3 types : (1) rotation round the longitudinal axis ; (2) backward and forward movements ; (3) flexion movements of the whole body, resulting in the production of secondary waves. The rotation or spinning movement is responsible for the backward or forward movements ; the primary spirals act like the blades of a propeller and drive the organism forward. No flagella have been demonstrated. In cultures the morphology is not so regular as in the animal body ; Noguchi (1912c) has described three types of *pallidum*—the thicker, the normal, and the thinner type. Whether these types are constant, or merely represent fluctuations round a mean, is not known ; Noguchi favours the former view. The organism stains rose-red with Giemsa. The organisms are held back by gradocol membranes having a pore size of 0·4 μ ; their narrowest diameter is therefore about 0·2 μ (Hindle and Elford 1933).

Cultivation.—Schereschewsky (1909) was the first to cultivate *Trep. pallidum in vitro*, but he did not succeed in obtaining pure cultures. Noguchi in 1911 was the first to do this. He used a medium of serum water to which a piece of sterile rabbit tissue had been added ; the medium was seeded with a fragment of syphilitic rabbit's testicle, and the whole was covered with a layer of liquid paraffin. Incubation was carried out anaerobically at 37° C. The primary mixed culture was later purified by growth in serum agar stabs containing fresh rabbit tissue ; in this medium a hazy zone around and above the tissue became perceptible in about 3 days due to proliferation of the spirochætes ; by subculture from this zone he eventually succeeded in obtaining pure cultures of the organism. The following year Noguchi (1912b) succeeded in cultivating *Trep. pallidum* directly from human lesions. The medium he used consisted of a mixture of 2 parts of nutrient agar and 1 part of ascitic or hydrocele fluid, put up in tubes 20 × 2 cm. in size, each containing at the bottom a piece of sterile rabbit kidney or testicle. Material from a chancre, condyloma, or skin papule was inoculated into the tube, and was covered with liquid paraffin. The organisms produced a slight haze round the kidney and could be picked off for purification. In fluid medium growth occurred very slowly and continued for several weeks. The pure cultures were inoculated into monkeys, and proved to be pathogenic. According to Gates (1923), surface colonies may be obtained on 6 per cent. rabbit blood agar plates incubated anaerobically. Colonies are said to be well developed in about a week at 37° C., and to be surrounded by a zone of complete hæmolysis. Other media have since been used with apparent success (Gates 1923, Weiss and Wilkes-Weiss 1924, Hoder 1930, Aksjanzew-Malkin 1933). It must be pointed out, however, that several reputable workers have entirely failed to cultivate *Trep. pallidum*. Among them is Jahnel (1934), who maintains that the so-called cultures of this organism are in fact cultures of a saprophytic spirochæte. The difficulty in practice of obtaining *in vitro* cultures is so great that for preserving the organism it is usual to employ *in vivo* methods. Brown and Pearce (1921b) found that if rabbits are infected with syphilis, the organisms are carried to the lymphatic glands and remain there indefinitely. When the strain is required for use, a popliteal gland is excised, ground up in a mortar with saline, and injected intratesticularly into fresh rabbits. Kolle and Schloszberger (1928) have recently shown that *Trep. pallidum* remains alive in the tissues of mice for an indefinite period, and can be recovered at any time from the glands, spleen, or brain. Using this method they made three passages through mice in 19 months, and found that the organisms remained fully virulent for rabbits.

Resistance.—Very susceptible to heat. According to Boak, Carpenter, and Warren (1932), saline suspensions of infected rabbit testicle are sterilized by exposure to 39° C. for 5 hours, 40° C. for 3 hours, 41° C. for 2 hours, and 41·5° C. for 1 hour.

Antigenic Structure.—Little known. Noguchi and Akatsu (1917), using agglutination and complement fixation, obtained evidence of an affinity of *Trep. pallidum* to *Trep. calligyrum*. They also observed a certain amount of heterogeneity between different strains of *pallidum*. There is said to be a strain-specificity in cultures of *pallidum* (see Georgi *et al.* 1929), but in view of the serious criticisms that have been made on the supposed cultivation of this organism, it would be dangerous to lay too much stress on this statement.

Pathogenicity of Treponema pallidum for Animals.

RABBITS.—Haensell in 1881 was the first to produce keratitis in rabbits by inoculation of syphilitic material into the anterior chamber of the *eye*. His observations were neglected for over 20 years, when they were confirmed by Bertarelli in 1906 ; the syphilitic nature of the lesions was proved by the demonstration in them of *Treponema pallidum*. The receptivity of the rabbit's *eye* has been confirmed by numerous workers. Bertarelli (1907, 1908) moreover showed that it was possible to carry over syphilis from one animal to another. According to Uhlenhuth and Mulzer (1913) inoculation of a small piece of syphilitic rabbit's cornea into the anterior chamber of the eye of a fresh rabbit is followed by complete healing of the local wound in 5 to 10 days. After 3 to 6 weeks, as a rule, pericorneal congestion commences, followed by pannus and keratitis. The keratitis increases to an acme, after which retrogression and healing occur ; this process may take weeks or months to complete, and may be interrupted by a relapse. Only a certain proportion of rabbits develop keratitis. The lesion is very much easier to produce by inoculation of rabbit than of human syphilitic material. Successive passages of the virus through the eye of rabbits resulted in an increase of virulence, manifested by a reduction in the incubation period from 6 to 8 weeks to 4 to 5 weeks.

Syphilis may also be conveyed to rabbits by inoculation into the *testicle* ; this method of transference was first successfully used by Parodi (1907). As with ocular injection, the implantation of human syphilitic material gives much less constant results than of that from the rabbit. Uhlenhuth and Mulzer (1913), for example, inoculated 27 rabbits intratesticularly with human syphilitic material—the juice from primary chancres—and obtained only 5 positive reactions. But after 15 passages through the rabbit the virulence had so increased that inoculation was almost uniformly successful, and the severity and extent of the disease were correspondingly greater. Brown and Pearce (1920a), using the method of intratesticular inoculation of ground-up syphilitic rabbit's testicle suspended in saline, were likewise uniformly successful in producing the disease. After an incubation period of about 3 to 4 weeks the testicle commences to swell, and soon reaches the size of a pigeon's egg ; the inflammation also affects the epididymis and cord. Sometimes a small superficial erosion may develop at the site of inoculation, covered with a dry yellowish-brown adhesive crust ; or an actual chancre may appear. According to Brown and Pearce (1920a) the testicular reaction pursues a cyclic or relapsing course, periods of active progression alternating with periods of quiescence or retrogression ; these phases apparently correspond with the variations in the number of spirochætes in the lesion. The length of time that the testicle is inflamed varies ; the lesion may disappear in 6 weeks, or it may last for over a year.

The method of intracutaneous or subcutaneous injection of rabbit syphilitic material into the *scrotum*, introduced by Tomasczewski (1910), gives rise after an incubation period of about a fortnight to a typical primary chancre with a central necrotic area and indurated edges. Sometimes a diffuse lesion of the scrotum follows. These scrotal lesions are invariably accompanied by marked inguinal lymphadenitis. The scrotal infection may spread, and numerous secondary lesions develop, lasting from 1 to 18 months.

Following on scrotal or testicular infection, generalized lesions may develop affecting practically any structure of the body (Brown and Pearce 1920b, 1921a, Brown et al. 1921). Thus there may be : papular or erythematous eruptions on the skin, sometimes appearing in successive crops ; granulomatous lesions of the skin passing on to ulceration ; alopecia, onychia, and paronychia ; necrotic and ulcerative lesions of the mucosæ and mucocutaneous borders ; localized lesions of the periosteum, bone, cartilage, tendons, and tendon sheaths, including such typical manifestations as destruction of the nasal septum and separation of the epiphyses ; conjunctivitis, keratitis, and iritis. Generalized lesions of syphilis may also be produced by the intravenous or intracardial injection of rabbits a few days old (Uhlenhuth and Mulzer 1913). For discussion of immunity in rabbit see p. 911, Chapter XLVIII.

Monkeys.—The experiments of Metchnikoff and Roux (1903, 1904a, b, 1905) amplified the earlier observations of Klebs in 1875–77 (see Klebs 1932), and showed that syphilis might be transmitted to the anthropoid apes, and with less certainty to monkeys. Of the apes the *chimpanzee* appeared to be the most susceptible. Altogether they inoculated 22 chimpanzees (*Troglodytes niger* and *T. calvus*) with syphilitic material, either of human origin or derived from experimental animals, and succeeded in producing disease in all of them. Inoculation was performed by scarification of the genitals, the thigh, or the eyebrow. After an incubation period of 15 to 49 days, generally 4 weeks, a primary chancre developed at the site of inoculation, and was followed in a few days by swelling of the focal lymph glands. Many of the animals developed lesions of secondary syphilis 3 to 9 weeks after the appearance of the chancre ; these comprised a papular eruption on the skin, palmar psoriasis, mucous plaques of the lips, tongue, and palate, and enlargement of the spleen.   Occasionally very severe syphilis developed, accompanied by alopecia, skin eruptions, emaciation, paresis of the hind-limbs, or even death.   No lesions of tertiary syphilis were ever found ; but it is to be noted that most of the animals died of broncho-pneumonia before they had been many weeks under observation, and in these tertiary lesions had no time to develop.   In macaques secondary lesions were never observed. According to Uhlenhuth and Mulzer (1913) apes are more difficult to infect than rabbits. These workers were successful in conveying human syphilis to rabbits, from rabbits to monkeys, and from a monkey back to rabbits.

OTHER ANIMALS.—For studying syphilitic lesions, chimpanzees and rabbits are the most useful experimental animals.   Infection can, however, be conveyed to certain other animals, such as pigs, guinea-pigs, rats and mice.   According to Tani, Kakishita, and Saito (1930), intratesticular inoculation of *guinea-pigs* gives rise to no obvious lesions, but intracutaneous inoculation, particularly into the perineal fold, is followed in about 11 days by the develop-ment of a swelling which persists for about 7 weeks (see also Mulzer and Hahn 1930).   In *rats* and *mice* a symptomless infection is usually produced, similar to that often seen in guinea-pigs.   The spirochætes remain latent in the tissues for months, as can be shown by inoculation of rabbits (Kolle and Schloszberger 1926, 1928).   Occasionally, however, a local chancre may be produced by inoculation of the scarified skin of the ano-scrotal region (Bessemans and de Potter 1930, 1931).

Treponema cuniculi

First observed by Bayon (1913).   Responsible for a disease known as " rabbit syphilis." Morphologically very similar to *Trep. pallidum*, but tends to be slightly longer and thicker. According to Noguchi (1922), dimensions are : length 7–30 μ, average 13 μ ; width 0·25 μ ; length of spirals 1–1·2 μ ; amplitude of spirals 0·6–1·0 μ.   Like *Trep. pallidum* it stains rose-red with Giemsa.   Inoculation of infective material on to the scarified skin of the genital region is followed, after an incubation period of 2 to 8 weeks, by characteristic lesions (see Chapter LXXVIII).

Notes on certain other Treponemata found in the Human or Animal Body.

Treponema pertenue.—Described by Castellani (1905).   Responsible for yaws.   Mor-phologically indistinguishable from *Trep. pallidum*.   Exact relation to this organism not yet fully understood.

Treponema refringens.—This organism was first described by Schaudinn and Hoff-mann (1905) in their original report on the discovery of *Trep. pallidum*.   It was observed in cases of syphilis complicated with such lesions as balanitis, ulcers, and papillomata, and in non-syphilitic lesions such as gonorrhœal papillomata.   Noguchi (1912d) culti-vated it from a condyloma.   According to him it grows luxuriantly in the deeper part of an ascitic agar tube, forming hazy colonies, denser than those of *Trep. pallidum*, which gradually extend from the deeper parts of the tube to the more superficial.   It is an anaerobe ; no growth occurs within 2 cm. of the surface.   Growth becomes visible in 4 days at 37° C. and proceeds for some weeks.   The addition of fresh tissue is not essential. In culture the organism is 6–24 μ long by 0·5–0·75 μ broad ; the middle part of the organism is wavy, but the two extremities are more regularly and deeply curved.   The ends are pointed.   It is non-pathogenic for rabbits and monkeys.

Treponema calligyrum.—This organism was observed by Noguchi in 1913 in two cases of condyloma, one syphilitic, the other not.   Pure cultures were obtained by the ascitic agar stab method.   In this medium growth is similar to that of *Trep. refringens*; the hazy colonies are more dense and diffuse than those of *Trep. pallidum*.   In culture the organisms are 6–14 μ long by 0·35–0·4 μ wide.   The primary spirals are regular and deep ; the length of each spiral is 1–6 μ, and the amplitude 1 to 1·5 μ.   The apex of the curve is not sharp and pointed as in *pallidum*, but more or less rounded.   It is non-pathogenic for rabbits and monkeys.

Treponema phagedenis.—This organism was cultivated by Noguchi (1912*f*) from a phagedenic ulcer on the labium of a woman. Growth occurred in ascitic agar medium under anaerobic conditions in the absence of kidney tissue. In the original lesion the spirochætes were 4–30 *μ* in length and 0·75 *μ* in thickness ; in culture their length was less variable, being 10–15 *μ*. The number of spirals varies from one to eight, and there is great variation in the length of each spiral. Some organisms appear nearly straight. The ends are pointed, but not drawn out. Other spirochætes have been described in ulcerative lesions round the genital regions, such as *Trep. balanitidis*, *Trep. pseudo-pallidum*, and *Trep. gangrenosa nosocomialis* (see Noguchi 1912*f*).

Spirochætes in the Human Mouth.—Spirochætes of different types have been described in the mouth ; they can generally be seen in scrapings from between the teeth. Sometimes organisms morphologically indistinguishable from *Trep. pallidum* are found. Noguchi (1912*a*) succeeded in cultivating what he regards as two separate species. *Trep. microdentium* is a short spirochæte about 3–4 *μ* long by 0·25 *μ* wide, having shallow rectangular curves of constant size. The ends are drawn out and pointed. In serum agar tissue medium it forms a haze near the bottom of the tube, gradually becoming denser and spreading upwards till it is within 2–3 cm. of the surface. Growth is anaerobic. *Trep. macrodentium* is a larger organism, varying from 3–8 *μ* long by 0·7–1·0 *μ* broad in young cultures, and having 2–8 irregular shallow curves ; the ends taper off abruptly. In older cultures the organisms are longer and thinner. In serum agar tissue medium growth occurs under anaerobic conditions in the form of a faint almost transparent haze.

Vinzent and Daufresne (1934), working mainly with pure cultures, have provisionally classified the mouth spirochætes into groups, which they label A to G. Group B corresponds to *Trep. microdentium* and Group F to *Trep. macrodentium*.

Treponema cobayae.—Found by Knowles and Basu (1935) in the blood of guinea-pigs. Blood parasite belonging to the relapsing fever group. Thin, delicate spirochæte, 13·5–23 *μ* in length, with finely tapering ends ; average length of spirals 3·6 *μ*. Can be cultivated in Galloway's medium. Inoculation of guinea-pigs with infected blood is followed, after an incubation period of 2 to 6 days, by a febrile disease accompanied by the presence of spirochætes in the blood. Fully virulent strains kill 30–60 per cent. of inoculated animals. Relapses may occur in animals that recover from the first attack. White rats and rabbits are also susceptible to infection.

Blood spirochætes have been described in other animals, such as the rabbit and the mouse (see Knowles and Basu 1935).

Leptospira icterohæmorrhagiæ

Isolation.—First adequate description given in 1915 by Inada and his colleagues in Japan (see Inada *et al.* 1916), who observed it in the blood and tissues of patients with Weil's disease.

Synonyms.—*Spirochæta icterohæmorrhagiæ ; Spirochæta icterogenes.*

Morphology.—Very delicate organism whose morphology can be studied satisfactorily only by dark-ground illumination. The spirals are too fine to be properly resolved in stained preparations. In length it is about 6–12 *μ*, and 0·1–0·15 *μ* in thickness ; forms as short as 4 *μ* and as long as 25 *μ* may sometimes be observed. It contains a number of perfectly regular closely-wound spirals, each of which is about 0·5 *μ* long or even less, and has an amplitude of 0·5 *μ*. Near the extremities the spirals become even closer. Secondary waves commonly appear during motion, but the spirochæte has a marked tendency to straighten itself out again. Apart from the primary spirals, which are set more closely than in any other group of spirochætes, the most characteristic feature of *Lepto. icterohæmorrhagiæ* is its sharp, tapering, hooked ends, which are set at an angle to the main axis, giving the whole organism a resemblance to the letter C or S. During the rotation that occurs when the organism is moving, these hooked ends are whirled round so rapidly that the organism appears to be furnished with a button-hole or an eye-splice at each extremity (Fig. 197). In fluid media the spirochætes may become entangled with each other and give rise to the characteristic picture of a "nest." This appears as a highly refractile ball composed of hundreds of interlaced organisms, some of which project radially from the circumference (Taylor and Goyle 1931). In dry-fixed films of blood or urine all sorts of forms may be seen, bearing a resemblance to the letters C, S, *l*, or *b*. Degeneration forms with thick, blunt, straight ends are not uncommon. According to Kaneko and Okuda (1917), the morphology of the spirochætes in man is less regular than in the guinea-pig ; they are often shrunken and atrophic, of varying thickness, with greater rigidity and less regular curves ; they may show circumscribed thickenings at two or three points, or they may resemble chains of granules. These irregular forms may perhaps result from the action of immune bodies on the organisms.

In suitable preparations the spirochætes may be stained by Giemsa or by one of the silver impregnation methods. In stained films the primary spirals are not visible. According to Hindle and Elford (1933), the organisms are held back by collodion membranes having a porosity of 0·25 μ ; this suggests that their diameter is 0·1 μ.

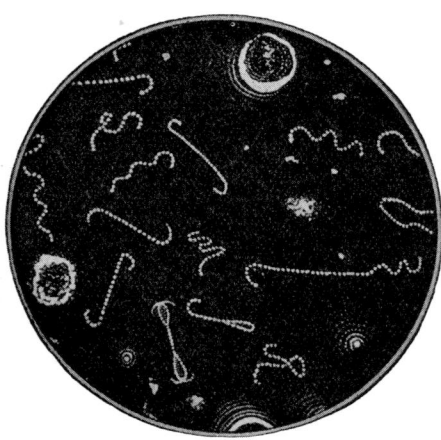

FIG. 197.—*Lepto. icterohœmorrhagiœ.*
Diagrammatic drawing showing primary and secondary spirals, and hooked and button-hole ends. (After Wenyon.)

Cultivation.—*Leptospira icterohœmorrhagiœ* was first cultivated by the Japanese workers (Inada *et al.* 1916) in Noguchi's ascitic fluid kidney medium. Subsequently Noguchi (1917) devised other media that were simpler to make and more satisfactory in practice. The first consists of rabbit serum 1 part, Ringer's solution 3 parts, and citrated rabbit plasma 0·5 parts ; the medium should be put up in tubes about ⅜-inch in diameter, and may or may not be covered with liquid paraffin. The second medium is similar to the first, but 0·5–1·0 parts of slightly alkaline 2 per cent. agar are added, at a temperature of 60–65° C., the whole medium being well mixed. From this semi-solid medium the citrated rabbit plasma may be omitted if necessary. The Noguchi-Wenyon medium is likewise satisfactory; it is made by mixing 9 parts of saline with 1 part of 2 per cent. nutrient agar, and adding 20 drops of fresh rabbit's blood to each 10 c.c. of the autoclaved medium cooled to 50° C. ; the tubes are not shaken. Very good results are obtained with Fletcher's (1928) medium. This is prepared by heating a 12 per cent. solution of rabbit serum in distilled water to 50° C., adding 6 c.c. of 2·5 per cent. nutrient agar to every 100 c.c. of serum-water mixture, adjusting the reaction to pH 7·4, tubing in 5 c.c. quantities, and sterilizing at 56° C. for 1 hour on 2 successive days. For inoculation, 0·1 c.c. of infected guinea-pig's blood, guinea-pig liver, or rat-kidney emulsion should be used. The tubes should be incubated at 25–30° C. ; growth occurs at 37° C., but degeneration rapidly sets in. Subcultures should be made every 4 to 6 weeks, and kept at 25° C. The optimum pH for growth is 7·6. The organism is aerobic ; in Noguchi's serum media, growth occurs at the top, giving rise to a slight haze, which stops abruptly a few centimetres from the surface.

Resistance.—*Leptospira icterohœmorrhagiœ* is killed by moist heat at 50–55° C. in half an hour ; it can withstand freezing. It is very sensitive to acid, being destroyed by human gastric juice in 30 minutes ; it will not grow in an even slightly acid medium. The organisms are rendered motionless in 10 to 15 minutes by 1/2000 HgCl₂ and are gradually dissolved. They are rapidly destroyed by bile. In defibrinated blood kept at room temperature in the light, the organisms remained virulent for 7 days, and in decomposing liver for 27 hours (Uhlenhuth and Fromme 1916). In infected guinea-pig liver kept in the ice-chest they remained virulent for 26 days (Buchanan 1927). Several observers have found that *Leptospiræ* may pass through Berkefeld candles (Inada *et al.* 1916, Bauer 1927, Buchanan 1927, Dimitroff 1927), but the results are variable. The more exact work of Hindle and Elford (1933) shows that they will pass through collodion membranes having an average pore size greater than 0·25 μ.

Antigenic Structure.—Our knowledge is very incomplete. If a large number of strains of *Lepto. icterohæmorrhagiæ* are tested against a number of sera from patients infected in different parts of the world, or against specially prepared immune sera, a considerable variation in their behaviour is noted. Most strains are agglutinated by most sera, though not always to titre, while some strains are agglutinated by certain sera but not by others (Schlossberger *et al.* 1935). This suggests that the *icterohæmorrhagiæ* spirochætes contain a number of partial antigens which are unevenly distributed in different strains. Antigenically *Lepto. icterohæmorrhagiæ* appears to differ from the other leptospiral strains that are pathogenic for human beings. Its relation to water spirochætes is still under discussion. Baermann and Zuelzer (1928) found that water strains were not agglutinated by the sera of convalescents from Weil's disease, or by the sera of animals inoculated experimentally with *Lepto. icterohæmorrhagiæ*, and that sera prepared against avirulent water strains did not agglutinate Weil strains. Brown and Davis (1927), using the adhesion test (see p. 718), found that *Lepto. icterohæmorrhagiæ* from rats or man behaved alike, while *Lepto. biflexa* was serologically distinct. Vaccination of guinea-pigs with cultures of *Lepto. biflexa* failed to immunize them against *Lepto. icterohæmorrhagiæ* (Uhlenhuth and Zuelzer 1921). According to Baermann and Zuelzer (1928), however, some water strains, the virulence of which has been raised by animal passage, behave antigenically like *Lepto. icterohæmorrhagiæ*. Some of the confusion is probably due to the lack of homogeneity among water strains. The majority of these are saprophytes and belong to the species *Lepto. biflexa*. Some of them, however, appear to be real *icterohæmorrhagiæ* strains, either in their normal virulent condition or in a degenerate avirulent condition. Passage through animals may succeed in restoring these to full virulence, rendering them indistinguishable antigenically from typical *icterohæmorrhagiæ* strains of parasitic origin. Since animals not infrequently act as leptospiral carriers, it is possible that apparent changes in antigenic structure and virulence brought about by passage are due to the isolation of an organism from the animal different from that which was inoculated. Caution must therefore be exercised in drawing conclusions from the type of evidence advanced by Baermann and Zuelzer (1928) and Zuelzer (1930).

Pathogenicity of Lepto. icterohæmorrhagiæ for Animals.

Lepto. icterohæmorrhagiæ is highly pathogenic for guinea-pigs, whether administered intraperitoneally, subcutaneously, cutaneously, or by the mouth. Rabbits, rats, and mice are only slightly susceptible, and usually remain perfectly well after inoculation (Martin and Pettit 1919). Cats, dogs, pigs, sheep, hens, pigeons, and monkeys are said to be refractory (Uhlenhuth and Fromme 1916, Martin and Pettit 1919), but recent evidence suggests that *Lepto. icterohæmorrhagiæ* is responsible for some cases of infectious jaundice in the dog (Dhont *et al.* 1934).

Intraperitoneal injection of guinea-pigs with 1–2 c.c. of infected human blood or ground-up rat's kidney is followed by an illness lasting for 5 to 12 days, and terminating in death. The chief symptoms of the disease are fever and jaundice. The fever commences the day after inoculation, reaches its acme in a few days, falls to normal, and finally to subnormal just before death. Jaundice first becomes visible when the temperature begins to fall— usually on the 4th or 5th day ; it increases till death, and is often accompanied by choluria. Anæmia and conjunctival congestion are frequent, and external hæmorrhages from the rectum, nose, and genitals may occur. Blood counts reveal a lymphocytosis during the first few days of the disease, and an anæmia (Buchanan 1927). Spirochætes appear in the blood about the 4th day, but are not easy to find microscopically. Post mortem, the animal shows generalized jaundice ; there are hæmorrhages into various parts of the body, particularly the lungs, intestinal walls, retroperitoneal tissues, and fatty tissues of the inguinal region. The hæmorrhages in the lungs form irregular spots of varying size, sharply demarcated from the surrounding tissue—giving the lungs a resemblance to the mottled wings of a butterfly (Inada *et al.* 1916). The spleen is enlarged and congested ; the kidneys show an acute parenchymatous nephritis and capsular hæmorrhages ; the suprarenals are often enlarged and hæmorrhagic. Histologically the chief lesions are cloudy swelling of the liver, sometimes accompanied by focal necroses, acute parenchymatous nephritis, endothelial cell proliferation in the spleen and lymph glands, and hæmorrhages in practically every structure of the body (Buchanan 1927). Spirochætes are most numerous in the liver, and are best demonstrated by Levaditi's or Fontana's method. They occur in the spaces between the cells, and when numerous are arranged about the cells like a garland.

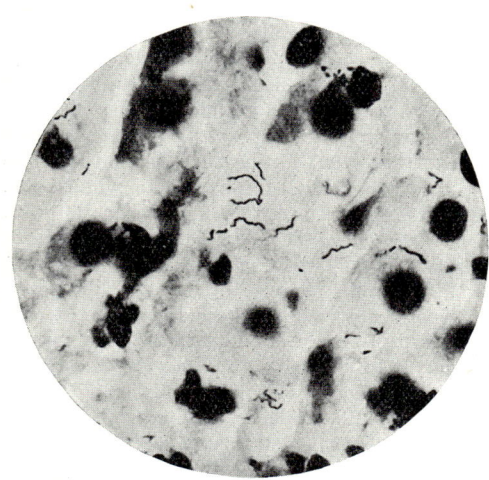

Their appearance is different from that seen under dark-ground illumination ; they are short and thick ; the primary spirals and tapering extremities are not evident, and numerous irregular undulations are seen. They are found in smaller numbers in the kidneys and adrenals.

By passage from guinea-pig to guinea-pig the virulence of the organism can apparently be increased. Stokes (Stokes *et al.* 1917), for example, found that the average time to death of animals inoculated intraperitoneally with human blood was 10 days, but that when passage strains were used it was only 5 days. Noguchi (1917) likewise noticed a reduction in survival time after passage of a strain through guinea-pigs.

Fig. 198.—*Leptospira icterohæmorrhagiæ.*
In section of liver of experimentally infected guinea-pig. Levaditi. (× 1000).

Notes on other species of Leptospira

Leptospira canicola. — This is a natural parasite of dogs, in which it gives rise either to infectious jaundice (see Okell *et al.* 1925), or to a disease affecting mainly the kidneys (see Chapter LXXIX). Is occasionally responsible for Weil's disease in human beings (Schüffner 1934). Closely resembles *Lepto. icterohæmorrhagiæ* but differs in its antigenic structure and in its lower virulence for guinea-pigs.

Leptospira grippo-typhosa.—Appears to be the causative agent of "swamp fever" in Eastern Europe (see Chapter LXXIX). Has been cultivated by Korthof (1932) in a peptone rabbit serum salt mixture medium. Differs antigenically from *Lepto. icterohæmorrhagiæ,* but apparently has some affinity with *Lepto. hebdomadis* (Tarassoff 1935). Is said to be avirulent for mice and only slightly virulent for guinea-pigs (Dinger and Verschaffelt 1930, Schüffner 1934).

Leptospira hebdomadis.—Described by Ido, Ito, and Wani (1918, 1919). Gives rise to the seven-day fever of Japan. Differs antigenically from *Lepto. icterohæmorrhagiæ,* and is less virulent than this organism for the guinea-pig.

Leptospira autumnalis.—Isolated from certain cases of Autumn fever or *Akiyami* in Japan. Two types have been described. The A type very closely resembles *Lepto.*

icterohæmorrhagiæ, and is quite possibly identical with it ; the B type is indistinguishable from *Lepto. hebdomadis* (Stéfanopoulo and Hosoya 1928, Yang and Theiler 1930, Inoue 1930). It is therefore doubtful whether the term *autumnalis* should be retained.

Leptospira biflexa.—Usually referred to by German workers as *Spirochæta pseudoictero-genes.* Widespread saprophyte found mainly in water. Described originally by Wolbach and Binger (1914). Often attached to other spirochætes and protozoa (Zuelzer 1928). Especially prevalent in the slime of ponds, lakes, and rivers, in the slime that collects on the ends of water taps and pipes, and in the roof slime of mines. Morphologically indistinguishable from *Lepto. icterohæmorrhagiæ* (Fig. 199). Is very easy to cultivate. Can thrive in tap or distilled water to which 0·1 per cent. potassium nitrate has been added, provided that the reaction is not acid (Zuelzer 1928). Grows readily in the media used for *Lepto. icterohæmor-rhagiæ* ; but Ringer's solution must be replaced by tap or dis-tilled water, since *biflexa* is very susceptible to even low con-centrations of sodium chloride (Uhlenhuth and Zuelzer 1921). The simplest and most efficient medium is 10 per cent. rabbit serum in distilled water. Isolation in pure culture is often

FIG. 199.—*Lepto. biflexa.*

Dark-ground illumina-tion (× 1500 ca.).

difficult. Hindle (1925) found that if 20 c.c. of water were added to a Petri dish con-taining a portion of human fæces about the size of a pea, and incubated at 25°–30° C. in the dark, *Lepto. biflexa* was generally observable microscopically in 10 days, and was abundant in 20 days. The leptospiræ were able to pass through an L5 candle. These observations formed the basis of several methods of isolation (Bauer 1927, Mochtar 1928, von Vagedes 1935). The general principle is to filter the water through a suitable candle and cultivate the filtrate. Is antigenically distinct from *Lepto. icterohæmorrhagiæ*. A specific precipitating substance of car-bohydrate nature has been extracted from it by Hindle and White (1934). Is non-pathogenic for animals. Is believed by certain workers to be an avirulent form of *Lepto. icterohæmor-rhagiæ*, which can be rendered virulent by suitable animal passage. Balance of evidence is against this view.

Spirillum minus

Sometimes referred to as *Spiro-chæta morsus muris.* Described by Futaki and his colleagues (1916, 1917) as the cause of rat-bite fever in man. According to Robertson (1924), it is a spirillum and not a spirochæte, and its correct name is *Spirillum minus.* Appears to be a natural parasite of rats, which act as healthy carriers of the organism. Morphologically the spirillum is short, rather thick, and has tapering ends, provided with one or more flagella. It is 2–5 μ long,

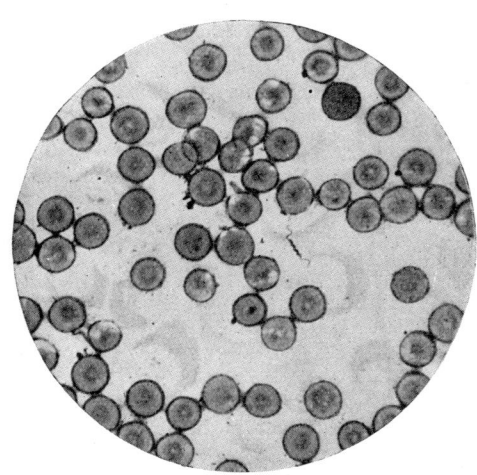

FIG. 200.—*Spirillum minus.*

In film of blood of experimentally infected mouse. Giemsa. (× 1000). [From specimen kindly sup-plied by Dr. J. G. Thomson.]

motile, and has regular spirals, each of which is about 1 μ in length. The movements are very rapid—like those of a vibrio. It is readily stained by ordinary aniline dyes, such as Loeffler's methylene blue, and by Giemsa. Cultures may be obtained in Shimamine's medium, but successive transfers have not been successful. The organism gives rise to one type of rat-bite fever in man. Intraperitoneal inoculation of infective human material into mice is followed by no clinical evidence of disease, but spirilla appear in the blood after 5 to 14 days. They are scarce at first, but later they increase, though they never become numerous ; it is uncommon to find two organisms in the same field (Theiler 1926). They persist indefinitely, though only in small numbers. Rats behave like mice, but the number of spirilla in the blood is fewer. Intraperitoneal inoculation of guinea-pigs produces a febrile disease. After an incubation period of 6 to 15 days spirilla appear in small numbers in the blood, and pyrexia sets in accompanied by enlargement of the lymph glands. There may be a marked inflammation of the subcutaneous tissue in the ano-genital region, involving the scrotal sacs, perianal tissue, and prepuce in males and the labia and perianal tissue in females. Later, after 3 or 4 weeks, alopecia, ulceration of the skin, and chronic conjunctivitis and keratitis may occur. The disease is generally chronic, lasting from about 2 to 4 months, but sometimes death occurs in the first 5 weeks (Ishiwara *et al.* 1917). Spirilla can be demonstrated in the blood, lymph glands, spleen, kidney, adrenal, and subcutaneous tissue. In Robertson's (1924) experience spirilla were never demonstrable in the blood, even by mouse inoculation, nor did any of the guinea-pigs die. Rabbits may be infected, but are less suitable for diagnostic purposes than mice or guinea-pigs. Monkeys are also susceptible (Inada *et al.* 1916).

REFERENCES

AKSJANZEW-MALKIN, S. (1933) *Zbl. Bakt.*, **129**, 405.
BAERMANN, G. and ZUELZER, M. (1927) *Klin. Wschr.*, **6**, 979 ; (1928) *Zbl. Bakt.*, **105**, 345.
BAUER, J. H. (1927) *Amer. J. trop. Med.*, **7**, 177.
BAYON, H. (1913) *Brit. med. J.*, ii. 1159.
BERTARELLI, E. (1906) *Zbl. Bakt.*, **41**, 320 ; (1907) *Ibid.*, **43**, 238, 448 ; (1908) *Ibid.*, **46**, 51.
BESSEMANS, A. and POTTER, F. DE. (1930) *C. R. Soc. Biol.*, **104**, 818 ; (1931) *Ibid.*, **107**, 279.
BOAK, R. A., CARPENTER, C. M., and WARREN, S. L. (1932) *J. exp. Med.*, **56**, 725.
BROWN, H. C. and DAVIS, L. J. (1927) *Brit. J. exp. Path.*, **8**, 397.
BROWN, W. H. and PEARCE, L. (1920*a*) *J. exp. Med.*, **31**, 475, 709, 729, 749 ; (1920*b*) *Ibid.*, **32**, 445, 473, 497 ; (1921*a*) *J. exp. Med.*, **34**, 167 ; (1921*b*) *Ibid.*, **34**, 185.
BROWN, W. H., PEARCE, L., and WITHERBEE, W. D. (1921) *J. exp. Med.*, **33**, 495, 515, 525.
BUCHANAN, G. (1927) *Spec. Rep. Ser. med. Res. Coun., Lond.*, No. 113.
CASTELLANI, A. (1905) *Brit. med. J.*, ii, 1280.
DHONT, C. M., KLARENBEEK, A., SCHÜFFNER, W. A. P., and VOET, J. (1934) *Ned. Tijdschr. Geneesk.*, **78**, 5197.
DIMITROFF, V. T. (1927) *J. infect. Dis.*, **40**, 508.
DINGER, J. E. and VERSCHAFFELT, F. (1930) *Ann. Inst. Pasteur*, **45**, 396.
DOBELL, C. (1912) *Arch. Protistenk.*, **26**, 117.
ELLERMANN, V. (1904) *Zbl. Bakt.*, **37**, 729 ; (1907) *Z. Hyg. InfektKr.*, **56**, 453.
FLETCHER, W. (1928) *Trans. roy. Soc. trop. Med.*, **21**, 265.
FUTAKI, K., TAKAKI, I., TANIGUCHI, T., and OSUMI, S. (1916) *J. exp. Med.*, **23**, 249 ; (1917) *Ibid.*, **25**, 33.
GALLOWAY, I. A. (1925) *C. R. Soc. Biol.*, **93**, 1074.
GATES, F. L. (1923) *J. exp. Med.*, **37**, 311.
GATES, F. L. and OLITSKY, P. K. (1921) *J. exp. Med.*, **33**, 51.
GEORGI, F., PRAUSNITZ, C., and FISCHER, O. (1929) *Klin. Wschr.*, **8**, 2007.
HAENSELL, P. (1881) *v. Graefes Arch. Ophthal.*, **27**, 93.
HINDLE, E. (1925) *Brit. med. J.*, ii. 57 ; (1931) " A System of Bacteriology," Med. Res. Counc., **8**, 148.
HINDLE, E. and ELFORD, W. J. (1933) *J. Path. Bact.*, **37**, 9.
HINDLE, E. and WHITE, P. B. (1934) *Proc. roy. Soc.*, B, **114**, 523.
HODER, F. (1930) *Z. ImmunForsch.*, **68**, 256.
IDO, Y., ITO, H., and WANI, H. (1918) *J. exp. Med.*, **28**, 435 ; (1919) *Ibid.*, **29**, 199.
INADA, R., IDO, Y., HOKI, R., KANEKO, R., and ITO, H. (1916) *J. exp. Med.*, **23**, 377.
INOUE, S. (1930) *Zbl. Bakt.*, **117**, 80.
ISHIWARA, K., OHTAWARA, T., and TAMURA, K. (1917) *J. exp. Med.*, **25**, 45.
JAHNEL, F. (1934) *Klin. Wschr.*, **13**, 550.
KANEKO, R., and OKUDA, K. (1917) *J. exp. Med.*, **26**, 325.
KLEBS, A. C. (1932) *Science*, **75**, 191.

KLIGLER, I. J. and ROBERTSON, O. H. (1922) *J. exp. Med.*, **35**, 303.
KNOWLES, R. and BASU, B. C. (1935) *Indian J. med. Res.*, **22**, 449.
KNOWLES, R., GUPTA, B. M. D., and BASU, B. C. (1932) *Indian J. med. Res.*, Memoir No. 22.
KOLLE, W. and SCHLOSZBERGER, H. (1926) *Dtsch. med. Wschr.*, **52**, 1245 ; (1928) *Ibid.*, **54**, 129.
KORTHOF, G. (1932) *Zbl. Bakt.*, **125**, 429.
LANDAUER, E. (1931) *Ann. Inst. Pasteur*, **47**, 667.
LAPIDARI, M. and SPARROW, H. (1928) *Arch. Inst. Pasteur, Tunis*, **17**, 191.
MARTIN, L. and PETTIT, A. (1919) " Spirochétose ictérohémorragique." Paris.
METCHNIKOFF, E. and ROUX, E. M. (1903) *Ann. Inst. Pasteur*, **17**, 809 ; (1904a) *Ibid.*, **18**, 1 ; (1904b) *Ibid.*, **18**, 657 ; (1905) *Ibid.*, **19**, 673.
MOCHTAR, A. (1928) *Zbl. Bakt.*, **107**, 374.
MORODER, J. (1929) *Arch. Schiffs- u. Tropenhyg.*, **33**, 603.
MULZER, P. and HAHN, C.-F. (1930) *Arch. Hyg.*, **103**, 95.
NOGUCHI, H. (1911) *J. exp. Med.*, **14**, 99 ; (1912a) *J. exp. Med.*, **15**, 81 ; (1912b) *Ibid.*, **15**, 90 ; (1912c) *Ibid.*, **15**, 201 ; (1912d) *Ibid.*, **15**, 466 ; (1912e) *Ibid.*, **16**, 199 ; (1912f) *Ibid.*, **16**, 261 ; (1912g) *Ibid.*, **16**, 620 ; (1913) *J. exp. Med.*, **17**, 89 ; (1917) *J. exp. Med.*, **25**, 755 ; (1922) *J. exp. Med.*, **35**, 391.
NOGUCHI, H. and AKATSU, S. (1917) *J. exp. Med.*, **25**, 765.
NORRIS, C., PAPPENHEIMER, A. M., and FLOURNOY, T. (1906) *J. infect. Dis.*, **3**, 266.
NOVY, F. G. and KNAPP, R. E. (1906) *J. infect. Dis.*, **3**, 291.
OBERMEIER, O. (1873) *Berl. klin. Wschr.*, **10**, 152, 378, 391, 455.
OKELL, C. C., DALLING, T., and PUGH, L. P. (1925) *Vet. J.*, **81**, 3.
PARHAM, J. C. (1922) *Amer. J. trop. Med.*, **2**, 341.
PARODI, U. (1907) *Zbl. Bakt.*, **44**, 428.
PLOTZ, H. (1917) *J. exp. Med.*, **26**, 37.
RIECKENBERG, H. (1917) *Z. ImmunForsch.*, **26**, 53.
ROBERTSON, A. (1924) *Ann. trop. Med. Parasit.*, **18**, 157.
SAKHAROFF, N. (1891) *Ann. Inst. Pasteur*, **5**, 564.
SCHAUDINN, F. and HOFFMANN, E. (1905) *Arb. ReichsgesundhAmt*, **22**, 527.
SCHEFT, G. (1935) *Zbl. Bakt.*, **134**, 35.
SCHERESCHEWSKY, J. (1909) *Dtsch. med. Wschr.*, **35**, 835, 1260, 1652.
SCHLOSSBERGER, H., GRILLO, J., and SCHEELE, L. (1935) *Klin. Wschr.*, **14**, 1133.
SCHUBERG, A. and SCHLOSSBERGER, H. (1930) *Klin. Wschr.*, **9**, 499.
SCHÜFFNER, W. (1934) *Trans. roy. Soc. trop. Med. Hyg.*, **28**, 7.
SINTON, J. A. (1924) *Indian J. med. Res.*, **11**, 825.
STÉFANOPOULO, G. J. and HOSOYA, S. (1928) *C. R. Soc. Biol.*, **98**, 1317.
STOKES, A., RYLE, J. A., and TYTLER, W. H. (1917) *Lancet*, i. 142.
TANI, KAKISHITA, M., and SAITO, K. (1930) *Zbl. Bakt.*, **117**, 73.
TARASSOFF, S. (1935) *Bull. Off. int. Hyg. publ.*, **27**, 683.
TAYLOR, J. and GOYLE, A. N. (1931) *Indian. med. Res. Memoirs*, No. 20.
THEILER, M. (1926) *Amer. J. trop. Med.*, **6**, 131.
TOMASCZEWSKI. (1910) *Dtsch. med. Wschr.*, **36**, 1025.
TUNNICLIFF, R. (1906) *J. infect. Dis.*, **3**, 148.
TWORT, F. W. (1921) *Lancet*, ii. 798.
UHLENHUTH and FROMME. (1916) *Berl. klin. Wschr.*, **53**, 269.
UHLENHUTH, P. and MULZER, P. (1913) *Arb. ReichsgesundhAmt.*, **44**, 307.
UHLENHUTH and ZUELZER. (1921) *Zbl. Bakt.*, **85**, Beiheft, 141.
VAGEDES, K. VON. (1935) *Zbl. Bakt.*, **133**, 401.
VINCENT, H. (1896) *Ann. Inst. Pasteur*, **10**, 488 ; (1899) *Ibid.*, **8**, 609.
VINZENT, R. and DAUFRESNE, M. (1934) *C. R. Soc. Biol.*, **116**, 490.
WEISS, C. and WILKES-WEISS, D. (1924) *J. infect. Dis.*, **34**, 212.
WENYON, C. M. (1926) " Protozoology," ii. London.
WOLBACH, S. B. and BINGER, C. A. L. (1914) *J. med. Res.*, **30**, 23.
YANG, K. and THEILER, M. (1930) *Amer. J. trop. Med.*, **10**, 407.
YUAN-PO, L. (1933) *Kitasato Arch. exp. Med.*, **10**, 78.
ZUELZER, M. (1925) " Die Spirochäten." " Handbuch der pathogenen Protozoen." Band **3**, 1627. Leipzig ; (1928) *Zbl. Bakt.*, **105**, 384 ; (1930) *Arch. Hyg.*, **103**, 282.

CHAPTER XXXVI

RICKETTSIA

DEFINITION.—*Rickettsia*.

Small, Gram-negative, bacterium-like organisms, usually less than half a micron in diameter. More or less pleomorphic. Stain rather poorly with aniline dyes, but well with Giemsa. Natural inhabitants of intestinal canal of arthropods; often occupy an intracellular position. Some species are parasitic in higher animals and are pathogenic for man. The type species is *Rickettsia prowazeki*.

Rickettsia is the name given to certain small bacteria-like bodies which are found in the alimentary canal of insects and other Arthropods, and which are frequently associated with disease in man and animals. As noted in a later section, not all workers are prepared to accept these bodies as living micro-organisms. There is a general consensus of opinion that the rickettsiæ do not pass through ordinary bacterial filters. Positive results have occasionally been reported when the coarser candles have been used, but there is no reason to believe that in this respect they differ from other very small bacteria.

The first-named species was described by da Rocha-Lima in 1916, who found these bodies in lice taken from patients with typhus fever; he proposed the name of *Rickettsia prowazekii* in honour of Ricketts and of Prowazek, both of whom died of typhus fever while investigating the disease. The second species was described by Töpfer (1916), also in 1916, in lice taken from patients suffering from Wolhynian fever—better known as Trench fever; this species has been given the alternative names of *Rickettsia quintana*—on account of the 5-day febrile paroxysms characteristic of this disease—and *R. wolhynica*; it appears to be closely related to, if not identical with, *R. pediculi*, which was found by da Rocha-Lima in the apparently normal human body louse. A third species, which was first described by Ricketts as far back as 1909 in Rocky Mountain spotted fever, has been called *Dermacentroxenus rickettsi* by Wolbach; as this organism appears to belong to the *Rickettsia* group, we shall refer to it as *Rickettsia rickettsi*. Sellards in 1923 claimed to have cultivated a fourth species, *R. nipponica*, from animals experimentally infected with tsutsugamushi fever in Japan. Cowdry has described a fifth species, *R. ruminantium*, associated with cases of heart-water of sheep, goats, and cattle in South Africa.

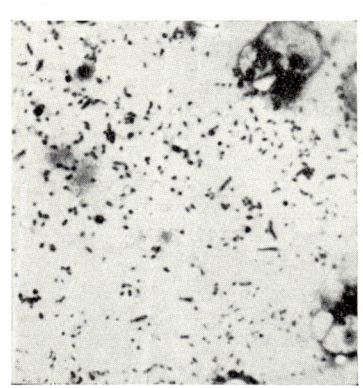

FIG. 201.—*Rickettsia melophagi*.
Smear preparation from gut of sheep-ked. Giemsa. (× 1000).

Besides these five species, which have been found in association with disease, thirty-nine other, apparently non-pathogenic, species of *Rickettsiæ* have been described in various insects and other arthropods.

As the rickettsiæ have been found both in blood-sucking and in non-blood-sucking insects it seems probable that they are primarily inhabitants of the alimentary canal of insects, and that infection of insects occurs by contamination with infected excreta (Hindle 1921). Some species are found not only in the lumen of the alimentary canal, but also in the epithelial cells lining the canal. A further invasion of the body may occur, leading to infection of the salivary glands and other tissues. Most species appear to be transmitted hereditarily to successive generations through infection of the eggs. There is a marked host specificity. Whether the rickettsiæ are to be regarded as simple commensals of insects, or as pathogens is not very clear; but the fact that the mortality in lice infected with *R. prowazeki* is very high suggests that their presence may be to some extent deleterious to the host. A few species appear to have become adapted to an alternate existence in insects and in animals; infection of insects occurs in these cases by blood-sucking. There is, however, no evidence to suggest that a separate cycle of development occurs in either host, as is so frequently observed with the protozoa.

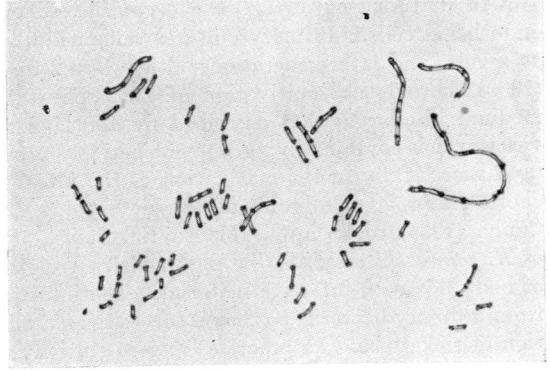

FIG. 202.—*Rickettsia prowazeki.*

Smear preparation from louse's gut, showing bacillary forms, and occasional thread-like chains. Magnification 2,000 diameters (approx.). (After Wolbach, Todd and Palfrey.)

Morphologically, in the gut of the louse rickettsiæ appear like very small cocci, diplococci, or short bacilli. Their size is generally given as 0·3–0·5 μ long by 0·3 μ broad, but the bacillary forms may reach a length of 1·5 or even 2·0 μ. Their arrangement is variable; single forms may occur; diploid forms are very common; and the small coccoid forms are often grouped in dense masses. Most species are non-motile. They stain very poorly with the ordinary aniline dyes, and are uniformly Gram-negative. They are best stained by Giemsa, with which they appear as purple dots, or frequently as bipolar-staining bacilli; sometimes they seem to be surrounded by a paler-staining substance. Other methods, however, of fixation and staining have been devised which under certain conditions are said to give more satisfactory results than Giemsa (Castaneda 1930, Lépine 1932). When very few in number, they cannot be recognized with certainty, since their resemblance to minute particles of detritus is too close; but when they are present in large numbers, their recognition is comparatively easy. It is by reason of the small numbers in which they occur in the blood of infected men and animals, that their demonstration in this medium has only rarely been accomplished. Arkwright, Bacot and Duncan (1919–20) lay down the following criteria for the recognition of *Rickettsia* in the louse's gut : (1) its minute size, $0.3–0.5 \mu \times 0.3 \mu$; (2) its irregularity in shape, round, oval, diplococcal, and bipolar-stained bacillary forms being seen ; (3) its occurrence in very large numbers, or even masses, especially on flakes of solid material in the excreta ; (4) its well-stained appearance and purple colour with Giemsa.

Cultivation.—With the possible exception of *R. nipponica*, none of the pathogenic species has yet been cultivated apart from living cells. Of the commensal species, *R. melophagi*, found in the sheep-ked, is said to have been grown on blood agar. Noguchi (1926) claimed to have cultivated some of the commensal rickettsiæ, found in ticks, on leptospiral medium containing 0·2 per cent. of a carbohydrate ; when 1 per cent. of agar was added, and the medium was slanted, surface colonies were obtained. Working with the rickettsiæ from Rocky Mountain fever and from typhus, Wolbach and Schlesinger (1923–24) succeeded in obtaining growth in tissue cultures. The organisms survived and multiplied only in the endothelial cells. Primary cultures remained alive and virulent for 1 to 2 weeks as a rule, and later-generation cultures for 2 to 4 weeks. Nigg and Landsteiner (1930) showed that cultivation of the typhus virus could be accomplished in a medium, similar to that described by Maitland and Maitland (1928) for vaccinia virus, which contains living but not actively proliferating cells. Another method used successfully in the cultivation of the filtrable viruses, namely growth on the chorio-allantoic membrane of the developing chick embryo, was found by da Cunha (1934) to be applicable to rickettsiæ. Pure, or practically pure, strains of *R. prowazeki* may also be obtained by Weigl's method of intrarectal injection of body lice with infective material. The intestine of the louse is practically free from ordinary bacteria, so that it serves as an almost sterile medium for the cultivation of rickettsiæ. In practice, *in vivo* cultivation in the tissues of a susceptible animal, such as the testicle of the guinea-pig or rabbit, is frequently employed for preserving strains of typhus virus ; according to Kodama and Takahashi (1931), viruses kept in this way undergo no change in antigenic structure or pathogenicity. Certain rickettsial strains, such as *R. nipponica*, can be cultivated in the anterior chamber of the rabbit's eye (Nagayo *et al.* 1930). After an incubation period of 4 to 8 days iritis develops, similar to that occurring naturally in tsutsugamushi fever. Histological examination reveals the presence of peculiar corpuscles in the endothelial cells of Descemet's membrane, consisting apparently of colonies of rickettsiæ. The optimum temperature for growth of the pathogenic species in tissue cultures seems to be about 32° C. (Pinkerton and Hass 1932).

The **Resistance** of *Rickettsia* has not been fully studied. The rickettsiæ of typhus, Rocky Mountain fever, and heartwater are said to be easily inactivated by heat, drying, and chemical disinfectants, but *R. quintana* is said to be more resistant (Cowdry 1926). The Trench fever Committee (Bruce 1921), however, found that the infectivity of louse excreta was destroyed by exposure to moist heat for 20 minutes at 60° C., and to dry heat for the same time at 100° C. Arkwright and Bacot (1923) found that *R. prowazeki* remained virulent for 11 days in louse excreta which had been kept dry at room temperature. The viability of rickettsiæ in infected tissues and in tissue cultures, as judged by their infectivity, seems to be considerably affected by the temperature at which they are kept. Spencer and Parker (1924), working with *R. rickettsi*, found that certain tissues remained infective in pure glycerol for as long as 10 months if preserved at − 10° C. Nigg (1935), working with the murine type of *R. prowazeki*, found that tissue cultures in a serum-Tyrode mixture remained alive and virulent for several months at 37° C. and at — 20° C., but generally died out in a week or two at the intermediate temperatures of 20° C. and — 4° C.

Antigenic Structure.—The difficulty of obtaining suspensions of rickettsiæ free from admixture with cells and other bacteria has rendered the study of the antigenic structure of these organisms peculiarly difficult. Ledingham (1920) and others have shown that inoculation of infective material or of rickettsial suspensions into rabbits is followed by the appearance of specific agglutinins. Advantage has been taken of this circumstance to study the relationship of the pathogenic rickettsiæ to *Proteus X* strains. Without entering here into the practical performance of the Weil-Felix test (see Chapter LXXX), it may be mentioned that the serum of patients suffering from typhus and typhus-like diseases frequently agglutinates *Proteus OX* 19 or one of its variant strains, *OX* 2 or *OX* K. Castaneda and Zia (1933), studying *R. prowazeki* and *Proteus X* 19 by the agglutination and absorption of agglutinins technique, found that these organisms behaved as if each possessed a specific and a group somatic antigen. White (1933), using in addition the precipitation test, obtained evidence of the existence in *X* 19 of two distinct somatic receptors : (1) an alkali-labile receptor (Castaneda's P factor), which is mainly responsible for the agglutination of this organism by its own antiserum ; (2) an alkali-stable receptor (Castaneda's X factor), which is responsible for the reaction of this organism with the sera of typhus patients. White's conclusion received confirmation from the further work of Castaneda (1934, 1935), who was successful in extracting specific soluble substances of polysaccharide nature from *X* 19 and *R. prowazeki*. These substances have already been referred to as P and X. It appears, therefore, as if *Proteus X* 19 and *R. prowazeki* possess a common alkali-stable antigenic factor (X), of polysaccharide nature, which is responsible for the Weil-Felix reaction. In addition, *Proteus X* 19 contains a specific alkali-labile receptor, also apparently of polysaccharide nature, which plays no part in this reaction (see Chapter XXVI). Whether *R. prowazeki* contains a specific receptor of its own similar to the P factor of *Proteus X* 19 is not yet clear.

The relationship of the different types of typhus virus to each other, and to the viruses of Rocky Mountain spotted fever, tsutsugamushi fever, fièvre boutonneuse, and tick-bite fever, has been studied partly by serological methods and partly by cross-protection tests in living animals The interpretation of the results is so closely bound up with the Weil-Felix reaction and with the clinical and epidemiological characteristics of these diseases that it is proposed to defer further discussion of this subject to Chapter LXXX. Suffice it to say that there appear to be at least three major receptors in *Proteus X* strains, represented by the *OX* 19, *OX* 2, and *OX* K types, which correspond to similar receptors in rickettsial strains isolated from different typhus and typhus-like diseases.

Pathogenicity.—As already mentioned, there are four known pathogenic species for man and one for cattle. Leaving aside this last species, *R. ruminantium*, about which comparatively little is known, we may refer briefly to the reproduction of the various rickettsial diseases in animals.

Pathogenicity of R. prowazeki for Animals.

A febrile disease simulating **typhus** can be reproduced in apes, monkeys, and guinea-pigs by the classical *louse-borne* type of virus ; rabbits and rats are relatively resistant to inoculation. According to Nicolle, Conor and Conseil (1911), chimpanzees are more sensitive than macaques ; subcutaneous inoculation of 1 c.c. of human blood is generally sufficient to infect chimpanzees, but for macaques 4–5 c.c. intra-peritoneally are required. The blood of human patients is most virulent towards the end of the fever, but it is said to be virulent from 2 days before the onset to 2 days after the decline of the fever (Arkwright *et al.* 1919–20).

After inoculation of typhus blood into *monkeys* there is an incubation period of about a week, followed by a rise of temperature, which continues to ascend gradually for some days, just as in man ; the temperature is maintained for 7 to 10 days, and then falls rapidly. A period of hypothermia may succeed, followed by a return to normal temperature. Accompanying the fever there are general constitutional symptoms, such as anorexia, ruffled coat, and conjunctival congestion ; on the 3rd or 4th day a rash sometimes breaks out on the face. Death may occur. During the early part of the fever there is a leucopenia, followed by a return to normal ; the leucocytes continue to rise, passing above normal during convalescence, and not returning to normal till about a month after inoculation. The disease can be passed indefinitely through monkeys. A single attack, provided it is severe, produces a solid immunity ; but after a mild attack the immunity is less marked. Instead of typhus blood, monkeys can be infected with a suspension of guinea-pig brain tissue, or with ground-up lice or louse excreta. Arkwright, Bacot and Duncan (1919) brought evidence to show that the monkey-louse, *Pedicinus longiceps*, became infected by feeding on typhus monkeys, or after rectal injection of typhus blood, and was able to transmit the disease to normal monkeys. The infected lice were found to contain rick-ettsiæ ; *Pedicini* from non-inoculated monkeys never contained rickettsiæ.

Guinea-pigs can be infected by virus from man, the louse, or infected guinea-pigs or monkeys. The incubation period is generally 6 to 14 days, but it may extend to 26 days (da Rocha-Lima 1920*a*) ; it is longer after subcutaneous than after intraperitoneal injection. The disease is characterized mainly by fever. The rectal temperature rises from 102° to 103° F. at the end of the incubation period, remains at between 103° and 106° F. for 3 to 14 days, and then falls to normal. According to Grünfeld, Serebrjannaja, and Neumann (1933), there is a mononuclear leucocytosis reaching its maximum as the fever declines ; the mononuclear cells rise from 2 per cent. to between 6 and 14 per cent. The animals recover, and are subsequently immune to a fresh inoculation. If killed, there is little to be seen macroscopically beyond slight enlargement and darkening of the spleen, and some-times slight congestion of the testicles, which may be covered with a gelatinous exudate. Microscopically, both in man and in guinea-pigs the main lesions are found in the blood capillaries, especially those in the skin, skeletal muscles and central nervous system. They consist of thromboses with perivascular accumulations of cells, often accompanied by small hæmorrhages. In the central nervous system characteristic nodules are found, simulating tubercles. The primary lesion is in the endothelial cells lining the walls of the capillaries. Rickettsiæ have been demonstrated in the lesions of the skin, kidneys, testicles, brain, and other organs in man (Wolbach *et al.* 1922). The height and duration of the fever in guinea-pigs is variable, and great care should be taken before concluding that it is definitely caused by the typhus virus. Ecker and Weed (1932) and Badger (1933*a*, *b*) point out that symptoms very suggestive of infection with *R. prowazeki* or *R. rickettsi* may be produced in guinea-pigs by certain organisms of the *Proteus* and Salmonella groups. Cultural, serological and cross-immunity tests may all be required to establish the real causative agent in any given febrile condition. According to Arkwright and Bacot (1923), the most certain way of establishing that an attack of fever in the guinea-pig is really due to the typhus virus is to inject lice intra-rectally with a suspension of the guinea-pig's platelets, and observe the development of rickettsiæ in the excreta. Infected guinea-pigs, it may be noted, do not give a positive Weil-Felix reaction, though natural agglutinins to *Proteus OX* 19 are sometimes present in a titre of 1/25 or less.

The typhus virus can be passed from man to monkeys, from monkeys to guinea-pigs, and from guinea-pigs to monkeys.

The *murine* typhus virus gives rise in *guinea-pigs* to a disease differing in certain respects from that caused by the classical louse-borne virus (Pinkerton 1929, 1931, Zinsser and Castaneda 1930). After intraperitoneal inoculation with the murine type the temperature rises rather earlier, about the 4th to 6th day, though the actual height reached may be less than with the louse-borne type. The scrotal and testicular reaction caused by the murine type, first described by Neill (1917) when investigating Mexican typhus, is much more intense, and microscopical examination reveals the presence of large numbers of rickettsiæ —sometimes known as Mooser (1928) bodies—in the tunica vaginalis. On the other hand, nodular lesions in the brain are more frequent in louse-borne than in murine type infections. Cross-immunity tests indicate that the two types of virus are very closely related, if not identical (Mooser and Dummer 1930, Nicolle and Laigret 1932, Zinsser and Castaneda 1934).

Pathogenicity of R. rickettsi for Animals.—The disease produced in *guinea-pigs* by inoculation of **Rocky Mountain spotted fever** virus is similar to that caused by the typhus virus, but is much more severe. After intraperitoneal inoculation with the Western type, the incubation period is usually only 2 to 4 days. The temperature rises rapidly to about 106° F., and death usually occurs within a week. From the 3rd or 4th day of the fever swellings and hæmorrhages of the scrotum and ears occur, which may go on to necrosis. Post-mortem examination shows a considerable enlargement of the spleen, and frequently a marked scrotal reaction with rickettsial bodies in the tunica vaginalis. The Eastern type is said to be less virulent, but both viruses produce a characteristic rash in the monkey (Badger 1933c).

Rabbits can be infected with the Rocky Mountain virus ; they develop a febrile disease ; rabbits inoculated with the typhus virus do not react at all. It is interesting to note, as indicating the closeness of the relationship between the two viruses, that rabbits experimentally infected with the Rocky Mountain virus may develop agglutinins to *Proteus X* 19 and give a positive Weil-Felix reaction ; rabbits inoculated with the typhus virus likewise develop agglutinins—usually to a rather higher titre (Munter 1928). But inoculation of a rabbit with typhus is said not to protect it against subsequent inoculation with Rocky Mountain virus ; indicating that though both viruses closely resemble each other antigenically, they are distinguishable by their virulence and by their immunizing properties. Experiments on guinea-pigs, however, indicate that inoculation with either virus provides a certain amount of protection against subsequent inoculation with the other (Breinl 1928). White *mice* and *rats* are said to develop a symptomless infection after intraperitoneal inoculation with Rocky Mountain spotted fever virus (Fukuda 1929).

Pathogenicity of R. nipponica for Animals.—The viruses of **tsutsugamushi fever, mite fever,** and **scrub typhus** appear to be closely related. They are not as a rule very infective for guinea-pigs, though occasional strains may prove highly fatal, giving rise to ascites and splenic enlargement after intraperitoneal inoculation. One of their most striking properties is their ability to give rise to an acute reaction, characterized by circum-corneal injection, iritis, turbidity of the aqueous humour, pannus, and the presence of rickettsial bodies in Descemet's membrane, on inoculation into the anterior chamber of the eye of *rabbits* (Nagayo *et al.* 1931, Lewthwaite and Savoor 1934). The serum of the animals often agglutinates *Proteus OX* K 10 days or so after inoculation. The viruses of this group are further distinguished by the ulceration and bubo formation which they cause on intracutaneous injection of *monkeys.* The virus of fièvre boutonneuse appears to be the only other known *Rickettsia* that can produce a marked local lesion in monkeys.

Pathogenicity of R. quintana for Animals.—We have little exact knowledge of the behaviour of the virus of **trench fever** in laboratory animals. Da Rocha-Lima (1920b) states that a small proportion of guinea-pigs may develop a low undulating fever after inoculation with material containing this organism, but that infection cannot be transmitted by passage to fresh animals.

Nature of Rickettsial Bodies.—Generally speaking, there are three main views on the nature of *Rickettsia* bodies. (1) By some workers, such as Woodcock (1921), the rickettsiæ are regarded as inanimate particles, resulting from the disintegration of red blood corpuscles and leucocytes under the influence of the specific virus of the disease. It is freely admitted that the rickettsiæ, when few in number, may be very difficult to recognize, and that they may be closely simulated by granular material ; but workers who have had most experience in the examination of lice maintain that they are able to distinguish rickettsiæ from other particles, especially when, as so frequently occurs, they are present in enormous numbers. Nicholson (1923) holds that they can be distinguished from mitochondria because the latter stain with aniline fuchsin and methyl green ; and from disintegrated nuclear or corpuscular particles, since these stain with iron hæmatoxylin. On morphological and cultural grounds there is evidence to show that the rickettsiæ are definite bodies capable of reproduction. (2) Some workers believe that *Rickettsia* is merely the form assumed in the louse by ordinary bacteria. This view has been developed particularly in relation to *R. prowazeki*. According to Fejgin (1924) this organism is merely a filtrable form of *Proteus X*, generated under the influence of the bacteriophage. The purpose of this hypothesis is to reconcile the finding of *Rickettsia* in the louse with agglutinins to *Proteus X* in the serum of typhus patients. No adequate experimental evidence has been put forward to support it (Hauduroy 1927). (3) The view held by the majority of competent workers is that the rickettsiæ are definite, independent, self-propagating micro-organisms, capable in some instances of giving rise to disease in man and animals. The evidence in favour of this last view is now so overwhelmingly strong that the onus of disproving it rests on its opponents.

Classification.—Admitting the claim of the rickettsiæ to be recognized as living organisms, we are faced with the problem of classifying them.

As regards their general position in the scheme of living things, they seem to occupy a position intermediate between the bacteria and the filtrable viruses. The fact that they can be resolved microscopically by visible light, and that they are held back by membranes which allow most of the filtrable viruses to pass through, brings them into line with the bacteria, but their failure to grow on ordinary culture media and their predilection, particularly marked with some members, for intracellular growth, indicate that their metabolic requirements are more closely allied to those of the filtrable viruses. Since we are as yet unable to study these organisms in pure culture free from all cellular material, it is very difficult to decide what relation the various members have to each other. Most of our information in this respect has been gleaned from examination of the sera of infected patients and from cross-immunity experiments in animals. These will be more conveniently described in Chapter LXXX, when the behaviour of the various causative agents of the typhus and typhus-like diseases will be discussed. It seems clear that the rickettsiæ represent micro-organisms which have undergone, and are probably in the process of undergoing, adaptation to numerous different hosts. Whereas a few years ago it was believed that typhus fever was an epidemic disease carried by the louse, we now know that it may exist in a number of endemic forms and may be carried by the rat-flea, the dog-tick, and certain mites. The viruses that have become adapted to these various hosts exhibit certain differences among themselves, and it has still to be decided whether these are sufficient to demand the creation of separate species, or whether the different typhus viruses should be regarded as merely varieties of one and the same species. Again the relation of the typhus fever group of viruses to those of Rocky Mountain spotted fever, tsutsugamushi fever, fièvre boutonneuse, certain types of tick fever, and so on is still in dispute, though the general lines of cleavage are becoming every year more distinct. For their description we must refer the reader to Chapter LXXX. (For general reviews on the rickettsiæ see Arkwright 1924, Wolbach 1925, Cowdry 1926.)

REFERENCES

ARKWRIGHT, J. A. (1924) *J. R. Army med. Cps*, **42**, 447.
ARKWRIGHT, J. A. and BACOT, A. W. (1923) *Brit. J. exp. Path.*, **4**, 70.
ARKWRIGHT, J. A., BACOT, A., and DUNCAN, F. M. (1919) *Trans. Soc. trop. Med. Hyg.*, **12**, 61 ; (1919–20) *J. Hyg., Camb.*, **18**, 76.
BADGER, L. F. (1933a) *Amer. J. trop. Med.*, **13**, 179 ; (1933b) *Publ. Hlth Rep., Wash.*, **48**, 677 ; (1933c) *Amer. J. publ. Hlth.*, **23**, 19.
BREINL, F. (1928) *J. infect. Dis.*, **42**, 48.
BRUCE, D. (1921) *J. Hyg., Camb.*, **20**, 258.
CASTANEDA, M. R. (1930) *J. infect. Dis.*, **47**, 416 ; (1934) *J. exp. Med.*, **60**, 119 ; (1935) *Ibid.*, **62**, 289.
CASTANEDA, M. R. and ZIA, S. (1933) *J. exp. Med.*, **58**, 55.
COWDRY, E. V. (1926) *Arch. Path. lab. Med.*, **2**, 59.
CUNHA, A.-M. DA. (1934) *C. R. Soc. Biol.*, **117**, 392.
ECKER, E. E. and WEED, L. A. (1932) *J. infect. Dis.*, **50**, 484.
FEJGIN, B. (1924) *C. R. Soc. Biol.*, **91**, 976.
FUKUDA, Y. (1929) *Zbl. Bakt.*, **111**, 408.
GRÜNFELD, A. A., SEREBRJANNAJA, A. I., and NEUMANN, M. W. (1933) *Zbl. Bakt.*, **129**, 56.
HAUDUROY, P. (1927) *Arch. Inst. Pasteur, Tunis*, **16**, 261.
HINDLE, E. (1921) *Parasitology*, **13**, 152.
KODAMA, M. and TAKAHASHI, K. (1931) *Zbl. Bakt.*, **119**, 311.
LEDINGHAM, J. C. G. (1920) *Lancet*, i. 1264.
LÉPINE, P. (1932) *C. R. Soc. Biol.*, **109**, 1162.
LEWTHWAITE, R. and SAVOOR, S. R. (1934) *Trans. 9th Congr., Far East. Assoc. trop. Med., Nanking*, **1**, 249.
MAITLAND, H. B. and MAITLAND, M. C. (1928) *Lancet*, ii. 596.
MOOSER, H. (1928) *J. infect. Dis.*, **43**, 241, 261.
MOOSER, H. and DUMMER, C. (1930) *J. exp. Med.*, **51**, 189.
MUNTER, H. (1928) *Z. Hyg. InfektKr.*, **109**, 124.
NAGAYO, M., MIYAGAWA, Y., MITAMURA, T., TAMIYA, T., SATO, K., HAZATO, H., and IMAMURA, A. (1931) *Jap. J. exp. Med.*, **9**, 87.
NAGAYO, M., TAMIYA, T., MITAMURA, T., and SATO, K. (1930) *C. R. Soc. Biol.*, **104**, 637.
NEILL, M. H. (1917) *Publ. Hlth Rep., Wash.*, **32**, 1105.
NICHOLSON, F. M. (1923) *J. exp. Med.*, **37**, 221.
NICOLLE, C., CONOR, A., and CONSEIL, E. (1911) *Ann. Inst. Pasteur*, **25**, 97.
NICOLLE, C. and LAIGRET, J. (1932) *Arch. Inst. Pasteur, Tunis*, **21**, 251.
NIGG, C. (1935) *J. exp. Med.*, **61**, 17.
NIGG, C. and LANDSTEINER, K. (1930) *Proc. Soc. exp. Biol., N.Y.*, **28**, 3.
NOGUCHI, H. (1926) *J. exp. Med.*, **43**, 515.
PINKERTON, H. (1929) *J. infect. Dis.*, **44**, 337 ; (1931) *J. exp. Med.*, **54**, 181.
PINKERTON, H. and HASS, G. M. (1932) *J. exp. Med.*, **56**, 131, 145, 151.
RICKETTS, H. T. (1909) *J. Amer. med. Ass.*, **52**, 379.
ROCHA-LIMA, H. DA. (1916) *Berl. klin. Wschr.*, **53**, 567 ; (1920a) Prowazek's " Handbuch der pathogenen Protozoen," ii, 990 ; (1920b) *Ibid.*, 1031.
SELLARDS, A. W. (1923) *Amer. J. trop. Med.*, **3**, 529.
SPENCER, R. R. and PARKER, R. R. (1924) *Publ. Hlth Rep., Wash.*, **39**, 55.
TÖPFER, H. (1916) *Münch. med. Wschr.*, **63**, 1495.
WHITE, P. B. (1933) *Brit. J. exp. Path.*, **14**, 145.
WOLBACH, S. B. (1925) *J. Amer. med. Ass.*, **84**, 723.
WOLBACH, S. B. and SCHLESINGER, M. J. (1923–24) *J. med. Res.*, **44**, 231.
WOLBACH, S. B., TODD, J. L., and PALFREY, F. W. (1922) " Report of Typhus Research Commission of League of Red Cross Societies to Poland." Harvard Univ. Press., Cambridge, Mass.
WOODCOCK, H. M. (1921) *J. R. Army med. Cps*, **37**, 418.
ZINSSER, H. and CASTANEDA, M. R. (1930) *J. exp. Med.*, **52**, 649 ; (1934) *Ibid.*, **59**, 471.

CHAPTER XXXVII

THE ORGANISMS OF PLEUROPNEUMONIA AND CONTAGIOUS AGALACTIA

The Organism of Pleuropneumonia

THIS organism, which is responsible for an infectious disease of cattle (see Chapter LXXXI), was first studied by Nocard and Roux (1898), who succeeded in cultivating it in Martin's broth containing 4 per cent. serum. Its extraordinarily complex morphology was described by Bordet (1910) and by Borrel and his colleagues (1910). The fact that Berkefeld filtrates often proved infective afforded ground for the belief that this organism was essentially a filtrable virus. Its recent intensive study, however, by Barnard (1926), Smiles (1926), Ørskov (1927), Nowak (1929), Wroblewski (1931), Ledingham (1933), Klieneberger (1934), Tang *et al.* (1935, 1936), Turner (1935), and Merling-Eisenberg (1935), has raised doubts as to whether it can any longer be included in the filtrable virus group. It is readily observable by ordinary microscopic methods, it can be cultivated *in vitro* in the complete absence of living cells, it is bile-soluble, and it gives rise to no inclusion bodies in the tissues. Its filtrability seems to depend largely on the occurrence of small granules and of plastic filamentous forms which, like leptospiræ, are able to pass through the pores of candles and membranes which are impermeable to the smaller bacteria. Its systematic position and its nomenclature are still under discussion. There is much to be said for Ledingham's suggestion of placing it in the family *Actinomycetaceæ*, and of Turner's suggestion of forming a new order of *Borrelomycetales*, closely allied to the *Actinomycetales*. For the moment we consider it best to treat it as belonging to a separate group, to which no name can as yet be assigned.

Cultivation.—The organism can be cultivated on a number of different media, but most workers have used serum broth or serum agar. Growth is said to occur under both aerobic and anaerobic conditions ; according to Turner (1935), micro-aerophilic conditions are most suitable. The optimum temperature for development is 37° C. ; no growth occurs below 30° C. (Tang *et al.* 1935). With freshly isolated strains, 2–3 day serum broth cultures often contain distinctive mucoid islands and threads visible to the naked eye, while dark-ground examination may reveal the presence of minute colonies about the diameter of a hen's red blood corpuscle (Tang *et al.* 1936). With older strains only a general cloudiness of the medium is seen. On solid media dew-drop colonies appear in 5 or 6 days. Under the microscope these are often umbonate, and consist of a yellowish-brown granular centre surrounded by a smooth transparent peripheral extension (Fig. 203). Well-developed colonies may reach a diameter of 2 mm. Cultivation is also successful on the chorio-allantoic membrane of the developing chick embryo (Tang *et al.* 1936).

Morphology.—The morphology of the organism is influenced by a number of factors, of which the age of the strain appears to be one of the most important (Tang *et al.* 1935). Generally speaking, freshly isolated strains pass through a filamentous stage of development, which, in strains kept for a long time under artificial conditions of cultivation, is often lacking. The microscopical appearances depend also on the method of preparing and examining the films. Nearly every observer has used a different method, and it is therefore not surprising that morphological descriptions of this organism are not always in strict agreement with each other. For the relative merits of examining unstained fluid cultures by dark-ground illumination, and stained impression preparations by transmitted illumination, reference must be made to Turner (1935) and Ledingham (1933). The description we shall give here is based largely on the appearances seen by the former method, mainly because the interpretation of impression films is not one that is familiar to

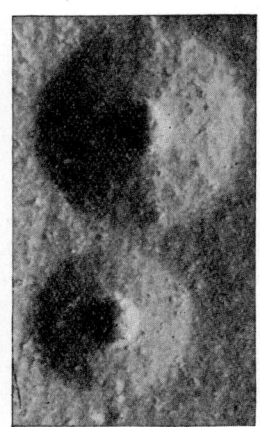

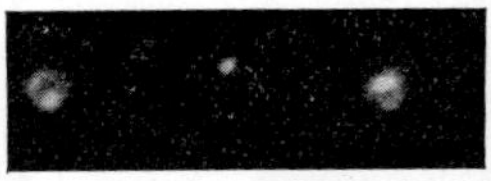

Fig. 204.—Organism of Pleuropneumonia.

Elementary bodies, granules, or conidioids. Dark-ground illumination (× 3600). (After Turner.)

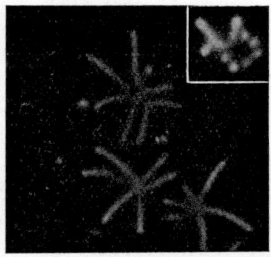

Fig. 206 (Inset).—Organism of Pleuropneumonia.
Spheroid showing multipolar germination. Dark-ground illumination (× 3600). (After Turner.)

Fig. 207.—Organism of Pleuropneumonia.

Fig. 203.—Organism of Pleuropneumonia.

Surface colonies on serum agar (× 140).

(After Tang *et al.*)

Fig. 205.—Organism of Pleuropneumonia.

Spheroid showing unipolar germination. Dark-ground iillumination (× 3600). (After Turner.)

Multipolar germination, showing how the buds have moved away from the parent spheroid and are developing into filaments. Dark-ground illumination (× 3600). (After Turner.)

most bacteriologists, nor one that is referred to elsewhere in this book (see Ledingham 1933, Klieneberger 1934).

At the risk of undue simplification, we shall follow Tang and his colleagues (1935) in describing five morphological stages in the growth of this organism. (*a*) *Granular stage.* Small granules, coccoid, diplococcoid, and cocco-bacillary bodies are seen, usually 0·15–0·4 μ in diameter. Turner refers to them as " conidioids." They stain deeply with Giemsa, and may be regarded as a resting stage (Fig. 204). (*b*) *Filamentous stage.* On inoculation into a fresh medium the granular bodies grow into spheroids about 0·4–0·8 μ in diameter, and develop on their periphery one or more spherical buds (Figs. 205, 206). These gradually move away from the parent body, but remain attached to it by a filament (Fig. 207). In old strains this filament is usually very short, and resembles with its terminal bud a sporing tetanus bacillus. In freshly isolated strains, however, enormously long filaments develop, sometimes crossing several fields of the microscope. Endomycelial protoplasmic streaming is often noticeable. The filaments stain very poorly with Giemsa. (*c*) *Stage of ramification.* During the process of streaming, areas of protoplasmic condensation appear at various points in the filament, and form the starting-point for the outgrowth of fresh filaments. A tangled branching mycelium is the result (Fig. 208). In older strains this stage is lacking. (*d*) *Stage of chain formation.* In this stage the streaming protoplasm condenses rapidly at multiple points, so that the filament takes on a streptococcal appearance (Fig. 209). (*e*) *Stage of disintegration.* The chains break up, and set free a multitude of granular and coccoid forms, thus completing the cycle of development. In old cultures, in which the filamentous stage is lacking, the buds in the second stage become detached from the parent body, and

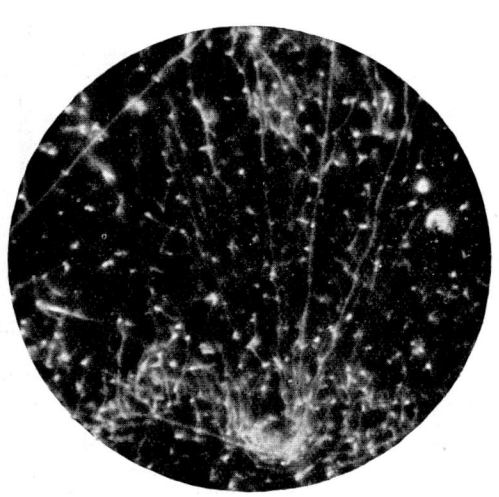

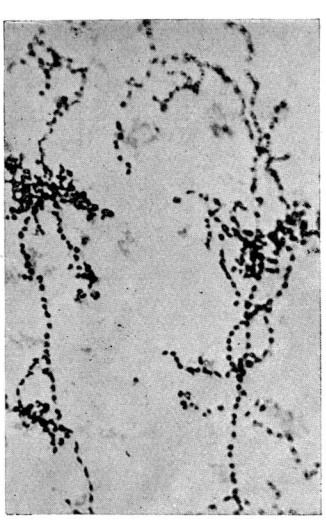

FIG. 208.—ORGANISM OF PLEUROPNEUMONIA.

Stage of ramification, showing nodes of protoplasmic condensation which form the starting-point for the outgrowth of fresh filaments. Dark-ground illumination (× 1114). (After Tang *et al.*)

FIG. 209.—ORGANISM OF PLEUROPNEUMONIA.

Stage of chain formation, showing condensation of protoplasm at multiple points of filament. Giemsa. (× 1640). (After Tang *et al.*)

either grow out again into spheroids which themselves start budding, or remain in the granular phase.

It will be seen that reproduction occurs partly by budding, and partly by fragmentation. Turner (1935) has described no fewer than five different methods of reproduction, and the reader who is interested will do well to refer to his beautifully illustrated paper. Again, reference must be made to Ledingham (1933) and Klieneberger (1934) for the mode of origin of the vibrionic forms, chromatic nodes, large oval swollen bodies, and other elements that are seen in preparations from colonies on solid media, and to Tang and his colleagues (1936) for a description of the apparently rare amœboid and giant ring forms. Fig. 210 represents diagrammatically the probable sequence of development. Though this appears to represent the general nature of the developmental cycle, it must be regarded in a purely tentative manner.   The interpretation of microscopical appearances in serum-containing media is notoriously difficult, and not all workers would be prepared to accept these appearances at their face value.

Resistance, Metabolism, Biochemical Reactions, and Antigenic Structure.— According to Tang and his colleagues (1935), serum broth cultures may remain viable for 45 days at 37° C., and for 98 days at 0°–5° C.   The organisms are bile-soluble, particularly in the filamentous stage, but are very resistant to ultra-violet irradiation and to the photodynamic action of methylene blue (Tang *et al.* 1936). They ferment glucose, maltose, and dextrin, and to a less extent sucrose, with the production of acid, but not mannitol, lactose, or salicin.   Hæmoglobin is reduced by freshly isolated strains.   The filaments are apparently more readily filtrable than the granular bodies.   Little is known of the antigenic structure of this organism,

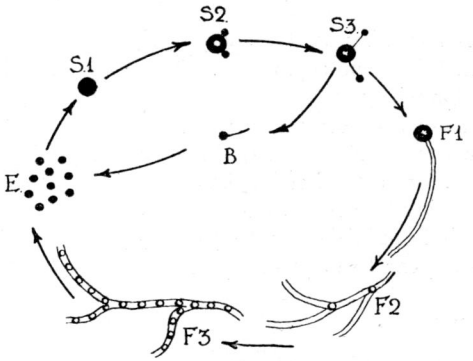

Fig. 210.—Organism of Pleuropneumonia.

Diagrammatic representation of developmental cycle.   Outer circle represents freshly isolated strain forming filaments.   Inner circle represents old laboratory strain not forming filaments.

E.   Elementary bodies, granules, or conidioids.
S_1.   Spheroid.
S_2.   Bipolar germination of spheroid.
S_3.   Spheroid with buds still attached to it by very short filaments—drum-stick appearance.
F_1.   Long filament growing out from spheroid.
F_2.   Filament showing ramification.
F_3.   Filament showing protoplasmic condensation, preparatory to liberation of condensed
          particles as elementary bodies.
B.   Buds detached from spheroid, and becoming elementary bodies.

but there is some evidence, based mainly on cross-protection tests, of the existence of more than one immunological type.

Pathogenicity.—The organism is naturally pathogenic to cattle.   Experimentally the subcutaneous inoculation of 0·5–1·0 c.c. of infected lymph or a virulent culture produces in 8 to 25 days a tense, hot, painful, inflammatory swelling accompanied by high fever and often followed by death.   Incisions of the skin over the affected part is followed by the exudation of a clear straw-coloured fluid, often amounting to several litres.   Post mortem, the connective tissue meshes of the lungs are distended with an immense quantity of clear yellow fluid, which is here and there coagulated into gelatinous trembling masses.   Microscopical examination of the freshly collected fluid reveals the presence of forms similar to those seen in culture ; the mycelial phase appears to predominate (Turner 1935).   It is interesting in this connection to note that only freshly isolated strains showing the filamentous phase of development are fully virulent.   There may be a little serous exudate in the pleural cavity, and the thoracic and inguinal lymphatic glands may be affected. According to Daubney (1935), the typical disease can be reproduced by inoculation into the jugular vein of lymph or culture mixed with a few cubic centimetres of 10 per cent. agar.   The emboli are held up in the lungs and form the starting-point of the disease.   Goats and buffaloes appear to be susceptible to experimental inoculation, but laboratory animals are resistant (Nocard and Roux 1898, Tang *et al.* 1935).

The Organism of Contagious Agalactia

This organism was isolated by Bridré and Donatien (1923, 1925) from infected sheep (see Chapter LXXXI).   It has been studied by Nowak and Wroblewski (1930), Wroblewski (1931), Ledingham (1933), and Nowak and Lominski (1934).   Its general characters are so similar to those of the pleuropneumonia organism that we do not propose to describe them separately.   The disease can be produced experimentally by inoculation with pure cultures.   The goat is more susceptible than the sheep.   The subcutaneous inoculation of 0·5–1·0 c.c. of a pure culture is followed in 4 to 7 days by the appearance of a small local swelling which disappears during the following week.   After a further incubation period of 1 to 4 weeks, localizing lesions appear in the joints, cornea, and, in lactating females, the udder.   The amount of milk secreted diminishes, and a yellowish purulent fluid takes its place. Laboratory animals appear to be insusceptible.

REFERENCES

BARNARD, J. E.   (1926) *J. R. micr. Soc.*, p. 253.
BORDET, J.   (1910) *Ann. Inst. Pasteur*, **24**, 161.
BORREL, DUJARDIN-BEAUMETZ, JEANTET, and JOUAN.   (1910) *Ann. Inst. Pasteur*, **24**, 168.
BRIDRÉ, J. and DONATIEN, A.   (1923) *C. R. Acad. Sci.*, **177**, 841 ; (1925) *Ann. Inst. Pasteur,* **39**, 925.
DAUBNEY, R.   (1935) *J. comp. Path.*, **48**, 83.
KLIENEBERGER, E.   (1934) *J. Path. Bact.*, **39**, 409.
LEDINGHAM, J. C. G.   (1933) *J. Path. Bact.*, **37**, 393.
MERLING-EISENBERG, K. B.   (1935) *Brit. J. exp. Path.*, **16**, 411.
NOCARD and ROUX.   (1898) *Ann. Inst. Pasteur*, **12**, 240.
NOWAK, J.   (1929) *Ann. Inst. Pasteur*, **43**, 1330.
NOWAK, J. and LOMINSKI, I.   (1934) *Ann. Inst. Pasteur*, **53**, 438.
NOWAK, J. and WROBLEWSKI, W.   (1930) *Trans. Congr. int. Microbiol.*, **1**, 619.
ØRSKOV, J.   (1927) *Ann. Inst. Pasteur*, **41**, 473.
SMILES, J.   (1926) *J. R. micr. Soc.*, p. 257.
TANG, F. F., WEI, H., and EDGAR, J.   (1936) *J. Path. Bact.*, **42**, 45.
TANG, F. F., WEI, H., MCWHIRTER, D. L., and EDGAR, J.   (1935) *J. Path. Bact.*, **40**, 391.
TURNER, A. W.   (1935) *J. Path. Bact.*, **41**, 1.
WROBLEWSKI, W.   (1931) *Ann. Inst. Pasteur*, **47**, 94.

CHAPTER XXXVIII

THE FILTRABLE VIRUSES : GENERAL PROPERTIES

Tentative Definition of Pathogenic Forms

Probably organized bodies which are usually invisible by ordinary microscopic methods of examination, which have a diameter of less than $0.2\,\mu$, which can often be filtered through candles and membranes impermeable to ordinary bacteria, which have not yet been cultivated in cell-free media but which multiply freely in the presence of susceptible cells *in vitro* or *in vivo*, which generally have a high resistance to glycerol, which frequently invade one particular species of host and tend to affect one particular tissue, which give rise to characteristic inclusion bodies in the tissues, and which cause a latent or overt infection followed as a rule by a lasting immunity.

THERE is a large group of diseases affecting man, animals, insects, and plants, which have most or all of the characteristics of infectious diseases, yet in which no visible microscopical organism has been satisfactorily demonstrated. That these diseases are infectious is shown by the fact that it is usually possible to reproduce them in normal hosts by inoculation, not only of the ground-up diseased tissue, but also of cell-free extracts or filtrates of the tissue. Since these cell-free extracts are most commonly obtained by filtration, the practice has grown up of referring to the specific infecting agents contained in them as "filtrable viruses." This term is sanctioned by usage, and is the one we shall employ ourselves ; but it is necessary to point out that as not all these viruses have yet been shown to be filtrable, and as the exact standardization of filtration has not yet proved possible, the term "filtrable" is necessarily a loose one. Alternative names, to which even greater objections can be raised, have been proposed, such as "ultramicroscopic viruses," "protista," "chlamydozoa," and "strongyloplasms."

Before describing the known properties of these viruses, it is desirable to touch on some of the technical difficulties in their study. Firstly, with regard to **filtration,** it may be stated categorically that the ability of a particulate body to pass through a filter is not a simple function of the relation of the size of the body to the size of the pores ; that is to say, a filter is not a mere mechanical sieve. Several factors other than the size of the filter pore determine whether a given body will pass through it or not. Thus, according to Rivers (1928), " the electrical charge on the virus, the electrical charge on the filter, the adsorption of the virus by aggregates of protein or by cell detritus, the amount of protein or other substances in the virus emulsion, the temperature at which the filtration is conducted, the amount of negative or positive pressure employed, the duration of filtration, and other factors . . . serve to influence the results of all filtration experiments." The ordinary porous bacterial filter consists of a positively charged alkaline earth cation, and a negatively charged silicate anion. If a simple basic dye, such as methylene blue, which consists of an organic colour cation united to an inorganic anion, is passed through a filter, a large amount of the dye will be adsorbed. The explanation of this is that the organic colour cation enters into combination with the silicate anion in the filter, forming an insoluble dye-silicate, which is retained ; the soluble salt, such as NaCl or KCl, formed by the union of the alkaline earth cation in the filter with the inorganic anion of the dye, passes through. A similar phenomenon is observed in protein solutions. In solutions more acid than the isoelectric point of the protein, the dissociated protein is chiefly in the form of multivalent cations capable of entering into combination with the silicate anions in the filter, and forming an insoluble combination, which is retained. On the other hand, in solutions more alkaline than the isoelectric point, the dissociated protein is chiefly in the form of multivalent anions, capable of entering into combination with the alkaline earth cations in the filter with the formation of soluble salts, which pass through. This is probably why enzymes, toxins, and viruses appear to pass more readily through filters in weakly alkaline than in acid solutions (see Mudd 1922–23, 1928).

The nature of the suspending fluid plays an important part in determining the result. Several workers have noted that viruses pass much more readily through filters when the suspension is made up with broth or serum than with saline or phosphate buffer (Grinnell 1929, Ward 1929, Sawyer and Frobisher 1929, Tallerman 1929, Marie and Urbain 1930, Galloway and Elford 1931). The mode of action of the broth is not known with certainty, but according to Elford (1933) it appears to be closely related to the ability of this medium to stabilize the dispersion of a lyophilic colloid. Soap has the opposite effect. Another factor, which is of special importance in comparing the filtrability of two different strains of virus, is the initial concentration of virus. The greater the number of virus particles present in the suspension, the more likely is virus to be found in the filtrate (Galloway and Elford 1931).

Cataphoresis experiments on such viruses as vaccinia, fowl-pox, foot-and-mouth, rabies, yellow fever, myxoma, and Rous sarcoma have agreed in showing that most viruses carry a negative charge in the neighbourhood of neutrality (Douglas and Smith 1928, Findlay 1930, Hindle and Findlay 1930, Poppe and Busch 1930, Natarajan and Hyde 1930, Sichert-Modrow 1930, Sankaran *et al.* 1934). It is true that Olitsky and Boëz (1927) stated that the foot-and-mouth virus carried a positive charge up to pH 8·0, but the results of these workers have not been confirmed. Most viruses have been studied over a range of about pH 5·0 to 9·0 ; they have been found to be negatively charged up to about pH 7·6, though the exact location of the isoelectric point has varied from pH 7·0 with the yellow fever virus to pH 9·3 with the virus of myxoma. The nature of the charge carried will affect, to some extent, the passage of the virus through a filter. Incidentally, use may be made of the electric charge carried by the virus to free it from other material in a tissue suspension, or at any rate to obtain it in a more concentrated form (Douglas and Smith 1928, Sankaran *et al.* 1934).

It is important to realize that the mere passage of an organism through a filter candle does not justify its inclusion in the group of filtrable viruses. Even under conditions of careful experimentation, small organisms, particularly slender flexible and motile organisms such as spirochætes, frequently appear in small numbers in the filtrate ; and conversely, the mere failure of an organism to pass through a filter candle does not justify its exclusion from the group of filtrable viruses. Some viruses, for example, such as those of varicella and herpes zoster, have not yet been shown to be filtrable, yet there is little doubt from what is known of their other properties that they should be included in this group. The term "filtrable virus" is one connoting a number of properties, the most important of which have already been defined at the head of this chapter.

In recent years the process of ultrafiltration has been introduced. In this process, thin collodion membranes are prepared with a given size of pore, the size being determined largely by the concentration of collodion used. In the development of these filters Elford (1931, 1933) has played a prominent part. Starting from the earlier work of Bechhold, he has been able by the use of appropriate solvent mixtures, and by the careful standardization of his technique, to prepare a series of membranes of very regular and accurately graded porosities by means of which determinations of the size of many of the commoner viruses have been successfully made, and subsequently confirmed by other workers (see also Elford, Grabar, and Ferry 1935). These filters—*Gradocol membranes*—approach nearer to the mechanical sieve than do ordinary filter candles ; they appear to be less influenced by the various secondary factors which we have mentioned, and to be capable, when properly used, of sorting out particles very largely according to their size ; though the influence of the pH of the suspending fluid, and of the electrical charge carried, must still be taken into account.

In calculating the size of the particle from the average pore diameter through which it just fails to pass, the effect of adsorption has to be considered. This effect is most influential in membranes with very small pores (Table LI). Thus a particle held back by a membrane with an average pore diameter of 30 mμ probably has a diameter of 10–15 mμ, while one held back by a membrane of 1,000 mμ probably has a diameter of 0·75–1·0 μ (see also Cox and Hyde 1932, Asheshov 1933 on ultrafiltration).

TABLE LI

RELATION OF SIZE OF RETAINED PARTICLE TO AVERAGE PORE DIAMETER OF GRADOCOL MEM-
BRANES (Elford 1933)

Membrane average pore diameter.	Size of Retained Particle.
mμ	
10–100	(0·33–0·5) d
100–500	(0·5–0·75) d
500–1,000	(0·75–1·0) d

d = average pore diameter of limiting membrane for optimum filtration conditions.

Secondly, there are certain difficulties in the **microscopical examination** of filtrable viruses. It has already been pointed out in Chapter II that under ordinary conditions of examination it is impossible to resolve particles less than 0·2 μ in diameter. Resolution, it will be remembered, is limited by the numerical aperture of the objective and the wave-length of the light used. Since there are serious difficulties in increasing the numerical aperture of the objective, it follows that the only way to resolve very small bodies is to use a wave-length shorter than any present in the visible spectrum. Resolution, however, is not always required, and considerable attention has been devoted of recent years to methods for rendering small bodies *visible*. Though certain filtrable viruses may be demonstrated in sections or smear preparations, their study is greatly facilitated by obtaining them in a suspension relatively free from tissue cells and other gross matter. Usually this is done by differential centrifugation, sometimes accompanied by filtration. The suspension can then be examined by one of the following methods : I. *Fixing and staining with a suitable dye.* Numerous workers, among whom Ledingham (1931) has been one of the foremost, have used this method. The dyes chosen are most frequently Giemsa's stain, or one of its modifications. By this means minute particles—the so-called elementary bodies—may be rendered visible in appropriate preparations. Since, however, it is impossible to demonstrate very small particles by transmitted light, even when they are deeply stained, it follows that this method is limited to the larger viruses. Its most conspicuous success has, in fact, been achieved hitherto with the virus of vaccinia, the diameter of which is about $0 \cdot 15 \, \mu$. It has proved of particular value in the microscopical observation of agglutination, where, of course visibility, and not resolution, of the aggregating particles is alone required ; II. *Dark-ground examination using visible light.* Provided the particles under examination can scatter enough light, and there is a sufficient difference of refractive index between them and the medium in which they are suspended, this method enables very small particles to be rendered visible, even though they are incapable of resolution. It provides a useful means of direct microscopic observation of virus particles ; III. *Photography in ultra-violet light.* Barnard (1925) has been the chief exponent of this method. After preliminary examination by method II, photographs are taken at particular wave-lengths in the ultra-violet spectrum (see Chapter II). Either transmitted or dark-ground illumination may be used. The former suffers from the disadvantage that the ability of viruses to absorb light is very low, and the image so obtained is smaller than it otherwise would be. With dark-ground illumination there is strong contrast, and sharply defined images are obtainable, though their size tends to be slightly too large. With a wave-length of $257 \, \mathrm{m}\mu$, particles as small as $75 \, \mathrm{m}\mu$ can be actually resolved. Their approximate size can then be determined from the mean of the images given by transmitted and dark-ground illumination. Theoretically, this method is open to almost unlimited extension, but in practice great technical difficulties are encountered. Barnard is already using wave-lengths at the lower limit of the ultra-violet spectrum, and is contemplating the use of soft X-rays. Provided the difficulties in manufacturing objectives, and utilizing other suitable optical methods, can be overcome, there is no reason why particles as small as the protein molecules should not be resolved and photographed.

Thirdly, with regard to **centrifugalization,** there are great mechanical difficulties in constructing a machine that is sufficiently powerful to throw down very fine suspended particles ; this difficulty is increased if the suspending fluid, as is usually the case, has a specific gravity greater than water. The centrifugal force of a machine varies with the square of the rate of rotation, and directly with the distance of the centrifuged material from the centre of the plate. But neither of these factors can be increased indefinitely, because with increasing rate of rotation, and with increasing diameter of the plate, a vibration develops that very largely counteracts the centrifugal force. Numerous other mechanical factors, such as the air-resistance and the heat generated in the machine, come into play when high speeds are developed, and limit the rate and time during which the machine may be run. Nevertheless, serious attempts have been made in recent years to overcome these difficulties, and very real progress has been registered. The introduction of higher speed electric motors, of the Lundgren angle centrifuge, and of the spinning-top centrifuge of Henriot and Huguenard (see McIntosh 1935) have each contributed to this end. Indeed with the spinning-top centrifuge, in which friction is diminished to a minimum, speeds of 80,000 r.p.m. have been reported. The greatest advance, however, has been made by Svedberg and his colleagues (1934), who have devised a centrifuge capable of revolving at 160,000 r.p.m. In this machine the rotor carries a cell which contains a column, 8 mm. in height, of the fluid to be centrifuged, situated 36 mm. from the centre. The cell has windows of crystalline quartz to allow of serial photographs being taken to register the progress of sedimentation. The rotor is driven by two twin turbines fed with oil at a pressure of 15 kgm. per sq. cm. Rotation takes place in an atmosphere of hydrogen at 20 mm. pressure, so as to avoid air friction and convection currents. In the original design (Svedberg and Nichols 1927) 240 litres of oil were required per minute to drive the turbines, and 7 litres of oil per minute to lubricate and cool the bearings. The cost of this machine has so far prohibited most laboratories from testing it, but in

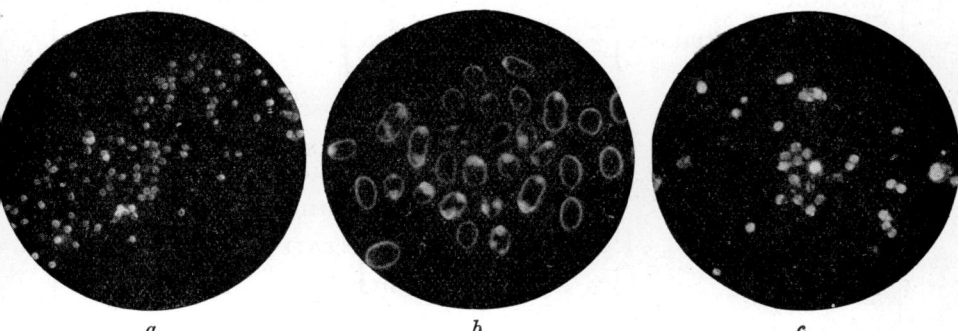

a   *b*   *c*

Fig. 211.—On left (*a*), elementary bodies of vaccinia from rabbit testis, and on right (*c*) elementary bodies of canary pox; in the middle (*b*) *Chromo. prodigiosum* for comparison. Photographed in ultra-violet light (× 3200). (After Barnard.)

Svedberg's hands it has been used with conspicuous success in estimating the molecular weight of proteins.

Not only is it possible, now, with some of the high-speed centrifuges, to throw down completely the larger viruses, but their approximate size can be calculated from measuring their rate of sedimentation. Bechhold and Schlesinger (1931) have worked out a formula from which the size of evenly dispersed spherical particles submitted to a constant centrifugal force may be determined. Further, by measuring the rate of concentration, it can be ascertained whether the particles are of uniform size. It can be shown, for instance, that the logarithm of the concentration of particles in the supernatant fluid is proportional to the length of time of centrifugation. If they are of unequal size, the larger particles will be thrown down rapidly, and the curve formed by plotting the logarithms of the concentrations against time will not be a straight line.

The larger viruses, of 0·1–0·2 μ in diameter, can be thrown down completely under suitable conditions in about half an hour by a centrifuge revolving at 10,000 r.p.m. (see Amies 1933), while particles of about 60 mμ, such as the staphylococcal bacteriophage, require a speed of 40,000 r.p.m. maintained for 1 to 1½ hours

(McIntosh 1935). Where centrifuges of only 3,000 r.p.m. are available, and it is desired to concentrate the suspension, the virus may sometimes be adsorbed on to kaolin or animal charcoal, and the deposit subsequently suspended in a protein-free medium (see Levadit and Nicolau 1923, Gins and Krause 1923, Tang 1932). Viruses vary, however in their reaction to different adsorbing agents (Lewis and Andervont 1927), and this method is therefore not always successful.

Morphology.—What little information we have on the shape of filtrable virus particles we owe almost entirely to Barnard, who has of recent years been successful in photographing some of the larger viruses in ultra-violet light. One of the most

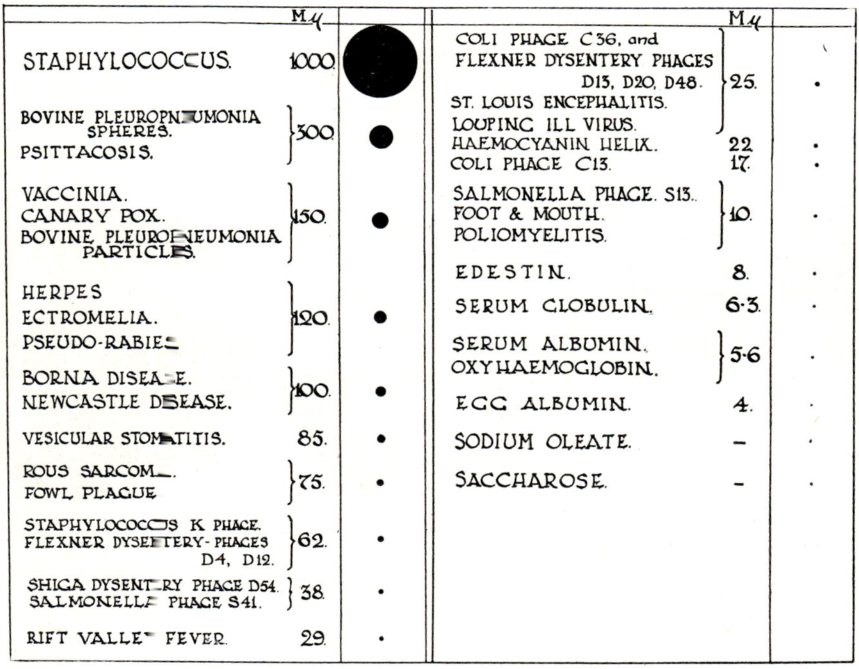

	Mμ			Mμ	
STAPHYLOCOCCUS.	1000.	●	COLI PHAGE C36, and FLEXNER DYSENTERY PHAGES D13, D20, D48.	25.	•
BOVINE PLEUROPNEUMONIA SPHERES. PSITTACOSIS.	300.	●	ST. LOUIS ENCEPHALITIS. LOUPING ILL VIRUS. HAEMOCYANIN HELIX. COLI PHAGE C13.	22. 17.	• •
VACCINIA. CANARY POX. BOVINE PLEUROPNEUMONIA PARTICLES.	150.	●	SALMONELLA PHAGE. S13. FOOT & MOUTH. POLIOMYELITIS.	10.	•
			EDESTIN.	8.	•
HERPES ECTROMELIA. PSEUDO-RABIES.	120.	●	SERUM GLOBULIN.	6.3.	•
BORNA DISEASE. NEWCASTLE DISEASE.	100.	●	SERUM ALBUMIN. OXYHAEMOGLOBIN.	5.6	•
			EGG ALBUMIN.	4.	•
VESICULAR STOMATITIS.	85.	•	SODIUM OLEATE.	—	•
ROUS SARCOMA. FOWL PLAGUE	75.	•	SACCHAROSE.	—	•
STAPHYLOCOCCUS K PHAGE. FLEXNER DYSENTERY- PHAGES D4, D12.	62.	•			
SHIGA DYSENTERY PHAGE D54. SALMONELLA PHAGE S41.	38.	•			
RIFT VALLEY FEVER.	29.	•			

Fig. 212.—SCHEMATIC REPRESENTATION SHOWING PROBABLE SIZE OF FILTRABLE VIRUSES AND CERTAIN BACTERIOPHAGES. (Modified from Elford.) The viruses of influenza and swine influenza are of the order of 80–120 mμ ; the lymphogranuloma virus is 125–175 mμ, the yellow fever viris 17–20 mμ.

carefully studied is that of ectromelia, a virus with a diameter of about 120 mμ (Barnard and Elford 1931). This organism is coccoid, and frequently occurs in pairs. Isolated organisms are spherical and highly refractile, the refractivity apparently decreasing with shortening of the wave-length used for illumination. Reproduction is by binary fission, and elongation is evident before division. The final separation of the two organisms takes place quickly, but a very fine connecting filament may be left between them. Ultra-violet photographs show a more highly refractive outline corresponding to the periphery of the cell, and often an increased density at the poles. Whether these appearances are due to the presence of a cell-wall and to polar condensation of the cytoplasm respectively, or are merely the effects of interfacial phenomena, it is impossible to say.

The size of many of the different viruses has now been calculated, mainly from

Elford's filtration work, and to a less extent from the microscopical photographs of Barnard, the results of high-speed centrifugation, and the rate of diffusion of the virus particles in a suitable medium. Figure 212, which we owe largely to the kindness of Mr. W. J. Elford, enables the size of these bodies to be visualized in relation to the bacteria on the one hand and the larger protein molecules on the other.

The method of reproduction of the filtrable viruses is still in doubt. The evidence so far obtained seems to favour binary fission. It is true that Bedson and Bland (1932, 1933) described a special developmental cycle for the psittacosis virus, but further observations led them to modify their original opinion.

Microchemical analysis of vaccinial elementary bodies has revealed the presence of ash, carbohydrate, fat, and nitrogen, a part of which was undoubtedly in the form of protein (Hughes *et al.* 1935). These results suggest that the composition of virus particles is essentially similar to that of ordinary bacteria.

Habitat.—With the exceptions noted below, all the filtrable viruses at present known are associated with living cells, whether in the animal or the vegetable kingdom. This does not mean that they are never found apart from disease processes, for their presence has been demonstrated in healthy carriers ; but it does mean that they are essentially parasitic. The existence, however, of saprophytic viruses is rendered highly probable by the recent work of Barnard (1935) and of Laidlaw and Elford (1936). Hitherto the only satisfactory criterion of the presence of a virus has consisted in the production of characteristic lesions in a susceptible animal by a suitably prepared filtrate. No technique has permitted the detection of a saprophytic virus, or of an avirulent variant of a parasitic virus. Barnard, however, by ultra-violet photography has been able to detect the presence of minute, reproducible bodies, about 150 mμ in diameter, in sterile tubes of serum broth ; while Laidlaw and Elford have demonstrated the occurrence of bodies from 0·15–0·5 μ in diameter in sewage, and have cultivated them indefinitely in Hartley's broth enriched with Fildes' extract.

Many of the viruses in the animal body appear to show a particular affinity for special tissues, such as nervous tissue or skin ; this resembles the affinity manifested by many of the known bacteria for special tissues. Even, however, when the lesions are confined to one tissue, the virus can frequently be demonstrated in other parts of the body. There is evidence, too, that the tissue localization is more apparent than real, depending on the mode of infection. Thus Ledingham (1924) found that in rabbits the virus of vaccinia, which usually affects the skin, was able to give rise to nodules on the peritoneum after direct inoculation into the spleen or the abdominal cavity. As well as their selective tissue localization, many viruses exhibit a species-specificity, giving rise to lesions only in one particular species of animal. Thus Cole and Kuttner's salivary gland virus is active only in guinea-pigs, Virus iii only in rabbits, and so on. On the other hand, there are viruses, such as those of rabies and foot-and-mouth disease, which are pathogenic not only to different species but also to widely separate groups of animals. Possibly too much weight has been laid in the past on the species-specificity of the viruses. It is now clear that most of the viruses are capable of infecting several different species of animal under experimental conditions.

Apart from the presence of a virus in a healthy carrier free from all clinical symptoms of disease, it has been shown that a virus may remain latent in the tissues after causing an initial infection. Thus, according to Gastinel and Reilly (1928) the herpes virus can sometimes be demonstrated in the brain of guinea-pigs that have recovered from a keratitis caused by inoculation of the cornea. Its presence gives rise to no symptoms, but can be shown by inoculation of the brain on to the cornea of a normal guinea-pig. It is possible that an attack of inter-current disease, or some artificial procedure such as vaccination, may activate such a latent virus, and cause it to give rise to clinical disease.

Whether the filtrable viruses occupy an intra- or an extracellular position in the body is not certainly known, but the indirect evidence so far accumulated suggests that their growth and multiplication occurs actually within the cells. The rinderpest virus, for example, appears to be contained within the leucocytes ; by centrifugalization of the blood, the virus is found to be concentrated mainly in the leucocytic layer. Similarly with the virus of fowl-plague, Todd (1928) found that in centrifuged blood the concentration of the virus was 100 times greater in the leucocytic layer than in the clear plasma or the washed red cells. Moreover there is evidence that for their multiplication the filtrable viruses often prefer young newly-formed cells ; many of the viruses acting on the skin, for example, give rise to lesions first along the lines of scarification, where repair is taking place. Further evidence in favour of this view is that certain viruses, *e.g.* Virus iii and vaccinia, have been found to grow in a transplantable rabbit tumour, in which the cells are in process of active multiplication, and to survive longer in the tumour than in the healthy tissues of the rabbit (Rivers and Pearce 1925). How far, in fact, the viruses are *cytotropic* and how far they are *cytotrophic* is a matter for dispute. Goodpasture (1930) believes that actual growth occurs only in the living cells of the body, while Ledingham (1932) is not prepared to go to this length. The viruses are very small, and it seems doubtful whether they have room enough to contain the necessary enzyme systems by which larger bodies, such as bacteria, obtain energy from complex substances in their environment. More probably they take advantage of ferment action in the body cells, and receive their nutritive material in a partly digested state. If this is so, then viruses, including the bacteriophage, must represent the most advanced and dependent state of parasitism of which we have knowledge in the unicellular world.

Inclusion Bodies.—Histological examination of the lesions occurring in filtrable virus diseases often reveals the presence within the cytoplasm or the nucleus, or sometimes both, of peculiar bodies whose nature is at present unknown, and which are usually referred to as " inclusion bodies." The appearance of these bodies varies in different diseases, and often in the same disease in different animals (Figs. 213, 214). The bodies may be rounded, oval, pyriform, or irregular in shape ; their substance may be hyaline or granular ; in structure they may be homogeneous, or they may contain one or more, often several, elementary corpuscles ; in their staining reactions they may be basophilic or acidophilic, and within the same inclusion body the granules or elementary corpuscles may stain differently from the ground substance ; lipoid substances staining with osmic acid are sometimes found. In many diseases affecting the skin, such as fowl-pox, human variola, and the common wart, the formation of inclusion bodies is restricted to the epidermis, but in others, such as zoster, varicella, and venereal herpes, they are found both in the epidermis and in the corium. Moreover, according to Lipschütz (1925), only certain layers of the epidermis may be affected ; thus in the common wart, inclusion bodies are found in the prickle- and horn-cell layers but not in the basal cell layer. Inclusion bodies can be produced experimentally only by the inoculation of living viruses ; they are not formed after inoculation of dead viruses, even though the latter have immunizing properties, *e.g.* vaccinia and herpes. After inoculation of the virus, the inclusion bodies appear at different times in different infections. Thus in common warts, the nuclear inclusion bodies are demonstrable only in the earliest stages ; in herpetic keratitis of rabbits the inclusion bodies appear within the first 24 hours ; in venereal herpes they are best seen on the third day, and so on. There appears to be some relationship between the presence of inclusion bodies and the infectivity of the tissue ; in herpetic keratitis of rabbits, for example, it is said that with the disappearance of the nuclear inclusion bodies the disease becomes no longer inoculable. Experimentally, the formation of inclusion bodies can be stimulated by the inoculation not only of infected tissue extracts, but often of filtered cell-free material. They can, moreover, often be demonstrated in tissue cultures (Andrewes 1929, Rivers *et al.* 1929).

The earlier workers regarded these inclusion bodies as protozoa, and pictured them as varying stages of an elaborate life-cycle. Subsequently they were believed to represent cellular degeneration products due to nucleolar extrusion, vacuolation of the cytoplasm, and other processes consequent on the attack
of the virus. Von Prowazek regarded them as of a dual nature,
consisting of micro-organisms

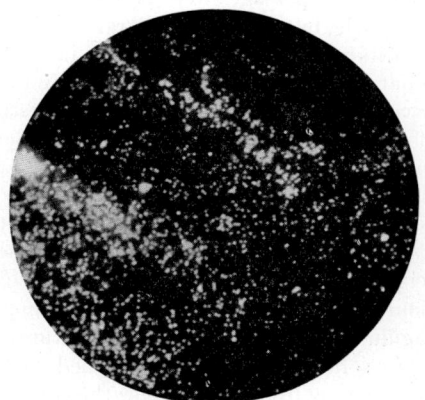

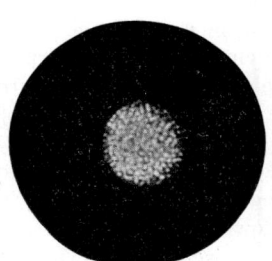

Ectromelia virus on left (Fig. 213), inclusion body from foot of mouse ; on right (Fig. 214), inclusion body after maceration, showing the liberated elementary bodies. Photographed in visible light (× 1250). (After Barnard.)

embedded in material deposited around them as the result of a reaction of the cell protoplasm ; for these bodies the term " Chlamydozoa "—literally cloak animals—was proposed. It is now, however, becoming increasingly clear that intracellular inclusion bodies are essentially colonies of the infecting virus. Since Woodruff and Goodpasture (1929, 1930) showed that the Bollinger inclusion body of fowl-pox consisted of 10,000–20,000 minute Borrel bodies, and that a single Bollinger body, washed free from surrounding virus, was capable of giving rise to a typical fowl-pox lesion on skin inoculation, it has been difficult to regard inclusion bodies as other than intracellular aggregations of elementary virus particles. By tryptic digestion, by maceration, by surface tension, or other means it has now been shown that the inclusion bodies of ectromelia (Barnard and Elford 1931), vaccinia (Ledingham 1931, Paschen 1932), and psittacosis (Bedson and Bland 1932, 1934) contain masses of elementary bodies which are apparently responsible for giving rise to characteristic intracellular changes. Whether the intranuclear acidophilic bodies, which are so common in infections caused by neutrotropic viruses, are of the same nature as the intracellular but extranuclear bodies has not yet been made clear either by morphological study or by the micro-incineration technique (see Cowdry 1933). Whatever the structure of inclusion bodies may be, however, there is no doubt whatever of their significance ; their presence in the tissue is a sure sign of infection, and is made use of in the routine diagnosis of certain of the filtrable virus diseases, such as rabies. (For a pictorial review of inclusion bodies see Findlay and Ludford 1926, and for a general account of their properties see Goodpasture 1929, 1929–30, Ledingham 1935. See also Figs. 273–276.

Cultivation.—With the exception of various saprophytic viruses described by Barnard (1935) and Laidlaw and Elford (1936), which can be grown on blood agar or in serum broth, the filtrable viruses have proved refractory to cultivation in the absence of living cells. In 1915 Noguchi succeeded in obtaining pure cultures *in vivo* of vaccinia virus, by growing it in the testicles of rabbits and bulls. The virus, obtained from skin scrapings, was first freed from bacteria by suitable means, and was then inoculated intratesticularly into rabbits. Transfers were made every four days. Several passages were necessary before the virus became adapted to growth in the testicle, but subsequently transfers were made without difficulty, and the virus reached its maximum multiplication in the testicle after 4 or 5 days ; it remained stationary in amount till the 8th day, and then decreased till after 5 weeks its presence could no longer be detected. By testicular cultivation, the virus did not lose its affinity for the skin ; both the testicular and the skin strains gave similar reactions in the skin, cornea, and testicles of rabbits, and in the skin of human beings. In 1925 Parker and Nye succeeded in growing the vaccinia and herpes viruses in tissue cultures prepared with normal rabbit testis and plasma. This was confirmed by Carrel and Rivers in 1927 working with the vaccinia virus. Infected rabbit testicle was ground up in a mortar, added to chick-embryo pulp, left for 24 hours in the ice-chest, and then inoculated into a Carrel flask containing a coagulum of hen plasma. The cultures were washed every 2 or 3 days with Tyrode's solution, and were nourished with a dilute fowl-embryo extract. After periods varying from 1 to 4 weeks the contents of the flasks were withdrawn, ground up in a mortar, and titrated on rabbits by the intradermal method. It was found that the cultures, which were seeded with 25 to 250 intradermal units of virus per c.c., contained after incubation for a week between 10,000 and 100,000 units per c.c., showing that actual multiplication of the virus had occurred. Haagen (1928) reported a modified method of *in vitro* cultivation of vaccinia virus in the presence of rabbit testicle, rabbit plasma, and rabbit spleen extract. Using this method, he carried the virus through 37 passages in a period of about 8 months. During the first 5 days of each subculture the virus multiplied about 1,000 times, and during the whole period its virulence remained approximately constant. Findlay (1928) reported similar success in the cultivation of the fowl-pox virus by Carrel's method. Craciun and Oppenheimer (1926) cultivated vaccinia virus in association with embryonic guinea-pig's cornea, and carried through nine successive transfers during a period of 71 days. Finally the *in vitro* cultivation of vaccinia virus in the apparent absence of proliferating cells was reported by the Maitlands (1928). Infected rabbit testicle was ground up, diluted with Tyrode's solution, added to minced hen's kidney, placed in the cold room for 4 hours, and then cultivated in a Carrel flask containing hen's serum. The flasks were incubated at 37° C., and subcultures made about once a week. Four passages were made in all. A 1/625 dilution of the last subculture, which represented a dilution of

$1/625 \times 10^8$ of the primary inoculum, produced vaccinia on inoculation into rabbits ; the original inoculum was active only in a 1/2500 dilution. Living tissue was, of course, not excluded, but no evidence of its multiplication was obtained.

Since these original observations, most of the common viruses, with the exception of rabies, have been grown in tissue culture. A more recent method is cultivation on the chorio-allantoic membrane of the developing chick embryo. Devised by Woodruff and Goodpasture (1931), the value of this method has already been demonstrated for the vaccinia and varicella viruses by Nauck and Paschen (1932) and by Taniguchi and his colleagues (1935), for the virus of vesicular stomatitis by Burnet and Galloway (1934), for the psittacosis virus by Burnet and Rountree (1935), and for the influenza virus by Burnet (1935), though according to Kunert (1935) the virulence of the vaccinia virus is not maintained under these conditions. As Rivers (1932) points out, many of the viruses in tissue culture exhibit both a species specificity and an affinity for certain kinds of cells. Fowl plague virus, for example, multiplies only in the presence of chick embryo skin and brain, but not in cultures of fibroblasts ; moreover, avian tissue appears to be essential.

None of the filtrable viruses has yet been cultivated in the absence of living cells. It is true that Eagles and McClean (1931) and Eagles (1935) state that they have grown vaccinia virus in a cell-free medium, but their results have not so far been confirmed (Maitland *et al.* 1932, Rivers and Ward 1933). It may indeed be questioned whether such highly parasitic organisms as the viruses appear to be are provided with sufficient enzyme systems to enable them to grow in the absence of the cellular activity of their host. The successful cultivation of the pathogenic viruses on lifeless media may well have to await the reproduction *in vitro* of the complete ferment mechanism of the living cell.

Resistance.—The filtrable viruses vary considerably in their resistance to nocuous agencies. Generally speaking, they resemble the vegetative bacteria more closely than the spore-bearing organisms ; that is to say they are generally destroyed by exposure to moist heat at 55–60° C. within half an hour, and succumb to fairly low concentrations of chemical disinfectants. On the whole, they appear to be more resistant than the vegetative bacteria to chemical agencies, but it must be remembered that experiments can never be performed in the complete absence of cellular, or at any rate, of protein material ; their apparently greater resistance may, therefore, be due to the protective action of substances in the medium.

The effect of desiccation varies, partly with the method employed, and partly with the particular 'virus in question. The Foot-and-Mouth Disease Research Committee (Report 1927) found that filtered vesicle fluid from the guinea-pig, if dried rapidly on slides at 37° C., was often inactivated immediately ; on the other hand, if dried slowly at room temperature, and kept at room temperature over H_2SO_4, it survived for 3 to 6 months. Noguchi (1918) found that, when dried, vaccinia virus remained alive for over a year, but its virulence was considerably decreased. One hour's exposure, to the August sun, of the foot-and-mouth virus, dried on a glass slide, inactivated it. Most viruses appear to be very resistant to cold. Vaccinia virus withstands a temperature of —180° C. for months, and even repeated freezing and thawing fails to destroy it. Frozen and dried, they may live for months (Sawyer *et al.* 1929). Vaccinia virus in dry powdered form withstands dry heat at 100° C. for 5 to 10 minutes. Moist heat at 55–60° C. for half to one hour is fatal to most viruses, but blood from swine fever is said to withstand a temperature of 58° C. for at least 2 hours ; it is inactivated, however, within an hour by a temperature of 78° C. Most viruses exhibit a fairly high resistance to glycerol, and one of the best methods of preserving infectious tissue is to suspend it in 50 per cent. glycerolated saline, cover it with liquid paraffin, and store it in the ice-chest (Perdrau 1927). Pure glycerol destroys the viruses fairly rapidly as a rule ; thus Noguchi (1918) found that vaccinia virus was destroyed by pure glycerol at 4° C. within 24 hours, though in 40 per cent. glycerol it survived for about 6 months. The preservative action of glycerol probably depends on the inhibition it exerts on autolysis of the infected tissue (Rivers 1928). Survival in distilled water, saline, or Ringer's solution, varies considerably. Vaccinia virus is said to survive in saline or in Ringer's solution at 4° C. for over a year ; the foot-and-mouth virus, on the contrary, rarely survives for more than 24 hours at 37° C. in saline. The optimum H-ion concentration for survival of the foot-and-mouth and the vaccinia virus is pH 7·6. Vaccinia virus is said to survive in 0·5 per cent. and 1·0 per cent. phenol solutions for over a year at 4° C., but to be destroyed by 2 per cent. phenol within 24 hours, and by a 1/30,000 solution of iodine within 1 hour at 37° C. (Noguchi 1918). Gordon (1925) found that vaccinia virus was destroyed by 50 per cent. ethyl alcohol, 50 per cent. methyl alcohol, and 50 per cent. acetone within an hour at room temperature ; 20 per cent. ethyl alcohol, 10 per cent. methyl alcohol, 10 per cent. acetone, and 20 per cent. ether failed to destroy it in 24 hours ; even 50 per cent. ether did not destroy it completely in this time. Potassium permanganate was found to be extremely viricidal, destroying it even in a 1/10,000 solution within an hour at room temperature. Chloroform is said to be very much more destructive than ether, alcohol, or acetone (Reynals 1928). The foot-and-mouth virus is resistant to concentrations of phenol, lysol, toluol, hydrogen peroxide, chlorine, iodine, acetone, and chloropicrin that rapidly destroy vegetative bacteria ; but it is killed by 0·1 per cent. formol at 26–27° C. in 24 hours, and by 2 per cent. antiformin or 0·4 per cent. $HgCl_2$ within 24 hours. On the other hand, a liver suspension from a mouse infected with ectromelia may remain virulent in 0·5 per cent. phenolized saline at 0° C. for several months. At low temperatures the presence of tissue cells seems to be beneficial to the survival of viruses, but at higher temperatures the reverse is probably true. Amies (1934), for example, found that vaccinia virus remained virulent much longer at 37° C. when stored in the form of a suspension of elementary bodies than in tissue culture. In general, the presence of serum or 0·5 per cent. agar is beneficial for survival, as is also storage under anaerobic conditions (Zinsser and Tang 1929, Zinsser and Seastone 1930, McClean and Eagles 1931). Viruses seem to be readily susceptible to photodynamic action (see Chapter V), and succumb in a few minutes when exposed to a concentration of about 1/100,000 methylene blue in the presence of light (Perdrau and Todd 1933, Herzberg 1933, Shortt and Brooks 1934).

Metabolism.—Practically nothing is known about the metabolism of the filtrable viruses, one of the great hindrances to its study being the impossibility of cultivating them in the absence of tissue cells. It has been shown by Warburg that normal cells seldom break down carbohydrates with the formation of lactic acid, even under aerobic conditions ; and when they do so the lactic acid formed is small in amount. According to Crabtree (1928), however, this character of aerobic glycolysis is manifested by tissues infected with certain of the filtrable viruses, particularly those, such as fowl-pox in pigeons, vaccinia in young chickens, and the human wart virus, which give rise to a considerable amount of cellular hyperplasia.   Whether the viruses, however, have any metabolism of their own has not yet been ascertained.

Antigenic Structure.—Although the study of the antigenic structure of viruses is as yet in its infancy, enough has been learned to show that, in this respect, viruses differ in no essential way from bacteria.   The presence of precipitins in the blood serum of animals inoculated with vaccinia virus has been reported by several workers (see Sobernheim 1925).   Gordon (1925) found agglutinins and complement-fixing bodies in the serum of rabbits inoculated with vaccinia, active up to a dilution of 1/100–1/200 ; both antibodies were specific in the sense that they reacted solely with vaccinia and variola virus suspensions, and gave no reaction with varicella virus, sterile pus, or brain suspensions from encephalitis lethargica.   In general, precipitins have been demonstrated more frequently than agglutinins or complement-fixing bodies.

Recent work, particularly with vaccinia, has revealed an antigenic complexity in the viruses similar to that present in many bacteria.   The elementary bodies of vaccinia appear to contain two agglutinogens, one of which, L, is destroyed by exposure to 56° C. for one hour, the other of which, S, withstands a temperature of at least 95° C. for this time.   By suitable methods precipitinogens can be extracted from infected material and from tissue cultures which appear to correspond to the agglutinogens in the elementary bodies.   There is evidence that the heat-stable precipitinogen is a polysaccharide hapten (Craigie 1932, 1935, Smith 1932, Craigie and Wishart 1934*a*, *b*, Ch'en 1934, Salaman 1934).

A further analogy with bacteria is furnished by the demonstration of multiple antigenic types in a single species of virus.   The most striking example of this is the foot-and-mouth virus, in which at least three specifically distinct types, differing in their infectivity, have been found (Vallée and Carré 1922, Waldmann and Trautwein 1926).   The existence of a group antigenic relationship such as that demonstrated between the viruses of influenza and swine influenza (see Chapter LXXI) is again reminiscent of the antigenic morphology of bacteria.

Besides stimulating the production of agglutinins, precipitins, and complement-fixing bodies—usually in comparatively low titres—the inoculation of viruses into suitable animals is often followed by the appearance of neutralizing antibodies in the serum.   The mode of action of these antibodies forms a constant subject of discussion.   Whether they destroy the virus, whether they merely inactivate it, whether they sensitize it, or whether they fail even to combine with it, is still not known with certainty.   Most of the evidence seems to be in favour of the occurrence of a slow union between virus and antibody leading to sensitization or actual destruction (see Chapter LII).

Pathogenicity.—The virulence of the pathogenic viruses is subject to variation. Some viruses appear to have become adapted to numerous different hosts ; there is evidence, for example, that all the animal poxes, with the possible exception of fowl-pox, are due to varieties of one and the same virus (Zwick 1924).   The properties of a virus may be considerably altered during the process of adaptation to a different host.   Inoculation of the calf with variola virus, and subsequent transference by passage through calves, modifies the virus in such a way that when reinoculated into human beings it gives rise not to small-pox but to vaccinia. Passage of the street virus of rabies through the brain of rabbits gives rise to the production of a fixed virus, which, though it kills rabbits on intracerebral inoculation more rapidly than the street virus, is yet much less virulent than the street virus on subcutaneous inoculation (Levaditi *et al.* 1924). This example illustrates another characteristic that is frequently observed in the study of viruses, namely, their adaptation not only to one particular host, but to one special tissue or route of inoculation.

Infection in most of the filtrable virus diseases appears to occur by direct contagion, the infective material gaining access to the body either by the nasopharynx or sometimes by the skin, as in rabies. In certain diseases the virus is inoculated into the blood stream by an insect vector ; yellow fever, for example, is carried by the mosquito *Aedes aegypti*, dengue fever by *Culex fatigans* Wied, and Pappataci fever by the sandfly, *Phlebotomus papatassii*. Laboratory infections are not infrequent, especially with yellow fever, psittacosis, rift valley fever, and louping ill.

The Nature of Filtrable Viruses.—We do not propose to review the various theories that have been advanced on this subject. Whether the filtrable viruses are organized living bodies reproducing themselves by binary fission or other means, whether they are unorganized semi-fluid menstrua capable of unlimited reproduction—the *contagium fluidum vivum* of Beijerinck—whether they resemble enzymes in being unorganized but capable of continuous survival and activity, or whether they behave like an inanimate poison which regenerates itself on contact with normal cells, is a matter that can be endlessly disputed without final agreement being reached. In our own view the evidence is becoming increasingly stronger that the filtrable viruses are essentially minute micro-organisms. Each of the various properties of the viruses can be paralleled by inanimate matter, but as Andrewes (1934) points out we know of nothing but a living organism that possesses at one and the same time *all* these various properties. Microscopical, filtration, and centrifugal observations leave no doubt that they are of particulate nature. In the case of the few viruses in which a comparison by these different methods has proved possible, the agreement between the results is very striking. It has, in fact, been so good as to make it necessary to conclude that, if the visible coccoid bodies are not the infective units of the virus, these must be particles of the same size, but for some unknown reason invisible either by direct observation or by ultra-violet photography (Dale 1935).

One of the chief stumbling-blocks to their admission into the world of living micro-organisms is their extremely small size. If the hæmoglobin molecule is taken as having a diameter of 5 mμ, it follows that a virus, such as that of foot-and-mouth disease, with a diameter of about 10 mμ, would have room for only $8\frac{1}{2}$ protein molecules. A staphylococcus, on the other hand, with a diameter of 1,000 mμ, could contain $8\frac{1}{2}$ million. It is difficult to understand how the foot-and-mouth virus, which incidentally has a complex antigenic structure (see Daubney 1934), could possibly carry out the functions characteristic of living matter. This virus, however, is very similar in its behaviour to that of vesicular stomatitis, which has a diameter of about 85 mμ. If we are going to draw an arbitrary dividing line, based solely on size, between the definitely living and the probably non-living, we shall have to draw it either below the level of the foot-and-mouth virus or above the level of the virus of vesicular stomatitis, because to assign the two to different classes would demand a greater break in continuity than would be intellectually justifiable. The truth is that we have no idea of the minimal degree of organization necessary for the lowest living creature. It may well be that, if practically the whole of the nutritive requirements of a given virus are supplied by the host cell in which it is a parasite, its total functional activity will be limited to absorption and division. For this purpose possibly a few protein molecules may suffice.

We have said nothing about the fascinating problem provided by the filtrable tumours. Here again we are on very difficult ground. There is evidence suggesting that filtrable virus particles are essential to their reproduction, and that tumours both of avian and mammalian origin are caused, to some extent at least, by infecting particles having many of the characteristics of the known filtrable viruses (see Gye 1925, Andrewes 1934, Ledingham and Gye 1935, and Chapter LXXXV).

REFERENCES

AMIES, C. R. (1933) *Lancet*, i. 1015 ; (1934) *Brit. J. exp. Path.*, **15,** 180.
ANDREWES, C. H. (1929) *Brit. J. exp. Path.*, **10,** 188 ; (1934) *Lancet*, ii. 63, 117.
ASHESHOV, I. (1933) *J. Bact.*, **25,** 323, 339.
BARNARD, J. E. (1925) *Lancet*, ii. 117 ; (1935) *Brit. J. exp. Path.*, **16,** 129.
BARNARD, J. E. and ELFORD, W. J. (1931) *Proc. roy. Soc.*, *B*, **109,** 360.
BECHHOLD, H. and SCHLESINGER, M. (1931) *Biochem. Z.*, **236,** 387.
BEDSON, S. P. and BLAND, J. O. W. (1932) *Brit. J. exp. Path.*, **13,** 461 ; (1933) *Ibid.*, **14,** 267 ; (1934) *Ibid.*, **15,** 243.
BURNET, F. M. (1935) *Med. J. Australia*, ii. 687.
BURNET, F. M. and GALLOWAY, I. A. (1934) *Brit. J. exp. Path.*, **15,** 105.
BURNET, F. M. and ROUNTREE, P. M. (1935) *J. Path. Bact.*, **40,** 471.
CARREL, A. and RIVERS, T. M. (1927) *C. R. Soc. Biol.*, **96,** 848.
CH'EN, W. K. (1934) *Proc. Soc. exp. Biol.*, *N.Y.*, **32,** 491.
COWDRY, E. V. (1933) *Amer. J. Path.*, **9,** 149.
COX, H. R. and HYDE, R. R. (1932) *Amer. J. Hyg.*, **16,** 667.
CRABTREE, H. G. (1928) *Biochem. J.*, **22,** 1289.
CRACIUN, E. C. and OPPENHEIMER, E. H. (1926) *J. exp. Med.*, **43,** 815.
CRAIGIE, J. (1932) *Brit. J. exp. Path.*, **13,** 259 ; (1935) *J. Immunol.*, **29,** 70.
CRAIGIE, J. and WISHART, F. O. (1934a) *Brit. J. exp. Path.*, **15,** 390 ; (1934b) *Trans. roy. Soc. Can.*, Section v. 91.
DALE, H. H. (1935) Huxley Memorial Lecture. Macmillan & Co., Ltd., London.
DAUBNEY, R. (1934) *J. comp. Path.*, **47,** 259.
DOUGLAS, S. R. and SMITH, W. (1928) *Brit. J. exp. Path.*, **9,** 213.
EAGLES, G. H. (1935) *Brit. J. exp. Path.*, **16,** 188.
EAGLES, G. H. and McCLEAN, D. (1931) *Brit. J. exp. Path.*, **12,** 97.
ELFORD, W. J. (1931) *J. Path. Bact.*, **34,** 505 ; (1933) *Proc. roy. Soc.*, *B*, **112,** 384.
ELFORD, W. J., GRABAR, P., and FERRY, J. D. (1935) *Brit. J. exp. Path.*, **16,** 583.
FINDLAY, G. M. (1928) *Brit. J. exp. Path.*, **9,** 28 ; (1930) *Brit. J. exp. Path.*, **11,** 109.
FINDLAY, G. M. and LUDFORD, R. J. (1926) *Brit. J. exp. Path.*, **7,** 223.
GALLOWAY, I. A. and ELFORD, W. J. (1931) *Brit. J. exp. Path.*, **12,** 407.
GASTINEL, P. and REILLY, J. (1928) *Bull. Méd.*, **42,** 839.
GINS, H. A. and KRAUSE, C. (1923) *Ergebn. allg. Path. path. Anat.*, **20,** ii. 805.
GOODPASTURE, E. W. (1929) *Arch. Path.*, **7,** 114 ; (1929–30) Harvey Lectures ; (1930) *Zbl. Ges. Neurol. Psychiat.*, **129,** 599.
GORDON, M. H. (1925) *Spec. Rep. Ser. med. Res. Coun., Lond.*, No. 98.
GRINNELL, F. B. (1929) *J. Bact.*, **18,** 175.
GYE, W. E. (1925) *Lancet*, ii. 109.
HAAGEN, E. (1928) *Zbl. Bakt.*, **109,** 31.
HERZBERG, K. (1933) *Z. ImmunForsch.*, **80,** 507.
HINDLE, E. and FINDLAY, G. M. (1930) *Brit. J. exp. Path.*, **11,** 134.
HUGHES, T. P., PARKER, R. F., and RIVERS, T. M. (1935) *J. exp. Med.*, **62,** 349.
KUNERT, H. (1935) *Z. Hyg. InfektKr.*, **117,** 216.
LAIDLAW, P. P. and ELFORD, W. J. (1936) *Proc. roy. Soc.*, *B*, **120,** 292.
LEDINGHAM, J. C. G. (1924) *Brit. J. exp. Path.*, **5,** 332.
LEDINGHAM, J. C. G. (1931) *Lancet*, ii. 525 ; (1932) *Brit. med. J.*, ii. 953 ; (1935) *Bull. Johns Hopkins Hosp.*, **56,** 247, 337 ; *Ibid.*, **57,** 32.
LEDINGHAM, J. C. G. and GYE, W. E. (1935) *Lancet*, i. 376.
LEVADITI, C. and NICOLAU, S. (1923) *C. R. Soc. Biol.*, **88,** 66.
LEVADITI, C., NICOLAU, S., and SCHOEN, R. (1924) *C. R. Soc. Biol.*, **91,** 423.
LEWIS, M. R. and ANDERVONT, H. B. (1927) *Amer. J. Hyg.*, **7,** 505.
LIPSCHÜTZ, B. (1925) *Zbl. Bakt.*, **96,** 222.
MAITLAND, H. B., LAING, A. W., and LYTH, R. (1932) *Brit. J. exp. Path.*, **13,** 90.
MAITLAND, H. B. and MAITLAND, M. C. (1928) *Lancet*, ii. 596.
MARIE, A. C. and URBAIN, A. (1930) *C. R. Soc. Biol.*, **103,** 866.

McClean, D. and Eagles, G. H. (1931) *Brit. J. exp. Path.*, **12**, 103.
McIntosh, J. (1935) *J. Path. Bact.*, **41**, 215.
Mudd, S. (1922–3) *Amer. J. Physiol.*, **63**, 429 ; (1928) " Filterable Viruses." T. M. Rivers, p. 55. Baillière, Tindall & Cox, London.
Natarajan, C. V. and Hyde, R. R. (1930) *Amer. J. Hyg.*, **11**, 652.
Nauck, E. G. and Paschen, E. (1932) *Zbl. Bakt.*, **124**, 91.
Noguchi, H. (1915) *J. exp. Med.*, **21**, 539 ; (1918) *Ibid.*, **27**, 425.
Olitsky, P. K. and Boëz, L. (1927) *J. exp. Med.*, **45**, 685.
Parker, F. and Nye, R. N. (1925) *Amer. J. Path.*, **1**, 325, 337.
Paschen, E. (1932) *Zbl. Bakt.*, **124**, 89.
Perdrau, J. R. (1927) *Brit. J. exp. Path.*, **8**, 167.
Perdrau, J. R. and Todd, C. (1933) *Proc. roy. Soc.*, B., **112**, 288.
Poppe, K. and Busch, G. (1930) *Z. ImmunForsch.*, **68**, 510.
Report. (1927) 2*nd Progr. Rep. Foot and Mouth Dis. Res. Comm. Ministry Agric. Fish.*, *Lond.*
Reynals, F. D. (1928) *J. exp. Med.*, **47**, 389.
Rivers, T. M. (1928) " Filterable Viruses," p. 3. Baillière, Tindall & Cox, London ; (1932) *Physiol. Rev.* **12**, 423.
Rivers, T. M., Haagen, E., and Muckenfuss, R. S. (1929) *J. exp. Med.*, **50**, 665.
Rivers, T. M. and Pearce, L. (1925) *J. exp. Med.*, **42**, 523.
Rivers, T. M. and Ward, S. M. (1933) *J. exp. Med.*, **57**, 51, 741.
Salaman, M. H. (1934) *Brit. J. exp. Path.*, **15**, 381.
Sankaran, G., Iyengar, K. R. K., and Beer, W. A. (1934) *Indian J. med. Res.*, **21**, 909.
Sawyer, W. A. and Frobisher, M. (1929) *J. exp. Med.*, **50**, 713.
Sawyer, W. A., Lloyd, W. D. M., and Kitchen, S. F. (1929) *J. exp. Med.*, **50**, 1.
Shortt, H. E. and Brooks, A. G. (1934) *Indian J. med. Res.*, **21**, 581.
Sichert-Modrow, I. (1930) *Zbl. Bakt.*, **119**, 12.
Smith, W. (1932) *Brit. J. exp. Path.*, **13**, 434.
Sobernheim, G. (1925) *Ergebn. Hyg.*, **7**, 133.
Svedberg, T., Boestad, G., and Eriksson-Quensel, I. B. (1934) *Nature*, **134**, 98.
Svedberg, T. and Nichols, J. B. (1927) *J. Amer. chem. Soc.*, **49**, 2920.
Tallerman, K. H. (1929) *Brit. J. exp. Path.*, **10**, 360.
Tang, F. F. (1932) *J. Bact.*, **24**, 133.
Taniguchi, T., Kogita, Y., Hosokawa, M., and Kuga, S. (1935) *Jap. J. exp. Med.*, **13**, 19.
Todd, C. (1928) *Brit. J. exp. Path.*, **9**, 19.
Vallée, H. and Carré, H. (1922) *C. R. Acad. Sci.*, **174**, 1498.
Waldmann, O. and Trautwein, K. (1926) *Berl. tierärztl. Wschr.*, **42**, 569.
Ward, H. K. (1929) *J. exp. Med.*, **50**, 31.
Woodruff, A. M. and Goodpasture, E. W. (1931) *Amer. J. Path.*, **7**, 209.
Woodruff, C. E. and Goodpasture, E. W. (1929) *Amer. J. Path.*, **5**, 1 ; (1930) *Ibid.*, **6**, 713.
Zinsser, H. and Seastone, C. V. (1930) *J. Immunol.*, **18**, 1.
Zinsser, H. and Tang, F. (1929) *J. Immunol.*, **17**, 343.
Zwick. (1924) *Dtsch. tierärztl. Wschr.*, **32**, 643.

PART III

INFECTION AND RESISTANCE

CHAPTER XXXIX

TYPES OF IMMUNITY

THE term *immunity*, used as we use it here, needs definition. As plain English, it does not mean what it says. This does not matter very much because, as Whitehead points out so aptly in his *Introduction to Mathematics*, the scientist shares with Humpty Dumpty the privilege of paying words extra and making them mean what he likes. But if we are to avoid confusion we must at least give our words definite orders and see that they are obeyed. It happens that the state suggested by the word that we have chosen as a generic label for the phenomena we wish to study is one about which we know very little, except that it exists. We have indeed not bothered very much about it. Complete natural insusceptibility to infection removes the relationship between the particular host and parasite concerned from our field of interest, except in so far as we can learn from any instance of this kind something of the genetic laws that determine the transmission of this innate and complete resistance. Our main business is with those interactions between parasite and host that are characterized by a fluctuating equilibrium, and with the factors that shift this equilibrium, so that sometimes the parasite, sometimes the host, gains the upper hand. *Resistance* would be a better word than *Immunity* ; but *Immunity* will serve well enough so long as we make it quite clear that we are using it to denote the resultant of two opposing systems, and that this resultant can assume any value from zero to infinity.

And our name misleads a little because of its associations. It happens to have been frequently applied to the data obtained by a particular kind of technique, and there has been a tendency to confuse technique with subject-matter. The special methods devised by the immunologist—if he must accept the unpleasing name that custom has given him—are applicable to problems with which he has no concern ; while the field proper to his study extends far beyond the limits that would be imposed by any definition in terms of the particular technique employed. The student of immunity is concerned with all data relating to the mechanisms involved in infective disease, by whatever means they are obtained. Any account given at the present time must stress unduly a particular set of phenomena, simply because they are the only phenomena that have as yet been adequately studied ; but this is a historical accident that will be remedied by time.

The phenomena that present themselves for study are derived from the most diverse sources.   Some come to us from epidemiology, using that term in its widest sense.   Under natural conditions different animal species show a widely differing incidence of certain infections.   Thus, anthrax is in the main a disease of herbivora. Of the animals dying of anthrax in this country in 1914, 733 were cattle, 5 were sheep, 32 were swine and 25 were horses.   In Australia and South America sheep are more commonly affected ; but Algerian sheep are stated to be highly resistant. Tuberculosis is one of the commonest natural infections of man and cattle.   It is common in pigs and in fowls.   It is relatively uncommon in sheep, goats, horses and dogs.   It is stated to be very uncommon as a natural disease in rabbits, guinea-pigs, rats and mice.   Among mankind there are well-marked racial differences in its incidence and severity.   In eight of the great cities of the United States in 1920 the mortality from tuberculosis among the white population varied from 0·794 to 1·216 per 1,000 living ; among the coloured population it varied from 2·855 to 4·205 per 1,000.   Such instances could be multiplied *ad nauseam*.

The epidemiologist also records differences in the incidence and fatality of various infective diseases at different ages, suggesting in many cases an increase in resistance with age.   He notes also that repeated attacks of the same infective diseases are in some instances very rare, as in measles, or smallpox, or diphtheria, or typhoid fever, while in others they are relatively common, as in influenza, or pneumonia, or the common cold.

Other data come to us from clinical medicine in the narrower sense.   Infections that, in their usual course, progress slowly to death or recovery sometimes assume a fulminating form.   Such a protean infection as tuberculosis shows the widest diversity in the varying prominence of its local and general manifestations.   And, in any infective disease, why do some patients die and others recover ?

For the immunologist these are crude data that require analysis.   Using his own methods he re-examines the phenomena presented by natural infection.   Sometimes he transforms the picture they present.   He finds, for instance, that the recorded frequency of natural tuberculosis in various animal species does not in all cases reflect their relative resistance to experimental infection (see Chapter LVI). He finds, also, that a clinical entity may correspond to an immunological diversity. This is true of tuberculosis ; there are different types of the tubercle bacillus, and a given host species is more resistant to one type than to another.   It is true of obar pneumonia.   For the immunologist this is not one disease but several, each caused by a significantly different type of pneumococcus ; and he notes that the statement that second attacks of pneumonia are not uncommon may belong to the Baconian category of a truth that has in it a mixture of a lie.   Again he finds that enteric fever is not one but many ; and his attempts at interference are planned accordingly.

Another important change that the immunologist makes in the clinical and epidemiological picture is in regard to the character and extent of the association between any given parasite and the host species that it infects.   He finds that the real range of interaction includes states of equilibrium in which the host shows no overt signs of disease.   Whether we call all these conditions latent infections, or refer to many of the hosts as healthy carriers, matters little.   No hair-splitting definition will help us much.   The significant thing we have learned is that in some infections, such as measles, contact between a previously uninfected host and the virus of the disease usually results in a clinically characteristic attack, so that the epidemiological picture gives us a reasonably adequate description of the biological association, while in other diseases, such as cerebrospinal meningitis or poliomyelitis, the clinically diagnosable cases form so small a fraction of the total number of infected persons that they might almost be regarded as occasional accidents in an association that, in its modal form, induces no such serious effects.

In re-examining the data that he receives from the field and from the ward, the immunologist relies in large part on experiments on animals. When he tries to interpret his data he is forced to rely almost entirely on this fundamental method of study. He cannot advance without some simplification of his problems, some control, at least, over the innumerable variables that determine the incidence and results of infective disease as it occurs in nature.

By such experiments he has found that he can increase the resistance of animals by infecting them with sublethal doses of a given pathogenic organism, or by injecting an organism that has lost its power to kill—though here he was forestalled by Jenner's experiment of vaccination in man—or, more safely and conveniently, by injecting dead organisms or their products. From analogy, and from the fact that he can demonstrate similar changes in the tissue fluids, he concludes that this artificial immunization in animals is essentially similar to the natural immunization that occurs during an attack of an infective disease. Since the tissues of the naturally infected or artificially immunized host play an active part in bringing about this increased resistance, he calls it *active immunity*. In some cases he finds that he can transmit this resistant state to a normally susceptible animal by injecting into it the serum of another animal that has been rendered immune. Since the tissues of the recipient appear to play a relatively passive part, he calls this *passive immunity*. He also finds that immunity of this kind is sometimes transmitted naturally from a mother to her young, either by the passage of the protective substances *via* the placental vessels, or by their ingestion during the first days or weeks of life in the colostrum. This he calls *congenital passive immunity*.

And so, if he has a taste for classification, the immunologist can draw up some such list as this :

1. Innate Immunity.

2. Acquired Immunity.
    (*a*) Active.
        (α) Naturally acquired.
        (β) Artificially induced.
    (*b*) Passive.
        (α) Naturally acquired (congenital).
        (β) Artificially induced.

Innate, or Genetic, Immunity.

Of innate as opposed to acquired immunity, little need here be said. We have noted that different animal species may display wide differences in their resistance to various bacterial parasites, or to their toxins. This species immunity is of great practical importance in relation to the communicability of infective disease from animals to man, or from one animal species to another.

There can be no doubt that differences in innate resistance also occur within any animal species, one individual differing from another in this biological character as in any other. Of the extent of these differences and of the laws that govern their inheritance we as yet know very little. Within recent years a number of workers have attempted to study this problem by direct experiment, and their results indicate that it is possible to increase or lower the average resistance of a given strain of rats, mice or other experimental animals, by selective breeding. (See for instance Webster 1923, 1924a, b, 1925, 1933a, b, Pritchett 1925, 1926a, b, Lambert and Knox 1928, Irwin 1929, 1933, Irwin and Hughes 1931, 1933, Lambert 1932, Schott 1932, Gowen 1933, Gowen and Schott 1933a, b, c, Schütze et al. 1936.)

Experiments of this type are, however, subject to great technical difficulties. The obvious method of obtaining a strain of animals with a high genetic resistance is to infect an adequate sample with the bacterium under study, breed from the survivors, and repeat the process through several subsequent generations. This plan has, in fact, been followed by some of the workers referred to above ; but it is clearly open to serious sources of error. In testing the resistance of our original generation we shall certainly alter it, and the effect of this alteration will not be confined to the parent animals. The surviving females will pass on a temporary passive immunity to their young ; and, since most of the species commonly employed in such tests attain sexual maturity within a few months at most, this congenital passive immunity may persist until the F_1 generation are tested. A much more serious source of error is that the survivors will often be carriers of the organisms with which they were infected. Either the male or female parent may thus infect the young, inducing in them an acquired active immunity, or adding it to the congenital passive immunity already present. If this source of error is avoided, by mating the original sample of animals at random, and testing them after they have been separated from their young, the number of animals that must be employed, and the resulting labour, are enormously increased ; since it will only be by chance that both parents of any one litter will be found to possess a resistance above, or below, the average.

The papers referred to above describe various attempts to overcome, or minimize, these technical difficulties ; and they are very fully discussed in a recent monograph by Hill (1934). His conclusion is that, while possible errors of the kind we have mentioned render doubtful many of the observations that have been recorded, a presumptive case has been established for the existence of genetic differences in resistance within a breed or species, as well as between breeds or between species. In regard to the degree of these genetic differences, within a strain or breed, it is much more difficult to arrive at any just conclusion. Some of the differences recorded have, in fact, been quite trivial ; but a few have been of a relatively high order.

As an example of the latter we may quote results recorded by Webster (1933b). By selective breeding, carried out through several generations, he was able to obtain a particularly resistant, and a particularly susceptible strain of mice, both originally derived from the strain that has been bred for many years at the Rockefeller Institute. The organism against which they were tested, in each successive generation, was *Bact. enteritidis*. The susceptible strain finally developed showed a mortality of 85 to 95 per cent. when infected with this organism, while the resistant strain showed a mortality of the order of 15 per cent. It is of interest to note that the difference in resistance between these two strains was non-specific, in the ordinary bacteriological sense. Thus the susceptible strain showed a mortality of 63 per cent., when tested against *Past. septica*, 80 per cent. when tested against Friedländer's bacillus, and 38 per cent. when tested against the pneumococcus, while the corresponding figures for the resistant strain were 35 per cent., 45 per cent. and 16 per cent. respectively. On the other hand the susceptible strain showed a mortality of 40 per cent., when tested against the virus of louping-ill, as compared with a mortality of 60 per cent. in the resistant strain ; so that the genetic factors concerned, whatever they may be, do not seem to operate against all types of infection, though they are operative against many.

Schütze, Gorer and Finlayson (1936), who have made tests on Webster's resistant and susceptible strains, record rather different results. The resistant strain showed a lower mortality than the susceptible when tested against *Bact. enteritidis* or *Bact. typhimurium* ; but when the two strains were tested against the pneumococcus, or against *Past. septica*, there was no significant difference in their behaviour. The discrepancy between these results and those recorded by Webster may be due to the fact that Schütze and his colleagues infected their mice by intraperitoneal injection, while Webster used the intranasal route. In Schütze's experiments, as in Webster's, both strains were equally susceptible to the virus of louping-ill.

Acquired Immunity.

It is with acquired immunity that we are here mainly concerned ; and our interest lies particularly in those reactions that we can induce, and study, in the laboratory. Before discussing these mechanisms in any detail, it will, however, be well to consider briefly the general difference in behaviour displayed by immune and susceptible animals.

Grades of Immunity.

We have noted that the kinds of immunity in which we are most interested are seldom absolute. To keep our ideas clear and precise we may consider briefly the grades of immunity that can, in fact, be demonstrated, remembering always that they shade into one another by imperceptible degrees.

Fig. 215 gives, in diagrammatic form, a rough classification that will be sufficient for our immediate needs. It represents an infection of the invasive type, associated with a bacteræmia (an invasion of the blood stream by micro-organisms) as well as with local lesions ; but it can easily be modified to meet the case of a toxæmic infection.

The width of the black wedge-shaped areas at any level may be taken to represent the chance of death, and the degree, or frequency, of bacteræmia, of local lesions, and of latent infections, in a sample of individuals possessed of approximately the same grade of immunity.

Thus, starting with the completely susceptible, we may assume that all, or almost all, infected individuals, will develop an acutely fatal bacteræmic infection. Local lesions will be infrequent, and minimal when they occur. There will be no latent infections.

Passing to our next arbitrary grade—partial immunity of low degree—we find fatal bacteræmic infections becoming less common, local lesions more frequent and more pronounced, and a small but increasing number of latent infections.

With partial immunity of a medium grade we find bacteræmia and death much less frequent, local lesions common and relatively extensive, and latent infections increasing in frequency.

With partial immunity of a high grade, death no longer occurs, bacteræmia is infrequent and, when it occurs, is slight and transient. Local lesions are becoming much less frequent and, when they occur, much less extensive. Latent infections reach a maximum frequency and then begin to decline.

Finally we reach the ideal—perhaps the dream ideal—of complete or solid immunity. The host is entirely impervious to all attacks of the parasite.

It will not have escaped attention that the grades of resistance that we have labelled as partial immunity are compatible with severe and often fatal infections, and that many infective diseases in their common clinical form might be regarded as occurring in partially immune persons. This view is almost certainly the right one. The syndromes that normally characterize such diseases as typhoid fever, or lobar pneumonia, are expressions of partial immunity. They would not occur

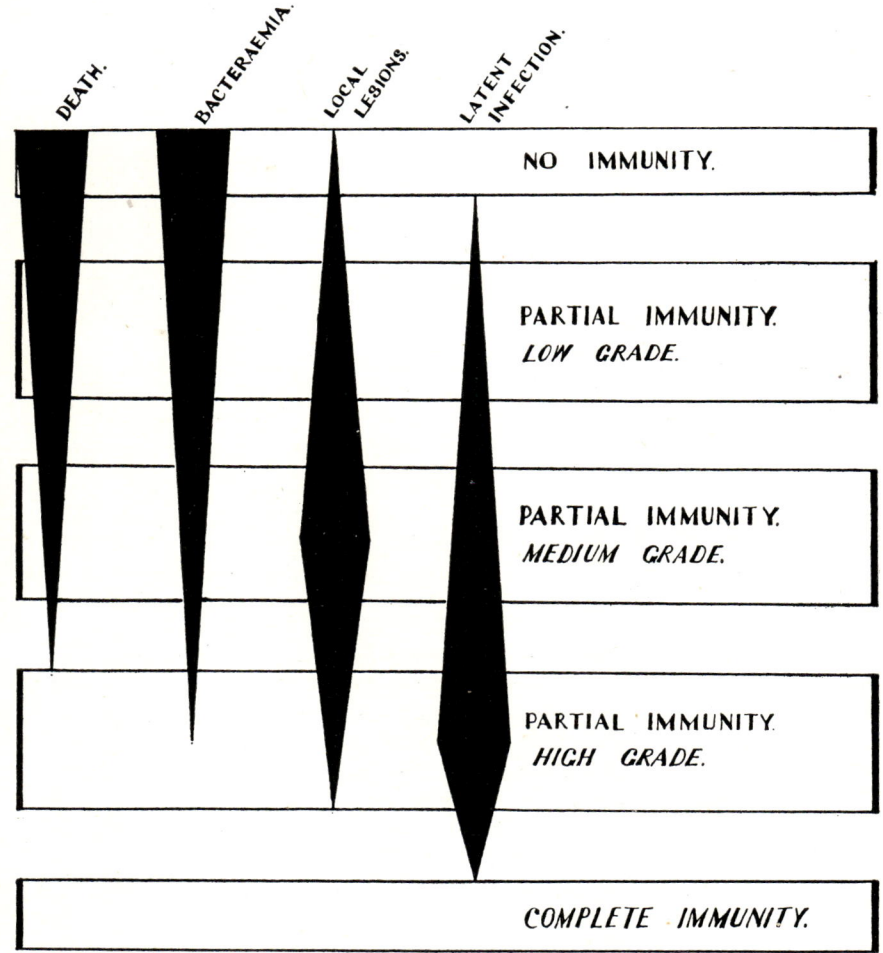

Fig. 215.

in a completely susceptible population attacked by a fully virulent parasite. The latter proviso is, of course, necessary. We may logically use the term immunity to express the relation of any given host to any given parasite, but events are determined by a balance—the balance between the virulence of the parasite and the resistance of the host.

The conception that infective disease, as we usually see it, is an expression of partial immunity, and that minor increases in immunity tend to increase the frequency of milder infections, is of sufficient importance to justify a few illustrative examples, drawn from experimental data.

It was noted by Smith and Moore (1892) that normal and actively immunized rabbits respond very differently to the subcutaneous inoculation of *Pasteurella septica*. Normal rabbits develop a rapidly fatal septicæmia. Immunized rabbits may develop large local abscesses, but show much less tendency to succumb to an acute generalized infection. More recent studies by Jones (1924) afford a good illustration of active immunity in all its grades. The normal rabbit is highly susceptible to *Pasteurella septica*, dying of a generalized septicæmia after the subcutaneous or intratracheal inoculation of 0·01 c.c. of a broth culture. In the latter case pulmonary lesions are slight or absent. In rabbits partially immunized by a single injection of a killed vaccine a similar intratracheal injection of living culture is followed, in most cases, by a severe and fatal pneumonia, usually associated with a suppurative pleurisy and pericarditis. In rabbits immunized by repeated doses of vaccine, intratracheal injections of living culture are usually without effect, while subcutaneous injections lead to the formation of localized abscesses followed by recovery.

Similar phenomena have been recorded in other bacterial infections. Thus Wadsworth (1904) found that the intratracheal injection of virulent pneumococci into normal rabbits was followed by a rapidly fatal septicæmia without local lesions, while similar injections in partially immunized rabbits were often followed by a characteristic pneumonic consolidation.

Differences of the same kind have been observed when strains of pneumococci of varying virulence have been injected intratracheally into normal rabbits. Thus Gaskell (1927) found that strains of high virulence gave rise to a rapidly fatal septicæmia without obvious pulmonary lesions ; those of lower virulence to a fatal lobar pneumonia ; those of still lower virulence to a patchy lobular consolidation, grading into an entire absence of reaction as the strains employed approached the region of entire avirulence.

The Relation of Immunity to Epidemiology and to Clinical Medicine.

Immunity is essentially an applied science. Its primary data are drawn from clinical medicine, and its outstanding achievement is that it enables us to do things, to interfere intelligently in the natural course of infective disease.

It must, therefore, remain in the closest touch with the field and with the ward. Its hypotheses, based largely on experiments in the laboratory, must stand their trial under field conditions. And here we are faced with a difficulty that is not shared by the more exact sciences. The relations of physics to the mechanical industries are superficially of the same kind as those of immunology to medicine, but actually they are very different. If a result obtained in the physical laboratory suggests a useful application to wireless reception or to aviation, or to any other practical and utilitarian end, it can be tried out with a reasonable certainty that its actual effect will be sufficiently obvious. It may succeed at once, or fail decisively at once, or succeed after adjustment ; but in any case definite answers will come back from the field to the laboratory, and both parties to the transaction will learn something from their success or their failure. In medicine this is not always the case, simply because the practice of medicine is a much more difficult thing than any kind of mechanical industry, or indeed than any industrial process at all.

It may be quite easy to tell when an immunological procedure is an unqualified practical success. It is much more difficult to tell whether it is a partial success, or an unqualified failure. And this cause of confusion, which in truth affects the immunologist in the laboratory almost as much as the physician in the ward, is so important that it deserves a separate chapter.

REFERENCES

GASKELL, J. F.　(1927) *Lancet*, ii. 951.

GOWEN, J. W.　(1933) *Quart. Rev. Biol.*, **8,** 338.

GOWEN, J. W. and SCHOTT, R. G.　(1933*a*) *J. Hyg., Camb.*, **33,** 370 ; (1933*b*) *Amer. J. Hyg.*, **18,** 674 ; (1933*c*) *Ibid.*, **18,** 688.

HILL, A. B.　(1934) *Spec. Rep. Ser. med. Res. Coun., Lond.*, No. 196.

IRWIN, M. R.　(1929) *Genetics*, **14,** 337 ; (1933) *J. Immunol.*, **24,** 285.

IRWIN, M. R. and HUGHES, T. P.　(1931) *Proc. Soc. exp. Biol., N.Y.*, **29,** 295 ; (1933) *J. Immunol.*, **24,** 343.

JONES, F. S.　(1924) *J. exp. Med.*, **39,** 725.

LAMBERT, W. V.　(1932) *J. Immunol.*, **23,** 229.

LAMBERT, W. V. and KNOX, C. W.　(1928) *Iowa State Coll. Sci.*, **2,** 179.

PRITCHETT, I. W.　(1925) *J. exp. Med.*, **41,** 195 ; (1926*a*) *Ibid.*, **43,** 161 ; (1926*b*) *Ibid.*, **43,** 143.

SCHOTT, R. G.　(1932) *Genetics*, **17,** 203.

SCHÜTZE, H., GORER, P. A., and FINLAYSON, M. H.　(1936) *J. Hyg., Camb.*, **36,** 37.

SMITH, T. and MOORE, V. A.　(1892) *U.S. Dep. Agric. Bur. anim. Indust. 8th and 9th ann. Rep.*, **45.**

WADSWORTH, A.　(1904) *Amer. J. med. Sci.*, **127,** 851.

WEBSTER, L. T.　(1923) *J. exp. Med.*, **38,** 45 ; (1924*a*) *Ibid.*, **39,** 129 ; (1924*b*) *Ibid.*, **39,** 879 ; (1925) *Ibid.*, **42,** 1 ; (1933*a*) *Ibid.*, **57,** 793 ; (1933*b*) *Ibid.*, **57,** 819.

CHAPTER XL

THE MEASUREMENT OF IMMUNITY REACTIONS IN THE LIVING ANIMAL

It is impossible to understand the present position of immunology, with its mixture of established fact, half-knowledge, hopeful guessings and frank bewilderment, without an adequate grasp of the difficulties involved in measuring immunity reactions in the living animal, and in assessing the significance of such measurements when they have been obtained.

That these difficulties should have been overlooked by the pioneers is not altogether surprising. The effects demonstrated in many of the earlier experiments were so dramatic as to need no exact measurement to establish their significance. The need for standardizing antitoxic sera did, indeed, provide an obvious opportunity for developing adequate biometrical methods; but the need was not realized, for reasons that will become apparent later in this chapter, and the opportunity was allowed to pass. As new methods of immunization were developed and tested in the laboratory, in the ward and in the field, the publication of violently conflicting reports as to their efficacy showed that something was amiss; but the remedy was not obvious, at least to the immunologist. The barriers that separate the different departments of science are not easy to break down, especially when the roads by which these departments are entered diverge widely in their course and are hedged by very different intellectual disciplines. It was natural enough that the laboratory worker and the clinician should show little eagerness to learn and apply the methods devised by the statistician. But the result has been a quite unnecessary amount of confusion; and the confusion is likely to persist so long as the need for such methods is ignored. It will not, therefore, be extravagant to devote a chapter to a brief discussion of the ways in which some of our present difficulties may be overcome—by avoiding the need for statistical methods where this is possible, and by using them intelligently when they cannot be escaped. It will be necessary to refer to many of the reactions that will be discussed in detail in later chapters; but, for the moment, their exact nature and significance does not concern us—we are regarding them merely as things that can be measured.

It is obviously beyond the scope of this book to describe, even in outline, the technical details of statistical measurement; for these reference may be made to one of the excellent textbooks available, such as those of Yule, of Pearl (on the more purely medical side), of Fisher (on the laboratory and experimental side), or the smaller primer of Woods and Russell. We must confine ourselves here to a brief discussion of general principles, with illustrative examples drawn from a few immunological problems.

The cause of our troubles is sufficiently obvious. It has been set out very clearly by Greenwood (1924) and by Yule (1924). The worker in the more exact sciences can reduce his uncontrollable variables to a minimum, or eliminate them altogether, and can so obtain constantly reproducible results. We cannot. In experiments on living animals, and still more in assessing the value of therapeutic or prophylactic procedures in man, we cannot exclude the interplay of factors about which we know little, except that they are certainly very numerous and may be very important. We cannot avoid an element of randomness in our observations ; but, if we have planned our experiments wisely and fortune has been kind in eliminating major disturbing factors that we could not have foreseen, this randomness will be of the kind that determines the number of heads and tails observed in a hundred tosses of a coin. The effect of such random variation can be calculated, and hence allowed for ; it is the assessment of the necessary allowance in any particular case that is our main concern.

It will simplify discussion to consider in turn a series of problems of the kind that are continually presenting themselves for solution.

THE MEASUREMENT OF RESISTANCE

To take the most obvious problem, though not the simplest, how can we measure the resistance of an animal to a particular parasite or to its toxin ? Suppose first that we wish to measure directly the resistance of the animal as a whole, taking death or survival as our test. Then it is only under quite exceptional conditions that we can obtain *any* measurement on a single animal. If we are dealing with a very powerful toxin that kills rapidly, within a few minutes or hours, it is sometimes possible to give repeated and increasing doses at short intervals and so to measure approximately the amount which is necessary to cause death. But if our toxin acts more slowly, or if we are dealing with a living bacterium, this method cannot be employed. If we start with a small dose and the animal fails to die during the period—usually measured in days—within which we should expect death to occur, we cannot test it again by giving a larger dose, because our first dose will almost certainly have changed its resistance. It is not, from our present point of view, the same animal as before. If we start with a large dose and the animal dies, we do not know how it would have reacted to a smaller dose ; if it lives, we know that it is resistant at that particular dose level, but we do not know and can never discover how it would have reacted to doses larger still. It is clear that, if we take death or survival as our test, we must deal with groups not with individuals. This condition is, in truth, usually implicit in the question we want to ask. We are not often interested in the resistance of a particular mouse, or guinea-pig, or rabbit, as such. We are almost always regarding the individual as a representative of a class—normal, or treated in some way that may, we think, have altered resistance to a particular bacterium or toxin—and we are none of us naïve enough to believe in a standard guinea-pig, even if we confine ourselves to animals of a given breed, sex, age and weight. What we sometimes fail to realize is that we must, in most cases, test large numbers of animals before we can regard our result as representing truly the average behaviour of the class from which those animals are drawn.

There are occasions, however, on which we do want to measure the resistance of an individual man or animal ; and, before discussing the methods to be adopted in measuring the resistance of groups, we may consider whether there is any way of solving this particular problem.

The Measurement of the Resistance of an Individual.

We cannot, as we have seen, obtain a direct measure of the resistance of any individual as an integral whole ; but we can sometimes measure the resistance of a particular tissue, provided that it is possible so to localize the effect of any one inoculum that the reactions to several inocula can be observed simultaneously. This method is commonly exploited in the determination of skin sensitiveness to bacterial toxins. The local effect of a small intradermic inoculation—0·2 c.c. is a convenient amount—is limited to the near neighbourhood of the site of injection. By spacing injections so as to leave a few centimetres between them it is easy to test several dilutions of a toxin on a comparatively small area of skin. In this way we can obtain an approximate measure of the smallest dose of toxin that will yield a characteristic reaction, and we can regard this as a measure of resistance —the smaller the dose that will produce such a result the less the resistance of the person or animal under test. Sometimes we rely on a different kind of skin test —the allergic—in which a positive reaction indicates not susceptibility but resistance, showing an increased energy and rapidity of response to a particular bacterial product.

There is another way in which we may attempt to estimate individual resistance —the demonstration and measurement of specific antibodies in the blood. In some cases we may measure the protective power of the serum against a toxin, or a virus, or occasionally against a living bacterium ; but this involves further tests on animals, so that we are faced with the same problem as before. Alternatively we may make use of *in vitro* antibody reactions—agglutination, complement fixation, the bactericidal power of the whole blood, and so on. But our measurement of resistance is now becoming very indirect, and we must watch our assumptions with corresponding care.

All these indirect methods of measuring *individual* resistance are, in fact, dependent on a preliminary knowledge of *average* behaviour. We cannot accept our skin tests, antitoxin titrations, agglutination reactions, and so on, as evidence of immunity until we have shown that such a correlation exists ; and, to establish the existence of this correlation, we must study the behaviour of groups.

The Measurement of the Average Resistance of a Group.

Let us start with the simplest problem. How can we determine whether a given procedure has made any difference at all in the resistance of a group of animals, even without measuring how large that difference is ? If the increase in resistance is of a very high order, our task is easy. We have only to administer to our treated animals a large dose of bacteria or toxin, which experience has shown to be certainly fatal to all untreated animals of the same species, age, weight, etc., and note that the treated animals survive. But we shall be wise to make very sure about our " certainly fatal " dose, especially if our group of treated animals is small. We shall, indeed, always test a few untreated controls to guard against any gross experimental error.

But the increase in resistance may not be of this dramatic kind. Our treated animals may be unable to withstand a dose of bacteria or toxin that will kill *all* untreated controls, though the mortality in treated and untreated groups may differ appreciably. Our problem is to determine whether this observed difference is likely to have occurred as the result of chance.

One method is to calculate the chances directly by straightforward but laborious arithmetic.

Suppose that we know, from an extended experience, that a particular experimental procedure causes a certain average death rate among large groups of animals. Let us express this death rate as p, using a decimal instead of a percentage notation (*i.e.* expressing a 50 per cent. death rate as 0·5). Then p will also be the chance of any particular animal dying. We should, in other words, expect to get death and recovery equally often if we made a series of tests, each on a single animal. Any animal under test must either live or die, so that, if the chance of death is p, the chance of life is q, where $q = 1 - p$. Expressed in figures, if the chance of death is 0·3 the chance of life must be 0·7 ; or, to revert to our more familiar percentages, if the percentage mortality is 30 the percentage survival must be 70.[*]

If we know the true average mortality rate, or chance of death, how often are we likely in any single test to meet with a death rate that differs from the average death rate by any specified amount ?

Suppose we make an experiment on two animals. Let us call them A and B. Using the notation referred to above, A's chance of dying is p. If A dies, B may either live or die ; and B's chance of death is also p. So the chance of both A and B dying is $p \times p$ or p^2.[†] The chance of both A and B living is clearly q^2. The chance of A living and B dying is $p \times q$; and this is also the chance of A dying and B living. So the chances of one animal dying and the other living, irrespective of which does which, is $2pq$. We have therefore :

Chance of two deaths . . . . p^2
Chance of one death . . . . $2pq$
Chance of no death . . . . q^2

These are the successive terms of the expansion of the expression $(p + q)^2$, and we can deal in exactly the same way with a group of any size, by substituting the number of animals

---

[*] Those who are unfamiliar with this notation may find a further illustration helpful. When we say that the probability of something happening—we usually call it the probability of an "event "—is 1 in 10, or 0·1, we mean that it will, on the average, happen once in ten trials. We may take the classical example of black and white balls in a bag. Suppose that there were in the bag 9 white balls and 1 black, and suppose that we drew all the balls from the bag one after another. Then we should, quite certainly, draw a black ball once, and a white ball nine times. If, after drawing a ball, we noted its colour, and then put it back in the bag, and went on doing this a very large number of times, we should, on the average, draw a black ball in one-tenth of the total number of draws. In other words the probability, or chance, of drawing a black ball is 1/10, and the chance of drawing a white ball is 9/10. In this case we must draw either a white or a black ball, and the chance of drawing one or the other is $1/10 + 9/10 = 10/10 = 1$, which is equivalent to certainty. We cannot draw a red ball, because there is no red ball in the bag, so the chance of doing this is $0/10 = 0$, which means that this particular event cannot possibly happen. Exactly the same principle would apply if there were balls of several colours in the bag, say 10 white, and 7 red, and 12 green and 21 black. The probabilities of drawing a ball of any given colour would then be 10/50 for white, 7/50 for red, 12/50 for green and 21/50 for black. In any case all the probabilities added together must equal unity ; and in any case the probability of any event *not* happening will be the sum of the probabilities of all the other possible events ; that is, it will be equal to unity minus the probability of the particular event in question. In this particular case, for instance, the probability of *not* drawing a black ball is $10/50 + 7/50 + 12/50 = 29/50 = 1 - 21/50$. To go back to our example of an animal under test, where we are concerned only with whether it lives or dies, if the probability of its death is p, then the probability of its living is $1 - p$, and this we call q.

[†] If the chances of two independent events are a and b respectively, the probability of both events happening is obtained by multiplying the separate probabilities together, *i.e.* in this case it is ab. A coin, for instance, is as likely to fall heads as tails ; so the chance of getting a head is 0·5. The chance of getting two heads, with two coins, is $0.5 \times 0.5 = 0.25$.

in the group for the 2 in the expression given above. For instance, if we had four animals in a group, our expression would become $(p + q)^4$ and the chance of getting 0, 1, 2, 3 or 4 deaths in any single test would be p^4, $4p^3q$, $6p^2q^2$, $4pq^3$ and q^4 respectively.

To take a numerical example, if our p were 0·5, representing an average 50 per cent. mortality, our q would also be 0·5, and our expression would be $(0·5 + 0·5)^2$ for 2 animals and $(0·5 + 0·5)^4$ for 4 animals. Working these out, our chances of getting 0, 1 or 2 deaths with 2 animals are 0·25, 0·5 and 0·25 respectively. Our chances of getting 0, 1, 2, 3 or 4 deaths with 4 animals are 0·0625, 0·25, 0·375, 0·25 and 0·0625 respectively. In each case, of course, all the terms taken together add up to unity ; since one or other of the possible events must happen. If we like to multiply these figures by 100, we shall get the per-centage frequency of the different events. Using 4 animals we should observe the true average mortality in 37·5 per cent. of our tests. In 31·25 per cent. (6·25 + 25) we should observe a mortality of 75 per cent. or more. In 6·25 per cent. of our tests we should observe a mortality of 100 per cent. In another 6·25 per cent. of our tests no animal would die.

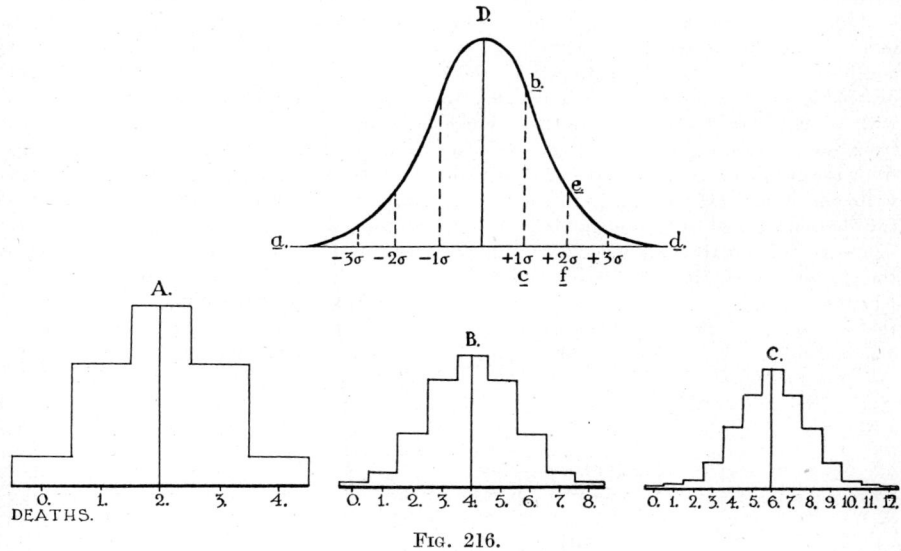

Fig. 216.

No one, of course, would really express the observed deaths in a group of 2 or 4 animals as percentage figures, or pay much attention to the results however they were expressed ; but these simple arithmetical examples will serve to illustrate the method of calculation. Whatever number of animals we use, we substitute that number for the n in the expression $(p + q)^n$ and carry out the necessary expansion.

The expression $(p + q)^n$ is, of course, an ordinary binomial expansion, and we can write down the successive terms, $p^n + np^{n-1}q + \dfrac{n(n-1)}{1,2} p^{n-2}q^2 \ldots$ and so on easily enough.

But the arithmetic that follows, when n is any number over 20, or thereabouts, is a laborious business. And, since we are seldom interested in the actual odds, but wish merely to know whether it is relatively unlikely, or very unlikely, that the result we have observed can have been due to chance in the statistical sense, we habitually take a short cut.

The nature of this short cut can most easily be explained by reference to Fig. 216. The diagrams in the lower half of the figure have been constructed as follows : In A the base line has been divided into 5 equal parts corresponding to the deaths of 0, 1, 2, 3 or 4 animals out of a group of 4. The chance, or frequency, of each event has been calculated as above, taking p as 0·5 ; and the height of the column above each specified number of deaths has been made proportional to this frequency. A vertical line has been drawn from the point on the abscissæ corresponding to the position of the mean. In B the same thing has been done for a group of 8 animals, and in C for a group of 12. As the number increases it will be noted that the figure alters its shape, becomes less grossly step-like, and shows a decreasing proportion of its total area at the extremities of the base line— the portions corresponding to no deaths at one end of the base line, and to a mortality of 100 per cent. at the other. If we made n very large, say 1,000, we should find that our diagram had approximated to the form shown at D in the upper part of the figure. This form is known as the *normal curve of error*, and it has properties that enable us to shorten the arithmetical calculations outlined above.

A function of this curve has been calculated that is known as the *standard deviation*, or *standard error*, and is usually written as σ. It is the *root mean square deviation*, or the square root of the figure obtained by squaring all the deviations from the mean, adding all the squares together and dividing the sum by the total number of observations.

Suppose that we take, as a very simple concrete example, a test carried out on 8 animals, in which the true average death rate would be 50 per cent., so that $p = 0.5$. We construct a table as follows (see Table LII). In the first column we write down the number of deaths that may be observed, from 0 to 8. In the second column we enter the frequencies with which these deaths will, on the average, be observed, calculating these frequencies from the expansion of $(0.5 + 0.5)^8$. In the third column (d) we write the deviations from the mean number of deaths (in this case 4 deaths). In the fourth column (d^2) we write the squares of the figures in the third column. In the fifth column (Fd^2) we write the quotients obtained by multiplying the figures in the second column by the corresponding figures in the fourth column. These quotients, when added together, give us the sum of the squares of all the deviations from the mean that will, on the average, be observed when we carry out this particular test on a group of this size. If we divide this sum by the sum of the figures in the second column we shall obtain the mean square deviation. The sum of the figures in the fifth column is 2, and the sum of the figures in the second

TABLE LII

No. of Deaths.	Frequency (F).	d.	d^2.	Fd^2.
0	0·00390625	− 4	16	0·0625
1	0·03125	− 3	9	0·28125
2	0·109375	− 2	4	0·4375
3	0·21875	− 1	1	0·21875
4	0·2734375	0	0	0·0
5	0·21875	+ 1	1	0·21875
6	0·109375	+ 2	4	0·4375
7	0·03125	+ 3	9	0·28125
8	0·00390625	+ 4	16	0·0625
Sum	1·0			2·0

column is 1. Thus the mean square deviation is $2/1 = 2$; and the standard deviation, or root mean square deviation, is $\sqrt{2} = 1.414$.

Now the mean square deviation (2) is equal to the product obtained by multiplying together the three values (n, p and q) that formed the basis of our binomial expansion $(p + q)^n$. In this particular instance $p = 0.5$, $q = 0.5$ and $n = 8$; so that

$$npq = 0.5 \times 0.5 \times 8 = 2.$$

This relation always holds, as will be clear to those who are familiar with the integral calculus, so that, in calculating our standard deviation in a case of this kind, we can avoid all the troublesome business of working out our frequencies from the binomial expansion, and simply determine the value of $\sqrt{npq}$.

Having obtained the standard deviation of the mean number of deaths, or as it is now more commonly called the standard error, we can use it to determine what we wish to know—the odds against an observed number, or proportion, of deaths having occurred as the result of chance. In the curve shown at D in Fig. 216 the base line has been divided in terms of this standard error (σ), starting from the mean and marking off multiples of σ in minus values to the left, and in plus values to the right. The proportions of the total area included by the curve and the base line that are cut off by the verticals erected at $+$ or -1σ, $+$ or -2σ, and so on, have been carefully calculated for each multiple of σ and can easily be obtained from the appropriate tables. The odds against observing a number of deaths that differs from the true average number of deaths by $+1\sigma$ or more is clearly given by the figure obtained by dividing the area enclosed by the curve from its commencement on the left to the vertical at $+1\sigma$ by the area enclosed by the curve from the vertical at $+1\sigma$ to the termination of the curve on the right, *i.e.* by the ratio area abc/area bcd (see Fig. 216). The odds against observing a number of deaths that differs from the average number by $+2\sigma$ or more are given by the ratio area aef/area efd, and so on.

Clearly, since the curve is symmetrical, the same relations hold for values that differ from the mean by -1σ or more, -2σ or more, and so on.

Table LIII gives the odds against observing a value that differs from the mean by $\pm 0.5\sigma$ or more, $\pm 1.0\sigma$ or more, and so on, up to $\pm 4.5\sigma$. At or beyond this point the odds are so high that their exact value is of no interest.

TABLE LIII

Deviation in Terms of the Standard Error ; or Ratio between a Difference and its Standard Error.	Odds against this Deviation or Difference being the Result of Random Chance.
0·5	0·6 to 1
1·0	2·15 to 1
1·5	6·5 to 1
2·0	20·98 to 1
2·5	79·53 to 1
3·0	369·4 to 1
3·5	2,149 to 1
4·0	15,773 to 1
4·5	147,188 to 1

Let us take an actual example to see how the table is used. Suppose we apply to 20 animals a test that will, on the average, kill 50 per cent. of them. What are the odds against our actually observing a mortality of 75 per cent. or more ?

In this case $p = 0.5$, $q = 0.5$, $n = 20$, and $\sqrt{npq} = \sqrt{20 \times 0.5 \times 0.5} = \sqrt{5} = 2.24$ approximately. A 50 per cent. mortality corresponds to the death of 10 animals out of 20. If 5 additional animals die the mortality will be 75 per cent. This differs from the mean number of deaths by 5/2·24 times (= 2·24 times) the standard error. Turning to our table we see that the odds against observing a result that differs from the average result by twice the standard error, or more, are approximately 21 to 1, while for 2·5 times the standard error the odds are approximately 80 to 1 ; so that the odds against observing a mortality of 75 per cent. or over, when we make our test on 20 animals, are somewhere between these figures.

We are, in practice, almost always concerned with the *proportion* of animals that die, not with absolute numbers. It is therefore convenient to express our standard error in terms of proportions, and to do this we simply substitute the expression $\sqrt{\dfrac{pq}{n}}$ for $\sqrt{npq}$. The answer we get is in decimal terms, so that to convert it to percentage figures we have to multiply by 100.

In the case we have just considered σ becomes

$$\sqrt{\frac{0\cdot5 \times 0\cdot5}{20}} = \sqrt{\frac{0\cdot25}{20}} = \sqrt{0\cdot0125} = 0\cdot1118 \text{ approx.} = 11\cdot18 \text{ per cent.}$$

We were assuming a percentage difference of $75 - 50 = 25$ per cent., and this is $25/11\cdot18$ ($= 2\cdot24$) times the standard error, which gives us the same answer as before.

The correctness of the odds given in Table LIII depends, of course, on the characters of the normal curve. If the curve with which we are concerned in any given experiment is not the normal curve, these odds will no longer hold exactly. There are two factors in the kind of experiment with which we are usually concerned that affect the form of the curve. One is the number of animals that we use. We shall never use enough to give us a really smooth curve. In fact our distribution will usually be nearer to that shown at C, Fig. 216, than to the true normal curve. The other factor is that while the normal curve is symmetrical, corresponding to the expansion of $(0\cdot5 + 0\cdot5)^n$, the curve with which we are actually concerned will usually be asymmetrical, corresponding, for example, to the expansion of $(0\cdot2 + 0\cdot8)^n$, since we shall not often be dealing with a test that gives, on the average, exactly a 50 per cent. mortality.

The only really accurate way of determining the odds in such cases is to work out the terms of the binomial expansion ; but if the number of animals in the group under test is not too small, say not less than 20, and the chance of the less likely event, life or death whichever it may be, is not less than 0·2, or thereabouts, the odds calculated on the basis of the standard error will not depart widely from the true odds, and will usually serve our purpose.

It will, however, have been noted that we have, throughout the preceding discussion, assumed the possession of one very important piece of knowledge—the true average mortality involved in the procedure under test. Usually we do not know this. The question that faces us is far more often as follows : In a particular test we have observed a mortality of, let us say, 40 per cent. among a group of 30 animals. What are the odds, if we did exactly the same experiment over again, that we should, in this second test, observe a mortality of 60 per cent. or more ? The only assumption on which we can proceed in this case is that our observed 40 per cent. mortality is the true average mortality ; but it is by no means a safe assumption, and for that reason among others we shall be wise to suspect that the real odds are shorter than those we calculate.

So far we have been considering what happens in a single group of animals ; but in most of our experiments we shall, in fact, be concerned with two groups : one that has been treated in some way that may, we think, have altered its average resistance, and another untreated group that we commonly speak of as a " control." We shall expose these two groups to the same risk, say the injection into each animal of a certain number of living bacteria, and note how many die in each group during some fixed time interval. The figure that will interest us here will not be the percentage of deaths in either group, but the difference in percentage mortality between the two groups. Similarly, the standard error that we want to calculate is the standard error of this difference. Since the proportion of deaths in each of the two groups will vary in repetitions of the test, the standard error of the difference will clearly be larger than the standard error of either percentage mortality taken alone. Actually, the standard error of a difference between two mean values is the square root of the sum of the squares of the standard errors of the two means.

Let us see how this works out in practice. Suppose we take a group of n treated animals and find that after the test injection x of them die, while of another group of n' untreated controls x' die. Let us assume that $\dfrac{x'}{n'}$ is greater than $\dfrac{x}{n}$. What are the odds against the lower death rate among our treated animals having arisen as the result of chance, instead of as the result of our treatment?

If the difference has arisen by chance, the two groups have not really differed in any significant way, so that the best measure we have of the real average chance of death is the mean of the values observed in our two groups. This is clearly $\dfrac{x + x'}{n + n'}$, and we call it p_0. The mean chance of survival is $q_0 = 1 - p_0$. The standard error of the proportion of deaths in our treated group is $\sqrt{\dfrac{p_0 q_0}{n}}$, and the standard error of the proportion of deaths in our control group is $\sqrt{\dfrac{p_0 q_0}{n'}}$. The squares of these values are $\dfrac{p_0 q_0}{n}$ and $\dfrac{p_0 q_0}{n'}$, and the square root of the sum of the squares, which is the standard error of the difference, is $\sqrt{p_0 q_0 \left(\dfrac{1}{n} + \dfrac{1}{n'} \right)}$, or if we are dealing in percentages

$$100 \sqrt{p_0 q_0 \left(\frac{1}{n} + \frac{1}{n'} \right)}.$$

Let us again take a concrete example. Thirty mice that had been repeatedly inoculated with a killed suspension of *Bact. typhi-murium* and 30 uninoculated mice to serve as controls were injected intraperitoneally with a constant dose (1,000 bacilli) of living *Bact. typhi-murium*. They were then observed over a period of 28 days. During this time 16 of the 30 vaccinated mice died of the infection, and 29 of the 30 controls. The survivors were killed on the 28th day and cultures were taken from their spleens. *Bact. typhi-murium* was recovered from 10 of the 14 surviving vaccinated mice, but not from the one surviving control. We may tabulate these results as follows :

Number of mice surviving on 28th day :

Vaccinated.	.	.	.	.	.	.	$14 = 46{\cdot}67$ per cent.
Controls	.	.	.	.	.	.	$1 = 3{\cdot}33$,, ,,
Difference .	.	.	.	.	.	.	$13 = 43{\cdot}33$,, ,,

Number of mice showing no evidence of infection (completely resistant) :

Vaccinated.	.	.	.	.	.	.	$4 = 13{\cdot}32$ per cent.
Controls	.	.	.	.	.	.	$1 = 3{\cdot}33$,, ,,
Difference .	.	.	.	.	.	.	$3 = 10{\cdot}00$,, ,,

The vaccinated mice show an advantage over the controls of 43·33 per cent. in regard to survival rate, but of only 10 per cent. in regard to their ability to resist completely the injection of this number of organisms. What are the odds against each of these observed differences in behaviour having been due to chance?

P.B.   C C*

Of 30 vaccinated mice 14 survived : of 30 control mice 1 survived.

$$q_0 = \frac{14 + 1}{30 + 30} = \frac{15}{60} = 0.25$$

$$p_0 = 1 - q_0 = 0.75$$

$$\sqrt{p_0 q_0 \left(\frac{1}{n} + \frac{1}{n'}\right)} = \sqrt{0.75 \times 0.25 \times \left(\frac{1}{30} + \frac{1}{30}\right)}$$

$$= \sqrt{\frac{0.75 \times 0.25}{15}} = 0.1118$$

The observed difference in mortality is 43·33 per cent., and the standard error, expressed as a percentage value, is 11·18. So the difference is equal to 43·33/11·18 (3·87) times its standard error.

Turning to Table LIII we find that the odds against observing such a difference as this as the result of chance are rather less than 15,000 to 1. These are very long odds, so that we shall conclude with considerable confidence that we have increased the ability of our mice to withstand the test dose of bacteria, by our preliminary injections of killed bacteria.

Have we increased their ability to resist the test dose completely ?

Of the 30 vaccinated mice, 4 proved completely resistant ; of the 30 control mice 1 proved completely resistant.

Taking q to express resistance—

$$q_0 = \frac{4 + 1}{30 + 30} = \frac{5}{60} = 0.0833$$

$$p_0 = 1 - q_0 = 0.9167$$

$$\sqrt{p_0 q \left(\frac{1}{n} + \frac{1}{n'}\right)} = \sqrt{\frac{0.0833 \times 0.9167}{15}} = 0.07136.$$

The observed difference in the proportion of mice completely resistant is 10·00 per cent., the standard error expressed as a percentage is 7·136. The observed difference is 10/7·136 (1·4) times its standard error.

Turning to Table LIII we find that the odds against observing such a difference as this as the result of chance are about 5 to 1. These are very short odds ; and we should clearly place no confidence in them. Taking our observations as a whole we should conclude that, by the method of immunization employed, we had almost certainly increased the ability of our mice to survive the test dose of living bacteria, but that the effect on their ability to resist infection entirely was relatively slight, and quite possibly insignificant.

This is one selected example. It may be useful to note how the odds vary according to the number of deaths or survivals observed in two groups, each of 20 animals, one group being treated by some procedure under test, the other serving as untreated controls. Both groups, of course, will be subjected to the same dose of living bacteria, toxin or other agent against which the treatment is directed. These odds are shown in Table LIV, very short odds being neglected and odds of over 1,000 to 1 being no further specified. No odds are shown for less than 5 deaths in one group or more than 15 deaths in the other group. Where the number of animals in each group is as small as 20, and the number of deaths in each group is very small (say 4 or less) or very large (say 16 or more) the assumptions

TABLE LIV

SHOWING (IN THE FORM $x : 1$, x ALONE BEING GIVEN) THE ODDS AGAINST DIFFERENT COMBINATIONS OF DEATHS IN TWO GROUPS, EACH OF 20 ANIMALS, ON THE ASSUMPTION THAT THE DIFFERENCE BETWEEN THE TWO GROUPS IS DUE TO ERRORS OF RANDOM SAMPLING.

Number of Deaths in First Group.	Number of Deaths in Second Group.															
	0	1	2	3	4	5	6	7	8	9	10	11	12	13	14	15
5	58	12	—			—	—	—	—	—	9	18	39	89	228	633
6	127	26	8	—		—	—	—	—	—	—	8	17	37	87	228
7	276	55	16	6	—	—	—	—	—	—	—	—	8	17	37	89
8	633	122	34	12	—	—	—	—	—	—	—	—	—	8	17	39
9	>1000	285	75	25	10	—	—	—	—	—	—	—	—	—	8	18
10	„	702	172	54	20	9	—	—	—	—	—	—	—	—	—	9
11	„	>1000	422	122	44	18	8	—	—	—	—	—	—	—	—	—
12	„	„	>1000	304	100	39	17	8	—	—	—	—	—	—	—	—
13	„	„	„	807	250	89	37	17	8	—	—	—	—	—	—	—
14	„	„	„	>1000	678	228	87	37	17	8	—	—	—	—	—	—
15	„	„	„	„	>1000	633	228	89	39	18	9	—	—	—	—	—
16	„	„	„	„	„	>1000	678	250	100	44	20	10	—	—		
17	„	„	„	„	„	„	>1000	807	304	122	54	25	12	6	—	
18	„	„	„	„	„	„	„	>1000	>1000	422	172	75	34	16	8	—
19	„	„	„	„	„	„	„	„	„	>1000	702	285	122	55	26	12
20	„	„	„	„	„	„	„	„	„	„	>1000	>1000	633	276	127	58

on which these calculations are based no longer hold. The example of the fully resistant mice among our groups of 30 was not above criticism in this respect.

In all the examples discussed above we have assumed that, so far as chance has entered into our observations at all, it has been in the form known to the statistician as " the error of random sampling " ; but there are other kinds of " chance," using that term in a broader and less technical sense. To take a crude example, suppose that we were testing a method of immunizing rabbits against a particular toxin, and failed to allow for the fact that different breeds of rabbit may differ significantly in their resistance to any agent of this kind. We might include in our " treated " group a majority of animals of the more resistant breed, and in our control group a majority of animals of the more susceptible breed. Under these conditions our " treated " group would probably show a statistically significant advantage, even if our treatment had, in reality, been quite without effect. " Chance " would be a charitable term for this particular piece of experimental carelessness ; but other factors, not nearly so obvious as differences in breed, or age, or sex, may influence the reaction of our experimental animals to the test we are employing. An essential part of a good experimental technique is, as Fisher emphasizes, that all possible means shall be used to " randomize " the conditions of test, *i.e.* to reduce the unknown variables to influences of the same type as those that determine whether a tossed coin shall come down " heads " or " tails."

It is of interest to inquire how far we can do this in practice. Not many workers have taken the trouble to test their technique in this way, but Lockhart (1926) records observations bearing directly on the point at issue. In four experiments, several groups, each of 20 mice, were injected with the same dose of the same culture of a pathogenic organism (*Bact. typhi-murium*) and the number dying in each group during the succeeding 14 days was noted. In one experiment 9 groups were injected ; the deaths were 16, 16, 17, 19, 18, 17, 15, 17 and 14. This gives 36 differences between pairs. The difference between 14 and 19 deaths, the largest observed in this group, should, as will be seen from Table LIV, occur on the average once in 27 comparisons. In a second series of 5 tests the deaths were 18, 17, 13, 16 and 13 ; this gives 10 differences between pairs. The difference between 13 and 18 deaths would be expected to occur, on the average, once in 17 comparisons.

In a third series of 5 groups the deaths were 5, 2, 4, 3 and 5 ; there is here no difference that would not be expected on our assumption, but the death rate is very low in all groups. In a fourth series of 5 groups the deaths were 19, 20, 19, 20 and 19 ; there is no unexpected difference, but the death rate was very high in all groups. Such a series of tests may be regarded as a trial of the adequacy of our experimental methods. If the distribution of deaths actually observed in different groups that have, within the limits of experimental control, been subjected to exactly the same treatment agrees closely with that expected on the assumption that the only differences that occur will be those due to the error of random sampling, then our technique may be regarded as highly satisfactory. If our observed distribution differs widely from that expected, then we have not succeeded in eliminating other disturbing factors, of unknown nature, which may mislead us when we come to apply a known procedure to one group in order to test its effect.

Lockhart's figures suggest that he was reasonably successful in randomizing his experimental conditions. It is, however, doubtful whether equally satisfactory results can always be attained in immunological tests of this kind, and it will perhaps be wise to make a practice of demanding rather long *calculated* odds before accepting an observed difference in behaviour as statistically significant. We might, for instance, fix an arbitrary limit for the ratio of a difference to its standard error at 3 : 1, which would give us calculated odds of 369 to 1 against the observed difference being due to chance. We are, of course, on the horns of a dilemma. If we fix our odds too high we shall tend to ignore differences that are possibly significant. If we fix them too low we may attach significance to differences that are, in fact, meaningless. In dealing with observations from the ward, or from the field, where fresh data cannot quickly or easily be collected, it is desirable that attention should be drawn to any points of possible interest or importance, with due emphasis where necessary on the allowance that must be made for sampling errors. In experimental work the case is rather different. The investigator will clearly be wise to take any hint that is offered by his quantitative results ; but if he desires to publish his findings and draw conclusions from them, it is reasonable to insist on a stricter standard. There is nothing to prevent him from repeating any experiment that has given a statistically dubious answer ; and this is clearly what he should do.

Experiments should, indeed, always be repeated, even when a single trial has given a result that passes all the conventional tests of statistical significance. The single trial cannot, except by analogy, tell us anything about happenings outside its own particular conditions ; and we can never be quite sure that these conditions do not include some determining factor other than that, the effect of which we are trying to investigate. By repeating an experiment several times, we are testing, in the only way we can, for the intrusion of unknown factors other than errors of random sampling. If each of several tests gives us a statistically significant answer, and each answer points in the same direction, we shall have some justification for stating our conclusion in general as opposed to particular terms ; but if some tests give different answers from others we must solve the problem of why these differences occur before we can accept the indication given by the original experiment.

The question thus arises, assuming a limit to the number of experimental animals that we have available, how we can use them to the best advantage in solving any particular problem. Shall we carry out one, or two, experiments with large numbers of animals in our test and control groups ? or, shall we make several experiments, each on a smaller scale ?

The answer would seem to be that each test should be made on a number of animals sufficiently large to enable us to detect a difference of the order we are expecting, making allowance for errors of random sampling. When this point has been reached we shall gain more by repeating the experiment, using groups of a similar size, than by doing one very large experiment, in which the effect of sampling errors would be considerably reduced, but which would give us no information in regard to other intrusive factors.

In most laboratory experiments, in which we are expecting a high mortality, usually approaching 100 per cent., in our control group, and are hoping for a much lower mortality, say 30–60 per cent., in our treated group, we shall gain more information by repeating our experiment six times, using 25 animals in each group, than by doing one experiment with 150 animals in each group. The best procedure, in any given case, will depend on the size of the difference we are expecting. Sometimes, particularly in the application of a therapeutic measure in human disease, quite a small difference in mortality is an objective well worth attaining ; and, if we wish to determine a difference of this size, our groups in any individual trial must be relatively large.

Let us take a concrete example. Certain laboratory experiments have led to the production of a serum which, on *a priori* grounds, may be expected to have some curative influence on a particular infective disease. Like all new curative measures it *must* be subjected to a period of trial before it is adopted for routine use. Our expectations may not be realized. The serum may be quite useless in practice. It is not a question of trial or no trial, but of a well-planned trial that will give us a definite answer as quickly as possible, as against a planless, haphazard series of trials that will take a long while to tell us very little, perhaps at a considerable expense in lives. Let us suppose that the real average effect of the serum is to reduce the case mortality of the disease from 30 per cent. to 20 per cent.—not, perhaps, a dramatic result but one that will save a large number of patients if the disease is a prevalent one. The only way in which the existence of such an effect can be quickly and certainly established is to test the serum on an adequate group of cases and compare the mortality in this treated group with the mortality in an untreated group. The two groups must if possible be compared over the same period of time and in the same place, since the case mortality of almost all acute infective diseases fluctuates from time to time and from one locality to another. They must also be similar in all relevant respects other than the administration of the serum ; for example, they must all be of the same race, and the age and sex distribution within the two groups must be approximately the same. Let us see what will happen if such a trial is carried out on two groups, each containing 10, 50, 100, 150, 200 or 250 patients. The relevant figures are set out in Table LV, the standard error being calculated on the percentage basis.

TABLE LV

SHOWING THE RATIO [DIFFERENCE IN MORTALITY/S.E.] FOR TREATED AND UNTREATED GROUPS IN THE CASE OF AN ANTISERUM WHICH PRODUCES A DECREASE IN CASE MORTALITY FROM 30 PER CENT. TO 20 PER CENT.

Number in Each Group.	Deaths in Treated Group.	Deaths in Untreated Group.	Difference. per cent.	S.E.	Difference in Mortality ÷ S.E.
10	2	3	10	19·365	0·52
50	10	15	10	8·660	1·15
100	20	30	10	6·124	1·63
150	30	45	10	5·000	2·00
200	40	60	10	4·330	2·31
250	50	75	10	3·873	2·58
500	100	150	10	2·739	3·65

Quite clearly a trial with 10 treated and 10 untreated patients is useless. In different trials on this scale, one observer will record more deaths in the treated group, another in the untreated. There will be hopeless confusion. The position with groups of 50 treated and 50 untreated patients is not much better. In about one of every four trials a difference such as this would be observed as the result of chance alone. There will be sharp differences of opinion as to whether the treatment does *any* good, and no possibility of assessing even approximately how much good it does. As the number of patients in each group increases the significance of the result recorded also increases—not proportionately to the number itself but in proportion to its square root. After a trial on two groups each of

100 patients we should begin to think it probable that the serum had done some good. After a trial on two groups each of 200 patients we should be inclined to adopt this view as a provisional conclusion pending further evidence. If trials on this scale were repeated we should be surprised if there were many unfavourable reports. After a trial on two groups of 500 patients we should have no reasonable doubt that our serum had reduced the case mortality. Moreover, with groups of this size we should begin to think that the benefit to be expected from our serum was appropriately represented by a decrease in case mortality from about 30 to about 20 per cent.—that is, by a saving of one patient in three who would otherwise have died—since the chance of the observed decrease differing from the real average by any given amount grows less and less as the number in the group increases.

It is of very real importance that trials of any new therapeutic measure should be planned and carried out on an adequate scale. Otherwise the period of so-called trial may be extended far beyond the necessary limits ; and a useless measure may be employed sporadically for years, or—what is far more serious—a useful measure may fail to obtain general recognition because the reports on inadequate trials are contradictory and confusing. Any student who cares to master the history of the use of anti-pneumococcal serum (see pp. 1319–1323) will find a case in point.

It should be noted that, in the case of a proposed method of prophylaxis, our field trials will often have to be carried out on a far larger scale, because the risk of contracting a particular infective disease is often far smaller than the risk of dying from it when contracted. If the attack rate of a disease is very low, our immunized and non-immunized groups must be greatly expanded—often to many thousands of persons—before the number of cases in our control group will be large enough for us to establish the significance of any difference in morbidity that may be noted.

If, however, we can select special groups that are for some reason exposed to a particularly high risk of infection—such for instance as the nurses or attendants in a fever hospital—we may be able to detect the effect of a given prophylactic method by the immunization of relatively small groups (see p. 1168). The same will hold, of course, for the population at large in the case of infections with a very high attack rate, such as the common cold (see p. 1306).

We have so far been concerned with problems in which each animal, or each patient, gives a qualitative result—death or survival, infection or no infection. There is obviously another kind of problem in which each animal may give a quantitative result : it may live so many days, or lose so much weight, or its temperature may rise so many degrees, and so on. We deal with a problem of this kind by a method that is essentially similar to that described above. We first obtain a measure of the variability of the response in each of our two groups by calculating the mean value recorded in each—say the mean time to death after a particular test inoculation—and the standard deviation of the observed distribution. For the latter purpose we make a table of the kind shown in Table LII, writing down in the first column the observed time to death in the units of time selected, say, days ; in the second column, the number of animals that die after these time intervals ; in the third column, the deviation from the mean time to death ; in the fourth the squares of these deviations and so on. The standard deviation calculated in this way is a measure of the *observed variation*. The value that we require is *the standard error of the mean, i.e.* the value that will enable us to calculate the chances, *if we performed exactly the same experiment over again*, of observing a mean value departing by more than the specified amount from the original mean value observed. This standard error of the mean is obtained by dividing the standard deviation of the distribution, calculated as above, by the square root of the number of animals in the group under test, *i.e.* :

$$\text{Standard Error (S.E.) of Mean} = \frac{\text{S.D}}{\sqrt{n}}.$$

Those who desire a mathematical proof of this formula should consult one of the standard textbooks.

Having obtained the mean, and the standard error of the mean, for a " treated " and " control " group we proceed just as before. We subtract one mean from the other and obtain the difference. The standard error of the difference is the square root of the sum of the squares of the standard errors of the two means.

The ratio of the difference to its standard error gives us the value we need in order to obtain, from Table LIII, the odds against the observed difference having been due to chance.

To take a concrete example, omitting the necessary calculations.

A group of 30 mice that had received certain immunizing injections, and 30 untreated mice as a control, were injected intraperitoneally with 1,000 *Bact. typhi-murium.* During the subsequent month 25 of the immunized mice died, and 28 of the controls. This was a trivial difference. But the mean time to death of the 25 immunized mice was 10·52 days with a standard error of 0·960 days, while the mean time to death of the 28 control mice was 5·93 days with a standard error of 0·924 days. The difference is 4·59 days, and the standard error of the difference is $\sqrt{0 \cdot 960^2 + 0 \cdot 924^2} = 1 \cdot 33$. The ratio of the difference to its standard error is $4 \cdot 59/1 \cdot 33 = 3 \cdot 45$, and the odds against observing such a difference as the result of chance (Table LIII) are about 2,000 to 1. The conclusion is that we have almost certainly made the disease less acutely fatal as the result of an immunization, although we have not increased the resistance of our mice to the point at which their chance of survival is significantly increased.

THE MEASUREMENT, OR COMPARISON, OF TOXICITY OR VIRULENCE

We often want to determine the minimal lethal dose of a bacterial toxin, or of a living bacterial culture. Still more often we want to compare the minimal lethal dose of two toxins, or of two cultures. The mathematical considerations involved in assessing the significance of the necessary *in vivo* titrations are beyond the scope of this book. Those who desire further information should consult the papers of Trevan (1927, 1929, 1930), and the recent monograph by Gaddum (1933).

We may note here that the dose that is actually measured, or compared, is the *average lethal dose, i.e.* the smallest dose that will kill 50 per cent. of a large group of test animals, and that the size of the group that must be employed to measure this dose within any specified limits of accuracy depends on what Trevan calls the *characteristic* of the toxin or culture, which is the curve relating increase in percentage mortality to increase in size of dose, or in log. doses. Clearly, the smaller the difference between the dose that kills no animals and the dose that kills 100 per cent. of animals, the more accurate will our estimation be for any given number of animals, and the smaller the number of animals we shall have to use to determine our average lethal dose within any required limits of accuracy. If a dose can be increased or diminished ten times or more without making much difference in the resulting mortality, then our estimation of the average lethal dose will become very inaccurate unless we use extremely large numbers of animals.

Two concrete examples will serve to illustrate the difficulties with which we are faced when we endeavour to determine the average lethal dose of a bacterial culture, or to compare the virulence of two bacterial strains.

A series of six dilutions were prepared from a culture of pneumococcus of moderate virulence, and the same amount of each dilution was inoculated into 40 mice. The doses administered, in terms of living pneumococci, were 10^6, 10^5, 10^4, 10^3, 10^2 and 10. Two of the mice that received each dose were then allotted at random to each of 20 numbered groups. Each group thus consisted of 12 mice, 2 for each dose tested. The deaths are recorded in Table LVI.

TABLE LVI

SHOWING THE NUMBER OF DEATHS IN 20 SAMPLES, EACH OF 12 MICE, INOCULATED WITH THE SAME SERIES OF GRADED DOSES OF THE SAME CULTURE OF PNEUMOCOCCUS.

Dose.	Group.																			
	1	2	3	4	5	6	7	8	9	10	11	12	13	14	15	16	17	18	19	20
10^6	2	2	2	2	2	2	2	2	2	2	2	2	2	2	2	2	2	2	2	2
10^5	2	2	2	2	2	2	2	2	2	2	2	2	2	2	2	2	2	2	2	2
10^4	1	2	1	1	2	1	2	1	1	2	2	2	1	2	1	0	1	0	2	1
10^3	1	0	0	0	0	1	0	0	0	1	1	0	0	0	0	0	0	0	0	0
10^2	0	0	0	0	0	0	0	0	0	0	0	0	0	0	0	0	0	0	0	0
10	0	0	0	0	0	0	0	0	0	0	0	0	0	0	0	0	0	0	0	0

Adding across the rows, the percentage mortality for the whole series was, with the falling doses, 100, 95·5, 65·0, 12·5, 0 and 0. The average lethal dose was probably something between 10,000 and 1,000 pneumococci. But if we had used two mice for each dose—and it would have been a highly conventional procedure—we should have said in the case of groups 10 and 11 that the average lethal dose was about 1,000 pneumococci; in the case of groups 1, 2, 5, 6, 7, 12, 14 and 19 that it lay somewhere between 1,000 and 10,000 pneumococci; in the case of groups 3, 4, 8, 9, 13, 15, 16, 17 and 20 that it was about 10,000 pneumococci; and in the case of group 18 that it was about 100,000 pneumococci. Had we been comparing 20 different strains of pneumococci, we might have been unwise enough to hazard the statement that strains 10 and 11 were about 100 times more virulent than strain 18; whereas, as this experiment showed, there would have been no adequate reason to assume any difference in virulence.

As an illustration of the comparison of the virulence of two different strains of a given bacterium we may take the data recorded by Lockhart (1926) in regard to the mortality produced by different doses of two strains of *Bact. typhi-murium*, " Ellinger " and " A52," all injections being given intraperitoneally. The figures are set out in Table LVII.

TABLE LVII

Dose.	Number of Mice in Each Group.	Mortality per cent. Strain A52.	Mortality per cent. Strain Ellinger.
10,000,000	25	92	96
100,000	25	48	88
1,000	25	44	56
10	25	16	24

We can feel fairly confident that the Ellinger strain is more virulent than the A52 strain; at each dose level it has given a higher mortality. But we clearly cannot express our result as any numerical ratio. If this is the best we can do with 200 mice, we must be satisfied to detect gross differences in virulence, so far as this organism is concerned.

THE STANDARDIZATION OF IMMUNOLOGICAL PRODUCTS

It may be noted here that the method of direct comparison is always employed when we wish to standardize an immunological reagent, *i.e.* to express its value in terms of some arbitrary unit. Thus if we wish to standardize an anti-diphtheria serum in terms of units of antitoxin, we compare its protective value with that of a particular antitoxic serum which is accepted by international agreement as the standard of reference. This standard serum has been submitted to very careful assay and has been allotted an agreed but arbitrary value in terms of antitoxin units. Once this value has been allotted it remains the permanent standard for the antitoxin, or other reagent, in question.

The statistical considerations involved in these comparative neutralization tests are of the same kind as those involved in comparisons of toxicity or of virulence ; but the size of the sampling errors, and hence the accuracy of our titrations, are modified by the actual procedure adopted in each particular case. Here again reference may be made to Gaddum's recent monograph and to the publications of Trevan.

A NOTE ON THE RECORDING OF QUANTITATIVE RESULTS

It is a common habit among immunological workers to record their quantitative results in the form of curves or charts. The advantage is obvious. The meaning leaps to the eye. The danger is that it sometimes leaps before one looks. It is a very safe rule never to trust the tale told by a curve until the quantitative data on which it is based have been critically examined. If the points through which a curve is drawn are based on figures which are subject to errors of random sampling, and if the data permit the standard deviation to be calculated, it is a good plan to mark off three times the standard deviation above and below each point on the curve, join up these points, and, realizing that the curve might run anywhere within the broad band thus demarcated, reconsider its actual significance.

Tables are duller things than curves, and rather more trouble to master. But they tell much more illuminating tales. They should always state quite plainly the number of observations made, never percentages without this information. If a table has a column headed " per cent." always look first at the columns giving the figures on which the percentages are based. Occasionally it will be found that 33·33 per cent. in the last column corresponds to a 1 and a 3 in the columns preceding it. In such cases, of course, the 33·33 per cent. is quite meaningless.

APOLOGIA

The student may, perhaps, feel that these biometrical difficulties have been laboured and elaborated *ad nauseam* ; but if he will note how often, in the following pages, it is necessary to record that A has reported such-and-such a series of observations, while B on repeating the experiment has obtained completely divergent results, and C attacking the same problem from a slightly different angle has obtained results that agree neither with A's nor with B's, he will realize that the point at issue is not without importance.

The crux of the matter is this : simple statistical principles of the kind we have been considering are not rules to be applied in drawing conclusions from an experiment that has been done—*they are part of the experiment itself, an essential factor in its proper planning.*

If an experiment on a particular scale is quite unlikely to give a significant answer, then it is better either to enlarge its scale to the extent required, or to abandon it.

The voyager who ignores tidal streams and compass deviations will arrive somewhere in the long run ; but he is less likely to identify correctly the place at which he has arrived than is another who allows for these variables by the accepted methods of elementary navigation.

REFERENCES

FISHER, R. A.   (1930) " Statistical Methods for Research Workers."   3rd Ed., Edinburgh ; (1935) " The Design of Experiments."   Oliver & Boyd, Edinburgh.

GADDUM, J. H.   (1933) *Spec. Rep. Ser. med. Res. Coun., Lond.*, No. 183.

GREENWOOD, M.   (1924) *Lancet*, ii. 153.

LOCKHART, L. P.   (1926) *J. Hyg., Camb.*, **25,** 50.

PEARL, R.   (1923) " Introduction to Medical Biometry and Statistics."   Philadelphia.

TREVAN, J. W.   (1927) *Proc. roy. Soc.*, B, **101,** 483 ; (1929) *J. Path. Bact.*, **32,** 127 ; (1930) *Ibid.*, **33,** 739.

WOODS, H. M. and RUSSELL, W. T.   (1931) " An Introduction to Medical Statistics."   London.

YULE, G. U.   (1924) *Med. res. Coun. indust. Fatigue Board, Rep.* 28 ; (1932) " An Introduction to the Theory of Statistics."   (10th Ed.)   London.

CHAPTER XLI

THE MECHANISMS OF BACTERIAL INFECTION

BEFORE we can discuss the mechanisms by which the host resists infection, it is necessary to build up as clear a picture as we can of the ways in which the parasite injures the host. The best picture we can produce at the moment is sadly confused in some places and extremely sketchy in others. But parts of the main outline are quite clear and definite, and it is with these that we shall be mainly concerned.

Specific Infection. Koch's Postulates.

Although not immediately pertinent to our main problem, a brief discussion of the kind of evidence which will justify the conclusion that a particular disease is caused by a particular parasite forms a convenient introduction to the consideration of infective processes in general, and raises points of some interest and importance.

A series of conditions, which must be fulfilled in order to establish such a causal relationship, are set out in most bacteriological textbooks under the title of " Koch's Postulates," though there is no clear evidence that Koch ever enunciated them in the categorical form in which they are usually quoted. They run in general terms as follows :

(1) The organism should be found in all cases of the disease in question, and its distribution in the body should be in accordance with the lesions observed.

(2) The organism should be cultivated outside the body of the host, in pure culture, for several generations.

(3) The organism so isolated should reproduce the disease in other susceptible animals.

We should to-day recognize additional ancillary criteria which help us to form an accurate judgment as to the relationship of a suspected organism to a given disease, as, for instance, the demonstration of specific antibodies in the blood of an infected man or animal.

It is obvious that technical difficulties may prevent us from fulfilling all Koch's postulates in every case. We may, for instance, be unable to cultivate the causative parasite although we can demonstrate its constant presence in the lesions by suitable staining methods ; this has hitherto been the case with regard to the bacillus of leprosy. Or the organism may be so small, and its morphology so doubtful, that we are unable to demonstrate its presence in the tissues, or to differentiate it with certainty from other bodies of the same order of size. If, to this difficulty, is added an inability to cultivate the organism *in vitro*, we may, as in the initial studies on most virus infections, be compelled to take a short cut, neglect the first two postulates, and rely on the reproduction of the disease in a suitable animal by the inoculation of filtrates from infected blood or tissue extracts, which are at least free from intact cells or living bacteria. In other cases the third postulate may be our stumbling-block. We may be able to demonstrate a characteristic bacterium in such a relation to the lesions of a particular disease that we can have no reasonable doubt that it is playing a causative rôle, and we may have learned how to propagate it in pure culture outside the body; but we may be quite unable to produce in any experimental animal lesions which bear any close resemblance to those which characterize the disease in man.

It is often possible, in the absence of complete proof, to establish the causative rôle of a particular organism with so high a degree of probability that there need be no hesitation in accepting this association as a reasonable provisional hypothesis. At the same time it must be recognized that any omission in the complete chain of evidence involves a risk of error; and much confusion has been caused by uncritical attempts to support the claims advanced on behalf of numberless bacteria isolated from different parts of the body in various diseases.

A little more may usefully be said with regard to the first and third postulates. In the early days of bacteriology the proposition that the causative organism of a disease should be present in every case adequately examined was held to imply its converse— that the organism should not be present in persons not suffering from the disease. And in some instances, such as the investigations that followed Loeffler's demonstration of the diphtheria bacillus, serious doubts were thrown on the claim of an authentic causal organism when it became clear that it could be isolated from the throats of persons who were quite certainly not suffering from diphtheria. Nowadays we have learnt to adopt a different standpoint. Our present conception of the probable distribution of any pathogenic parasite is that it will be found in every case of the specific infection that is clinically obvious, and is adequately investigated under satisfactory conditions; in many cases of minor infection that show little resemblance to the fully developed disease; and in a certain proportion of apparently healthy persons, especially in contacts.

With regard to the third postulate, we should not expect complete identity between the clinical picture in man and the lesions produced in an experimental animal. The picture presented by any infective process depends as much upon the reactions of the host's tissues as upon the activities of the infecting parasite; and in this, as in other respects, one animal species differs from another. Sometimes this is a small matter. No one who had any knowledge of the morbid anatomy of tuberculosis in man or cattle would hesitate in identifying the experimental disease in the rabbit or guinea-pig, in spite of minor superficial differences. But the lesions produced in experimental animals by the typhoid bacillus, or by the scarlatinal streptococcus, bear little obvious resemblance to the corresponding human diseases.

The student should note very carefully that there are two distinct stages in the use of experimental animals in the study of infective disease. In the first we are trying to reproduce a particular infection in a form which is clinically or pathologically recognizable as identical with the natural disease. This is the kind of reproduction demanded by Koch's third postulate. In the second we are utilizing our susceptible animal for an intensive study of the particular infective process with which we are concerned. This is really the more significant and interesting part of our investigations. The lesions produced in the guinea-pig by the subcutaneous inoculation of cultures or filtrates of the diphtheria bacillus bear little resemblance to diphtheria as it appears in man; but almost the whole of our present knowledge of immunity in relation to that disease, which has at last placed us in a position to exert effective control, has been built up on knowledge gained from experiments on that small laboratory animal.

It should be noted, also, that there is a shifting of emphasis from the clinical to the bacteriological side as our knowledge progresses. At the start of our inquiry we are presented with a clinical or epidemiological entity, and our task is to discover the microbial parasite that is the essential cause. We may, as in the case of diphtheria, or syphilis, or tetanus, find that a single specific parasite is involved ; indeed this is far the most frequent solution if we neglect racial variations within the causative microbial species. We may, however, find that a disease which is a clinical entity involves several distinct bacterial species as alternative infecting agents. Secondary pneumonia affords one example, bacillary dysentery another. Once the connection between a particular parasite and a particular disease has been firmly established, the tendency of the bacteriologist is to focus his attention on the organism, rather than on the clinical condition to which it most frequently gives rise, and to try to build up a picture of the reactions between that organism and a susceptible host species in general. Thus we should think in terms of pneumococcal infection, rather than in terms of pneumonia ; and regard that particular condition merely as one example of the reaction between the pneumococcus and the human tissues, including in our generalized picture such lesions as middle-ear disease, sinusitis, meningitis, peritonitis, suppurative arthritis, etc., and keeping constantly in mind the part played by bacteræmic spread and selective localization.

It will be convenient, in this and the immediately succeeding chapters, to deal exclusively with bacterial infections, since most of our knowledge has been acquired in studying infections of this type. In a later chapter we shall discuss how far our conceptions have to be modified in the case of infections with the filtrable viruses. Protozoal and helminthic infections are beyond the scope of this book ; though there is a growing tendency for the methods that have been elaborated by the student of bacterial disease to be applied in this extended field.

Invasion of the Tissues by Bacteria.

With very few exceptions, bacteria and other microbial parasites must gain access to the host's tissues and multiply in them before they can produce any harmful effect ; and we may for the moment regard the capacity to pass through some protective covering layer—most commonly through one of the mucous surfaces of the body—and to multiply in the subjacent tissues, as an essential attribute of a pathogenic organism. The " passing through " must not, of course, be interpreted too literally, or as necessarily implying any active motion on the part of the parasite. Apart from mechanical injuries to the skin or mucous membranes, micro-organisms probably gain access to the tissues by the same routes and by the same methods as inert particles of non-living matter, particularly in those areas where lymphatic tissue lies near the surface and lymphatic drainage is abundant, as in the naso-pharyngeal region, the tonsils, and the lymphoid follicles of the intestine. In other cases they appear to reach the crypts of mucous glands, and then, after local multi-plication, to penetrate to the subepithelial tissue. In any event it is probable that the capacity for invasion depends in considerable part on a capacity to with-stand the conditions existing on the particular surface where lodgment is first made, or in the channels or viscera through which the parasite must pass before it gains contact with a penetrable surface. It happens that the logical point of departure in a description of the reaction between a pathogenic parasite and its host—the transit from the outside world to the host's tissues—is the part of the picture which is most sketchy and unfinished. Only a few details have as yet been filled in, and their significance is not always obvious. It will be more convenient to deal with this aspect of the question in a separate chapter, and to pass at once to the events which follow the passage of the parasite into the tissues.

A broad distinction can be made between those parasites which tend to remain localized at or about their point of entry, and those which are rapidly disseminated throughout the body and produce a generalized infection associated with a bacteræmia. It is unlikely, as we shall see later, that any bacterial parasite multiplies freely in the blood stream, and the presence of large numbers of bacteria in the circulating blood would seem, in most cases, to be the expression of a loss of equilibrium, in which a rapid overflow of organisms from extensive or numerous foci of infection cannot be effectively balanced by the mechanism which removes them, or in which a less rapid overflow results in a similar accumulation because the clearing mechanism is in some way put out of action.

The property of invasiveness is one of the characters which distinguish one bacterial species from another, or one strain from another within the same species. Since, in many cases, the pathogenicity of a particular bacterial parasite appears to be mainly determined by its relative rapidity of spread within the tissues, it is logical enough to refer to those species which spread rapidly as *virulent* and to those which spread slowly, or not at all, as *avirulent* ; and this usage is generally followed. The term *virulent* is sometimes used as though it were completely synonymous with *invasive* ; but this usage is unjustified by derivation and singularly inconvenient in practice. If rigidly adhered to it would involve the exclusion from the class of virulent bacteria of all those organisms that exert their lethal effect by the production, in localized foci, of powerful toxins. We could, for instance, no longer speak of virulent and avirulent diphtheria bacilli. It is better practice to retain the term *virulent* in its correct sense of *poisonous*, without any implication as to how the poisonous effect is produced, and to apply it to any organism which gives rise to a rapidly fatal infection. The particular attributes on which virulence depends can be described in other terms.

It may, then, be stated that multiplication of bacterial cells within the tissues is one of the essential factors on which infection depends. Some species can produce a fatal infection without any wide dissemination within the body, others only cause death when such widespread dissemination occurs. Some part of the mechanism of resistance will clearly be concerned with the killing and removal of the bacterial cells as such.

Bacterial Localization.

Apart from the generalized bacteræmic invasion referred to above, most bacteria tend to lodge and multiply in tissues remote from their point of entry to the body ; and certain species, or groups of species, differ sharply from one another in regard to the particular tissues or organs in which such localization occurs.

The site of the primary lesion and the direction of the initial spread of infection are largely determined by the portal of entry to the body, and by the local anatomy, particularly by the direction of the lymph flow. But the portal of entry in its turn is determined by the natural habitat of the parasite, and this by its potentialities for life under different environmental conditions.

Thus, some types of staphylococci are normal inhabitants of the skin. Those types, or races, that are potentially pathogenic, may gain access to the underlying tissues by the hair follicles, or by the ducts of the sebaceous glands, and cause the characteristic pustules or boils.

Many of those bacteria that lead a parasitic existence in the nasopharynx, and are spread from host to host by droplet infection, tend in consequence of this common portal of entry to show a rough similarity in the distribution of the lesions they produce ; but the similarity is very incomplete, and breaks down altogether on a close analysis. Thus, pneumococci, hæmolytic streptococci, influenza bacilli, diphtheria bacilli and meningococci are all spread by droplet infection. Diphtheria bacilli and hæmolytic streptococci both tend to lodge and multiply in the tonsils, the former giving rise to the characteristic lesions of faucial diphtheria, the latter to tonsillitis. Both produce soluble toxins, which diffuse widely from the initial lesion. But the tendency to invasive spread is much greater in the case of the streptococcus than in that of the diphtheria bacillus. Pneumococci, hæmolytic streptococci and influenza bacilli may all spread to the lungs and cause pneumonic lesions, but their rôle in this regard is very different. The pneumococcus fully merits its name by its pre-eminence as an invader of the pulmonary tissue. It is the sole important bacterial agent in the primary pneumonia of adolescence and adult life. In the secondary pneumonias associated with such infections as measles, whooping cough and influenza, it shares its honours with the influenza bacillus and the hæmolytic streptococcus. The meningococcus, although it is a nasopharyngeal parasite and spreads by droplet infection, produces its characteristic lesion in the meninges. Pneumococci, hæmolytic streptococci and influenza bacilli may also give rise to meningitis ; but whereas this is the modal reaction of the meningococcus, when it produces clinically obvious infection, it is a relative rarity among the host of pathogenic reactions caused by the three other bacterial parasites.

The common sites of the primary lesions of syphilis are obviously determined by the usual mode of infection ; but the secondary and later stages are the same whether the primary chancre was genital or extragenital, and the tissues affected and the lesions produced are highly characteristic of the disease.

Instances could be multiplied *ad nauseam*. The point that needs emphasis is that the distribution of infective lesions depends in large part on the biological characters of the infecting parasite. It is a very safe prophecy that these differences in selective localization will in time be traced to differences in the biochemical behaviour of the pathogenic bacteria. Such differences must, of course, have their counterpart in variations in the local metabolic processes in the different tissues of the host. We are, at the moment, almost blankly ignorant of the factors concerned.

The Stimulation of Specific Cellular Reactions.

The differences between the infections produced by the various pathogenic micro-organisms are not confined to the distribution of lesions within the body. The lesions themselves are different and may be highly characteristic. The tendency of certain bacterial species to stimulate a localized polymorphonuclear reaction, associated with pus formation, has earned for them the title " pyogenic." Such experimental evidence as is available indicates that the migration of polymorphonuclear leucocytes to the focus of infection is the direct result of an attractive (chemotactic) effect, exerted by some diffusible bacterial product. Equally characteristic lesions, which differ among themselves, are produced by the various non-pyogenic organisms. The diphtheria bacillus, the typhoid bacillus and the *Treponema pallidum* give rise to tissue reactions which are so distinct that any competent histologist could differentiate them without bacteriological assistance. The special case of tuberculosis is of particular interest, in that a beginning has been made in tracing the connection between the various chemical products of the bacterial cell and the type of tissue reactions to which they give rise (see p. 294).

It is not, of course, the case that every pathogenic bacterium provokes a distinct and characteristic cellular response, or that the pathologist unaided can often arrive at an exact bacteriological diagnosis from a histological examination of the infected tissue ; but, as Kettle (1927) has pointed out so clearly, there is a broad correlation between certain types of lesion and certain groups of bacteria, and the groups which the pathologist would recognize on the basis of the distribution and type of the lesions produced are, in many cases at least, those which the bacteriologist would recognize as containing closely related bacterial species.

All this may seem very obvious and elementary ; but it is of the first importance to realize that different pathogenic parasites have different points of attack, and different methods of attacking.

Bacterial Toxins.

There is no apparent reason why the mere presence in the tissues, or blood stream, of any reasonable number of cells of an order of size expressed in low multiples of μ should exert any harmful effect on the host that harbours them. No mechanical theory of the pathogenic action of bacteria is compatible with our knowledge of the way in which the tissues deal with inert particles which have gained access to them. The basis of all harmful effects of bacterial infection is quite certainly chemical ; and only when the chemist has replaced the immunologist shall we be able to give an intellectually satisfying account of what happens when a particular parasite invades a particular host. In the meantime we must do what we can with the crude data at our disposal.

It has long been known that certain bacterial species produce highly poisonous substances which give rise to characteristic lesions or symptoms when injected into susceptible animals. These are the bacterial toxins. A convention has become established according to which those toxins which diffuse readily from the bacteria that produce them are referred to as *exotoxins*, while poisonous substances which remain attached to the protoplasm of the bacterial cells are referred to as *endotoxins*. As knowledge has accumulated, it has been possible to correlate this character with others, and a broad distinction may be made between characteristic members of the two groups.

A typical exotoxin is readily separated from a bacterial culture, in a suitable fluid medium, by simple filtration through a candle of porcelain or diatomaceous earth. It shows a characteristic affinity for certain cells of a susceptible host, producing easily recognizable symptoms during life, or lesions which can be detected after death. Thus one exotoxin can usually be distinguished from another by what we may term its pharmacological action. Instances of this specific effect are afforded by the action of tetanus toxin on the motor nerve cells, by the ocular and pharyngeal paralyses caused by the toxin of *Cl. botulinum*, and by the acute fatty degeneration of the cardiac muscle, the hæmorrhagic lesions of the adrenals, and the late paralysis in animals that survive, which are a characteristic of experimental diphtheritic toxæmia.

An exotoxin is usually fatal in a very small dose. The *Minimal Lethal Dose* of a potent diphtheria toxin for a guinea-pig is about 0·002 c.c., of a potent tetanus toxin about 0·0005 c.c., and of a potent botulinum toxin about 0·0001 c.c. Such toxins are usually relatively thermolabile. Diphtheria toxin is inactivated by heating at 58°–60° C. for 1–2 hours ; tetanus toxin by heating at 60° C. for 20 minutes. Lastly—and this is a matter which will be considered more fully in a subsequent chapter—exotoxins are usually highly antitoxinogenic ; that is, on inoculation into a suitable animal they stimulate the production of antitoxins which neutralize them specifically and in accordance with the law of multiple proportions.

The typical endotoxin is not liberated into the fluid medium in which the bacterium producing it is growing, and hence cannot be separated from the bacterial cells by simple filtration. The usual method of preparing a solution, or suspension, of an endotoxin is to break up the bacterial cells by prolonged grinding, with or without salt, by alternate freezing and thawing, or by merely allowing them to autolyse in a fluid medium. Toxins of this type may in most cases be demonstrated by the injection into a susceptible animal of the unaltered bacterial cells. In this case it is assumed that the liberation of the toxin is brought about by the lysis of the cells *in vivo*. The endotoxins do not, in general, give rise to diagnostic symptoms or lesions in experimental animals, so that it is not usually possible to recognize any particular endotoxin by its pharmacological action. The *Minimal Lethal Dose* of a typical endotoxin is in general far larger than that of a typical exotoxin; sometimes the ratio is of the order of 1,000,000 to 1. Thus the M.L.D. of a killed broth culture of the cholera vibrio is about 0·5 c.c. for the guinea-pig, the M.L.D. of meningococcus for the mouse is about 2 mgm. of bacillary substance, and the M.L.D. of the gonococcus for the same animal is about 10 mgm. of bacillary substance. Endotoxins are usually relatively thermostable. Cholera endotoxin requires 1 hour's heating at 80°–100° C. for its inactivation; the endotoxin of the meningococcus requires 1 hour's heating at 120° C.; while the same treatment has failed to inactivate the endotoxin of the gonococcus. Finally, the endotoxins are seldom actively antitoxinogenic. In some cases it has proved impossible to prepare anti-endotoxic sera. A more common experience is that the prolonged immunization of an animal results in the production of an antiserum which is able to neutralize a few M.L.D.'s of the endotoxin; but the law of neutralization in multiple proportions usually fails : x c.c. of serum may protect an animal against y M.L.D. of toxin, where x is some such amount as 0·1–0·5 c.c. and y is a low number such as 1–5 ; but nx c.c. of serum will not protect against ny M.L.D. of toxin where n is any large number. Indeed, in many cases, a relatively small increase in y brings us to a limit at which no amount of anti-endotoxic serum will afford protection. It would seem that the anti-endotoxins must differ qualitatively from the anti-exotoxins—their mode of action must be different.

Although this broad distinction can be made by comparing typical exotoxins with typical endotoxins, our difficulties become very great if we attempt to assign each toxic bacterial product to its correct group, and we soon find it necessary to jettison several of the differential criteria which we have mentioned above. Thus, the toxin of *Cl. botulinum* is a typical exotoxin, filtrable, with a very small M.L.D., with a characteristic pharmacological action, and antitoxinogenic; but it is relatively heat-resistant (75°–80° C. for 10 mins.). The toxin of *Cl. welchii* is filtrable, has a characteristic local action on the tissues, and is antitoxinogenic; but its M.L.D. is relatively large (0·02–0·1 c.c. for the pigeon), and it is relatively heat-resistant (70° C. for 30 mins.). The erythema-producing toxin of the hæmolytic streptococcus—the toxin which is responsible for the rash in scarlet fever, and is employed in the Dick reaction—is filtrable, has a characteristic action on the skin of a susceptible person, and is antitoxinogenic; but its M.L.D. is very large (5–10 c.c. or more of an unconcentrated filtrate for the rabbit) and it is very resistant to heat (96° C. for 45 mins.). The hæmolytic streptococcus also produces another filtrable toxic constituent which differs from the Dick toxin in being thermolabile (55° C. for 30 mins.), in causing lysis of red blood cells, and perhaps of leucocytes, though the identity of streptococcal hæmolysin and leucocidin is not accepted by all observers. Its M.L.D. is large, of about the same order as the thermostable toxin, but in this dose it kills susceptible rabbits within 24–36 hours with an associated hæmoglobinuria and characteristic evidence of intravascular hæmolysis at necropsy (M'Leod and M'Nee 1913, Channon and M'Leod 1929). Until recently it appeared to be non-antitoxinogenic; but Todd (1932) has shown that, by the use of suitable reagents, antihæmolysin can be demonstrated to high titre in the serum of immunized animals. The toxin of Shiga's dysentery bacillus has a selective action on the mucosa of the large intestine and on the central nervous system in the rabbit, and it is antitoxinogenic. But its M.L.D. is relatively large as compared with the more typical exotoxins (0·1–1 c.c. of filtrate or fluid culture for the rabbit ; 0·002 mgm. of dried bacterial substance for the mouse) and it is relatively heat-resistant (75°–90° C. for 1 hr.). Its distribution between the bacterial cells and the culture fluid is curious. It is present in filtrates from an autolysed broth culture ; but it is also present in the bacterial cells themselves and the toxin is commonly preserved in the form of dried bacterial substance.

One implication which has sometimes—though without justification—been attached to the term " exotoxin " is very probably misleading. Toxins of this type have been described in words which suggest that they are of the nature of active secretions of the bacterial cells. There is little definite evidence that this is so. Though some exotoxins, as that of *Cl. welchii*, are produced in high concentration during the phase of active bacterial growth, others, such as diphtheria, tetanus and Shiga toxins, only attain a high concentration in a fluid culture when the phase of active growth has passed, and the majority of the bacteria present are dead or dying. How far autolytic processes may be concerned in toxin-production is quite uncertain. We have, in fact, no real knowledge of what exotoxins are, or how they are produced. We can detect them only by their toxic action.

In almost all our studies on bacterial toxins we have had to be content with crude reagents—filtrates, autolysates or extracts which quite certainly contain a multitude of substances besides those which we desire to investigate. We have not yet succeeded in isolating any bacterial exotoxin in a chemically pure state, although a considerable degree of concentration has been attained by various methods of fractional precipitation. Within the last few years, however, we have obtained some indication of the chemical structure of a class of bacterial constituents which must be regarded as endotoxins in the usually accepted sense.

Boivin and his colleagues (1933–1935) and Raistrick and Topley (1934) (see also Delafield 1934, Martin 1934) have investigated, independently, the immunological activities of various constituents extracted from bacteria of the Salmonella group. Both groups of workers have succeeded, by somewhat different methods, in isolating from the bacteria substances that contain a complex polysaccharide component, combined with a non-protein component containing nitrogen, phosphorus and fatty acids.

The substances, in their intact form, are toxic for mice and for rabbits. When they are split into its two components by mild acid hydrolysis they lose almost all their toxicity. The polysaccharide component is entirely non-toxic. The phosphatide, or nucleotide, component is toxic for mice only in very large doses (4 mgm. or more).

These toxic bacterial components are of considerable interest. There is little doubt that they are identical with the specific somatic antigens of the bacteria concerned, the antigenic specificity being conferred by the polysaccharide components which may perhaps be regarded as haptens. Toxic antigens of this type, characterized by different polysaccharide haptens, are widely distributed among the Gram-negative bacilli of the coli-typhoid group, and perhaps among other more distantly related bacteria. Moreover, we now know something of the effects produced by these particular endotoxins ; and it seems likely that they all act in much the same way, irrespective of the particular bacterium from which they have been derived.

The latter conclusion is based on results obtained in recent studies on blood chemistry in relation to experimental infection. Several observers have reported changes in the concentration of blood sugar, or of some other chemical constituent, following the injection into an animal of bacteria or bacterial products (Menten and Manning 1925, Zeckwer and Goodell 1925, Menten 1926, Levine and Kolars 1926, Menten and King 1930), but many of these earlier findings are difficult to correlate and interpret. Delafield (1931, 1932) has recently recorded a more detailed and systematic study, which confirms and extends certain of the earlier observations, and presents a more orderly picture of the modal reaction concerned. He finds that the intravenous injection into rabbits of killed suspensions of various Gram-negative bacilli is followed by a sharp rise in blood sugar, reaching its maximum (300 mgm. per cent. or more) within a few hours. Following this transient hyperglycæmia, the blood sugar returns to the normal level, and in most cases falls significantly below it. This hypoglycæmic phase, when it occurs, usually attains its lowest level (70 mgm. per cent. or less) in about 24 hours. If the animal survives, there is then a rapid return to the normal level. The inorganic blood phosphorus usually fluctuates inversely as the blood sugar, falling when the latter rises, rising when the latter falls. The bacterial components that induce this characteristic response are stable to heat and to many chemical reagents. Bacterial suspensions remain active after steaming, after short periods in the autoclave at 120° C., or after extraction with alcohol or acetone. As noted above, the active substances seem to be present in most Gram-negative bacteria, but absent, or latent, in most Gram-positive species (Delafield 1932). Working with the complex antigenic component isolated from *Bact. typhi-murium* (Delafield 1934) it was possible to demonstrate the same type of chemical response, and confirmatory findings have since been recorded by Boivin and Mesrobeanu (1934*b*).

We know nothing as yet of the mechanism by which these chemical changes are induced. It is possible (see Evans and Zeckwer 1927) that adrenal stimulation may play some part. But the whole problem awaits further inquiry.

Other Active Constituents or Products of Bacteria.

In addition to exotoxins and endotoxins bacteria may contain, or produce, other active substances that influence the course of an infection without exerting a directly harmful effect on any living cell.

Thus pyogenic staphylococci produce a *coagulase* that accelerates the clotting of human plasma (Much 1908, Gross 1931*a*, *b*, Chapman *et al.* 1934). They also (Duran-Reynals 1933) produce a " spreading-factor " that increases the permeability of the tissue capillaries.

Tillett and Garner (1933) have shown that most strains of hæmolytic streptococci that are pathogenic for man produce an active substance that dissolves human fibrin. This *fibrinolysin* though possessing many of the characters of an enzyme is relatively heat-stable (see Tillett, Edwards and Garner 1934, Tillett 1935).

There is no doubt (see, for instance, Reimer 1936) that active substances of the coagulase and fibrinolysin type may be produced by a variety of bacteria ; and that a single bacterium may produce both types of substance, or exert both types of activity, accelerating the clotting of plasma and dissolving the fibrin clot when it has been formed. Again, each type of activity shows some degree of host-specificity. A given strain of streptococcus, for instance, may be actively lytic for human fibrin, but quite inactive for rabbit or fowl fibrin. It is highly probable that bacterial constituents or products of these, or related, types play an important part in determining the histological reaction associated with different types of infection (see in addition to references above, Goodner 1931, 1933).

It seems altogether probable that other bacterial enzymes, catalysts, or activators, play an important part in infective processes. We have described in some detail in Chapter III various enzyme systems concerned in bacterial metabolism, and, in particular, a variety of substrates. It was noted that the activity of many of these systems is not dependent on the life of the bacterial cell.   Dead bacteria, provided that they are not too greatly altered, are able to activate many of the chemical changes that have been observed.

It seems quite possible that, wherever there is formed in the tissues a nidus of bacterial cells, alive or dead, there may result in the immediate neighbourhood a diversion of the normal metabolic processes sufficiently serious to derange the local cell activities.   It is not impossible that the diffusion of bacterial enzymes might convert such a local effect into a more general one.   It may be noted that enzymes appear to be relatively ineffective antigens, in the sense that they do not usually induce the formation of specific anti-enzymes.

We should then regard the bacterial cell as endowed with an extensive armoury of chemical weapons of attack.   These include (*a*) the filtrable toxins, diffusing freely from the site of infection and acting specifically on certain sensitive tissue cells.   These are often lethal in extremely small doses ; (*b*) the hæmolysins and leucocidins, acting directly on red cells and leucocytes, and hence influencing the course of an infection ; (*c*) toxic substances contained in the bacterial cells, and not freely liberated into the surrounding fluid.   Among these endotoxins are some, at least, of the somatic bacterial antigens, that are lethal in moderate doses and induce characteristic changes in the chemical constitution of the circulating blood ; (*d*) various active substances which, though not directly toxic, influence the reactions of the tissues by inducing or inhibiting the clotting of plasma or lymph, or by dissolving the fibrin of a clot already formed, or by increasing the permeability of the tissue spaces, or by any combination of these effects ; (*e*) a wide variety of bacterial enzymes, many of which remain active after the death of the bacteria. Some, at least, of these may modify the local tissue metabolism of the host.

Hypersensitiveness and Allergy.

There are reasons, which will be discussed more fully elsewhere, for believing that the tissues may become sensitized during the course of a bacterial infection, so that a bacterial constituent which before called forth little or no response may act as a powerful stimulus.   In some cases the vigorous response evoked is injurious to the host, so that a bacterial product which possesses little or no toxicity for a normal animal may be highly toxic for an animal which has become sensitized by infection.   The well-known tuberculin reaction in the guinea-pig is a case in point.

Some Illustrative Examples.

We have described above the various bacterial factors which, so far as we know at the moment, are certainly, probably, or possibly concerned in the pathogenesis of infective diseases.

A few illustrative examples may serve to emphasize the more important points.

Botulism may be placed at one end of the scale, as an example of a pure toxæmia. It is not a true infection, but is closely analogous to the effects that may follow the consumption of such vegetable poisons as those produced by certain fungi or plants. There is no certain evidence that *Cl. botulinum* ever invades the tissues, or multiplies in them.   Man is affected by eating food in which the organism has grown and produced its toxin.

Tetanus is one step removed, in that the bacillus must gain access to the tissues and multiply in them in order to produce its toxic effects ; but its invasive powers are very slight.   It usually gains access to the body as the result of some mechanical injury, and the local multiplication of the organism is in many cases assisted by gross injury to the tissues, by the injurious effects of some associated infection, or by the presence of some chemical agent, such as a calcium salt, which alters the local conditions to the advantage of the parasite.

Diphtheria takes us a little further along the scale. The bacillus is capable of implanting itself in the faucial region, and of spreading from host to host, by ordinary droplet infection or in similar ways. It has relatively slight but quite definite invasive powers. It causes a characteristic local lesion, and may occasionally invade other tissues and organs. Its lethal effect, however, depends almost entirely on its activity as a toxin-producer.

The hæmolytic streptococcus combines the activities of a typically toxigenic organism with those of the highly invasive group of bacteria. It produces a relatively heat-stable toxin, with a characteristic action on the skin, which is the cause of the typical toxic rash in scarlet fever; but it also invades the tissues freely. Indeed, highly virulent strains of the organism are among the most rapid and vigorous tissue-invaders with which we are acquainted in human pathology. In relation to this tissue invasion it is very probable that the hæmolysin, the leucocidin, the fibrinolysin and the spreading factor produced by pathogenic streptococci play a significant part.

As we move along the scale we meet a variety of organisms whose pathogenicity seems to depend entirely on their power of spread and multiplication in the tissues, and whose more important effects seem to be localized to the areas in which such multiplication occurs. These differ among themselves in selective localization, and in the tissue reactions to which they give rise. Thus, staphylococci most commonly cause localized suppurative lesions, with a varying degree of lymphatic spread, which may sometimes be rapid and extensive. More rarely they give rise to a generalized infection of the pyæmic type, in which the cocci are carried from the original focus of infection in detached fragments of an infected thrombus. Here again, hæmolysin, leucocidin, coagulase, fibrinolysin and the so-called spreading factor must play a part in determining the type of lesion in any particular case.

Finally, there are organisms, such as the tubercle bacillus, the leprosy bacillus and the *Tr. pallidum*, that tend to produce more chronic lesions of the granulomatous type. We know little as yet of the bacterial constituents that determine this particular type of tissue response, except in the case of the tubercle bacillus—see Chapter LVI; and even there our knowledge is as yet very scanty. It seems probable that it is conditioned in large part by the absence of those bacterial constituents that determine the more rapid and vigorous response induced by organisms of the acutely toxic, pyogenic, or invasive type.

The defence mechanisms brought into play, and their relative importance, will clearly differ according to the type of infection. It is with these mechanisms that we shall be concerned in the following chapters.

SUMMARY

(1) An ability to gain access to the tissues, and to multiply in them to a lesser or greater degree is an essential attribute of a pathogenic organism. Some organisms produce their effects by the local production of a powerful toxin which passes into the tissues, and produces its toxic effects on cells remote from its site of origin. Others produce their main pathological effects at the site, or sites, in which they are multiplying. Of these latter, some give rise mainly to lesions limited to the near neighbourhood of their point of entry; others to lesions remote from this point,

but characteristically localized in certain tissues or organs ; others, again, to a generalized bacteræmic infection. These different modes of attack are often combined in the case of a single infecting bacterium.

(2) The selective localization of bacteria in particular organs or tissues of the body is determined in part by characters inherent in the bacteria themselves. The anatomy of the infected host, the biochemical reactions of different tissues, and the defence mechanisms brought into play, combine with these inherent bacterial characters in determining the exact distribution of lesions encountered in each particular case.

(3) Pathogenic bacteria differ in the cellular reactions to which they give rise. These differences may be highly characteristic.

(4) Among the bacterial toxins are some which are characterized by the ease with which they may be separated from the bacterial cells which produce them. Under suitable conditions they diffuse into a fluid medium and may be obtained from the cells by simple filtration. Toxins of this class are commonly referred to as *exotoxins*. They are usually characterized by possessing a specific pharmacological action, and by being actively antitoxinogenic. Their Minimal Lethal Dose is generally small, sometimes very small. They are in many cases thermolabile, being inactivated by temperatures in the neighbourhood of 55° C.

(5) Apart from these toxins there is another class of toxic bacterial products which are characterized by remaining incorporated in the substance of the bacterial cells. They can be obtained in a state of solution, or perhaps suspension, only by methods which result in the disintegration of the cells. They do not, in general, exert any characteristic pharmacological action by which they can be differentiated from one another. They are feebly antitoxinogenic, and the antitoxins to which they give rise do not obey the law of combination in multiple proportions. Their Minimal Lethal Dose is usually large. They are relatively heat-stable, withstanding temperatures of 80°–120° C. for an hour or more. They are often referred to as *endotoxins*.

(6) Although it is often an easy matter to assign a toxic bacterial product to one of these categories, this is not always the case, since the criteria referred to above are by no means constant. It would, indeed, be very difficult to give any satisfactory definition of an endotoxin. Within this category, it would seem that we must include certain of the somatic antigens of bacteria that have been found to be highly toxic in the form in which they occur in the bacterial cell.

(7) There are other constituents, or products, of bacterial cells, which, though not directly toxic, exert an influence on the course of the infective process. These include substances that induce or inhibit the coagulation of lymph, or plasma ; substances that dissolve the fibrin of a clot already formed ; substances that increase the local permeability of the tissues and probably other substances of a related kind.

(8) It is at least possible that the various enzymes concerned in bacterial metabolism exert an influence on infection by intervening in the normal metabolism of the tissues.

(9) As the result of infection the tissues of the host may become hypersensitive to the infecting bacteria or to their products. Such sensitization may play an essential part in some of the phenomena of infective disease.

REFERENCES

BOIVIN, A. and MESROBEANU, L. (1933) *C. R. Soc. Biol.,* **112,** 76 ; (1934a) *Ibid.,* **115,** 304, 309 ; (1934b) *Ibid.,* **117,** 273 ; (1934c) *C. R. Acad. Sci.,* **198,** 2211 ; (1935a) *C. R. Soc. Biol.,* **118,** 612 ; (1935b) *C. R. Acad. Sci.,* **201,** 168.

BOIVIN, A., MESROBEANU, I., and MESROBEANU, L. (1933a) *C. R. Soc. Biol.,* **113,** 490 ; (1933b) *Ibid.,* **114,** 307 ; (1934a) *Ibid.,* **115,** 306 ; (1934b) *Ibid.,* **117,** 271 ; (1935) *Arch. roum. Path. exp. Microbiol.,* **8,** 45.

CHANNON, H. A. and M'LEOD, J. W. (1929) *J. Path. Bact.,* **32,** 283.

CHAPMAN, G. H., BERENS, C., PETERS, A., and CURCIO, L. (1934) *J. Bact.,* **28,** 343.

DELAFIELD, M. E. (1931) *J. Path. Bact.,* **34,** 177 ; (1932) *Ibid.,* **35,** 53 ; (1934) *Brit. J. exp. Path.,* **15,** 130.

DURAN-REYNALS, F. (1933) *J. exp. Med.,* **58,** 161.

EVANS, C. L. and ZECKWER, I. T. (1927) *Brit. J. exp. Path.,* **8,** 280.

GOODNER, K. (1931) *J. exp. Med.,* **54,** 847 ; (1933) *Ibid.,* **58,** 153.

GROSS, H. (1931a) *Zbl. Bakt.,* **122,** 354 ; (1931b) *Ibid.,* **123,** 212.

KETTLE, E. H. (1927) *Lancet,* i. 1169, 1225.

LEVINE, V. E. and KOLARS, J. J. (1926) *Proc. Soc. exp. Biol., N.Y.,* **24,** 36.

M'LEOD, J. W. and M'NEE, J. W. (1913) *J. Path. Bact.,* **17,** 524.

MARTIN, A. R. (1934) *Brit. J. exp. Path.,* **15,** 137.

MENTEN, M. L. (1926) *J. infect. Dis.,* **38,** 354.

MENTEN, M. L. and KING, C. G. (1930) *J. infect. Dis.,* **46,** 275.

MENTEN, M. L. and MANNING, H. M. (1925) *J. infect. Dis.,* **37,** 400.

MUCH, H. (1908) *Biochem. Z.,* **14,** 143.

RAISTRICK, H. and TOPLEY, W. W. C. (1934) *Brit. J. exp. Path.,* **15,** 113.

REIMER, K. (1936) *Zbl. Bakt.,* **136,** 84.

TILLETT, W. S. (1935) *J. Bact.,* **29,** 111.

TILLETT, W. S., EDWARDS, L. B., and GARNER, R. L. (1934) *J. clin. Invest.,* **13,** 47.

TILLETT, W. S. and GARNER, R. L. (1933) *J. exp. Med.,* **58,** 485.

TODD, E. W. (1932) *Brit. J. exp. Path.,* **13,** 248.

ZECKWER, I. T. and GOODELL, H. (1925) *J. exp. Med.,* **42,** 43, 57.

CHAPTER XLII

THE MECHANISMS THAT HINDER OR PREVENT THE ACCESS OF BACTERIA TO THE TISSUES

As noted in the previous chapter, an ability to gain access to the tissues and to multiply in them to a lesser or greater degree is an essential attribute of a pathogenic organism. It is logical to commence our study of the defence mechanisms of the host by considering the barriers that are opposed to the ingress of bacterial parasites from the outside world. Unfortunately our knowledge is here at its sketchiest. Most studies of experimental infections in animals have been concerned with reactions that take place within the tissues. It is only within recent years, and in the hands as yet of relatively few workers, that any serious attempt has been made to study systematically the mechanisms involved in the first line of defence.

It will be convenient to take in turn the various body surfaces and portals of entry, and to summarize very briefly our scanty knowledge of their behaviour towards bacteria that establish contact with them.

The Skin.—It needs only the most casual acquaintance with the ordinary chances of life to establish the value of an intact skin as a barrier against bacterial infection. The inability of the deeper tissues to protect themselves against the free access of bacteria from the outside world set a sharp limit to major surgical interference in pre-Listerian days. There can be little doubt that the skin functions in the main as a simple mechanical barrier, but it has recently become clear that the efficacy of this barrier is enhanced by a complex biological mechanism which enables the skin surface to free itself rapidly from the majority of those bacteria that are continually impinging upon it.

Our knowledge of this mechanism has been derived from two independent sources ; the observations of Arnold, Gustafson and others (1930), which form part of a systematic study of the self-disinfecting mechanisms of the body surfaces, and those of Colebrook (1930) on the sterilization of the hands. Colebrook found that hæmolytic streptococci were rapidly killed on the skin of the normal hand. Three minutes after swabbing a finger lightly with a broth culture—by which time the skin was apparently dry—30,000,000 cocci could be recovered by thorough swabbing with sterile broth. One hour later 1,722,000 viable cocci were recoverable ; two hours later 7,000 cocci. Similar observations were made with *Proteus vulgaris*, Friedländer's pneumobacillus and *Bact. coli*. Simple control experiments, in which glass surfaces were swabbed, allowed to dry and sampled at intervals thereafter, showed that the bactericidal effect could not be attributed to simple desiccation. While the skin of the normal hand shows this striking capacity for freeing itself—at least partially—from bacteria which form no part of its normal flora, its reactions are entirely different towards those species that habitually live upon it. Thus, Colebrook found that no amount of washing, nor any of the chemical disinfectants commonly employed for sterilizing the hands in obstetrical practice, would remove from the skin the numerous staphylococci and less numerous bacilli that normally vegetate thereon.

Arnold, Gustafson and others (1930) (see also Karns and Arnold 1931) record a more detailed series of observations along similar lines. Taking *Chromobacterium prodigiosum* as the test organism, they found that 90 per cent. of the bacteria placed on the skin of the hands were killed within 10 minutes, about 99 per cent. within 20 minutes, and that none could be recovered in most cases after 30 minutes. Many other bacterial species behaved in the same way. Using the palmar surface of the clean hand *Bact. coli, Bact. typhosum,* and *Bact. enteritidis* could not be recovered 10 minutes after application. Certain regions, such as the lateral margins of the dorsal surface of the finger-nails and the region under the nail tip, freed themselves far more slowly from the bacteria applied to them. Dirty skin in any situation had relatively little power of autosterilization. Using *Bact. enteritidis* as a test organism on the hands of workmen (electricians and plumbers) before and after washing the hands at the end of the day, it was found that the dirty hands gave no reduction in the number of recoverable bacteria in 10 minutes, a 5 per cent. reduction in 20 minutes, and a 15 per cent. reduction in 30 minutes. After washing there was an 85 per cent. reduction in 10 minutes, and a complete disappearance after 20 minutes. The dead skin, tested on cadavers within 15 minutes of death, had lost most of its bactericidal action. With *Bact. coli* there was a 12 per cent. reduction in 10 minutes, a 16 per cent. reduction in 20 minutes, and a 50 per cent. reduction in 30 minutes. As in Colebrook's experience it was noted that staphylococci could constantly be isolated from the normal human skin. When *Staph. aureus* was applied experimentally to the clean palmar skin, there was an initial rapid reduction (82 per cent. in 10 min.), but the organism was still recoverable after much longer periods.

The mechanism of this autosterilizing action is as yet quite uncertain. It seems probable that the chemical properties of the sweat are the determining factors. Arnold and his colleagues note that the pH of the normal skin is markedly acid (5·8–5·2, see Schade and Marchionini 1928) and are inclined to attach considerable importance to this factor ; but they found it impossible to test this thesis experimentally, since they were not able to alter the pH of the superficial layer of the skin by any method that did not involve injury to the epidermis with exposure of the deeper layers, or gross interference with the vascular supply.

Fleming (1922, 1929, 1932) has recorded the presence in tears, in nasal secretion, and in many tissues including the skin, of a relatively thermolabile substance which, in high dilution, causes the lysis of certain non-pathogenic bacteria, and in particular of an organism to which he gave the name of *Micrococcus lysodeikticus*. This substance, *lysozyme*, is also active against some strains of staphylococci and intestinal streptococci of human origin. In high concentration it acts, though less energetically, on other pathogenic bacteria. It is natural to inquire whether it plays any part in the self-disinfecting action of the human skin. If so, it would seem that its rôle is relatively unimportant ; since Colebrook (1930) records that many of the bacteria that are rapidly removed are not susceptible to its action, while *Micrococcus lysodeikticus* itself disappears less rapidly from the skin than such species as *Str. hœmolyticus, Bact. coli* or *Proteus vulgaris*.

The Mouth, Stomach and Intestinal Tract.—When bacteria gain access to the mouth, provided that they are not introduced as constituents of some food or drink that is immediately swallowed, they adhere to the mucus with which the lining epithelium is plentifully covered.

A series of careful studies by Bloomfield (1922*a, b, c*) have enabled him to trace in some detail their subsequent fate. In an initial series of experiments carbon particles were placed on the tongue, on the palate, in the sublingual space, on the mucosa of the cheek, on the posterior pharyngeal wall, or on the tonsil, and their subsequent movement was carefully observed. It was found that there was little or no tendency for the particles to spread at large over the surface of the mouth, but that they were removed from the various sites of implantation in an orderly manner. The general path of removal was directly backwards. There was no forward dissemination nor was there any tendency to wide lateral spread—carbon placed well to one side of the tongue near its tip did not, for instance, cross the mid-line. The paths of transit from the tongue, sublingual space and palate all converge at the base of the tongue. The tonsils, protected by the faucial pillars, occupy a position that is out of the way of these lines of passage so that under normal conditions particles that are deposited on the tongue are swept past them. The currents that bear the particles backwards are almost certainly the result of suction, set up by the lips, cheek, tongue and palate ; and particles are removed with particular rapidity from the sublingual space and from the lateral buccal mucosa, where the flow of saliva is maximal and the local formation of the mucosa is least favourable to retention. Particles placed directly on the tonsils are in part removed rapidly by the general flushing action of the saliva ; but those that once gain lodgment remain relatively stagnant for a considerable period of time. Having reached the base of the tongue the particles are periodically swallowed. In general, carbon particles are almost completely removed from the mouth within 15 to 30 minutes. Subsequent experiments with *Sarcina lutea* showed that bacteria introduced into the mouth were removed in the same fashion as carbon particles. Attempts were made to alter the flora of the tongue by thorough and repeated washing. It was found that the greater part of any bacteria artificially implanted could be rapidly removed in this way, but no amount of washing would produce any significant change in the character or number of the normal lingual flora. It would appear that bacteria entering the mouth are unable to persist on any of the mucous surfaces for more than a few hours unless their biological characters are such as to allow of successful colonization. Once colonized they become part of the local flora, and can no longer be dislodged by any simple mechanical means, nor probably by any ordinary disinfectant.

Once bacteria have been swallowed they are subjected in the stomach and upper part of the duodenum to the action of the gastric juice, with its high hydrogen-ion concentration. It has long been recognized that the gastric secretion imposes a barrier to the passage of bacteria from the mouth to the intestine, but the recent studies of Arnold and his colleagues (Arnold 1926, 1927, 1928, 1929, Arnold and Brody 1926*a, b*) have placed our knowledge on a more detailed basis. By fixing various segments of the gastro-intestinal tract of the dog to the skin of the abdomen they were able to withdraw samples of the contents by sterile puncture as desired, and thus to determine the nature of the normal flora in relation to the acidity or alkalinity of the intestinal contents, and also the fate of other bacteria when administered by the mouth.

Table LVIII shows the relation between the hydrogen-ion concentration of the intestinal contents and the prevailing bacterial flora at different levels.

TABLE LVIII

Portion of Small Intestine.	pH of Contents.	Bacterial Flora.
Duodenum	5·2–6·0	Few Gram-positive cocci.
Jejunum, upper half . .	5·5–6·5	,, ,, ,, ,,
Jejunum, lower half . . .	6·0–7·0	Gram-positive cocci, few Gram-positive and Gram-negative bacilli.
Ileum	6·8–8·0	Rich and varied bacterial flora.

Using as test organisms *Chromobacterium prodigiosum* and *Ps. pyocyanea*, it was found that these bacteria, when introduced in watery suspensions into the empty stomach of a dog 12 to 18 hours after a meal, failed to reach the cæcum. Introduced in an alkaline buffered watery suspension or in alkaline buffered milk they reached the cæcum in large numbers. (See also Teale 1934.)

Whether the bactericidal action of the duodenal contents is entirely determined by its hydrogen-ion concentration, is, perhaps, open to question (see Meyer and Löwenberg 1928).

With regard to the possible effect of Fleming's lysozyme in the stomach and intestine, Goldsworthy and Florey (1930) have studied the distribution of this substance in mucus and mucosal extracts from several animal species, using as test organisms *Micrococcus lysodeikticus* and a series of unidentified susceptible bacteria isolated from the air of the laboratory. In the cat, no lysozyme could be detected in mucus from the stomach or colon, though small amounts could be demonstrated in saline extracts of the dried mucosæ. In the dog, detectable amounts were present in the mucosa of the intestinal tract, more in the colon than in the stomach. In the rabbit, the mucosal extracts were actively lytic. The colon was more active than the stomach, the small intestine falling between the two. In the guinea-pig, on the other hand, the mucosa from the stomach was more active than that from the intestine. What part this substance plays in eliminating susceptible species from the intestinal flora it is however impossible to say.

Quite apart, however, from the action of the contained lysozyme, there can be no doubt that the mucus itself provides a very efficient and important cleansing and protective mechanism. Florey (1933) has studied this mechanism in some detail. He finds that the mucus does not form a uniform coating over the epithelial cells of the mucosa, but is present in the form of a lace-like mesh-work spread over the mucosal surface. The villi free themselves from any small adherent particles by movements that bring the particles into contact with the mucus, to which they adhere. The mucus, with the adherent particles, is then rolled up into small masses by the intestinal movements, and is propelled onwards by the peristaltic movements of the bowel. Non-pathogenic bacteria, when introduced into the intestinal lumen, appear to behave very much as inert particles, except that those sensitive to lysozyme are dissolved when lysozyme is present. When a thick suspension of a pathogenic organism, such as *Bact. typhi-murium*, is introduced into an intestinal loop the resulting changes are very different. There is a considerable exudation of phagocytic cells into the gut lumen, and in places the epithelial cells desquamate, leaving bare the underlying stroma. Most of the mucosa, however, preserves its epithelial covering completely ; and it would appear that the bacteria not infrequently enter, and pass through, the epithelial cells themselves.

It is of obvious interest to inquire whether those procedures that alter the normal conditions in such a way as to allow bacteria to pass alive through the stomach and duodenum to the lower segments of the intestine have any effect in promoting their passage through the intestinal mucosa to the lymphatics and blood stream.

Arnold (1928) has studied this problem experimentally. *Bact. coli* and *Chromobacterium prodigiosum* were injected with minimal injury into a dog's duodenum, and counts were made of the bacteria in the lymph collected from a canula inserted into the thoracic duct. The results are summarized in Table LIX. It will be noted that alkalinization alone does not suffice to induce the transit of bacteria from the intestinal lumen to the lymphatics, but that addition of bile, or still better of egg white, so alters the conditions at the mucosal surface that such passage occurs. The negative findings with the other suspending fluids employed are in accord with those of Neisser (1896) and of Teale and Embleton (1914). It would appear that only under quite exceptional conditions is the intestinal mucosa permeable to living bacteria ; and it would seem (Nedzel and Arnold 1931) that raw egg albumin is peculiarly potent in inducing the passage of bacteria not only from the intestinal lumen to the lymphatics and the blood, but in the reverse direction from the blood stream to the intestinal lumen.

TABLE LIX

Solution injected with Bacteria.	Average No. of Bacteria in Lymph per c.c.	Time of Appearance after Injections.
Alkaline solution and egg white. .	500 to 1,000	First 5 mins. and lasting for 30 mins.
Neutral solution and egg white . .	None	—
Alkaline solution	None	—
Neutral solution	None	—
Alkaline solution and bile . . .	50 to 100	First 5 mins. and lasting for 20 mins.
Neutral solution and bile	3 to 5	During first 30 mins.
Alkaline solution and dog's serum .	None	—
Neutral solution and dog's serum .	None	—

The Nose, Nasopharynx and Respiratory Tract.—The nasal cavities are in part protected from air-borne bacteria by the anatomy of the anterior nares. The greater part of the inhaled bacteria appear to be arrested at or near the nasal orifices (see Thomson and Hewlett 1896). Those that pass beyond this point adhere to the film of mucus that covers the nasal mucosa, and are then swept back—in this case by the current set up by the ciliated epithelium—towards the naso- and oro-pharynx, where they join the bacteria being swept back by suction currents from the mouth (see Bloomfield 1919, 1922*d*).

Whether this mechanical clearance is the only factor concerned is again uncertain. Arnold, Ostrom and Singer (1928) introduced *Chromobacterium prodigiosum* and *Bact. coli*, by spraying, into the nose of men, rabbits, dogs and guinea-pigs, and noted their rapid disappearance. They state that swabs taken from the posterior pharyngeal wall gave no indication that there was any extensive passage of the bacteria to the throat; but they were unable to detect in nasal washings or secretions any substance that was bactericidal to the test organisms employed. It may be noted that the rate of disappearance recorded by Arnold and his colleagues—a diminution in numbers during the first 5 minutes, and total disappearance within half an hour—was more rapid than that recorded by Bloomfield— little change in 2 hours but almost complete disappearance in 24. This slower rate of elimination was also noted by Bloomfield in the case of particles of kieselguhr placed on the nasal septum.

Lysozyme is known to be present in high concentration in the nasal secretions, and it is altogether probable that it plays a part in freeing the nasal cavities from those species of bacteria against which it is active.

Whatever may be the nature of the complex of mechanisms involved there is every reason to suppose that the same result is attained in the nose as in the mouth. The majority of bacteria that enter at the external nares are removed or destroyed, and fail to obtain any but the most transient footing among the normal nasal flora; those that survive and multiply do so because they are in some way adapted for successful colonization, and once such colonization has occurred they may persist for an indefinite period of time.

The conditions in the nasopharynx have been sufficiently dealt with in considering the elimination of bacteria from the mouth.

It would appear (Calamida and Bartarelli 1902) that the accessory nasal sinuses are normally sterile.

There is little doubt that in health the trachea and bronchi contain few if any living bacteria (see Thomson and Hewlett 1896, Bloomfield 1922*d*) ; and it is probable that the main protective mechanism consists in the filtering action of the nasal passages combined with the adherence of bacteria which pass the posterior nares, or are drawn in *via* the mouth, to the pharyngeal or upper laryngeal mucosa. It is however quite certain, from the ordinary experience of the *post-mortem* room, that dust particles, and hence presumably bacteria, reach the lungs in numbers that, if minimal in any short period of time, attain a considerable total in the course of months or years.

Under exceptional conditions (see Nenninger 1901, Paul 1902, Quesnil 1902, Bloomfield 1922*d*) bacteria may reach the lungs in relatively large numbers, though those that penetrate so deeply never form more than a small fraction of the total number inspired.   Once past the vocal cords, the inspired organisms are probably dealt with mechanically in three ways. They may adhere to mucus and be expectorated ; they may perhaps be driven upwards by the ciliated epithelium ; they may reach the deeper bronchi or lung alveoli and be removed, probably by phagocytic cells, to the regional lymph glands.   Whether any immediately bactericidal mechanism is at work we do not know.

The Conjunctivæ.—It is convenient to consider the conjunctivæ in connection with the upper respiratory tract.   The mechanical flushing action of the tears is an obvious phenomenon, and there is little doubt that the main route of removal is *via* the lachrymal duct.

Maxcy (1919) was able to recover *Chromobacterium prodigiosum* from the nose within 5 minutes after its introduction into the conjunctival sac.   Stort (1891) failed to recover *Bact. coli* from the rabbit's conjunctiva 1 hour after its implantation ; but found that it persisted for a much longer time if the lachrymal duct were previously tied.

Tears have the highest lysozyme content of any secretion yet examined.   At a dilution of 1 : 40,000 they may cause complete lysis of a suspension of *Micrococcus lysodeikticus*.   There can be little doubt that this agent suffices to rid the conjunctiva of many of the organisms that come in contact with it, and that it plays a part in the local defence of this region against certain pathogenic bacteria (see Ridley 1928).

The Genital Tract.—It is probable, though there is no definite evidence on the point, that the external genitals, so far as they are covered with a complete dermal layer, share the bactericidal action of the skin elsewhere.   There are probably additional selective factors—favourable or inhibitory for particular bacterial species—resulting from localized glandular secretions, or from differences in the amount of moisture in the skin.

The urethra in the male and female is normally sterile, or contains in the neighbourhood of the meatus a few staphylococci and diphtheroid bacilli.   The mechanical flushing action of the urine, combined perhaps with its slightly acid reaction (pH 6·0), is probably an important factor.

The vagina has a highly characteristic flora, consisting largely of aciduric bacilli of the Döderlein type (see Küster 1929).   The normal vaginal secretion has a marked bactericidal action on many species of bacteria.   Thus Menge (1894) found that *Ps. pyocyanea*, staphylococci and streptococci introduced experimentally into the vagina could not be recovered after 21 to 26 hours.

The Efficiency of the Bactericidal or Inhibitory Mechanisms Operating on Body Surfaces.

It is extremely difficult to assess the relative protective value of the factors that we have described above, as compared with the mechanisms that we shall discuss in subsequent chapters. It is obvious that they often fail ; but how frequently they succeed we cannot tell.

That they are of real importance can easily be shown experimentally by noting the different doses of bacteria that are required to induce experimental infection by different routes.

To take a single example from many available, the dose of *Bact. typhi-murium* that will, on the average, lead to a fatal infection when injected intraperitoneally into a mouse of 18–22 gm. is somewhere between 1,000 and 1,000,000 times smaller than the dose that will lead to the same result when administered by the mouth. A series of observed figures for groups of 85 mice per dose (intraperitoneal injection) and of 75 mice per dose (*per os* infection) are given in Table LX.

TABLE LX

Showing the Percentage Mortalities observed in Groups of Mice after the Administration of Various Doses of a Virulent Strain of *Bact. typhi-murium* intraperitoneally or *per os*.

Number of Bacilli administered.	Mortality per cent.	
	Intraperitoneal.	Per os.
1,000,000,000	Not tested	48·75
10,000,000	98·8	28·25
100,000	84·7	22·50
1,000	65·9	15·00
10	28·2	Not tested

SUMMARY

There are a series of mechanisms, concerning the exact nature of which we as yet know relatively little, that tend toward the mechanical removal or local destruction of most of those bacteria that reach the various body surfaces from the outside world. These mechanisms vary in nature from one locality to another ; each body surface—the skin, the conjunctivæ, the mucous membranes of the nose, mouth, pharynx, intestinal tract, genital tract and so on—tends to develop and maintain its own characteristic bacterial flora, the flora of any one locality differing both qualitatively and quantitatively from that of another, and the flora of a particular locality (say the nasopharynx) showing minor but significant differences as we pass from one person to another, or study a single person over a prolonged period of time.

The resistance thus afforded to colonization of bacterial immigrants is certainly an important factor in the body's first line of defence, but its effectiveness in relation to any particular natural infection, or under any specified set of conditions, cannot at present be estimated with any accuracy. We know only that this barrier is, in fact, often penetrated, and that the fate of the host then depends on the mechanisms of antibacterial or antitoxic immunity that we shall consider in subsequent chapters.

REFERENCES

ARNOLD, L. (1926) *J. infect. Dis.*, **38**, 246 ; (1927) *Amer. J. publ. Hlth*, **17**, 918 ; *J. Amer. med. Ass.*, **89**, 789 ; (1928) *Amer. J. Hyg.*, **8**, 604 ; (1929) *J. Hyg., Camb.*, **29**, 82.
ARNOLD, L. and BRODY, L. (1926a) *Amer. J. Hyg.*, **6**, 672 ; (1926b) *J. infect. Dis.*, **38**, 249.
ARNOLD, L., GUSTAFSON, C. J., MONTGOMERY, B. E., HULL, T. G., and SINGER, C. (1930) *Amer. J. Hyg.*, **11**, 345.
ARNOLD, L., OSTROM, M. L., and SINGER, C. (1928) *Proc. Soc. exp. Biol., N.Y.*, **25**, 624.
BLOOMFIELD, A. L. (1919) *Amer. Rev. Tuberc.*, **3**, No. 9, 553 ; (1922a) *Ibid.*, **5**, No. 11, 903 ; (1922b) *Johns Hopk. Hosp. Bull.*, **33**, 61 ; (1922c) *Ibid.*, **33**, 145 ; (1922d) *Ibid.*, **33**, 252.
CALAMIDA, U. and BARTARELLI, E. (1902) *Zbl. Bakt.*, **32**, 428.
COLEBROOK, L. (1930) *Min. Hlth Inter. Rep. Dep. Comm. Matern. Mortal. Morb.*, Appendix D.
FLEMING, A. (1922) *Proc. roy. Soc., B*, **93**, 306 ; (1929) *Lancet*, i. 217 ; (1932) *Proc. roy. Soc. Med.*, **24**, (Sect. Path.), 1.
FLOREY, H. W. (1933) *J. Path. Bact.*, **37**, 283.
GOLDSWORTHY, N. E. and FLOREY, H. W. (1930) *Brit. J. exp. Path.*, **11**, 192.
KARNS, R. and ARNOLD, L. (1931) *Proc. Soc. exp. Biol., N.Y.*, **28**, 375.
KÜSTER, E. (1929) Kolle and Wassermann, " Hdb. path. Mikroog." (3te Abt.), **6**, 372.
MAXCY, K. F. (1919) *J. Amer. med. Ass.*, **72**, 636.
MENGE, K. (1894) *Dtsch. med. Wschr.*, **20**, 867, 891, 907.
MEYER, K. and LÖWENBERG, W. (1928) *Klin. Wschr.*, **7**, 984.
NEDZEL, A. J. and ARNOLD, L. (1931) *Proc. Soc. exp. Biol., N.Y.*, **28**, 358, 360, 361, 364.
NEISSER, M. (1896) *Z. Hyg. InfektKr.*, **22**, 12.
NENNINGER, O. (1901) *Z. Hyg. InfektKr.*, **38**, 94.
PAUL, L. (1902) *Z. Hyg. InfektKr.*, **40**, 468.
QUESNIL, U. (1902) *Z. Hyg. InfektKr.*, **40**, 505.
RIDLEY, F. (1928) *Proc. roy. Soc. Med.*, **21** (Sect. Ophthal.), 55.
SCHADE, H. and MARCHIONINI, A. (1928) *Klin. Wschr.*, **7**, 12.
STORT, A. G. (1891) *Arch. Hyg.*, **13**, 395.
TEALE, F. H. (1934) *J. Path. Bact.*, **39**, 391.
TEALE, F. H. and EMBLETON, D. (1914) *Proc. roy. Soc. Med.*, **7** (Sect. Path.), 69.
THOMSON, ST. C. and HEWLETT, R. T. (1896) *Lancet*, i. 86.

CHAPTER XLIII

THE MECHANISMS OF ANTITOXIC IMMUNITY

For our immediate purpose this type of immunity may be dealt with very briefly.

Apart from certain cases of natural insusceptibility, such as the insusceptibility of birds and of cold-blooded animals to tetanus toxin (Vaillard 1892), immunity to bacterial exotoxins depends on the presence in the circulating blood of antitoxins which exert a specific neutralizing action. These antitoxins may have been naturally acquired, as the result of past infections, overt or latent ; or they may have been produced in response to purposeful immunization with modified or unmodified toxin. They can be passively transferred from one animal to another—naturally from mother to offspring *via* the placental vessels or in the colostrum, artificially by injecting an antitoxic serum into a susceptible host.

The original observations on this type of immunity were made by von Behring and Kitasato (1890), who showed that the sera of animals that had received repeated injections of non-lethal doses of tetanus toxin or of diphtheria toxin had acquired the property of specifically neutralizing these toxins and thus preventing their poisonous effects.

Since that time a host of antitoxic sera have been prepared, and applied in prophylaxis or treatment. We are here concerned only with anti-exotoxins—in the sense in which these were defined in Chapter XLI. Among these we should include —in addition to diphtheria and tetanus antitoxins—the antitoxins that neutralize the erythrogenic toxin produced by the hæmolytic streptococcus and the toxins of the *Staphylococcus aureus*, of Shiga's dysentery bacillus, and of a variety of pathogenic anaerobes, such as *Cl. welchii, Cl. septique, Cl. œdematiens* and the lamb-dysentery bacillus. The antitoxin which neutralizes the toxin of *Cl. botulinum* is, of course, a typical anti-exotoxin ; but, as we have explained above, it is doubtful whether *Cl. botulinum* should be included among the pathogenic bacteria in the ordinary sense, since there is little evidence that it is capable of giving rise to infection *in vivo*.

A characteristic of antitoxic immunity is the relatively low concentration of antitoxin in the circulating blood which suffices to afford protection against natural infection, provided that it has been produced as the result of active immunization. In the particular case of diphtheria in man, we have good reasons for believing that less than 0·01 unit of antitoxin per c.c. of blood serum will render a person immune to the natural disease (see Glenny 1925). Under such conditions the initial toxin produced is neutralized as it passes from the site of infection before it reaches the susceptible cells. But it is clear that this small amount of circulating antitoxin will not suffice for long, and that more will be needed to neutralize additional toxin as and when it is produced. An actively immune person or animal differs from a non-immune not only in possessing circulating antitoxin but in the readiness and rapidity with which more antitoxin is produced in response to the stimulus provided by the access of toxin to the tissues (see Chapter XLVII).   The equilibrium between the rate of toxin-production by the bacterium and the rate of antitoxin-production by the host is, in the immune animal, readjusted to the host's advantage.   A degree of antitoxic immunity that afforded ample protection against infection with a toxigenic organism could of course be broken down by the inoculation, in a single dose, of an overwhelming amount of toxin.

Although the efficacy of antitoxic immunity is, in the main, determined by quantitative relationships of this kind, there can be little doubt that qualitative differences between one antitoxin and another affect the firmness of toxin-antitoxin union, and so the degree of protection afforded.

It was pointed out many years ago that the curative effect of antidiphtheria sera, as judged by experiments on laboratory animals, did not always run parallel to the antitoxin content as assessed by the ordinary technique (see, for instance, Kràus and Schwoner 1908, Kraus and Baecher 1913).   Kraus and his colleagues suggested that one important quality of an antitoxic serum, not measured or expressed in the official standardization in terms of Antitoxin Units, was the character that determined the *rate* of neutralization, and for this character they proposed the name *avidity*.   The conception of avidity has been considerably modified, and rendered far more precise, by recent observations recorded by Madsen and Schmidt and by Glenny and his colleagues.

Madsen and Schmidt (1929) found that, with some antitoxic sera, toxin-antitoxin mixtures that were neutral as judged by subcutaneous injection in the guinea-pig might produce a fatal toxæmia when injected intravenously into rabbits.   Glenny and his colleagues (see Glenny and Barr 1932*a*, *b*, Glenny *et al.* 1932) note that, with sera of this kind, it is possible to prepare mixtures such that rabbits will survive the intravenous injection of 10 c.c. but not of amounts varying from 0·001 c.c. to 0·5 c.c.   The greater dilution of the small inocula in the rabbit's circulating blood apparently results in the dissociation of a lethal dose of toxin.   Glenny and his colleagues have devised a method for estimating the avidity of antitoxic serum in terms of a *dilution-ratio*, which they define as the ratio of the amount of antitoxin necessary to form a neutral mixture with one L_r dose of toxin in a total volume of 2 c.c., to the amount necessary to form a neutral mixture with the same amount of toxin in a total volume of 200 c.c., neutrality being determined in each case by the injection of 0·2 c.c. of the mixture into the skin of a guinea-pig.   Although Glenny and Barr, in agreement with Madsen and Schmidt, note that avid sera commonly give rapid flocculation when examined by Ramon's method, they regard firmness of union, rather than rapidity of reaction, as the essential character in avidity.   They note that the avidity of antitoxic sera appears to be determined, at least in part, by the type of serum protein with which the antitoxin is associated.   Thus (Barr and Glenny 1931*a*, *b*, Glenny and Barr 1932*a*, Glenny *et al.* 1932), if successive globulin fractions are precipitated with increasing amounts of ammonium sulphate, the earlier fractions are more avid than the later.   These phenomena are by no means confined to the particular case of diphtheria toxin and antitoxin.   It would seem indeed that non-avid sera are more frequently met with among antitoxic sera of other types (Glenny *et al.* 1932).   [See also Chapter LII for analogous observations in the case of antiviral sera.]

The increased resistance afforded by specific antitoxic immunity is determined almost entirely by the interception and neutralization of the toxin before it reaches the susceptible cells.   Once these have been attacked, the antitoxin is relatively ineffective.

Glenny and Hopkins (1925) have studied the effect of the administration of various doses of antitoxin at different times after the intradermal injection of a Schick dose of diphtheria toxin into a guinea-pig. This amount of toxin produces a characteristic local reaction at the site of inoculation ; 0·001 unit of antitoxin is sufficient to prevent this reaction if the toxin and antitoxin are mixed together before inoculation. If, however, the toxin is injected before the antitoxin, neither 10 units of antitoxin injected intravenously 15 minutes later, nor 1,000 units injected intravenously 30 minutes later, are sufficient to prevent the appearance of a small reaction at the site of the injection of the toxin. The size of the reaction is, however, very greatly reduced as compared with that which occurs when no antitoxin is given. If 10 units of antitoxin are administered intravenously 30 minutes after the intradermal injection of the toxin, or 1,000 units intravenously after $1\frac{1}{2}$ hours, or intramuscularly after 45 minutes, the size of the lesion is reduced to about half its usual diameter. A slight reduction in the size of the reaction is obtained if 1,000 units are injected intravenously after $2\frac{1}{2}$ hours, or intramuscularly after $1\frac{3}{4}$ hours ; but the subcutaneous injection of this amount of antitoxin 15 minutes after the intradermal inoculation of toxin leads to no reduction in the size of the reaction. We may note the relatively enormous dose of antitoxin that is required to neutralize the effect of the toxin under the conditions of this experiment ; 1,000 units of antitoxin are equivalent to 1,000,000 times the dose of toxin injected into the skin, yet this amount administered intravenously 30 minutes after the intradermal injection fails to suppress completely the local toxic effect.

A purely antitoxic immunity affords effective protection against such an infection as diphtheria, in which the tissue invasion is minimal and the ill effects are due almost entirely to the toxæmia. Does it afford effective protection against those bacteria that are invasive as well as toxigenic ? We should expect that it would protect only against that part of the total pathological effect that is due to the action of the toxin itself. If the toxin plays any important part in the invasive process, the antitoxin might to that extent lessen the extent of infection. But we should expect modification of the infection rather than complete immunity. The available evidence is in accord with our expectations.

The presence of circulating antitoxin, active against the rash-producing toxin of the hæmolytic streptococcus, affords protection against clinical scarlet fever, that is, against the obvious effects of the toxin itself ; but it does not appear to protect against the local lesion in the throat—the acute tonsillitis (Okell 1932). Again, it would seem (Burt-White, Colebrook and others 1930, Baird and Cruickshank 1930, Stent 1930) that the presence of circulating antitoxin, as revealed by a negative Dick test (see p. 1162) in pregnant women during the later stages of gestation, affords little if any protection against a severe or fatal infection with hæmolytic streptococci during the puerperium. These clinical findings are borne out by the results of experiment. Thus, Parish and Okell (1927) found that a potent antitoxic serum, which would protect rabbits against acute toxæmic death following the intravenous injection of large doses of living cultures of hæmolytic streptococci, did not prevent a fatal infection, leading to death after a week or more, associated with multiple foci of infection.

Closely analogous results have been obtained in experimental staphylococcal infections in the rabbit (Burnet 1929, Burnet and Kellaway 1930, Kellaway, Burnet and Williams 1930). The potent staphylococcal toxin is neutralized, in multiple proportions, by the specific antitoxin ; and a rabbit can be actively or passively immunized against the poisonous effect of a toxin-containing filtrate. But such immunized animals are still susceptible to the injection of living staphylococci and succumb to a pyæmic infection, though they survive rather longer than non-immunized controls.

Thus, we may say that antitoxic immunity is highly effective *so far as it goes* —much more effective, within its own sphere, than the specific antibacterial immunity discussed in the next chapter ; for it is direct in its action, does not depend on the efficient functioning of a complex system of phagocytic cells, and is complete and final in its effect on the noxious agent.   If the invasive power of an infecting toxigenic organism is so low that the normal antibacterial defence mechanism can be relied on to suppress it, or to hold it in check, an added antitoxic immunity will afford almost complete protection against the corresponding disease.

It will be observed that the characteristic mechanisms of antitoxic immunity, as here defined, are brought into play only against those toxins that diffuse freely from a locus of infection.   Reactions between endotoxins and the corresponding antibodies undoubtedly play a part, perhaps a large part, in infection and resistance ; but it is at the moment hardly possible to differentiate clearly between anti-endotoxic and antibacterial immunity.   It has, for instance, been noted in Chapter XLI that some endotoxins are identical with the surface somatic antigens that determine the immunological reactions of the intact bacterial cells.

This chapter is itself a summary.

REFERENCES

BAIRD, D. and CRUICKSHANK, R.   (1930) *Lancet*, ii. 1009.
BARR, M. and GLENNY, A. T.   (1931*a*) *J. Path. Bact.*, **34**, 539 ; (1931*b*) *Brit. J. exp. Path.*, **12**, 337.
BEHRING, E. VON, and KITASATO, S.   (1890) *Dtsch. med. Wschr.*, **16**, 1113.
BURNET, F. M.   (1929) *J. Path. Bact.*, **32**, 717.
BURNET, F. M. and KELLAWAY, C. H.   (1930) *Med. J. Aust.*, **2**, 295.
BURT-WHITE, H., COLEBROOK, L., MORGAN, G., JERVIS, B. J. W., and HARRE, G. E. (1930) *Brit. med. J.*, i. 240.
GLENNY, A. T.   (1925) *J. Hyg., Camb.*, **24**, 301.
GLENNY, A. T. and BARR, M.   (1932*a*) *J. Path. Bact.*, **35**, 91 ; (1932*b*) *Ibid.*, **35**, 142.
GLENNY, A. T., BARR, M., and STEVENS, M. F.   (1932) *J. Path. Bact.*, **35**, 495.
GLENNY, A. T. and HOPKINS, B. E.   (1925) *J. Path. Bact.*, **28**, 261.
KELLAWAY, C. H., BURNET, F. M., and WILLIAMS, F. E.   (1930) *J. Path. Bact.*, **33**, 889.
KRAUS, R. and BAECHER, ST.   (1913) *Zbl. Bakt., Ref.* **57**, Beiheft 106.
KRAUS, R. and SCHWONER, J.   (1908) *Zbl. Bakt.*, **47**, 124.
MADSEN, T. and SCHMIDT, S.   (1929) *C. R. Soc. Biol.*, **102**, 1091, 1093.
OKELL, C. C.   (1932) *Lancet*, i. 761, 815, 867.
PARISH, J. and OKELL, C. C.   (1927) *J. Path. Bact.*, **30**, 521.
STENT, L.   (1930) *Lancet*, i. 1066.
VAILLARD, L.   (1892) *Ann. Inst. Pasteur*, **6**, 224.

CHAPTER XLIV

THE MECHANISMS CONCERNED IN SPECIFIC ANTIBACTERIAL IMMUNITY

THE only sound basis for a discussion of this subject would be to treat it as a problem in comparative pathology, describing in turn the reaction to infection of unicellular organisms, of simple multicellular animals, of the invertebrates, and of the vertebrates, culminating in the mammals and man. It happens that, owing to the classical studies of Metchnikoff, our earlier knowledge of the cellular reactions involved in immunity was developed largely along these lines ; and any serious student of the subject should make himself familiar with the work of Metchnikoff and his school (see Metchnikoff 1901). For our present purpose, however, it will suffice to note that the mechanisms that are described in this chapter are clearly traceable, in their gradually increasing complexity and differentiation, from the simplest to the most highly organized of animal hosts. In the pages immediately following we shall be concerned almost entirely with happenings in the small mammals of the laboratory ; and it will be convenient to deal first with the reactions of normal animals, and then to consider how these reactions are modified by active or passive immunization.

The Reactions which follow the Intravenous Injection of Dyes or Suspensions of Inert Particles into Normal Animals.

The simplest introduction to a discussion of the mechanisms involved in antibacterial immunity is a brief description of the way in which the living tissues deal with certain dyes and suspensions.

In pre-bacteriological days Hoffmann and von Recklinghausen (1867) and Ponfick (1869) noted that particles of carmine and vermilion, when injected intravenously into animals, were not eliminated in the urine or the bile, but were deposited in various organs such as the spleen, liver, lymph nodes and bone-marrow, where they remained recognizable for weeks. More recently, and particularly within the last decade, extensive and detailed studies have been carried out on the effects of intravital staining with a variety of dyes such as trypan blue, vital red, pyrrhol blue (isamine blue), diaminefast scarlet and benzopurpurin, or with suspensions of finely divided carbon (Indian ink) or colloidal ferric oxide (saccharated oxide of iron). An account of a recent investigation along these lines and a good review of the literature will be found in a series of papers by Cappell (1929, 1930).

Briefly, these studies have shown that the various dyes are stored, in the form of granules or in intracellular vacuoles, by certain cells that have a characteristic distribution throughout the body. The histologist calls these cells *histiocytes*, the immunologist knows them best by Metchnikoff's name, *macrophages*. The most active may be divided into two main types, the sessile and the wandering. The most active of the sessile histiocytes are those found in certain specialized areas of the vascular or lymphatic endothelium—the endothelium of the liver capillaries (Kupffer cells), of the spleen sinuses, of the venous sinusoids of the bone-marrow, of the capillaries and medullary sinusoids of the adrenals, of the capillaries of the pituitary gland, and of the sinuses of the lymph glands throughout the body. Somewhat less active in this respect are the reticulocytes, which do not form a lining to blood or lymphatic channels, but are disposed about the reticulum fibres in the interstices of the tissues. The wandering histiocytes are found throughout the tissue spaces, and some of them find their way into the circulating blood, particularly into the vessels of the internal organs.

The common character of dye-storage possessed by cells of this type has led many observers, and particularly Aschoff (1924), to regard them as an integrated system of cells fulfilling a particular bodily function. Aschoff has coined for them the generic term of *reticulo-endothelial system* (R.-E. system, for short). This system, as described by him, is summarized in schematic form as follows.

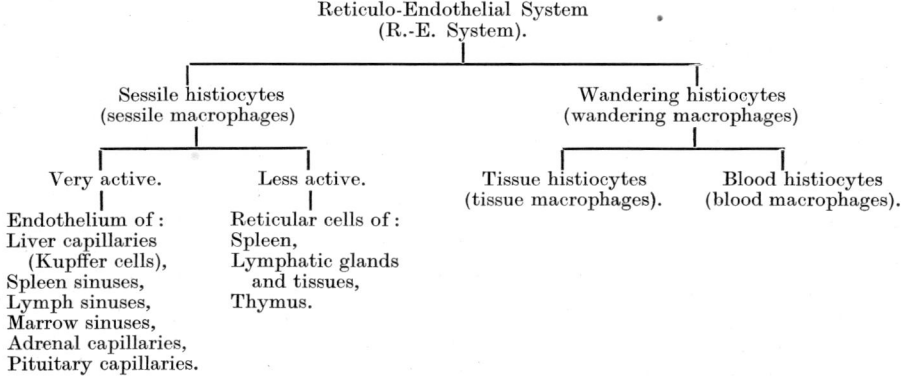

We are here concerned mainly with the more active phagocytic cells, and particularly with the sessile histiocytes of the lymph glands, liver, spleen and bone-marrow, and with the wandering histiocytes in general.

As Cappell emphasizes, there is no gradual transition from the less specialized endothelium to that in which the sessile histiocytes are found. The endothelium of the lymph sinuses abruptly assumes a pronounced vital-staining capacity, in marked contrast to that of the endothelium of the afferent and efferent lymphatics ; while the same contrast exists between the endothelium of the spleen sinuses, liver capillaries, etc., and the vascular endothelium in general.

There is probably some degree of functional differentiation between different parts of the reticulo-endothelial system. Some histiocyte depôts may be more active in removing effete blood corpuscles or leucocytes, others in removing bacteria or smaller particles. There is also a difference between one animal species and another in the relative activity of the various depôts of sessile histiocytes. Thus the bone-marrow of the mouse is far less active than the bone-marrow of the rabbit (Cappell 1930). In birds, the mass of the reticulo-endothelial system is concentrated in the liver.

The histiocytes are not, however, the only phagocytic cells with which we are concerned. The polymorphonuclear leucocytes of the blood, although they do not take up vital stains in the same way as the cells of the reticulo-endothelial system, play an active part in removing particulate material from the circulation under certain specialized conditions.

The intervention of these cells is, for instance, brought about by the injection, directly into the blood stream, of an Indian ink suspension or of some similar material. Following such an inoculation, the polymorphonuclear cells accumulate in certain areas—most abundantly in the pulmonary capillaries, to a less extent in the veins and sinusoids of the liver, spleen and other viscera. The abundance of polymorphonuclear cells in the lungs, which may be associated with a definite leucopænia in the peripheral circulation, is so characteristic a feature of the reaction as to make it quite clear that some mechanism is at work which temporarily retains the circulating leucocytes in this particular situation. While in the lungs the polymorphonuclear cells take up a certain number of the injected carbon particles ; but the degree of phagocytosis is relatively slight, and in marked contrast to the active engorgement of particles by the histiocytes of the reticulo-endothelial system (Dudgeon and Goadby 1931). In the course of a few hours the majority of the polymorphonuclear cells leave the lung capillaries. Some of them pass into the alveolar spaces, some along the lymphatics to the regional lymph glands ; but the great majority appear to make their way back into the general circulation and so pass to the spleen sinuses, where they appear to be taken up by macrophages.

There is still another mechanism at work in freeing the general circulation from injected foreign particles, in which no cellular elements are primarily concerned. Many suspensions, including carmine and Indian ink, are unstable when introduced into the blood stream. The dispersed particles are rapidly agglutinated into larger masses, and these appear to be filtered off from the circulating blood, during its passage through the finer capillaries. These aggregates are themselves phago-cytosed at later stages. It has been noted that the aggregates of carbon particles contain large numbers of blood-platelets (Delrez and Govaerts 1918), and their formation is associated with a definite peripheral thrombopænia (Dudgeon and Goadby 1931). Whether the platelets play any active part in the process of flocculation is, however, very doubtful. The phenomenon of aggregation—certainly in the case of bacteria and presumably in that of any particulate material—appears to be unaffected after the elimination of platelets by the injection of an antiplatelet serum (Govaerts 1921a, b, Bull and McKee 1922).

Confining ourselves for the moment to the particular case of the direct introduction of particulate matter into the blood stream, we may inquire in what ways our description needs modification or extension when our injected particles are living bacterial cells.

The Reactions which follow the Intravenous Injection of Bacteria into Normal Animals.

There is no doubt at all that the mechanism brought into play in clearing the blood stream from bacterial cells is in the main identical with that which frees it from inert particles of the same order of size (Wyssokowitch 1886, Werigo 1894, Opitz 1898, Bardach 1889, Métin 1900, Bail 1905, Bull 1914–16, Kyes 1916, Bartlett and Ozaki 1917, 1918, Wright 1927 and many others). The reticulo-endothelial cells, particularly those of the liver, spleen and bone-marrow, actively phagocytose the injected bacteria. The mechanism of aggregation, followed by the removal of the bacterial aggregates from the general circulation by their retention in the lung capillaries, is sometimes very prominent (Bull 1914–16, Bartlett and Ozaki 1917, 1918, Wright 1927, Dudgeon and Goadby 1931). This is accompanied, as in the case of the intravenous injection of carbon particles, by an accumulation of polymorphonuclear cells in the lung capillaries, associated with a temporary peripheral leucopænia (see Levaditi 1901, Andrewes 1910). But the polymorphonuclear cells appear to play a more active part in phagocytosing bacteria than in phagocytosing carbon particles (Dudgeon and Goadby 1931). It is probable that these cells with their ingested bacteria are subsequently carried to the reticulo-endothelial depôts in the spleen, liver and elsewhere, and are there phagocytosed by the sessile histiocytes. Such wandering histiocytes as are present in the lung capillaries ingest the bacterial cells, or cell-aggregates, directly.

So far then as we can regard bacteria merely as foreign particles, our description of the reaction of the tissues to the intravenous injection of vital stains or carbon particles needs little modification. But, in fact, the bacteria we inject are alive and capable of multiplication ; and it is the balance between their capacity to multiply and the capacity of the tissues to remove them that determines the fate of the animal host.

Bull (1914–16) counted the viable bacteria in the systemic blood stream of dogs and rabbits at various intervals after the intravenous inoculation of a bacterial suspension. Using pneumococci and streptococci he found that there was at first a sharp and progressive fall in the number of organisms in the circulating blood, lasting until about the 5th hour. After this there was in most cases a secondary rise, varying in degree and persistence with the virulence of the organism and the resistance of the host. With strains of low virulence the numbers then declined until the blood became sterile. Typhoid bacilli, injected directly into the blood stream, showed a similar rapid fall in numbers within a few minutes of inoculation. In one experiment they fell from 10,000,000 per c.c. 1 minute after injection to 40 per c.c. at the end of 15 minutes.

Wright (1927) has carried out a very detailed series of experiments on experimental pneumococcal septicæmia in the rabbit, and the following illustrative examples are taken from his paper.

TABLE LXI

Living Pneumococci per c.c. of Circulating Blood at Stated Times after Inoculation of Avirulent, Slightly Virulent, and Highly Virulent Pneumococci into Normal Rabbits.

Time.	Avirulent.	Slightly Virulent.	Highly Virulent.
Immediately	8,900,000	1,030,000	1,070,000
2 hours	206	20,800	137,000
5 ,, ...	2	340	25,000
24 ,, ...	0	1,300	1,510,000
48 ,, ...	—	134	Dead
96 ,, ...	—	0	—

In Table LXI are set out the numbers of living pneumococci per c.c. of circulating blood at varying intervals after the intravenous injection of (a) an avirulent, (b) a slightly virulent, and (c) a highly virulent strain. In Fig. 217 the same series of observations are set out in chart form, the logarithms of the numbers of pneumococci per c.c. of circulating blood being plotted as ordinates against time as abscissæ. The figures need no comment. With an avirulent strain the clearance of the organisms from the blood stream is rapid and permanent. With a slightly virulent strain there is the same initial rapid clearance, so that

99·97 per cent. of the injected organisms have been removed from the blood stream by the end of the 5th hour.   There is then a period during which the capacity of this strain of pneumococcus to multiply in the tissues—limited though it is—makes itself felt, and the number of viable organisms rises from 340 per c.c. at the 5th hour to 1,300 per c.c. at the 24th hour.   But the clearing mechanism is now removing the newly generated bacterial cells at a greater rate than this particular strain can produce them.   The number of organisms per c.c. sinks to 134 at the 48th hour, and the blood is sterile by the 96th.   The

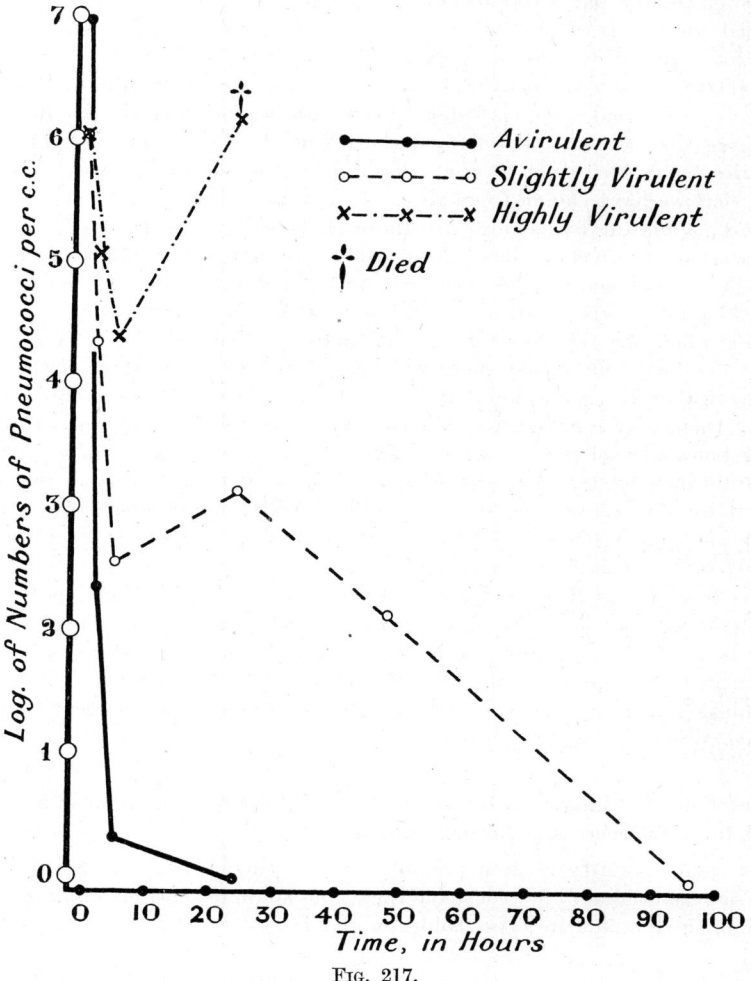

FIG. 217.

highly virulent strain is not proof against the initial action of the clearing mechanism. By the 5th hour 97·7 per cent. of the injected pneumococci have been removed from the blood stream.   But when the parasite's capacity for multiplication is brought fully into play it overwhelms the defence mechanism of the host.   By the 24th hour the number of pneumococci per c.c. of circulating blood has risen to 1,510,000 ; and between the 24th and 48th hours the rabbit dies from acute pneumococcal septicæmia.

It is probable (Wright 1927) that the initial rapid clearing which follows the intravenous injection of a large dose of virulent pneumococci is the result of the lag phase in bacterial growth (see Chapter IV). Wright has shown that this initial clearance of virulent pneumococci can be almost eliminated by injecting a culture that is still in the logarithmic phase.

In the argument from analogy, which plays so large a part in the construction of our concepts of infection and resistance, we must be very careful to allow for the effects of our experimental technique. The reactions which we have described above are those that follow the sudden introduction into the blood stream of a relatively enormous number of bacteria—a number of the order of 1,000,000,000. Such an occurrence must be of extreme rarity in natural infection, and it is possible that some part of the mechanism we have described—for instance, the aggregation of bacterial cells and the retention of the aggregates in the lung capillaries—may have been over-emphasized by the particular experimental procedure that we have chosen to employ. In any case there seems little doubt that the most significant happenings are those that occur between the 5th and 24th hours after an intravenous inoculation, when the fate of the host is being determined by the balance between bacterial multiplication, on the one hand, and the removal of the newly produced bacterial cells on the other.

Even when the tide has for the moment turned decisively in favour of the host, it does not follow that there will be a complete sterilization of the tissues. Bacteria will have been caught up in the liver, spleen and elsewhere, and there some of them may remain alive, but relatively inactive, for considerable periods.

Our knowledge of the exact method by which bacteria are *killed* in the tissues is woefully incomplete. There is no doubt at all that the majority of the bacteria taken up by phagocytic cells are destroyed by intracellular digestion ; but the tacit assumption that a bacterium phagocytosed is, of necessity, a bacterium finally disposed of is certainly unwarranted.

It is possible, as Rous and Jones (1916) have suggested, that ingestion by a phagocytic cell may sometimes protect a bacterium against bactericidal substances in the body fluids, and that wandering phagocytes may sometimes play a part in the spread of infection within the tissues. But it is probable that any such happenings represent a chance and local breakdown in a mechanism that under most conditions is highly efficient.

The Reactions that follow the Intraperitoneal Injection of Bacteria or of Suspensions of Inert Particles into Normal Animals.

The small quantity of fluid present in the normal peritoneal cavity, or other serous sac, contains very few cells, and these consist almost entirely of mononuclears, mainly of the lymphocyte type (Dudgeon and Ross 1906, Cappell 1930, and many others).

Durham (1897), in his classical paper on the reaction to intraperitoneal infection, described the course of events that follows the injection of bacterial and other suspensions into the peritoneum of the guinea-pig. As regards the changes in the cellular contents of the exudate, there is a preliminary period lasting for about 1 hour or less during which no increase in cells can be detected. The cellular reaction, when it occurs, differs widely in degree and in character according to the kind of inoculum employed. With injections of dead bacteria, or of living strains of low virulence, there is a rapid emigration into the peritoneal cavity of polymorphonuclear leucocytes (or *microphages*, if we employ the terminology of Metchnikoff) which ingest the bacterial cells. These cells increase in number up to the 8th hour or later, and then slowly decline. As they decline, their place is taken by large mononuclear phagocytes (*macrophages*), which ingest those bacteria that still remain free in the fluid, together with many of the polymorphonuclear cells and the bacteria that they have already phagocytosed. Durham puts the duration of the whole period of peritoneal reaction, from the time of the first appearance of the microphages to the final disappearance of the macrophages and the return to normal, as 4 to 7 days.

Although this microphage-macrophage succession may be regarded as the modal reaction in the peritoneal exudate following the injection of a bacterial suspension, it requires considerable modification in the light of subsequent studies (Dudgeon and Ross 1906, Buxton and Torrey 1906*a*, *b*, *c*, *d*, Cappell 1930). The cellular content of the exudate during the earlier hours of the reaction is by no means confined to polymorphonuclear cells, and other cells present during this period may be actively phagocytic. Cappell (1930) believes that the appearance of typical macrophages during the later stages of the reaction is due not to the emigration of fully formed cells of this type from some neighbouring depôt of histiocytes, such as the omentum, but to the gradual maturation of the small mononuclears that are present in the exudate from the earliest stages. These he regards as immature macrophages, and he believes them to be derived mainly from the small mononuclear cells that are so plentiful in the *tâches laiteuses* and adventitial sheaths of the omentum and mesenteries.

These events in the fluid exudate form only a part, perhaps only a minor part, of the general peritoneal reaction. Certain specialized regions of the peritoneal membrane, and of the tissues which are subjacent to it, play a very important rôle. Among these specialized tissues the omentum is pre-eminent (Durham 1897, Buxton and Torrey 1906*d*, Dudgeon and Ross 1906). Just as particulate material injected into the circulation tends to be aggregated into masses that are caught up in the lung capillaries, so the particles or cells in a suspension injected into the peritoneum are aggregated into masses that are deposited on the omental surface ; and, just as the polymorphonuclear cells of the circulating blood tend to collect in the lung capillaries together with the aggregated particles, so such cells as are present in the peritoneal exudate tend to collect on the surface of the omentum. On this surface, and in the interstices of the underlying tissue, macrophages are normally present, especially in the milk-spots, or *tâches laiteuses* ; and these cells play from the first an active part in the phagocytosis of the deposited particles or cells. Ingestion completed, these cells migrate into the deeper omental tissues, changing in shape as they do so from the spheroidal or slightly irregular form of the macrophage of the body fluids or surfaces to enormously elongated trailing cells, which make their way through the interstices of the tissues. When such cells have phagocytosed large amounts of some indigestible material, such as carbon particles, they may be detected in the tissues for periods of weeks or months. The part played by polymorphonuclear cells in the omental reaction appears to vary with different inocula. According to the observations of Buxton and Torrey, they are absent or very scanty during the first few hours or so, but they then begin to collect in increasing numbers and to play their part in the phagocytic reaction.

These reactions at the surface of the omentum, and in its interstices, are rendered doubly effective as a clearing mechanism by the movements of the omentum as a whole following the injection of a suspension of particles or bacteria into the peritoneal cavity. Disposed at first as a more or less extended fold, hanging down among the intestinal coils, it is gradually gathered up into a closely folded band, extending across the peritoneum, and carrying with it, as in a retracted net, the particles caught on its surface layers. The mechanism of these movements has been studied by Florey and Carleton (1926). They find that the omentum is totally incapable of any intrinsic movement. The movements that it undergoes are impressed on it by (*a*) posture, (*b*) the peristaltic movements of the intestines, and (*c*) the movements of the diaphragm. The retraction into a tightly gathered transverse band is due to the alteration in the character of the omental surface, and particularly to the deposition of fibrin, which causes the omental folds that are brought into apposition to adhere to one another, instead of extending again in response to the next passive movement.

The reaction that follows an intraperitoneal injection is not, however, limited to the peritoneal cavity. Indeed, it spreads beyond it with surprising rapidity.

Muscatello (1895) injected carmine suspensions into the peritoneum, killed the inoculated animals after various intervals, and studied the distribution of the dye. Within 1–2 hours he found particles of carmine in the liver and spleen. Similar particles, in smaller numbers, were found in the lungs, pancreas and testis. Durham (1897) noted the rapid passage of bacteria from the peritoneal cavity to the blood stream, and concluded that the most important route of transit was *via* the diaphragmatic lymphatics, the anterior mediastinal glands and the right lymphatic duct. The importance of the diaphragmatic route was also noted by Dudgeon and Ross, and the correctness of Durham's conclusions has been confirmed by many subsequent observers, notably in the careful studies of Buxton and his co-workers, and in the more recent studies of Bolton (1921). Buxton and Torrey (1906*b*) found that, almost immediately after the intraperitoneal injection of an Indian-ink suspension, there was a rush of carbon particles into and through the lymphatics of the diaphragm. Thence they passed rapidly through the anterior mediastinal lymphatics and the corresponding lymph glands, reaching the blood stream within a very few minutes. During the earliest stages of this transit there was very little evidence of phagocytosis in the mediastinal glands or elsewhere ; but, as time passed, an increasing number of carbon particles were found within the histiocytes of the lymph nodes.

In other experiments (Buxton 1906, Buxton and Torrey 1906*a*) the fate of living typhoid bacilli, injected intraperitoneally into rabbits, was followed by quantitative plating methods. The living bacilli passed into the general circulation almost immediately ; and their numbers per c.c. of circulating blood reached a maximum after about an hour. After this there was a rapid decrease, and few bacilli could be recovered from the blood after about the 6th hour. When suspensions of liver and spleen tissue were plated it was found that there was a rapid accumulation of bacilli in these organs, and particularly in the liver, within a few minutes after an intraperitoneal injection. There was then a transitory decrease in the numbers of viable organisms, followed by a secondary increase lasting from the 2nd to the 6th hour, *i.e.*, the bacilli were increasing in the liver and the spleen while they were decreasing in the blood. After about the 6th hour there was a general decrease, lasting for several days, and more rapid in the liver than in the spleen. When animals were killed 4 days after injection viable bacilli were still recovered from the liver, though in small numbers ; larger numbers were recovered from the spleen, and very large numbers from the mediastinal glands. Many observations on laboratory animals have shown that living bacilli may be recovered from the spleen weeks or months after experimental infection (Topley and Wilson 1923, Price-Jones 1927).

It may be noted that the rapid transit of particles or bacteria from the peritoneum to the blood stream is almost certainly the result of the mechanical pumping action of the rise and fall of the diaphragm in breathing. This is probably assisted by a special arrangement of the endothelial cells of the peritoneal membrane covering the diaphragm, which provides for a rapid passage of particles to the underlying lymphatics (Florey 1927).

The Reactions that follow the Injection of Bacteria or Inert Particles into Normal Animals by Other Routes.

It is not necessary to describe in any detail the course of events which follow the injection of particulate material by other routes, such as the intramuscular or subcutaneous. Cappell (1929) gives a full description of the spread of soluble and colloidal dyes, or of carbon particles, from the local site of injection, and reference may be made to his paper for fuller details on this point. It suffices for our present purpose to note that spread is slower and more restricted than after intraperitoneal inoculation, and that the injected particles or bacterial cells may pass so slowly on their centripetal journey that the great majority of them are caught up in the histiocyte depôts of the regional lymphatic glands before they can reach the blood stream. The centripetal transit is more rapid after intramuscular than after subcutaneous inoculation, owing to the increased rate of lymph flow resulting from muscular contractions.

It should be noted that it does not follow that the injection of bacteria directly into the blood stream is necessarily more fatal to the host than injection by other routes. Indeed, it would appear that the reverse is often the case when small inocula are employed.

Lange and Gutdeutsch (1928) found that pneumococci, streptococci and *Pasteurella* were more fatal to mice when injected intraperitoneally than when injected subcutaneously or intravenously, and that the subcutaneous was rather more fatal than the intravenous route. In the case of *Erysipelothrix rhusiopathiæ*, the bacillus causing swine erysipelas and mouse septicæmia, the subcutaneous route of injection was found to be more fatal than the intraperitoneal or intravenous. According to Sobernheim and Murata (1924), the dose of *B. anthracis* required to kill a guinea-pig after intravenous or intraperitoneal inoculation is about ten times the dose that will produce a fatal infection when injected by the subcutaneous or intracutaneous routes.

The probable reason for this apparent anomaly is that bacteria injected intravenously are at once exposed to the full force of the highly efficient clearing mechanism that protects the blood stream. If the number of bacilli injected is small, they may all be removed without a nidus of infection being established in the tissues. As we have seen, it is the progressive secondary infection of the blood stream from a centre of bacterial multiplication established somewhere in the tissues that is the usual precursor of a fatal septicæmic infection.

The Reactions that follow the Administration of Pathogenic Bacteria to Normal Animals by the Mouth.

Ørskov and his colleagues (Ørskov, Jensen and Kobayashi 1928, Ørskov and Moltke 1928, Ørskov and Lassen 1930), extending the observations of Müller (1912), have recorded a series of experiments in which they fed mice with *Bact. typhi-murium* and allied strains of the Salmonella group by dropping measured amounts of a broth culture, or of a saline suspension, into the open mouth. The animals so treated were killed after intervals varying from a few hours to a month or more, and cultures were prepared from the blood, liver, spleen, mesenteric glands, the small intestine at different levels, and certain other situations. In this way it was possible to follow the spread of infection throughout the body. These observations are of particular interest because they are concerned with a natural disease of mice, and because the portal of entry is that by which the parasite gains access to its host in the natural spread of the disease.

It would seem that the bacilli, when they gain access to the body by the mouth, fail to establish any immediate foothold in the intestine, and for the most part rapidly succumb. A certain number, however, enter the tissues from the alimentary tract and are carried to the mesenteric lymph glands. Later they enter the blood stream, probably *via* the thoracic duct, but are rapidly removed from the circulation by the reticulo-endothelial cells, particularly those of the liver and the spleen. During this phase the blood taken from the heart is sterile, and *Bact. typhi-murium* cannot usually be recovered from the intestine ; while the liver, spleen and mesenteric glands show its presence in increasing numbers. In many animals this stage is followed by a secondary bacteræmia, which increases in intensity until the animal succumbs. The intestine, which as stated above is rapidly freed from the invading bacteria during the primary stage of the infection, becomes secondarily infected during its later stages, probably by way of the bile-duct.

A similar series of experiments were carried out using *Bact. paratyphosum B* as the infecting agent—an organism closely related to *Bact. typhi-murium*, but far less pathogenic for the mouse. The same rapid disappearance from the intestine was noted, and the same localization in the lymphatic glands ; but in this case there appeared to be no tendency for the infection to spread beyond this primary focus, though the bacilli might persist in the mesenteric glands for weeks or months. A relatively avirulent variant of *Bact. typhi-murium* behaved in the same way as *Bact. paratyphosum B.*

Bactericidal and Bacteriolytic Reactions.

It is very difficult to assess with any accuracy the part played by the lytic action of complement on sensitized bacterial cells. There is little doubt that this purely humoral effect is much less important than was at one time supposed, but it is certainly operative to some degree with certain organisms and under certain conditions.

Thus, apart from Pfeiffer's classical experiments with *V. choleræ*, Buxton and Torrey (1906*d*) note that many of the typhoid bacilli that collect on the surface of the omentum after an intraperitoneal inoculation are destroyed by extracellular lysis instead of being ingested by macrophages, and many workers have recorded analogous observations. In the case of Gram-positive organisms, such as pneumococci or streptococci, it would seem, however, that this purely humoral mechanism plays no part.

THE REACTION OF ACTIVELY IMMUNIZED ANIMALS AS COMPARED WITH THAT OF NORMAL ANIMALS

We have so far been concerned only with the reaction of normal animals to bacteria of varying virulence ; and we have seen that the normal clearing mechanism, while highly effective against a strain that has little capacity for multiplication within the tissues, may be overwhelmed by a more virulent strain that is capable of establishing multiple or extensive foci of active infection from which the circulation is continuously flooded.

So far as this particular mechanism is concerned, we can summarize the difference between an actively immunized and a normal animal very briefly, by saying that an immunized animal behaves towards a virulent strain of a particular pathogenic bacterium in the same way as a normal animal behaves towards an avirulent, or slightly virulent, strain of the same bacterial species. Without any attempt to recapitulate in detail, we may quote a few illustrative examples.

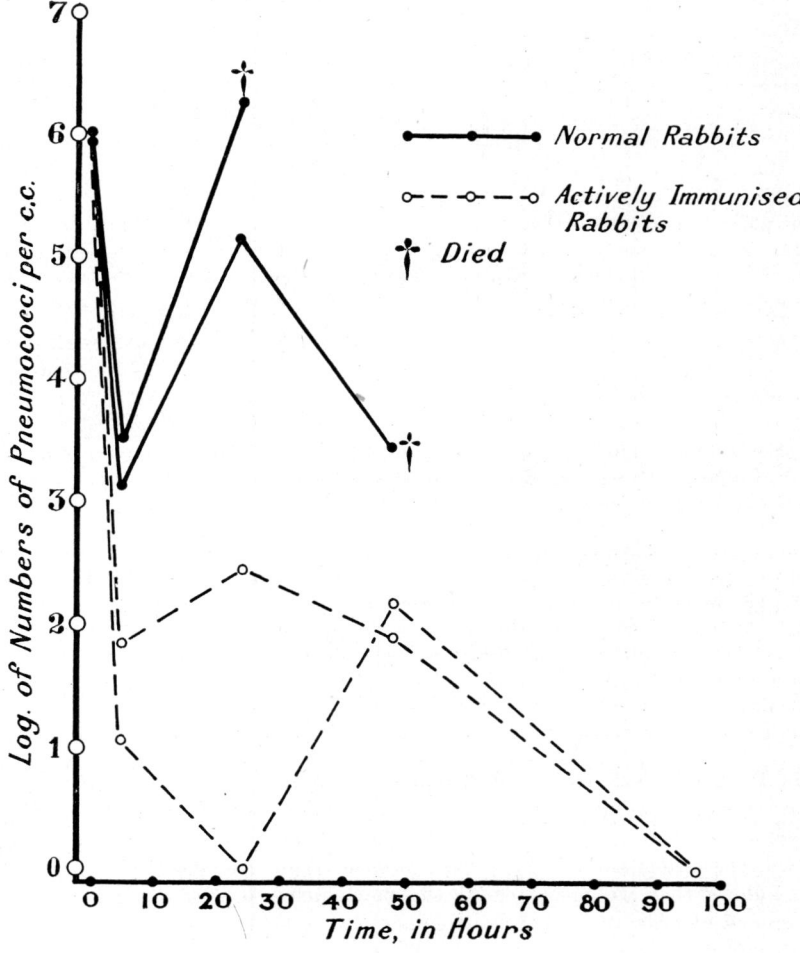

Fig. 218.

Wright (1927) studied the response, to the intravenous injection of virulent pneumococci, of rabbits that had been immunized by the injection, at various intervals before the test inoculation, of a killed culture of the same strain. Table LXII and Fig. 218 show the results obtained in two rabbits that had been immunized 3 months previously, and in two normal controls injected with the same dose of the same living culture. Comparison with Table LXI and Fig. 217 will show that the immunized rabbits dealt with the highly virulent culture in the same way as the normal rabbit of Table LXI dealt with the slightly virulent strain.

TABLE LXII

SHOWING THE NUMBER OF PNEUMOCOCCI PER C.C. OF CIRCULATING BLOOD AT VARIOUS TIMES AFTER INOCULATION OF A VIRULENT STRAIN INTO NORMAL AND INTO ACTIVELY IMMUNIZED RABBITS.

Time after Injection.	Normal.		Immunized.	
	Rabbit 247.	Rabbit 248.	Rabbit 299.	Rabbit 300.
Immediately	870,000	1,100,000	1,000,000	1,000,000
5 hours	1,300	3,300	12	68
24 ,, ...	142,000	1,953,000	0	289
48 ,, ...	2,800	Innumerable	149	79
96 ,, ...	Dead	Dead	0	0

The phagocytic reactions that we have described are illustrated in Figs. 219, 220, 221, and 222, for which we are indebted to Professor H. D. Wright.

The reaction in the lung capillaries in these immunized animals is illustrated by the following figures (Wright 1927) obtained from a film preparation.

Total number of pneumococci seen 893
Phagocytosed by polymorphonuclear cells 297
Phagocytosed by mononuclear cells 340
Total phagocytosed 637
Total outside phagocytes 256
In unphagocytosed aggregates associated with platelets . . . 206
In free aggregates 53

The results that have been obtained when immunized animals have been injected with virulent bacteria by other routes—by intraperitoneal or subcutaneous injection or by the mouth—are in entire conformity with those described above. An immunized animal reacts to a highly virulent bacterium as does a normal animal to one of lower virulence. The exact degree of difference in behaviour depends on the grade of immunity that has been established.

The immunity with which we are here concerned is, it should be noted, strictly specific. The influence of non-specific factors on immunity is considered in Chapter XLIX.

The Passive Transference of Antibacterial Immunity.—The increased resistance that an actively immunized animal enjoys in virtue of the increased efficiency of the defence mechanism considered above can be passively transferred from an immunized to a normal animal by injecting into the second the blood serum of the first.

It follows that we must regard the mechanism by which virulent bacteria are disposed of when once they have gained access to the tissues of an immunized animal as involving an integrated system of cellular reactions conditioned by the presence of specific antibodies in the blood or tissue fluids.

Again, a few illustrative examples will suffice.

Bull (1915a, b) found that, in a rabbit in which a bacteræmia had been established by the intravenous injection of pneumococci, the bacteria were removed from the circulation within about 15 minutes after the intravenous injection of 0·2–0·5 c.c. of antipneumococcus serum per kilo-body-weight of the rabbit.

Wright (1927) showed that the clearing mechanism of a normal rabbit could be rendered highly effective against virulent pneumococci by the intravenous injection of the serum of an actively immunized animal. The results of one such experiment are set out in

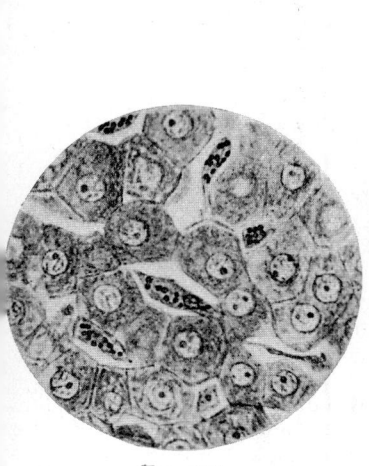

FIG. 219.

howing phagocytosis of pneumococci by macrophages in the liver of an immunized rabbit.

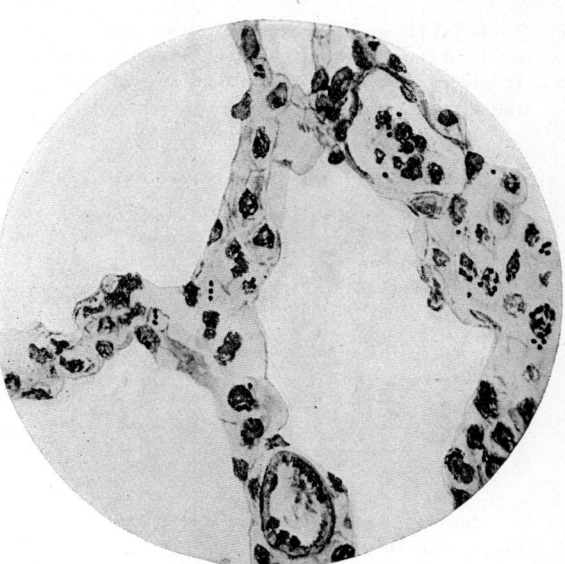

FIG. 222.

Lung of an immunized rabbit, showing phagocytosis of pneumococci in capillaries of alveolar walls.

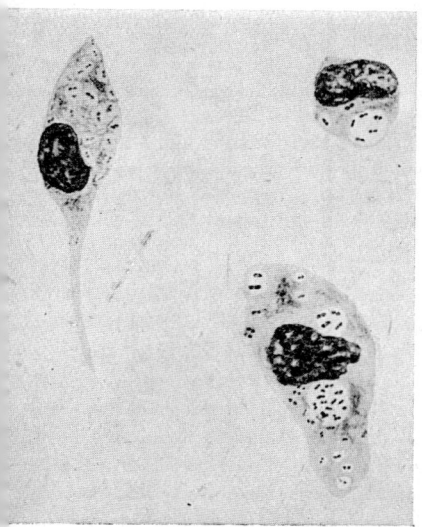

FIG. 220.

showing phagocytosis of pneumococci by the Kupffer cells, from the liver of an immunized rabbit.

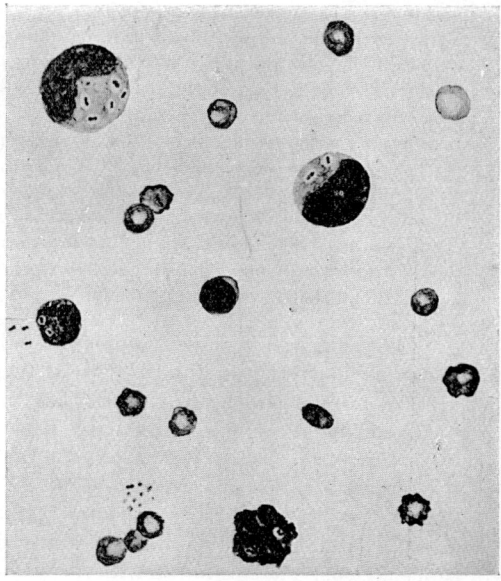

FIG. 221.

Blood from the liver of an immunized rabbit, showing phagocytosis of pneumococci.

Table LXIII and Fig. 223. The two passively immunized rabbits received 1 c.c. respectively of the serum of an actively immunized rabbit 1 hour before the test dose of culture. It will be noted that the normal animal died between the 5th and 24th hours, so that the secondary rise in the number of bacteria was not actually observed.

TABLE LXIII

SHOWING THE NUMBERS OF PNEUMOCOCCI PER C.C. OF CIRCULATING BLOOD AT VARIOUS TIMES AFTER INOCULATION OF A VIRULENT STRAIN INTO ONE NORMAL AND TWO PASSIVELY IMMUNIZED RABBITS.

Time after Injection.	Normal.	Pass. Imm. 1.	Pass. Imm. 2.
Immediately	2,300,000	2,300,000	2,000,000
5 hours	43,000	2	52
24 ,, ...	Dead	8	14
48 ,, ...	—	0	1
96 ,, ...	—	0	0

Manwaring and Coe (1914) perfused a normal liver with a dilute suspension of pneumococci, with and without the addition of an antipneumococcal serum, and found that the retention of pneumococci within the liver capillaries was very marked in the former case, but very slight in the latter.

There are many earlier observations of an analogous kind.

Bordet (1897) showed that an antistreptococcal serum would protect a guinea-pig against the intraperitoneal injection of a lethal dose of living streptococci. By withdrawing samples of the peritoneal exudate at various intervals after the inoculation, he was able to show that the recovery of the passively immunized animal was associated with a greatly increased degree of phagocytosis, mainly by the polymorphonuclear cells. By a very ingenious experiment he demonstrated that the relatively slight degree of phagocytosis in the peritoneal exudate of the normal animal could not be ascribed to an absence of activity on the part of the leucocytes. If a suspension of *Proteus* bacilli were injected into the peritoneum of a normal guinea-pig at a time when virulent streptococci were multiplying actively therein without undergoing any considerable degree of phagocytosis, the leucocytes at once ingested the *Proteus* bacilli in enormous numbers.

Pfeiffer and his colleagues (Pfeiffer 1893a, b, 1894a, b, 1895, Pfeiffer and Issaeff 1894, Issaeff 1894) showed that an anticholera serum would protect a guinea-pig against the intraperitoneal injection of living cholera vibrios ; but in this instance the protective effect would appear to depend mainly on a lysis of the vibrios, brought about by the combined action of antibody and complement.

It has, then, been shown quite clearly that specific antibodies play an important rôle in antibacterial immunity. Are they always concerned, or is there some other defence mechanism of the tissues that functions independently of them ?

The evidence at present available does not allow us to give any decisive answer to this question ; and reference to the literature shows a wide divergence between the tentative conclusions sponsored by different observers. One reason for this is that the point at issue has not always been clearly defined. Sometimes the problem actually submitted to experimental study has been the correlation between resistance to a particular bacterium and the presence of the corresponding antibodies in the circulating blood. But we shall see, when studying anaphylaxis, that specific antibodies readily become fixed to tissue cells ; so that the demonstration of immunity in the absence of circulating antibodies, or a failure to find any correlation between antibody titre and degree of resistance, cannot be accepted as satisfactory evidence that specific antibodies are not involved.

As an illustrative example of the relations that have been found to hold in experiments of this kind we may refer again to the careful studies of Wright (1927).

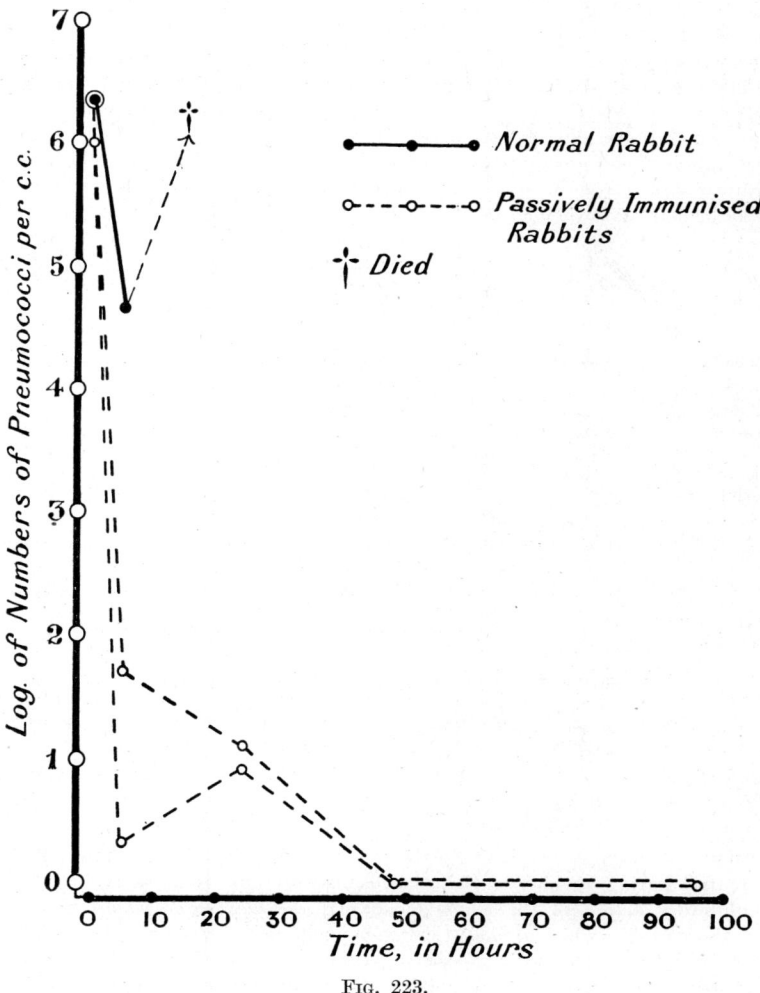

FIG. 223.

In these experiments, a large series of rabbits were immunized by a single intravenous inoculation of killed culture and were tested at various intervals thereafter by determining the rate at which virulent pneumococci disappeared from the blood stream, after the intravenous injection of 1 c.c. of living culture. The results suggested that there was a slight, but definite, improvement in the clearing capacity within a few hours. This became well established on the 3rd day, was still marked at the end of a month, and might persist for 3 to 6 months, though in diminishing degree. The serum of many of these rabbits was tested for the presence of agglutinins, opsonins, and precipitins. It was found that the production of these antibodies was inconstant, and that the times of their appearance and disappearance in the blood in no way corresponded to the duration of the improved clearing capacity. In many cases no antibodies were ever demonstrable, although the rabbit showed a well-marked clearing reaction. In others, agglutinins appeared to low titre on the 4th day, increased in amount to the 7th or 10th day, and disappeared by the end of the 3rd week. Thus they first appeared after the increased clearing capacity had become well established, and vanished while it was still present in a marked degree. In connection with these experiments Wright also determined the inhibiting action of whole blood (heparinized) on the growth of pneumococci, using a modification of the methods employed by earlier workers in determining the bactericidal action of whole blood on this organism. He found that the results of this *in vitro* test were far more closely correlated with the clearing capacity of the rabbits, and with the power of their serum to confer this clearing capacity on normal rabbits, than were the results obtained by agglutination or precipitin reactions.

A protocol, taken from his paper, and slightly modified in form, affords a clear illustration of the general type of his results. (Table LXIV).

TABLE LXIV

Rabbits.	Immune A.	Immune B.	Immune C.	Immune D.	Immune E.	Normal.	Normal.
Action of Serum.							
Agglutinins . .	—	—	—	—	—		
Precipitins . .	—	+	—	—	+		
Inhibition of growth by whole blood . . .	+	+ +	+ +	+ +	+ +		
Passive protection of normal rabbits . . .	+	+ +	+	slight	+ +		
Clearing capacity of rabbit :	No. of organisms per c.c. after intravenous injection.						
At once . . .	1,030,000	1,170,000	1,170,000	1,250,000	840,000	950,000	1,070,000
2 hours . . .	20,800	0	0	0	0	210,000	137,000
5 ,, . . .	340	0	0	0	0	25,000	25,000
24 ,, . . .	1,300	0	0	0	116	1,400,000	1,510,000
48 ,, . . .	134	0	0	0	0	Dead	Dead
96 ,, . . .	0						

The lack of correspondence between the presence of agglutinins and precipitins on the one hand, and clearing capacity on the other, is obvious ; but the association between the growth-inhibitory action of the whole blood and the clearing capacity is very close. Similarly, those rabbits which are able to remove pneumococci rapidly and completely from their own circulating blood are in a position to confer a similar ability on normal rabbits, by the transference to the latter of a relatively small proportion of their blood serum. The correspondence, in this case, is not absolute ; but the association is well-marked.

It should, perhaps, be noted that other workers have reported the occurrence of an effective active immunity in the entire absence of circulating antibodies, as judged by all available tests, including the bactericidal power of the whole blood (see, for instance, Teale 1935).

Evidence of an essentially different kind has sometimes been appealed to in the discussion of this problem. It has been pointed out that there may be little if any correspondence between the protective power of an antiserum and its antibody content as determined by agglutination, or other *in vitro* tests (see, for instance,

Wadsworth 1917, Avery *et al.* 1917). So far as this is so, it is clearly not an argument in favour of a tissue immunity as against an immunity depending on humoral antibodies—the passive transference of protection is proof enough that some humoral factor is concerned. The most that can be concluded from such observations is that the protective power of the serum is not determined by the particular antibodies measured by the *in vitro* tests. The force of most arguments of this kind has been greatly weakened during recent years by the demonstration that antibacterial immunity is dependent on the antibodies acting on particular antigenic components of the bacterial cell, while other antibodies, though giving agglutination or precipitation *in vitro*, may have no protective effect *in vivo* (see below). It has been shown too that many of the quantitative methods used by the earlier workers were very ill-adapted for the accurate assay of the antibodies concerned ; and the employment of a more adequate technique has resulted, in many cases, in the demonstration of a close correspondence between the protective power of a serum and its content in a particular antibody (see Smith 1932).

Perhaps the strongest argument in favour of the essential rôle of the serum antibodies in antibacterial immunity is the fact that such immunity is specific. It is true that a non-specific active immunity can sometimes be induced ; but it is almost always of the relatively trivial and transient type described in Chapter XLIX. Effective and durable active immunity is usually narrowly specific ; and in many cases we can identify the particular antigenic component, or components, on which it depends. If there is an immunity that has nothing to do with antibody formation, then we must invoke an additional specific mechanism, in which the same antigenic components are in some way involved. There is nothing very unlikely in such an assumption, and it may well prove to be correct ; but it will accord with the sound principle of economy of hypothesis, to reserve judgment pending the accumulation of further evidence.

The Dependence of Effective Antibacterial Immunity upon Particular Antibodies.

On which of the various serum antibodies does antibacterial immunity depend ? This question was answered, in respect to one particular infection, long before anyone realized that it had been asked. Neufeld and Händel (1909), in their classical paper on the testing of antipneumococcal sera, first showed the existence of different serological types of pneumococci by noting that a given serum would protect a mouse against one strain of pneumococcus but not against another.

The demonstration of the presence of two separable antigenic components in the pneumococcal cell—the type-specific polysaccharide and the non-specific nucleo-protein —afforded an obvious opportunity of approaching this problem along more satisfying lines ; and the results obtained were unequivocal. The antibody corresponding to the polysaccharide hapten was found to have a high protective value : the antibody corresponding to the nucleo-protein antigen had little, if any, protective effect (Avery and Morgan 1925, Avery and Neill 1925). A decisive demonstration of the protective action of the antibody acting on the specific polysaccharide, in the absence of antibodies acting on any other constituent or product of the pneumococcal cell, has recently been recorded by Avery and Goebel (1931). They prepared a synthetic antigen by obtaining purified polysaccharide from a culture of Type III pneumococcus and linking it to horse globulin, and with this antigen they immunized rabbits. The antisera so obtained protected mice against Type III pneumococci, but not against Type I or Type II pneumococci. We must not, of course, infer that no other antibody plays any part in antipneumococcal immunity ; but we may certainly infer that this particular antibody is effective when acting by itself.

In this connection an observation of considerable interest was made by Sugg, Richardson and Neill (1929). It was found that a particular variety of yeast contained the specific polysaccharide component of the Type II pneumococcus. Vaccination of mice with a heated suspension of this yeast significantly increased their resistance to Type II pneumococcus, but not to Type I or Type III.

Julianelle (1926) has reported entirely analogous findings in the case of Friedländer's bacillus. A serum containing antibodies for one of the type-specific polysaccharides protects mice against the corresponding serological type. A serum containing only antibodies corresponding to the common nucleo-protein antigen affords no protection.

It was, however, in the case of the motile bacilli, possessing flagellar and somatic antigens, that the problem of the different immunizing value of different bacterial antigens was first stated in its clearest and most explicit form by Felix and his colleagues (see Felix 1924). The results of experimental studies carried out during the past few years have afforded strong support to his contention that the flagellar antigens, and the corresponding antibodies, play little if any part in the mechanism of specific antibacterial immunity, while the heat-stable somatic antigens and the antibodies that react with them are all-important.

Arkwright (1927) immunized guinea-pigs by the injection of vaccines prepared from different strains of *Bact. typhosum* and *Bact. paratyphosum A*, and subsequently tested their resistance by the injection of living virulent bacilli.

In the case of *Bact. typhosum*, a vaccine prepared with a smooth, motile, virulent strain (containing the flagellar antigen and the surface antigen IX) produced a significant increase in resistance. A vaccine prepared from a rough, motile variant (containing the flagellar antigen but not the surface antigen IX) did not. In the case of *Bact. paratyphosum A* four vaccines were used : (1) a smooth, motile strain, with the flagellar antigen and the surface antigens I, II, (2) a non-motile, smooth variant, with no flagellar antigen but retaining the surface antigens I, II, (3) a rough, motile variant, with the flagellar antigen but without the surface antigens I, II, and (4) a rough, non-motile variant containing neither the flagellar antigen nor the surface antigens I, II. Vaccines (1) and (2), containing the antigens I, II, produced a marked increase in resistance. Vaccines (3) and (4), from which this antigen was absent, did not.

Ibrahim and Schütze (1928) obtained analogous results in the immunization of mice against *Bact. typhi-murium*. They used seven different vaccines derived from smooth and rough strains and killed by heating for different times at different temperatures. They found that the rough variants, in which the specific polysaccharide antigen was absent, were ineffective as immunizing agents. The smooth variants, containing the specific polysaccharide antigen, produced a significant increase in resistance ; but prolonged heating at 100° C. (2 hours) reduced their immunizing value.

Robertson and Felix (1930) have recently reported that an antiserum to *Cl. septique*, containing antibodies against the heat-stable, somatic antigen, but none acting on the heat-labile, flagellar antigen, has a high protective value as tested in mice. Henderson (1932) has recently recorded analogous results with *Cl. chauvœi*.

Experiments, in which untreated mice and mice vaccinated with different bacterial suspensions were submitted to the risk of natural infection during a long-continued experimental epidemic of mouse typhoid, have yielded entirely concordant results (Greenwood, Topley and Wilson 1931). The total numbers in each of the vaccinated groups were large —over 300 mice—so that the difference noted may be regarded as certainly significant. The results are summarized in Table LXV.

The column giving the antigenic structure shows the components on the surface of the bacterial cells and those carried by the flagella. All vaccines except E were saline suspensions, killed by heat and formalin. Vaccine E—a killed broth culture—was included because of the possibility that some bacterial product of immunizing value might be liberated into the culture fluid. The measure of resistance—the mean survival time in the epidemic cage limited to 60 days—was selected for reasons that will be referred to later. The significance of the standard error, which is attached to each survival time, has been considered in Chapter XL.

TABLE LXV

Group.	Vaccine.	Antigens.	Mean Survival Time in Epidemic Cage. Limited to 60 Days.
C	*Bact. typhi-murium* . . . . . (Smooth—Type and Group)	Surface, IV, V, (XII). Flag. i. Flag. 1, 2, 3.	35·31 ± 0·884
E	*Bact. typhi-murium* . . . . . (Smooth—Type and Group— Broth culture)	Surface, IV, V, (XII). Flag. i. Flag. 1, 2, 3.	34·97 ± 0·845
F	*Bact. paratyphosum B* . . . . (Smooth—Group)	Surface, IV, V, (XII). Flag. 1, 2.	35·06 ± 0·845
G	*Bact. paratyphosum B* . . . . (Smooth—Type)	Surface, IV, V, (XII). Flag. b.	33·71 ± 0·853
D	*Bact. typhi-murium* . . . . . (Rough—Type and Group)	Surface, R. Flag. i. Flag. 1, 2, 3.	29·44 ± 0·771
B	*Bact. typhosum* . . . . . . (Rough)	Surface, R. Flag. d.	29·28 ± 0·732
A	*Staph. albus*	—	29·86 ± 0·714
H	Unvaccinated Controls	—	26·26 ± 0·641

It will be seen that the control and vaccinated groups can be divided into three classes on the basis of their survival time. The unvaccinated mice lived, on the average, for 26·26 days, and were thus significantly less resistant than any other group. The groups D, B and A were slightly more resistant. This increased resistance was clearly not specific. The rough polysaccharide antigen was not concerned, for the *Staph. albus* vaccine did not contain it. The flagellar antigens of *Bact. typhi-murium* were not concerned, for neither the *Staph. albus* nor the rough *Bact. typhosum* contained them. The groups C, E, F and G were definitely more resistant ; their mean survival time varied from 33·71 to 35·31 days. They all differed from the other groups in that they contained the specific polysaccharide surface antigens of *Bact. typhi-murium* (IV and V). They differed among themselves with regard to their flagellar antigens. The results indicate quite clearly that the specific polysaccharide surface antigen is the most important immunizing agent.

We may, then, take it as a general rule—a rule that we could have foretold in view of the facts considered in Chapter VII—that the antibodies acting on the surface antigens of virulent, smooth bacilli are essential agents in effective antibacterial immunity ; and that the efficiency of any bacterial vaccine depends in large part on the presence of these antigens.

In the particular case of the typhoid bacillus it will be necessary to discuss the significance of the Vi antigen and Vi antibody, recently described by Felix and Pitt (1934*a*, *b*) ; but since the relation of these observations to the more general problems of active and passive immunization is still uncertain, it will be more convenient to postpone this discussion to Chapter LXVI.

The Efficacy of Antibacterial Immunity.

As we emphasized in the earliest pages of this book, immunity may be of very varying grade. The first effect of the mechanisms that we have discussed in this chapter is to free the circulating blood from bacteria, and so save the host from a fatal bacteræmia. The effect on the local foci of infection is less pronounced, and much less rapid. Bacteria may remain latent in such foci over considerable periods.

Thus (Topley 1929) of 64 vaccinated mice that had survived in apparent health for 28 days after an intraperitoneal injection of 1,000 virulent *Bact. typhi-murium*, 31 were found to be harbouring that organism in the spleen. We need not doubt that a complete sterilization of the tissues often occurs ; but we must not identify the absence of overt illness with a complete absence of infection, or illness followed by recovery with infection followed by a return to the uninfected state.

There is another factor which may limit the efficacy of immunity of this type. There are regions of the body in which bacterial infections are particularly dangerous, and when foci are established at these sites an immunity that is effective against lesions elsewhere seems to be of little avail. Thus Bull (1915b) notes that immunized animals, after rapidly freeing their blood stream of pneumococci and remaining in apparent health for several days, may later succumb to a pneumococcal meningitis.

In general, antibacterial immunity is, as we should expect, found to be more variable and often less effective than antitoxic immunity.

Active Antibacterial Immunization as the Result of Infection.

We may close this chapter by considering what happens when a bacterium of moderate virulence obtains access to the tissues of a host that makes a successful immunizing response, and so recovers. We will take as an example a disease, such as typhoid fever, in which the bacterial parasite gains access to the blood stream and so is spread throughout the tissues during the early stages of the attack.

Fig. 224 shows diagrammatically the probable progress of an infection of this type. At A is represented the initial phase, during which the bacteria gain access through a mucous surface and pass to a regional lymphatic gland. At B the bacteria are proliferating in the gland, and there is an intermittent escape of some of them into the blood stream. At C these bacteria are shown as collecting in the liver and spleen, these organs being taken as examples of tissues rich in reticulo-endothelial cells, and hence concerned in the normal clearing mechanisms of the blood. At D the bacteria are proliferating in those situations in which they have collected during the initial phases of infection, which correspond to the incubation period of a clinical attack of disease. At E there is a re-invasion of the blood stream from these foci of bacterial proliferation, a well-marked bacteræmia, and a transport of bacteria to other tissues, not previously infected. This corresponds to the phase of clinical illness, and, in a fatal case, persists till death. Up to this stage no antibodies have appeared in the circulating blood ; but at this point they usually make their appearance in cases that recover. At F is represented the phase of clinical recovery. The improved clearing mechanism, consequent on an efficient antibody-producing response, has terminated the bacteræmic stage ; and we are left with a few scattered foci of infection, in the spleen, liver and lymph nodes, and perhaps in other tissues.

As we have seen, there is reason to believe that the persistence of this state of affairs over prolonged periods is consistent with the maintenance of apparent health. At G is represented the final stage of complete restitution, with the disappearance of all infecting bacteria, and the persistence in the tissues or body fluids of protective antibodies. It is probable that a proportion of infections may be terminated at

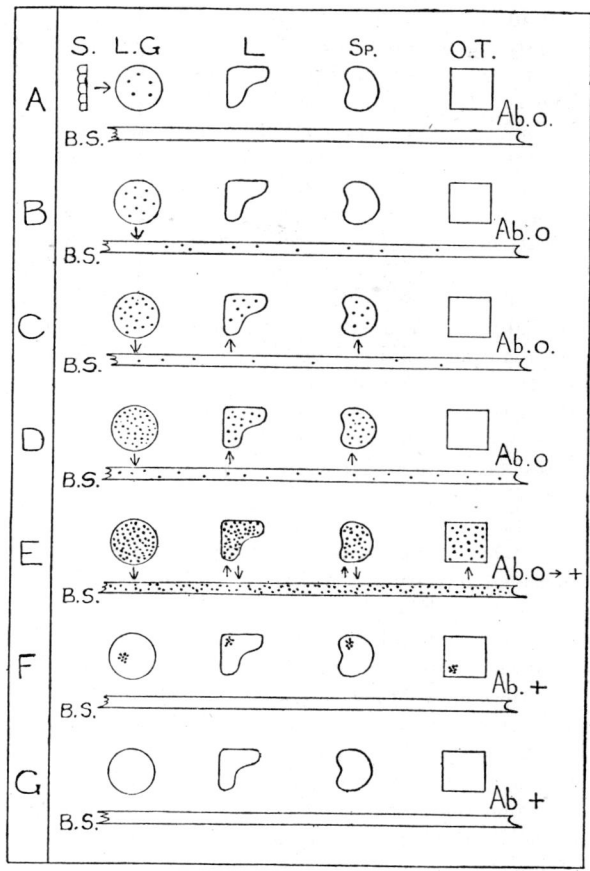

FIG. 224.

S = Mucous Surface. L.G. = Regional Lymphatic Glands. L = Liver. Sp. = Spleen. O.T. = Other Tissues. B.S. = Blood Stream. Ab.0. = Circulating Antibodies Absent. Ab. + = Circulating Antibodies present.

one of the initial stages, A, B, C or D, without ever passing to E, the stage of clinical illness ; and there are reasons for believing that such abortive infections, especially if repeated, may lead to the acquirement of an effective degree of immunity to reinfection. With suitable modifications our diagram could be adapted to other bacterial infections, differing in regard to the primary focus of infection and the direction and extent of the secondary spread.

SUMMARY

(1) The mechanism brought into play in the removal of bacteria from the tissues is, in its main outlines, identical with that employed in the removal and storage of inert particles of the same order of size.

(2) When large numbers of bacteria are introduced directly into the blood stream they are in part taken up by the sessile histiocytes in such reticulo-endothelial depôts as the liver and the spleen, in part phagocytosed by polymorphonuclear cells and by macrophages in the lungs, in part flocculated into aggregates which are filtered off in the lung capillaries and later phagocytosed.

(3) With avirulent bacteria, that have little power of multiplication within the issues, this mechanism results in a rapid and permanent clearing of the circulation. With virulent bacteria an initial partial clearing is followed by a stage of bacterial multiplication in the foci to which the bacteria have been removed, resulting in a secondary invasion of the blood stream. The fate of the host is determined by the balance between this bacterial multiplication and the efficiency of the clearing mechanism. With slightly or moderately virulent strains there is a secondary bacteræmia followed by a secondary clearing. With highly virulent strains the secondary bacteræmia increases and the animal dies of an acute septicæmia. Even when secondary clearing occurs, and the animal remains in apparent health, foci of infection may remain in the various histiocyte depôts, and living bacteria may persist in these situations over long periods of time.

(4) When bacteria gain access to the body by other routes they are dealt with in part by local mechanisms of the same general character as that described under (3). The extent to which invasion of the blood stream occurs depends upon the anatomy and functional activity of the tissues first invaded, and upon the virulence of the invading organism. The blood stream is invaded very rapidly after intraperitoneal inoculation, less rapidly after intramuscular inoculation, and still less rapidly after subcutaneous inoculation. In all cases the passage from the primary site of infection to the blood stream is mainly by way of the lymphatics, and the histiocyte depôts in the regional lymphatic glands play a prominent part in the removal of the invading bacteria. When relatively avirulent bacteria gain access to the tissues at some site from which passage to the blood stream is slow, infection may never pass beyond the first line of defence in the regional lymphatic glands ; but here, as in the case where a generalized infection has become established, localized foci of infection may persist over long periods of time.

(5) In addition to this process of removal by phagocytic cells, a direct bactericidal action of the serum plays a part in ridding the tissues of bacteria. The importance of this purely humoral immunity appears to differ widely in different bacterial infections ; but it is probably always subsidiary to the phagocytic mechanism, and is seldom, if ever, the main factor in defence.

(6) The efficiency of the clearing mechanism of a normal animal may be increased, *vis-à-vis* a particular bacterial parasite, by active immunization with a killed culture of that particular organism. The immunity so produced is specific in the serological sense. The actively immunized animal deals with a virulent strain of the bacterium against which it has been immunized in the same way as a normal animal deals with an avirulent or slightly virulent strain of the same bacterial species.

(7) Immunity of this type may be passively transferred by the inoculation into a normal animal of the serum obtained from an animal that has been actively immunized.

(8) The antibodies by which this passive immunity is conferred are those that unite with the surface antigens of the virulent bacteria ; and in order to induce an effective active antibacterial immunity the immunizing agent employed must contain these surface antigens.

(9) The mechanisms described above come into play during the later stages of any bacterial infection that is associated with the development of an antibacterial immunity.

REFERENCES

ANDREWES, F. (1910) *Lancet*, i. 1737 ; (1910) *Ibid.*, ii. 8, 83, 153.
ARKWRIGHT, J. A. (1927) *J. Path. Bact.*, **30**, 345.
ASCHOFF, L. (1924) *Ergebn. inn. Med. Kinderheilk.*, **26**, 1.
AVERY, O. T., CHICKERING, H. T., COLE, R., and DOCHEZ, A. R. (1917) *Monogr. Rockefeller Inst.*, No. 7.
AVERY, O. T. and GOEBEL, W. F. (1931) *J. exp. Med.*, **54**, 437.
AVERY, O. T. and MORGAN, H. J. (1925) *J. exp. Med.*, **42**, 347.
AVERY, O. T. and NEILL, J. M. (1925) *J. exp. Med.*, **42**, 355.
BAIL, O. (1905) *Arch. Hyg.*, **52**, 272.
BARDACH, J. (1889) *Ann. Inst. Pasteur*, **3**, 577.
BARTLETT, C. J. and OZAKI, Y. (1917) *J. med. Res.*, **35**, 465 ; (1918) *Ibid.*, **37**, 139.
BOLTON, C. (1921) *J. Path. Bact.*, **24**, 429.
BORDET, J. (1897) *Ann. Inst. Pasteur*, **11**, 177.
BULL, C. G. (1914) *J. exp. Med.*, **20**, 237 ; (1915a) *Ibid.*, **22**, 457 ; (1915b) *Ibid.*, **22**, 466 ; (1915c) *Ibid.*, **22**, 475 ; (1915d) *Ibid.*, **22**, 484 ; (1916) *Ibid.*, **24**, 7, 25.
BULL, C. G. and McKEE, C. M. (1922) *Amer. J. Hyg.*, **2**, 208.
BUXTON, B. H. (1906) *J. med. Res.*, **15**, 18.
BUXTON, B. H. and TORREY, J. C. (1906a) *J. med. Res.*, **15**, 5 ; (1906b) *Ibid.*, **15**, 41 ; (1906c) *Ibid.*, **15**, 55 ; (1906d) *Ibid.*, **15**, 73.
CAPPELL, D. F. (1929) *J. Path. Bact.*, **32**, 595 ; (1930) *Ibid.*, **33**, 429.
DELREZ, L. and GOVAERTS, P. (1918) *C. R. Soc. Biol.*, **81**, 53.
DUDGEON, L. S. and GOADBY, H. K. (1931) *J. Hyg., Camb.*, **31**, 247.
DUDGEON, L. S. and ROSS, M. (1906) *Trans. Path. Soc. Lond.*, **57**, 155.
DURHAM, H. E. (1897) *J. Path. Bact.*, **4**, 338.
FELIX, A. (1924) *Z. ImmunForsch.*, **39**, 127.
FELIX, A. and PITT, M. (1934a) *J. Path. Bact.*, **38**, 409 ; (1934b) *Lancet*, ii. 186.
FLOREY, H. W. (1927) *Brit. J. exp. Path.*, **8**, 479.
FLOREY, H. W. and CARLETON, H. M. (1926) *J. Path. Bact.*, **29**, 97.
GOVAERTS, P. (1921a) *C. R. Soc. Biol.*, **85**, 667 ; (1921b) *Arch. int. Physiol.*, **16**, 1.
GREENWOOD, M., TOPLEY, W. W. C., and WILSON, J. (1931) *J. Hyg., Camb.*, **31**, 257.
HENDERSON, D. W. (1932) *Brit. J. exp. Path.*, **13**, 421.
HOFFMANN, F. A. and RECKLINGHAUSEN, F. VON. (1867) *Zbl. med. Wiss.*, No. 31, 481.
IBRAHIM, H. M. and SCHÜTZE, H. (1928) *Brit. J. exp. Path.*, **9**, 353.
ISSAEFF. (1894) *Z. Hyg. InfektKr.*, **16**, 287.
JULIANELLE, L. A. (1926) *J. exp. Med.*, **44**, 113, 683, 735.
KYES, P. (1916) *J. infect. Dis.*, **18**, 277.
LANGE, B. and GUTDEUTSCH, H. (1928) *Z. Hyg. InfektKr.*, **109**, 253.
LEVADITI, C. (1901) *Ann. Inst. Pasteur*, **15**, 894.
MANWARING, W. H. and COE, H. C. (1914) *J. Immunol.*, **1**, 401.
METCHNIKOFF, E. (1901) " L'Immunité dans les maladies infectieuses." Paris.
MÉTIN. (1900) *Ann. Inst. Pasteur*, **14**, 415.
MÜLLER, M. (1912) *Zbl. Bakt.*, **62**, 335.
MUSCATELLO, G. (1895) *Virchows Arch.*, **147**, 327.
NEUFELD, F. and HÄNDEL, L. (1909) *Z. ImmunForsch.*, **3**, 159.
OPITZ, E. (1898) *Z. Hyg. InfektKr.*, **29**, 505.
ØRSKOV, J., JENSEN, K., and KOBAYASHI, K. (1928) *Z. ImmunForsch.*, **55**, 34.
ØRSKOV, J. and LASSEN, H. C. A. (1930) *Z. ImmunForsch.*, **67**, 137.
ØRSKOV, J. and MOLTKE, O. (1928) *Z. ImmunForsch.*, **59**, 357.
PFEIFFER, R. (1893a) *Z. Hyg. InfektKr.*, **11**, 393 ; (1893b) *Ibid.*, **13**, 357 ; (1894a) *Ibid.*, **16**, 268 ; (1894b) *Ibid.*, **18**, 1 ; (1895) *Ibid.*, **19**, 75.

PFEIFFER, R. and ISSAEFF.   (1894) *Z. Hyg. InfektKr.*, **17**, 355.
PONFICK.   (1869) *Virchows Arch.*, **48**, 1.
PRICE-JONES, C.   (1927) *J. Path. Bact.*, **30**, 45.
ROBERTSON, M. and FELIX, A.   (1930) *Brit. J. exp. Path.*, **11**, 14.
ROUS, P. and JONES, F. S.   (1916) *J. exp. Med.*, **23**, 601.
SMITH, W.   (1932) *J. Path. Bact.*, **35**, 509.
SOBERNHEIM, G. and MURATA, H.   (1924) *Z. Hyg. InfektKr.*, **103**, 691.
SUGG, J., RICHARDSON, L. V., and NEILL, J. M.   (1929) *J. exp. Med.*, **50**, 579.
TEALE, F. H.   (1935) *J. Immunol.*, **28**, 133.
TOPLEY, W. W. C.   (1929) *Lancet*, i. 1337.
TOPLEY, W. W. C. and WILSON, J.   (1923) *J. Hyg., Camb.*, **21**, 237.
WADSWORTH, A. B.   (1917) *J. exp. Med.*, **25**, 629.
WERIGO, M.   (1894) *Ann. Inst. Pasteur*, **8**, 1.
WRIGHT, H. D.   (1927) *J. Path. Bact.*, **30**, 185.
WYSSOKOWITCH, W.   (1886) *Z. Hyg. InfektKr.*, **1**, 3.

CHAPTER XLV

THE AGGRESSIVE ACTION OF BACTERIA

In the preceding chapters we have considered the ways in which bacteria injure the tissues of an animal host, and the ways in which the host defends itself against attack. In the present chapter we are concerned with certain bacterial products that exert an aggressive effect, not so much by acting directly on the host's tissues, as by interfering with its defence mechanisms.

The available data are, as is so commonly the case, sadly confused by the fact that we have been forced to work with the crudest and most complex of reagents. The easiest way of disentangling, to some extent, the confused threads of this particular problem is to take as our starting-point a series of observations recorded by Bail and his colleagues (Bail 1900, 1902–3, 1904a, b, c, 1905, Bail and Pettersson 1902, 1903, Bail and Weil 1906, 1911, Weil 1905a, b). Working with the anthrax bacillus, with organisms of the *Pasteurella* group, with the cholera vibrio and with the typhoid bacillus, they found that exudates produced in experimental animals by the inoculation of these bacteria had characteristic properties, which Bail attributed to the presence of special bacterial products to which he gave the name *aggressins*; these aggressins were, he believed, produced in the tissues of the infected host, but seldom, if ever, *in vitro*.

The properties of aggressins, as described by Bail, may be summarized as follows :

(1) Sub-lethal doses of bacteria are rendered lethal by the addition of aggressins.

(2) A lethal dose of bacteria, which alone would produce a slowly fatal infection, causes a rapidly fatal infection associated with characteristic lesions when aggressins are added to the inoculum.

(3) The addition of cholera aggressins neutralizes the bactericidal action of an anticholera serum, as tested by intraperitoneal injection in the guinea-pig.

(4) By the injection of aggressins an immunity is produced which is far more effective than that produced by the inoculation of bacteria and is different in kind. This immunity can be passively transferred.

According to Bail, the aggressins are not themselves toxic. They produce their effects, which are in the main specific, solely by aiding the rapid multiplication of bacteria within the tissues. He states also that they are extremely thermolabile, being completely inactivated by 30 minutes' exposure to a temperature of 55° C. and markedly affected by any temperature above 44° C.

Bail's contention, that the results of his experiments required for their interpretation the assumption of the existence of a hitherto unrecognized bacterial product of peculiar importance in infection and immunity and deserving the new title of " aggressin," did not long remain unchallenged. Wassermann and Citron (1907) recorded their reasons for believing that the aggressins were simply products of bacterial growth, or of bacterial autolysis, which could be prepared in the test tube by suitable methods. Citron (1906) recorded experiments which showed that the addition of bacterial extracts to living bacteria increased their virulence ; that by the use of such extracts it was possible to immunize animals against experimental infection ; and that the serum of such immunized animals conferred passive immunity on others. Bail and Weil (1906) maintained that the immunity produced by Citron with his bacterial extracts was far less effective than that produced by natural aggressins, and that it was different in kind ; though it is not entirely clear on what differential criteria they relied in distinguishing anti-aggressin immunity from the varieties previously recognized.

Doerr (1906) criticized the aggressin theory on somewhat similar grounds, but emphasized particularly the fact that large doses of dead bacilli may cause death in experimental animals with the lesions described by Bail as characteristic of the aggressin effect. He also noted that if sub-lethal doses of killed cultures were added to sub-lethal doses of living bacteria the combined inoculum might cause a fatal infection of the aggressive type. This additive effect did not appear to be in any way specific, but some killed cultures were more effective than others. For instance, dead typhoid or dysentery bacilli were more aggressive than dead staphylococci. In addition, Doerr demonstrated that aggressive exudates did, in fact, contain ordinary bacterial antigens ; since a typhoid exudate gave well-marked precipitation with an ordinary antityphoid serum.

Sauerbeck (1907) has also criticized Bail's hypothesis. He concludes, from the results of a large series of experiments, that aggressive exudates are not lacking in toxicity, since two or three times the amount that produces the characteristic aggressive effect will kill an animal within a few days in the absence of living bacteria ; that the activity of a given aggressive exudate is in no way proportional to the virulence of the organism that produced it, but rather to its toxigenicity ; that characteristic aggressive effects can be produced with toxic bacterial products that have been prepared in the test tube ; and that aggressive action, whatever its cause, is entirely non-specific. His findings as regards the heat-stability of the aggressive bacterial products also differ from Bail's, since he states that they are reduced in potency, but not completely inactivated by heating at temperatures between 55° C. and 70° C.

The detailed studies of Dudgeon (1912) on the properties of exudates obtained from natural infections in man and from experimental infections in animals made it clear that one of the mechanisms involved in the total aggressin effect was a specific anti-opsonic action.

The method he adopted in the majority of his experiments was as follows. He obtained exudates from natural infections in man or from experimental infections in animals. The exudate, after the separation of as much material as possible by centrifugation, was mixed in a capillary tube with an equal volume of normal serum, or of serum from an immunized man or animal. After 1 hour's incubation at 37° C. leucocytes and bacterial suspension were added to each mixture, the tubes were re-incubated for 15 minutes and films were prepared from the contents, the degree of phagocytosis being determined in the usual way. In control tubes the exudate was replaced by saline. In each case the opsonic effect of the serum, and of the serum-exudate mixture, was determined against the bacterium causing the infection and against some related organism. The results shown in Table LXVI illustrate an effect that was commonly observed. The exudate came from a subcutaneous staphylococcal abscess ; the immune serum was from the infected patient ; the normal serum was from an uninfected control. The sera and the serum-exudate mixtures were tested against the strain of staphylococcus grown from the abscess and against a strain of Bact. coli.

TABLE LXVI

Mixture.	Number of Bacteria ingested by 50 Leucocytes.	
	Staph. aureus.	*Bact. coli.*
Normal Serum + Saline	240	229
Immune Serum + Saline	294	203
Normal Serum + Exudate	139	200
Immune Serum + Exudate	139	237
Exudate + Saline	61	21

The exudate alone had a slight opsonic effect, but it specifically reduced the opsonic action of normal or of immune serum on *Staph. aureus*, leaving unaffected their opsonic action on *Bact. coli*.

The substances responsible for this specific anti-opsonic effect were found, in many cases at least, to be markedly thermostable. Table LXVII shows the effect of adding a boiled exudate, obtained from an experimental infection with *Bact. enteritidis*, to the serum of the infected animal.

TABLE LXVII

Mixture.	Number of Bacteria ingested by 50 Leucocytes.	
	Bact. enteritidis.	*Bact. coli.*
Serum + Saline	248	130
Serum + Boiled Exudate	27	102

In further experiments Dudgeon submitted exudates to boiling, removed the coagulum by centrifugation, added excess of alcohol to the clear supernatant fluid, collected the precipitate by centrifugation, and redissolved it in saline. The preparation so obtained still showed specific anti-opsonic action.

These results bore an obvious analogy to an earlier series of observations (Dudgeon, Panton and Wilson 1909–1910, 1910–1911). Extracts were prepared from various bacteria by grinding or by alternate freezing and thawing, and these extracts were shown to have a specific anti-opsonic effect. The anti-opsonic substances were markedly thermostable, remaining active after boiling for 30 minutes. A considerable series of control tests showed that they had no direct action on the leucocytes.

In addition to these heat-stable specific anti-opsonic substances, Dudgeon found that many infective exudates contained directly toxic substances, as judged by injection into experimental animals. In this respect, however, they varied widely, according to the infecting bacterium. It may be noted that certain highly toxic exudates, such as those obtained in experimental infections with *Bact. enteritidis*, retained their toxicity after boiling.

Further light has been thrown on the probable nature of the anti-opsonic substances in aggressive exudates during the prolonged and detailed study of the factors involved in antipneumococcal immunity.

Rosenow (1907) found that extracts or autolysates of virulent pneumococci had the power of inhibiting the phagocytosis of relatively avirulent pneumococci, and he suggested the name *virulins* for the active substances concerned.

Cole (1917) observed that empyema fluids from pneumococcal infections contained soluble substances which specifically neutralized the protective antibodies in an antipneumococcal serum, and that similar substances might be present in the blood of rabbits suffering from experimental pneumococcal infection. He showed that, when an antipneumococcal serum was injected intravenously into a rabbit previously infected with the same type of pneumococcus, the protective antibodies disappeared very rapidly from the blood, and that a similar phenomenon could be demonstrated in patients severely ill with lobar pneumonia.

The more recent studies on the antigenic components of bacterial cells that we have outlined in Chapter VII, and the demonstration that sensitization to the phagocytic action of polymorphonuclear cells, and presumably of macrophages, depends upon the union of antibody with an antigenic component situated at the surface of the bacterial cell, offer the obvious suggestion that the substances responsible for the specific anti-opsonic effects of aggressive exudates are dissolved bacterial antigens. Landsteiner's demonstration of the inhibition of antigen-antibody reactions by simple haptens (see pp. 180–183), and the *in vitro* reactions of specific bacterial polysaccharides that fail to stimulate antibody production *in vivo*, indicate that bacterial haptens, as well as complete antigens, may be expected to exert this anti-opsonic effect.

There is good evidence that this is actually the case. Sia (1926) has studied the action of the type-specific polysaccharides of Type II and Type III pneumococci on the growth of these organisms in serum-leucocyte mixtures from the rabbit and from the cat. The pneumococci were of relatively low virulence and developed very poorly in either of the serum-leucocyte mixtures employed. The addition of minute amounts of Type II polysaccharide greatly increased the growth of Type II pneumococci, but had little effect on the growth of the Type III organisms. The addition of minute amounts of Type III polysaccharide greatly increased the growth of Type III pneumococci, but not of Type II.

Felton and Bailey (1926) have demonstrated the aggressive action of Type II polysaccharide by injecting it into mice together with relatively avirulent pneumococci of the same type, and inducing a fatal infection.

Ward (1932) has recently shown that the inhibitory action of extracts from pneumonic lungs on the bactericidal action of whole blood is greater than that of the specific polysaccharide as prepared in the laboratory. It may be that the polysaccharide hapten as developed in the tissues is in a more active state, or it may be that more than one hapten or antigen is involved. In any case it seems highly probable that dissolved antigenic components play an important part in neutralizing the natural antibodies, or the antibodies formed by the host during the course of an infection, and so in reducing the effectiveness of the defence mechanisms. Cole (1917) and Park and Cooper (1928) record evidence suggesting that a fatal outcome in cases of lobar pneumonia in man is frequently associated with the presence in the blood of specific soluble antigen in amounts greater than can be neutralized by the antibodies that the patient has produced.

In addition to these dissolved haptens or antigens it is clear that some infective exudates will contain bacterial toxins that interfere with the defence mechanism of the host by an attack delivered against the cellular rather than against the humoral defences. Two pathogenic species at least, the pyogenic staphylococcus and the hæmolytic streptococcus, produce a specific leucocidin that attacks the polymorphonuclear cells. We know little as yet with regard to the action of bacterial toxins on the cells of the reticulo-endothelial system ; but it is quite probable that we shall find that certain bacterial species are capable of producing toxins that have a selective action on the macrophages.

There are also the bacterial coagulases, fibrinolysins and " spreading factors," which have been included among the bacterial toxins. It is clear that they might, perhaps with better justification, have been described as aggressins.

In summary : it would seem that we are justified in recognizing the following factors as involved, to a varying degree, in the defence rupture that is produced by the injection of sterile infective exudates, of dead bacteria, or of bacterial extracts, in association with non-lethal doses of living bacilli.

(1) *Dissolved bacterial haptens or antigens, or similar components still attached to bacterial protoplasm.* These act specifically by uniting with the corresponding antibody, and so preventing the effective sensitization of the living bacterial cells. Many of these haptens are of the nature of polysaccharides. Many of them appear to be thermostable. It is probably only those haptens or antigens that are situated at the surface of the bacterial cell that are able to function in this way ; since it is the surface components that are concerned in sensitization.

(2) *Bacterial toxins that selectively attack the cells concerned in tissue defence.* Their action is non-specific *qua* the infecting bacterium, since the injury to the phagocytic cells will reduce the efficacy of the defence mechanism against all types of invading bacteria. Many of these toxins are thermolabile ; others, perhaps, are thermostable.

(3) *Other toxic bacterial products, bacterial enzymes, fibrinolysins, etc.,* that may act in any of the ways that we have considered in Chapter XLI. In many such instances the effect may be merely additive—the tissues may have to deal simultaneously with a toxæmia and an invasive infection which have no direct connection with one another. In other cases the bacterial toxins, enzymes or hormone-like products may interfere with the defence mechanism of the host in various ways. In any case such action is probably non-specific in the immunological sense, though it is quite likely that a particular bacterial product may favour one type of infection more than another.

To which of these bacterial products, if any, should we attach the label *aggressin* ? There seems little advantage in using it at all ; it describes an effect, not an entity. There is, perhaps, something to be said for the term *aggressive action*, if we can so define it as to make it fill a gap in our terminology. It would seem to be most usefully employed as indicating an action on the cells or body fluids that is not directly injurious, or of which the directly injurious effects are minimal, but which so interferes with the defence mechanism of the host as to favour, specifically or non-specifically, the multiplication of bacteria within the tissues.

Used in this sense, it may be compared with the term *defence rupture*, employed to describe the action of certain chemical agents such as calcium and silica (see pp. 942–944).

REFERENCES

Bail, O. (1900) *Zbl. Bakt.*, **27**, 10, 517 ; (1902–3) *Ibid.*, **33**, 343, 610 ; (1904a) *Ibid.*, **35**, 102 ; (1904b) *Ibid.*, **35**, 247 ; (1904c) *Ibid.*, **37**, 270 ; (1905) *Arch. Hyg.*, **52**, 272.

Bail, O. and Pettersson, A. (1902) *Zbl. Bakt.*, **33**, 756, 759 ; (1903) *Ibid.*, **34**, 167.

Bail, O. and Weil, E. (1906) *Ibid.*, **40**, 371 ; (1906) *Ibid.*, **41**, 536 ; (1911) *Arch. Hyg.*, **73**, 218.

Citron, J. (1906) *Zbl. Bakt.*, **40**, 153 ; (1906) *Ibid.*, **41**, 230 ; (1906) *Z. Hyg. InfektKr.*, **52**, 238.

Cole, R. (1917) *J. exp. Med.*, **26**, 453.

Doerr, R. (1906) *Zbl. Bakt.*, **41**, 497, 593.

Dudgeon, L. S. (1912) *Lancet*, i. 1593, 1671, 1737 ; ii. 1.

E E*

DUDGEON, L. S., PANTON, P. N., and WILSON, H. A. F. (1909–10) *Proc. roy. Soc.*, B, **82**, 406 ; (1910–11) *Ibid.*, **83**, 33.

FELTON, L. D. and BAILEY, G. H. (1926) *J. infect. Dis.*, **38**, 131.

PARK, W. H. and COOPER, G. (1928) *J. Amer. med. Ass.*, **90**, 1349.

ROSENOW, E. C. (1907) *J. infect. Dis.*, **4**, 285.

SAUERBECK, E. (1907) *Z. Hyg. InfektKr.*, **66**, 81.

SIA, R. H. P. (1926) *J. exp. Med.*, **43**, 633.

WARD, H. K. (1932) *Ibid.*, **55**, 511, 519.

WASSERMANN, A. and CITRON, J. (1907) *Zbl. Bakt.*, **43**, 373.

WEIL, E. (1905a) *Arch. Hyg.*, **52**, 412 ; (1905b) *Ibid.*, **54**, 149.

CHAPTER XLVI

THE NATURAL ANTIBODIES: THEIR NATURE, ORIGIN AND BEHAVIOUR

In the preceding chapters we have discussed the part played by antitoxins and antibacterial antibodies in the defence mechanisms of the host. We assumed, in that discussion, that these specific antibodies had been produced in response to artificial immunization or to natural infection. An adequate survey of any host species living under natural conditions will, however, show that many of the individuals composing it contain in their blood serum substances that react, *in vitro* and *in vivo*, in the same way as specifically induced agglutinins, or bactericidins, or antitoxins. The frequency of any particular antibody will be found to vary widely from one animal species to another, and often from group to group within the same species in accordance with age, or with some environmental circumstance.

The problems that concern us in this chapter are : (*a*) How do these natural antibodies arise ? and (*b*) what part do they play in determining differences in natural immunity ?

The Natural Antitoxins

The extensive evidence that we now possess with regard to the origin and significance of the natural antitoxins has, for the most part, been obtained in the study of two human infections, diphtheria and scarlet fever. It would, perhaps, be more natural to consider the relevant data in the chapters dealing with these two diseases ; but it would be impossible to discuss our more general problem without frequent references to these particular instances, and it will therefore be more convenient to set out the evidence here.

That normal human beings may contain diphtheria antitoxin in their blood has long been known (Abel 1894, Wassermann 1895), but no extensive data on the distribution of antitoxin among the population at large were collected until after the description by Römer (1909) of the convenient intradermal technique for the measurement of small amounts of toxin and antitoxin. This was soon followed by the studies of Karasawa and Schick (1910), Schick (1911) and von Groer and Kassowitz (1915, 1917, 1919), which gave us a fairly detailed knowledge of the frequency of the presence of antitoxin among different age groups. The elaboration of the Schick test (Michiels and Schick 1913, Schick 1913), in which the presence of circulating antitoxin is detected by the insensitiveness of the skin to the intradermal injection of a small amount of toxin (the *negative* Schick reaction), has provided a still simpler method of detecting the presence of antitoxin above a certain level (1/100 to 1/30 unit of antitoxin per c.c. of blood).

The proportion of persons who possess diphtheria antitoxin in the circulating blood varies in a striking and characteristic way as we pass from birth through childhood and adolescence to maturity and old age. Table LXVIII sets out the extensive data recorded by Zingher (1923). It will be noted that the percentage of positive reactors is tabulated, *i.e.* the percentage that possess less than 0·01–0·03 units of antitoxin per c.c. of blood.

At about 6 months of age just over half the infants tested react positively to the Schick test. The percentage of positive reactors then rises rapidly and between 8 months and 3 years fluctuates about an average value of approximately 88 per cent. After this period there is a continuous fall, at first rapid, then more gradual ; between the 6th and 7th year the positive reactors number 50·4 per cent., by 12–13 they have fallen to 26·6 per cent., by 20–30 to 11·7 per cent., and at the allotted three-score years and ten to approximately 5 per cent.

TABLE LXVIII

Showing Percentage of Schick-Positive Reactors (*i.e.*, Persons containing less than 0·01 Unit of Diphtheria Antitoxin per c.c. of Blood) in Various Age Groups.

Age Group.	Number Tested.	Per cent. Positive.
6–7 months	53	56·6
7–8 ,, ...	41	63·4
8–9 ,, ...	62	83·8
9–10 ,, ...	58	93·1
10–11 ,, ...	61	87·0
11–12 ,, ...	34	91·1
1–3 years	1,727	83·2
4–6 ,, ...	1,328	58·6
6–7 ,, ...	13,754	50·4
7–8 ,, ...	16,180	43·5
8–9 ,, ...	17,126	36·6
9–10 ,, ...	18,065	32·2
10–11 ,, ...	18,057	29·3
11–12 ,, ...	17,994	28·2
12–13 ,, ...	16,258	26·6
13–14 ,, ...	14,138	23·1
14–15 ,, ...	9,650	19·7
15–16 ,, ...	4,861	17·8
16–17 ,, ...	369	18·4
20–30 ,, ...	1,253	11·7
30–40 ,, ...	1,488	10·6
40–50 ,, ...	1,220	8·2
50–60 ,, ...	920	6·4
60–70 ,, ...	662	5·4
Over 70 ,, ...	181	5·5

The Origin of the Natural Antitoxins.

The most generally accepted view with regard to the succession of immuno-logical events that underlie this observed fluctuation in skin-sensitivity to diph-theria toxin is as follows. At birth the majority of infants are endowed with circulating antitoxin which they have acquired passively from their mothers—mainly by passage of this antibody through the placental membrane, in part perhaps with the colostrum in the early days of suckling. This passive congenital immunity, like all other types depending on the passive acquirement of antibodies, will be relatively short-lived. A careful study of the disappearance of antitoxin from the blood of an infant whose mother was highly immune is recorded by Neill and his colleagues (1932). From infancy onwards the child will be exposed to the risk of infection, increasing from year to year during the earlier part of school life. The result of this exposure will be that some children will contract the typical disease, while others will escape with mild and atypical infections, or with infections so slight that they fall wholly within the bacteriological as opposed to the clinical sphere. Each of these infections will stimulate the production of antitoxin, so that there will result a gradual process of natural immunization, the transitory passive immunity of early infancy being thus replaced, after a period of susceptibility, by a lasting active immunity.

This description, it should be noted, is not based on the results of Schick testing alone ; it is supported by a considerable body of evidence. Observations carried out by Römer's technique, and particularly the extensive series of observations made by von Groer and Kassowitz (1915), have shown clearly that the results of the skin test afford a reliable indication of the frequency of circulating antitoxin in the different age groups. Thus 84 per cent. of infants at birth were found to have diphtheria antitoxin in their blood in a concentration of 1/200 A.U. or over, at ages 9–18 months the proportion had fallen to 32 per cent. and by $2\frac{1}{2}$–$3\frac{1}{2}$ years to 28 per cent. It then rose steeply and by 17–18 years was back at the birth figures of 84 per cent. (See also Jensen 1933.)

There is, moreover, direct evidence that antitoxic immunity to diphtheria in infants results from transference of antitoxin from mother to child. Von Groer and Kassowitz tested the blood of 143 mothers and their new-born children. In 96 per cent. of cases antitoxin was present in both mother and child, or absent in both. It should be noted, however, that in some instances discrepancies have been noted between the result of the skin test in infancy and the presence of antitoxin in the blood, a proportion of Schick-negative infants showing little if any circulating antitoxin (Kellogg 1926-7, Friedberger and Heim 1929, Okell 1932, see also Cooke and Sharma 1932).

The mechanism of passive congenital immunity has been studied experimentally in animals. Ehrlich (1892), for instance, demonstrated the transference of anti-abrin and antiricin from female mice to their young by both the transplacental and mammary routes. It would seem that the relative importance of the two routes of transference depends upon the number of tissue layers that separate the maternal and fœtal circulation in different animal species. Table LXIX, taken from a recent paper by Mason, Dalling and Gordon (1930), sets out this relation in summary form.

TABLE LXIX

THE RELATIVE IMPORTANCE OF THE PLACENTAL AND MAMMARY ROUTES IN THE PASSIVE TRANS-
MISSION OF ANTIBODIES FROM MOTHER TO OFFSPRING. (After Mason, Dalling and Gordon.)

Species.	Layers of Tissue between Maternal and Fœtal Circulation.	Importance of Placental Transmission.	Importance of Transmission by Colostrum.
Pig	5	—	+++
Ruminants	4	—	+++
Carnivores	2	+−	+
Rodents, apes, man . . .	1	+++	+−

Before considering the significance of the findings in the later age groups we may note that the distribution of scarlatinal antitoxin among the different age groups, as judged by the Dick test, appears to be essentially similar to that of diphtheria antitoxin.   Table LXX gives the results obtained by Zingher (1924) in testing 7,700 persons.

TABLE LXX

PERCENTAGE OF POSITIVE DICK REACTIONS IN DIFFERENT AGE GROUPS (ZINGHER).

Age Group.	Number of Persons Tested.	Per cent. Positive.
0–6 months	29	44·8
6–12 ,, ...	52	65·3
1–2 years	233	71·6
2–3 ,, ...	204	64·2
3–4 ,, ...	241	60·5
4–5 ,, ...	264	48·4
5–10 ,, ...	1,955	33·6
10–15 ,, ...	2,965	22·8
15–20 ,, ...	981	16·8
Over 20 ,, ...	776	14·4

It would seem that a negative Dick test during the first few months of life is as likely to be due to an insusceptibility of the infant skin to scarlatinal toxin as to the presence of antitoxin in the blood and tissue fluids.   Cooke and others (1927, 1928) tested 200 mothers and their offspring.   The results confirmed the rarity of positive Dick reactions in new-born infants ; but the mothers of some of the negatively-reacting infants reacted positively, and some of the infants had no detectable antitoxin in their blood.   When tested six weeks to three months later these infants were usually found to have become Dick-positive, while later still they became Dick-negative again.   This reversion to the Dick-negative state was always associated with the appearance of antitoxin in the circulating blood.

Returning to the course of events from infancy onwards, are we justified in accepting the view that the acquirement of antitoxic immunity with increasing age is entirely due to natural active immunization resulting from the reception from without of specific stimuli in the shape of clinical or subclinical infections ? This hypothesis has certainly not been placed beyond dispute.   It has indeed been vigorously disputed, particularly by Hirszfeld (1926) and his colleagues.

Hirszfeld believes that all the normal antibodies should be regarded as " biochemical organs," with which the individual is endowed as the result of his evolutionary history. These " biochemical organs " ripen, or come to maturity, at different periods in his own individual development ; just as the various organs and tissues of the body come to full maturity at different ages.   As we speak of a " morphogenesis " through which each individual passes, so we should think of a " serogenesis " which forms an integral part of normal development.   The time at which any particular antibody normally makes its appearance may be regarded as the period of " immunological crisis " for that particular antibody, and marks the establishment of a " biochemical reflex " on which the production of that antibody depends.   Until the biochemical reflex has become established attempts at immunization with the particular antigen concerned will have little effect.   Hirszfeld does not deny that specific, or non-specific, stimuli from without may play some part in accelerating the production of particular antibodies, or in increasing their concentration ; but he would relegate such influences to a very secondary place.   He would not regard the presence in the blood stream of antibodies acting on a particular bacterium as valid evidence of past or present infection with the bacterium in question.   Above all, he would not accept the view that the antibody-forming apparatus is a *tabula rasa*, on which environmental stimuli can write at will.   It is a complex mechanism with its possible activities fixed and ordered by the phylogeny of each animal species ; and it will therefore respond to the appropriate stimuli and to no others.

It will be simpler to discuss the more general aspects of Hirszfeld's views when we have dealt with the origin of antibacterial sensitizers, and to confine our immediate attention to antitoxic immunity, noting in passing that the problem is in no sense a purely academic one but has important bearings on many problems of diagnosis and prevention.

Perhaps the most significant data, supporting Hirszfeld's contention, are to be found in observations (Hirszfeld, Hirszfeld and Brokman 1924, Hirszfeld and Hirszfeld 1927) which suggest a linkage between the inheritance of the power to produce antitoxin and the power to produce the iso-agglutinins which determine the human blood-groups (see p. 853). From these records Hirszfeld draws the following conclusions. Where both parents are Schick-negative the children will be Schick-negative, except during the first few years of life. Where both parents are Schick-positive the children will be Schick-positive, and will remain so throughout life. Where one parent is Schick-negative and the other Schick-positive the children who belong to the same blood-group as the Schick-negative parent tend to be Schick-negative, those who belong to the same blood-group as the Schick-positive parent tend to be Schick-positive. The validity of these observations has, however, been questioned by Rosling (1928), who examined 50 children over one year of age whose parents belonged to different blood-groups and reacted differently to the Schick test. He found that 23 children gave the same Schick reaction as the parent to whose blood-group they belonged, while 27 reacted differently.

A negative is notoriously difficult to prove ; and we cannot assert that no child has ever developed diphtheria antitoxin except in response to the specific stimulus provided by diphtheria toxin. We can, however, study the frequency of negative and positive Schick reactors in different samples of the population, and correlate our findings with the history of exposure to infection, so far as such a history is obtainable. If we find that free or frequent exposure to infection is consistently associated with a high percentage of negative reactors, while population groups that have been relatively free from any risk of infection show a notably low percentage of negative reactors, we shall be inclined to attach great importance to the part played by environmental stimuli, and to be a little sceptical as to the occurrence of spontaneous antitoxin production. The same holds, of course, in antiscarlatinal immunity and the Dick test.

Zingher (1923) noted that the proportion of Schick-positive children in different New York schools fluctuated very widely (14·62–70·13 per cent.), and that the schools with the highest percentage of positive reactors were those attended by the children of the more fortunate classes, who would have been less likely to have contracted the infection during early life, while a low percentage of positive reactors was found in schools attended by children of the poorer classes, and particularly in orphan asylums. The effect of institutionalism on the frequency of the Dick reaction is similar. Table LXXI gives a series of observations recorded by Dyer and others (1926).

We might hope to obtain data of the same kind by comparing the frequency of Schick-positive reactions in countries where diphtheria is common with their frequency in countries where it is rare ; but the presence or absence of a particular disease among native races, and especially among their children, is less easy to determine than might be supposed, and such evidence as we have is conflicting.

Smits (1926) states that diphtheria is a very rare disease among the natives in the Dutch Indies, and it might therefore be expected that a high proportion of the native population would give a positive Schick reaction. This, he found, was not the case. Among 600 Javanese natives positive results were obtained in only 2 per cent. of the men and 8 per cent. of the women, while 41 per cent. of the children reacted positively. If the statement of the rarity of diphtheria could be accepted, this striking decrease in the proportions of Schick-positives with age would clearly support the view that antitoxin may be elaborated in the absence of any external specific stimulus. Kirschner (1929), however, records a detailed study of the prevalence of diphtheria in the Preanger district of Java during the period 1921–27, and notes the great increase in the number of recorded cases which followed the provision of facilities for bacteriological diagnosis in 1923. He produces evidence that the disease is an important cause of mortality among native children and that a mild form is relatively common. We cannot, therefore, accept the findings with regard to the Schick test as supplying valid evidence in support of Hirszfeld's views.

TABLE LXXI

PERCENTAGE OF DICK-POSITIVE CHILDREN IN CERTAIN SCHOOLS IN WASHINGTON. (After Dyer, Caton and Sockrider.)

School.	Age in Years.	No. Tested.	Per cent. Positive.
Suburban	3–15	75	77·3
Suburban	6–15	59	74·5
33 Rural Schools	4–21	1,147	72·5
33 Rural Schools	6–15	1,039	73·6
Episcopal Home	6–15	47	38·3
Orphan Asylum	3–14	80	32·5
Orphan Asylum	5–15	148	8·1

Smits' observations do not stand alone. Heinbecker and Irvine-Jones (1928) performed Schick tests on 49 Eskimos ; only 12 gave positive reactions, and of these 11 were under 12 years of age. Antitoxin was demonstrated in some of the negative reactors. Yet diphtheria is said to be unknown among the Eskimos.

Kleine and Kroó (1930) tested 101 East African natives by the Schick reaction ; 95 of these were children between the ages of 6 and 15, the remaining 6 were adults. In no case was a positive reaction obtained. The toxin employed was subsequently retested and found to have lost none of its activity. Specimens of serum were obtained from 11 of the natives and tested for antitoxin ; 10 of these contained antitoxin in considerable amount (0·05 A.U. to more than 1 A.U. per c.c.). It is clear therefore that the East African native frequently forms diphtheria antitoxin early in life ; yet, according to Kleine and Kroó, this population is not, so far as is known, exposed to infection with diphtheria. (See also Parr and Avery 1926–27, Parr, Goodale and Kirschner 1930.)

Grasset and his colleagues (1933) record a high frequency of natural diphtheria immunity among South African natives, as judged both by Schick tests and antitoxin titrations. They note, however, the occurrence of diphtheria among the populations concerned, and adopt without question the view that the antitoxin has been produced in response to infection.

In only a few instances do such surveys include a record of the carrier rate of diphtheria bacilli, or of hæmolytic streptococci, among the population concerned. Wells (1933) records a study of the Schick reactions of central and polar Eskimos, in which a proportion of tests were confirmed by antitoxin titrations, and throat swabs were obtained from all persons examined. He reports the frequent presence of bacilli morphologically resembling *C. diphtheriæ*, and states that four strains gave the typical fermentation reactions, and one strain showed some degree of virulence. These findings clearly tend to throw doubt on the significance of the observations recorded by Heinbecker and Irvine-Jones (1928), but it can hardly be said that the presence of toxigenic diphtheria bacilli was established with certainty.

A study by Asbelew and Margo (1932) of the Schick and Dick reactions of 103 of the 250 inhabitants of the Arctic island of Kolgujew is very difficult to reconcile with the *Durchseuchung* hypothesis—the view that antitoxin is produced only or mainly as the result of infection. With the exception of one girl of 8 years all persons examined were Schick-negative, and with the exception of one doubtful case all were Dick-negative. The antitoxin content of the blood was unfortunately not determined. Diphtheria and scarlet fever had never been reported on the island. Swabs were obtained from the throats of 168 persons, and from the noses of 93. No diphtheria bacilli were isolated, and hæmolytic streptococci were only found in four swabs.

There is great need of further studies in which full bacteriological and immunological tests are carried out on isolated or semi-isolated populations.

Although it is not complete, in this particular sense, the recent study by Dungal (1932) of diphtheria in Reykjavik is particularly instructive. From 1926 onwards diphtheria has been very rare, not only in Reykjavik but in Iceland as a whole ; but in the preceding years

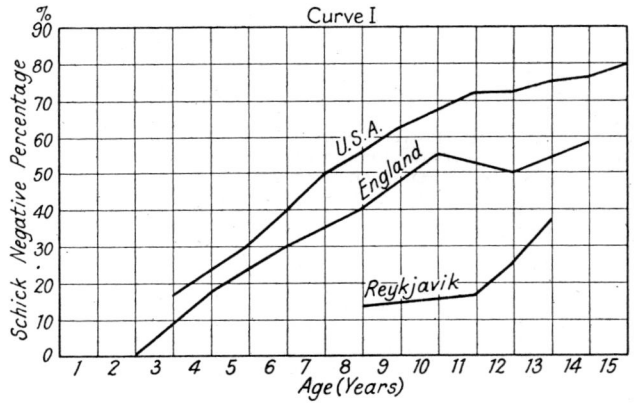

FIG. 225.

there was a moderate prevalence, reaching its peak in Reykjavik in 1921 with an attack rate of 6·9 per 1,000, and subsiding rapidly during the following 5 years. In December 1931 and during the early months of 1932 Dungal tested 814 school children in Reykjavik between the ages of 8 and 14 years. Of these, 81·9 per cent. gave a positive Schick reaction, a figure differing widely from that recorded in cities such as New York or London, where diphtheria is endemic. Still more significant, the curve describing the development of Schick immunity with age was of a very different kind. There was a trivial rise in the proportion of negative reactors from 13·97 per cent. in the 8-year age group to 17·24 per cent. in the 11-year age group ; but there was a sudden rise to 26·36 per cent. among the 12-year-olds, and a further rise to 37·50 per cent. at 13 years. This clearly corresponds with the inclusion of children who had experienced the epidemic prevalence of 1921 and the neighbouring years. Fig. 225, reproduced from Dungal's paper, illustrates these facts very plainly. Such an experience as this is clearly a weighty piece of evidence in favour of the dominant rôle played by latent infection in the stimulation of antitoxin production.

Taking the evidence from isolated, or semi-isolated, populations as a whole it can hardly be said to tell decisively for, or against, the *Durchseuchung* hypothesis. Its balance will depend, for each of us, on the particular records that inspire us with most confidence.

Another very instructive way in which we may obtain evidence with regard to the influence of environment on antitoxin production is to study *the rate of change* from the Schick-positive to the Schick-negative state under different conditions.

A good example is given by Zingher (1923), who records the percentage of Schick-positive children in different age groups among the inmates of a particular institution, dividing them into those who had been resident there for more or less than 3 months. The figures are set out in Table LXXII. The numbers examined in some of the groups were small so that the corresponding percentages must be accepted with caution ; but there can be no doubt as to the significance of the marked difference between the recently admitted inmates and the older inhabitants. The institutional environment had clearly induced a swing from positive to negative reactiveness, with a velocity far higher than could be accounted for by changing age.

Perhaps the most conclusive evidence of the effect of environment and infection is provided by such studies as those of Dudley (1923, 1926), who observed a small semi-isolated community of boys through a period of several years during which it was visited by three waves of diphtheria. By testing the Schick reactions at different periods he was able to demonstrate a wave of antitoxic immunization associated with each wave of disease.

TABLE LXXII

PERCENTAGE OF CHILDREN GIVING POSITIVE SCHICK REACTIONS AMONG THOSE WHO HAD RESIDED IN A CERTAIN INSTITUTION, (*a*) FOR MORE THAN 3 MONTHS, AND (*b*) FOR LESS THAN 3 MONTHS, ACCORDING TO AGE GROUP. (After Zingher.)

Age Group.	Over 3 Months.	Under 3 Months.
4–5 years	23·8	66·6
5–6 ,, ...	27·3	33·3
6–7 ,, ...	17·0	43·0
7–8 ,, ...	13·9	43·7
8–9 ,, ...	4·6	33·3
9–10 ,, ...	3·8	9·0
10–11 ,, ...	1·6	33·3
11–12 ,, ...	5·0	25·0

There is no doubt at all that the frequency of Schick and Dick reactors in any population or community in which diphtheria and scarlet fever are prevalent is determined very largely by the degree of exposure to infection ; and active immunization certainly plays a large part in natural antitoxin production under such conditions. It seems unlikely that antitoxin would be produced in the entire absence of such specific stimuli ; but we are not in a position to deny this possibility.

It is of some interest to note that numerous observers have recorded the presence of diphtheria antitoxin in the blood of normal horses. Sordelli (1920) found antitoxin in the blood of horses under 9 months old, presumably resulting from passive congenital immunization. No horse between 1 and 5 years of age possessed antitoxin, but the blood of all horses over 10 years of age contained detectable amounts. Glenny (1925) found 0·1 A.U. or more per c.c. in 70 per cent. of horses over 7 years of age tested between the years 1907 and 1915, but in only 35 per cent. of those tested after 1917. He suggests that this difference may be due to the greatly lessened concentration of horses in towns during the later period, and a resulting diminution in the risk of infection. A few well-documented instances are on record showing that horses are liable to natural infection with diphtheria bacilli. In most cases the organisms have been isolated from superficial wounds (Minett 1922, Kliewe and Westhues 1925, Parish and Okell 1926) ; only in a few instances have they been demonstrated in the throat (Cobbett 1899, Ramon 1925, Zurukzoglu and Mündel 1935a, b).   We have, however, no adequate evidence with regard to the frequency of such infections, so that we cannot tell whether the frequency of antitoxin in the blood, as recorded by Glenny, can reasonably be attributed to external stimuli of this kind.

The Immunological Significance of the Natural Antitoxins.

Whatever the mechanism of their production, there is no doubt that the natural antitoxins confer on their possessors a significant degree of immunity.   Direct experimental evidence is, of necessity, scanty ; but so far as it goes it is demonstrative.

Guthrie, Marshall and Moss (1921) collected 8 volunteers and determined their reaction to the Schick test ; 4 reacted positively and 4 negatively (including 2 pseudo-reactions). The throat of each of these 8 volunteers was swabbed with a virulent culture of the diphtheria bacillus.   The four positive reactors developed clinical diphtheria ; the 4 negative reactors, possessing natural antitoxin at or above the Schick-immune level, developed no illness, though 3 of them became carriers.

The main body of evidence on which we rely in concluding that natural antitoxin confers natural immunity has, however, been collected during the course of extensive clinical and epidemiological studies on diphtheria and scarlet fever (see Chapters LVIII and LXIII).   There is no doubt that a person whose blood contains antitoxin at or above the Schick-immunity level is very unlikely to contract diphtheria, even when exposed to serious risk of infection.   If he does so, the attack will almost always be of a mild and clinically atypical type.   The nature of the evidence that associates natural antitoxic immunity with effective resistance to scarlatinal infection is of the same general kind as in the case of diphtheria.

The Natural Antibacterial Antibodies

It has long been known that there are naturally occurring agglutinins, bactericidins and other sensitizing antibodies, just as there are naturally occurring antitoxins ; but the ground that has been surveyed in the two cases is rather different. We have seen that our knowledge of the distribution and mode of origin of the natural antitoxins is, in the main, derived from the study of diphtheria and scarlet fever in man.   Our knowledge of the distribution and mode of origin of the antibacterial sensitizers is, in the main, derived from studies on their occurrence in different species of animals.

One of the earliest studies of this kind was recorded by Bürgi (1907).   He tested sera from the dog, guinea-pig, rabbit, goose, hen, sheep, goat, horse, ox and man against suspensions of various bacteria, including *V. choleræ*, *Bact. typhosum*, *Bact. coli*, *Past. aviseptica*, *Staph. aureus* and *Proteus vulgaris*, and noted well-marked agglutination in many instances, often to a relatively high titre.   He found, however, that the various sera tended to be arranged in very much the same order of activity, against whichever species of organism they were tested ; and, in further experiments, that this order was in general maintained when the sera were tested for their ability to flocculate suspensions of mastic.

Gibson (1930) carried out similar experiments with sera from the ox, rabbit, guineapig, horse, sheep, pig, rat, cat and man, tested against *Proteus* X19, *Ps. pyocyanea*, *Bact. typhosum*, *Bact. paratyphosum A*, *Bact. paratyphosum B*, *Bact. enteritidis*, *Bact. flexneri*, *Bact. shigæ*, *Proteus morgani*, *Bact. friedländeri*, several strains of *Bact. coli* and *V. choleræ*.   He found, as Bürgi had done, that the sera tested tended to fall in a definite order with regard to their power of agglutinating a wide variety of bacteria.   Ox sera were the most active ; pig and horse sera were somewhat less active ; sheep serum was next in order ; while human, cat, rabbit and guinea-pig sera, in that succession, showed progressively weaker effects. Rat serum was the weakest of all. Similarly the different bacterial species showed a definite order of sensitivity to agglutination. *Bact. flexneri, Bact. friedländeri* and *Ps. pyocyanea* were the most sensitive, while certain strains of *Bact. coli* were least sensitive. By absorption experiments, Gibson was able to show that this agglutination was dependent on the presence of specific antibodies ; but since any one organism, in addition to removing completely the specific agglutinin acting on itself, might reduce the titre of the serum for other organisms, and a similar general reduction in titre might be produced by adsorption with some non-specific agent such as charcoal, he concluded that another non-specific serum constituent was concerned in the full effect obtained with the untreated sera. In later experiments (Gibson 1932), in which the H and O antigens and antibodies were differentiated, he obtained results suggesting that the specificity was due mainly to the H agglutinins, while the O agglutinins for any one bacterium might be greatly reduced by absorption with an antigenically unrelated organism.

Timmerman (1930) tested sera from the guinea-pig, rabbit, hare, goat, sheep, buffalo and man against *Bact. typhosum* and was able to demonstrate the presence of both somatic (O) and flagellar (H) agglutinins in one or more specimens of serum from each species, except in the case of the guinea-pig, in which 2 of 20 animals showed O but no H agglutinins.

Lovell (1932) tested the sera of 202 normal swine, 23 cattle, 46 sheep and 20 horses for flagellar agglutinins against 7 different types of Salmonella bacilli. Normal agglutinins against one or more of these types were present in 190 swine, 13 cattle, 36 sheep and 18 horses, usually at relatively low titre. Absorption experiments indicated that these agglutinins were in most cases specific. In further studies (Lovell 1934) he tested the sera of 263 normal swine, 163 cattle, 71 sheep, 40 horses and 40 rabbits for H and O agglutinins against *Bact. typhi-murium, Bact. newport, Bact. choleræ-suis* and *Bact. enteritidis*. The great majority of the pig, cattle, sheep and horse sera showed the presence of flagellar agglutinins for some, or all, of these species. A rather smaller, and more variable, proportion showed the presence of somatic agglutinins. As in the earlier study, absorption tests gave clear indication of specificity, though in some instances there were minor degrees of cross-absorption. The rabbit sera seldom showed the presence either of flagellar or somatic agglutinins. Mackie and Finkelstein (1930, 1931, 1932) (see also Finkelstein 1933) have tested the serum of a number of normal animals, such as the ox, sheep, horse, pig, rabbit, rat, cat, guinea-pig, pigeon and man, against a variety of bacteria, including *V. choleræ, Bact. typhosum* and other members of the Salmonella group, dysentery bacilli, proteus bacilli, influenza bacilli, *Br. abortus, Br. melitensis*, meningococci and so on. They have also (Mackie *et al.* 1932) tested the bactericidal action of whole blood and of serum-leucocyte mixtures. They were able to demonstrate complement fixation and bactericidal action in a large number of cases, and to show that the bactericidal effect depended on the joint action of complement and a heat-stable factor that could be removed by absorption. This absorption was specific, in the sense that it was often possible to demonstrate the removal of bactericidal power against the absorbing organism while the absorbed serum was still bactericidal for other bacteria.

Gordon and Carter (1932) record results which lead them to a different conclusion. Testing rabbit and guinea-pig sera against cholera vibrios, typhoid and other Salmonella bacilli, and dysentery bacilli, they were able to demonstrate a well-marked bactericidal action that depended on the interaction of complement and some heat-stable factor; but they failed to demonstrate any specific absorption of the latter. Their results suggested that the bactericidal activity against the less sensitive organisms could be removed by absorption with many different bacteria, leaving in each case an effective residuum of bactericidal action against those organisms, such as the cholera vibrio and the dysentery bacillus that are particularly sensitive to serum lysis.

To summarize these findings : the serum of most normal animals contains substances that react with bacteria in the test tube giving agglutination, complement fixation and bacteriolysis (bactericidal action). The sera of some animals, such as pigs and cattle, seem to react with a wider variety of bacteria than do the sera of other animals, such as the rabbit and guinea-pig. Different species of bacteria also vary in their sensitiveness to normal sera. Some species are agglutinated, or lysed, by normal serum from many different animals, others are sensitive only to a few. The specificity of the flagellar agglutinins in normal sera seems to have been clearly established, and the evidence is definitely in favour of the specificity of some, at least, of the agglutinins acting on the antigens at the surface of the bacterial cells. These agglutinins, flagellar and somatic, are, it should be noted, usually present to low titre only (1 : 5–1 : 40 or thereabouts). The evidence with regard to the specificity of the bactericidal antibodies is more conflicting ; but results indicating specificity have been recorded, and if somatic agglutinins are present we should expect them to exert a bactericidal action in the presence of complement.

In view of the divergence of evidence and opinion referred to above, it may be well to discuss this question of specificity a little more fully. The conclusion that the natural antibacterial sensitizers are specific does not, of course, imply any particular hypothesis as to their mode of origin ; it assumes only that they unite with certain bacteria because of a chemical affinity conferred by certain specific combining groups.

We need not, therefore, assume that the natural antibodies are in all cases identical with those induced by active immunization. A " natural " antibody and an " immune " antibody, both acting on the same bacterium, must each possess chemical groupings with a specific affinity for groupings borne by the bacterium ; but, if the natural antibody has arisen in some way other than in response to infection with the actual bacterium concerned, it is quite possible that the chemical correspondence between its active groupings and those on the bacterial surface will be less close than in the case of an antibody produced in response to infection or artificial immunization. There are certain experimental findings that are in accord with such a possibility. It is, for instance, a very general experience that some, at least, of the " natural " antibodies require, for their removal from a serum, an absorbing dose of bacteria very much larger than that required for the removal of the same amount of an " immune " antibody.

If we adopted this view we should expect that the antibacterial antibodies demonstrable in any random sample of a human or animal population would be of two kinds, those arising as the result of infection with the bacterium on which they act, and those arising in some other way. This brings us directly to the question of their origin under natural conditions.

The Origin of the Natural Antibacterial Antibodies.

It is, of course, well established that certain kinds of " natural antibodies " are produced in the absence of any environmental stimulus, and in accordance with definite genetic laws.

The best example is perhaps provided by the isohæmagglutinins that divide mankind into different blood-groups.

Landsteiner (1901) distinguished the principal blood-groups into which the human race may be divided, and showed that this grouping depends, in the main, on the distribution, of two different antigenic constituents, which may be present together, or

separately, or may both be absent. There are two corresponding antibodies, and these
are so distributed that neither antibody is present in the blood of an individual whose
red cells contain the corresponding antigen. By determining the antigens present in any
sample of blood it is therefore possible to assign it to its correct group. It happens that
two classifications of the four main blood-groups are in common use in different countries,
that of Jansky (1908) and that of Moss (1910). The fact that the numbering differs, so
that Group I of Jansky corresponds to Group IV of Moss, has led to much confusion. For
our present purpose we may adopt the terminology suggested by von Dungern and Hirszfeld
(1910–11), in which the antigens are represented by capital letters, the antibodies by Greek
letters, and the absence of both antigens or of both antibodies by the cipher O. The
groups may then be conveniently named by their antigenic constituents, a method which
can cause no confusion. The constituent factors of the four groups can then be set out
as follows :

Antigens	.	.	.	.	O	A	B	AB
Antibodies	.	.	.	.	$\alpha\beta$	β	α	O

The serum of a Group O blood will agglutinate the corpuscles of Groups A, B and AB,
for it contains the antibodies α and β ; but the corpuscles of this group will not be agglutinated by the serum of any group, since they contain neither of the antigens A and B. A
person belonging to this group is a " universal donor " ; his blood can be transferred
with safety to any recipient, but he can only receive with safety the blood of a person
belonging to the same group as himself. The interactions of the other groups will be
obvious, and it will be noted that a member of Group A can receive blood from Groups
O and A, a member of Group B from Groups O and B, while a member of Group AB can
receive blood from any group, since his serum contains no antibodies, but can donate
blood only to a member of his own group.

There are marked racial differences in the relative frequency of the different groups.
Thus among Europeans Group A is far commoner than Group B, while among Asiatics,
and particularly among the Indians, the reverse is the case. There is evidence (von
Dungern and Hirszfeld 1910a, b, Hirszfeld 1926) that the antigenic constituents A and B
are inherited along Mendelian lines, the presence of each factor being dominant to its
absence.

In addition to these isoagglutinins and isolysins—antibodies acting on the
corpuscles of other individuals within the same species—the sera of all animal
species that have been examined have been found to contain antibodies acting
on the red cells of certain other animal species. The kind, number and activity of
these antibodies vary from one species to another in the same way as the bacterial
sensitizers described earlier in this chapter. The pioneer researches of Ehrlich and
Morgenroth (1899, 1900a, b) established quite clearly, by means of absorption tests,
the specificity of the antibodies concerned.

In this connection and because it has a direct bearing on the problem with which
we are mainly concerned—the origin and nature of the natural antibacterial sensitizers
—brief reference must be made to an antigen-antibody reaction of a curious and interesting
kind which was first described by Forssman (1911), who observed that the injection into
rabbits of organs obtained from the guinea-pig, or from certain other animals, led to the
production of hæmolysin for sheep's red corpuscles. These observations have been confirmed and extended by many subsequent workers (see Taniguchi 1919–20, 1921, 1922,
Browning 1931) ; and it is now known that the so-called *heterophile* or *Forssman* antigen,
which is responsible for this reaction, is widely distributed among different animal species, and
in a curiously random fashion. Thus the organs of the guinea-pig, horse, dog, cat, mouse,
fowl and tortoise stimulate the production of heterophile antibody when injected into the

rabbit, while the organs of man, rabbit, ox, sheep, rat, goose, pigeon, eel and frog do not. The organs and tissues that have been examined with regard to the presence or absence of heterophile antigen include kidney, liver, lung, adrenal, testicle, heart, skeletal muscles, lymph glands and serum, though not all of these have been tested in the case of each of the species enumerated above. It is noteworthy that the organs of the sheep, freed of all red corpuscles, do not stimulate the production of heterophile antibody ; and it appears to be a general rule that those species that contain heterophile antigen in their red corpuscles do not contain it in their tissues, at least in the full and effective antigenic form.

It soon became clear, from absorption experiments of the usual type, that the hæmolysin produced by the rabbit in response to the injection of guinea-pig's kidney was not identical with that produced in response to injection with sheep's corpuscles. The hæmolytic serum in the latter case contains a mixture of hæmolysins, only one of which corresponds to the heterophile antigen.

It appears (Iwai 1917, Georgi 1919, Taniguchi 1921) that the specific component (hapten) of the heterophile antigen is contained in the lipoid constituents of the tissues, especially in those which are soluble in alcohol and ether and insoluble in acetone—the so-called " lecithin fraction." The heterophile antibody, in addition to acting as a hæmolysin for sheep's red cells, forms a precipitate and fixes complement when mixed with an emulsion of the lecithin fraction derived from a tissue containing the heterophile antigen. The lipoid extract does not stimulate the formation of the heterophile antibody when injected into the rabbit, but when mixed with a suitable foreign protein it regains its full antigenic property (Landsteiner and Simms 1923). It should be noted that only animals of the rabbit type—those not containing heterophile antigen in their tissues—are capable of producing heterophile antibody in response to the injection of guinea-pig's kidney or other suitable tissue. It is also of particular interest from our present point of view that certain normal antibodies are of the heterophile type—for instance, the natural hæmolysin for sheep's red cells that is found in the serum of rabbit and man (Friedemann 1917).

It is clear therefore that, during the normal course of its development, any animal will produce a number of " natural antibodies " which we may assume to be serum proteins, probably serum globulins, differentiated from one another by possessing different specific combining groups. It would not be in any way surprising if certain of these combining groups happened to have a chemical affinity for the combining groups of certain bacterial antigens. It has indeed already been noted that many bacteria contain an antigenic component that is immunologically identical with, or closely similar to, Forssman's heterophile antigen (see p. 194).

We may note that normal hæmolysins and hæmagglutinins are absent from the blood of very young animals, and are developed during the process of normal growth (Hirszfeld 1926, Friedberger, Bock and Fürstenheim 1929). The same is apparently true of the natural antibacterial agglutinins (Kraus and Low 1899, Lüdke 1905, Braun 1909, Gibson 1930 ; see also Mackie and Finkelstein 1928, 1930). Observations made by Bailey (1923) add a point of considerable significance. In studying the development of the normal hæmagglutinins of the fowl, he noted their absence in the young chick and their appearance during the normal process of growth, but he also found that chickens failed to respond to immunization with foreign red cells until they had spontaneously developed some agglutinating capacity. The inability of the antibody-forming apparatus to respond effectively to an antigenic stimulus during the earliest period of life would seem to be a general rule. Thus, Blum (1932) and others have noted the failure of young infants to produce diphtheria antitoxin in response to the injection of toxoid.

In Chapter VI we have given reasons for believing that antibodies are specialized serum globulins. It is therefore of particular interest to find that the serum of new-born animals is markedly deficient in globulin, particularly in euglobulin, that this deficiency is temporarily made good in certain species by the transfer of globulin from mother to young in the colostrum, and that the capacity for producing euglobulin from its own tissues is developed by the young animal at a later stage of growth (Toyama 1919, Howe 1922, Lewis and Wells 1922). The appearance of the natural antibodies and the increase in serum globulin are closely correlated with one another (see Famulener 1912). Orcutt and Howe (1922) have observed the passage of natural agglutinins for *Br. abortus* from a cow to her calf in the globulins of the colostrum ; and Timmerman (1931) has demonstrated the presence of agglutinins for the typhoid bacillus in human colostrum during the first 5 days of suckling.

The acceptance of the view that some of the natural antibodies that act on bacteria may arise during the normal production of serum proteins, simply because of an accidental chemical affinity between certain of these proteins and certain bacterial antigens, does not involve the assumption that this is the usual method of production. It is much more likely that environmental stimuli play an important part. The most obvious of such stimuli is that provided by natural infection with the bacteria on which the natural antibodies are found to act. How does this conception of their origin accord with the available evidence ?

If we turn back to the observations of Bürgi, of Gibson, and of Lovell on normal agglutinins we seem to be met with almost insuperable difficulties. Can we really believe that such animals as the ox and the pig are infected during their relatively short lives with such a variety of organisms as *Proteus* X19, *Bact. typhosum*, *Bact. paratyphosum A*, *Bact. paratyphosum B*, *Bact. enteritidis*, *Bact. flexneri*, *Bact. shigæ*, *V. choleræ* and, doubtless, a host of other pathogenic organisms that are only absent from the list because they have not been tested ? It is proverbially difficult to prove a negative ; and it would be rash to assert that even so extensive an infection-experience as this is impossible. Perhaps the best answer is that it seems altogether unlikely—so unlikely that any other alternative hypothesis would be welcome. If we confine ourselves to the Salmonella group, for instance, we find (Lovell 1932, 1934) that agglutinins for a variety of the flagellar and somatic antigenic components of the members of this group may be demonstrated in the blood of a high percentage of young swine, and that these agglutinins can, in the majority of cases, be specifically absorbed ; yet cultures of the fæces and organs of the animals from which the specimens of blood were obtained have in no instance yielded a growth of the corresponding organisms. Moreover the cultural results recorded by other observers are almost all of the same negative kind, at least in those instances in which the strains isolated were adequately identified.

We have noted that antibodies of this type often show certain peculiarities. They tend to be present in low titre, and they tend to be very difficult to remove by absorption with the bacteria on which they act. So far as these particular antibodies are concerned the evidence appears to us to be definitely against the view that they are produced in response to natural infection.

This conclusion does not, however, apply to natural antibodies in general. Though the greater part of the evidence bearing on this problem has been obtained by studies of the kind outlined above, some of it has emerged from surveys of the normal agglutinins present in the sera of human groups, living under different environmental conditions. It has sometimes been possible to correlate the results of such surveys with the associated epidemiological records, as in the studies on the distribution of diphtheria, or scarlatinal antitoxin referred to above ; and it has been shown quite clearly that the frequency of natural agglutinins for a particular bacterium, among a random sample of the human population living in a particular locality, is closely associated with the frequency of infections due to that bacterium in that locality. Examples are provided in the epidemiology of enteric infection (Chapter LXVI), or of undulant fever (Chapter LXXII).

A few surveys of a similar kind have been made in laboratory animals. Thus Bailey (1927) examined 81 rabbits taken from a laboratory stock among which cases of snuffles were occurring, due to infection with *Pasteurella lepiseptica*. Three rabbits were suffering from acute snuffles ; cultures from the nose gave a copious growth of *Past. lepiseptica*, and agglutinins and complement-fixing antibodies were demonstrated in the blood stream. Nine had chronic snuffles ; all of these showed the presence of *Past. lepiseptica* in the nares and agglutinins and complement-fixing antibodies in the serum. Three had suppurative lesions from which *Past. lepiseptica* was isolated ; agglutinins and complement-fixing antibodies were demonstrated in their serum. Six showed no clinical symptoms of infection, but *Past. lepiseptica* was isolated from the nares ; in all six agglutinins and complement-fixing antibodies were found. Ten showed no symptom of infection and cultures from the nares yielded no *Past. lepiseptica* ; in none of these could agglutinins or complement-fixing antibodies be demonstrated. Six rabbits were then taken, one of which yielded a scanty growth of *Past. lepiseptica* and showed the presence of complement-fixing antibodies to low titre, while the other five showed no evidence of infection. All six were infected with *Past. lepiseptica* by nasal instillation. All six became carriers without any symptoms of snuffles. The rabbit which was already infected showed a rise in titre of complement-fixing antibodies, and these antibodies appeared in each of the other five rabbits during the course of the succeeding three months.

There is then no doubt that the members of a herd, or population, submitted to a constant or recurrent risk of infection with a particular bacterium will tend to form antibodies acting on that particular organism in response to the stimuli provided by infection of varying severity ; and the natural working of this mechanism will certainly play a large part in determining the frequency distribution of the antibodies concerned.

Do these two modes of origin—the formation of serum globulins with an accidental affinity for certain bacterial antigens, and the production of specific antibodies in response to natural infection—exhaust the possibilities ? Our present knowledge of the factors determining antigen-antibody reactions lends no support to such a view. Antigenic specificity depends, as we have seen, on chemical structure. Its biological or, in the narrower sense, its bacteriological significance is determined simply by the actual distribution of the specific chemical groupings—the haptens —among existing species of micro-organisms. Our knowledge of this distribution is scanty in the extreme. We know something of the detailed antigenic structure of certain groups of closely related bacteria, but almost nothing as regards the possible sharing of antigenic components by species that show no other obvious relationship. What little we do know suggests that such a possibility cannot be ignored (see p. 194).

We must, then, accept the possibility that the antibodies which we detect in the blood of a high proportion of animals of a particular species, and which act specifically on bacteria A, B and C, may have been produced in response to infection with some other organisms, X, Y and Z. Lovell (1934) explored this possibility in the case of the natural agglutinins of young swine, and found in two instances that coliform bacilli isolated from the mesenteric glands induced, on injection into rabbits, the formation of agglutinins acting on certain bacilli of the Salmonella group. Though these observations can, at the moment, be regarded as no more than suggestive, they indicate the desirability of further work along similar lines. Nor should we limit the possibilities to actual infection with an unrelated bacterium possessing a common antigenic grouping. In defining an antigen we excluded administration by the digestive tract when demanding that it should give rise to the production of antibodies on injection into a suitable animal, because the antigen might be chemically altered while in the digestive tract, and we should in any case have no assurance that it would pass from the intestine into the tissues in an active form. But recent studies on oral immunization have made it clear that the antigenic components of dead bacterial cells do, in some cases at least, pass from the intestines to the tissues and stimulate antibody formation. It is at least possible that among the unlimited variety of other antigenic materials which gain access to the intestinal tract, some, under favourable conditions, may behave in the same way. Were this the case, there would be little cause for surprise if some few of the multiplicity of reactive groupings produced by an antibody-forming apparatus subjected to an infinite succession of widely varied stimuli should happen to show affinities to the antigenic groupings of certain species of bacteria. Nor need we limit the possibilities to the intestinal tract. There is good evidence that inhalation of antigenic material may result in an effective antibody response ; and under suitable conditions similar material may gain access to the tissues through the skin.

We must then accept the view that the naturally occurring antibacterial sensitizers, and perhaps also the natural antitoxins, may owe their origin to any one of four mechanisms : actual infection with the corresponding bacterium ; infection with some other organism that shares a common antigenic component ; the entrance to the tissues *via* the intestinal tract, or possibly by other routes, of non-living antigenic material capable of stimulating the production of an antibody with the active group in question ; or the formation of such antibodies as a by-product in the normal functioning of the antibody-forming apparatus altogether apart from any specific external stimulus.

The Immunological Significance of the Natural Antibacterial Antibodies.

Do naturally occurring antibodies of the type considered above confer a relative immunity to the risk of natural infection, analogous to that conferred by the natural antitoxins ? The evidence available does not allow of any but the most tentative answer. So far as it goes it suggests that there is sometimes a relation between the presence in the blood of a particular antibacterial sensitizer and a relatively high resistance to the corresponding bacterium ; but that this relation is not a generalized one, and that many antibodies of this type are quite without effect on the resistance of the animal possessing them. This is not surprising. We have given reasons for believing that the natural antibacterial sensitizers acting on a single bacterium—even on the surfaces of a single type of bacterial cell—may be of several different kinds, and it seems not unlikely that some of these may have a protective value while others have not.

Kyes (1916) showed that, when virulent pneumococci were inoculated into the naturally immune pigeon, the organisms were rapidly withdrawn from the blood stream and phagocytosed by macrophages in the liver and spleen. Heist, Solis-Cohen and Solis-Cohen (1918) found that the whole blood of the pigeon was actively bactericidal for the pneumococcus while the whole blood of the susceptible mouse or rabbit was not. The serum of the pigeon was not bactericidal alone, indicating that the killing power depended on the leucocytes as well as on the constituents of the serum. That serum constituents are in fact concerned, and that among these constituents are specific antibodies, would seem to follow from the observations of Bull and McKee (1921), who studied the passive transfer of immunity from the normally resistant chicken to the normally susceptible mouse. They found that chicken serum would protect mice against virulent pneumococci of Types I, II and III ; and that absorption of the chicken serum with Type I pneumococci removed its protective power against Type I but not against Type II. Similarly absorption with Type II removed the protective power against this type, leaving the protective power against Type I.

Robertson and Sia (1924) found a marked inhibition of the growth of pneumococci in serum-leucocyte mixtures from the resistant cat or dog, but no such inhibition in similar mixtures from the susceptible rabbit or guinea-pig. More recently they have reported experiments which suggest that this bactericidal action is due to sensitization followed by phagocytosis (Robertson and Sia 1927). They sensitized pneumococci by prolonged contact with large amounts of the serum under test, and then determined the degree of phagocytosis by the leucocytes of various resistant and susceptible animals. They found that sensitization with serum from the resistant cat, sheep, pig and horse rendered the pneumococci susceptible to phagocytosis by the leucocytes of these animals, or by those of the susceptible rabbit or guinea-pig ; while treatment with serum from such susceptible species as the rabbit, guinea-pig or man, did not sensitize the pneumococci for the leucocytes of these animals, or for those from the resistant cat, sheep, pig or dog.

The actual number of sera from each species examined by Robertson and Sia was not large, and it would seem that their original conclusions require some modification, at least in regard to man. Thus, Robertson and Cornwell (1930), using serum-leucocyte mixtures, studied the presence of antibodies for various types of pneumococci in the serum of normal persons. All the sera examined showed the presence of antibodies for one or more of the serological types employed, but any given serum might be inactive against some types though active against others. It would seem, moreover, that the presence of antibodies against a particular type does not afford complete protection against infection with that type, since Robertson and others (1930) found that the serum of patients in the first 48 hours of an attack of lobar pneumonia often contained sensitizing antibodies for the infecting type of pneumococcus.

Some of the findings recorded in earlier sections with regard to the frequency distribution of various normal agglutinins make it very difficult to believe that they have any protective value. Thus somatic agglutinins for various organisms of the Salmonella group are frequently present in the blood of swine, cattle and sheep ; but these species are relatively susceptible to infection with certain of these organisms (Lovell 1934). A particularly striking example of this kind of anomaly is afforded by the observation that the great majority of normal horse sera agglutinate the glanders bacillus to high titre, though glanders is bacteriologically a disease of equines (see Wilson 1934).

SUMMARY

(1) Antibodies of various kinds—antitoxins, agglutinins, bactericidal antibodies and so on—are frequently found in the serum of normal men and animals. The origin of these naturally occurring antibodies is still a matter in dispute ; but it seems possible that they may arise in several different ways.

(2) The new-born animal, when born of a naturally immune mother, is endowed with a congenital passive immunity, due to transference of specific antibodies from the maternal blood through the placenta, or by way of the colostrum during

the early days of suckling. This, like other types of passive immunity, is of relatively short duration.

(3) Young animals from whose blood these congenitally acquired antibodies have disappeared and young animals in whom they are not present at birth often develop them with advancing years.

(4) There are reasons for believing that this production of antibodies is dependent on the activity of an antibody-forming apparatus that is imperfectly developed at birth, but reaches functional maturity at a relatively early period of life.

(5) It is certain that this apparatus, apart from any external stimuli, will form various antibodies—such as the normal hæmagglutinins or hæmolysins—which distinguish one animal species from another. It is possible that certain of the antibodies acting on bacteria or their products may be formed in the same way, as the result of a normal serogenesis determined by purely genetic factors.

(6) The more commonly accepted view is that these antibodies arise as the result of the response of the antibody-forming apparatus to external environmental stimuli, and that such stimuli usually consist of overt or latent infections with the bacterium in question. This view has been upheld particularly in relation to natural antitoxic immunity against diphtheria and scarlet fever, and in this regard there can be little doubt that it is correct.

(7) In the case of specific antibacterial immunity there are greater difficulties in accepting this hypothesis in its entirety. Samples of sera collected from a given animal species may contain antibodies active against an enormous number of different bacteria, and it seems difficult to believe that a single animal can have been infected with so many different organisms, some of which are not known to be natural parasites of the species to which it belongs. There are, however, good reasons for believing that some at least of the agglutinins or other antibodies found in normal men or animals have been produced in response to infection, overt or latent.

(8) It is possible that other forms of external stimuli may be concerned, such as (a) infection with a different species of bacterium, which shares a common antigenic factor with the bacterium with which the antibody in question has been shown to act, or (b) the absorption from the intestinal canal or through the lungs or skin of some antigenic material containing a similar reactive chemical group.

(9) The presence of natural antitoxin in the circulating blood usually confers an effective protection against clinical infection, at least in the case of diphtheria and scarlet fever.

(10) The relation between the presence of antibacterial sensitizers and resistance to infection with the corresponding bacteria is very uncertain. It seems probable that some of these natural antibodies exert a protective effect, while others do not.

REFERENCES

ABEL, R. (1894) *Dtsch. med. Wschr.*, **20**, 899, 936.
ASBELEW, W. N. and MARGO, A. A. (1932) *Zbl. Bakt.*, **126**, 212.
BAILEY, C. E. (1923) *Amer. J. Hyg.*, **3**, 370.
BAILEY, G. H. (1927) *Amer. J. Hyg.*, **7**, 370.
BLUM, J. (1932) *Med. Offr*, **47**, 245.
BRAUN, H. (1909) *Arch. Hyg.*, **68**, 116.
BROWNING, C. (1931) " System of Bacteriology." *Med. Res. Coun. Lond.*, **6**, 501.
BULL, C. G. and McKEE, C. M. (1921) *Amer. J. Hyg.*, **1**, 284.
BÜRGI, E. (1907) *Arch. Hyg.*, **62**, 239.

COBBETT, L. (1899) *Lancet*, ii. 332.
COOKE, J. V., BRINKERHOFF, N., and WOODS, P. E. (1928) *Amer. J. Dis. Child.*, **35**, 772.
COOKE, J. V., ERMATINGER, L., and BRINKERHOFF, N. (1928) *Amer. J. Dis. Child.*, **35**, 762.
COOKE, J. V., KEITH, H. R., and ERMATINGER, L. (1927) *Amer. J. Dis. Child.*, **34**, 969.
COOKE, J. V. and SHARMA, B. M. (1932) *Amer. J. Dis. Child.*, **44**, 40.
DUDLEY, S. F. (1923) *Spec. Rep. Ser. med. Res. Coun., Lond.*, No. 75 ; (1926) *Ibid.*, No. 111.
DUNGAL, N. (1932) *Brit. J. exp. Path.*, **13**, 360.
DUNGERN, F. VON, and HIRSZFELD, L. (1910a) *Z. ImmunForsch.*, **4**, 531 ; (1910b) *Ibid.*, **6**, 284 ; (1911) *Ibid.*, **8**, 526.
DYER, R. E., CATON, W. P., and SOCKRIDER, B. T. (1926) *Publ. Hlth Rep., Wash.*, **41**, 1159.
EHRLICH, P. (1892) *Z. Hyg. InfektKr.*, **12**, 183.
EHRLICH, P. and MORGENROTH, J. (1899) *Berl. klin. Wschr.*, **36**, 6, 481 ; (1900a) *Ibid.*, **37**, 453 ; (1900b) *Ibid.*, **37**, 681.
FAMULENER, L. W. (1912) *J. infect. Dis.*, **10**, 332.
FINKELSTEIN, M. H. (1933) *J. Path. Bact.*, **37**, 359.
FORSSMAN, J. (1911) *Biochem. Z.*, **37**, 78.
FRIEDBERGER, E., BOCK, G., and FÜRSTENHEIM, A. (1929) *Z. ImmunForsch.*, **64**, 294.
FRIEDBERGER, E. and HEIM, FR. (1929) *Dtsch. med. Wschr.*, **55**, 132.
FRIEDEMANN, U. (1917) *Biochem. Z.*, **80**, 333.
GEORGI, W. (1919) *Arb. Inst. exp. Ther., Frankfurt*, **9**, 33.
GIBSON, H. J. (1930) *J. Hyg., Camb.*, **30**, 337 ; (1932) *J. Immunol.*, **22**, 211.
GLENNY, A. T. (1925) *J. Hyg., Camb.*, **24**, 301.
GORDON, J. and CARTER, H. S. (1932) *J. Path. Bact.*, **35**, 549.
GRASSET, E. and PERRET-GENTIL, A. (1933) *C. R. Soc. Biol.*, **113**, 1457, 1460.
GRASSET, E., PERRET-GENTIL, A., FRIEDMAN, J., and GROSS, I. (1933) *S. Afr. med. J.*, **7**, 779.
GROER, F. VON and KASSOWITZ, K. (1915) *Z. ImmunForsch.*, **23**, 108 ; (1917) *Ibid.*, **26**, 277 ; (1919) *Ibid.*, **28**, 327.
GUTHRIE, G. C., MARSHALL, B. C., and MOSS, W. L. (1921) *Johns Hopk. Hosp. Bull.*, **31**, 388.
HEINBECKER, P. and IRVINE-JONES, E. I. M. (1928) *J. Immunol.*, **15**, 395.
HEIST, G. D., SOLIS-COHEN, S., and SOLIS-COHEN, M. (1918) *J. Immunol.*, **3**, 261.
HIRSZFELD, H. and HIRSZFELD, L. (1927) *Z. ImmunForsch.*, **54**, 81.
HIRSZFELD, H., HIRSZFELD, L., and BROKMAN, H. (1924) *J. Immunol.*, **9**, 571.
HIRSZFELD, L. (1926) *Ergebn. Hyg. Bakt.*, **8**, 367.
HOWE, P. E. (1922) *J. biol. Chem.*, **53**, 479.
IWAI, S. (1917) *Mitt. med. Fak. Kyushu*, **4**, 130.
JANSKY, J. (1908) *Folia serol.*, **3**, 316.
JENSEN, C. (1933) *Acta med. scand.*, Suppl. No. 14.
KARASAWA, M. and SCHICK, B. (1910) *Jb. Kindheilk.*, **72**, 264.
KELLOGG, W. H. (1926–27) *Proc. Soc. exp. Biol., N.Y.*, **24**, 141.
KIRSCHNER, L. (1929) *Meded. Dienst Volksgezondh. Ned.-Ind.*, **18**, 164.
KLEINE, F. K. and KROÓ, H. (1930) *Dtsch. med. Wschr.*, **56**, 46.
KLIEWE, H. and WESTHUES, M. (1925) *Münch. med. Wschr.*, **72**, 587.
KRAUS, R. and LOW, L. (1899) *Wien. klin. Wschr.*, **12**, 95.
KYES, P. (1916) *J. infect. Dis.*, **18**, 277.
LANDSTEINER, K. (1901) *Wien. klin. Wschr.*, **14**, 1132.
LANDSTEINER, K. and SIMMS, S. (1923) *J. exp. Med.*, **38**, 127.
LEWIS, J. H. and WELLS, H. G. (1922) *J. Amer. med. Ass.*, **78**, 863.
LOVELL, R. (1932) *J. comp. Path.*, **45**, 27 ; (1934) *Ibid.*, **47**, 107.
LÜDKE, H. (1905) *Zbl. Bakt.*, **38**, 81.
MACKIE, T. J. and FINKELSTEIN, M. H. (1928) *J. Hyg., Camb.*, **28**, 172 ; (1930) *Ibid.*, **30**, 1 ; (1931) *Ibid.*, **31**, 35 ; (1932) *Ibid.*, **32**, 1.
MACKIE, T. J., FINKELSTEIN, M. H., and ROOYEN, C. E. VAN. (1932) *J. Hyg., Camb.*, **32**, 494.
MASON, J. H., DALLING, T., and GORDON, W. S. (1930) *J. Path. Bact.*, **33**, 783.
MICHIELS, J. and SCHICK, B. (1913) *Z. Kinderheilk.*, **5**, 255.
MINETT, F. C. (1922) *J. comp. Path.*, **35**, 71, 291.
MOSS, W. L. (1910) *Johns Hopk. Hosp. Bull.*, **21**, 63.
NEILL, J. M., GASPARI, E. L., RICHARDSON, L. V., and SUGG, J. Y. (1932) *J. Immunol.*, **22**, 117.
OKELL, C. C. (1932) *Lancet*, i. 761, 815, 867.
ORCUTT, M. L. and HOWE, E. P. E. (1922) *J. exp. Med.*, **36**, 291.
PARISH, H. J. and OKELL, C. C. (1926) *Brit. J. exp. Path.*, **7**, 173.
PARR, L. W. and AVERY, M. S. (1926–27) *J. prev. Med., Baltimore*, **1**, 529.
PARR, L. W., GOODALE, R. H., and KIRSCHNER, H. (1930) *J. prev. Med., Baltimore*, **4**, 39.
RAMON, G. (1925) *Bull. Soc. Cent. méd. vét.*, **101**, 227.
ROBERTSON, O. H. and CORNWELL, O. A. (1930) *J. exp. Med.*, **52**, 267.
ROBERTSON, O. H. and SIA, R. H. P. (1924) *J. exp. Med.*, **39**, 219 ; (1924) *Ibid.*, **40**, 467 ; (1927) *Ibid.*, **46**, 239.

ROBERTSON, O. H., TERRELL, E. E., GRAESER, J. B., and CORNWELL, M. A.   (1930) *J. exp. Med.*, **52,** 421.

RÖMER, P. H.   (1909) *Z. ImmunForsch.*, **3,** 208.

ROSLING, E.   (1928) *Z. ImmunForsch.*, **59,** 521.

SCHICK, B.   (1911) *Naturf. Aerzte, Wiesbaden,* **27,** 212 ; (1913) *Münch. med. Wschr.*, **60,** 2608.

SMITS, E.   (1926) *Tijdschr. Geneesk. Ned.-Ind.*, **66,** 634.

SORDELLI, A.   (1920) *Rev. Inst. Bact.*, **2,** 5.

TANIGUCHI, T.   (1919–20) *J. Path. Bact.*, **23,** 368 ; (1921) *Ibid.*, **24,** 122, 217, 241, 356, 456 ; (1922) *Ibid.*, **25,** 77.

TIMMERMAN, W. A.   (1930) *Brit. J. exp. Path.*, **11,** 447 ; (1931) *Z. ImmunForsch.*, **70,** 388.

TOYAMA, I.   (1919) *J. biol. Chem.*, **38,** 161.

WASSERMANN, A.   (1895) *Z. Hyg. InfektKr.*, **19,** 408.

WELLS, J. R.   (1933) *Amer. J. Hyg.*, **18,** 629.

WILSON, G. S.   (1934) *J. Hyg., Camb.*, **34,** 361.

ZINGHER, A.   (1923) *Amer. J. Dis. Child.*, **25,** 392 ; (1924) *Amer. J. publ. Hlth.*, **14,** 955.

ZURUKZOGLU, S. and MÜNDEL, O.   (1935a) *Schweiz. med. Wschr.*, **65,** 559 ; (1935b) *Z. ImmunForsch.*, **85,** 314.

CHAPTER XLVII

THE ANTIBODY-FORMING APPARATUS AND ITS REACTIONS

In the preceding chapters we have referred freely to the serum antibodies without any attempt to describe the mechanism by which they are produced. Any adequate description is, indeed, impossible. We know too little. It is, for instance, quite clear that the formation of antibodies is associated in some intimate way with the formation of the serum proteins, but we are quite ignorant as to how these proteins are produced, or where. The scanty data at our disposal with regard to the cells and tissues probably involved and the way in which they respond to specific and non-specific stimuli are, however, well worth considering; since they throw light on several problems of practical as well as theoretical importance.

The Site of Formation of Antibodies

Ehrlich's conception of antibodies was that they were shed " cell-receptors." The antigen gained effective contact with the cell by becoming anchored, through specific chemical groupings of its own, to specific chemical groupings on " side-chains " carried by the tissue cells. This theory seemed to imply, by logical extension, the view that antibodies were produced by those cells to which particular antigens, by reason of their chemical structure, were most likely to become attached —that an antitoxin, for instance, was produced by the cells that were most susceptible to the corresponding toxin. A further implication seemed to be that any cell in the body was endowed with the potentiality of forming antibodies, should antigens with suitable side-chains present themselves to it. It would be rash to say that the possibility of such a generalized distribution of function has been excluded, but the trend of opinion, especially in recent years, has quite clearly been towards a different conception, which would regard the antibody-forming apparatus as an integrated system of cells, together constituting a functional though not a structural entity. The evidence on which this view is based may be summarized as follows.

The Local Formation of Antibodies.—Experiments designed to demonstrate the local formation of antibodies, at or in the immediate neighbourhood of the site of inoculation, have given negative or equivocal results.

Römer (1901) recorded observations which he regarded as demonstrating the formation of anti-abrin in the rabbit's conjunctiva; and von Dungern (1902) injected crab-plasma into the anterior chamber of one eye of each of several rabbits and recorded, in one instance, the appearance of a precipitin for crab-plasma in the aqueous humour of the injected eye before its appearance in the blood serum. But these observations have never been confirmed; and, at least in the case of Römer's results, they are open to criticism on technical grounds (see Hektoen 1911). Similarly, the results recorded by Wassermann and Citron

(1905), who injected typhoid bacilli into rabbits intrapleurally and intraperitoneally, and compared the antibody titre of the local exudate and of the blood serum at various times thereafter, afford no convincing evidence of any formation of antibodies in the serous cavities. Hektoen (1911) conducted a very careful series of experiments on the immunization of dogs with rat or goat corpuscles. He was unable to obtain any evidence of antibody formation in the anterior chamber of the eye, in the pleural or peritoneal cavity, or in the connective or muscular tissue of the leg. In every case antibodies appeared in the blood, but there was no evidence that these were produced at the site of inoculation. Thus, amputation of a leg 48 hours after a suspension of red cells had been injected into the muscles made no difference to the time at which antibodies appeared in the blood, or to the titre which they attained.

Cannon and Sullivan (1932) record experiments which they regard as indicating the local formation of antibodies at the site of an intradermal injection ; and Trawinski (1932) concludes, from his experimental findings, that the skin is involved in agglutinin production irrespective of the site of inoculation of the antigen. In each case, however, the part played by the dermis is ascribed to its richness in reticulo-endothelial cells ; so that these observations are in accord with those described in the following section.

The Rôle of the Reticulo-Endothelial System in the Formation of Antibodies.

Hektoen and Carlson (1910) injected dogs with rat or goat corpuscles and bled them dry from the carotid artery during the latent period of immunization, before any rise had occurred in the antibody titre of the serum ; immediately thereafter they restored their blood volume by transfusion from a normal dog. This procedure appeared to have, if anything, a stimulating effect on the subsequent antibody production, indicating that the injected antigen was rapidly removed from the blood. This suggestion was confirmed in other experiments in which normal dogs were bled dry and transfused with blood from other dogs in the latent stage of immunization (3 to 48 hours after inoculation of the antigen). When the dose of red cells injected into the donor had been of the usual optimal amount the recipient showed no rise in antibody titre, indicating that no appreciable amount of antigen remained in the circulating blood even after so short an interval.

We need only recall the description of the clearing mechanism given in Chapter XLIV to evoke the suggestion that the cells of the reticulo-endothelial system, which we know to be concerned in the removal of foreign particulate material from the blood stream, are also concerned directly or indirectly in the formation of antibodies.

The view that certain of the organs or tissues which we now group together under this system might be specially concerned in antibody formation is by no means new. Pfeiffer and Marx (1898) stated that in rabbits, which were undergoing immunization against cholera vibrios, bacterial antibodies might be present in the spleen, the bone-marrow, and perhaps the lungs, in higher concentration than in the blood (see also Tsurumi and Kohda 1913, Cary 1922).

Deutsch (1899) studied the effect of splenectomy on the production of agglutinins and protective antibodies after intraperitoneal injection of typhoid bacilli into guinea-pigs, and found that splenectomy before the injection of the bacterial antigen had little or no effect on the subsequent antibody production, while splenectomy carried out 3 to 5 days after the immunizing injection led to a significant decrease in the concentration of antibodies. He added the interesting observation that, when the spleen was extirpated from a recently immunized guinea-pig and transferred to the peritoneum of a normal guinea-pig, anti-typhoid agglutinins appeared in the blood of the latter though to a relatively low titre. Luckhardt and Becht (1911) studied this question in greater detail. Dogs were injected intravenously with rat or goat corpuscles. Shortly afterwards the spleen was removed, emulsified, and injected into the peritoneum of a normal dog. The recipients showed the typical rise in the antibody titre of the blood serum. The animals from which the spleen had been removed after injection of the red cells produced hæmolysins, hæmagglutinins and hæmopsonins less rapidly and to a lower titre than did the control animals not submitted to splenectomy.

Some recent experiments on agglutinin formation in rabbits (Topley 1930) have given analogous results, and afford the additional suggestion that, after minimal doses of antigen, the reticulo-endothelial cells do not release the antigen in an unaltered form. Rabbits received intravenous injections of killed paratyphoid bacilli in a dose of 10^5 bacilli per kilo. body weight. At varying intervals thereafter, 24 hours to 216 days, they were bled and killed. The spleen, emulsified in saline, was in each case injected into a normal rabbit. The serum from a rabbit killed 24 hours after the injection of bacilli contained no agglutinins. The rabbit that received the spleen tissue from this animal developed agglutinins to low titre, but the time relations of the response differed from those of the typical response to active immunization (see pp. 868–875) in several ways. The highest titre was reached earlier, and the agglutinins disappeared far more rapidly from the blood stream. Reactions of the same general type were noted in the normal rabbits injected with the spleens removed from the immunized animals after longer intervals. Moreover, these rabbits, when injected 21 to 62 days after receiving the spleen tissue with a minimal dose of the same bacilli, showed no evidence of the energetic secondary response (see pp. 872–874) which might have been expected if they had received a previous stimulus with unaltered antigen. These results are more compatible with the view that the histiocytes of the spleen themselves form antibodies or some intermediate product than with the view that they merely retain the antigen and afterwards liberate it in a form which provides an antigenic stimulus to other antibody-forming cells.

Scarff (1931) has recorded experiments suggesting that the reaction of the spleen to foreign blood corpuscles is different from its reaction to bacteria ; and it may be that we should consider different antigenic materials—foreign cells, bacteria, antigens in solution and so on—in relation to different depôts of histiocytes, rather than antigens in general in relation to histiocytes in general.

The rôle of the reticulo-endothelial system in the production of antibodies has also been investigated by the method known as *blockade* alone or combined with splenectomy. In this method large amounts of Indian ink or colloidal iron are injected intravenously, with the object of engaging the activities of as large a quota as possible of the reticulo-endothelial system, and so rendering it less able to deal with a subsequent injection of antigenic material. The results recorded show some divergence. Bieling and Isaac (1921, 1922a, b) reported an inhibitory effect of blockade on antibody production, and several workers have obtained analogous results (Siegmund 1922, Gay and Clark 1924, Vanucci 1924, Jungeblut and Berlot 1926, Lewis and Loomis 1926, Meyer 1926, Tuft 1934). Others, however, have failed to detect any difference between the behaviour of normal and blockaded animals (Rosenthal and Fischer 1922, Fränkel and Grunenberg 1924, Ross 1926). Such discrepancies need cause no surprise. In the case of a system of cells so widely distributed throughout the body, the effectiveness of any method of blockade must vary according to the conditions obtaining in each particular case. Blockade that falls short of completeness may, as some authors have suggested (Standenath 1923), have a stimulating rather than a depressing effect.

Other methods of injuring or disabling the cells of the reticulo-endothelial system have been utilized in attempts to study the part played by these cells in antibody production— the action of X-rays (Benjamin and Sluka 1908, Läwen 1909, Hektoen 1915, 1918, 1920), of thorium X (Hektoen and Corper 1920), and of radium emanation (Hektoen and Corper 1922), of benzene (Rusk 1914, Simonds and Jones 1915, Hektoen 1916a), of toluene (Hektoen 1916b) and of mustard gas (dichlorethyl sulphide) (Hektoen and Corper 1921). The results of these experiments, taken as a whole, lend support to the view that any procedure which severely injures the cells of the reticulo-endothelial system will markedly, or sometimes completely, inhibit the formation of antibodies. Their significance is, perhaps, rendered a little dubious by the fact that the doses required to produce a clear-cut inhibitory effect were of an order which makes it unlikely that their action was confined to the cells of the reticulo-endothelial system and the hæmopoietic tissues.

The Rôle of Other Organs or Tissues in the Formation of Antibodies.

It may be noted that the effect on antibody formation of the removal of other organs —unconnected with the reticulo-endothelial system—has been studied by various observers. The removal of the thyroid has apparently no inhibitory effect (Fjeldstad 1910, Hektoen and Curtis 1915, Ecker and Goldblatt 1921, Houssay and Sordelli 1921, Clevers 1921, Také 1923). An increase in antibody production has occasionally been recorded as a result of this procedure (Ecker and Goldblatt 1921, Houssay and Sordelli 1921, Clevers 1921). Hektoen and Curtis (1915) state that complete removal of the stomach or of the small intestine does not interfere with the formation of hæmopsonins or hæmagglutinins ; simultaneous removal of the spleen and pancreas appears to have the same depressing effect on antibody production in dogs as removal of the spleen alone ; adrenalectomy in dogs, at the height of the antibody curve, does not alter the antibody content of the blood serum ; in rats, removal of one half of the liver appears to have no effect on the production of hæmolysin.

The Formation of Antibodies in Tissue Cultures.—A method which offers obvious possibilities for the study of antibody formation is that of tissue culture.

Carrel and Ingebrigsten (1912) cultivated fragments from the bone-marrow and lymph glands of guinea-pigs in the homologous blood plasma, and added to the cultures small amounts of red cells from the goat, against which the serum of the guinea-pig showed no lytic action. Hæmopsonins appeared in the culture on the 3rd day, as judged by direct observation of the degree of phagocytosis. Hæmolysins were detectable on the 4th day, and had increased markedly in activity on the 5th. The hæmolysins could be specifically absorbed from the fluid by the usual technique. Lüdke (1912) injected killed cultures of typhoid or dysentery bacilli into rabbits, removed fragments of the spleen or bone-marrow after 1 to 5 days, and cultivated them in homologous plasma. After 2 to 5 days' incubation he was able to detect lysins and agglutinins in the culture fluid. In a similar way he succeeded in producing hæmolysin for ox or sheep corpuscles. His results were for the most part negative when he added the antigenic materials directly to the tissue cultures. Przygode (1913, 1914), Reiter (1913) and Schilf (1926) have also recorded positive results. Meyer and Loewenthal (1928) record experiments in which they were able to demonstrate a significant rise in agglutinins in tissue cultures prepared from rabbits that had been inoculated with typhoid bacilli. The tissues examined were the spleen, the lymph glands and the milk spots from the omentum. The latter observation is highly significant, since the omental milk spots, in addition to fibroblasts, contain only cells of the reticulo-endothelial type.

Conclusions with regard to the Site of Formation of Antibodies.—Taking the data as a whole the conclusions to be drawn do not seem to be in doubt in spite of minor discrepancies. There is ample evidence that the organs and cells which have been shown to be concerned in the clearing mechanism of the tissues are also concerned in some way with antibody formation. There is no clear evidence that any other organ or tissue plays a similar rôle.

If we inquire more closely as to the part which the cells of the reticulo-endothelial system play in antibody formation, we must be content with vague hints rather than detailed answers. We know that they remove from the blood stream particulate antigenic material, and probably similar material in colloidal solution. Do they themselves produce the corresponding antibodies, or do they merely retain the antigen temporarily, yielding it up in an altered or unaltered state to the tissue fluids, and thus passing it on to some other cells in which the actual antibody synthesis occurs ?

Of the experiments outlined above, some of those dealing with the rôle of the spleen in antibody production, and the results obtained by Meyer and Loewenthal with cultures from the omentum, seem to offer the suggestion that the histiocytes themselves are capable of producing antibodies in the fully formed state.

The Mechanism of Antibody Formation

As to how antibodies are formed we have no positive knowledge that is based on direct experiment. In the early days of immunology the hypothesis that the injected antigen was in some way incorporated in the antibody was tentatively advanced. It had the obvious merit of offering a possible explanation of specificity, but was soon abandoned because of the enormous quantitative disparity between the antigen injected and the antibody formed. More recently it has been revived in a less direct form ; but it is difficult to accept in any form at all.

In certain of the experiments recorded above it was calculated that the dose of active antigenic material injected into a 2,000 gm. rabbit was of the order of 0·000,000,5–0·000,005 mgm., yet this dose might result in the production of agglutinin to a titre of 1 : 500. Hooker and Boyd (1931) have calculated that, taking such relationships into account, one molecule of active antigenic substance must give rise to an amount of antibody globulin sufficient to agglutinate 600 bacteria ; and, since the surface relationship between one molecule of globulin and 600 bacteria is of the order of 1 : 25,000,000, there seems no room for any hypothesis which assumes the permanent incorporation of any fraction of the antigen in the antibody complex. Berger and Erlenmeyer (1931) and Hooker and Boyd (1931, 1932) have examined this question experimentally, using a linked synthetic antigen containing arsenic, and testing for the presence of arsenic in the antibody-containing serum. These tests were entirely negative and the limits thus set to the amount of antigen present in the antiserum appear to render it impossible that a molecule of antibody can contain any grouping derived from the antigen. If the antigen is incorporated in the antibody at any stage in the formation of the latter, it must apparently be released again, perhaps leaving its impress on the complex of which it once formed a part, and by repeated reassimilation modifying successive fractions of the serum globulin (see Topley 1930).

A working hypothesis of the method of antibody formation, that has a reasonable *a priori* probability and accords well with our present knowledge of the structure of antigens and antibodies, has been put forward independently by Breinl and Haurowitz (1930), Alexander (1931) and Mudd (1932). Ignoring minor differences in the views of its sponsors, this hypothesis assumes that all antibodies *are* globulins, and that they are *new* globulins, synthesized under the directing influence of the antigen. This influence is exerted through a union, physical or chemical, between the peptides or amino-acids and the active groupings of the antigen, during the globulin synthesis. Mudd lays special stress on the point that this synthesis occurs at the interface between the antigen and the surrounding fluid, a point of particular interest in view of the observation that the antibody content of an antibacterial serum seems to be largely determined by the nature of the active groupings at the cell surface. The globulin thus formed is assumed to be dissociated from the antigen after a certain stage has been reached, and the latter is thus able to leave its stereochemical imprint on successive molecules of antibody globulin, synthesized under the same conditions. Breinl and

Haurowitz would locate this synthesis in the reticulo-endothelial cells, the antibody globulin being released when these cells disrupt. This hypothetical localization would, at least, accord quite well with our knowledge of the activity of the reticulo-endothelial system.

The Distribution of Antibodies

Wherever and however antibodies are formed they soon gain access to the blood stream and are distributed throughout the body. Their concentration remains highest in the blood serum, but they are present in the lymph and in most other body fluids, with the possible exception of the cerebrospinal fluid.

Thus Pagano (1894), Falloise (1903) and Batelli (1904) found that the concentration of hæmolysin was lower in the thoracic lymph than in the blood serum. Hughes and Carlson (1908), working with normal dogs, horses and cats, found that the concentration of hæmolysin for rabbit corpuscles formed a descending series, in the order—serum, thoracic lymph, neck lymph, pericardial fluid, aqueous humor. Becht and Greer (1910) studied the distribution of normal and immune antibodies in dogs. They also studied the rate of transference of antibodies from the circulating blood to the tissue fluids after passive immunization by the intravenous route. Their findings with regard to the distribution of normal and immune antibodies were in accord with those of Hughes and Carlson. In the actively immunized animals they observed a marked rise in the antibody titre of the serum, thoracic lymph and neck lymph, the relative concentrations in the different fluids maintaining the same order as in the normal animals. After passive immunization, by transfusion of blood from an immunized to a normal dog, the characteristic distribution of antibodies was established within $4\frac{1}{2}$ hours. These findings were confirmed in all essentials by Hektoen and Carlson (1910).

The antibodies are not, however, confined to the blood plasma and tissue fluids. We shall see, when considering the phenomena of anaphylaxis and hypersensitiveness, that they are taken up by various cells, and that these cells are, as a result, rendered sensitive and responsive to the corresponding antigens.

It is very probable that the cellular distribution of the various antibodies is an important factor in the defence mechanisms of the tissues as a whole ; but our knowledge of this distribution is, as yet, in its infancy (see, for instance, Freund 1930).

The Response of the Antibody-forming Apparatus to Specific Stimuli

The Primary Response to a Specific Stimulus.—It will simplify discussion to consider first the response to the injection of an antigenic material directly into the blood stream. It will also be convenient to select an example in which the antibody concerned is not present *ab initio* in the blood of the experimental animal employed. The production of flagellar agglutinins by the rabbit in response to a single intravenous injection of a killed suspension of *Bact. paratyphosum B* affords a convenient illustrative example. Fig. 226 shows a typical reaction.

There is an initial induction phase, not shown in this particular diagram because the first reading after the injection of the antigen was taken on the fifth day. This induction phase usually lasts for 24 to 48 hours, by the end of which time agglutinin is usually detectable to very low titre (1 : 5 to 1 : 20). The titre then rises rapidly as shown in the figure, until about the 16th day. The time limits between which the maximum titre is usually attained may be put at about the 10th to 22nd day. It then falls, at first rapidly, then more slowly, agglutinins still being present in the blood 100 days after the inoculation. It will be noted that, in this chart, the titres are plotted as ordinates on a logarithmic scale, time as abscissæ on an arithmetical scale. Equal rises and falls in the curve represent not equal increments or losses of agglutinins but equal proportionate increases or decreases—for example, doublings or halvings of the amount present.

The Effect of Dosage.—As regards the relation between the dose of antigen administered and the amount of antibody produced, Table LXXIII sets out some figures for the particular case we are considering.

The minute dose of 10,000 bacilli per kilo. body weight, administered to rabbits varying from 1,380 to 3,750 gm., results in no detectable formation of agglutinins. When we increase the dose ten times we pass the threshold and obtain an average titre of 1 : 330. Over the range 10^5 to 10^8 bacilli a thousandfold increase in dose results in about a tenfold increase in

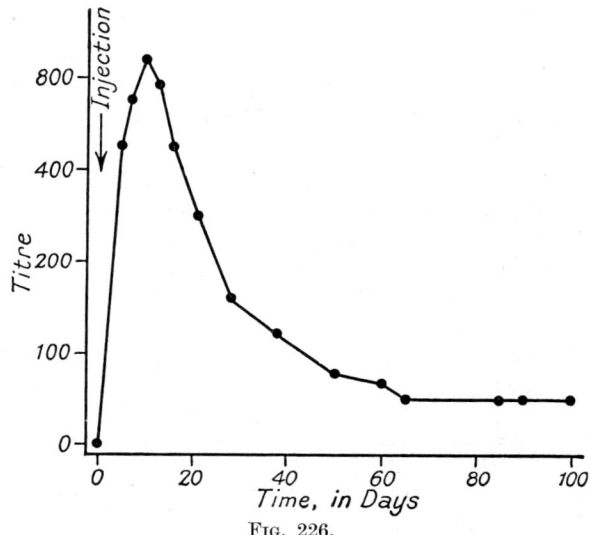

Fig. 226.

Production of agglutinins in rabbit after single injection of *Bact. paratyphosum B.*

titre—the critical student glancing at the numbers in the second column will not place too much reliance on the mean values recorded in the third. If we increase our dose still further we shall get still higher titres ; but we shall be reaching the point where our inoculum attains an appreciable toxicity, and we shall, apart from this, be subject to the law of diminishing returns. However high we push our dose, up to the limit that will kill our rabbit, we are unlikely, after any single inoculation, to reach a titre of more than 1 : 10,000–1 : 20,000.

TABLE LXXIII

SHOWING THE MEAN VALUES OF THE HIGHEST TITRE OF FLAGELLAR AGGLUTININS IN SMALL GROUPS OF RABBITS INJECTED INTRAVENOUSLY WITH DIFFERENT DOSES (PER k.b.w.) OF *Bact. paratyphosum B.*

No. of Bacilli injected per k.b.w.	No. of Rabbits tested.	Highest Titre. (Mean Value).
10^8	3	3,540
10^7	3	1,860
10^5	6	330
10^4	4	0 .[1]

[1] = no agglutination at a dilution of 1 : 4.

We may sum up in general terms by stating that there is a minimal threshold value, below which no response is obtained. Above this value the titre attained varies with the dose administered but in such a way that the increase in titre is relatively much smaller than the increase in dose required to produce it. Eventually a point is reached at which further increase in dose results in little or no increase in antibody production.

In connection with the problem of dosage, we may note some recent observations by Hartley (1935), which indicate that the total volume of an immunizing injection, as well as its content in antigenic material, has a significant influence on the antibody response. A series of guinea-pigs were injected with a constant dose of diphtheria toxoid made up in a total volume of 0·5 c.c. or 5·0 c.c. of saline. In repeated tests it was found that the animals receiving the larger volume gave a far better immunizing response.

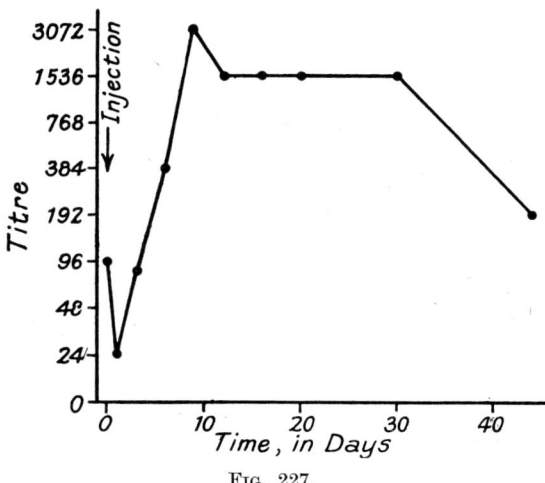

FIG. 227.

Production of hæmagglutinin in a dog after a single injection of rat corpuscles.
(After Hektoen and Carlson.)

Variations in Response to Different Antigens.—Fig. 227 shows the effect of injecting into an animal (a dog) a particular antigen (rat corpuscles) against which it possesses a normal antibody (hæmagglutinin).

It will be noted that the immediate effect of the injection is to cause a fall in the normal antibody titre, followed by a rapid rise of the type depicted in Fig. 226. This *negative phase* is a characteristic result of injecting any large amount of antigen into an animal that possesses the corresponding antibody in its circulating blood.

The response to a single dose of an antigen in colloidal solution is illustrated in Fig. 228, which shows the course of precipitin formation in the rabbit following a single injection of horse serum.

There is a rather protracted induction period lasting for some 8 days, followed by a rise in antibody titre to a maximum about the 16th day and then a slower fall, till precipitin ceases to be detectable about the 37th day.

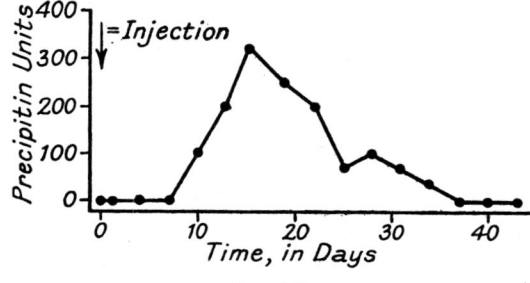

FIG. 228.

Precipitin production : response of a rabbit to single injection of horse serum.
(After Dean and Webb.)

It should be noted that this curve is not comparable, at a mere glance, with those given earlier in the chapter since the titres are plotted as an arithmetical not as a geometrical or logarithmic series. To make the curve comparable with those describing agglutinin or hæmolysin production the logarithms of the number of precipitin units would have to be plotted as ordinates.

The Response of the Antibody-forming Apparatus to the Simultaneous Injection of Several Antigens.

It is clear that the capacity of the antibody-forming apparatus must have some limit. The question at issue is at what stage that limit is reached. Will antibodies be formed as readily against two or three or n antigens, all injected at the same time, as against a single antigen ? The answer is of considerable practical interest, since mass immunization against a multiplicity of diseases could be envisaged more cheerfully if syringes could be loaded on the blunderbuss principle. The evidence is conflicting.

There are records (Benjamin and Witzinger 1912, Huntoon and Craig 1921) which suggest that the injection of more than one antigen, simultaneously or in rapid succession, lessens the production of one or other of the corresponding antibodies. Corrigan (1925),

and Hektoen and Boor (1931), on the other hand, have recorded results which indicate a far less restricted range of activity. The latter observers immunized rabbits by repeated intravenous injections of mixtures containing large numbers of different antigens, each in a relatively pure state. These included hæmoglobin from the ox, cat, dog, hog, horse, man, sheep and turkey, horse pseudoglobulin, serum albumin from chicken and man, egg albumin and other constituents. One of the mixtures contained 14 different antigenic constituents, the other 35. Precipitins were produced

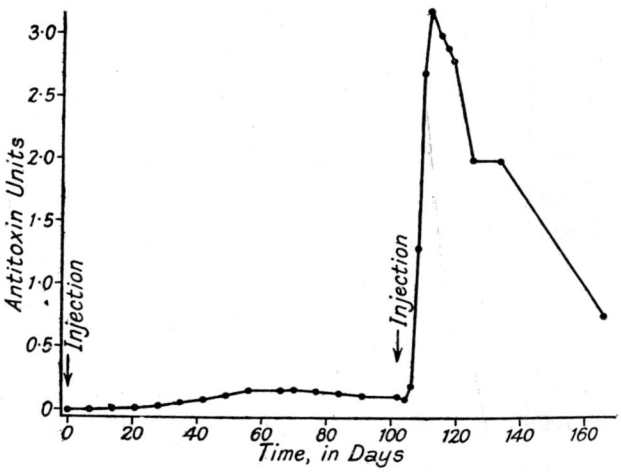

Fig. 229.

Antitoxin production in the horse : showing difference between primary and secondary response. (After Glenny and Südmersen.)

against almost all the antigens injected, and in most cases to high titre.

In the particular case of antitoxins the careful work of Glenny and his colleagues (Glenny 1925a, Glenny, Hopkins and Waddington 1925, Glenny and Waddington 1926, 1928) makes it clear that the simultaneous injection of several antigens may considerably reduce the titre of antitoxin obtained. It seems likely, as Glenny suggests, that this " crowding out " effect is particularly prone to occur when any one antigen is present in great excess.

With optimal doses of each constituent, and a total inoculum which is not unduly large, it seems probable that an effective response can be obtained against a reasonable number of different antigens, even if the titre of some or all of the corresponding antibodies is relatively reduced. From the practical point of view the problem will clearly differ according as we are attempting to induce an active immunity in man or animal, or to produce a high titre serum for passive immunization. In the former case a reduction in the antibody titre attained might be of minor importance, in the latter it would be a grave disadvantage. Each case, as it arises, should be subjected to experimental trial.

The Difference in Response to Primary and Secondary Stimuli.—Having considered the response of the antibody-forming apparatus to an initial injection of antigen we may inquire how it responds to repeated stimuli, and it will be convenient to take as our first instance the response of a horse to the injection of

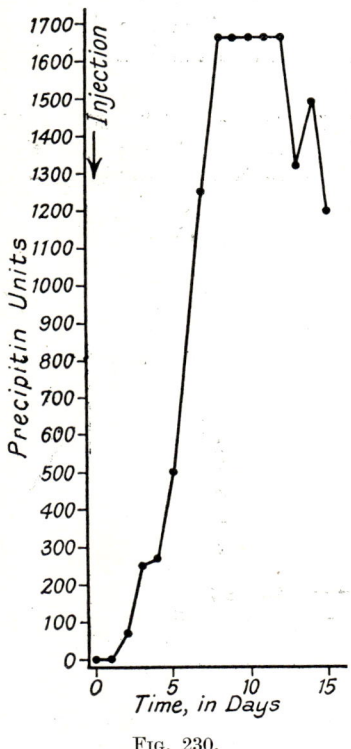

FIG. 230.

Precipitin production: response of a previously sensitized rabbit to a single injection of horse serum—secondary response.
(After Dean and Webb.)

diphtheria toxin, selecting an animal whose blood, at the time of the initial injection, is devoid of antitoxin. This particular reaction has been studied in great detail by Glenny and his colleagues (Glenny 1925*b*, 1931, Glenny and Südmersen 1921) and forms the basis of his insistence on the fundamental difference between a primary and a secondary response. Fig. 229 shows a typical example.

The primary injection is followed by an induction period of some 14 days, after which there is a very slow rise in the antitoxin content of the blood, reaching a low maximum of 0·16 units per c.c. between the 9th and 10th weeks, and sinking slowly to 0·11 units by the middle of the 15th week, at the time of the second injection. The response to this second injection is of an altogether different character. Within 4 days a distinct rise in the titre of antitoxin is observable, and the curve then rises steeply to a maximum of 3·2 units per c.c. on the 10th day, followed by a fairly rapid decline. It may be added that with repeated and increasing doses the antitoxin content of a horse's serum may be raised to well over 1,000 units per c.c.

This difference in response to primary and subsequent injections of the same antigenic material is not limited to the production of diphtheria antitoxin, though it is particularly well marked in this case. Fig. 230, showing the response to an injection of horse serum in a rabbit which had previously been injected with that antigen, but whose precipitin titre had since sunk to zero, may be compared with Fig. 228 above.

The same holds true, in regard to the comparative titre attained, though not in regard to the prolonged induction period after the primary stimulus, when the antigenic material is particulate, as in the case of a bacterial suspension. Table LXXIV sets out the primary and secondary response of rabbits to the intravenous injection of 10^5 *Bact. paratyphosum B* per kilo. body weight. It will be noted that the titres given are not the maximum attained but the average titre during the 50 days after inoculation. This value was selected because the curve of agglutinin titre after a secondary inoculation tends not only to rise higher than after a primary injection, but to remain high over a longer period.

TABLE LXXIV

Showing the Average Titre over a Period of 50 Days after Primary and Secondary Injections into Rabbits of 10^5 *Bact. paratyphosum B* per k.b.w.

Rabbit.	Primary Average Titre.	Interval between 1st and 2nd Injections.	Secondary Average Titre.
R11	280	147 days	2,720
R19	37	147 ,,	1,720
R25	130	147 ,,	430
R30	130	133 ,,	1,230
R31	91	133 ,,	1,230
R33	110	133 ,,	2,010

The difference between the primary and secondary response is sufficiently obvious and needs no comment. With very small doses there may be no detectable primary response, antibodies appearing first after the second or later injection of a bacillary suspension. An illustrative example is given in Table LXXV.

The tendency for the antibody titre to be maintained at a high level for a longer

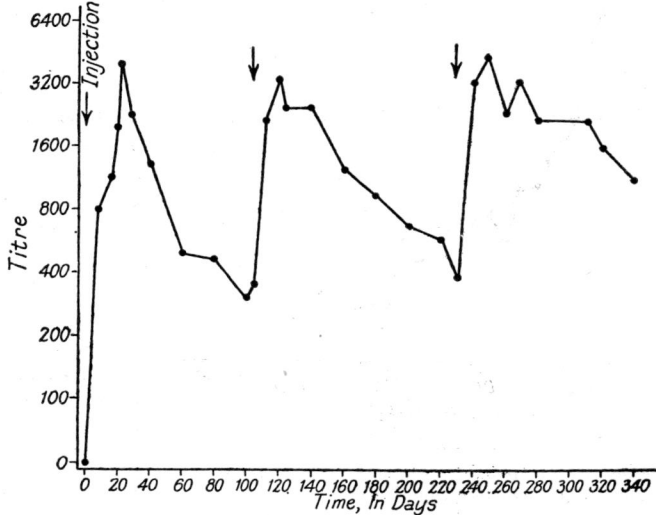

Fig. 231.

Agglutinin production : response of a rabbit to widely spaced injections of *Bact. typhosum.*

time after secondary and subsequent responses than after a primary response is illustrated in Fig. 231, showing the response of a rabbit to three widely spaced injections of *Bact. typhosum*, Fig. 232, showing the response of an uninoculated person to an injection of typhoid vaccine, and Fig. 233, showing the response of a previously inoculated person to the same antigenic material.

P.B.   F F*

TABLE LXXV

Showing the Highest Titre attained after 1st, 2nd and 3rd Injections of 10⁴ *Bact.*
paratyphosum B per k.b.w.

Rabbit.	Highest Titre after 1st Injection.	Interval between 1st and 2nd Injections.	Highest Titre after 2nd Injection.	Interval between 2nd and 3rd Injections.	Highest Titre after 3rd Injection.
R16 . . .	0	28 days	8	92 days	40
R32 . . .	0	28 ,,	32	92 ,,	319
R46 . . .	0	28 ,,	7	92 ,,	20
R47 . . .	0	28 ,,	0	92 ,,	0

It must not be supposed that the differences between a primary and secondary response are always so clear-cut as those depicted here. The curves may, however, be regarded as giving a true picture of the kind of differences observed. It will be noted in Figs. 231 and 232 that the primary response may be quite brisk and result in a high titre of agglutinins. This, for instance, is the usual experience as regards the production of H agglutinins in response to the injection of an optimal dose of flagellated bacilli.

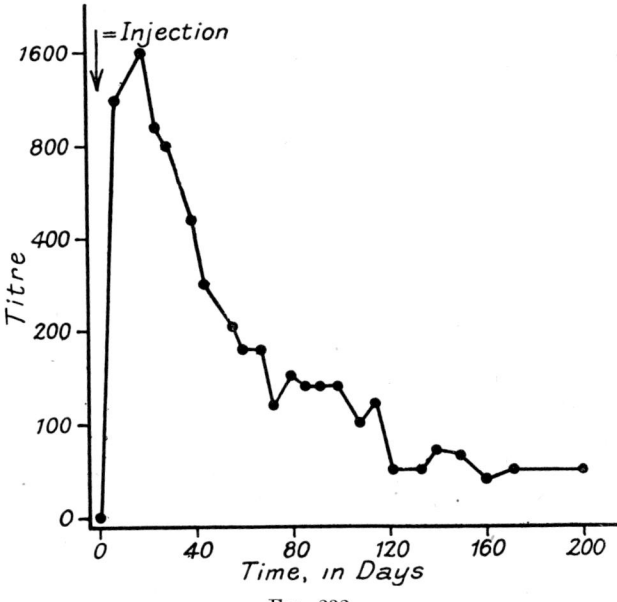

Fig. 232.

Agglutinin production : response of an uninoculated person to a single injection of typhoid vaccine.

We have noted that increases in the dose of antigen administered at a single injection are subject to the law of diminishing returns : in just the same way the repetition of injections, beyond a certain number, is usually found to produce less and less effect with each successive dose. When the titre of a particular antibody has been forced up to a certain level, which varies widely with the nature of the antigen employed and the responsiveness of the animal injected, it becomes impossible to induce any further rise in the concentration of antibody in the circulating blood.

Fig. 234 shows the effect of repeated subcutaneous injections of typhoid bacilli in the rabbit (Goldberg 1901). It will be noted that each successive injection raises the agglutinin titre, but that the increments tend to become proportionately smaller and smaller, the last injection on the 35th day producing a relatively trivial effect.

The Negative Phase.—Just as the injection of a considerable dose of a particular antigen into an animal that possesses a corresponding normal antibody may result in a temporary decrease in the concentration of that antibody in the circulating blood, the injection of a large dose of antigen into an animal that has already developed a certain concentration of antibody in response to earlier injections may be followed by a well-marked negative phase, which is usually followed in its turn by a rise in titre above the previous level. An illustrative example is afforded by the response of an immunized rabbit to two injections of horse serum, given intravenously at an interval of 5 days (Fig. 235).

The importance of avoiding this negative phase in therapeutic immunization has been emphasized particularly by Wright and his co-workers (Wright 1909).

The Response of the Antibody-forming Apparatus to the Administration of Antigens otherwise than by Injection into the Tissues.

In defining the properties of an antigen on p. 137, it was stated that it should stimulate the formation of an antibody when introduced *parenterally* into the body. This caveat was included in the definition because administration *via* the intestinal tract does not ensure the passage of the antigen to the tissues in an unaltered and effective form. It may be broken down by the digestive enzymes. If it is not acted on by them it may never pass through the intestinal mucosa. Whether, in fact, any particular antigenic material administered by this route reaches the tissues in an unaltered form can only be determined by direct experiment. The available evidence suggests that some bacterial antigens, but not all, induce the formation of specific antibodies when administered by the mouth.

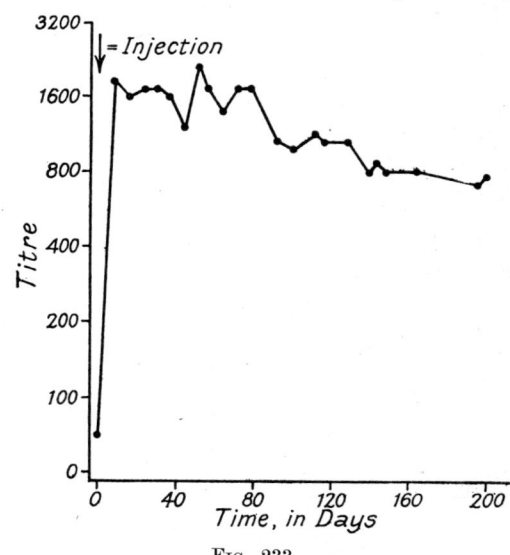

FIG. 233.

Agglutinin production : response of a previously inoculated person to a single injection of typhoid vaccine.

Thus, the administration *per os* of killed suspensions of flagellated bacilli of the typhoid-paratyphoid group results in the production of somatic (O) agglutinins, but flagellar (H) agglutinins are either not produced at all, or only to low titre (Pijper and Dau 1930, Greenwood, Topley and Wilson 1931). The same difference between the formation of H and O agglutinins appears to hold in the case of the cholera vibrio (Pfeiffer and Lubinski 1930). Dysentery bacilli, which are non-flagellated, induce the formation of somatic agglutinins when administered by the mouth (Kanai 1921, Otten and Kirschner 1927) ; and it is probable that analogous effects are produced by many other bacterial cells (see for instance Ross 1926, 1930, 1931, 1932, 1934).

In all cases it would seem that administration *per os* is far less effective than inoculation into the tissues, in the sense that much larger doses have to be given and the antibody titre attained is usually lower.

As regards other routes of entry, Stillman (1927, 1930) has shown that protective anti-bodies are produced in rabbits after the administration of living pneumococci by inhalation, but here we may be dealing with an active infection and consequent tissue invasion by living bacterial cells.   In so far as resistance to toxin can be taken as a proof of the formation of antitoxin, there is evidence (Hosmer-Zambelli 1931) that the intranasal instillation of toxoid acts as an effective stimulus.

It seems justifiable to conclude that the administration of non-living antigenic material by various routes other than directly into the blood stream or tissue

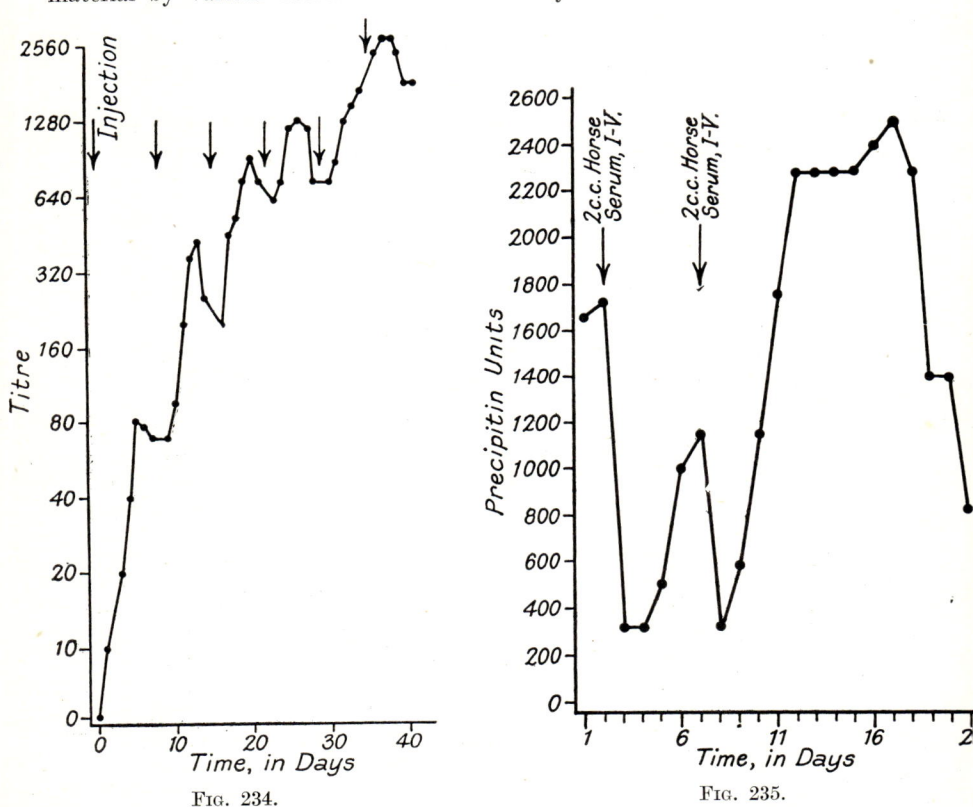

FIG. 234.

Effect of repeated injections of *Bact. typhosum* on agglutinin production in a rabbit. (After Goldberg.)

FIG. 235.

Precipitin production: effect of intravenous inj- tion of horse serum into an immunized rab (Dean and Webb, 1928.)

spaces will often result in antibody production, but that none of these alternative routes are so certain or so effective.

The Nature of the Substances that stimulate Antibody Production.

In the preceding discussion we have been concerned with antigens of the chemi-cally complex type, ranging from purified proteins to crude suspensions of bacteria or other cells.   It has frequently been stated that only proteins, or substances containing a protein component, can function as complete antigens and induce an immunizing response when injected into the tissues.   Protein-free derivatives of these complete antigens—the haptens, of varying complexity—retain the property of specific union with the antibodies produced in response to the injection of the complete antigens, and, in some cases, give specific precipitation *in vitro* (see Chapter VI) and specific anaphylactic reactions *in vivo* (see Chapter XLVIII). There can be no doubt of the validity of Landsteiner's broad distinction between complete antigens and haptens, or of the association between decreasing chemical complexity, or molecular size, and a progressive loss of antigenic function ; but observations that have been recorded within the past few years have caused us to modify our views in regard to the dependence of immunizing power on the presence of a protein component.

All the early studies on the purified polysaccharide components isolated from various bacteria, and in particular from pneumococci, suggested that these substances had the properties of haptens, and induced no immunizing or antibody-forming response when injected into the tissues. But observations have since accumulated which are difficult to reconcile with such a view.

Schiemann and Casper (1927) reported that the purified specific polysaccharide of the Type I pneumococcus, when injected into mice, produced an active immunity against living Type I pneumococci, but not against other types. They noted that this immunity was induced by the injection of small, but not of larger, doses. Schiemann (1929) recorded the immunization of mice by the injection of Type II pneumococcal polysaccharide, and noted that the blood of these immunized mice contained protective antibodies ; though he was unable to demonstrate antibody production in rabbits. Francis and Tillett (1930) recorded observations suggesting that persons who were given repeated intradermal injections of the purified polysaccharide of Type I, II or III pneumococcus, developed a specific local response which took the form of an immediate wheal and erythema ; and that this response was associated with the appearance of specific antibodies in the blood. Similar observations have been recorded by Finland and Sutliff (1932) and by Zozaya and Clark (1932). Zozaya and Clark (1933) recorded the immunization of mice with polysaccharide fractions from Types I, II and III pneumococci, and noted that small doses were more effective than larger ones ; but their results were irregular except when the polysaccharides were adsorbed on collodion particles or on carbon.

Recent studies by Avery and Goebel (1933) have thrown further light on this question. They were able to show that the Type I pneumococcal polysaccharide, as it occurs in the bacterial capsule, possesses an acetyl grouping. This grouping is lost during the separation and purification of the polysaccharide by the methods which have been commonly employed. The acetylated form was found to induce active immunity in mice, while the deacetylated form was effective in small, but not in large doses. It did not induce antibody production in rabbits.

Analogous results have been recorded in relation to organisms of the Salmonella group by Boivin and his colleagues (1933–36) and by Raistrick and Topley (1934). From these organisms fractions can be isolated that contain a complex polysaccharide united to a phosphatide, or nuclein, component, but no protein. These fractions are toxic, and fully antigenic. They induce active immunity in mice, and antibody production in the rabbit. They would appear to be identical with the specific somatic antigens of these bacterial species, or types. The separated and purified polysaccharide component is non-toxic. Boivin and his colleagues state that it is non-antigenic ; but recent (unpublished) experiments by Topley, Raistrick and Wilson have given different results.

These findings are important because they provide a method of studying the comparative immunizing value of different chemical components derived from crude bacterial antigens, and so of placing practical prophylaxis on a sounder and more scientific basis.

The Response of the Antibody-forming Apparatus to Active Infection

The examples given above all refer to the response of the antibody-forming apparatus to the experimental injection of non-living antigenic substances. We may close this section with a few examples of its response to natural infections of the clinically obvious type. For simplicity we may confine our attention to acute infections, noting, however, that in the case of subacute and relapsing diseases, such for instance as tuberculosis, there is evidence that the antibody titre fluctuates as the infection varies from quiescence to activity.

As a typical example of an antibody curve during the course of an acute febrile infection we may take some of the numerous observations that have been made on patients suffering from typhoid fever. Figs. 236 and 237, constructed from data recorded by Jörgensen (1905), show the fluctuations in typhoid agglutinins during a typical attack of the disease, and during the terminal stage of a primary attack and the two relapses which in this case immediately followed it. The clinical course of the disease is, in each case, indicated by the fluctuations in temperature. It will be noted that, in the second of these cases, the agglutinin response during the primary attack was unusually feeble.

The Response of the Antibody-forming Apparatus to Non-Specific Stimuli.

Since the serum antibodies react specifically with their corresponding antigens, it is natural to suppose that they will be formed *de novo* only in response to the specific stimulus provided by the introduction into the tissues of the antigen concerned. In making this supposition we must, however, be very careful to limit its implications. We must recollect, as has been emphasized in Chapter VII, that we are concerned with chemical entities, and not with particular species of bacteria or particular types of cell. We know that certain antigens are shared by several bacterial species ; and the production, in response to the introduction into the tissues of one bacterium containing antigens a and x, of antibodies acting on another bacterium containing the antigens b and x is, in so far as it depends on the production of antibody X, a strictly specific response in the only sense with which we are here concerned. With these limitations, our supposition is in accord with all the recorded facts. The available literature contains no instance in which the introduction into the tissues of a substance of known chemical constitution has led to the production *de novo* of an antibody reacting specifically with a second substance, the chemical constitution of which bears no relation to that of the first.

If we turn to the production of a normal antibody in increased amount, a rise in the titre of an antibody previously produced in response to a specific stimulus, or the reappearance of such an antibody after the titre has fallen to zero, it is clear that our supposition no longer holds on *a priori* grounds. There would be nothing remarkable in an antibody-forming apparatus that had once produced, and possibly stored, a particular antibody, turning that antibody into the circulation anew, or in greater amount, in response to some non-specific stimulus which increased the activity of the apparatus without directing it into any particular channel. Whether or not this type of non-specific stimulation occurs can be settled only by empirical trial.

In this connection we may note a terminological confusion which has sometimes arisen in the literature. The production, in response to an antigenic stimulus, of an antibody that has been produced in the tissues on some previous occasion, is often referred to as an *anamnestic reaction* (*anamnesis*—recollection). Sometimes this term is used in connection

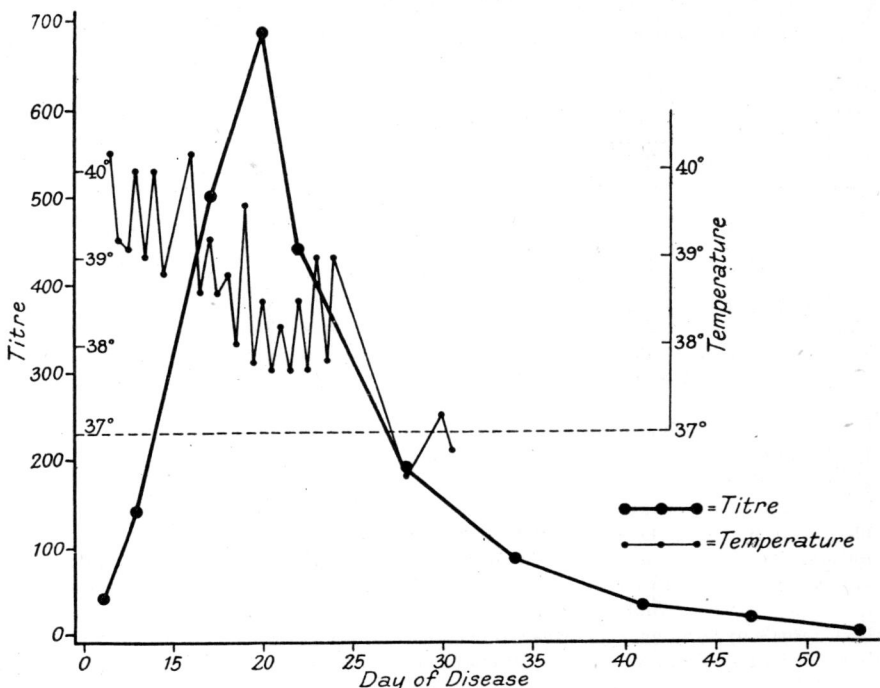

Fig. 236.

Rise and fall of agglutinins in blood of patient during an attack of typhoid fever.
(After Jörgensen.)

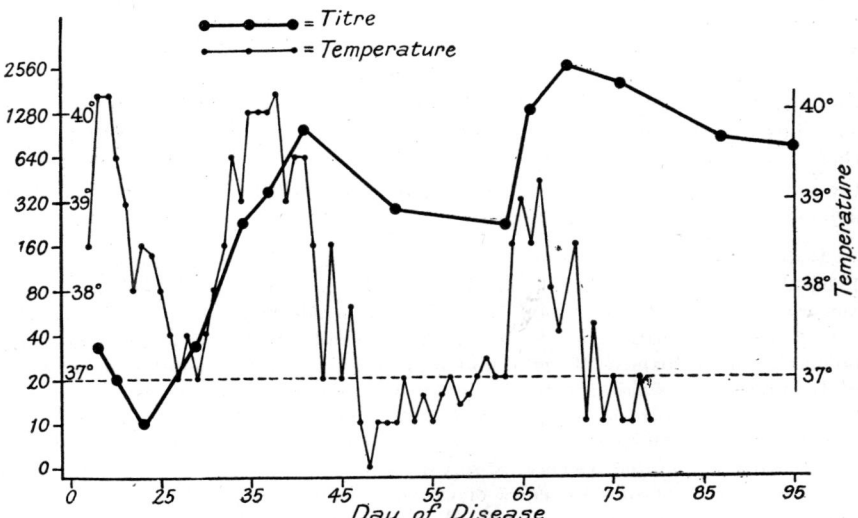

Fig. 237.

Fluctuations of agglutinins in blood of patient during attack of typhoid fever, followed by
two relapses.
(After Jörgensen.)

with the type of non-specific stimulus to which we have just referred—the tissues are stimulated to general activity, in which is included the renewed production of a particular antibody that had been formed at some time in the past. Sometimes, perhaps more accurately, it is employed in reference only to those instances in which the particular chemical stimulus concerned formed part of the earlier experience of the antibody-producing cells. In this limited sense it is clearly synonymous with the secondary response, in the sense defined above, and has no reference to the problem with which we are here concerned.

Several observers have recorded a stimulation of antibody production as the result of excessive or repeated bleeding.

Friedberger and Dorner (1905) stated that the withdrawal of considerable amounts of blood, either shortly before an immunizing injection, or within a few days thereafter, had a definitely stimulating effect on the subsequent antibody production. Hektoen and Carlson (1910), in the experiments already referred to, found that bleeding a dog dry during the initial latent stage of active immunization and immediately transfusing it with the blood of a normal dog appeared to increase the production of antibodies. Hahn and Langer (1917) have reported experiments in which they observed a marked increase in agglutinin titre in 4 rabbits as the result of repeated daily bleedings. Trommsdorf (1921) has recorded an increase in agglutinins for the diphtheria bacillus as the result of daily bleedings. Other workers (Klinger 1918, Landau 1918) have however failed to confirm these results. It may be noted that an opposing factor is brought into play when an immunized animal is subjected to massive repeated bleeding. The mere withdrawal of considerable quantities of blood would, of itself, tend to lower the titre of the circulating antibodies if the antibody-forming apparatus did not share in the subsequent activity of the hæmopoietic tissues. That immunized animals may suffer extensive bleedings without any detectable and lasting fall in antibody titre has long been known (Roux and Vaillard 1893).

It may be accepted that bleeding does act as a stimulus to antibody production in the same sense that it acts as a stimulus to the production of the serum proteins in general ; that is, there is an active response tending to make good the loss sustained. Whether this particular stimulus suffices to force the titre, transitorily or for longer periods, far above the pre-existing level is more doubtful.

Another procedure that has been stated to supply a non-specific stimulus to the antibody-forming apparatus is the injection of various metallic salts, colloidal solutions or other substances. We may ignore, from our present point of view, those instances in which the effect of such injections is limited to an increase in the bactericidal power of the blood. Such effects will be more conveniently considered in Chapter XLIX.

Walbum and his collaborators (Walbum and Morch 1923, Walbum and Berthelsen 1925, Walbum 1925, 1926, Schmidt 1926, Ørskov and Schmidt 1928) have recorded numerous experiments along these lines. They conclude that the inoculation of salts of certain metals, especially those of cobalt, manganese and beryllium, causes an increase in the production of antitoxin, or of agglutinins, if given early in the course of immunization, and leads to a secondary rise in titre, if injected when the antibody titre has commenced to fall. Several investigators have, however, failed to confirm these observations (McIntosh and Kingsbury 1924, Horgan 1925), and the protocols included in some of Walbum's reports suggest that the response is very irregular.

Steaben (1925) studied the effect of various colloids on antibody production. Using agar, gelatin, a silver sol and an iron sol, she found that the injection of these colloids had no power to increase the antibody titre when this had become steady, though the injection of such a colloid at the same time as the bacterial antigen might increase the antibody response.

Obermayer and Pick (1904) recorded that animals immunized 3 months previously showed a fresh formation of precipitin after the injection of a 5–10 per cent. solution of peptone. Fleckseder (1916) stated that the injection into human beings of deutero-albumose or nucleic acid gave rise to an increase in the agglutinins for typhoid bacilli which were already present in detectable amount in the subjects in question. Weichardt and Schräder (1919) noted a definite increase in agglutinin titre after the injection of deutero-albumose, sodium nucleinate or milk; and Matsuda (1924) reported that the injection of deuteroalbumose was followed by a secondary increase in the disappearing viricidal antibodies in the blood of vaccinia-immune animals. An excellent summary of the data with regard to the effect of protein substances as non-specific stimuli is contained in a review by Weichardt (1922). Here again we may note the irregularity of the results obtained, and the absence of any large increase in antibody content such as usually follows a specific stimulus.

Finally we may consider those cases in which the non-specific stimulus is pro-vided by a complex antigen, similar in type to that providing the initial specific stimulus but possessing no known common antigenic factor. So far as this anti-genic dissimilarity is in fact complete the case does not differ in its essentials from those we have considered above.

Dreyer and Walker (1909) recorded a secondary rise in agglutinins for *Bact. coli*, follow-ing the intraperitoneal injection of killed staphylococci into previously immunized rabbits. Conradi and Bieling (1916) state that rabbits immunized against *Bact. typhosum* show a secondary rise in agglutinins after various non-specific stimuli, such as those provided by the injection of *Bact. coli*, dysentery bacilli and *C. diphtheriæ*. Tsukahara (1921) records a series of experiments which are highly suggestive. He injected rabbits with typhoid, paratyphoid and dysentery bacilli, using one organism as the primary specific stimulus and another as the secondary non-specific stimulus, and noted many instances of a secondary rise in agglutinins. A careful perusal of his protocols however indicates very clearly that, where the secondary response was well marked, there was some antigenic relationship between the two kinds of bacteria employed, indicated by the fact that a primary inoculation with one of them was followed by a slight but definite production of antibodies acting on the other. This fact, of course, excludes these particular examples from the category which we are considering.

Rosher (1924) was unable to detect non-specific stimulation of antibody production in any of the following instances: primary specific antigen *Bact. coli*, secondary non-specific inoculum *Staph. aureus*; primary specific antigen *Bact. coli*, secondary non-specific inoculum sheep's red cells; primary specific antigen *Bact. paratyphosum A*, secondary non-specific inoculum suspension of mixed unrelated bacteria; primary specific antigen *Bact. typhosum*, secondary non-specific inoculum *Bact. paratyphosum B*; primary specific antigen *Bact. enteritidis*, secondary non-specific stimulus infection with living tubercle bacilli. In all cases in which this point was examined, the secondary inoculum acted as an effective primary specific stimulus, inducing the production to a relatively high titre of antibodies reacting with its own antigenic components, while leaving the titre of antibodies acting on the previously injected antigen unaltered. Analogous results had been noted by many of the observers referred to above.

To summarize, we may say that there is some evidence that non-specific stimuli —extensive bleeding, or the injection of metallic salts or colloids or protein solutions or unrelated bacteria—may induce (a) an increase in the titre of a normal antibody, (b) an increase in the production of immune antibodies when administered during the early stages of immunization, or (c) a secondary rise in titre when administered after the effect of the preliminary specific immunization has reached its zenith, or declined from it. The responses falling within this category are, however, exceedingly irregular, usually trivial, and never comparable to those which follow the reinjection of the specific antigen. It is quite certain also that the injection of a given antigen may stimulate the antibody-forming apparatus to the energetic production of the corresponding antibody, without any detectable production or mobilization of antibodies acting on an unrelated antigen to which it had previously responded.

The Fate of Antibodies when injected into a Normal or Immunized Animal.

This is a convenient place in which to note a series of observations which, while not immediately related to the phenomena that we have been discussing, are of considerable practical importance.

When we inject an antibody-containing serum into a normal animal, the rate at which it reaches the blood stream and the maximum concentration which it there attains are in great part determined by the route of injection. Obviously we shall obtain the most rapid effect by injecting our antiserum intravenously. Injection by any other route will involve a lag period before the maximal concentration is reached in the circulating blood ; and since the antibody-containing serum is being slowly eliminated throughout the whole period the concentration in the blood and tissue fluids in general will reach a lower level.

Smith (1907) records a series of experiments that serve to illustrate these points.

Fig. 238 shows the disappearance of agglutinins for *Bact. coli* from the blood of a rabbit after an intravenous injection of the serum of an immunized goat.

Fig. 239 shows the effect of inoculating the same serum subcutaneously. It will be noted that the maximal concentration of agglutinin in the circulating blood is not reached until 53 hours after the injection.

Fig. 240 shows the concentration of antitoxin in the circulating blood of a human subject at varying intervals after the subcutaneous injection of an antitoxic serum. It will be noted that the peak is not reached until the 3rd or 4th day.

It may be noted that an antiserum injected into the peritoneum rapidly reaches the blood stream *via* the thoracic duct, so that the effect does not differ greatly from that of an intravenous injection. After an intramuscular injection an antiserum reaches the blood stream more slowly than after an intraperitoneal injection but more rapidly than after a subcutaneous injection.

Another point of some importance in connection with passive immunization is illustrated in Figs. 241 and 242 (Glenny and Hopkins 1922).

In Fig. 241 is recorded the rate of disappearance of antitoxin from the circulation of 3 normal rabbits after the intravenous injection of 0·5 c.c. of diphtheria antitoxin, derived from the horse. Fig. 242 gives a similar record in the case of 3 rabbits that had received previous inoculations of horse serum. These were " immune " or " sensitized " to horse serum—the relation of the immune to the sensitized state is discussed in Chapter XLVIII—and in consequence eliminated the antibody from their circulation much more rapidly than did the normal rabbits. The same phenomenon will occur when a person who has previously received an injection of horse serum is given an antitoxic or antibacterial serum derived from that animal (see Hooker and Follensby 1931).

The influence of previous sensitization may be even more marked when an antiserum is injected by the subcutaneous or intramuscular route. The cells of a sensitized or immunized animal take up, or fix, some of the antibody distributed throughout the tissues *via* the circulating blood.   As a result these cells, or some of them, are able to combine specific-

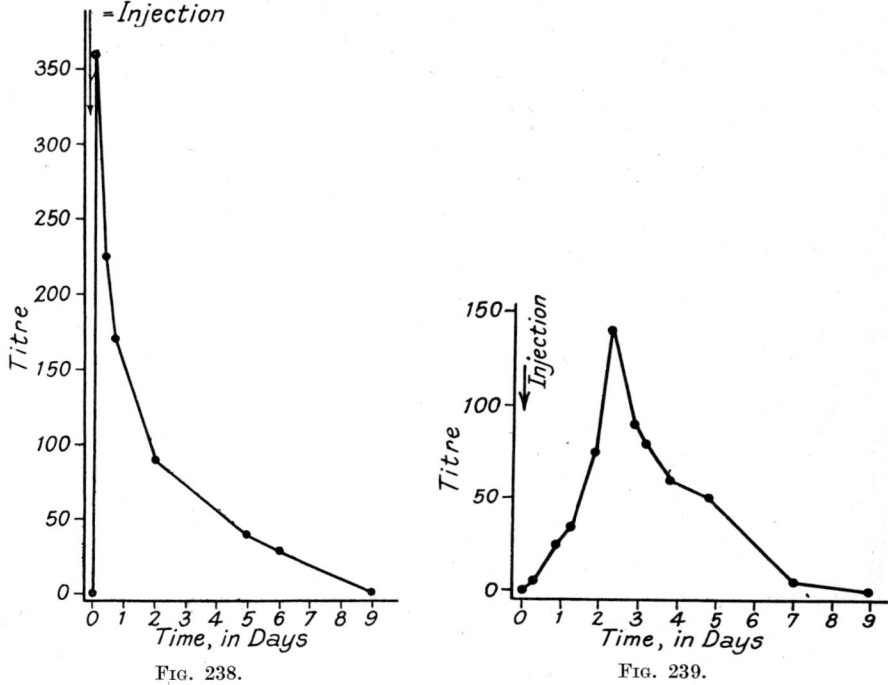

Fɪɢ. 238.

Disappearance of agglutinins from circulation of a rabbit after intravenous
injection of agglutinating serum.
(After Smith.)

Fɪɢ. 239.

Rise and fall of agglutinins in blood of a rabbit
after subcutaneous injection of agglutinating
serum.

(After Smith.)

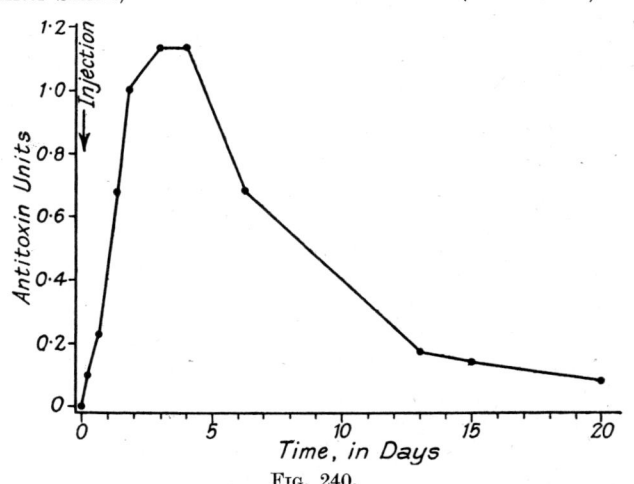

Fɪɢ. 240.

Rise and fall of antitoxin in blood of human subject after subcutaneous injection of antitoxic
serum.
(After Smith.)

ally with the corresponding antigen. The intracutaneous, subcutaneous or intramuscular injection of an antiserum prepared in the horse into an animal already sensitized to horse

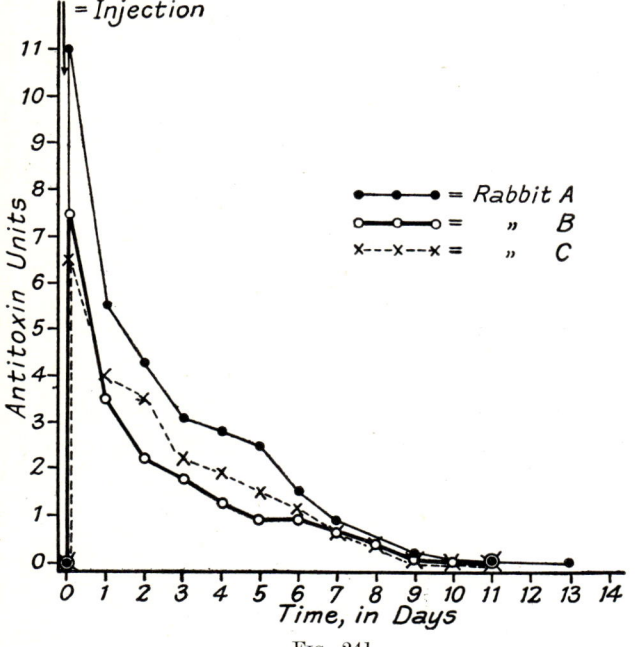

Fig. 241.

Disappearance of antitoxin from blood of three normal rabbits, after intravenous injection of antitoxic horse serum.

(After Glenny and Hopkins.)

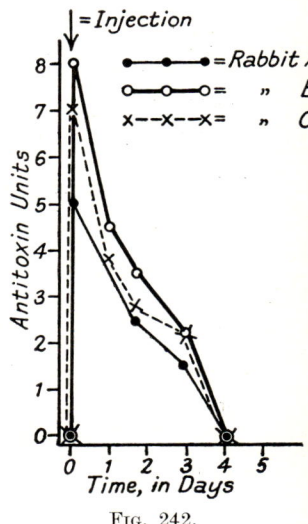

Fig. 242.

Disappearance of antitoxin from blood of three rabbits, previously sensitized to normal horse serum, after intravenous injection of antitoxic horse serum.

(After Glenny and Hopkins.)

serum, appears to be followed by the fixation of a large proportion of the serum at, or in the neighbourhood of, the site of injection, with a consequent reduction in its therapeutic or prophylactic effect (see Kahn and McDermott 1934, Kahn 1934).

SUMMARY

(1) The available evidence indicates that the cells of the reticulo-endothelial system, which are known to remove injected antigenic material from the blood and tissue fluids, play an essential part in the production of antibodies. Whether these cells themselves produce the antibodies in their final and complete form, or whether their rôle is confined to the temporary retention of antigen and its subsequent liberation in an altered or unaltered state, the actual synthesis of antibodies occurring elsewhere, cannot yet be determined. The present indications are that the part played by the reticulo-endothelial system is not confined to the retention and release of unaltered antigens.

(2) The antibody-forming apparatus responds in a characteristic way to a specific stimulus provided by the introduction of an antigen into the tissues. This response differs as regards its time relations, extent and even its occurrence or non-occurrence, in different animals and with different antigens, but its general form

is of a well-defined type. Following an optimal injection of an antigen which evokes an effective primary response there is a lag period of a few days followed by the appearance in the blood of the corresponding antibody. The titre of this antibody rises rapidly to a maximum which is usually attained between the 10th and 22nd day after inoculation. It then falls, at first rapidly then more slowly, reaching a level which is maintained with little alteration for several months. The final disappearance of antibodies from the blood stream may not occur for many months, or even years.

(3) The amount of antibody produced in response to a single injection of antigen varies with the amount of antigen injected. There is a threshold dose—often extremely small—below which no response is obtained. With increasing doses there is an increase in antibody production as judged by the maximal titre attained in the blood, but the increase is not in simple proportion ; a large increase in dosage usually results in a relatively smaller increase in titre. As the dose increases still further the ratio of increase in titre to increase in dose grows smaller and smaller, until a maximum effective dose appears to be attained, provided that a lower limit of dosage is not imposed by the toxicity of the antigenic material.

(4) The antibody-forming apparatus is capable of responding simultaneously to the injection of several different antigens, but the multiple response tends to be less effective against any one antigen than if it were responding to that antigen alone.

(5) The antibody-forming apparatus displays a characteristic difference in its response to primary and subsequent injections of the same antigen. Following a secondary stimulus antibody production is usually more rapid and more copious than after the primary stimulus, and the decline in titre of circulating antibodies after a maximum has been reached is usually delayed. An immunized differs from a normal animal, not only in the possession of a particular antibody, but in its capacity to produce that antibody rapidly and in large amount in response to the specific stimulus.

(6) Repeated inoculations are on this account more effective in raising the antibody titre to a high level than a single injection, even of a very large dose. Just as there appears to be a limit to the titre that can be attained by increasing the size of a single dose of antigenic material so there is a limit beyond which repeated injections fail to force the titre.

(7) The injection of a large dose of antigen into an animal in whose blood the corresponding antibody is present frequently results in a temporary fall in the concentration of that antibody, followed in most cases by a secondary rise.

(8) Antibody formation may be induced by the administration of antigens by the mouth, by inhalation, or by intranasal instillation. Administration by these routes is, in general, less effective than direct inoculation into the tissues. In the case of administration *per os* there is evidence that antibodies may be produced against certain antigenic components but not against others.

(9) Although the majority of naturally occurring antigens are proteins, or contain protein components, recent observations have shown that other substances, such as complex polysaccharides, are capable of inducing an active immunity, and, in some cases at least, of stimulating antibody production.

(10) There is evidence that non-specific stimulation of the antibody-producing apparatus may under certain conditions result in some increase in the concentration of a normal antibody or in the renewed production or mobilization of an antibody

previously produced in response to a specific stimulus ; but such evidence is conflicting.   It is clear that this non-specific response occurs very irregularly, is usually trivial or transitory in its effect, and is never comparable to the response to a further injection of the specific antigen.

(11) The rate at which antibody, contained in any foreign antiserum, reaches the blood and tissue fluids of a normal animal and the concentration there attained depend in great part on the route by which the antiserum is injected.   If the animal or man has received a previous injection of any serum of the same animal origin the antibody will be eliminated at a greatly increased rate.

REFERENCES

ALEXANDER, J. (1931) *Protoplasma*, **14**, 296.
AVERY, O. T. and GOEBEL, W. F.   (1933) *J. exp. Med.*, **58**, 731.
BATELLI, F.   (1904) *C. R. Soc. Biol.*, **56**, 199.
BECHT, F. C. and GREER, J. R.   (1910) *J. infect. Dis.*, **7**, 127.
BENJAMIN, E. and SLUKA, E.   (1908) *Wien. klin. Wschr.*, **21**, 311.
BENJAMIN, E. and WITZINGER, O.   (1912) *Z. Kinderheilk.*, **3**, 73.
BERGER, E. and ERLENMEYER, H.   (1931) *Z. Hyg. InfektKr.*, **113**, 79.
BIELING, R. and ISAAC, S.   (1921) *Z. ges. exp. Med.*, **25**, 1 ; (1922*a*) *Ibid.*, **26**, 251 ; (1922*b*)
    Ibid., **28**, 154.
BOIVIN, A., MESROBEANU, I., and MESROBEANU, L.   (1933*a*) *C. R. Soc. Biol.*, **113**, 490 ;
    (1933*b*) *Ibid.*, **114**, 307 ; (1934*a*) *Ibid.*, **115**, 306 ; (1934*b*) *Ibid.*, **117**, 271.
BOIVIN, A., MESROBEANU, I., and MESROBEANU, L.   (1935) *Arch. roum. Path. exp. Microbiol.*,
    8, 45.
BOIVIN, A. and MESROBEANU, L.   (1933) *C. R. Soc. Biol.*, **112**, 76 ; (1934*a*) *Ibid.*, **115**, 304,
    309 ; (1934*b*) *Ibid.*, **117**, 273 ; (1934*c*) *C. R. Acad. Sci.*, **198**, 2211 ; (1935*a*) *C. R. Soc.
    Biol.*, **118**, 612 ; (1935*b*) *C. R. Acad. Sci.*, **201**, 168.
BRIENL, F. and HAUROWITZ, F.   (1930) *Z. physiol. Chem.*, **192**, 45.
CANNON, P. R. and SULLIVAN, F. L.   (1932) *Proc. Soc. exp. Biol., N.Y.*, **29**, 517.
CARREL, A. and INGEBRIGSTEN, R.   (1912) *J. exp. Med.*, **15**, 287.
CARY, W. E.   (1922) *J. med. Res.*, **43**, 399.
CLEVERS, J.   (1921) *C. R. Soc. Biol.*, **85**, 659.
CONRADI, H. and BIELING, R.   (1916) *Dtsch. med. Wschr.*, **42**, 1280.
CORRIGAN, M.   (1925) *J. infect. Dis.*, **37**, 549.
DEAN, H. R. and WEBB, R. A.   (1928) *J. Path. Bact.*, **31**, 89.
DEUTSCH, L.   (1899) *Ann. Inst. Pasteur*, **13**, 639.
DREYER, G. and WALKER, E. W. A.   (1909) *J. Path. Bact.*, **14**, 28.
DUNGERN, F. VON.   (1902) " Die Antikörper."   Jena.
ECKER, E. E. and GOLDBLATT, H.   (1921) *J. exp. Med.*, **34**, 275.
FALLOISE, A.   (1903) *Bull. Acad. roy. de Belg.*, p. 521.
FINLAND, M. and SUTLIFF, W. D.   (1932) *J. exp. Med.*, **55**, 853.
FJELDSTAD, C. A.   (1910) *Amer. J. Physiol.*, **26**, 72.
FLECKSEDER, R.   (1916) *Wien. klin. Wschr.*, **29**, 637, 641.
FRANCIS, T. J. and TILLETT, W. S.   (1930) *J. exp. Med.*, **52**, 573.
FRÄNKEL, E. and GRUNENBERG, K.   (1924) *Z. ges. exp. Med.*, **41**, 581.
FREUND, J.   (1930) *J. exp. Med.*, **51**, 889.
FRIEDBERGER, E. and DORNER.   (1905) *Zbl. Bakt.*, **38**, 544.
GAY, F. P. and CLARK, A. R.   (1924) *J. Amer. med. Ass.*, **83**, 1296.
GLENNY, A. T.   (1925*a*) *J. Path. Bact.*, **28**, 241, 252 ; (1925*b*) *J. Hyg., Camb.*, **24**, 301 ; (1931)
    " System of Bacteriology."   *Med. res. Coun., Lond.*, **6**, 106.
GLENNY, A. T. and HOPKINS, B. E.   (1922) *J. Hyg., Camb.*, **21**, 142.
GLENNY, A. T., HOPKINS, B. E., and WADDINGTON, H.   (1925) *J. Path. Bact.*, **28**, 305.
GLENNY, A. T. and SÜDMERSEN, H. J.   (1921) *J. Hyg., Camb.*, **20**, 176.
GLENNY, A. T. and WADDINGTON, H.   (1926) *J. Path. Bact.*, **29**, 118 ; (1928) *Ibid.*, **31**, 403.
GOLDBERG, S. J.   (1901) *Zbl. Bakt.*, **30**, 605.
GREENWOOD, M., TOPLEY, W. W. C., and WILSON, J.   (1931) *J. Hyg., Camb.*, **31**, 484.
HAHN, M. and LANGER, H.   (1917) *Z. ImmunForsch.*, **26**, 199.
HARTLEY, P.   (1935) *Brit. J. exp. Path.*, **16**, 468.

HEKTOEN, L. (1911) *J. infect. Dis.*, **9**, 103 ; (1915) *Ibid.*, **17**, 415 ; (1916*a*) *Ibid.*, **19**, 69 ; (1916*b*) *Ibid.*, **19**, 737 ; (1918) *Ibid.*, **22**, 28 ; (1920) *Ibid.*, **27**, 23.
HEKTOEN, L. and BOOR, A. K. (1931) *J. infect. Dis.*, **48**, 588.
HEKTOEN, L. and CARLSON, A. J. (1910) *J. infect. Dis.*, **7**, 319.
HEKTOEN, L. and CORPER, H. J. (1920) *J. infect. Dis.*, **26**, 330 ; (1921) *Ibid.*, **28**, 279 ; (1922) *Ibid.*, **31**, 305
HEKTOEN, L. and CURTIS, A. C. (1915) *J. infect. Dis.*, **17**, 409.
HOOKER, S. B. and BOYD, W. C. (1931) *J. Immunol.*, **21**, 113 ; (1932) *Ibid.*, **23**, 465.
HOOKER, S. B. and FOLLENSBY, E. M. (1931) *J. Immunol.*, **20**, 269.
HORGAN, E. S. (1925) *Brit. J. exp. Path.*, **6**, 108.
HOSMER-ZAMBELLI, F. (1931) *G. Batt. Immun.*, **6**, 165.
HOUSSAY, B. A. and SORDELLI, A. (1921) *C. R. Soc. Biol.*, **85**, 679.
HUGHES, W. T. and CARLSON, A. J. (1908) *Amer. J. Physiol.*, **21**, 236.
HUNTOON, F. M. and CRAIG, S. H. (1921) *J. Immunol.*, **6**, 235.
JÖRGENSEN, A. (1905) *Zbl. Bakt.*, **38**, 556.
JUNGEBLUT, C. W. and BERLOT, J. A. (1926) *J. exp. Med.*, **43**, 613, 797 ; (1926) *Ibid.*, **44**, 129.
KAHN, R. L. (1934) *J. Immunol.*, **27**, 143.
KAHN, R. L. and MCDERMOTT. (1934) *J. Immunol.*, **27**, 125.
KANAI, S. (1921) *Brit. J. exp. Path.*, **2**, 256.
KLINGER, R. (1918) *Z. ImmunForsch.*, **27**, 532.
LANDAU, H. (1918) *Z. Hyg. InfektKr.*, **86**, 260.
LÄWEN. (1909). See HEKTOEN. (1915).
LEWIS, P. A. and LOOMIS, D. (1926) *J. exp. Med.*, **43**, 263.
LUCKHARDT, A. B. and BECHT, F. C. (1911) *Amer. J. Physiol.*, **28**, 257, 274.
LÜDKE, H. (1912) *Berl. klin. Wschr.*, **49**, 1034.
MCINTOSH, J. and KINGSBURY, A. N. (1924) *Brit. J. exp. Path.*, **5**, 18.
MATSUDA, T. (1924) *Z. ImmunForsch.*, **41**, 44.
MEYER, H. (1926) *Z. Hyg. InfektKr.*, **106**, 124.
MEYER, K. and LOEWENTHAL, H. (1928) *Z. ImmunForsch.*, **54**, 409.
MUDD, S. (1932) *J. Immunol.*, **23**, 423.
OBERMAYER, F. and PICK, E. P. (1904) *Wien. klin. Wschr.*, **17**, 265.
ØRSKOV, J. and SCHMIDT, A. (1928) *Z. ImmunForsch.*, **55**, 69.
OTTEN, L. and KIRSCHNER, L. (1927) *Z. Hyg. InfektKr.*, **107**, 314.
PAGANO, G. (1894) *Arch. ital. Biol.*, **20**, 110.
PFEIFFER, R. and LUBINSKI, H. (1930) *Zbl. Bakt.*, **118**, 152.
PFEIFFER, R. and MARX. (1898) *Z. Hyg. InfektKr.*, **37**,, 272.
PIJPER, A. and DAU, H. (1930) *Brit. J. exp. Path.*, **11**, 112.
PRZYGODE, P. (1913) *Wien. klin. Wschr.*, **26**, 841 ; (1914) *Ibid.*, **27**, 201.
RAISTRICK, H. and TOPLEY, W. W. C. (1934) *Brit. J. exp. Path.*, **15**, 113.
REITER, H. (1913) *Z. ImmunForsch.*, **18**, 5.
RÖMER, P. H. (1901) *v. Graefes Arch. Ophthal.*, **52**, 72.
ROSENTHAL, F. and FISCHER, M. (1922) *Klin. Wschr.*, **1**, 2265.
ROSHER, A. B. (1924) *Lancet*, ii. 110.
ROSS, V. (1926) *J. Immunol.*, **12**, 237 ; (1930) *J. exp. Med.*, **51**, 585 ; (1931) *Ibid.*, **54**, 875, 899 ; (1932) *Ibid.*, **55**, 1; (1934) *J. Immunol.*, **27**, 235, 249, 273, 307.
ROUX, E. and VAILLARD, L. (1893) *Ann. Inst. Pasteur*, **7**, 65.
RUSK, G. Y. (1914) *Univ. Calif. publ. Path.*, **2**, 139.
SCARFF, R. W. (1931) *J. Path. Bact.*, **34**, 119.
SCHIEMANN, O. (1929) *Z. Hyg. InfektKr.*, **110**, 567.
SCHIEMANN, O. and CASPER, W. (1927) *Z. Hyg. InfektKr.*, **108**, 220.
SCHILF, F. (1926) *Zbl. Bakt.*, **97**, 219.
SCHMIDT, S. (1926) *Z. ImmunForsch.*, **45**, 305.
SIEGMUND, H. (1922) *Klin. Wschr.*, **1**, 2307, 2566.
SIMONDS, J. P. and JONES, H. M. (1915) *J. med. Res.*, **33**, 197.
SMITH, H. (1907) *J. Hyg., Camb.*, **7**, 205.
STANDENATH, F. (1923) *Z. ImmunForsch.*, **38**, 19.
STEABEN, D. B. (1925) *Brit. J. exp. Path.*, **6**, 1.
STILLMAN, E. G. (1927) *J. exp. Med.*, **45**, 1057 ; (1930) *Ibid.*, **52**, 215, 225.
TAKÉ, M. N. (1923) *J. infect. Dis.*, **32**, 138.
TOPLEY, W. W. C. (1930) *J. Path. Bact.*, **33**, 339.
TRAWINSKI, A. (1932) *Zbl. Bakt.*, **123**, 336.
TROMMSDORF, R. (1921) *Z. ImmunForsch.*, **32**, 379.
TSUKAHARA, I. (1921) *Z. ImmunForsch.*, **32**, 410.
TSURUMI, M. and KOHDA, K. (1913) *Z. ImmunForsch.*, **19**, 519.
TUFT, L. (1934) *J. Immunol.*, **27**, 63.
VANUCCI, D. (1924) *Sperimentale*, **78**, 23.
WALBUM, L. E. (1925) *Z. ImmunForsch.*, **43**, 433 ; (1926) *Ibid.*, **47**, 213.

WALBUM, L. E. and BERTHELSEN, K.   (1925) *Z. ImmunForsch.*, **42,** 467.
WALBUM, L. E. and MORCH, J. R.   (1923) *Ann. Inst. Pasteur*, **37,** 397.
WASSERMANN, A. and CITRON, J.   (1905) *Z. Hyg. InfektKr.*, **50,** 331.
WEICHARDT, W.   (1922) *Ergebn. Hyg.*, **5,** 275.
WEICHARDT, W. and SCHRÄDER, E.   (1919) *Münch. med. Wschr.*, **66,** 289.
WRIGHT, A. E.   (1909) " Studies in Immunization."   London.
ZOZAYA, J. and CLARK, J.   (1932) *Proc. Soc. exp. Biol., N.Y.*, **30,** 44 ; (1933) *J. exp. Med.*, **57,** 21.

CHAPTER XLVIII

ANAPHYLAXIS, HYPERSENSITIVENESS AND ALLERGY

In the preceding chapters we have considered a series of reactions most of which have as a common factor the property of affording specific protection against bacteria or their products. Numerous observations, both clinical and experimental, have afforded instances of the contrary condition, in which an individual is, or may be rendered, more susceptible to some noxious agent than are the generality of his own species. In some cases an individual may become highly sensitive to an agent which is entirely innocuous to his normal fellows. The phenomenon of hypersensitiveness is presented in its clearest and least ambiguous form when the exciting agent is some non-living material, so that there is no question of multiplication within the body, or of the complex and variable tissue reactions that are associated with bacterial infection. It will be convenient to consider first the data relating to this type of abnormal sensitivity, and then to discuss its bearing on the phenomena of bacterial disease. It will also simplify matters to start with the most striking and clear-cut case of hypersensitiveness—the phenomenon of acute anaphylactic shock.

ANAPHYLACTIC SHOCK

The detailed study of this curious reaction dates from the beginning of the present century, though several observations are on record in the earlier literature which with our fuller knowledge we can recognize as undoubted examples of anaphylaxis. The observations of Richet and his co-workers (Portier and Richet 1902, Richet 1907) first drew general attention to the experimental facts ; though the issue was at this stage obscured by the chance that the agent selected for study was itself toxic for the experimental animal employed. Richet observed that dogs which had survived a single injection of an extract of certain actinians might succumb rapidly, and with a curious and characteristic symptom complex, to a second injection of the same material given after days or weeks. It was this substitution of increased susceptibility for the increased resistance which usually follows the injection of sublethal doses of a toxic material that led him to coin the term *anaphylaxis*.

At about the same time Theobald Smith in America had noted the abnormal sensitiveness of guinea-pigs to widely spaced injections of toxin-antitoxin mixtures. He communicated these observations to Ehrlich in 1904 ; and Otto in 1905 published the results obtained in a detailed study of this phenomenon. He showed that the horse serum in the mixtures, not the toxin, was the essential agent ; that an interval of 10 days elapsed after the sensitizing dose before hypersensitiveness was established ; and that no hypersensitiveness resulted when large injections of serum were given at short intervals.

The same phenomenon was studied independently by Rosenau and Anderson (1906, 1907), who established the strict specificity of the reaction. They found that guinea-pigs sensitized to horse serum showed little if any hypersensitiveness to the serum of other animals, such as the rabbit, cat, dog, pig, sheep, chicken or man. Similarly, guinea-pigs sensitized to horse serum did not respond in any abnormal way to the subsequent injection of egg-white, vegetable protein or milk. They noted also that the amount of serum required to produce sensitization was extremely small ; as little as 0·000,001 c.c. sometimes induced typical hypersensitiveness. The amount required to produce anaphylactic shock in a sensitized animal was, however, considerably greater (0·01–0·1 c.c.). They confirmed the existence of a latent period of 10–12 days between the sensitizing injection and the establishment of the anaphylactic state, and noted that, once established, this state lasted for an indefinite period, extending over several months at least.

These observations have been repeatedly and consistently confirmed by later workers. Animals may be actively sensitized by the injection of any substance that is antigenic in the full sense. The sensitizing injection may be given by any route. Often a single sensitizing dose suffices. In some animals, and with some antigens, it is necessary to give more than one sensitizing injection, and to use doses far larger than the minute amount that suffices in the particular case of the sensitization of the guinea-pig to horse serum ; but the same principle holds—the injections must not be too large, nor too often repeated.

As regards the shock-inducing, or " assaulting " injection, either the antigen used for sensitization, or certain types of separated haptens containing the specific reactive grouping, are effective in eliciting the characteristic symptoms. The route of injection is important. Intravenous inoculation gives the most constant results ; in some animals it is the only effective route for this purpose. In the guinea-pig, which is peculiarly susceptible in this respect, shock may be produced by intraperitoneal inoculation, but larger doses are required.

A curious and significant fact emerged early in the widespread investigation which followed the opening-up of this new field of research. The symptoms and lesions of anaphylactic shock were found to be constant for a given animal species, irrespective of the nature of the sensitizing antigen ; while these symptoms and lesions differed sharply from one animal species to another. Thus the guinea-pig reacts in the same way when anaphylactic shock is produced with horse serum, egg albumin, milk or various bacterial antigens ; but the reactions of the sensitized guinea-pig, rabbit and dog to horse serum differ sharply and characteristically from one another.

Anaphylactic Shock in the Guinea-pig.—After a sensitized guinea-pig has received an intravenous injection of the specific antigen, it at first remains quiet ; but within a minute marked restlessness develops. The hair begins to bristle over the head and neck, and the animal usually rises on its hind legs, rubs its nose vigorously, and emits loud spasmodic sneezes. Often it gives a jump, or a series of jumps. Within a few minutes tonic and clonic convulsions set in, and the animal falls on its side. The respiration becomes slow, the mouth opening with each violent inspiratory effort ; and breathing ceases within a few minutes. The heart continues to beat for several minutes after breathing has ceased.

The post-mortem findings were first described in any detail by Gay and Southard (1908) ; but it is to Auer and Lewis (1910) that we owe the first adequate account of the physiological reactions that lead up to the fatal issue. In guinea-pigs examined immediately after death from fatal anaphylactic shock, these observers confirmed the presence of intestinal congestion and the occurrence of active peristaltic movements that had been previously noted. They observed the frequency of hæmorrhages on the under side of the diaphragm, and noted, as Gay and Southard had done, the distension of the lungs ; but they showed that this distension was not due to simple emphysema. The lungs remained distended long after the thorax was freely opened. Even when removed from the body they showed no sign of collapse ; and portions cut off from the pulmonary lobes, if not too small, remained in their condition of dilatation. More detailed examination showed that the distension was caused by contraction of the bronchioles, which retained the inspired air in the dilated alveoli. The death of the animal was clearly referable to suffocation consequent on this obstruction to respiration. Auer and Lewis showed that the bronchiolar contraction was not prevented by section of the vagi or by the administration of curare, and was therefore of muscular or immediately neuro-muscular origin. They showed also that the blood pressure during anaphylactic shock at first rose considerably and then fell slowly but steadily till death, as one would expect in asphyxia.

Anaphylactic Shock in the Rabbit.—The rabbit, like the guinea-pig, suffers from acute anaphylactic shock if the sensitization is adequate, and if a sufficient amount of antigen is subsequently administered by the intravenous route. The reaction is not, however, so readily elicited. The symptoms of shock differ in several important respects. The preliminary signs of irritation, the coughing and the violent inspiratory efforts are absent. The animal lies with outstretched legs or falls on its side, gives a series of convulsive movements often associated with the passage of urine and fæces, and dies. In many cases irregular respiratory movements continue for a brief period after the heart has ceased to beat—a reversal of the order of cessation observed in the guinea-pig. At necropsy the pulmonary dilatation, which is so striking a feature in the guinea-pig, is absent in the rabbit. The most characteristic abnormality found in the latter is the extreme dilatation of the right side of the heart. Coca (1919) showed that this dilatation was associated with marked obstruction to the pulmonary circulation, evidenced by the increased pressure required to drive fluid from the pulmonary artery to the left auricle. He concluded that acute anaphylactic death in the rabbit was due to a spasmodic constriction of the branches of the pulmonary artery, followed by rapid dilatation of the right side of the heart and acute heart failure. His observations and conclusions have been confirmed by other workers (Drinker and Bronfenbrenner 1924, Grove 1932a, b).

Anaphylactic Shock in the Dog.—A sensitized dog, after receiving an intravenous injection of the specific antigen, shows marked signs of restlessness and excitement. Within a few minutes the animal vomits and usually passes urine and fæces, the latter sometimes blood-stained. It then collapses and lies prone. The muscles of the limbs are relaxed, and the dog appears extremely weak. Respiration is slow, and often deep and laboured. Stridor may be heard, and a little froth may exude from the lips. In rapidly fatal shock the weakness progresses, renewed diarrhœa and vomiting set in, and coma, occasionally associated with epileptiform convulsions, leads on to death. It has been pointed out by Dean and Webb (1924) that the reaction almost always occurs in two stages, the initial acute symptoms being followed by some signs of recovery. In fatal cases these soon give place to the second stage of increasing collapse. In other instances severe initial shock is followed by a rapid return to normal.

As pointed out by Biedl and Kraus (1909), anaphylactic shock in the dog is associated with a progressive fall in blood pressure ; later investigations (Pearce and Eisenbrey 1910, Dale 1920b) have made it clear that this is not due to any failure of output from the heart or to any influence of the central nervous system, but to the collection and stagnation of the blood somewhere in the tissues. The studies of Dale and his colleagues (Dale 1920b) render it highly probable that capillary dilatation is the essential factor.

Manwaring (1910) performed a large number of experiments in an attempt to localize the site of reaction ; and, having found that shock did not occur when the abdominal vessels were ligated, proceeded to explore the rôle of the various abdominal viscera by a series of operative experiments designed to exclude each in turn. He found that the exclusion of the liver inhibited acute shock in dogs; and his observations have been amply confirmed by subsequent workers (Voegtlin and Bernheim 1911, Denecke 1914). These results accord well with the findings at necropsy. The congestion of the abdominal viscera has been noted by many observers; and Weil (1917) points out that in dogs dying of anaphylactic shock in its acutest form the single outstanding feature at necropsy is the enormous distension and congestion of the liver.

We may briefly note certain additional phenomena, which seem to be general to anaphylactic shock as displayed by any of the species so far investigated, though not developed to an equal degree in all of them. There is commonly a marked leucopænia; and this, as Webb (1924) has shown, is associated with an aggregation of polymorphonuclear cells in the capillaries of the lungs, a phenomenon clearly analogous to that which follows the intravenous injection of bacteria in immunized animals. There is a decrease in the coagulability of the blood, most marked in the dog. There appears to be a decrease in the amount of complement in the circulating blood. There is a marked fall in body temperature.

Anaphylactic Shock in Other Animals.—Although the guinea-pig, rabbit and dog have been studied more extensively than any other species in regard to their anaphylactic reactions, a considerable number of experiments have been carried out on other animals; and it is instructive to note that, in addition to striking differences in behaviour and physiological reaction during anaphylactic shock, various species differ widely from one another in the ease with which they can be sensitized. Thus, among rodents, the rat appears to occupy a peculiar position in that it is extremely refractory to sensitization (Longcope 1922, Parker and Parker 1924, Spain and Grove 1925); though an anaphylactic response can be demonstrated under suitable conditions (Kellaway 1930). Birds, so far as they have been examined, may be sensitized by the usual procedures (Friedberger and Hartoch 1909); and the anaphylactic reaction in the pigeon has been studied in some detail (Gahringer 1926, Hanzlik and Stockton 1927). Sensitization to foreign proteins, associated with phenomena which are anaphylactic in kind but do not include typical shock, has been described in cold-blooded animals such as the frog (Goodner 1926). In monkeys, and this is of particular interest for the student of human pathology, sensitization appears to be induced irregularly and with considerable difficulty. Zinsser (1920) reports his failure to sensitize *rhesus* or ringtail monkeys with a single injection of horse serum; and he could produce only mild anaphylactic symptoms after treatment with repeated doses of antigen.

The problem of human anaphylaxis will be most conveniently considered in relation to the problem of natural hypersensitiveness.

Passive Anaphylaxis.

It was noted by some of the earliest workers in this field that female guinea-pigs which had been actively sensitized gave birth to young that were themselves hypersensitive. Otto (1907) first demonstrated that the anaphylactic state could be passively transferred by injecting the serum from an anaphylactic into a normal animal, and in so doing placed anaphylactic shock in the category of the *in vivo* antigen-antibody reactions. His findings were soon confirmed and extended by other workers, in particular by Doerr and Russ (1909), and the numerous observations which have since been recorded place the following propositions on a firm basis of experimental fact, so far at least as the guinea-pig is concerned. A normal animal that has received an injection of the serum of an actively sensitized animal will respond to the subsequent injection of the corresponding antigen by developing acute anaphylactic shock. Passive sensitization may be effected with equal or even greater certainty by an injection of the serum of an animal that has been

" immunized " against a given antigen by repeated injections, so that it is not itself sensitive to the antigen in question. In either case the injection of the serum is not followed by the *immediate* sensitization of the recipient. An interval of some hours must elapse between the injection of the sensitizing serum and the injection of the corresponding antigen if typical shock is to be regularly obtained. For maximal sensitization the interval is even longer—4 to 6 days (Kellaway and Cowell 1922).

It may be noted that, under suitable experimental conditions, an analogous reaction, " reversed passive anaphylaxis," may be induced in the guinea-pig by injecting antigen first and antibody later (see Kellett 1935).

The efficacy of an antiserum in the induction of passive anaphylaxis appears to be closely related to its content in specific antibody as recorded by precipitin tests (Doerr and Russ 1909), and there seems no reason for supposing that the reagents involved differ from those with which our other immunological studies have made us familiar. The experimental study of this phenomenon has, however, brought to light a relationship that is probably of fundamental importance in immunological mechanisms. Different antisera, produced by the immunization, or sensitization, of animals of different species against a single antigen, differ widely in their ability to induce passive sensitization in a given species of animal.

Thus, Avery and Tillett (1929) and Brown (1934b) found that guinea-pigs could be sensitized to pneumococcal polysaccharides by the injection of antipneumococcal sera prepared in the rabbit, but not by antipneumococcal sera prepared in the horse. Again (see Friedberger and Hartoch 1909, Scott 1931), guinea-pigs cannot be sensitized with the serum of fowls, and pigeons cannot be sensitized with the serum of rabbits. The mouse would appear to resemble the guinea-pig, in that it can be passively sensitized with antipneumococcal serum prepared in the rabbit but not with antipneumococcal horse sera (Mehlman and Seegal 1934).

It will be seen in later sections of this chapter that there are reasons for believing that the fixation of the injected antibody by the tissue cells of the recipient is an essential factor in passive anaphylaxis ; and it is not surprising to find that the serum globulins of different species behave differently in a reaction of this kind.

The phenomena of active and passive anaphylaxis appear, as we have seen, to depend on specific reactions of the antigen-antibody type, and there seems no purpose in burdening our vocabulary with additional labels, such as " anaphylactogens " or " anaphylactic antibodies." It is, however, of interest to inquire how partial antigens, or haptens, behave in this reaction.

The Rôle of Haptens in Anaphylaxis.—Tomcsik and Kurotchkin (1928) immunized rabbits against *Bact. aerogenes*, the pneumobacillus, and a yeast. In each case they were able to obtain a high-titre precipitating serum for the polysaccharide hapten extracted from the corresponding organism. Guinea-pigs injected with these rabbit antisera developed acute anaphylactic shock when subsequently injected with the corresponding hapten. Lancefield (1928) sensitized guinea-pigs with the sera of rabbits immunized against hæmolytic streptococci, and induced acute shock by the injection of the separated haptens. Enders (1929) obtained similar results with a polysaccharide fraction from the tubercle bacillus. Avery and Tillett (1929) and Brown (1934a) have studied the anaphylactic action of the pneumococcal polysaccharides. These haptens will not induce active sensitization in the guinea-pig, but they will induce acute anaphylactic shock in animals passively sensitized by the injection of precipitating antisera prepared in the rabbit, and these reactions are type-specific.

Tillett, Avery and Goebel (1929) have tested the anaphylactic response to synthetic sugar-proteins. They prepared p-aminophenol glucoside and p-aminophenol galactoside and linked these to serum globulin and to egg albumin. Preliminary precipitation tests showed that antisera produced in rabbits reacted specifically *in vitro* with the carbohydrate groupings. Guinea-pigs passively sensitized by the injection of an anti-glucoside-globulin serum developed typical anaphylactic shock when subsequently injected with glucoside-albumin. Guinea-pigs sensitized with anti-galactoside-globulin serum reacted similarly when injected with galactoside-albumin. In each case the reaction was shown to be specific. Active sensitization with the globulin compounds, followed after 11 days by injection of the corresponding albumin compounds gave similar results. The unconjugated glucoside or galactoside did not induce shock when injected into sensitized animals, but each inhibited anaphylactic shock when injected immediately prior to the injection of the corresponding carbohydrate-protein compound. Klopstock and Selter (1929) carried out similar experiments and obtained similar results, using compounds of protein with atoxyl, or with the sodium salt of metanilic acid. Landsteiner and Levine (1930) sensitized guinea-pigs to the d- and l-isomers of p-amino-tartranilic acid, in each case coupled to horse globulin. The subsequent injection of the corresponding active groupings coupled to chicken globulin induced anaphylactic shock. The shock could be specifically inhibited by a preliminary injection of a compound of resorcinol with the active grouping concerned. Similar results were obtained with guinea-pigs passively sensitized to p-amino-arsanilic acid, the active substance being coupled to tyrosine for the inhibition tests.

Specific Desensitization.—The specific desensitization of sensitized animals was recorded by many of the earlier investigators (Otto 1905, Rosenau and Anderson 1906, 1907, 1908, Besredka and Steinhardt 1907, Gay and Southard 1908). Desensitization—as then observed, and in the sense in which this term is now commonly employed—differs from the inhibitory effect induced by simple haptens in that the desensitizing agent is the complete antigen, which is capable, when administered intravenously in adequate doses, of inducing typical shock. The desensitizing effect is obtained, in place of acute shock, if a very minute dose of antigen is given and repeated, or if rather larger doses are given by a route, such as the subcutaneous, which ensures slow absorption. The essential conditions for success appear to be the administration of an amount of antigen that is adequate in total by some method that prevents any rapid accumulation in the circulating blood. It would seem that desensitization, however it is induced, is purely temporary, the anaphylactic, or hypersensitive state being re-established in a few days or weeks (Valléry-Radot *et al.* 1936, Adelsberger 1936, Gernez 1936).

The Mechanism of Anaphylactic Shock.

It is clear that acute anaphylactic shock, as induced by any of the procedures that have been described above, belongs to the category of the specific antigen-antibody reactions. The only question at issue is the mechanism by which this primary reaction gives rise to the series of events that characterize acute shock in any given animal species.

Two opposing views have been put forward. According to one the reaction between antigen and antibody, occurring in the circulating blood or in the tissue fluids, gives rise to a toxic product, anaphylatoxin, which, acting on susceptible cells, gives rise to the characteristic syndrome. According to the other the primary reaction occurs not in the blood or tissue fluids but on or in the tissue cells ; and the reactions that characterize acute shock are due not to any toxicity of the antigen-antibody compound itself, or of any derivative from it, but to cellular disturbances initiated by the antigen-antibody reaction. As we shall see, the picture that has been pieced together during the last ten years derives, in all its essential outlines, from the cellular school, though it contains details reminiscent of the anaphylatoxin hypothesis.

The Humoral or Anaphylatoxin Hypothesis.—The chief protagonist of this conception of the mechanism of acute anaphylactic shock was Friedberger (1910, 1912, 1913), who had at an earlier period been one of the sponsors of the cellular hypothesis. Certain difficulties in the latter theory, not easily explicable in the light of the knowledge then available, had caused him to modify his views ; but his complete *volte-face* was largely determined by the observation of Friedemann (1909) that a guinea-pig could be poisoned with the characteristic symptoms of acute shock by injecting a mixture of an antigen and its homologous antibody after a brief period of incubation *in vitro*.

The humoral theory in its original form postulated a union of antigen with antibody in the circulating blood, followed by a cleavage of the resulting complex, presumably of the hydrolytic type, and the setting free of toxic degradation products—a conception which seemed to accord well with the findings of Vaughan and Wheeler (1907) on the toxicity of the intermediate products of proteolytic degradation in general. Friedemann's observations, which have been repeatedly confirmed, seemed at first to afford a direct demonstration of the production of anaphylatoxin from antigen and antibody *in vitro* ; but it soon became clear that sera could be rendered toxic, in this sense, by a variety of procedures in which antigen and antibody played no part. Thus anaphylatoxin can be produced by incubating normal serum with kaolin (Ritz and Sachs 1911, Keysser and Wassermann 1911, Mutermilch 1913), barium sulphate (Mutermilch), talc (Mutermilch), starch (Ritz and Sachs 1918), inulin (Nathan 1914), or agar (Bordet and Zuntz 1914). The humoral theory in its earlier form was often described in terms of Ehrlich's hypothesis—the linkage of complement to antigen by an intermediary amboceptor followed by a proteolysis in which complement acted as an enzyme—and a certain air of probability was lent to this view by the observation that the free complement in the circulating blood may be greatly diminished during anaphylactic shock. But there is no evidence that complement can play such an enzymic rôle ; and the *in vitro* toxification of serum by non-specific adsorbents is clearly not explicable in such terms as these. As an alternative hypothesis it was suggested that the formation of an antigen-antibody compound, or the addition to serum of kaolin, starch or similar reagents, might remove some stabilizing constituent, perhaps antitrypsin, and so initiate a process of auto-digestion—a kind of serum autolysis. The work of Jobling and Petersen (1914) and of Bronfenbrenner (1915), among others, is in accord with this possibility ; but there are almost insuperable objections to its acceptance as an explanation of the *in vitro* toxification of serum, and still more to the view that it forms the essential mechanism of anaphylactic shock *in vivo*. Thus, there has been an almost universal failure to show any relation between the increase in the toxicity of serum under the influence of a toxifying material and chemical changes indicative of proteolysis (de Kruif and German 1917, Dale 1920*b*, Doerr 1922) ; while the rapidity of toxification—under favourable conditions a serum may be rendered highly toxic within a few minutes—is hardly compatible with the known behaviour of proteolytic enzyme reactions. Still more is this the case in acute anaphylactic shock. As early as 1908 Wells pointed out the extreme improbability of the view that the minute amount of egg albumin that suffices to produce almost immediate shock in the sensitized guinea-pig could, in the short interval available, undergo proteolysis with the liberation of a toxic dose of degradation products. The substitution of the serum proteins for the antigen as the supposed substrate removes the quantitative difficulty, but greatly increases that introduced by the time factor. We cannot believe in the formation of an antigen-antibody compound, the adsorption by it of a stabilizing serum constituent, and a consequent digestion of the serum proteins, all occurring within a very few minutes. Moreover, substances that produce *in vitro* toxification of serum may fail to produce anaphylactic symptoms when injected intravenously into animals (Dale 1920*b*, Doerr 1922).

The exact nature of the process which underlies the *in vitro* toxification remains obscure ; but it appears to be related in some way to the redistribution of the plasma constituents that occurs during clotting (Novy, de Kruif and Novy 1917, Novy and de Kruif 1917, de Kruif 1917, de Kruif and German 1917).

Anaphylactoid Shock.—Apart altogether from the difficulties referred to above, it is very doubtful how far the acute and fatal reaction that follows the intravenous injection of a toxified serum can be identified with true anaphylactic shock. The resemblances are certainly striking, and it seems certain that common factors are involved ; but there are certain differences. At necropsy the emphysema of the lungs may be rather less striking, while œdema and hæmorrhage into the pulmonary tissue are more frequent. For this reason there is general agreement that " anaphylactic " should be replaced by the ambiguous but convenient " anaphylactoid " as a descriptive term for this type of shock, and that " anaphylatoxin " should be replaced by " serotoxin " as a designation for the active agent in toxified serum.

There are, in truth, many agents other than toxified sera that may produce a fatal anaphylactoid reaction when injected intravenously into the guinea-pig. A list of such substances given by Harzlik and Karsner (1920, 1924) includes a wide variety of organic colloids and of salts of heavy metals. The syndrome produced differs a little from one anaphylactoid agent to another ; and with none does it resemble completely and in detail that of true anaphylactic shock. The spasm of the bronchioles—the most dramatic of the anaphylactic reactions in the guinea-pig—is in general a prominent feature, though it may vary in degree. There is, however, a high frequency, with these anaphylactoid reagents, of capillary thromboses and embolism in the lungs.

Among such anaphylactoid reagents—and this has been a source of error in several experiments supposed to support the humoral view—must be included all antisera that contain a high concentration of Forssman antibody (see Doerr and Pick 1913, Taniguchi 1922, Scott 1931). The toxic effect is here due, in part at least, to a direct action of the heterophile antibody on the heterogenetic antigen contained in the guinea-pig's tissues. When the serum is injected by the ordinary intravenous route the first stress of this reaction falls on the endothelium of the lung capillaries, resulting in lesions which appear to be identical with those produced by the serotoxins.

Peptone Shock.—Another anaphylactoid reagent is ordinary peptone (de Waele 1907, Biedl and Kraus 1909, Hirschfelder 1910, Doerr 1914, 1922, Dale 1920*a*, 1929, Manwaring, Clark and Chilcote 1923). The resemblance of peptone shock to true anaphylactic shock is very striking. In the guinea-pig there is the typical contraction of the bronchioles, in the dog the fall in blood pressure, and the congestion of the liver. In both there may be found the loss of coagulability of the blood and the multiple small subserous hæmorrhages that are characteristic features of acute anaphylaxis in general. It is probable that peptone, like the serotoxins, acts as a direct endothelial poison (see Dale 1929). In the case of the dog there appears to be an additional action on the liver cells.

Histamine Shock.—Histamine is an amine derived by decarboxylation from histidine. It was isolated from ergot by Barger and Dale (1911) and its pharmacological action has been studied in considerable detail by Dale and his colleagues, and by others (Dale 1913, 1920*a*, *b*, 1929, Dale and Laidlaw 1919, Maunter and Pick 1915, Longcope 1922, Voegtlin and Dyer 1924).

The toxic syndrome produced by histamine reproduces very faithfully several of the characteristic features of acute anaphylaxis. In the guinea-pig the spasm of the bronchioles is constantly present in its most typical form. In the dog (Maunter and Pick 1915, Dale 1929) the muscular walls of the efferent hepatic veins are very sensitive to histamine ; in response to traces of this substance they constrict and dam back the blood in the capillary spaces of the liver. But there are also quite definite points of difference. The loss of the coagulability of the blood and the capillary hæmorrhages that are associated with anaphylactic shock do not occur in histamine poisoning ; and the distension of the dog's liver with blood and lymph in anaphylaxis is far more severe and persistent than that produced by histamine.

The importance of these observations lies in the fact that histamine is a relatively simple substance of known chemical constitution, the pharmocological action of which has been studied in considerable detail. It can hardly be a mere coincidence that on intravenous injection it mimics so closely the syndrome produced by the injection of a non-toxic antigen into a sensitized animal.

Summarizing the evidence up to this point we may say that sera may be treated in various ways that render them toxic, in the sense that they produce when injected intravenously into the guinea-pig a syndrome that closely resembles, but is not identical with, that of acute anaphylactic shock. There is, however, no evidence that an " anaphylatoxin " is produced as the result of an antigen-antibody reaction occurring in the blood stream, nor has any mechanism for the production of such an anaphylatoxin been yet suggested which is compatible with all the known facts. Moreover, many reagents other than toxified sera will produce similar anaphylactoid reactions ; and one reagent of known chemical composition will give rise to some of the most characteristic features of acute shock. It seems clear that the apparent uniformity of the major symptoms of these different *in vivo* reactions is misleading, if we regard it as denoting an identity of underlying mechanism, though we can hardly be mistaken in supposing that some common factor runs through them all. It will be convenient to consider the cellular hypothesis of anaphylactic shock before discussing what this factor is likely to be.

The Cellular Hypothesis.—The essence of this hypothesis is that, for the production of anaphylactic shock, the primary antigen-antibody reaction must occur, not in the blood stream or tissue fluids, but in or on the tissue cells. Why this cellular reaction should give rise to the striking syndrome that characterizes acute shock is a separate problem that we may consider later.

The earliest experiments made it clear that those procedures that led to a high concentration of antibodies in the circulating blood were not those that produced the anaphylactic state. Repeated injections of antigen into a normal animal lead to a high antibody content but not to hypersensitiveness. In passive sensitization the highest concentration of antibody in the blood occurs immediately after the sensitizing injection of antiserum ; but it is only after the lapse of a latent period, during which most of the antibody has disappeared from the blood stream (Fenyvessy and Freund, see Doerr 1922, Weil 1913), that hypersensitiveness is established.

Such facts as these clearly suggested that " fixed," not " circulating " antibody was concerned in the reaction. But far more decisive support for the cellular hypothesis was derived from experiments carried out with isolated tissues from actively and passively sensitized animals.

P.B.   G G

Schultz (1910) excised portions of intestine from sensitized guinea-pigs, suspended them in a bath of Ringer's solution, and studied their response to the addition of the specific antigen. He found that such isolated muscle contracted far more vigorously, when the antigen was added to the bath, than did similar preparations from normal animals when submitted to the action of similar amounts of the same foreign protein. These observations were confirmed and greatly extended by Dale (1913), using an improved technique in which one horn of the guinea-pig's uterus was substituted for the intestinal preparation, and this technique has since been used by Dale and his colleagues (Dale 1920a, b, 1929, Dale and Hartley 1916, Dale and Kellaway 1922), and by Weil (1913–17) in attempts to determine the underlying mechanism of the acute anaphylactic reaction.

The reaction of the sensitized uterine horn is extraordinarily delicate ; a typical contraction may occur after the addition of as little as 1 c.c. of a 1 : 10,000,000 dilution of horse serum to a bath containing 150 c.c. of Locke's solution. It is also sharply specific ; not only does the uterus removed from a guinea-pig sensitized against horse serum fail to respond to the serum of cat, rabbit, dog or man, but it is possible to sensitize separately against the euglobulin, pseudoglobulin and albumin fractions of horse serum (Dale and Hartley 1916).

All the essential features of anaphylaxis can, indeed, be demonstrated *in vitro.* Uterine horns removed from guinea-pigs sensitized either actively or passively respond specifically to the addition of the specific antigen to the bath of Ringer or Locke solution in which they are suspended. Perfusion of the uterus with warm Ringer solution before removal from the body does not abolish its sensitiveness. After a single maximal response to the addition of a relatively large amount of antigen, followed by a change to fresh Ringer's solution, the uterus no longer responds to the addition of fresh antigen : it has been specifically desensitized. If such a desensitized uterus is again washed, soaked for $2\frac{1}{2}$ hours in a 10 per cent. dilution of the specific antiserum, washed in numerous changes of Ringer's solution, and again tested by the addition of antigen, it will give a typical contraction, showing that it has been passively sensitized *in vitro.* The uteri of normal guinea-pigs may be rendered hypersensitive by prolonged perfusion with diluted serum from anaphylactic or immunized guinea-pigs. This hypersensitiveness is hardly perceptible after 1 hour's perfusion, but it is easily perceptible after 5 hours' perfusion, thus affording a striking analogy to the latent period in passive sensitization in the living animal.

A fact of great significance was established by Dale while investigating the response of the uteri from immunized guinea-pigs. These animals had received repeated injections of horse serum increasing in amount. Some of them were injected intraperitoneally with 5 c.c. of horse serum but showed no sign of shock. Nevertheless, the uterine horns, removed from other animals of the same series, reacted with a typical contraction on the addition of horse serum to the bath, thus showing that fixed antibody is present in the immune as well as in the hypersensitive animal, and lending strong support to the view that the immune guinea-pig is protected by the excess of antibody in its circulating blood.

The protective function of circulating antibody is clearly shown in some of Weil's experiments (see Fig. 243, p. 899). A series of guinea-pigs were passively sensitized by the intraperitoneal injection of 0·1 c.c. of rabbit-v-horse serum, i.e. the serum from a rabbit immunized by repeated injections of horse serum. Three days later one animal received 2 c.c. of this antiserum (20 sensitizing doses) and immediately thereafter 0·01 c.c. of horse serum (1–2 anaphylactic doses). This guinea-pig showed slight symptoms only. It was killed ; its uterus was tested by Dale's technique, and its serum was injected into another normal guinea-pig which was tested 24 hours later by the injection of horse serum. The uterus of the first animal gave a typical reaction, showing that it had anchored the antibody injected 3 days previously, and that this fixed antibody had not combined to any appreciable extent with the 0·01 c.c. of antigen subsequently injected under cover of a protective dose of antibody. The second guinea-pig developed typical shock, showing that a considerable amount of the antibody injected into the first guinea-pig immediately prior to the injection of the antigen had remained unneutralized in the circulation. Another sensitized guinea-pig

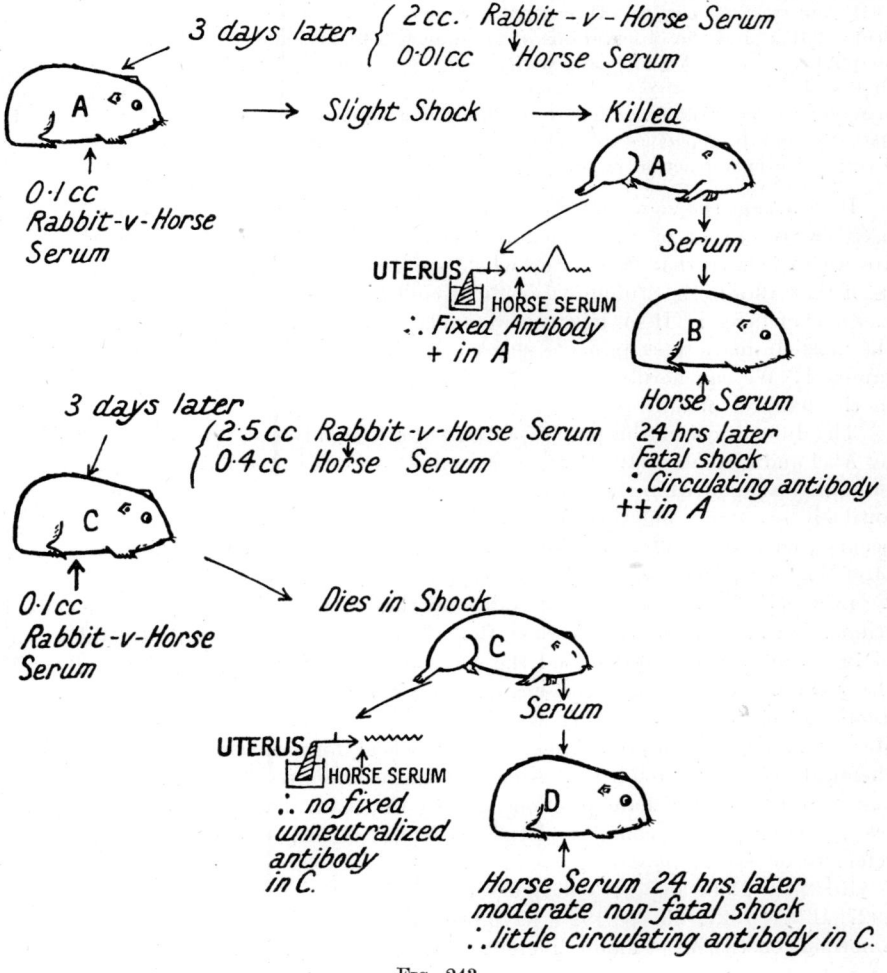

Fig. 243.

of the same series received 2·5 c.c. of the rabbit-v-horse serum (25 sensitizing doses) and immediately thereafter 0·4 c.c. of horse serum (52 anaphylactic doses). It died in acute shock, showing that the amount of antibody present was not sufficient to protect the cells containing the fixed antibody from this excessive dose of antigen. The uterus, removed immediately after death, showed itself to be desensitized. A normal guinea-pig was injected with the serum of this animal and 24 hours later received an injection of horse serum. It developed moderate symptoms only, showing that the greater part of the circulating antibody in the animal that died of acute shock had been neutralized by the large dose of antigen.

We may state with some confidence that, so far as the guinea-pig is concerned, the different behaviour of the hypersensitive and " immune " animal may be explained by postulating a difference in the relative concentration of fixed and circulating antibody.

If, however, we turn to other animals the evidence is more confused (see Dale 1920b, Scott 1931) ; and the observations of Manwaring and his colleagues (1923–28) on acute anaphylaxis in the dog are particularly difficult to fit into the relatively simple picture that we have drawn above. It seems, however, altogether unlikely that the mechanism of acute anaphylaxis differs fundamentally from one animal to another ; and it is probable that apparent discrepancies will in time resolve themselves into the expression of secondary divergencies in a reaction of one essential type.

If we accept the view that the cellular responses that characterize acute anaphylaxis are the result of an antigen-antibody reaction occurring on or in the cells, are we to believe that this is the whole story—that it is this reaction in and by itself that affords the stimulus to cellular contraction, or produces all the localized vascular changes ? If so, how can we explain the fact that those tissues that play the most dramatic part in acute shock are exactly those that are sensitive to histamine ? We can hardly believe that these cells, and these alone, are concerned in the fixation of antibody.

The difficulty would in part be explained if it could be shown, as was suggested by Abel and Kubotka (1919), that histamine itself was produced by some form of protein cleavage within the cell as the result of the injury inflicted by the antigen-antibody reaction ; but there is no adequate evidence that such an enzyme action occurs (see Dale 1929). The probable solution of our problem has come, as so often happens, from work along quite different lines.

Lewis (1927), in his classical studies on the reaction of the skin to a localized stimulus or injury, was able to show that the local reddening, due to the dilatation of the minute blood vessels, and the succeeding local wheal, were independent of the local neuro-vascular mechanism, whereas the surrounding flare, due to the dilatation of the neighbouring arterioles, was dependent on a local axon reflex. He concluded that the reddening and the wheal formation were the result of a chemical stimulus provided by some substance liberated from the injured cells ; and he found that histamine, alone among the many known substances that he tested, reproduced in complete detail the effects of this cell constituent, which he refers to as the *H-substance*.

Recently Dale and his colleagues (see Dale 1929, Dale, Dudley and Thorpe 1927, Harris 1927, Thorpe 1928) have been able to show that histamine is in truth a normal constituent of many different tissues ; and the evidence available strongly supports the view that it exists as such during life, and is not formed from some mother-substance after cell-death. Whether it is present in the free uncombined state, in which it is readily diffusible, is more doubtful. There are reasons for believing that it may, in certain circumstances at least, be present, and be liberated from the cell, in loose combination with cell-constituents of high molecular weight and low diffusibility.

The relative histamine content of different tissues is interesting and suggestive. Using a physiological method of assay (see Thorpe 1928, Harris 1927) the lungs have been found to contain between 35 and 75 mgm. of histamine per kilo, the liver between 2·5 and 6·6 mgm., the skin as a whole about 6 mgm. (24 mgm. in the epidermis and 4 mgm. in the dermis). Other tissues contain much less. The voluntary muscles contain about 1 mgm. per kilo, the testis about 1·8 mgm., the submaxillary gland about 0·5 mgm., and the thyroid about the same.

There is thus strong presumptive evidence that cellular injury, however it is produced, is liable to liberate histamine into the immediately surrounding tissue fluids. The amount liberated will depend on the extent of the injury, and on the type of tissue injured. The extent of the resulting histamine effect—its localization to the site of injury or its generalization with the resulting stimulation of histamine-sensitive cells throughout the body—will depend in part on the amount of histamine liberated, in part perhaps on the form in which it is liberated—whether uncombined and highly diffusible or in a loose combination of low diffusibility.

If we look back on the anaphylactic and anaphylactoid reactions in the light of this dual conception—cell injury on the one hand, histamine effect on the other —they become far less puzzling. We need not, indeed we cannot at the moment, attempt a histological disentanglement of the two reactions. Whether the cells that are injured and liberate histamine are themselves histamine-sensitive, whether minimal injury may so disturb the internal economy of a cell that it becomes reactive to its own contained histamine, or whether we should locate the injury and liberation of histamine in one type of cell, the response to the liberated his-tamine in another, are problems which are not soluble at the moment. In some cases there are suggestive hints. Isolated plain muscle from the sensitized dog gives no significant response to the specific antigen. Yet the plain muscle of the dog is sensitive to histamine. It would seem that in the dog, as opposed to the guinea-pig, the sensitization to the antigen is limited mainly to the liver.

We may then, in general terms, describe the acute anaphylactic reaction as consisting of two different but related effects—cell injury determined by an antigen-antibody reaction occurring on or in those cells by which antibody has been fixed, and a secondary histamine effect determined by the response of the histamine-sensitive cells.

It should perhaps be noted that, if we want to generalize our statement as completely as possible, we should write *histamine or histamine-like* effect. It has been observed (see Grant and Jones 1929, Dale 1929) that the frog's skin reacts to minimal injuries in much the same way as the skin of man ; but this reaction is not produced by histamine. Extracts of frog's skin, however, reproduce this response as closely as histamine reproduces the injury response in man. The active principle of the frog's skin is not histamine, though it appears to be a base that resembles it in some of its chemical properties.

As regards the anaphylactoid reactions, they differ from acute anaphylactic shock in that the cell injury is not determined by an antigen-antibody reaction ; they resemble it in that the secondary histamine effect is essentially the same. It should be noted that most of the anaphylactoid reagents, such as toxified sera, do not stimulate contraction of the isolated guinea-pig uterus. This histamine-liberating injury presumably occurs elsewhere when these agents are injected *in vivo*. Peptone, on the other hand, has a direct stimulating effect on plain muscle, which suggests that it may contain histamine.

The complete picture of an anaphylactic or anaphylactoid reaction will thus consist of a description of cellular injury, differing from case to case according to the reagent employed and the susceptibilities of the experimental animal, and a histamine effect, differing from one animal species to another according to the distribution of the histamine-sensitive cells, but common to all reactions in one animal species, by whatever reagents they are caused.

Local Anaphylactic Reactions

Within a year of the original observations of Portier and Richet, and before the phenomenon of acute anaphylactic shock had been submitted to any detailed study, Arthus (1903) described a curious reaction in the rabbit, which was soon recognized as belonging to the same order of exaggerated response to a foreign antigen. Inoculating rabbits subcutaneously with repeated doses of horse serum, he noted that the initial injections were without any detectable effect, but that, as one injection succeeded another with suitable intervals between them, the local reactions became more intense and more persistent. After a few injections the site of inoculation became swollen and œdematous. These local swellings were at first transient, but with each successive injection they lasted longer, with more definite induration, until finally the response took the form of a firm indurated swelling which progressed to a localized necrosis. This altered response was not confined to the tissues in the immediate neighbourhood of the earlier injections. The rabbit, as a whole, had become so sensitized that it reacted in this characteristic and abnormal way to the injection of the specific antigen at any site (see also Seegal, Seegal and Jost 1932, Davidoff, Seegal and Seegal 1932). It may be noted that this reaction, in its typical form, appears to be peculiar to the rabbit. Nicolle (1907) failed to reproduce it in the guinea-pig, and Opie (1924) failed to elicit it in either the guinea-pig or the dog.

HYPERSENSITIVENESS IN MAN

Clinical observations have long been on record containing descriptions of reactions in human subjects that present obvious analogies to the anaphylactic reaction in experimental animals.

Serum Sickness.—It has been known for many years that a proportion of those persons who receive injections of antitoxic or antibacterial serum for prophylactic or therapeutic purposes develop a curious and characteristic condition which has been given the name of " serum sickness." An excellent description of the disease and a detailed discussion of its significance are contained in the monograph of von Pirquet and Schick (1905). For our immediate purpose we need refer only to the following points.

The reaction occurs after primary as well as after subsequent injections. It is in no way related to the antibody content of the injected serum, but is a response to the foreign protein as such, which is usually horse serum. There is, in the great majority of cases, an incubation period of 8 to 12 days between the injection of the serum and the onset of the symptoms. The illness itself is characterized by rashes, especially of an urticarial type and often commencing at the site of the inoculation, by fever, joint pains, slight œdema without albuminuria (or with a mere trace of albumin in the urine), and by a varying degree of glandular swelling usually confined to the regional glands that receive the lymphatics from the site of inoculation. The illness is variable in duration, protean in its symptoms, and seldom of a serious nature, though it may be associated with severe discomfort. It is probably never fatal.

In a tiny minority of cases an entirely different reaction follows the injection of serum, the patient dying within a few minutes with symptoms resembling those of acute anaphylactic shock. Park (1908) records two such cases among 50,000 persons who received serum injections in New York.

The Idiosyncrasies.—Another group of reactions, which clearly come into the general category of hypersensitiveness, are the so-called idiosyncrasies, in which certain persons develop a characteristic symptom-complex as the result of natural contact with some particular substance, or range of substances. The substances that may evoke this response are of the most varied nature : in hay fever, pollens of various species ; in asthma, pollens, horse dander or the cutaneous débris from other animals ; in the food idiosyncrasies, a wide range of different materials ; in the drug idiosyncrasies, a whole series of chemical compounds which seem to have no characteristic or common structure.

One of the most striking features of the idiosyncrasies as a group is that— as in the anaphylactic reaction—the symptom-complex bears no relation to the particular type of substance by which it is evoked. In spite of the varied nature of the exciting materials concerned, the syndrome induced shows an essential uniformity ; though there are minor differences which seem to depend in the main on the particular route by which the reacting substance gains access to the tissues. It is particularly striking that, in the case of drugs, the response exhibited by the hypersensitive subject—using hypersensitive in this particular sense—bears no relation to the pharmacological action of the drug in question.

The reactions induced may be either local or general. Among the former are the local reaction to the intracutaneous injection of horse serum or to the application to the skin of such a drug as iodoform, the coryza of hay fever and perhaps the associated asthma, and the acute vomiting and gastro-intestinal disturbance that follow the ingestion of a particular food-stuff. Among the latter are the generalized urticarial eruptions or œdema that may follow the administration by any route of a substance to which a person is hypersensitive, the occasional pyrexia, and the asthmatic symptoms that sometimes follow the entry of the exciting substance by a route other than the respiratory tract.

There are obvious points of similarity between this group of reactions on the one hand and anaphylactic hypersensitiveness on the other, but there are also obvious divergencies.

Among the points of similarity we may include the following (see Coca 1920a) :—

In both cases the reaction is specific. Although the naturally hypersensitive person may react to several different substances the range is usually limited, and may be confined to a single chemical substance. In both cases the type of response is essentially the same for a single animal species irrespective of the nature of the exciting substance.

Among the features that have been held to differentiate between the two conditions are the following. The exciting agent in anaphylaxis is always an antigenic substance ; the exciting agent in human hypersensitiveness is often non-antigenic. Anaphylactic hypersensitiveness is induced by the injection of a sensitizing dose of antigen ; hypersensitiveness in man is often exhibited upon first contact with the exciting agent. The anaphylactic state, apart from congenital passive anaphylaxis, is not a heritable condition ; natural human hypersensitiveness shows a definite tendency to run in families, though the hypersensitiveness is often exhibited towards different substances in parents and offspring. Specific desensitization is far more easily demonstrated in anaphylaxis than in hypersensitiveness.

Taking these points of difference *seriatim* we may attempt to assess their significance in the light of the evidence now available. Coca and his colleagues, who would regard the differences between the two conditions as sufficient to justify a formal separation into different categories, employ the term *atopy* to denote the natural hypersensitive state, and the term *atopen* to denote the exciting agent (see Coca and Cooke 1923). We may define our first problem as the determination of the differences between atopens and antigens.

Atopens and Antigens.—It is certain that many substances are at the same time antigenic and atopic. Horse serum forms an excellent example, though we should note that Coca and Cooke separate serum sickness from the true atopies. If, however, we confine ourselves to the more typical atopens we still find that a single substance commonly displays both types of activity.

Alexander (1924) found that guinea-pigs could be rendered anaphylactic to rye pollen, though he could not induce the formation of precipitating or complement-fixing antibodies in detectable amount. Parker (1924) reports the production of precipitins for ragweed pollen in rabbits and guinea-pigs, and Ramsden (1926) obtained similar results. Walzer and Grove (1925) showed that the pollens of timothy-grass and ragweed have definite antigenic properties, since both induce the anaphylactic state in guinea-pigs, demonstrable either by intravenous inoculation or by Dale's technique. They note, however, that sensitization with pollens is far more difficult and uncertain than with such an antigen as horse serum, and they failed to demonstrate precipitins in the serum of the sensitized animals. Caulfeild and his colleagues (1926) prepared various fractions from ragweed, timothy-grass and birch pollens, and obtained with them active and, in some cases, passive sensitization. Ramsden (1926) demonstrated both active and passive sensitization of guinea-pigs to pollen. Longcope and others (1925, 1927) have demonstrated the active sensitization of guinea-pigs to extracts of horse dander, and have succeeded in specifically desensitizing such animals by the usual procedures. There seems little doubt that many of the reagents that have been classed as typical atopens have a definite antigenic action.

There is, of course, no doubt at all that many of the substances that function as atopens—for example many drugs—are non-protein in nature and are therefore not antigenic in the full sense. Moreover, it has been found (Grove and Coca 1925) that the removal of all proteins and other detectable nitrogenous substances from extracts of pollen, or of house dust, does not cause any appreciable loss of atopic activity, as tested by intracutaneous inoculation in susceptible persons. On the other hand, the tryptic digestion of the proteins of horse dander, or of the green pea, caused a loss of atopic activity corresponding with the loss of protein.

The fact that non-protein substances can excite a specific response in the hypersensitive person cannot, however, be taken as a proof that antigens and atopens differ in any essential respect. We have seen that many haptens, when injected intravenously into actively or passively sensitized guinea-pigs, will induce acute anaphylactic shock, so that it would be in no way surprising if a fundamentally similar reaction were produced in naturally sensitive persons by contact with antigenic components of a similar kind.

There remain instances of drug idiosyncrasies that are not so readily explicable along these lines, since the chemical structure of the exciting agent is not of the relatively complex kind which characterizes those haptens that are capable of inducing acute shock in a sensitized animal.

Recent observations have, however, indicated a possible mechanism by which such simple compounds might come to function as complete or partial antigens. It has been found that animals may be sensitized by the injection of atoxyl and serum, or even of arsenical compounds alone (see Klopstock and Selter 1929, Mayer and Sulzberger 1931, Sulzberger and Mayer 1931); and it seems probable (Landsteiner and Levine 1930) that in such cases a preliminary union occurs between the simple arsenical compounds and some serum or tissue protein, with the formation of an effective antigenic complex. Jacobs (1932) succeeded in sensitizing guinea-pigs to iodinated sera by injecting them with guinea-pig serum mixed with Lugol's iodine solution, and suggested that a similar mechanism might be involved in the development of iodine sensitiveness in man. Horsfall (1934) injected formolized rabbit serum into rabbits, and found that the animals developed skin sensitivity to uncombined formaldehyde.

Active and Passive Sensitization in Man.—The second criterion that has been accorded differential significance is the mode of sensitization. There is no question that human hypersensitiveness occurs naturally and apart from any known previous contact with the particular antigen to which the sensitive subject reacts, just as the " natural " antibodies may be found in persons who, so far as we can tell, have never been infected with or immunized against the particular bacterium on which their sera react.

There is, however, good evidence that this condition frequently arises as the result of active sensitization.

Hooker (1924) tested a large number of persons by the intracutaneous injection of horse serum before and after they had been immunized by the injection of toxin-antitoxin mixtures. Of 367 persons tested before immunization 308 failed to react to horse serum. Of these, 100 were found to be Schick-positive and were immunized by toxin-antitoxin injections. On retesting these 100 persons at a later date, 66 gave positive reactions to horse serum. Park (1924) carried out a similar series of observations, in which he tested the sensitiveness to horse serum of immunized and non-immunized groups of children. He found that 84 of 116 children who had received toxin-antitoxin injections reacted positively to horse serum, while of 90 children who had not been immunized 45 were sensitive, giving a difference of 22·5 per cent. between the two groups. Other observers (Cowie 1914, Longcope and Rackeman 1918, Gordon and Creswell 1924, Mackenzie 1924) have obtained results that point in the same direction. It would appear that the injection of horse serum significantly increases the percentage of sensitive persons in a sample of the normal population. As we have already noted (p. 877), the intradermal injection of pneumococcal polysaccharides may induce a specific skin-sensitivity, so that this effect is not limited to protein substances.

Again (see von Pirquet and Schick 1905), while the serum sickness that develops in a naturally hypersensitive person, apart from previous sensitization, is almost always of the delayed type described above, a proportion of those cases that occur in persons who have received previous injections of horse serum show a characteristic acceleration of the response. In some cases the localized œdema, the generalized urticaria, the febrile reaction and all the symptoms of severe serum sickness may develop within 24 hours.

The most striking evidence in favour of the view that experimental anaphylaxis and natural hypersensitiveness depend on essentially similar mechanisms has, perhaps, been provided by the demonstration that hypersensitiveness to a particular atopen or antigen can be passively transferred from one person to another, since this clearly places human hypersensitiveness with anaphylaxis in the category of the antigen-antibody reactions.

Ramirez (1920) reported the case of a man who was sensitive to horse dander. He was employed as the donor in the transfusion of an anæmic patient who received 600 c.c. of his blood. The recipient, who gave no history of such an idiosyncrasy, thereafter developed marked hypersensitiveness to horse dander. The evidential value of this case is somewhat lessened by the fact that the same donor was used in another transfusion without rendering the recipient hypersensitive.

An observation that has provided a basis for the experimental study of passive sensitization in man was recorded by Prausnitz and Küstner in 1921. Küstner himself was markedly sensitive to the cooked flesh of certain fish. Using an extract of cooked fish as antigen these observers failed to demonstrate the presence of precipitins in Kustner's serum, nor could they produce passive sensitization of guinea-pigs. If, however, a little of Kustner's serum was injected into the skin of a normal person and the antigen was injected into the same site 24 hours later, a marked local reaction was produced. This reaction did not occur if the antigen and the serum were injected simultaneously, a finding strikingly analogous to the latent period in the passive anaphylactic sensitization of the guinea-pig.

The detailed study of this passive atopic sensitization has been taken up by Coca and his colleagues and by other investigators. Coca and Grove (1925) gave the name *atopic reagins* to the antibodies present in the serum of naturally hypersensitive persons, through the agency of which the specific hypersensitiveness can be passively transferred to the skin of normal non-sensitive persons. They record that these reagins have been demonstrated in the serum of all those subjects of hay fever or of asthma in whom the reaction to the intradermal injection of the specific atopen is positive. They find, however, that not all normal skins are receptive, about 11 per cent. failing to react at all, and some 5 per cent. giving slight or doubtful reactions. The remaining 84 per cent. are fully receptive, and the local passive sensitization lasts for at least 4 weeks once it has been established. They find that the reagin may be neutralized by the specific atopen in the test tube, but that it gives no precipitin reaction *in vitro*, nor will it induce passive anaphylaxis in the guinea-pig. In a control series of experiments they noted that the normal human skin could not be passively sensitized to egg white or to ragweed-pollen with rabbit antisera, although these contained specific precipitins. Exactly similar phenomena have, however, been noted in the case of passive anaphylaxis—neither horse antisera nor chicken antisera are effective in the passive anaphylactic sensitization of the guinea-pig, though antisera prepared in the rabbit are highly efficient from this point of view.

Clarke and Gallagher (1926) give a very clear-cut demonstration of the latent period in passive atopic sensitization and of the *in vivo* neutralization of reagin by atopen without the production of any tissue reaction. They injected 0·05 c.c. of atopen into one area of skin, and 5 minutes later they injected 0·05 c.c. of reagin-containing serum into the same site and 0·05 c.c. of the same serum into a second site some distance from the first. No reaction occurred after these injections, showing that the union in the tissues of atopen and reagin under conditions that give no time for the preliminary fixation of the reagin does not produce the typical response. Next day each site was reinjected with the same quantity of atopen. At the second site, where no atopen had previously been injected, a typical reaction occurred. At the first site no obvious response was elicited, showing that the reagin had been neutralized by the atopen that was present when the sensitizing injection was given.

Levine and Coca (1927) found that there was a proportional relationship between the degree of sensitivity of the skin and the reagin content of the serum in 33 cases of hay fever.

Reagins and Antibodies.—The observations quoted above do not suggest that any clear separation can be made between these two types of antibody. It is true that reagins may be demonstrated in sera that give no precipitation with the specific antigen ; but, as we have seen, passive anaphylaxis may be induced with sera in which no precipitins can be detected. It is by no means clear, therefore, that reagins and precipitins are different antibodies ; the apparent qualitative differences may in reality be quantitative—as they appear to be in anaphylaxis—depending on a difference in delicacy between the *in vivo* and *in vitro* tests. De Besche (1918), for instance, has reported the presence of precipitins in the serum of a considerable proportion of a small group of asthmatics who were sensitive to the proteins of the horse, cat, dog or cow. He notes that patients who showed the presence of precipitins at one time might fail to do so at another. The antibodies appeared to fluctuate above and below the level at which they were demonstrable *in vitro.*

Otto and Adelsberger (1931) have recently recorded a careful series of observations on the relation between the atopic reagins and the anaphylactic antibodies. They note that the typical reagin, as exemplified in the sera of persons sensitive to horse dander, is extremely effective in the transference of specific sensitivity to a localized area of the normal human skin. It is less effective in sensitizing the skin of the guinea-pig, and quite ineffective in sensitizing that animal to anaphylactic shock. The sera of persons suffering from serum sickness, or of those who have been injected with horse serum without suffering from the clinical disease, are effective—though somewhat less effective—in the transference of sensitivity to the normal human skin. They are far more effective in sensitizing the guinea-pig's skin ; and are not infrequently effective in inducing generalized anaphylactic sensitization. Anti-horse sera, prepared in rabbits or guinea-pigs, are relatively—but not entirely—ineffective in the transference of sensitivity to the human skin, but are uniformly effective in inducing passive anaphylaxis in the guinea-pig.

The evidence as a whole suggests minor differences in the antibodies with which these various workers have been concerned—differences perhaps connected with the proteins in antisera obtained from different animal species rather than with the active grouping of the antibody ; but there seems no adequate reason for regarding reagins and anaphylactic antibodies as belonging to essentially different types. *Atopens* and *reagins* might well give place to *antigens* and *antibodies* in immunological nomenclature, except where some convenient term is required to denote the way in which an antigen or antibody is functioning at a particular time.

The Genetic Factor in Anaphylaxis and Hypersensitiveness.—The third character that has been held to differentiate human hypersensitiveness from anaphylaxis is concerned with the part played by inheritance in the two conditions. There is evidence (Cooke and Veer 1916, Coca 1920a, Spain and Cooke 1924, Clarke, Donnally and Coca 1928) that human hypersensitiveness tends to run in families. There is at present no evidence that the anaphylactic state, as induced in the sensitized guinea-pig, occurs naturally or is determined by genetic factors. Does this indicate any essential difference in the nature of the two phenomena ?

Even if we accepted the premises as warranting such a conclusion we should require much more evidence than we have before we accepted the second premise as valid. Anaphylaxis in its usual experimental form is, of course, never inherited ;

since one of the necessary conditions for its study is that the injection of the antigen into the unsensitized animal shall not produce shock, *i.e.*, the experimental animal selected must not be naturally sensitive to the antigen under test. Whether there are any cases in which the injection of an antigen into an animal that has not been artificially sensitized produces typical anaphylactic shock, demonstrably due to an antigen-antibody reaction, we do not know, because no systematic search has ever been made. In the absence of such knowledge we cannot tell what part inheritance plays in the natural anaphylactic state, if that state occurs. As Doerr (1922) points out, we have for obvious reasons studied natural hypersensitiveness in man and anaphylaxis in experimental animals. It is at least possible that the differences noted are referable in large part to the different universes selected for study.

With regard to the inheritance of human hypersensitiveness we have already noted (see Cooke and Veer 1916, Spain and Cooke 1924) that the genetic factor appears to be concerned with a tendency to develop atopic hypersensitiveness in general, rather than a sensitiveness to any one atopen in particular. It appears to be unusual to find that parents and offspring, or several members of the same family, are all hypersensitive to the same substance ; one may respond to ragweed pollen, another to horse dander, another to cat hairs, and so on. It has also been noted (Clarke, Donnally and Coca 1928) that the type of reaction to atopic substances in general appears to be in some degree inherited ; the tendency to develop asthmatic symptoms, for instance, being particularly frequent in certain families.

There seem insufficient grounds for postulating an essential difference between anaphylaxis and hypersensitiveness on the premises of our present knowledge of the influence of genetic factors in the two conditions.

Desensitization in Hypersensitiveness and Idiosyncrasy.

Fourthly, some observers, and particularly Coca (1920*b*), would lay great stress on the difficulty of desensitization in the sensitive human subject as compared with its relative ease and certainty in the anaphylactic animal. While admitting that a degree of lessened sensitivity to natural contact with the specific atopen may be attained in a hypersensitive person by suitably graded injections, Coca points out that the further administration of the atopen by subcutaneous or intracutaneous inoculation will always demonstrate the persistence of the hypersensitive state.

It seems doubtful, however, whether this criterion has any greater differential value as between the atopic and anaphylactic states than those we have discussed above. It is true that desensitization may readily be demonstrated in the anaphylactic guinea-pig ; but even here it depends on a strict observance of the necessary quantitative and time relationships, as may be seen in many of Weil's experiments. In other species the problem is far less simple ; it is for instance notoriously difficult to desensitize the rabbit.

In the hypersensitive human subject, as in the experimentally sensitized animal, the available evidence indicates that desensitization induces a temporary change in the immunological balance of the tissues, with a subsequent reversion to the hypersensitive state (see Vallery-Radot *et al.* 1936, Adelsberger 1936, Gernez 1936).

We cannot of course apply the results obtained in our animal experiments, without modification, to our clinical problems. The relief of a case of hay fever

or the desensitization of a serum-sensitive patient as a preliminary to the administration of antitoxin, demands the application of a technique that can be elaborated
only on a basis of empirical trial, and which may or may not be successful. This
does not, however, justify the conclusion that there is any essential qualitative
difference in the underlying mechanism.

ALLERGIC REACTIONS IN BACTERIAL INFECTIONS

The term *allergy* is almost impossible to define. Here we are using it in a loose,
but widely accepted sense to cover a group of reactions characterized by a heightened
or accelerated response to a particular type of antigen, irrespective of the balance
of harm, or benefit, that the altered response confers on the allergic host.

All the phenomena of hypersensitiveness could obviously be included under
this general label. In the present section we are concerned with those instances
in which an allergic state develops in relation to a bacterial infection.

It has already been noted that bacterial haptens may induce acute anaphylactic
shock in a sensitized guinea-pig; but before discussing allergic reactions in the
wider sense we may refer briefly to the question of anaphylactic sensitization with
bacterial antigens.

The available data may be summarized by stating that active sensitization has been
induced with various bacterial antigens and passive sensitization with the corresponding
antibodies as demonstrated by the occurrence of acute shock (Rosenau and Anderson 1907,
Kraus and Doerr 1908, Holobut 1909, Kraus and Admiridzibi 1910, Zinsser and Parker 1917,
Tomcsik and Kurotchkin 1928, Lancefield 1928, Enders 1929, Avery and Tillet 1929), or by
Dale's technique with the isolated uterus (Zinsser and Parker 1917, Zinsser and Mallory
1924, Tomcsik and Kurotchkin 1928). The reactions are specific and desensitization
can be demonstrated. Sensitization to bacterial antigens cannot, however, be produced
with the same ease as can sensitization to such antigens as horse serum or egg
white. A single injection of bacteria frequently fails to produce any demonstrable sensitization, and the most successful results have been obtained by giving repeated small injections
of antigen, followed by an interval of three weeks or so before the intravenous injection of
the test dose, which should be relatively large. A technical difficulty in work of this
kind is introduced by the fact that many of the bacterial suspensions employed are themselves toxic when administered in any considerable dose, and the symptoms that develop
in normal animals after the injection of massive doses of bacteria or bacterial products
may be very similar to anaphylactic shock. The difference in the response of normal and of
sensitized animals may, therefore, be relatively difficult to detect.

Turning to those instances in which specific sensitization occurs during the
course of a bacterial infection—the type of hypersensitiveness with which we are
most closely concerned—the classical example of an allergic response to a non-
living bacterial antigen is afforded by the tuberculin reaction in its various forms.

This experimental allergic reaction is readily demonstrated in the guinea-pig. The
injection into a normal guinea-pig of 2 c.c. of Koch's old tuberculin—a culture of tubercle
bacilli in 5 per cent. glycerine broth, grown for 6–8 weeks at 38° C., concentrated to 1/10th
volume at 100° C., and freed from bacilli by filtration through a clay or kieselguhr candle
—has little effect. But the injection of 0·01 c.c. into a guinea-pig in the 8th or 10th week
of tuberculous infection may kill it within a few hours. At necropsy, supposing the injection
to have been given subcutaneously, the site of inoculation is found to be very congested,
dark red or almost violet in colour. The focal glands are swollen and congested, the liver

and spleen show on their surface numerous dark red spots, particularly in the neighbourhood of the multiple tuberculous lesions which are commonly present. Microscopically these red spots are seen to consist of enormously dilated capillaries. Thus the tuberculin produces a local reaction at the site of inoculation, numerous scattered focal reactions in the immediate neighbourhood of pre-existing tuberculous foci, and a rapidly fatal toxæmic effect, probably secondary to the widespread focal reactions.

This fatal generalized tuberculin reaction in the guinea-pig exemplifies the allergic response in its severest form. The development of hypersensitiveness in an infected animal may, however, be demonstrated quite as clearly by means of the localized reaction that follows the intracutaneous injection of 0·2 c.c. of a high dilution (1 : 800 to 1 : 4,000) of tuberculin (see Römer and Joseph 1909, 1910, Lewis and Aronson 1923, Eagleton and Baxter 1923). For further details with regard to the tuberculin reaction, and its diagnostic use in human and veterinary medicine, see Chapter LVI.

We have so far been concerned with the allergic response to a non-living antigenic material ; but there is abundant evidence that the sensitized tissues respond differently from the non-sensitized to contact with living bacteria. Here again, the classical example is afforded by Koch's observations on experimental tuberculosis (Koch 1891).

When a normal guinea-pig is injected subcutaneously with living tubercle bacilli, a localized nodule appears at the site of inoculation after 10–14 days. This nodule increases in size, involves the skin, and undergoes necrosis, leaving an indurated ulcer that persists until the animal's death. Meanwhile there occurs the characteristic lymphatic spread of infection, involving first the regional lymphatic glands and later the more remote tissues and organs. But if living tubercle bacilli are injected into a guinea-pig that is already infected with tuberculosis of some weeks' duration the result is quite different. On the 1st or 2nd day following the reinoculation the site of injection shows an area of acute superficial inflammation 0·5–1 cm. in diameter, without the formation of any nodule in the underlying subcutaneous tissue. Next day the affected area of skin is found to be necrotic, and finally it sloughs, leaving a flat, shallow ulcer which undergoes rapid healing. The regional lymph glands are not affected ; and there is no evidence of the spread of infection from the localized focus caused by the second inoculation. This rapid and energetic response does not, in this case, confer any permanent benefit on the guinea-pig, for it is destined to die from the primary infection ; but it affords a striking example of a reaction that betrays at one and the same time the character of hypersensitiveness and of immunity.

Although tuberculosis happens to afford the classical illustration of allergy developing as the result of infection, there are numberless other examples. There is, indeed, little doubt that an increased sensitivity, associated with an increased vigour of response, is of frequent, perhaps of almost constant, occurrence at one stage or another of every infective disease ; and it is very probable that this sensitization plays a part in pathogenesis, particularly in subacute or chronic infections.

The allergy of infection, it will be noted, may be regarded as a state of partial immunity, as well as of increased sensitivity ; and the all-inclusive classification of Doerr (1922), who would place acute anaphylaxis, natural hypersensitiveness and immunity in a single generic group, with sub-groups clearly marked by certain features but shading into each other when the focus of attention is shifted from the obvious manifestation to the underlying mechanism, offers the most reasonable as well as the most coherent picture of the phenomena that we have considered in this chapter.

So far as our present knowledge goes it seems very probable that anaphylaxis, hypersensitiveness, and immunity of the type dependent on specific antibodies, all result from the working of a single underlying mechanism, the character of the total reaction being determined in each particular case by a variety of secondary factors. Anaphylactic shock, for instance, is an experimental curiosity of high informative value to the student of immunity but not of any obvious significance in determining the survival or extinction of a species during the course of its evolution. The sudden introduction of a foreign antigenic substance into the circulating blood is not an event that is likely to menace any living thing, unless it is subjected to intentional human interference. It is neither paradoxical nor surprising that a mechanism, which in natural circumstances tends directly towards immunity, should react to the disadvantage of its possessor when exposed to a stimulus that formed no part of the environment in which it was evolved.

Infection-Immunity.

This is as convenient a place as any in which to mention a conception that is often found in current bacteriological literature—the hypothesis that there is a kind of immunity that is associated with existing, but not with past infection. In its extreme form this conception suggests that so long as an infection with a particular bacterial parasite exists, even though that infection is latent, the host will be immune to reinfection with that particular bacterium, but that once the host's tissues are freed altogether from the infecting parasite susceptibility will return.

We have already noted Koch's observation that a guinea-pig behaves differently towards a primary and a secondary infection with living tubercle bacilli. The studies of many subsequent workers have confirmed and greatly extended his findings, and have shown quite clearly that a subacute or chronic tuberculous infection is associated with a considerable resistance to reinfection.

Significant evidence bearing on the problem of infection-immunity has been obtained during the study of experimental syphilis in the rabbit. In this infection it is possible, by administering an adequate dose of neosalvarsan, or of one of the related arsenical drugs, to cure the initial infection and observe the effect of so doing on the resistance of the rabbit to reinfection.

A syphilitic keratitis may be induced in the rabbit by the injection of *Trep. pallidum* into the anterior chamber of the eye (see Bertarelli 1906, 1907, 1908), a chancre may be produced by injection into the skin of the scrotum (Tomasczewski 1910), and a characteristic lesion follows injection into the testicle (Parodi 1907).

When an infected rabbit is reinoculated with the same strain of *Trep. pallidum* after a relatively short interval a local chancre does not develop (Truffi 1910); but reinfection with a different strain may induce a typical local lesion (Kolle and Schloszberger 1926). Brown and Pearce (1921) infected a number of rabbits and treated some of them with arsphenamine shortly after the development of the primary chancre. Five days later these rabbits were injected with the same strain of *Trep. pallidum*. Most of the treated animals developed chancres. The untreated animals did not.

Kolle (1922, 1924) treated rabbits with neosalvarsan at various stages of infection. He found that rabbits treated within about 6 weeks after the initial infection usually responded to a subsequent injection by developing a new chancre. When treatment was delayed beyond this point, reinfection seldom gave rise to a chancre. When treatment was delayed for about 3 months a new chancre could very rarely be produced.   Rabbits that were treated and reinfected at long intervals after the primary infection (75–250 days) were not, however, completely resistant to reinfection (see Kolle and Prigge 1927, 1929).   Tissue extracts from treated rabbits that had not been reinfected were non-infective for normal rabbits, but similar extracts from treated and reinfected rabbits gave rise to characteristic lesions, showing that the spirochætes had gained access to the tissues and were presumably multiplying in them, at least to a limited extent.   On these grounds Kolle and his colleagues maintain that the immunity to reinfection displayed by rabbits that have been treated in this way is only a " chancre immunity."   The exact significance of this term is a little dubious.   We have noted many examples of a partial antibacterial immunity in which bacteria may persist for long periods in the tissues without giving rise to any of the lesions that they produce in non-immunized animals.   Moreover, the evidence suggests that a more complete immunity against *Trep. pallidum* may be induced under optimal conditions.   Uhlenhuth and Groszmann (1928) treated syphilitic rabbits with neosalvarsan 107 to 506 days after the primary infection.   Attempted reinfection 3 to 10 months after treatment gave rise to no obvious lesions ; and in only 4 of 11 rabbits could spirochætes be demonstrated in the tissues.   (For a more detailed discussion and further references see Chapter LXXVIII.)

In summary, we may say that immunity to reinfection appears to be established within a short time after the appearance of the initial lesion.   At this stage the maintenance of immunity depends on the maintenance of infection ;   complete chemotherapeutic cure is followed by a return of susceptibility.   But after a longer period of infection a partial immunity is established that may persist after complete chemotherapeutic cure ;   and, after still longer periods of infection, a complete immunity may be established that is independent of the persistence of infection.

Whether it is necessary to assume the existence of some mechanism other than those we have considered in this and in preceding chapters, in order to account for the immunity to reinfection— or, as it is more appropriately termed, to " super-infection "—during the early stages of the initial infection, is a question that cannot yet be answered.   We may, at least, note that this resistance to superinfection appears to be type-specific.   As regards the resistance developed during the later stages of infection, it seems highly probable that it can be accounted for by a slow acquirement of an immunity of the usual antibacterial type.

SUMMARY

(1) Acute anaphylactic shock may be produced by inoculating into an animal any antigen to which it has previously been sensitized.   The symptoms and lesions associated with shock in any particular case are determined by the anatomical and functional peculiarities of the species of animal employed, not by the character of the antigenic material injected.

(2) Sensitization is specific.   It may be induced either actively or passively, and hence must depend, at least in part, on some form of antigen-antibody reaction.

(3) Active sensitization is induced—in the case of such an animal as the guinea-pig and such an antigen as horse serum—by a single minimal injection of antigen. After this injection there follows a latent period during which hypersensitiveness

develops, and during this period no further injections of antigen must be given. Once the anaphylactic state has been actively induced it lasts for months or years.

(4) Passive sensitization is induced by the injection into a normal animal of the serum from a sensitized or from an immunized animal—that is by any serum containing the specific antibody. There is a correlation between the antibody content of a serum and its effectiveness as a sensitizing agent ; and for this reason the serum of an immune animal is more effective (*i.e.*, sensitizes in smaller doses) than the serum of a hypersensitive animal. The anaphylactic state that is induced by the injection of an antibody-containing serum takes some hours to develop. To ensure typical shock the assaulting dose of antigen should not be injected until 8 to 24 hours have elapsed after the injection of the antiserum. During this latent period the antibodies have, for the most part, disappeared from the blood and become fixed on or in the tissue cells. The anaphylactic state when passively induced passes off in a few days or weeks.

(5) To produce typical shock in either an actively or passively sensitized animal, the assaulting dose of antigen must be introduced into the blood stream rapidly and in adequate, though not necessarily in large amount. Intravenous injection gives the most consistent results, and in many cases is the only route by which typical shock can be induced.

(6) The injection of haptens, or partial antigens, fails to induce active sensitization, just as it fails to induce active immunity. Complex haptens, such as the bacterial polysaccharides, will induce acute shock when injected into an animal actively sensitized by the injection of the corresponding full antigen, or passively sensitized by the injection of a specific antiserum. Less complex haptens will neither induce active sensitization nor induce shock in a sensitized animal ; but when injected into such an animal they will inhibit the induction of shock by the corresponding antigen. In a sensitized animal antigens and haptens behave *in vivo* as they behave in the precipitin reaction *in vitro*.

(7) The sensitized animal may be desensitized by the injection of the specific antigen in amounts too small to induce acute shock or by a route that ensures slow absorption so that there is no rapid transport to the circulating blood.

(8) The anaphylactic state can be demonstrated in an isolated tissue or organ as well as in the animal as a whole ; thus, the uterus of a sensitized guinea-pig reacts *in vitro* to contact with the antigen employed in sensitization.

(9) The balance of experimental evidence is strongly in favour of the view that the anaphylactic response is the result of an antigen-antibody reaction occurring on or in the cells that have removed the antibody from the blood and in some way fixed it themselves. The anaphylactic state is associated with the presence of fixed antibody and the absence of circulating antibody. The immune state is associated with the presence of circulating antibody in a concentration sufficient to protect the fixed antibody that is also present.

The difference between the anaphylactic and immune state is quantitative rather than qualitative, depending upon the balance between circulating and fixed antibody.

(10) Many of the most dramatic features of the syndrome of anaphylactic shock are the result not of the antigen-antibody reaction itself but of the liberation of histamine by the injured cells, and the secondary response of the histamine-sensitive cells throughout the body.

(11) A great variety of substances, when injected intravenously, may give rise

to a syndrome resembling, in many but not in all particulars, that of anaphylactic shock.   These reactions are spoken of as anaphylactoid reactions.   The resemblance is not due to any similarity in the underlying mechanism, but to the fact that, in each case, cellular injury is followed by the liberation of histamine, and this by the characteristic syndrome of histamine shock.

(12) Apart from acute anaphylactic shock there are other examples of hypersensitiveness, among them the natural idiosyncrasies that have been observed in man to contact with particular materials, such as pollens, horse serum, horse dander, and certain drugs.

(13) In spite of obvious superficial differences between this condition and experimental anaphylaxis in the guinea-pig, the knowledge that has been gained in recent years—and particularly the demonstration that skin sensitivity to these atopic substances can be passively transferred—has lent support to the view that the underlying mechanism is essentially the same.

(14) Specific hypersensitiveness may also develop in the course of natural or experimental bacterial infection.   This type of hypersensitiveness—which is sometimes referred to as *allergy*—is characterized by an accelerated and exaggerated reaction to contact with the infecting bacterium or its products.   It partakes of the character of hypersensitiveness in these respects.   It partakes of the character of immunity in that the allergic reaction is often associated with the localization of infection.   This type of reaction may sometimes be demonstrated in animals that have been immunized by the injection of bacteria or bacterial products, as well as in animals that are suffering from an active or quiescent infection.   It is probably an important factor in the development of natural or artificial immunity.

(15) Acute anaphylaxis, natural hypersensitiveness, the allergic response and specific antibacterial immunity would appear to depend on the same fundamental mechanism—the union of an antigen with its specific antibody.   The differences between them depend on the nature of the antigen concerned (living parasite, toxic substance or intrinsically inert material), the nature of the animal into whose tissues it penetrates, the rate and route of penetration, the distribution of the antibody in the animal's tissues and body fluids, the secondary effects of the primary cellular reactions, and a variety of other factors.

REFERENCES

ABEL, J. J. and KUBOTKA, S.   (1919) *J. Pharmacol.*, **13**, 243.
ADELSBERGER L.   (1936) *Rev. Immunol., Paris*, **2**, 14.
ALEXANDER, M. E.   (1924) *J. Immunol.*, **8**, 457.
ARTHUS, M.   (1903) *C. R. Soc. Biol.*, **55**, 817.
AUER, J. and LEWIS, P. A.   (1910) *J. exp. Med.*, **12**, 151.
AVERY, O. T. and TILLETT, W. S.   (1929) *J. exp. Med.*, **49**, 251.
BARGER, G. and DALE, H. H.   (1911) *J. Physiol.*, **41**, 499.
BERTARELLI, E.   (1906) *Zbl. Bakt.*, **41**, 320 ; (1907) *Ibid.*, **43**, 238, 448 ; (1908) *Ibid.*, **46**, 51.
BESCHE, A. DE.   (1918) *J. infect. Dis.*, **22**, 594.
BESREDKA, A. and STEINHARDT, E.   (1907) *Ann. Inst. Pasteur*, **21**, 117, 384.
BIEDL, A. and KRAUS R.   (1909) *Wien. klin. Wschr.*, **22**, 363.
BORDET, J. and ZUNTZ, E.   (1914) *Z. ImmunForsch.*, **23**, 42, 49.
BRONFENBRENNER, J.   (1915) *J. exp. Med.*, **21**, 480.
BROWN, R.   (1934*a*) *Proc. Soc. exp. Biol., N.Y.*, **31**, 699 ; (1934*b*) *Ibid.*, **31**, 700.
BROWN, W. H. and PEARCE, L.   (1921) *J. exp. Med.*, **33**, 553.
CAULFEILD, A. H. W., COHEN, C., and EADIE, G. S.   (1926) *J. Immunol.*, **12**, 153.
CLARKE, J. A. and GALLAGHER, M. G.   (1926) *J. Immunol.*, **12**, 461.

CLARKE, J. A., DONNALLY, H. H., and COCA, A. F. (1928) *Ibid.*, **15**, 9.
COCA, A. F. (1919) *Ibid.*, **4**, 209, 219 ; (1920a) *Ibid.*, **4**, 363 ; (1920b) *Proc. Soc. exp. Biol.*, *N.Y.*, **18**, 71.
COCA, A. F. and COOKE, R. A. (1923) *J. Immunol.*, **8**, 163.
COCA, A. F. and GROVE, E. F. (1925) *Ibid.*, **10**, 445.
COOKE, R. A. and VEER, A. V. (1916) *Ibid.*, **1**, 201.
COWIE, D. M. (1914) *Amer. J. Dis. Child.*, **7**, 253.
DALE, H. H. (1913) *J. Pharm. exp. Ther.*, **4**, 167 ; (1920a) *Bull. Johns Hopk. Hosp.*, **31**, 257 ; (1920b) *Ibid.*, **31**, 310 ; (1929) *Lancet*, i. 1179, 1233, 1285.
DALE, H. H., DUDLEY, H. W., and THORPE, W. V. (1927) *J. Physiol.*, **62**, 397.
DALE, H. H. and HARTLEY, P. (1916) *Biochem, J.*, **10**, 110.
DALE, H. H. and KELLAWAY, C. H. (1922) *Philos. Trans.*, **202**, 273.
DALE, H. H. and LAIDLAW, P. P. (1919) *J. Physiol.*, **52**, 355.
DAVIDOFF, L. M., SEEGAL, B. C., and SEEGAL, D. (1932) *J. exp. Med.*, **55**, 163.
DEAN, H. R. and WEBB, R. A. (1924) *J. Path. Bact.*, **27**, 51, 65.
DENECKE, G. (1914) *Z. ImmunForsch.*, **20**, 501.
DOERR, R. (1914) *Ergebn. Hyg. Bakt.*, **1**, 257 ; (1922) *Ibid.*, **15**, 71.
DOERR, R. and PICK, E. P. (1913) *Z. ImmunForsch.*, **19**, 251.
DOERR, R. and RUSS, V. K. (1909) *Ibid.*, **3**, 181, 706.
DRINKER, C. K. and BRONFENBRENNER, J. (1924) *J. Immunol.*, **9**, 387.
EAGLETON, A. J. and BAXTER, E. M. (1923) *J. Hyg., Camb.*, **22**, 107.
ENDERS, J. F. (1929) *J. exp. Med.*, **50**, 777.
FRIEDBERGER, E. (1910) *Ibid.*, **4**, 636 ; (1912) *Ibid.*, **15**, 475 ; (1913) *Ibid.*, **18**, 227.
FRIEDBERGER, E. and HARTOCH, O. (1909) *Ibid.*, **3**, 581.
FRIEDEMANN, U. (1909) *Z. Immunol.*, **2**, 591.
GAHRINGER, J. E. (1926) *J. Immunol.*, **12**, 477.
GAY, F. P. and SOUTHARD, E. E. (1908) *J. med. Res.*, **19**, 17.
GERNEZ, C. (1936) *Rev. Immunol., Paris*, **2**, 27.
GOODNER, K. (1926) *J. Immunol.*, **11**, 335.
GORDON, J. E. and CRESWELL, S. M. (1929) *J. prev. Med., Baltimore*, **3**, 21.
GRANT, R. T. and JONES, T. O. (1929) *Heart*, **14**, 337.
GROVE, E. F. (1932a) *J. Immunol.*, **23**, 125 ; (1932b) *Ibid.*, **23**, 147.
GROVE, E. F. and COCA, A. F. (1925) *J. Immunol.*, **10**, 471.
HANZLIK, P. J. and KARSNER, H. T. (1920) *J. Pharm. exp. Ther.*, **14**, 379, 425, 449, 479 ; (1924) *Ibid.*, **23**, 173.
HANZLIK, P. J. and STOCKTON, A. B. (1927) *J. Immunol.*, **13**, 395.
HARRIS, K. E. (1927) *Heart*, **41**, 161.
HIRSCHFELDER, A. D. (1910) *J. exp. Med.*, **12**, 586.
HOLOBUT, T. H. (1909) *Z. ImmunForsch.*, **3**, 639.
HOOKER, S. B. (1924) *J. Immunol.*, **9**, 7.
HORSFALL, F. L. (1934) *J. Immunol.*, **27**, 553.
JACOBS, J. (1932) *J. Immunol.*, **23**, 361.
JOBLING, J. W. and PETERSEN, W. (1914) *J. exp. Med.*, **19**, 480.
KELLAWAY, C. H. (1930) *Brit. J. exp. Path.*, **11**, 72.
KELLAWAY, C. H. and COWELL, J. S. (1922) *Ibid.*, **3**, 268.
KELLETT, C. E. (1935) *J. Path. Bact.*, **41**, 479.
KEYSSER, F. and WASSERMANN, M. (1911) *Z. Hyg. InfektKr.*, **68**, 535.
KLOPSTOCK, A. and SELTER, G. E. (1929) *Z. ImmunForsch.*, **63**, 463.
KOCH, R. (1891) *Dtsch. med. Wschr.*, **17**, 101.
KOLLE, W. (1922) *Ibid.*, **48**, 1301 ; (1924) *Ibid.*, **50**, 1074, 1235.
KOLLE, W. and PRIGGE, R. (1927) *Ibid.*, **53**, 1499 ; (1929) *Ibid.*, **55**, 985.
KOLLE, W. and SCHLOSZBERGER, H. (1926) *Ibid.*, **52**, 1245.
KRAUS, R. and ADMIRIDZIBI, F. S. (1910) *Z. ImmunForsch.*, **4**, 607.
KRAUS, R. and DOERR, R. (1908) *Wien. klin. Wschr.*, **21**, 1008.
KRUIF, P. H. DE. (1917) *J. infect. Dis.*, **20**, 717.
KRUIF, P. H. DE and GERMAN, W. H. (1917) *Ibid.*, **20**, 833.
LANCEFIELD, R. C. (1928) *J. exp. Med.*, **47**, 91, 469, 857.
LANDSTEINER, K. and LEVINE, P. (1930) *Ibid.*, **52**, 347.
LEVINE, P. and COCA, A. F. (1927) *J. Immunol.*, **11**, 411, 435.
LEWIS, P. A. and ARONSON, J. D. (1923) *Amer. Rev. Tuberc.*, **7**, 404.
LEWIS, T. (1927) " The Blood Vessels of the Human Skin and their Responses." London.
LONGCOPE, W. T. (1922) *J. exp. Med.*, **36**, 627.
LONGCOPE, W. T., O'BRIEN, D. P., and PERLZWEIG, W. A. (1925) *J. Immunol.*, **10**, 599 ; (1927) *Ibid.*, **13**, 253.
LONGCOPE, W. T. and RACKEMAN, F. M. (1918) *J. exp. Med.*, **27**, 341.
MACKENZIE, G. M. (1924) *J. Immunol.*, **9**, 333.
MANWARING, W. H. (1910) *Z. ImmunForsch.*, **8**, 1 ; (1926) *J. Immunol.*, **12**, 177 ; (1928) *J. Amer. med. Ass.*, **90**, 2090.

MANWARING, W. H. and BRILL, S. (1923) *J. Immunol.*, **8,** 47.
MANWARING, W. H., BRILL, S., and BOYD, W. H. (1923) *Ibid.*, **8,** 121.
MANWARING, W. H., CHILCOTE, R. C., and HOSEPIAN, V. M. (1923) *Ibid.*, **8,** 233.
MANWARING, W. H., CLARK, W. S., and CHILCOTE, R. C. (1923) *Ibid.*, **8,** 191.
MANWARING, W. H., FRENCH, W. O., and BRILL, S. (1923) *Ibid.*, **8,** 211.
MANWARING, W. H., HOSEPIAN, V. M., and BEATTIE, A. C. (1923) *Ibid.*, **8,** 229.
MANWARING, W. H., HOSEPIAN, V. M., ENRIGHT, J. R., and PORTER, D. F. (1925) *Ibid.*, **10,** 567.
MANWARING, W. H., HOSEPIAN, V. M., O'NEILL, F. I., and BING MOY, H. (1925) *Ibid.*, **10,** 575.
MANWARING, W. H. and MARINO, H. D. (1927) *Ibid.*, **13,** 69.
MANWARING, W. H., MARINO, H. D., and AZEVEDO, J. L. (1928) *Ibid.*, **15,** 109.
MANWARING, W. H., MARINO, H. D., AZEVEDO, J. L., and TORBERT, H. C. (1928) *Ibid.*, **15,** 351.
MANWARING, W. H., MARINO, H. D., McCLEAVE, T. C., and BOONE, T. H. (1927) *Ibid.*, **13,** 319, 357.
MANWARING, W. H., REEVES, D. L., MOY, H. B., SHUMAKER, P. W., and WRIGHT, R. W. (1927) *Ibid.*, **13,** 63.
MANWARING, W. H., SHUMAKER, P. W., WRIGHT, R. W., REEVES, D. L., and MOY, H. B. (1927) *Ibid.*, **13,** 59.
MANWARING, W. H. and WILLIAMS, T. B. (1923) *Ibid.*, **8,** 75.
MANWARING, W. H., WRIGHT, R. W., and SHUMAKER, P. W. (1926) *J. Amer. med. Ass.*, **86,** 1271.
MAUNTER, H. and PICK, E. P. (1915) *Münch. med. Wschr.*, **62,** 1141.
MAYER, R. L. and SULZBERGER, M. B. (1931) *Arch. Derm. Syph., Berl.*, **163,** 245.
MEHLMAN, J. and SEEGAL, B. C. (1934) *J. Immunol.*, **27,** 81.
MUTERMILCH, S. (1913) *Ann. Inst. Pasteur*, **27,** 83.
NATHAN, E. (1914) *Z. ImmunForsch.*, **23,** 204.
NICOLLE, M. (1907) *Ann. Inst. Pasteur*, **21,** 128.
NOVY, F. G. and KRUIF, P. H. DE. (1917) *J. infect. Dis.*, **20,** 536, 566, 589, 618, 629, 776.
NOVY, F. G., KRUIF, P. H. DE, and NOVY, R. L. (1917) *Ibid.*, **20,** 499, 657.
OPIE, E. L. (1924) *J. Immunol.*, **9,** 231, 247, 255, 259.
OTTO, R. (1905) *v. Leuthold Gedenkschr.*, 1 ; (1907) *Münch. med. Wschr.*, **55,** 1665.
OTTO, R. and ADELSBERGER, L. (1931) *Z. Hyg. InfektKr.*, **113,** 16.
PARK, W. H. (1908) "Diphtheria." Nuttall and Graham-Smith. Camb. ; (1924) *J. Immunol.*, **9,** 17.
PARKER, J. T. (1924) *Ibid.*, **9,** 515.
PARKER, J. T. and PARKER, F. (1924) *J. med. Res.*, **44,** 263.
PARODI, U. (1907) *Zbl. Bakt.*, **44,** 428.
PEARCE, R. M. and EISENBREY, A. B. (1910) *J. infect. Dis.*, **7,** 565.
PIRQUET, C. VON and SCHICK, B. (1905) "Die Serumkrankheit." Leipzig.
PORTIER, P. and RICHET, C. (1902) *C. R. Soc. Biol.*, **54,** 170.
PRAUSNITZ, C. and KÜSTNER, H. (1921) *Zbl. Bakt.*, **86,** 160.
RAMIREZ, M. A. (1920) *N.Y. med. J.*, **112,** 115.
RAMSDEN, S. G. (1926) *J. Immunol.*, **12,** 231.
RICHET, C. (1907) *Ann. Inst. Pasteur*, **21,** 497.
RITZ, H. and SACHS, H. (1911) *Berl. klin. Wschr.*, **48,** 987 ; (1918) *Z. Hyg. InfektKr.*, **86,** 235.
RÖMER, P. H. and JOSEPH, K. (1909) *Berl. klin. Wschr.*, **48,** 1300 ; (1910) *Münch. med. Wschr.*, **57,** 229, 1685.
ROSENAU, M. J. and ANDERSON, J. F. (1906) *Bull. U.S. hyg. Lab.*, **29,** 1 ; (1907) *J. infect. Dis.*, **4,** 552 ; (1908) *Ibid.*, **5,** 85.
SCHULTZ, W. H. (1910) *J. Pharmacol.*, **2,** 221.
SCOTT, W. M. (1931) "System of Bacteriology." Med. Res. Coun., **6,** 457.
SEEGAL, D., SEEGAL, B. C., and JOST, E. J. (1932) *J. exp. Med.*, **55,** 155.
SPAIN, W. C. and COOKE, R. A. (1924) *J. Immunol.*, **9,** 521.
SPAIN, W. C. and GROVE, E. F. (1925) *Ibid.*, **10,** 433.
SULZBERGER, M. and MAYER, R. L. (1931) *Arch. Derm. Syph., Berl.*, **24,** 537.
TANIGUCHI, T. (1922) *J. Path. Bact.*, **25,** 77.
THORPE, W. V. (1928) *Biochem. J.*, **22,** 94.
TILLETT, W. S., AVERY, O. T., and GOEBEL, W. F. (1929) *J. exp. Med.*, **50,** 551.
TOMASCZEWSKI, E. (1910) *Dtsch. med. Wschr.*, **36,** 1025.
TOMCSIK, J. and KUROTCHKIN, T. J. (1928) *J. exp. Med.*, **47,** 379.
TRUFFI, M. (1910) *Zbl. Bakt.*, **54,** 337.
UHLENHUTH, P. and GROSZMANN, H. (1928) *Z. ImmunForsch.*, **55,** 380.
VALLERY-RADOT, P., MAURIC, G., and HUGO, A. (1936) *Rev. Immunol., Paris*, **2,** 6.
VAUGHAN, V. C. and WHEELER, S. M. (1907) *J. infect. Dis.*, **4,** 476.
VOEGTLIN, C. and BERNHEIM, B. M. (1911) *J. Pharm. exp. Ther.*, **2,** 507.

VOEGTLIN, C. and DYER, H. A. (1924) *J. Pharmacol.*, **24**, 101.
WAELE, H. DE. (1907) *Bull. Acad. med. Belg.*, **21**, 715.
WALZER, M. and GROVE, E. F. (1925) *J. Immunol.*, **10**, 483.
WEBB, R. A. (1924) *J. Path. Bact.*, **24**, 79.
WEIL, R. (1913) *J. med. Res.*, **27**, 497 ; **28**, 243 ; (1914) *Ibid.*, **29**, 233 ; **30,** 87, 299; (1916)
  J. Immunol., **1,** 1, 19, 35, 47 ; (1917) *Ibid.*, **2,** 95, 109, 399, 469, 525, 571.
WELLS, H. G. (1908) *J. Infect. Dis.*, **5,** 449.
ZINSSER, H. (1920) *Proc. Soc. exp. Biol., N.Y.*, **18,** 57.
ZINSSER, H. and MALLORY, T. B. (1924) *J. Immunol.*, **9,** 75.
ZINSSER, H. and PARKER, J. (1917) *J. exp. Med.*, **26,** 411.

CHAPTER XLIX

CERTAIN NON-SPECIFIC MECHANISMS IN GENERAL IMMUNITY

The integrated protective mechanisms which we have described in the preceding chapters are specific in their action. When fully established, by nature or by art, they increase the resistance of the body against some particular bacterial infection, not against bacterial infections in general. In the present chapter we shall consider certain mechanisms from which this element of specificity is absent.

β **Lysins, Leukins and Plakins.**—Among the earliest records of experimental immunity are a series of observations on anthrax infection, which establish clearly the presence in the serum of certain animal species of bactericidal substances different in kind from the bactericidal complex formed of specific sensitizer and complement. Thus the serum of the rat is actively bactericidal for the anthrax bacillus, and this activity remains after heating the serum at a temperature of 56–60° C. for 30–40 minutes (von Behring 1889, 1892, Malvoz 1902, Pirenne 1904). The name β *lysins* has since been applied to these relatively thermostable bactericidal serum constituents.

Another series of observations, dating from the same early period, have shown that similar thermostable bactericidal substances can be extracted from suspensions of polymorphonuclear leucocytes. Like the β lysins these *leukins* are restricted in their range of activity, some bacterial species, in particular the spore-bearing aerobes such as *B. anthracis* and *B. subtilis*, being highly sensitive to their action, other species being relatively or entirely resistant. There is some divergence of evidence with regard to the susceptibility or insusceptibility of different bacteria, and it seems possible that the leukins derived from one animal species may differ in this respect from those derived from another. Nor can it be said that there is yet any certainty as to whether the β lysins and leukins are relatively simple substances, or complex systems like serum complement, with its end-piece, mid-piece and third and fourth components. (See Hahn 1895, Schattenfroh 1897, 1899, Pettersson 1906, 1908a, b, Hiss 1908, Hiss and Zinsser 1908, Zinsser and Hiss 1908, Schneider 1909, Zinsser 1910, Kling 1910, Weil 1911, Blum 1922, Haussmann 1925, Mackie and Finkelstein 1932, Mackie et al. 1932.)

There are observations which suggest that substances with a general similarity to leukins may be extracted from blood platelets (see Pettersson, above, Gruber and Futaki 1907, Barreau 1909), and these have been called *plakins*. It is not certain what relation the β lysins bear to the leukins or to the plakins. There are apparent differences in thermostability—the β lysins are inactivated at temperatures between 65° and 70° C., the leukins not below 75° C. But these differences have hardly been established with sufficient sharpness, or with sufficient regard to possible effects of differences in the containing medium, to be accepted as a clear differential criterion. It seems certain, however, that many animal species may contain no demonstrable β lysins in their serum, although leukins may readily be derived from their leucocytes.

Our present knowledge may be summarized by the statement that there exist in the normal sera of certain animal species thermostable bactericidal substances which are non-specific in their action, in the sense in which immunological specificity is generally understood—though their range of activity is limited by the varying sensitiveness of different bacterial species—and which are not increased in amount as the result of immunization. Bactericidal substances having very similar properties may be extracted from leucocytes and perhaps from blood platelets.

The relation of these substances to effective immunity is by no means clear. To take the case of anthrax, the relatively resistant rat has β lysins in its serum, so has the susceptible rabbit, while the relatively resistant dog has none (see Ledingham 1922).

The significance of the leukins and plakins is still more difficult to assess. That the leukins—using that term for the moment as a generic name for the antibacterial substances present in or derived from leucocytes—play some part in resistance to infection, seems a highly probable assumption ; but we do not know whether their rôle is primary or secondary, nor how it is related to the defence mechanisms that we have considered in more detail above.

We may note, in this connection, an observation by Buxton and Torrey (1906) which suggests that the polymorphonuclear cells play a significant rôle as bactericidal agents, even when they are not concerned in the primary phagocytic reaction. The injection of typhoid bacilli into the peritoneal cavity of the rabbit is followed by the rapid deposition of a large proportion of the injected bacteria on the surface of the omentum. Here they are in part destroyed by extracellular lysis, in part ingested by the omental histiocytes. During the first 4–6 hours the polymorphonuclear cells play little if any part in the events on the omental surface, but after that interval there is a marked and increasing polymorphonuclear reaction which varies in intensity in different animals, and the fate of the rabbit appears to depend in part on the successful mobilization of the polymorphonuclear cells. When they collect rapidly and in large numbers the clearance of typhoid bacilli is complete, and the animal recovers. When they are scanty or slow in arrival secondary centres of bacterial multiplication appear, and the animal dies with a generalized bacteræmic infection. These observations have not been repeated in detail by later observers, and are not therefore established on a sufficiently broad basis to allow of any general induction ; but they are clearly suggestive.

Variations in the Phagocytic Power of the Leucocytes.—We have seen that one animal differs from another in the phagocytic power of its whole blood and that this difference is determined, at least in part, by the presence or relative concentration of sensitizing antibodies, the opsonins or bacteriotropins, whose action is increased in effectiveness by the normal serum complement. This opsonizing action is specific, so far as the sensitizing antibody is concerned, and may be increased or induced *de novo* as the result of specific immunization. But the phagocytic activity of the leucocytes, as was first shown clearly by Shattock aud Dudgeon (1908), is itself variable. Leucocytes from different persons, and particularly from persons suffering from various infections, show a significant difference in their ability to ingest not only various bacteria, but also inert particles, such as melanin. The latter observation is of importance, since it indicates that such variations in phagocytic activity are independent of the nature of the phagocytable object (see also Glynn and Cox 1909–10, Boughton 1910, Rosenow 1910, Hektoen 1911, Wright 1931).

Lysozyme.—In Chapter XLII we referred to the bactericidal substance described by Fleming under the name of lysozyme and noted that, in high concentration, it has some bactericidal effect on pathogenic bacteria as well as on those non-pathogenic organisms that are particularly susceptible to its action. What part this substance plays in the defence mechanisms of the tissues it is, at the moment, impossible to say.

Induced Variations in the Non-specific Bactericidal Power of the Blood.—This leads us to a consideration, necessarily brief, of the possibility of inducing an effective immunity by increasing the non-specific bactericidal mechanisms of the cells and fluids of the body. Within recent years Wright and his collaborators (see Wright, Colebrook and Storer 1923, Wright 1931) have been active in exploring this field. Using specially devised *in vitro* methods of testing the bactericidal power of the whole blood, they have found that the addition of living or killed bacterial suspensions to blood in the test tube, or the injection of similar suspensions into the living animal, results in a very rapid increase in bactericidal power. This increase they attribute, in greater part, to the liberation by the leucocytes of directly bactericidal substances, in lesser part to increased opsonic power. Although this response is not specific—in the sense that there need be no antigenic relationship between the bacterium employed to induce the response and the bacterium against which the bactericidal effect is exerted—some bacterial suspensions have been found to provide a more effective stimulus than others.

This increased bactericidal power is developed with great rapidity—within a few minutes or hours—and is relatively transient, lasting at most for a period of days. It may be induced by a wide variety of stimuli.

Thus Prausnitz and Meissner (1925) record an increase in the bactericidal power of the whole blood after the injection of yatren and aolan. Fleming (1926) records a characteristic response after the injection of salt solutions into rabbits, or after the injection of nuclein (1928). Colebrook, Eidenow and Hill (1924) have recorded a similar response after exposure to ultra-violet light or to dark heat, and also after the application of a mustard plaster.

In some instances, at least, this temporary increase in the bactericidal power of the blood would seem to be due to, or associated with, an increase in the opsonic power of the serum (see Ledingham and Bulloch 1906, Bedson 1915). Thus, Bedson found that an injection of nuclein was followed by an increase in the normal opsonic action, which was detectable within 20–30 minutes, was still demonstrable after 24 hours, but then rapidly faded.

The value of this reaction as a protective mechanism is exceedingly difficult to determine. It may be concerned in some, at least, of those instances in which a temporary, or trivial, increase in resistance has been observed to follow a procedure which could not have resulted in the production of specific antibodies.

H. D. Wright, for example, has noted that rabbits may show an increased resistance to the intravenous injection of virulent pneumococci within 5 hours of the injection of a killed suspension of the same organism, a time interval too short to permit of antibody production. Similarly, Teague and McWilliams (1917) report that the intravenous injection of killed typhoid bacilli into rabbits is followed, within 24 hours, by a slight resistance to the injection of living bacilli. In other instances, the injection of a killed suspension of a given bacterium has been observed to induce a slight, or transient, increase in resistance to some antigenically unrelated organism (H. D. Wright 1927, Nukada and Arifuku 1931, and many others). The triviality, or transitoriness, of this non-specific increase in resistance should be stressed ; and in this connection we may recall the effect of non-specific immunization in protecting mice against natural infection with *Bact. typhi-murium* (see Table LXV, p. 831). The limited mean survival time of control unvaccinated mice, in an infected herd, was 26.26 ± 0.641 days, that of mice vaccinated with *Staphylococcus aureus* (an entirely unrelated organism) was 29.86 ± 0.714 days. Mice immunized with a specific vaccine lived on the average 35.31 ± 0.884 days. The difference between the non-specifically immunized and the control mice was trivial, barely attaining statistical significance, but two other non-specific vaccines gave a closely similar result, while a third, not included in Table LXV, gave no protection at all. It would seem that the increase in resistance afforded by non-specific stimulants of this class is too slight, and altogether too transient, to have any significant prophylactic value. Whether they can be usefully exploited therapeutically is a different problem.

The Shwartzman Phenomenon.

In the preceding paragraphs we have considered various reactions that are associated with a non-specific increase in resistance. In concluding this chapter it will be convenient to refer briefly to an experimental procedure that is associated with a localized and non-specific increase in sensitivity. Shwartzman (1928, 1929*a*, *b*, 1931, 1932, 1933) has described a curious phenomenon that has become known by his name, and has been studied in considerable detail by a number of other workers (see Gratia and Linz 1931, 1932, Gross 1931, Peck and Sobotka 1931, Gratia 1932, Peck 1933, 1934, Freund 1934*a*, *b*, Gerber 1936, Ogata 1936).

If a rabbit is injected intradermally with a small amount of a filtrate of a culture of *Bact. typhosum*, and 24 hours later is injected intravenously with the same filtrate, the intravenous injection is followed, within a few hours, by the development of a hæmorrhagic lesion at the site of the intradermal injection. It is not, however, necessary that the same organism should be used for the intradermal injection and for the subsequent intravenous injection, or that the organisms used for the two injections should be antigenically related. Filtrates from, or suspensions of, a variety of bacteria will sensitize the skin to the intravenous injection of an equally wide variety of bacteria or bacterial filtrates. Not all bacteria contain effective sensitizing substances, nor is the local sensitizing effect the result of a simple inflammatory reaction. Thus (Shwartzman 1928), the injection of uninoculated culture media, of turpentine or of filtrates of various strains of streptococci, failed to sensitize the skin to the subsequent intravenous injection of filtrates of typhoid cultures. The sensitizing substances, whatever they may be, appear to be relatively thermostable, resisting heat at $100°$ C. for one hour, and, in some instances, autoclaving for 45 minutes.

What part this mechanism plays in natural infection and resistance, or in artificial immunization, it is at the moment impossible to say.

SUMMARY

(1) In addition to the specific factors that determine antibacterial immunity, there are certain non-specific factors which appear to play some part in the reaction of the tissues to invading bacteria. The exact significance of these factors, and their relation to the general defence mechanism, are at the moment doubtful.

(2) Among these factors are certain thermostable bacteriolysins—the β lysins

—which are present in the sera of certain animal species. Their bactericidal action is limited to particular bacterial species, and it seems doubtful whether they confer an effective immunity even against these. They are not increased in amount as the result of immunization.

(3) Bactericidal substances may be extracted from leucocytes (the leukins) and perhaps from blood platelets (the plakins). These substances bear many resemblances to the β lysins, and appear to be even more thermostable. They probably play some part in antibacterial immunity, but what that part is remains, at the moment, an unsolved problem.

(4) Leucocytes vary in their phagocytic activity, and it seems likely that such variations may be induced in response to infection, and perhaps to immunization.

(5) Various non-specific stimuli are capable of inducing a rapid but transient increase in the bactericidal power of the blood, probably determined by some of the factors referred to above. The resulting increase in resistance is too slight, and too temporary, to be of practical prophylactic value.

(6) The phenomenon described by Shwartzman provides an example of non-specific sensitization.

REFERENCES

BARREAU, E. (1909) *Arch. Hyg.*, **70**, 331.
BEDSON, S. P. (1915) *J. Path. Bact.*, **19**, 191.
BEHRING, E. VON. (1889) *Z. Hyg. InfektKr.*, **6**, 117 ; (1892) *Ibid.*, **12**, 1.
BLUM, K. (1922) *Arch. Hyg.*, **91**, 373.
BOUGHTON, T. H. (1910) *J. infect. Dis.*, **7**, 111.
BUXTON, B. H. and TORREY, J. C. (1906) *J. med. Res.*, **15**, 73.
COLEBROOK, L., EIDENOW, A., and HILL, L. (1924) *Brit. J. exp. Path.*, **5**, 24.
FLEMING, A. (1926) *Ibid.*, **7**, 174 ; (1928) *Proc. R. Soc. Med.*, **21**, 861.
FREUND, J. (1934a) *J. exp. Med.*, **60**, 661. (1934b) *Ibid.*, **60**, 669.
GERBER, I. E. (1936) *Arch. Path.*, **21**, 331.
GLYNN, E. E. and COX, G. L. (1909–10) *J. Path. Bact.*, **14**, 90.
GRATIA, A. (1932) *Ann. Inst. Pasteur*, **49**, 131.
GRATIA, A. and LINZ, R. (1931) *C. R. Soc. Biol.*, **106**, 1290 ; (1932) *Ibid.*, **109**, 585.
GROSS, H. (1931) *Zbl. Bakt.*, **122**, 96.
GRUBER, M. and FUTAKI, K. (1907) *Dtsch. med. Wschr.*, **33**, 1588.
HAHN, M. (1895) *Arch. Hyg.*, **25**, 105.
HAUSSMANN, A. (1925) *Ibid.*, **95**, 69.
HEKTOEN, L. (1911) *J. infect. Dis.*, **9**, 103.
HISS, P. H. (1908) *J. med. Res.*, **19**, 323.
HISS, P. and ZINSSER, H. (1908) *Ibid.*, **19**, 399, 429.
KLING, C. A. (1910) *Z. ImmunForsch.*, **7**, 1.
LEDINGHAM, J. C. G. (1922) *Lancet*, ii. 898.
LEDINGHAM, J. C. G. and BULLOCH, W. (1906) " Studies in Pathology." Aberdeen.
MACKIE, T. J. and FINKELSTEIN, M. H. (1932) *J. Hyg., Camb.*, **32**, 1.
MACKIE, T. J., FINKELSTEIN, M. H., and VAN ROOYEN. (1932) *Ibid.*, **32**, 494.
MALVOZ, E. (1902) *Ann. Inst. Pasteur*, **16**, 625.
NUKADA, S. and ARIFUKU, S. (1931) *Z. ImmunForsch.*, **70**, 1.
OGATA, T. (1936) *J. exp. Med.*, **63**, 59.
PECK, S. M. (1933) *J. Immunol.*, **25**, 447 ; (1934) *Ibid.*, **27**, 89.
PECK, S. M. and SOBOTKA, H. (1931) *J. exp. Med.*, **54**, 407.
PETTERSSON, A. (1906) *Zbl. Bakt.*, **42**, 56 ; (1908a) *Ibid.*, **45**, 235 ; (1908b) *Ibid.*, **46**, 405.
PIRENNE, Y. (1904) *Zbl. Bakt.*, **36**, 256, 368, 388.
PRAUSNITZ, C. and MEISSNER, G. (1925) *Ibid.*, **94**, 376.
ROSENOW, E. C. (1910) *J. infect. Dis.*, **7**, 429.
SCHATTENFROH, A. (1897) *Arch. Hyg.*, **31**, 1 ; (1899) *Ibid.*, **35**, 135.
SCHNEIDER, R. (1909) *Ibid.*, **70**, 40.
SHATTOCK, S. G. and DUDGEON, L. S. (1908) *Proc. roy. Soc.*, B, **80**, 165.

SHWARTZMAN, G.   (1928) *J. exp. Med.*, **48**, 247 ; (1929a) *J. infect. Dis.*, **45**, 232 ; (1929b) *J. Amer. med. Ass.*, **93**, 1965 ; (1931) *J. infect. Dis.*, **48**, 183 ; (1932) *J. exp. Med.*, **56**, 291, 687 ; (1933) *Ibid.*, **57**, 857.
TEAGUE, O. and MCWILLIAMS, H.   (1917) *J. Immunol.*, **2**, 185.
WEIL, E.   (1911) *Arch. Hyg.*, **74**, 289.
WRIGHT, A. E.   (1931) *Lancet*, ii. 225, 277, 333.
WRIGHT, A. E., COLEBROOK, L., and STORER, E. J.   (1923) *Ibid.*, i. 365.
WRIGHT, H. D.   (1927) *J. Path. Bact.*, **30**, 185.
ZINSSER, H.   (1910) *J. med. Res.*, **22**, 397.
ZINSSER, H. and HISS, P. H.   (1903) *Ibid.*, **19**, 411.

CHAPTER L

LOCAL IMMUNITY

THE defence mechanisms with which we have hitherto been concerned have all exerted a generalized effect. By whatever route bacteria or their products gain access to the tissues these mechanisms will tend to protect the body as a whole.

Another type of immunity may be conceived, confined to one particular area of the body, or to one particular kind of tissue. Such a heightened local resistance may or may not result in, or be associated with, a significant increase in the resistance of the body as a whole. There has been a tendency to confuse the issue by an inadequate definition of the problem to be solved. The concept of a local immunity as such has been imperfectly separated from hypotheses regarding the mechanisms on which it depends. In some cases the term has been used as though it implied a tissue or cellular immunity, not conditioned by humoral factors. In others there has been a failure to distinguish clearly between specific and non-specific effects. It will simplify discussion if we consider the available evidence from each point of view in turn.

What evidence is there for the existence of a local as opposed to a general immunity ?

As long ago as 1887 Meierowitsch (1888) noted that rabbits which had recovered from an experimental attack of erysipelas were resistant to subsequent inoculations of the causative streptococcus during periods up to 2 months. This observation was confirmed by many later workers, and Gromakowsky (1895) noted that animals which had become resistant to a local cutaneous inoculation did not always withstand an intraperitoneal inoculation.

This phenomenon was studied in much greater detail by Cobbett and Melsome (1895, 1898). They concluded, on the basis of a considerable series of experiments, that an attack of erysipelas in the rabbit completely protects the area of skin affected against a subsequent inoculation of the specific streptococcus; ; while on the rest of the body it confers an immunity which is usually less marked and is sometimes entirely absent. They noted also that, when streptococci were inoculated into the skin of a rabbit's ear after the subsidence in that ear of an attack of erysipelas, an inflammatory reaction quickly appeared but subsided before the typical erysipelatous lesion had made any appreciable progress in a control rabbit. This rapid but transitory inflammatory reaction was most marked in ears that had been locally immunized, less marked in ears that shared in a general protection. Gay and Rhodes (1922) have recorded experiments bearing on the same problem. They concluded from their results that a rabbit which had recovered from an attack of erysipelas was completely protected against subsequent intracutaneous injections of the causative streptococcus, irrespective of its exact locality, for a period of at least 3 months. They were unable to obtain a similar immunity by the intracutaneous injection of cultures killed by heat or by alcohol. Immunity against intracutaneous inoculation was not associated with immunity against intravenous inoculation ; while immunization by the intravenous route was found to afford more protection against subsequent intravenous inoculation than against intracutaneous inoculation. Rivers (1925) carried out a series of experiments in which rabbits were given repeated intracutaneous injections of living hæmolytic streptococci derived from a case of erysipelas. He noted that the reactions following successive injections showed a progressive decrease in severity. After several such injections the sera of the rabbits were tested for the presence of protective antibodies. The serum to be tested was mixed with a suspension of living streptococci and injected into the skin of a normal rabbit ; at another site in the same animal another injection was made consisting of a mixture of the same streptococcal suspension and normal serum. The sera from the immunized rabbits had a marked protective action, normal serum had none. The studies of Amoss and Bliss (1927) bring out further points of interest. Like other observers they found that an area of skin which had been involved in an erysipelatous reaction was definitely more resistant to a subsequent injection of the causative strepto-coccus, and that if the injections were repeated the degree of resistance progressively increased. They noted that the primary lesion in the skin of the rabbit's flank tended to spread ventrally from the site of inoculation in the direction of the lymph flow ; and they found that when the area involved in the primary reaction and the skin in its immediate neighbourhood were tested by subsequent intradermal inoculations the area of increased resistance extended ventrally beyond the area of primary reaction, but not anteriorly, posteriorly or dorsally. At this period no increased resistance could be demonstrated in the skin of the opposite flank. After prolonged immunization the skin at a distance from the site of inoculation might show increased resistance, but this generalized skin immunity was associated with a humoral immunity, evidenced by the appearance of specific antibodies in the blood.

Taking these observations as a whole it would appear that a local immunity to hæmolytic streptococci may exist in the absence of a general immunity, and that, when repeated local injections lead to a general immunizing response, the level of immunity may, for a time at least, be higher in the immediate neighbourhood of the site of inoculation than in the tissues generally. It may be noted that the severe inflammatory reaction associated with an attack of erysipelas is more effective in inducing a local immunity than is the relatively trivial reaction that follows the injection of a killed suspension of streptococci ; and that there is evidence that the tissues become allergic during the immunizing infection.

Although experimental erysipelas provides the best-documented example of a local as opposed to a general immunity, many analogous observations have been recorded in relation to other infections. Cooper (1926), for instance, states that rabbits may be im-munized against the injection of virulent pneumococci into the buccal mucosa by repeated injections, into the same tissue, of a killed pneumococcal vaccine, but not by injections of the same vaccine given subcutaneously or intradermally. Other examples of a similar kind will be noted in the succeeding paragraphs.

There are also many experimental observations in relation to virus diseases (see Chapter LII) which suggest that a local immunity plays an important part in determining the reaction of the body as a whole.

We need not doubt that a local immunity exists, in the sense that one area of the tissues is more resistant than another to the introduction into it of a living bacterium or virus. The problem at issue is whether these localized differences in resistance can be accounted for by local variations in the effectiveness of the mechanisms we have considered in previous chapters, or whether some essentially different mechanism is involved.

*Is the distribution of a local immunity confined to a particular type of cell or tissue,
affecting that type of cell or tissue wherever it occurs in the body, or is this distribution determined by the site of inoculation, affecting all cells or tissues in the
immediate neighbourhood of that site ?*

We may particularize our question in regard to the phenomena considered in
the preceding section by inquiring whether it is the skin, as such and apart from
other tissues, that is rendered resistant by the intracutaneous injection of living
hæmolytic streptococci, or whether the effect is limited to the area of the initial
erysipelatous reaction, affecting in that area all the cells or tissues involved in the
inflammatory process.

The evidence is somewhat conflicting. The observations of Gay and Rhodes
appear to favour the view that the skin as such irrespective of its nearness or
remoteness to the site of the primary inflammatory reaction is rendered resistant
by a localized experimental erysipelas. The findings of most other workers, and
particularly those of Amoss and Bliss, suggest that the distribution of resistance
is, in the first instance, confined to the area affected by the erysipelatous reaction,
though other areas of skin share in the more general immunity that may be induced
by repeated injections of streptococci.

The question posed leads naturally to the one that follows it, and data relevant
to its solution will be considered under this and other heads.

*Does the local immunity as such, and apart from an associated humoral immunity,
confer an increased resistance on the body as a whole ?*

It will be convenient to commence our discussion of this question by setting
out, in their baldest terms, the views that have been put forward by Besredka
(1919, 1920, 1921).

He notes that many, if not all, pathogenic bacteria show a marked tendency to specific
localization in particular tissues of the body. Thus the typhoid, paratyphoid and dysentery
bacilli cause intestinal infection, while the anthrax bacillus commonly causes infection
of the skin. He would, however, carry this argument much further than those who regard
such frequency distributions as the expression of a modal type of infection, determined
by a variety of interacting factors and often departed from in particular instances. He
believes, for instance, that the localization is in no way dependent on the route by which
the bacteria enter the body. By whatever path typhoid, paratyphoid or dysentery bacilli
gain access to the tissues they pass to the intestines, and there produce their distinctive
lesions. Similarly, for a fatal anthrax infection to result, the anthrax bacillus however
introduced must reach the skin.

As a logical corollary, a naturally immune or an actively immunized animal owes its
increased resistance to the local immunity possessed by the particular tissues which are,
in susceptible animals, specifically liable to attack. If these susceptible tissues are rendered
immune then the whole animal is immune, because the specific localization which is an
essential feature of bacterial infection can no longer occur. Thus, in the last analysis,
general immunity is simply the expression of effective local immunity. The various
antigen-antibody reactions that have been observed are, in reality, of altogether minor
importance.

These conclusions are clearly revolutionary and provocative ; and like all provocative
conclusions based on experimental study they have acted as a stimulus to further research.
Taken as they stand, it seems hardly necessary to do more than confront them with the
evidence set out in the preceding chapters in order to demonstrate that they cannot be

accepted as an adequate picture of the facts. Whether a localized immunity in Besredka's sense plays any part in resistance to bacterial infection is another matter.

Taking the case of experimental typhoid, paratyphoid or dysentery infection in rabbits, Besredka lays emphasis on the point that these animals can be effectively immunized by feeding with dead or living cultures. When dead bacterial cells are used for immunization, it is sometimes necessary to administer in addition a small dose of bile, which causes minimal lesions of the mucous membrane. The fact that an increased resistance can be induced in this way does not, however, afford any evidence in favour of the conception of a specific induced immunity of the intestinal mucosa. We have seen (p. 875) that the administration of dead or living bacteria by the mouth is often followed by the passage of bacterial antigens from the intestines to the tissues and this, in its turn, by the usual antibody-forming response. The argument on which Besredka lays most stress in this particular instance is the following. He states that when dysentery bacilli are administered to rabbits by the mouth agglutinins may appear in the blood after the first administration, but they soon disappear, and do not reappear after any subsequent administration. He records analogous observations in the case of rabbits immunized by the oral administration of typhoid bacilli after preliminary treatment with bile ; and, in both cases, he interprets the early disappearance of agglutinins, their failure to reappear after subsequent administration of bacteria *per os*, and the increasing resistance to infection by any route, to the establishment of a local immunity of the intestinal mucosa, which presents an impenetrable barrier to the passage of bacteria from the intestines to the tissues, and at the same time prevents the essential selective localization of the bacilli should they gain access to the tissues by some other route. The few experiments recorded by Besredka seem quite inadequate to form a basis for such an important and far-reaching conclusion ; and, as Otten and Kirschner (1927) have pointed out, the crucial observation of the disappearance of antibodies from the blood during a series of repeated administrations of vaccine *per os* finds no adequate confirmation in the results obtained by other workers.

Turning to the case of anthrax, controversy has centred round Besredka's contention that the skin alone is susceptible to this infection. Balteano (1922) states that he has confirmed Besredka's findings. Plotz (1924) carried out a series of experiments in which cultures of *B. anthracis* were enclosed in thin-walled glass bottles and introduced into the subcutaneous tissue of rabbits. The wounds were allowed to heal and at various periods thereafter the bulbs were broken *in situ* and the contained culture was allowed to escape into the surrounding tissues. The majority of such animals survived, and Plotz concludes that the rabbit can resist a large subcutaneous inoculation of *B. anthracis*, provided that the bacilli do not come into contact with any wound of the skin.

Other investigators have, however, recorded quite different results. Sobernheim and Murata (1924) estimated the minimal lethal dose of a culture of *B. anthracis* when administered by different routes. They found that about 1/10,000 of a loopful would produce death when introduced intraperitoneally or intravenously, about 1/100,000 of a loopful when introduced subcutaneously or intracutaneously and about 1/1,000,000 of a loopful when injected intramuscularly.

It is obviously difficult to avoid infecting the skin when making injections into any subjacent tissue, and this objection has been urged against those who have recorded successful infection by some route other than the intracutaneous ; but Besredka's assumption can hardly be reconciled with the observation that a *smaller* dose of bacilli is required to produce a fatal infection when the inoculation is made into the muscles than when it is made directly into the skin. Similarly, Basset (1925) was unable to demonstrate any superiority of the intracutaneous as compared with the subcutaneous or intramuscular route. Müller (1925) has recorded results which are directly opposed to those obtained by Plotz. He states that, several years before his paper was published, he had inoculated a pigeon's egg with anthrax bacilli, sealed the opening, and introduced the egg into the peritoneal cavity of a rabbit. Five weeks later this animal died from anthrax. Unable to reconcile this result with Besredka's views he carried out further experiments of the same type, but with a slightly different technique. Finding that anthrax bacilli would grow slowly through the pores of an L_1 candle, he placed cultures of the organism in such candles, sealed them carefully, and introduced them into the peritoneal cavities of nine rabbits. Seven of these animals died after intervals varying from 6 to 51 days. This long incubation period would appear to preclude an infection of the skin occurring at the time of the introduction of the candles. Burke and Barnes (1931) have utilized the bactericidal action of gentian violet in an attempt to produce an initial subcutaneous infection with *B. anthracis* unassociated with any primary infection of the skin. A guinea-pig was injected with a young culture of *B. anthracis* by introducing the needle through the skin of the abdominal wall in one flank, and then passing it subcutaneously across the abdomen to the other flank, where the inoculum was deposited. The point of the needle was then withdrawn to just beneath the skin puncture, the syringe barrel was detached, another barrel containing a 1 per cent. solution of gentian violet was attached, and the dye was introduced into the puncture as the needle was withdrawn. The guinea-pig died in 56 to 72 hours. The characteristic gelatinous infiltration occurred at the point where the inoculum had been deposited, not at the point where the needle had been inserted. Cultures from the dye-stained area about the site of the skin puncture remained sterile. It seems fair to conclude that Besredka's contention with regard to the unique susceptibility of the skin to anthrax has not been proved. Besredka and his colleagues (Besredka 1924a, b, Besredka and Urbain 1924) have also attempted to immunize the skin against other bacteria. They applied filtrates from broth cultures of staphylococci or streptococci to the shaved skin of rabbits, and tested the resistance of these areas of skin to subsequent infection with the homologous organisms. From their results they conclude that this procedure confers a high degree of local immunity. In later reports they, and others, have recorded valuable curative properties in these filtered cultures—the so-called " antivirus " preparations—but these observations do not bear directly on the problem at issue, and need not be further considered.

We need not doubt that various procedures of this kind may raise the resistance of local areas of skin to subsequent infection ; but it by no means follows that this is associated with an increase in the resistance of the body as a whole.

Thus, Hach, Borodaj and Melnyk (1928) state that staphylococci, after intravenous inoculation into rabbits, tend first ($3–3\frac{1}{2}$ hours) to accumulate in the spleen, few remaining in the blood and few being present in the skin. As the infection progresses towards its rapidly fatal issue the distribution changes ; the number of cocci in the spleen rapidly diminish, the number present in the skin show an enormous increase. Multiple intradermal inoculations of a staphylococcal filtrate, preceding the intravenous injection, prevented this rapid accumulation of staphylococci in the skin (Hach and Melnyk 1928) ; but there was no effective immunity, the rabbits dying of typical acute staphylococcal infection.

Is local immunity specific or non-specific ?

We may now return to the more general question of the nature of the mechanisms that determine those types of local immunity that have been shown to exist, and enquire particularly whether they are in the main specific or non-specific.

Cobbett and Melsome (1898) found that a local non-specific inflammatory reaction, such as that following the injection of mustard oil, would effectively protect the skin of a rabbit's ear against subsequent attempts to produce experimental erysipelas.

Amoss and Bliss (1927) noted that the localized resistance following an erysipelatous lesion was not sharply specific. It was effective against strains of hæmolytic streptococci antigenically dissimilar from the strain producing the initial lesion, and to a less extent against *Staphylococcus aureus*. Rivers and Tillett (1925), studying the properties of the serum derived from the rabbits in which they had produced a localized antistreptococcal immunity, found that such immune serum injected into the skin 24 to 48 hours before the injection of living streptococci into the same site rendered this site relatively refractory to infection. Similar results were, however, obtained by the injection of normal serum, or of ordinary nutrient broth, though the protection in this case was less effective and quite non-specific. Mallory and Marble (1925) prepared filtrates from cultures of staphylococci and streptococci. With these they infiltrated localized areas in the skin of a rabbit, and found that such treatment conferred a strictly localized but non-specific immunity lasting for 5–6 weeks. This increased resistance was, however, little if any greater than that conferred by the infiltration of the skin with sterile broth. Analogous results have been recorded by Miller (1927), Freedlander and Toomey (1928), Hanger (1930) and Toomey and Freedlander (1931).

Freedlander and Toomey carried out a detailed histological study of the reactions induced in the cutaneous tissues by the application of compresses of sterile broth, and of the reactions that followed the subsequent injection of *Staphylococcus aureus* into these treated areas. They found that the application of the broth compresses to the abdominal wall of the guinea-pig, for a period of 48 hours, produced a localized œdema, a marked proliferation of histiocytes and a moderate exudation of polymorphonuclear and small mononuclear cells. The cellular response to the subsequent injection of *Staphylococcus aureus* differed widely in treated and untreated animals. In the broth-prepared animals there was an increase in the histiocytes and fibroblasts with a dense exudation of polymorphonuclear cells, which showed little tendency to degenerate. The histiocytes phagocytosed the staphylococci at an early stage of the reaction, while the proliferating fibroblasts tended to wall off the lesion. In the control animals the œdema following the bacterial infection was more marked, there was little proliferation of histiocytes or fibroblasts, and the polymorphonuclear cells, which collected in considerable numbers during the earlier stages of the reaction, showed a marked tendency to undergo degeneration at a later period. The reaction was in general more severe and destructive and far less localized.

It would seem justifiable to conclude that there is an important non-specific element in the local immunity that follows the injection into the skin of various reagents, or its treatment with compresses, etc., and that this non-specific increase in resistance is determined in large part by the mobilization of various phagocytic cells, and perhaps by changes in the local capillaries and lymphatics. It should be noted, moreover, that a non-specific immunity of this type is by no means limited to the skin.

Pfeiffer and Issaeff (1894) showed that the injection of such materials as broth, peptone solutions or urine into the peritoneum of the guinea-pig would so alter the local conditions that the animal became resistant to the intraperitoneal injection of living cholera vibrios in doses fatal to untreated control animals. It is not justifiable to regard this particular non-specific immunizing reaction as local, in the same sense as the cutaneous reactions considered above, since material injected into the peritoneum is rapidly transferred to the blood stream, and a generalized non-specific response of the type discussed in Chapter XLIX may well be concerned, in addition to any possible local effect.

Gay and Morrison (1923) injected various substances intraperitoneally into rabbits, and injected living streptococci 24 hours later. They found that certain substances, such as meat-extract broth, afforded marked protection, while others, such as aleuronat, did not. They noted that the substances which conferred protection were those that produced exudates in which macrophages were particularly numerous, while those that produced exudates containing numerous polymorphonuclear cells but few macrophages were far less effective.

The existence of this non-specific element in local immunity does not, of course, exclude the possibility that specific factors are also involved. On this point the evidence is, at the moment, too scanty to allow of any definite conclusion.

P.B.   H H

*Is local immunity necessarily associated with a cellular or tissue immunity in the
strict sense ?*

There is, as has been pointed out above, no necessary correlation between
local immunity and cellular immunity in the sense here implied—an immunity
which belongs to the cell as such apart from its immediate environment and, in
particular, apart from any antibodies which may be present in the tissue fluids
in its immediate neighbourhood. A cellular immunity might well be widespread in
its distribution, and effects. A local immunity may be due to a variety of factors
other than an acquired resistance of particular cells.

None of the observations outlined above necessitates the assumption that a
cellular immunity is involved ; but all of them are quite compatible with its
existence.

In this relation we may recall certain facts in regard to the formation and
distribution of antibodies, and the phenomenon of anaphylaxis and hypersensitiveness. The serum antibodies, wherever they are produced, are rapidly distributed throughout the tissues, and are in part fixed by various tissue cells. We
know almost nothing of the mechanism of this fixation, or of how the antibodies
are distributed among the tissue cells. We do know, however, that a cell that has
taken up its quota of a given antibody reacts specifically to the presence of the
corresponding antigen ; and this mechanism would seem to be involved in those
allergic reactions that are associated with infection and immunity. A " cellular
immunity " of this type, and conditioned in this way, almost certainly occurs ;
though we have, at the moment, no knowledge of what part it plays in the mechanisms of immunity in general.

SUMMARY

The evidence available appears to justify the following conclusions.

(1) By the injection of various materials into the tissues, and by certain analogous procedures, it is possible to induce an immunity which is confined to the
neighbourhood of the treated area, and is not shared by the body as a whole.

(2) This immunity appears to be distributed in accordance with the area involved in the original inflammatory reaction, not in accordance with the distribution
throughout the affected part or throughout the body generally of one particular
type of cell. There is good evidence of a localized immunity affecting an *area* of
skin, or a particular serous sac. There is no adequate evidence of an immunity
affecting the skin as a whole, or the intestinal mucosa as a whole, or serous surfaces
as a whole.

(3) It follows that we cannot accept the conclusion that a localized immunity
of the latter type is an essential factor in a general immunity. Even had an induced skin immunity, or mucous membrane immunity, been shown to exist, our
knowledge of the general defence mechanisms of the body would prevent us from
regarding such a local increase in resistance as the essential factor in antibacterial
immunity.

(4) All the evidence suggests that non-specific factors are of primary importance in those instances of local immunity that have been submitted to experimental
study. It would appear to be the initial inflammatory reaction as such, and the
cellular changes which persist for some time after it has subsided, that determine

the relative resistance of the treated area to subsequent experimental infections. In particular it would seem that any treatment which induces a local mobilization and concentration of histiocytes will confer on the treated area an increased resistance, which will last as long as the local cellular changes persist.

(5) When a localized area is repeatedly treated with a particular bacterium, a general immunity is often superimposed on the local immunity. There is nothing in the evidence at present available to suggest that such general immunity, in so far as it is specific, differs essentially from the specific antibacterial immunity that we have considered in earlier chapters.

(6) The problem of the existence of a cellular, as opposed to a humoral, immunity is distinct from that of the existence of a local, as opposed to a general, immunity. There is nothing that compels us to assume the existence of a cellular immunity ; but it would accord well with several experimental findings. If such a mechanism plays an essential part in immunity, it seems quite possible that it is conditioned by the fixation by various tissue cells of specific antibodies, and is hence only a humoral immunity at one remove.

REFERENCES

AMOSS, H. L. and BLISS, E. A. (1927) *J. exp. Med.*, **45**, 411.
BALTEANO, L. (1922) *Ann. Inst. Pasteur*, **36**, 805.
BASSET, J. (1925) *C. R. Soc. Biol.*, **93**, 1513, 1515, 1517.
BESREDKA, A. (1919) *Ann. Inst. Pasteur*, **33**, 301, 557, 882 ; (1920) *Ibid.*, **34**, 361 ; (1921) *Ibid.*, **35**, 421 ; (1924a) *Ibid.*, **88**, 565 ; (1924b) *C. R. Soc. Biol.*, **89**, 7.
BESREDKA, A. and URBAIN, A. (1924) *Ibid.*, **89**, 506.
BURKE, V. and BARNES, L. A. (1931) *J. Immunol.*, **20**, 173.
COBBETT, L. and MELSOME, W. S. (1895) *J. Path. Bact.*, **3**, 39 ; (1898) *Zbl. allg. Path. path. Anat.*, **9**, 827.
COOPER, M. L. (1926) *J. infect. Dis.*, **38**, 491.
FREEDLANDER, S. O. and TOOMEY, J. A. (1928) *J. exp. Med.*, **47**, 663.
GAY, F. P. and MORRISON, L. F. (1923) *J. infect. Dis.*, **33**, 338.
GAY, F. P. and RHODES, B. (1922) *Ibid.*, **31**, 101.
GROMAKOWSKY, D. (1895) *Ann. Inst. Pasteur*, **9**, 620.
HACH, IW., BORODAJ, M., and MELNYK, V. (1928) *Z. ImmunForsch.*, **54**, 251.
HACH, IW., and MELNYK, V. (1928) *Z. ImmunForsch.*, **54**, 269.
HANGER, F. M. (1930) *J. exp. Med.*, **52**, 485.
MALLORY, T. B. and MARBLE, A. (1925) *Ibid.*, **42**, 465.
MEIEROWITSCH. (1888) *Zbl. Bakt., Ref.*, **3**, 406.
MILLER, C. P. (1927) *Z. Hyg. InfektKr.*, **107**, 253.
MÜLLER, L. (1925) *C. R. Soc. Biol.*, **93**, 1243.
OTTEN, L. and KIRSCHNER, L. (1927) *Z. Hyg. InfektKr.*, **107**, 314.
PFEIFFER, R. and ISSAEFF. (1894) *Ibid.*, **17**, 355.
PLOTZ, H. (1924) *Ann. Inst. Pasteur*, **38**, 169.
RIVERS, T. M. (1925) *J. exp. Med.*, **41**, 179.
RIVERS, T. M. and TILLETT, W. S. (1925) *Ibid.*, **41**, 185.
SOBERNHEIM, G. and MURATA, H. (1924) *Z. Hyg. InfektKr.*, **103**, 691.
TOOMEY, J. A. and FREEDLANDER, S. O. (1931) *J. exp. Med.*, **53**, 363.

CHAPTER LI

THE INFLUENCE OF DIET, FATIGUE, CHANGES IN TEMPERATURE AND HUMIDITY, CHEMICAL AGENTS AND OTHER FACTORS ON GENERAL OR LOCAL IMMUNITY

The Influence of Diet on Immunity

IT will be convenient to discuss first the effects produced by deficiency or excess of those accessory food factors that have come to be grouped together under the name of *vitamins*.

Variations in the Intake of Vitamin A.—In 1909 Knapp described a curious condition of the eyes developing in rats fed on a deficient diet. This condition (xerophthalmia) is characterized by a thickening and drying of the superficial epithelial covering of the eye, patchy in distribution, and associated in its later stages with a subacute bacterial infection of the underlying tissues. Knapp did not ascribe these lesions to any specific dietary deficiency ; but we know now that the essential factor in its causation is lack of the fat-soluble Vitamin A, and Knapp's protocols show that the diet he employed was, in fact, deficient in this constituent. Similar lesions have since been described by many other observers, not only in the rat but in other animals, such as the rabbit (Nelson and Lamb 1920, Boock and Trevan 1922) and the dog (Steenbock, Nelson and Hart 1921). Particularly interesting is the account of Bloch (1921, 1928) of the occurrence of numerous cases of xerophthalmia in Danish children during the Great War, when the supply of animal fats to the general population, and in particular to the dwellers in large towns, was greatly restricted. The increased susceptibility to bacterial infection that results from Vitamin A deficiency is, however, by no means limited to the superficial tissues of the eye. In describing the condition of the children in Copenhagen Bloch remarks : " It is absolutely characteristic of these dystrophic children how little they are able to withstand infections, and how quickly they die of serious intercurrent fever." The most important killing disease that developed among them was broncho-pneumonia. Blegvad (1923) records the following incidence of serious complicating infections among the cases of xerophthalmia—broncho-pneumonia 63, bronchitis 45, pyuria 42, otitis media 30. These clinical observations are in entire accord with the results obtained in dietary experiments on animals.

The liability of rats fed on a diet deficient in Vitamin A to develop intercurrent infections, such as glandular abscesses, suppurative arthritis, suppurative otitis, pyelonephritis and broncho-pneumonia, has been noted by many observers (Drummond 1919, Hess *et al.* 1921, Cramer 1923, 1924, 1927, Gross 1924, Wolbach and Howe 1925, Green and Mellanby 1928, 1930, Gudjónsson 1930). The more precise knowledge that has accrued within recent years in regard to the chemical nature of certain of the vitamins has made it possible to demonstrate clearly that the fat-soluble vitamin concerned is A, not D (see Goldblatt and Benischek 1927, Green and Mellanby 1928) ; and to establish, in this respect as in others, the functional similarity of Vitamin A and carotene (Green and Mellanby 1930).

These observations on the increased frequency of spontaneous infections have been confirmed and extended by testing the resistance of animals kept on an A-deficient diet to experimental infection (Werkman 1923*b*, Hotta 1928, Reiter 1929, Lassen 1930, 1931, 1932, McClung and Winters 1932, Greene 1933, Robertson 1934). Lassen's studies are of particular interest, since the course of infection in the avitaminotic and control animals was followed in considerable detail. Rats were reared on a diet lacking Vitamin A, and were then infected, together with control rats of the same age fed on a complete diet, by administering living cultures of *Bact. typhi-murium* by the mouth, or by subcutaneous or intravenous injections. The avitaminotic rats showed a significantly lower resistance than the normal controls. In the experiments in which the bacilli were administered by the mouth, the course of the infection was studied by the technique employed by Ørskov, Jensen and Kobayashi (see p. 821). The rats were killed at various intervals after infection and cultures taken from the intestines, Peyer's patches, mesenteric glands, liver, spleen, lungs and heart's blood. In the normal rats the infection tended to be limited to the Peyer's patches and mesenteric glands, with some extension to the liver and spleen. In the avitaminotic rats it tended to become generalized, and to produce a fatal bacteræmic infection. In the few experiments in which the bacilli were injected intravenously, the avitaminotic rats showed the same initial clearing of the blood stream as did the normal controls, but in the former this initial clearance was followed by a secondary bacteræmia and a fatal generalization of infection.

By adding irradiated ergosterol to the Vitamin A-deficient diet and noting that this procedure did not prevent the fall in resistance to experimental infection, Lassen (1931) was able to show—as Green and Mellanby had done in the case of spontaneous infections—that the effect of removing all fat-soluble vitamins from the diet was due to the absence of Vitamin A.

It may be noted, and this is a point of some importance, that Lassen found it necessary to induce a pronounced degree of avitaminosis before he could demonstrate a well-marked break in resistance. He states that a slight decrease in resistance occurs after 2 to 3½ weeks on a Vitamin A-free diet, at a time when the animal shows no clinical evidence of avitaminosis, but that the clear and significant fall in resistance sets in suddenly at a later stage, coincidentally with the appearance of xerophthalmia.

The mechanism that underlies the decreased resistance of animals deprived of Vitamin A is as yet far from clear. Cramer (1923, 1924) has described atrophic changes in the intestinal mucosa of avitaminotic rats, and believes that the lesions facilitate the passage of bacteria from the intestines to the tissues. Wolbach and Howe (1925) record striking changes in the surface epithelium in certain situations, though they locate these lesions in the lining membranes of the nares, trachea, bronchi and genito-urinary tract, rather than in the intestine. These observations would suggest that the increased susceptibility to infection associated with A-avitaminosis may be due, in part at least, to a failure of the first-line defence mechanisms discussed in Chapter XLII ; but such a view is difficult to reconcile with other evidence on record. Thus Lassen (1931) found no difference in the rate at which bacteria passed from the intestine to the mesenteric glands *via* the Peyer's patches and lymph follicles, as between normal and avitaminotic rats. It was in the subsequent course of events—the fatal generalization of infection as opposed to its successful localization—that the avitaminotic animals displayed their lack of effective resistance. Moreover (Hotta 1928, Reiter 1929, Lassen 1930, 1931, 1932) such animals are more susceptible than normal controls to the subcutaneous, intraperitoneal and intravenous injection of bacteria—in which the first line of defence is artificially ruptured—as well as to the administration of pathogenic bacteria by the mouth.

It would seem, therefore, that there must be some defect in the defence mechanisms of the tissues—in the efficient functioning of the reticulo-endothelial system itself, or in the conditioning or accessory action of the humoral antibodies—but of the nature of that defect we have as yet no knowledge. It may be noted in this connection that most workers have failed to find any satisfactory evidence that deprivation of Vitamin A—or indeed of any other vitamin—reduces the efficiency of antibody production in response to a specific stimulus (see Zilva 1919, Werkman 1923*a*, *b*, Werkman, Nelson and Fulmer 1924, Cramer and Kingsbury 1924, Simola and Brunius 1933), though Greene (1933) records an apparently significant decrease in the ability of A-avitaminotic rabbits to produce hæmolysins for sheep's red cells. Lassen (1931, 1932) notes that the sharp difference in resistance between normal and avitaminotic rats cannot be demonstrated when both groups have been previously immunized by the injection of a heat-killed vaccine, which indicates that the antibody-producing mechanism is still functioning with effect.

It may be noted, as further evidence that some deep-seated break in resistance is involved, that observations have been recorded suggesting that the deprivation of Vitamin A renders animals more susceptible to the injection of bacterial toxins, as well as to the invasive action of living bacterial cells (Werkman, Baldwin and Nelson 1924, Schubert 1928).

We have been concerned so far with a comparison between animals fed on a normal diet and those deprived of Vitamin A. The former have clearly an advantage ; but it is by no means a necessary corollary that an excess of Vitamin A will raise the resistance above normal level.

There are as yet no adequate experimental or field data on which a sound opinion on this further problem can be based. It is intrinsically a difficult one, since it really resolves itself into comparisons of resistance over a wide range of different levels of Vitamin A intake. The amount that is required for normal growth may fall short—even if not far short—of the amount required for optimal resistance.

Among other experiments that have a bearing on this point are those of Webster and Pritchett (1924) on the influence of diet on susceptibility to experimental infection with *Bact. typhi-murium*. They compared the resistance of mice fed on the ordinary diet of the Rockefeller Institute—a daily ration of bread, soaked in fresh, pasteurized, Grade B milk, supplemented by two weekly feedings of an oatmeal and buckwheat mixture and one weekly feeding of dry biscuit—with that of mice fed on a modified McCollum diet containing wheat flour, casein, milk powder, butter fat and salts. Mice kept on these diets were tested in groups of 10–36 animals, by the injection through a stomach tube of 2–5 million *Bact. typhi-murium*. The results indicated that the mice fed on the McCollum diet were significantly more resistant than those fed on the ordinary laboratory diet. Pritchett (1927) records a more numerous series of experiments along similar lines, in which an attempt was made to assess the influence of the different constituents of the McCollum diet. The increased resistance of the mice fed on this diet was in general confirmed ; but the effects produced by varying its constitution were not easy to interpret. For instance, the entire withdrawal of butter fat—the only source of Vitamin A—left the mice more resistant than the mice on the ordinary laboratory diet, though less resistant than those on the full McCollum diet. On the other hand the addition of butter fat to the normal laboratory diet was followed, in four of seven trials, by a lowering of mortality as compared with the control group ; and a similar result was obtained by the addition of cod-liver oil. In a later series of experiments on the effect of diet on the epidemic spread of mouse typhoid Webster (1930) records results from which he concludes that the substitution of the McCollum diet for the ordinary laboratory diet increases the resistance of mice to contact infection.

In another series of observations along similar lines (Topley, Greenwood and Wilson 1931) different results were obtained. Mice fed on a basal diet of whole-wheat flour, casein, butter and a salt mixture showed no advantage over mice fed on a diet of whole oats, milk and water as regards their ability to resist infection during an experimental epidemic of *Bact. typhi-murium* infection. The addition of an excess of fat, butter or lard, or of a Vitamin-A concentrate to this diet appeared to react unfavourably on the mice at risk. The unfavourable action of these artificial diets was not manifest when the mice were infected by intraperitoneal inoculation. Under these conditions there was a suggestion that the mice fed on the usual laboratory diet of oats, milk and water were slightly less resistant than the other groups, but the differences observed were quite insignificant. In order to avoid the possible complication introduced by the excess of fat in the vitamin-rich diets, other experimental epidemics were initiated in which the vitamin content of the normal laboratory diet was increased by the addition of a ration of carrot or of cabbage. The mice receiving carrots appeared to be at a disadvantage as compared with those on the normal diet ; the addition of cabbage produced no significant change in mortality. It may be noted that Lassen (1931) records that a considerable excess of shark-liver oil in the diet caused a slight decrease in the resistance of rats to experimental paratyphoid infection.

These experiments are considered here because some of them at least have a bearing on the effect of an excess of Vitamin A over the amount required to maintain growth and apparent well-being ; but it would in truth be unwise to lay much stress on their significance, since it is clear that the diets employed varied in many ways besides their differences in Vitamin A content. It does, however, seem fair to conclude that no adequate experimental evidence has yet been produced that an excess of Vitamin A over the level required to prevent all overt signs of avitaminosis induces an increased resistance to bacterial infection.

Little evidence is available with regard to the effect of increasing the amount of Vitamin A supplied to human subjects. The collection of such evidence clearly demands special conditions. The infections associated with child-birth afford opportunities for such a trial, and are of particular interest because of the obvious possibility that pregnancy may make a large call on the vitamin reserves. Mellanby, Green and their colleagues (Green *et al.* 1931) record a trial in which 275 women received a Vitamin-A concentrate by mouth during the last month of pregnancy, the incidence of varying degrees of morbidity among this group during the puerperium being compared with the corresponding figures for a control group of 275 women not so treated. In every comparison the treated group fared better than the untreated. Thus 19·2 per cent. of the treated women suffered from pyrexia, as against 30·9 per cent. of the untreated ; while for severe pyrexia the figures were 1·5 per cent. and 3·6 per cent. respectively. The evidence so far as it goes clearly suggests that the administration of Vitamin A in large amounts has some prophylactic value against the risk of puerperal infection.

There is no obvious reason for supposing that the administration of excess of Vitamin A would exert a beneficial effect on an already established infection ; and most of the scanty evidence available is in accord with the *a priori* probabilities. Mellanby and Green (1929) reported a few cases from which they concluded that a therapeutic effect was exerted in puerperal fever ; but the studies of Thomas (1931) on a far larger series of puerperal cases showed no benefit, either in mild or serious infections. Orenstein (1932) failed to find any evidence that the administration of a highly potent preparation of Vitamin A has a beneficial effect on cases of pneumonia occurring among the native workers on the Rand mines. Over a 1-year period alternate cases were treated with this preparation. Of 375 treated cases 10·13 per cent. died ; of 389 untreated cases 10·28 per cent. died.

Variations in the Intake of Vitamin B.—It would appear both from clinical records and from experimental studies that a deficiency in the intake of Vitamin B —the antineuritic vitamin—has no effect on resistance to infection at all comparable to that produced by a lack of Vitamin A. There have been suggestions that B-avitaminosis is associated with a minor increase in susceptibility to infection, but the evidence is of very doubtful significance (see Werkman 1923*a*, *b*, Werkman, Baldwin and Nelson 1924, Lassen 1929, 1931, 1932, Robertson 1934).

Variations in the Intake of Vitamin C.—The evidence with regard to the effect of Vitamin C on resistance is peculiarly confusing and discrepant.

On the clinical side Hess (1920) stresses the frequency of infective complications in scurvy, while Bloch (1928) states that scorbutic children show no tendency to infection in any way comparable to that displayed by children suffering from xerophthalmia.

As regards spontaneous infections in guinea-pigs suffering from experimental scurvy, Hamburger and Goldschmidt (1922–23), Grant (1926, 1930) and Schmidt-Weyland and Költzsch (1927) state that they are very common. On the other hand, Holst and Frölich (1912) state that they are uncommon. The observations of Glenny and Allen (1921) on the occurrence of epidemic infection among a stock of guinea-pigs on a vitamin-deficient diet, and its suppression by the addition of a ration of green stuff, may perhaps be taken as relevant evidence, though we clearly cannot assume that C-avitaminosis was the determining factor.

As regards the resistance of scorbutic guinea-pigs to experimental infection, Findlay (1923), Werkman, Nelson and Fulmer (1924), Grant (1926) and Schmidt-Weyland and Költzsch (1927) record a slight increase in susceptibility. Findlay would ascribe this to the degenerative changes and feeble leucoblastic reaction seen in the bone-marrow of guinea-pigs suffering from chronic scurvy. Werkman, Nelson and Fulmer stress the association between lowered resistance and lowered body temperature.

The observations of Zinsser and Castaneda (1931) on the increased susceptibility of guinea-pigs and rats on a vitamin-deficient diet to experimental typhus infection may be referred to here. It is probable that the guinea-pigs were suffering from some degree of C-avitaminosis ; but the fact that rats, which are generally regarded as being relatively insensitive to the deprivation of this vitamin, showed the same decrease in resistance makes it difficult to assess the significance of these results.

Variations in the Intake of Vitamin D.—The similar behaviour of Vitamin A and the anti-rachitic vitamin as regards their fat-solubility makes many of the earlier observations on the effect of a Vitamin D-deficient diet of doubtful significance.

Certain of the experimental studies that we have summarized above show that the addition of Vitamin D to a diet from which the fat-soluble vitamins have been removed does not prevent the lowering of resistance : indeed there is a suggestion in some of them (see Lassen 1931) that the addition of irradiated ergosterol increases the susceptibility of the animals receiving it. In other experiments Lassen found that rats on a rachitogenic diet not entirely lacking in Vitamin A showed no appreciable lowering of their resistance to experimental infection *per os*, even when the macroscopic and histological evidence of rickets was clear and unmistakable ; and Freund (1932) was unable to demonstrate any significant difference in the resistance of rats and mice maintained on normal, Vitamin D-free or Vitamin D-excess diets.

If we attempt to assess the significance of the data at present available with regard to the influence of variations in vitamin intake on resistance to infection, we shall probably conclude (1) that there is good evidence that gross deficiency of Vitamin A produces a serious lowering of resistance ; (2) that it is doubtful whether the addition of any extra source of Vitamin A to an ordinary unrestricted human or animal diet is likely to lead to any significant increase in resistance, save, possibly, in the special conditions of pregnancy, but that this question must await the answer of properly controlled trials carried out on an adequate scale ; (3) that the evidence with regard to the effect of Vitamin C deficiency is so divergent that no sound conclusion is possible at the moment, though there are definite suggestions that animals such as the guinea-pig, that are peculiarly susceptible to the deprivation of this vitamin, are rendered more susceptible to infection when it is withheld ; and (4) that there is at present no satisfactory evidence that either Vitamin B or Vitamin D are in any way associated with the factors that determine resistance or susceptibility. (For more detailed general reviews of the literature see Lassen 1931, and Robertson 1934.)

The Influence of Other Dietary Factors on Resistance.

Before reviewing the scattered, but not inconsiderable, literature dealing with the possible effects of various dietetic factors, other than deficiency or excess of one or other of the vitamins, we may summarize recent observations by Watson (1936), which seem to provide an unequivocal experimental demonstration of an increase in resistance due to a change in diet, though the mechanism involved is, at the moment, quite obscure.

These experiments were carried out as part of a systematic study of the influence of diet on the resistance of mice to bacterial infection, and the significant results were obtained during the comparison of two diets which differed in that 50 per cent. of the oatmeal supplied in one diet was, in the other, replaced by dried milk. In each case the diets were otherwise adequate and vitamins were supplied in the form of yeastrel and cod-liver oil. In repeated tests, carried out on statistically adequate groups of mice, it was found, with few exceptions, that the mice fed on the diet containing dried milk were significantly more resistant to the intraperitoneal injection of a toxic fraction isolated from *Bact. typhi-murium*. They were also more resistant to the administration by the mouth of living cultures of *Bact. typhi-murium*. They were not significantly more resistant to the intraperitoneal injection of living bacilli. The resistance to the injection of the toxin, and to the oral administration of moderately virulent cultures, was fully developed only in mice that had been fed since birth on the diet containing dried milk. It was detectable in mice that received the diet for three months before the test inoculation, but was in this case barely significant.

Reference to the protocols recorded by Webster and Pritchett (1924), by Pritchett (1927), and by Topley, Greenwood and Wilson (1931) will show that the results obtained were entirely compatible with the view that the milk powder in the McCollum diet was the component that determined the increased resistance of the mice receiving it, though this possibility was not in fact envisaged or discussed.

How the effect is exerted it is not, as yet, possible to say. It seems, perhaps, more likely to be due to the effect on metabolism of a well-balanced diet, than to traces of any accessory substance in the dried milk ; and it would appear that the tissue changes on which increased resistance depends takes some time to develop.

Turning to studies that have so far yielded less definite and clear-cut results we may first consider certain surveys of a quite general kind, in which an attempt has been made to establish preliminary correlations that will serve to define problems rather than to answer them.

In this category fall the studies of Orr and Gilks (1931) on the health of two African tribes—the Masai and the Kikuyu—and related studies (Orr, MacLeod and Mackie 1931) on the effect of nutritional variations on the resistance of sheep. The Masai, particularly the males, live mainly on a diet of milk, meat and raw blood. The Kikuyu live almost entirely on cereals, roots and fruits. Apart from a marked difference in physique—the adult male Masai is 5 inches taller, 23 lb. heavier and 50 per cent. stronger than the Kikuyu —there appears to be a significant difference in the frequency of certain types of infective disease ; though the facilities for obtaining statistical data among native tribes are not of the kind that allow the collection of entirely convincing evidence. With this reservation, it would seem that pulmonary infections (bronchitis, pneumonia and phthisis) and tropical ulcer are far more frequent among the Kikuyu than among the Masai, while the latter are more prone to arthritis, presumably of an infective type. This difference in susceptibility to particular kinds of infection is associated with a low calcium content of the blood in the Kikuyu (9·4 mgm. per 100 c.c. as against 11·4 mgm. among a small sample of Europeans in Kenya and 10–10·5 mgm. among Europeans in general). Samples of Masai blood could not be obtained on account of a tribal tabu. In the experiments on sheep, which were carried out in Scotland, animals were allowed to graze on different types of pasture, or fed on different diets in pens, and studies were made of the blood calcium, blood phosphorus, and (as an index of immunity *faute de mieux*) of certain of the natural agglutinating or lytic antibodies. The results, as one would expect, are by no means easy to interpret ; but there appears to be a definite correlation between ample pasturage, a high calcium and low phosphorus content of the blood, and general well-being, and there is a suggestion that these conditions are associated with active lytic properties of the serum, while the agglutinins in certain experiments appear to have varied inversely as the lysins. In later experiments (Mackie *et al.* 1932) a slight indication was obtained that the animals on the poor pasture were more susceptible than controls to the intradermal injection of the toxin of the lamb dysentery bacillus.

The possibility that variations in the intake of *mineral salts* may have an influence on resistance has been explored by various experimental workers (Zilva 1919, Lange 1925, 1927*a*, *b*, Pritchett 1927, Hotta 1928, Kligler and Geiger 1928, Mayer and Sulzberger 1931, Sulzberger and Mayer 1931), but the evidence is highly confusing. We can, at the moment, do little more than suspend judgment, and note that a question has been asked, but not answered.

We may pass to the effect of a general deficiency of food, apart from qualitative changes. We are here in little better case, so far as experimental evidence is concerned. Hotta (1928) records a definite decrease in the resistance of mice kept on a starvation diet, while Lassen (1931) finds only a trivial decrease in resistance of rats suffering from a relative but well-marked inanition for a period of 17 weeks (see also Müller and Simons 1919, Bieling 1925, Bickert 1931).

Apart altogether from their effect on the defence mechanisms of the tissues, there can be no question that variations in diet alter the local conditions in the gastro-intestinal tract. We know (see Rettger and Cheplin 1921, Dudgeon 1926) that the ingestion of certain food-stuffs produces characteristic changes in the gastro-intestinal flora ; and Arnold (1926,

1927a, b, 1929) has stressed the importance of various food materials in deranging or maintaining the efficacy of the gastro-duodenal bactericidal mechanism, particularly in infants. He suggests that such results as those recorded by Webster and Pritchett (1924) and Pritchett (1927) may be due in part to effects of this kind.

The Influence of Fatigue on Resistance

In spite of the abundant clinical experience that establishes beyond question the conclusion that bodily rest is an important factor in the treatment of any infective disease, the experimental evidence with regard to the effect of fatigue on resistance to infection is more than a little puzzling.

Spaeth and his colleagues (Oppenheimer and Spaeth 1922, Nicholls and Spaeth 1922, Spaeth 1925) have published a series of observations carried out on rats and guinea-pigs, from which they conclude that the resistance of these animals to tetanus toxin, and to experimental infection with the pneumococcus, is increased as the result of the fatigue induced by making the animals run for a long period in a revolving cage. Friedberger and others (1931) have injected rats and guinea-pigs intraperitoneally with El Tor vibrios and have compared the fate of resting animals with that of others fatigued before, or after, or both before and after, the inoculation. There was no significant difference in mortality among the different groups. In the same series of experiments these authors studied the effect of fatigue on antibody production. The results were entirely negative. Such observations must clearly be interpreted conservatively, and without uncritical generalization. They emphasize the stability of the defence mechanisms of the tissues under a variety of different stresses ; but they do nothing to lessen the significance of our common experience that fatigue is harmful in established infections, and it would be very unwise to conclude from them that fatigue has no influence on the liability to contract an infection under natural conditions.

More illuminating are the experiments recorded by Boycott and Price-Jones (1926). It may be noted that the infection they studied—that produced by *Bact. enteritidis* in the rat—is a natural disease of that animal, and therefore far more analogous in its pathogenesis to natural human infections than are the experimental conditions selected for study by the workers referred to above. When rats were infected with *Bact. enteritidis* by subcutaneous or intraperitoneal inoculation, fatigue induced before the inoculation, or during the first few days after it, appeared to have very little effect on the subsequent mortality rate. But when the rats were infected by feeding and then fatigued on several occasions during the subsequent few days the results were quite different. Twenty-seven rats were treated in this way and of these 13 died. Twenty control rats were fed on the same cultures, but were not subsequently fatigued ; of these none died. The animals that survived the whole period of observation were submitted to necropsy, and it was found, in conformity with the findings recorded by many other observers, that the majority of them were still harbouring *Bact. enteritidis* in the spleen. There is an obvious suggestion that fatigue has a significant effect in activating a latent infection and favouring its fatal generalization.

The Effect of Variations in Temperature, Humidity and Other Physical Conditions of the Environment

The evidence available under this head is concerned mainly with the effect of these environmental factors on the first-line defence mechanisms of the kind considered in Chapter XLII. Arnold and his colleagues (Arnold 1927b, 1928, 1929, Arnold and Brody 1927) have studied in considerable detail the effect of high temperature, especially when associated with high humidity, on the gastro-duodenal bactericidal mechanism of the dog. They find that such conditions are associated with a decrease in gastric secretion, a consequent fall in the acidity of the gastric and duodenal contents, and an increased passage of bacteria from the stomach or duodenum to the cæcum.

There are in the literature many other records of experiments on the effect of temperature and humidity on resistance to infection (for recent papers see McDowell 1923, Kligler and Olitzki 1931, Robertson and Weld 1932), but the numbers of animals in the comparable groups are so small, and the effects of these two factors seem so difficult to disentangle, that the significance of the results reported cannot be assessed.

Hill and Muecke (1913) have shown that the mucosa of the human nose becomes turgid with blood and covered with a thick, mucous secretion when subjects are exposed to a warm, moist atmosphere, and that when such subjects pass immediately to a cold atmosphere the mucosa pales quickly as the result of a constriction of the vessels, but remains swollen and œdematous for a considerable period. Mudd and his colleagues (1921) have found that chilling of the body surface is associated with a marked fall of temperature in the nasal and post-nasal cavities, and that the return to the normal temperature in these situations is at first rapid, but then very slow, when the body surface is again warmed. There is, then, good evidence of significant changes in the physiological conditions of the nose and nasopharynx in response to changes in temperature and humidity, and it may well be that some of these changes are associated with a lowering of the local resistance ; but such a correlation will clearly be very difficult to establish by any statistical survey of naturally occurring infections, and we have as yet no experimental data bearing directly on this point.

Among other physical agencies mention may be made of the possible effect of ultra-violet irradiation of the body surface since this procedure has been advocated as a means of increasing resistance to infection. We have noted (p. 920) that Colebrook, Eidenow and Hill (1924) have demonstrated a temporary increase in the bactericidal power of the blood as the result of exposure to ultra-violet rays, and a similar effect after exposure to dark heat, or to the blistering of the skin with a mustard plaster. The general experience of the beneficial effect of sunlight as enjoyed under optimal natural conditions, combined with such observations as the above, made it natural to inquire whether any isolated constituent of the solar radiation, and particularly the rays of short wave-length, would produce a significant increase in resistance to infection. Some favourable views have been recorded (Maughan and Smiley 1928, 1929, Hill and Laurie 1931) ; but the balance of evidence appears to be very definitely against the view that exposure to such rays has any significant effect.

Barenberg and Lewis (1928) report entirely negative results in a small group of infants. Colebrook, D. (1929), in a very careful and detailed study carried out on school children of 5–7 years of age, compared the frequency of infection (1) in a group of 101 children irradiated 3 times a week with light from a carbon arc lamp with a high output of ultra-violet rays, (2) in a group of 94 children irradiated under the same conditions except that light of wavelength shorter than 3,200 Å.U. was cut off by a glass screen, and (3) in a group of 92 children who received no irradiation. Over the period of observation—August 1927 to March 1928—the number of colds per 100 child-weeks' exposure to risk was 20·2 in the group irradiated without screening, 18·7 in the group irradiated with the screened lamp, and 18·6 in the control group. The average duration of each cold was 7·5, 7·5 and 7·1 days respectively. The incidence of measles among those exposed to risk and not previously attacked —a small group—showed no significant difference between the treated and untreated : the attack rates were 80·0 per cent. in those irradiated without screening, 70·6 per cent. in those irradiated but screened, and 68·2 per cent. in the unirradiated controls. In the case of whooping cough the attack rates were 8·8 per cent., 7·7 per cent. and 8·6 per cent. In no case did the irradiated group show any benefit. A later report by Doull, Hardy, Clark and Herman (1931) is entirely confirmatory. It deals with a careful study of the frequency of colds among irradiated and unirradiated groups of volunteer students, or members of the staff, at Johns Hopkins University. Every statistical precaution was taken in planning the trial and in assessing its results. These were unequivocal. Among 169 persons in the irradiated group, the attack rate during the period September 29, 1929 to May 31, 1930 was 78·6 per 1,000 student-weeks ; among 184 persons in the unirradiated control group it was 71·9. Whatever test was employed—duration of colds, the presence of fever, the presence of cough or sputum—or whatever allowance was made for previous history or differences in physical conditions, the result was the same, the irradiated group showed no advantage.

The experimental data available are, so far as they go, in accord with field observations. Chapman and Hardy (1931) were unable to obtain any evidence that irradiation increases the resistance of rabbits to the subcutaneous injection of *Pasteurella lepiseptica*. Hill, Greenwood and Topley (1930) found that irradiation conferred no benefit on mice submitted to contact infection with *Pasteurella muriseptica*.

Seasonal Variations in Resistance

Seasonal variations in the frequency of particular infective diseases are a commonplace of epidemiology. How far such variations are dependent on fluctuations in the average resistance of the host species, how far on environmental factors that increase the opportunities for the spread of infection, and how far on factors the nature of which we cannot even guess, are problems to which we can as yet give no answer.

Observations are on record from which the conclusion has been drawn that seasonal changes in the efficacy of the normal defence mechanisms do in fact occur (see Pritchett 1925, 1926, Glenny and Waddington 1928, Blake and Okell 1929, Mayer and Sulzberger 1931, Sulzberger and Mayer 1931, Orr, MacLeod and Mackie 1931). Wilson (1930) has noted synchronous fluctuations in the mortalities following the injection of three different strains of *Bact. typhi-murium* into mice during a sixteen months' period, each strain being tested on 15 occasions. It appeared impossible to relate these synchronous changes in mortality to any common factor acting on the three bacterial strains, and it seemed difficult to escape from the view that they must have been due to synchronous transient fluctuations in the resistance of the mice, but these fluctuations showed no definite seasonal distribution.

Even if the occurrence of seasonal variations in resistance were clearly established, it would be an exceedingly difficult task to disentangle the various factors involved ; and without such disentanglement there could be little hope of intelligent interference. The vitamin content of foodstuffs, and many other dietetic variables, are subject to seasonal influences ; the condition of the nasal mucosa and the efficiency of the gastro-duodenal bactericidal mechanism are, as we have seen, affected by changes in temperature and in humidity ; and there is little doubt that many other types of physiological response, of which as yet we know little or nothing from the immunological viewpoint, may be subject to influences of a similar kind. Until our knowledge of the relative significance of these factors, working in isolation, is much more accurate and detailed than it is at present we can hardly hope to construct a useful working chart of the total effect of the environmental changes associated with the changing seasons.

The Effect of Certain Chemical Substances in Favouring Bacterial Infection

We may include in this chapter a brief survey of a series of observations that have, during recent years, focussed attention on certain chemical substances that play a significant part in the local pathogenesis of infective lesions. It is becoming increasingly clear that some of these factors exert an important influence on the frequency and severity of naturally occurring infections, particularly in industrialized communities.

As a first example we may cite the observations of Bullock (Gye) and Cramer (1919) on the effect of calcium salts in certain anaerobic infections, and the more recent studies of Fildes (Fildes 1927, 1929a, b, Knight and Fildes 1930, Campbell and Fildes 1931). Bullock and Cramer found that ionizable salts of calcium, inoculated together with the washed spores of *Cl. welchii*, of *Cl. tetani* or of certain other anaerobes, led to the development of the corresponding infections in their most typical and fatal forms, while the washed spores alone showed no tendency to develop in the tissues after inoculation. The chlorides of sodium, potassium, ammonium, strontium or manganese had no such effect. They were unable to determine the exact mechanism by which this effect, to which they gave the name *kataphylaxis*, was brought about ; though they were able to show that it was not due to an absence of leucocytes from the lesions, nor to a lack of phagocytic activity on the part of the cells that collected at the site of inoculation. Fildes (1927), attacking the particular problem of experimental tetanus in the guinea-pig, studied the vegetation of spores in the normal testicle, after ligation of the blood vessels. He found that the injection of tetanus spores into the ligated testicle was followed by a rapidly fatal toxæmia, indicating rapid vegetation in the tissues. Comparison of sections from ligated and unligated testicles, at various intervals after the injection of the spores, showed that active vegetation had occurred in the ligated testicle at a period when emigration of leucocytes was at its earliest stage in the unligated testicle, and therefore before any significant degree of phagocytosis could in any case have occurred. He concluded that there must be some definite stimulus to vegetation in tissues cut off from their blood supply, either by ligation of vessels or by the vascular injury following the injection of calcium salts, and suggested that this stimulus was probably the result of the diminished oxygen tension, although Bullock and Cramer had tentatively rejected this view. Later (Fildes 1929b) he carried out a detailed study of the oxidation-reduction potential of the tissue fluids under different conditions using suitable indicator dyes. He found that oxidized methylene blue injected into the subcutaneous tissues of the living guinea-pig is not reduced, while reduced methylene blue is rapidly oxidized. In the dead animal the oxidized methylene blue undergoes a slight reduction, while the reduced methylene blue is not oxidized. Analogous results were obtained with thionin and with indophenol I. The general conclusion may be drawn that, in the subcutaneous tissues of the living guinea-pig the oxidation-reduction potential (Eh) at the prevailing pH of about 7·0 is in the neighbourhood of $+ 0·12$ volts, while, as shown in a previous communication (Fildes 1929a), tetanus spores will not germinate readily at a potential more oxidizing than $+ 0·01$ volts at this pH (see also Knight and Fildes 1930). In further experiments it was shown that the injection of solutions of calcium chloride led to the production of localized areas of oxygen deficiency, with an Eh on the negative (reducing) side of that of methylene blue, thus providing conditions suitable for the germination of tetanus spores. Campbell and Fildes (1931) studied the effect of other methods of varying the oxygen pressure of the tissues. Guinea-pigs were maintained in atmospheres containing different partial pressures of oxygen (60 per cent., 20 per cent. and 7 per cent.) and in air containing 0·15 per cent. of carbon monoxide. Control experiments showed the corresponding pressures of oxygen in the subcutaneous tissues (in mm. Hg) to be approximately 26, 20, 5 and 6. When animals subjected to these atmospheres were injected intramuscularly with a mixture of tetanus spores and aleuronat the animals maintained in atmospheric air (20 per cent. oxygen) showed a mortality of 45 per cent., those maintained in an atmosphere of 60 per cent. oxygen a mortality of 6 per cent., those contained in 7 per cent. oxygen, or in air containing 0·15 per cent. CO, a mortality of 75 per cent. These results clearly support the view that the oxygen pressure of the tissues controls the germination of the tetanus spores.

Bullock (Gye) and Cramer (1919) noted that the local defence rupture produced by the injection of calcium salts favoured infection with streptococci, as well as with anaerobic bacilli. The nature of the effect has been studied in more detail by Kettle (1927). Here again there is no evidence of any diminished emigration of leucocytes, or lessened phagocytic activity, and the main effect of the calcium, as revealed by histological examination of the lesions, is a striking increase in the rate of bacterial multiplication. As Kettle points out, the streptococcal-calcium lesions in the mouse bear a close resemblance to the rapidly spreading streptococcal cellulitis that occurs in man. It would appear that the characteristic exudative lesion that is caused by the calcium salt provides peculiarly favourable cultural conditions for streptococci, as it does for anaerobic bacilli ; though it does not, of course, follow that the two effects are determined by identical chemical or physical factors.

Calcium is not the only substance which produces defence rupture. That silica has an injurious effect on the lungs and that there is an association between silicosis and tuberculosis has been known for some 30 years, and Gardner (1920) has shown experimentally that a dust containing a high percentage of silica has a significant effect on pulmonary tuberculosis in the guinea-pig. The factors concerned in this enhancement of tuberculous infections by silica have been studied in detail by Kettle (see Gye and Kettle 1922, Kettle 1924, 1926, 1927, 1930, 1932).

The majority of these experiments have been carried out on mice. These animals are normally far more resistant to tuberculosis than is the guinea-pig ; and the selective action of silica can be readily demonstrated by subcutaneous injection of the material under test followed by an intravenous injection of living tubercle bacilli. Silica, or silica-containing material, is injected at one spot, some other substance to act as a control at another. If the control substance is an irritant, such as calcium chloride or turpentine, the bacilli that are injected intravenously appear in both the silica and control lesions, but it is in the silica lesion that they show the most active proliferation. The specific action of the silica is clearly evidenced by the fact that the more extensive calcium lesion provides far less favourable conditions for the growth of the tubercle bacillus. It is further evidenced by the results of careful comparative tests on a large number of industrial dusts (Kettle 1932), which show that it is the presence of silica, or of a silicate, that determines the characteristic effect. Crystalline silica, unlike colloidal or amorphous silica, is very slowly dissolved in the tissues, and only when dissolved does it exert its injurious action. Silica crystals coated with oxide of iron are not dissolved in the tissues, and they remain inert and harmless.

The pathogenesis of the lung lesions of silicosis, and the association of this condition with tuberculosis, have been studied in numerous experiments in which dusts have been brought in contact with the lung tissue of guinea-pigs or rabbits, either by repeated or prolonged inhalation, or by the direct injection of a suspension of the dust into the trachea (Kettle 1930).

An interesting experiment is recorded by Gardner (1930). Guinea-pigs were infected, by inhalation, with a strain of tubercle bacillus of unusually low virulence, which normally produces in these animals a retrogressive type of tuberculosis confined to the lungs and bronchial glands. The infection is practically never fatal. When animals so infected were exposed for 8 hours a day to quartz dust an entirely different picture was produced. After 3 to 5 months the bacilli in the lungs began to proliferate actively. The infection spread to all parts of the lungs and to the abdominal viscera, producing large and progressive lesions. The bacilli had not become more virulent, since cultures isolated from the dusted animals produced the usual type of retrogressive tuberculosis when administered to normal undusted guinea-pigs.

Until recently it had been generally assumed that the silica, and the lesions it produced, sensitized the tissues to tuberculous infection. The silica, that is to say, had been regarded as the primary active agent. Recent studies by Kettle (1934) have shown that this view needs considerable modification.

Different groups of guinea-pigs were injected intratracheally with a suspension of silica alone, a suspension of avirulent tubercle bacilli alone, and a mixture of silica and avirulent tubercle bacilli. The dust alone produced a catarrhal reaction, but relatively little fibrosis, and nothing resembling the characteristic nodular silicosis of man. The avirulent tubercle bacilli alone produced relatively little tissue reaction. The mixture of silica and tubercle bacilli produced a characteristic nodular tuberculo-silicosis, closely similar to the human disease. It would seem that the typical silicotic lesions are induced not by silica acting on a normal lung but by the joint action of silica and some bacterial infective agent ; and Kettle suggests that the natural human disease should be known as infective silicosis.

Experimental studies of the kind outlined above open up wide fields for further exploration, and we may reasonably hope to obtain light on many problems by studying the ways in which infections may be modified as the result of the local or general action of various chemical agents. Two recent contributions along these lines may be noted.

Findlay (1928) has attempted to test the tentative hypothesis that the localization of pathogenic bacteria, or of filtrable viruses, at the site of localized tissue injury might be the result of the liberation of histamine, or of histamine-like substances, from the injured tissues, leading to a localized dilatation of the capillaries and an increased permeability of the capillary endothelium. Animals of a susceptible species were inoculated intravenously with an infective agent—the virus of fowl-pox, or of vaccinia, or of the Rous sarcoma, *Staph. aureus*, *Str. hæmolyticus*, or the pneumococcus—and histamine acid phosphate in a 0·5 per cent. solution was then injected into a site suitable for the observation of any lesion, the same amount of phosphate-buffer solution being inoculated into a corresponding site on the opposite side of the body to serve as a control. In each of the experiments the lesions appearing at the site of the histamine injections were significantly more frequent and more severe than those appearing at the site of injection of the phosphate-buffer solution. The latter were indeed infrequent in occurrence and minimal in degree.

Rosher (1931) has studied the effect of the growth-promoting factors (X and V) on experimental infection with *H. influenzæ* in mice. When a suspension of influenza bacilli in ordinary nutrient broth was used for intraperitoneal inoculation, 26 per cent. of 45 strains killed one or more of five mice. When 0·05 c.c. of Fildes' solution (containing both growth factors) was added to the inoculum, 71 per cent. of these strains killed one or more mice.

In more recent (unpublished) studies, Rosher has found that the X and V factors, acting together, enhance the toxic action of dead influenza bacilli ; so that we are not, in this case, dealing with a pure growth-promotion effect.

The Rôle of the Bacteriophage in Infection and Resistance

This is, perhaps, as convenient a place as any to summarize the available evidence with regard to the rôle played by the bacteriophage, or rather by bacteriophages, in infection and resistance. In Chapter X we discussed the nature of these lytic agents, and concluded that the balance of evidence was definitely in favour of the view that they are filtrable viruses, parasitic on, or symbiotic with, various species or strains of bacteria. The relationship between the various types of phage and the bacteria that are sensitive to their action is often highly specific ; and this specificity seems to be determined, in many cases at least, by the nature of the antigenic components that are situated at the bacterial surface.

The existence of living viruses, specifically attacking various pathogenic bacteria, offered an obvious possibility that they might be employed in the prevention or cure of infective disease. That they can, in fact, be so employed, and are highly effective, has been claimed by d'Herelle (1926) ; and in recent years several observers have reported favourable results in field trials of cholera phage as a prophylactic in India (see Morrison 1932). There are also various observations in the literature with regard to the use of phages as therapeutic reagents in human infections ; but these are discrepant, and not of the kind that provide us with the evidence we need.

On the experimental side the problem has not yet been submitted to the detailed and extensive study that it clearly deserves. This is probably because such results as have been recorded have been the reverse of encouraging.

There are a few observations which suggest that phages may have some slight protective value if injected into an animal simultaneously with such organisms as the typhoid bacillus, or the colon bacillus (Wollman 1925, Arnold and Weiss 1926, Walker 1929). But the great majority of observers, including many who have worked with bacteria that are natural pathogens of the rodents of the laboratory, have recorded almost consistently negative results.

Thus there has so far been a general failure to demonstrate any protective or curative action of phage filtrates against *Bact. typhi-murium* or *Bact. enteritidis* when tested in mice (Topley and Wilson 1925, Topley *et al.* 1925, Levy 1925, Wollman 1925, Richet and Hauduroy 1925, Bronfenbrenner and Korb 1925–26, Ebert and Peretz 1929, Greenwood *et al.* 1936). Similarly, phage filtrates have shown little or no protective or curative action in Salmonella infections in fowls (Pyle 1926), in experimental plague in rats (Compton 1928, 1930, Doorenbos 1929), in hæmolytic streptococcal infections in rabbits (Clark and Clark 1927), or in guinea-pigs (Colvin 1932), or in experimental anthrax in the mouse (Cowles and Hale 1931). Nor is there any experimental evidence that the presence in the intestines of mice of a phage acting on *Bact. typhi-murium* prevents the spread of natural contact infection with that organism (Topley and Wilson 1925, Topley *et al.* 1925, Greenwood *et al.* 1936).

Such observations as these are sufficient to show that a phage that produces lysis in the test tube is often quite inactive *in vivo*. Discouraging as these results are, however, they cannot be regarded as conclusive evidence that the phage is an entirely ineffective agent in the body ; though they should make us very sceptical of claims coming from the ward or from the field. The problem as to why a phage, which is so active *in vitro*, appears to be so inactive in the tissues, is one that must be attacked by the method of properly controlled experiments in animals ; and very little has as yet been done in this direction.

The obvious suggestion that the failure of a phage to protect against infection is due to the development in the tissues of bacteria resistant to its action, just as resistant bacteria develop in a lysed broth culture, has as yet no experimental support. Strains of *Bact. typhi-murium*, isolated from mice that have died of infection in spite of the presence of phage in the tissues, have proved just as sensitive to that phage as the bacteria originally inoculated (Topley and Wilson 1925, Topley *et al.* 1925, Greenwood *et al.* 1936).

It may be (see Zdansky 1924) that the cells or colloids of the body fluid exert *in vivo* an inhibiting effect on phage lysis similar to the inhibition exerted *in vitro* by high concentrations of gelatin or agar (Bail 1922, Doerr and Berger 1922, Otto and Munter 1923, Bronfenbrenner and Korb 1925) ; but there is as yet no clear evidence that this is so.

In any case, until we know more than we do of the factors that prevent the phage from exerting any protective effect in the tissues, we cannot justifiably conclude that it is impossible so to adjust the conditions that its activity might be restored.

SUMMARY

(1) With regard to the effect on resistance of variations in diet, the one fact that stands out clearly is that a gross deficiency in the intake of Vitamin A, especially during the period of rapid bodily growth, is associated with a marked increase in susceptibility to infection. There are suggestions that C-avitaminosis, in animals peculiarly liable to this condition, may be associated with a similar break in resistance ; but the evidence is highly confusing. There is no evidence that a deficiency of Vitamin B or of Vitamin D has any significant effect on resistance. There is little if any evidence that an excess of Vitamin A, above the limit required to prevent the occurrence of detectable avitaminosis, has any prophylactic or therapeutic effect in infective disease, with the possible exception that some prophylactic effect may be exerted by the administration of Vitamin A during the late stages of pregnancy.

(2) Our knowledge of the influence of other dietetic factors on resistance to infection is as yet too scanty to justify any general conclusions. Recent observations show that the addition of dried milk to an otherwise adequate diet increases the resistance of mice to certain bacterial toxins, and certain bacterial infections ; and it seems clear that this is not a vitamin effect. Studies of this kind are, however, in their infancy.

(3) The experimental evidence with regard to the influence of fatigue on resistance suggests that it is more important as a factor leading to the activation of a latent infection than as predisposing to infection *ab initio*.

(4) The data with regard to the effect of variations in the physical environment are scanty. It is certain that fluctuations in temperature and humidity affect the local conditions in the upper part of the respiratory tract, and it seems possible that the changes produced may in some cases lower the local resistance. There is evidence that similar environmental changes may derange the gastro-duodenal bactericidal mechanism. There is no satisfactory evidence that irradiation with ultra-violet rays produces any significant increase in resistance to natural or experimental infection.

(5) There are suggestions that a seasonal variation may occur in the general resistance to infection. If this be the case, such fluctuations are probably dependent on variations considered in the previous sections ; but which factors are concerned or what their relative importance may be we cannot tell.

(6) Evidence is accumulating with regard to the importance of certain chemical substances as agents favouring local infective processes. Thus ionizable calcium salts favour the germination of tetanus spores in the tissues, and this fact is of importance in aiding the natural pathogenesis of tetanus in wounds grossly contaminated with soil. Silica favours the local proliferation of the tubercle bacillus

in the tissues, and is an important predisposing cause to this infection in certain industrial populations. The mechanisms upon which these kataphylactic effects depend have been subjected to detailed study with results of considerable interest and importance.

(7) There is as yet no experimental evidence that the bacteriophages exert any protective or curative action *in vivo* ; but this possibility needs further study.

REFERENCES

ARNOLD, L. (1926) *J. infect. Dis.*, **38**, 246 ; (1927*a*) *Amer. J. publ. Hlth.*, **17**, 918 ; (1927*b*) *J. Amer. med. Ass.*, **89**, 789 ; (1928) *Amer. J. Hyg.*, **8**, 604 ; (1929) *J. Hyg., Camb.*, **29**, 82.
ARNOLD, L. and BRODY, L. (1927) *Proc. Soc. exp. Biol., N.Y.*, **24**, 832.
ARNOLD, L. and WEISS, E. (1926) *J. Lab. clin. Med.*, **12**, 20.
BAIL, O. (1922) *Wien. klin. Wschr.*, **35**, 722, 743.
BARENBERG, L. H. and LEWIS, J. M. (1928) *J. Amer. med. Ass.*, **90**, 504.
BICKERT, F. W. (1931) *Arch. Hyg.*, **106**, 271.
BIELING, R. (1925) *Z. Hyg. InfektKr.*, **104**, 518.
BLAKE, A. V. and OKELL, C. C. (1929) *Brit. J. exp. Path.*, **10**, 175.
BLEGVAD, O. (1923) " Om Xerophthalmia." Copenhagen.
BLOCH, C. E. (1921) *J. Hyg., Camb.*, **19**, 283 ; (1928) *Acta Pediatr.*, **7** (Suppl. 2), 61.
BOOCK, E. and TREVAN, J. (1922) *Biochem. J.*, **16**, 780.
BOYCOTT, A. E. and PRICE-JONES, C. (1926) *J. Path. Bact.*, **29**, 87.
BRONFENBRENNER, J. and KORB, C. (1925) *J. exp. Med.*, **42**, 483 ; (1925–26) *Proc. Soc. exp. Biol. Med.*, **23**, 3.
BULLOCK, W. E. and CRAMER, W. (1919) *Sixth Sci. Rep. Imp. Cancer Res. Fund*, pp. 40, 57.
CAMPBELL, J. A. and FILDES, P. (1931) *Brit. J. exp. Path.*, **12**, 77.
CHAPMAN, J. and HARDY, M. (1931) *Amer. J. Hyg.*, **11**, 404.
CLARK, P. F. and CLARK, A. S. (1927) *Proc. Soc. exp. Biol., N.Y.*, **24**, 635.
COLEBROOK, D. (1929) *Spec. Rep. med. Res. Coun., Lond.*, No. 131.
COLEBROOK, L., EIDENOW, A., and HILL, L. (1924) *Brit. J. exp. Path.*, **5**, 54.
COLVIN, M. G. (1932) *J. infect. Dis.*, **51**, 17.
COMPTON, A. (1928) *J. infect. Dis.*, **43**, 448 ; (1930) *Ann. Inst. Pasteur*, **45**, 754.
COWLES, P. P. and HALE, W. M. (1931) *J. infect. Dis.*, **49**, 264.
CRAMER, W. (1923) *Lancet*, i. 1046 ; (1924) *Ibid.*, i. 633 ; (1927) *Ibid.*, ii. 774.
CRAMER, W. and KINGSBURY, J. N. (1924) *Brit. J. exp. Path.*, **5**, 54.
DOERR, R. and BERGER, W. (1922) *Z. Hyg. InfektKr.*, **97**, 422.
DOORENBOS, W. (1929) *Ned. Tijdschr. Geneesk.*, **2**, 5472.
DOULL, J. A., HARDY, M., CLARK, J. H., and HERMAN, N. B. (1931) *Amer. J. Hyg.*, **13**, 460.
DRUMMOND, J. C. (1919) *Biochem. J.*, **13**, 95.
DUDGEON, L. S. (1926) *J. Hyg., Camb.*, **25**, 119.
EBERT, B. P. and PERETZ, L. H. (1929) *Zbl. Bakt.*, **115**, 71.
FILDES, P. (1927) *Brit. J. exp. Path.*, **8**, 387 ; (1929*a*) *Ibid.*, **10**, 151 ; (1929*b*) *Ibid.*, **10**, 197.
FINDLAY, G. M. (1923) *J. Path. Bact.*, **26**, 1 ; (1928) *Ibid.*, **31**, 633.
FREUND, R. (1932) *Z. Hyg. InfektKr.*, **113**, 361.
FRIEDBERGER, E., ANDERSEN, O., CALLERIO, C., and RUTCHKO, I. (1931) *Z. ImmunForsch.*, **72**, 225.
GARDNER, L. U. (1920) *Amer. Rev. Tuberc.*, **4**, 734 ; (1930) *Proc. int. Silicosis Conf.*, Johannesburg.
GLENNY, A. T. and ALLEN, K. (1921) *J. Path. Bact.*, **24**, 6.
GLENNY, A. T. and WADDINGTON, H. (1928) *J. Path. Bact.*, **31**, 403.
GOLDBLATT, H. and BENISCHEK, M. (1927) *J. exp. Med.*, **46**, 699.
GRANT, A. H. (1926) *J. infect. Dis.*, **39**, 502 ; (1930) *Amer. Rev. Tuberc.*, **21**, 102, 115.
GREEN, H. N. and MELLANBY, E. (1928) *Brit. med. J.*, ii. 691 ; (1930) *Brit. J. exp. Path.*, **11**, 81.
GREEN, H. N., PINDAR, D., DAVIS, G., and MELLANBY, E. (1931) *Brit. med. J.*, ii. 595.
GREENE, M. R. (1933) *Amer. J. Hyg.*, **17**, 60.
GREENWOOD, M., HILL, A. B., TOPLEY, W. W. C., and WILSON, J. (1936) *Spec. Rep. Ser. med. Res. Coun., Lond.*, No. 209.
GROSS, L. (1924) *J. Path. Bact.*, **27**, 27.
GUDJÓNSSON, S. V. (1930) " Exper. on Vitamin A Deficiency in Rats and the Quantitative Determination of Vitamin A." Copenhagen.
GYE, W. E. and KETTLE, E. H. (1922) *Brit. J. exp. Path.*, **3**, 241.

HAMBURGER, R. and GOLDSCHMIDT, L. (1922–23) *Jahrb. Kinderheilk.*, **100**, 210.
D'HERELLE, F. (1926) " The Bacteriophage and its Behaviour." Eng. Transl. London.
HESS, A. F. (1920) " Scurvy—Past and Present." Philadelphia.
HESS, A., McCANN, G. F., and PAPPENHEIMER, A. M. (1921) *J. biol. Chem.*, **47**, 395.
HILL, L., GREENWOOD, M., and TOPLEY, W. W. C. (1930) *Brit. J. exp. Path.*, **11**, 182.
HILL, L. and LAURIE, A. R. (1931) *Lancet*, i. 182.
HILL, L. and MUECKE, F. F. (1913) *Lancet*, i. 1291.
HOLST, A. and FRÖLICH, T. (1912) *Z. Hyg. InfektKr.*, **72**, 1.
HOTTA, Y. (1928) *Zbl. Bakt.*, **108**, 413.
KETTLE, E. H. (1924) *Brit. J. exp. Path.*, **5**, 158 ; (1926) *J. industr. Hyg.*, **8**, 491 ; (1927)
    Lancet, i. 1169, 1225 ; (1930) *Proc. roy. Soc. Med.*, **24**, Sect. Path., 1 ; (1932) *J. Path.
    Bact.*, **35**, 395 ; (1934) *Ibid.*, **38**, 201.
KLIGLER, I. J. and GEIGER, A. (1928) *Proc. Soc. exp. Biol., N.Y.*, **25**, 385.
KLIGLER, I. J. and OLITZKI, L. (1931) *Amer. J. Hyg.*, **13**, 349.
KNAPP, P. (1909) *Z. exp. Path.*, **5**, 147.
KNIGHT, B. C. J. G. and FILDES, P. (1930) *Biochem. J.*, **24**, 1496.
LANGE, L. B. (1925) *Amer. Rev. Tuberc.*, **11**, 206 ; (1927a) *Ibid.*, **15**, 629 ; (1927b) *Tubercle*,
    London, **8**, 422.
LASSEN, H. C. A. (1929) *Z. ImmunForsch.*, **63**, 110 ; (1930) *J. Hyg., Camb.*, **30**, 30 ; (1931)
    " Exper. Studies on the Course of Paratyphoid Infections in Avitaminotic Rats with
    Special Reference to Vitamin A Deficiency." Copenhagen ; (1932) *Z. ImmunForsch.*,
    73, 221.
LEVY, M. M. (1925) *C. R. Soc. Biol.*, **93**, 395.
McCLUNG, L. S. and WINTERS, J. C. (1932) *J. infect. Dis.*, **51**, 469.
McDOWELL, C. (1923) *Amer. J. Hyg.*, **3**, 521.
MACKIE, T. J., FRASER, A. H. H., FINKELSTEIN, M. H., and ANDERSON, E. J. M. (1932)
    Brit. J. exp. Path., **13**, 328.
MAUGHAN, G. H. and SMILEY, D. F. (1928) *J. prev. Med.*, **2**, 69 ; (1929) *Amer. J. Hyg.*,
    9, 466.
MAYER, R. L. and SULZBERGER, M. B. (1931) *Arch. Derm. Syph., Berl.*, **163**, 245.
MELLANBY, E. and GREEN, H. N. (1929) *Brit. med. J.*, i. 984.
MORRISON, J. (1932) " Bacteriophage in the Treatment and Prevention of Cholera."
    London.
MUDD, S., GOLDMAN, A., and GRANT, S. B. (1921) *J. exp. Med.*, **34**, 11.
MÜLLER, J. and SIMONS, H. (1919) *Z. Biol.*, **70**, 231.
NELSON, V. E. and LAMB, A. R. (1920) *Amer. J. Physiol.*, **51**, 530.
NICHOLLS, E. E. and SPAETH, R. A. (1922) *Amer. J. Hyg.*, **2**, 527.
OPPENHEIMER, E. H. and SPAETH, R. A. (1922) *Amer. J. Hyg.*, **2**, 51.
ORENSTEIN, A. J. (1932) *S. Afr. med. J.*, **6**, 685.
ORR, J. B. and GILKS, J. L. (1931) *Spec. Rep. Ser. med. Res. Coun., Lond.*, No. 155.
ORR, J. B., MACLEOD, J. J. R., and MACKIE, T. J. (1931) *Lancet*, i. 1177.
OTTO, R. and MUNTER, H. (1923) *Z. Hyg. InfektKr.*, **100**, 402.
PRITCHETT, I. W. (1925) *J. exp. Med.*, **41**, 209 ; (1926) *Ibid.*, **43**, 161, 173 ; (1927) *Ibid.*,
    46, 557.
PYLE, N. J. (1926) *J. Bact.*, **12**, 245.
REITER, H. (1929) *Z. ImmunForsch.*, **61**, 433.
RETTGER, L. H. and CHEPLIN, H. A. (1921) " A Treatise on the Transformation of the
    Intestinal Flora." Yale Univ. Press.
RICHET, C. and HAUDUROY, P. (1925) *C. R. Soc. Biol.*, **93**, 222.
ROBERTSON, E. C. (1934) *Medicine*, **13**, 123.
ROBERTSON, E. C. and WELD, C. B. (1932) *Proc. Soc. exp. Biol., N.Y.*, **30**, 33.
ROSHER, A. B. (1931) *Brit. J. exp. Path.*, **12**, 133.
SCHMIDT-WEYLAND, P. and KÖLTZSCH, W. (1927) *Z. Hyg. InfektKr.*, **108**, 199.
SCHUBERT, J. (1928) *Dtsch. med. Wschr.*, **54**, 472.
SIMOLA, P. E. and BRUNIUS, E. (1933) *Biochem. Z.*, **258**, 228.
SPAETH, R. A. (1925) *Amer. J. Hyg.*, **5**, 839.
STEENBOCK, H., NELSON, E. M., and HART, E. B. (1921) *Amer. J. Physiol.*, **58**, 14.
SULZBERGER, M. B. and MAYER, R. L. (1931) *Arch. Derm. Syph., N.Y.*, **24**, 537.
THOMAS, M. (1931) *Rep. med. Offr Hlth Glasgow*, 1930, p. 112.
TOPLEY, W. W. C., GREENWOOD, M., and WILSON, J. (1931) *J. Path. Bact.*, **34**, 163.
TOPLEY, W. W. C. and WILSON, J. (1925) *J. Hyg., Camb.*, **24**, 295.
TOPLEY, W. W. C., WILSON, J., and LEWIS, E. R. (1925) *J. Hyg., Camb.*, **24**, 17.
WALKER, J. E. (1929) *J. infect. Dis.*, **45**, 73.
WATSON, M. (1936) *In Press.*
WEBSTER, L. T. (1930) *J. exp. Med.*, **52**, 901, 909, 931.
WEBSTER, L. T. and PRITCHETT, I. W. (1924) *J. exp. Med.*, **40**, 397.
WERKMAN, C. H. (1923a) *J. infect. Dis.*, **32**, 247 ; (1923b) *Ibid.*, **32**, 255.
WERKMAN, C. H., BALDWIN, F. M., and NELSON, V. E. (1924) *J. exp. Path.*, **35**, 549.

WERKMAN, C. H., NELSON, V. E., and FULMER, E. I.   (1924) *J. exp. Med.*, **34,** 447.
WILSON, G. S.   (1930) *J. Hyg., Camb.*, **30,** 196.
WOLBACH, S. B. and HOWE, P. R.   (1925) *J. exp. Med.*, **42,** 753.
WOLLMAN, E.   (1925) *Ann. Inst. Pasteur*, **39,** 789.
ZDANSKY, E.   (1924) *Z. Hyg. InfektKr.*, **103,** 164.
ZILVA, S. S.   (1919) *Biochem. J.*, **13,** 172.
ZINSSER, H. and CASTANEDA, M. R.   (1931) *J. exp. Med.*, **53,** 493.

CHAPTER LII

IMMUNITY IN VIRUS DISEASES

THE virus diseases of man and animals are described in Chapters LXXXII–LXXXV, and that description includes the immunity reactions that occur in each particular infection. It is, however, even at the cost of some repetition, desirable to summarize and discuss the available data with regard to immunity to virus diseases as a whole, as contrasted with immunity to bacterial infections. There was a tendency among earlier workers to differentiate somewhat sharply between immunity to these two classes of parasite ; and this differentiation involved, mainly by assumption, the mechanisms brought into play as well as the quality and duration of the immunity induced. The problem that mainly concerns us here is the extent to which this differentiation is justified. Almost all experiments on the transmission of virus infections, and on immunity reactions *in vivo* or *in vitro*, have of necessity been carried out with tissue extracts or with other crude material containing host products as well as virus. Under these conditions the qualitative or quantitative analysis of such reactions is rendered very difficult, and for this reason the study of antiviral immunity has tended to lag behind that of antibacterial immunity at just those points in which the latter has become most precise. We have, however, learned enough of the mechanisms concerned to construct a useful working outline which can be filled in rapidly when our technical difficulties have been overcome, and which has already passed the sound empirical test of enabling us to interfere with considerable success in the natural propagation of infection.

Antiviral Immunity as Observed under Natural Conditions.

The first fact that forces itself on our attention when we examine the natural history of virus diseases is the frequency with which an effective and lasting immunity is afforded by a single attack (see Andrewes 1931). Smallpox, chickenpox, measles, mumps, cattle plague, swine fever, and dog distemper—all these are common virus diseases, and all confer an immunity that, in the great majority of cases, appears to last throughout life. There are exceptions. Herpes simplex is one ; influenza and the common cold are others. Not long ago foot-and-mouth disease would have been placed in this non-immunizing or poorly immunizing class ; but we have had to reconsider our views in that regard, and perhaps the relations that have misled us in this instance have misled us in others also. It would, however, be unwise to stress the value of the relative effectiveness of immunity as a differential criterion between virus and bacterial diseases, if only because we really know very little of the immunizing value of generalized bacterial infections.

There is another way in which bacterial and virus diseases have been thought to differ in their natural behaviour. We shall note in Chapter LIII the frequency of latent or atypical bacterial infections, emphasizing the fact that a clinical survey of diphtheria or scarlet fever or enteric fever gives a quite inadequate picture of the frequency of infection with the bacteria concerned. The current clinical conception of many of the commoner virus diseases would seem to minimize the significance of latent, or even of atypical, infections, suggesting by implication that every infected person provides a frank case of disease, or at least a case that is clinically diagnosable if suspicion is aroused. Those who hold this view would base it in part on the high attack rate among the previously-not-attacked during an epidemic prevalence of such a disease as measles, in part on their belief that it is unnecessary to assume the existence of healthy carriers of infection, or of individuals who have undergone a process of latent immunization, in order to explain observed epidemic happenings. But the attack rate among the previously-not-attacked exposed to risk, even in so highly contagious a disease as measles, is certainly not 100 per cent.; and there are good reasons for a belief in the existence and importance of latent immunization.

Stocks (1928, 1930a, b), in a series of careful analyses of the relevant data, has shown that the morbidity figures for measles, for chicken-pox and for German measles are inexplicable except on the assumption of immunization in the absence of diagnosed disease, or of an effective inherited immunity. That the former factor is involved can be demonstrated by comparing, during any epidemic prevalence, the attack rate among children who have previously been intimately exposed to risk without contracting the disease with that among children who have previously been less intimately exposed. The natural history of these widely prevalent virus diseases, as developed by Stocks, presents striking analogies to the natural history of diphtheria or of scarlet fever.

In other virus diseases the intervention of atypical cases and of the healthy carrier has obtained general recognition. In poliomyelitis the specific virus has been demonstrated in the nasal secretions obtained from healthy carriers, from persons long convalescent from an attack of the disease, and from atypical cases (Kling, Wernstedt and Pettersson 1912, Flexner, Clark and Fraser 1913, Lucas and Osgood 1913, Kling and Pettersson 1914, Taylor and Amoss 1917, Flexner and Amoss 1919, Paul and Trask 1932).

There is still a divergence of views with regard to the frequency of healthy carriers of poliomyelitis virus, though there can now be none in regard to the frequency of atypical cases. The epidemiological evidence, especially when viewed from a statistical angle, is in entire accord with the suggestions offered by the bacteriological findings. Wickman (1907) pointed out that it was impossible to account for the epidemiological behaviour of the disease without assuming the existence of latent and atypical infections; and Stocks (1932), examining the available data of recent outbreaks, calculates that the ratio of those developing latent immunizing infections to those developing clinical attacks of the disease is probably of the order of 100 to 1 or more. In the case of another virus disease, encephalitis lethargica, he would put this ratio in the neighbourhood of 800 to 1.

In this connection it may be noted that protective antibodies acting on the virus of poliomyelitis are widely distributed among the population at large.

Aycock and Kramer (1930a, b, c), using the highly susceptible monkey as a test animal, determined the protective power of samples of serum obtained from convalescent cases and from normal persons. Some 90 per cent. of the former and just over 50 per cent. of the latter showed protective antibodies in the serum. Similar tests were later carried out on normal persons, giving no history of poliomyelitis, living in another area of the

United States. Of 21 adults, 18 showed neutralizing antibodies in their blood. Brodie (1932) has recently recorded similar findings in Montreal.

If we accept the view that the presence of such antibodies indicates previous contact with the virus of poliomyelitis we can hardly escape the corollary that mild atypical attacks, or a purely immunizing carrier infection, must be an exceedingly common event in this particular disease. Some authorities, however, believe that protective substances occur in the serum of normal persons apart altogether from any specific stimulus (see Jungeblut and Engle 1932, 1933, 1934, Jungeblut 1933, 1934). The problem is analogous to that of the origin of the natural antibacterial antibodies (see Chapter XLVI).

A similar method has recently been employed in mapping out endemic centres of yellow fever infection in West Africa. Using protection tests in the monkey (Beeuwkes, Bauer and Mahaffy 1930), or in the mouse (Russell 1932, see also Theiler 1930, 1931, Sawyer and Lloyd 1931), it has been found that in areas in which clinical cases of yellow fever are infrequent and sporadic a high proportion of the children show neutralizing antibodies in their blood, indicating that the overt cases of disease give a quite inadequate picture of the real frequency of infection.

Recent observations by Duran-Reynals (1931) provide an interesting laboratory analogy to the field observations summarized above. In the course of certain experiments on vaccinial infection he found that some of his control rabbits showed the presence of neutralizing antibodies in their blood. Of 21 controls, 8 were shown to be immune. These controls had been injected with material that did not contain vaccinia virus, but they were housed in the same room as other rabbits that had active vaccinial lesions. Fourteen normal rabbits, housed in another room, were treated in the same way as these 21 controls ; none developed any immunity to vaccinia. The conclusion that this spontaneous immunity had developed in the infected room as the result of latent or unrecognized infection was confirmed by the discovery, on one of the immune controls, of three or four very small papules which were proved, by transfer to another rabbit, to be vaccinial in nature.

The Mechanism of Virus Infections.

It would appear that the general process of tissue invasion in virus diseases does not differ in any essential way from that described in the case of bacterial infections. There would seem, in many cases at least, to be the same sequence of local proliferation, blood-stream invasion and secondary foci of infection, each phase varying in prominence according to the virulence of the virus and the susceptibility or resistance of the host.

Thus, Todd and White (1914) note that, when cattle are injected subcutaneously with a small dose of the virus of rinderpest, the blood usually remains non-infective for 72 hours, becoming infective coincidently with the onset of illness ; and Andrews and others (Report 1931) note that the virus of foot-and-mouth disease does not appear in the blood of experimentally infected cattle until shortly before the commencement of the febrile reaction, though it may be present in high concentration some hours before the temperature begins to rise, or before vesicles appear. The virus then tends to persist in the blood throughout the febrile period, though the degree and persistence of blood-stream infection varies widely in different animals (see also Waldmann, Trautwein and Pyl 1931). In the case of yellow fever, Hudson and Philip (1929) record that monkeys bitten by infected mosquitoes show the presence of virus in their blood 1 to 2 days after infection, and at about the same interval before the onset of fever.

Vaccinia, as regards its obvious lesions, is commonly limited to the site of inoculation into the skin ; though the virus may be recovered from the blood after intradermal inoculation in the rabbit (Ohtawara 1922, Rivers and Tillett 1923, Gildemeister and Heuer 1927), and Gins and his colleagues (1929) have reported its presence in the nasal secretion of children after ordinary cutaneous vaccination. With highly potent strains of virus a generalized vaccinia may occur after dermal inoculation in the rabbit, with a widespread eruption, pocks on the lips and tongue, and lesions in the lungs, liver and other organs (Douglas, Smith and Price 1929).   When such a virus is injected intravenously this severe, and sometimes fatal, generalization occurs with considerable frequency, and there is a rough proportionality between the dose of the virus administered and the degree of resultant generalization.   When less potent viruses are injected intravenously there is frequently some degree of generalization, evidenced by an eruption of pocks on previously shaved areas of skin or on the mucosa (Calmette and Guérin 1901, Camus 1917–18, Levaditi and Nicolau 1923).

In certain other respects the pathogenesis of virus diseases appears to differ more or less sharply from bacterial infections.   The tendency to selective localization appears to be more definite ; and it has become customary to use such terms as *dermotropic* or *neurotropic* to define the special, but by no means exclusive, affinities of a given species or strain.   This tropism is very probably related to another peculiarity of the viruses—their tendency to produce characteristic inclusion bodies in certain cells.   (For a good and full description of these bodies and a discussion of their probable nature, see Ludford 1928, Findlay and Ludford 1926.)   *It seems very possible that this habit of functioning as intracellular parasites has an important bearing on antiviral immunity.*

The histopathology of the virus diseases, while it differs in certain aspects from that of most bacterial infections, does not differ so sharply and fundamentally as to require a separate generic description.   No such generic description could, in fact, be given ; for one virus infection differs widely from another in the type and distribution of the cellular reactions produced.   We have referred above to the formation of characteristic intracellular inclusion bodies.   In general, however, the tissue lesions that are associated with virus infections—inflammatory, necrotic, degenerative, granulomatous and proliferative—are of the same kind as those that follow infection with one or other of the pathogenic bacteria ; and the stress of the reparative reaction appears to fall on the same cells of the reticulo-endothelial system (see Ledingham 1924, 1926*a, b*, 1927, Ledingham and Barratt 1929).

Of the ultimate mechanisms by which the filtrable viruses produce their harmful effects we as yet know little or nothing.   We do not, for instance, know whether any of them produce soluble toxins with a characteristic pharmacological action, such as are produced by certain bacteria.   Until our technique has developed to the point at which we can secure mass cultivation *in vitro*, in a cell-free medium, this problem is likely to remain unanswered.   We can at the moment go no further than the statement that no instance has as yet obtruded itself upon our notice in which it seems necessary to assume the presence of a soluble toxin acting at a distance from any focus of living virus.

Antiviral Immunity.

Before discussing the mechanism of antiviral immunity it will be convenient to consider briefly the ways in which such immunity may be induced ; since it is held by many that, in this respect, there is a significant difference between the behaviour of the filtrable viruses and bacterial cells.

Active Antiviral Immunity.—As regards active immunity, we have seen that this is conferred under natural conditions by a typical attack of the disease, and probably by atypical attacks of varying severity or by a carrier infection.   Artificially it may be induced by the injection of a sublethal dose of living virulent virus (a dangerous and uncertain method, even when injections are made by an unusual route), by the injection of a virus that has changed its disease-producing characters, but not its antigenic structure, during adaptation to a different host-species—the classical example is the use of vaccinia to protect against variola—or by an initial injection of a fully attenuated virus followed by injections of less and less attenuated samples until the fully virulent virus is resisted—the classical example is the Pasteurian method of protection against rabies by the injection of rabbit-cord virus attenuated by drying. The question at issue is whether we can induce an effective antiviral immunity by the injection of killed virus alone, in the way that we can produce an antibacterial immunity by the injection of killed bacterial cells. The question really reduces itself into two others. Can we produce an effective resistance by the injection of virus-containing material so completely inactivated that it produces no detectable infection when injected in large doses into a fully susceptible animal ? If this is possible, may we assume that the inactivated virus is actually dead ?

We may answer the first question with a qualified affirmative.

Semple (1912) has shown that the classical Pasteurian methods of rabies prophylaxis may be replaced by injections of rabbit-brain virus inactivated by treatment with 1 per cent. phenol. Boynton (1918, 1928) records successful immunization against cattle plague with a phenolized vaccine, Curasson and Delpy (1926) and Daubney (1928) with a vaccine inactivated with formol. Ducloux and Cordier (1926) report successful immunization against sheep-pox with vaccines inactivated by formol or by ethanol. Bedson, Maitland and Burbury (1927) record the partial immunization of guinea-pigs against foot-and-mouth virus by the injection of formolized virus, and the complete immunization of a proportion of animals after prolonged treatment. Todd (1928*b*), having failed to immunize fowls by the injection of heat-killed or formolized fowl plague virus, succeeded in producing an effective immunity by the injection of three doses of a phenolized vaccine. Bedson (1931) produced a high degree of immunity in guinea-pigs against herpes by the injection of a formolized virus and records similar results with inactivated psittacosis virus (see Discussion 1932).

There are, however, a large number of observations that suggest—although the evidence is not always entirely convincing—that the resistance induced by such inactivated vaccines is in many cases trivial and transitory, and that to secure an effective and lasting immunity it is necessary to supplement the initial injection of inactivated vaccine by a later injection of active virus, in a dose that the partially protected animal will be able to resist. A particularly well-documented account of this method will be found in the studies of Laidlaw and Dunkin (1928*a, b*) on dog distemper.

It would seem a fair conclusion that the injection of inactivated virus material almost always confers some degree of specific resistance, provided that a suitable method of inactivation is employed ; but that the resistance so conferred varies widely in effectiveness in different virus diseases. In some it is of a high order. In others it must be reinforced by injections of active virus ; and it is probable that such reinforcement always increases the solidity and duration of the resistant state.

When we inquire whether an inactivated virus may be assumed to be a dead virus, we are on very difficult ground. The immediate and logical answer is quite clearly in the negative—the assumption is certainly unjustified on the evidence at present available. Some at least of that evidence tells against the view that " inactivated " and " killed " are even approximately equivalent terms. There is general agreement that the application of violent, and therefore certain, methods of killing—such as heating to high temperatures for long periods—destroys the antigenic value of virus-containing material. Indeed, as we have seen above, inactivation by such a chemical agent as formol may remove the antigenic value of one virus but not of another. Such facts are, perhaps, in favour of the view that attenuation rather than death marks the limit beyond which we cannot pass if an effective antigenic stimulus is to be obtained ; but they are also explicable on the assumption that the lack of immunizing effect is due to some alteration in an important antigenic constituent rather than to the killing of the virus. If all effective vaccines were attenuated, not killed, we might expect occasional infections with our treated vaccines. In some instances at least such accidents seem never to occur. Thus (see Harvey and McKendrick 1930), the testing of 500 samples of Semple's phenolized rabies vaccine by the injection of 1 c.c. intramuscularly into rabbits did not result in a single infection. Similarly, if a symptomless infection occurred in an animal injected with an inactivated vaccine, it might be possible by passage from that animal through others to produce characteristic symptoms or lesions. Bedson (1931) notes that his formolized herpes vaccine produced no lesions when introduced into the plantar skin of guinea-pigs, nor was it possible by passage from animal to animal by this route to restore its activity. It is unlikely that we shall solve this problem until we have at our disposal methods of *in vitro* cultivation that will allow us to deal freely with the filtrable viruses apart from cells and tissue fluids, and to apply to them the criteria of viability on which we rely in the case of bacteria.

Whatever the final verdict may be, it is the common practice at the moment to rely on the injection of living virus under the protection either of a partial active immunity induced by the previous injection of virus inactivated in some appropriate way, or of a temporary passive protection induced by the injection of serum from an immunized animal. The latter method is very commonly employed, and its practical exploitation has led to some interesting observations. These have been admirably summarized by Andrewes (1931). Virus-serum mixtures incubated until infection can no longer be produced by any route seem to be useless as immunizing agents. To be effective they must be slightly under-neutralized. In this state they will produce immunity against some virus diseases. A more generally effective method is the so-called side-to-side inoculation—virus into one site, serum into another. Depending upon the ratio of antiserum to virus, this procedure may be followed by a mild and atypical infection or may produce no detectable general reaction. In some cases effective immunity is secured only if the serum-virus ratio is within the range at which a generalized reaction occurs ; in others, such as dog distemper (Laidlaw and Dunkin 1931), an excess of antiserum sufficient to suppress such a reaction does not prevent a successful immunizing response. Side-to-side immunization has been successfully employed in cattle plague (Kolle and Turner 1898, see also Carmichael 1928), swine fever (Dorset *et al.* 1919) and dog distemper (Laidlaw and Dunkin 1931). Theiler (1907–1909) records the successful immunization of horses and mules against African horse sickness by the simultaneous intravenous injection of virus and antiserum.

Another effective method is to administer the antiserum after the virus. This involves a mild immunizing attack of the disease, and for this reason it will clearly never be a method of choice where times and conditions may be determined at will ; but it has an important application when exposure to risk of infection has already occurred, or is an imminent and unavoidable danger. By the administration of antiserum in adequate amount, and at the correct interval after exposure, it is possible to avoid a severe and typical attack, replacing it by a trivial infection that will confer a lasting immunity. The modern methods of measles prophylaxis (see Chapter LXXXIV) afford an excellent example of successful action along these lines.

Passive Antiviral Immunity.—Turning to passive immunity, enough has already been said to indicate that antiviral sera are at least as effective in affording protection against the homologous virus as is an antibacterial serum in protecting against the homologous bacterium. It may be noted that, while antibacterial sera are commonly prepared by the immunization of some conveniently large animal, usually the horse, it has become the practice to prepare antiviral sera by the immunization of an animal of the same species as those it is desired to protect. This is in part due to the fact that much of the work on virus diseases has been carried out within the province of veterinary medicine, and that the original observations on the protective power of immune sera were made with the blood obtained from convalescent animals, or from such animals after further treatment with large injections of active virus. These hyperimmunized animals, when of a conveniently large kind, provide a supply of highly effective antiserum. There are, moreover, many observations which suggest that homologous antisera may be more effective than those prepared in animals of another species. Thus an antidistemper serum prepared in the dog will protect both dogs and ferrets against distemper virus, but protection in the ferret is much less effective and less consistent than in the dog (Laidlaw and Dunkin 1931). [Cf. the efficacy of different antisera in passive anaphylaxis, p. 893.]

As in antibacterial immunity, the passive immunity so obtained is transient —too transient to be of any prophylactic value except under narrowly limited conditions that only occasionally occur in practice.

There are observations on record—some of them contained in the papers already referred to—indicating that antiviral sera may have a definite if limited therapeutic value.

The Mechanisms of Antiviral Immunity.

We know very little of what happens when a virus is introduced into the tissues of a resistant animal, or when a relatively avirulent strain is injected into a relatively susceptible animal. We cannot, therefore, construct any detailed pictures of the kind outlined in Chapter XLIV in the case of bacterial infections.

Our ignorance on this point is due to technical difficulties rather than to lack of interest. In the case of bacterial infections we can, by staining and by cultivation, trace the distribution of the parasites in the tissues with considerable accuracy. In virus diseases neither method is available in a form suitable for this purpose, and we are thrown back on the inoculation of a susceptible animal whenever we wish to demonstrate the presence of virus in a given tissue. If we desire our results to be quantitative—as we usually do—we are in further difficulties unless the virus produces a characteristic skin reaction. If it does, we can titrate it with some approach to accuracy. If it does not we have to rely on producing infection or death in an adequate sample of animals with each dose tested, and our task becomes formidable. Nor do our troubles end here. The material we inject contains not only virus, but products derived from the host; and the possible effects of the latter cannot be neglected. The assumption that the result obtained by the injection of virus-containing material into a susceptible animal is determined by the virus alone is, as we shall see, quite unjustified.

Such knowledge as we have has been gained mainly by experiments on normal animals. So far as it goes it suggests that the immediate clearing mechanism involved in freeing the blood stream and tissue fluids from virus is the same as that brought into play in the case of bacteria, and that, in a naturally immune animal, or in a relatively susceptible animal injected by a route that does not allow the virus to gain easy access to the tissues for which it has a special affinity, this clearing mechanism is capable of functioning very effectively.

Thus Gins and Weber (1916) found, in conformity with the results of earlier workers, that vaccinia virus of ordinary potency disappeared rapidly from the blood stream after intravenous injection. When large amounts of virus were injected, and the organs were tested within 5 hours, virus could usually be recovered from the spleen, less frequently from the liver, but never from the bone-marrow. Douglas, Smith and Price—who were, it will be remembered, working with a highly potent strain of virus—record four experiments in which various organs were tested for virus within a few days after an intravenous injection. In these the virus was recovered in each case from lungs and spleen, in 3 of 4 cases from the liver, and in 3 of 4 cases from the bone-marrow ; but the fact that infection was in all cases widely generalized makes the significance of these findings doubtful. Of more interest are the relative frequencies of vaccinial lesions in the different organs and tissues. Of 36 rabbits injected intravenously the numbers showing lesions at different sites were as follows : skin 31, mucosa of lips or nose 26, tongue 24, lungs 35, liver 24, spleen 24, adrenals 14, œsophagus 1, bladder 1, intestine 1, muscles 2, heart 1, pericardium 1, peritoneum 3. Lesions were also relatively frequent in the testes among the males, and in the ovaries among the females. Thus we find the highest frequencies in those tissues for which vaccinia virus is known to have a special affinity and in those organs—lungs, liver, spleen and adrenals—which are primarily concerned in freeing the blood stream from inanimate foreign particles or from bacteria.

Flexner and Amoss (1914) record that the injection of poliomyelitis virus into the veins of monkeys—a route that does not commonly lead to the production of the typical disease—is followed by the prompt deposition of the virus in the spleen and bone-marrow, but not in the kidneys. Galloway (Report 1931) has recorded a few experiments in which the infectivity of various organs was determined 24–48 hours after the injection of foot-and-mouth virus into the pad of the guinea-pig's foot. The concentration of virus was highest in the blood, but the spleen, liver and lungs contained virus in detectable amount, while the mesenteric glands, ovary, testis and muscles did not. In dog distemper (Laidlaw and Dunkin 1928a, b), organs rich in reticulo-endothelial cells, such as the spleen, show a high virus content.

A review of the available data appears to justify the following conclusions. Where the virus concerned has an affinity for some special tissue in which it causes its characteristic lesions, it will, naturally enough, be found in the greatest concentration in those lesions or in their immediate neighbourhood. Thus we find vaccinia virus in the highest concentration in the lymph of the pustules, the virus of foot-and-mouth disease in the fluid of the vesicles, the virus of rabies, or of poliomyelitis, or of Borna disease, in the central nervous system, and so on ; but even in these diseases the other tissues in which the virus is most frequently present, if we except the blood, are those concerned in the normal clearing mechanism— the spleen, liver, lungs, bone-marrow or adrenals. In generalized infections, in which localization in the skin or nervous system is not a feature of the disease, the reticulo-endothelial tissues frequently show the highest virus content.

The blood we must consider in rather more detail. That the virus may often be demonstrated in blood withdrawn during the febrile stage of illness, or even at other times, we have already seen ; but many of the results recorded, particularly in the later stages of experimental infections, have been curiously irregular. It would appear that these irregularities have been due in part to the fact that the virus is often present in the cellular elements—particularly in the leucocytes— rather than in the plasma, and that viricidal antibodies may appear in the plasma, while virus is present in the cells.

As long ago as 1899 Kolle showed that the infective agent in the citrated blood of an animal suffering from cattle plague was readily removed by centrifugation. The supernatant plasma was non-infective ; the deposit, containing the blood cells, infective to a high degree. Todd and White (1914) studied this phenomenon in greater detail and showed that the virus was mainly associated with the leucocytes, and Schein (1917) and Daubney (1928) recorded similar findings. Russ (1906) (see also Landsteiner and Russ 1906) found that the virus of fowl plague was present in greater amount in the cellular constituents of the blood than in the plasma, and Todd (1928*a*) has shown that the concentration is highest in the leucocytic layer, though Doerr and Gold (1932) record experiments which they interpret as indicating an adsorption of the virus by the red cells.

Smith (1929) has studied this problem in some detail in experimental vaccinia in the rabbit. Comparing the infectivity of the whole blood, the plasma, and the washed deposit of cells during the early days of a generalized infection he found that the washed cells were most infective, and the plasma non-infective. By fractional centrifugation it was possible to show that the red cells played no part in fixing the virus. The results suggested strongly that the leucocytes alone were concerned, but the possible participation of the blood platelets could not be entirely excluded. At a later stage—and this is the immediately significant point—the washed cells might be infective while neither the whole blood nor the plasma produced any lesion in susceptible rabbits. After intradermal inoculation of virus the washed cells might be found infective in animals whose whole blood gave consistently negative results.

In further experiments it was found that specific antibodies made their appearance in the plasma of infected rabbits as early as the 3rd day after infection and thereafter rapidly increased in concentration. There was, therefore, a period during which the leucocytes contained active virus while the plasma contained protective antibodies. Infectivity tests carried out with the whole blood during this period gave irregular and often negative results, depending on the balance between virus and antibody. But if washed cells, freed from antibody, were used for the test inoculation, virus could regularly be demonstrated in the blood up to the 8th day after infection. Berry and Kitchen (see Russell 1932) in a case of yellow fever noted the simultaneous presence of virus and protective antibodies in the blood on the 4th and 5th days of disease. Such observations indicate clearly that caution should be exercised in assuming that any tissue extract or body fluid is necessarily free from living virus because it is non-infective.

The data that enable us to compare the fate of a virus when injected into an immunized animal with its fate when injected into a normal animal of the same species are even more scanty. There is the clear and significant fact that the characteristic signs of infection do not occur, or are very greatly modified ; but beyond that fact we know relatively little.

In the particular case of foot-and-mouth disease, Bedson, Maitland and Burbury (1927) have shown that three stages—not of course sharply demarcated from each other—can be recognized in the active immunization of the guinea-pig. In the first, the animal resists the intramuscular injection of a dose of virus that uniformly causes a generalized infection in controls, but responds to inoculation into the pad of the foot by developing a local vesicle followed by generalized lesions. In the second the solid resistance to intramuscular injection is associated with a heightened resistance to intradermal injection, so that the local vesicle is not followed by generalization. In the third and final stage the guinea-pig is immune to the inoculation of the virus by any route. There is here a clear suggestion of an improved clearing mechanism that, in the partially immunized animal, is able to protect the sensitive tissues if these have not been directly infected at the time of inoculation. Analogous observations have been made during the period of fading immunity in cattle and pigs (Andrewes and others ; Report 1931). Recent experiments by Galloway (Report 1931) on the survival of foot-and-mouth virus after inoculation into the tissues of immunized animals are in general accord with this view. Virus injected into the mucous membrane of the tongue of immunized rabbits could not be recovered from the blood at any time from the 2nd to the 36th hour after inoculation. Similarly, virus inoculated into the tongue or pads of immunized guinea-pigs could never be recovered from the blood. It could be recovered from the local lesions from 30 minutes to 24 hours after injection, but not after 36 hours.

Of particular interest is an isolated experiment recorded by Smith (1929). Vaccinia virus was injected intravenously into an immunized rabbit, and the washed blood cells were tested for infectivity after 30 minutes, 1, 2, 4, 6 and 8 hours. The cells were infective up to and including the 4th hour, after which they were non-infective. This rapid disappearance of virus from the blood of an immunized animal contrasts sharply with the course of events in a normal rabbit.

The Nature and Reactions of the Antiviral Antibodies.

In discussing the rôle of the serum antibodies in antibacterial immunity, we were able to draw on our extensive knowledge of the ways in which antibodies and bacteria react *in vitro*. Our knowledge of the *in vitro* reactions of filtrable viruses and their specific antisera is as yet rudimentary ; but it will help us in the present discussion if we summarize the scanty evidence available, comparing it with that set out in Chapter VI.

In the particular case of vaccinia virus, it has been shown that the serum of an immunized rabbit reacts *in vitro* with virus-containing material from the pocks of variola or vaccinia in man, giving complement fixation and, under suitable conditions, visible precipitation (Gordon 1925, Burgess, Craigie and Tulloch 1929, Bedson and Bland 1929, Craigie and Tulloch 1931, Havens and Mayfield 1931). These reactions are specific—suspensions of material from the lesions of chickenpox do not react with anti-vaccinial sera—and they confirm the antigenic similarity or identity of the viruses of vaccinia and variola. It will be noted that the antigenic material employed is extremely crude. Vaccine lymph contains substances derived from the tissues of the calf and a number of non-pathogenic contaminating bacteria as well as the vaccinia virus itself, and antigenic substances of similar kinds are present in material derived from human skin lesions.

It has been suggested that the reactions referred to above may be due to foreign contaminating bacterial antigens rather than to antigens derived from the virus ; but this criticism has been adequately met.

Bedson and Bland (1929) showed that antivaccinial sera did not fix complement in the presence of bacteria derived from calf-lymph, nor did antisera prepared against those bacteria fix complement in the presence of the lymph (see also Havens and Mayfield 1931). Craigie and Tulloch (1931) record the failure of antisera prepared against the secondary bacterial infectors, found in vaccinia and variola crusts, to give visible flocculation with crust extracts. They note, moreover, that antisera prepared by injecting rabbits with extracts of the bacteriologically sterile organs of an animal suffering from generalized experimental vaccinia give good flocculation with crust extracts, and that antisera prepared against dermal vaccine lymph gives good flocculation with extracts of virus-containing organs. Similar observations have been recorded by Thompson, Hazen and Buchbinder (1932). The conclusion that these reactions depend on antigens present in or derived from the virus itself is confirmed by the observation of Gilmore (1931) that antivaccinial sera prepared in the rabbit, or human serum derived from cases of variola minor, give specific complement fixation in the presence of vaccinia virus which has been propagated through 17 to 24 successive subcultures in an appropriate tissue medium.

Recent observations by Ledingham (1931) and by others have an important bearing on this problem. The tissues of animals infected with vaccinia may be shown by appropriate staining methods to contain minute granules, the Paschen bodies, which almost certainly represent the actual virus—such bodies may be demonstrated in this and other virus diseases as optically resolved images by the beautiful methods devised by Barnard (1919, 1926, 1932, Barnard and Elford 1931–32). By differential centrifugation Ledingham has been able to prepare suspensions of these elementary bodies almost entirely freed from extraneous material, and finds that, in this state, they are specifically agglutinated by an antivaccinial serum.

Craigie (1932) has recorded experiments which indicate that the flocculation that occurs in a mixture of vaccinia virus and antivaccinial serum is not wholly, or even mainly, an agglutination reaction ; but is due in large part to the interaction of a soluble specific substance derived from the virus with a corresponding antibody in the serum. In the precipitate so formed the virus particles are entangled. The virus particles separated from the soluble substance are agglutinable by the serum, and absorption experiments suggest that the precipitation and agglutination reactions are dependent upon the same antigenic components.

Smith (1932) has recorded experiments that indicate the close similarity between the filtrable substance described by Craigie and the bacterial haptens described in Chapter VI. Rabbits were injected intratesticularly with vaccinia virus, and autolysates were prepared from the infected testicular tissue. From these autolysates a soluble specific substance was obtained, which would withstand boiling, but not autoclaving. It gave a positive biuret test, positive reactions for arginine and tyrosine, negative reactions for tryptophan and cystine, and a positive Molisch test for carbohydrate. It therefore contains both protein and carbohydrate radicles. It shares with the bacterial haptens the capacity to give specific precipitation *in vitro*, and the incapacity to stimulate antibody production *in vivo*.

Douglas and Smith (1930) have studied the action of whole blood and of serum-leucocyte mixtures on vaccinia virus. They find that leucocytes take up the virus *in vitro* ; that immune is significantly more viricidal than normal blood ; and that normal cells in the presence of immune plasma appear to be more viricidal than immune cells in the presence of normal plasma.

It happens that the greater part of the available data with regard to the *in vitro* antigen-antibody reactions of the filtrable viruses refers to the particular case of vaccinia ; but we shall probably not err in regarding this as an illustrative example of the behaviour of viruses in general. All the evidence that we have points in this direction.

Thus Bedson and Bland (1929) have demonstrated specific complement fixation with herpes virus and an antiherpes serum, Ciuca (1929) with foot-and-mouth virus and the corresponding antiserum, Frobisher (1929) with yellow-fever virus and the sera of convalescent men and monkeys, Laidlaw and Dunkin (1931) with the virus of dog distemper, and Broom and Findlay (1932) with the virus of Rift Valley fever and the sera of men, monkeys, sheep, rats and mice that have recovered from natural or experimental infection. Ledingham (1931) has demonstrated the agglutination of suspensions of the Borrel bodies of fowl-pox by the sera of fowls that have recovered from that infection, and Bedson (1932) has demonstrated agglutination and complement-fixation reactions between the elementary bodies of psittacosis virus and a specific antiserum.

It would seem, then, safe to conclude that naturally infected men and experimentally infected animals produce specific antibodies to a filtrable virus, which react with that virus *in vitro* in the same specific way as an antibacterial serum reacts with the homologous bacterium, or with its products.

Certain observations on the neutralization of a filtrable virus by an antiviral serum—as studied by inoculation tests in susceptible animals—have raised doubts as to whether the antigen-antibody reaction involved is entirely similar to that which occurs between a bacterium and the corresponding sensitizing antibody.

Andrewes (1928*b*) found that mixtures of vaccinia virus with antivaccinial serum might fail to give rise to lesions when injected intradermally, indicating effective neutralization, though they proved infective when injected intratesticularly, intracerebrally or intravenously. He found also that virus could be recovered from a neutral serum-virus mixture for periods as long as 24 hours by simple dilution, and that the specific neutralizing antibodies could be recovered from the mixture by filtration through a candle that held back the virus. Todd (1928*c*) found that mixtures of fowl-plague virus and anti-fowl-plague serum, which were just neutral when undiluted, regained their infectivity on tenfold dilution with normal saline. This phenomenon was observable after 4 hours' contact between virus and serum at 37° C., but not after 24 hours' contact at 28° C. The effect of dilution at the earlier period was also evidenced by the fact that a mixture that was inactive when injected intramuscularly was infective when injected intravenously. Bedson (1928) records similar experiments with herpes virus and an antiherpes serum, and concludes that there is a slow union between the virus and the viricidal antibodies *in vitro,* the effect of dilution being limited to the period during which this union is incomplete. In later experiments (Bedson 1929) he demonstrated that collodion particles would adsorb the specific antibodies from an antiherpes serum, and that particles so treated would adsorb herpes virus more readily than untreated particles, or than particles treated with normal serum. From this he concluded that the antigen must have united with the antibody. Andrewes (1930*a*) re-examining the reaction between vaccinia virus and an antivaccinial serum in the light of these results found that it became less and less easy to recover active virus from serum-virus mixtures as the period of contact was prolonged, but that the time required for complete irreversible inactivation of the virus was of the order of 24 to 48 hours at 37° C., or 4 to 8 days at room temperature. The observation of Smith (1930) that it is possible by the use of optimal amounts of absorbing material to absorb separately the antibodies acting on herpes and vaccinia virus from a mixture of antiherpes and antivaccinial serum indicates quite clearly that, under suitable conditions, an effective antigen-antibody union occurs ; though Sabin (1935) records experiments from which he draws quite different conclusions.

It would seem probable that antibodies acting on the filtrable viruses form with them a union which is at first of a loose kind, easily dissociable on simple dilution, and which attains stability and firmness only after the lapse of a considerable period of time, probably as the result of some secondary change in the antigen-antibody complex. Closely analogous relations have been shown to hold between bacterial toxins and certain antitoxic sera.

As is the case with the antibodies acting on bacteria and their products, the antibodies in antiviral sera appear to be confined to the globulin fractions.

Hartley (1914) concluded from the results obtained in the fractional precipitation of anti-cattle-plague serum that the antibodies were contained in the euglobulin. Maitland and Burbury (1927) found that the antibodies in the serum of guinea-pigs immunized against foot-and-mouth virus were associated with the serum globulin. Weyer, Park and Banzhaf (1929) concluded that the antibody of poliomyelitis antiserum was contained in the pseudoglobulin, while Morgan and Fairbrother (1930) found the euglobulin the most potent. Henseval (1919) found the antibodies of a vaccinial antiserum to be distributed throughout the serum proteins, but describes the euglobulin fraction as especially potent. Ledingham, Morgan and Petrie (1931) found antibody in both the euglobulin and pseudoglobulin fractions of an antivaccinial horse serum ; the highest concentration was in the euglobulin, but the greatest absolute amount was in the large pseudoglobulin fraction. Laidlaw and Dunkin (1931) found the antibody of distemper antiserum to be confined to the globulin fraction ; further study showed that the antibody was associated with a globulin fraction that was insoluble in water, but soluble in weak acids or alkalies and in water saturated with CO_2, thus behaving like the pneumococcal antibody described by Felton (1925, 1926, 1928).

There can be no dispute that humoral factors play an important part in anti-viral, as in antibacterial, immunity ; but there has been a tendency to suggest that a specific cellular immunity is even more important. It may be so. It would be folly to dogmatize in our present state of ignorance. But the scanty evidence at present available hardly favours such a view.

Andrewes (1929a) cultivated a particular virus (known as Virus III) in tissue cultures prepared from rabbit testis, and found that the characteristic intranuclear inclusion bodies associated with this infection *in vivo* were also formed *in vitro*. Rivers, Haagen and Muckenfuss (1929a, b) later described the formation of characteristic inclusion bodies in cultures of vaccinia and of herpes virus, grown in association with cells of the rabbit's cornea. Andrewes (1929b) employed this method in an attempt to study the relative importance of cellular and humoral immunity in Virus III infection. Cultures were pre-pared containing the virus associated with (a) normal testicular cells and normal serum, (b) normal testicular cells and the serum from an immune animal, (c) testicular cells from an immune animal in association with normal serum and (d) immune testicular cells with immune serum. With immune testis and immune serum no inclusion bodies were formed. With immune serum and normal testis the same result was obtained, provided that the serum was allowed to come into contact with the testicular tissue before the virus was added. If, however, the virus was allowed to remain in contact with the tissue for 10 minutes or longer at 37° C. before the immune serum was added inclusion bodies developed, though they were always scantier than in control cultures in normal serum. When immune testis was combined with normal serum inclusion bodies usually developed ; when the immune testis was well washed by a preliminary soaking in Tyrode's solution inclusion bodies were constantly obtained. Similar results were later obtained with herpes virus and an antiherpes serum (Andrewes 1930b). These observations indicate very clearly that, in the case of the viruses studied and under the experimental conditions obtaining, the humoral factor is decisive, while there is little evidence of an increased resistance of the cells from the immunized animal. In the case of vaccinia virus Rivers, Haagen and Muckenfuss (1929b) record observations which show apparent divergencies from Andrewes' findings, but these may have been due mainly to differences in the technique employed.

It is perhaps a plausible guess, though certainly no more, that the main difference between antiviral and antibacterial immunity lies in the fact that an essential element in virus infections is entry into and multiplication within particular sus-ceptible cells, and that an adequate concentration of antibody in, or in the neigh-bourhood of, these cells protects them from the virus, and so presents an effective barrier to the spread of infection within the tissues.

This difference we may note involves the existence in virus diseases of a type of local immunity that is absent in bacterial infections. Some of the observations recorded in this chapter, and such findings as those recorded by Laidlaw and his colleagues in experimental influenza (p. 1309), would accord with a localized immunity of this kind.

The Antigenic Structure of the Filtrable Viruses.

We know almost nothing of the antigenic structure of the viruses. It seems a reasonable enough assumption that living cells so small must have relatively few antigenic components ; and it is, perhaps, not an abuse of the argument from analogy to suppose that, as in the bacteria, the particular component that is con-centrated at the surface of the virus particle will dominate the picture from the point of view of effective immunity. We have seen that, in the particular case of vaccinia virus, there is evidence of the existence of a heat-stable, soluble antigenic component, having the properties of a bacterial hapten, and it is altogether probable that we shall in time be able to separate similar haptens from other viruses and so to apply the same chemical methods of analysis that have proved so fruitful in the study of bacterial antigens.

There is one direction in which we already have evidence of antigenic differences of a kind entirely analogous to those existing within a pathogenic bacterial species. Just as there are different serological types of pneumococci, each type acting as a specific entity so far as its more important immunity reactions are concerned, so there are at least three types of the virus of foot-and-mouth disease, each type producing the same clinical syndrome in susceptible animals but producing immunity only against itself. By cross-immunity experiments Vallée and Carré (1922*a*, *b*) demonstrated the existence of two types of foot-and-mouth virus, to which they gave the labels A and O. Waldmann and Trautwein (1926) and Trautwein (1927) described three immunologically distinct types of virus which they called A, B and C. It has been found that the A type of Vallée and Carré is identical with the B type of Waldmann and Trautwein, and the O type of the former observers with the A type of the latter (see Report 1928). These immunological differences may be demonstrated either by active or passive immunization of susceptible animals, and the antibodies may also be differentiated by complement-fixation tests *in vitro* (Ciuca 1929, Rep. 1931).

It is clear that observations of this kind should make us very cautious in accepting statements with regard to the effectiveness of the immunity that follows a single attack of a particular virus disease. One attack of foot-and-mouth disease does not always protect against a second ; because foot-and-mouth disease is a clinical but not an immunological entity. One attack of O foot-and-mouth infection protects against another infection with that strain of virus, though we cannot yet assess with any accuracy the exact degree or duration of the protection afforded, but an attack of O infection does not protect against a subsequent attack of A infection.

No other instances of clear-cut antigenic differences, such as those that exist between the different types of foot-and-mouth disease virus, have as yet been put on record. Burnet and Macnamara (1931) have reported observations that suggest, but do not prove, the existence of antigenic differences between different strains of poliomyelitis virus, and Flexner (1932) has recorded experiments that suggest an antigenic modification of this virus as the result of repeated passage in the monkey. The available evidence (see Chapter LXXI) suggests that the viruses of human and swine influenza are antigenically related, though not identical, and that the swine virus may originally have been derived from man. This is a field that is as yet almost unexplored, but there seems no reason to suppose that the picture finally constructed will differ in kind, though it may differ in emphasis, from that which we have described in the case of bacteria.

Allergy in Virus Diseases.

The characteristic response to reinoculation with vaccinia virus affords one of the classical examples of an allergic reaction. The typical sequence of events after a successful primary inoculation commences with an incubation period lasting about 3 days, followed by the appearance of papules at the sites of inoculation on about the 4th day. These develop into compound vesicles during the next 5 days, become definitely pustular about the 10th day, and heal by the well-known scabbing process between the 14th and 21st days. If a person who has been successfully vaccinated is again injected with calf-lymph during the period of waning immunity, but before he has again become fully susceptible, the most noticeable feature in the local reaction is an acceleration of all stages. The papules appear earlier, sometimes within 24 hours ; and vesiculation and pustulation, when they occur, are in evidence at a far earlier period than after primary vaccination. Very frequently, however, the reaction ceases at the papular stage, and this may be so transitory as to be missed unless daily examinations are made. In any case, the induration round the papules or vesicles is usually far less marked after a secondary than after a primary vaccination, and the constitutional symptoms are slighter. We have, in fact, the typical allergic combination of accelerated response with localization of infection. It would appear (Andervont and Rosenau 1930) that vaccinia virus killed by heating to high temperatures is capable of producing the characteristic immediate reaction with papule formation in persons previously vaccinated ; while it has no effect in unvaccinated persons, nor does it produce an active immunity. There are, of course, many analogous observations in the case of bacterial allergy and hypersensitiveness.

There is no reason to believe that other virus infections differ from vaccinia in their ability to induce the allergic state, though this aspect of antiviral immunity has not yet been studied in any detail. A few observations are on record. Thus, Andrewes (1928a) records an allergic reaction in rabbits infected with Virus III. Animals that had been solidly immunized showed a relatively small local lesion when reinoculated in the testes, but no nuclear inclusions were present in these lesions. Partially immunized rabbits developed more pronounced testicular lesions, as judged histologically, than did either normal or solidly immunized animals. These lesions, however, unlike those produced in normal rabbits, were usually free from nuclear inclusion bodies.

Other Factors in Virus Infections.

Our knowledge of the interplay of factors other than those we have referred to above is very scanty ; but so far as it goes it suggests no fundamental differences between the mechanisms involved in antiviral and antibacterial immunity.

We have seen that the reticulo-endothelial cells are intimately concerned in the pathogenesis of the virus infections, and it seems altogether probable that they play an important rôle in the production of antiviral antibodies. The time relations of the antibody response to virus infections would seem to be of the same general type as those that occur in bacterial infections, or in active immunization against a bacterial antigen (see Ciuca 1929, Ledingham 1932).

In virus as in bacterial infections there is evidence that ancillary factors may play an important part. Duran-Reynals (1928) records the enhancing effect of extracts of embryonic or sarcoma tissue, or of suspensions of kieselguhr, on the dermal infectivity of partially inactivated vaccinia virus. He also (1929) notes a similar effect produced by extracts of testicular tissue. This latter phenomenon has been studied by McClean (1930) who finds that the active principle in testicular extract produces a local increase in the permeability of the skin, and thus increases the area of diffusion of the virus.

A series of observations by M. Maitland (see Report 1928) on the factors determining the localization of the virus in experimental foot-and-mouth disease in the guinea-pig are of considerable interest. Seeking an explanation of the limitation of the vesicles to the mouth and the hairless part of the feet, she transferred strips of hairy skin to the soles of guinea-pigs' feet and found that vesicles developed in the hairy skin so transferred, whether the virus was injected directly into it or introduced elsewhere in the body. She also showed that, when virus was inoculated intramuscularly, vesicles failed to appear on the sole of one hind foot, if that foot was protected by cotton-wool and a bandage. On the unprotected feet vesicles appeared as usual. Again, when the bottom of the cage was made of wire mesh, the pressure on the toes and anterior part of the feet resulted in the appearance of vesicles on these parts, though they are not the usual sites of vesicle formation.

SUMMARY

It is perhaps a fair summary of the evidence presented in this chapter to suggest that it is compatible with the view that there is no essential difference between the mechanisms involved in antiviral and antibacterial immunity. In so far as immunity to virus infections is more effective than immunity to bacterial invasion, it seems possible that the difference is due rather to the greater limitations imposed on the virus by its habit of intracellular parasitism than to any special reaction on the part of the host.

REFERENCES

ANDERVONT, H. B. and ROSENAU, M. J. (1930) *J. Immunol.*, **18**, 51.

ANDREWES, C. H. (1928a) *J. Path. Bact.*, **31**, 461 ; (1928b) *Ibid.*, **31**, 671 ; (1929a) *Brit. J. exp. Path.*, **10**, 188 ; (1929b) *Ibid.*, **10**, 273 ; (1930a) *J. Path. Bact.*, **33**, 265 ; (1930b) *Ibid.*, **33**, 301 ; (1931) *Lancet*, i. 989, 1046.

AYCOCK, W. L. and KRAMER, S. D. (1930a) *J. prev. Med.*, **4**, 189 ; (1930b) *Ibid.*, **4**, 201 ; (1930c) *J. exp. Med.*, **52**, 457.

BARNARD, J. E. (1919) *J. R. micr. Soc.*, p. 1 ; (1926) *Ibid.*, p. 253 ; (1932) *Ibid.*, **52**, 230.

BARNARD, J. E. and ELFORD, W. J. (1931–32) *Proc. roy. Soc.*, B, **109**, 360.

BEDSON, S. P. (1928) *Brit. J. exp. Path.*, **9**, 235 ; (1929) *Ibid.*, **10**, 364 ; (1931) *Ibid.*, **12**, 254 ; (1932) *Ibid.*, **13**, 65.

BEDSON, S. P. and BLAND, J. O. W. (1929) *Ibid.*, **10**, 393.

BEDSON, S. P., MAITLAND, H. B., and BURBURY, Y. M. (1927) *J. comp. Path.*, **40**, 5.

BEEUWKES, H., BAUER, J. H., and MAHAFFY, A. F. (1930) *Amer. J. trop. Med.*, **10**, 305.

BOYNTON, W. H. (1918) *Philipp. J. Sci.*, B, **13**, 127 ; (1928) *Ibid.*, **36**, 1.

BRODIE, M. (1932) *J. exp. Med.*, **56**, 507.

BROOM, J. C. and FINDLAY, G. M. (1932) *Lancet*, i. 609.

BURGESS, W. L., CRAIGIE, J., and TULLOCH, W. J. (1929) *Spec. Rep. Ser. med. Res. Coun. Lond.*, No. 143.

BURNET, F. M. and MACNAMARA, J. (1931) *Brit. J. exp. Path.*, **12**, 57.

CALMETTE, A. and GUÉRIN, C. (1901) *Ann. Inst. Pasteur*, **15**, 161.

CAMUS, L. (1917–18) *J. Physiol. Path. gén.*, **17**, 244.

CARMICHAEL, J. (1928) *J. comp. Path.*, **41**, 185.

CIUCA, A. (1929) *J. Hyg., Camb.*, **28**, 325.

CRAIGIE, J. (1932) *Brit. J. exp. Path.*, **13**, 259.

CRAIGIE, J. and TULLOCH, W. J. (1931) *Spec. Rep. Ser. med. Res. Coun., Lond.*, No. 156.

CURASSON, G. and DELPY, L. (1926) *Rec. Méd. vét.*, **102**, 297.

DAUBNEY, R. (1928) *J. comp. Path.*, **41**, 228, 263.

Discussion. (1932) *Proc. R. Soc. Med.*, **25**, 451.

DOERR, R. and GOLD, E. (1932) *Z. Hyg. InfektKr.*, **113**, 645.

DORSET, M., McBRIDE, C. N., NILES, W. B., and REITZ, I. H. (1919) *J. Amer. vet. med. Ass.*, **55**, 55, 259, 272.

DOUGLAS, S. R. and SMITH, W. (1930) *Brit. J. exp. Path.*, **11**, 96.

DOUGLAS, S. R., SMITH, W., and PRICE, L. R. W. (1929) *J. Path. Bact.*, **32**, 99.

DUCLOUX, E. and CORDIER, G. (1926) *C. R. Acad. Sci.*, **183**, 486.

DURAN-REYNALS, F. (1928) *J. exp. Med.*, **47**, 389 ; (1929) *Ibid.*, **50**, 327 ; (1931) *J. Immunol.*, **20**, 389.

FELTON, L. D. (1925) *J. infect. Dis.*, **37**, 199 ; (1926) *Johns Hopk. Hosp. Bull.*, **38**, 33 ; (1928) *J. infect. Dis.*, **43**, 543.

FINDLAY, G. M. and LUDFORD, R. J. (1926) *Brit. J. exp. Path.*, **7**, 223.

FLEXNER, S. (1932) *J. Amer. med. Ass.*, **99**, 1244.

FLEXNER, S. and AMOSS, H. L. (1914) *J. exp. Med.*, **20**, 249 ; (1919) *Ibid.*, **29**, 379.
FLEXNER, S., CLARK, P. F., and FRASER, F. R. (1913) *J. Amer. med. Ass.*, **60**, 201.
FROBISHER JR., M. (1929) *Proc. Soc. exp. Biol.*, *N.Y.*, **26**, 846.
GILDEMEISTER, E. and HEUER, G. (1927) *Zbl. Bakt.*, **105**, 86.
GILMORE, E. ST. G. (1931) *Brit. J. exp. Path.*, **12**, 165.
GINS, H. A. and WEBER, R. (1916) *Z. Hyg. InfektKr.*, **82**, 143.
GINS, H. A., HACKENTHAL, L., and KAMENTZEWA, N. (1929) *Z. Hyg. InfektKr.*, **10**, 110.
GORDON, M. H. (1925) *Spec. Rep. Ser. med. Res. Coun., Lond.*, No. 98.
HARTLEY, P. (1914) *Mem. Dep. Agric. Ind. Vet.*, **1**, No. 4, 178.
HARVEY, W. F. and MCKENDRICK, A. G. (1930) " System of Bacteriology." *Med. Res. Coun.*, **7**, 198.
HAVENS, L. C. and MAYFIELD, C. R. (1931) *Amer. J. publ. Hlth.*, **21**, 329.
HENSEVAL, M. (1919) *C. R. Soc. Biol.*, **82**, 889.
HUDSON, N. P. and PHILIP, C. B. (1929) *J. exp. Med.*, **50**, 583.
JUNGEBLUT, C. W. (1933) *J. Immunol.*, **24**, 157 ; (1934) *Ibid.*, **27**, 17.
JUNGEBLUT, C. W. and ENGLE, E. T. (1932) *J. Amer. med. Ass.*, **99**, 2091 ; (1932) *Proc. Soc. exp. Biol.*, *N.Y.*, **29**, 879 ; (1933) *J. Immunol.*, **24**, 267 ; (1934) *J. exp. Med.*, **59**, 43.
KLING, C. and PETTERSSON, A. (1914) *Dtsch. med. Wschr.*, **40**, 320.
KLING, C., WERNSTEDT, W., and PETTERSSON, A. (1912) *Z. ImmunForsch.*, **14**, 303.
KOLLE, W. (1899) *Z. Hyg. InfektKr.*, **30**, 33.
KOLLE, W. and TURNER, G. (1898) *Ibid.*, **29**, 309.
LAIDLAW, P. P. and DUNKIN, G. W. (1928a) *J. comp. Path.*, **41**, 1 ; (1928b) *Ibid.*, **41**, 209 ; (1931) *Ibid.*, **44**, 1.
LANDSTEINER, K. and RUSS, V. K. (1906) *Z. Bakt., Ref.*, **38**, 540.
LEDINGHAM, J. C. G. (1924) *J. Path. Bact.*, **27**, 345 ; (1926a) *J. State Med.*, **34**, 125 ; (1926b) *J. Path. Bact.*, **29**, 309 ; (1927) *Brit. J. exp. Path.*, **8**, 12 ; (1931) *Lancet*, ii. 525 ; (1932) *J. Path. Bact.*, **35**, 140.
LEDINGHAM, J. C. G. and BARRATT, M. M. (1929) *Lancet*, ii. 515.
LEDINGHAM, J. C. G., MORGAN, W. T. J., and PETRIE, G. F. (1931) *Brit. J. exp. Path.*, **12**, 357.
LEVADITI, C. and NICOLAU, S. (1923) *Ann. Inst. Pasteur*, **37**, 1.
LUCAS, W. P. and OSGOOD, R. B. (1913) *J. Amer. med. Ass.*, **60**, 1611.
LUDFORD, R. J. (1928) *Proc. roy. Soc., B*, **102**, 406.
MAITLAND, H. B. and BURBURY, Y. M. (1927) *J. comp. Path.*, **40**, 93.
MCCLEAN, D. (1930) *J. Path. Bact.*, **33**, 1045.
MORGAN, W. T. J. and FAIRBROTHER, R. W. (1930) *Brit. J. exp. Path.*, **30**, 512.
OHTAWARA, T. (1922) *Sci. Rep. Govt Inst. infect. Dis., Tokyo*, **1**, 203.
PAUL, J. R. and TRASK, J. D. (1932) *J. exp. Med.*, **56**, 319.
Report. (1928) *Min. Agric. Fisher. 3rd Prog. Rep. Foot-and-Mouth Dis. Res. Comm.* ; (1931) *Min. Agric. Fisher. 4th Prog. Rep. Foot-and-Mouth Dis. Res. Comm.*
RIVERS, T. M., HAAGEN, E. and MUCKENFUSS, R. (1929a) *J. exp. Med.*, **50**, 665 ; (1929b) *Ibid.*, **50**, 673.
RIVERS, T. M. and TILLETT, W. S. (1923) *J. Exp. Med.*, **38**, 673.
RUSS, V. K. (1906) *Arch. Hyg.*, **59**, 286.
RUSSELL, F. F. (1932) *Amer. J. med. Sci.*, **183**, 87.
SABIN, A. B. (1935) *Brit. J. exp. Path.*, **16**, 70, 84, 158, 169.
SAWYER, W. A. and LLOYD, W. (1931) *J. exp. Med.*, **54**, 533.
SCHEIN, H. (1917) *Ann. Inst. Pasteur*, **31**, 571.
SEMPLE, D. (1912) *Sci. Mon. med. san. Dept Ind.*, No. 44.
SMITH, W. (1929) *Brit. J. exp. Path.*, **10**, 93 ; (1930) *J. Path. Bact.*, **33**, 273 ; (1932) *Brit. J. exp. Path.*, **13**, 434.
STOCKS, P. (1928) *Ann. Eugenics*, **3**, 361 ; (1930a) *Lancet*, i. 796 ; (1930b) *Proc. roy. Soc. Med. Sect. Epidem.*, **23**, 65 ; (1932) *J. Hyg., Camb.*, **32**, 219.
TAYLOR, E. and AMOSS, H. L. (1917) *J. exp. Med.*, **26**, 745.
THEILER, A. (1907–1909) *Transv. Dept Agric. Rep. Vet. Bact.*, (1907–1908) ; (1909) *Transv. Dept Agric. J.*, **7**, 175, 355.
THEILER, M. (1930) *Ann. trop. Med. Parasit.*, **24**, 249 ; (1931) *Ibid.*, **25**, 69.
THOMPSON, R., HAZEN, E. L., and BUCHBINDER, L. (1932) *J. Immunol.*, **22**, 189.
TODD, C. (1928a) *Brit. J. exp. Path.*, **9**, 19 ; (1928b) *Ibid.*, **9**, 101 ; (1928c) *Ibid.*, **9**, 244.
TODD, C. and WHITE, R. G. (1914) " Experiments on Cattle Plague." Cairo. (Govt. Press.)
TRAUTWEIN, K. (1927) *Arch. wiss. prakt. Tierheilk.*, **56**, 505.
VALLÉE, H. and CARRÉ, H. (1922a) *C. R. Acad. Sci.*, **174**, 207 ; (1922b) *Ibid.*, **174**, 1498.
WALDMANN, O. and TRAUTWEIN, K. (1926) *Berl. tierärztl. Wschr.*, **42**, 569.
WALDMANN, O., TRAUTWEIN, K., and PYL, G. (1931) *Zbl. Bakt.*, **121**, 19.
WEYER, E. R., PARK, W. H., and BANZHAF, E. J. (1929) *Amer. J. Path.*, **5**, 517.
WICKMAN, I. (1907) " Beiträge zur Kenntnis der Heine-Medinschen Krankheit." Berlin.

CHAPTER LIII

HERD INFECTION AND HERD IMMUNITY

In the preceding chapters we have taken as our host unit the individual man or animal. It is clearly possible to work with a different unit—the herd. If we wish to study the epidemic spread of infection, and the factors that favour or prevent it, then it is with this larger unit that we must deal.

The herd, like each of its members, has a characteristic structure; and this structure, from our present point of view, includes not only the hosts belonging to the herd species, and their spatial relationships to one another, but the presence and distribution of alternative animal hosts and possible insect vectors of infection, as well as all those environmental factors that favour or inhibit the spread of infection from host to host. This herd structure, apart altogether from the susceptibility or resistance of the individual hosts, may play a decisive part in the immunity of the herd as such. A herd may be immune to a particular disease—in the logical sense that it will resist the introduction of infection from without—although each of its members is fully susceptible, and would fall an easy victim if he strayed to a herd with a structure that allowed an endemic prevalence of the disease in question. In this sense the English herd is immune to plague; because the association of man, the rat and the flea is not now of a kind to allow spread along natural routes. It is probably immune to cholera, as the result of an adequate system of water purification. It is not—nor does it seem likely to become—immune to any of those diseases that are spread by droplet infection. It would take us altogether beyond our present scope to consider the known or problematical effects on herd resistance of such changes in environmental conditions; but we may at least note that many of the most striking successes of preventive medicine have been attained by altering herd structure without inducing any increased resistance in its individual members. By attacking insect vectors of infection, such as the mosquito, by preventing the frequent passage of bacteria from one person's intestine to another person's mouth by way of water and food, and by a general improvement in environmental conditions, we have succeeded in eliminating, or reducing to negligible proportions, diseases that formerly took a heavy toll of lives, and still take that toll in areas where such measures are not applied.

The type of herd immunity with which we are here concerned is that in which this freedom from the spread of infection has not yet been attained, so that contact with the bacterial parasite is at least an occasional event in the normal experience of the host species. Under such conditions the course of events in any infected herd will be determined mainly by the distribution of the parasite and the distribution of those kinds of specific immunity that we have considered in earlier chapters. Intelligent interference with the course of events is impossible without a clear idea as to what is actually happening.

We may recognize, in theory, at least six categories of hosts among any infected herd. Four of these categories include individuals who are themselves infected, (1) the typical case, (2) the atypical case, (3) the latent infection, and (4) the healthy carrier ; while two categories are not themselves infected, or infective, (5) the uninfected immune and (6) the uninfected susceptible. The division between (2), (3) and (4) is formal rather than actual—these conditions shade into each other by imperceptible degrees. It is doubtful whether the division between (3) and (4) is justifiable even for convenience of description, since many, perhaps most, of the class commonly described as healthy carriers are in reality suffering from a symptomless, and often negligible, infection. It may be noted that the individuals falling in categories (3) and (4) are in general, though in a very varying degree, resistant to further infection from without ; so that the only fully susceptible hosts at risk are those in class 6.

Fig. 244 may help the student to visualize the kind of distribution, both of infection and of immunity, that may be met with in infected herds under different epidemic conditions. No distinction has been made in the diagram between latent infections and healthy carriers. A few arrows have been introduced to indicate the direction of effective spread—effective in the sense of producing new cases of disease or in converting susceptibles to immunes. As we shall see, an epidemic of an infective disease is usually accompanied by an epidemic of symptomless immunization.

In this figure, A may be taken as an example of an epidemic phase in an endemic-epidemic prevalence, that is, as representing the state of affairs during an outbreak of an infective disease from which the affected herd is never completely free, epidemics of varying severity recurring at more or less frequent intervals. B may be regarded as a later stage of A, or as a small epidemic wave occurring in a herd in which susceptibles are few, while carriers are frequent. C may be taken as representing the state of affairs during a severe epidemic occurring in a herd with little initial immunity. An extreme example of this catastrophic type of prevalence has occasionally been afforded by the introduction of such a disease as measles into an isolated island community that has either never experienced the infection before, or has been free from it for many years. D may be regarded as representing a stage of relative quiescence between two outbreaks of the type depicted in A. It will be noted that the proportion of susceptibles is higher than in A or B, and with such a distribution as this a fresh outbreak of the A type is likely to occur.

As an illustration of the types of distribution depicted in A, B and D, no better example could be selected than that of diphtheria. We are here dealing with a disease that is essentially a toxæmia ; and, as we have seen, an effective antitoxic immunity will in this case protect the host against clinically detectable infection. In the Schick test we have a method which allows us to divide the members of any herd into susceptibles and immunes. Except in the case of very young children a negative reaction may be taken as an indication that an individual has something over 0·01 A.U. of antitoxin per c.c. of circulating blood, and also that he will produce further antitoxin briskly and effectively in response to any entry of toxin into his tissues. We may, if we wish, obtain a more exact picture of the distribution of antitoxin, by collecting samples of blood and titrating them by a modified Römer technique (see Jensen 1933). By swabbing throats and noses, and testing the virulence of any morphologically typical diphtheria bacilli cultivated, we can determine with some approach to accuracy the distribution of the parasite among the hosts at risk ; and we are thus in a position to give a description of the course

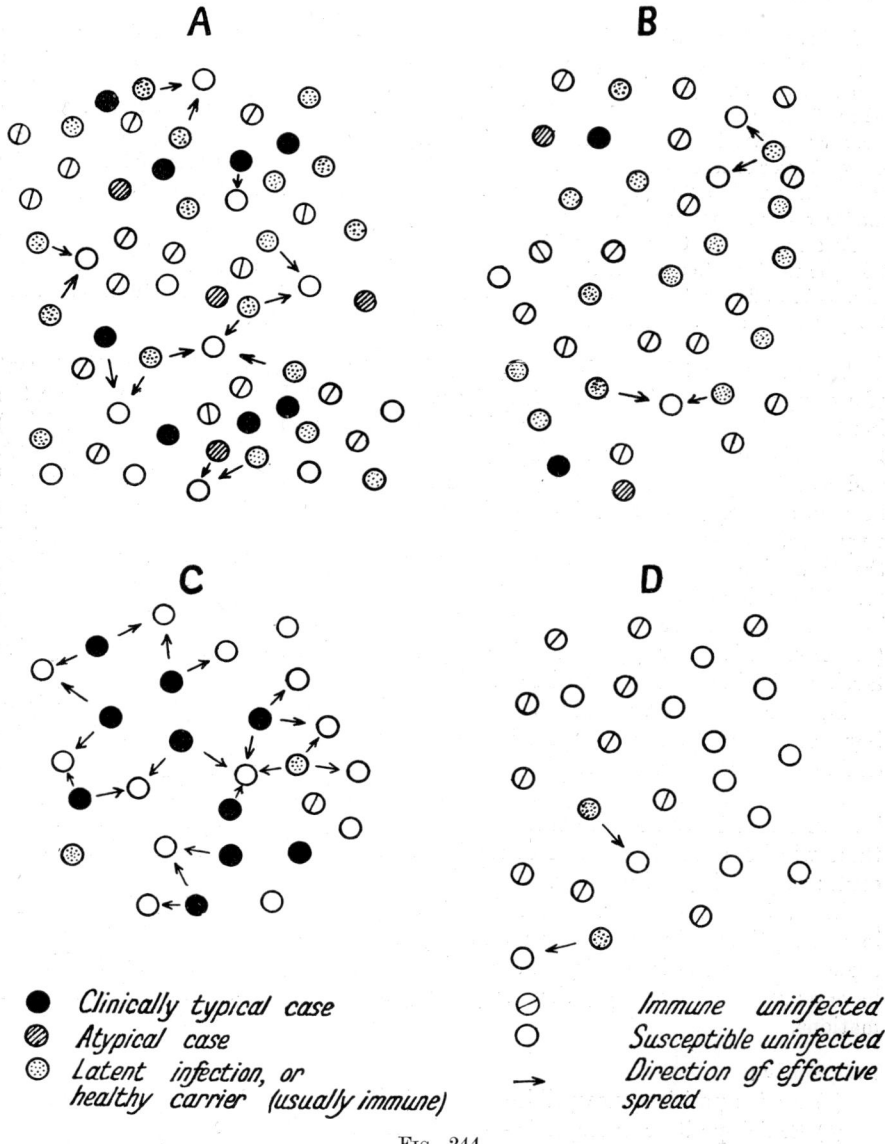

● Clinically typical case	⊖	Immune uninfected
⊘ Atypical case	○	Susceptible uninfected
⊛ Latent infection, or healthy carrier (usually immune)	→	Direction of effective spread

Fig. 244.

of events in any particular community that is vastly more informative than we can at the moment supply for most other diseases.

It has of course long been recognized that the diphtheria bacillus is not confined to those who are suffering from the clinical disease in its typical form. It is frequently isolated from cases of mild sore throat associated with an epidemic of typical diphtheria, less frequently from healthy contacts, and still less frequently from non-contacts.

Kober (1899) records the isolation of diphtheria bacilli from 70 per cent. of 139 contacts who were themselves suffering from mild sore throat, and from 8 per cent. of 123 contacts who had apparently normal throats. Closeness and continuity of contact, here as in other diseases, have a considerable influence on the carrier rate. The collected figures recorded in the Medical Research Council's monograph on diphtheria (see Monograph 1923) show a 15 per cent. carrier rate of virulent diphtheria bacilli among 610 contacts in barracks or hospital wards, a 7 per cent. carrier rate among 10,883 home contacts, and a 0·6 per cent. carrier rate among the general non-contact population.

As a measure of the risk to which an ordinary urban population is submitted we may take the carrier rate of virulent diphtheria bacilli among children attending the elementary schools in and about London. During the last 10 years or so it has fluctuated between 2·5 per cent. and 5 per cent. (see Dudley 1923, Forbes 1927).

The events that follow the passage of virulent diphtheria bacilli from the throat of a case, or of a carrier, to the throat of a non-infected person will depend on the immunological condition of the recipient. If he is susceptible (Schick-positive) he will either respond by developing antitoxin and so becoming more resistant, and eventually Schick-negative, or else he will develop clinical diphtheria and become a case. Hence Schick-positive carriers of virulent diphtheria bacilli are very rare. They are not non-existent—they cannot be if we accept the view that the transition from the susceptible to the immune class is usually the result of latent infection—but we may take it that a person who is carrying virulent bacilli in sufficient number to be detectable by an ordinary swabbing is (a) immune (Schick-negative), or (b) undergoing rapid immunization to the Schick-negative level, or (c) incubating the disease.

If, then, we take the case of a relatively isolated community, such as a large boys' school, and trace the spread of infection and the development of immunity during an epidemic of diphtheria, we shall observe the following sequence of events.

At the start we may suppose that we have 50 to 70 per cent. Schick-negative immunes and 30 to 50 per cent. Schick-positive susceptibles. Among these boys there will be a certain number of carriers of virulent diphtheria bacilli, say 3 per cent. ; these will be immunes.

When these bacilli spread to uninfected boys they may obtain lodgment either in a susceptible or in an immune ; and, depending on the dose of bacilli transferred, the exact degree of immunity of the recipient and many other factors of which we have as yet no knowledge, they may bring about any of the following transformations.

Frequently :
    (a) Schick-positive susceptible—→ case (mild or severe).
    (b) Schick-positive susceptible—→ Schick-negative immune
                           (a) without detectable carrying,
                           (b) with detectable carrying.
    (c) Schick-negative immune—→ Schick-negative immune carrier.

Very rarely :
    (d) Schick-positive susceptible—→ Schick-positive carrier.
    (e) Schick-negative immune—→ mild " bacteriological " case.

As an illustrative example of the findings that have actually been recorded in work of this kind, we may cite the illuminating studies of Dudley (1923, 1926, 1932) on diphtheria prevalence during a series of years in the Royal Naval School at Greenwich, a school of some 1,000 boys.

Between January and May 1919—the period at which Dudley's record starts—there were 65 cases of diphtheria. From then onwards until May 1921 there were no cases. Between May and July of that year 20 cases were recorded, and in the September-to-December term the outbreak reached epidemic proportions, with 77 cases. Between January and April 1922, 831 of the boys were Schick-tested. The results obtained are summarized in Table LXXVI.

TABLE LXXVI

SHOWING RELATION BETWEEN SCHICK REACTION AND PREVIOUS EXPERIENCE AMONG BOYS TESTED JANUARY TO APRIL 1922.

Previous Residence in School.	Experienced 1919 Epidemic.	Experienced 1921 Epidemic.	Per cent. Immune (Schick-negative).
None (new boys) . . .	No	No	58
6 months–2 years . . .	No	Yes	85
Over 3 years	Yes	Yes	95

The relation between experience and immunity is obvious. Moreover, the fluctuations in the immunity rate as plotted by terms of entrance were discontinuous. For entrants during the four terms September 1917 to September 1918 inclusive the percentage giving negative reactions in 1922 were 100 per cent., 92 per cent., 100 per cent. and 98 per cent. respectively. For the entrants during the period May 1919 to May 1921 inclusive the rates by terms of entrance were 82 per cent., 90 per cent., 82 per cent., 85 per cent., 83 per cent., 82 per cent. and 86 per cent. as compared with the 58 per cent. in boys joining in January 1922. It would appear that there had been two waves of immunization in the school, coinciding with the waves of clinical infection.

A sample swabbing of the school during the latter part of the 1921 epidemic showed 28 carriers of diphtheria bacilli in addition to the 77 cases. During the period January to July 1922 the carrier rate for virulent diphtheria bacilli was 2·2 per cent., during September to December of the same year it rose to 4·5 per cent., and during this period cases of diphtheria were still occurring. But immunization of susceptibles was proceeding synchronously with the spread of clinically detectable infection. Of 88 boys who had given positive reactions on first testing 24 reacted negatively when retested 3 months later. Similar findings are recorded for later years, with carrier rates of virulent diphtheria bacilli varying from 1·0 to 4·5 per cent., and with recurrent cases of diphtheria that never attained the epidemic frequency of September to December 1921. Thus of 35 Schick-positive entrants in March 1924, 13 had become negative within 4 months ; and 2 years' residence in the school had increased the 58 per cent. immunity rate of the new boys entering in January 1922 to 84 per cent. It may be noted that this rapid immunization was confined to the boarders, forming the population of about 1,000 to which all the figures quoted above refer. There were at the school some 120 day boys, who did not share in the continuous exposure to risk of infection experienced by the boarders. Among these the rate of immunization was relatively slow. Over a 4-months' period only one of 24 Schick-positive day boys became Schick-negative.

The increasing ratio of carriers to cases as a herd becomes more and more immune is well illustrated by the case rates and carrier rates in one group of some 160 boys during the winter term of 1921 and the winter term of 1922.

	Case Rate.	Carrier Rate.
1921	7 per cent.	2 per cent.
1922	0·6 ,, ,,	6 ,, ,,

In 1921 during a severe epidemic, following on a period in which the school had been free from diphtheria for 2 years, the spread of virulent bacilli produced 3·5 cases to one carrier ; in the winter of 1922 after this severe exposure, and in spite of the entrance of 43 new boys during the post-epidemic period, the spread of infection produced 10 carriers to one case.

In judging the significance of such figures we must remember that the real carrier : case rate over any considerable interval of time is always higher than that given by comparing the recorded case rate with the recorded carrier rate over that period—a point that has recently been stressed by Dudley (1932). All clinical cases of diphtheria will be recorded. A case rate of 3 per cent. per annum in a particular community means that 3 persons in every hundred of those exposed to risk develop diphtheria during the year in question. But a carrier rate of 7 per cent. does not mean that 7 per cent. become carriers during the year ; it means that at any one swabbing of an adequate sample 7 persons in each hundred are, on the average, found to be harbouring diphtheria bacilli. The total number of persons that become carriers during the period in which the seven cases of diphtheria occur will be much higher. Thus, over one yearly period, Dudley records an average carrier rate of 6·6 per cent. with small fluctuations above or below this level ; but repeated swabbing (7–8 times) of a large sample of boys showed that at least 40 per cent. were harbouring the diphtheria bacillus at one time or another during this period.

The general significance of the picture presented by such studies as these is clear enough ; but we must remember that the two categories—immunes and susceptibles—that are divided from one another by simple Schick testing present a very incomplete picture of the graduations in resistance that actually exist in a herd at risk. Glenny (1925) defines five grades of immunity, which are set out in Table LXXVII. These are, of course, not exhaustive ; nor are they sharply demarcated from one another.

TABLE LXXVII

SHOWING VARYING GRADES OF RESISTANCE TO DIPHTHERIA. (After Glenny.)

	Group.				
	1	2	3	4	5
Schick test . . .	—	+	+	+	+
Antitoxin in blood .	> 1/30 A.U.	< 1/30 A.U.	0	0	0
Earlier stimuli . .	Many	Many	Many	Few	None
Response to further stimuli	Rapid	Rapid	Rapid	Slow	Very slow
Description . . .	Immune	Immune	Potentially immune	Sub-immune	Fully susceptible

If we could elaborate our study of a population at risk by estimating at regular intervals the exact amount of antitoxin in each person's circulating blood ; and if, dealing with a very large population, we could withdraw an adequate sample of persons at frequent intervals and determine the response of each Schick-positive person to small injections of toxoid, we should be able to build up a far more detailed picture of what was really happening. Adopting Glenny's classification, we should be able to detect the transformation from the fully susceptible to the sub-immune, and thence through the Schick-positive immune to the fully developed Schick-negative immune, as well as transference from the Schick-positive to the Schick-negative class.

Our rare Schick-positive carriers would be found in the immune or potentially immune sub-groups, and would rapidly pass into the Schick-negative class. We should almost certainly find that severe cases tended to arise from the fully susceptible Schick-positives, mild " bacteriological " cases from the sub-immunes or potentially immunes.

A point of great importance is the reaction of the Schick-immunes to the reception of virulent diphtheria bacilli. We know that they very rarely contract clinical diphtheria, and then only in a mild form. We know that many of them become carriers. Is a point reached in natural immunization at which a person resists carrier infection as well as infection in the clinical sense ? Can we grade our Schick-immunes as we grade our Schick-susceptibles, putting at the lower end of the scale those who have just attained to the Schick level of immunity, and at the upper end of the scale those who are so resistant that virulent diphtheria bacilli are unable to gain lodgment in their throats ? If a human herd is rendered 100 per cent. Schick-negative, either by natural immunization or by prophylactic inoculation, will infection with the diphtheria bacillus be eliminated in the bacteriological sense, or will a freedom from clinical diphtheria be associated with a persistent carrier rate not much below that of the population at large, and perhaps with carrier epidemics ? Is complete immunity, of the kind that would render a herd entirely free from infection, likely to be attained by immunization of this kind, however far it is pushed ?

We cannot yet answer these questions. There is a suggestion in some of Dudley's recent studies (Dudley 1932) that Schick-immunes who have been exposed to risk for long periods carry virulent diphtheria bacilli less frequently than Schick-immunes with a shorter experience in the infected environment. But as yet we have no statistically decisive figures. In so far as we are dealing with a purely antitoxic immunity—and this is the case in our artificial Schick-immunes—we should not expect freedom from the carrier state unless, as seems unlikely, successful lodgment in the throat depends on a local toxic effect. In so far as our natural Schick-immunes possess an antibacterial as well as an antitoxic immunity we must remember that the diphtheria bacillus is separable into many antigenically different types, though all types produce the same toxin (Durand 1918, 1920, Havens 1920, Smith 1923, Eagleton and Baxter 1923), so that we should expect any antibacterial immunity to be type-specific. Moreover, it is very doubtful whether the mechanisms discussed in Chapter XLIV would have any appreciable effect in preventing a localized tonsillar infection.

Scarlet fever is another disease in which, by the aid of the Dick test and the examination of throat swabs for hæmolytic streptococci, we can obtain information of the same general kind as that now available in the case of diphtheria ; but we have not yet any records comparable in detail and duration with those afforded by Dudley's work at Greenwich. So far as our fragmentary records go they look like pieces of a very similar picture, with one essential difference. The production of the erythrogenic toxin forms a relatively small part of the pathogenic potentialities of hæmolytic streptococci ; and an antitoxic immunity that will suffice to prevent the occurrence of the clinical syndrome that we label scarlet fever will not suffice to prevent the spread of tonsillitis, or of other clinically obvious streptococcal infections (see Okell 1932). For effective immunity against all the clinical manifestations of infection with hæmolytic streptococci we need an antibacterial as well as an antitoxic immunity ; and this antibacterial immunity will almost certainly be type-specific.

Turning to diseases in which antitoxic immunity, in the strict sense in which we are using that term, plays no apparent part, we are not in a position to give any adequate description of the course of events in a naturally infected herd. This is because we have no such simple tests as the Schick and Dick reactions by which to separate our immunes from our susceptibles. There are good reasons for believing that by an adequate survey, including a careful study of the distribution of the infecting organism and tests for the presence of specific antibodies in the blood of the hosts at risk, we could add greatly to our knowledge of what is happening during an endemic or epidemic prevalence. But we have not got that knowledge yet.

Some things we do know. We know that in certain diseases, such as cerebrospinal meningitis, the ratio of carriers to cases is very high (see for instance Glover 1918), so that it seems probable that the immunes greatly outnumber the susceptibles. The same general relationship—a widespread carrier epidemic associated with relatively few clinical cases—seems to hold in certain virus diseases, such as poliomyelitis and encephalitis lethargica.

In other diseases, such as typhoid fever, the ratio of carriers to cases is not so high (see Chapter LXVI). But we know that atypical cases of typhoid fever occur during an epidemic, and that many carriers of typhoid bacilli give no history of ever having suffered from a typhoid-like disease. It is a fairly safe assumption that an endemic or epidemic prevalence of typhoid fever is associated with the occurrence of sub-clinical immunizing infections. We know quite certainly that such a prevalence leaves behind it infected healthy carriers who may be a potent source of further spread.

THE EXPERIMENTAL STUDY OF HERD INFECTION AND IMMUNITY

It is clearly possible, by selecting a convenient host species and a parasite that spreads naturally among them, to submit problems of the kind we have considered above to direct experimental study—initiating an epidemic of a particular disease among our test population, and studying the reactions of new entrants, of old members of the herd, or of migrants from one herd to another, by any available means (see Greenwood *et al.* 1936). We can, under such conditions, observe the effects of any intentional interference we choose, splitting a herd into smaller units, reaggregating these units after any selected interval, varying the rate of immigration of susceptibles, actively immunizing some or all of our animals by vaccines of different kinds administered by different routes, and so on as new problems suggest themselves for attack. In this way we gain enormously in an increased control over many of our unknown variables ; but we lose, in so far as we wish to argue from our experimental herds to happenings in the natural world outside our cages, by having to rely on analogies that are certainly incomplete, and may well be misleading. Because our control is still far from complete we must use large numbers of animals and make constant use of statistical methods in trying to assess the meaning of our results. We must, therefore, use a small, easily controlled and relatively inexpensive animal, and the mouse fulfils these requirements. Experiments of this kind have been carried out during the last decade, in England and in America, on mouse typhoid—caused by infection with *Bact. typhi-murium* or less frequently with *Bact. enteritidis*—, on mouse pasteurellosis, and on a virus disease known as ectromelia. The American workers have also studied the spread of infection among rabbits and fowls housed in laboratories, or maintained as breeding stock by dealers. It will be convenient to consider the data thus obtained in direct relation to the observations on human herds, noting carefully the points at which particular caution must be exercised in applying the argument from analogy and in generalizing from an isolated experience.

Is there, in the spread of infection among mice, the same distribution of typical cases, atypical cases, latent infections and carriers, and the same natural immunization associated with natural infection, that occurs among human herds ?

In the particular case of mouse typhoid—and almost certainly in other epidemic infections—it is quite certain that the great majority of the mice at risk are infected by the bacterial parasite at some period or other during a prolonged epidemic prevalence.

In a particular experiment (Topley, Ayrton and Lewis 1924) 5 mice were fed on a culture of *Bact. typhi-murium*. As soon as they were found to be excreting the bacillus in their fæces, 20 normal mice were added, and thereafter 1 normal mouse was added to the cage each day for 115 days. The fæces of every mouse were examined on 6 days a week during the course of the experiment ; each mouse that died was examined bacteriologically, and at the termination of the experiment all surviving mice (55 in number) were killed, cultures were taken from their spleens, and their blood was tested for agglutinins. The existence of non-fatal, and apparently mild or trivial, infections was clearly demonstrated. Some mice that excreted *Bact. typhi-murium* on several occasions remained in apparent health during the whole period of their residence in the cage. When these were killed at the end of the experiment some gave negative spleen cultures and showed no agglutinins in their blood, others gave negative spleen cultures but possessed agglutinins, others gave positive spleen cultures with or without agglutinins in the serum. Taking, as criteria of infection, death from the infective disease, excretion of the organism in the fæces, and the isolation of the organism, or the demonstration of agglutinins, in the surviving mice, it was found that of 128 mice which had resided in the cage for periods of 14 to 115 days, 122 had become infected. Of these infected mice 46 were surviving in apparent health on the day when the experiment terminated, but 25 of them (54·3 per cent.) were found to be harbouring *Bact. typhi-murium* in their spleens. The collected figures for eleven different epidemics of mouse typhoid, lasting from 60 to 117 days, show that of 267 surviving mice 190 (71·2 per cent.) were latently infected (Topley 1926).

Similarly (Greenwood *et al.* 1936), the results obtained in experiments with the virus disease, ectromelia, indicated that some 80 per cent. of the mice entering the herd were infected with the virus within three weeks of entry.

The way in which the bacterial parasites are distributed among the hosts at risk is then of the same general kind as obtains in natural epidemics in man, differing mainly in the fact that fewer hosts escape infection. Is there any evidence that the spread of infection results in immunization as well as, or in place of, the production of overt disease ? That survivors from an epidemic are, on the average, more resistant than new-comers to an infected herd is certain ; for they live longer —usually much longer—when exposed to a subsequent wave of mortality (Topley 1921, Amoss 1922).

This increase in resistance with increasing herd experience under epidemic conditions can be studied in greater detail by constructing life tables for the mice submitted to risk of infection during a long-continued prevalence of such a disease as mouse typhoid. It is convenient in calculating the expectation of life to limit it to 60 days, regarding any mouse living for longer periods as dying on the 60th day, since the use of the unlimited expectation of life gives undue weight to the relatively few mice that live for much longer periods, and also because we have a normal standard of comparison for the shorter period, but none for the latter.

Employing this value ($_{60}E_x$) we find in a particular experiment, in which 3 normal mice were added to an infected herd each day from March 6th, 1921, to June 30th, 1923, that the limited expectation of life drops slightly (from 22·49 to 21 days) during the first week of herd life and then rises, at first slowly, but more steeply after the 15th day, until by the 33rd day it reaches the figure of 34·75 days. It fluctuates round this figure up to the 100th day of herd residence; after which the numbers of survivors are too small to give a reliable average. In general then, we may say that a mouse that has survived about 30 days' exposure to risk will live more than half as long again as a new-comer to the cage (Greenwood and Topley 1925, Greenwood *et al.* 1936).

We can ask the same question in another way, using a direct experimental comparison instead of a life table. In a particular experiment (Greenwood, Newbold, Topley and Wilson 1926) in which mouse pasteurellosis was the infection selected for study, two parallel epidemics (A and B) were initiated on November 11th, 1924, and were maintained by the addition of normal mice until December 1925. At regular intervals groups of mice that had survived for 10, 20, 30, 40, 50 days or more in Herd A were transferred to Herd B, and with them were added a numerically equal group of normal mice that had had no previous experience of pasteurellosis. Averaging the results, the figures shown in Table LXXVIII were obtained:

TABLE LXXVIII

Length of Life in Herd A.	Expectation of Life in Herd B ($_{60}E_x$).
Nil (normal entrants to B)	22·37 ± 0·36 days
10 days	21·34 ± 1·10 ,,
20 ,, ...	25·50 ± 1·13 ,,
30 ,, ...	32·55 ± 1·28 ,,
40–45 days	33·08 ± 1·52 ,,
50–60 ,, ...	37·39 ± 1·69 ,,

Here, again, survival through a testing period of 30 days or more added some 50 per cent. to a mouse's expectation of life under severe epidemic conditions.

But clearly we cannot, in the absence of further evidence, assume from such results that the mice have been actively immunized. We are dealing with fatal diseases, and natural selection has certainly been at work. In the mouse typhoid experiment, of every 1,000 mice living on day 0 (their day of entry to the herd) only 256 survived for 30 days. Death had by then removed some 75 per cent. of those at risk; and, if no active immunization had occurred, the surviving 25 per cent. would have a higher average resistance than new-comers to the herd, assuming only that the natural resistance of mice differs *inter se*, and that this difference plays some significant part in determining survival during the first 30 days—an assumption that may be very safely made. Webster and his colleagues (see Webster 1923*a*, *c*, *d*, 1924*a*, *b*, 1926, Pritchett 1925, 1926) consider that this natural, inborn resistance is the dominant factor in determining death or survival during an epidemic. That it plays some part there can be no reasonable doubt, but there are reasons for doubting its dominance, and for believing that active immunization is exerting an effect similar in kind, if less in degree, to that exerted in the spread of diphtheria in man.

Thus (Greenwood *et al.* 1926, 1928, Newbold 1927), if the method of partial correlation is applied to the data for mouse typhoid and mouse pasteurellosis, and correlation coefficients are calculated for : (A) length of after-life and length of previous exposure, keeping constant the death rate during previous exposure and the death rate during after-life, and (B) length of after-life and death rate during previous exposure, keeping constant the length of previous exposure and the death rate during after-life, we get the figures set out in Table LXXIX.

TABLE LXXIX

Coefficient.	Nature of Epidemic.		
	Pasteurellosis. (1)	Pasteurellosis. (2)	Mouse Typhoid.
A	0·194 ± 0·016	0·150 ± 0·015	0·307 ± 0·014
B	0·029 ± 0·017	− 0·018 ± 0·016	− 0·282 ± 0·014

Coefficient A is positive and significant in all cases, indicating that the longer a mouse has survived within limits under constant conditions as regards death rate, the longer it will continue to survive under continued exposure to infection. Coefficient B is insignificant in the two pasteurellosis experiments, significant but negative in the mouse typhoid experiment, indicating that, with equal lengths of exposure to risk, the survivors from a period of high mortality have no significant advantage over the survivors from a period of lower mortality. This latter finding clearly suggests that the elimination by death of the more susceptible mice is not a very important factor in raising the average resistance of the survivors, while the advantage derived from prolonged exposure at a constant death rate is compatible with the view that active immunization is important. The exact significance of these results is, however, uncertain. It is probable that some at least of the mice emerging from a period of high mortality will already be suffering from an infection which will cause their death in a few days or weeks, apart altogether from any subsequent risks, while it may be that fewer of the mice emerging from a more prolonged exposure to a lower rate of herd mortality are in this particular position.

The probability that active immunization is an important factor is, perhaps, increased by the observation that, in the transfer experiment with pasteurellosis, mice that had lived in herd A only during periods of low death rates—less than one-third the average death rate for the whole epidemic period—still showed a marked advantage over normal mice on transference to herd B. The limited expectation of life of those normal immigrants that entered herd B on the same days as these particular groups of migrants from herd A was 20·9 ± 0·49 days, for those migrants that had spent 50 days in herd A it was 34·6 ± 4·10 days.

It may be noted also that such evidence as is available (Topley, Wilson and Lewis 1925, Greenwood and Topley 1925) indicates that the increased resistance gained by survival in an infected herd, or after experimental infection by feeding or inoculation, is specific in the ordinary bacteriological sense. A mouse that has survived infection with *Bact. typhi-murium* appears to be no more resistant than normal mice to infection with *Pasteurella muriseptica*. This, of course, accords well with epidemiological experience in general, but not with the view that the determining factor in increasing the average resistance of a herd at risk is the selection by the sieve of death of those individuals possessing an innate non-specific resistance. If differences in innate resistance are of major importance it would appear that they must either be specific or must be differences of immunizability rather than that of immunity.

Whether or not active immunization is the main factor that determines the increased average resistance of surviving mice, the grade of antibacterial immunity produced can excite little enthusiasm.

As stated above, the expectation of life limited to 60 days was selected in these and subsequent experiments in part because there is an available standard of reference for this period (Greenwood, Topley and Wilson 1931b). On October 4th, 1929, 20 normal mice were assembled in a cage of the same type as that used in all epidemic experiments. From then onwards until January 17th, 1930, daily additions of normal mice were made, and the herd was then observed until May 27th, 1930. The 329 mice of this experiment were living under exactly the same conditions as the infected herd, except that no infection was present at any time during the period of observation. Of these 329 mice 56 died. The limited expectation of life, as was to be expected, remained practically constant at all cage ages from day 0 to day 170—the last day for which figures were available. The lowest $_{60}E_x$ figure was 56·69 days, the highest 59·27 days. The figure rose slowly from just under 57 days on the day of entry to over 58 days on the 40th day of cage life—presumably as the animosities of first acquaintance were replaced by the toleration of later herd life and fighting grew less frequent. Thereafter it hardly varied.

Taking a figure of 58 as our normal $_{60}E_x$, we note that the best that natural immunization against mouse typhoid or mouse pasteurellosis can do—so long as surviving mice are exposed to a continuous risk of heavy infection—is to raise the expectation of life from a little under a half to a little over two-thirds of the normal figure. This is a very different picture from that presented by our study of diphtheria in man—even allowing for the fact that in the latter case we are dealing with a disease of relatively low fatality. Either mice differ in some fundamental way from men ; or the conditions in mouse cages differ fundamentally from those in schools and institutions—an obvious possibility ; or natural immunization against enteric infection or against pasteurellosis is less efficient than natural immunization against diphtheria or scarlet fever. Perhaps, though by no means certainly, this might be expanded to the conclusion that natural antitoxic immunization is much more effective than natural antibacterial immunization.

There is no known disease of mice that presents any close analogy with such toxæmic human infections as diphtheria and scarlet fever ; but the description by Marchal (1930) of a natural virus disease of mice—ectromelia—that gives rise to severe and fatal epidemics under experimental conditions has afforded an opportunity for the study of natural immunization against a virus infection. The results obtained present a striking contrast to mouse typhoid or mouse pasteurellosis (Greenwood et al. 1936).

Adopting the same plan of starting an epidemic in a herd of mice and thereafter adding 3 mice a day, two epidemics of this disease have been observed over a period of some 18 months. Applying the ordinary life-table method it was found in one of these epidemics —the results in the other were entirely analogous—that the limited expectation of life ($_{60}E_x$) on entry to the infected herd was 30·71 days. It fell until the 7th day when it was 25·39 days, this fall obviously depending on the average time taken to contract infection. From then onwards the $_{60}E_x$ value rose ; but instead of reaching a maximal value in some 30 days at a figure far below the normal expectation of life it continued to rise until, on the 100th day after entry, it had reached the figure of 54·69 days, and thereafter fluctuated slightly above and below this value over a period of some 15 months. In other words, instead of experience and survival in the infected herd resulting, at the best, in an expectation of life of some two-thirds of the normal span, those mice that lived through some

3 months or more of the epidemic prevalence had an expectation of life little inferior to the normal $_{60}E_x$ value of 58 days, though they continued to live in a herd in which the specific infection was causing a high and continuous death rate.

A more prolonged experience of the same epidemic prevalence has shown that waves of exceptionally high mortality occur during which many of the old survivors succumb ; but this fact does not abolish the significance of the marked difference in behaviour between a bacterial and a virus infection over epidemic periods that last through a large part of the lifetime of a normal mouse. It seems fairly clear that, even under conditions of severe and continuous exposure to infection, a mouse can develop a relatively effective immunity to ectromelia.

How far may the course of events in an infected herd be modified by the artificial immunization of some or all of the hosts at risk ?

We shall discuss in later chapters the evidence with regard to the efficacy of different kinds of prophylactic vaccination in human herds. So far as experimental epidemiology is concerned we can, at the moment, attempt an answer only in mouse typhoid and, with far scantier data, in ectromelia.

It is quite certain that active immunization with a killed culture of *Bact. typhimurium* will increase the resistance of mice to that organism ; and although some of the earlier observations (Loeffler 1906, Wolf 1908, Yoshida 1909, Brückner 1910, Webster 1922, Ornstein 1922, Neufeld 1924, Lange and Yoshioka 1924) suggest that the immunity obtained in this way is relatively poor and inconstant, repeated trials with considerable numbers of mice, and with carefully adjusted doses of vaccine and of living culture, indicate that a quite significant increase in resistance can regularly be obtained (Topley 1929, Topley, Wilson and Lewis 1925).

Thus, in one experiment, 50 mice were immunized by two intraperitoneal injections of 5×10^8 *Bact. typhi-murium* killed by formalin and heat. A week after the second injection these 50 immunized mice, together with 50 normal controls, were injected intraperitoneally with 1,000 living *Bact. typhi-murium*. The results are shown in Table LXXX.

TABLE LXXX

	No. Inoculated.	No. Dead in 28 Days.	Average Time to Death of Mice that Died.	No. Survivors with Positive Spleen Cultures.
Normal . . .	50	50	5·0 days	—
Vaccinated . . .	50	29	18·3 ,,	12

This vaccine had, therefore, produced the following effects : a proportion of the immunized mice showed a partial but ineffective immunity in that they lived on the average far longer than the controls but succumbed to the disease during the period of observation ; 24 per cent. showed a more effective resistance by living in apparent health throughout the period of observation, but post-mortem examination showed that they were suffering from a latent infection ; 18 per cent. appeared to have been rendered completely immune to this dose of bacteria, in that they remained in apparent health for 28 days and showed no evidence of infection when killed and examined by spleen culture. These results may be taken as representative of a considerable number of similar experiments.

We should not perhaps expect an immunity of this order to be very effective as a prophylactic measure in herds submitted to a continuous risk of infection, and actual trial confirms our lack of faith.

An epidemic of mouse typhoid was started on January 1st, 1928, and was continued until September 17th, 1929, by the addition of 3 normal mice a day (Greenwood, Topley and Wilson 1931a). Every 7th day 10 additional normal mice, and several groups, each of 10 mice, that had been immunized with different vaccines were added to the cage. The results, as they concern the relative efficacy of different antigenic components, have already been noted on p. 831. We are concerned here only with the results obtained with the most effective vaccines employed.

The limited expectation of life ($_{60}E_x$) of the normal mice on entry was $26·26 \pm 0·641$ days ; for the four immunized groups that had received vaccines containing the smooth surface antigen the $_{60}E_x$ figures were $32·10 \pm 0·432$, $34·97 \pm 0·845$, $35·06 \pm 0·845$ and $33·71 \pm 0·853$ days respectively. Thus by active immunization with a killed vaccine an increase in average resistance was obtained of the same order as that attained naturally by normal mice after living for some 30–50 days in an infected herd under the joint influence of active immunization and mortuary selection.

After 60 days' residence in the cage the $_{60}E_x$ figures for the vaccinated and unvaccinated groups have, as we should expect, largely levelled up, though the vaccinated mice still show a slight advantage. The figure for the unvaccinated group has risen to 36·47 days, those for the vaccinated groups to 40·17, 37·39, 36·90 and 47·54 days respectively.

Very similar results were obtained in another experiment in which a comparison was made between the effect of administering a killed *Bact. typhi-murium* vaccine by the mouth, or by intraperitoneal inoculation (Greenwood, Topley and Wilson 1931c). A larger dose was used for *per os* than for intraperitoneal immunization ($5,000 \times 10^6$ as against 500×10^6 bacilli). In each case two doses of vaccine were given with a week's interval between them, and the mice were added to the infected herd 1 week after the second dose of vaccine. The experiment lasted from December 12th, 1929, to June 26th, 1930. The death rate in this epidemic was rather lower than in those referred to above, and the expectation of life of the normal mice on entry was therefore somewhat longer. The $_{60}E_x$ figures on the day of entry were as follows : normal mice $31·18 \pm 1·04$ days, mice vaccinated *per os* $35·30 \pm 1·22$ days, mice vaccinated intraperitoneally $38·19 \pm 1·17$ days.

The immunity to ectromelia induced by vaccinating mice with a formolized virus is far more effective than the immunity to mouse typhoid induced by vaccination with a killed suspension of *Bact. typhi-murium*. Thus, in one series of tests (Greenwood *et al.* 1936), 173 of 180 vaccinated mice survived a dose of ectromelia virus that killed all of 60 controls.

The expectations raised by these results were fulfilled, up to a point, in the single experiment in which the effect of active immunization against the virus disease has been tested under epidemic conditions (Greenwood *et al.* 1936).

For this experiment, a herd was selected in which ectromelia was actively spreading, and causing a high mortality. On 21.10.32, and on every seventh day thereafter for a period of 70 days, 30 immunized and 30 non-immunized mice were added to the herd. From 21.10.32 to 27.3.33 three additional normal mice were added daily. The experiment was terminated on 16.3.34. Taking the 300 immunized mice, the 300 normal controls added with them and the 210 normal mice added daily over the same period, the $_{60}E_x$ values for the day of entry to the herd were : immunized mice 49·1 days, normal controls added with immunized 20·8 days, normals added daily 21·4 days. This shows a very great advantage to the immunized mice, and it was maintained throughout later cage-ages until the combined effects of natural immunization and selection, which are so effective in this disease, had raised the $_{60}E_x$ of the surviving normal entrants to the same high level.

In the final stages of this epidemic there were many deaths among the artificially immunized mice, and among the naturally immunized survivors. Whether these deaths were in all cases due to ectromelia it is very difficult to say. It will, in any case, be wise to withhold any final opinion as to the efficacy of immunization in affording permanent protection against ectromelia under these very severe conditions of exposure until further data are available.

The evidence so far recorded may conveniently be summarized in tabular form (Table LXXXI). The $_{60}E_x$ figures for the surviving mice have been recorded after that period of exposure (30–100 days) when the full advantage appears to have been attained, and the limited expectation of life has reached relative stability. For the uninfected standard herd the figure of 58 days has been taken both for new entrants and for survivors at all periods. The two sets of figures for the vaccinated mice in the second mouse typhoid experiment refer to the least and most effective of the four antigenically similar vaccines employed.

TABLE LXXXI

SHOWING LIMITED EXPECTATION OF LIFE ($_{60}E_x$), IN DAYS, FOR VARIOUS GROUPS OF MICE SUBMITTED TO EPIDEMIC INFECTION.

Infection.	Normal.		Vaccinated.			
			I.P.		P.O.	
	N.E.	S.	N.E.	S.	N.E.	S.
None	58·00	58·00	—	—	—	—
Mouse Typhoid (a) . .	22·49	34·75	—	—	—	—
Mouse Typhoid (b) . .	26·26	36·47	32·10 35·06	40·17 36·90	—	—
Mouse Typhoid (c) . . .	31·18	42·40	38·19	49·52	35·30	44·87
Pasteurellosis	22·37	37·39	—	—	—	—
Ectromelia (a)	30·71	54·69	—	—	—	—
Ectromelia (b)	20·8	52·8	49·1	51·6	—	—

I.P. = Intraperitoneal. P.O. = *Per os.*
N.E. = New Entrants. S. = Survivors after 30–100 days.

The significance of the figures is obvious. With such bacterial infections as mouse typhoid and pasteurellosis residence and survival in an infected herd increases resistance, as measured by expectation of life, but never raises it to the normal level. However long a mouse has lived in such a herd it is never indifferent to the risk that it continues to run. There is no solid immunity.

In the particular case of mouse typhoid, active immunization, by the intra-peritoneal injection of two massive doses of a vaccine with an optimal antigenic character, will induce an increase in resistance of the same order as that attained after long residence in the herd.   This increased resistance on entry is augmented by life in the infected herd ; but vaccination followed by exposure to risk never raises the resistance to the normal level.   Here, again, solid immunity is not attained.   The effect of *per os* immunization is similar in kind to that of intra-peritoneal immunization, though the resistance induced is slightly inferior.

In the case of the virus disease, ectromelia, the natural immunizing response is far more effective.   The immunity attained is not complete—old survivors some-times die of typical ectromelia, even though they have passed through a charac-teristic attack many months earlier—but it is of a high order.   In conformity with this, vaccination with a formolized virus greatly increases the expectation of life of the mice exposed to risk.

It is clearly of interest to determine the effect of immunizing all entrants to an infected herd.   Will this procedure result in the elimination of the disease, at least in its overt form ?   In the particular case of mouse typhoid, it will not.

In an experiment designed to test this point (Greenwood, Topley and Wilson 1931c) 3 normal mice were added daily to an infected herd from March 15th, 1929, to May 12th, 1929.   The limited expectation of life on entry of these mice was $27 \cdot 00 \pm 1 \cdot 019$ days. From May 13th, 1929, to October 20th, 1929, 3 immunized mice were added daily instead of the 3 normal mice, and from October 21st, 1929, to June 29th, 1930, 1 immunized mouse was added daily to see whether slowing the rate of immigration would have any significant effect on the epidemic prevalence.   The $_{60}E_x$ figure for the immunized mice added during the three-a-day period was $34 \cdot 92 \pm 0 \cdot 684$ days, for those added during the one-a-day period it was $36 \cdot 38 \pm 0 \cdot 938$ days—results very similar to those recorded above.   But mouse typhoid was spreading and killing as actively in June 1930 as it was in March 1929.   The mice at risk lived a little longer, but that was all.

It would, of course, be quite wrong to conclude—even if we may justifiably argue from mice to men—that active immunization of such a kind is useless.   As has been noted above, it is capable of completely protecting a proportion of mice against a single experimental infection with a dose of living bacilli that is fatal to unvaccinated controls.   Under conditions in which exposure to risk is slight, transient or intermittent, a resistance of this order may make all the difference between escape and infection, or between life and death.   The lesson, so far as it is applicable, would appear to be that such resistance does not allow its possessor to ignore the risk of infection.   We could not, by universal immunization of such a kind, stamp out a disease irrespective of the sanitary environment.

The Rôle of Bacterial Variation in Herd Infection and Immunity.

This problem, which may well be of major significance for the student of in-fective disease, is at the moment in a rather curious position.   Judging from much of the current epidemiological literature one would assume that the primary question —Do changes in bacterial characters play an important part in epidemic happen-ings ?—had been answered clearly and decisively on a basis of incontrovertible evidence.   There is free reference to " epidemic " strains of particular bacteria, to loss and gain of virulence and infectivity during an epidemic prevalence, to secular changes in the pathogenic powers of a particular parasite.   But nearly all such writing is really only the writer's way of saying that the disease in question was more prevalent, or more fatal, or spread more rapidly at one time than at another.   The difficulty, which has seldom been faced, is that a description of epidemic events is, of necessity, a description of a fluctuating equilibrium between parasite and host. For an increase in bacterial virulence we can substitute a decrease in host resistance, or *vice versa* ; the effect, *on balance,* is the same. If our descriptions are to be used as evidence in solving this particular problem the rise in virulence, or the fall in resistance, must be proved, not assumed ; and the proof is no easy matter.

That changes in host resistance are quite certainly of primary importance will be obvious from our consideration of the natural history of diphtheria or scarlet fever in man, and of the happenings in herds of mice. Is there any evidence that changes in the infectivity or virulence of the bacterial parasite play an equally significant part ?

Of indirect and suggestive evidence there is plenty. We know that bacteria frequently undergo variation in the laboratory ; and we know that avirulent or atoxigenic variants may be isolated from man or animals (see for instance Reimann 1927, Wadsworth and Sickles 1927, Okell 1929). We know also that antibodies acting on the surface antigens of the smooth virulent forms of bacteria are in many cases capable of inducing the S $\rightarrow$ R variation (see for instance Griffith 1923). We know that many epidemic diseases have displayed wide secular fluctuations in their fatality. Taking our biological and epidemiological knowledge as a whole, the conclusion that bacterial variation plays an important part in epidemic happenings seems so probable that an experimental answer in the opposite sense would certainly be suspect—suspect to the extent that we should want to be very sure that our experiments had been properly planned, and that our conclusions had not been arrived at by an unjustifiable inductive generalization from a few particular instances. Experiment, combined with carefully controlled bacteriological and immunological observations in naturally occurring epidemics, must, of course, be our final court of appeal ; but neither from this source nor from any other should we accept hasty judgments.

The experimental data at present available may be summarized as follows.

Webster and his colleagues (Webster 1923*a, b, c, d,* 1924*a, b, c, d,* 1925, 1926, 1927, 1928, 1930*a, b, c,* Webster and Burn 1926, 1927*a, b*) have shown quite clearly that different strains of the same bacterium, isolated at different periods of the same epidemic prevalence, may possess an approximately equal virulence as judged by direct inoculation tests, including inoculation into the stomach through an œsophageal tube. This, indeed, was their constant finding with the strains they examined. They conclude that changes in bacterial virulence play no part in the fluctuations in mortality that may be observed at different stages of a long-continued epidemic prevalence. These they would regard as due to changes in the average host resistance, and particularly to innate differences among the hosts at risk, or to seasonal or dietetic factors, that affect resistance in some non-specific way. They have, however, recorded differences in virulence among strains of the same bacterial species isolated from different epidemic prevalences of the same infective disease (Webster 1930*d,* Hughes 1930, Hughes and Pritchett 1930, Pritchett, Beaudette and Hughes 1930*a, b*), and they would regard these differences in virulence as determining certain observed differences in behaviour between one epidemic and another —for instance, differences in the proportion of carrier infections to fatal cases of the disease. Recently Webster and Clow (1933) have recorded an interesting series of observations on the variations in the virulence of pneumococci for mice. They found that a strain of high virulence, as judged by intraperitoneal injection, might be of low virulence as judged by injection into the nasal cavity ; and that a strain of high initial intranasal and intraperitoneal virulence might, as the result of passage from nose to nose, lose all, or almost all, its intranasal virulence, without affecting its intraperitoneal virulence. These findings did not, however, lead them to modify their earlier conclusions.

We have so far considered variations in *virulence* ; but virulence may not be the only factor concerned. If we assume the possible existence of another factor, labelling it *infectivity* and defining it as the *capacity to spread from one host to another under any specified conditions of exposure to risk of infection*, we may inquire whether infectivity is so highly correlated with virulence that we may regard them as synonymous terms.

The evidence available (Topley, Greenwood, Wilson and Newbold 1928) suggests, as would be expected, that those strains of *Bact. typhi-murium* that are capable of spreading rapidly among a herd of mice, giving rise to severe epidemics of mouse typhoid with a high mortality rate, are always of relatively high virulence as judged by direct intra-peritoneal inoculation, and that strains of low virulence are incapable of giving rise to severe epidemics, or of spreading widely among the herd at risk, although they may persist for long periods in the tissues of the originally infected hosts, and may give rise to a few latent infections, or even to an occasional death, among the normal mice exposed to risk.

The correlation between virulence and the power to induce severe epidemics by contact infection does not however hold with all strains of *Bact. typhi-murium*. A particular strain of this organism, isolated originally from an infected mouse, was found to possess an unusual combination of characters (Topley, Greenwood and Wilson 1931). It was of moderately high virulence, killing in repeated tests some 65–75 per cent. of mice inoculated with 100–1,000 bacilli, but it possessed little power of producing severe epidemics by contact infection. In six closed epidemics, in each of which 100 normal mice were exposed to infection from 25 infected companions, the average limited survival time of the exposed mice ($_{60}E_x$) was 51·27 days—not far short of the normal limit. The proportion of the survivors harbouring *Bact. typhi-murium* in their spleens at the end of the period of observation was however high—an average of 31 per cent. for the six epidemics. Data were available for two other groups of epidemics, initiated with two strains of *Bact. typhi-murium* of low virulence as tested by direct inoculation. In one group the average $_{60}E_x$ was 52·62 days, in the other 52·21 days—figures almost identical with those obtained with the more virulent strain—but the percentage of infected survivors was 9·7 in one group and 9·0 in the other, less than one-third of the figure recorded for the relatively virulent strain. This strain had therefore the following combination of characters : a relatively high virulence when injected into the tissues, a considerable power of contact spread with the production of latent infections, but a relatively slight power of producing fatal contact infections.

It was of obvious interest to test the resistance to contact infection, with a highly virulent and infective strain, of survivors from these six epidemics of latent infection, and to compare it with the resistance of survivors from more fatal epidemics and with that of artificially immunized mice. An experiment carried out along these lines gave the results shown in Table LXXXII.

TABLE LXXXII

	Average $_{60}E_x$.	Per cent. Surviving on 60th Day.
Normal mice	37·49 ± 2·613	36·7
Vaccinated mice	41·95 ± 1·529	53·0
Survivors of severe epidemics	48·31 ± 1·836	66·0
Survivors of mild epidemics	48·75 ± 1·861	69·0

Thus the survivors from these mild epidemics were much more resistant than normal mice, significantly more resistant than vaccinated mice, and just as resistant as the survivors from epidemics of greater severity, involving a more stringent mortuary selection. The strain that gave rise to these mild epidemics might, perhaps, be regarded as one in which the natural immunizing activity was greater than the natural killing power. Clearly, *if* a strain of this character made its appearance during an epidemic prevalence it *might* exert a significant influence on the course of events. But we cannot disregard the *if*.

In recent experiments on epidemic pasteurellosis (Greenwood *et al.* 1936) results have been obtained that seem to afford a satisfactory proof that changes in infectivity do occur during the epidemic spread of a bacterial parasite. Certain strains of *Pasteurella* that originally possessed little power of contact infection, though they were of moderately high virulence as judged by direct inoculation into mice, have, during their slow and limited spread in an experimental herd, given rise to variants in which the capacity for rapid and fatal spread was well developed. These experiments, like that recorded above, do not indicate a complete correlation between virulence and infectivity. If we adopt a term that is very commonly, though a little loosely, employed in current literature, and speak of an *epidemic strain* of a particular bacterial species, defining it as a *strain that has the capacity to spread naturally among a herd at risk giving rise to a severe and fatal epidemic*, we might hazard the guess that an epidemic strain is characterized by two attributes, high virulence and high infectivity, and that it may lose its epidemic character by losing either attribute. On what infectivity, as apart from virulence, depends we have as yet no knowledge. It does not depend primarily on an ability to multiply *in the tissues* ; for a strain may be highly virulent but not highly infective. It must presumably depend on adaptations that enable it to meet those environmental changes that are associated with transfer from host to host, and to establish in the recipient host a primary focus of infection from which subsequent tissue invasion can occur. But to say this is merely to define our problem a little more closely.

In summary ; variations in virulence in a bacterial parasite during an epidemic prevalence have often been sought for with negative results. There is, however, experimental evidence that different strains of the same bacterial parasite, possessing different degrees of virulence or of infectivity, produce very different results when they are allowed to spread by natural infection among a susceptible herd. There is also evidence that a bacterial parasite may vary in infectivity during an experimental epidemic. Taking the experimental evidence as a whole, it would seem to accord quite well with the view, expressed by many epidemiologists, that variations in the characters of the parasite are of major importance in the spread of human infections, and that an outbreak of disease may be initiated by the evolution, or importation, of an " epidemic strain " of the causative organism.

The Rôle of other Factors in Herd Infection and Herd Immunity.

All those factors that affect the resistance of the individual will affect the average resistance of the herd of which he is a member. Those factors that have been adequately studied have been considered more or less briefly in earlier chapters.

There are, as we have said, special factors, such as the spatial distribution of the hosts at risk, the duration of the intermittency of contact, and other conditions of arrangement or environment, that affect herds but not individuals. Some of these have been studied, in a tentative and preliminary fashion, by direct experiment (see Greenwood *et al.* 1936). Many have been studied in far greater detail but with less control under field conditions. Some day we may be able to work these factors into our immunological picture in terms of the effects produced by changes in the rate at which infection is received, or in the rate at which immunization proceeds (see for instance Dudley 1923) ; but that day has not come yet.

The Control of Herd Infection.　The study of herd infection and herd immunity by the methods described above is as yet in its infancy but it has already modified many of our conceptions with regard to the administrative control of epidemic disease.　Isolation and quarantine, for instance, have, in the past, played a major part in public health administration.　A very cursory consideration of the various types of distribution of a bacterial parasite within an infected herd that have been described earlier in this chapter, and of the results obtained in experimental epidemics, will raise serious doubts as to the probable efficacy of such measures. In the case of quarantine, it is clear that it can succeed only where it is complete ; and the history of sanitary control suggests that successful quarantine is possible only under very exceptional conditions, and over relatively short periods of time. The carrier and the atypical case defeat a sanitary barrier, just as they defeat isolation ; and, under the conditions of modern transit, there seems little possibility of preventing the introduction into any one part of the inhabited world of any infective parasite which is prevalent in another.　Once the barrier is passed, the subsequent course of events will depend upon the conditions obtaining within the community into which infection has been introduced.

The policy of the isolation of sick persons within a community is based on a similar failure to realize that the clinical picture provides a very incomplete description of the true state of affairs.　If isolation removed from the community the whole, or even the great majority, of the infected individuals, it might be expected to exert a considerable influence on the prevalence of an infective disease.　But if the ratio of latent or atypical infections to clinically recognizable cases is high, we cannot hope to effect any marked reduction in the morbidity rate by removing to hospital those cases which exhibit the typical stigmata of the disease.　We may indeed effect a smaller reduction in the total infective material than the ratio of isolated to non-isolated, among infected individuals, would suggest ; for the sick person would, in any case, move less freely among his fellows than the apparently healthy carrier.　As in the case of quarantine, we should expect a policy of isolation to be successful only in exceptional circumstances, when the recognizable cases form a very high proportion of the total infected, and when the total mass of infection to be dealt with is small.　Once a given infective disease has assumed an endemic-epidemic prevalence within a herd, we should expect no appreciable result from the isolation hospital, so far as a reduction in morbidity is concerned.　It is interesting to find that the expectations based on bacteriological and experimental findings are borne out by administrative experience.　Thus, an attempt has been made, by an analysis of the available records, to answer the question : Does hospital isolation have any effect upon the incidence of scarlet fever ?　All applications of the calculus of correlations have wholly failed to bring out any connection whatever between the incidence rate of scarlet fever and the extent of isolation (see Greenwood and Topley 1925).　The value of the isolation hospital must apparently be judged by the benefit which it confers on the sick within its walls ; for it would seem to have little effect on the health of the community as a whole.

Turning to those administrative measures which bring about a general reduction in the opportunities for the transference of infection from host to host, theoretical considerations suggest that action along these lines is likely to be effective.　Any improvement in sanitation, which ensures a clean water, or milk, or food supply, which reduces the frequency of insect vectors of infection, or which lessens the opportunities for close contact between individuals, may be expected to lead to a reduction in the incidence of those infections, with the transference of which that particular measure of sanitation interferes. This expectation has been fulfilled whenever an effective method of reducing the general opportunities for the transference of a particular infection has been adopted.

It may be noted that it is in the case of infections of the respiratory tract that it is particularly difficult, under modern conditions of civilization, to devise any effective means of preventing transit of the parasite from host to host, and that it is exactly these diseases which have so far defied the attacks of preventive medicine.

Finally, the whole trend of our present knowledge stresses the importance of the susceptible host. Any measure which increases the average resistance of a herd, whether it depends on specific immunization, or on some factor which confers an increased immunity less specific in its range, will exert a direct influence on the incidence of the corresponding infections. The accurate determination of the conditions which must be fulfilled, in order that induced variations in immunity should exert their optimal effect, and the development of methods by which such immunity can be induced, are two of the most important problems which await solution.

REFERENCES

Amoss, H. L. (1922) *J. exp. Med.*, **36**, 45.
Brückner, G. (1910) *Dtsch. med. Wschr.*, **36**, 2047.
Dudley, S. F. (1923) *Spec. Rep. Ser. med. Res. Coun., Lond.*, No. 75 ; (1926) *Ibid.*, No. 111 ; (1932) *J. Hyg., Camb.*, **32**, 193.
Durand, P. (1918) *C. R. Soc. Biol.*, **81**, 1011 ; (1920) *Ibid.*, **83**, 613.
Eagleton, A. J. and Baxter, E. M. (1923) *J. Hyg., Camb.*, **22**, 107.
Forbes, G. (1927) *Spec. Rep. Ser. med. Res. Coun., Lond.*, No. 115.
Glenny, A. T. (1925) *J. Hyg., Camb.*, **24**, 301.
Glover, J. A. (1918) *J. Hyg., Camb.*, **17**, 350.
Greenwood, M., Hill, A. B., Topley, W. W. C., and Wilson, J. (1936) *Spec. Rep. Ser. med. Res. Coun., Lond.*, No. 209.
Greenwood, M., Newbold, E. M., Topley, W. W. C., and Wilson, J. (1926) *J. Hyg., Camb.*, **25**, 336 ; (1928) *Ibid.*, **28**, 127.
Greenwood, M. and Topley, W. W. C. (1925) *J. Hyg., Camb.*, **24**, 45.
Greenwood, M., Topley, W. W. C., and Wilson, J. (1931a) *J. Hyg. Camb.* **31**, 257; (1931b) *Ibid.*, **31**, 403 ; (1931c) *Ibid.*, **31**, 484.
Griffith, F. (1923) *Rep. publ. Hlth med. Subj., Lond.*, No. 18, p. 1.
Havens, L. C. (1920) *J. infect. Dis.*, **26**, 388.
Hughes, T. P. (1930) *J. exp. Med.*, **51**, 225.
Hughes, T. P. and Pritchett, I. W. (1930) *J. exp. Med.*, **51**, 239.
Jensen, C. (1933) " The intracutaneous rabbit method of measuring diphtheria toxin and antitoxin." *Acta path. microbiol. scand.*, Suppl. 14.
Kober, M. (1899) *Z. Hyg. InfektKr.*, **31**, 433.
Lange, B. and Yoshioka, M. (1924) *Z. Hyg. InfektKr.*, **101**, 451.
Loeffler, F. (1906) *Dtsch. med. Wschr.*, **32**, 289.
Marchal, J. (1930) *J. Path. Bact.*, **33**, 713.
Monograph. (1923) *Med. Res. Coun., Lond.*, Diphtheria.
Neufeld, F. (1924) *Z. Hyg. InfektKr.*, **101**, 466.
Newbold, E. M. (1927) *J. Hyg., Camb.*, **26**, 19.
Okell, C. C. (1929) *J. Hyg., Camb.*, **29**, 309 ; (1932) *Lancet*, i. 761, 815, 867.
Ornstein, O. (1922) *Z. Hyg. InfektKr.*, **96**, 48.
Pritchett, I. W. (1925) *J. exp. Med.*, **41**, 195 ; (1926) *Ibid.*, **43**, 161.
Pritchett, I. W., Beaudette, F. R., and Hughes, T. P. (1930a) *J. exp. Med.*, **51**, 249 ; (1930b) *Ibid.*, **51**, 259.
Reimann, H. A. (1927) *J. exp. Med.*, **45**, 807.
Smith, J. (1923) *J. Hyg., Camb.*, **22**, 1.

TOPLEY, W. W. C. (1921) *J. Hyg., Camb.*, **20,** 103 ; (1926) *Lancet*, i. 477, 531, 645 ; (1929) *Ibid.*, i. 1337.

TOPLEY, W. W. C., AYRTON, J., and LEWIS, E. R. (1924) *J. Hyg., Camb.*, **23,** 223.

TOPLEY, W. W. C., GREENWOOD, M., and WILSON, J. (1931) *J. Path. Bact.*, **24,** 523.

TOPLEY, W. W. C., GREENWOOD, M., WILSON, J., and NEWBOLD, E. M. (1928) *J. Path. Bact.*, **27,** 396.

TOPLEY, W. W. C., WILSON, J., and LEWIS, E. R. (1925) *J. Path. Bact.*, **23,** 421.

WADSWORTH, A. B. and SICKLES, G. M. (1927) *J. exp. Med.*, **45,** 807.

WEBSTER, L. T. (1922) *J. exp. Med.*, **36,** 71 ; (1923*a*) *Ibid.*, **37,** 231 ; (1923*b*) *Ibid.*, **37,** 781 ; (1923*c*) *Ibid.*, **38,** 33 ; (1923*d*) *Ibid.*, **38,** 45 ; (1924*a*) *Ibid.*, **39,** 129 ; (1924*b*) **39,** 843 ; (1924*c*) **39,** 857 ; (1924*d*) **40,** 117 ; (1925) *Amer. J. Hyg.*, **5,** 335 ; (1926) *J. exp. Med.*, **43,** 573 ; (1927) *Ibid.*, **45,** 529 ; (1928) *Ibid.*, **47,** 685 ; (1930*a*) *Ibid.*, **51,** 219 ; (1930*b*) *Ibid.*, **52,** 901 ; (1930*c*) *Ibid.*, **52,** 909 ; (1930*d*) *Ibid.*, **52,** 931.

WEBSTER, L. T. and BURN, C. G. (1926) *Ibid.*, **44,** 359 ; (1927*a*) *Ibid.*, **45,** 911 ; (1927*b*) *Ibid.*, **46,** 887.

WEBSTER, L. T. and CLOW, A. D. (1933) *J. exp. Med.*, **58,** 465.

WOLF, K. (1908) *Münch. med. Wschr.*, **55,** 270.

YOSHIDA, E. (1909) *Arch. Hyg.*, **69,** 21.

PART IV

THE APPLICATION OF BACTERIOLOGY TO MEDICINE AND HYGIENE

CHAPTER LIV

ACTINOMYCOSIS, ACTINOBACILLOSIS, AND RELATED DISEASES

INTRODUCTORY

THE term Actinomycosis was originally given by Bollinger in 1877 to a disease in cattle characterized by the formation of a hard wooden swelling of the tongue or a fusiform enlargement of the jaw. In the lesions of this disease he found numerous opaque slightly yellowish bodies of coarsely granular or mulberry-like appearance, which were found to consist of a fungus. His colleague Harz, a botanist, to whom he referred for an opinion on this organism, decided that it was a true mould and suggested for it the name of ray fungus or *Actinomyces bovis*. A similar mycotic disease in man was described the following year by Israël (1878, 1879); and in 1879 Ponfick suggested that the two diseases were identical. From seven cases of actinomycosis in cattle, Bostroem in 1891 isolated an aerobic filamentous organism showing true branching; and from two cases in human beings, Wolff and Israël in the same year (1891) isolated a similar branching organism, which was, however, anaerobic. In 1902 Lignières and Spitz described a new disease in cattle, differentiated from actinomycosis chiefly by its tendency to invade the lymph glands. From the affected animals they cultivated a very small, non-branching, Gram-negative bacillus, to which they gave the name actinobacillus. The disease they called actinobacillosis.

As early as 1874 Vandyke Carter drew attention to a disease in India known as Madura foot. Microscopical examination revealed the presence of a fungus, but attempts to cultivate it were unsuccessful till 1894 when Vincent succeeded in isolating an aerobic branching filamentous organism, similar in many respects to *Actinomyces bovis*, which he called *Streptothrix maduræ*.

From the disease known as " Farcy of cattle," Nocard in 1888 cultivated an aerobic branching filamentous organism, which likewise resembled Bostroem's *Actinomyces*. Similar branching organisms have been encountered in a number of diverse lesions in human beings and other animals.

From this brief description, it will be realized that there are several diseases from which actinomyces-like organisms have been isolated. In one group of diseases, their proliferation occurs in the form of colonies which have a definite ray structure; such colonies are seen in the pus as granules or *Drusen*. In another group the organisms form a felted mycelium without any radial arrangement, and without any formation of granules. Some authors prefer to limit the term actinomycosis to diseases of the former group, denoting those of the latter group by such terms as Streptothricosis, Cladothricosis, Oosporosis, Pseudotuberculosis, Para-actinomycosis, or Pseudo-actinomycosis. In Chapter XIII we have given our reasons for including all the filamentous branching organisms in the *Actinomyces* group. The logical sequence of this is to classify all diseases caused by these organisms under the name of Actinomycosis. This term, however, is often used in a broad sense to include chronic granulomata characterized by club formation. Such granulomata are in fact sometimes caused by *Staph. aureus* or *C. pyogenes*, and though their inclusion may be justified on clinical grounds, it leads to great confusion bacteriologically. We therefore propose to exclude from Actinomycosis the granulomatous lesions of cattle and swine that are caused by organisms other than those belonging to the *Actinomyces* group. The staphylococcal lesions are better referred to as Botriomycosis (see Chapter LXIV).

ACTINOMYCOSIS.

A. Due to *Actinomyces bovis* of Wolff and Israël. True ray-fungus disease in man and cattle. Granules or *Drusen* formed in tissues. Anaerobic.
B. Due to *Actinomyces*—aerobic types.
    (1) Non-acid-fast group. Madura foot—granules found in tissues. Other lesions in man and animals—no granules found in tissues.
    (2) Acid-fast group—chiefly pulmonary and abdominal infections in man. No granules formed in tissues. Farcy of cattle—no granules formed in tissues.
C. Due to *Actinomyces muris*. Rat-bite fever (one type) in man, and infective arthritis in mice. No granules formed in tissues.

ACTINOBACILLOSIS.

Due to bacilli.
    (1) *Actinobacillus lignieresi* of Lignières and Spitz. Actinobacillosis in cattle. Granules or *Drusen* formed in tissues.
    (2) *Actinobacillus actinoides* of Theobald Smith. Broncho-pneumonia of calves : pneumonia of rats. No granules formed in tissues.

ACTINOMYCOSIS

A. Due to Actinomyces bovis Wolff and Israël

Epidemiology.—Actinomycosis in man is not a common disease. Of 87 cases collected by Harbitz and Gröndahl (1911), 56 were in males and 27 in females ; in 4 the sex was not noted. Persons of all ages are attacked, but the disease appears to be most common in the third decade of life. Country folk supply the majority of cases, but the disease is by no means confined to rural districts. The cervico-facial region is the commonest situation. Table LXXXIII, which we have compiled from cases observed by Illich and by Leith (see Delépine 1915), and Colebrook (1921), indicates the distribution of the lesions.

The mortality of the disease depends largely on the site affected. Of 10 cases of cervico-facial infection observed by Colebrook (1921), 9 recovered : on the other hand 12 out of 14 thoracic and abdominal infections proved fatal. Of 87 cases recorded by Harbitz aud Gröndahl (1911), 42 died or remained unhealed.

TABLE LXXXIII

DISTRIBUTION OF ACTINOMYCOTIC LESIONS IN MAN.

	Cases.	Percentage.
Head and neck	234	51·4
Tongue	16	3·5
Abdomen	99	21·8
Thorax	65	14·3
Skin	11	2·4
Other situations and doubtful . .	30	6·6
	455	100·0

The extent to which *cattle* are infected is difficult to ascertain, largely because the disease has so frequently been confused with actinobacillosis. According to Jelenevski (see Hutyra and Marek 1926) the morbidity, as estimated in various abattoirs from 1896 to 1911, was as follows : Berlin 0·31 per cent., Vienna 0·01 per cent., Moscow 3·34 per cent., Kief 0·67 per cent., and Warsaw 0·65 per cent. ; but the mild form of lingual actinomycosis was apparently not included in these statistics. Of 85,445 tongues imported from the Argentine and examined by MacFadden (1913) in London from August to October 1913, 4,949 or 5·8 per cent. showed lesions, but there is evidence to suggest that many of these were infected with the actinobacillus. In this country the disease is not infrequent. It is stated to be commoner in low-lying marshy districts, and to affect stall-fed cattle more frequently than those fed on pasture. According to Magnusson (1928), it affects almost exclusively the jaw bone, which develops a typical fusiform swelling ; but Albiston and Pullar (1934) state that the soft tissues—tongue, lymph and salivary glands, muscle—may be affected. Certainly the jaw seems to be the common site. Primary lesions of the internal organs are rare (Hutyra and Marek 1926). Generalization of the infection is not uncommon in man, but is rarely seen in cattle. So-called actinomycosis of the udder in cattle seems to be almost invariably due to staphylococcal infection (Magnusson 1928, Albiston 1930).

Actinomycosis is by no means infrequent in *swine.* The udder is attacked. Magnusson (1928) states that two types of *Actinomyces*, both anaerobic, may be found, which differ from the *bovis* variety. Some cases are due to staphylococci, and are more correctly termed botriomycosis. The disease occurs rarely in sheep, goats, and dogs. Most carnivora are resistant. We have met with one case in a mouse, in which the liver showed typical actinomycotic lesions.

Mode of Infection.—The mode of infection both in man and animals is obscure. In the days when Bostroem's organism was held to be the cause of the disease, it was generally thought that infection was conveyed by grasses, which lodged in the mucosa and provided a suitable nidus for the development of the organism. This view appeared probable because the organism was found to lead a saprophytic existence outside the body, being frequently isolated from grasses and cereals, and because awns of grasses, or barley spikes, are not uncommonly found in the actual lesions.   But now that Bostroem's organism is regarded as an accidental contaminant, and the organism isolated by Wolff and Israël as the true cause of the disease, this hypothesis has been abandoned.   Wolff and Israël's organism appears to be a strict parasite ; it has never been found outside the animal body, and its survival in artificial culture is brief.   These facts suggest that the disease is transmitted by infected pus, saliva, or nasal discharge.

Strong evidence in favour of this view is provided by the work of Naeslund (1925, 1926, 1929) who, in a study of the flora of the human mouth, succeeded in isolating both aerobic and anaerobic types of *Actinomyces*.   The anaerobic types were indistinguishable from *Actinomyces bovis*, and were more frequently met with than the aerobic types.   They were, moreover, isolated from a high proportion of salivary calculi, thus supporting Söderlund's (1921) view that the formation of these calculi must be regarded as a specific result of actinomycotic infection.   The same organisms also seemed to play an important part in the development of dental tartar. Naeslund believes that the *bovis* type is a normal inhabitant of the human mouth, while the aerobic types merely gain access to the mouth through chance contamination of the food.   If this view is correct—and it is supported by the observations of Lord and Trevett (1936)—the factors predisposing to the development of actinomycosis have still to be determined. Possibly suitable necrotic foci, such as septic teeth, have to be present in which the organisms can develop under anaerobic conditions.

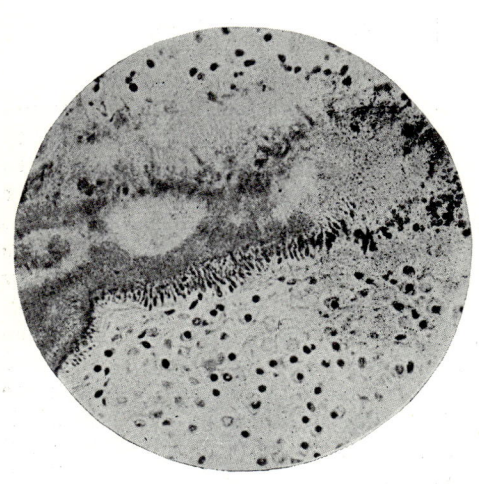

Fig. 245.

Part of the edge of a colony of *Actinomyces bovis* in the jaw of an ox, showing the peripheral zone of clubs (× 350).

Bacteriology. — In the tissues *Actinomyces* grows in the form of colonies or *Drusen*, which macroscopically have the appearance of small granules.   A section suitably stained reveals the presence of a central mass of partly necrotic material, in which branching filaments may be recognized, and a peripheral zone of swollen bodies looking like clubs and arranged radially.   The clubs are surrounded by pus cells, outside of which there are aggregations of mononuclear cells and dense masses of fibrous tissue.   The colony often presents a characteristically scalloped edge.   The mode of formation of the clubs is still under dispute, some workers maintaining that they represent the swollen extremities of the filaments, others that they are due to a reaction on the part of the tissues.   The fact that they occur in so-called actinomycotic lesions due to staphylococci, and that they may be formed under experimental conditions around dead masses of tubercle bacilli and actinomyces, suggests that the second explanation is more probably correct.   The disease spreads by contiguity ; the surrounding tissues, no matter of what type, are invaded and destroyed.

The pus discharged from these lesions is not usually abundant ; it is yellow, often bloody, thick or thin, and sometimes tough and viscous. If shaken up with water in a test tube it will be seen to contain small granules, which rapidly sink to the bottom. They vary greatly in size, but are generally about 0·25 to 1 mm. in diameter ; they are opaque, spherical bodies, greyish-white by reflected and yellowish by transmitted light, and have an oily appearance. Generally they are soft and can be readily crushed, but in cattle they may be hard or even calcified. In pus from old lesions they are darker in colour, and not infrequently brown. Microscopical examination of these granules reveals the presence of a felted mycelium, together with rod-shaped and coccoid bodies, surrounded by radially disposed clubs. The filaments are irregularly Gram-positive ; the clubs are usually Gram-negative. Clubs are said to be more conspicuous in lesions of cattle than in those of man.

Though all observers are agreed on the microscopical appearance of the organism in the tissues, attempts to cultivate it have led to divergent results. Bostroem in 1891 was the first to report positive results. By inoculating several hundred tubes of medium from a few cases of actinomycosis in cattle he succeeded in obtaining about 12 cultures of an aerobic, branching, pigmented, filamentous organism. Although he was unable to reproduce the disease in animals by injection with this organism, he had no hesitation in concluding that it was the cause of the disease. A little later in the same year Wolff and Israël (1891) reported the isolation of an anaerobic, branching, filamentous organism from 2 cases of human actinomycosis. (For a description of these organisms see Chapter XIII.) They inoculated cultures of this organism into 22 animals—generally by planting in the peritoneal cavity small pieces of agar on which growth had occurred. After 4 to 7 weeks, 18 of the animals—most of which were rabbits—were killed. All of them showed tumours in the peritoneal cavity, abdominal wall, or in one of the viscera, varying in size from a millet seed to a plum ; the larger tumours had knob-like prominences on the surface. Section revealed the presence of a capsule containing tallow-like material, sometimes intersected by anastomosing septa. The typical granules were found in the contents. Cultures were made from 6 of the animals ; of these 4 proved successful. In the remaining 4 animals, which were left alive, tumours could be felt through the abdominal wall 7 to 9 months after inoculation. From a study of the protocols provided, one gathers that in many instances the tumours were very small ; in some, however, especially those in which more than one tumour developed, there seems to be little doubt that the organisms actively multiplied in the tissues and gave rise to a true actinomycotic lesion.

Levy in 1899 isolated the Wolff-Israël *Actinomyces* from 5 human cases. In 1905 Wright in Boston carried out a more thorough investigation. From 13 cases of actinomycosis in human beings and from 2 in cattle he isolated in pure culture an organism of the Wolff-Israël type. Inoculation experiments were performed, chiefly on guinea-pigs and rabbits. Intraperitoneal injection of broth cultures of recently isolated strains resulted in the appearance of localized lesions, situated mostly in the great omentum. The largest of the nodules was about 6 mm. in diameter. Microscopically they consisted of connective tissue, often enclosing one or more cavities filled with pus and containing the characteristic clubbed colonies of *Actinomyces*. There was, however, no evidence of actual multiplication of the organisms in the tissues. These inoculation experiments are not very

P.B.   K K convincing. Wright believed that this could be explained by the difference in the conditions prevailing in experimental infection from those in the natural disease, particularly in the absence of secondary micro-organisms. From a critical résumé of the literature he came to the conclusion that the Wolff-Israël organism was the true cause of actinomycosis. Bostroem's organism he regarded as an example of the numerous saprophytic group of fungi which are common on grains and grasses, and which are therefore liable to gain access as contaminants to actinomycotic lesions.

Recent work has tended more and more to confirm Wright's conclusions. Henry in 1910 isolated an organism of the Wolff-Israël type from a case of actinomycosis in a man, which, starting in the upper jaw, had invaded the meninges. In 1911 Harbitz and Gröndahl in Norway isolated the Wolff-Israël organism from 10 out of 19 human cases and from a single case in a cow. Cole-brook (1920) in this country reported on 30 cases of human actinomycosis. From 27 he obtained cultures, but of these only 24 were studied in detail. Twenty-one of the strains proved to be of the Wolff-Israël type ; 2 strains resembled this type, but differed in certain cultural points ; the last strain was aerobic. Agglutination tests showed that the serum of the severely infected patients reacted with a suspension of the Wolff-Israël type. Bosworth (1923) cultivated this organism from 13 out of 34 cattle affected with actinomycotic lesions ; the remaining 21 cases proved to be due to the actinobacillus. Finally, Magnusson (1928) isolated *Actinomyces bovis* from 54 out of 61 cases of actinomycosis of the jaw in cattle in which the granules contained Gram-positive filaments, and showed that, though the disease could not be satisfactorily reproduced in small animals, it was possible to set up typical actinomycotic lesions in cattle by the inoculation of pure cultures of this organism.

It will be seen that the Wolff-Israël type of organism has been isolated from a number of cases of actinomycosis both in man and cattle in different parts of Europe and America. That it has not been cultured from all cases is probably explained by the technical difficulties associated with its isolation, especially when the lesion is invaded with secondary organisms, and by the fact that granules from old lesions not infrequently prove to be sterile.

We may conclude that the evidence in favour of the ætiological rôle of the *Actinomyces bovis* described by Wolff and Israël is sufficient to justify us in accepting this organism as the cause of that variety of actinomycosis which is characterized by the presence in the tissues of the typical ray fungus.

One further point in connection with the bacteriology of the disease may be mentioned. In the characteristic granules it is not unusual to encounter, as well as the branching filaments of *Actinomyces*, densely packed masses of Gram-negative cocco-bacilli. These organisms were first described and isolated by Klinger in 1912 who named them *B. actinomycetem comitans* ; and they have been subsequently noted by Colebrook (1920) in this country, and Bayne-Jones (1925) in America. What relation these organisms bear to *Actinomyces bovis* is not clear. (For further information see Chapter XIII.)

Diagnosis, Prophylaxis and Treatment.—Diagnosis is made by microscopical and cultural examination of the affected tissues. The granules should be crushed between slides and stained by Gram's method. If calcified, they should first be treated with hydrochloric acid. The presence of a mycelium of Gram-positive filaments surrounded by radially disposed Gram-negative clubs is characteristic of actinomycosis. Cultures are made from fresh young granules only ; after thorough washing, they are seeded into a number of tubes containing blood broth (Gordon 1920), glucose agar, or serum agar ; incubation is carried out under both aerobic and anaerobic conditions, preferably in an atmosphere to which 5–10 per cent. CO_2 has been added. Primary cultures are frequently contaminated ; single colonies should therefore be picked off to obtain pure cultures. Examination of the agglutinating power of the patient's serum to the organism isolated should be carried out if possible. In pulmonary actinomycosis in man the sputum is tough, often viscous, and sometimes hæmorrhagic ; the typical granules can be found on examination (Harbitz and Gröndahl 1911). Most of the abdominal cases commence in the appendix. In the rare cases of actinomycotic meningitis, the primary lesions are generally in the lungs and bronchial glands (Henry 1910).

As we are still ignorant of the factors determining the development of the disease, it is difficult to lay down prophylactic measures against it. It is clear, however, that the discharge from the lesions should be considered dangerous, and every care taken to prevent its coming into contact with man or other animals.

B. Infections due to, or associated with, the Aerobic Members of the Actinomyces Group

(1) Madura Disease.

This disease, which is peculiar to man, was first thoroughly investigated by Vandyke Carter of Bombay in 1874. It occurs chiefly in India, but cases have been reported in Algiers, Italy, Roumania, America, and other countries. The lesions are commonest in the foot, and are of a chronic granulomatous nature, characterized by swelling, suppuration, and sinus formation. The pus contains granules, which in some cases are yellowish in colour, in others black. These granules are generally larger than those seen in actinomycosis—up to 1 mm. in diameter ; they may be aggregated into masses looking not unlike fish-roe (Kanthack 1893). Under the microscope, those from the pale or ochroid variety of the disease consist of a central irregularly staining felted mycelium, showing true branching ; sometimes they are surrounded by a ray formation of club-like structures. Vincent (1894) cultivated from them an aerobic filamentous organism, which gave a pink or rose coloration on potato (see Chapter XIII). It proved to be practically non-pathogenic for laboratory animals. He called it *Streptothrix maduræ* ; its correct name is *Actinomyces maduræ*.

Wright (1898) found that the granules from the black or melanoid type of the disease consisted of a mycelium of hyphæ or fungoid elements, more or less degenerated, embedded in a hyaline brown-coloured refringent substance, which itself formed more or less of a reticulum. The pigment could be dissolved by sodium hypochlorite solution, leaving the mycelium unaltered. Cultures resulted in the development of a mould, consisting of a branching septate mycelium, and forming typical mould-like colonies. Wright concludes that the pale variety of the disease is due to an organism of the *Streptothrix* (*Actinomyces*) group, while the black variety is due to a mould or hyphomycete. It is probable that several types of organism are responsible for the disease, and that the pale variety, at least, may be caused either by an *Actinomyces* or by a fungus.

(2) Other Lesions in Man.

Eppinger (1891) described a case of brain abscess in a glass-grinder due to a branching filamentous organism. Old calcified abscesses were found in the bronchial and supraclavicular glands, and pseudotubercles were noticed in the lungs and pleura. The organism grew abundantly on ordinary media under aerobic conditions (see Chapter XIII). Injection into rabbits and guinea-pigs proved fatal in 1 to 4 weeks ; post mortem the lungs, liver, and spleen were studded with small white nodules. He called the organism *Cladothrix asteroides* (*Actinomyces asteroides*) and the disease Pseudotuberculosis cladothrichica. Later MacCallum (1902) recorded a case of peritonitis in a negro child due to infection with the same organism. According to Claypole (1913) this organism is mildly acid-fast.

Henrici and Gardner (1921) isolated a similar organism from the sputum of a woman, which differed however in certain particulars, and which they called *Actinomyces gypsoides*. From the literature they were able to gather accounts of 26 cases of infection with acid-fast *Actinomyces*. Infection probably occurs by inhalation ; the first lesions are in the peribronchial nodes. Later, caseous broncho-pneumonia develops, followed by central softening and cavity formation. Metastases may occur. The duration of the illness is generally about 6 months. These cases are liable to be confused with tuberculosis. The differential diagnosis is effected by cultivation of the organism, and the exclusion of tuberculosis by injection of the sputum into guinea-pigs.

Another strain, called *Actinomyces variabilis*, was isolated by Cohn (1913) from the bladder and prostate of a man with pyuria. Namyslowski (1912) describes a strain cultivated by Rosenhauch from the purulent cornea of a child who had received a blow in the eye. He says this is the sixth case in the literature of the finding of *Actinomyces* in lesions of the cornea.

Thjøtta and Gundersen (1925) isolated a strain from the blood of a young man with acute rheumatic fever ; it was non-pathogenic to rabbits and guinea-pigs, and the authors concluded that it had no relation to the disease.

Organisms of the *Actinomyces* group have been found in smear preparations and in serial sections of the contents of carious teeth in persons showing no clinical evidence of actinomycosis (Lord 1910). Berestnew (1898) describes the finding of such organisms in the tissues. Organisms simulating the *Actinomyces* group in certain respects have been isolated from the cerebrospinal fluid of children with purulent meningitis (Gerbasi 1927). An organism, apparently identical with *Actinomyces graminis*, has recently been isolated by Biggart (1934) from a fatal case of actinomycosis in a woman. The primary lesion was in one lung, but secondary involvement of both lungs, and of the liver, spleen, kidneys, and subcutaneous tissue of the left thigh and right arm had occurred. Typical *Drusen* forms were lacking.

Numerous other cases might be quoted in which an *Actinomyces* of the aerobic type has been found in lesions of different parts of the body.

(3) Cattle Farcy. Farcin du bœuf.

Cattle farcy is characterized by the appearance—generally on the medial surface of the extremities—of firm, painless perivascular nodes, which later suppurate. When incised, they discharge a whitish, odourless mass resembling soft cheese (Report 1913). The regional lymph glands become converted into firm, painful tumours. It is a chronic disease lasting for a year or more, and marked in the later stages by severe cachexia. From the pus of an affected animal Nocard (1888) isolated an aerobic branching organism, now known as *Actinomyces farcinicus*. Intravenous injection of pure cultures into a cow and a sheep resulted in the development of miliary nodules. The disease is not common in Europe ; it is very prevalent in Guadeloupe, and has been recorded in India, and recently in Kenya (Daubney 1927).

(4) Other Lesions in Cattle.

Evans (1918) has recorded an infection of the udder of cows with an organism of the aerobic *Actinomyces* group. She succeeded in isolating it from 18 out of 21 samples of milk, in which it was present in considerable numbers.

(5) Goats and Horses.

Silberschmidt (1899) isolated a member of this group from three goats; this organism is called *Actinomyces capræ*. The same organism was later cultivated by Galli-Valerio from the lung of a goat. Dean (1900) cultivated a member of the group from an abscess in the submaxillary region of a horse.

C. Infections due to, or associated with, the Facultative Aerobic Members of the Actinomyces Group.

(1) Rat-bite Fever.

For many years there has been great confusion over the ætiology of this disease. Schottmüller (1914), Blake (1916), Tileston (1916), and others described the isolation of a streptothrix—*Streptothrix muris ratti*—from the blood of patients suffering from rat-bite fever, while Japanese workers (see Chapter LXXIX) brought strong evidence to show that the disease was due to a spirochætal organism known as *Spirochæta morsus muris* or *Spirillum minus*. There seems to be no question now that both organisms may be responsible, and that rat-bite fever may be of at least two different types. The evidence for this conclusion is based on a careful study of the literature.

In 1925 Levaditi, Nicolau, and Poincloux in France described an organism, to which they gave the name *Streptobacillus moniliformis*. It was isolated from the blood of a laboratory worker who was suffering from an acute disease characterized by fever, sore throat, papular erythema, and multiple arthritis. The following year Parker and Hudson (1926) gave an account of an epidemic disease occurring in Haverhill, Massachusetts. This disease they referred to as Erythema arthriticum epidemicum or Haverhill fever. An organism was isolated—*Haverhillia multiformis* —which was subsequently proved to be identical with *Streptobacillus moniliformis*. In neither instance was there any suspicion of infection having occurred through rats. In 1933 Strangeways accidentally encountered the same organism in mice that had died after intraperitoneal inoculation with the blood of rats infected with *Trypanosoma equiperdum*. Investigation showed her that *Streptobacillus moniliformis* was an inhabitant of the nasopharynx of the rat, in which it normally led an apparently harmless existence. A very similar organism had already been reported by Tunnicliff (1916) in the lungs of white rats affected with bronchopneumonia. It would therefore appear that *Streptobacillus moniliformis* is no other than the *Streptothrix muris ratti* of the earlier workers. Both organisms appear to be closely related to the *Actinomyces* group, and we have therefore suggested for them the name *Actinomyces muris*. Since this organism is pathogenic for man and is a normal parasite of the rat, it is not difficult to understand how it may be responsible for human infection. *Spirillum minus* is also a normal parasite of the rat, and may likewise cause rat-bite fever. We shall restrict ourselves at the moment to the description of the type of disease caused by *Actinomyces muris*. For the type caused by *Spirillum minus* see p. 1451.

It is not yet clear whether the clinical picture is the same in the two infections. Generally speaking, however, rat-bite fever is a paroxysmal febrile disease of the relapsing type. The wound heals readily, but after an incubation period of probably not more than a fortnight (in the *muris* type), it becomes inflamed and painful. Lymphadenitis and lymphangitis develop, and are quickly followed by symptoms of systemic infection ushered in by a chill and rapid rise of temperature. There is extreme prostration, severe generalized muscular pain and tenderness, headache, weakness, and a widespread macular eruption. Multiple arthritis may appear. After a few days the temperature falls by crisis, and the disease then assumes the relapsing type, febrile paroxysms occurring usually at about weekly intervals. The case mortality may be as high as 10 per cent. Little is known of the post-mortem appearances of fatal cases, but it is interesting to note that Blake's case showed an ulcerative endocarditis and a subacute myocarditis. Diagnosis during life is made by cultivation of the causative organism from the blood stream during a febrile attack. About 20 c.c. of blood are withdrawn, and are distributed partly into serum broth, and partly over a number of plates of Lœffler's serum. The cultures may be incubated either aerobically or anaerobically—preferably in the presence of 5 per cent. CO_2. Though infection usually follows a rat-bite, the outbreak of Haverhill fever studied by Parker and Hudson (1926) was traced to the consumption of raw milk, as was also another milk-borne outbreak involving 86 persons which has been described more recently by Place and Sutton (1934). How the milk becomes contaminated it is difficult to say, but the fact that the organism may be excreted by the urine of infected mice and perhaps rats seems to afford a possible explanation. Little is known about treatment, but it is doubtful whether salvarsan, which is often successful in the spirochætal type of the disease, is likely to have any beneficial effect in the *muris* type.

(2) Infective Arthritis of Mice.

The natural disease produced in mice by *Actinomyces muris* has been described by Levaditi, Selbie, and Schoen (1932) and Mackie, van Rooyen, and Gilroy (1933). It may occur in either sporadic or epidemic form, and may be of an acute septicæmic or a more chronic polyarticular type. The mortality is high. Infection probably results either through bites, or through contamination with urine, which may contain the organism. In acute cases the animal appears ill and has a lustreless coat. The eyes may be glued together by a semipurulent conjunctival discharge. Death occurs in a few days, and nothing characteristic is found at necropsy. The subacute or chronic type is characterized by polyarthritis and myocarditis, the former evidenced by swelling of the joints, the latter by cyanosis of the tail and extremities. One of the commonest manifestations is œdematous swelling of the feet and legs, sometimes confined to one or both hind limbs. Ulceration of the feet may occur, but gangrene is rarely observed. Paralysis of the hind limbs, enlargement of lymphatic glands, subcutaneous swellings, and keratitis are other manifestations that are not infrequently encountered. The conjunctivitis may suggest infection with *Ery. muriseptica*, the swelling and ulceration of the feet ectromelia. Diagnosis is made by culture. The organism can often be isolated from the blood, even in chronic cases, and from the spleen, liver, glands and joints. Serum agar or Lœffler's serum should be used. Experimental reproduction of the disease in normal mice is readily accomplished by inoculation of pure cultures (see p. 275).

ACTINOBACILLOSIS

In 1902 Lignières and Spitz described under the term actinobacillosis a disease that had occurred in epizootic form amongst cattle in the Argentine during the summer of 1900–01. Once a herd had become infected the disease spread rapidly, attacking 15–25 per cent., sometimes even 50 per cent., of the animals in the course of a few weeks. After a short time the epizootic died down, but sporadic cases, generally of a mild form, occurred at intervals. The main animals attacked were cattle ; sheep were rarely, and horses never attacked. In cattle all ages were affected, from calves of 1 month to animals several years old.

In about 80 per cent. of the cases the lesion was in the subcutaneous tissue of the neck ; in about 5 per cent. in the tongue. With the exception of the lungs, the internal organs were not often affected. The most striking difference from actinomycosis lay in the frequency with which the regional lymphatic glands were invaded. In the neck the lesion commences as a rounded subcutaneous nodule of fibrous consistence, adherent to the skin, with a smooth but later pro-tuberant nodular surface. During the next few days the lesion grows rapidly, softens in the centre, and becomes converted into a cold abscess. In this state it persists for weeks or months, gradually enlarging. Eventually it ulcerates and discharges a highly viscous, milky-white or slightly green, almost odourless pus, containing little greyish-white opaque granules up to 0·4 mm. in diameter. The pus is so viscous that it is rarely discharged completely ; it forms crusts on the surface of a fungat-ing ulcer, which persists indefinitely.

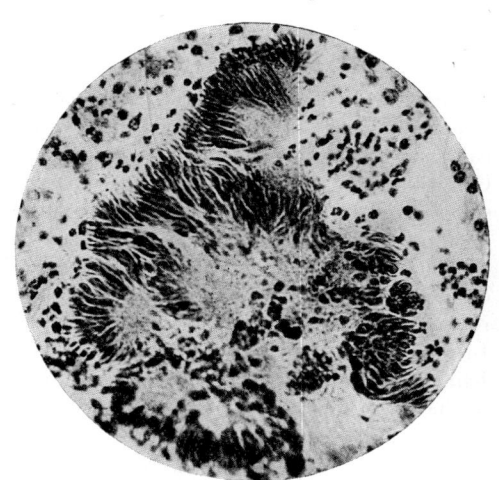

FIG. 246.

A colony of *Actinobacillus lignieresi* in the tongue of an ox, showing the long, finger-shaped clubs (× 350).

The abscesses are usually multiple, and frequently occur in different situations simultaneously—such as the tongue, glands, and lungs. Fibrous tissue is formed around the lesions—as in actinomy-cosis. On examination the granules are seen to be simple or composite. They consist of tufts of radiating clubs varying in size from about $16 \times 8 \mu$ to $99 \times 24 \mu$. They are stained best by glycerol picrocarmine ; in a few seconds the clubs take on a yellow colour, while the pus appears pink. No mycelium is found. If, however, the granule is stained with carbol-fuchsin, it is sometimes possible to distinguish small bacilli in the granular detritus that occupies the centre. Both clubs and bacilli are Gram-negative. A very pretty picture is obtained by staining with Ziehl-Neelsen and decolorizing cautiously with 1 per cent. H_2SO_4. The interior of the colony is blue, while the clubs, being weakly acid-fast, are stained red.

Cultures made from the granules revealed the presence of a very small

Gram-negative, non-motile, cocco-bacillus, which Lignières and Spitz called the actinobacillus—now called *Actinobacillus lignieresi*. (For description see Chapter XIII.) In this country the disease is less acute, and the lesions are more localized, though the glands are almost invariably affected.

Reproduction of the Disease in Animals.—Subcutaneous inoculation of a pure culture into cattle leads to the formation of an abscess similar to that occurring in the natural disease, though not all strains are virulent. Fluctuation is apparent about the 10th day. The abscess enlarges, and eventually the skin gives way, allowing a small quantity of pus to exude. Fungating masses spring up around the opening and obstruct drainage. The animals gradually waste. The pus contains typical granules. Feeding has not been successful in transmitting the disease. A local abscess develops after subcutaneous inoculation of pure cultures into pigs and sheep. In horses a large œdematous swelling is formed, which discharges pus after a few days.

The work of Lignières and Spitz has been confirmed by workers in several countries. Nocard (1902) recognized the disease in France. He pointed out that in actinomycosis of cattle the granules in the pus are yellowish in colour and often calcified, whereas in actinobacillosis they are greyish-white and rarely calcified. Griffith (1916) examined the diseased tongues and lymphatic glands of 44 cattle slaughtered in this country. Of these no fewer than 40 showed lesions of actinobacillosis. From 23 of these he isolated a Gram-negative bacillus which had the characters of *Actinobacillus lignieresi*. One of the cultures inoculated subcutaneously into a calf caused a local lesion containing typical granules. The remaining 4 cases, affecting the lower jaw, were due to the *Actinomyces bovis*. In an examination of 34 specimens of " actinomycosis " in cattle slaughtered at Islington, Bosworth (1923) recognized *Actinobacillus lignieresi* 21 times ; from 17 of the cases he isolated it in pure culture. The other 13 specimens were examples of actinomycosis.

Diagnosis.—The important points are : (1) The location : practically all jaw lesions appear to be due to *Actinomyces bovis*, while lesions of the soft parts— tongue, cheek, gum, palatal mucosa, skin, and lymphatic glands—are due to the actinobacillus. (2) The frequent involvement of the lymph glands in actinobacillosis ; in actinomycosis the glands are swollen only as the result of secondary infection from open lesions. (3) Granules are rarely found in the glands in actinomycosis, very frequently in actinobacillosis. (4) In actinobacillosis the granules are paler in colour, and rarely calcified ; in actinomycosis the granules are darker in colour and often calcified. (5) In actinobacillosis the granules consist of a central mass of detritus containing minute Gram-negative bacilli surrounded by long, radially disposed clubs ; in actinomycosis the granules contain a central Gram-positive mycelium, together with Gram-positive rods and coccoid forms, surrounded by short, radially disposed clubs. (6) In actinobacillosis cultures reveal the presence of a small Gram-negative, aerobic cocco-bacillus ; in actinomycosis a Gram-positive, branching, filamentous organism, often assuming rod forms in culture, not unlike *C. diphtheriæ*, is isolated under anaerobic conditions. During life the agglutination reaction may be of value. The serum of animals suffering from actinobacillosis frequently agglutinates the causative organism to a titre of 1/50 or over.

According to Ravaglia (1934), who observed actinobacillosis in *sheep*, affecting the subcutaneous tissue and lymphatics of the neck, the pus discharged contained no definite granules, while microscopically colonies were rare and club formation was inconspicuous.

Prophylactically, Lignières and Spitz (1902) found that segregation and killing of infected animals was the best procedure. Immune horse serum was employed in the treatment of some cases—though without conspicuous success. Iodide is said to be of much more value in the treatment of actinobacillosis than of actino-mycosis.

So far as we know actinobacillosis is very rare in man. Ravaut and Pinoy (1911), Thompson and Willius (1932), and Beaver and Thompson (1933) have each described a case, but in no instance has the identification of the causative organism with *Actinobacillus lignieresi* been entirely satisfactory.

Pneumonia in Calves due to Actinobacillus actinoides.—Smith (1918, 1921) has described an epizootic broncho-pneumonia in calves, most common in the 2nd and 3rd months of life, characterized by areas of consolidation, focal necroses, and other lesions. From the lungs of a number of fatal cases in two separate out-breaks he isolated an organism which he called *B. actinoides* (see Chapter XIII). In some cases it was present in pure culture, in others it was associated with *C. pyogenes, Br. bronchiseptica,* or other organisms. On microscopical examination of the lungs, it was seen in the form of slender bacilli situated at the periphery of necrotic areas, aggregated into masses in the alveoli and alveolar ducts, or in the proliferating epithelium that occupied the smaller bronchioles. On coagulated horse serum, tiny whitish flocculi appeared in the water of condensation ; these consisted of radiating filaments terminating in clubs. The organism was non-pathogenic to laboratory animals, but intratracheal injection into calves was sometimes followed by the appearance of small necrotic foci in the lungs, indistinguishable from those observed in the natural disease. What relation this organism has to the actino-bacillus of Lignières and Spitz has not been determined. Jones (1922) has isolated it from the pneumonic lungs of white rats.

REFERENCES

ALBISTON, H. E. (1930) *Aust. vet. J.*, **6**, 2.
ALBISTON, H. E. and PULLAR, E. M. (1934) *Aust. vet. J.*, **10**, 146.
BAYNE-JONES, S. (1925) *J. Bact.*, **10**, 569.
BEAVER, D. C. and THOMPSON, L. (1933) *Amer. J. Path.*, **9**, 603.
BERESTNEW, N. (1898) *Z. Hyg. InfektKr.*, **29**, 94.
BIGGART, J. H. (1934) *Bull. Johns Hopk. Hosp.*, **54**, 165.
BLAKE, F. C. (1916) *J. exp. Med.*, **23**, 39.
BOLLINGER. (1877) *Zbl. med. Wiss.*, **15**, 481.
BOSTROEM, E. (1891) *Beitr. path. Anat.*, **9**, 1.
BOSWORTH, T. J. (1923) *J. comp. Path.*, **36**, 1.
CLAYPOLE, E. J. (1913) *J. exp. Med.*, **17**, 99.
COHN, T. (1913) *Zbl. Bakt.*, **70**, 290.
COLEBROOK, L. (1920) *Brit. J. exp. Path.*, **1**, 197 ; (1921) *Lancet*, i. 893.
DAUBNEY, R. (1927) *J. comp. Path.*, **40**, 195.
DEAN, G. (1900) *Trans. path. Soc. Lond.*, **51**, 26.
DELÉPINE, A. S. (1915) " Encyclopædia Medica," 2nd edit., Vol. i. p. 157. Edinburgh and London.
EPPINGER, H. (1891) *Beitr. path. Anat.*, **9**, 287.
EVANS, A. C. (1918) *J. infect. Dis.*, **23**, 373.
GERBASI, M. (1927) *Zbl. Bakt.*, **101**, 369.
GORDON, M. H. (1920) *Brit. med. J.*, i. 435.
GRIFFITH, F. (1916) *J. Hyg., Camb.*, **15**, 195.
HARBITZ, F. and GRÖNDAHL, N. B. (1911) *Beitr. path. Anat.*, **50**, 193.

HENRICI, A. T. and GARDNER, E. L.   (1921) *J. infect. Dis.*, **28**, 232.
HENRY, H.   (1910) *J. Path. Bact.*, **14**, 164.
HUTYRA, F. and MAREK, J.   (1926) " Special Pathology and Therapeutics of the Diseases of Domestic Animals," **1.**   Chicago and London.
ISRAËL, J.   (1878) *Virchows Arch.*, **74**, 15 ;   (1879) *Ibid.*, **78**, 421.
JONES, F. S.   (1922) *J. exp. Med.*, **35**, 361.
KANTHACK, A. A.   (1893) *J. Path. Bact.*, **1**, 140.
KLINGER, R.   (1912) *Zbl. Bakt.*, **62**, 191.
LEVADITI, C., NICOLAU, S., and POINCLOUX, P.   (1925) *C. R. Acad. Sci.*, **180**, 1188.
LEVADITI, C., SELBIE, F. R., and SCHOEN, R.   (1932) *Ann. Inst. Pasteur*, **48**, 308.
LEVY, E.   (1899) *Zbl. Bakt.*, **26**, 1.
LIGNIÈRES, J. and SPITZ, G.   (1902) *Bull. Soc. Méd. vét.*, **20**, 487, 546.
LORD, F. T.   (1910) *Boston med. surg. J.*, **163**, 82.
LORD, F. T. and TREVETT, L. D.   (1936) *J. infect. Dis.*, **58**, 115.
MACCALLUM, W. G.   (1902) *Zbl. Bakt.*, **31**, 529.
MACFADDEN, A. W. J.   (1913) *Rep. med. Offr Hlth Port Lond.*, Nov. 13th.
MACKIE, T. J., ROOYEN, C. E. VAN, and GILROY, E.   (1933) *Brit. J. exp. Path.*, **14**, 132.
MAGNUSSON, H.   (1928) *Acta path. microbiol., scand.*, **5**, 170.
NAESLUND, C.   (1925) *Acta path. microbiol. scand.*, **2**, 110, 244 ;   (1926) *Ibid.*, **3**, 637 ;   (1929) *Ibid.*, **6**, 66, 78.
NAMYSLOWSKI, B.   (1912) *Zbl. Bakt.*, **62**, 562.
NOCARD, E.   (1888) *Ann. Inst. Pasteur*, **2**, 293 ;   (1902) *Bull. Soc. Méd. vét.*, **20**, 695.
PARKER, F. and HUDSON, N. P.   (1926) *Amer. J. Path.*, **2**, 357.
PLACE, E. H. and SUTTON, L. E.   (1934) *Arch. intern. Med.*, **54**, 659.
RAVAGLIA, F.   (1934) *Nuova Vet.*, **12**, 20.
RAVAUT, P. and PINOY.   (1911) *Pr. méd.*, **19**, 49.
Report.   (1913) *Rep. med. Offr Hlth Port Lond.*, Nov. 13th.
SCHOTTMÜLLER, H.   (1914) *Derm. Wschr.*, **58**, suppl. p. 77.
SILBERSCHMIDT.   (1899) *Ann. Inst. Pasteur*, **13**, 841.
SMITH, T.   (1918) *J. exp. Med.*, **28**, 333 ;   (1921) *Ibid.*, **33**, 441.
SÖDERLUND, G.   (1921) *Acta Chir. scand.*, **53**, 189.
STRANGEWAYS, W. I.   (1933) *J. Path. Bact.*, **37**, 45.
THOMPSON, L. and WILLIUS, F. A.   (1932) *J. Amer. med. Ass.*, **99**, 298.
THJØTTA, T. and GUNDERSEN, E.   (1925) *J. Bact.*, **10**, 1.
TILESTON, W.   (1916) *J. Amer. med. Ass.*, **66**, 995.
TUNNICLIFF, R.   (1916) *J. infect. Dis.*, **19**, 767.
VINCENT, H.   (1894) *Ann. Inst. Pasteur*, **8**, 129.
WOLFF, M. and ISRAËL, J.   (1891) *Virchows Arch.*, **126**, 11.
WRIGHT, J. H.   (1898) *J. exp. Med.*, **3**, 421 ;   (1905) *J. med. Res.*, **13**, 349.

CHAPTER LV

SWINE ERYSIPELAS, ERYSIPELOID, AND MOUSE SEPTICÆMIA

SWINE ERYSIPELAS

INTRODUCTORY

SWINE erysipelas is a disease affecting mainly pigs, and caused by the slender Gram-positive bacillus, *Erysipelothrix rhusiopathiæ*. Adolescent animals seem to be most frequently affected, but it occurs at all ages except during the first 3 months of life, when it is uncommon. The finer breeds of pigs are particularly susceptible. Four clinical types of the disease are described (Craig 1926). (1) The acute or septicæmic form. After an incubation period of 1 to 5 days, illness commences with prostration and high fever, anorexia, thirst, occasional vomiting, and conjunctivitis. Twenty-four hours later bright or dark red patches appear on the skin over the ears, snout, neck, abdomen, and inner sides of the forelegs. The mortality is about 80 per cent., death occurring usually in 3 or 4 days. (2) The urticarial form, or " The Diamonds." This is a mild form accompanied by slight malaise and fever, and characterized by the eruption on the 2nd or 3rd day of well-defined, quadrangular or rhombic patches on the skin of the sides, back, and buttocks ; the patches are slightly swollen, deep red or violet in colour, sometimes with a pale centre, from 1–5 cm. in diameter, and may become covered with dry crusts which are afterwards cast off. Recovery occurs in a few days ; death is unusual. (3) The chronic or cardiac form. This may follow either of the previous types, or may arise independently. Warty vegetations develop on one of the heart valves, generally the mitral. Death may occur suddenly, or the animals may live for several weeks with symptoms of cardiac insufficiency. (4) The joint or arthritic form. This may follow the urticarial form, accompany the cardiac form, or arise independently. The joints of the limbs become enlarged, due to a synovitis ; the animals are stunted, prefer the recumbent posture, and when induced to get up, walk in a stiff fashion on their toes with the back arched. This form is not usually fatal, but interferes with growth and fattening.

Morbid Anatomy.—In animals dying of the septicæmic form the spleen is enlarged, the lymphatic glands are congested, the gastric and intestinal mucosæ are reddened, and the lungs are œdematous ; there are sometimes small hæmorrhages on the serous and mucous membranes and beneath the endocardium. The bacilli are found in small numbers in the blood, spleen, kidneys, and other organs, and in the secretions and excretions. In the cardiac form they are chiefly found in, and may be confined to, the vegetations on the valves.

Epidemiology.—Swine erysipelas is common in this country and throughout Europe ; in America, on the other hand, it is rare. It occurs particularly in valleys and low-lying districts, and during the summer and autumn months. In this country, as a rule, only a few pigs in a herd are affected, but on the Continent large epidemics may occur. The causative bacillus has also been found to be responsible for outbreaks of polyarthritis in sheep, joint-ill in lambs, and for occasional infections in cattle and turkeys (see Beaudette and Hudson 1936).

The natural disease in pigs is apparently due to intestinal infection, though infection by the skin appears possible. The bacilli have been found in the gall-bladders of animals that have recovered from the mild type of the disease (Pitt 1908*b*), and from the tonsils and intestinal mucosa of normal swine (Pitt 1908*a*, Tenbroeck 1920), so that carriers may play an important part in the spread of infection. The bacilli are very resistant to the changes associated with putrefaction, and may remain alive for months in carcases of buried animals (Lösener 1896) ; it is possible, therefore, that infection may occur by food or water contaminated with infected soil.

The disease can be experimentally reproduced in swine by inoculation with pure cultures (see Chapter XIV).

Diagnosis.—The bacteriological diagnosis of swine erysipelas is made by microscopic examination of the blood during life, and of the blood and viscera after death, for the characteristic slender Gram-positive bacilli. If the organisms are too few to be seen microscopically, they may be cultivated on agar, in broth, and in gelatin stabs. If contaminated or putrefying material alone is available for examination, then the mouse inoculation test should be performed (see p. 284). The agglutination test may be of value, particularly in animals showing evidence of joint involvement. The antigen should be prepared from a smooth strain (see Schoening and Creech 1936).

Prophylaxis and Serum Treatment.—General prophylactic methods are similar to those for anthrax (see Chapter LXXIII).

The routine vaccination of herds has been attempted by two or three different methods (Voges and Schütz 1898). Pasteur and Thuillier (Pasteur 1882, Pasteur and Thuillier 1883) were responsible for the first method. They stated that if the virus was passed through rabbits, it gradually lost its virulence for pigs ; on the other hand, if it was passed through pigeons, its virulence was so exalted that the final passage virus was more virulent for pigs than even the most infectious products of pigs dying naturally from swine erysipelas. Their first vaccine, therefore, consisted of the avirulent rabbit passage virus ; their second, which was given about 12 days after the first, consisted of the hypervirulent pigeon passage virus. Though it is quite impossible from the available statistics (Chamberland 1894) to assess the value of this method, there is a general consensus of opinion that so long as its use is restricted to the more resistant commoner breeds of pigs and to areas in which the disease is rife, it results in a general lowering of the mortality from swine erysipelas. When, however, it is used for protection of the less resistant finer breeds, it frequently causes severe losses, amounting to 5 or 10 per cent. of the animals inoculated. For this reason its use has been very largely abandoned.

The methods now employed are those of sero-vaccination. In Lorenz's method (1893, 1894, 1896), a dose of immune serum is injected, followed after about 4 and 14 days by injections of living virulent bacilli. The serum provides a passive immunity, which is converted by the living vaccines, given subsequently, into an active immunity. In Leclainche's method the living vaccine is mixed with the serum, and the two are injected together. A second injection of vaccine alone is given 10 or 12 days later. Both these methods have been widely used, and appear to give satisfactory results. Both of them are open to the objection that living bacilli are introduced into the body, with the result that the animals may become healthy carriers of the disease. Immunization by the use of dead bacilli has not yet proved practicable.

In the actual treatment of swine that have already developed the disease the injection of 10–30 c.c. of immune serum is recommended.

ERYSIPELOID

Infection of man with the bacillus of swine erysipelas was first described by Rosenbach in 1884 (see Rosenbach 1909). Though, according to Verge (1933), a cutaneous, an intestinal, and a generalized form of the disease may occur, the first type, usually referred to as " erysipeloid," is undoubtedly the commonest. It is met with in cooks, kitchen workers, butchers, and in those who handle fish, game, or cheese (Klauder 1926). Epidemics of the disease have been reported. Stefansky and Grünfeld (1930) describe an outbreak at Odessa involving about 200 persons engaged in handling freshwater fish brought by sailing ships from the Dnieper and Bug ; while Lawson and Stinnett (1933) in the United States report 247 cases of erysipeloid occurring among workers employed in sawing and polishing bones in the manufacture of buttons.

Klauder (1932) says that infection can invariably be traced to contact with animals, fish, shell-fish, dead matter of plant or animal origin, or matter derived from animals such as hides, pelts, bones, and manure. The organism usually gains access through injuries on the skin, including the bites of animals, fish, and crustacea. Where the organism comes from, however, is not so clear. Direct transmission to man from swine suffering from erysipelas appears to be uncommon (Bierbaum and Gottron 1929), while actual infection of fish and crustaceans has not so far been demonstrated (Verge 1933). The organism is known to be very resistant to salting and putrefaction, and to survive for a long time outside the body. Possibly it leads a saprophytic existence in favourable surroundings.

However it reaches the skin, it gives rise, after an incubation period of 1–4 days, to an erysipeloid lesion characterized by a sharply defined, slightly elevated, purplish-red zone, which extends peripherally at the same time as it fades and desquamates centrally. The rash is accompanied by considerable swelling, itching, burning, and pain. Regional lymphangitis and lymphadenitis may develop. Arthritis of the finger joints is not unusual. Relapses are common, and second attacks may occur. The milder forms last 2–4 weeks, but the disease may continue for months. It rarely proves fatal.

The bacilli may be cultivated from the deep layer of an excised piece of skin. Alternatively tissue fluid may be obtained for culture by injecting saline into the skin at the border of the lesion, and re-aspirating it without withdrawal of the needle.

The most satisfactory form of treatment seems to consist in the inoculation of immune serum. It is advisable to inject 1–2 c.c. per kilo. of body-weight intramuscularly (Klauder 1926). This treatment may be supplemented by multiple inoculations of serum around the local lesion.

MOUSE SEPTICÆMIA

Infection with *Ery. muriseptica*—an organism closely related to, if not identical with, *Ery. rhusiopathiæ*—gives rise to a natural infection in mice, which spreads readily among a herd of these animals, sometimes assuming epidemic proportions. The disease was originally described by Koch (1880) as *mouse septicæmia.*

The experimental disease produced in mice by the inoculation of *Ery. muriseptica* corresponds exactly with that produced by *Ery. rhusiopathiæ* (see p. 284).

REFERENCES

BEAUDETTE, F. R. and HUDSON, C. B. (1936) *J. Amer. vet. med. Ass.*, **88**, 475.
BIERBAUM, K. and GOTTRON, H. (1929) *Derm. Z.*, **57**, 5.
CHAMBERLAND, C. (1894) *Ann. Inst. Pasteur*, **8**, 161.
CRAIG, J. F. (1926) *Annu. Congr. nat. vet. Med. Ass. G.B.I.*, p. 163.
KLAUDER, J. V. (1926) *J. Amer. med. Ass.*, **86**, 536 ; (1932) *J. industr. Hyg.*, **14**, 222.
KOCH, R. (1880) "Investigations into the Etiology of Traumatic Infective Diseases," New Sydenham Society. London.
LAWSON, G. B. and STINNETT, M. S. (1933) *Sth. med. J.*, **26**, 1068.
LOEFFLER. (1886) *Arb. ReichsgesundhAmt.*, **1**, 46.
LORENZ. (1893) *Zbl. Bakt.*, **13**, 357 ; (1894) *Ibid.*, **15**, 278 ; (1896) *Ibid.*, **20**, 792.
LÖSENER, W. (1896) *Arb. ReichsgesundhAmt.*, **12**, 448.
PASTEUR, L. (1882) *C. R. Acad. Sci.*, **95**, 1120.
PASTEUR and THUILLIER. (1883) *C. R. Acad. Sci.*, **97**, 1163.
PITT, W. (1908a) *Zbl. Bakt.*, **45**, 33, 111 ; (1908b) *Ibid.*, **46**, 400.
ROSENBACH, F. J. (1909) *Z. Hyg. InfektKr.*, **63**, 343.
SCHOENING, H. W. and CREECH, G. T. (1936) *J. Amer. vet. med. Ass.*, **88**, 310.
STEFANSKY, W. K. and GRÜNFELD, A. A. (1930) *Zbl. Bakt.*, **117**, 376.
TENBROECK, C. (1920) *J. exp. Med.*, **32**, 331.
VERGE, J. (1933) *Rev. gén. Méd. vét.*, **42**, 65.
VOGES, O. and SCHÜTZ, W. (1898) *Z. Hyg. InfektKr.*, **28**, 38.

CHAPTER LVI

TUBERCULOSIS

Villemin in 1868 published his masterly study on the epidemiology of tuberculosis, and succeeded in transmitting the disease to animals by direct inoculation. Koch in 1882, after an investigation that will always remain as a classical example of thorough and accurate bacteriological technique, showed conclusively that the tubercle bacillus was the one essential cause of tuberculosis. The bacillus was resistant to all ordinary stains ; but Koch succeeded in staining it by an alkaline solution of methylene blue, kept in contact with the tuberculous tissue for 24 hours. The bacillus would not grow on any ordinary medium ; but he devised a new medium—inspissated blood serum—on which, after a delay of 10 days or so, growth first became apparent. Finally by a large series of inoculations with pure cultures of the bacillus, several generations removed from the primary one, he transmitted the disease to numerous animals of different species. Henceforward the demonstration of the bacillus afforded the sole infallible criterion for the diagnosis of all the manifold lesions of tuberculosis.

THE BACTERIOLOGY OF TUBERCULOSIS IN MAN

Tubercle bacilli may be divided by cultural and pathogenicity reactions into four types—human, bovine, avian, and cold-blooded (see Chapter XV). Of these only the first two are found in natural infections of man.

It is true that natural infections with the avian type have occasionally been described by continental workers, but the bacteriological evidence provided has not always been convincing. In this country, where the most thorough examinations have been made, not a single case has been reported. If avian infections do occur, they must be very rare (see Tulloch 1936). The extensive work of the Royal Commission on Tuberculosis (Report 1911a), supplemented by the more recent findings of A. S. Griffith and of several other workers, have afforded us a knowledge of the frequency of tuberculosis in patients of different ages. This knowledge is best summarized in tabular form (Table LXXXIV).

This table refers only to English cases. In Scotland the percentage of all forms of tuberculosis due to the bovine type is higher—often considerably so (see Griffith 1932a, 1934, Blacklock 1932, Griffith and Summers 1933, Blacklock and Griffin 1935, Munro and Scott 1936). Taking all ages into consideration, it will be seen that the majority of infections are due to the human type. Bovine infections are highest during the first 5 years of life ; in adults infections due to this type are uncommon. The main organs affected by the bovine type are the gastro-intestinal tract and its associated lymphatic glands, particularly those of the cervical and mesenteric group. Primary abdominal tuberculosis is almost invariably due to

TABLE LXXXIV

Frequency of Bovine Tuberculosis in Human Beings.

(A. S. Griffith 1932a, 1934, Cumming *et al.* 1933.)

Variety of Tuberculosis.	All Ages.		0 to 4 Years.		5 to 14 Years.	
	Number of Cases.	Per cent. Bovine.	Number of Cases.	Per cent. Bovine.	Number of Cases.	Per cent. Bovine.
Cervical glands	116	45·7	21	85·7	54	48·1
Lupus	177	48·6	75	57·3	87	47·1
Meningeal	214 [1]	24·3	23	34·8	29	31·0
Bone and joint	520	18·0	88	27·3	351	18·5
Genito-urinary	23	17·4	—	—	3	33·3
Pulmonary	869	2·1	—	—	—	—
Miscellaneous	23	8·7	3	33·3	11	9·1
Autopsies	183	22·3 [2]	101	29·7 [3]	55	14·3 [4]

[1] Including 151 cases in which age distribution is not recorded.
[2] ,, 4 cases ,, " human " bacilli were also present.
[3] ,, 1 case ,, ,, ,, ,, ,, ,,
[4] ,, 1 case ,, ,, ,, ,, ,, ,,

the bovine type (Griffith 1925b) ; but secondary abdominal tuberculosis, which occurs most frequently as a late complication in pulmonary tuberculosis, is generally due to the human type. Lupus occupies a peculiar position ; 52·4 per cent. of the strains are of bovine and 47·6 per cent. of human type. But generally both human and bovine strains are atypical ; their cultural reactions conform to the standard of one or other type, but their virulence for animals is lowered. Since these atypical variants are found almost exclusively in lupus, it is probable that the degradation in virulence results from the sojourn of the organisms in the skin (Report 1911b). There is no evidence that it is due to the effect of light, as might be supposed, since organisms of lowered virulence are isolated both from exposed and unexposed areas. A. S. Griffith (1924) concludes that the changes occurring in the organisms cultivated from lupus lesions are not merely degenerative, but are the result of adaptation of the bacilli to sojourn in the skin. As a rule, by passage of atypical bovine strains through calves or rabbits, their full virulence is regained. Passage of atypical human strains through guinea-pigs or monkeys has not been successful in restoring their virulence (A. S. Griffith 1924). Atypical strains may be found in conditions other than lupus ; thus in an investigation of 261 strains isolated from human cases of bone and joint tuberculosis Eastwood and F. Griffith (1916) encountered 10 atypical strains. Sometimes these atypical strains are found on further investigation to consist of a mixture of bovine and human bacilli (Report 1911c).

Approximately one-quarter of all cases of tuberculous meningitis and cerebral tuberculosis appear to be due to the bovine type (see Griffith 1932b, 1934, Blacklock and Griffin 1935, Griffith and Menton 1936). The proportion is greater in the lower than in the higher age groups.

Pulmonary tuberculosis has been generally held in the past to be due almost exclusively to the human type of bacillus. A. S. Griffith (1914), for example, collected figures referring to 938 cases in which the causative organism had been typed, and found that in only six had a bovine type been isolated ; in three of these it had been associated with a bacillus of human type. Of recent years, however, this conception has been challenged (see Munro and Griffith 1928, Griffith 1930, Griffith and Munro 1933, Cumming *et al.* 1933, Walker 1934, Griffith and Smith 1935, Tobiesen *et al.* 1935*a*, *b*). It has been found that in Scotland and in Northern England an appreciable proportion of cases are due to infection with the bovine type (Table LXXXV).

TABLE LXXXV

FREQUENCY OF BOVINE TUBERCLE BACILLI IN PULMONARY TUBERCULOSIS IN DIFFERENT PARTS OF GREAT BRITAIN.

Area.	No. of Strains Examined.	Percentage Bovine.
Scotland, North-East	103	12·6
Scotland, South-West	595	4·03
England, North	391	3·58
England, South	657	0·61

The reason for the differences between different parts of the country will be most conveniently discussed in the next section. *Summarizing,* we may say that infections in this country with bovine tubercle bacilli occur mainly in children ; in adults they are less common. The usual types of infection due to the bovine bacillus are glandular and alimentary tuberculosis, together with miliary tuberculosis and meningitis in infants. In pulmonary tuberculosis, though it is very much less common than the human bacillus, it is sufficiently frequent to demand serious attention.

EPIDEMIOLOGY

Tuberculosis is an infectious disease that spares neither age, sex, race, nor nationality. The pulmonary form was described by Hippocrates, and spinal caries has been observed in the mummies of ancient Egypt (Smith, E., 1909). With the spread of civilization it became more rife ; but now, in the more highly civilized countries of the world, it is declining. The main features of its epidemiology, as enumerated by Villemin (1868), are still generally true :

(1) Tuberculosis is uncommon in mountainous areas. It is comparatively rare in the mountains of Hungary and Styria, in the Carpathians, the Engadine, the Pyrenees, the high plateaux of Abyssinia and Armenia, in the Western Ghats and the Nilghiries, in the Himalayas, the Rockies, the Andes, and the high plateau of Mexico.

(2) It increases proportionately to the degree of crowding, and is especially common in the capitals, and great commercial and manufacturing towns.

(3) It attacks particularly persons who live in closed communities, such as prisoners, soldiers, and religieux.

(4) It spares those people who live in small communities, in the open air, or in a savage or nomadic state. The wandering Arabs, for example, rarely contract tuberculosis ; but it is common amongst the Arabs who have exchanged their tents for stone houses.

(5) It is very common among troops living in barracks, but is uncommon in the field and among troops who are not living in barracks. At the time at which Villemin wrote, the mortality from tuberculosis in the Army during peace time was from 5 to 12·5 per 1,000 ; in the field, however, the mortality was very much lower. As an example, he quotes the case of the Allied Armies before Sebastopol during the winter of 1854–5 ; even though they were living under most unhygienic conditions, and were subject to poor food, severe cold, and excessive fatigue, cases of tuberculosis were very rare.

(6) Close contact in small, badly ventilated dwellings leads to the development of the disease.

(7) Though at one time unknown in Australia, New Zealand, North America and parts of Polynesia, it has become a scourge in these countries since the advent of Europeans.

(8) Bovine tuberculosis, like human, increases with close contact and over-crowding ; when it appears in a byre it generally attacks large numbers of animals.

All these facts bring tuberculosis into line with the other zymotic diseases.

Mortality from Tuberculosis.—Table LXXXVI shows the annual mortality from tuberculosis of all forms and of the respiratory system in this country during the last 80 years.

TABLE LXXXVI

Showing the Annual Mortality per 1,000 Persons living in England and Wales from Tuberculosis. (Standardized Death Rates.)

Years.	Tuberculosis (all forms).	Tuberculosis of Respiratory System.
1851–55	3·638	2·890
1856–60	3·328	2·663
1861–65	3·316	2·625
1866–70	3·217	2·558
1871–75	2·956	2·327
1876–80	2·818	2·141
1881–85	2·558	1·922
1886–90	2·342	1·704
1891–95	2·138	1·504
1896–1900	1·912	1·337
1901–05	1·739	1·208
1906–10	1·556	1·082
[1] 1911–15	1·389	1·005
[1] 1916–20	1·359	1·009
1921–25	1·065	0·816
1926–30	0·922	0·721
1931	0·869	0·686
1932	0·815	0·636
1933	0·799	0·639
1934	0·740	0·586

[1] Mortality refers to civilians only.

It will be seen that the mortality has steadily declined since 1851—the first year for which standardized death rates are recorded. Several causes have been alleged for this decrease, such as better housing and sanitary conditions, improved social habits, diminished drunkenness, higher standard of living, earlier diagnosis, segregation of advanced cases, sanatorium treatment, and the development of a racial immunity. It is extremely difficult to assess the importance of these factors. Greenwood and Wolff (1928) are of the opinion that greater weight must be ascribed to social, hygienic, and cultural improvements than to biological factors, such as the progressive increase in the resistance of the race through natural selection and acquired immunity.

Wolff (1935) points out that the tuberculosis mortality has declined more in the industrialized States of Europe than in those which are still mainly agricultural. The main reason for this, he believes, is that the standard of living and general social hygiene are on a higher level in the industrially developed than in agricultural countries. Much the same thesis is put forward by Baskett (1931), who maintains that in all civilized countries the phthisis mortality is inversely correlated with the level of real wages. That biological factors are also operating, however, is almost certain. Ostenfeld, Heitmann, and Neander (1931), for example, point out that in Sweden during the past century there has been a centrifugal spread in the frequency of the disease. A hundred years ago the highest death rate from tuberculosis was in Södermanland, where now it is lowest ; while Norbotten, which 100 years ago was relatively free from the disease, is now specially affected. The suggestion is that the resistance of a population in which the disease has been prevalent for some generations is greater than that of a population coming into contact with tuberculosis for the first time. Further evidence in support of this thesis will be found in a later section dealing with tuberculosis in native races.

Among the social factors that are of importance, Wolff (1930b) lays great stress on diet. During the Great War the death rate from tuberculosis in German cities, which was only 1·57 per 1,000 in 1913, rose in 1918 to 2·87. In Warsaw by 1917 it had reached 8·4 per 1,000, and in Belgrade, as the result of the military occupation and want of food, it rose to the enormous figure of 14·0 per 1,000 (Dublin, see Opie 1929). Experimentally, there is some evidence that animals fed on a plentiful diet are more resistant to infection than those on a meagre diet, and that vitamin A deficiency may lower their resistance (see Robertson 1934, Clausen 1934, and Chapter LI).

Without in any way minimizing the desirability of active public measures against tuberculosis, it may be pointed out that the decline in the tuberculosis death rate in this country set in long before the establishment of hospitals, sanatoria, or dispensaries for the treatment of patients suffering from the disease, indicating that the underlying social, economic, and biological causes were able by themselves to effect a considerable reduction in the mortality from tuberculosis in the absence of any *ad hoc* public health interference.

Some Factors affecting the Mortality from Tuberculosis.

Occupation.—Occupation is of importance. In this country the mortality from pulmonary tuberculosis is below the average for all males in fishermen and coalminers, but is high in stone and slate quarrymen, in cutlers, file-makers, earthenware manufacturers, and highest of all in the Cornish tin-miners. All trades, in fact, in which the men are exposed to the inhalation of particles of metallic or stone dust, particularly dust containing silica, have a high mortality rate from pulmonary tuberculosis. Both experimental and field work have shown the predisposing action of silica towards tuberculosis (Gye and Kettle 1922, Kettle 1924, 1930).

Age and Sex.—We have no space to analyse the age and sex incidence fully. Table LXXXVII shows the high mortality of the disease in the 0–5 age group ; the fall during the period of adolescence ; the great increase in mortality, especially in women between the ages of 15 and 30 ; and the high mortality in men between the ages of 40 and 55 from what is known as the late adult type of tuberculosis.

TABLE LXXXVII

Deaths from Tuberculosis in 1934 in England and Wales classified according to Age and Sex.

Age Group.	Tuberculosis (all forms).		Tuberculosis of Respiratory System.	
	Males.	Females.	Males.	Females.
All ages	17,448	13,434	14,734	10,948
0–1	242	171	39	18
1–5	693	615	83	65
5–10	337	349	69	59
10–15	335	414	101	214
15–20	901	1,412	688	1,198
20–25	1,843	2,194	1,604	1,983
25–30	1,748	1,905	1,570	1,757
30–35.	1,678	1,485	1,527	1,369
35–40	1,494	1,118	1,371	1,022
40–45	1,473	900	1,378	796
45–50	1,707	776	1,624	705
50–55	1,662	624	1,576	546
55–60	1,402	510	1,316	435
60–65	927	382	889	333
65–70	637	289	580	229
70–75	232	168	209	131
75–80	102	80	85	63
80 and upwards	35	42	25	25

During the present century a great change has come over the age and sex distribution of tuberculosis. Reference to Fig. 247 will show that during last century and the first decade of the present century the mean annual death rate per 100,000 living was highest in infancy and early childhood, while in 1933 it was highest in the 20–25 age group.

The fall in the death rate during the early years of life has been most striking. This is almost certainly attributable to some extent to the much greater care now exercised in infant welfare, and to the more general provision of pasteurized milk (see Drolet 1930). It may be noted that the highest tuberculosis mortality in children occurs during the 1–2 age group, and is due to various types—respiratory, meningeal, abdominal, miliary, and chronic disseminated. Meningitis alone is responsible for about 50 per cent. of the total deaths during the first 10 years of life.

The death rate in young adults, on the other hand, has undergone much less alteration. Most of the deaths in this group are due to pulmonary tuberculosis, and as Fig. 248 shows, the death rate from this form is much higher in females than in males in the 10–30 age group. Indeed the female pulmonary tuberculosis death rate in the 20–25 age group is practically identical with that in the first years of the century.

After the age of 30 the male pulmonary tuberculosis death rate increases, till in the 45–55 age group it is nearly three times that of the female death rate. The reasons for these differences are not apparent, and though they are often lightly attributed to changes in the general mode of life of young women during the present century, and to the greater strain of competitive existence among men, the reasons are undoubtedly complex, and we shall do well to refrain from attempting to simplify them unduly. We may note that the changes in the age and sex distribution of tuberculosis are not confined to this country, but are reflected in greater or less degree in the statistics of many other European countries and of the United States of America (see Dow and Lloyd 1930, Drolet 1930, Whitney 1931, Macnalty 1932).

Race and Civilization.—Certain races seem to be more susceptible than others; thus the Negroes in North America suffer much more severely than the white population. In eight of the great cities of the United States, the mortality from tuberculosis in 1920 amongst the white population varied from 0·794 to 1·216 per 1,000

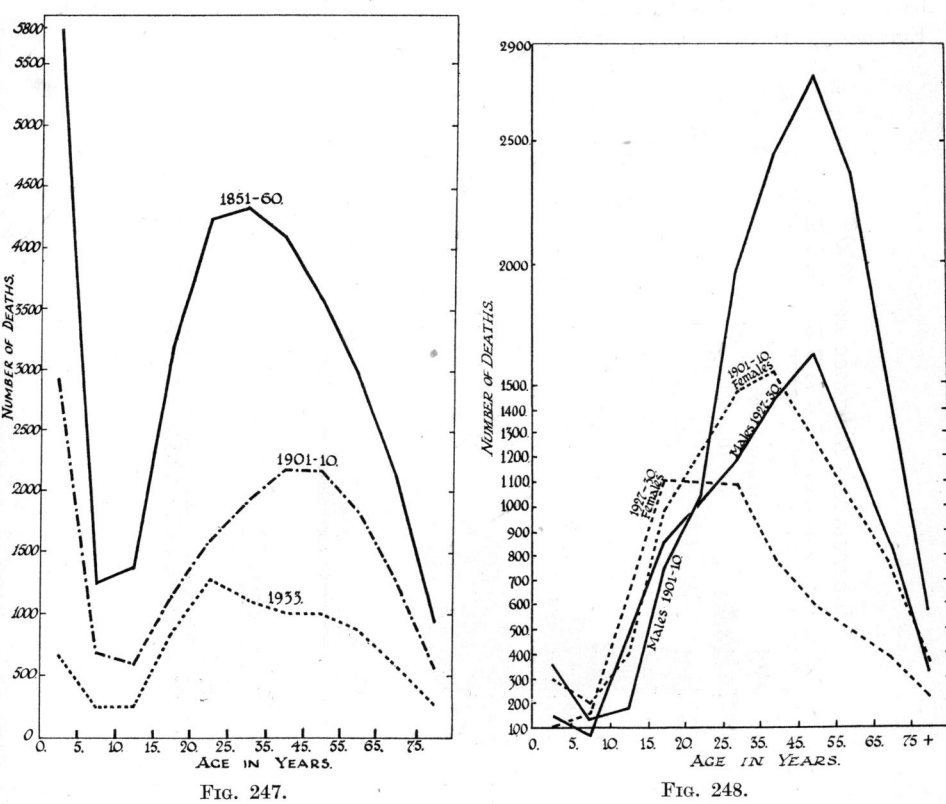

FIG. 247.

Death rates per million from tuberculosis (all forms) at ages. England and Wales 1851–60, 1901–10, and 1933.

FIG. 248.

Death rates per million from pulmonary tuberculosis at ages for each sex. England and Wales 1901–10 and 1927–30.

living, whereas amongst the coloured population it varied from 2·855 to 4·405 per 1,000 (Mossell 1923). Jews, on the other hand, are said to have a high resistance. In Fig. 249 is represented the incidence per 1,000 from tuberculosis amongst different races living under military conditions.

It will be seen that the differences in mortality between different races are very striking. There are so many factors influencing the distribution and mortality of tuberculosis that it would be unjustifiable to conclude that all these differences are due to a lower *genetic* resistance of the coloured than of the white races. The environment in which the two races live, the level of personal and social hygiene, the nature of the diet, and numerous other factors vary widely, and we know of no data in which the mortality of the disease is compared in coloured and white subjects living under identical conditions and exposed to the same risk of infection from birth upwards (see Krause 1928, Johnson and Myers 1933, Scott 1935).

In primitive peoples living in their native countries tuberculosis either does not occur or is comparatively uncommon. This freedom from tuberculosis appears to be not an expression of the inherent resistance of man living under natural conditions, but is rather due to the lack of opportunity of infection with the tubercle bacillus. Once this organism is imported—generally by the advent of infected Europeans—the disease may spread rapidly, provided the environmental conditions

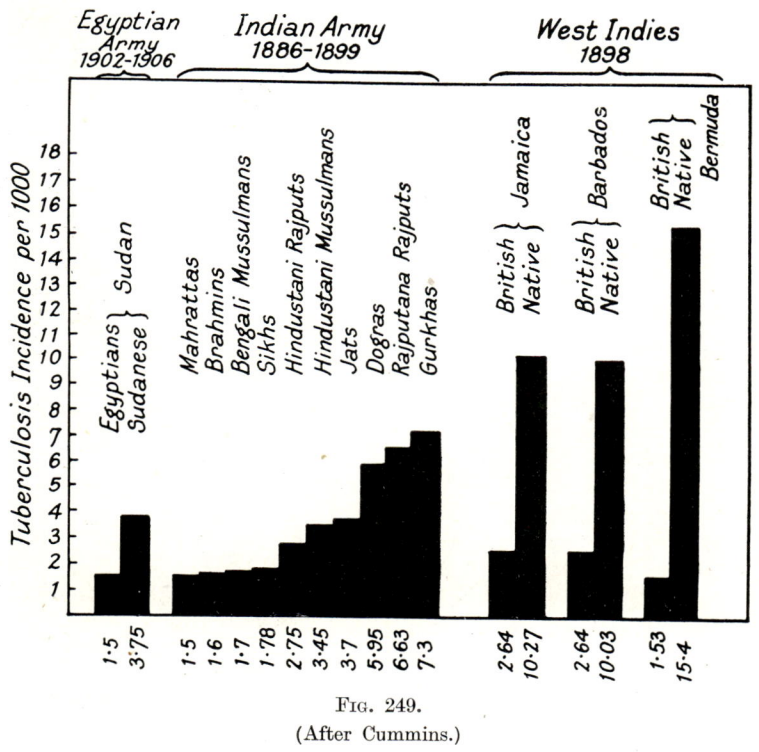

Fig. 249.
(After Cummins.)

are suitable. The same happens when primitive peoples leave their native country and take up residence in a civilized area. Many of them become infected, contract a severe form of the disease, and die.

This sequence of events has been noticed by several competent observers. Cummins (1908) found that the death rate from tuberculosis amongst the Sudanese in the Egyptian Army was considerably higher than amongst the Egyptians (Fig. 249). In their native country tuberculosis was rare; but when they were brought into contact with more civilized peoples, they proved to be very susceptible to the disease. Metchnikoff, Burnet, and Tarassevitch in 1911 reported that the nomadic Tartar Kalmuks 50 years ago were practically free from tuberculosis; but that under the influence of increasing contact with the Russians, they were becoming more and more infected by the disease. In the central parts of the Steppes cases were uncommon, but at the periphery, where contact with civilization occurred most freely, tuberculosis was very frequent. Coleman, reporting on the North American Indians, brought evidence to show that tuberculosis was unknown before the advent of Europeans. With the advance of civilization, however, it has become increasingly common. The toll of life levied by the disease in some tribes is enormous ; in 1896, for example, amongst the Oglalas the incidence of tuberculosis was 148·7 per 1,000, and the death rate 24·88 per 1,000. Borrel's (1920) observations on the Senegalese troops during the War are of great interest. In the villages and interior of Senegal tuberculosis is rare ; but when the Senegalese troops were brought to France, large numbers of them developed tuberculosis. The longer their stay was in France, the higher was the incidence of tuberculosis amongst them.

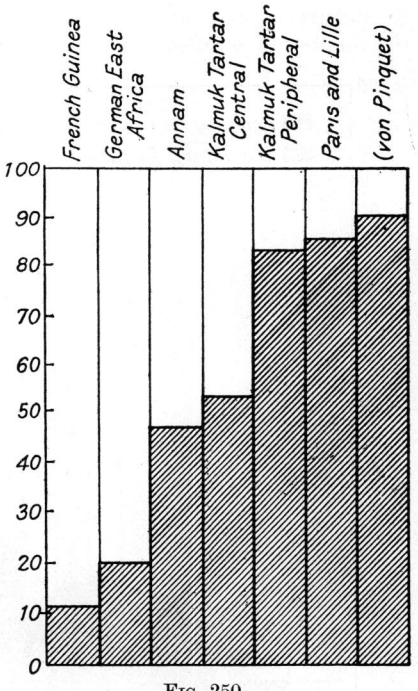

FIG. 250.

Comparative percentages of positive cutaneous tuberculin reactions in primitive and civilized peoples. (After Cummins.)

After 1 year's stay the mortality from tuberculosis was 2 per 1,000 ; after 3 to 4 years' stay it was 16 per 1,000. In 1918 the case incidence was as high as 36·1 per 1,000. (For references to these and other observations see Cummins 1911–12, Westernhoeffer 1911, Bushnell 1920.) A study of the tuberculin reaction (see p. 1016) shows that in primitive peoples the proportion of positive reactors is low ; but that the more they come into contact with civilization, the greater is the proportion of reactors (Fig. 250).

Not only, however, is the mortality from tuberculosis high amongst primitive peoples brought into contact with civilization, but the type of disease is entirely different from that usually met with in civilized countries. Instead of the localized, slowly spreading, ulcerative type of phthisis, the disease often pursues a rapid course, fatal in a few weeks to a few months. Pathologically, the glands at the site of infection—generally the tracheo-bronchial group—are enormously enlarged and caseating, and there are miliary tubercles throughout the body. The tissues seem to be devoid of resisting power ; there is no fibrosis, no limitation of the lesions, and no attempt at healing.

This acute type of tuberculosis recalls the type that is met with in infants of civilized peoples. A fairly high proportion of infants who become infected with the tubercle bacillus develop an acute, fatal disease, generally of the miliary type. That this is true is shown by the combined evidence of the tuberculin test, the mortality statistics, and post-mortem findings (see p. 1019). After the first year of life in civilized peoples, tuberculosis assumes a sub-acute or chronic course, and the miliary spread is seen only as a fatal termination, not as a primary manifestation of the disease. But in uncivilized races brought for the first time into contact with tuberculosis, the acute, fatal, miliary type is seen quite commonly even in adults.

At the present time there must be very few native races left that have not had some degree of contact with civilization. Tuberculin surveys carried out in recent years have shown that most native races are now undergoing a process of tuberculization, and it is to be expected that the acute miliary type so often met with in peoples brought into contact with tuberculosis for the first time will gradually give way to the more chronic types characteristic of civilized peoples. See Paneth (1928), Scott (1929, 1935), Editorial (1929), Duchêne (1929), Goodale and Krischner (1930), Kleine (1930), Schwetz (1930), Schwetz *et al.* (1930), Grasset and Perret-Gentil (1930), Whitney (1931), Pinner and Kasper (1932), Report (1932*b*), Review (1933), Sauvan (1935), Rodríguez Pastor *et al.* (1935), Long (1935).

The Frequency of Tuberculosis.

In this country tuberculosis is a notifiable disease, and it might be thought that the number of notified cases would afford a fair estimate of the frequency of the disease. In fact, however, this is not so. For various reasons —medical and social—large numbers of cases are not notified, and the resulting figures sometimes scarcely exceed the deaths. They are in fact so unreliable that, since 1931, the Registrar-General has ceased to publish them in his Annual Report. Neither the morbidity nor the mortality statistics afford any adequate idea of the prevalence of tuberculous infection. To obtain a satisfactory idea of this, it is necessary to resort to three other sources of information, namely, the tuberculin test, post-mortem statistics, and X-ray examination.

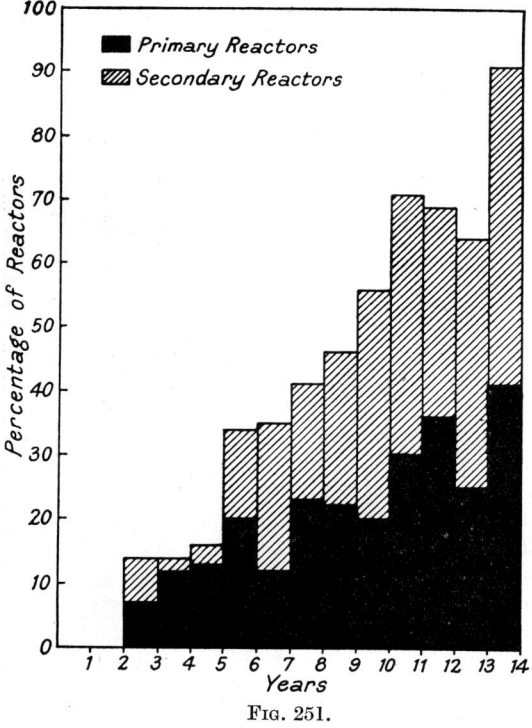

Fig. 251.
(Modified from von Pirquet.)

Latent Tuberculosis as revealed by the Tuberculin Test. —The tuberculin test as used by von Pirquet (1907) consists in placing a drop of tuberculin on the forearm and a drop of 50 per cent. glycerine adjacent to it as a control. With a small lancet a scratch is made through each of the drops. A positive reaction is denoted by the appearance within 24 or 48 hours of a bright red papule, at least 5 mm. in diameter at the site of inoculation of the tuberculin; later the colour becomes dark red, and the lesion disappears in about a week. This may be called a primary positive reaction. In some persons, however, the reaction is delayed for a few days, or occurs only after a second inoculation a week later—torpid or secondary reaction. From a large series of tests, it would appear that a primary positive reaction is evidence of the existence in the body of a comparatively recent tuberculous lesion, which may or may not be actively progressing. A torpid or secondary reaction is believed to indicate the existence of an old tuberculous lesion in the process of healing. Complete failure to react is regarded as evidence that the person has never come into contact with tuberculosis, or that healing has occurred. Von Pirquet's original technique has been modified by many subsequent observers, some of whom lay stress on the advantages to be gained by using varying dilutions of tuberculin, and so obtaining quantitative results.

Using this test, von Pirquet (1909) examined 1,134 clinically non-tuberculous infants and children in the Escherich Clinic at Vienna. The patients belonged to the lower classes, and were probably more heavily infected with tuberculosis than were the children of the higher social classes. It is important to remember in interpreting the results, given in Table LXXXVIII and Fig. 251, that tuberculosis was at the time of the investigation exceedingly rife in Vienna ; it is not justifiable, therefore, to regard them as generally applicable to every urban population.

TABLE LXXXVIII

SHOWING THE PERCENTAGE OF CHILDREN WHO REACTED TO THE TUBERCULIN TEST IN VIENNA.
(Modified from von Pirquet.)

Age	0–1	1–2	2–3	3–4	4–5	5–6	6–7	7–8	8–9	9–10	10–11	11–12	12–13	13–14
No. of cases . .	388	89	75	87	62	66	61	39	72	45	44	45	36	22
Primary positive.	—	—	7%	12%	13%	20%	12%	23%	22%	20%	30%	36%	25%	50%
Torpid or secondary positive .	—	—	7%	2%	3%	14%	23%	18%	24%	36%	41%	33%	39%	41%
Total reactors .	—	—	14%	14%	16%	34%	35%	41%	46%	56%	71%	69%	64%	91%

The figures for the older age groups are rather small ; but it is clear that by the age of 10 years about 70 per cent., and by the age of 14 probably over 90 per cent., of children were infected with tuberculosis. It will be noticed that torpid or secondary reactions were uncommon under 5 years, but gradually increased with age ; this may be taken to indicate that quite a high proportion of children between 5 and 14 had old, and probably healing, tuberculous foci.

Similar investigations undertaken by various workers have shown that in the large cities of Europe, such as Paris, Vienna, and Prague, about 20 per cent. of children are infected at the age of 2, 55 per cent. at 5, and 90 per cent. at 15 ; of adults 97 per cent. are infected (Mantoux 1910, Calmette *et al.* 1911).

The von Pirquet test is now being gradually displaced by the *graded intradermal or Mantoux test.* In surveying a given population it is usual to inoculate 0·1 c.c. of a 1/10,000 dilution of old tuberculin intradermally into the forearm. A positive reaction is characterized by the development within 48–96 hours of an area of erythema or erythematous infiltration at least 5 mm. in diameter ; many workers insist on a minimal diameter of 10 mm. If the reaction is negative after 48 hours, a second injection is given using 0·1 c.c. of a 1/1000 dilution, and if still negative 48 hours later, a third injection is given using 0·1 c.c. of a 1/100 dilution. Sometimes a fourth injection of a 1/10 dilution may be required. A control test made with broth is unnecessary except with the 1/10 dilution. Non-specific reactions are not infrequent, but usually disappear within 24 or 48 hours. Though in this country it is usual to refer to the actual dilution injected, in the United States the dose is expressed in milligrams of tuberculin ; by this notation 1 mgm. of tuber-culin is supposed to be contained in 0·1 c.c. of a 1/100 dilution.

In general, it may be taken that a reaction to the intradermal inoculation of 1/1000 tuberculin corresponds to a positive von Pirquet test, though perhaps the former is slightly more delicate. In ordinary survey work it will generally be found that about 85–90 per cent. of the total positive reactors respond to the 1/1000 dilution ; by using a 1/100 dilution a further 5–15 per cent., and by using a 1/10 dilution a further 3–5 per cent., of reactors may be detected (Hetherington *et al.* 1929, Dow and Lloyd 1931, Hart 1932). It will thus be seen that the intra-dermal test made with the lower dilutions is more sensitive than the von Pirquet test.

Some of the results obtained during recent years by the graded intradermal test are reproduced in graphical form in Fig. 252.

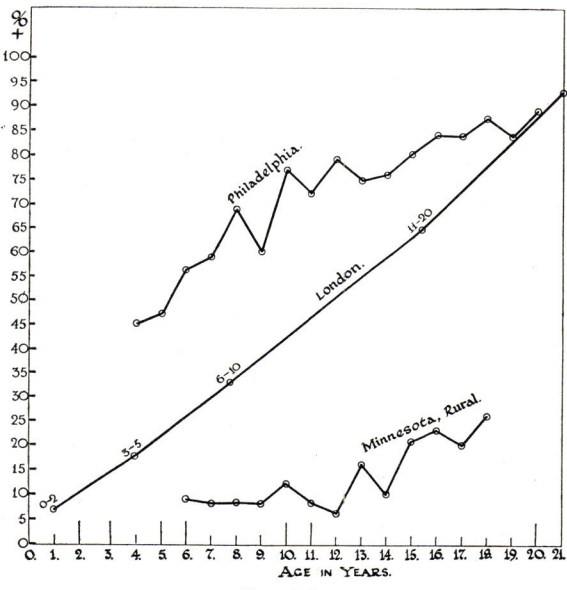

Fig. 252.

Percentage of children and adolescents reacting to the intradermal inoculation of old tuberculin·
   (1) Philadelphia school children reacting to 1/100 dilution (Hetherington *et al.* 1934).
   (2) London hospital children reacting to 1/100 dilution (Hart 1932).
   (3) School children in wealthy rural community in Minnesota reacting to 1/1000 dilution
      or to von Pirquet test (Slater and Jordan 1932).

It is apparent that in the large industrial cities of Europe and America most children are infected with tuberculosis by the time they reach 18 years of age, but in rural areas infection is much less frequent. Since only a comparatively small proportion of reacting children develop clinical tuberculosis or die of the disease, it is clear that in the majority of them the infection must remain latent. This deduction is of fundamental importance to a proper understanding of the mechanism of immunity in tuberculosis.

It has been shown by a number of workers that children brought up in contact with open cases of tuberculosis react to tuberculin at a much earlier age than normal children. Fig. 253, taken from Dow and Lloyd (1931), shows that over 70 per cent. of children of such parents react positively by the age of 5 years. In children brought up in contact with tuberculous parents having a negative sputum the proportion of tuberculin-positives is little higher than in normal children.

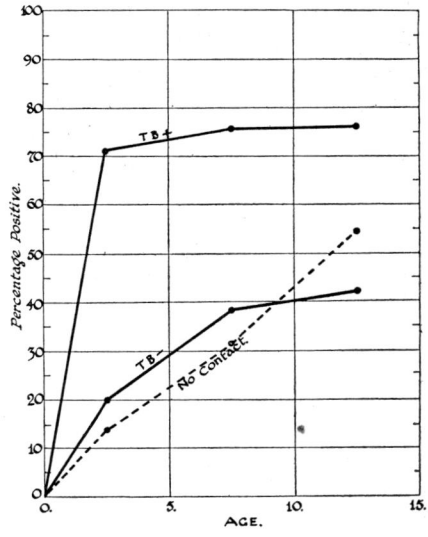

Further references to tuberculin surveys will be found in papers by Scheel (1929) Myers (1930), Myers *et al.* (1934), Brink *et al.* (1933), Cummins and Evans (1933), Drolet (1934), van den Berg (1936).

Latent Tuberculosis as revealed by Post-mortem Statistics.—It is one of the commonest experiences of the post-mortem room to find evidence of tuberculosis in persons who presented no clinical evidence of the disease during life, and who died from some other cause. The lungs and lymphatic glands are the organs that are usually affected. For purposes of classification we may divide tuberculosis as found at autopsy into three classes : (1) Fatal tuberculosis, in which the disease has been directly responsible for death. (2) *Latent active tuberculosis,* in which advancing, generally caseous, lesions are found, but

Fig. 253.

Percentage of contact and non-contact children reacting to the intradermal tuberculin test at ages. (Dow and Lloyd 1931).

which do not appear to be the immediate cause of death. (3) *Latent inactive tuberculosis,* in which the lesions are apparently healed and often calcified.

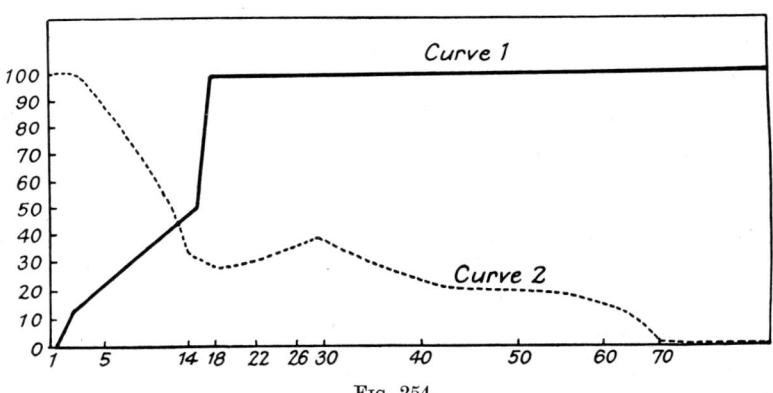

Fig. 254.

Curve 1 = frequency of tuberculous lesions in every 100 autopsies of the same age group.
Curve 2 = frequency of fatal tuberculosis in relation to all cases of tuberculosis.
(After Naegeli.)

In 1900 Naegeli published the results of an investigation at Zürich, made to determine the frequency of tuberculous lesions in subjects coming to autopsy. A very careful examination was made of every cadaver, and all doubtful lesions were subjected to microscopic examination. Caseation and calcification were accepted as evidence of tuberculosis ; the oblique, distorted indurations at the lung apex were considered tuberculous or not, according to histological examination and the presence of other tuberculous lesions in the body. Table LXXXIX and Fig. 254 show his general results.

TABLE LXXXIX

MODIFIED FROM NAEGELI (1900), SHOWING THE FREQUENCY OF TUBERCULOSIS (TB.) OF ALL FORMS IN POST-MORTEM SUBJECTS AT ZÜRICH.

	Autopsies.	Tb. not found.	Tb. found.	Percentage Tb.	Of Tb. Patients.			
					Died of Tb.	Percentage.	Non-lethal Tb.	Percentage.
Children 0–18 years .	88	73	15	17·04	11	73·3	4	26·7
Adults 18 years and over	420	29	391	93·11	110	28·13	281	71·84

The surprising observation was made that, in adults, 93·11 per cent. showed evidence of tuberculosis. In his first series of 136 adults, only 113 or 83·1 per cent. were found to be tuberculous ; but in his last series of 284 adults, probably owing to his greater experience, as many as 278 or 97·9 per cent. were found to be tuberculous. It will be observed that of the children who showed tuberculosis, 73·3 per cent. had died of the disease (Table LXXXIX). In other words, latent or non-lethal tuberculosis is very much commoner in adults than in early life. Naegeli came to the following conclusions : (1) Tuberculosis is very infrequent in infancy, reaches 96 per cent. by the 18th year, and 100 per cent. by the 50th year. (2) In infancy 100 per cent. of cases of tuberculosis are fatal ; at 18 years of age 29 per cent. are fatal ; 38 per cent. at 30 years ; 22 per cent. at 40 years ; 10 per cent. at 65 years, and practically none at 70 years. (3) Latent active tuberculosis is uncommon in children ; reaches 33 per cent. at puberty ; 40 per cent. at 30 years ; and falls to 25 per cent. in later years. (4) Latent inactive or healed tuberculosis is infrequent before 18 ; reaches 25 per cent. in the 3rd decennium ; 40 per cent. in the 4th decennium ; and 75 per cent. in the 70th year. (5) The disposition towards fatal tuberculosis is therefore highest in infancy ; falls to puberty ; rises towards 30 years ; and later falls again. After 18 years, immunity increases more or less proportionally to age.

A similar, but more extensive series of autopsies, was reported on by Burkhardt in 1906. The material examined came from the Dresden-Friedrichstadt Hospital, and to a less extent from the Kgl. Frauenklinik. It is important to notice that the autopsies were made on the working-class population. Since the mortality from tuberculosis amongst patients of this class was 35 per cent., while amongst the general population of Dresden it was only 13–14 per cent., it is clear that the results he obtained are not absolutely representative of the population as a whole. His figures are shown in Table XC.

These figures agree fairly well with Naegeli's. The chief differences are that the incidence of tuberculosis in children is higher, the mortality from tuberculosis in children is less, and that in adults is higher than in Naegeli's figures. Both

TABLE XC

	Autopsies.	Tb. not found.	Tb. found.	Percentage Tb.	Of Tb. Patients.			
					Died of Tb.	Percentage.	Non-lethal Tb.	Percentage.
Children 0–18 years .	190	118	72	38	35	48·6	37	51·4
Adults 18 years and over	1,262	113	1,149	91	466	40·6	683	59·4

agree in showing that in persons of 18 and onwards the incidence of tuberculosis exceeds 90 per cent.

Burkhardt gives a very instructive table recording the incidence of latent tuberculosis in the different age groups (Table XCI).

From this table it is seen that, though the percentage of persons with latent active tuberculosis does not vary greatly in the different age groups, the percentage with latent inactive or healed tuberculosis increases progressively with age.

TABLE XCI

SHOWING THE FREQUENCY OF LATENT TUBERCULOSIS IN PERSONS CLASSIFIED ACCORDING TO AGE.

Percentages reckoned on every 100 persons of the same age coming to autopsy.

Age Group.	Latent Active Tb.	Latent Inactive Tb.
	Per cent.	Per cent.
1–5	9	4
5–14	25	11
14–18	5	24
18–30	12	26
30–40	14	34
40–50	18	38
50–60	19	44
60–70	21	50
70–80	22	57
80–90	22	61

The general inferences which appear to be justified by these results are as follows :

(1) The great majority of persons living in civilized countries, and particularly in urban communities, have been infected with some form of tuberculosis by the time they attain adult life.

(2) Between 10 and 20 per cent. of persons of all ages living in such communities are suffering from some focus of tuberculous infection which, though latent, is active.

(3) A large proportion of these latent active lesions must heal spontaneously, since evidence of healed tuberculosis increases with age.

It must be understood that Naegeli's and Burkhardt's figures refer to all forms of tuberculosis. For the frequency of pulmonary tuberculosis, see p. 1030 and Tables XCIV and XCV (p. 1030).

The conclusions of these two workers on the Continent have received support from the careful observations of Blacklock (1932, 1935) at the Royal Hospital for Sick Children, Glasgow. Blacklock made post-mortem examinations on 1,800 children under 13 years of age dying from various causes during the years 1924–34. He found (1) that practically all children under 2 years of age showing tuberculous lesions had actually died of tuberculosis, whereas in children 4–13 years of age only about 75 per cent. had died of this disease, and (2) that the percentage of positive tuberculin reactors in the first two years of life was nearly the same as the percentage incidence of tuberculous lesions found at autopsy, indicating again that at this age practically all children who became infected died of the disease. These figures refer to a low social class in Scotland in which tuberculosis is undoubtedly a very severe disease, and it would be unjustifiable to conclude that they are valid for all classes and for all countries.

In considering the *fatality of tuberculous infection in early life*, it must be remembered that the type of case seen by Naegeli, by Burkhardt and by Blacklock, was not representative of the whole infantile population, but merely of that portion of the infantile population which showed symptoms of disease of sufficient severity to demand admission to hospital. If an equal number of apparently healthy infants could have been examined, it is quite conceivable that many would have shown latent tuberculous lesions. All our figures hitherto have been selective. The diagnosis of tuberculosis in infancy is extremely difficult, and only advanced and fatal cases are recorded. The result is that we have come to believe that infection in infancy is usually fatal. That this conclusion is wrong is shown very clearly by the observations made at Lübeck on the infants who were vaccinated by the mouth during the first few days of life with the B.C.G. strain (see p. 1050). The vaccine had by mischance become contaminated with virulent human tubercle bacilli and a large number of the infants became infected (Report 1935b). Out of 251 vaccinated infants, 72 died of tuberculosis, 5 died of other causes, while 174 were alive two to three years later. It is probable that all the surviving children had been infected to a greater or less extent, and radiographical examination actually showed the presence of calcified mesenteric glands in 127 of them. It is interesting to note that practically all cases that developed a primary lung lesion died, while the majority, which had primary alimentary lesions, survived.

We may conclude tentatively that tuberculous infection in infancy is often liable to cause death, particularly if it occurs by the respiratory tract. Infection is, however, by no means uniformly fatal. Provided the environmental conditions are good, and exposure to infection is not too severe or repeated, it seems probable that latent lesions may result of a type similar to those met with in later years.

Latent Pulmonary Tuberculosis as revealed by X-ray Examination.

In recent years X-ray examination of the chest has come to play an important part in the diagnosis of pulmonary tuberculosis, since it is possible by this means to detect lesions before clinical manifestations have developed. In several countries surveys are now being made to determine the frequency of pulmonary lesions in different classes of the population. Table XCII, taken from Hetherington, McPhedran, Landis and Opie (1929), affords an example of the type of result obtained.

It refers to the roentgenological examination of school children, both white and

TABLE XCII

SHOWING PERCENTAGE OF PULMONARY LESIONS RECOGNIZED BY X-RAY EXAMINATION IN SCHOOL CHILDREN IN PHILADELPHIA, U.S.A., MOST OF WHOM REACTED TO 1/10,000 TUBERCULIN. (Hetherington *et al.* 1929, and Opie 1930.)

Age Group.	No. of Children Examined.	Tb. Foci in Lungs and Lymphatic Glands—mainly Calcified.	Childhood Type of Tuberculosis.		Adult Type of Tuberculosis.		Total Lesions.
			Latent Infiltration.	Clinically Manifest.	Latent Apical.	Clinically Manifest.	
5–9 . . .	124	5·9	1·2	0·6	0·0	0·0	7·7
10–14 . . .	452	13·9	2·1	0·5	0·5	0·1	17·1
15–19 . . .	1,060	20·1	1·9	0·2	1·0	0·5	23·7

coloured, in Philadelphia, Pa. The figures are selective, and refer almost exclusively to those children who reacted to an intradermal injection of 0·1 c.c. of 1/10,000 tuberculin. It will be noted that in the older children over 20 per cent. showed pulmonary or associated glandular lesions. Of these, 0·7 per cent. actually had clinical symptoms of disease. The distinction between the childhood and the adult type of pulmonary tuberculosis may be neglected for the moment; it will be referred to later (p. 1030).

What proportion of latent lesions progress to a stage at which they give rise to clinical tuberculosis is at present unknown. It is quite clear from the post-mortem evidence that has already been given that many of them must remain latent or gradually retrogress. Special *ad hoc* surveys to follow the history of children with such lesions are at present being made, and it is hoped that in 10 years' time or so we shall be in a better position to answer this question.

Numerous other figures might be quoted to show the high frequency of latent active and overt tuberculosis in medical students and nurses, both of whom are often exposed to an unusually high risk of infection (see Heimbeck 1927, 1932, 1933, Ross 1930, Hetherington *et al.* 1931, 1935, Herman *et al.* 1932, Shipman and Davis 1933, Geer 1934, Kramer 1934, Stiehm 1935). Reference may also be made to similar surveys conducted by X-ray examination, sometimes in association with the tuberculin test, in school children and other classes of the population (see Chadwick 1927, Opie *et al.* 1929, Hewitt and Cutts 1932, Martin *et al.* 1934, Fellows 1934, Rouvillois 1934, Harrington *et al.* 1935, Weber *et al.* 1935).

Frequency of Tuberculosis in relation to Degree of Exposure to Infection.

It has already been pointed out that in children exposed to contact with patients suffering from open tuberculosis the proportion reacting to tuberculin reaches a high figure in the early years of life (see Fig. 253, p. 1019). Observations by numerous workers on families containing one or more members with a positive sputum have now shown that the children in these families have a much higher morbidity and mortality rate from tuberculosis than children in families with sputum-negative patients, and still more so than children in families completely free from tuberculosis. In this country Cox (1929) analysed the histories of 1,486 children under 5 years of age in Lancashire exposed to contact in the home with open tuberculosis. In these children the death rate from non-pulmonary tuberculosis was 9 times greater in the 0–1 year age group, 14 times greater in the 1–2 age group, and 19 times greater in the 2–5 age group than that of a control child population in the County of Lancaster. The excess deaths, it may be noted, were mainly due to tuberculous meningitis. In households containing one or more persons suffering from tuberculosis but having a negative sputum, the death rate of the exposed children was rather greater than that in control children, but the differences were not statistically significant. Cox's figures have received general confirmation from the observations of Turner in Worcestershire (193_).

In the United States even more convincing evidence is available from the extensive observations of Opie (1928–29, 1935) and his colleagues (see Opie and McPhedran 1935, McPhedran and Opie 1935), and of such workers as Evarts, Potter, and Dunn (1934). The following figures furnished by Opie, McPhedran, and Putnam (1935), which refer to the development of pulmonary tuberculosis, are of interest in showing not only the much greater frequency of the disease in subjects exposed to open cases of tuberculosis, but also the proportion developing pulmonary tuberculosis in relation to the age of exposure.

(1) Of persons first exposed between 0 and 9 years to contact with sputum-positive patients, 9·92 per cent. of those living 12–14 years after the beginning of exposure had acquired pulmonary tuberculosis, whereas among those exposed to contact with sputum-negative patients, only 1·97 per cent. subsequently developed the disease.

(2) Of persons first exposed between 10 and 14 years to contact with sputum-positive patients, 20 per cent. of those living 10–14 years after the beginning of exposure had acquired pulmonary tuberculosis.

(3) Of persons first exposed after 15 years of age to contact with sputum-positive patients, 9·68 per cent. had acquired pulmonary tuberculosis, while the corresponding figure for persons exposed to sputum-negative patients was 6·86 per cent.

As the result of these observations we may conclude with Opie and his colleagues that the spread of tuberculosis in the community is, in great part, the result of slowly progressive household epidemics, which often transmit the disease by contagion from one generation to another.

TUBERCULOSIS OF HUMAN ORIGIN. METHODS OF INFECTION

Tubercle bacilli may gain entrance to the body by various routes.

The possibility of *congenital* infection seems to be very small. Sitzenfrey (see Ghon *et al.* 1925) examined 26 placentas from tuberculous mothers, and found tuberculous lesions in 7 of them ; on the basis of these results Moll (see Ghon *et al.* 1925) argues that there are two types of infantile tuberculosis : (1) an early form due to hæmatogenous infection of the fœtus from the placenta ; and (2) a later form, of respiratory origin, occurring in extra-uterine life. The former type he would regard as definitely congenital. But Ghon, Kudlich and Winternitz (1925), who have recently investigated this subject, found no evidence to support the occurrence of congenital infection ; in 87 infants investigated at autopsy they found a primary focus of disease indicative of post-natal infection ; in none of them was a picture found corresponding to Moll's early form.

Tubercle bacilli may gain access to the body by *direct inoculation,* as by an infected needle or knife, or through an abraded pustule (von Eiselberg 1887). Cases of direct inoculation of tuberculosis are uncommon, but are seen occasionally in butchers, post-mortem attendants, and laundresses.

Infection may occur by passage of the bacilli through the various mucous surfaces of the body, but except for that part of the mouth and pharynx which is more or less common to the respiratory and alimentary tracts, this route of infection is probably of minor importance.

Pulmonary Tuberculosis.—We now come to the much-discussed question of the mode of infection in the most common of all tuberculous diseases—pulmonary tuberculosis. There are two main hypotheses : the first, advocated by von Behring and by Calmette and his colleagues, maintains that infection occurs primarily through the mucosa of the alimentary tract ; the second, advocated by Cornet, Flügge, and in this country by A. S. Griffith and Cobbett particularly, maintains that infection occurs primarily by the respiratory tract. We must consider briefly the evidence in favour of each of these opposing views.

Von Behring in 1904 advanced the hypothesis that the pulmonary tuberculosis of adolescent and adult life is the end-result of an infantile infection contracted by the absorption through the mucosa of the alimentary tract of bacilli ingested with the food. In childhood the infection is manifested by caseous glands, particularly cervical and mesenteric ; in adult life by caseous apical tuberculosis of a chronic type. This hypothesis was supported to some extent by the work of Calmette and Guérin (1905).

Pregnant goats were injected into each udder with 0·02 gm. of a fresh bovine culture. Severe lesions resulted, confined to the udder, and proving fatal in 40–60 days. From one such animal two kids were raised ; one of these was killed in a sickly condition on the 45th day, and the other died on the 51st day after birth. This second animal, besides showing enlarged mesenteric glands at necropsy, also had miliary tubercles in the lungs ; the peribronchial glands were normal. In a second experiment, performed on two kids 5 days old, they delivered 0·05 gm. of a fresh bovine culture directly into the stomach ; two or four doses were given. One of the animals died about 10 weeks later ; post mortem, the mesenteric glands were greatly enlarged ; the lungs were riddled with tubercles ; and the peribronchial and posterior mediastinal glands were very large and were filled with caseous tubercles. In a third experiment, the same procedure was adopted on adult goats. When killed 7 to 9 weeks later, these animals showed little or no swelling of the mesenteric glands ; the peribronchial and posterior mediastinal glands were not affected ; but the lungs were tuberculous. On the basis of these results they conclude that, in the immense majority of cases, pulmonary tuberculosis is contracted, not by inhalation, but by ingestion of dust or products containing tubercle bacilli ; the bacilli pass through the mucosa of the alimentary tract and are carried to the lung. They dissent, however, from von Behring's suggestion that adult pulmonary tuberculosis is due to the slow evolution of an intestinal infection contracted in infancy : on the contrary, they think that adults develop pulmonary tuberculosis more easily than children after intestinal infection ; children are better protected by their lymph-glandular system. Dust, they consider, is infective, not because it is inhaled, but because it is swallowed.

Further experiments by Calmette and Guérin (1906a, b) showed that the lungs might become involved after intra-œsophageal infection of heifers and cows with bovine bacilli. Vallée (1905) found that the bronchial glands of young calves might be infected by feeding the animals on tuberculous milk, but he failed by this method to produce lesions in the lungs. One further piece of evidence adduced by Calmette in favour of the intestinal origin of infection in tuberculosis is the analogy presented by glanders. He states that it is impossible to produce the usual pulmonary type of glanders in horses by intratracheal injection of the bacilli ; but if the glanders bacilli are given to the horse in its drinking water, pulmonary glanders consistently results. He concludes (1920) that in all susceptible animals, including man, tuberculosis in its manifold varieties of localization—glandular, pulmonary, alimentary, etc.—results in the great majority of cases from an infection, primarily lymphatic, then hæmatogenous, having its origin in the absorption of tubercle bacilli by the digestive tract—principally by the buccal, pharyngeal, and intestinal mucosæ.

It will be realized that the evidence adduced by Calmette is entirely derived from experiments on animals. There is no doubt that pulmonary lesions may follow intestinal infection of goats and heifers ; but to infer from this that pulmonary tuberculosis in man is usually secondary to an alimentary infection seems to us to be unjustifiable.

The evidence in favour of the respiratory hypothesis, on the other hand, is largely derived from observations made on human patients ; it depends partly on the anatomical distribution of the lesions, and partly on the types of infecting bacilli.

The workers on the Royal Commission, and subsequently A. S. Griffith, Eastwood, and F. Griffith, examined in all 260 children under 12 years of age who had died of tuber-culosis. From 32 of these children, bovine tubercle bacilli were isolated. In all the cases infected with bovine bacilli in which there were lesions, the anatomical evidence pointed definitely to the alimentary tract as the portal of entry of the bacilli (Griffith, A. S., 1925b). In these cases the mesenteric glands were the most severely affected regional lymphatic glands ; the bronchial glands either were not macroscopically tuberculous, or showed disease of slighter degree and in an earlier stage. The anatomical picture of the disease in children from whom human tubercle bacilli were obtained was less uniform than in the bovine cases. They could be divided into three groups : (1) In the first group the respiratory tract was evidently the portal of entry ; the bronchial glands were the most severely affected regional lymphatic glands ; the mesenteric glands either not being affected, or showing more recent disease obviously secondary to the thoracic disease. (2) In the second group, both the bronchial and the mesenteric glands were severely affected, and there was nothing to indicate that one set of glands had been infected previously to the other. Probably infection had occurred simultaneously by both the respiratory and the alimentary tracts. (3) The third group was a small one, and contained those cases in which the alimentary tract was the sole portal of entry of the human bacillus ; the distribution of disease was the same as in the bovine cases.

From these results the following conclusions were drawn : (1) The path of infection of the *bovine* tubercle bacillus is almost exclusively the alimentary tract. (2) The chief portal of entry of the *human* tubercle bacillus is the respiratory tract. (3) Primary abdominal tuberculosis due to the human tubercle bacillus is rare.

We know that pulmonary tuberculosis is, with few exceptions, due to the human tubercle bacillus ; and we have evidence, founded on post-mortem results, to show that the human tubercle bacillus generally enters the body by the respiratory tract. We may therefore conclude that in most cases of pulmonary tuberculosis infection has occurred by the respiratory and not by the alimentary tract.

Further evidence of the inhalation hypothesis is obtained by considering the types of tubercle bacilli that are found in different situations of the body (Table XCIII).

It will be seen that 98 per cent. of infections of the lungs and 95 per cent. of infections of the bronchial glands are due to the human type of bacillus. On the other hand, as many as 50 per cent. of abdominal and 46 per cent. of cervical gland infections are due to the bovine bacillus. If, as von Behring and Calmette suppose, pulmonary tuberculosis

TABLE XCIII

Showing the Proportion of Bovine and Human Infections in different Varieties of Tuberculosis. (Modified from Cobbett 1922.)

Type of Tuberculosis.	Type of Tubercle Bacillus.	
	England. All Ages.	
	Human.	Bovine.
	Per cent.	Per cent.
Pulmonary	97·9	2·1
Bronchial glands	94·5	5·5
Abdominal	50	50
Cervical glands	54	46

were due to bacilli that had gained access to the body through the alimentary tract, it would be reasonable to expect that about 50 per cent. of infections of the lungs and bronchial glands would be due to the bovine bacillus. This is clearly not the case. The figures in the table afford no evidence that the bacilli pass downwards from the cervical, or upwards from the mesenteric, glands to invade the bronchial glands and lungs ; on the contrary, the fact that bovine bacilli are uncommon in these organs suggests that infection must occur by some other route, namely the respiratory tract.

If the lungs are infected by the respiratory tract it is not difficult to understand why bacilli of the human type should almost invariably be found in pulmonary tuberculosis. The most common source of infection with the bovine type is milk, and this is invariably ingested by the mouth ; human tubercle bacilli, on the other hand, are often present in the air in the form of cough-spray or in dust from dried sputum, and are in a suitable state to be inhaled. The almost invariable presence of human bacilli in tuberculous lungs strongly suggests that infection occurs by inhalation.

Another argument in favour of the respiratory mode of infection in pulmonary tuberculosis is based on a comparison of the frequency of mesenteric tuberculosis in this country and America. Examining 67 young British adults, Opie (1925) found healed tuberculous lesions of the mesentery in 27 per cent.—a finding that he ascribes to the high incidence of bovine tuberculosis in this country. In America, where bovine tuberculosis is much less frequent, lesions of the mesentery are uncommon in human beings. Yet both in this country and in America, pulmonary tuberculosis is very frequent. If the lungs were infected from the alimentary tract, pulmonary tuberculosis should be much commoner in this country than in America. But this is not so.

Finally we may refer to the very careful studies of Ghon (1916) in Vienna, and of Opie (1917a, b, 1924a, b, 1925) in America, on the anatomical distribution of the lesions in the pulmonary tuberculosis of childhood. Dissection of the lungs after death, aided by preliminary examination with the X-rays, showed that the primary lesion occurred in the substance of the lungs, and that the bronchial glands were infected only secondarily. This clearly points to the respiratory tract as the portal of infection. If the bacilli reached the lungs from the alimentary tract *via* the lymphatics, the bronchial glands should show the primary, and the lungs the secondary lesions.

From these various sources of evidence we conclude that, with the exception of those cases of miliary tuberculosis in which the lungs have been infected from the blood stream, the vast majority of cases of pulmonary tuberculosis are due to infection by the respiratory tract. In the light of recent work a further exception should perhaps be made for those cases of tuberculosis of bovine origin in which the pulmonary disease is apparently secondary to lesions in the glands. Further work is required on the exact mechanism of infection in these cases, but there is no reason to modify substantially the general conclusions that have just been reached.

Dust and Droplet Infection.

Accepting the inhalation hypothesis, we are faced with the problem of how the bacilli gain entrance to the respiratory tract. The evidence brought to bear on this problem is so extensive that we can give nothing more than a brief outline of the conclusions drawn from it. According to Cornet (1889), the chief source of infection is the *dust arising from dried sputum*. Examining 140 specimens of dust taken from various situations—chiefly hospitals, public buildings, and the private rooms of tuberculous patients—he found tubercle bacilli in 40 of them. He believes that tubercle bacilli may remain alive and virulent in dust for 3 or 4 months. He maintains that, apart from his sputum, a patient suffering from pulmonary tuberculosis is harmless. The main objections to this view are : (1) For the tubercle bacilli to be set free by the desiccation of sputum the air must be absolutely dry ; if it is at all moist, complete desiccation does not occur. In Europe, at any rate, the atmospheric conditions during most of the year are unfavourable for complete desiccation. (2) During the process of drying there is evidence that the tubercle bacilli, especially if exposed to sunlight, are liable to die (Heymann 1901, Mayer, E., 1921, Caldwell 1925, Eidinow 1927).

According to Flügge (1899) and members of his school (Moeller 1899, Heymann 1901, Findel 1907, Ziesché 1907, Hollmann 1924), the tubercle bacilli gain entrance to the respiratory tract in the form of *minute droplets* expelled from the mouth and nose of patients suffering from open pulmonary tuberculosis. Buchner showed that bacteria suspended in a very fine spray could be conveyed through several metres of rubber tubing, even when only a light current of air was used. Laschtschenko found that sprayed tuberculous sputum carried tubercle bacilli in suspension over a considerable distance when propelled by an air-current of only 3 mm. per second. By taking suspensions of *Chr. prodigiosum* into his mouth, he showed that organisms were expelled to a slight extent during speaking, to a greater extent in coughing, and to a still greater extent in sneezing. Numerous workers have found that tuberculous patients when coughing expel droplets containing tubercle bacilli ; these droplets are projected for varying distances, but not further as a rule than $1\frac{1}{2}$ metres. Guinea-pigs placed about half a metre from the mouth of tuberculous patients, and exposed freely to their cough-spray, not uncommonly contract tuberculosis.

To this view Lange and Keschischian (1925) raise objections on the ground that the droplets expelled during the act of coughing are so large that they rapidly fall to the ground. Using a Buchner spray they found that droplets of an aqueous solution of eosin of 200 μ or over in diameter remained in suspension for a few seconds ; droplets of 20 μ and under for a few minutes, and droplets of only a few μ for 1 to 3 hours. But since the droplets expelled in coughing are said to be fairly large, they conclude that primary lung infection by droplets must be uncommon. Their measurements of the size of the droplets were made on glass slides ; but as Strausz (1926) points out, the diameter of a droplet that has settled on a slide is not the same as its diameter when suspended in the air ; in fact it is about three times as great. He concludes, from a series of measurements he made, that the diameter of droplets of sputum suspended in the air is about 50–250 μ, the majority being 70–85 μ. Droplets of this size can probably remain in suspension for a minute or two, and are consequently liable to be inhaled.

Wells (1934) notes that the falling velocity of a small droplet is proportional to the square of its diameter. He calculates that the time taken for droplets of various sizes to fall 2 metres—rather over the height of a tall man—is as follows : droplets with a diameter of 0·1 mm. 6 seconds, of 0·01 mm. 10 minutes, of 0·001 mm. 16·6 hours. But as these droplets fall they evaporate, and the rate of evaporation is again proportional to the square of the diameter. Water droplets with a diameter of 1 mm., falling in unsaturated air at a temperature of 18° C., will evaporate in 165 secs., those with a diameter of 0·1 mm. in 1·7 secs., those with a diameter of 0·05 mm. in 0·4 secs. Droplets expelled from the human mouth in coughing, sneezing or loud talking will clearly not evaporate so rapidly as droplets of water, since they contain in solution substances that tend to retain water ; but the same general relations will hold. The larger droplets, those of 0·1 mm. or over in diameter, will tend to behave as above. They will settle rapidly, and while settling, and for some little time after, they will retain their droplet form. Smaller droplets will behave quite differently. They will remain suspended in the air for much longer periods ; but, since they soon lose their water by evaporation, they will quickly cease to be droplets and will become what the author refers to as " droplet nuclei," *i.e.* the bacteria or other particles contained in the droplet together with any substances in solution, the whole in a desiccated or semi-desiccated state. The physical properties of these " droplet nuclei " are not precisely calculable, but all analogies suggest that they might remain suspended in air for a very considerable time. They would, moreover, be carried long distances by air currents.

This wide difference in behaviour between large and small droplets is, as the author emphasizes, of obvious significance in relation to the spread of infection. The term " droplet infection," as commonly employed in medical literature, should be regarded as applying to the spread of infection by larger droplets. It is spread of this sort that will usually be measured in experiments where Petri dishes are exposed at various distances from a coughing or speaking person. Spread by the smaller droplets and their nuclei is best described as " air-borne " infection. It will obey quite different laws and may, under certain conditions, be of great epidemiological importance. (See also Wells and Stone 1934.)

From animal experiments there is no doubt that tubercle bacilli, whether in the form of dry dust, of moist droplets, or of droplet nuclei, can penetrate the respiratory passages and reach the lung (Lange and Nowoselsky 1925). It is probable therefore that Cornet and Flügge are both right. The only question is which mode of infection is the more common—dust or droplet infection. Considering that in this country the atmospheric conditions are seldom suitable for the formation of absolutely dry dust, whereas the opportunities for droplet infection must be extremely common in such situations as trains, 'buses, trams, theatres, meeting-places, and crowded rooms of all sorts, droplet infection, including air-borne infection by droplet nuclei, is probably of far greater importance than infection by dust. The discussion may seem to be of purely academic interest ; but from the standpoint of preventive medicine it is of considerable importance. Injunctions against spitting are numerous ; but if Flügge's view is correct, it would be of far greater value to educate the public never to cough or sneeze without putting a handkerchief in front of the mouth. If this were done, not only would the risk of contracting tuberculosis be diminished, but a check would be put on all the diseases that are spread by inhalation.

Pathogenesis of Pulmonary Tuberculosis. Childhood and Adult Types.

Evidence has already been brought to show that pulmonary tuberculosis of adults is usually due to respiratory infection. We must now consider the different types of pulmonary disease that occur in childhood and adult life, and decide whether adult pulmonary tuberculosis is a continuation or recrudescence of the childhood form, or is due to a re-infection in later years.

As previously stated, Ghon (1916) came to the conclusion that the primary lesion in tuberculosis of infants and children occurs in the substance of the lungs, and that secondary to this infection the adjacent lymphatic glands become involved. Opie (1917*a*, *b*, 1924*a*, *b*, 1925), besides confirming this conclusion, carried out a large series of examinations on the lungs of persons of all ages who had died of non-tuberculous diseases. The pulmonary tuberculosis of children up to 10 years of age was, he found, essentially of a *focal* type ; the lesions were situated in any part of the lungs, and were accompanied by caseation or calcification of the regional lymphatic glands. In older children, and in adults, two types of tuberculous lesions were found : focal lesions, similar to those in infants and young children ; and apical lesions, situated at the apex of the lungs, and not accompanied by caseation of the regional glands. Focal lesions developed in early childhood, and increased in frequency throughout life, as can be seen by reference to Table XCIV.

TABLE XCIV

FREQUENCY OF HEALED TUBERCULOUS LESIONS (FOCAL OR APICAL) IN THE LUNGS OF PERSONS IN ST. LOUIS, DYING OF DISEASES OTHER THAN TUBERCULOSIS.

Age.	Frequency.
2–5 years	42·8 per cent.
5–10 ,, ...	45·5 ,,
10–18 ,, ...	55·5 ,,
18–30 ,, ...	83·3 ,,
30–50 ,, ...	91·3 ,,
50–70 ,, ...	93·3 ,,

Apical tuberculous lesions were not encountered in young children, but increased with advancing age (Table XCV).

TABLE XCV

FREQUENCY OF LATENT APICAL TUBERCULOSIS IN 50 AUTOPSIES ON PERSONS IN ST. LOUIS, DYING OF DISEASES OTHER THAN TUBERCULOSIS.

Age.	Frequency.
18–30 years	16·7 per cent.
30–50 ,, ...	13 ,,
50–70 ,, ...	26·7 ,,
70 and over	50 ,,

The question naturally arises : Have the apical lesions of adult life developed from the focal lesions of childhood ? Opie brings evidence to disprove this : (1) apical tuberculosis is more common in later life when the focal lesions of childhood have in most instances completely healed ; (2) in adults the focal lesions of childhood are almost invariably calcified and healed, and no longer contain living tubercle bacilli (Opie and Aronson 1927), whereas the apical lesion is relatively fresh and caseous ; (3) in at least half of the cases examined, the focal lesion was in one lung and the apical lesion in the opposite lung. Moreover, the characters of active pulmonary tuberculosis in childhood and in adult life are different.

Characters of Active Pulmonary Tuberculosis of Childhood.	*Characters of Active Pulmonary Tuberculosis of Adults.*
1. No particular localization.	1. Apical localization.
2. Hilum glands involved.	2. Hilum glands not involved.
3. Little or no tendency to cavity formation or deposition of fibrous tissue.	3. Tendency to cavity formation and deposition of fibrous tissue within the lung substance.
4. Rapid course.	4. Chronic course.
5. Similar to infection of normal guinea-pig.	5. Similar to infection of tuberculous guinea-pig.

We may conclude therefore that, though in most cases of apical tuberculosis a focal lesion is present, the apical lesion is not an extension of the focal disease. In other words, the phthisis of adults is not the result of tuberculosis acquired in childhood.

Additional evidence in support of this view has been advanced by Opie (1928–29, 1935) and by Opie, McPhedran, and Putnam (1935). Following up children exposed to contact with open tuberculosis at some time between birth and 9 years of age, these workers found that the maximum proportion of infiltrating lesions of the childhood type detectable by X-ray examination was reached at about 3 years of age, after which it fell gradually to zero by 11 years of age. On the other hand, latent apical lesions of the adult type were not seen before 4 or 5 years of age, but after this they rose progressively as the age of the child increased. In other words, the two types of lesions behaved as if they were entirely unrelated. Further observations showed that children first exposed to infection after 15 years of age usually developed the typical adult apical type of pulmonary disease.

All these findings suggest that the pulmonary tuberculosis of adults is not usually a continuation of childhood disease, but is due to a re-infection some time during late childhood or early adolescent life. It must be pointed out, however, that the lesions so produced often remain latent, and clinically manifest tuberculosis may not develop for months or years after re-infection.

TUBERCULOSIS OF BOVINE ORIGIN. FREQUENCY AND MODE OF INFECTION

Frequency.—The frequency of this type of tuberculosis varies greatly in different countries and in different parts of the same country, depending in general on the incidence of tuberculosis in cattle and the quantity of raw milk consumed. In Scotland the percentage of bovine infection in all forms of tuberculosis is higher than in England. Taking Great Britain as a whole, there were in 1931 about 2,600 deaths and 6,250 notifications (Report 1934). Of the deaths, about three-quarters occurred in children under 15 years of age. These figures are calculated on the proportion of bovine infections in different forms of tuberculosis, and are subject to the error of random sampling. Making allowance, however, for such an error, and for the fact that the notifications probably underestimate the true number of cases, it is clear that the bovine tubercle bacillus is responsible in Great Britain for a large number of deaths and for an immense amount of suffering, invalidity, and often permanent deformity.

In England and Wales about 6·0 per cent. of all deaths from tuberculosis are due to infection of bovine origin. The frequency in other countries is less certain. In the United States Park and Krumwiede (1910), who examined 436 strains of tubercle bacilli, of which 291 were derived from patients with pulmonary tuberculosis, found that 7·57 per cent. were of the bovine type. This percentage, however, is not applicable to the present frequency of tuberculosis of bovine origin. Since 1917 an intensive campaign has been carried out under the Federal Government to eradicate tuberculosis in cattle, and the extent to which these animals are infected is now on an average, probably only about one-tenth of that in Great Britain. Clinical observers are unanimous in agreeing on the comparative infrequency in the United States of cervical and mesenteric glandular tuberculosis in young children, both of which manifestations in this country are generally due to the bovine bacillus (see Reichle 1936). In Germany, Austria, Denmark and Holland the disease appears to be fairly frequent, though probably less so than in Great Britain (see Klimmer 1931, Lange 1932, Blacklock 1932, Tobiesen *et al.* 1935*a, b,* de Lange and de Bruin 1935).

Source of Infection.—Cattle form the great reservoir of infection with the bovine bacillus. In this country about 40 per cent. of all milch cows react to the tuberculin test ; about 40 per cent. slaughtered in public abattoirs show naked-eye lesions of tuberculosis ; and about 0·5 per cent. are actually excreting tubercle bacilli in their milk (Report 1932*a,* 1934, Savage 1933). The proportion of milk samples containing virulent tubercle bacilli varies with the nature of the sample and the part of the country from which it is derived. On an average about 7 per cent. of samples of mixed milk from individual farms contain tubercle bacilli, the proportion varying from about 2 per cent. in Somerset to about 21 per cent. in Cheshire (Report 1932*a,* Gloyne 1932, Pullinger 1934, 1935, Parry and Hall 1935). In Scotland the proportion seems to be even higher (Report 1933*a*).

We have no space to furnish the complete evidence incriminating milk as the main cause in man of tuberculosis of bovine origin. The general nature of the evidence rests on (1) the parallelism in different countries between the frequency of tuberculosis in cattle and of tuberculosis of bovine origin in man ; (2) the high proportion of alimentary infections in man due to the bovine type ; (3) the frequency of non-pulmonary tuberculosis of bovine origin in infancy and childhood ; (4) the comparative infrequency of tuberculosis of bovine origin in areas in which the majority of the milk, even though heavily infected, is pasteurized or boiled before use. The most convincing evidence is afforded by the observations of Price (1932, 1934) in Toronto on the frequency of the bovine type of bacillus in non-pulmonary tuberculosis of childhood. Of 300 tuberculous children examined under 14 years of age, 15 per cent. were found to be infected with the bovine type. Without exception, these children came from parts of Ontario outside Toronto where pasteurization of milk was not carried out, and all had a history of being fed for some time on raw milk. In Toronto, where pasteurization has been compulsory since 1915, not a single case of tuberculosis of bovine origin was found, in spite of the fact that 26 per cent. of pooled samples of raw milk coming into the town contained tubercle bacilli.

The bacilli in the milk may pass through the lymphoid tissue of the mouth and nasopharynx, and reach the cervical glands, where they give rise to disease. The tonsil seems to be not uncommonly infected (Saenz *et al.* 1933). Alternatively they may pass through the intestinal mucosa and invade the mesenteric group of glands. There seems to be little doubt that the organisms may traverse the mucous membrane without giving rise to any lesions in the mucosa itself. Once they have gained access to the lymphatic system, they may be distributed in the body either by direct spread, by the lymph stream, or by the blood stream. Blood-borne infection appears to be mainly responsible for miliary tuberculosis, meningitis, bone and joint disease, and genito-urinary tuberculosis.

With regard to pulmonary tuberculosis of bovine origin, the mode of infection is not quite so clear. Most of the work in this country suggests that this disease follows on glandular tuberculosis acquired through alimentary infection, but in Germany Lange (1931, 1932) has brought evidence to show that in farm workers infection may result from the inhalation of tubercle bacilli expectorated by tuberculous cattle.

Summarizing, we may say that practically all non-pulmonary, and a variable proportion of pulmonary, cases of bovine origin are contracted through the agency of raw milk or cream. Cheese and butter, it may be noted, probably play a quite insignificant part in the transmission of infection, since tubercle bacilli die out in these products within about a month—at a time before they are usually put on the market.

It is of interest to recall the changes that our views on this type of tuberculosis have undergone in the present century. At the London Congress on Tuberculosis in 1901, Koch asserted, on the basis of quite inadequate experimentation, that bovine bacilli were virtually non-pathogenic to human beings. As the result of considerable opposition, he modified his views at the Washington Congress in 1908, to the extent of admitting that human beings might be infected with bovine tubercle bacilli, though he maintained that serious disease due to these organisms was very rare, and that preventive measures to protect the human population against tuberculosis of bovine origin were quite unnecessary. The extensive labours of the Royal Commission on Tuberculosis in this country, and of continental and American workers, revealed the fallacy of Koch's teaching, and showed that non-pulmonary tuberculosis in childhood was frequently caused by the bovine bacillus. The more recent work of Griffith, Munro, Lange, and others has now drawn attention to the occurrence of bovine bacilli in pulmonary tuberculosis ; and infections of bovine origin as a whole must be regarded as a serious menace to the human population in those countries where tuberculosis of cattle is common. The evidence suggests that the bovine bacillus is quite as virulent for man as the human bacillus, and possibly even more so (see Griffith 1925b). The result of Koch's teaching was of more than academic importance. By exonerating cows from all blame in the causation of tuberculosis in man, it put back the clock of veterinary preventive medicine to a degree far greater than is generally appreciated. It further removed the rationale for boiling milk, which had hitherto been accepted on empirical grounds, and delayed for a long time the adoption of pasteurization. Even now we are not free from its trammels, and the public health expert has to fight a continuous battle against the ignorance and prejudice resulting from an authoritative statement made on inadequate evidence 35 years ago. (For general review of tuberculosis of bovine origin, besides those already quoted, see Griffith 1927, 1932c, Report 1931b.)

DIAGNOSIS

Microscopical Examination in Diagnosis.—Tuberculosis is one of the few diseases in which a diagnosis can often be made by microscopical examination alone. The simplest method is to stain a film of sputum, pus, or other pathological product with Ziehl-Neelsen's stain, using 25 per cent. sulphuric acid for decolorization, and 1 per cent. aqueous methylene blue for counterstaining. Numerous other methods of staining, however, have been recommended from time to time, such as Herman's (1908), Mori's (1911), Bozzelli's (1914), and Schulte-Tigge's. When the bacilli are present in very small numbers, attempts may be made to concentrate them by the antiformin method, or by such methods as those of Faisca (1921), Grysez and Bernard (1920), Mayer, G. (1926), and S. R. Douglas and Meanwell (1925); the last method is applicable to milk.

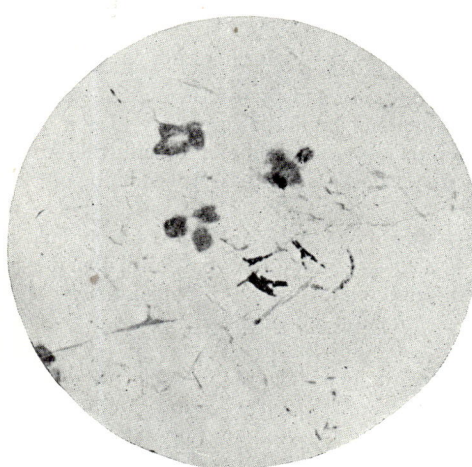

Fɪɢ. 255.—*Mycobacterium tuberculosis,* in urine, showing the characteristic clumps (× 1000).

Urine should be centrifuged, and films made from the deposit (Fig. 255). When examining the cerebrospinal fluid, it is best to allow the fluid to stand till a fibrinous clot forms; this should be removed with a platinum loop, spread on a slide, and stained in the usual manner for acid-fast bacilli.

In both pulmonary and non-pulmonary tuberculosis the bacilli may often be found in the fæces (Alexander 1910, Costa 1926, Sergent 1926, Sykes 1926, Verdina 1926); for their detection some concentration method, such as the ligroin method, should be employed. Examination of the fæces is chiefly of use in children, who generally swallow their sputum, and in cases of closed pulmonary tuberculosis in which there is no sputum. It has been suggested that the bacilli may be excreted from the blood into the bile, and thus reach the fæces (Alexander 1910, Calmette 1920, Remlinger 1923, Koizumi 1924, Verdina 1926).

Examination of the stomach contents obtained by gastric lavage is also extensively used in the diagnosis of tuberculosis in children (Kereszturi *et al.* 1932, 1933, Collis and Brockington 1933, Poulsen and Andersen 1934, Gourley 1934, Nalbant 1934). The actual process of lavage is unpleasant for the child, and it may quite well be replaced by the much simpler methods of obtaining sputum described by Behmann (1930) and Wood (1936), in which the child is made to cough by the insertion of a swab or laryngeal mirror into the throat. The material so obtained can be rubbed thoroughly over a slide, and stained in the usual way. According to Mishulow and her colleagues (1934), repeated examination of fæces is probably as satisfactory as that of gastric lavage specimens.

In pus the bacilli are often very difficult to demonstrate; Gardner (1926) recommends the use of half-saturated aqueous picric acid as a counterstain.

The microscopical method of examination, though very simple, must not be undertaken without due regard to the errors of the technique employed. Microscopical examination alone cannot distinguish between tubercle bacilli and other types of acid-fast bacilli. Besides saprophytic acid-fast bacilli of the *Mycobacterium* group, which are widespread in hay, straw, dust, animal litter, soil, and water, there are a number of other organisms, such as the leprosy bacillus, Johne's bacillus, and some species of *Actinomyces*, which are acid-fast and which may occasionally give rise to confusion.

In order to avoid contamination of the material with these organisms, strict attention must be paid to the preparation of the actual films. In particular, all stains and reagents should be made up with fresh glass-distilled water ; and all glass-ware should be soaked in 50 per cent. nitric acid for at least 15 minutes. Only new slides should be employed, since there is no simple method of removing acid-fast bacilli from slides on to which they have been fixed and stained, and every slide should be thoroughly flamed in a Bunsen burner immediately before use. If the material has to be rubbed up in a drop of water on the slide fresh glass-distilled water or water from a hot tap in constant use should be used, since acid-fast bacilli are usually abundant in cold-water taps (see Chapter XV). Care must be taken to avoid contamination of the cedar-wood oil reservoir from the surface of a previous film, and the oil-immersion objective should always be cleaned after examining a positive film. All apparatus, particularly if made of metal or rubber, used in the collection of catheter and other specimens, should be kept under conditions that will prevent the growth of saprophytic acid-fast bacilli on their surface (see Wells 1936).

When all these precautions have been taken, the importance to be attached to the finding of acid-fast bacilli will vary with the nature of the material examined. While acid-fast bacilli in sputum or cerebrospinal fluid may be regarded as almost certainly diagnostic of tuberculosis, their presence in fæces or urine must be interpreted with far greater caution, since the presence of saprophytic acid-fast, including smegma, bacilli cannot with certainty be excluded. In blood so many artefacts are liable to be present that it is extremely doubtful whether the search for acid-fast bacilli is justified at all.

Cultural Methods in Diagnosis.—Increasing use is now being made of cultural methods in the diagnosis of tuberculosis. Uncontaminated material should be seeded directly on to a suitable medium. Contaminated material, such as sputum, should be first treated for about 15 minutes with 15 per cent. antiformin, 15 per cent. H_2SO_4, or some other agent capable of killing off non-acid-fast organisms. Many different media have been recommended, particularly by American workers.

A. S. Griffith and F. Griffith (1907), working for the Royal Commission on Tuberculosis many years ago, made a careful comparison of whole egg, egg yolk, egg yolk agar, and various serum media, and found that the most satisfactory medium for *primary* cultivation was Dorset egg (3 parts egg to 1 part saline, sloped and inspissated at 75° C. for 2 hours on 2 successive days). Our own experience bears this out. Dorset's egg medium, which was prepared independently by A. S. Griffith and F. Griffith (1907), or a medium made up with 1–2 parts of egg yolk to 1 part of tap water, has proved superior to all the other media—Petroff, Petragnani, Löwenstein, Herrold, Corper and Uyei, Woolsey—commonly recommended. Many of these more complex media contain dyes, which have some inhibitory action on the growth of the organisms, and many contain glycerol, which has a selective action favouring the growth of the human tubercle bacillus at the expense of the bovine. The plain Dorset or egg yolk medium is free from these defects, and is equally suitable for the growth of both human and bovine types (see also Griffith, A. S., 1935).

Great care must be used to avoid contamination of the material with saprophytic acid-fast bacilli. Glass-stoppered vessels sterilized in the dry oven or the autoclave should be used. Rubber corks, and certainly bark corks, are to be avoided, since they may contain acid-fast bacilli. Even using the greatest precautions, it is impossible to avoid occasional contamination of the material with saprophytic acid-fast bacilli, and numerous workers have recorded the development of these organisms in otherwise sterile cultures (see Tiedemann 1931, Beaven and Bayne-Jones 1931, Pinner 1932, Cummins and Williams 1933, Griffith 1933, Bruynoghe and Adant 1933, Pinner 1935). The fact that they usually are contaminants, and are not derived from the tissues, is evident from the fact that Schwabacher (1933) obtained them in cultures from normal rabbit blood.

Under favourable conditions the cultural method is more delicate than the microscopic method for the demonstration of acid-fast bacilli. Corper and Cohn (1933) estimate that for the rapid microscopic detection of these bacilli in sputum there must be about 100,000 per c.c., whereas for their detection by the cultural method 10–100 organisms per c.c. suffice. Some workers regard the cultural as more delicate even than the animal inoculation method (see Norton *et al.* 1932). The great drawback to the cultural method is that it provides no proof that the acid-fast bacilli which have been cultivated are really tubercle bacilli or are derived from the material under examination. No organism should, in fact, ever be reported as a tubercle bacillus until it has been finally identified by animal inoculation.

Of recent years, mainly owing to the assertion of Löwenstein that tubercle bacilli can be isolated from the blood of a high proportion of patients suffering not only from pulmonary and non-pulmonary tuberculosis, but also from such diseases as articular rheumatism, polyarthritis, chorea, multiple sclerosis, schizophrenia, and retro-bulbar neuritis, great attention has been paid to the subject of *tuberculous bacillæmia*. We do not propose to discuss this work in detail. Though tubercle bacilli may be demonstrated by cultural and animal inoculation methods in as many as 5–10 per cent. of severe, advanced and progressive cases of pulmonary tuberculosis, in 30–40 per cent. of cases of miliary and meningeal tuberculosis, and in 50 per cent. of fatal tuberculous cases examined post mortem, they can very rarely be found in the early stages of pulmonary or non-pulmonary tuberculosis. A search for these organisms in the blood is therefore of little value in diagnosis. The great majority of workers have entirely failed to substantiate Löwenstein's findings, which were almost certainly due to gross errors in technique. The whole subject has been critically reviewed by G. S. Wilson (1933).

Serological Methods in Diagnosis.—Serological methods of diagnosis are not, on the whole, satisfactory.

Arloing and Courmont (for references see Wilson, G. S., 1925) in 1898 recommended the *agglutination test*. They obtained a homogeneous suspension of tubercle bacilli by growth of a special strain—now known to be of avian type (Wilson, G. S., 1925)—in glycerine broth. The reaction was considered positive when the organisms were agglutinated by the patient's or animal's serum in a dilution of 1–5 to 1–20. Positive results were obtained in 95 per cent. of early cases of pulmonary tuberculosis and in 50 per cent. of cases of surgical tuberculosis. The percentage, however, of normal persons and of patients suffering from non-tuberculous diseases who reacted positively was as high as 30–67 per cent. Numerous other workers (Mongour and Buard 1898, 1899, Beck and Rabinovitsch 1900, 1901, Bendix 1900, Neisser 1900, Koch 1901, Chang 1922, Courmont and Papacostas 1923, Spehl 1923, Karmann 1924) have reported on this test, and the general consensus of opinion is that as a method of diagnosis it is unreliable ; many patients with tuberculosis fail to react, and many persons who appear perfectly well do react.

The *complement-fixation reaction* stands on a slightly firmer basis, though its value is still very much disputed. Numerous methods of performing the test have been devised, and still more numerous antigens. The French generally employ

Calmette and Massol's technique with Besredka's antigen. Table XCVI, taken from Rieux (1926), gives some of the results that have been obtained.

TABLE XCVI

COMPLEMENT FIXATION IN TUBERCULOSIS.

Type of Disease.	Positive Results.
Pulmonary tuberculosis with positive sputum . . .	85%
Clinically tuberculous pleurisy	46·6%
Tuberculous peritonitis	80%
Tuberculous meningitis	Rarely positive
Glandular tuberculosis	38%
Bone and joint tuberculosis.	50%
Renal tuberculosis	90%
Healthy persons	10–15%
Persons suffering from non-tuberculous diseases . . .	10%

Rieux concludes that every patient giving a strongly positive reaction, and who is not suffering from syphilis, leprosy, or malaria, is tuberculous. Besredka and Manoukhine (1914) conclude that in the first stage of tuberculosis the reaction is always positive ; in the second stage it is generally positive ; in the third stage it is often weakly positive or negative—especially before death. In this country the reaction is not held in such favour. Coulthard (1923) obtained the highest percentage of positive reactions in chronic pulmonary tuberculosis ; he regards a strongly positive reaction as indicative of a relatively high degree of immunity, irrespective of the extent of the disease. In acute forms of tuberculosis, such as the miliary and acute pneumonic forms, and in tuberculous meningitis, the reaction was generally negative. In early pulmonary tuberculosis and in actively progressive pulmonary tuberculosis the results were disappointing. Sellers and Ramsbottom (1922) concluded that the test was of little value in diagnosis.

That the test is generally positive in chronic pulmonary tuberculosis there is little doubt ; but these cases can generally be diagnosed by other means. In the early stages of the disease, when diagnosis by the usual methods is in doubt, the complement-fixation reaction is unreliable. It can at best be used only as a subsidiary method, and even as such it must be interpreted with great reserve. (For further literature on the test, see Calmette and Massol 1914, Dudgeon, Meek and Weir 1914, Meek 1914, Radcliffe 1915, Urbain and Fried 1921, Brocq-Rousseu, Urbain and Cauchemez 1923, von Gutfeld and Weigert 1924, Douglas, S. R., and Meanwell 1925, Salomon and Valtis 1925, Valtis 1925, Wadsworth *et al.* 1930, Hünigen 1932, Rice *et al.* 1933, Urgoiti and Beato 1934).

The *precipitin reaction*, obtained by mixing the patient's serum with tuberculin, is of little or no practical importance. It is of interest to note that the antigen responsible for the complement-fixation and the precipitin reactions is a non-protein gum (Laidlaw and Dudley 1925, Mueller 1926).

Allergic Reactions in Diagnosis.—The tuberculin reaction may be performed in various ways ; the tuberculin may be (1) rubbed on to the scarified skin—cutaneous reaction of von Pirquet (1907) ; (2) incorporated in an ointment and rubbed into the skin—percutaneous reaction of Moro ; (3) injected intracutaneously—Mantoux's reaction (1910) ; (4) dropped into the conjunctiva—Calmette's ophthalmic reaction ; (5) injected subcutaneously—Koch's original method (1890) (see p. 1042). Both the von Pirquet and the graded intradermal test have already been described. There is no question that the latter method is to be preferred. Nearly all persons with either a latent or an active tuberculous infection react positively to tuberculin, except when suffering from advanced disease, severe cachexia, or one of the infectious exanthemata. A positive reaction indicates the presence of a tuberculous focus in the body, but does not distinguish between an active and an inactive lesion. Except in the first few years of life a positive reaction is of very limited value in the diagnosis of clinical tuberculosis. On the other hand, a negative intracutaneous reaction, particularly to a 1/100 or 1/10 dilution, practically excludes the existence of tuberculous infection at any age (see Hart 1932).

We have purposely refrained from any attempt at interpreting different degrees of reactivity to tuberculin in terms of either diagnosis or prognosis (see von Gröer 1932, Johnston *et al.* 1934). So little definite information is at present available on the subject that a discussion of it is hardly justifiable. It may be noted that in childhood a positive reaction may become negative with complete healing of the lesion, though the frequency with which this occurs is not known (see Lloyd and Macpherson 1933, Opie 1935). The allergic condition is frequently maintained as a result of the persistence of tubercle bacilli in quiescent or healed lesions. According to Opie and Aronson (1927), tubercle bacilli are often detectable by guinea-pig inoculation even in apparently normal lung tissue.

Animal Inoculation Tests in Diagnosis.—The most delicate test for tubercle bacilli is animal injection, and the most suitable animal is the guinea-pig. The susceptibility of the guinea-pig is extremely high ; even minute amounts of infective material will render this animal tuberculous. The material—sputum, pus, milk, etc.—should be injected subcutaneously or intramuscularly into the thigh ; the advantage of intramuscular injection is that the local abscess which forms does not ulcerate through the skin. It is wise to inject at least two animals, in case one dies of secondary infection—an occurrence which is very common after the inoculation of urine or fæces. One animal should be killed 3–4 weeks later, and if no signs of tuberculosis are apparent, the other should be kept for 6–8 weeks after inoculation before being killed.

In positive cases killed at 6–8 weeks there will be found (1) a caseous local lesion ; (2) enlargement and caseation of the femoral, inguinal, sublumbar, portal, mediastinal, and cervical glands, the severity of the lesions diminishing as the distance from the site of inoculation increases ; (3) enlargement of the spleen with the presence of irregular necrotic areas ; (4) yellowish-green necrotic areas in the liver ; (5) a few discrete spherical tubercles in the lungs (for further details see p. 308). In animals killed after 3 or 4 weeks the lesions are less severe, and are restricted mainly to the lower portion of the chain of glands and to the spleen and liver. However experienced the worker may be, it is of paramount importance to make a microscopical examination for the presence of acid-fast bacilli. Direct smear preparations should be made from two or three enlarged lymphatic glands, as well as from the spleen, liver, and lungs, and a diagnosis of tuberculosis should not be made unless acid-fast bacilli are found in the internal organs or in glands not directly draining the site of inoculation. The reason for this is that saprophytic acid-fast bacilli may be present in the local lesion and the regional lymphatic glands, though they are usually incapable of penetrating further into the tissues after inoculation by the intramuscular route. It is dangerous to make a diagnosis of tuberculosis unless at least one gland shows caseation. In all doubtful cases cultures should be put up on ordinary media for the diagnosis of Salmonella, *Brucella*, *Pasteurella*, and pyogenic infections, and on to suitable media for the growth of tubercle and saprophytic acid-fast bacilli. Whenever necessary, a fresh animal should be inoculated intramuscularly with some ground-up pathological material, and with any acid-fast bacillus that may develop in culture. Special care must be taken in the microscopic examination of material to guard against the presence of acid-fast bacilli derived from water or from tuberculous tissue on the instruments used for making a post-mortem examination, since boiling does not destroy their property of acid-fastness. Heating the instruments in a Bunsen flame to dull redness usually suffices for this purpose.

The tuberculin test, made by inoculating 0·1 c.c. of a 1/100 dilution of old tuberculin into the skin of the flank, may be used for the diagnosis of tuberculosis in a guinea-pig during life (see p. 1042). It is of particular value in furnishing a guide to the time at which the animal should be killed. The test is usually very reliable, provided no reaction is considered positive unless the local lesion reaches 10 mm. in diameter. Tuberculosis, however, should never be diagnosed on a tuberculin test alone ; the result should always be confirmed by post-mortem examination.

IMMUNITY IN TUBERCULOSIS

Our knowledge of the defensive mechanism of the animal body against the tubercle bacillus is very incomplete. A study of the humoral antibodies—notably agglutinins, complement-fixing bodies, and opsonins—has failed to throw much light on the subject ; there is apparently no strict relationship between the antibody content of the person's serum and his resistance to tuberculosis. Most of the knowledge that we have gained consists of isolated observations, which it is impossible as yet to piece together except in the form of a purely tentative hypothesis. A summary of these observations must necessarily be disjointed.

Koch's Phenomenon.—If a healthy guinea-pig is injected subcutaneously with a pure culture of tubercle bacilli, the slight local lesion caused by the injection heals in a few days ; in 10 to 14 days, however, a hard nodule appears, which breaks down and remains as an ulcerating sore till the animal dies ; the regional lymphatic glands swell considerably and undergo caseation. But if a tuberculous guinea-pig—one that has been injected 4 to 6 weeks previously—is injected subcutaneously into the opposite thigh with a pure culture of tubercle bacilli, the slight local lesion heals rapidly, but no nodule forms. Instead, on the 1st or 2nd day after inoculation, a circular dark-coloured area of induration, about $\frac{1}{2}$ to 1 cm. in diameter, appears at the site of injection. The next day the skin over this ecchymotic area undergoes necrosis ; and later it is thrown off leaving a shallow ulcer, which heals quickly ; the focal lymphatic glands remain unaffected. This reaction was first observed by Koch (1891a), and is known as Koch's phenomenon. For its success three conditions are necessary (von Löwenstein 1913) : (1) the primary infection must be a slight one, so that the disease runs a chronic course ; (2) the re-infecting dose must be given as late as possible after the sensitizing dose ; the longer the animal has been infected the higher is its resistance ; (3) the re-infecting dose must not be too large.

It is clear that the reaction of a tuberculous guinea-pig to a fresh infection is different from that of a normal guinea-pig to a primary infection. Some experiments conducted by Debré and Bonnet (1922) will make this clearer.

A. One group of guinea-pigs was injected with 0·1 mgm. of tubercle bacilli every day for 5 days. *Result.*—Five nodules appeared, identical in their period of incubation (8 to 10 days), in their evolution, and in their accompanying glandular reaction. *B.* Another group of guinea-pigs was injected with 0·1 mgm. of tubercle bacilli every 5 days for five successive times. *Result.*—The first two nodules and their accompanying glandular reaction were identical with those in Series *A*. The third nodule appeared after a shorter incubation period than the first two, was much smaller—the size of a lentil instead of a nut—did not ulcerate, and caused only a slight glandular swelling. The fourth and fifth nodules were identical with the third. *C*. Another group of guinea-pigs was injected with 0·1 mgm. of tubercle bacilli every 10 days on five successive occasions. *Result.*—The first nodule and its accompanying glandular reaction were similar to those in Series *A*. The second and third nodules resembled the 3rd, 4th, and 5th nodules of Series *B*. The fourth nodule produced either a typical Koch's phenomenon, or rapid abscess formation followed by cicatrization, without any glandular enlargement. The fifth nodule constantly provoked the typical eschar described by Koch. With these particular doses, it will be seen that Koch's phenomenon did not appear till about 6 weeks after the first injection. The main lesson to be learnt from this experiment is that the " clinical " re-infection of a tuberculous guinea-pig is impracticable after the appearance of the local abscess. Before the local lesion has appeared the animal reacts to a fresh infection just as a normal animal ; but once the local lesion due to the first injection has developed—generally in 8 to 10 days—the lesions produced by subsequent injections become less and less, till after 6 weeks the freshly injected organisms call forth an acute reaction, quite unlike the chronic process that follows a primary infection.

These observations are similar to those made on experimental syphilis, which have shown that it is possible to produce in the ape a series of chancres, so long as the second injections are made before the appearance of the primary chancre ; once the primary chancre has appeared, further inoculation of syphilitic material fails to produce a fresh chancre. The guinea-pig that has developed a local tuberculous lesion, or the ape that has developed a primary chancre, reacts differently from a normal animal to a fresh infection. It is, so to speak, at once more sensitive and more resistant to the infective material than the normal animal. This state of supersensitiveness is generally known as *allergy*. Whether the immunity is only a symptom-immunity, or whether it is sufficiently high to prevent the actual invasion of the organisms at the site of the second injection is not known, but the experiments of Thomsen and Pedersen-Bjergaard (1933) suggest that it may be of the latter type.

Koch (1891*a*) found that his phenomenon could be reproduced even when dead tubercle bacilli were employed for the second injection. Killed suspensions of tubercle bacilli, when injected subcutaneously into normal guinea-pigs, give rise merely to a local sterile abscess ; there is no constitutional disturbance whatever. But if they are injected into a tuberculous guinea-pig, one of two things happens, depending on the dose : if a large dose is used the guinea-pig dies in 6 to 48 hours ; if a smaller dose is used, there is a local necrosis of the skin—Koch's phenomenon. The allergic guinea-pig, in fact, responds to the injection of dead tubercle bacilli in very much the same way as to that of living bacilli. Koch therefore argued that the reaction must in each case be due to some chemical substance present alike in living and dead bacilli. This active principle he endeavoured to obtain in a soluble form (Koch 1891*b*).

Tuberculin : Preparation, Purification, and Standardization.—Koch grew tubercle bacilli for 6 to 8 weeks at 38° C. in flat-bottomed flasks containing 5 per cent. glycerine broth. The culture was then placed in a water-bath at 100° C., evaporated to 1/10 of its volume, and freed from bacilli by filtration through a clay or kieselguhr candle. The resulting filtrate was a clear, brown, syrupy fluid ; as it contained 40–50 per cent. of glycerine, no antiseptic was required for its preservation. It is generally known as Koch's *old* or *original tuberculin*, and contains all the substances in the culture medium, including those formed from the medium by the bacilli, and the disintegration products of the bacilli themselves, not precipitated by 50 per cent. glycerine. This old tuberculin was found to contain in an impure form the toxic constituents that Koch had been looking for. It is heat-stable, and, when undiluted, will resist autoclaving for half an hour.

Later, owing to the failure of old tuberculin in the treatment of tuberculosis, Koch (1897) prepared a series of tuberculins in the hope of obtaining one that should be immunizing without being toxic. Though we are not at the moment concerned with their action, it will be convenient to refer briefly to their nomenclature and method of preparation.

Tuberculin A.—Tubercle bacilli are treated with $\frac{N}{10}$ NaOH for 3 days at room temperature with frequent shaking, and filtered through paper ; the filtrate, when neutralized, constitutes Tuberculin T.A. It contains numerous bacilli, and on subcutaneous injection gives rise to abscess formation. For this reason Koch subsequently filtered off the bacilli through candles ; the resulting product was not so active ; and as it did not keep for long, and had to be prepared fresh each time, he abandoned it.

Tuberculin O.—Tubercle bacilli from a freshly isolated virulent culture are dried in a vacuum desiccator, and ground up in an agate mortar till only a few acid-fast bacilli are left. The powder is then suspended in distilled water, centrifuged at 4,000 r.p.m. for $\frac{1}{2}$ to $\frac{3}{4}$ hour, and the whitish opalescent supernatant fluid, now free from bacilli, is drawn off, and 20 per cent. glycerine added for preservation. This constitutes T.O., or *Obertuberculin*.

Tuberculin R.—The sediment from T.O. is dried, ground up in a mortar, suspended in water, and centrifuged ; the supernatant fluid is removed and kept. The sediment is again dried, ground up, suspended, and centrifuged, and the supernatant fluid removed and kept. This process is repeated till no more sediment is thrown down on centrifugalization. The supernatant fluids are mixed, 20 per cent. glycerine is added, and the resulting product constitutes T.R. or the residual tuberculin.

Koch's New Tuberculin or Tuberculin B.E.—The tubercle bacilli are ground up by a mechanical mill in water containing 50 per cent. glycerine, till a homogeneous suspension results. This is the *Bazillenemulsion*, and is really nothing but a simple bacterial vaccine.

Numerous other tuberculins have been prepared by different workers.

Of recent years considerable attention has been paid to the mode of preparation, purification, and standardization of *old tuberculin* so as to render it suitable for quantitative tuberculin skin reactions. Without describing these processes in detail, we may say that synthetic media are now generally used, so as to eliminate non-specific reactions caused by protein constituents of the broth (see Douglas and Hartley 1934*b*). The tuberculo-protein, which appears to be mainly responsible for the skin reaction, can be obtained in relatively pure form, either by the trichloracetic acid method (see Seibert and Munday 1932, Seibert 1934, Seibert *et al.* 1934, Clark *et al.* 1934), or by the benzoic acid method of Gough (1934). The purified tuberculin so obtained is usually referred to by the term T.P.T.

Besides the tuberculo-protein, a proteose-like substance has been isolated from old tuberculin by Gough (1934), and a polypeptide-like substance by Seibert (1934) and Reichel and Clark (1934). Both of these substances differ from the tuberculo-protein in being non-antigenic, but both are as highly potent and specific in the tuberculin skin test as the original proteins. It seems probable that the active principle of tuberculin is, in fact, a protein derivative of low molecular weight.

Old tuberculin is most conveniently standardized against a standard tuberculin —hitherto issued by the Frankfurt Institute but now stored at the State Serum Institute, Copenhagen (see Report 1931*a*)—using the intradermal inoculation of sensitized guinea-pigs (see Okell and Parish 1927).

This method, originally described by Römer (1909), consists in inoculating the tuberculin into the animal's flank. As many as 12 or 16 injections can be made on the depilated skin of the same animal. Twenty-four hours after injection a large papule is seen with a hæmorrhagic necrotic centre—the so-called cockade reaction. The reaction reaches its height after 48 hours, and later necrosis becomes more marked. Slight infiltration and swelling cannot be regarded as positive. Römer's test is positive about 3 weeks after infection. Dilutions of the tuberculin to be tested are compared with the standard tuberculin, and the relative potencies of the two products determined.

Tuberculo-protein preparations are standardized against old tuberculin, either by using the guinea-pig method or by making titrations on human subjects (see Lichtenstein 1934, Appel *et al.* 1934, Barnwell and Pollard 1934, Aronson 1934, Long 1934, Long *et al.* 1934).

The Reaction to Tuberculin.—Koch found that 2 c.c. of old tuberculin injected subcutaneously into a normal guinea-pig had very little effect on it ; but the injection of as small a quantity as 0·01 c.c. into a tuberculous guinea-pig—infected 8 to 10 weeks previously—killed it within a few hours. Post mortem, the local lesion at the site of the tuberculin injection was very congested, and often dark or almost violet in colour ; the focal glands were also very congested ; the liver and spleen, besides their tuberculous lesions, showed on the surface numerous puncti-form dark red spots looking like ecchymoses, but which microscopically were found to consist of enormously distended capillaries in the neighbourhood of the tuberculous foci, filled with red blood corpuscles. That is to say, the effect of the tuberculin was to produce (1) a local lesion, at the site of injection ; (2) a focal lesion, around the tubercles in the tissues ; and (3) a constitutional reaction, terminating in death (see also p. 909).

Analogous observations were made on man. A new-born infant, which has never come into contact with tuberculosis, can withstand the injection of 1 c.c. of old tuberculin. A healthy adult, who has been infected, but who is not suffering from clinical tuberculosis, can withstand the injection of about 0·01 c.c. without suffering from more than transient malaise and slight pains in the limbs. But the same quantity injected into a clinically tuberculous patient gives rise to a severe reaction, characterized by malaise, pains in the limbs, cough, dyspnœa, rigor, vomiting, and a high fever ; the temperature begins to rise about 4 hours after the injection, reaches a maximum of 102° to 104° F., and passes off in 12 to 15 hours. As in the guinea-pig, the reaction is (1) local—an inflammatory reaction occurs at the site of injection (*Stichreaktion*) : (2) focal—acute congestion occurs around tuberculous foci ; this can be actually observed in lupus patients ; an injection causes redness and swelling of the lesion, lasting for 2 or 3 days, followed by the formation of crusts of dried exuded serum, which drop off in 2 or 3 weeks leaving a clean red scar : (3) a constitutional reaction, already described.

The tuberculin reaction can be obtained not only in animals actually infected with the tubercle bacillus, but also in animals that have been injected with dead tubercle bacilli. Bessau (1916), for example, was able by the intraperitoneal injection of 1 mgm. of human tubercle bacilli killed by heat at 65° C. for 2 hours, or by the subcutaneous injection of 5–15 mgm., to produce a skin sensitivity to tuberculin in guinea-pigs ; the tuberculin reaction was often as strong as in tuberculous animals. But this hypersensitiveness did not develop immediately ; it took as a rule 2 to 3 weeks, and sometimes as long as 4 months, to develop. These observations have been frequently confirmed (Nakayama 1924, Zinsser and Petroff 1924, Lange and Freund 1926).

Unlike dead bacilli, old tuberculin, even after a long course of injections, usually fails to sensitize the guinea-pig (but see Aronson and Nicholas 1933). According to Seibert (1932), this is due partly to the fact that the dosage is inadequate, and partly to a diminution in the antigenic activity of the protein in old tuberculin as the result of the heat used in its preparation. Tuberculo-protein, on the other hand, if given in a total dosage of about 30 mgm., corresponding to about 60 c.c. of pure tuberculin, is capable of bringing about typical skin sensitiveness in the guinea-pig. Rabbits can also be sensitized if larger doses are used, but the tuberculin reaction in the rabbit is less constant than in the guinea-pig, and not all tuberculous rabbits react to tuberculin (see Report 1913).

It is very difficult to regard Seibert's explanation as wholly satisfactory, as she herself realizes. Why is it, for example, that guinea-pigs can be sensitized to tuberculin by a single dose of 0·1–0·5 mgm. of dead tubercle bacilli (see Tytler 1930, Douglas and Hartley 1934a), when it requires as much as 30 mgm. of purified protein to produce the same effect ?

Bovine and human tuberculin appear to be similar in their toxic effects (Wolbach and Ernst 1904). Moreover, tuberculins prepared from strains differing in virulence have apparently the same potency (see Seibert and Morley 1933). There is evidence, however, that human and bovine tuberculins are not identical ; a difference between them can be detected by means of cross-anaphylactic reactions in the guinea-pig (see Lewis and Seibert 1931.)

Since dead bacilli are able to sensitize animals to tuberculin, some sensitizing substance, tuberculin or tuberculin-like, must be liberated from the bacilli in the tissues. These substances sensitize the cells of the body, which are then able to react more strongly to the subsequent injection of tuberculin. The generalized tuberculin reaction has been held to differ from anaphylaxis in that (1) the passive transference of tuberculin sensitivity from an infected to a normal animal has never yet been satisfactorily demonstrated : (2) the focal reaction, which occurs in the immediate neighbourhood of foci of active tuberculous infection after the injection of tuberculin, has no counterpart in anaphlyactic shock : (3) the reaction to tuberculin is delayed for some hours ; in anaphylaxis the shock occurs directly after the injection : (4) after tuberculin there is a rise in temperature ; in anaphylactic shock there is a fall in temperature (see Chapter XLVIII).

It is doubtful whether much attention should be paid to these differences. Lewis and Seibert (1931), for example, have apparently been able to produce fatal anaphylactic shock in guinea-pigs by the use of tuberculo-protein in place of tuberculin (see also Enders 1929). The sensitizing dose was 0·1–15·0 mgm. and was given intraperitoneally ; the " shocking " dose was 5–15 mgm. and was given intravenously. Similar shock could be produced by the intravenous inoculation of tuberculo-protein into tuberculous guinea-pigs. Passive sensitization was also successfully accomplished by the intravenous inoculation of guinea-pigs with the serum of other guinea-pigs that had been actively immunized by repeated inoculation with tuberculo-protein. Twenty-four hours after the receipt of the serum, the passively sensitized animals were inoculated with 10–15 mgm. of tuberculo-protein. Most of them died of shock within 5 minutes. The serum of tuberculous guinea-pigs, however, was unable to convey passive sensitization to normal animals. Lewis and Seibert believe that bacterial protein preparations are usually bad anaphylacto-gens, because in their native state they are very insoluble, and when brought into solution they are either denatured, altered, or hydrolysed, particularly if they are exposed to heat, cold, sunlight, acids, or alkalies. Ultra-filtration and precipitation with ammonium sulphate are free from these defects, and were used for the prepara-tion of the tuberculo-proteins in the experiments just described. Most workers have used old tuberculin, which has been submitted to prolonged heating, and it is probable that their failure to obtain anaphylactic shock may be attributable to this cause. On the whole it seems likely that the differences between the generalized tuberculin reaction and the typical anaphylactic reaction are dependent far more on solubility and rapidity of absorption of the protein than on any fundamental differences in the nature of the two reactions.

The Relation between Allergy and Immunity.

Allergy may be defined as a state resulting from one or more previous infections, and manifested by an accelerated reaction to subsequent contact with the bacillus, or with certain of its antigenic constituents (see p. 909). There seems to be little doubt that allergy is an expression of immunity. We know that animals infected with tuberculosis—provided the disease is not acute—are more resistant to subsequent infections than normal animals. There is evidence that animals with a high tuber-culin sensitivity are more resistant to subsequent infections than animals with a low tuberculin sensitivity. And it has been stated that by prophylactic injections of guinea-pigs with tuberculin R. it is possible to afford some protection against repeated inoculations with virulent tubercle bacilli (Koch 1897) (see p. 1049). It is known too that in human beings the absence of the allergic state is coupled with a high susceptibility to tuberculosis ; thus infants of civilized, and both infants and adults of uncivilized races, who react negatively to the tuberculin test, are liable to contract a particularly severe form of tuberculosis ; moreover, patients in an advanced stage of tuberculosis, who have little or no resistance to the disease, generally give a negative tuberculin reaction.

The higher resistance of tuberculin-positive persons and the lower resistance of tuberculin-negative persons is well exemplified by recent experience in Norway. Stimulated by Scheel's observations at the Ullevaal Communal Hospital at Oslo on the frequency of tuberculosis in probationer nurses, Heimbeck (1927, 1932, 1933) tested every nurse entering the hospital with tuberculin. This hospital has 2,000 beds, 300–400 of which are set aside for tuberculous patients. The training course for the nurses lasts 3 years and comprises a period of service in the tuberculosis wards. Of 762 probationers submitted to the von Pirquet test, 496 gave a positive and 266 a negative reaction. This large proportion of non-reactors was partly due to the circumstance that many of the nurses came from country districts, where presumably they had not been exposed to infection. The tests were commenced on January 1st, 1924, and up to the time of publication in 1933, 118 of these nurses are said to have developed signs of tuberculosis ; 10 had died. Of the 118 cases, no fewer than 94 belonged to the group that gave a negative von Pirquet reaction on entering hospital. That is, the incidence of tuberculosis was over 7 times as high in the positive as in the negative group. Moreover, all the deaths were in the latter group.

From 1927 onwards Heimbeck endeavoured to protect the von Pirquet negative nurses by vaccinating them subcutaneously with B.C.G. (see p. 1050). As the result of this procedure many of the nurses developed a positive tuberculin reaction, but some did not. The two groups were followed up, and it was found that of 164 nurses who became von Pirquet positive, only 3 developed tuberculosis, while of 94 nurses that remained negative, no fewer than 22 developed tuberculosis. The incidence of tuberculosis was therefore nearly 13 times as high in the negative as in the positive group.

Heimbeck's figures, which are supported by those of Scheel (1935) on medical students in Oslo, strongly suggest that a negative reaction to the von Pirquet test is indicative of a lower degree of resistance to tuberculosis than a positive reaction. Jacobson (1933), however, in Denmark, who made a similar investigation on 149 probationers, was unable to arrive at any definite conclusion as to the value of the von Pirquet test in assessing the probability of the development of tuberculosis, while Shipman and Davis (1933) in California found that a higher proportion of initially tuberculin-positive nurses developed tuberculosis than of tuberculin-negative nurses.

Reference must also be made to the extensive investigations carried out among the mine labourers on the Witwatersrand (Report 1932b). These labourers, or " boys," came from native territories in which tuberculosis was endemic. On arrival at the mine, they were submitted to a cursory physical examination in order to eliminate those with obvious disease, and were tested intradermally with 0·1 c.c. of a 1/5000 dilution of old tuberculin. Their after-history is summarized in Table XCVII.

TABLE XCVII

SHOWING PROPORTION OF POSITIVE AND NEGATIVE REACTORS TO 1/5000 TUBERCULIN DEVELOPING CLINICAL TUBERCULOSIS. (S. African gold miners.)

Type of Reaction.	Number.	No. developing Tuberculosis.	Incidence of Tuberculosis per 100,000.
(a) Negative	32,864	114	347
(b) Weakly or moderately positive .	57,236	391	683
(c) Strongly positive.	3,879	60	1,547
(b and c) Positive	61,115	452	738

It will be seen that the incidence of tuberculosis was more than twice as high in the positive as in the negative reactors, and that the stronger the reaction was to tuberculin, the greater was the liability to clinical tuberculosis.

Before concluding that these figures are in direct contradiction to those of Heimbeck, it is important to realize that the two populations concerned differed in several respects. Heimbeck's nurses had all presumably undergone a thorough physical examination before being accepted for service, whereas the South African " boys " had undergone a much less rigorous inspection. As a result, probably a number of the positive reactors were in the incipient stage of tuberculosis. This probability is borne out by the fact that one-third of the strongly positive reactors broke down within 3 months of their admission to the mines. Again, the injection of 0·1 c.c. of a 1/5000 dilution of tuberculin is probably not quite as delicate an index of infection as the von Pirquet test. Consequently some of the negative reactors among the " boys " would have been classed by the von Pirquet test as positive. If we accept Heimbeck's conclusions that negative reactors are more susceptible than positive, then the inclusion of a number of weakly positive reactors in the negative group would have the effect of making the results in this group more favourable than they would otherwise have been. Clinical observations showed that, though the incidence of tuberculosis was higher in the positive than the negative group of Rand labourers, nevertheless the severity of the disease and the case-mortality rate were both considerably greater among the initially negative reactors. The lesions showed little or no tendency to fibrosis, and the disease rapidly became generalized, whereas in the positive reactors fibrosis occurred and the lesions often remained localized to the lungs. Thus, in 24 per cent. of tuberculous cases in the negative group the disease ran a septicæmic course, as opposed to 4 per cent. in the strongly, and 5 per cent. in the moderate and weakly positive, tuberculin reactors.

It is important to point out that a high proportion of Heimbeck's tuberculous nurses were suffering from erythema nodosum—a condition which, though regarded by Heimbeck as tuberculous, is still of very doubtful ætiology. If, as would be done in this country, these cases were excluded from the tuberculous group, the difference between the von Pirquet positive and negative reactors would be very much less striking.

In considering the interpretation of the findings among the Rand labourers, it is necessary also to take into account certain other factors. There is a good deal of evidence derived from clinical and radiographical observations to suggest that, though allergy serves as a valuable protective mechanism against re-infection in normal persons with inactive latent foci of tuberculosis, in patients suffering from the disease or in persons with latent active foci, it may have the reverse effect. Such persons, when exposed to re-infection, of either exogenous or endogenous origin, react much more strongly than normal persons. A severe inflammatory disturbance is liable to develop around the active focus, and lead to general toxæmia and extension of the local lesion. It seems probable that many of the Rand labourers had latent active foci on arrival, with often a high degree of allergy, and that the severe physical exercise in the mines led to mobilization of the tubercle bacilli in the body and to rapid progression of the disease. How much of this activation of latent lesions was due to the allergic condition of the tissues, and how much to the effect of physical fatigue and possibly other environmental conditions in lowering the general resistance of the body, it is impossible to say. We must, however, realize that the Rand labourers differed from the Norwegian nurses in many other ways than in their degree of allergy.

It would therefore be unjustifiable to compare directly the South African figures with those obtained by Heimbeck at Oslo. It would be equally unjustifiable to close our eyes to the different results of the two investigations. On the whole, we think the right conclusion is that persons who have never been in contact with the tubercle bacillus are more likely to develop tuberculosis, when exposed to a fairly severe infection, than persons who have had previous experience of the bacillus which has led to the development of retrogressive tuberculous foci. The latter type is probably more resistant than the former as the result of some degree of acquired immunity. If, however, allergy is accompanied by latent active lesions (see p. 1019), or if exposure to infection is frequent or severe, then the opposite conclusion may well hold true.

If this conception is correct it will be seen that there is no simple relationship existing between allergy and the liability to develop clinical tuberculosis. The relationship is dependent on a number of variable factors, among which the state of the lesions, the general environmental conditions, and the risk of exposure to infection are probably three of the most important. If we are to gauge the liability of individual persons to develop clinical tuberculosis, a knowledge of their sensitivity to tuberculin is clearly insufficient. In addition we shall want to know the number, extent, and degree of activity of all tuberculous foci in the patient's body, together with his general environmental conditions and mode of living. Whether such knowledge, if obtained, would enable us to assess, in terms of probability, the likelihood of tuberculosis developing, we are not in a position to say, but investigations are now on foot which it is hoped will provide an answer to this question—at any rate so far as pulmonary tuberculosis is concerned.

Turning to the experimental study of allergy, we find that many workers have endeavoured to simplify the problem unduly. Rich (1929, 1930, 1931, 1933a, b), in particular, and his colleagues (Rich and McCordock 1929, Rich and Brown 1930, Rich, Chesney, and Turner 1933, Rich, Jennings, and Downing 1933), and followers (Rothschild *et al.* 1934) at Baltimore have tried to dissociate allergy from immunity. We have no space here to enter into a critical discussion of the arguments used to support his thesis. The most important single piece of experimental evidence is based on the observation that guinea-pigs, which had been submitted to a mild tuberculous infection and then desensitized by repeated massive doses of tuberculin, were just as resistant to superinfection with virulent tubercle bacilli as a control group of animals that had received the same primary infection but had not been desensitized. The fallacy of this argument seems to us to lie in the assumption that the only effect produced was the desensitization of the animals. The possible immunizing effect of the tuberculin itself is altogether ignored.

The whole attempt to dissociate allergy from immunity is curiously reminiscent of the old controversy that raged between the protagonists of the humoral and those of the cellular theory of immunity. Our present conception of immunity to infection rests on both a cellular and a humoral basis. The preliminary sensitization, mechanical clumping, and sometimes lysis of the bacteria appear to depend on antibodies, which are either free in the circulation or are concentrated on the surface of the tissue cells. The ingestion of the bacteria, their removal from the circulation, and their subsequent disintegration are accomplished mainly by phagocytic cells of various types. Generally speaking, the presence of a high content of circulating antibody is indicative of a considerable degree of immunity, while the existence of fixed antibody with relatively little circulating antibody is indicative of immunity of a lower grade. The evidence suggests that the meeting of antigen and antibody on the surface of the cells is often accompanied by a severe reaction of anaphylactic type, while when the union occurs in the circulation this type of reaction is forestalled. There seems to be no valid reason for excluding resistance to tuberculosis from this general picture. Our present knowledge is compatible with the view that allergy represents a stage in the development of immunity when the antibodies are concentrated mainly on the surface of the cells, whereas so-called immunity is a stage further on, when there is a considerable amount of free antibody in the circulation, and the local disturbances caused by the meeting of antigen and antibody in the tissues are therefore less severe. This conception is supported by the observations of Sewall, de Savitsch, and Butler (1934), who, by superinfecting guinea-pigs at varying times after the first infection, found that immunity was more or less inversely proportional to the degree of skin hypersensitiveness. These results suggest that allergy is merely a stage in the development of immunity. They explain why allergy may be present without any considerable increase in resistance to infection, and why immunity may be present without any definite allergic manifestations.

Summarizing, we believe that the experimental and field evidence suggest that allergy is a step on the road to immunity. Though, in general, allergic subjects will be found less liable to develop clinical tuberculosis than those who have never been in contact with the tubercle bacillus, there are large numbers of individual exceptions. Allergic persons with latent active lesions, particularly if exposed to unfavourable environmental conditions, are probably more liable to develop clinical manifestations of disease than those who are completely non-allergic. The relationship between allergy and the liability to develop tuberculosis is complex, and depends on a number of factors, of which the state of the lesions, the risk of exposure to infection, and the general environmental conditions are probably among the most important. (For general discussion on relation of allergy to immunity see Chapter XLVIII.)

Our knowledge of immunity to tuberculosis is very deficient. On the whole we think the evidence favours the view that variations in genetic resistance are less important than the development of acquired immunity. Neither type is absolute ; both are subject to fluctuations ; and acquired immunity, in particular, rarely seems to be of a high order or of long duration. The logical development of these conclusions will be dealt with in the next section.

THE PROPHYLAXIS AND TREATMENT OF TUBERCULOSIS

Prevention of Infection.—General hygienic measures include the prevention of spitting, except into a suitable receptacle, which can be sterilized or burnt ; the prevention of coughing, except into a handkerchief ; the segregation of advanced cases of open tuberculosis ; the prevention of overcrowding ; the protection of infants and children from contact with tuberculous parents ; the pasteurization or boiling of all milk except that coming from tubercle-free herds ; and education in personal hygiene and in diet (see Discussion 1935).

In view of the conclusions reached in the last section we believe that avoidance of exposure to massive and repeated infection and unfavourable environmental conditions is of greater importance than the attempt to develop an acquired immunity. There has in the past been a great tendency to overlook the fact that tuberculosis is an infectious disease. Little or no attempt has been made to protect nurses, medical students, and doctors against the unduly high risk of infection that practice of their profession entails, with the result that the incidence of tuberculosis has been unnecessarily high among these classes of the population. Again, too rigid an interpretation of Koch's phenomenon has led to the conclusion that tuberculous patients cannot be re-infected, regardless of the possible danger that a highly allergic patient may incur from an acute local inflammatory disturbance of a pulmonary focus resulting from re-infection. Exposure to any disease, even those in which recovery is followed by a high degree of immunity, is always accompanied by danger, and is not justified except in such an instance as measles in which an attenuated attack can be ensured by appropriate serum treatment. The avoidance of unnecessary exposure to infection is particularly desirable in the case that we are now considering, where infection never seems to be followed by a high degree of immunity, and is sometimes followed by clinical disease from which complete recovery is uncommon.

The argument is sometimes advanced that tuberculous milk is not an unmixed evil. The tubercle bacilli that it contains are presumed to cause mild infections in infants and children which serve to protect them against subsequent infection with the human bacillus. This argument cannot be too strongly condemned. The bovine tubercle bacillus is no less virulent than the human (see Griffith 1925*b*), and many of the infections to which it gives rise are severe and fatal. The argument involves the assumption that the exposed population, as a whole, benefits from the development of an acquired immunity, and ignores altogether the process played by natural selection in weeding out the least resistant members of the population. Even if it were true, the price to be paid, in terms of lives and suffering, for any such advantage is far too high (see p. 1031 and Griffith 1925*b*, Report 1934). If acquired immunity is to be developed, let us at least endeavour to produce it in some more intelligent way, less fraught with danger of active disease and death.

Prophylactic Vaccination against Tuberculosis.--Numerous attempts have been made to vaccinate animals against tuberculosis. Koch (1897), using tuberculin R., stated that by giving large doses, about 2–3 mgm., he was able to immunize a considerable number of guinea-pigs, so that they withstood repeated injections of virulent tubercle bacilli without becoming infected. These results, however, have never been satisfactorily confirmed.

Koch likewise tested the immunizing value of tubercle bacilli boiled in dilute mineral acids or strong alkalies ; other workers have simply boiled or heated them to 70° C. ; others have treated them with glycerine or 25 per cent. lactose ; Löwenstein used formalin, Loeffler applied dry heat, Rappin used sodium fluoride, Noguchi sodium oleate, Deycke and Much choline and neurine, but all without result. More recently Dreyer has treated the bacilli with formalin, and subsequently extracted them with acetone ; as a result the organisms lose their acid-fast property. This so-called *diaplyte* vaccine has not been found of value for immunizing guinea-pigs (Bronfenbrenner and Straub 1925, Douglas, J. S. C. *et al.* 1925), but Dreyer, Vollum, and Ammitzböll (1934) have reported favourable results from its use in the vaccination of cattle.

The general outcome of most of these attempts has been disappointing, and Calmette, in particular, has concluded that dead vaccines are useless for purposes of immunization. How far this conclusion is justifiable, it is difficult to say. Most of the earlier workers were undoubtedly hoping for the production of an immunity similar to that obtainable in certain other diseases. The knowledge that we have since gained shows that such a hope was unduly optimistic. Recent experiments, made mostly on guinea-pigs with heat-killed bacilli, suggest very strongly that vaccination with dead organisms does lead to a definite increase in the resistance of the animals to infection, as judged by comparison of mortality, average survival time, and certain other criteria with those in control unvaccinated animals (Petroff 1927, Petroff, Branch, and Jennings 1929, Freund 1932, Hughes 1933, Westenrijk

1933, Branch and Enders 1935), but this increase of resistance falls far short of absolute immunity.

An attempt to improve the antigenic quality of the vaccine has been made by Spahlinger (1932), who grows the bacilli on media containing proteins specific to the type of animal to be vaccinated, and allows them to die out naturally during a period of some months. Adequately controlled experiments with this vaccine have not yet been made, but there is evidence to suggest that it may have some action in raising the resistance of animals to infection (Report 1935a).

Vaccination with the B.C.G. Strain.—Believing that dead tubercle bacilli are useless for purposes of immunization, and that acquired immunity depends upon the persistence in the body of living bacilli, Calmette introduced a living vaccine consisting of a bovine strain that had become avirulent as the result of several years' subculture on a glycerol bile potato medium. This B.C.G. (Bacille Calmette-Guérin) strain can be injected into animals without giving rise to more than a small retrogressive local lesion, and its presence in the body usually renders the animal sensitive to tuberculin. According to Calmette, calves and heifers vaccinated with 50 mgm. subcutaneously become resistant to tuberculosis, and during the following year are able to withstand an intravenous injection of 5 mgm. of living virulent tubercle bacilli, sufficient to kill unvaccinated animals in 2 months.

The success of his laboratory experiments led Calmette to the vaccination of human subjects. In order to forestall natural infection, he considered it important to vaccinate infants directly after birth. For this purpose he recommended 3 doses, each of 10 mgm., to be given by the mouth on alternate days during the first 10 days of life. Moreover, in order to prevent infection before immunity had become established, he recommended that the infant should be removed from all sources of infection for 2 months after vaccination.

This vaccine has now been tried out on an extensive scale with results that are extremely difficult to assess. The great difficulty is that, with one or two exceptions to be mentioned later, there has been a general failure to realize the necessity of comparing the vaccinated infants with a control group belonging to the same social class, brought up in the same environment, and treated in exactly the same way as the vaccinated group. The usual practice has been to compare the tuberculosis or general mortality in the vaccinated infants with the estimated mortality for non-vaccinated infants in similar surroundings or in the country as a whole. Such comparisons, as Greenwood (1928), Rosenfeld (1928), Wolff (1930a, b), and Berghaus (1930, 1931) have pointed out, are grossly unfair. In the first place no exact figures exist for the mortality in unvaccinated infants brought up in a tuberculous environment, and the estimates that have been made differ enormously. In the second place, the unvaccinated infants are not strictly comparable with the vaccinated group, partly because they are not kept sheltered from infection during the first 2 months of life, and partly because they receive less parental, medical, and nursing attention than those infants which, after vaccination, are kept under more or less continuous observation. For these reasons, the reproduction, even if it were possible, of the immense pile of data that has accumulated on this subject in France and French-speaking countries, would serve no useful purpose, since from a statistical point of view it is practically worthless.

The realization of these fallacies has now led to the institution by other workers of a few experiments in which an attempt has been made to provide a control group with which the vaccinated group can be more strictly compared. It must be noted that the difficulties of obtaining an absolutely identical control group are almost insuperable, and some allowance has therefore got to be made when considering the results. We have already (p. 1045) drawn attention to the favourable results recorded by Heimbeck following the vaccination of von Pirquet-negative probationer nurses with B.C.G. Similar results have also been obtained by Scheel (1935) with medical students. We may now briefly consider the data collected by other workers on the vaccination of infants.

Park, Kereszturi, and Mishulow (1933) in New York vaccinated infants born into tuberculous families with B.C.G., the vaccine being given by the mouth during the first 10 days of life. A control group of infants was left unvaccinated. The two groups were not strictly comparable, (1) because the vaccinated infants were removed from their parents for 1 month after immunization, while the control infants were left at home ; and (2) because the control infants were rather more heavily exposed to tuberculous infection than the vaccinated group. Some of the infants were kept under observation for 5 years, but with most of them the observational period was shorter. Altogether 3 out of 239 vaccinated, and 7 out of 189 control infants died of tuberculosis. The non-tuberculous mortality, on the other hand, was considerably higher in the vaccinated than in the control group—in contradiction of Calmette's assertion that B.C.G. vaccination lowers both the tuberculosis and the general mortality. Another series of children from tuberculous families was vaccinated parenterally—the vaccine being given intracutaneously or subcutaneously some time after birth. All the vaccinated children reacted negatively to tuberculin before immunization. Of the control children, some had a positive and some had a negative reaction. During the observational period none of the 150 vaccinated children died of tuberculosis. Of the 155 control children with an initially positive Mantoux reaction 5 died of tuberculosis, while of 269 control children with an initially negative reaction 4 died of tuberculosis. While admitting that the differences are not significant, the authors conclude that B.C.G. vaccination apparently confers some measure of protection against tuberculosis in early life.

A similar experiment has been reported by Aronson and Dannenberg (1935), in which both white and coloured infants were observed. No data, however, are provided to indicate how the children were selected, or what degree of similarity existed between the control and the vaccinated groups. The vaccinated infants were given B.C.G. by the mouth during the first 10 days of life. Observations on the infants were made as far as possible at 3-monthly intervals during the first year, and at 6-monthly intervals subsequently. The results are summarized in Table XCVIII.

TABLE XCVIII

DEATHS FROM TUBERCULOSIS IN CHILDREN VACCINATED WITH B.C.G. AND IN A CONTROL GROUP.
(Aronson and Dannenberg 1935.)

Type of Exposure.	Vaccinated Group.			Control Group.		
	No.	Mean Age at Time of Last Observation in Months.	Deaths from Tuberculosis.	No.	Mean Age at Time of Last Observation in Months.	Deaths from Tuberculosis.
Exposed to contact with tuberculous patients having a positive sputum	41	31·4	1	84	40	10
Exposed to contact with tuberculous patients having a negative sputum	15	28·3	0	45	39·3	2
Not exposed to known contact with tuberculous patients	14	—	0	38	—	0

The numbers are few, and it will be observed that the mean age at the time of last observation was higher in the control than in the vaccinated group. Since tuberculous mortality is higher in the second than in the first year of life, this may obviously have affected the control group unfavourably. The results, however, do suggest that B.C.G. vaccination tends to confer some protection against the risk of death from tuberculosis during the first year or two of life. Radiographical observations, moreover, showed that whereas only 16·6 per cent. of 36 vaccinated children in the first group had lesions in the lungs, 56·6 per cent. of 83 control children in the same group showed pulmonary lesions.

It will be observed that neither of these investigations yielded very striking results, but both of them afford some evidence that B.C.G. vaccination may bring about a slight increase in resistance to tuberculosis. How long the increased resistance is likely to last we are unable to say, but Calmette himself advised re-vaccination at 3, 7, and 15 years of age.

If we admit the beneficial effect of B.C.G. vaccination, we have still to decide what value it is likely to be in practice. Tuberculosis mortality has been falling so rapidly, particularly in the lowest age groups, that in this country it is now of very much less importance than it used to be. In 1929, for example, only 1·4 per cent. of the total infantile mortality was due to tuberculosis, and the chances against dying from tuberculosis during the first year of life were about 1,000 to 1. In face of such a slight risk, general vaccination of all infants with B.C.G. is out of the question. If vaccination is to be employed, it will have to be restricted to infants who are born into tuberculous families, and possibly to other classes of the population, such as nurses and medical students, who are exposed to a special risk of infection. The evidence, particularly of Scandinavian and American workers, suggests that vaccination is more effective if performed by the intracutaneous or subcutaneous than by the oral route, and that the degree of allergy resulting is higher. Parenteral vaccination is, however, not without its disadvantages. A cold abscess forms, which persists for months, and may sometimes break down and ulcerate through the skin.

We may add that there is no evidence to prove that organisms of the B.C.G. strain may regain their virulence by residence in the body. The virulence of the strain seems to be actually falling, and it is doubtful how long it will retain its protective properties. The Lübeck catastrophe, in which 72 out of 251 vaccinated infants died of tuberculosis (see Report 1935*b*), was almost certainly due to the contamination of the vaccine with another strain of tubercle bacilli. Animal experiments, with the exception of those on cattle (see p. 1058), have on the whole not given a very convincing answer to the prophylactic value of B.C.G. vaccination, and we shall not therefore refer to them further. A few of the papers in the enormous bibliography that has now arisen on this subject may be quoted (see Calmette 1924, 1930, 1931, 1932, Calmette and Guérin 1924, Calmette *et al.* 1924, 1926, Weil-Hallé and Turpin 1925, Wilbert 1925, Gamna and Giordano 1926, Heymans 1926, Tsekhnovitzer 1926, Gerlach 1927, Kraus 1927, Petroff *et al.* 1927, 1929, Gerlach and Kraus 1929, Kraus and Gerlach 1929, Debré and Cofino 1929, Gerlach 1930, Begbie 1930, 1931, Neufeld 1930, Uhlenhuth and Seiffert 1930, Griffith 1931, Birkhaug 1933, Clawson 1933, Meiszner and Prausnitz 1934, Irvine 1934, Shaffer 1935, Naeslund 1935, Besta and Lenneberg 1935, Rist 1936).

Therapeutic Immunization against Tuberculosis.—The introduction of tuberculin by Koch in 1890 was the first of a long series of attempts to cure tuberculosis by the use of vaccines of tubercle bacilli or their products. Koch's old tuberculin, which has already been described (p. 1040), gave rise to such severe reactions—both focal and constitutional—that it was for a time practically abandoned. It is now used chiefly for stimulating chronic cases of tuberculosis that have passed into a torpid state, in which neither advance of the disease nor progress towards recovery is occurring (Burnand *et al.* 1922). Extremely small doses are employed. Jaquerod (see Burnand *et al.* 1922) starts with 0·1 c.c. of a 1/100,000 dilution of old tuberculin; he repeats the injection every 2 days, increasing the dose by 1/10 c.c., provided the reaction is not too severe. After about 5 months the patient is able to withstand 0·5 c.c. of the undiluted tuberculin; this dose is repeated 3 or 4 times, after which the treatment is finished. The fundamental rule of all tuberculin treatment is never to provoke a febrile reaction of any importance.

TUBERCULOSIS IN ANIMALS

Frequency and Bacteriology.—Tuberculosis is widespread throughout the animal kingdom. It is common among certain species of domesticated animals, and though rarely encountered in wild animals living under feral conditions, it is not infrequent amongst them when they are brought into captivity (see Griffith 1928*a, b,* Scott 1928, Scott and Beattie 1928). Cattle, and pigs, and to a less extent fowls, are the most frequently affected of stock animals. Sheep and goats rarely suffer naturally from the disease. Horses, dogs, and cats are occasionally affected.

Bacteriologically, human, bovine, and avian types are found with varying degrees of frequency (see Table XCIX which has been compiled from the results of A. S. Griffith 1924, 1925*a,* 1926, 1928*a, b,* Stableforth 1929, Cornell and A. S. Griffith, 1930, Lovell 1930, and Schwabacher (1934), together with some of our own results).

Cattle are almost invariably infected with the bovine type. The avian bacillus may give rise to localized lesions particularly in calves (see Minett 1932, Gloyne 1933); it has been occasionally isolated from the sputum and the milk of cows (Wolters 1931). Pigs suffer from infection with all three warm-blooded types but mainly the bovine and avian. Nearly all strains isolated from the horse have been of bovine type, but these equine strains are often atypical, showing a lowered virulence for calves and rabbits. In the dog both human and bovine types are found, but all strains isolated from the cat have so far proved to be of bovine type. Sheep may be infected with the bovine or avian types; Harshfield and Roderick (1934) in the United States have described 6 cases of avian type infection. Parrots kept as pets are usually infected with the human type, but those living in aviaries with other birds may be infected with the avian type (see Cobbett 1917). Fowls and most other birds are infected almost exclusively with the avian type of bacillus.

Tuberculosis of Cattle.—Tuberculosis is one of the most serious diseases of cattle. In this country it is extremely common. As already mentioned, about 40 per cent. of cattle react to the tuberculin test, about 40 per cent. of animals slaughtered in public abattoirs show macroscopic lesions of tuberculosis, and about 0·5 per cent. of all milch cows excrete tubercle bacilli in their milk (Report 1932*a,* 1934, Savage 1933). The disease is common throughout Europe, but in the United States and Canada it is very much less frequent, except in a few areas where the cattle population is fairly dense.

The incidence of the disease increases with the age of the animal; it is un-

TABLE XCIX

Species of Animal.	No. of Cases.	Type of Tubercle Bacillus.		
		Bovine.	Human.	Avian.
Anthropoid Apes	6	—	6 [1]	—
Lemurs	2	—	2	—
Monkeys	26	8	18 [2]	—
Cattle	52	50	1	1
Horse	38	37 [3]	—	1
Sheep	4	2	—	2
Goat	2	2	—	—
Deer	3	3	—	—
Gnu	3	2	1	—
Antelope	3	3	—	—
Pig	258	183 [4]	5 [5]	70 [6]
Cat.	25	25 [7]	—	—
Dog	20	7	13	—
Rabbit	8	4	—	4
Guinea-pig	6	5	1	—
Parrot	1	—	1	—
Fowls, and other birds . . .	20	—	1	19

[1] Including 1 strain of sub-standard virulence.
[2] Including 1 dysgonic strain.
[3] Including 14 strains of sub-standard virulence.
[4] Including 4 cases in which avian, and 1 case in which human, bacilli were also present.
[5] Including 1 case in which bovine bacilli were also present.
[6] Including 4 cases in which bovine bacilli were also present.
[7] Including 1 strain of sub-standard virulence.

common in calves, fairly common in bullocks and heifers, and very common in cows —particularly the older animals. Table C, compiled by Delépine (see Cobbett 1917) on the basis of tuberculin tests controlled by post-mortem examination, will make this clear.

TABLE C

Frequency of Tuberculosis in Cattle classified according to Age.

Age.	Number Examined.	Percentage Tuberculous.
0–1 years	29	3·4
1–2 ,, ...	68	13·2
2–3 ,, ...	112	24·1
3–5 ,, ...	51	23·5
5–9 ,, ...	94	48·9
9–13 ,, ...	25	76·0

The organs most frequently infected in cattle are the lungs, pleura, and thoracic lymph glands ; less often the lymph glands and organs of the abdominal cavity. Tuberculosis of the udder is frequent, especially in the later stages of the infection. According to Vallée (1905), who gives records of over 43,000 tuberculous cattle, pulmonary lesions were present in 75 per cent., and hepatic lesions in 28 per cent., of all cases of localized tuberculosis ; in generalized tuberculosis the lungs were always invaded, and the liver was invaded in 83 per cent. of cases. It is important to realize that tuberculous cattle may excrete bacilli in their milk even though no evidence of disease of the udder, as judged by microscopical examination after death, is to be found (Report 1909, Gaiger and Davies 1933). Cattle form the chief source of infection for other domesticated animals.

Diagnosis of Tuberculosis in Cattle.—The diagnosis of tuberculosis in cattle follows much the same lines as that of human tuberculosis. An attempt may be made either to demonstrate tubercle bacilli directly in the animal's secretions or excretions, or to arrive at an indirect diagnosis by some form of immunity reaction, such as the tuberculin test, which, if positive, may be interpreted as evidence of infection. The direct method is restricted largely to the examination of sputum and milk. Sputum is not always easy to obtain, but if the cow has a cough, small particles of sputum can often be found on the wall of the byre opposite the animal's head (Riddoch 1903).

Demonstration of Tubercle Bacilli in Milk.—Microscopical, cultural, serological, and animal inoculation tests are available, the last method being the commonest and most delicate.

Microscopical examination is of value mainly for the milk of individual cows suspected of suffering from udder tuberculosis.

The most satisfactory method is to draw off quarter samples from the udder, and to spin each sample separately a short time at low speed, to spread a film on a slide, to fix and de-fat with a combination of heat, alcohol and ether, and to stain with carbol-fuchsin (see Cowan and Maddocks 1935). The work of Torrance (1922, 1927), Matthews (1931), and Davies (1933) has shown that tubercle bacilli in milk are generally associated with the presence of characteristic endothelial cell clumps. It is therefore only necessary to examine the film with a low power for the presence of these clumps, and to reserve the oil-immersion lens for films in which these clumps are present. The clumps themselves are not diagnostic of tuberculosis, but they afford a good indication of the locality of the tubercle bacilli in the film. It would appear that about 50 per cent. or so of milks from individual cows shown to contain tubercle bacilli by guinea-pig inoculation can be detected by the microscopic method (Cowan and Maddocks 1935).

Cultivation is not often used as a routine, since it is less delicate than the guinea-pig method and not as rapid as the microscopic method. It is suitable mainly for the milk of individual cows collected under aseptic conditions.

The sediment resulting from high-speed centrifugation should be treated with an equal volume of 15 per cent. HCl for 10–15 minutes, and inoculated on to suitable media (see Wolters and Dehmel 1931).

The main value of the method seems to be in the occasional detection of the avian tubercle bacillus, which might be missed by the animal inoculation method.

Serological methods are still in the experimental stage. German workers have reported favourably on the value of the complement-fixation test carried out on the milk whey in the diagnosis of udder tuberculosis, but it is as yet too early to assess their possible sphere of usefulness (see Karsten 1933, 1935, Söntgen and Menck 1933, Rautmann 1934, Rautmann and Hartwigk 1934, Schultz 1935, Paarmann 1936, Kuhlmann 1936).

Guinea-pig inoculation constitutes the most generally useful and most delicate method of detecting tubercle bacilli in milk.

About 50–100 c.c. of milk, either mixed or from individual animals, should be centrifuged at 3,000 r.p.m. for 30 minutes. The sediment and the cream should be mixed, and 3 c.c. of the mixture should be inoculated intramuscularly into the left thigh of each of two animals, which should previously have been shown to be free from tuberculosis by means of the intradermal tuberculin test. One animal should be killed 3–4 weeks after inoculation; if the results are negative, the other animal should be left for 6–8 weeks. The post-mortem appearances of animals inoculated with tubercle bacilli have already been referred to (p. 1038), and it need only be mentioned here that no animal should be regarded as tuberculous unless characteristic lesions containing acid-fast bacilli are demonstrated.

The Tuberculin Test in the Diagnosis of Cattle Tuberculosis.—This test may be carried out in a number of different ways, but each method consists in noting a reaction, local or constitutional, to the injection of tuberculin. In this country the double intradermal test is generally used, but in the United States the single intradermal test, made by inoculating tuberculin into the skin of the caudal fold, is officially recommended. For the full technique of the double intradermal test the following references may be consulted (Report 1925, Buxton and MacNalty 1928).

Briefly the test consists in injecting 0·1 c.c. of old tuberculin into the deeper layers of the dermis of a shaved area on the side of the neck. The animal is examined 48 hours later, and if a large diffuse œdematous swelling is found, hot and tender, the reaction is regarded as positive. If no more than a pea-like swelling is present, a second injection of 0·1 c.c. should be made into the centre of the nodule, and the animal should be inspected after a further 48 hours. The true criteria of a positive reaction are swelling, heat, and tenderness, and as these are liable to variation, the interpretation of the test demands considerable experience.

A positive tuberculin reaction generally denotes that the animal contains a tuberculous focus somewhere in the body. It gives no information on the activity of the focus. The test is used mainly to determine whether the animal is *infected*, not whether it is *infective*. A negative reaction, while not absolutely excluding the presence of infection, is strong evidence against it. In calves the tuberculin test does not appear to be so reliable as in older animals. The test has been strongly criticized by a number of workers, and there is no question that it is not entirely satisfactory. The presence of infection with avian tubercle bacilli, which appear to be not uncommon, particularly in Denmark, is sufficient to give rise to a positive reaction, even though avian bacilli rarely cause more than a localized, retrogressive type of tuberculosis. Similarly, a reaction may sometimes be obtained in animals showing skin infiltrations and nodules due to an acid-fast bacillus different from the tubercle bacillus; this condition has been described in the United States (see Daines and Austin 1934). The test, it will be understood, is not absolutely specific for tuberculosis, and is often given by animals containing insignificant foci of disease. Border-line reactions are not infrequent; possibly the replacement of old tuberculin with a purer type of tuberculin may diminish the difficulty caused by non-specific reactions. In careful hands, however, it is of very real value, and is indispensable in the detection of tuberculous infection (see Teipel 1925, Ernest and Lash 1928, Haring and Traum 1929, Hastings *et al.* 1930, 1933, Mohler 1931, Fowler and Wright 1931, Glover 1932–33, Buxton and Glover 1932–33, Minett 1932, McEwen and Roberts 1934).

Control of Tuberculosis in Cattle.—Opinions on the measures to be taken to control tuberculosis in cattle are very divided. In this country and in Germany the practice has been to rely on the detection of definitely tuberculous animals by clinical inspection, combined with bacteriological examination of the milk, and to remove all open cases of disease. Though this method may, if prosecuted with real thoroughness, bring about a diminution in the total number of animals suffering from open tuberculosis, it probably has little or no effect on the total incidence of infection. The reason for this, of course, is that by the time a tuberculous animal has been diagnosed by the methods just described, it has already been excreting tubercle bacilli for some time and has acted as a focus of infection for other animals in the herd.

In the Scandinavian countries, largely owing to the initiative of Bang (see Bang 1928, 1929, 1930, 1932), and in the United States and Canada, a more radical method has been adopted, aiming at the elimination not only of open cases of tuberculosis, but of all animals infected with the tubercle bacillus. The general method is to test every animal in the herd with tuberculin, to segregate, remove, or slaughter the positive reactors, and to build up the herd exclusively from negatively reacting animals. The tuberculin test must be repeated at 3- or 6-monthly intervals to detect any fresh reactors in the clean herd. This method, if accompanied by complete removal or slaughter of the reacting animals, is often highly successful in eradicating tuberculosis and in maintaining a tuberculosis-free herd. Where, however, segregation alone is practised, and two herds are kept on the same farm (Bang's method), the results are less satisfactory.

The respective merits of the two methods of controlling tuberculosis in cattle cannot be fully discussed here ; opinion is sharply divided upon them. The eradication method is undoubtedly much the more effective, and should be recommended whenever sufficient money is available to meet the cost. The cost, however, is a very real consideration, and many agriculturists regard tuberculosis as of insufficient economic importance to justify a radical scheme. They would rather rely on the rapid detection of open cases of tuberculosis, and the restriction of the herd to comparatively young animals, in which the disease is less frequent than in the older animals (see Table C, p. 1054). The question must be decided by the agriculturists themselves. From the point of view of human medicine, safeguarding of the milk supply is much more satisfactorily effected by pasteurization than by reliance on any eradication scheme (see Haring 1929, Mohler *et al.* 1929, Hilton 1929, Günzel 1929, Glover and Spencer 1930, Seiferle 1930, Regner 1930, Holth 1930, Wight 1930, Kiernan and Wight 1930, Jordan 1933).

Vaccination of Cattle against Tuberculosis.—If an eradication scheme is impracticable, it is clearly desirable to aim at the diminution of advanced and open cases of tuberculosis. Besides the measures already discussed for this purpose, the possibility of vaccinating the animals so as to raise their general level of resistance to tuberculous infection has long occupied the minds of veterinary and other workers. Von Behring introduced the method of vaccinating calves with living bacilli of the human type. The method was successful in rendering the animals allergic, and fairly successful in protecting them—for a few months at least—against natural tuberculosis ; but it had to be discarded, since it was found that the bacilli remained alive in the tissues and were excreted by the milk, which was, of course, dangerous for human beings (Report 1911c, Griffith, A. S., 1912–13, 1916–17). Attempts have been made to vaccinate cattle with avian bacilli, but the results have not been so successful—probably because avian bacilli do not set up the same focal lesions in cattle that human bacilli do (Gamna and Giordano 1926). Friedmann introduced his turtle bacillus for vaccination, but this organism was found to provide little or no protection for warm-blooded animals.

More recently the claims put forward by Calmette for his B.C.G. vaccine have attracted considerable attention. Many different workers have now carried out experiments to test the prophylactic value of this vaccine. Since the technique of different workers has varied very considerably, it is impossible to summarize quantitatively the results that have been obtained, and we must refer our readers to the original papers in which they are described (see Watson 1928, 1930, Schroeder and Crawford 1928–29, Rankin 1929, Rankin *et al.* 1932, Haring *et al.* 1930, Bang, O. *et al.* 1931, Cotton and Crawford 1932, Jundell and Magnusson 1933, Buxton and Griffith 1931, Griffith, Buxton, and Glover 1931, 1935, Buxton 1936).

The results, however, are sufficiently concordant to justify a few tentative general conclusions. There seems to be little doubt that if B.C.G. is given to uninfected calves shortly after birth, preferably by the parenteral route, their resistance both to experimental and natural infection with the tubercle bacillus is definitely increased compared with that of unvaccinated control animals. The immunity produced is by no means absolute, and does not seem to be sufficient as a rule to prevent actual infection from occurring. It is, however, often sufficient for a time to keep the infection from becoming active. There is evidence that the immunity resulting from the primary vaccination gradually diminishes with passage of time, and wears off to a greater or less extent after 12 months. Re-vaccination may partially restore the lost immunity, but there is not yet sufficient evidence to justify an opinion on its real value.

From these results it is clear that vaccination of calves with B.C.G. deserves a trial under field conditions. Whether the limited increase in immunity that it is likely to produce will be sufficient to bring about any considerable diminution in the number of active cases of tuberculosis among animals that are exposed to frequent infection from their fellows, it is impossible to predict, and we must await the verdict of actual experience. It is important to realize that B.C.G. vaccination renders the animal allergic, so that the tuberculin test can no longer be used to indicate the presence of infection with virulent bacilli. B.C.G. vaccination is therefore incompatible with an eradication policy.

Mention may perhaps be made of the Spahlinger vaccine (see p. 1050) which has recently been credited with some success in preliminary experiments in the North of Ireland (Report 1935a).

Tuberculosis of Pigs.—The exact incidence of this disease is unknown, but slaughter-house records leave no doubt of its frequency in this country. Ellison (1930) found that 12·09 per cent. of 72,350 pigs supplied to a bacon factory at Ipswich showed macroscopic lesions of tuberculosis. Other figures showed that 7·6 per cent. of 44,000 pigs coming into another bacon factory over a period of 2 years contained lesions of tuberculosis (Report 1933b). The glands draining the alimentary tract are mainly affected, particularly the submaxillary and mesenteric group. In about 84 per cent. of carcasses in Ellison's series the lesions were confined to the head and neck, and in about 5 per cent. to the plucks or offal or both. In only 0·15 per cent. of animals was the disease generalized or advanced.

The bovine type of tubercle bacillus is found in about two-thirds and the avian bacillus in about one-third of the cases ; the human tubercle bacillus is very much less common (Griffith, A. S., 1928a, Cornell and Griffith 1930). Submaxillary glands infected with avian or human bacilli are often not appreciably enlarged, and contain discrete caseo-calcareous tubercles ; those infected with bovine bacilli are generally enlarged and composed wholly or in part of caseous or caseo-calcareous material surrounded by fibrous tissue. Generalized tuberculosis is almost invariably due to the bovine type.

Pigs become infected from various sources, the chief being raw cow's milk, infected cow dung, slaughter-house offal, and the droppings of tuberculous fowls. Infection occurs by the mouth. The disease can be diagnosed during life by the intradermal inoculation of tuberculin into the ear, but in most animals infection is not diagnosed, and often not even suspected, till they come to the abattoir. Prevention consists in avoiding contamination of the food with tubercle bacilli ; boiling all food, including milk, that may possibly be infected ; and keeping the animals separate from tuberculous cattle and poultry (see Mohler and Washburn 1930).

Tuberculosis in Fowls.—Comparatively little is known of the frequency with which tuberculosis attacks fowls in this country. It is met with in farmyard birds, but is uncommon on poultry farms. In Germany, however, Klimmer (quoted by Knorr 1932) stated that of 75 million hens, $7\frac{1}{2}$ million were tuberculous, and that 3 per cent. of market eggs, and 10 per cent. of eggs from tuberculous hens, contained tubercle bacilli. In the United States a survey of 115,700 flocks of poultry in 40 States revealed the presence of tuberculosis in 6,690 (5·8 per cent.) ; the actual number of fowls affected was estimated at over 8 million (Mohler and Washburn 1930). The organs most frequently involved are the liver, spleen, intestines, lungs, bones, joints, peritoneum, kidneys, and ovary (Gallagher 1926). The disease can be diagnosed by the intradermal tuberculin test using avian tuberculin. The slaughter policy seems to be the most suitable method of dealing with the disease when it is extensive, but an eradication plan based on the use of tuberculin may be tried if the disease is less extensive or the birds valuable. (For a general survey of avian tuberculosis see Gloyne 1933.) Acid-fast organisms have been reported in bumble-foot of chickens, but their exact nature is unknown (see Bunyea 1936).

REFERENCES

ALEXANDER, D. M. (1910) *J. Hyg., Camb.*, **10**, 37.
APPEL, J. M., DOUGLAS, B. H., ROSENBUSCH, T., and WILLIS, H. S. (1934) *Amer. Rev. Tuberc.*, **30**, 478.
ARONSON, J. D. (1934) *Suppl. Amer. Rev. Tuberc.*, **30**, 727.
ARONSON, J. D. and DANNENBERG, A. M. (1935) *Amer. J. Dis. Child.*, **50**, 1117.
ARONSON, J. D. and NICHOLAS, R. V. (1933) *J. Immunol.*, **25**, 483.
BANG, B. (1928) *J. Amer. vet. med. Ass.*, **72**, 20 ; (1929) *Tierärztl. Rdsch.*, **35**, 745, 766 ; (1930) *Vet. Rec.*, **10**, 557 ; (1932) *Z. Tuberk.*, **64**, 87.
BANG, O., JUNDELL, I., and MAGNUSSON, H. (1931) *Ann. Inst. Pasteur*, **47**, 386.
BARNWELL, J. B. and POLLARD, H. M. (1934) *Amer. Rev. Tuberc.*, **30**, 482.
BASKETT, B. G. M. (1931) *The Times*, March 25th.
BEAVEN, P. W. and BAYNE-JONES, S. (1931) *J. infect. Dis.*, **49**, 399.
BECK, M. and RABINOVITSCH, L. (1900) *Dtsch. med. Wschr.*, **26**, 400 ; (1901) *Z. Hyg. InfektKr.*, **37**, 205.
BEGBIE, R. S. (1930) *Edin. med. J.*, **37**, 187 ; (1931) *Ibid.*, **38**, 173.
BEHMANN, H. (1930) *Münch. med. Wschr.*, **77**, 62.
BEHRING, E. VON. (1904) *Dtsch. med. Wschr.*, **30**, 193.
BENDIX, E. (1900) *Dtsch. med. Wschr.*, **26**, 224.
BERG, M. R. H. VAN DEN. (1936) *Ned. Tijdschr. Geneesk.*, **80**, 945.
BERGHAUS, W. (1930) *Dtsch. med. Wschr.*, **56**, 1771 ; (1931) *Z. Tuberk.*, **59**, 230.
BESREDKA, A. and MANOUKHINE, J. (1914) *Ann. Inst. Pasteur*, **28**, 569.
BESSAU, G. (1916) *Berl. klin. Wschr.*, **53**, 801.

BESTA, B. and LENNEBERG, L. (1935) *Z. Hyg. InfektKr.*, **117**, 7.
BIRKHAUG, K. E. (1933) *Amer. Rev. Tuberc.*, **27**, 6.
BLACKLOCK, J. W. S (1932) *Spec. Rep. Ser. med. Res. Coun., Lond.*, No. 172 ; (1935) *Brit. J. Tuberc.*, **2**, 69.
BLACKLOCK, J. W. S and GRIFFIN, M. A. (1935) *J. Path. Bact.*, **40**, 489.
BORREL, A. (1920) _nn. Inst. Pasteur*, **34**, 105.
BOZZELLI, R. (1914) *Ann. Staz. Mal. Best. Napoli*, **2**, 77.
BRANCH, A. and ENDERS, J. F. (1935) *Amer. Rev. Tuberc.*, **32**, 595.
BRINK, G. C., BROWN M. H., and GRAY, K. G. (1933) *Canad. publ. Hlth J.*, **24**, 471.
BROCQ-ROUSSEU, URBAIN, A., and CAUCHEMEZ. (1923) *Ann. Inst. Pasteur*, **37**, 872.
BRONFENBRENNER, J. J. and STRAUB, E. L. (1925) *J. exp. Med.*, **41**, 257.
BRUYNOGHE, R. and ADANT, M. (1933) *C. R. Soc. Biol.*, **111**, 1051.
BUNYEA, H. (1936) ". *Amer. vet. med. Ass.*, **88**, 386.
BURKHARDT, A. (1933) *Z. Hyg. InfektKr.*, **53**, 139.
BUSHNELL, G. E. (1920) " A Study in the Epidemiology of Tuberculosis," New York.
BURNAND, GROSJEAN, JAQUEROD, PIGUET, REYNIER DE, ROSSELL, SILLIG, and BERGEN. (1922) " Études sur la Tuberculose." Paris.
BUXTON, J. B. (1936 *Edin. med. J.*, **43**, 160.
BUXTON, J. B. and GLOVER, R. E. (1932–3) *3rd Rep. Inst. Anim. Path. Univ. Camb.*, p. 227.
BUXTON, J. B. and GRIFFITH, A. S. (1931) *Lancet*, i. 393.
BUXTON, J. B. and MACNALTY, A. S. (1928) *Spec. Rep. Ser. med. Res. Coun., Lond.*, No. 122.
CALDWELL, M. E. (1 25) *J. infect. Dis.*, **37**, 465.
CALMETTE, A. (1920) " L'infection bacillaire et la tuberculose chez l'homme et chez les animaux." Paris.
CALMETTE, A. (1924) *Rev. belge Tuberc.*, **15**, 293.
CALMETTE, A. (1930) *er. Congr. int. Microbiol.*, **1**, 39 ; (1931) *Proc. R. Soc. Med.*, **24**, 85 ; (1932) *Ann. Inst. Pasteur*, **49**, Suppl.
CALMETTE, A. and GUÉRIN, C. (1905) *Ann. Inst. Pasteur*, **19**, 601 ; (1906a) *Ibid.*, **20**, 353 ; (1906b) *Ibid.*, **20**, 89 ; (1924) *Ibid.*, **38**, 371.
CALMETTE, A. and MASSOL, L. (1914) *Ann. Inst. Pasteur*, **28**, 338.
CALMETTE, A., BOQUET, A., and NÈGRE, L. (1924) *Ann. Inst. Pasteur*, **38**, 399.
CALMETTE, A., GRYSEZ, V., and LETULLE, R. (1911) *Pr. Méd.*, **19**, 651.
CALMETTE, A., GUÉRIN C., NÈGRE, L., and BOQUET, A. (1926) *Ann. Inst. Pasteur*, **40**, 89.
CHADWICK, H. D. (1927) *Amer. Rev. Tuberc.*, **15**, 601.
CHANG, P. Y. (1922) *Nat. med. J. China*, **8**, 256.
CLARK, L. T., EMMETT A. D., and BIRD, O. D. (1934) *Amer. Rev. Tuberc.*, **30**, 471.
CLAUSEN, S. W. (1932) *Physiol. Rev.*, **14**, 309.
CLAWSON, B. J. (1935 *Proc. Soc. exp. Biol., N.Y.*, **31**, 165.
COBBETT, L. (1917) " Causes of Tuberculosis," Cambridge ; (1922) *Lancet*, i. 979.
COLLIS, W. R. F. and BROCKINGTON, C. F. (1933) *Lancet*, i. 127.
CORNELL, R. L. and GRIFFITH, A. S. (1930) *J. comp. Path.*, **43**, 56.
CORNET, G. (1889) *Z. Hyg. InfektKr.*, **5**, 191.
CORPER, H. J. and COHN, M. L. (1933) *J. Lab. clin. Med.*, **18**, 515.
COSTA, G.-J. G. (1926 *C. R. Soc. Biol.*, **95**, 330.
COTTON, W. E. and CRAWFORD, A. B. (1932) *J. Amer. vet. med. Ass.*, **80**, 18.
COULTHARD, H. L. (1923) *J. Path. Bact.*, **26**, 350.
COURMONT, P. and PALACOSTAS. (1923) *C. R. Soc. Biol.*, **89**, 521.
COWAN, S. T. and MADDOCKS, L. (1935) *J. Path. Bact.*, **41**, 373.
COX, G. L. (1929) *Rep. Lancs. County Council.*
CUMMING, W. M., FOSTER, W. M., GIRDWOOD, R. O., and GRIFFITH, A. S. (1933) *J. Path. Bact.*, **36**, 153.
CUMMINS, S. L. (1908) *Brit. J. Tuberc.*, **2**, 35 ; (1911–12) *Trans. Soc. trop. Med. Hyg.*, **5**, 245.
CUMMINS, S. L. and EVANS, A. C. (1933) *Brit. med. J.*, i. 815.
CUMMINS, S. L. and WILLIAMS, E. M. (1933) *Tubercle, Lond.*, **15**, 49.
DAINES, L. L. and AUSTIN, H. (1934) *Amer. Rev. Tuberc.*, **30**, 209.
DAVIES, G. O. (1933) *Vet. Rec.*, **13**, 1046.
DEBRÉ, R. and BONNET, H. (1922) *C. R. Soc. Biol.*, **87**, 449.
DEBRÉ, R. and COFINO, E. (1929) *C. R. Soc. Biol.*, **102**, 513, 516.
Discussion. (1935) *Proc. R. Soc. Med.*, **28**, 1297.
DOUGLAS, J. S. C., EDINGTON, J. W., and SIMSON, F. W. (1925) *J. Path. Bact.*, **28**, 633.
DOUGLAS, S. R. and HARTLEY, P. (1934a) *Tubercle, Lond.*, **16**, 100 ; (1934b) *Ibid.*, **16**, 105.
DOUGLAS, S. R. and MEANWELL, L. J. (1925) *Brit. J. exp. Path.*, **6**, 203.
DOW, D. J. and LLOYD, W. E. (1930) " Tuberculosis Mortality in Children." Brompton Hosp. Rep. No. 1 ; 1931) *Brit. med. J.*, ii. 183.
DREYER, G., VOLLUM, R. L., and AMMITZBÖLL, H. H. (1934) *J. comp. Path.*, **47**, 1.

DROLET, G. J. (1930) *J. prev. Med., Baltimore*, **4**, 115 ; (1934) *Amer. Rev. Tuberc.*, **30**, 1.
DUCHÊNE. (1929) *Bull. Off. int. Hyg. publ.*, **21**, 775.
DUDGEON, L. S., MEEK, W. O., and WEIR, H. B. (1914) *J. Hyg., Camb.*, **14**, 72.
EASTWOOD, A. and GRIFFITH, F. (1916) *J. Hyg., Camb.*, **15**, 257.
Editorial. (1929) *Pr. méd.*, **37**, 1175.
EIDINOW, A. (1927) *Brit. med. J.*, ii. 160.
ELLISON, G. (1930) *J. roy. san. Inst.*, **50**, 669.
EISELBERG, A. VON. (1887) *Wien. med. Wschr.*, **37**, 1729.
ENDERS, J. F. (1929) *J. exp. Med.*, **50**, 777.
ERNEST, L. B. and LASH, E. (1928) *Circ. U.S. Bur. Anim. Ind.*, No. 249.
EVARTS, H. W., POTTER, R. G., and DUNN, E. G. (1934) *Amer. Rev. Tuberc.*, **29**, 123.
FAISCA, J. B. R. (1921) *C. R. Soc. Biol.*, **84**, 1002.
FELLOWS, H. H. (1934) *Amer. Rev. Tuberc.*, **30**, 109.
FINDEL, H. (1907) *Z. Hyg. InfektKr.*, **57**, 104.
FLÜGGE, C. (1899) *Z. Hyg. InfektKr.*, **30**, 107.
FOWLER, A. B. and WRIGHT, N. C. (1931) *Bull. Hannah Dairy Inst.*, No. 2.
FREUND, J. (1932) *Proc. Soc. exp. Biol., N.Y.*, **29**, 1200.
GAIGER, S. H. and DAVIES, G. O. (1933) *Vet. Rec.*, **13**, 900.
GALLAGHER, B. A. (1926) *Fmrs' Bull. U.S. Dep. Agric.*, No. 1200.
GAMNA, C. and GIORDANO, C. (1926) *G. Batt. Immun.*, **1**, 173.
GARDNER, A. D. (1926) *Lancet*, i. 1090.
GEER, E. K. (1934) *Amer. Rev. Tuberc.*, **29**, 88.
GERLACH, F. (1927) *Zbl. Bakt.*, **104**, 61 ; (1930) *Ergbn. Hyg. Bakt.*, **11**, 775.
GERLACH, F. and KRAUS, R. (1929) *Z. ImmunForsch.*, **59**, 306.
GHON, A. (1916) " The Primary Lung Focus of Tuberculosis in Children," trans. by King. London.
GHON, A., KUDLICH, H., and WINTERNITZ, F. (1925) *Z. Tuberk.*, **42**, 3, 97.
GLOVER, R. E. (1932–33) *3rd Rep. Inst. Anim. Path. Univ. Camb.*, p. 200.
GLOVER, A. J. and SPENCER, W. T. (1930) *J. Amer. vet. med. Ass.*, **76**, 374, 380.
GLOYNE, S. R. (1932) *Tubercle, Lond.*, **13**, 443, 488 ; (1933) *Bull. Hyg. Lond.*, **8**, 39.
GOODALE, R. H. and KRISCHNER, H. (1930) *Amer. Rev. Tuberc.*, **21**, 223.
GOUGH, G. A. C. (1934) *Brit. J. exp. Path.*, **15**, 237.
GOURLEY, I. (1934) *Amer. Rev. Tuberc.*, **29**, 461.
GRASSET, E. and PERRET-GENTIL, A. (1930) *Ann. Inst. Pasteur*, **44**, 659.
GREENWOOD, M. (1928) *Brit. med. J.*, i. 793.
GREENWOOD, M. and WOLFF, G. (1928) *Z. Tuberk.*, **52**, 97.
GRIFFITH, A. S. (1912–13) *J. Path. Bact.*, **17**, 323 ; (1914) *Brit. med. J.*, i, 1171 ; (1916–17) *J. Path. Bact.*, **21**, 329 ; (1924) *Tubercle, Lond.*, **5**, 569 ; (1925a) *J. comp. Path.*, **38**, 157 ; (1925b) *Trans. Nat. Ass. Prov. Tuberc.*, *11th Ann. Conf.* ; (1926) *J. comp. Path.*, **39**, 71 ; (1927) *Proc. nat. Conf. Mat. and Inf. Welf., Lond.* ; (1928a) *Ibid.*, **41**, 53, 109 ; (1928b) *J. Hyg., Camb.*, **28**, 198 ; (1930) *J. Path. Bact.*, **33**, 1145 ; (1931) *Spec. Rep. Ser. med. Res. Coun., Lond.*, No. 152 ; (1932a) *Edin. med. J.*, **39**, 177 ; (1932b) *J. Path. Bact.*, **35**, 97 ; (1932c) *Brit. med. J.*, ii. 501 ; (1933) *Tubercle, Lond.*, **15**, 53 ; (1934) *Lancet*, i. 1382 ; (1935) *Acta. tuberc. scand.*, **9**, 229.
GRIFFITH, A. S., BUXTON, J. B., and GLOVER, R. E. (1931) *2nd Rep. Inst. Anim. Path. Univ. Camb.*, p. 46 ; (1935) *Lancet*, i. 451.
GRIFFITH, A. S. and GRIFFITH, F. (1907) *Roy. Comm. Tuberc., 2nd interim Rep.*, ii. 3.
GRIFFITH, A. S. and MENTON, J. (1936) *Brit. med. J.*, i. 524.
GRIFFITH, A. S. and MUNRO, W. T. (1933) *Lancet*, i. 399.
GRIFFITH, A. S. and SMITH, J. (1935) *Lancet*, ii. 1339.
GRIFFITH, A. S. and SUMMERS, G. J. (1933) *Lancet*, i. 875.
GRÖER, F. VON. (1932) *Wien. med. Wschr., Sonder-Abdruck.*, No. 39.
GRYSEZ, V. and BERNARD, A. (1920) *C. R. Soc. Biol.*, **83**, 1506.
GÜNZEL. (1929) *Berl. tierärztl. Wschr.*, **45**, 281.
GUTFELD, F. VON, and WEIGERT, E. (1924) *Zbl. Bakt.*, **93**, 436.
GYE, W. E. and KETTLE, E. H. (1922) *Brit. J. exp. Path.*, **3**, 241.
HARING, C. M. (1929) *Circ. Calif. agric. Ext. Serv.*, No. 33.
HARING, C. M. and TRAUM, J. (1929) *Circ. Calif. agric. Ext. Serv.*, No. 21.
HARING, C. M., TRAUM, J., HAYES, F. M., and HENRY, B. S. (1930) *Hilgardia*, **4**, 307.
HARRINGTON, F. E., MYERS, J. A., and LEVINE, I. (1935) *J. Amer. med. Ass.*, **104**, 1869.
HARSHFIELD, G. S. and RODERICK, L. M. (1934) *J. Amer. vet. med. Ass.*, **85**, 597.
HART, P. D'A. (1932) *Spec. Rep. Ser. med. Res. Coun., Lond.*, No. 164.
HASTINGS, E. G., BEACH, B. A., and THOMPSON, I. (1930) *Amer. Rev. Tuberc.*, **22**, 218.
HASTINGS, E. G., WISNICKY, W., BEACH, B. A., and McCARTER, J. (1933) *J. Amer. vet. med. Ass.*, **82**, 565.
HEIMBECK, J. (1927) *Lancet*, ii. 290 ; (1932) *Pr. méd.*, **40**, 528 ; (1933) *Med. Klin.*, **29**, 1731.
HERMAN, M. (1908) *Ann. Inst. Pasteur*, **22**, 92.

HERMAN, N. B., BAETJER, F. H., and DOULL, J. A. (1932) *Bull. Johns Hopk. Hosp.*, **51**, 41.
HETHERINGTON, H. W., MCPHEDRAN, F. M., LANDIS, H. R. M., and OPIE, E. L. (1929) *Amer. Rev. Tuberc.*, **20**, 421 ; (1931) *Arch. intern. Med.*, **48**, 734 ; (1934) *Amer. Rev. Tuberc.*, **29**, 142 ; (1935) *Arch. intern. Med.*, **55**, 709.
HEWITT, E. S. and CUTTS, R. E. (1932) *Amer. Rev. Tuberc.*, **25**, 525.
HEYMANN, B. (1901) *Z. Hyg. InfektKr.*, **38**, 21.
HEYMANS, J.-F. (1926) *C. R. Soc. Biol.*, **95**, 242.
HILTON, G. (1929) *J. Dairy Res.*, **1**, 58.
HOLLMANN, R. (1924) *Z. Tuberk.*, **41**, 127.
HOLTH, H. (1930) *Off. int. Epizooties*, **3**, 576.
HUGHES, J. (1933) *J. Immunol.*, **25**, 103.
HÜNIGEN, W. (1932) *Z. Tuberk.*, **64**, 447.
IRVINE, K. N. (1934) " The B.C.G. Vaccine," Humphrey Milford, London.
JACOBSON, C. J. (1933) *Hospitalstidende*, **76**, 763.
JOHNSON, W. M. and MYERS, J. A. (1933) *Amer. Rev. Tuberc.*, **28**, 381.
JOHNSTON, J. A., HOWARD, P. J., and MARONEY, J. (1934) *Amer. Rev. Tuberc.*, **29**, 652.
JORDAN, L. (1933) *Spec. Rep. Ser. med. Res. Coun., Lond.*, No. 184.
JUNDELL, I. and MAGNUSSON, H. (1933) *Acta path. microbiol. scand.*, Suppl. 16, p. 183.
KARMANN, P. (1924) *Zbl. Bakt.*, **93**, 368.
KARSTEN. (1933) *Dtsch. tierärztl. Wschr.*, **41**, 561 ; (1935) *Ibid.*, **43**, 101.
KERESZTURI, C., HAUPTMANN, D., SCHICK, B., and MISHULOW, L. (1933) *J. Amer. med. Ass.*, **100**, 1481.
KERESZTURI, C., MISHULOW, L., SCHICK, B., and BEHNER, D. (1932) *J. Amer. med. Ass.*, **98**, 1879.
KETTLE, E. H. (1924) *Brit. J. exp. Path.*, **5**, 158 ; (1930) *Proc. R. Soc. Med.*, **24**, 79.
KIERNAN, J. A. and WIGHT, A. E. (1930) *Fmrs' Bull. U.S. Dep. Agric.*, No. 1069.
KLEINE, F. K. (1930) *Dtsch. med. Wschr.*, **56**, 130.
KLIMMER, M. (1931) *Klin. Wschr.*, **10**, 1994.
KNORR, M. (1932) *Arch. Hyg.*, **108**, 181.
KOCH, R. (1882) *Berl. klin. Wschr.*, **19**, 221 ; (1890) *Dtsch. med. Wschr.*, **16**, 1029 ; (1891a) *Ibid.*, **17**, 101 ; (1891b) *Ibid.*, **17**, 1189 ; (1897) *Ibid.*, **23**, 209 ; (1901) *Ibid.*, **27**, 829.
KOIZUMI, T. (1924) *Z. Tuberk.*, **41**, 173.
KRAMER, H. (1934) *Z. Tuberk.*, **71**, 165.
KRAUS, R. (1927) *Zbl. Bakt.*, **104**, 65.
KRAUS, R. and GERLACH, F. (1929) *Z. ImmunForsch.*, **62**, 339.
KRAUSE, A. K. (1928) *Amer. Rev. Tuberc.*, **18**, 208.
KUHLMANN, H. (1936) *Münch. tierärztl. Wschr.*, **87**, 229.
LAIDLAW, P. P. and DUDLEY, H. W. (1925) *Brit. J. exp. Path.*, **6**, 197.
LANGE, B. (1931) *Z. Hyg. InfektKr.*, **112**, 298 ; (1932) *Brit. med. J.*, ii. 503.
LANGE, B. and FREUND, R. (1926) *Z. Hyg. InfektKr.*, **105**, 571.
LANGE, B. and KESCHISCHIAN, K. K. (1925) *Z. Hyg. InfektKr.*, **104**, 256.
LANGE, B. and NOWOSELSKY, W. (1925) *Z. Hyg. InfektKr.*, **104**, 286.
LANGE, C. DE and BRUIN, M. DE. (1935) *Ned. Tijdschr. Geneesk.*, **79**, 652.
LEWIS, J. H., and SEIBERT, F. B. (1931) *J. Immunol.*, **20**, 201.
LICHTENSTEIN, M. R. (1934) *Amer. Rev. Tuberc.*, **30**, 214.
LLOYD, W. E. and MACPHERSON, A. M. C. (1933) *Brit. med. J.*, i. 818.
LONG, E. R. (1934) *Suppl. Amer. Rev. Tuberc.*, **30**, 757 ; (1935) *Puerto Rico J. publ. Hlth*, **10**, 270.
LONG, E. R., ARONSON, J. D., and SEIBERT, F. B. (1934) *Suppl. Amer. Rev. Tuberc.*, **30**, 733.
LOVELL, R. (1930) *J. comp. Path.*, **43**, 205.
LÖWENSTEIN, E. (1913) See Kolle and Wassermann's " Hdb. path. Mikroorg.," 2te Abt., 1912–13, **5**, 660.
MCEWEN, A. D. and ROBERTS, R. S. (1934) *J. comp. Path.*, **47**, 32.
MACNALTY, A. S. (1932) *Rep. publ. Hlth med. Subj., Lond.*, No. 64.
MCPHEDRAN, F. M. and OPIE, E. L. (1935) *Amer. J. Hyg.*, **22**, 565.
MANTOUX, C. (1910) *Pr. méd.*, **18**, 10.
MARTIN, D. C., PESSAR, H. T., and GOLDBERG, J. A. (1934) *Amer. Rev. Tuberc.*, **29**, 182.
MATTHEWS, H. T. (1931) *Vet. Rec.*, **11**, 403.
MAYER, E. (1921) *Amer. Rev. Tuberc.*, **5**, 75.
MAYER, G. (1926) *Zbl. Bakt.*, **100**, 10.
MEEK, W. O. (1914) *J. Hyg., Camb.*, **14**, 76.
MEISZNER, I. and PRAUSNITZ, C. (1934) *Zbl. Bakt.*, **132**, 23.
METCHNIKOFF, E., BURNET, E., and TARASSEVITCH, L. (1911) *Ann. Inst. Pasteur*, **25**, 785.
MINETT, F. C. (1932) *J. comp. Path.*, **45**, 317.
MISHULOW, L., KERESZTURI, C., and HAUPTMAN, D. (1934) *Amer. Rev. Tuberc.*, **29**, 471.
MOELLER, A. (1899) *Z. Hyg. InfektKr.*, **32**, 205.
MOHLER, J. R. (1931) *Misc. Publ. U.S. Dep. Agric.*, No. 59.

MOHLER, J. R. and WASHBURN, H. J. (1930) *Fmrs' Bull., U.S. Dep. Agric.* No. 781.
MOHLER, J. R., WRIGHT, A. E., and ERNEST, L. B. (1929) *Misc. Publ. U.S. Dep. Agric.*, No. 66.
MONGOUR and BUARD. (1898) *C. R. Soc. Biol.*, **50**, 1142 ; (1899) *Ibid.*, **51**, 564.
MORI, N. (1911) *Ann. Staz. Mal. Best. Napoli*, **1**, 327.
MOSSELL, S. T. (1923) " A Study of the Negro Tuberculosis Problem in Philadelphia." Philadelphia.
MUELLER, J. H. (1926) *J. exp. Med.*, **43**, 1, 9.
MUNRO, W. T. and GRIFFITH, A. S. (1928) *Lancet*, i. 384.
MUNRO, W. T. and SCOTT, H. (1936) *Lancet*, i. 393.
MYERS, J. A. (1930) *Amer. Rev. Tuberc.*, **21**, 479.
MYERS, J. A., DIEHL, H. S., and LEES, H. D. (1934) *J. Amer. med. Ass.*, **102**, 2086.
NAEGELI, O. (1900) *Virchows Arch.*, **160**, 426.
NAESLUND, C. (1935) *Lancet*, i. 1512.
NAKAYAMA, J. (1924) *Z. Hyg. InfektKr.*, **102**, 581.
NALBANT, J. P. (1934) *Amer. Rev. Tuberc.*, **29**, 481.
NEISSER, M. (1900) *Wien. med. Wschr.*, **50**, 2263.
NEUFELD, F. (1930) *Dtsch. med. Wschr.*, **56**, 1599.
NORTON, J. F., THOMAS, J. G., and BROOM, N. H. (1932) *Amer. Rev. Tuberc.*, **25**, 378.
OKELL, C. C. and PARISH, H. J. (1927) *Brit. J. exp. Path.*, **8**, 170.
OPIE, E. L. (1917a) *J. exp. Med.*, **25**, 855 ; (1917b) *Ibid.*, **26**, 263 ; (1924a) *Amer. Rev. Tuberc.*, **10**, 249 ; (1924b) *Ibid.*, **10**, 265 ; (1925) " Widespread Tuberculous Infection of Healthy Individuals and its Significance." Philadelphia ; (1928–9) *Harvey Lectures* ; (1929) *Amer. Rev. Tuberc.*, **20**, 141 ; (1930) *J. Amer. med. Ass.*, **95**, 1151 ; (1935) *Amer. Rev. Tuberc.*, **32**, 617.
OPIE, E. L. and ARONSON, J. D. (1927) *Arch. Path. Lab. Med.*, **4**, 1.
OPIE, E. L., LANDIS, H. R. M., MCPHEDRAN, F. M., and HETHERINGTON, H. W. (1929) *Amer. Rev. Tuberc.*, **20**, 413.
OPIE, E. L. and MCPHEDRAN, F. M. (1935) *Amer. J. Hyg.*, **22**, 539.
OPIE, E. L., MCPHEDRAN, F. M., and PUTNAM, P. (1935) *Amer. J. Hyg.*, **22**, 644.
OSTENFELD, HEITMANN, and NEANDER. (1931) " Tuberculosis in Denmark, Norway and Sweden." League of Nations, Hlth. Organisation, C.H. 957, Geneva.
PAARMANN, E. (1936) *Tierärztl. Rdsch.*, **42**, 1.
PANETH, O. (1928) " Tuberculosis in the Karo-districts." G. Kolff and Co., Weltevreden.
PARK, W. H., KERESZTURI, C., and MISHULOW, L. (1933) *J. Amer. med. Ass.*, **101**, 1619.
PARK, W. H. and KRUMWIEDE, C. (1910) *J. med. Res.*, **23**, 205.
PARRY, R. H. and HALL, I. W. (1935) *Lancet*, i. 1127.
PETROFF, S. A. (1927) *J. Amer. med. Ass.*, **89**, 285.
PETROFF, S. A., BRANCH, A., and JENNINGS, F. B. (1929) *J. Immunol.*, **16**, 233.
PETROFF, S. A., BRANCH, A., and STEENKEN, W. (1927) *Proc. Soc. exp. Biol., N.Y.*, **25**, 14; (1929) *Amer. Rev. Tuberc.*, **19**, 9.
PINNER, M. (1932) *Proc. Soc. exp. Biol., N.Y.*, **30**, 214 ; (1935) *Amer. Rev. Tuberc.*, **32**, 424.
PINNER, M. and KASPER, J. A. (1932) *Amer. Rev. Tuberc.*, **26**, 463.
PIRQUET, C. VON. (1907) *Berl. klin. Wschr.*, **48**, 644, 699 ; (1909) *J. Amer. med. Ass.*, **52**, 675.
POULSEN, V. and ANDERSEN, A. O. (1934) *Amer. J. Dis. Child.*, **47**, 307.
PRICE, R. M. (1932) *Amer. Rev. Tuberc.*, **25**, 383 ; (1934) *Canad. publ. Hlth J.*, **25**, 13.
PULLINGER, E. J. (1934) *Lancet*, i. 967 ; (1935) *Ibid.*, i. 1342.
RADCLIFFE, J. A. D. (1915) *J. Hyg., Camb.*, **15**, 36.
RANKIN, A. C. (1929) *Canad. J. Res.*, **1**, 48.
RANKIN, A. C., OWER, J. J., SHAW, R. M., TALBOT, P. R., and VANGO, H. M. (1932) *Canad. J. Res.*, **6**, 177.
RAUTMANN, H. (1934) *Z. InfektKr. Haustiere*, **45**, 250.
RAUTMANN, H. and HARTWIGK, H. (1934) *Z. InfektKr. Haustiere*, **45**, 233.
REGNER, G. (1930) *Off. int. Epizooties*, **3**, 582.
REICHEL, J. and CLARK, L. T. (1934) *Suppl. Amer. Rev. Tuberc.*, **30**, 721.
REICHLE, S. (1936) *Arch. Path.*, **21**, 79.
REMLINGER, P. (1923) *C. R. Soc. Biol.*, **88**, 409.
Report. (1909) 3rd *Int. Rep. roy. Comm. Tuberc.*, H.M. Stat. Off., Lond.; (1911a) *Final Rep. roy. Comm. Tuberc.*, H.M. Stat. Off., Lond. ; (1911b) *Ibid.*, Part 2, Append. Vol. II ; (1911c) *Ibid.*, Part 2, Append. Vol. III ; (1913) *Ibid.*, Append. Suppl. Vol., p. 59 ; (1925) *Spec. Rep. Ser. med. Res. Coun., Lond.*, No. 94 ; (1931a) *Rep. perm. Comm. biol. Standardization Hlth. Organiz.*, League of Nations, Geneva ; (1931b) *Rep. publ. Hlth med. Subj., Lond.*, No. 63 ; (1932a) " A Survey of Tuberculosis of Bovine Origin in Great Britain," People's League of Health, London ; (1932b) " Tuberculosis in South African Natives with special reference to the Disease amongst the Mine Labourers on Witwatersrand,"

S. Afr. Inst. med. Res., No. 30 ; (1933*a*) *Spec. Rep. Ser. med. Res. Coun., Lond.*, No. 189 ; (1933*b*) *Rep. Chief med. Offr., Min. Hlth., Lond.*, for 1932 ; (1934) *Economic Advisory Coun., Comm. Cattle Diseases*, H.M. Stat. Off., Lond. ; (1935*a*) " Report on the Spahlinger experiments in Northern Ireland," H.M. Stat. Off., Lond. ; (1935*b*) " Die Säuglingstuberkulose in Lübeck." *Arb. ReichsgesundhAmt.*, **69**, 1.

Review. (1933) *Bull. Hyg., Lond.*, **8**, 346–9.

RICE, C. E., ORR, J. H., and BREED, G. B. (1933) *J. Immunol.*, **25**, 19.

RICH, A. R. (1929) *Arch. intern. Med.*, **43**, 691 ; (1930) *Bull. Johns Hopk. Hosp.*, **47**, 189 ; (1931) *Trans. nat. Tuberc. Ass.,N.Y.*,**27**, 149 ; (1933*a*) *Bull. Johns Hopk. Hosp.*, **52**, 203 ; (1933*b*) *Lancet*, ii. 521.

RICH, A. R. and BROWN, J. H. (1930) *Proc. Soc. exp. Biol.*, *N.Y.*, **27**, 695.

RICH, A. R., CHESNEY, A. M., and TURNER, T. B. (1933) *Bull. Johns Hopk. Hosp.*, **52**, 179.

RICH, A. R., JENNINGS, F. B., and DOWNING, L. M. (1933) *Bull. Johns Hopk. Hosp.*, **53**, 172.

RICH, A. R. and McCORDOCK, H. A. (1929) *Bull. Johns Hopk. Hosp.*, **44**, 273.

RIDDOCH, J. (1903) *J. comp. Path.*, **16**, 357.

RIEUX, J. (1926) " La Tuberculose pulmonaire latente." Paris.

RIST, E. (1936) *Edin. med. J.*, **43**, 172.

ROBERTSON, E. C. (1934) *Medicine*, **13**, 123.

RODRÍGUEZ PASTOR, J., MORALES OTERO, P., PAYNE, G. C., RAMÍREZ SANTOS, R., SILVA, E., and ARRUZA, J. (1935) *Puerto Rico J. publ. Hlth*, **10**, 451–542.

RÖMER, P. H. (1909) *Beitr. klin. Tuberk.*, **13**, 1.

ROSENFELD, S. (1928) *Wien. klin. Wschr.*, **41**, 800.

ROSS, E. L. (1930) *Canad. med. Ass. J.*, **22**, 347.

ROTHSCHILD, H., FRIEDENWALD, J. S., and BERNSTEIN, C. (1934) *Bull. Johns Hopk. Hosp.* **54**, 232.

ROUVILLOIS, H. (1934) *Bull. Acad. Méd.*, **112**, 115.

SAENZ, A., LE MÉE, J. M., COSTIL, L. (1933) *C. R. Soc. Biol.*, **113**, 564.

SALOMON, M. and VALTIS, J. (1925) *C. R. Soc. Biol.*, **93**, 1145.

SAUVAN, A. (1935) *Marseille méd.*, **72**, 529.

SAVAGE, W. G. (1933) *Brit. med. J.*, ii. 905.

SCHEEL, O. (1929) *Ann. Inst. Pasteur*, **43**, 394.

SCHEEL. (1935) *Bull. Acad. Méd.*, **114**, 149.

SCHROEDER, E. C. and CRAWFORD, A. B. (1928–29) *J. Amer. vet. med. Ass.*, **74**, 773.

SCHULTZ, C. (1935) *Dtsch. tierärztl. Wschr.*, **43**, 113.

SCHWABACHER, H. (1933) *Spec. Rep. Ser. med. Res. Coun., Lond.*, No. 182, Appendix A ; (1934) *J. comp. Path.*, **47**, 214.

SCHWETZ, J. (1930) *Bull. Soc. Path. exot.*, **23**, 283.

SCHWETZ, J., CABU, F., and BAUMANN, H. (1930) *Bull. Soc. Path. exot.*, **23**, 279.

SCOTT, H. H. (1928) *Proc. Zool. Soc. Lond.*, i. 249 ; (1929) *Brit. J. Tuberc.*, **23**, 179 ; (1935) *Proc. R. Soc. Med.*, **28**, 1343.

SCOTT, H. H. and BEATTIE, J. (1928) *J. Path. Bact.*, **31**, 49.

SEIBERT, F. B. (1932) *J. infect. Dis.*, **51**, 383 ; (1934) *Suppl. Amer. Rev. Tuberc.*, **30**, 713.

SEIBERT, F. B. and MORLEY, N. (1933) *J. Immunol.*, **24**, 149.

SEIBERT, F. B. and MUNDAY, B. (1932) *Amer. Rev. Tuberc.*, **25**, 724.

SEIBERT, F. B., ARONSON, J. D., REICHEL, J., CLARK, L. T., and LONG, E. R. (1934) *Suppl. Amer. Rev. Tuberc.*, **30**, 713.

SEIFERLE, E. (1930) *Off. Int. Epizooties*, **4**, 435.

SELLERS, A. and RAMSBOTTOM, E. N. (1922) *J. Path. Bact.*, **25**, 247.

SERGENT, E. (1926) " Nouvelles études cliniques et radiologiques sur la tuberculose et les maladies de l'appareil respiratoire." Paris.

SEWALL, H., SAVITSCH, E. DE, and BUTLER, C. P. (1934) *Amer. Rev. Tuberc.*, **29**, 373.

SHAFFER, M. F. (1935) *J. Path. Bact.*, **40**, 107.

SHIPMAN, S. J. and DAVIS, E. (1933) *Amer. Rev. Tuberc.*, **27**, 474.

SLATER, S. A. and JORDAN, K. (1932) *Amer. Rev. Tuberc.*, **25**, 218.

SMITH, E. (1909) *Brit. med. J.*, ii. 1532.

SÖNTGEN and MENCK. (1933) *Tierärztl. Rdsch.*, **39**, 189.

SPAHLINGER, H. (1932) *Lancet*, i. 309.

SPEHL, P. (1923) *C. R. Soc. Biol.*, **88**, 987.

STABLEFORTH, A. W. (1929) *J. comp. Path.*, **42**, 91, 163.

STIEHM, R. H. (1935) *Amer. Rev. Tuberc.*, **32**, 171.

STRAUSZ, W. (1926) *Z. Hyg. InfektKr.*, **105**, 416.

SYKES, K. A. H. (1926) *Lancet*, i. 273.

TEIPEL, H. (1925) *J. comp. Path.*, **38**, 73.

TIEDEMANN, H. J. (1931) *Zbl. Bakt.*, **122**, 483.

THOMSEN, O., and PEDERSEN-BJERGAARD, K. (1933) *Exp. Studies of Immun. in Tuberculosis*, **76**, 661.

TOBIESEN, F., JENSEN, K. A., and LASSEN, H. C. A. (1935a) *Ugeskr. Laeg.*, **97**, 293 (*Bull. Hyg., Lond.*, **10**, 441); (1935b) *Tubercle, Lond.*, **16**, 385.
TORRANCE, H. L. (1922) *Vet. Rec.*, **2**, 289; (1927) *Ibid.*, **7**, 875.
TSEKHNOVITZER, M. (1926) *Ann. Inst. Pasteur*, **40**, 827.
TULLOCH, W. J. (1936) *Edin. med. J.*, **43**, 144.
TURNER, H. M. (1931) *Tubercle, Lond.*, **12**, 145.
TYTLER, W. H. (1930) "A System of Bacteriology." *Med. Res. Coun. Lond.*, **5**, 246.
UHLENHUTH, P. and SEIFFERT, W. (1930) *Z. ImmunForsch.*, **69**, 187.
URBAIN, A. and FRIED, B. (1921) *Ann. Inst. Pasteur*, **35**, 294.
URGOITI, A. and BEATO, F. (1934) *Rev. San. Hyg. publ.*, **9**, Part 2, 1.
VALLÉE, H. (1905) *Ann. Inst. Pasteur*, **19**, 619.
VALTIS, J. (1925) *Ann. Inst. Pasteur*, **39**, 365.
VERDINA, C. (1926) *G. Batt. Immun.*, **1**, 34.
VILLEMIN, J. A. (1868) "Études sur la tuberculose." Paris.
WADSWORTH, A. B., MALTANER, E. J., and STEVENS, B. S. (1930) *Amer. Rev. Tuberc.*, **22**, 539.
WALKER, G. (1934) *Brit. med. J.*, i. 371.
WATSON, E. A. (1928) *J. Amer. vet. med. Ass.*, **73**, 799; (1930) 11th *Int. vet. Congr., Lond.*
WEBER, G. W., MURPHY, K. M., and HOLCOMB, F. W. (1935) *Amer. Rev. Tuberc.*, **32**, 331.
WEIL-HALLÉ, B. and TURPIN, R. (1925) *Paris méd.*, **15**, 20.
WELLS, A. H. (1936) *Amer. Rev. Tuberc.*, **33**, 91.
WELLS, W. F. (1934) *Amer. J. Hyg.*, **20**, 611.
WELLS, W. F. and STONE, W. R. (1934) *Amer. J. Hyg.*, **20**, 619.
WESTENRIJK, N. (1933) *Beitr. klin. Tuberk.*, **83**, 515.
WESTERNHOEFFER. (1911) *Berl. klin. Wschr.*, **48**, 1063.
WHITNEY, J. S. (1931) "Facts and Figures about Tuberculosis," Nat. Tub. Assoc., N.Y.
WIGHT, A. E. (1930) *J. Amer. vet. med. Ass.*, **76**, 366.
WILBERT, J. (1925) *Ann. Inst. Pasteur*, **39**, 641.
WILSON, G. S. (1925) *J. Path. Bact.*, **28**, 69; (1933) *Spec. Rep. Ser. med. Res. Coun., Lond.*, No. 182.
WOLBACH, S. B. and ERNST, H. C. (1904) *J. med. Res.*, **12**, 295.
WOLFF, G. (1930a) *Dtsch. med. Wschr.*, **56**, 1644; (1930b) *Z. Tuberk.*, **57**, 1; (1935) *Acta Med. scand.*, **84**, 526.
WOLTERS. (1931) *Dtsch. tierärztl. Wschr.*, **39**, 548.
WOLTERS, K. L. and DEHMEL, H. (1931) *Z. InfektKr. Haustiere*, **39**, 102.
WOOD, W. B. (1936) *Tubercle, Lond.*, **17**, 162.
ZIESCHÉ, H. (1907) *Z. Hyg. InfektKr.*, **57**, 50.
ZINSSER, H. and PETROFF, S. A. (1924) *J. Immunol.*, **9**, 85.

CHAPTER LVII

LEPROSY, RAT LEPROSY, AND JOHNE'S DISEASE

LEPROSY

History and Epidemiology.—Leprosy is a disease of great antiquity ; when or where it originated is not known, but according to Rogers and Muir (1925) it is probable that the original focus was in the northern belt of Central Africa. The disease was described in Asia Minor about 345 B.C. ; thence it spread gradually westwards, till in the Middle Ages practically every country in Europe was affected. During the fourteenth and fifteenth centuries leprosy in Europe declined rapidly ; about the same time, however, it was carried to the Western Hemisphere. During the last 70 years the disease has appeared in Oceania, where it has spread widely ; in Hawaii, for example, it was estimated in 1909 that 1 in every 40 natives was a leper (Brinckerhoff and Moore 1909).

At the present time the highest incidence of the disease is confined to tropical countries, particularly (1) Equatorial Africa ; (2) the long belt stretching from Assam and Burma, through the Malay States and Indo-China to the islands of the Pacific ; and (3) the West Indian Islands and the northern part of South America. Males appear to be more commonly affected than females. Infection seems to be most frequent in youth and early adult life ; Rogers and Muir (1925) state that probably over 50 per cent. of cases are infected before the age of 20. The lower social classes are more frequently infected than the higher. The incubation period may be almost any time, from a few weeks to several years ; the commonest period is 2 to 4 years, but it is said that it may extend even to 40 years. The disease is extremely chronic and may be of lifelong duration ; after it has lasted for a variable length of time it may retrogress as the result of a naturally acquired immunity ; on the other hand, after remaining chronic for years, it may take on an acute course. The mortality from the disease itself is comparatively low.

The way in which leprosy is conveyed is uncertain. Most workers are agreed that it is infectious, but the manner in which infection is spread is still largely a matter of conjecture. Considering the long incubation period of the disease, this is not surprising. The restriction of the lesions to the skin suggests that the bacilli gain entrance through cuts, abrasions, and fissures, but it is possible that the nasal mucosa may be primarily infected. Lepers suffering from the tubercular form are very much more infective than those suffering from the anæsthetic form ; this is because lepra bacilli are numerous in the nodules of the skin, but are uncommon in the anæsthetic patches. Blood-sucking flies and other insects have been suspected as carriers of infection, but no convincing evidence against them has been brought forward. On the whole the infectivity of the disease

1066

is low ; close and long-standing contact with lepers has generally to be maintained before infection is contracted.

The **bacteriology** of the disease has already been described in Chapter XV.

Experimental Reproduction of the Disease in Animals.—A few workers claim to have reproduced leprosy in monkeys.   Nicolle in 1905 inoculated two bonnet monkeys subcutaneously in front of the left ear with ground-up tissue from a patient with generalized nodular leprosy.   A nodule appeared 62 days later at the site of inoculation, and a fortnight after its appearance it was partly excised ; histologically it consisted of several small nodules made up of lymphocytes and mononuclears ; there were no giant cells and no caseation ; lepra bacilli were present in moderate numbers, almost exclusively within the cells.   Inoculation by scarification of the skin, or by rubbing on to the nasal and conjunctival mucosa, was without effect.   More recently, Reenstierna (1926) inoculated two monkeys (*Macacus sinicus* and *M. rhesus*) with a suspension of ground-up lepromata from two untreated patients with generalized nodular leprosy ; the inoculations were made in the supraorbital and malar regions of both sides of the face, into both nostrils, and in the pubic region.   On the 39th day, a small, round, hard nodule was visible over the right malar bone ; similar swellings appeared later over the other sites of inoculation, with the exception of the nasal mucosa, which remained intact.   The nodules increased till the 70th day, when they varied in size from a small pea to a nut.   Pieces were excised from some of these and injected into guinea-pigs and monkeys ; both sets of animals remained well.   Microscopically, the nodules consisted of granulation tissue with large mononuclear cells, often vacuolated, containing leprosy bacilli.   Shortly after excision of the nodules, the remaining lesions began to decrease in size ; ultimately they disappeared.   Similar results were obtained with 6 other monkeys.   The nodules appeared in 5 to 8 weeks, sometimes reached the size of a small plum, and disappeared as a rule in 6 to 10 weeks.   Passage experiments were unsuccessful.   Soule and McKinley (1932) likewise found that *Macacus rhesus* and *Cebus olivaceus* monkeys, inoculated intradermally over the eyebrow, developed firm, hard, nodular swellings in 18–20 days, which increased gradually in size for 10–14 days, then retrogressed, and disappeared entirely within another 3 or 4 weeks.   The injection of pure cultures, made according to their technique, also resulted quite frequently in the production of transient nodular lesions (see also McKinley 1934).

There appears to be little doubt from these experiments that a localized form of leprosy can be conveyed to monkeys by inoculation of leprous material ; but the disease is transient and rapidly cures itself.

Diagnosis.—In the tubercular form, a piece of skin over one of the nodules should be examined microscopically for leprosy bacilli (Fig. 256).   With a sharp pair of scissors curved on the flat, a piece of skin 3 mm. long and 2 mm. deep is clipped off the surface.   The corium is pressed downwards on to a clean new slide, and a film preparation made, and stained with Ziehl-Neelsen (Rogers and Muir 1925) ; or the skin may be fixed, embedded in paraffin, and sections cut in the usual way. If acid-fast bacilli cannot be found in the nodules, it is advisable to examine the nasal mucosa.   The most satisfactory method is to scrape the mucosa gently with a blunt scalpel, and make ordinary film preparations.   The bacilli can frequently be demonstrated in this situation in the tubercular form, and may be found in some cases of the anæsthetic form of the disease.   Sometimes they are present in the nasal mucosa before skin nodules have developed ; thus they are said to be demonstrable occasionally in apparently healthy contacts. In early cases of generalized leprosy, the bacilli can often be demonstrated in clippings from the lobule of the ear. If there is any doubt as to whether the organisms found in the nose or skin are true leprosy bacilli, it is advisable to inject a suspension of the ground-up material into guinea-pigs ; if they are leprosy bacilli, there will be no result ; if on the other hand they are tubercle bacilli, the animals will develop the usual form of experimental tuberculosis.

When the lungs are involved, the sputum may contain lepra bacilli, which are most easily distinguished from tubercle bacilli by animal inoculation.

The complement-fixation test has been employed for the diagnosis of leprosy, but it does not appear to be of much value in practice, since a positive reaction may be obtained with antigens made from tubercle bacilli (Row 1925–26).

Lepers frequently give a positive Wassermann reaction ; doubtless this is often due to the co-existence of syphilis, but there appears to be little doubt that the Wassermann reaction may be positive in leprosy in the complete absence of syphilitic infection. In countries in which the positive Wassermann reaction rate varies from 7 to 20 per cent. amongst the general population, many observers have found that the rate amongst lepers varies from 15 to 95 per cent. (Rogers and Muir 1925). The great variation in the percentage of positive reactions amongst the leprous population seems to depend largely on the type of antigen employed. Thus Hasseltine (1924) examined the serum of 236 lepers in Hawaii. Using an acetone-insoluble antigen he obtained 17·8 per cent. of positive results ; with an antigen consisting of an alcoholic extract of beef heart to which 0·4 per cent. of cholesterol had been added, he obtained 50 per cent. of positives ; and with Kolmer's (1922) new antigen he obtained 21·6 per cent. of positives. The greatest number of positive reactions occurred in lepers with the nodular type of

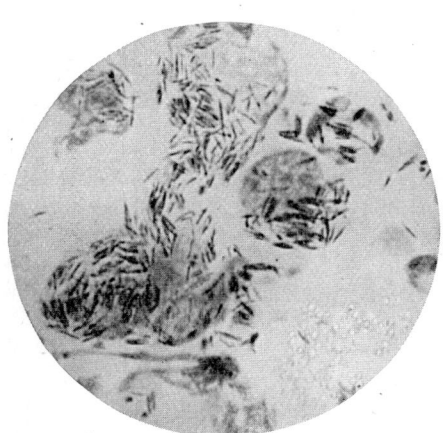

FIG. 256.

Leprosy bacilli in the tissues. The bacilli are seen in dense clumps, mostly intracellular (× 1000).

disease, the smallest number in those with the anæsthetic type. In each form, lepers in the advanced stage of the disease gave more positive results than those in an early stage. Of the general population about 12 per cent. showed evidence of syphilis. It seems clear from these findings that (i) a large number of undoubted lepers give a negative Wassermann reaction, even when a highly sensitive cholesterolated antigen is used ; (ii) if a cholesterolated antigen is used, a higher proportion of lepers react positively than when an acetone-insoluble antigen without addition of cholesterol is used. Hasseltine found that many lepers with a positive reaction improved under anti-syphilitic treatment. In the differential diagnosis of leprosy and syphilis, he regards a positive reaction with an acetone-insoluble antigen or with Kolmer's antigen as strong presumptive evidence of syphilis ; in the absence of definite evidence of leprosy, such patients should be given anti-syphilitic treatment before being declared lepers. Fletcher (1915), working in the Federated Malay States, obtained 13·6 per cent. of positive Wassermann reactions in lepers with no history of syphilis, and only 3·4 per cent. in non-lepers who also had no history of syphilis. The luetin skin test was uniformly negative in leprosy, even when the Wassermann reaction was positive. Since the luetin test may be negative when the

Wassermann reaction is positive, and more positive Wassermann reactions occur in lepers than in non-lepers, Fletcher concludes that leprosy itself may be responsible for a positive Wassermann reaction.

Recently attempts to diagnose leprosy by means of a specific allergic reaction with a substance known as *lepromin* have been made by Bargehr (1926), but it is as yet too early to pronounce on the value of this method.

Prophylaxis and Treatment.—The prophylaxis of leprosy is at present a hygienic problem, and rests on the detection and isolation of infected persons, and on their adequate control.

In the treatment of leprosy, vaccines of several different types have been used. Tuberculin was tried as early as 1891, but without result. Nastin is a preparation made by ethereal extraction of an acid-fast streptothrix, and used largely by Deycke; the results do not appear to be very promising. Vaccines have been prepared from the numerous acid-fast bacilli isolated from leprous lesions, also without any marked benefit. With all these vaccines a certain number of patients improve temporarily, but this improvement seems to be largely due to a non-specific reaction, and is most marked when a severe constitutional reaction is produced. Several workers have used the bacilli present in lepra nodules. Hasson (1925–26), for example, employs a vaccine consisting of an autolysate of lepra bacilli, obtained from artificial blisters in lepers, mixed with *Ps. pyocyanea*; this latter organism is added to provoke a febrile reaction. His own reports are very favourable; improvement is said to begin after the third injection, and to be progressive. Patients treated for 18 months have not relapsed. It is doubtful how far this treatment is specific; Row (1925–26) states that he has observed great improvement by the use of a vaccine consisting of autolysed tubercle bacilli.

RAT LEPROSY

Rat leprosy is a disease that was first described by Stefansky (1903) in 1901 at Odessa. Rats were being slaughtered in large numbers, consequent on the outbreak of human plague, and rat leprosy was found in 4–5 per cent. of them. This frequency is very much higher than that reported by other observers. McCoy (1913) found it in 186 out of about 200,000 rats caught in San Francisco, Cal., an incidence of only 0·093 per cent.; Wherry (1908) found it in 20 out of 9,631 rats caught in Oakland, Cal., an incidence of only 0·21 per cent.; and in Japan Ota and Asami (1932) found it in 0·7 per cent. of *Rattus norvegicus* and in 0·1 per cent. of *Rattus rattus*.

The disease exists in two forms—the glandular type and the musculo-cutaneous type—but there appears to be no sharp division between them. In the *glandular type* one or more of the groups of subcutaneous glands—inguinal, axillary, or cervical—is enlarged, hard, and of whitish colour. On section the glands are uniform and hard; there are no nodules or necrotic areas visible macroscopically. Microscopically, the capsule and trabeculæ are thickened; the sinuses are filled with dense aggregations of irregularly polygonal cells, which have a large nucleus and much cytoplasm—probably macrophages; the cytoplasm is packed with acid-fast bacilli, so that the contours of the cell-body are often invisible. A few giant cells, with several peripheral nuclei, containing numerous bacilli in their cytoplasm are also visible. Some organisms may be found free.

In the *musculo-cutaneous type* the rat is emaciated ; the skin presents one or more irregularly round or oval areas of alopecia, commonest on the head ; occasionally ulcers are seen, about 0·5 cm. in diameter, covered with a mealy-looking discharge containing acid-fast bacilli. At the site of these areas of alopecia the skin is atrophic. The subcutaneous tissues are devoid of fat, and show the presence of a greyish-white, granular material, which Stefansky regards as altered muscle tissue ; it contains numerous acid-fast bacilli. Sometimes nodular masses are found in the muscles, covered with particles of stretched atrophic skin. Stefansky believes that the primary lesion begins in the subcutaneous muscle fibres, and sometimes spreads to the skeletal muscles. Histologically, numerous acid-fast bacilli are found in the corium and subcutaneous tissue ; some are free, but most are situated in the cells of the granulation tissue, and in large cells rich in cytoplasm, which resemble the lepra cells of Virchow, but contain no vacuoles. Acid-fast bacilli invade the muscle fibres, collect around the nuclei, and lead to destruction of the tissue. Lesions of the internal organs are rare ; but McCoy (1913) states that nephritis is very common ; the kidneys are enlarged, yellowish-brown, friable, and often cystic, but no acid-fast bacilli are found in them. In an examination of 186 leprous rats, McCoy (1913) noted alopecia in 47·5 per cent., cutaneous ulcers in 22 per cent., diffuse subcutaneous infiltration in 97·9 per cent., enlarged lymphatic glands in 87 per cent., and nephritis in 53·8 per cent.

Not infrequently the disease appears to be latent. Lampe and de Moor (1935), for example, in an examination of 5,000 rats trapped in Batavia, found that about 10 per cent. were carrying acid-fast bacilli in their lymph glands, while only a few showed manifest skin lesions.

The **bacteriology** of the disease has already been discussed in Chapter XV.

Reproduction of the Disease in Animals.—Stefansky failed to infect rats or guinea-pigs, but Dean was more successful. He inoculated 30 rats with suspensions of infiltrated skin and enlarged lymphatic glands. Many of the animals died of intercurrent disease, but 9 of them developed marked lesions. In 3 cases the infection was passed in series from one rat to another, and from this to a third. The experimental disease ran a slow course, lasting from 6 months to a year. Post mortem, after subcutaneous inoculation, there was sometimes a local lesion containing semi-caseous material and acid-fast bacilli ; in these cases the regional lymphatic glands were sometimes invaded by bacilli. After intraperitoneal inoculation the lesions were more extensive ; the epiploon was infiltrated with grey masses of opaque material, which consisted of collections of cells containing bacilli. The liver was not usually involved, but in some animals there were small, pale, sharply circumscribed areas, composed chiefly of acid-fast bacilli. The capsule of the spleen was often thickened and contained bacilli, but in only one case was the organ itself involved. In 3 animals there was a tumour-like mass in the anterior mediastinum, consisting of pale-yellow material, which contained large numbers of bacilli. Small nodules in the lungs were found in two cases. The organism proved non-pathogenic to guinea-pigs, rabbits, mice, and a macaque monkey.

The way in which natural infection occurs is not known, but the presence of lesions in the skin and subcutaneous tissues suggests that it is contracted through cutaneous fissures and abrasions. Wayson and Masunaga (1935), however, suggest that infection may occur through the nose. Examination of wild rats affected with leprosy, and of white rats inoculated subcutaneously, revealed the presence of acid-fast bacilli in the nasal mucosa. Moreover, nasal instillation of a lepromatous suspension was followed by development of rat leprosy. Against this suggestion is the fact that in the natural disease the bacilli seem to be commonest in the inguinal and axillary rather than in the cervical glands. The same objection applies to conjunctival infection, which Marchoux and his colleagues (1935) have shown to be successful under experimental conditions. Further observations are clearly desirable.

JOHNE'S DISEASE

SYNONYMS.—*Enteritis chronica pseudotuberculosa bovis; Entérite spécifique chronique des bœufs; Chronischer infektiöser Darmkatarrh des Rindes;* chronic bovine pseudo-tuberculous enteritis.

Johne's disease is a specific enteritis affecting cattle, and less frequently sheep and deer, caused by an acid-fast organism known as Johne's bacillus. It was first described by Johne and Frothingham in 1895 at Dresden. They regarded it as a peculiar form of tuberculosis, possibly due to the avian type of bacillus.

The disease is fairly common in Northern Europe, and has been observed in America. It affects particularly young cows, but no age is exempt. Since, however, the incubation period is lengthy—up to about 18 months—it is uncommon to meet with the disease in cows less than 2 years old. Latent infection is apparently quite frequent, and according to Minett (1933) 30–40 per cent. of animals in affected herds may react to johnin. Sheep are less frequently attacked. In this country the disease is prevalent in cattle, especially those on marshy or boggy land. Natural infection probably occurs through the ingestion of fodder that has been soiled with fæces of infected animals.

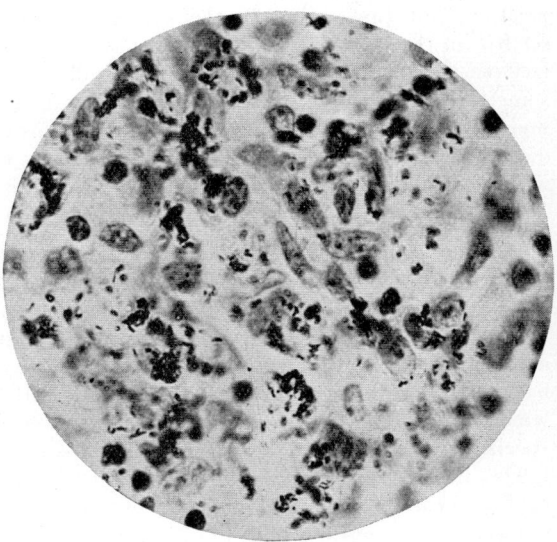

FIG. 257.

Section of intestine of cow with Johne's disease. The bacilli are seen in dense clumps, mostly intracellular (× 1000).

Clinically the disease runs a chronic course, subject often to long periods of intermission, and characterized by unthriftiness, a falling off in the milk yield, diarrhœa of varying severity, and progressive emaciation; there is no fever.

Pathologically, the main lesions are situated in the last 50 feet of the small intestine, and in the neighbourhood of the ileocæcal junction, but sometimes the whole gut is affected. The intestine is thick and rigid, looking not unlike a hose pipe; the mucosa is greatly thickened and is thrown into regular corrugations, resembling the convolutions of the cerebrum. The mucosa is smooth and pale or pink in colour, and covered with slimy material; on the surface of the corrugations it is dotted with red spots or hæmorrhages ; between the folds it often has a warty appearance.   Occasionally small nodules are seen, due to enlargement of solitary lymphoid follicles.   There is no ulceration of the mucosa, and the peritoneal surface appears normal.   The mesenteric lymph glands are usually enlarged, œdematous and pigmented.   Histologically, the mucosa, and to a less extent the submucosa, are infiltrated with lymphoid and epithelioid cells, which are responsible for the thickening.   Near the surface of the gut the mucosa is absolutely structureless ; all traces of nuclei and cell outlines have disappeared.   Giant cells are rare ; there is no caseation, ulceration, fibrosis, or calcification.   Short acid-fast bacilli, often in enormous numbers, are found in the mucosa lying between the glands and in the lymphoid tissue of the solitary follicles ; they may invade the submucosa, and very occasionally the underlying muscle layer.   The bacilli are arranged in dense clumps, and may be intra- or extracellular.   Johne and Frothingham were of the opinion that they were primarily intracellular in position, but that owing to the subsequent disintegration of the cell, they were set free in the tissue.   The cellular reaction around the bacilli is diffuse, not localized as in tuberculosis.   Bacilli are generally found in the mesenteric glands and sometimes in the sublingual and submaxillary glands.   In sheep there may be very much less thickening and corrugation of the intestinal mucosa than in cattle.   The disease can be reproduced in cattle and sheep by feeding or parenteral inoculation with pure cultures of Johne's bacillus (see Chapter XV).

The **bacteriology** of the disease has already been described in Chapter XV.

Diagnosis and Prophylaxis.—Differential diagnosis has to be made from strongylosis, coccidiosis, and particularly tuberculous enteritis.   The tuberculin test with bovine tuberculin is negative, but a reaction often follows the injection of avian tuberculin (see Bang 1909, 1914).   Twort and Ingram (1913) advocate the use of a preparation like tuberculin, but made from glycerine broth cultures of Johne's bacillus.   M'Fadyean, Sheather and Edwards (1912) prepared a similar preparation, which they termed *johnin*.   These products, however, do not appear to be strictly specific ; reactions may be obtained in tuberculous animals.   Recently, Dunkin (1928) has recorded successful results with johnin prepared by growing Johne's bacillus in a special broth medium containing dead *phlei* bacilli.   The culture is reduced by evaporation to 1/10 of its volume, and filtered through sand and paper pulp.   For diagnosis the double intradermal test is used.   0·2 c.c. of the concentrated johnin is injected as deeply as possible into the dermis on the side of the neck, and a second injection of 0·2 c.c. is made into the same site 48 hours later. Measurements of the skin fold are recorded before inoculation, and 48 and 72 hours after inoculation.   A positive reaction is characterized by a diffuse swelling, which is usually hot and tender.   The skin fold increases in thickness from an initial measurement of about 5 mm. to a final measurement of 13 to 18 mm.   In a nonreactor the swelling is like a pea, definitely circumscribed, and is never tender.   The test, as judged by both laboratory and field experience, has, in Dunkin's hands, proved specific, and is stated not to interfere with the simultaneous application of the intradermal tuberculin test.   Minett (1933) also reports favourably on this method.   More recently still Dunkin (1933) has prepared johnin from cultures in a synthetic medium free from extracts of acid-fast bacilli.   This preparation does not give rise to the non-specific swellings that sometimes follow the use of johnin made from phlei-containing media.   Interpretation of allergic reactions in Johne's disease is, however, by no means straightforward.   In some animals avian tuberculin causes a stronger reaction than johnin, while in other animals the reverse holds true. Doubtful reactions are not uncommon, and present considerable difficulty.

The bacilli are sometimes found throughout the intestine ; in such cases diagnosis is often possible by microscopical examination of a piece of rectal mucosa removed with forceps or a Volkmann's spoon. The bacilli are sometimes found in the fæces, generally in very small numbers (M'Fadyean *et al.* 1912) ; but it is impossible without cultural examination to distinguish them from saprophytic acid-fast bacilli. In any case in which acid-fast bacilli are found, it is advisable to inject them into a guinea-pig, in order to exclude the possibility of their being tubercle bacilli. Agglutination and complement fixation are said to be of little value in distinguishing Johne's bacillus from the tubercle bacillus (Twort 1912).

The disease is usually fatal, but numerous instances of apparent recovery or of long intermissions in its course are known. In some of these animals post-mortem examination has revealed the presence of intense cellular reactions in the mesenteric glands, which had apparently resulted in the disappearance of the bacilli.

According to Vallée, Rinjard, and Vallée (1934), subcutaneous vaccination of non-infected animals with 5–10 mgm. of living virulent cultures of Johne's bacillus affords a high degree of protection against the disease. This statement awaits confirmation. Destruction of animals suffering from obvious disease is of little value in preventing its further spread. A more hopeful policy is to test all members of the herd with johnin, to segregate and ultimately remove the reactors, to disinfect stalls and buildings, and to raise the non-infected animals on clean pastures (Hutyra and Marek 1926, Minett 1933).

REFERENCES

BANG, O. (1909) *Zbl. Bakt.*, **51**, 450 ; (1914) *Proc. 10th int. vet. Confr., Lond.*, **3**, 157.
BARGEHR, P. (1926) *Z. ImmunForsch.*, **49**, 346.
BRINCKERHOFF, W. R. and MOORE, W. L. (1909) *Publ. Hlth Bull., Wash.*, No. 27.
DUNKIN, G. W. (1928) *J. comp. Path.*, **41**, 94 ; (1933) *Ibid.*, **46**, 159.
FLETCHER, W. (1915) *J. Hyg., Camb.*, **15**, 102.
HASSELTINE, H. E. (1924) *Publ. Hlth Bull., Wash.*, No. 141, p. 37.
HASSON, J. (1925–6) *Trans. roy. Soc. trop. Med. Hyg.*, **19**, 349.
HUTYRA, F. and MAREK, J. (1926) "Special Pathology and Therapeutics of the Diseases of Domestic Animals," 3rd Amer. edit., i. Chicago and London.
JOHNE and FROTHINGHAM. (1895) *Dtsch. Z. Thiermed.*, **21**, 438.
KOLMER, J. A. (1922) *Amer. J. Syph.*, **6**, 496.
LAMPE, P. H. J. and MOOR, C. E. DE. (1935) *Geneesk. Tijdsch. Ned-Ind.*, **75**, 634.
McCOY, G. W. (1913) *Publ. Hlth Bull., Wash.*, No. 61, p. 27.
M'FADYEAN, J., SHEATHER, A. L., and EDWARDS, J. T. (1912) *J. comp. Path.*, **25**, 217.
McKINLEY, E. B. (1934) *Medicine*, **13**, 377.
MARCHOUX, E., CHORINE, V., and KOECHLIN, D. (1935) *Ann. Inst. Pasteur*, **55**, 632.
MINETT, F. C. (1933) *Vet. Rec.*, **45**, 1074.
NICOLLE, C. (1905) *C. R. Acad. Sci.*, **140**, 539.
OTA M., and ASAMI, S. (1932) *C. R. Soc. Biol.*, **111**, 287.
REENSTIERNA, J. (1926) *Ann. Inst. Pasteur*, **40**, 78.
ROGERS, L. and MUIR, E. (1925) "Leprosy." Bristol.
ROW, R. (1925–26) *Trans. roy. Soc. trop. Med. Hyg.*, **19**, 407.
SOULE, M. H. and McKINLEY, E. B. (1932) *Amer. J. trop. Med.*, **12**, 1.
STEFANSKY, W. K. (1903) *Zbl. Bakt.*, **33**, 481.
TWORT, C. C. (1912) *Zbl. Bakt.*, **66**, 316.
TWORT, F. W. and INGRAM, G. L. Y. (1913) "A Monograph on Johne's Disease." London.
VALLÉE, H., RINJARD, P., and VALLÉE, M. (1934) *C. R. Acad. Sci.*, **199**, 1074.
WAYSON, N. E. and MASUNAGA, E. (1935) *Publ. Hlth Rep., Wash.*, **50**, 1576.
WHERRY, W. B. (1908) *J. infect. Dis.*, **5**, 507.

CHAPTER LVIII

DIPHTHERIA AND OTHER DISEASES DUE TO CORYNEBACTERIA

THE modern conception of diphtheria as a clinical entity may be regarded as dating from the observations of Bretonneau in 1826. The conception of the disease as a bacteriological entity dates from the publication of Loeffler's classical paper in 1884. Klebs had described the bacillus in the diphtheritic membrane in the previous year, but he had brought forward no convincing evidence of its ætiological rôle. The best possible introduction to a discussion of the bacteriological aspects of diphtheria is a brief summary of Loeffler's experiments. He demonstrated the presence of the bacillus, which we now know as *C. diphtheriæ*, in the throats of 13 of 22 persons suffering from clinical diphtheria. From 6 of these cases he isolated the organism in pure culture. With these strains, and with remote subcultures from them, he inoculated mice, rats, guinea-pigs, rabbits, finches, pigeons, fowls and monkeys. The mice and rats proved completely resistant. The guinea-pigs died in 2 to 5 days, after subcutaneous inoculation, showing at necropsy a localized area of hæmorrhagic œdema at the site of inoculation, pleural effusions which were often blood-stained, areas of pulmonary consolidation, and marked congestion of the suprarenals. The small birds died in every case within a few days, showing at necropsy an area of œdema, hæmorrhage and necrosis in the breast muscles, where the inoculation had been made. Many of the rabbits were inoculated into the trachea, or into the cornea ; in several of these typical false membranes developed. Similar false membranes were produced by intratracheal inoculation in pigeons. The introduction of cultures of *C. diphtheriæ* into the vagina of guinea-pigs, after minimal injury of the mucosa, was also followed in some cases by typical membrane formation, with local œdema ; and sometimes by generalized symptoms terminating in death. Attempts to produce infection without injury to surface epithelium were not, however, successful. The simple application of cultures of virulent bacilli to the mucosa of the nose or throat, or to the conjunctiva, of rabbits or guinea-pigs was without result ; nor did a monkey whose throat was vigorously brushed with a living culture develop more than a moderate inflammatory lesion which healed in a few days. Attempts to infect rabbits, guinea-pigs, fowls and pigeons by exposing them to a spray of living culture were unsuccessful. No clear case of paralysis, similar to that encountered as a sequela of human diphtheria, was observed in any of these animals. One highly significant point was noted ; in most of those animals which died the bacilli could be recovered only from the tissues in the neighbourhood of the site of infection. Cultures taken from the lesions in the internal organs or tissues usually remained sterile. Loeffler concluded that death was due not to the dissemination of bacilli throughout the body, but to the effect of some substance elaborated in the local lesion.

Thus Loeffler had shown that, in certain animals and under suitable conditions, the bacillus which he had isolated would produce lesions closely resembling those of human diphtheria. This demonstration was the logical extension of the results recorded by Trendelenburg in 1869 and by Oertel in 1871, both of whom had succeeded in producing false membranes in rabbits and pigeons by inoculating them with material from human lesions. He had further shown that the subcutaneous or intramuscular inoculation of cultures of the bacillus into susceptible animals was followed by death associated with lesions which, while they bore little superficial resemblance to human diphtheria, were in themselves highly characteristic ; that these lesions were not the direct result of tissue invasion by the bacilli ; and that certain animal species were highly resistant to infection by any route.

The next important step in our knowledge of diphtheritic infection was the discovery by Roux and Yersin in 1888 that sterile filtrates from cultures of the diphtheria bacillus would kill guinea-pigs with lesions identical with those which follow the injection of the living organism. This demonstration of the presence of a potent extracellular toxin afforded an explanation of Loeffler's observation that death was not associated with any spread of bacteria beyond the local lesion. In rabbits inoculated with such filtered cultures Roux and Yersin noted the occurrence of late paralysis.

Later investigations have confirmed and extended these pioneer observations, and we now have a fairly detailed knowledge of the reaction of a large number of animal species to the diphtheria bacillus and to its toxin.

The lesions produced in experimental animals have been described on pp. 336 and 337. We are here concerned with them only in so far as they throw light on the pathogenesis of diphtheria in man. The epidemiology of diphtheria, the way in which the disease attacks herds as opposed to individuals, will be more conveniently considered in a later section of the chapter, when we have discussed the diagnostic methods on which our present knowledge largely depends.

It will be recalled that experimental diphtheritic toxæmia in the guinea-pig is associated with fatty degeneration of the heart muscle and diaphragm, and with congestion and hæmorrhage in the adrenal glands. There can be little doubt (see Bolton 1905, Dudgeon 1906, Jaffé 1920, Andrewes *et al.* 1923) that the direct action of diphtheria toxin on the heart muscle is one of the most important causes of death in human diphtheria.

With regard to the adrenal lesions, it may be noted that the gross changes, which are so characteristic of diphtheritic toxæmia in the guinea-pig, are not found in fatal cases in man. There is, however, a growing body of evidence which suggests that suprarenal congestion, with small extravasations of blood, and degenerative changes in the cortical or medullary cells, is of frequent occurrence in fatal human infection ; though these lesions are revealed only by careful histological examination (Andrewes *et al.* 1923). So far as the nervous lesions are concerned we need only indicate the obvious analogy between the late paralysis of experimental diphtheria in the rabbit, guinea-pig or dog, and the characteristic paralysis in man.

We may, then, regard diphtheria as an infection in which a characteristic local lesion, the membranous inflammation of the fauces, is associated with an equally characteristic toxæmia, in which a powerful exotoxin exerts a selective poisonous action on certain groups of cells.

We have already referred to Loeffler's observation, that the diphtheria bacillus can be recovered from the local experimental lesion, but not usually from the internal organs. These findings have been generally confirmed by subsequent investigators, though a few discordant results have been recorded (Andrewes *et al.* 1923). In human diphtheria it would appear that some degree of tissue invasion is of fairly frequent occurrence, though *C. diphtheriæ* has very rarely been isolated from the blood during life ; Andrewes and his colleagues (1923) note 3 positive results in the records of 313 cases studied by Leede, Roedelius, and Reiche in Hamburg. The bacteriological findings at autopsy are somewhat discordant, and difficult to interpret. That *C. diphtheriæ* has, on occasion, been cultivated from most of the internal organs examined there is little doubt ; but the technique employed has varied widely ; and, with the single exception of the general agreement that the diphtheria bacillus may be isolated from the lungs in a considerable proportion of cases of fatal diphtheria, there is little agreement as to the frequency with which it may be found in the various organs and tissues. As Andrewes and his colleagues point out, the presence of *C. diphtheriæ* in the lungs may well be due to direct inhalation, rather than to active spread. The evidence, as a whole, clearly suggests that natural diphtheria in man, like experimental diphtheria in the guinea-pig, rabbit, or pigeon, is to be regarded as essentially a toxæmia, in which tissue invasion is minimal ; and in which individual resistance or susceptibility to infection, and recovery or death when infected, are largely determined by the presence or rapid production of antitoxin.

This does not mean that invasiveness, as a character of the bacterium, plays no part in the natural or experimental disease. Where the *materies morbi* consists of living bacilli, some degree of local tissue invasion and bacterial proliferation must occur if a significant amount of toxin is to be elaborated and absorbed. It follows that the virulence of a particular strain of *C. diphtheriæ* is not completely defined by determining its toxigenicity.

That this is so has been demonstrated very clearly by recent observations on the case-fatality rates associated with infections caused by different types of *C. diphtheriæ*.

The Gravis, Mitis and Intermediate Types of C. diphtheriæ in Relation to Diphtheria in Man.

We have already referred (pp. 341–343) to the description by McLeod and his colleagues (Anderson, Happold, McLeod and Thomson 1931) of three different types of *C. diphtheriæ*, and have noted that the *gravis* and *intermediate* types are associated with a high case-fatality rate, while infections caused by the *mitis* type are far milder.

The differences recorded are very striking. To take two examples, Anderson, Cooper, Happold and McLeod (1933a), working in Leeds, record a case-fatality rate of 13·1 per cent. among 425 *gravis* infections, of 8·7 per cent. among 24 *intermediate* infections, and of 0·0 per cent. among 113 *mitis* infections ; and Robinson and Marshall (1935), working in Manchester, record a case-fatality rate of 15·1 per cent. among 443 *gravis* infections, of 7·7 per cent. among 168 *intermediate* infections, and of 0·5 per cent. among 198 *mitis* infections. Numerous other records give analogous findings (Anderson *et al.* 1933b, Carter 1933, Leete *et al.* 1933, Menton *et al.* 1933, Ali 1934, Christison 1934, Robinson 1934, Robinson and Marshall 1934, Gundel and Liebetruth 1935, Schiff and Werber 1935).

As would be expected, the frequency of complications, such as albuminuria or paralysis, shows differences of a similar kind. Thus, Anderson, Cooper, Happold and McLeod (1933a) record a 52·6 per cent. incidence of albuminuria among their *gravis* cases, 52·1 per cent. among their *intermediate* cases, and 28·4 per cent. among their *mitis* cases. For the frequency of paralysis, their figures are : *gravis* cases 20·5 per cent., *intermediate* cases 21·7 per cent., *mitis* cases 1·9 per cent. Robinson and Marshall (1935) note a 16·5 per cent. incidence of paralysis among their *gravis* cases, 10·1 per cent. among their *intermediate* cases, and 3·0 per cent. among their *mitis* cases.

The sharp difference between the severity of the *mitis* cases and those due to infection with the *gravis* and *intermediate* types emerges clearly from the available records. It is much less clear that there is any consistent difference between the severity of *gravis* and *intermediate* infections. There is at least a suggestion (Robinson and Marshall 1934, 1935) that whichever of these two types assumes temporary dominance during a particular epidemic prevalence gives rise to the higher case-fatality rate.

All these figures, it should be noted, refer to cases treated with antitoxin. It would seem to be established that, under these conditions, the mortality associated with *mitis* infections is almost negligible. The case-fatality rate associated with any particular epidemic will, therefore, be determined by the proportion of the cases that are infected with the *gravis* and *intermediate* types.

That wide variations occur in the frequency of the different types at different times and in different places has been clearly established. Thus, Anderson, Cooper, Happold and McLeod (1933a) record the following frequencies in Leeds : *gravis* infections 75·62 per cent., *intermediate* infections 4·27 per cent., *mitis* infections 20·11 per cent. In 1934 Robinson and Marshall, working in Manchester, observed 23·8 per cent. of *gravis* infections, 54·6 per cent. of *intermediate* infections, and 19·2 per cent. of *mitis* infections. A few infections were mixed. In the same city in the following year they observed 50·9 per cent. of *gravis* infections, 19·9 per cent. of *intermediate* infections and 27·8 per cent. of *mitis* infections.

The figures just quoted vary in regard to the proportion of *gravis* to *intermediate* strains, rather than in the proportion of those highly pathogenic types to the relatively non-pathogenic *mitis* strains ; but there seems no doubt that the proportion of *mitis* infections may also vary within wide limits. Thus Schiff and Werber (1935) record only 8·2 per cent. of *mitis* infections in Berlin, Murray (1935b) 40 per cent. in Dundee, and Whitley (1935) no less than 92 per cent. in Maryland.

The evidence at present available does not allow of any definite conclusion in regard to the factors that determine the greater virulence of *gravis* and *intermediate* as compared with *mitis* strains. The *mitis* strains are highly toxigenic ; indeed they would seem to produce toxin *in vitro* more actively than *gravis* strains. The toxins produced by *gravis* and *mitis* strains appear to be identical in regard to their neutralizability by antitoxin ; and, so far at least as the guinea-pig is concerned, antitoxin would appear to be about equally effective in controlling experimental *gravis* or *mitis* infections (see Parish, Whatley and O'Brien 1932a, b, Anderson, Cooper, Happold and McLeod 1933a). We cannot therefore ascribe the difference in virulence between these strains to a difference in the amount or kind of exotoxin produced. When *gravis*, *intermediate* and *mitis* strains are tested for virulence by injecting them into guinea-pigs which are not protected by antitoxin, no significant differences in mortality are noted with doses of the customary size. Povitsky, Eisner and Jackson (1933), however, report that the minimal lethal dose of *gravis* strains for the guinea-pig is smaller than that of *mitis* strains ; and, in contrast to the observations referred to above, find that antitoxin is somewhat more effective in controlling *mitis* than *gravis* infections. It would appear (see Anderson *et al.* 1933a, Parish 1936, Stallybrass 1936) that avirulent variants are more common among any large sample of *mitis* strains than among a corresponding sample of *gravis* or *intermediate* strains. The rabbit, unlike the guinea-pig, would seem to be significantly more susceptible to *gravis*, or *intermediate*, than to *mitis* strains (see Anderson *et al.* 1933*a*, Leete, McLeod and Morrison 1933, Murray 1935*a*). This difference is more marked when the injections are given intravenously than when they are given subcutaneously. Even under these conditions, however, it is not of the same order as the difference in case fatality observed in natural infections in man. Why *gravis* strains are more fatal for the rabbit than *mitis* strains is as yet unknown. There are scattered statements in the literature that suggest that the factor concerned may be an increased power of tissue invasion ; but this problem still awaits solution.

Before the *gravis, intermediate* and *mitis* types of *C. diphtheriæ* had been differentiated by McLeod and his colleagues, observations were on record which indicated that the pathogenicity of a strain of *C. diphtheriæ* for laboratory animals was not completely determined by its toxigenicity, as assessed by its capacity for producing toxin *in vitro*. The highly toxigenic " Park 8 " strain, for instance, was found to be of relatively low virulence for the guinea-pig, as judged by the smallest number of living bacilli that would produce toxæmic death on inoculation. Barratt (see Andrewes *et al.* 1923) carried out a careful comparison between the virulence and toxigenicity of 14 strains of *C. diphtheriæ*, testing the former property by determining the M.L.D. of saline suspensions of once-washed bacilli, and the latter by a similar series of tests carried out with broth filtrates. The results showed a variation between 0.25×10^6 and 16.25×10^6 in the M.L.D. of the washed bacilli and between 0.02 c.c. and 0.5 c.c. in the M.L.D. of the toxic filtrate. (A single strain which produced death after the injection of 17×10^6 bacilli gave a toxin which contained less than one M.L.D. in 4 c.c. of filtrate.) There was little correlation between virulence and toxigenicity, with the exception that the two strains with the highest M.L.D. of bacilli were the poorest toxin producers. The conclusion which appears to be justified by these, and by similar results, is that all strains which are virulent, in the usually accepted sense, are toxigenic, and that very weak toxin producers are generally of relatively low virulence ; but that, given an adequate toxigenicity, virulence is determined in part by other factors (see also Feierabend and Schubert, 1929, 1930).

The Diagnosis of Infection in Diphtheria.

The laboratory diagnosis of infection with *C. diphtheriæ* depends on the isolation of the causative organism. We are here concerned with details of procedure only in so far as they involve general principles.

Direct Microscopy.—Taking first the laboratory diagnosis of a case that is suspected, on clinical grounds, to be diphtheria, we may note that the causative organism happens to possess a distinctive morphology. Though a cultural test must never be omitted, it is possible to make a presumptive diagnosis if characteristic *C. diphtheriæ* are found in a suitably stained film made directly from a swab taken from the suspected lesion. As a method of confirming or refuting a clinical diagnosis of diphtheria this procedure has little to recommend it. Failure to find the diphtheria bacillus has no diagnostic value ; and the time consumed in searching large numbers of direct films greatly increases the labour of routine diagnostic work. It cannot be too strongly emphasized, in regard to the administration of antitoxin, that a clinical diagnosis should be acted on at once, without waiting for confirmation from the laboratory.

The examination of a direct film from a throat swab has, however, one advantage, not directly concerned with the diagnosis of diphtheria itself. The spirilla and fusiform bacilli associated with Vincent's angina are readily recognizable in such films, and their presence will assist in a clinical diagnosis of this condition. Even in such cases, however, it is very unsafe to rely solely on the film findings. Some cases that show the presence of spirilla and fusiform bacilli in direct films will be found to yield typical *C. diphtheriæ* on culture. Such advantage as is gained is, in any case, limited to swabs taken from the throat. Whether it justifies the serious addition in time and labour that is involved in the routine examination of direct films from all throat swabs, or whether it should be left to the clinician to indicate those cases in which he desires an examination for spirilla and fusiform bacilli, in addition to *C. diphtheriæ*, must remain a matter of opinion.

Cultivation.—In regard to the preparation and examination of cultures, the procedure until recently followed in all laboratories, and still followed in most, is to inoculate a slope of Lœffler's inspissated serum medium with the swab taken from the suspected lesion, incubate it overnight, and examine it next morning by direct inspection of the growth for characteristic colonies, and by the examination of stained films prepared from suspicious colonies, where these are present, or from the confluent growth. The finding of the characteristic bacilli, showing metachromatic granules when stained by an appropriate method, justifies a confirmatory diagnosis in a clinically suspected case. The actual report given should be " morphologically typical *C. diphtheriæ* present," or some similar formula ; since, from the clinical standpoint, a diphtheria bacillus means a toxigenic diphtheria bacillus, and toxigenicity has not yet been proved.

The modifications that have been introduced into this procedure during recent years concern the substitution of various selective and differential media for the Loeffler's serum.

All these media contain potassium tellurite, and their differential value depends on the black or grey colour developed by colonies of *C. diphtheriæ*, which, combined with the other colonial characteristics, makes it possible to identify them with considerable accuracy by direct examination with the aid of a hand lens. These tellurite-containing media have also a selective action, since the growth of many of the normal nasopharyngeal organisms is inhibited. Since recognition of the characteristic appearance of isolated colonies is the essential feature of this technique, plate cultures are used instead of slopes. A disadvantage of these media is that *C. diphtheriæ*, when growing on them, often fails to develop its characteristic morphology ; so that the examination of stained films has not the same diagnostic value as when Loeffler's medium is employed. It is now customary, in some laboratories at least, to rely on a macroscopic diagnosis based on colonial appearances alone. It has been found that this method yields reliable results in the hands of experienced workers ; but it should not be attempted until this experience has been gained.

Of the various media that have been employed that devised by Clauberg (1929, 1931, 1933, 1935, 1936) has been subjected to the most extensive trials. It consists, in its latest modification, of inspissated ox or sheep serum, containing glycerol and potassium tellurite. This medium has been reported on favourably by many observers in addition to Clauberg himself.

Weigmann and Degn (1932), for instance, examined 1,200 swabs in parallel on Loeffler's and Clauberg's media ; 10·25 per cent. were positive on the former, 13 per cent. on the latter. Lewis (1933) records a similar investigation on 509 swabs ; 10·8 per cent. were positive on Loeffler slants, 14·14 per cent. on Clauberg plates. Kairies (1933), Kemkes (1934) and Hasenbach (1935) record very similar results ; though a few workers (see Waldhecker 1934) have found little difference between the two media.

Allison and Ayling have described a serum agar medium containing tellurite and copper sulphate with which they record satisfactory results (see Allison and Ayling 1929, Allison 1930).

The heated-blood tellurite medium described by Anderson, Happold, McLeod and Thomson (1931) fulfils a similar purpose, and has the advantage that it is particularly favourable for the differentiation of *gravis*, *mitis* and *intermediate* strains ; but it may be noted that it needs careful preparation if optimal results are to be obtained. Whether it has quite so great an advantage over the ordinary Loeffler slope, in regard to the proportion of positive results, as has Clauberg's medium is perhaps doubtful (see McClure 1933, Piazecka-Zeyland 1933, Ali 1934).

Horgan and Marshall (1932) describe a blood-agar tellurite-containing medium, which they report as being easy to prepare, and as giving a high proportion of positive results. On this medium they were able to differentiate between the *gravis* and *mitis* types. This medium has been favourably reported on by Smyth (1934).

Many other forms of tellurite-containing media have been described in the literature ; but most of them have been less extensively tested.

There can be little doubt that the use of any satisfactory form of tellurite medium will increase the proportion of positive findings as compared with the use of Loeffler slopes. The technique has one other outstanding advantage, on which there is general agreement. It very greatly facilitates the isolation of *C. diphtheriæ* in pure culture, and hence the performance of virulence tests when these are required. The main point still at issue would seem to be the reliability of a bacteriological diagnosis based on colonial appearances on a tellurite-containing medium, without microscopical confirmation. This is a question that only time and experience can settle. At the moment, there would seem to be considerable advantages in the method, followed in some laboratories, of planting all swabs both on a slope of Loeffler's serum and on a plate of tellurite medium. Next day the tellurite plates are examined first. Any case in which the plate fails to show suspicious colonies is regarded as negative, and the corresponding Loeffler slope is discarded. The number of positive findings missed in this way is certainly very small. Where the tellurite plate shows characteristic or suspicious colonies, a film is prepared from the corresponding Loeffler slope for microscopic examination. The extra labour involved in the use of the tellurite plates is largely compensated by the great saving in the preparation and examination of films. There will remain a very few cases in which suspicious colonies are present on the tellurite plate, but no characteristic bacilli are found in the film from the Loeffler slope. A subculture of the suspicious colonies to Loeffler's medium and a microscopical examination of the resulting growth will usually solve these occasional discrepancies.

There remains the question as to when it is necessary to confirm a presumptive diagnosis, based on the morphology of the bacilli from a Loeffler slope, or on the colonial appearances on tellurite medium, or on both, by additional tests, particularly by a test for virulence. Although the fermentation reactions of *C. diphtheriæ* have considerable differential value, from the systematist's point of view, they fail to differentiate between toxigenic and non-toxigenic strains ; and, since this is the essential point at issue from the clinical or epidemiological point of view, they are not often employed in routine diagnostic work. If we desire additional evidence, we proceed directly to a virulence, or toxigenicity, test.

Virulence Tests.—Two methods are in common use. Subcutaneous injections of a broth culture of the suspected organism may be made in two guinea-pigs, one of which has been protected by the previous injection of antitoxin. The death of the unprotected animal, with the characteristic lesions, and the survival of the protected control, are evidence of toxigenicity. Alternatively we may employ the Römer method, giving small injections of bacilli intradermally, and observing the characteristic skin reaction. Here, again, we use a control guinea-pig that has been protected with antitoxin. The latter method is particularly valuable when many strains have to be tested, since several intradermal injections may be made in a single animal. If this is done a small *following* dose of antitoxin may be given, to prevent the death of the animal before the skin lesions have time to develop. This will not prevent the development of the skin lesions themselves, though they will be inhibited in the control, in which the antitoxin is given *before* the intradermal injections (see p. 810).

As a general working rule it may be stated that virulence tests are unnecessary when a bacillus with characteristic microscopic, or colonial, morphology has been isolated from a case of faucial infection that is clinically suggestive of diphtheria. Virulence tests should always be performed on bacilli isolated from the nose, or from any situation other than the fauces, and on bacilli isolated from suspected carriers.

It is possible that these general rules may require some modification when the practice of differentiating between the *gravis, intermediate* and *mitis* types becomes a routine procedure. We have noted above that avirulent strains are far commoner among *mitis* organisms than among the other two types. The most recent records indicate that this difference is a very wide one. Parish (1936) reports 96·9 per cent., 99·5 per cent. and 99·7 per cent. of virulent cultures among large samples of *gravis* strains examined by different workers, and 94·1 per cent., 99·1 per cent. and 99·9 per cent. for *intermediate* strains, as against 80·0 per cent., 86·6 per cent. and 87·5 per cent. for *mitis* strains. Stallybrass (1936), quoting Wright's findings in Liverpool, reports one avirulent culture among 145 *gravis* strains, and 4 avirulent cultures among 116 *intermediate* strains, as against no less than 100 avirulent cultures among 231 *mitis* strains. It may, therefore, be found with extended experience that virulence tests can be confined to *mitis* strains. But the figures quoted above refer to large mixed samples, most of which were presumably isolated from the throat in cases of suspected diphtheria ; and, until we have far more information with regard to the proportion of avirulent cultures among *gravis* and *intermediate* strains isolated from carriers, or from situations other than the throat, it would be unwise to change our present rules.

The Diagnosis of Susceptibility or Immunity to Diphtheria.

Modern methods of diphtheria control depend quite as much on distinguishing between the susceptible and resistant members of the human herd, as on diagnosing cases and carriers. The technique that first enabled us to do this on an adequate scale was the test introduced by Schick (Michiels and Schick 1913*a, b*, Schick 1913). It is performed as follows.

The test toxin is stored in a relatively concentrated solution, and when required for use is diluted so that one Schick dose is contained in 0·2 c.c. Part of this diluted toxin is heated to 70° C. for 5 minutes, to serve as a control. Into the flexor surface of one arm 0·2 c.c. of the unheated toxin is injected intradermally, care being taken that the injection is made into the substance of the dermis in such a way as to raise a definite bulla. Into the flex or surface of the opposite arm is injected 0·2 c.c. of the heated toxin. Readings should be taken daily until the 4th or 5th day ; the readings made on the 4th day give the

best differentiation between the various reactions.   The following types of reaction may
be observed :

   (*a*) The negative reaction—no reaction of any kind in either arm.

   (*b*) The positive reaction—no reaction in the control arm.

> In the test arm a circumscribed red flush appears after 24 to 36 hours, reaching its
> maximum development on the 4th day.   At this time there is a circular
> circumscribed area, 1–2 cm. in diameter, slightly raised above the general
> surface of the skin.   This slowly fades during the following few days or more,
> leaving an area of brownish pigmentation, with a desquamating epidermis.

   (*c*) The pseudo-reaction (negative).—This reaction, which is of the characteristic allergic
type, develops equally in both arms during the first 24 hours.   It is less sharply
circumscribed than the true positive reaction, and fades much more rapidly.
By the 4th day it has usually disappeared, leaving some slight degree of reddish
or brownish discoloration.

   (*d*) The combined reaction (pseudo + positive).

> The control arm shows the succession of changes referred to under the pseudo-
> reaction.   The reaction in the test arm is almost indistinguishable from that in
> the control arm during the first 24 hours.   After this time the reaction in the
> test arm continues to develop, while that in the control arm commences to fade.
> By the 4th day the difference between the two arms is usually quite distinctive.

   The positive and combined reactions indicate susceptibility ; or more precisely they
show that antitoxin is either absent from the circulating blood, or is present in a concentration of less than some limiting value, which is usually stated to be 1/30 A.U. per c.c.
of serum, but which is probably of the order of 1/100 A.U.   The negative and pseudo-
reactions indicate the presence of antitoxin in a concentration of 1/30 A.U. or more per
c.c. of blood.

   The Schick test, within its limits, is a quantitative one ; and the test dose must
therefore be defined, and the test toxin standardized.

   The Schick dose was originally defined on an empirical basis as 1/50th of the guinea-
pig M.L.D. ; but, as Glenny (1925) has pointed out, we are concerned in the Schick test
not only with toxicity but with combining power.   We want to know how much toxin
the subject's tissue fluids can neutralize.   The M.L.D. is not a satisfactory unit for this
purpose since it is not a measure of combining power ; but an adequate degree of toxicity
must be ensured, since the dermal reaction depends on the presence of free toxin.

   The subject was considered by the Biological Standardization Commission of the
League of Nations in 1931 (see Report 1931), and two alternative definitions of the Schick
dose were adopted.   One reads as follows :

   " The Schick test-dose, for injection in a volume of 0·2 c.c., shall be that quantity
of toxin which, when mixed with 1/750th part or more of an international unit of antitoxin
and injected intracutaneously into a normal guinea-pig, causes no local reaction ; but,
when mixed with 1/1,250th part or less of an international unit and similarly injected,
causes a marked reaction of the type of a ' positive ' Schick reaction ; *provided that* the
toxin is such that 1/25th of the Schick test-dose as above determined, without admixture
with antitoxin, when injected intracutaneously into a normal guinea-pig, causes a definite
local reaction of the type of a ' positive ' Schick reaction ; but that 1/50th of the Schick
test-dose, similarly injected without admixture, causes no local reaction of this type."

   In the alternative definition the main clause defines the Schick dose in terms of the
M.L.D., and the proviso deals with combining power.   Both conditions must be fulfilled
under the Regulations (1931) made in Great Britain in accord with the Therapeutic Substances Act (1925).

   As a possible alternative to the Shick test, the actual amount of circulating
antitoxin in a person's blood may be determined by titration, using the Römer

technique. This is clearly a more accurate method, and involves a single withdrawal of blood compared with the intradermal injections and their observation during the following few days. The necessary animal inoculations might be supposed to prevent the adoption of this method as a routine. Jensen (1933b), however, who uses rabbits instead of guinea-pigs, for the intracutaneous injections, thus increasing the number of tests that can be carried out on a single animal, considers it the method of choice both for convenience and accuracy.

The evidence now available leaves no reasonable doubt that a person who reacts negatively to the Schick test, or who has been shown to possess an equivalent amount of antitoxin in the circulating blood, will resist all ordinary risks of infection. This evidence has in part been obtained by keeping under observation samples of the general population whose Schick reaction has been determined, in part by observing the behaviour of negative and positive reactors when exposed to high risks of infection. The evidence available under the latter head is more impressive, and more readily obtained, than that under the former, for the simple reason that, where the risk of infection and consequently the incidence of disease are high, the observation of relatively small samples over relatively short periods of time will serve to reveal statistically significant differences, if such exist. This problem will be referred to again in discussing the efficacy of active immunization.

We may note here the single instance of a direct experiment on man which has, so far as we are aware, been placed on record. Guthrie, Marshall and Moss (1921) collected eight volunteers and determined their reaction to the Schick test ; four reacted positively, two negatively, and two gave pseudo-reactions which were read as negative. The throat of each of these eight volunteers was swabbed with a virulent culture of *C. diphtheriæ*. The organism established itself on the tonsils of the four positive reactors, and of three of the four negative reactors. The four positive reactors developed clinical diphtheria ; the three negative reactors became temporary carriers without showing any sign of the disease.

In discussing the nature and origin of the normal antibodies in Chapter XLVI, we have already described the observations of Zingher and of others on the results obtained in the application of the Schick test to large samples of the normal population, and have considered the opposing theories of the origin of normal antitoxin as the result of latent infection, or as a phase of normal biochemical ontogeny, in the absence of any specific stimulus ; and we have expressed our personal view that it is impossible to account for the observed distribution of natural antitoxic immunity among the population in general, and among certain isolated groups in particular, without assuming that natural immunization plays a highly important rôle.

The Treatment of Diphtheria with Antitoxin.

The nature of antitoxic immunity and the general principles that determine its practical application have been discussed in Chapter XLIII. We are here concerned with the methods that are employed in the particular case of diphtheria in man, and the available data with regard to their efficacy.

As regards the commercial preparation of antitoxic sera, we need only note that the animal almost universally employed is the horse, and that immunization is usually carried out by the administration of increasing doses of toxic filtrates, administered at intervals of a few days. The initial dose must be minute, 0·01 c.c.

or thereabouts. The final dose, usually reached within a period of 6 weeks to 2 months, may be very large, 1 litre or more. When a satisfactory titre has been attained the horse is bled from the jugular vein, with strict precautions as regards sterility ; the serum, after separation from the clot, is filtered through a coarse porcelain candle, and 0·3 to 0·5 per cent. tricresol is usually added as a further precaution to maintain sterility (Dean 1908). The average serum so obtained contains between 600 and 800 units of antitoxin per c.c.

Apart from its great theoretical interest, the isolation of antitoxin in a state of chemical purity would be an important advance from the practical point of view. This has not yet been achieved, but considerable success has been attained in the concentration of the active constituents (Brieger and Ehrlich 1893, Brieger and Cohn 1893, Brieger and Boer 1896, Pick 1902, Gibson 1905, Banzhaf and Gibson 1907, 1908–9, Banzhaf 1912–13, Andrewes *et al.* 1923). The methods employed, which vary in minor points of technique, depend on the demonstration that the major part of the antitoxin is contained in that fraction of the serum globulin which is precipitated by half saturation with ammonium sulphate, but redissolved when the precipitate is extracted with a saturated solution of sodium chloride. This so-called " pseudoglobulin " fraction can be separated from the euglobulin, and from the serum albumin. The process is accompanied by the loss of an appreciable fraction of the antitoxin originally present in the serum ; but the concentra‍tion of antitoxin in the finished product may be increased six or eight times as compared with the untreated serum ; and there is a relative elimination of non-effective protein material, though the protein content per c.c. is appreciably increased during the process of concentration.

Our object in treatment will obviously be to introduce as much antitoxin as we can, at the earliest possible moment, since we must act on the assumption that the beneficial result of our interference will probably be limited to the neutralization of the toxin which has not yet been firmly anchored to the cells which are susceptible to its action.

In support of this view we may cite such experimental results as those recorded by Glenny and Hopkins (see p. 810). For the same reason we should give thera‍peutic injections of antitoxin intravenously or intramuscularly, never subcutane‍ously, since the relatively slow absorption from the subcutaneous tissues will defeat our main objective (see p. 882).

It is sometimes taught that the administration of antitoxin is without effect after the 5th or 6th day of disease, a dictum based mainly on the figures recorded by Faber (1904), which show a progressive increase in case mortality from 7·1 per cent. in patients receiving antitoxin on the first day of disease, to 17.0 per cent., 21·3 per cent. and 19·9 per cent. among those treated on the 6th, 7th and later days respectively. It has, however, been pointed out that such hospital statistics are of little value, because there is an important element of selection of which they take no account. Cases admitted to hospital on the 5th day or after will, *ipso facto*, include a large number of severe infections ; since the delay in admission will in most cases be due either to delayed diagnosis, often resulting from failure to obtain a medical opinion, or to an unwillingness to resort to hospital. In either case those patients who are well on the way to recovery by the 5th or 6th day will never be admitted, while those who are seriously ill will be transferred to hospital, either because a late diagnosis has been arrived at, or because the serious condition of the patient has alarmed his friends.

There is no justification for withholding antitoxin because a case is in an advanced stage, though every effort should be made to ensure that it is given early in the disease.

A system of dosage in common use is that advocated by Park (1921) (see Table CI) ; but there has been a tendency to increase the amount of antitoxin given in the severer type of case as the result of the experience of recent years, and this tendency seems likely to continue. Thus, Bie (1922), in an admirable review of the evidence in regard to the value of antitoxin treatment in diphtheria, advocates the administration of very large total doses (92,000—170,000 units).

TABLE CI

UNITS OF ANTITOXIN TO BE ADMINISTERED TO CASES OF VARYING GRADES OF SEVERITY.
(After Park.)

Age or Weight of Patient.	Mild Cases.	Early Moderate.	Late Moderate and Early Severe.	Severe and Malignant.
Under 2 years. 10–30 lbs. wt.	2,000–3,000	3,000–5,000	5,000–10,000	7,500–10,000
2–15 years. 30–90 lbs. wt.	3,000–4,000	4,000–10,000	10,000–15,000	10,000–20,000
Adults. 90 lbs. or over .	3,000–5,000	5,000–10,000	10,000–20,000	20,000–50,000
Route of administration .	Intramuscular	Intravenous	Intravenous	Intravenous

It might be expected that after some 40 years it would be easy to produce irrefutable statistical evidence of the beneficial effects of the antitoxin treatment of diphtheria in man. The evidence does, in truth, seem decisive to most of us ; that it is still possible to bring forward contrary arguments that are not altogether specious is due to the fact that once a strong presumptive case has been made out in favour of a particular therapeutic measure it is not justifiable to continue the period of trial at a risk of human lives.

Of the classical studies from the early days of antitoxin treatment, the only one that affords an entirely satisfactory basis for comparison is that of Fibiger (1898). For a period of one year all cases of diphtheria admitted to hospital were divided into two groups by separating those admitted on alternate days. All cases admitted on one day were given antitoxin, all those admitted on the next day were treated without antitoxin, and so on throughout the period of trial. The results were as follows : of 239 cases treated with antitoxin 8 died, a mortality of 3·5 per cent. ; of 245 cases treated without anti-toxin 30 died, a mortality of 12·25 per cent. Applying the formula given on p. 777, the difference between the case mortality in the two groups is 8·75 per cent. and the standard error of this difference is 2·445 per cent., so that the odds against the difference being due to random sampling are several thousands to one.

Other results recorded during the early and middle 'nineties—comparisons between the case-fatality rates in hospitals in which antitoxin was given and others in which it was not, or between the experience in one hospital before and after the introduction of antitoxin—all pointed in the same direction ; and the period of trial ended with the adoption of antitoxin as a routine method of treatment.

If we survey the course of events since that time we find that they strongly support the view that the use of antitoxin has resulted in a significant lowering of the case-fatality rate ; but they would hardly be accepted as demonstrative proof in the absence of the earlier and controlled trials.

There is, for instance, the decline in the case-fatality rate as shown by the returns of the hospitals of the Metropolitan Asylums Board (see Table CII).

Antitoxin came into general use about 1895, and the figures suggest that it had produced its full effect on the case-fatality rate about 10 years later ; since when this rate has been kept down to a figure of about one-third of that prevailing in pre-antitoxin days. But, if we are disposed to be critical, we shall note that the downward trend had shown itself before the introduction of the antitoxin, and that secular trends in case fatality are known to occur apart altogether from the introduction of new therapeutic measures—as in the classical example of scarlet fever.

There is another factor which would add to our doubt. At about the same time as antitoxin was coming into general use the basis of diagnosis of diphtheria was changing. The introduction of bacteriological methods made it possible to recognize as diphtheria many cases that would earlier have been regarded as non-diphtheritic anginas. For this reason the total of recorded cases would tend to be increased by the inclusion of many mild infections, and the recorded case mortality would automatically fall.

TABLE CII

Year.	Case Mortality per cent.	Year.	Case Mortality per cent.
1889	40·7	1909	9·4
1890	33·5	1910	7·8
1891	30·6	1911	8·4
1892	29·3	1912	6·2
1893	30·4	1913	6·2
1894	29·3	1914	7·9
1895	22·8	1915	8·4
1896	21·2	1916	6·8
1897	17·7	1917	6·7
1898	15·4	1918	7·7
1899	13·9	1919	9·3
1900	12·3	1920	8·6
1901	11·1	1921	8·8
1902	11·0	1922	8·7
1903	9·7	1923	6·8
1904	10·0	1924	7·0
1905	8·3	1925	5·0
1906	8·8	1926	4·9
1907	9·6	1927	4·0
1908	9·7		

Somewhat better evidence is afforded by the figures for the mortality rates in cases of laryngeal diphtheria, excluding those cases treated by tracheotomy. This gives a series of cases in which the clinical signs were alone sufficient to establish a diagnosis, and in which the infection may be regarded as uniformly serious. In 1894 the mortality in this class of case, in the M.A.B. hospitals, was 62 per cent. ; after 1895 it fell, at first rapidly, then less steeply, until in 1910 it was 11·7 per cent. (Andrewes *et al.* 1923). Even here, however, the possible intrusion of other factors, such as changes in the proportion of all laryngeal cases treated by tracheotomy, and in the period at which tracheotomy is performed, make it difficult to assess the real significance of the record figures.

In any case, the clear historical evidence of long-period fluctuations in the severity of diphtheria, as of other infective diseases, forbids us to place too great an emphasis on a progressive fall in mortality lasting for a few decades ; and, in recent years, there have been signs that the disease is still able to reassert its killing power. Deicher and Agulnik (1927), for instance, give figures for a Berlin hospital and for one of the districts of that city (see Table CIII).

TABLE CIII

RUDOLF VIRCHOW HOSPITAL.				
Year	1923	1924	1925	1926
Total cases	132	140	114	172
Deaths	8	7	10	30
Mortality per cent.	6·1	5·0	8·7	17·4

ALT BERLIN.				
Year	1923	1924	1925	1926
Total cases	1,068	1,016	1,109	1,421
Mortality per cent.	7·58	5·9	8·1	11·1

It is tempting to suggest that this change has been caused by an increase in the proportion of cases due to the *gravis* or *intermediate* types. During the period 1930–32, for instance, a severe form of diphtheria was prevalent in Leeds. It was during this epidemic that McLeod and his colleagues differentiated the three types, and we have already noted that the *gravis* cases showed a case mortality of 13·1 per cent., while no deaths occurred among the *mitis* infections. The case-mortality rate for all infections in this series of cases, *gravis*, *intermediate* and *mitis* combined, was 10·3 per cent., a figure that may be compared with those given in Table CII. Similar figures have been quoted from other observers. It is very possible that this explanation is the true one ; but, since we have no information with regard to the relative proportion of *gravis*, *intermediate* and *mitis* infections during the earlier years of this century, when the prevailing case mortality of diphtheria was low, we must wait for further experience before granting it definite acceptance.

We are thus left with a mass of statistical data all of which is compatible with the view that the use of antitoxin has had a considerable effect in lowering the mortality from diphtheria, but most of which is indecisive. Taking the general trend of this evidence with Fibiger's early observations and adding to it the decisive results obtained in animal experiments, we have a sound basis for the conclusion that antitoxin provides the best available method of treatment, and that its early administration is the essential factor in controlling the clinical disease. The failure to establish a statistical case that is beyond criticism merely shows how hard it is to assess the real effect of any remedy in any human disease, unless that effect is so dramatic as to be immediately and consistently evident.

In view of recent experience, in Germany, in England and elsewhere, there is, however, an obvious need to re-examine the problem with a view to improving, or adding to, our present therapeutic reagents.

The Standardization of Diphtheria Antitoxin.

We have already referred to the standardization of diphtheria antitoxin, in our discussion of the toxin-antitoxin reaction (pp. 168–170). We noted that the instability of a toxic filtrate renders it quite unsuitable as a standard of reference, and that, for this reason among others, Ehrlich's original definition of the unit of antitoxin (A.U.) as *the smallest amount of antitoxin that will neutralize* 100 *M.L.D. of toxin,* using the guinea-pig as the test animal, had soon to be abandoned, and has been replaced by a unit defined in terms of a standard antitoxin. Such a standard antitoxic serum, when dried and preserved *in vacuo* in the presence of phosphorus pentoxide, maintains its potency over long periods of time. It has, moreover, become a general principle in biological standardization that a reagent shall, wherever possible, be assayed by comparing its potency with that of a standard preparation of the same reagent, to which some unit value has been assigned by international agreement. In the case of diphtheria, Ehrlich's original antitoxin was adopted as the international standard. The correct definition of a unit of diphtheria antitoxin is as follows.

One unit of diphtheria antitoxin (1 *A.U.*) *is contained in that amount of an antitoxic serum that has the same total combining capacity, for toxin and toxoid, as one unit of the standard antitoxin.*

Standard antitoxin is now preserved and issued by selected Institutes, and is tested from time to time under the auspices of the Biological Standardization Commission of the League of Nations (see Report 1923).

The methods employed in measuring the potency of an antitoxic serum, and the knowledge that has been acquired in their development and use, have played so large a part in the evolution of our present methods of controlling the disease that, at the cost of some repetition, it is desirable to summarize them here. Three such methods are available. Two of them depend on *in vivo* tests, the third on an *in vitro* titration.

The first is Ehrlich's classical method of injecting mixtures of toxin and antitoxin subcutaneously into guinea-pigs ; and this method is still the official one in many countries (see Report 1923, Prausnitz 1929). It has been found convenient to employ the end-point of toxæmic death rather than the end-point of complete neutralization—the L+ rather than the Lo dose of toxin (see p. 170). The first procedure is, then, to determine the smallest amount of a suitable toxic filtrate that, when mixed with one unit of standard antitoxin and injected into a 250 gm. guinea-pig, will, on the average, kill the animal by the 4th day. In practice batches of guinea-pigs are injected with each mixture prepared and the mixture producing a 50 per cent. mortality, or thereabouts, is regarded as containing the L+ dose of toxin. The procedure is then reversed. The amount of toxin is held constant at the L+ dose, and the amount of the serum to be tested is varied, again using an adequate number of guinea-pigs for each dose in the range within which the L+ mixture is expected to fall. The amount of serum in the mixture that gives a 50 per cent. mortality within 4 days contains one unit of antitoxin. The number of guinea-pigs that must be inoculated with any such mixture in order to give an estimate of the unit value of an antitoxic serum within a specified margin of error depends on the factors considered in Chapter XL. In practice a rough preliminary titration is made, and the exact value of the serum is then assessed using larger numbers of guinea-pigs.

The second method depends upon the observation of Römer (1909) that the intradermal injection into a guinea-pig of 1/250–1/500 M.L.D. of toxin is followed by a localized swelling and erythema. With slightly larger doses, this erythematous reaction is followed by definite necrosis. The neutralization of toxin by antitoxin prevents this reaction. The great advantage of this method is that it allows the toxicity of several different mixtures to be tested on a single guinea-pig, and thus not only economizes animals but eliminates much of the difficulty due to differences in susceptibility between one guinea-pig and another. The successive steps in the process of standardization do not differ in any essential from those followed in the Ehrlich method. Varying amounts of a suitable toxin are first mixed with one unit of the standard antitoxin and 0·2 c.c. of each mixture is injected into the depilated skin of a guinea-pig. The amount of toxin in the mixture that gives a minimal skin reaction is noted. This amount of toxin has been defined by Glenny and Allen (1921) as the Lr dose. A series of mixtures is now prepared in which the Lr dose of toxin is mixed with varying amounts of the serum under test, and 0·2 c.c. of each of these mixtures is injected intradermally into another guinea-pig. The amount of serum in that mixture that gives a minimal skin reaction contains one unit of antitoxin. In practice it is customary to use fractions of 1.A.U. and corresponding fractions of the Lr dose of toxin, in order to avoid the administration of lethal doses of toxin in the mixtures containing toxin in excess.

The third method depends on the observation of Ramon (1922) that a satisfactory measure of the combining power of an antitoxic serum can be obtained by mixing falling amounts of the serum with a constant amount of toxin and noting the ratio of one reagent to the other in the tube that first shows flocculation. This is the method of optimal proportions (see p. 146). Glenny and Okell (1924) (see also Glenny and Wallace 1925) have suggested that the amount of toxin corresponding to one unit of antitoxin in the mixture that shows optimal flocculation when tested by the Ramon method should be called the Lf dose. The procedure with this *in vitro* test is essentially the same as with either of the *in vivo* methods. The Lf dose of a suitable toxic filtrate is determined by titration against the standard antitoxin. The amount of the serum under test that gives optimal flocculation with the Lf dose of toxin is determined by a second titration. This amount of serum contains one unit of antitoxin.

Table CIV (see Glenny 1925) sets out the units (or named doses) employed in testing diphtheria toxin and antitoxin. The meaning to be attached to the Schick dose is considered later.

TABLE CIV

(After Glenny 1925.)

Character measured.	Unit or Dose.		Result of Inoculation in Guinea-pig.
	Toxin.	Antitoxin.	
Toxicity . . .	M.L.D.	—	Death on 4th day.
,, . . .	M.R.D.	—	Minimal skin reaction.
Combining power	L + dose	1 A.U.	Mixture causes death on 4th day.
,, ,,	Lo ,,	1 A.U.	Mixture causes minimal œdema.
,, ,,	Lr ,,	1 A.U.	Mixture causes minimal skin reaction.
,, ,,	Lf ,,	1 A.U.	Mixture gives optimal proportions for flocculation.
,, ,,	Schick ,,	0·001 A.U.	

The comparison of large numbers of different antitoxic sera—natural or concentrated—by these different methods has brought to light facts of considerable theoretical and practical importance. The L+ dose of toxin is always appreciably larger than the Lo dose. The Lr dose of toxin always approximates closely to the Lo dose, as would be expected, since a very small excess of unneutralized toxin will elicit the Römer reaction. The Lf dose is, in general, slightly less than the Lr dose. Glenny (1925) notes the following relation between the various doses of an average toxic filtrate: L+ dose = 0·21 c.c., Lo dose = 0·18 c.c., Lr dose = 0·175 c.c., Lf dose = 0·155 c.c. The ratio of the Lf dose to any of the *in vivo* doses is not constant for all toxic filtrates. Antitoxin gives flocculation with both toxin and toxoid while the determination of the L+, Lo and Lr doses depends on the presence of unneutralized toxin, and is hence affected by differences in the proportion of toxin to toxoid. Moreover, as was shown by Glenny, Pope and Waddington (1925), not only does the Lf/Lr ratio vary from one toxic filtrate to another, when these are tested against the same serum, but the Lf/Lr ratio of a single toxic filtrate varies when it is tested against different antitoxic sera. It follows that, when sera are compared with one another by *in vivo* and *in vitro* methods, their apparent relative potency may vary according to the method of comparison employed ; and, with such sera, the ratio $\dfrac{in\ vitro\ \text{value}}{in\ vivo\ \text{value}}$ will vary from one serum to another.   Glenny and his colleagues note that they have obtained *in vitro/in vivo* ratios varying from 0·4 to 2·0 with different antitoxic sera, and that, in general, if the Ehrlich value is considerably higher than the Ramon value *i.e.* if the *in vitro/in vivo* ratio is low, the serum will be found to give rapid flocculation ; while, if the Ramon value is higher than the Ehrlich value, the serum will be found to give very slow flocculation and the toxin-antitoxin complex will show considerable dissociation on simple dilution.   In their later papers, Glenny and his colleagues use the inverse ratio—*in vivo/in vitro*—so that a serum with a ratio greater than unity has a greater protective action than its flocculation value would lead one to expect.

Such findings as these clearly raise the question as to whether the protective action of an antitoxic serum is determined solely by its antitoxic content, as measured by one or other of the methods commonly employed.   This question has been discussed on p. 810, where it was noted that antitoxic sera may differ in *avidity*, as well as in their total capacity for neutralizing toxin.   It was noted also that this avidity appears to be determined by the firmness of the toxin-antitoxin union, and that avid sera (those that unite firmly with toxin) are more effective than non-avid sera, those that form a loose union with toxin.

The avidity of antitoxic sera appears to be determined, at least in part, by the type of serum protein with which the antitoxin is associated.   Thus (Barr and Glenny 1931*a*, *b*, Glenny and Barr 1932, Glenny *et al.* 1932) if successive globulin fractions are precipitated with increasing amounts of ammonium sulphate, the earlier fractions show a higher *in vivo/in vitro* ratio, a higher dilution ratio and a greater curative power in rabbits than the original serum, while the avidity as judged by these tests decreases with each successive fraction precipitated.

Non-avid sera do not form a high proportion of the antidiphtheria sera obtained in routine serum production, and Glenny and his colleagues note that they are usually derived from horses that have proved difficult to immunize.   With other antitoxic sera (see Glenny *et al.* 1932) it would seem that they may occur more frequently.

These findings do not, of course, lessen the importance of determining the antitoxin content of a serum in terms of standard units, or of producing sera with the highest possible antitoxin content   We clearly want to know how many units we are giving, and to give as many units as we can.   They do suggest that the protective or curative value of a serum is not always completely described by stating the number of units it contains ; and it may prove desirable in the future to adopt some standard of avidity in addition to our standard of content.

The Epidemiology of Diphtheria.

Before discussing the prophylaxis of diphtheria it is necessary to have in our minds a picture of how the disease behaves under natural conditions.   This picture, as it has been presented to us by the combined studies of bacteriologists and epidemiologists, using the Schick test and the throat swab, is far more detailed and informative than the corresponding picture that we possess for other diseases. For this reason it was selected as an illustrative example in our general discussion of herd infection and herd immunity in Chapter LIII, and reference should be made to that chapter.   We may add here a few additional particulars with regard to the natural history of the disease, that were not relevant to the more general discussion.

Diphtheria is a disease which shows a characteristic age incidence.   Greenwood (see Andrewes *et al.* 1923) has calculated the probability of being attacked by diphtheria at different ages for three samples of the population, in different places and at different times. The figures selected were those for Breslau (1886–90), Manchester (1911–12), and London (1910–12). In the case of London the rates for males and females were calculated separately. In Breslau the peak of the curve falls in the age group 2–3, with a slight decline in the group 3–4. In Manchester the maximum is at 3–4, with a slight decline at 4–5. In London the maximum for both sexes is at ages 4–5. All four curves are definitely skew, the mode falling well to the left. Diphtheria is rare during the first year of life, and then becomes increasingly frequent until the maximum frequency is reached somewhere between the 2nd and 5th year. The incidence declines slowly until the age group 5–10, then rapidly during the age group 10–15, after which the probability of contracting diphtheria is small. It becomes still smaller in the age group 15–20, and remains at a very low level during the rest of life.

Apart from this variation in susceptibility at different ages, diphtheria shows a curious capriciousness in its incidence among small communities containing many members of susceptible age. The attack rate among those exposed to risk may be very low, and varies very widely from one outbreak to another.

Diphtheria is not markedly associated with density of population, if we measure that elusive variable by computing the total population within some unit area ; indeed, over considerable periods in its history, the disease has shown a marked predilection for rural as opposed to urban conditions. It is, however, typically a disease of schools, and of institutions where children are herded together at susceptible ages. Moreover, a particular school or institution may form an endemic centre of the disease for a period of months or years.

The persistence of infection within a particular community is, of course, accounted for by the presence of one or more chronic carriers. We have previously given figures for the frequency of carriers of *C. diphtheriæ* among various classes of contact, and among the population at large. The carrier state is by no means confined to those who have themselves passed through an attack of disease ; but, since the diagnosis of clinical diphtheria at once brings a patient under observation, and involves some degree of control and a considerable degree of responsibility on the part of the medical authorities, it is of interest to note the rate at which the proportion of carriers decreases during and after convalescence.

An investigation carried out by Hartley and Martin (1919–20) has yielded valuable information on this point. The study was carried out on 457 young adults suffering from diphtheria. A swab was taken on the day of admission, and every 7th day thereafter, till three successive negative results were obtained. The time at which any individual ceased to carry *C. diphtheriæ* was calculated as being half-way between the last positive and the first of three successive negative swabs. The data were complete for the first 50 days, after which some of the patients were no longer under observation. The results were plotted in the ordinary way, using either the numbers still carrying, or the logarithms of those numbers, as ordinates, and time as abscissæ. It was found that the latter curve after the first five days from admission, gave a close approximation to a straight line. The general form of the equation of such a curve is $\dfrac{\log n_1 - \log n_2}{t_2 - t_1} = K$, where n_1 and n_2 are the numbers carrying at times t_1 and t_2. If we take time as measured from the fifth day after admission, this may be expressed in the form

$$\log n = \log n' - Kt,$$

where n is the number carrying on any given day, n' is the number carrying on the 5th day, and t is the time interval in days measured from the fifth.   The equation to the curve which gave the best fit was calculated by Greenwood as

$$\log n = 2 \cdot 6002 - 0 \cdot 0218\ t.$$

The observed and calculated number of carriers for the first 50 days were as given in Table CV.

TABLE CV

Days after Admission.	Number carrying (observed).	Number carrying (calculated).
5	392	—
10	302	310
15	232	242
20	194	189
25	156	147
30	118	115
35	92	89
40	70	70
45	52	54
50	41	42

The agreement is obviously very close, and such a relationship between lapse of time and the disappearance of bacilli suggests that this disappearance is due to the operation of a large number of small causes acting independently, in other words to chance.   It would seem that a person who has carried *C. diphtheriæ* for 6 weeks or more is, on the average, just as likely to become free during the next few days as another who has carried for only a week.   There are, however, as Hartley and Martin point out, a few persons with obviously unhealthy tonsils who carry persistently, but cease to carry after tonsillectomy.

It may be noted that the constant 0·0218 in the formula quoted above indicates that about 5 per cent. of those carrying on any one day have ceased to carry on the day following.   In order to determine whether this rate of clearing held true in general, or applied only to this particular sample, data collected from various published reports were analysed in the same way.   It was found that the general form of the curve was very similar in each case, *i.e.* the logarithmic relation between carrier rate and time held good, but the value of the constant varied very widely, such figures as 0·018, 0·093, and 0·202 being obtained.   Some adjustment is necessary because, in certain of these series, the test of clearance was a single negative swab, but the value of the constant in Hartley and Martin's series would only be altered to 0·032 on this basis, so that the rate of clearing under different conditions varies considerably, a fact which seems to merit further investigation.

These figures refer to the ordinary faucial diphtheria.   The curious, but not uncommon, condition of nasal diphtheria, in which a subacute or chronic rhinitis with or without membrane formation is associated with the presence of virulent *C. diphtheriæ*, follows a far more chronic course ; and the control of nasal carriers forms an administrative problem of the greatest difficulty.   The fact that consti- tutional symptoms may be slight or absent suggests the presence of some factor which prevents free absorption of toxin from the nasal cavity (Andrewes *et al.* 1923).   The same absence of symptoms makes it easy to overlook the presence of a nasal carrier when investigating an outbreak, and a thorough search should always be made with this possibility in mind.

We have already noted the effect of closeness of contact on the carrier rate.

It may be added that the investigation of epidemics in institutions suggests that this factor is of great importance, both in regard to the production of carriers and of actual cases of disease. It would seem that duration of contact must be considered as one aspect of this problem ; and there is good evidence that contact of the type which is exemplified by the case of boys sleeping in a single dormitory is enormously more important than casual or momentary contact during working hours (Dudley 1923).

In concluding this section we may consider the importance of fomites in the spread of diphtheria. From the case of the child's box of bricks, reported by Abel in 1893, there have been instances in which it seemed possible to incriminate a particular article as a disseminator of infection. Very occasionally, as in the case of the common supply of penholders for a number of schoolboys recorded by Dudley (1923), it would appear that such a mode of transmission may have played a significant part. In general, however, the balance of evidence would appear to be heavily against the view that fomites play any significant rôle in the spread of the disease ; and there is nothing to suggest that stringency of disinfection would make any appreciable impression on its incidence. Provided that ordinary cleanliness is practised, and the elementary precautions of sick-nursing strictly observed, it would appear that time and money will be more fruitfully expended along other lines.

The Spread of Diphtheria by Domestic Animals.—It was at one time believed that certain domestic animals played a significant part in the spread of diphtheria, but most of the evidence on which this belief was based has been shown to be erroneous. It is now clear that Klein's (1889) statements with regard to diphtheria in the cat were incorrect, and Savage (1919–20) has shown that this animal is extremely resistant to infection by feeding, by intranasal injection, or by swabbing the throat with living culture. There is, indeed, no evidence that it ever contracts or transmits the disease. The domestic fowl was credited with similar malign potentialities, a belief that probably arose as the result of a superficial similarity between " fowl diphtheria " and the human disease. The fowl disease is now known to be caused by a filtrable virus, and the generally accepted view is that fowls can be disregarded as a potential source of infection. A report by Litterer (1925) does, however, suggest that these birds may sometimes harbour virulent *C. diphtheriæ*. In two instances he isolated diphtheria bacilli from the throat of several fowls, kept by families among which a case of diphtheria had occurred. The bacilli were fully virulent as tested by the inoculation of guinea-pigs, controlled by protection with diphtheria antitoxin. Some of these fowls were obviously ill, and showed typical membranes. They recovered rapidly after injection with antitoxin. Attempts to reproduce the disease in healthy fowls by swabbing the throat with virulent *C. diphtheriæ*, with or without previous scarification, were uniformly unsuccessful. Thirty fowls suffering from roup were treated in a similar manner. In five cases a typical membrane was produced. If similar results are recorded by other investigators it may be necessary to consider the possibility of the fowl playing some part in the spread of the disease in exceptional circumstances ; but it seems altogether unlikely that this part is a significant one from the epidemiological point of view.

We have referred (see Chapter XLVI) to the occasional isolation of virulent diphtheria bacilli from the horse, but here again there is no evidence that such infection has any appreciable effect on the incidence of the disease in man.

Similarly, the demonstration by Ramon and Erber (1934) and by Dold and Weigmann (1934) of virulent diphtheria bacilli in the throats of monkeys has little significance in relation to human infection under ordinary conditions of life.

The cow is in a different category, since the general consumption of milk renders any infection of this animal of particular importance. The earlier records of diphtheria in the cow may be safely disregarded, since the nature of the disease was never fully established, and the conditions described were, in most instances, subsequently shown to be due to quite different causes. It is now reasonably certain that the cow does not naturally suffer from any form of infection with *C. diphtheriæ*, and that the only lesion in this animal which has any significance in the spread of the disease is the occasional infection of pre-existing superficial lesions on the teats from the hands of a milker who is suffering from the disease, or is carrying virulent bacilli. The existence of these lesions has been recorded by Dean and Todd (1902), Ashby (1906) and Henry (1920), and the authors have met with one instance of this condition. In all cases the virulence of the bacilli has been established. Such infected wounds, when they occur, are of obvious importance as forming a persistent focus from which the milk is likely to be infected; and in the cases recorded the lesions have been detected during the investigation of a milk-borne epidemic. In the majority of the cases in which an epidemic of diphtheria is traceable to an infected milk supply it is probable that the original source of the bacilli has been a human carrier, who has handled the milk at some time during its preparation. It may be added that the incrimination of the milk rests, in almost all instances, on epidemiological evidence. The isolation of *C. diphtheriæ* from milk, even when a particular supply is under grave suspicion, is a very rare event. This is due, in part at least, to the fact that the actual milk which conveyed the infection is seldom, if ever, available for examination at the time when attention has been drawn to it, and all the evidence suggests that the infection of a supply from any particular source is probably of the nature of an infrequent accident, rather than a persistent contamination. It must be emphasized that the identification of a diphtheria-like bacillus isolated from milk requires the most stringent tests. No organism derived from such a source should be reported as *C. diphtheriæ* until its character has been established by a properly controlled virulence test.

Prophylaxis in Diphtheria.

Our present methods of controlling diphtheria as a herd disease depend almost entirely on active immunization. Passive immunization, because of its transitory nature, has a very restricted application in this field, and may be shortly dismissed.

To meet particular, and transitory emergencies, such as the accidental admission to a children's ward of a child suffering from diphtheria, the administration of 500–1,000 units of antitoxin to each of the other children thus exposed to risk, the injection being given by the subcutaneous or intramuscular route, has been found an effective method of stopping the spread of the disease. The introduction of the Schick test has enabled us to differentiate between susceptibles and immunes, and only the positive reactors need be given antitoxin. Even under such conditions as these active immunization has the great advantage of conferring a lasting immunity; but the length of the induction period makes it less effective as a method of ensuring that no spread of infection shall occur within the ward.

For all ordinary field purposes active immunization is employed; and an adequate understanding of the principles that govern the application of this method in the control of the disease is so important to the medical practitioner and to the medical officer of health that the relevant data must be set out in some detail.

As early as 1892 von Behring and Wernicke had shown that susceptible animals might be safely immunized by inoculating them with increasing doses of living culture after a protective dose of antitoxic serum. Six years later Nikanaroff reported successful immunization by the inoculation of a few doses of toxin neutralized with antitoxin; and Dreyer, in 1900, proposed the use of toxin-antitoxin mixtures during the early stages of antitoxin production in horses. The long lag in the application of similar methods to man appears to have been in part due to the fact that the reported results of toxin-antitoxin mixtures in the horse were unfavourable, while unmodified toxin was clearly too dangerous a reagent for use in human subjects. More recent work (see for instance Glenny and Waddington 1928) has shown quite clearly that laboratory animals, such as the guinea-pig, may be rendered immune to diphtheria toxin, as judged by the intradermal test, by a few injections of toxin-antitoxin or of toxoid.

Von Behring (1913) reported the successful use of a toxin-antitoxin mixture in the immunization of children; but the exact nature of his preparation was not described. From 1913 onwards the use of such mixtures for the active immunization of children developed very rapidly, particularly in America and owing largely to the work of Park and Zingher (Park 1913, 1918, 1922, Park and Zingher 1915, 1916, Zingher 1921, 1922). Although these toxin-antitoxin mixtures have proved effective and are entirely safe as long as they are accurately prepared and are stored and used under optimal conditions there are latent possibilities of danger if these conditions are not fulfilled.

In one instance, involving 5 deaths and 40 serious reactions (see Forbes 1927), it was found that the toxin had been added in fractions to obtain the correct toxin-antitoxin ratio, in forgetfulness of the Danysz phenomenon. In another instance it was found that a particular phial of toxin-antitoxin mixture that had been frozen had caused severe constitutional reactions, while other phials of the same batch, which had not been frozen, had been used without any untoward results. Further investigations showed that the freezing of such mixtures frequently resulted in a marked rise in toxicity. It has been shown by Pope (1927) that this phenomenon is dependent, in part at least, on a separation of phenol during freezing; this leads to a local concentration greatly in excess of the 0·5 per cent. or so added for preservative purposes, and to a consequent destruction of antitoxin, which is more sensitive than toxin to phenolization. Observations recorded by Robinson and White (1928) indicate that, even in the absence of added phenol, dissociation of toxin-antitoxin mixtures may occur on freezing, the degree of dissociation apparently depending on the concentration of the mixture.

There are obvious advantages in using a prophylactic in which the chance of such a dissociation is eliminated, and recent investigations have shown that various forms of toxoid, or of toxoid-antitoxin mixtures, are highly efficient antigens (see Hartley 1926, Watson and Langstaff 1926, Glenny and Pope 1927, Glenny and Waddington 1928). Ramon in 1924 employed, under the name of " anatoxin," a toxoid prepared by adding 0·4 per cent. formalin to a toxic filtrate and incubating for 1 month at a temperature of 37° C., and this " anatoxin " has been extensively used as a prophylactic in many countries. The relative advantages, or disadvantages, of these various reagents will be discussed very briefly in a later section. For the moment we may turn to the question of the effectiveness of active immunization in general.

Since the Schick test provides us with a method of separating susceptible persons from immunes, and is frequently employed in determining whether a given person does, or does not, require active immunization, we may first note the evidence with regard to the efficiency of this method in converting Schick-positive to Schick-negative reactors.

Using one of the recognized methods of immunization, such as the injection of three doses of formolized toxin (0·5 c.c., 1·0 c.c. and 1·5 c.c.) with an interval of 2–3 weeks between the injections, it is possible to induce Schick-immunity in 88–98 per cent. of Schick-susceptibles within 6–8 weeks. (See Park and Zingher 1915, 1916, Ramon 1926, Lagrange 1926, Kundratitz 1927, Progulski and Redlich 1927, Martin, Loiseau and Laffaile 1928, Parish and Okell 1928, van Boeckel 1928, Pagani-Cesa 1931, Ramon, Debré *et al.* 1931, Ray 1931, Seligmann 1931, Cerruti 1931, Faberi and Giuseppi 1931, Maggiora-Vergano 1931, Nicolle 1933, Greengard 1934, Nélis 1934 and many others.)

The results obtained in some of these trials have given us valuable hints with regard to the probable duration of the immunity so induced. Thus (Parish and Okell 1928) 440 children who were Schick-positive when first tested were rendered Schick-negative by immunization. When retested 1–7 years later approximately 5 per cent. had become positive again. But these " relapsed " Schick-positives still showed the effect of immunization by rapidly producing circulating antitoxin in response to very small amounts of diphtheria toxin ; they would fall into the " sub-immune " or " potentially immune " classes of Glenny's classification (see p. 972).

The results of active immunization may also be followed by periodic titrations of the amount of antitoxin in the circulating blood, using the Römer method (Ramon and Debré *et al.* 1930, Fischer and Pockels 1933, Andolz Aquilar 1935). Jensen (1933a, b) has been particularly active in the development of this method, using the rabbit as a test animal for the Römer titrations, and has recorded a series of very valuable curves showing the rate of disappearance from the blood of the antitoxin produced in response to the immunizing injections. It would appear from these that the antitoxin titre attained and the rate of antitoxin loss are subject to very wide individual variations. The fall that occurs, after the maximum titre is reached, can be described by the equation for a bimolecular reaction, $kt = \dfrac{x}{a\,(a-x)}$ where a is the original amount of antitoxin, x is the amount lost in time t, and k is a constant. The value of k varies from person to person ; and Jensen (1933a), analysing his observations on the basis of this formula, concludes that the duration of effective immunity after active immunization may vary from a few weeks or months to 60 years or more.

The ultimate court of reference in determining the efficacy of active immunization must, however, be the observation of the behaviour of immunized persons when exposed to the risk of natural infection.

In examining the evidence with regard to this question it must be noted that immunization is often, but not always, preceded by Schick testing, only the Schick-positive reactors receiving the subsequent immunizing injections of toxoid. In such cases the " treated " group consists of natural and artificial immunes, and the " control " group consists, in general, of a sample of the community having approximately the same age distribution as the treated group, but neither Schick-tested nor immune. In other cases the comparison is between those who have been artificially immunized and those who have not, irrespective of the distribution of natural immunity in the untreated groups.

Bieber (1920) reported the after-history, from 1913, of 1,097 immunized and 3,275 non-immunized children in villages near Magdeburg. Of the former, 52 (4·8 per cent.) had contracted diphtheria ; of the latter, 493 (15·1 per cent.). Park (1922) records the history over a shorter period of 90,000 immunized or naturally immune children and 90,000 controls. During the period of observation 14 of the former contracted diphtheria as against 56 of the latter. Adams (see Fitz-Gerald 1928) records the history during the years 1926 and 1927 of 11,000 children who had received two immunizing doses of toxoid, and of 9,000 non-immunized controls. Among the immunized the incidence of diphtheria was 1·55 per 1,000, among the non-immunized it was 11·44 per 1,000. Isabolinski and others (1931) describe the results of immunization in Smolensk. Of 4,185 children, immunized with toxoid, 0·14 per cent. contracted diphtheria during the eleven months following immunization ; of 19,000 control children in the same town 1·5 per cent. contracted diphtheria during the same period. McKinnon and others (1931) and Fitz-Gerald and others (1932) record the results of immunization in Toronto. Among a group of 36,189 children who had passed through the immunization centres and had been found to be Schick-negative, or had received one or more immunizing doses of toxoid, or had been found to be sensitive to a preliminary injection of toxoid and so received no further treatment, there were 120 cases of diphtheria during the period of observation (December 1926–June 1929). As a control the prevailing rates of diphtheria morbidity at ages among the non-immunized population were applied to each age group of the immunized. This gave 478 as the expected number of cases. Of the 36,189 children, 16,829 had received three doses of toxoid. Among this group 222 cases of diphtheria would have been expected ; only 23 occurred. There are many other records of an analogous kind ; for a recent summary see Forbes (1932).

Still more demonstrative evidence is obtained if we confine our attention to groups of persons who are exposed to an unusually high risk of contracting diphtheria. Fever hospitals supply an environment in which such a risk occurs, and the history of attempts to immunize the nursing and domestic staff is correspondingly instructive (see, for instance, Benson 1928, Woods 1928, Harries 1930). We may take the figures given by Harries for the Birmingham City Fever Hospital as an illustrative example (Table CVI).

TABLE CVI

SHOWING THE DIPHTHERIA INCIDENCE AMONG THE NURSING AND DOMESTIC STAFF AT
BIRMINGHAM CITY FEVER HOSPITAL. (Modified from Harries.)

Year.	Diphtheria Incidence per cent.		
	Nursing.	Domestic.	Combined.
1919	15·6	9·4	13·5
1920	24·5	16·3	21·8
1921	13·0	11·1	12·4
1922 (a)	6·5	6·7	6·5
1923 (b)	3·7	8·9	5·2
1924	0·93	11·1	3·9
1925 (c)	—	—	0·77
1926	—	—	0·76
1927	—	—	0
1928	—	—	0
1929	—	—	0·6

(a) Schick testing of nursing staff commenced.
(b) Active immunization of nursing staff commenced.
(c) Active immunization of domestic staff commenced.

The significance of such figures cannot be in doubt. The decline of diphtheria among the nurses coincident with the commencement of Schick testing and immunization, the persistence of diphtheria among the domestic staff until similar measures were applied to them, and the subsequent lowering of incidence until during 3 years, only 1 case of diphtheria occurred among a staff increasing from 130 to 166, indicate clearly that adequate immunization of all susceptibles will reduce to insignificance the incidence of this disease among a community exposed to particularly severe risks.

Orphan asylums, children's homes and boarding schools, where persons of a susceptible age are congregated together, afford another example of an environment in which the risk of infection is above the average ; and the experience in such institutions confirms that obtained in fever hospitals. Nassau (1930), for instance, records the effect of active immunization in a children's home near Berlin ; and Dudley (1923, 1926, 1932) has provided a very fully documented account of the control of diphtheria in the Royal Naval School at Greenwich.

There is, then, no reasonable doubt that active immunization, properly performed, is highly effective in protecting the individual against diphtheria, and in eliminating diphtheria from any small closed community in which all the inmates can be Schick-tested and, if necessary, immunized. It may be noted that, in the few instances in which diphtheria in an immunized person, or in a fully immunized community, has been recorded, the infection has almost always been of the *gravis* type, and even then the infection has not been severe (see, for instance, Dudley *et al.* 1934).

The Control of Institutional Epidemics.

Before considering the effect of mass immunization on the incidence of diphtheria among the community as a whole, we may interpolate a brief description of the steps that should be followed in order to control an outbreak of diphtheria in a school or similar institution (see Okell, Eagleton and O'Brien 1924).   The steps that should be taken immediately the first case of diphtheria occurs are as follows :

(1) Perform a Schick test on all inmates and take swabs from the nose and throat.

(2) Next day take a preliminary reading of the Schick tests, and isolate in one ward all negative reactors. The results of the swabs, based on morphological appearances, will be available on this day. Those who are Schick-negative—swab-positive should be regarded as carriers and retained in isolation. Those who are Schick-negative—swab-negative are uninfected and immune, and can be released from isolation. Those who are Schick-positive—swab-positive (they will be a very small group, if they are found at all) should be regarded as probably incubating diphtheria : they should be kept under close and constant observation, and treated with antitoxin immediately any clinical signs develop. Those who are Schick-positive—swab-negative are uninfected but susceptible : they should be kept under observation and swabbed again if any signs of infection develop. The immunization of all susceptibles should be commenced at once.

(3) All cultures of morphologically typical *C. diphtheriæ* should be tested for virulence. Those Schick-negative persons who are harbouring avirulent diphtheria bacilli may be released from isolation, leaving those immunes who are carriers of virulent bacilli and who must be regarded as potential disseminators of infection until they cease to carry. Any susceptible person who was, at the time the swabs were taken, harbouring virulent diphtheria bacilli will probably have developed the disease before the results of the virulence tests are known. Those Schick-positives who are harbouring avirulent bacilli may be regarded as uninfected susceptibles.

Mass Immunization against Diphtheria.

We may now turn to the question, will Schick testing and immunization significantly reduce, or altogether eliminate, the incidence of diphtheria in the community at large if applied on the widest possible scale ? It must be realized that the emphasis is on the final limiting clause. There is no reason to doubt that, if all susceptibles in the community could be tested and if necessary immunized, the reduction in the incidence of diphtheria would be of the same order as that attained in closed or semi-closed communities. But we are dealing with practical politics, and what we want to know is the probable effect of an administratively possible policy. We are here faced with a problem of great statistical difficulty. It will not do to cite a few instances in which the inauguration of mass-immunization of school children has been associated with a decline in the general diphtheria morbidity rate, because we know quite well that most infective diseases are subject to secular trends in frequency, and a falling rate for any one of them might well have no significant association with any particular preventive measure adopted at the time the fall occurred.

Woods (1928), for instance, has pointed out that the fall in the diphtheria morbidity rate which followed the introduction of mass immunization in New York in 1918 cannot be accepted as certainly significant. The rate was already falling before the immunization began ; and if a straight line is fitted to the trend of mortality for the years prior to 1917, and is then extrapolated beyond 1918, this extended line approximates very closely to that which would describe the actual course of events during the following decade.

Godfrey (1932), in an admirable review of the available evidence, discusses the possible reasons for such divergent results as those recorded in New York City and Philadelphia, where immunization was followed by a marked decrease in morbidity, and in Newark, Detroit and Buffalo, where similar measures failed. Tracing in detail the course of events in eleven different districts in New York State he arrives at the conclusion that the crucial point is to be found in the immunization of the child of pre-school age (the age group 1–5). The earlier attempts at mass immunization were, for obvious administrative reasons, confined mainly to children of school age (the age groups 5–9 and 9–14). Godfrey can find no evidence that the immunization of 50 per cent. or over of the children in these age groups produces a definite fall in the incidence of diphtheria in the community as a whole. When, however, the immunization of 30 per cent. or more of the age group 1–5 is superimposed on that of the later age groups there is an immediate and striking decline in the general prevalence of the disease. Godfrey found only two exceptions to this rule in the eleven areas from which his data were obtained.

The same point is made by Lee (1931) who has studied the trend of diphtheria mortality in Philadelphia and in New York City from 1870 to 1930. Fitting an exponential curve to the recorded death rates, he finds that for neither city was there any significant departure from the general trend between the end of the period (1890–1900), when the use of antitoxin as a therapeutic measure was becoming general, and 1929. But in 1930, following the extension of the immunization campaign to children of pre-school age, there was a dramatic change in both cities. In Philadelphia the expected death rate on the basis of the previous trend would have been 10·5 per 100,000, with odds of 20 : 1 that it would fall between 8·1 and 13·6. Actually it was 2·86. In the case of each city the odds against the observed difference between the actual and the expected death rates being due to chance are of an astronomical order.

It is possible that the effect of immunizing children of school age alone may be offset, so far as its influence on the *general* morbidity is concerned, by the creation of healthy carriers who may infect the younger susceptibles in their homes. We have, here, an admirable example of the necessity for considering the factors that determine herd immunity, as well as those that determine immunity in the individual.

It may be pointed out as a matter of practical politics that, in conducting mass immunization, it is customary to omit Schick testing in children under 8 years of age. So few children below this age are Schick-negative that the extra visit to the clinic involved by the Schick testing is hardly justified. Children over 8, on the other hand, should be Schick tested, and only the Schick-positive reactors immunized. It is advantageous, especially in older children, to test their sensitivity to formol toxoid at the same time as their Schick reaction is determined. This may be done by means of the Moloney test (Moloney and Fraser 1927), in which an injection of 0·2 c.c. of a 1/20 dilution of formol toxoid is given intradermally. This injection may replace the control injection of heated toxin given in the ordinary Schick test. Any person giving more than a minimal local reaction at the site of the toxoid injection should be immunized very cautiously, starting with a dose of about 0·1 c.c. of prophylactic instead of the customary 0·5 c.c., or using toxin-antitoxin floccules, which have less tendency to give a local reaction.

In summary, we have in the modern method of antidiphtheria immunization a measure that is based on well-attested immunological principles, involves the use of a reagent of proved potency, is supported by the results of numerous animal experiments, has been shown to be effective in raising the resistance of the individual and in controlling the incidence of the disease in isolated or semi-isolated communities, and is almost certainly capable of greatly reducing the incidence in the community as a whole, if due attention is paid to herd reactions.

The Various Forms of Diphtheria Prophylactic.

We have already noted that toxin-antitoxin mixtures have been very generally abandoned because of the risk, small as it is, of their dissociation during preparation or storage.

There can be no question that, in the formol toxoid that has so largely displaced them, we have a reagent that is at least as effective (see, for instance, Park and Schroder 1932).

Of the chemical changes involved in the conversion of toxin into toxoid by formalin we know relatively little. It is a natural assumption that the action of formaldehyde on amino-acid groupings is in some way concerned, and it has been stated that a large proportion of these groupings disappear during the preparation of formol toxoid from a toxic broth filtrate (see Kissin and Bronstein 1928, 1930). But Hewitt (1930) has criticized these findings on technical grounds, and states that some 85 per cent. of the amino-nitrogen remains free. He points out, moreover, that the amount of formalin used in the preparation of toxoid—the usual practice is to incubate a toxic filtrate with 0·4 per cent. of formalin for several weeks at 37° C.—is approximately the amount required to combine with all the amino-nitrogen present ; and since only about 15 per cent. is in fact so combined, it would seem that the formalin must have some other action. While not discarding the possibility that such action on amino-nitrogen as occurs may be the essential factor in detoxication, Hewitt suggests as an alternative possibility that the formaldehyde may cause the union of two or more toxin molecules to produce a non-toxic molecule of a higher molecular weight (see also Bunney 1931, Schmidt 1933*a*, *b*, *c*).

The addition of antitoxin to toxoid, giving the toxoid-antitoxin mixture which is extensively used in England, is an empirical attempt to obtain a reagent which induces an effective immunity without giving a troublesome local reaction. It may be that a difference in the rate of absorption, and perhaps a slow dissociation of the compound in the tissues, has an effect on the stimulus provided. In any event there can be no doubt that this form of prophylactic is an effective one. In its refined form of toxoid-antitoxin floccules, in which much of the non-specific serum protein is eliminated, there is general agreement that it combines effectiveness with a minimum of unpleasant local effects (see Glenny and Pope 1927, Swyer 1931, Dudley 1932, Underwood 1934 and others).

The use of alum-precipitated toxoid for active immunization in man followed the demonstration by Glenny (1930) that this reagent was extremely effective in inducing an active immunity in experimental animals (see also Glenny and Barr 1931, and Glenny *et al.* 1931). He suggests that this high efficiency is probably due to delayed absorption of the precipitated toxoid from the site of inoculation, with a consequent prolongation of the antigenic stimulus. These results, combined with those obtained in the use of this reagent in man, have awakened hopes that it may be possible to induce an effective immunity with a single inoculation. The administrative advantages of such a method are obvious. It cannot be said that the experience at present available is sufficient to justify the abandonment of the older methods, and their replacement by a single dose of 1 c.c. of alum-precipitated toxoid. Many of the published reports are favourable, some more so than others, and it seems possible that the one-dose method may become the routine procedure (see Schmidt 1931, Saunders 1932, Graham *et al.* 1933, Havens and Wells 1933, White and Schlageter 1934, Baker and Gill 1934, Keller and Leathers 1934, McGinnes *et al.* 1934, Monroe and Volk 1934, Underwood 1935, Volk 1935, Isabolinski *et al.* 1935, Report 1935) ; but there are records that indicate the wisdom of suspending judgment until we have a far more extensive experience (see Fraser and Halpern 1935). We have already noted that the alum-precipitated toxoid tends to produce a small and quite harmless indurated nodule at the site of inoculation. In persons who are unusually susceptible to toxoid the large single injection may in addition give rise to an extensive and unpleasant local reaction. For this reason it is advisable to do a preliminary Moloney test, particularly in older children and adults. Mention should perhaps be made of the method advocated by Löwenstein (1929) of administering toxoid made into an ointment by inunction. Some favourable results with this method have been recorded ; but more recent reports, taken as a whole, suggest that this method is much less effective than that of subcutaneous injection (see Abt and Feingold 1931, Kegel and Gasul 1931, Seligmann 1931, Nélis 1932, Hassmann 1932, Bürgers 1933). It has also been stated (Lesné *et al.* 1927, Hosmer-Zambelli 1931) that formol toxoid is effective when administered by the intranasal route, but no extensive trial has been made of this method.

The Standardization of Diphtheria Prophylactics.

The flocculation test of Ramon (1922) provides an obvious method of determining the amount of toxoid in any prophylactic, and Glenny, Pope and Waddington (1925) found that the immunizing value of a modified toxin was closely related to its Lf value. It has, indeed, become a common practice to state the dose of toxoid contained in a prophylactic in terms of Lf units, when the actual dose of toxoid is stated at all, which is not often the case. But it would obviously be preferable, were it possible, to measure the actual immunizing potency of all preparations by direct comparison with some arbitrarily selected standard reagent.

The technical differences involved in such a comparison are, however, very great. For the reasons discussed in Chapter XL, a comparison carried out on a small number of animals is quite valueless ; and, in spite of a few reports in a different sense, it is very doubtful whether the accurate standardization of a reagent used for inducing active immunity is as yet within the realm of practical politics.

The relevant regulations in force in Great Britain, under the Therapeutic Substances Act, are as follows :

" Diphtheria Prophylactic shall be submitted to the following tests :

(a) *Tests to determine that the specific toxicity of the toxin used in its preparation has been so reduced that it does not exceed the prescribed maximum.*—Five human doses of the Diphtheria Prophylactic under test shall be injected into each of 5 normal guinea-pigs each weighing 250–350 grammes. This injection must not cause the death of any of the guinea-pigs within 6 days following the injection. If all the guinea-pigs injected survive for 6 days but any of them die within 30 days following the injection from the specific toxæmia, one human dose of the Diphtheria Prophylactic under test shall be injected into each of 5 normal guinea-pigs, each weighing 250–350 grammes. This injection must not cause the death of any of the guinea-pigs within 30 days following the injection.

If a batch of Diphtheria Prophylactic is shown by either of these tests to have a greater toxicity than the maximum hereby indicated, it shall not be issued unless and until the toxicity has been so reduced by further treatment that it does not exceed that maximum.

(b) *Test for potency as an immunizing antigen.*—A quantity of Diphtheria Prophylactic not exceeding five human doses shall be injected on one occasion into each of 10 normal guinea-pigs ; or, alternatively, a quantity of Diphtheria Prophylactic not exceeding one-tenth of a human dose shall be injected into each of 10 normal guinea-pigs on each of two occasions, separated by an interval of not more than 4 weeks. The guinea-pigs shall be tested for immunity to diphtheria toxin, if they have received the single injection hereinbefore prescribed, at a date not later than 6 weeks after injection, and if they have received the two injections hereinbefore prescribed, at a date not later than 3 weeks after the second injection.

The test for immunity may be made by either of the two following methods :

(i) by intracutaneous injection into each guinea-pig of one test-dose of Schick Toxin. If more than 2 out of the 10 guinea-pigs exhibit a positive Schick reaction, the batch of Diphtheria Prophylactic shall be treated as insufficiently potent, and shall not be issued ; or

(ii) by subcutaneous injection into each guinea-pig of five minimal lethal doses of diphtheria toxin. If more than 2 out of the 10 guinea-pigs die as the result of this injection the batch of Diphtheria Prophylactics hall be treated as insufficiently potent, and shall not be issued."

This, it will be noted, is the prescription of limits of toxicity and antigenic efficiency, not standardization in terms of units.

Other Diseases caused by Corynebacteria

Diphtheroid bacilli of various types have frequently been isolated from the sites of pathological conditions in man. They have been cultivated from the conjunctiva in various forms of subacute or chronic conjunctivitis, from the external auditory meatus in cases of ear disease, from the lesions of acne vulgaris, from other lesions of the skin, from the urine in cases of subacute or chronic urethritis, and from lymphatic glands in a variety of conditions, particularly in lymphadenoma. In a few instances, including perhaps acne vulgaris, the evidence suggests that the association is a causative one, but in the vast majority of cases the early claims to have established an ætiological relationship have broken down in the light of subsequent investigations. There is, as yet, no satisfactory evidence that any *Corynebacterium*, other than *C. diphtheriæ*, with the possible exception of *C. acnes*, plays any significant rôle as a pathogenic parasite of man ; though various species form an important constituent of his normal bacterial flora (Andrewes *et al.* 1923, Harris and Wade 1915).

Diphtheroid Infections in Animals.

There are at least two diseases which occur naturally in animals other than man, and are caused by infection with *Corynebacteria*.

Ulcerative Lymphangitis of Horses and Pseudotuberculosis of Sheep.—Both these diseases are the result of infection with *C. ovis*, or, as it is more commonly called, the Preisz-Nocard bacillus. The characters of this organism and the lesions that it produces in experimental animals have been described in Chapter XVI. It may be noted that this organism, unlike *C. diphtheriæ*, is pyogenic and invasive, as well as toxigenic. The exotoxin produced by it differs from the exotoxin of *C. diphtheriæ* both in the character of the lesions produced in experimental animals and in its antigenic relationships. The pathogenesis of the natural disease in horses and sheep seems to be determined mainly by the invasive and pyogenic activities of the causative organism. The part played by the toxin is at present doubtful. It may be noted that pseudotuberculosis of sheep is an important disease, from this stand-point, in certain parts of the world, particularly in Australia (see Bull and Dickinson 1931, 1933, 1935, Dickinson and Bull 1931, Discussion 1934).

Infections caused by C. pyogenes.—This organism has been isolated from suppura-tive pneumonia, suppurative arthritis and other suppurative lesions, in cattle, swine, and occasionally sheep (see p. 339).

Infections caused by C. renale.—This organism appears to give rise to cystitis and pyelitis in cattle (see p. 339).

Pseudotuberculosis of Mice.—This is a natural disease of mice caused by *C. pseudotuberculosis murium*. So far as it is known, no other animal species is susceptible. Since, in this instance, the animal used for experimental purposes has been the natural host, the lesions of the disease have been described in Chapter XVI (p. 340).

REFERENCES

ABEL, R. (1893) *Zbl. Bakt.*, **14**, 756.
ABT, A. F. and FEINGOLD, B. F. (1931) *Amer. J. Dis. Child.*, **41**, 8.
ALI, M. (1934) *J. Egypt. med. Ass.*, **17**, 77.
ALLISON, V. D. (1930) *Brit. J. exp. Path.*, **11**, 244.
ALLISON, V. D. and AYLING, T. H. (1929) *J. Path. Bact.*, **32**, 299.
ANDERSON, J. S., COOPER, K. E., HAPPOLD, F. C., and MCLEOD, J. W. (1933a) *J. Path. Bact.*, **36**, 169; (1933b) *Lancet*, i. 293.
ANDERSON, J. S., HAPPOLD, F. C., MCLEOD, J. W. and THOMSON, J. G. (1931) *J. Path. Bact.*, **34**, 667.
ANDOLZ AQUILAR, F. (1935) *Riv. Igiene Sanit. pubbl.*, June, 529.
ANDREWES, F. W., *et al.* (1923) Monograph on Diphtheria. *Med. res. Coun. Lond.*
ASHBY, A. (1906) *Publ. Hlth.*, **19**, 145.
BAKER, J. N. and GILL, D. G. (1934) *Amer. J. publ. Hlth.*, **24**, 22.
BANZHAF, E. J. (1912–13) *Coll. Stud. Dept. Hlth., N.Y. Cy.*, **7**, 114.
BANZHAF, E. J. and GIBSON, R. B. (1907) *J. biol. Chem.*, **3**, 253; (1908–09) *Coll. Stud. Dept. Hlth., N.Y. Cy.*, **4**, 202.
BARR, M. and GLENNY, A. T. (1931a) *J. Path. Bact.*, **34**, 539; (1931b) *Brit. J. exp. Path.*, **12**, 337.
BEHRING, E. VON. (1913) *Dtsch. med. Wschr.*, **39**, 873.
BEHRING and WERNICKE. (1892) *Z. Hyg. InfektKr.*, **12**, 10.
BENSON, W. T. (1928) *Edin. med. J.* (New Ser.), **35**, 617.
BIE, V. (1922) *Acta med. scand.*, **56**, 537.
BIEBER, W. (1920) *Dtsch. med. Wschr.*, **46**, 1184.
BOECKEL, L. VAN. (1928) *Ann. Inst. Pasteur*, **42**, 1098.
BOLTON, C. (1905) *Lancet*, i. 278.

BRETONNEAU, P. (1826) " Des inflamm. spéc. du tissu muqueux et en partic. de la diph., etc." Crevot, Paris.
BRIEGER, L. and BOER, O. (1896) *Dtsch. med. Wschr.*, **22**, 783.
BRIEGER, L. and COHN, G. (1893) *Z. Hyg. InfektKr.*, **15**, 1.
BRIEGER, L. and EHRLICH, P. (1893) *Z. Hyg. InfektKr.*, **13**, 336.
BULL, L. B. and DICKINSON, C. G. (1931) *Aust. J. exp. biol. med. Sci.*, **8**, 45 ; (1933) *Aust. vet. J.*, **9**, 82 ; (1935) *Ibid.*, **11**, 126.
BUNNEY, W. E. (1931) *J. Immunol.*, **20**, 47.
BÜRGERS. (1933) *Klin. Wschr.*, **12**, 775.
CARTER, H. S. (1933) *J. Hyg., Camb.*, **33**, 542.
CERRUTI, C. (1931) *Alti. III. Congr. naz. Microbiol.*, Milano, 114.
CHRISTISON, M. H. (1934) *Zbl. Bakt.*, **133**, 59.
CLAUBERG, K. W. (1929) *Zbl. Bakt.*, **114**, 539 ; (1931) *Ibid.*, **120**, 324 ; (1933) *Ibid.*, **128**, 153 ; (1935) *Ibid.*, **134**, 271 ; (1936) *Ibid.*, **135**, 529.
DEAN, G. (1908) See " Bacteriology of Diph." Nuttall & Graham-Smith, Camb., p. 513.
DEAN, G. and TODD, C. (1902) *J. Hyg., Camb.*, **2**, 194.
DEICHER, H. and AGULNIK, F. (1927) *Dtsch. med. Wschr.*, **53**, 825.
DICKINSON, C. G. and BULL, L. B. (1931) *Aust. vet. J.*, **8**, 83.
Discussion. (1934) *Proc. roy. Soc. Med.*, **27**, 1335.
DOLD, H. and WEIGMANN, F. (1934) *Z. Hyg. InfektKr.*, **116**, 154.
DREYER, G. (1900) " Exper. Undersogelser over Difterigiftens Toxoner." Copenhagen.
DUDGEON, L. S. (1906) *Brain*, **29**, 227.
DUDLEY, S. F. (1923) *Spec. Rep. Ser. med. Res. Coun., Lond.*, No. 75 ; (1926) *Ibid.*, No. 111 ; (1932) *Quart. J. Med.*, **1**, 213.
DUDLEY, S. F., MAY, P. M. and O'FLYNN, J. A. (1934) *Spec. Rep. Ser. med. Res. Coun., Lond.*, No. 195.
FABER, E. E. (1904) *Jb. Kinderheilk.*, **59**, 620.
FEIERABEND, B. and SCHUBERT, P. (1929) *Z. ImmunForsch.*, **62**, 283 ; (1930) *Trav. Inst. d'Hyg. publ. Tchécosl.*, **1**, 48.
FIBIGER, J. (1898) *Hospitalstidende*, 4. Ser., **6**, 309, 337.
FISCHER, W. and POCKELS, W. (1933) *Med. Klin.*; **29**, 666.
FITZ-GERALD, J. G. (1928) *Ann. Inst. Pasteur*, **42**, 1089.
FITZ-GERALD, J. G., DEFRIES, R. D., and FRASER, N. E. (1932) *Amer. J. publ. Hlth.*, **22**, 25.
FORBES, J. G. (1927) *Spec. Rep. Ser. med. Res. Coun., Lond.*, No. 115 ; (1932) *Bull. Hyg., Lond.*, **7**, 669, 737.
FRASER, D. T. and HALPERN, K. C. (1935) *Canad. publ. Hlth J.*, **26**, 469.
GIBSON, R. B. (1905) *J. biol. Chem.*, **1**, 161.
GLENNY, A. T. (1925) *J. Hyg., Camb.*, **24**, 301 ; (1930) *Brit. med. J.*, ii. 244.
GLENNY, A. T. and ALLEN, K. (1921) *J. Path. Bact.*, **24**, 61.
GLENNY, A. T. and BARR, M. (1931) *J. Path. Bact.*, **34**, 131 ; (1932) *Ibid.*, **35**, 91.
GLENNY, A. T., BARR, M., and STEVENS, M. F. (1932) *J. Path. Bact.*, **35**, 495.
GLENNY, A. T., BUTTLE, G. A. H., and STEVENS, M. F. (1931) *J. Path. Bact.*, **34**, 267.
GLENNY, A. T. and OKELL, C. C. (1924) *J. Path. Bact.*, **27**, 187.
GLENNY, A. T. and POPE, C. G. (1927) *J. Path. Bact.*, **30**, 587.
GLENNY, A. T., POPE, C. G., and WADDINGTON, H. (1925) *J. Path. Bact.*, **28**, 279.
GLENNY, A. T. and WADDINGTON, H. (1928) *J. Path. Bact.*, **31**, 403.
GLENNY, A. T. and WALLACE, U. (1925) *J. Path. Bact.*, **28**, 317.
GODFREY, E. S. (1932) *Amer. J. publ. Hlth.*, **22**, 237.
GRAHAM, A. H., MURPHREE, L. R., and GILL, D. G. (1933) *J. Amer. med. Ass.*, **100**, 1096.
GREENGARD, J. (1934) *Amer. J. Dis. Child.*, **47**, 799.
GUNDEL, M. and LIEBETRUTH, E. (1935) *Z. Hyg. InfektKr.*, **117**, 66.
GUTHRIE, G. C., MARSHALL, B. C., and MOSS, W. L. (1921) *Johns Hopk. Hosp. Bull.*, **31**, 388.
HARRIES, E. H. R. (1930) *Lancet*, i. 802.
HARRIS, W. H. and WADE, H. W. (1915) *J. exp. Med.*, **21**, 493.
HARTLEY, P. (1926) *Brit. J. exp. Path.*, **7**, 55.
HARTLEY, P. and MARTIN, C. J. (1919–20) *Proc. roy. Soc. Med.*, **13** (Sect. Epidem.), 277.
HASENBACH, I. (1935) *Zbl. Bakt.*, **134**, 137.
HASSMANN, K. (1932) *Münch. med. Wschr.*, **79**, 871.
HAVENS, L. C. and WELLS, D. M. (1933) *J. infect. Dis.*, **53**, 138.
HENRY, J. E. (1920) *J. Amer. med. Ass.*, **75**, 1715.
HEWITT, L. F. (1930) *Biochem. J.*, **24**, 983.
HORGAN, F. S. and MARSHALL, A. (1932) *J. Hyg., Camb.*, **32**, 544.
HOSMER-ZAMBELLI, F. (1931) *G. Batt. Immun.*, **6**, 165.
ISABOLINSKI, M. P., KARPATSCHEWSKAJA, B. P. and TOWJANSKAJA, W. F. (1931) *Z. ImmunForsch.*, **73**, 27.
ISABOLINSKI, M. P., JUDENITSCH, W., and LEWZOW, I. (1935) *Z. ImmunForsch.*, **85**, 218.

JAFFÉ. (1920) *Arb. Inst. exp. Ther.* (*Frankfurt am M.*), **11,** 5.
JENSEN, C. (1933*a*) *Acta. path. microbiol., scand.,* **10,** 137 ; (1933*b*) *Ibid., Suppl.,* No. 14.
KAIRIES, A. (1933) *Med. Klin.,* **29,** 709.
KEGEL, A. H. and GASUL, B. M. (1931) *Amer. J. Dis. Child.,* **41,** 45.
KELLER, A. E. and LEATHERS, W. S. (1934) *J. Amer. med. Ass.,* **103,** 478.
KEMKES, B. (1934) *Dtsch. med. Wschr.,* **60,** 1631.
KISSIN, D. and BRONSTEIN, L. (1928) *Z. ImmunForsch.,* **56,** 11 ; (1930) *Ibid.,* **66,** 210.
KLEBS, E. (1883) *Verh. Kongr. inn. Med.,* 139.
KLEIN, E. E. (1889) *Rep. loc. Govt Bd publ. Hlth,* **19,** 143.
KUNDRATITZ, K. (1927) *Wien. klin. Wschr.,* **40,** 933.
LAGRANGE, E. (1926) *Rev. prat. Mal. Pays chauds,* **6,** 277.
LEE, W. W. (1931) *J. prev. Med., Baltimore,* **5,** 211.
LEETE, H. M., McLEOD, J. W., and MORRISON, A. C. (1933) *Lancet,* ii. 1141.
LESNÉ, MARQUEZY, LEMAIRE, and MONMIGNANT. (1927) *C. R. Soc. Biol.,* **96,** 1205.
LEWIS, E. S. (1933) *J. Lab. clin. Med.,* **18,** 413.
LITTERER, W. (1925) *S. med. J.,* **18,** 577.
LOEFFLER, F. (1884) *Mitt. ReichsgesundhAmt.,* **2,** 421.
LÖWENSTEIN, E. (1929) *Dtsch. med. Wschr.,* **55,** 53.
McCLURE, W. B. (1933) *Canad. publ. Hlth J.,* **24,** 546.
McGINNES, G. F., STEBBINS, E. L., and HART, C. (1934) *Amer. J. publ. Hlth.,* **24,** 1141.
McKINNON, N. E., ROSS, M. A., and DEFRIES, R. D. (1931) *Canad. publ. Hlth J.,* **22,** 217.
MAGGIORA-VERGANO, R. (1931) *Boll. Sezione Ital., Soc. Internaz. Microbiologia, Milan,* **3,** 409.
MARTIN, L., LOISEAU, G., and LAFFAILE, A. (1928) *Ann. Inst. Pasteur,* **42,** 1010.
MENTON, J., COOPER, T. V., DUKE, F. W., and FUSSEL, W. H. (1933) *J. Hyg., Camb.,* **33,** 414.
MICHIELS, J. and SCHICK, B. (1913*a*) *Z. Kinderheilk.,* **5,** 255 ; (1913*b*) *Ibid.,* **5,** 349.
MOLONEY, P. J. and FRASER, C. J. (1927) *Amer. J. Publ. Hlth.,* **17,** 1027.
MONROE, J. D. and VOLK, V. K. (1934) *Amer. J. publ. Hlth.,* **24,** 342.
MURRAY, J. F. (1935*a*) *Brit. J. exp. Path.,* **16,** 384 ; (1935*b*) *J. Path. Bact.,* **41,** 97.
NASSAU, E. (1930) *Dtsch. med. Wschr.,* **56,** 741.
NÉLIS, P. (1932) *Rev. Hyg. Police sanit.,* **54,** 729 ; (1934) *Ibid.,* **56,** 206.
NICOLLE, M. (1933) *C. R. Soc. Biol.,* **113,** 1467.
NIKANAROFF, P. J. (1898) *Arch. Ser. Biol., St. Petersb.,* **6,** 57.
OERTEL. (1871) *Dtsch. Arch. klin. Med.,* **8,** 242.
OKELL, C. C., EAGLETON, A. J., and O'BRIEN, R. A. (1924) *Lancet,* i. 800.
PAGANI-CESA, A. (1931) *Terapia,* **20,** 289.
PARISH, H. J. (1936) *Proc. R. Soc. Med.,* **29,** 481.
PARISH, H. J. and OKELL, C. C. (1928) *Lancet,* ii. 322.
PARISH, H. J., WHATLEY, E. E., and O'BRIEN, R. A. (1932*a*) *J. Path. Bact.,* **35,** 653 ; (1932*b*) *Brit. med. J.,* ii. 915.
PARK, W. H. (1913) *Amer. J. Obstet. Gynaec.,* **68,** 1213 ; (1918) *N.Y. med. J.,* **108,** 221 ; (1921) *J. Amer. med. Ass.,* **76,** 109 ; (1922) *Ibid.,* **79,** 1584.
PARK, W. H. and SCHRODER, M. C. (1932) *Amer. J. publ. Hlth.,* **22,** 7.
PARK, W. H. and ZINGHER, A. (1915) *J. Amer. med. Ass.,* **65,** 2216 ; (1916) *Amer. J. publ. Hlth.,* **6,** 431.
PIAZECKA-ZEYLAND, E. (1933) *Ann. Inst. Pasteur,* **50,** 754.
PICK, E. P. (1902) *Beitr. chem. Physiol. Path.,* **1,** 351.
POPE, C. C. (1927) *J. Path. Bact.,* **30,** 301.
POVITSKY, O. R., EISNER, M. and JACKSON, E. (1933) *J. infect. Dis.,* **52,** 246.
PRAUSNITZ, C. (1929) Mem. on Standardization of Therap. Sera, etc. League of Nations Hlth. Organization. Geneva.
PROGULSKI, S. and REDLICH, F. (1927) *Wien. klin. Wschr.,* **40,** 284.
RAMON, G. (1922) *C. R. Soc. Biol.,* **86,** 661, 711, 813 ; (1924) *Ann. Inst. Pasteur,* **38,** 1 ; (1926) *Arch. Inst. Pasteur Algér.,* **4,** 61.
RAMON, G. and ERBER, B. (1934) *C.R. Soc. Biol.,* **116,** 726.
RAMON, G. and DEBRÉ, R., with MOZER, M. and G., and PICHOT, G. (1930) *Ann. Inst. Pasteur,* **45,** 326 ; (1931) *Amer. J. Dis. Child.,* **41,** 1.
RAY, H. H. (1931) *Amer. J. med. Sci.,* **182,** 251.
Report. (1923) *Biological Standardization Comm. League of Nations* ; (1931) *Ibid.* ; (1935) *Amer. J. publ. Hlth.,* **25,** 712.
ROBINSON, D. T. (1934) *J. Path. Bact.,* **39,** 551.
ROBINSON, D. T. and MARSHALL, F. N. (1934) *J. Path. Bact.,* **38,** 73 ; (1935) *Lancet,* ii. 441.
ROBINSON, E. S. and WHITE, B. (1928) *J. Immunol.,* **15,** 381.
RÖMER, P. H. (1909) *Z. ImmunForsch.,* **3,** 208.
ROUX, E. and YERSIN, A. (1888) *Ann. Inst. Pasteur,* **2,** 629.
SAUNDERS, J. C. (1932) *Lancet,* ii. 1047.
SAVAGE, W. G. (1919–20) *J. Hyg., Camb.,* **18,** 448.

Schick, B. (1913) Münch. med. Wschr., **60**, 2608.
Schiff, F. and Werber, M. (1935) Dtsch. med. Wschr., **60**, 2608.
Schmidt, S. (1931) C. R. Soc. Biol., **107**, 330 ; (1933a) Z. ImmunForsch., **78**, 27 ; (1933b) Ibid., **78**, 323 ; (1933c) Ibid., **78**, 339.
Seligmann, E. (1931) Dtsch. med. Wschr., **57**, 1573.
Smyth, F. G. A. (1934) J. R. Army med. Cps, **62**, 391.
Stallybrass, C. O. (1936) Proc. R. Soc. Med., **29**, 487.
Swyer, R. (1931) Lancet, i. 632.
Trendelenburg. (1869) Arch. klin. Chir., **10**, 720.
Underwood, E. A. (1934) Lancet, i. 678 ; (1935) Ibid., i. 137.
Volk, V. K. (1935) Amer. J. publ. Hlth., **25**, 430.
Waldhecker, M. (1934) Z. Hyg. InfektKr., **116**, 337.
Watson, A. F. and Langstaff, E. (1926) Biochem. J., **20**, 763.
Wergmann, F. and Degn, J. (1932) Zbl. Bakt., **125**, 374.
White, J. L. and Schlageter, E. A. (1934) J. Amer. med. Ass., **102**, 915.
Whitley, O. R. (1935) J. Lab. clin. Med., **20**, 1024.
Woods, H. M. (1928) J. Hyg., Camb., **28**, 147.
Zingher, A. (1921) Arch. Pediat., **38**, 336 ; (1922) J. Amer. med. Ass., **78**, 1945.

CHAPTER LIX

GLANDERS AND MELIOIDOSIS

GLANDERS

NUMEROUS investigators during the nineteenth century brought evidence to show that glanders was infectious ; and that the disease in man was the same as that in the horse. The causative agent, however, was not isolated till 1882, when Loeffler and Schütz (Loeffler 1886) succeeded in cultivating *Pf. mallei* from a horse dying of acute glanders. They isolated it in pure culture from the liver and spleen, and produced characteristic lesions in the guinea-pig, rabbit, and field mouse by injection of the bacilli. The organisms were demonstrated histologically in the lesions, and isolated in pure culture.

Epidemiology in Animals.—Glanders is primarily a disease of equine animals. Pigs and cattle are absolutely resistant. Goats, sheep, dogs, and cats sometimes contract the disease naturally ; it has also occurred in zoological gardens amongst carnivora, such as lions and tigers, which have been fed on infected horse-flesh.

There are two clinical types of the disease in horses and asses—glanders and farcy. In **glanders,** which may be acute or chronic, the lungs are almost invariably affected. Rounded, greyish, firm nodules, about ½ to 1 cm. in diameter, appear in small numbers—often not more than a dozen or so. They are embedded in the lung tissue, from which they are not easy to enucleate. When recent they have a dirty white centre and a dark red, or sometimes yellow, gelatinous periphery ; the central part consists of thick pus. In older nodules the greyish central zone is surrounded by dryish crumbling material, or by a fibrous capsule. In acute cases there may be an actual pneumonic infiltration of the lung. Histologically the young lesions consist of polymorphonuclear cells, surrounded by a zone of congestion. It is stated that, in the older nodules, there is frequently a zone of epithelioid and giant cells around the central necrotic area, and surrounding the whole there is a layer of fibrous tissue. Occasionally calcification may occur (Riegler 1905, Reinhardt 1919). Glanders may invade other organs as well as the lungs, particularly the nasal mucosa and trachea ; nodules first appear, which later ulcerate and discharge a greenish-yellow serous fluid, sometimes streaked with blood (Hutyra and Marek 1926). Subcutaneous abscesses are not uncommon ; and in the acute disease nodules are distributed throughout the spleen, liver, and other organs.

In the mule glanders is almost invariably acute, death occurring in 3 or 4 weeks (Mason 1918).

Farcy may result from direct infection of the skin, or it may be a secondary manifestation of glanders. Swellings appear in the skin or subcutaneous tissues, particularly of the extremities and flanks, which break down and ulcerate. The lymphatic vessels leading from these swellings become firm and enlarged, standing out beneath the skin a hard cords—farcy pipes. These can be traced to the lymphatic glands, which likewise become prominent—farcy buds. Along the course of the lymphatic vessels fresh swellings may appear, so that there may be a chain of nodules connected by firm cords, looking not unlike a rosary.

Incidence.—Glanders is widespread throughout Europe, but of recent years, owing to precautionary measures, it has steadily diminished in most countries. It is still prevalent, however, in Russia, where as many as 4 per cent. of the horses are said to be infected (Hutyra and Marek 1926). The disease occurs in Asia, Africa, and America ; Australia has so far remained free. In Great Britain it was very common previous to the passing of the Glanders or Farcy Order in 1907 ; since then it has decreased, so that now no more than occasional sporadic cases are reported (Table CVII).

TABLE CVII

PREVALENCE OF GLANDERS AND FARCY IN GREAT BRITAIN.

Year	No. of Outbreaks.	Horses Attacked.	Year.	No. of Outbreaks.	Horses Attacked.
1893 . .	1,381	2,133	1910 . .	351	1,014 [1]
1894 . .	965	1,437	1911 . .	209	504 [1]
1895 . .	964	1,594	1912 . .	172	315 [1]
1896 . .	817	1,294	1913 . .	162	438 [1]
1897 . .	900	1,629	1914 . .	97	286 [1]
1898 . .	748	1,385	1915 . .	49	85 [1]
1899 . .	853	1,472	1916 . .	46	117 [1]
1900 . .	1,119	1,858	1917 . .	25	63 [1]
1901 . .	1,347	2,370	1918 . .	34	98 [1]
1902 . .	1,155	2,040	1919 . .	25	61 [1]
1903 . .	1,456	2,499	1920 . .	15	22 [1]
1904 . .	1,529	2,658	1921 . .	11	45 [1]
1905 . .	1,214	2,068	1922 . .	4	4 [1]
1906 . .	1,066	2,012	1923 . .	9	16 [1]
1907 . .	854	1,921	1924 . .	3	4 [1]
1908 . .	789	2,433 [1]	1925 . .	2	2 [1]
1909 . .	533	1,753 [1]			

[1] Includes horses that reacted to the mallein test, and on post-mortem examination showed glanders lesions.

Both the mule and the ass are very susceptible to glanders, and in them the disease generally takes an acute form. In spite of the high susceptibility of asses, however, these animals do not appear to be as frequently affected as horses and mules. Thus, during the War, Mason (1918) stated that the incidence of glanders in Cairo and Alexandria was approximately 1 in every 4 horses and mules, but only 1 in every 100 asses.

In considering the incidence of glanders, it must be remembered that in many respects the disease resembles tuberculosis. For every clinical case there are a number of latent cases, revealed only by the mallein test or one of the numerous other reactions that are now employed in diagnosis. Occult glanders, in fact, is the rule, not the exception (M'Fadyean 1905). Months may elapse between infection and the onset of symptoms ; and in many animals it would appear that the disease may lie permanently dormant, or undergo spontaneous cure. As with most diseases affecting the respiratory tract, glanders is commonest in cities and in places where large numbers of animals are kept in close contact. During the first 5 years of this century, for example, about 75 per cent. of all cases reported in Great Britain occurred in London (M'Fadyean 1905). The disease used to be especially prevalent in the large studs of horses owned by the Municipal Omnibus Companies ; once the infection had been introduced, it spread rapidly throughout the stud. Apart from clinical cases there was an even larger number of carriers, which served to propagate the disease and to render its control extremely difficult.

Mode of Infection.—The mode of infection is not at all clear. Though primary disease of the lung appears to be very common, the belief has grown up that infection does not occur by the respiratory tract. It is difficult to gather from the literature the real incidence of primary glanders of the lung. There are many other diseases that give rise to lesions closely resembling the glanders nodule (Riegler 1905, Joest 1915) ; and our impression is that in the past many true cases of glanders have been classified under other headings and *vice versa*. Experimentally, most attempts to produce chronic pulmonary glanders *via* the respiratory tract have failed ; intratracheal and intranasal injection of the bacilli have resulted in the acute disease. Most workers have therefore concluded that infection does not ordinarily occur by this route. On the other hand, typical pulmonary lesions have followed infection by the mouth (M'Fadyean 1904, Bonome 1906). In animals infected in this way, however, it is usual to find some degree of inflammatory reaction in the intestinal mucosa and submucosa, together with hyperplasia and necrosis of the mesenteric glands. As these lesions are uncommon in horses dying naturally, it is by no means certain that the disease set up in this way corresponds to that occurring spontaneously. Bonome (1906) tries to explain the discrepancy by assuming that the intestinal and mesenteric glandular lesions rapidly retrogress so that in about 2 months only the pulmonary lesions are apparent.

Without discussing this question any further, we may point to the close analogy with tuberculosis, in which much the same arguments have been advanced for and against the respiratory route of infection (see Chapter LVI). Whether the infectious material in glanders reaches the lungs by direct inspiration, by absorption through the pharyngeal mucosa, or by passage through the intestine and mesenteric glands, it is impossible to say with certainty. The important point is that the nasal and pulmonary discharges, and sometimes the urine and fæces, of animals suffering from glanders are infectious, and that any other susceptible animal coming into contact directly or indirectly with these discharges is liable to contract the disease.

Reproduction of the Disease.—Farcy may be transmitted by subcutaneous inoculation. Under natural conditions, it is probable that some cases occur by direct infection of the skin—as in grooming—while others are really metastatic infections of pulmonary origin. In nearly every case of farcy, glanders nodules are present in the lungs at necropsy (M'Fadyean 1904).

Glanders may be reproduced in horses, asses, and mules by feeding with cultures of the bacillus, and by subcutaneous inoculation. Sheep and goats are easily infected, but cows and pigs are absolutely resistant. Of laboratory animals the guinea-pig and the field mouse (*Arvicola arvalis*) are the most susceptible to experimental inoculation ; rabbits and dogs are less so ; rats, birds, and perhaps white mice, are comparatively resistant. (See Chapter XVIII.)

Epidemiology in Man.—Glanders in man is uncommon. Robins in 1906 succeeded in collecting reports of 156 cases. It is a protean disease, and probably many real cases that occur are diagnosed wrongly. It may be acute or chronic, and it may be localized chiefly in the respiratory organs, or in the skin and subcutaneous tissues. In acute glanders there is generally fever, a muco-purulent discharge from the nose, and a degree of prostration out of all proportion to the clinical signs (Bernstein and Carling 1909) ; a generalized pustular eruption is very frequent. Death invariably occurs in a week or 10 days. In the chronic disease there may be coryza ; there may be multiple subcutaneous and intramuscular abscesses, often associated with enlargement of the lymphatic glands and vessels ; nodules may form in the mucosa of the respiratory and alimentary tracts, and may break down and ulcerate ; necrotic foci may appear in the bones, and nodular lesions in the viscera. The disease may remain active for weeks, months, or even years ; it is usually but not invariably fatal. Sometimes after apparent recovery the disease may break out again ; latent periods up to 10 years have been observed (Bernstein and Carling 1909). (For an account of a case in a veterinary surgeon see Gaiger 1913, 1916.)

The disease attacks chiefly those who come into close contact with horses such as ostlers, grooms, and coachmen. Infection results most frequently from contamination of a scratch or wound with a glanderous discharge, but primary infection of the nasal mucosa may occur. Several cases of glanders have been reported in laboratory workers ; indeed, probably no organism, with the possible exception of *Br. tularensis*, is so dangerous to work with as the glanders bacillus. In the Czernowitz laboratory the disease broke out amongst several members of the staff a few days after the breaking of a centrifuge tube. Numerous other laboratory infections are on record (Bernstein and Carling 1909). When one considers the infectivity of the organism in artificial culture, it is surprising that the disease is not more common amongst those who come into contact with glandered animals. M'Fadyean stated in 1905 that, during the past 12 years, a single firm of knackers in London had dealt with from 800 to 2,000 diseased carcasses ; yet not a single case of glanders had occurred amongst the men. There are several statements in the literature suggesting that the virulence of the organism is subject to rapid variation (Gamaléia 1890, Motta 1906, Bernstein and Carling 1909, Dudgeon *et al.* 1918). It may be that the bacilli in chronic lesions of the horse are relatively avirulent to man, in much the same way as they are to the guinea-pig. If this is so, they may be incapable of giving rise to clinical disease. In this connection it may be noted that Babes, while making autopsies on persons who had come into contact with horses and who had died from diseases other than glanders, observed the presence of encapsulated glanders nodules in the internal organs, especially the lungs. This suggests that occult glanders may occur in man as well as in the horse (M'Fadyean 1905). The incubation period varies from a few hours to several weeks.

Diagnosis.

In acute glanders or farcy a microscopical examination should be made of the pus or discharge. Bacilli are fairly numerous in fresh lesions, but may be difficult to find in older ones. Their demonstration in sections of the tissues is often very difficult, and special staining methods have usually to be adopted ; the bacilli are more easy to find in smears. Cultures should be put up on agar, glycerine agar, and potato. If the material is grossly contaminated, it is best to inject it sub-cutaneously into a guinea-pig, recover the bacillus from the enlarged glands, and inject it intraperitoneally in pure culture into fresh guinea-pigs. In any case the culture should be tested for virulence, and the characteristic Straus re-action noted (see p. 363). Not all strains of *Pf. mallei* are virulent on isolation ; sometimes two or three passages have to be made before the typical disease develops (Dudgeon *et al.* 1918). As a rule material from the acute disease in horses proves virulent, but from the chronic disease it is generally avirulent.

The Straus reaction is not diagnostic of glanders ; swelling of the testicles and periorchitis may occur after injection of guinea-pigs with organisms of the *Brucella* group, with *Actinobacillus lignieresi*, with Preisz-Nocard's *C. ovis*, with *Pf. whitmori*, and with a few other species less commonly met with.

Mallein Test.—This is used for the diagnosis of latent or chronic glanders in horses. Mallein is prepared by growing the glanders bacillus in flasks of peptone veal broth containing 4 per cent. of glycerol. After 15 to 20 days' incubation the cultures are sterilized in the autoclave, concentrated to one-tenth of their volume in a water bath, and filtered through paper (Nocard 1895). The resultant product is a syrupy brown liquid ; before injection, this crude mallein has to be diluted about 1/10 with sterile water or 0·5 per cent. phenolized saline. The *subcutaneous test* is made by injecting 2·5 c.c. of the diluted mallein under the skin of the neck. Sometimes mallein is prepared by simple filtration, without concentration, of a broth culture ; in this case 1 c.c. is used for injection. A positive reaction is characterized by (1) a local swelling, congestion, and œdema, often very extensive and painful, appearing some hours after the inoculation, increasing for 30 to 36 hours, and lasting for a week or more ; it never suppurates ; (2) a systemic disturbance, with a rise of temperature, dullness, depression, shivering, anorexia and other symptoms of illness ; the temperature rises about the 8th hour, reaches its maximum from the 10th to the 18th hour, and subsides after 36 or 48 hours. The interpretation of the reaction is largely a matter of experience. Generally speaking, a marked local reaction with a rise of temperature of 2° C. or over can be considered positive. A rise of only 1° to 2° C. may be accounted positive if the local reaction is typical ; otherwise it should be considered doubtful. If the rise of temperature is less than 1·0° C., the reaction is negative. A rapid rise of temperature, however high, if succeeded by an equally rapid fall, is of no importance. Old horses may fail to react. In doubtful cases the test should be repeated after 4 weeks. In normal horses the injection of mallein causes a very slight reaction ; the small local œdematous tumour disappears in 24 to 30 hours.

A definitely positive reaction, even in the absence of clinical disease, may be taken as proof that the horse is glandered. Extensive use of the reaction has shown that, judged by post-mortem findings, a positive result is correct in about 92 per cent., a negative in 96 per cent. of cases. (For interpretation of the reaction see Babes 1891, M'Fadyean 1893, Bonome 1894, Foth 1894*a*, *b*, Report 1915, Mason 1918, Hutyra and Marek 1926.)

The subcutaneous reaction is inapplicable to horses suffering from fever. It has also the great disadvantage that it is followed by the appearance of antibodies in the blood ; hence serological tests cannot be used in horses that have been injected with mallein. For these reasons it has largely been abandoned, and replaced by the cutaneous and the conjunctival tests. In the *conjunctival mallein test* pure mallein is rubbed on the inner surfaces of the lids with a soft paint brush. In a positive case the reaction appears 4 to 6 hours later, reaches a maximum in 8 to 12 hours, and disappears gradually after 24 to 48 hours. There is a secretion of purulent yellow or greenish-yellow material at the inner canthus ; this over-flows and runs down the face. The palpebral conjunctiva is red and swollen. In 50–75 per cent. of the cases a rise of temperature occurs to over 38·5° C. (Rein-hardt 1919). In a negative reaction the secretion, if any, is serous or mucoid. The test is contra-indicated in horses suffering from conjunctivitis, and from other diseases in which conjunctivitis may develop spontaneously. Horses recently infected, within 4 to 20 days, do not react ; nor do horses with advanced glanders, especially if weak or exhausted. On the other hand, the reaction may be positive in horses that have recovered from the disease. In doubtful cases the test may be repeated immediately.

The *cutaneous mallein test* is not used much ; but it is of real value, especially when the conjunctival test is inadvisable or yields a doubtful result. Mallein is rubbed into the shaved and scarified skin on the side of the neck. In a positive reaction there is a marked local swelling. A modification of this method, known as the *intradermal palpebral test*, in which the mallein is injected into the cutaneous surface of the eyelid, was employed during the War. In a positive reaction a well-marked sensitive œdema of the eyelid is observed about the 9th or 10th hour after injection, accompanied by conjunctival congestion, a mucous discharge from the eye, and closure of the eyelids. The reaction reaches its height between the 24th and 36th hours, and may persist for 3 or 4 days. In normal animals there may be very slight swelling of the eyelid 2 to 6 hours after injection, disappearing about the 12th hour.

Serological Tests.—The **complement-fixation test** is the most reliable laboratory test for glanders. According to Reinhardt (1919) it gives false positives in 4 per cent. of healthy horses, and false negatives in 2 per cent. of glandered horses. According to Poppe (1919), who reports on 2,669 animals, it gave incorrect results in 0·97 per cent. of cases in which glanders was present, and in 2·21 per cent. of cases in which it was absent. It is stated to be sometimes positive in horses suffering from strangles, horse influenza, or petechial fever, and in emaciated animals not suffering from glanders. It may also be positive in normal donkeys, mules, and pregnant mares.

The **agglutination reaction** is less reliable. Though various workers (see Bourges and Méry 1898, Collins 1908, Nevermann 1910) have regarded a titre of 1/1000–1/2000 as practically diagnostic of glanders, it is quite clear that the serum of perfectly normal horses frequently reacts to this level (see Wilson 1934). Much depends on the agglutinability of the strain used and the technique adopted. Without adequate standardization of these factors, the interpretation of the results of different workers is impossible. As in other diseases, the higher the titre, the greater is its significance. The agglutination test, however, should never be relied on exclusively for diagnosis. Repeated tests are of value ; if, in a series of tests at intervals of several weeks, the titre remains the same, it is unlikely that the animal is glandered.

The **precipitin reaction** is not trustworthy enough for practical diagnosis, prob-ably because of the presence of non-specific nucleo-protein substances in the organisms. Sakamoto (1930) has, however, extracted a soluble polysaccharide from cultures of *Pf. mallei*, with which a specific precipitation test is said to be obtainable.

A number of other tests have obtained prominence during recent years, such as the conglutination reaction, and the combined complement-fixation and hæmagglutination reaction or so-called K.H. reaction of Pfeiler and Scheffler (see Poppe 1919). These reactions are said to be of particular value in the diagnosis of the disease in mules, asses, and pregnant mares, the blood of which not infrequently has a marked anticomplementary action.

It will be realized that a large number of tests are available for the diagnosis of glanders. In practice it is unwise to rely exclusively on any one alone. For ordinary routine work the best combination is the complement-fixation and the conjunctival mallein tests. If these give a doubtful result, the other tests may be employed.

In man the mallein test has been used so seldom that it is difficult to gain any idea of its value. Sabolotny (1926) reports a case in which it was positive. The agglutination test is not very reliable, as the serum of normal persons may have a titre up to 1/100. In glanders it may rise to as high as 1/2000 (Galtier 1881, Collins 1908, Dudgeon *et al.* 1918) ; but on the other hand it may be extremely low. Several cases have been reported in which no agglutination occurred at all, or only up to 1/60 (Gabriélidès and Remlinger 1902, Bernstein and Carling 1909). The complement-fixation reaction is sometimes of value (Watson 1923, Sabolotny 1926). A leucocytosis is often present in acute glanders (Gabriélidès and Remlinger 1902, Bernstein and Carling 1909).

Immunity and Prophylaxis.

There is a considerable amount of evidence to show that horses may recover spontaneously from glanders (Nocard 1900). Only a small proportion of apparently healthy horses that give a positive mallein reaction subsequently develop clinical signs of the disease (M'Faydean 1900). If they are carefully observed, many of them are found to lose their reaction to mallein. It must be noted, however, that the disappearance of the mallein reaction is no proof of cure (M'Fadyean 1901, Bonome 1906). Spontaneous recovery from glanders does not leave the animals with a high degree of immunity. If exposed to natural infection or experimentally inoculated with glanders material, they not infrequently again contract the disease (M'Fadyean 1900, Nocard 1900, Mohler and Eichhorn 1914).

Numerous attempts have been made to produce an active immunity to glanders. Using graded doses of *morvine*—a substance similar to mallein—Babes (1892) stated that he was able to immunize guinea-pigs. Nicolle (1906) likewise claimed to have immunized guinea-pigs (1) by repeated doses of dead bacilli ; (2) by repeated injection of living organisms in very small doses ; (3) by a single injection of living organisms in a non-fatal dose. But attempts to render horses immune by vaccination or injections of mallein have not been successful (M'Fadyean 1901). Mohler and Eichhorn (1914) vaccinated horses with 3 or 4 doses of dried bacilli ; these animals developed agglutinins and complement-fixing bodies, but were still susceptible to natural and experimental infection with glanders.

Mallein has been tried in the curative treatment of horses and of man ; some authors report promising results (Babes, V. 1891, Babes, A. 1892, Pilavios 1893, Bonome 1894), but the mass of evidence does not support their conclusions. It must be remembered that both in horses and in man the disease may retrogress spontaneously, so that it is difficult to estimate the value of any curative treatment.

Serum therapy has been tried in human glanders (Watson 1923), but the number of cases treated is too small to allow of any conclusions.

For the control of glanders in horses the best results have followed the procedure laid down in the Glanders or Farcy Order of 1907. Briefly this provides that every animal with clinical evidence of glanders, and every animal giving a positive mallein test, shall be regarded as a diseased animal, and shall be slaughtered. The diseased carcass shall be buried or suitably destroyed, and thorough disinfection of the infected premises shall be carried out. Contacts shall be tested by mallein, and all positive reactors shall be slaughtered. Since the coming into force of this order in 1908, glanders in Great Britain has diminished steadily, till now it may be considered as completely eradicated (see Table CVII, p. 1108.)

MELIOIDOSIS

The first descriptions of this glanders-like disease in man were given by Whitmore and Krishnaswami in 1912, and Whitmore in 1913, who encountered it at Rangoon. Clinically it appeared to be a septicæmia or pyæmia ; post mortem, suppurating or caseous deposits were found in the viscera. A slender, motile, Gram-negative bacillus was isolated from the lesions, which reproduced the characteristic disease in guinea-pigs. The disease has been named Melioidosis by Stanton and Fletcher (1921, 1925) and the causative organism *B. whitmori (Pfeifferella whitmori)*. Melioidosis has been reported not only from Burma and British Malaya, but also from Cochin China, Ceylon, and Tonkin (see Denny and Nicholls 1927, Pons 1927, Pons and Advier 1927, Mesnard, Joyeux, and Gaulene 1929, Souchard and Ragiot 1933, Roton 1933). In their monograph published in 1932 Stanton and Fletcher were able to collect records of 83 cases.

In man the clinical course is brief, death generally occurring within 3 or 4 weeks of the onset of symptoms. At autopsy the commonest findings are localized areas of consolidation in the lungs, composed of aggregations of small suppurating foci, and abscesses or caseous deposits of varying size in the spleen, liver, and sometimes kidneys. In one case in a European recorded by Stanton, Fletcher, and Kanagarayer (1925), the only lesions were two abscesses in the liver with walls consisting of shaggy necrotic material, resembling those found in amœbic dysentery. In several cases the lesions have been confined to the lungs. Histologically they are indistinguishable from those of glanders.

The disease appears to be primarily one of *rodents*. At Kuala Lumpur in the Federated Malay States, Stanton and Fletcher (1925) stated that it had been present first epidemically and later in a sporadic form amongst their stock of laboratory animals during the past 12 years. The earliest symptom in rabbits and guinea-pigs is a white milky discharge from the eyes and nose ; later dyspnœa occurs, followed by death. At post-mortem in acute cases, there are few signs except yellow miliary nodules on the nasal septum. When the disease has lasted for some time, minute caseous nodules of focal necrosis are found in the lungs, spleen, and sometimes in the liver.

Cases of natural infection have been recorded in wild rats, one case in a cat, and one in a horse. Rodents can be infected experimentally by feeding and by injection of the bacilli into the tissues. (See Chapter XVIII.)

How man becomes infected is not clear. Some cases have undoubtedly followed contamination of the skin, as in morphia addicts, but Stanton and Fletcher (1932) regard the alimentary tract as the most probable route by which the organisms usually gain access to the body.

Diagnosis of the disease in man during life is not always easy. The organisms can be cultivated from the blood, from abscesses and sinuses, superficial pustules, and the urine. Splenic or hepatic puncture may be useful for obtaining infective material. In one case Martin (1931) isolated the organism from the cerebrospinal fluid. Suspected material should be cultivated on glycerol agar and inoculated into guinea-pigs. One patient tested gave a positive mallein reaction. Agglutination is not of much value, partly because most patients die before agglutinins have had time to develop, and partly because normal agglutinins to 1/80 or over are sometimes present in healthy persons. At autopsy the organisms can be readily isolated from the visceral lesions. (For general review of the disease see Stanton and Fletcher 1932, de Moor *et al.* 1932, Souchard 1932, Couture 1935.)

REFERENCES

BABES, A. (1892) *Arch. Méd. exp.*, **4**, 450.
BABES, V. (1891) *Arch. Méd. exp.*, **3**, 619.
BERNSTEIN, J. M. and CARLING, E. R. (1909) *Brit. med. J.*, i. 319.
BONOME, A. (1894) *Dtsch. med. Wschr.*, **20**, 703, 725, 744 ; (1906) *Zbl. Bakt.*, **38**, 97.
BOURGES and MÉRY. (1898) *C. R. Soc. Biol.*, **5**, 165.
COLLINS, K. R. (1908) *J. infect. Dis.*, **5**, 401.
COUTURE, E. (1935) *Rev. Hyg.*, **57**, 190.
DENNY, C. R. and NICHOLLS, L. (1927) *Ceylon J. Sci., D.*, **2**, 37.
DUDGEON, L. S., SYMONDS, S. L., and WILKIN, A. (1918) *J. comp. Path.*, **31**, 43.
FOTH. (1894*a*) *Zbl. Bakt.*, **16**, 508 ; (1894*b*) *Ibid.*, **16**, 550.
GABRIÉLIDÈS and REMLINGER. (1902) *C. R. Soc. Biol.*, **54**, 1147.
GAIGER, S. H. (1913) *J. comp. Path.*, **26**, 223 ; (1916) *Ibid.*, **29**, 26.
GALTIER, V. (1881) *C. R. Acad. Sci.*, **92**, 303.
GAMALÉIA, N. (1890) *Ann. Inst. Pasteur*, **4**, 103.
HUTYRA, F. and MAREK, J. (1926) " Special Pathology and Therapeutics of the Diseases of Domestic Animals." 3rd Amer. edit. Chicago and London.
JOEST. (1915) *Z. InfektKr. Haustiere*, **16**, 239.
LOEFFLER. (1886) *Arb. ReichsgesundhAmt.*, **1**, 141.
M'FADYEAN, J. (1893) *J. comp. Path.*, **6**, 36 ; (1900) *Ibid.*, **13**, 55 ; (1901) *Ibid.*, **14**, 265 ; (1904) *Ibid.*, **17**, 295 ; (1905) *Ibid.*, **18**, 23.
MARTIN, P. H. (1931) See Stanton and Fletcher (1932).
MASON, F. E. (1918) *J. comp. Path.*, **31**, 58.
MESNARD, J., JOYEUX, B., and GAULENE, M. (1929) *Bull. Soc. méd.-chir. Indochine*, **7**, 32.
MOHLER and EICHHORN. (1914) *J. comp. Path.*, **27**, 183.
MOOR, C. E. DE, SOEKARNEN, and WALLE, N. V. D. (1932) *Geneesk. Tijdschr. Ned.-Ind.*, **24**, 1618.
MOTTA, C. (1906) *Zbl. Bakt., Ref.* **38**, 414.
NEVERMANN. (1910) *J. comp. Path.*, **23**, 62.
NICOLLE. (1906) *Ann. Inst. Pasteur*, **20**, 625, 698, 801.
NOCARD, E. (1895) *J. comp. Path.*, **8**, 227 ; (1900) *Ibid.*, **13**, 80.
PILAVIOS. (1893) *J. comp. Path.*, **6**, 187.
PONS, R. (1927) *Ann. Inst. Pasteur*, **41**, 1338.
PONS, R. and ADVIER, M. (1927) *J. Hyg., Camb.*, **26**, 28.
POPPE. (1919) *Berl. tierärztl. Wschr.*, **35**, 173.
REINHARDT, R. (1919) *Berl. tierärztl. Wschr.*, **35**, 453, 465.
Report. (1915) *Ann. Rep. Chief vet. Offr Bd Agric. Fish.*, for year 1914.
RIEGLER, M. (1905) *J. comp. Path.*, **18**, 277.
ROBINS, G. D. (1906) *Stud. R. Victoria Hosp., Montreal*, **2**, No. 1.
ROTON. (1933) *Bull. Soc. méd.-chir. Indochine*, **11**, 7.
SABOLOTNY, S. S. (1926) *Zbl. Bakt.*, **97**, 168.
SAKAMOTO, K. (1930) *J. Immunol.*, **18**, 331.
SOUCHARD, L. (1932) *Arch. Inst. Pasteur Indochine*, No. 16, 193.
SOUCHARD and RAGIOT. (1933) *Bull. Soc. Path. exot.*, **26**, 567.
STANTON, A. T. and FLETCHER, W. (1921) *Trans. 4th Congr. Far East Ass. trop. Med.*, **2**, 196 ; (1925) *J. Hyg., Camb.*, **23**, 347 ; (1932) *Studies Inst. med. Res., F.M.S.*, No. 21.
STANTON, A. T., FLETCHER, W., and KANAGARAYER, K. (1925) *J. Hyg., Camb.*, **23**, 268.
WATSON, E. A. (1923) *J. Amer. med. vet. Ass.*, **64**, 146.
WHITMORE, A. (1913) *J. Hyg., Camb.*, **13**, 1.
WHITMORE, A. and KRISHNASWAMI, C. S. (1912) *Indian med. Gaz.*, **47**, 262.
WILSON, G. S. (1934) *J. Hyg., Camb.*, **34**, 361.

CHAPTER LX

CHOLERA

HISTORY.—Though cholera has been endemic in India for centuries, there is no record of its spread to the rest of the world previous to 1817 (Kirchner 1906). Between 1817 and 1823 it invaded many parts of Asia. The second pandemic, 1826–37, was more widespread. Starting in India, it spread to Russia in 1829, and thence to Poland, Germany, Austria, Sweden, and England. Throughout the years 1832–33 the whole of Europe was ravaged. Four thousand deaths occurred in London alone, and 7,000 in Paris. Canada and New York were infected by Irish immigrants fleeing from their native country. The population of Cuba was decimated, and there was a heavy toll of life in Mexico. The third pandemic, 1846–62, again invaded Europe and America. In 1854 the number of deaths in England was 20,000, in Italy 24,000, and in France 140,000. America was infected by way of New Orleans in 1848 ; thence the disease spread up the Mississippi valley and reached California. In the fourth pandemic, 1864–75, the disease prevailed widely over Asia, Africa, Europe, and America. The fifth pandemic, 1883–96, spread over Egypt, Asia Minor, and Russia ; there was a severe outbreak at Hamburg in 1892 ; and several ports in France, Italy, and Spain were infected. The present or sixth pandemic, which started in 1902, has been confined chiefly to Asia, Egypt, and the Southern countries of Europe. Though the disease has frequently been imported into England and America, since 1873 it has not succeeded in gaining a foothold. With the improved sanitary arrangements of our Western civilization, cholera is being gradually restricted in its field ; and it will probably not be long before it is forced back and confined once more to a few endemic foci, such as those in Lower Bengal (Craster 1913a, Elkington 1916).

Bacteriology.—At the Berlin Conference of July 1884 Koch (1886a) announced his discovery of the causative organism of cholera—the comma bacillus or *Vibrio choleræ*. During the previous year in Egypt and in India he had examined the fæces of 32 patients during life, and the intestinal contents at autopsy of 62 patients who had succumbed to the disease. In not a single instance had he failed to demonstrate the comma bacillus. The organisms were most numerous in the lower half of the small intestine. In acute cases they were present in almost pure culture, but in cases that had lasted longer, and in whom secondary changes had occurred, the vibrios were few and more difficult to find. In a smear from the rice-water stools or the intestinal contents of typical cases, the comma bacilli were arranged with their long axes parallel to one another, presenting a picture similar to that of fish in a stream. The organisms were found in the intestinal contents, in the lumen of the glands, and even between the epithelium and the basement membrane of the mucosa. They were apparently confined to the gut ; the mesenteric glands and the blood were sterile. As a control, Koch examined the intestinal contents of more than 30 cadavers of patients dying from non-choleraic—mostly intestinal —diseases, but he failed to demonstrate the vibrio in a single instance. Though unable to reproduce the disease in lower animals by administration of the vibrio, he came to the conclusion that it was definitely the cause of cholera.

This conclusion was challenged by a number of authorities holding one or other of the multitudinous theories of disease current previous to the bacteriological era. During the next few years their position was strengthened by the discovery of vibrios in all sorts of situations—cheese, dirty well, river and sea water, intestinal abscesses of pigs, diarrhœal fæces of patients with cholera nostras or dysenteric diseases, and other animal and saprophytic sources (see Chapter XXI). Since many of these vibrios bore a close resemblance to Koch's comma bacillus, and since their differentiation by means of the morphological, cultural, and pathogenicity tests that were then available was difficult or even impossible, grave suspicion was cast on the ætiological significance of the cholera vibrio.

Later on, however, with the introduction of a more highly specialized technique —especially the agglutination and complement-fixation reactions and Pfeiffer's phenomenon—it was possible to show that the majority of these vibrios differed in one or more essential respects from the comma bacillus. Even then the confusion was not altogether cleared up ; for vibrios were isolated from persons who had been in contact with cholera patients, and from water supplies in areas where cholera was epidemic, which, though conforming to the true cholera type in most respects, yet failed to agglutinate with a specific serum. Intensive study of these inagglutinable strains has rendered it probable that many of them belong to the cholera species, but that through the effect of environment they have undergone slight changes which render their identification when first isolated peculiarly difficult. By frequent subculture in the laboratory and passage through the peritoneal cavity of guinea-pigs or mice many of these strains have recovered their agglutinability (Zlatogoroff 1909, Craster 1914, Taylor and Ahuja 1935).

Koch's observations have been repeatedly confirmed in all parts of the world. In large outbreaks of cholera, the comma bacillus has been found in nearly every case ; and the further study of the vibrio has left no doubt that it is the specific cause of the disease.

Bacteriologically, the disease is essentially due to the growth, often in almost pure culture, of cholera vibrios in the intestine. On their autolysis the organisms liberate toxic bodies that have an extremely irritating effect on the intestinal tract, leading to severe and repeated purging, exhaustion, and death.

Experimental Reproduction of the Disease in Animals and Man.—Natural cholera in animals is unknown, but there are certain experimental procedures by which a disease closely resembling cholera can be reproduced in guinea-pigs and rabbits.

Using dogs and rabbits, Nicati and Rietsch (1884) found that the direct injection of comma bacilli into the duodenum was followed by a fatal disease, characterized by the presence of vibrios in large numbers in the small intestine. Koch (1886*b*) confirmed this observation on guinea-pigs, but pointed out that the frequency of a fatal termination depended on the amount of trauma accompanying the injection. He tried to infect the animals by the mouth ; and in order to enable the vibrios to pass through the stomach unharmed, he rendered the gastric contents alkaline by the administration of 5 c.c. of 5 per cent. sodium carbonate solution. Twenty guinea-pigs treated in this way were shortly afterwards fed with 10 c.c.

of a broth culture of cholera. Only one died—an animal that had recently aborted. This suggested to Koch that the relaxation of the animal's intestine might have been responsible for the infection. Into his next batch of 35 guinea-pigs, therefore, besides giving the sodium carbonate and the cholera culture, he injected 1 c.c. of *Tinct. opii* intraperitoneally to paralyse the gut, and to prolong the stay of the vibrios in the small intestine. The result was that 30 of the animals died, displaying before death weakness of the hind limbs and collapse. At necropsy, the small intestine was deeply injected and filled with a flocculent colourless fluid, containing the vibrios in almost pure culture.

Metchnikoff (1894), working at first with the Massauah bacillus, and later with a true cholera strain, was able to convey the disease to sucking rabbits by rubbing the vibrios on the mother's teats. Diarrhœa usually followed, and about half of the animals died —in 2 to 5 days. What was even more interesting was that if the animals, shortly after they became ill, were put alongside litters of normal rabbits, many of the latter became infected. Sanarelli (1921), from experiments on very young rabbits, concluded that the vibrios were absorbed by the bucco-pharyngeal mucosa, passed through the cervical lymphatic glands, entered the blood stream, and were excreted into the cæcum and colon, whence they ascended the small intestine, and gave rise to the typical lesions of the disease. After the rabbits were 10 days old they could no longer be infected by the mouth. In man, however, tissue invasion appears to be very uncommon. Adult rabbits can also be infected experimentally, though by a different route. Thomas (1893) found that if they were injected intravenously with living vibrios, most of them died within 36 hours ; diarrhœa was present as a rule only in those that lived longer than 24 hours. Post mortem, however, in all the animals there was a creamy, soup-like fluid in the duodenum, and rice-water in the jejunum and ileum, containing vibrios in large numbers. Small ecchymoses of the mucosa were also seen. These findings were confirmed by Issaeff and Kolle (1894), who pointed out that the most typical picture occurred in those rabbits which survived for 3 or 4 days after injection. At the post-mortem examination of these animals, as well as the changes already described, most of the epithelium was found to be detached, so that the internal surface of the small gut was lined by the basement membrane. Isolated patches of epithelium were packed with vibrios. Of 35 rabbits inoculated with doses varying from 1/20 loopful to 9 loopfuls of an 18-hours' agar culture, 27 died.

In man there have been numerous cases of laboratory infection, both intentional and unintentional, resulting from cholera cultures. Koch (1886b) recorded the case of a medical man who attended a bacteriological course in Berlin, and developed cholera. Since there was no cholera at the time either in Berlin or the rest of Germany, it is practically certain that he contracted his infection in the laboratory. Dr. Oergel of Hamburg infected himself with the peritoneal exudate of a guinea-pig that had been injected with cholera vibrios ; a drop spurted up and entered his mouth. The following day he was ill, and a few days later he died in coma. There was no cholera in Germany at that time. Pfeiffer and Pfuhl (see Kolle 1894) both contracted infection in the laboratory. Pfeiffer, who infected himself at Berlin while making animal experiments with a strain freshly isolated from a cholera case in Hamburg, developed a sharp attack ; vibrios were found in his fæces and persisted till the 33rd day of the disease. Antibodies to *V. choleræ* were demonstrated in his serum. Pfuhl had only a mild attack, vibrios persisting in his fæces for 8 days. Numerous other instances are recorded of similar laboratory infections (Kolle and Schürmann 1912).

Amongst the intentional cases, the best known are those of von Pettenkofer and

Emmerich. Doubting the value of Koch's work, both these observers decided to test the effect of the vibrio on themselves. After a preliminary dose of sodium bicarbonate, they drank some water to which a small amount of fresh cholera culture had been added. Von Pettenkofer suffered from diarrhœa only ; but his less fortunate companion developed a severe attack of cholera. As well as having diarrhœa with typical rice-water stools, he passed into a profound state of toxæmia with suppression of urine and the *vox cholerica*. Many attempts to produce artificial infection in man have, however, been fruitless. Metchnikoff (1893) carried out a number of experiments on himself and others, sometimes with positive, but more often with negative results. So far as the ætiology of the disease is concerned, negative experiments are, as Koch pointed out, of little value. We do not know all the factors that are necessary for the reproduction of the disease, and quite often the conditions in individual experiments must be unsuitable. The experiments that Nature provides on a large scale are far more convincing.

The Toxins of Vibrio Choleræ.—These have already been described in Chapter XXI.

Epidemiology.

In India cholera is most prevalent during the hot weather. Thus in Lower Bengal the maximum incidence is reached from February to May ; in the Punjab from May to October (Rogers 1911). The disease is commoner in men than in women. The case mortality is lowest in the 11–20 age group, and increases with age ; in the figures cited by Rogers the case mortality in patients between 11 and 20 years of age was 51·3 per cent., in those over 50 years of age it was 73·7 per cent. The effect of atmospheric conditions seems to vary in different parts of India ; those who are interested will do well to study the very careful statistical analyses made by Russell and Sundararajan (1928). The disease in India occurs with a certain periodicity, and by calculations based on the relevant data it is said to be possible to predict an epidemic 2 or 3 months ahead of its occurrence (Russell and Sundararajan 1926–27).

The true home of cholera is the delta of the Ganges. Here the disease has occurred year after year for centuries. Previous to 1817 it had apparently never spread widely from this area, but since that year it has manifested an increasing disposition to invade not only other parts of India, but almost the whole world. The disease now recurs so constantly in certain areas, such as the West Indies, Southern China, the Philippines, Persia, Arabia, and South-East Russia, that these must be regarded as endemic foci. In other areas it usually dies out, though it may be reimplanted from time to time. In India alone the number of deaths from cholera during the 10 years 1898–1907 was 370,000 or 1·64 per 1,000 of the population. It is the low-lying alluvial tracts and the seaports that are most invaded ; on high land the disease spreads less readily.

Mode of Spread.—There are many ways in which infection can be transmitted from the sick to the healthy person. A study of the epidemiology of cholera indicates, however, that outbreaks can be divided into those dependent on (1) water-borne infection, and (2) case or carrier infection.

The classical example of a *water-borne* outbreak is the Hamburg epidemic of 1892. Hamburg, and two of its suburbs—Altona and Wandsbeck—were provided each with a different water supply. Hamburg drew its water from the river Elbe at a point above the city, and did not filter it. Altona drew its water from the

Elbe below Hamburg, after the fluid refuse and fæces of nearly 800,000 people had been poured into it, but it took the precaution to instal a highly efficient sand-filtration plant. Wandsbeck received its supply from a relatively non-polluted lake, and likewise filtered it. On August 16, 1892, a case of cholera was reported in Hamburg. Others occurred in rapid succession, till by the end of the month there were about 1,000 fresh cases a day. When the epidemic came to an end, on October 23, the figures were : Cases 18,000 ; deaths 8,200. The incidence of cholera in Altona and Wandsbeck was in comparison very low. Altona reported 516 cases, but there is reason to believe that most of these acquired their infection in Hamburg. On the Hamburg-Altona frontier the line of demarcation between the two towns was very irregular, and there was much overlapping of the water supplies. It was observed that in the same street the houses that were supplied with the Hamburg water were invaded by cholera, whereas those supplied with the Altona water were spared. The Elbe was probably infected originally from the excreta of cholera patients on board the numerous barges anchoring opposite the Hamburg water intake. During the outbreak, cholera vibrios were isolated from the river not far below the mouth of the main Hamburg sewer (Koch 1894). There is here a perfectly clear demonstration of the ability of water to convey the cholera vibrio, and of the efficacy of sand-filtration in protecting a town against a highly polluted source of water. Numerous other outbreaks are on record in which the water supply has become infected and has led to the development of cholera.

Epidemics originating in this way are generally explosive ; the ascending limb of the incidence curve rises very steeply ; the epidemic soon reaches its maximum, and with the cleansing of the water begins to fall. The decline is, however, less steep than the ascent, probably because a number of contact infections occur that are not directly dependent on the water-borne infection at all, and therefore continue to arise even after the water is clean again.

The second method of infection—*case or carrier infection*—is the one by which the disease is spread from place to place, and attains its widespread distribution. Infected material is conveyed from the sick to the healthy person, either by water, food, or infected linen. Milk, raw fruits and vegetables, and other uncooked food are all able to serve as media for the transference of the vibrio. Clothing, especially linen, if kept moist, can retain its infectivity for several days or even weeks. Numerous experiments have been made to test the survival time of the cholera vibrio under natural conditions.

Greig (1913–14b) in India stored the rice-water stools of 94 patients in a dark cupboard at room temperature, taking care to prevent evaporation. The average life of the vibrio was 7 to 8 days in the cooler weather, and 1 to 2 days in the hot weather. The longest survival time was 17 days. Gamaléia (1893) found that on linen strips kept moist in a water-saturated atmosphere the vibrios lived for about 5 weeks ; when the strips were dried in a desiccator, they died in 17 hours. Dried on silk threads the vibrios rarely live for more than a few hours, but sometimes they may survive for 3 or 4 days (Kitasato 1889). Berckholz (1889), however, found that on threads dried in air they might live for as long as 30 days. In water *V. choleræ* remains viable for a variable time. Houston (1909), who added cultures of the vibrio to raw river water, found that 99·9 per cent. of the organisms were dead in a week ; none survived longer than 2 weeks. Haffkine and Simpson (1895) in Calcutta brought evidence to show that the survival time of the vibrio in water was less than 5 weeks. Some natural waters, such as the Jumna and the Ganges (Hankin 1896), appear to be unfavourable to its survival. Probably much depends on the purity of the water. In spring water the vibrios lived for 30 days, in Berlin sewer water for 6 to 7 days, and in cesspool water for less than 24 hours (Koch 1886*b*).

Speaking generally, we may say that heat and desiccation are rapidly destructive ; but that under suitable conditions of moisture and temperature the cholera vibrio may survive outside the body for a considerable time.

Patients who have recovered from cholera may continue to excrete the vibrio —often very irregularly—for some weeks. As a rule about 90 per cent. become free from infection within a fortnight, and 99 per cent. in a month. But occasionally the vibrios may persist for 3 to 4 months, or even—as in one recorded case —for a year. It is not only convalescents, however, who are infective ; healthy persons who have been in contact with cholera cases may become infected and excrete the vibrios without manifesting any sign of the disease. Sometimes cholera eventually develops in these healthy carriers—possibly owing to an alimentary indiscretion—and if this occurs some time after their contact with cholera patients it may be very puzzling to trace the source of their infection. Munson (1915), for example, discovered three healthy carriers in a prison in Manila. These were isolated and examined daily. Two of them, after having been carriers for 16 and 17 days respectively, developed cholera, and the third developed it after 18 days and died in 8 hours. As Munson points out, this man might have travelled half-way round the world scattering his infection broadcast during his 18-day period as a carrier, and died of true cholera in a place many thousands of miles from any other source of infection. These cases are probably exceptional, but there is evidence to suggest that many persons do not develop the disease clinically for some hours—24 or more—after the vibrios are demonstrable in the fæces (Crendiropoulo 1912). It is probable that the cholera vibrio often survives in the gall-bladder, and from there is excreted into the intestine. Greig (1913), who examined the bile of 271 fatal cases of cholera, isolated the specific vibrio from 80 of these, and found evidence of cholecystitis in 12 of the 80 positive cases. Similar results are reported by Schobl, Kulescha, Hunter and others (see Elkington 1916). Sometimes it is excreted in the urine (Greig 1913–14*a*).

The spread of contact infection may be aided to some extent by flies. Cholera vibrios have been isolated from flies taken in infected houses, from flies caught in a post-mortem room in which cholera corpses had been examined, and from the feet of flies caught 17 hours after their experimental contamination (Elkington 1916).

Contact infection is responsible for the usual *chain-spread* of cholera. Cases occur in different localities, often widely separated from each other, exhibiting a regular sequence of infection. With the rapidity of modern transport it is often very difficult to ascertain all the links in a given chain. When it is remembered that infection may be carried and transmitted by apparently healthy persons, the magnitude of this difficulty will be appreciated. An excellent example of this chain-spread is afforded by the Hamburg epidemic of 1892. This, as we have already stated, was due to an infected water supply ; but from Hamburg the disease was carried by infected persons to nearly 300 places in Germany and other countries.

Often the presence of a carrier in a community is rendered probable by the development at intervals of clinical cholera cases for which no obvious source of infection is recognizable. The production of these " cholera nests," as they are called, is particularly frequent in the East, where the sanitary conditions are poor.

The two methods of infection described may be, and frequently are, combined.

In the suburbs of Calcutta, for example, the tanks, which supply a large proportion of the native population with water, are freely open to pollution from cholera cases, so that whenever a tank belonging to a given household becomes contaminated, a small outbreak may result. Since the water in these tanks is used not only for drinking, but for washing, bathing, and sewage disposal, it is not surprising that they are frequently responsible for the conveyance of infection.

Diagnosis.

The bacteriological diagnosis of cholera may be very easy, or remarkably difficult. Here we can indicate only the outline of the methods to be employed. (For further details see Koch 1886a, 1894, Ellermann 1904, Crendiropoulo 1912, Craster 1913a, b.)

The fæces or intestinal contents should be examined microscopically. A flake of mucus, for preference, should be spread on a slide and stained with dilute carbol-fuchsin. If comma bacilli are present in pure or almost pure culture—especially if they present the typical fish-in-stream appearance—a provisional diagnosis of cholera can be made directly. By this means alone Koch (1894) was able to diagnose about 50 per cent. of the specimens sent for examination to the Institute for Infectious Diseases at Berlin. If, however, other bacilli are present, it is advisable to suspend judgment till further examination has been made.

The fæces should be seeded immediately on reception into a tube of ordinary peptone water (1 per cent. peptone, 0·5 per cent. NaCl). In this medium, cholera vibrios are able to grow more rapidly than other intestinal bacilli. Multiplication occurs chiefly at the surface, where a thin pellicle forms in the course of a few hours. After 6 to 12 hours' incubation at 37° C., a loopful taken from the surface should be filmed, and if vibrios are present, a fresh tube of peptone water should be seeded and an agar plate streaked with a loopful taken from the surface of the culture. Alternatively a selective medium, such as Dieudonné's (see Vedder and van Dam 1932), or the phenolphthalein starch medium described by Yen (1932–33), may be used. After 12 to 18 hours' incubation, the peptone water culture should be tested by the addition of pure sulphuric acid for the cholera-red reaction. The colonies on the agar plate should be examined after 12 hours, and filmed. If they consist of vibrios, 1·5 mgm. (about a loopful) of culture should be rubbed up in 1 c.c. of broth and injected intraperitoneally into a guinea-pig. At the same time 2 or 3 tubes of broth should be seeded with single colonies, and incubated at 37° C. After 3 days they should be tested for hæmolysin production by the addition of 1 c.c. of culture to an equal quantity of a 5 per cent. suspension of washed goat or sheep red blood cells ; this mixture should be incubated for 2 hours at 37° C. and kept over-night in the cold before reading. A suspension of colonies on the agar plate should be made in 0·2 per cent. formol, and tested against an agglutinating serum containing the specific cholera O (sub-group I) antibody (see Gardner and Venkatraman 1935). For practical purposes the isolation of a non-hæmolytic vibrio with the specific O antigen of sub-group I may be regarded as diagnostic of cholera. Vibrios having the O antigen of sub-group I, but hæmolysing sheep or goat red cells, belong to the El Tor group. Not too much weight, however, should be placed on the hæmolytic or non-hæmolytic activity of the organism, since the ability to produce an active hæmolysin seems to depend on a number of factors which are not always easy to control (see Chapter XXI).

The final identification of the organism should be made by the absorption of agglutinins test and by Pfeiffer's (1895) reaction. For this 4 guinea-pigs are required. (1) 1 loopful of an 18 hours' agar culture at 37° C., suspended in 1 c.c. of broth, is mixed with 0·001 c.c. of a high-titre cholera antiserum and injected intraperitoneally. (2) The same inoculum, with 0·002 c.c. of antiserum. (3) The same inoculum, with 0·01 c.c. of normal serum. (4) 1 loopful of culture alone is injected. The 3rd and 4th animals act as controls. Immediately after injection, and 20, 40 and 60 minutes later, a drop of peritoneal exudate is removed by a fine Pasteur pipette from each of the four animals, and examined in a hanging-drop preparation. If the reaction is positive, in animals 1 and 2 the vibrios will lose their motility, swell up, and undergo granular degeneration ; in animals 3 and 4 the drop will be seething with actively motile, comma-shaped vibrios. The reaction may alternatively be carried out *in vitro*. Pfeiffer's reaction is highly specific. If a mixture of *V. choleræ*, and *V. metchnikovi*, for example, is added to an immune anti-cholera serum and injected into a guinea-pig, only the cholera vibrios undergo lysis ; the others are unaffected, multiply, and kill the animal.

During an epidemic of cholera the bacteriological diagnosis can usually be made by simple microscopical and cultural examination, supplemented, if necessary, by the cholera-red and the agglutination reaction. But in non-epidemic times, or at the beginning of an epidemic, especially in a country usually free from cholera, the diagnosis should never be made till all the tests described have been performed and found positive.

The identification of vibrios from carriers or cholera contacts, and from non-human sources such as water or milk, is often very difficult, and has to be performed with the utmost care. Vibrios are often found under these conditions (Dunbar 1893, Kutscher 1893, 1895, Gotschlich 1895, 1906, Haffkine and Simpson 1895, Neufeld and Haendel 1907, Ruffer 1907, Zlatogoroff 1909, Crendiropoulo 1912, Craster 1913*a, b,* 1914, Jermoljewa 1926) that bear an extremely close resemblance to the cholera vibrio, and can be differentiated from it only by extensive study. Even in cholera stools, antigenically atypical forms, such as those described by Chen (1932–33), Yang and White (1934), Aoki and Oshiro (1934), and White (1935), are often found. In the examination of such vibrios, attempts should be made by repeated subculture and intraperitoneal inoculation of mice or guinea-pigs to bring about a change to the typical antigenic form. Most non-cholera vibrios are harmless to guinea-pigs, but the pathogenicity test cannot be relied on exclusively.

In the examination of suspected convalescents, besides looking for the vibrio in the fæces, it is well to test the serum for agglutinins and bactericidins. Where a large-scale investigation has to be carried out in the search for carriers, a rectal swab should be taken from each person and inoculated into peptone water. Subcultures and plates are made from this after 6 to 9 hours' incubation. Using this method Craster (1913*b*) at the Quarantine Station, New York, examined nearly 27,000 immigrants in 4 months, and identified 31 as carriers.

Prophylaxis and Treatment.

The prevention of cholera is similar to that of typhoid. Owing to the serious nature of the disease stringent precautions have been taken, particularly at seaports, to prevent its introduction into countries usually free from cholera and its subsequent dissemination. (For an account of these see Elkington 1916.)

Vaccination.—Ferran (1885) in Spain was the first to attempt vaccination against cholera. He injected small doses up to about 0·5 c.c. of a living broth culture subcutaneously ; a severe local and general reaction followed. The results were not satisfactory ; and the work was suppressed by the Government.

Haffkine, a pupil of Pasteur's, then took up the problem. He (1892) prepared two living vaccines : (1) consisting of vibrios whose virulence had been attenuated by frequent cultivation in a constantly aerated atmosphere ; (2) consisting of vibrios whose virulence had been exalted by 20 to 30 passages through the peritoneal cavity of guinea-pigs. These vaccines were used on a fairly large scale in India ; sometimes only the first vaccine was given, sometimes both. The figures have been published by Haffkine (1895*a*, *b*, 1913), and critically discussed by Kolle (1896*b*). It is impossible here to give the results in tabular form. The injections were made on numerous tea estates, in regiments, gaols, and families. The numbers of inoculated and uninoculated were often unequal ; the two sets were unevenly exposed to risk of infection ; in some instances the inoculation was performed during the progress of the epidemic ; in others the disease did not break out for a year or more after inoculation ; and the cases that did occur were too few to afford a correct idea of the comparative immunity of the two groups. Haffkine's statistics have been carefully examined by Greenwood and Yule (1915), who point out the variability of the results of inoculations performed in different areas. They conclude, however, that certain of the results establish a presumption in favour of the value of Haffkine's inoculation.

Later (1911, 1913), Haffkine abandoned his living vaccines, and recommended the use of his vaccine ii, killed by heat at 50° C. for a few minutes, and preserved with 0·5 per cent. phenol. Kolle (1896*a*) was the first to introduce the killed vaccine. By experiments on himself and his colleagues, he showed that the injection of 1/10 to 1/5 of a 24-hours' agar culture, killed by chloroform vapour or heat, stimulated the production of specific bactericidal antibodies. His vaccine has been employed on a fairly large scale by Murata (1904) in Japan, and by Savas (1914) in Greece. The significance of Murata's results is very doubtful, since only one inoculation was given, and there is some doubt as to the homogeneity of his statistics (see Greenwood and Yule 1915). Savas employed anti-cholera vaccination in the Grecian Army during the second Balkan War. As the greater part of the inoculations were made during the progress of the cholera epidemic, it follows that the exposure to risk of infection was different amongst the inoculated and the uninoculated. For this reason statistical analysis of most of Savas' figures is not likely to afford much information as to the value of vaccination. An exception must be made for the Sanitary Corps, nearly every member of which received two inoculations before the disease broke out. A comparison made between the incidence of cholera among the members of the Sanitary Corps and among the combatants is recorded in Table CVIII (taken from Greenwood and Yule 1915).

TABLE CVIII

	Not Attacked.	Attacked.	Total.
Sanitary Corps	2,884	13	2,897
Combatants	112,613	2,192	114,805
Total	115,497	2,205	117,702

$\chi^2 = 32\cdot79$.   P = less than 0·0001.

The value of χ^2 is high ; and the probability that the difference in the attack rates between the two groups is attributable to chance is much less than 1 in 10,000 (see p. 1224). Greenwood and Yule (1915) conclude from these results that " anti-cholera inoculation . . . is a prophylactic step of importance, although an exact statistical measure of the degree of relative immunity conferred cannot be provided."

Kolle's vaccine—a 24-hours' agar culture killed by heat at 55° C. for 1 hour, and preserved with 0·5 per cent. phenol—has now replaced all others. It should be standardized to contain 1,000 million total organisms per c.c. ; two doses of 0·5 and 1·0 c.c. should be given at a week's interval.

Bacteriophage Treatment.—Administration of bacteriophage is now being tried both prophylactically and therapeutically in the treatment of cholera. The data so far collected are scanty and refer to native populations, amongst whom the collection of exact records presents peculiar difficulties (see Morison 1932, Asheshov et al. 1930, Asheshov 1933). What is usually regarded as the ideal method— that of treating alternate cases—is not only generally impossible but may be undesirable, since under primitive conditions of sanitation rapid transference of the bacteriophage from treated to untreated persons is likely to occur. Comparisons have usually to be made (1) between a group of treated and another of untreated patients in any given epidemic ; unless the two groups are practically identical in age, sex, time of exposure, risk of exposure, and other relevant factors, such a comparison may yield very misleading results ; (2) between the mortality in treated cases in one epidemic and that in untreated cases in a previous epidemic ; since the case mortality in different epidemics is subject to considerable variation alto- gether apart from any active interference on the part of man, this method is likewise unsatisfactory. For the moment, therefore, we must reserve our judgment on the value of bacteriophage treatment. In view of the favourable light in which this method is regarded by many clinicians, it seems probable that it does favourably affect the course of the disease, but in this, as in other similar problems, we must await the collection of adequate statistical material before coming to a definite decision.

Serum Therapy.—Antisera to cholera are readily prepared by the injection of goats or horses with dead, followed by living, vibrios. The resultant serum has a marked prophylactic effect when tested by the intraperitoneal method in guinea- pigs, but unfortunately its therapeutic powers are low. Injected more than an hour or so after the vibrios, it fails to save the animal's life (Pfeiffer 1894). This is doubtless because the antibodies in the serum are chiefly bactericidal, and are unable to neutralize the toxins liberated by the disintegration of the vibrios. For the treatment of cholera cases, a serum is required that has a high anti-endotoxic titre. Several attempts have been made to produce such a serum. Macfadyen (1906) used an extract of young agar cultures ground up in liquid air for immunizing rabbits and goats. Tested on guinea-pigs 0·5 c.c. of the rabbit's serum, after inoculation of toxin, protected against 8 lethal doses, and 0·002 c.c. of the goat's serum protected against 3 lethal doses. Schurupow (1909) immunized horses with an alkaline extract of 2-days' cholera cultures, and apparently succeeded in obtaining an anti-endotoxic serum. Unfortunately these sera have not been used on a large scale in practice, and it is impossible, in spite of the favourable reports (Savas 1914) that have been made on them, to estimate their value in treatment.

REFERENCES

Aoki, K. and Oshiro, T. (1934) *Z. ImmunForsch.*, **83**, 291.
Asheshov, I. N. (1933) *Rep. sci. advis. Board Ind. Res. Fund Ass.*, 1932–33, p. 38. Govt. India Press, Simla.
Asheshov, I. N., Asheshov, I., Khan, S., and Lahiri, M. N. (1930) *Ind. J. med. Res.*, **17**, 971.
Berckholz. (1889) *Arb. ReichsgesundhAmt.*, **5**, 1.
Chen, W. K. (1932–33) *Proc. Soc. exp. Biol., N.Y.*, **30**, 887.
Craster, C. V. (1913a) *J. infect. Dis.*, **12**, 472 ; (1913b) *J. Amer. med. Ass.*, **61**, 2210 ; (1914) *J. exp. Med.*, **19**, 581.
Crendiropoulo. (1912) *Bull. Cons. sanit. marit. quar. Egypte.*
Dunbar. (1893) *Dtsch. med. Wschr.*, **19**, 799.
Elkington, J. S. C. (1916) *Comm. Aust. Quar. Serv.*, No. 7.
Ellermann, V. (1904) *Zbl. Bakt.*, **37**, 729.
Ferran, J. (1885) *C. R. Acad. Sci.*, **100**, 959.
Gamaléia, N. (1893) *Dtsch. med. Wschr.*, **19**, 1350.
Gardner, A. D. and Venkatraman, K. V. (1935) *J. Hyg., Camb.*, **35**, 262.
Gotschlich, F. (1895) *Z. Hyg. InfektKr.*, **20**, 489 ; (1906) *Ibid.*, **53**, 281.
Greenwood, M. and Yule, G. U. (1915) *Proc. R. Soc. Med.*, **8**, Sec. Epidem. and State Med., p. 113.
Greig, E. D. W. (1913) *Indian med. Gaz.*, **48**, 8 ; (1913–14a) *Indian J. med. Res.*, **1**, 90 ; (1913–14b) *Ibid.*, **1**, 481.
Haffkine, W. M. (1892) *C. R. Soc. Biol.*, **4**, 635, 671 ; (1895a) *Rep. to Govt. India*, Calcutta ; (1895b) *Brit. med. J.*, ii. 1541 ; (1911) " Epidemiological Notes," Calcutta ; (1913) " Protective Inoculation against Cholera," Calcutta.
Haffkine, W. M. and Simpson, W. J. (1895) *Indian med. Gaz.*, **30**, 89.
Hankin, M. E. (1896) *Ann. Inst. Pasteur*, **10**, 511.
Houston, A. C. (1909) *4th Res. Rep. met. Water Bd.*
Issaeff and Kolle, W. (1894) *Z. Hyg. InfektKr.*, **18**, 17.
Jermoljewa, S. (1926) *Zbl. Bakt.*, **100**, 170.
Kirchner, M. (1906) *Klin. Jahrb.*, **16**, 1.
Kitasato, S. (1889) *Z. Hyg. InfektKr.*, **5**, 134.
Koch, R. (1886a) *New Sydenham Soc.*, **115**, 327 ; (1886b) *Ibid.*, **115**, 370 ; (1894) " The Bacteriological Diagnosis of Cholera," trans. by Duncan. Edinburgh.
Kolle, W. (1894) *Z. Hyg. InfektKr.*, **18**, 42 ; (1896a) *Zbl. Bakt.*, **19**, 97 ; (1896b) *Ibid.*, **19**, 217.
Kolle, W. and Schürmann, W. (1912) See Kolle and Wassermann's " Hdb. path. Mikroorg.," 2te Abt., 1912–13, **4**, 1.
Kutscher. (1893) *Dtsch. med. Wschr.*, **19**, 1301 ; (1895) *Z. Hyg. InfektKr.*, **19**, 461.
Macfadyen, A. (1906) *Lancet*, ii. 494.
Metchnikoff, E. (1893) *Ann. Inst. Pasteur*, **7**, 562 ; (1894) *Ibid.*, **8**, 529.
Morison, J. (1932) " Bacteriophage in the Treatment and Prevention of Cholera." H. K. Lewis & Co., Ltd., Lond.
Munson, E. L. (1915) *Philipp. J. Sci., B*, **10**, 1.
Murata, N. (1904) *Zbl. Bakt.*, **35**, 605.
Neufeld and Haendel. (1907) *Arb. ReichsgesundhAmt.*, **26**, 536.
Nicati, W. and Rietsch, M. (1884) *C. R. Acad. Sci.*, **99**, 928.
Pfeiffer, R. (1894) *Z. Hyg. InfektKr.*, **18**, 1 ; (1895) *Ibid.*, **19**, 75.
Rogers, L. (1911) " Cholera and its Treatment." Oxford.
Ruffer, M. A. (1907) *Bull. Cons. sanit. marit. quar. Egypte.*
Russell, A. J. H. and Sundararajan, E. R. (1926–27) *Indian J. med. Res.*, **14**, 901 ; (1928) *Indian med. Res. Mem.*, No. 12.
Sanarelli, G. (1921) *Ann. Inst. Pasteur*, **35**, 745.
Savas, C. (1914) *Bull. Off. int. Hyg. publ.*, **6**, 1653.
Schurupow, J. S. (1909) *Zbl. Bakt.*, **49**, 623.
Taylor, J. and Ahuja, M. L. (1935) *Indian. J. med. Res.*, **23**, 531.
Thomas. (1893) *Arch. exp. Path. Pharm.*, **32**, 38.
Vedder, A. and Dam, W. van. (1932) *Zbl. Bakt.*, **126**, 145.
White, P. B. (1935) *J. Hyg., Camb.*, **35**, 347.
Yang, Y. N. and White, P. B. (1934) *J. Path. Bact.*, **38**, 187.
Yen, A. C. H. (1932–33) *Proc. Soc. exp. Biol., N.Y.*, **30**, 884.
Zlatogoroff, S. J. (1909) *Zbl. Bakt.*, **48**, 684.

CHAPTER LXI

MENINGITIS

INTRODUCTORY

MENINGITIS is an inflammatory affection of the membranes surrounding the brain and spinal cord, which occurs sometimes as a primary disease, and sometimes secondarily to disease of some other part of the body.

Prior to the advent of bacteriology the tuberculous form was recognized, the cerebrospinal form when it occurred in epidemics, and the post-basic form in children.

The discovery of the tubercle bacillus by Koch in 1882 provided a bacteriological means of differentiating the tuberculous from other forms of meningitis. Pneumococci were shown by Fraenkel (1886), Foà and Bordoni-Uffreduzzi (1886), and others to be responsible for the meningitis which occasionally complicates lobar pneumonia. In 1887 Weichselbaum of Vienna published his classical paper on the finding of a Gram-negative diplococcus in six cases of acute cerebrospinal meningitis ; this organism he named the *Diplococcus intracellularis meningitidis*. The same year his work was confirmed by Goldschmidt (1887) and by Edler (1884–88). Jaeger (1895), in describing the differences between the pneumococcus and the meningococcus, assigned to the latter characters which it does not possess, and numerous papers were published during the following 10 years dealing with the differences between his description and that of Weichselbaum (Scherer 1895, von Hibler 1896, Heubner 1896, Kiefer 1896, Kister 1896, Still 1898, Councilman *et al.* 1898, Faber 1900, Jaeger 1903*a, b*, Albrecht and Ghon 1901, 1902, 1903). The correctness of Weichselbaum's observations was finally established by the extensive studies of von Lingelsheim (1905*a, b*) during an epidemic of cerebrospinal fever in 1904–5. Since that date the *Diplococcus intracellularis meningitidis* of Weichselbaum, or, as it is now called, *Neisseria meningitidis*, has been recognized as the causative organism of the disease. Still showed in 1898 that the post-basic meningitis of children is due to a Gram-negative diplococcus apparently identical with Weichselbaum's, and subsequent work has shown that the two organisms are the same.

Other forms of meningitis will be dealt with at the end of the present chapter.

Cerebrospinal Meningitis

This is an infectious disease characterized by inflammation of the meninges, particularly at the base of the brain. It may be acute or chronic, and may occur sporadically or epidemically. The causative agent is the meningococcus. The disease can be reproduced experimentally by the intrathecal inoculation of virulent meningococci into monkeys and rabbits (see Chapter XXII). There is reason to believe that the pathological manifestations are due mainly to the presence of endotoxic substances, which are contained in the bacterial cells and are liberated when these undergo autolysis.

Epidemiology.

I. History and Incidence.—The first definite knowledge that we have of cerebro-spinal fever is due to Vieusseux, who in 1805 described an outbreak of the disease at Geneva. In the following year it appeared in Medfield, Massachusetts, and during 1806–07 it attacked the Prussian Army. Since then it has invaded most countries in the world, rising at one time to epidemic proportions, subsiding at other times to remain dormant for long periods, but inevitably reappearing in outbreaks of greater or less severity. The disease has, in fact, shown a gradual increase, both in its geographical range and in the number of persons it has attacked. Thus, according to Hirsch (1886) from 1805 to 1830 the disease was most prevalent in the United States ; from 1837 to 1850 France was attacked most severely ; from 1854 to 1874 epidemics occurred both in Europe and in America, and from 1875 down to the present time not only these two continents but Asia, Africa, and Australia have been invaded (Low 1916).

The first undoubted case reported in Great Britain occurred in 1830. From that date the disease remained endemic in this country, giving rise to occasional small outbursts. Our knowledge of the disease previous to 1912, the year in which compulsory notification was introduced, is largely furnished by the death returns ; these record a gradual rise from 1900, when 9 deaths were recorded in England and Wales, to 1911, when 134 were recorded. In 1907 there was an outbreak of epidemic proportions in Scotland and Ireland ; Edinburgh had 206 cases with 135 deaths, Glasgow 998 cases with 715 deaths, and Belfast 623 cases with 495 deaths.

The first large epidemic recorded in England occurred in 1915. It began late in 1914 amongst the Canadian Expeditionary Force (Reece 1916) quartered on Salisbury Plain, and rapidly spread, involving both the civil and the military population. The following figures are instructive (Rolleston 1919) (Table CIX).

TABLE CIX
ENGLAND AND WALES

	Cases.	Deaths.
1912	272	142
1913	304	163
1914	300	206
1915	2,343	1,521
1916	1,278	838
1917	1,385	906

During the War the British Expeditionary Force in France was attacked with some severity ; the French Army suffered less, and the German Army hardly at all.

New York suffered severely in 1904–05. In the latter year there were 2,755 cases with 2,026 deaths (Flexner 1907a). Extensive outbreaks were reported in France in 1909–10, and in Texas in 1912. Recently the disease has been increasing in some countries. There was a particularly severe outbreak in the United States in 1928–30. In England and Wales the incidence rose from 1923 with 300 cases and 284 deaths, to 1931 with 2,152 cases and 1,440 deaths.

The disease attacks particularly children and adolescents. Compton (1918) finds that the most susceptible age is 0 to 5 years ; the susceptibility is slightly less from 5 to 10, distinctly less from 10 to 15, and for the remainder of life it remains fairly low—at about 1/5 of that of the 0 to 5 age period. In the Danzig epidemic of 1865, 93 per cent. were under 5 years of age. The disease is unusual, however, in the first 3 months of life. It is somewhat commoner amongst males, but this appears to be related more to increased opportunity for infection than to any special sex predisposition. Miners and soldiers are the two occupational classes on which the disease falls most heavily. The seasonal incidence is very marked, the greater proportion of cases occurring in winter and spring ; during 1915 and 1916 in England, 77 per cent. of the cases were in the first six months of the year. Much has been written about weather conditions. A low temperature, a cold wind, and increased humidity of the atmosphere appear to be predisposing agents (Dopter 1921), but it seems probable that these act mainly by leading to overcrowding indoors. Fatigue exerts a powerful influence ; it is the recruits, unaccustomed to the rigours of military life, who furnish the greatest number of cases in the Army. Dopter tells an impressive story of a party of recruits who made a long, fatiguing march to join their regiment at Versailles. On reaching their destination cerebrospinal fever broke out, and of a total strength of 153 men no fewer than 79 developed the disease.

II. Mode of Spread of the Disease.—The disease is endemic in large towns, from which, at least in the post-basic form, it rarely disappears. Every winter and spring a few fresh cases occur—sporadic cases affecting children, less frequently young adults—which appear at widely separated points having no apparent connection with each other. In villages the endemic state is practically unknown.

Every now and then an epidemic breaks out. As a rule it starts insidiously by the occurrence of one or two cases at intervals of a week or more ; it then begins to advance by the formation of small multiple foci in families, schools, barracks, or gaols. Often it works itself out in one focus before passing on to another. Thus, at Strassburg (Dopter 1921) in 1840 the 7th line regiment was attacked in October ; three months later it spread to the 69th regiment, of which two companies were quartered with a part of the 7th. In January the 29th line regiment and the 11th artillery were attacked ; in February the 34th line regiment and the 1st artillery ; and in March, 6 months after the commencement of the outbreak, it invaded the pontonniers.

In a town the cases are not aggregated together, but occur widely scattered, as if there were no causal relationship between them. Thus in Hamburg between 1880 and 1885 the 180 cases of cerebrospinal fever that occurred were distributed over 131 streets.

The spread of the epidemic is irregular and capricious ; often groups, which from their situation appear certain to be attacked, escape, whereas others, situated remotely from the primary focus, are attacked. Similarly with regard to time ; the successive outbreaks of an epidemic are irregular ; there are paroxysms of intensity followed by remissions or intermissions. The decline of the epidemic takes place slowly, fewer and fewer foci remaining, till finally the endemic state is regained (Dopter 1921).

It is remarkable what a predilection the disease has for the military population ;

frequently garrisons have been attacked without a single case amongst the neigh-bouring civilians. Of 75 epidemics in France, collected by Hirsch (1886), 39 were confined to the troops. In Germany the miners of Westphalia and Silesia have suffered severely. In India it is the gaols that appear to have furnished most of the cases.

Two of the most striking points about an epidemic of cerebrospinal fever are the low morbidity and the high case mortality. Dopter (1921) says that the morbidity varies between 0·01 and 0·3 per cent. of the population at risk, though occasionally it may rise higher. The case mortality is generally about 70 per cent. ; it may be as low as 37 per cent., or as high as 90 per cent.

Long before the discovery of the causal organism, it had been noticed that over-crowding favoured the development of the disease. The reason for this was not known. At a post-mortem examination of a case of cerebrospinal fever, Weigert noticed the presence of a purulent rhinitis, and on the basis of this observation von Strumpell suggested that the nasopharynx might serve as a portal of entry for the infective material. Weichselbaum (1887) in his original paper likewise mentioned that one of his cases had a purulent sinusitis, and expressed the opinion that the organisms might find their way to the meninges *via* the nose. While working with meningococci Kiefer (1896) developed a purulent right-sided rhinitis from which he cultivated Weichselbaum's diplococcus ; he did not develop menin-gitis. During the next few years a number of workers claimed to have isolated the organism from the nose, not only of patients but of healthy contacts. Further work rendered it clear that not only were meningococci frequently present in the nasopharynx of patients suffering from cerebrospinal fever—about 60 per cent. of cases in the first week of the disease—but also in the nasopharynx of contacts and even of non-contacts (Albrecht and Ghon 1901, von Lingelsheim 1905a, Kutscher 1906, Ostermann 1906). It became clear therefore that the meningococcus was able to vegetate in the nasopharynx—frequently without giving rise to menin-gitis—and that it could be transmitted from patients to healthy persons in the vicinity.

Certain observers, notably Dopter (1921), have come to the conclusion that the real disease to which the meningococcus gives rise is rhinopharyngitis ; the meningitis which occasionally develops is to be regarded, not as the main disease, but as a complication, in much the same way as nephritis is often grafted on scarlatina or paralysis on diphtheria. Actual rhinopharyngitis does not appear to be a common sequel to meningococcal invasion, and it is probably more accurate to speak of this invasion as a " carrier epidemic." There is some evidence, however, that the meningococcus does not act as a pure commensal, because antibodies are sometimes formed as a result of its presence in the nasopharynx (Rake 1935a).

During the Great War observations of considerable interest were made on the carrier rate. By swabbing large numbers of the military population in camps and depots, it was found that previous to an outbreak of cerebrospinal fever the propor-tion of carriers of the meningococcus increased steadily. The normal carrier rate amongst troops was recorded as 2–4 per cent., but preceding an epidemic, it rose till it reached 20–30 per cent. Soon after it had passed the 20 per cent. limit, isolated cases of meningitis began to appear, and as the epidemic gained foot-hold the carrier rate likewise rose, sometimes to as high as 88 per cent.

Investigating the cause of this " warning rise " in the carrier rate, Glover

(1920) was led to suspect a relationship between it and overcrowding in the sleeping huts. These huts were at the best poorly ventilated (Eagleton 1919–20), and during the stress of war the mobilization standard had been over-stepped, so that beds, instead of being separated by 1 ft. 4 in., were practically touching each other. Glover (1920) noticed that the carriers in a given hut tended to be aggregated together ; three Type II carriers were in adjacent beds, two Type I carriers, and so on. This pointed strongly to the direct transmission of the meningo-coccus from one man to another sleeping in the next bed. Finding that the spraying capacity during normal sleep was not more than about 3 ft., Glover tried the effect of spacing out the beds in the hope that the infection would be diminished. The results obtained seemed to be in accordance with expectation. The effect of the distance between the beds was not confined to the carrier rate. At Caterham depot, where there was severe overcrowding, an outbreak of cerebrospinal fever had occurred during each winter of the War, but subsequently to the adoption of the spacing-out policy in 1917–18, not a single case occurred.

Because of the far-reaching conclusions on the relation between overcrowding and the carrier rate, and the importance of detecting the " warning rise," Glover's work has received a great deal of attention. Few satisfactory observations have been recorded, but amongst them there has been a noteworthy absence of confirma-tion of his main theses. In the Detroit epidemic of 1928–29, Norton and Baisley (1931) found no correlation between the degree of overcrowding in the home and the contact carrier rate. During the outbreak of 1931 at Aldershot, Armstrong and his colleagues (1931), from a study of the position of carriers in dormitory barrack rooms, were unable to obtain any evidence that infection occurred mainly at night. The carriers were scattered quite irregularly without any particular relation to the position of the beds. Our own nasopharyngeal surveys of the civilian population carried out during the past few years have shown us that the carrier rate in institu-tions may be as high as 20 per cent. and over, without any outbreak of cerebrospinal fever occurring. Rake (1934) has made the same observation. Perhaps the most striking figures, however, are afforded by Dudley and Brennan (1934). Working at the Chatham naval hospital, they found that between January, 1932, and March, 1933, there were 11 cases of cerebrospinal meningitis with a carrier rate of about 13 per cent. During the period March, 1933, to May, 1934, the carrier rate was 54 per cent., yet not a single case of meningitis occurred. During the same period at the Royal Naval Hospital, Portsmouth, there were 6 cases of meningitis with a carrier rate of only 5 per cent. Analysis of the distribution of carriers at Chatham showed no constant relationship between the density of the population and the carrier rate. The senior ratings with the most spacious sleeping accommodation had as high a carrier rate—60 per cent.—as the recruits with the worst sleeping quarters.

That Glover's observations were correct, no one has questioned ; but it may be doubted whether Glover was justified in attaching to them a general rather than a local significance. It is reasonable to suppose that overcrowding must increase the frequency of exchange of nasopharyngeal flora. Whether, however, this neces-sarily results in a high carrier rate, and if so to what extent overcrowding favours the development of cerebrospinal meningitis, it is at present impossible to say.

Routes of Infection.—There is now no doubt that the meningococcus gains access to the body *via* the nasopharynx. Several early observers claimed to have found the organism in various parts of the respiratory tract, and it was not long before its predilection for the nasopharynx was demonstrated. It is unusual to find it in the nose itself or in the saliva, where, as Gordon (see Report 1917) showed, the salivary streptococci exert an inimical action on its growth ; it may be isolated from the throat, but the most important site is undoubtedly the nasopharynx. It is here that it multiplies, and sometimes sets up a rhinopharyngitis.

Whereas there is now general agreement that the nasopharynx is the portal of entry, it is still uncertain by what route the organism gains access to the meninges. There are two main views : the first, supported by Netter and Debré (1911), postulates the direct transmission of the organism from the nose to the meninges ; the second, upheld by several workers in Germany, America and England (Westenhoeffer 1906, Elser and Huntoon 1909, Herrick 1918, Baeslack *et al.* 1918, Rolleston 1919), is that it is carried to the meninges by the blood stream. The available evidence is as follows.

(*a*) Direct Extension from the Nose.—The advocates of this view draw attention to the close relation existing between the subarachnoid space and the nose. Around each of the 15 to 18 branches of the olfactory nerve which pierce the cribriform plate of the ethmoid there is a sheath ; between this sheath and the nerve itself there is a space which is in direct communication with the subarachnoid space.

Clark (1929) found that a solution of potassium ferrocyanide and iron ammonium citrate, instilled into a rabbit's nose, reached the surface of the brain within an hour. The distribution of the blue granules indicated that the path followed had been the perineural spaces of the olfactory nerves. Further work showed that material might pass from the nasal to the intracranial cavity by way of the blood vessels piercing the cribriform plate. Fine canaliculi, representing prolongations of the subarachnoid space into the olfactory mucosa, have also been described traversing the cribriform plate, homologous with similar prolongations found in the internal ear and around the optic nerve ; but Clark was unable to satisfy himself that these canaliculi had any direct communication with the nasal lymphatic vessels. Methylene blue injected into the subarachnoid space beneath the frontal lobe of a dog colours not only the perineural prolongations, but also the lymphatic plexus of the nasal mucosa. The lymph flow appears to be centrifugal, whereas the flow of fluid (not lymph) in the perineural spaces may, as Clark's observations have shown, be centripetal, and thus carry particulate material from the nose to the brain (see also Findlay and Clarke 1935).

Another possibility is that the organisms may invade the nasal sinuses, set up a purulent sinusitis, and reach the skull by the lymphatics, or by direct extension through the bone. Numerous observers have found a sinusitis in cases of cerebrospinal fever, particularly of the sphenoidal sinus. Embleton and Peters (1915) examined three patients who had died of the disease, and found in each a sphenoidal empyema due to the meningococcus. Against this view are the facts that, though not uncommon, sinusitis is by no means constant in cerebrospinal fever, and that in children, in whom the disease is commoner than in any other class, the sphenoidal sinus does not develop before the third year of life. Moreover it is possible that the involvement of the nasal sinuses may be secondary to the meningitis, the organism being carried by the natural flow of the lymph stream to the nose. Flexner (1907*b*) found in monkeys, injected intraspinally, that the organisms might find their way from the meninges to the nasopharynx.

As well as the transethmoidal and the sphenoidal routes, it has been suggested that spread may occur *via* the Eustachian tube to the middle ear and thence to the brain. This seems unlikely because of the rarity of otitis media in cerebrospinal fever, and of the lateness of its development when it does occur.

The advocates of direct lymphatic spread from the nose to the meninges object to the hæmatogenous route of infection on the ground that blood cultures are frequently sterile, that positive results are not more common at the beginning of the disease than during its later stages, and that the arthropathies and visceral lesions which sometimes appear as complications occur fairly late in the course of the disease, suggesting that the blood has become secondarily infected from the meninges ; that this may occur in animals has been shown by Flexner (1907*b*), who found meningococci in the blood subsequent to intraspinal injection.

(*b*) THE HÆMATOGENOUS ROUTE.—Meningococci were found in the blood by Salomon in 1902 ; Jacobitz in 1905 reported two cases ; Elser (1905–06) obtained 10 positive blood cultures out of 41—mostly in the first week of the disease ; Dieudonné (1906) was successful in 4 cases out of 5. During the War Baeslack (1918) and his co-workers cultivated the meningococcus 8 times from 22 consecutive cases, and Barber and Fleming (see Herrick 1918) 12 times from 15 consecutive cases. Moreover the organism has been cultivated from the petechial spots (Muir 1919), from the swollen periarticular lesions (Still 1898), from the endocardial vegetations, and from other situations clearly infected by the blood stream.

From these records it is clear that an infection of the blood is frequently present. It must be remembered that the meningococcus is not an easy organism to grow, and that if it is present in only small numbers the chances of obtaining it in blood culture are not great. With ordinary care, however, at least 25 per cent. of the blood cultures may be expected to be positive in the first week of the disease.

As well as the finding of the meningococci in the blood, other reasons have been advanced in favour of the hæmatogenous route. Clinical evidence shows that a meningococcal septicæmia may occur without the development of meningitis. Herrick (1918) states that 4 per cent. of patients with septicæmia fail subsequently to develop meningitis.

Westenhoeffer (1906), who at one time favoured the direct method of spread, but who later abandoned this view in favour of the hæmatogenous route, was struck by the presence in two cases of cerebrospinal fever of miliary abscesses in the myocardium and in the renal medulla ; by the occurrence of cases of purulo-hæmorrhagic encephalitis ; and by the finding of pus around the small arteries of the pia in a brain that otherwise appeared normal—all points suggestive of blood infection.

It is clear that the demonstration of meningococci in the blood cannot be regarded as evidence in favour of the hæmatogenous route, unless it can be shown that the blood is generally infected before the meninges ; otherwise it is legitimate to argue that the bloodstream infection is secondary to the meningeal invasion. So far the number of cases that have been studied with a view to determining the sequence of events is insufficient to enable any definite conclusions to be drawn.

Summing up, it may be said that the most probable sequence of events is as follows : The organisms reach the nasopharynx by air-borne infection ; here they may set up a rhinopharyngitis, but more usually appear to give rise to no trouble. In some cases, however, the meningococci gain access to the meninges—whether by direct invasion or *via* the blood stream is not yet known. In a few instances lesions in other parts of the body develop, generally in the late stage of the disease, such as endocarditis, arthropathies, and renal abscesses. These are probably due to a secondary infection of the blood stream from the meninges.

Diagnosis.

In cerebrospinal meningitis the causative organism is always present in the cerebrospinal fluid ; in a considerable proportion of cases it is also present in the nasopharynx. In this latter situation Elser (1905–06) found it in 6 out of 22 patients ; Weichselbaum and Ghon (1905) in 18 out of 19 patients (not fully identified) ; Goodwin and von Sholly (1906) found it in 12 out of 22 patients in the first week of the disease, and in 5 out of 15 in the second week. Von Lingelsheim

(1908) found it in 46 out of 49 patients in the early stage of the disease. Gordon (see Report 1920) states that it can always be found in the early stage of the disease, but that its isolation is more difficult later. For diagnostic purposes, therefore, it is essential to perform a lumbar puncture, and desirable to take a nasopharyngeal swab.

Examination of the Spinal Fluid.—The spinal fluid should be withdrawn and divided into three portions, which should be treated as follows :

(1) *Examination of centrifuged deposit for cells and organisms, and of the supernatant fluid for specific precipitinogens.* The fluid is centrifuged, the deposit stained by Gram, and examined microscopically for the presence of the oval Gram-negative diplococci. These vary greatly in numbers ; sometimes they are present in every field, but in others they are not found until after a prolonged search ; in this respect the picture is very different from that of septic meningitis, in which the pneumococci or streptococci are present in large numbers, and can be found without difficulty. In cerebrospinal meningitis the majority of the cocci are situated within the polymorphonuclear cells. Dissolved antigenic material, probably of polysaccharide type, may frequently be demonstrated in the spinal fluid. A few drops of the supernatant fluid are layered gently on to a similar quantity of monovalent or polyvalent antimeningococcal precipitating serum in a Dreyer's tube. Usually a fine white opaque ring of precipitation becomes apparent in a few minutes. If it does not, the tube is incubated in a water-bath for 1–2 hours at 37° C. Both Rake (1933*b*) and Maegraith (1935) have obtained very satisfactory results with this method. In Maegraith's series of 120 cases, a positive reaction occurred in 116, while of 180 control fluids, all but 2 were negative. No other method affords such a rapid diagnosis.

(2) *Immediate plating.* As soon as the spinal fluid is withdrawn, it should be streaked in quantities of 1 c.c. over 2 or 3 plates of ascitic agar or Gordon's trypagar (Gordon *et al.* 1916). These plates should be incubated immediately, or if this is impossible, they must be transmitted to the laboratory in a warm container. The less their temperature falls below 37° C., the more likely is growth to occur, and the shorter will be its lag period. Growth is often favoured by the addition of 5–10 per cent. CO_2 to the atmosphere. In favourable circumstances colonies should be formed within 18 hours. These are examined with a hand lens, and films are made in the usual manner. A growth of Gram-negative diplococci having been obtained, it is important to ascertain their serological type. If there is a heavy growth on the plates, this may be suspended in a small quantity of saline, heated to 65° C. for 1 hour, standardized to 500 million per c.c., and tested against the type sera ; incubation should be performed by the partial immersion method in a water-bath for 4 hours at 55° C. If the growth is insufficient, or if an immediate diagnosis is essential, Bell's (1920*b*) quick-typing method may be used. Ultra-specific type sera are used, *i.e.* sera from which all co-agglutinins have been removed. With a platinum loop or fine Pasteur pipette one drop of each of these sera is placed on a glass slide ; a distance of about 1–2 cm. should be left between the drops. A few colonies are picked off the plate, suspended in the smallest possible quantity of saline, and heated to 65° C. for 30 minutes ; the suspension should contain at least 4,000 million organisms per c.c. One drop of suspension is then mixed with each drop of serum on the slide, and the mixtures are observed carefully with a hand lens. In many cases agglutination will be visible in one of the drops within 2 or 3 minutes. If after 5 minutes there is no agglutination, a fresh series of mixtures should be put

up, containing 2, 3 or 4 drops of sera with 1 drop of suspension. In either case, if the resulting agglutination is not specific, another series of mixtures should be made, containing 1 drop of serum with 3, 6 or 12 drops of suspension. Agglutination will no longer appear with the heterologous serum. This method is very useful for quick diagnosis, and is rarely incorrect. The results should always be checked by the slow method at 55° C. If there is insufficient growth on the primary plates to allow of either method of agglutination, subcultures must be made on to fresh plates, and the growth examined after 24 hours. The fact must not be forgotten that one variety of organism found in meningitis, *N. flavescens*, may produce a golden-yellow pigment (Branham 1930).

It must be pointed out that not all strains are readily agglutinable by the available type sera. Strains from sporadic cases are usually less readily agglutinated than those isolated during an epidemic. Much depends upon the strains selected for the preparation of the agglutinating sera (see Griffith 1917, Scott 1917, Bell 1920a, Murray 1929, Branham 1932, Rake 1933a).

It is important to test the fermentation reactions of the organisms isolated. For this purpose colonies should be inoculated into glucose, maltose, and sucrose peptone water, containing 10 per cent. of ascitic fluid or blood serum. The meningococcus produces acid in glucose and maltose, but not in sucrose ; *N. flavescens* is without action on any of the sugars. The final identification of any strain must be made on the basis of morphological, cultural, fermentation, and serological reactions.

(3) *Incubation of the spinal fluid with subsequent subcultivation.* It is always wise to incubate 5 c.c. of the fluid at 37° C. in a sterile tube, in case direct plating proves negative. Sometimes the organisms develop in the fluid itself, when they fail to do so in cultures made at the time of lumbar puncture. As soon as turbidity appears, the fluid should be subcultured on to suitable media, and the resulting colonies identified in the usual way.

The frequency with which positive cultures are to be expected depends partly on the stage of the disease and partly on the carefulness of one's technique. Flack (see Report 1917), in an examination of 55 specimens of cerebrospinal fluid, obtained the following results :

	No.	Culture Positive. Per cent.
In clear fluids	15	33 per cent.
In slightly turbid fluids . .	13	61 per cent.
In turbid fluids	27	96 per cent.

In the early stages of the disease before the spinal fluid is purulent, the proportion of positive cultures is much lower than in the later stages. In chronic cases the fluid, after being frankly purulent, may clear again, and the organisms become increasingly difficult to isolate. Ultimately they disappear and can no longer be demonstrated.

Cultivation from the Nasopharynx.—At the time of lumbar puncture a nasopharyngeal swab should be taken. There are two advantages in this practice. First, a positive culture may be obtained from the nasopharynx, especially in the early stages of the disease, when the spinal culture is negative. Second, the nasopharyngeal swab may yield a heavier growth than the spinal plate, and so enable the serological typing of the organisms to be carried out more rapidly. Since the nasopharyngeal and spinal strains are almost invariably of the same type, there is little danger of error in this procedure.

For examining the nasopharynx, West's swab should be used ; this consists of a wire curved at one end, fitted with a pledget of cotton-wool, and enclosed in a glass tube.   As soon as the swab has been taken it should be streaked over a plate of ascitic agar or Gordon's trypagar ; if the latter medium is used, it is advisable to smear 2 or 3 drops of fresh blood over the surface.   The plates must be incubated immediately, or kept in a warm container.   The following day they are examined for the typical lenticular colonies of meningococci.   The further examination of these colonies should be performed in the same way as that of the spinal colonies.

The serological typing of meningococci isolated from the nasopharynx often presents difficulties, particularly during inter-epidemic periods (see Chapter XXII). During the course of an epidemic, the proportion of agglutinable to inagglutinable strains may rise considerably, depending probably upon the selection of a virulent epidemic strain of well-defined antigenic specificity (Report 1920).   The higher the carrier rate is, the more likely are the organisms to be agglutinated.

Examination of the Blood.—(1) *Cultivation.*—An attempt may be made to cultivate the meningococcus from the blood, although this procedure is not adopted as a routine.   For this purpose 10 c.c. of blood should be withdrawn from the median basilic vein, and distributed in 1 c.c. quantities over a series of 10 ascitic agar plates ; or two flasks containing 150 c.c. of 33 per cent. ascitic fluid broth may each be seeded with 5 c.c. blood.   Positive results may be expected in 25 per cent. of cases examined during the first week of the disease.

(2) *Demonstration of Antibodies.*—The blood may be examined for specific antibodies in special cases ; but the diagnostic value of such tests is very doubtful, and they must never be regarded as a substitute for the direct cultural examination.

It has been found that agglutinins are frequently present in the blood serum of patients suffering from cerebrospinal fever (Dieudonné 1906, MacGregor 1910).   Von Lingelsheim (1908) examined the sera of 593 patients.   On the 1st day of disease 24·1 per cent. gave a positive agglutination reaction ; from the 6th to the 20th day, 52·7 per cent. ; after the 21st day, only 26·7 per cent. of positive reactions were obtained.   The titre varies considerably.   Bettencourt and França (1904) found that it was usually 1–10 to 1–50 ; occasionally titres of 1–200 or even 1–1000 were met with.   Von Lingelsheim (1905a) gives the following figures :

146 agglutinated at	.	.	.	.	.	.	.	.	.	1–10
86 ,, ,,	.	.	.	.	.	.	.	.	.	1–25
30 ,, ,,	.	.	.	.	.	.	.	.	.	1–50
8 ,, ,,	.	.	.	.	.	.	.	.	.	1–100
1 ,, ,,	.	.	.	.	.	.	.	.	.	1–200
149 failed to agglutinate at	.	.	.	.	.	.				1–10

Gates (1918) found agglutinins almost constantly in the blood of carriers of 4 to 16 weeks' standing ; the titre was generally 1–16 to 1–32.

It is seen that agglutinins are not present in more than 50 per cent. of cases as a rule. MacGregor (1910) found that when marked toxæmia was present, there were generally no agglutinins ; likewise in chronic and in abortive cases.   They were present in greatest quantities in cases with an acute onset and fairly high fever.   Other observers (Elser and Huntoon 1909) have found the agglutination reaction to be too irregular for diagnosis.

Houston and Rankin (1907), studying the opsonic content of the serum of patients suffering from cerebrospinal fever, found that it was raised in 25 per cent. of patients on the 2nd day of the disease, in 60 per cent. on the 5th day, and in 96·1 per cent. after the 6th day. They stated that the opsonin test was of great value in the diagnosis of suspected cases. MacGregor (1910) found opsonins present in greatest quantity during the 2nd and 3rd weeks of the disease ; like agglutinins, they are said to be most abundant in cases with acute onset.

Post-mortem Examination.—In the examination of bodies at autopsy, it is important to take cultures within 12 hours of death if possible ; the meningococcus dies out rapidly, and though it may be found microscopically in smears from the meninges, cultures often prove to be sterile. For cultural purposes, it is best to use the pus on the meninges ; if there is no pus visible in this situation, the interior of the lateral ventricles should be carefully examined ; occasionally some may be found in the posterior horn. In cases of doubt the spinal cord should be removed, and a careful search made, especially of the posterior aspect.

Prophylaxis.

We have seen that the meningococcus lives as a parasite in the nasopharynx. Under normal conditions it will be found in a certain proportion of apparently healthy persons. Mathews and Herrold (1918) found it in 4·4 per cent. of non-contacts in a military camp during an epidemic ; Ponder (1918) in 13 per cent. of non-contact civilians in a non-epidemic period ; Scott (1916) in 22 per cent. of non-contact hospital out-patients ; Nabarro (1917) in 6·3 per cent. of children attending a hospital. As a conservative estimate we may say that in non-epidemic times the meningococcus is present in 2–8 per cent. of healthy civilians ; the actual proportion will depend to a certain extent on the time of year.

We have also seen that the meningococcus is transmitted from carriers to normal persons around them. The carrier is clearly of great importance in the continued propagation of infective material. It is of interest, therefore, to ascertain how long the organism survives in the nasopharynx. Gordon and Flack (see Report 1917) and Mathews and Herrold (1918) observed that there are two classes of carriers ; in the one class, only a few colonies of meningococci are found on the plates streaked from a nasopharyngeal swab ; in the other class, there is an almost pure growth of meningococci. The former class clears up rapidly ; the latter may carry the organism for months.

Flack (see Report 1917) gives the following table relative to the length of time that carriers may remain infective (Table CX).

TABLE CX

	Contact Carriers.	Per cent.	Non-contact Carriers.	Per cent.
Under 2 weeks	20	16·1	12	19·7
From 2–4 ,,	45	36·3	32	52·5
,, 4–6 ,,	26	21·0	5	8·2
,, 6–8 ,,	14	11·3	2	3·3
,, 8–10 ,,	4	3·2	7	11·5
,, 10–12 ,,	5	4·0	—	—
Over 12 ,,	10	8·1	3	4·9

Thus the percentage of carriers of more than 4 weeks' duration was 47·6 per cent. in the case of 124 true contacts, and 27·9 per cent. in the case of 61 non-

contact carriers.   A comparison of the persistence of different serological types
of the meningococcus in the nasopharynx failed to reveal any marked variation
between them.   Norton and Baisley (1931) in the civilian epidemic at Detroit
found that 72·4 per cent. of contact carriers became negative within a fortnight.
Not all carriers, however, clear up.   During inter-epidemic times some persons
carry the meningococcus for months and even years ; the organism, in fact, takes
its place in the normal nasopharyngeal flora.

Apart from droplet infection by carriers, it is possible that indirect infection
may play a small part in the spread of the disease.   Dopter (1921) considers that
this may occur occasionally by handkerchiefs, bedding, clothes, and drinking
vessels contaminated with nasal mucus.   It is difficult to say how frequent such
indirect infection may be, but in view of the extreme susceptibility of the meningococcus to drying and to cold, we may regard it as negligible.   Neither in barracks
nor in civilian households is this method of infection to be compared with the
direct infection by nasal mucus sprayed from the carrier.

In connection with the prevention of cerebrospinal fever much has been
written on the advisability of detecting and isolating carriers.   Hachtel and
Hayward (1911) were able to eliminate the disease from an orphan children's
home by isolating the carriers, treating them with topical applications of antimeningococcal serum, and not releasing them till after two negative swabs.
Apart from occasional instances of this sort it will be realized that, however
effective such an isolation policy might be, its rigid application in civil or military
life would be quite impracticable, owing to the high proportion of carriers in a
given population.   Wherever possible, however, it is advisable to prevent carriers
from coming into contact with infants and young children, particularly in dormi-
tories and bedrooms.

In preventing an outbreak, or in limiting its spread, it is desirable on general
grounds to reduce overcrowding as much as possible, to ensure adequate ventilation,
and to induce people, as far as the weather and other conditions permit, to lead
an open-air life.   Flack (see Report 1917) found that carriers became negative
much more rapidly during fine weather and sunshine than during dull rainy weather.
Attempts at nasal disinfection generally prove fruitless ; neither local treatment
with antiseptics nor with immune serum appears to be of any definite value in
achieving this end.

Prophylactic Vaccination.—The value of prophylactic vaccination is difficult
to ascertain.   No definite conclusions can be drawn from the earlier attempts (see
Sophian and Black 1912, Greenwood 1916, Gates 1918).   More recently Zrůnek
and Feierabend (1931) endeavoured to immunize the Czechoslovak army.   Soldiers
whose names began with A-M were vaccinated, while those with names beginning
with N-Z were left as controls.   Three doses—2,000, 4,000, and 4,000 million—of
a vaccine prepared from recently isolated local strains killed at 60° C. for 1 hour
were given.   The inoculations were made in December, just prior to the usual
seasonal outbreak of the disease.   Of 21,280 subjects vaccinated in 1926 and 1927,
5 developed meningitis and 3 died.   Of 19,684 controls, 6 developed meningitis
and 3 died.   Unfortunately for the success of the experiment, meningitis was much
less prevalent in 1927 and 1928 than in previous years.   The evidence, so far as it
goes, does not however suggest that vaccination confers a high degree of immunity
to the disease.   Riding and Corkill (1932) carried out a large series of vaccinations
on natives in the Northern Sudan.   One group of 10,691 men received a polyvalent

meningococcal vaccine, another group of 10,451 received T.A.B. vaccine, while 245,058 served as controls. No significant protection was afforded by either of the vaccines.

Serum Treatment.—The results of this treatment recorded by different observers are somewhat confusing, and their significance is by no means easy to assess.

Jochmann (1906) was the first to introduce this method of treatment. He prepared a polyvalent serum by injecting horses, first with dead then with living cultures, and found that it would protect mice against 4–6 M.L.D., provided it was given 24 hours beforehand in a dose of 0·5 c.c. subcutaneously or intraperitoneally. He showed that the serum contained agglutinins, bactericidins and bacteriotropins. He then employed his serum for the treatment of human patients ; he gave it in 20 c.c. doses subcutaneously or intrathecally ; 12 out of the 17 cases treated recovered.

Kraus and Doerr (1908) prepared a serum by the injection of goats and horses with broth filtrates and endotoxin ; the resulting product was able to neutralize the endotoxin *in vitro*, and to protect guinea-pigs against subsequent injection with a lethal dose of toxin.

In spite of the work done by the early observers, it is to Flexner (1907c, 1912, 1913, Flexner and Jobling 1908a, b) more than to any other, that we owe our present knowledge of the value of serum treatment. In 1907 he (1907c) prepared sera from the goat, horse, rabbit and guinea-pig. He found that in monkeys the simultaneous injection of serum and of meningococci intraspinally was not followed by the development of severe symptoms, although the organisms persisted for a time in the spinal fluid ; further, by injecting serum 6 hours after the infecting dose, the monkey—already seriously ill—could be saved from apparently impending death. Encouraged by these results he proceeded to try the serum on human cases. Together with Jobling (Flexner and Jobling 1908a) he prepared his serum by subcutaneous injection into horses at weekly intervals of living cocci and auto- lysate alternately ; an attempt to standardize it was made by titrating it according to the complement-fixation test, and against the autolysate in guinea-pigs, but neither method was found to be quantitatively reliable. The serum was distributed from the Rockefeller Institute in New York to all parts of the world ; reports were received from the practitioners using it, and in 1913 these were finally collected and analysed (Flexner 1913).

Excluding fulminant cases dying within 24 hours of serum injection, cases with mixed infection of the meninges, cases of intercurrent infections, and hope- lessly chronic cases, of a total of 1,294 patients treated by their serum, 894 recovered and 400 died, giving a mortality of 30·9 per cent. This mortality must be compared with that of untreated cases, *from which, however, similar deductions have not been made.* At this time the mortality of cerebrospinal fever in Great Britain was from 70–80 per cent., in Germany 42–67 per cent., in France 75 per cent., in Belgium 77·7 per cent., and in Italy 55·6 per cent., in Palestine over 80 per cent., in Greece 58·6 per cent., and in the Transvaal 74 per cent. From these figures it may be concluded that the mortality of non-serum-treated cases was about 70 per cent. In 1,211 treated cases the reports were sufficiently full to permit an analysis of the effect of the time of administration (Table CXI, p. 1140).

This table brings out very strikingly the beneficial effect of early treatment. The mortality of cases in which serum treatment was commenced before the 4th day was only half that of cases not treated till the 2nd week or later.

TABLE CXI

Time of Injection.	No. of Cases.	Recovered.	Died.	Per cent. Recovered.	Per cent. Died.
1–3 days	199	163	36	81·9	18·1
4th–7th day . . .	346	252	94	72·8	27·2
Later than 7th day .	666	423	243	63·5	36·5
Totals	1,211	838	373	69·2	30·8

Another interesting point is the fatality of serum-treated patients at different ages (Table CXII).

TABLE CXII

MORTALITY ACCORDING TO AGE IN SERUM-TREATED PATIENTS.

Age.	No. of Cases.	Recovered.	Died.	Per cent. Recovered.	Per cent. Died.
Under 1 year . .	129	65	64	50·4	49·6
1–2 years .	87	60	27	69·0	31·0
2–5 ,, .	194	139	55	71·6	28·4
5–10 ,, .	218	185	33	84·9	15·1
10–20 ,, .	360	254	106	70·6	29·4
Over 20 ,, .	288	180	108	62·5	37·5
Age not given . .	18	11	7	61·1	38·9
Totals	1,294	894	400	69·1	30·9

From this table it is seen that infants under 1 year of age have the highest mortality, and children between 5 and 10 years the lowest. The high infantile mortality may be largely due to the difficulty of diagnosis, so that serum treatment is often not commenced till after the disease has lasted a week, and partly also to the technical difficulties inherent in lumbar puncture and in serum administration in the very young.

A further study of the records seemed to show that in cases favourably influenced by serum, recovery occurred fairly rapidly; not infrequently the temperature, which in untreated patients generally falls by lysis, fell by crisis. This was especially noticeable in cases treated early.

Following the injection of serum, the blood leucocytosis fell from a figure of 20,000–40,000 to normal within a week or so; the spinal fluid became progressively clearer, the pus cells grew fewer, and the meningococci disappeared. On the other hand, in cases not influenced by serum the leucocytosis remained high; the spinal fluid showed an increase in the turbidity, and in the number of pus cells and living meningococci.

In cases untreated by serum which did not prove rapidly fatal, the disease often passed into a chronic stage lasting for months; or if recovery occurred, it was apt to be followed by a relapse. In serum-treated cases, however, it was found that the patients either died or recovered completely. Only very rarely did the disease become chronic. Relapses were likewise uncommon; they occurred in only 8 per cent. of cases, and frequently yielded to further serum treatment.

Another favourable indication of the value of serum was the diminution in the proportion of patients who developed complications. These complications—irido-choroiditis, panophthalmitis, deafness due to internal ear disease, pleurisy, pericarditis, endocarditis, arthropathies, insanity and others—are not uncommon in patients who recover naturally. In serum-treated patients such complications were few ; the only one which occurred with any frequency was deafness ; this was doubtless due to the early spread of the disease to the internal ear ; the sooner serum treatment was begun, the less likely was this spread to occur.

Summing up Flexner's results, it would appear that by serum treatment the mortality was considerably reduced, the frequency of relapses diminished, the incidence of chronic cases abolished, and the proportion and the severity of the complications lowered very considerably.

Dopter (1921) analyses 882 cases treated during 1909–11 in various parts of France by sera which he prepared at the Pasteur Institute. The number of deaths was 129, giving a crude death rate of 14·5 per cent. Deducting 28 cases treated *in extremis* or not till a few hours before death, and 4 cases succumbing to secondary infections after the meningeal symptoms had receded, there remain 850 cases with 97 deaths, or a corrected death rate of 11·7 per cent. The mortality of the non-serum-treated cases at the same period was about 65 per cent.

Netter and Debré (1911) give records of 133 patients. The first 33 were not given serum treatment, the last 100 were injected intraspinally. The results are given in Table CXIII.

TABLE CXIII

	No. of Cases.	"Crude D.R."	"Corrected D.R."
		Per cent.	Per cent.
Untreated . . .	33	48·5	37·0
Treated . . .	100	28·0	10·9

In the serum-treated patients the disease was shortened ; thus, 66 per cent. recovered within a week, as against 18 per cent. of non-serum-treated patients. The frequency of complications and sequelæ was likewise diminished ; in serum-treated patients they amounted to 6·3 per cent., in patients who had not received serum to 23·5 per cent. The time of injection was also found to be important, as is shown in Table CXIV.

TABLE CXIV

Time of Serum Injection.	No. of Cases.	"Crude D.R."	"Corrected D.R."
		Per cent.	Per cent.
1st–3rd day	44	20·9	5·55
4th–7th day	32	33·3	15·4
Later than 1 week . .	23	26·0	15·0

Adshead (1918) treated a series of 71 patients in the Royal Naval Hospital, Haslar, during 1915–17. The serum used in the first 22 cases came from various sources ; in the last 49 cases, the Rockefeller polyvalent serum was used almost exclusively. It was found advisable to give 3 or 4 doses of 20 c.c. on consecutive days. Serum given late in the disease appeared to cause a rise in intracranial pressure. Frequent lumbar puncture and depletion of cerebrospinal fluid led to wasting, slow convalescence, and sometimes death. Of the total of 71 patients, 19 died—a mortality of 26·8 per cent. The main complications were suppurative irido-cyclitis, which occurred twice, pericarditis 4 times, and acute synovitis of the larger joints 6 times. Sequelæ were practically absent.

Hine (see Report 1920) analysed 267 cases of cerebrospinal fever in soldiers treated during the War by mono-typical serum prepared in this country. From these, 18 are subtracted who died from fever or from another serious intercurrent disease, and 48 who were not given the correct serum—owing to failure to type the coccus. Of the remaining 201 cases, 57 died, *i.e.* a mortality of 28·4 per cent. During 1914–18 the average male civilian death rate from cerebrospinal fever in London, without similar deductions, was 60·1 per cent. These cases Hine divides into two groups (Table CXV).

TABLE CXV

	Cases.	Deaths.	Percentage Mortality.
Group A. Cases in which serum was given on the 6th day or earlier	141	27	19·1
Group B. Delayed exhibition of serum. Insufficient dosage. Moribund or with severe complications	39	15	38·5
	10	9	90·0 } 50·0
	11	6	54·5

Table CXVI shows the effect of the type of serum administered.

TABLE CXVI

	Cases.	Deaths.	Percentage Mortality.
Type I . . .	65	6	9·2
Type II . . .	104	41	39·4
Type III . . .	28	7	25·0
Type IV . . .	4	3	75·0
Untyped . . .	48	22	45·8

From this it is seen that the best results were obtained with Type I serum ; this, in spite of the fact that Kennedy and Drought (1917) found that cases infected by Type I were considerably more fatal than those infected by Type II.

The mortality of 152 cases treated within the first 6 days was 25 per cent. ; of 44 treated later 43 per cent. This agrees with Flexner and Jobling's results. Rolleston (1918) on the other hand found little difference in the mortality of cases in the Navy treated before or after the 7th day. He points out with justice that cases which survive without serum treatment until after the 7th day are not fulminating, and probably some are so mild as to recover spontaneously.

Wadsworth (1931) recorded the treatment of cases during the years 1920–30 with a 6-strain serum prepared in the New York State laboratory. Making the same exceptions as in Flexner's series, 108 deaths occurred in a series of 606 patients, *i.e.*, a case mortality of 17·8 per cent. In this country Sturdee and Scott (1933) reported a crude death rate of 38·8 per cent. in a series of 859 cases receiving serum treatment during 1931–33.

Before judging the value of serum treatment there are certain factors of importance to be considered.

The first concerns the **mode of preparation** of the serum. This has varied in different countries.

Flexner and Jobling (1908*a*) used subcutaneous injection of living diplococci and of an autolysate alternately ; this method, though effective, requires considerable time— 10 months or more—before the serum is sufficiently potent for use. Amoss and Wollstein (1916) described a more rapid procedure, yielding a polyvalent serum of high titre in 8 to 12 weeks ; the essential feature of their method consists in giving 3 successive intravenous injections of living meningococci at daily intervals, followed by a rest of 8 days, before the administration of a fresh series. Numerous strains of different types are included. A. S. Griffith (see Report 1920) followed this method in his preparation of sera for the Medical Research Council, with the exception that he used strains of only one type for each horse ; the resulting sera were therefore monovalent. It is important in selecting the cultures to be used for immunization to choose strains which are representative of those present during an epidemic. F. Griffith (1917) advises the use of the highly complex strains which are found more commonly at the height of an epidemic than at any other period. In the preparation of a polyvalent serum Wadsworth and Kirkbride (1926) favour the use of 4–6 carefully selected strains rather than of larger numbers. On the ground that meningococci produce a soluble toxin (see Ferry, Norton, and Steele 1931), Ferry (1932, 1934) recommends antitoxic sera prepared by injecting horses with the type-specific toxins. The evidence, in his opinion, suggests that antitoxic are of more importance therapeutically than antibacterial sera. The antibody content of sera may be concentrated by suitable fractionation (Neal *et al.* 1928, Murdick and Cohen 1933, 1935), but whether such sera are more efficacious in practice than ordinary sera still remains to be seen.

The next point to be considered is the **titration** of the serum. As yet there is no laboratory method by which the therapeutic power may be correctly gauged.

Flexner and Jobling (1908*a*) relied partly on the complement-fixation test, and also on titration against autolysate in guinea-pigs. Nicolle, Debains and Jouan (1918) used the complement-fixation test alone ; Jobling (1909) the opsonin content ; Amoss and Wollstein (1916) the agglutinin content ; Hitchens and Robinson (1916) a mouse-protection test ; Gordon (see Report 1920) the anti-endotoxic value ; and de la Rivière and Roux (1925) a precipitin test. As the results given by these different methods vary considerably, it is clear that they cannot all be satisfactory. Experience during more recent years has similarly failed to reveal any substantial agreement between different workers on the best method of titration. Wadsworth (1931) favours agglutination, Zozaya (1932) and Mishulow (1935) precipitation, Ferry, Norton and Steele (1931) and Konowa and Nikolsky (1934) toxin-neutralization, Sickles (1933) a neutralization test based on skin reactivity, and Zdrowdowsky and Voronine (1932), Branham (1935), and Rake (1935*b*) some form of protection test. Standardization in terms of some significant unit is clearly desirable before liberation of a serum from the laboratory ; otherwise normal sera, or sera containing only a minimal antibody content, may be distributed by certain agencies. What this unit is to be still awaits international agreement. (For general discussion, see Murray 1929.)

Another point is the **dose** of serum to be injected.

In an acute case in an adult it is advisable to inject 20–30 c.c. of serum to start with, after having drawn off rather more than an equivalent amount of cerebrospinal fluid. The quantity of fluid which should be withdrawn varies from case to case ; if it is under great pressure, it may be allowed to run until it is coming at the rate of 1 drop per second. Sometimes 120 c.c. may flow away before this rate is reached. But the patient must be watched very carefully during the process, and if any untoward signs are observed, the flow must be stopped immediately. Generally it is better, if the fluid is under great pressure, to withdraw about 50 c.c., and to repeat the lumbar puncture 12 hours later. The serum should be injected at least once a day for the first 4 or 5 days ; sometimes it is desirable to give it twice daily. As in diphtheria, the amount given must be judged by the clinical condition of the patient. In fulminant cases, for example, greater risks may be taken than in less acute cases.

The **route** of injection is also of importance. Since meningococci are frequently present in the blood stream it has been advised that the serum should be given not only intra-thecally but also intravenously. Herrick (1918) treated 137 cases by spinal injections with a mortality of 34·3 per cent. ; and 128 cases by combined spinal and intravenous injections with a mortality of only 14·8 per cent. Further, he found that the greater the amount of serum injected, the lower was the mortality. He advises giving about 100 c.c. intrathecally and 400–600 c.c. intravenously. Fewer complications were encount-ered when the combined method was employed. In the pure meningococcal septicæmias without coincident meningitis, the serum should always be administered intravenously. In chronic cases, with blockage of the spinal canal, serum should be injected sub-occipit-ally into the cisterna magna (see Report 1931). Very favourable results are said to follow this method (Cassoute *et al.* 1933, Alliezand and Carbonel 1933, Sepet *et al.* 1933, Robertson 1935). In cases that develop arthropathies, serum may be advantageously injected into the inflamed joints.

These are the main factors influencing serum treatment—the mode of prepara-tion, the method of titration, the amount injected, and the route of injection. Taking all these into consideration, the results obtained must be considered as relatively favourable. It would seem that in cases adequately treated with a good monovalent serum, Type I in particular, the mortality may be reduced by over 50 per cent. The adjustments that have been made in arriving at certain of these figures are, however, clearly unjustifiable, and so far as we know serum has never been tested under statistically satisfactory conditions. To do this, it would be necessary to give the serum to alternate cases in an epidemic, and to treat both series of cases in other respects in identically the same way. This would mean performing a lumbar puncture on the control cases with the same frequency as on the serum-treated cases, and replacing the fluid withdrawn by normal serum. The effect of lumbar puncture alone is probably of value. Until such a series is tried, we shall not be able to form a just opinion of the specific activity of the serum itself. The facts, however, that the earlier the serum is administered, the better are the results ; that certain batches of sera appear to be more efficacious than others ; and that the combined intrathecal and intravenous method gives a lower mortality than the intrathecal method alone, seem to us to point in favour of the therapeutic value of the serum itself.

Pneumococcal Meningitis

This form of meningitis occurs as a complication of lobar or broncho-pneumonia, and is commoner in children than in adults. Not infrequently in children it is secondary to middle-ear disease. Sometimes a primary pneumococcal meningitis is seen. The pneumococci are present in large numbers in the cerebrospinal fluid, which is turbid and full of pus cells ; the cocci may be recognized by their appear-ance as Gram-positive, lanceolate, capsulated, and mostly extra-cellular diplococci. Cultures are best taken on to blood agar or ascitic agar. The type of coccus may be determined in the usual way. Serum treatment with monovalent type serum may be carried out, preferably by the combined intravenous and intrathecal method. The disease, however, is almost uniformly fatal.

Streptococcal Meningitis

Streptococcal meningitis is most frequently due to extension from middle-ear disease, especially in children, and to perforated wounds of the skull. The cerebrospinal fluid is turbid, and contains large numbers of pus cells and of streptococci, which are usually of the β-hæmolytic type. Recovery is very rare.

Tuberculous Meningitis

Tuberculous meningitis is probably always secondary to a tuberculous focus in some other part of the body, but, as it is often difficult to determine the site of the primary lesion, even at autopsy, the disease not infrequently appears to be primary. Osler (Osler and McCrae 1920) states that it may occur during the 1st year of life, but is commonest between the 2nd and 5th years ; it is, however, not uncommon in adults, particularly as a terminal infection in pulmonary tuberculosis. The laboratory diagnosis is often difficult. Lumbar puncture reveals a fluid which may be limpid, and may contain only mononuclear cells. The protein content is, however, always raised, while both the sugar and the chloride content are much diminished. The number of cells is generally increased, the most usual count being between 50 and 400 per c.mm. In most cases these cells consist chiefly of lymphocytes, but these are almost always associated with numerous polymorphonuclear and often with some plasma cells. If the fluid is allowed to stand at room temperature, a clot not infrequently forms ; this should be spread on a slide, and stained by Ziehl-Neelsen. If no clot forms, the fluid should be centrifuged at high speed for half an hour, the deposit spread on albuminized slides, or fixed with methyl alcohol, and stained with Ziehl-Neelsen. It is often only after prolonged search that a group of tubercle bacilli is found. As well as being examined microscopically, the clot or centrifuged deposit should be injected intramuscularly into a guinea-pig, which is killed after 4–8 weeks (see Chapter LVI). Sometimes it is possible to culture the organisms when none are visible microscopically ; for this purpose the deposit should be distributed over 3 or 4 Dorset egg tubes, and incubated for a month. The bovine type is responsible for about 23 per cent. of cases in this country.

The disease is uniformly fatal. A few cases have been reported which have recovered, but it is possible that they are explicable by an error in diagnosis.

Influenzal Meningitis

This form may be met with sporadically or during the progress of an influenza epidemic. Most cases appear to be primary. It was first described by Slawyk (1899), and has since been recognized by a number of workers (see particularly Cohen 1909, Ritchie 1910, Henry 1912, Rivers 1922, Schnyder 1925, Koch and Krämer 1931, Eddy 1933, Neal *et al.* 1934, Dahr 1934). Neal and her colleagues met with 111 cases of this type among a total of 2,727 cases of meningitis. The incidence is highest in childhood. It is rare under 2 months or over 6 years of age (Fothergill and Wright 1933). About 60–80 per cent. of cases occur during the first 2 years of life. The disease closely simulates cerebrospinal meningitis. It usually lasts 10–20 days, and has a case mortality rate of about 95 per cent. The cerebrospinal fluid is under pressure, is cloudy or purulent, has a high cell count, especially of polymorphs, and shows a variable increase in protein and often a marked decrease in sugar. Gram-negative bacilli are present with the typical Pfeiffer morphology, but sometimes accompanied by long thread forms. In the early stage of the disease they are intracellular, but later they become free in the fluid. On suitable media they can be cultivated from the spinal fluid, and often from the blood, and from the purulent joint exudates that occur not infrequently as a complication of this disease. In their nutritional requirements and their indole production they resemble *H. influenzæ*, but they differ from this organism in their high pathogenicity for laboratory animals. Inoculated intraperitoneally into rabbits, guinea-pigs, rats, and mice, they often give rise to a fatal septicæmia and to purulent effusions in the serous cavities.

Other Forms of Meningitis

Occasionally meningitis may be caused by organisms, such as *B. anthracis*, *Bact. coli*, Friedländer's bacillus (Gordon and Norton 1930), *Bact. typhosum*, *Bact. enteritidis* (Stevenson and Wills 1933), *Pf. mallei*, *Br. suis* (Hartley *et al.* 1934, Hansmann and Schencken 1932), the gonococcus (Strumia and Kohlhas 1933), *Actinomyces bovis* (Henry 1910), and *Leptospira icterohæmorrhagiæ* (Marie and Gabriel 1935, Mollaret and Erber 1935).

Rivers and Scott (1935) have described a case due to a filtrable virus.

REFERENCES

ADSHEAD, G. P. (1918) *Spec. Rep. Ser. med. Res. Coun., Lond.*, No. 17.
ALBRECHT, H. and GHON, A. (1901) *Wien. klin. Wschr.*, **14**, 984 ; (1902) *Ibid.*, **15**, 1219 ; (1903) *Zbl. Bakt.*, **33**, 496.
ALLIEZAND, J. and CARBONEL, J. (1933) *Marseille-Méd.*, **70**, 838.
AMOSS, H. L. and WOLLSTEIN, M. (1916) *J. exp. Med.*, **23**, 403.
ARMSTRONG, C., FOTHERINGHAM, J. B., HOOD, A., LITTLE, C. J. H., and THOMPSON, T. O. (1931) *J. R. Army med. Cps*, **57**, 321.
BAESLACK, F. W., BUNCE, A. H., BRUNELLE, G. C., FLEMING, J. S., KLUGH, G. F., MCLEAN, E. H., and SALOMON, A. V. (1918) *J. Amer. med. Ass.*, **70**, 684.
BELL, A. S. G. (1920a) *Spec. Rep. Ser. med. Res. Coun., Lond.*, No. 50, p. 57 ; (1920b) *Ibid.*, No. 50, p. 63.
BETTENCOURT, A. and FRANÇA, C. (1904) *Z. Hyg. InfektKr.*, **66**, 463.
BRANHAM, S. E. (1930) *Publ. Hlth Rep., Wash.*, **45**, 845 ; (1932) *J. Immunol.*, **23**, 49 ; (1935) *Publ. Hlth Rep., Wash.*, **50**, 768.
CASSOUTE, MONTUS, and LEGRAND. (1933) *Marseille-Méd.*, **70**, 836.
CLARK, W. E. LE G. (1929) *Rep. publ. Hlth med. Subj., Lond.*, No. 54.
COHEN. (1909) *Ann. Inst. Pasteur*, **23**, 273.
COMPTON, A. (1918) *J. R. Army. med. Cps*, **31**, 241.
COUNCILMAN, W. T., MALLORY, F. B., and WRIGHT, J. H. (1898) *Rep. State Bd Hlth Mass.*
DAHR, P. (1934) *Dtsch. med. Wschr.*, **60**, 782.
DIEUDONNÉ. (1906) *Zbl. Bakt.*, **41**, 418.
DOPTER, C. (1921) " L'infection meningococcique." Paris.
DUDLEY, S. F. and BRENNAN, J. R. (1934) *J. Hyg., Camb.*, **34**, 525.
EAGLETON, A. J. (1919–20) *J. Hyg., Camb.*, **18**, 264.
EDDY, B. E. (1933) *J. infect. Dis.*, **52**, 242.
EDLER. (1884–88) *San. Ber. Preusz. Armee.*
ELSER, W. J. (1905–06) *J. med. Res.*, **14**, 89.
ELSER, W. J. and HUNTOON, F. M. (1909) *J. med. Res.*, **20**, 371.
EMBLETON, D. and PETERS, E. H. (1915) *J. R. Army med. Cps*, **24**, 468.
FABER, E. E. (1900) *Z. Hyg. InfektKr.*, **34**, 253.
FERRY, N. S. (1932) *J. Immunol.*, **23**, 315, 325 ; (1934) *Ibid.*, **26**, 133.
FERRY, N. S., NORTON, J. F., and STEELE, A. H. (1931) *J. Immunol.*, **21**, 293.
FINDLAY, G. M. and CLARKE, L. P. (1935) *J. Path. Bact.*, **40**, 55.
FLEXNER, S. (1907a) *J. exp. Med.*, **9**, 105 ; (1907b) *Ibid.*, **9**, 142 ; (1907c) *Ibid.*, **9**, 168 ; (1912) *J. State Med.*, **20**, 257 ; (1913) *J. exp. Med.*, **17**, 553.

FLEXNER, S. and JOBLING, J. W. (1908a) *J. exp. Med.*, **10**, 141 ; (1908b) *Ibid.*, **10**, 690.
FOÀ, P. and BORDONI-UFFREDUZZI, G. (1886) *Dtsch. med. Wschr.*, **12**, 249, 568.
FOTHERGILL, L. D. and WRIGHT, J. (1933) *J. Immunol.*, **24**, 273.
FRAENKEL. (1886) *Dtsch. med. Wschr.*, **12**, 209.
GATES, F. L. (1918) *J. exp. Med.*, **28**, 449.
GLOVER, J. A. (1920) *Spec. Rep. Ser. med. Res. Coun., Lond.*, No. 50, p. 133.
GOLDSCHMIDT, F. (1887) *Zbl. Bakt.*, **2**, 649.
GOODWIN, M. E. and SHOLLY, A. I. VON. (1906) *J. infect. Dis.*, Suppl. 2, p. 21.
GORDON, J. E. and NORTON, J. F. (1930) *J. prev. Med., Baltimore*, **4**, 339.
GORDON, M. H., HINE, T. G. M., and FLACK, M. (1916) *Brit. med. J.*, ii. 678.
GREENWOOD, M. (1916) *Proc. roy. Soc. Med., Epidem. Sect.*, **10**, 44.
GRIFFITH, F. (1917) *Rep. loc. Govt Bd, New Ser.*, No. 111, p. 52.
HACHTEL, F. W. and HAYWARD, E. H. (1911) *J. infect. Dis.*, **8**, 444.
HANSMANN, G. H. and SCHENCKEN, J. R. (1932) *Amer. J. Path.*, **8**, 435.
HARTLEY, G. A., MILLICE, G. S., and JORDAN, P. H. (1934) *J. Amer. med. Ass.*, **103**, 251.
HENRY, H. (1910) *J. Path. Bact.*, **14**, 164 ; (1912) *Ibid.*, **17**, 174.
HERRICK, W. W. (1918) *J. Amer. med. Ass.*, **71**, 612.
HEUBNER, O. (1896) *Dtsch. med. Wschr.*, **22**, 423.
HIBLER, E. VON. (1896) *Zbl. Bakt.*, **19**, 33, 113.
HIRSCH, A. (1886) " Handbook of Geographical and Historical Pathology," Trans. New Sydenham Soc., Vol. 3, p. 547. London.
HITCHENS, A. P. and ROBINSON, G. H. (1916) *J. Immunol.*, **1**, 345.
HOUSTON, T. and RANKIN, J. C. (1907) *Brit. med. J.*, ii. 1414.
JACOBITZ. (1905) *Münch. med. Wschr.*, **52**, 2178.
JAEGER, H. (1895) *Z. Hyg. InfektKr.*, **19**, 351 ; (1903a) *Zbl. Bakt.*, **33**, 23 ; (1903b) *Ibid.*, **33**, 681.
JOBLING, J. W. (1909) *J. exp. Med.*, **11**, 614.
JOCHMANN, G. (1906) *Dtsch. med. Wschr.*, **32**, 789.
KENNEDY, A. M. and DROUGHT, C. C. W. (1917) *Brit. med. J.*, i. 261.
KIEFER, F. (1896) *Berl. klin. Wschr.*, **33**, 628.
KISTER, J. (1896) *Zbl. Bakt.*, **20**, 148.
KOCH. (1882) *Berl. klin. Wschr.*, **19**, 221.
KOCH, F. E. and KRÄMER, E. (1931) *Münch. med. Wschr.*, **78**, 1131.
KONOWA, A. and NIKOLSKY, A. (1934) *Zbl. Bakt.*, **132**, 187.
KRAUS, R. and DOERR, R. (1908) *Wien. klin. Wschr.*, **21**, 12.
KUTSCHER, K. (1906) *Dtsch. med. Wschr.*, **32**, 1071.
LINGELSHEIM, VON. (1905a) *Dtsch. med. Wschr.*, **31**, 1017 ; (1905b) *Ibid.*, **31**, 1217 ; (1908) *Z. Hyg. InfektKr.*, **59**, 457.
LOW, R. B. (1916) *Rep. loc. Govt Bd, New Ser.*, No. 110, p. 115.
MACGREGOR, A. S. M. (1910) *J. Path. Bact.*, **14**, 503.
MAEGRAITH, B. G. (1935) *Lancet*, i. 545.
MARIE, J. and GABRIEL, P. (1935) *Bull. Mém. Soc. méd. Hôp., Paris*, **51**, 1454.
MATHEWS, G. and HERROLD, R. D. (1918) *J. infect. Dis.*, **22**, 523.
MISHULOW, L. (1935) *Science*, **81**, 383.
MOLLARET, P. and ERBER, B. (1935) *Bull. Mém. Soc. méd. Hôp. Paris*, **51**, 1632.
MUIR, R. (1919) *J. R. Army med. Cps*, **33**, 404.
MURDICK, P. P. and COHEN, S. M. (1933) *J. Immunol.*, **24**, 531 ; (1935) *Ibid.*, **28**, 205.
MURRAY, E. G. D. (1929) *Spec. Rep. Ser. med. Res. Coun., Lond.*, No. 124, p. 111.
NABARRO, D. (1917) *Rep. loc. Govt Bd, New Ser.*, No. 114, p. 207.
NEAL, J. B., JACKSON, H. W., and APPELBAUM, E. (1934) *J. Amer. med. Ass.*, **102**, 513.
NEAL, J. B., JACKSON, H. W., APPELBAUM, E., and BANZHAF, E. J. (1928) *J. Amer. med. Ass.*, **91**, 1427.
NETTER, A. and DEBRÉ, R. (1911) " La méningite cérébro-spinale." Paris.
NICOLLE, M., DEBAINS, E., and JOUAN, C. (1918) *Ann. Inst. Pasteur*, **32**, 150.
NORTON, J. F. and BAISLEY, I. E. (1931) *J. prev. Med.*, **5**, 357.
OSLER, W. and MCCRAE, T. (1920) " The Principles and Practice of Medicine," 9th edit. London.
OSTERMANN, A. (1906) *Dtsch. med. Wschr.*, **32**, 414.
PONDER, C. (1918) *J. Hyg., Camb.*, **17**, 247.
RAKE, G. (1933a) *J. exp. Med.*, **57**, 561 ; (1933b) *Ibid.*, **58**, 375 ; (1934) *Ibid.*, **59**, 553 ; (1935a) *Ibid.*, **61**, 545 ; (1935b) *Proc. Soc. exp. Biol., N.Y.*, **32**, 1175.
REECE. (1916) *Rep. loc. Govt Bd, New Ser.*, No. 110.
Report. (1917) *Spec. Rep. Ser. med. Res. Coun., Lond.*, No. 3 ; (1920) *Ibid.*, No. 50 ; (1931) *Rep. publ. Hlth med. Subj., Lond.*, No. 65.
RIDING, D. and CORKILL, N. K. (1932) *J. Hyg., Camb.*, **32**, 258.
RITCHIE, J. (1910) *J. Path. Bact.*, **14**, 615.
RIVERS, T. M. (1922) *Amer. J. Dis. Child.*, **24**, 102.
RIVERS, T. M. and SCOTT, T. F. M. (1935) *Science*, **81**, 439.

RIVIÈRE, D. DE LA, and ROUX, E. (1925) *Ann. Inst. Pasteur*, **39**, 368.
ROBERTSON, D. (1935) *Brit. med. J.*, i. 445.
ROLLESTON, H. (1918) *Lancet*, i. 87 ; (1919) *Ibid.*, i. 541, 593, 645.
SALOMON. (1902) *Berl. klin. Wschr.*, **39**, 1045.
SCHERER. (1895) *Zbl. Bakt.*, **17**, 433.
SCHNYDER, W. (1925) *Ann. Inst. Pasteur*, **39**, 769.
SCOTT, W. M. (1916) *Rep. loc. Govt Bd, New Ser.*, No. 110, p. 56 ; (1917) *Ibid.*, No. 114, p. 111.
SEPET, VAGUE, and HENRY. (1933) *Marseille-Méd.*, **70**, 843.
SICKLES, G. M. (1933) *Amer. J. Hyg.*, **17**, 412.
SLAWYK. (1899) *Z. Hyg. InfektKr.*, **32**, 443.
SOPHIAN, A. and BLACK, J. (1912) *J. Amer. med. Ass.*, **59**, 527.
STEVENSON, F. N. and WILLS, L. K. (1933) *Lancet*, ii. 1084.
STILL, G. F. (1898) *J. Path. Bact.*, **5**, 147.
STRUMIA, M. M. and KOHLHAS, J. J. (1933) *J. infect. Dis.*, **53**, 212.
STURDEE, E. L. and SCOTT, W. M. (1933) *Bull. Off. int. Hyg. publ.*, **25**, 1721.
WADSWORTH, A. (1931) *Amer. J. Hyg.*, **14**, 630.
WADSWORTH, A. and KIRKBRIDE, M. B. (1926) *Amer. J. Hyg.*, **6**, 507.
WEICHSELBAUM, A. (1887) *Fortschr. Med.*, **5**, 573, 620.
WEICHSELBAUM, A. and GHON, A. (1905) *Wien. klin. Wschr.*, **18**, 625.
WESTENHOEFFER. (1906) *Berl. klin. Wschr.*, **43**, 1267, 1313.
ZDRODOWSKI, P. and VORONINE, E. (1932) *Ann. Inst. Pasteur*, **48**, 617.
ZOZAYA, J. (1932) *J. infect. Dis.*, **50**, 310.
ZRŮNEK, K. and FEIERABEND, B. (1931) *Trav. Inst. Hyg. publ. Tchécosl.*, **2**, 1.

CHAPTER LXII

GONORRHŒA

HISTORY.—That gonorrhœa is a disease stretching back into antiquity we know, but we are entirely ignorant of the time and place of its first appearance. There is little to suggest that the disease has altered in its nature during the passage of time ; it appears to run its course now in the same way as it has done for hundreds of years. It therefore differs from many diseases in which the clinical picture alters with the centuries. The explanation of this may lie in the absence of both natural and acquired immunity in man.

The causal agent, the gonococcus, was discovered by Neisser in 1879, who found it in 35 cases of gonorrhœa which had lasted for varying lengths of time, from 3 days to 13 weeks. He failed to find it in non-gonorrhœal pus, such as that accompanying chancres, buboes, etc., or in simple vaginal discharges ; he demonstrated its presence in 7 cases of ophthalmia neonatorum, and in 2 cases of adult ophthalmia. Though unable through illness to complete his investigation, he placed the ætiological rôle of the gonococcus on a footing which has never since been seriously challenged. It was left, however, to Bumm (1885a, b) to cultivate the organism, and by inoculation experiments on human subjects to demonstrate its pathogenicity in pure cultures.

Gonorrhœa in Adults.

Gonorrhœa is an acute infectious disease, generally characterized by primary invasion of the genito-urinary tract, and frequently complicated by secondary disturbances of greater or less severity.

By far the commonest method of infection is by sexual intercourse. In man the anterior urethra is first attacked. After an incubation period of 2 to 3 days, a mucoid discharge appears, which rapidly becomes purulent. At first the gonococci are mostly extra-cellular, but soon they are taken up by the pus cells, which ingest them in large numbers ; as many as 100 may be counted in a single cell.

In cases not successfully treated at this stage, the gonococci pass backwards to the posterior urethra, where they infect the glands ; from this situation they are extremely difficult to dislodge. The prostate, too, is frequently infected ; indeed it is generally a prostatitis which is responsible for the chronicity of the disease.

In women the disease starts with an acute urethritis ; later the cervix uteri becomes infected, and may remain so for a number of years.

Complications of Gonorrhœa in Adults.—Though infection may remain localized to a small area of the genito-urinary tract, it is quite common for it to spread either by direct continuity or by the blood stream to other parts of the body, and set up complications. This may occur during either the acute or the chronic stage of the disease. Thus the gonococcus has been found in epididymitis (Colombini 1898, Witte 1900), in proctitis (Bumm 1884), in salpingitis, in arthritis (Bordoni-Uffreduzzi 1894, Neisser 1894), in tenosynovitis (Hocheisen 1906), in vesiculitis (Wynn 1905), in cystitis, in ophthalmia (Neisser 1879), less frequently in peri-renal abscesses (Colombini 1898), in pyelonephritis, and in peritonitis.

In rare instances the disease may be very acute, the organisms gaining access to the blood stream and giving rise to a bacteræmia, which may be followed by pyæmia. In these cases, which may prove fatal, there is widespread infection throughout the body, and post mortem there may be found endocarditis, myocarditis, less frequently pericarditis, subcutaneous and intra-muscular abscesses in different situations, polyarthritis, phlebitis, pleurisy, general adenitis, pneumonia, and septic infarcts in the spleen and kidneys. Several such cases have been reported (Leyden 1893, Ghon and Schlagenhaufer 1898, Thayer and Lazear 1899, Strong 1904, Duval and Lewis 1905, Wynn 1905, Hocheisen 1906, Jenkins 1922). Gonococci have been demonstrated in nearly all these lesions, and have often been obtained in pure culture from the blood stream both during life and after death (Thayer and Lazear 1899, Duval and Lewis 1905, Wynn 1905, Jenkins 1922). Meningitis is a rare complication (see Strumia and Kohlhas 1933). A few cases are on record of a gonococcal stomatitis (Crosby 1905), or parotitis (Colombini 1898) ; from the latter situation the organisms have actually been cultivated.

Gonorrhœa in Children.—Children suffer from ophthalmia neonatorum and from vulvo-vaginitis. The former is due to infection at birth with gonococci present in the maternal passages ; the latter to infection of towels in infants' hospitals.

At one time ophthalmia neonatorum was responsible for a large proportion of cases of blindness, but since the introduction of the Credé preventive treatment it has become much less common.

Vulvo-vaginitis is essentially a hospital disease. Like puerperal fever and the old hospital gangrene, it is very much more frequent in institutions where large numbers of patients are collected together. Thus Fischer (1895), reporting in 1895 on the incidence during the past 2 years of the disease in the children's hospital at Altona, said that of 50 cases all but 10 were contracted in the hospital ; of these 10, some had apparently been imported from other hospitals. Holt (1905) reported on no fewer than 273 cases of the disease in the Babies' Hospital, New York, during the preceding 11 years. The disease is spread from one cot to another by the use of towels and other linen, which are imperfectly sterilized. Once introduced into a hospital or institution, it is a most difficult disease to eradicate ; only scrupulous care in technique, constantly maintained for months on end, will prove successful eventually. The disease has a way of cropping up after it has lain dormant for weeks ; to relax precautions too soon is but to court disaster.

It will be seen that the parts of the body attacked are not the same in adults as in children. Gonorrhœal ophthalmia is common in infants, rare in adults ; gonorrhœal vaginitis is common in infants and children up to 5 or 6 years old, but is uncommon in adults. A similar difference is noted in the complications ; thus in adults the internal genito-urinary organs are frequently attacked ; in children these are rarely attacked, but on the other hand acute peritonitis is fairly common in female children, but rare in adults. Thus we may say that the vagina and conjunctiva are specially susceptible during infancy, and the internal genital organs during adult life. The mucosa of the urethra and rectum are susceptible throughout life. Both in adult gonorrhœa in the female, and in vulvo-vaginitis of children, the rectum is stated to be frequently involved—in 20–30 per cent. of the cases.

Reproduction of the Disease in Man.—Direct experiments on man to ascertain the pathogenicity of the gonococcus have been almost entirely confined to urethal injection. By this route, using pure cultures of the organism, it is comparatively easy to set up a typical attack of gonorrhœa, both in males and in females (Bumm 1885a, Wertheim 1891, Bordoni-Uffreduzzi 1894, Finger *et al.* 1895, Colombini 1898). The injection of a young culture into the urethra is followed in two or three days by a purulent urethritis, which pursues a course similar to that occurring in the natural disease, often lasting for months in spite of treatment. Gonococci are present in the pus cells, and may be recovered in pure culture.

Not only is it possible to convey the disease to a normal person by injection of pure cultures, but it is possible to incite an acute attack in a patient who is suffering from chronic gonorrhœa. There is apparently little, if any, immunity acquired to the disease. Injection into the human urethra of killed gonococci gives rise to a transitory purulent inflammation (Scholtz 1900).

Steinschneider and Schäffer (1895) injected large numbers of living gonococci into the subcutaneous tissues of healthy persons, and found that no reaction of any sort occurred.

Using gonotoxin, de Christmas (1897) found that the injection of 1 c.c. into the human urethra gave rise to a urethritis, coming on in 2 hours, and subsiding after about 2 days. No immunity was established ; the same effect was reproduced after each of 5 successive injections. Wassermann (1898) injected 0·1 c.c. of toxin subcutaneously into himself ; 4 hours later a reaction set in, characterized by local inflammation, slight shivering, an evening rise of temperature, headache, and pains in the limbs and joints. He then injected the same dose subcutaneously into two patients suffering from chronic gonorrhœa ; similar results followed, accompanied by swelling of the local glands. No immunity to the toxin was established ; the same reaction was repeated after 5 separate injections at 4-day intervals.

Diagnosis.

The diagnosis of gonorrhœa depends in the main on the demonstration of the causative organism. The characteristic morphology and staining reaction of the gonococcus, and the fact that a considerable proportion of the cocci are always intracellular, make it possible to identify the organism by a direct microscopical examination of the purulent discharge in *acute* infections (Fig.

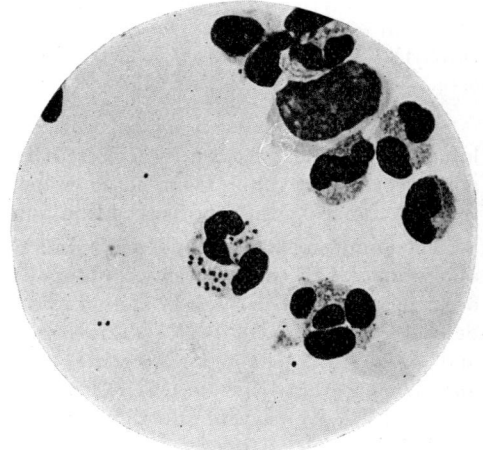

Fig. 258.—*Neisseria gonorrhœœ* in film of pus from acute gonorrhœa (× 1000).

258). Wherever any element of doubt exists, cultures should be prepared on a suitable medium (see Chapter XXII). In *chronic* cases it may be extremely difficult to demonstrate the gonococcus in films, or to isolate it in culture. This holds particularly true for the female, where a diagnosis on microscopic grounds alone can rarely be made. Appropriate measures must be taken to obtain material for examination from the situation most likely to be the seat of chronic infection—the deep urethral glands and the prostate in the male, the Bartholinian glands and the cervical glands in the female. It may be noted that the fluid withdrawn from the joints in gonorrhœal arthritis is frequently sterile, and that the same is true of pus withdrawn from the Fallopian tube in chronic cases of gonorrhœal salpingitis.

For diagnostic cultivation the method described by McLeod and his colleagues (1934) is to be strongly recommended. The medium used is a 10 per cent. heated blood agar prepared from broth made according to Wright's (1929, 1933) method, *i.e.*, extraction of the minced meat for 45 minutes at 60° C. in the presence of 1 per cent. peptone and 0·2 per cent. Na_2HPO_4, followed by steaming. The broth should have a reaction of pH 7·4, and the minimum amount of agar necessary to give stability to the medium should be added. The plates are first incubated for 18 hours at 36° C. in a closed jar containing air, 8 per cent. of which has been replaced by CO_2, and then for 24 hours under ordinary aerobic conditions. A 1 per cent. solution of tetramethyl-*p*-phenylenediamine hydrochloride is then poured over the plate and run off immediately. The effect of this solution is to turn gonococcal colonies a bright purple colour. Medium-sized convex translucent colonies that rapidly turn bright purple and are found microscopically to consist of Gram-negative diplococci may be provisionally accepted as gonococci. For further identification, when necessary, the colonies are picked off, and studied culturally and biochemically. Occasionally colonies giving the oxydase reaction and consisting of Gram-negative diplococci are isolated from the genito-urinary tract which subsequent examination shows are not true gonococci. Organisms of this type are unlikely to give rise to more than 1–5 per cent. of erroneous diagnoses. Though this method of culture is considerably more delicate than direct microscopical examination of smears, a certain number of cases do occur in which the smear method is positive when the cultural method is negative. The greatest caution, however, must be taken in chronic cases in identifying the gonococcus on morphological appearances alone. As Beck (1933) points out, confusion is often caused by staphylococci and streptococci, which may occur in pairs and fail to retain the Gram stain.

In chronic or latent gonorrhœa, or in cases of rheumatism, iritis, etc., in which a latent gonococcal infection is suspected, failure to demonstrate the presence of the gonococcus can never be regarded as definite evidence that this organism is absent from the tissues. In such cases certain indirect methods of diagnosis are available.

The Complement-Fixation Test.—Müller and Oppenheim (1906) were the first to apply this test to clinical practice, obtaining a positive result in a case of gonorrhœal arthritis. Since then it has been used by a large number of workers (Watabiki 1910, Schwartz and McNeill 1911, 1912, Keyes 1912, Kolmer and Brown 1914, Irons and Nicoll 1915, Dixon and Priestley 1919, Priestley 1919, Magner 1920, Smith and Wilson 1920, Herrold 1921, Torrey and Buckell 1922, Torrey *et al.* 1922, Walker 1922, Rubenstein and Gauran 1923, Osmond and Oliver 1929, Kristjansen 1931, Price 1933, Thjøtta and Waaler 1933, Schröpl 1934).

The technique of the reaction requires extreme care, and for a detailed description of the various methods employed the student is referred to the Medical Research Council's Report (1918)—a report which has been largely drawn on in the present section on diagnosis. It is generally recognized that a polyvalent antigen and an anti-sheep hæmolytic system are most satisfactory.

Great care is necessary in the interpretation of the reaction. The following points must be borne in mind : (1) the reaction does not become positive for at least 2 weeks after infection ; (2) it is often negative in simple cases of anterior urethritis in the male, and of urethritis in the female ; (3) it is generally positive in cases in which complications are present ; (4) it remains positive for about 3 months after clinical cure ; (5) a single negative reaction is of little importance ; (6) two or three successive negative reactions during the course of 4 to 6 weeks are of considerable importance in excluding the presence of the disease ; (7) a positive reaction becoming negative about 3 months after clinical cure is strong evidence in favour of real cure ; (8) a positive reaction denotes the recent activity in the body of a focus of living gonococci.

Sera of patients who have never had gonorrhœa are said to be consistently negative. The injection of vaccines interferes with the test, as the gonococcal antigen itself is able to stimulate the production of specific immune bodies ; the reaction is therefore valueless in vaccine-treated patients. Only in one other disease may the reaction be positive—namely in cerebrospinal meningitis ; the two diseases are so easily differentiated on clinical grounds that confusion is unlikely.

Table CXVII shows the percentage of positive reactions which may be expected in certain gonococcal infections. It has been compiled largely from the results of Schwartz and McNeill (1911, 1912), Kolmer and Brown (1914), Smith and Wilson (1920), Walker (1922), Torrey, Wilson and Buckell (1922), and Rubenstein and Gauran (1923).

TABLE CXVII

Acute Gonorrhœa, 2–4 weeks	48% positive reactions
Subacute and Chronic Gonorrhœa	61% ,, ,,
Epididymitis	82% ,, ,,
Prostatitis	80% ,, ,,
Vesiculitis	88% ,, ,,
Metritis	68% ,, ,,
Salpingitis	77% ,, ,,
Vulvo-vaginitis	50% ,, ,,
Arthritis	82% ,, ,,

It is seen that complications in the male genital system and in the joints give the highest percentage of positive results. The test is therefore of considerable value in those cases in which microscopic and cultural tests are most likely to fail. It is of especial value in chronic pelvic disease.

The complement-fixation test is being regarded with increasing favour. The more recent reports record a very small proportion of false positive reactions— usually under 1 per cent.—and a higher proportion of positive results than is given in Table CXVII. Price (1933) in particular, using a modified technique, claims to have obtained a very high proportion of positive results, ranging from 27 per cent. in the 1st week after exposure to 100 per cent. in the 5th week.

The figures given by Tulloch (1929) from Dundee may also be quoted.

Complement fixation positive : microscopical findings positive : 433
    ,,   ,,   negative :   ,,   ,,   negative : 737
    ,,   ,,   positive :   ,,   ,,   negative : 163
    ,,   ,,   negative :   ,,   ,,   positive : 215

The figures given in the last row refer mainly to early cases in which the complement-fixation reaction had not had time to become positive. Those in the third row refer mainly to chronic cases, and it is in such cases that the complement-fixation test finds its main value.

P.B.   P P

Precipitin Reaction.—This method was advocated by Robinson and Meader (1920) who found that discharges from gonorrhœal inflammations gave a precipitin reaction with antigonococcus serum, even when no gonococci were to be found microscopically. Kelley (1922), who tried this reaction, was unable to confirm their results. The test cannot yet be relied on for diagnosis.

More recently Meinicke (1931) has introduced his *Klärungsreaktion* (MKR test) and Müller (1932) his *Ballungs-Reaktion* (Im.B.R. test) for the diagnosis of gonorrhœa. According to Schröpl (1934), who made comparative observations on these tests, both of them give a higher proportion of non-specific reactions than the complement-fixation test, especially with syphilitic sera. One or other of them may be used, however, in conjunction with the complement-fixation reaction in order to amplify and control the results obtained by this test.

Skin Reaction.—Bruck (1909) found that patients with gonorrhœa showed a marked skin reaction to dead gonococci. Kohler employed this test in diagnosis, and found it to be valuable in many cases.

Irons (1912) prepared a glycerinated suspension from several strains of gonococci, which he called gonococcin. Inoculation was made on the skin with the point of a needle. After a few hours, in positive cases, a papule appears, surrounded by hyperæmia, reaching its maximum size in 24 hours, and disappearing after several days. The diameter of the papule and the hyperæmic zone around it is 5 mm. or more. The reaction was found to be generally positive at some time during the course of the disease, but in cases of severe infection, it might remain consistently negative. On the whole, it does not appear to be sufficiently regular to be of value in diagnostic work.

Prevention and Treatment.

Prevention is intimately associated with early diagnosis and efficient treatment. The mode of infection indicates sufficiently clearly the ways in which the disease can be avoided, and the reservoirs of infection which exist in any community. The problem is one of personal and social hygiene.

Opinions as to the value of vaccine treatment differ considerably. The evidence available does not lend itself to statistical analysis (see Aronstam 1908, Ballenger 1908, Butler and Long 1908, Churchill and Soper 1908, Hamilton and Cooke 1908, Bruck 1912, Lees 1919, Thomson 1919).

Antibacterial sera have been employed in the treatment of gonorrhœa, but without any conspicuous success. The infection is not of a type in which we should expect such sera to be of value (see Rogers 1906, Torrey 1906, Jötten 1921).

Of recent years a method of treatment by artificial pyrotherapy has been introduced, depending on the fact that in culture the gonococcus is almost completely destroyed by exposure for 2 hours to a temperature of 41·5°–42° C. (see Carpenter *et al.* 1933). The patient's temperature is raised by placing him in a special cabinet heated with carbon filament lamps, or by passing high-frequency currents through his trunk. The aim is to keep his temperature at a sufficiently high level for a sufficient length of time to bring about *in vivo* sterilization of the gonococci. It is as yet too early to pronounce on the value of this form of treatment. Some favourable results have been reported (see Warren and Wilson 1932, Hench *et al.* 1935).

REFERENCES

ARONSTAM, N. E. (1908) *J. Amer. med. Ass.*, **51**, 1419.

BALLENGER, E. G. (1908) *J. Amer. med. Ass.*, **50**, 1784.

BECK, A. (1933) *Zbl. Bakt.*, **130**, 281.

BORDONI-UFFREDUZZI. (1894) *Zbl. Bakt.*, **15**, 742.

BRUCK, C. (1909) *Dtsch. med. Wschr.*, **35**, 470 ; (1912) See Kolle and Waessermann's " Hdb. d. path. Mikroorg.," 2te Abt., 1912–13, **4**, 721.

BUMM, E. (1884) *Arch. Gynaek.*, **23**, 327 ; (1885*a*) *Dtsch. med. Wschr.*, **11**, 508 ; (1885*b*) *Ibid.*, **11**, 910.

BUTLER, W. J. and LONG, J. P. (1908) *J. Amer. med. Ass.*, **50**, 744.

CARPENTER, C. M., BOAK, R. A., MUCCI, L. A., and WARREN, S. L. (1933) *J. Lab. clin. Med.*, **18**, 981.

CHRISTMAS, J. DE. (1897) *Ann. Inst. Pasteur*, **11**, 609.

CHURCHILL, F. S. and SOPER, A. C. (1908) *J. Amer. med. Ass.*, **51**, 1298.

COLOMBINI, P. (1898) *Zbl. Bakt.*, **24**, 955.

CROSBY, D. (1905) *Amer. J. med. Sci.*, **129**, 880.

DIXON, H. B. F. and PRIESTLEY, A. H. (1919) *Lancet*, ii. 964.

DUVAL, C. W. and LEWIS, P. A. (1905) *J. med. Res.*, **13**, 535.

FINGER, E., GHON, A., and SCHLAGENHAUFER, F. (1895) *Arch. Derm. Syph.*, Wien, **33**, 141, 323.

FISCHER, W. (1895) *Dtsch. med. Wschr.*, **21**, 861.

GHON, A. and SCHLAGENHAUFER, F. (1898) *Wien. klin. Wschr.*, **11**, 580.

HAMILTON, A. and COOKE, J. M. (1908) *J. infect. Dis.*, **5**, 158.

HENCH, P. S., SLOCUMB, C. H., and POPP, W. C. (1935) *J. Amer. med. Ass.*, **104**, 1779.

HERROLD, R. D. (1921) *J. Amer. med. Ass.*, **76**, 225.

HOCHEISEN. (1906) *Arch. Gynaek.*, **79**, 415.

HOLT, L. E. (1905) *N.Y. med. J.*, **81**, 521.

IRONS, E. E. (1912) *J. infect. Dis.*, **11**, 77.

IRONS, E. E. and NICOLL, H. K. (1915) *J. infect. Dis.*, **16**, 303.

JENKINS, J. A. (1922) *Brit. med. J.*, i. 641.

JÖTTEN, K. W. (1921) *Z. Hyg. InfektKr.*, **92**, 9.

KELLEY, M. F. (1922) *J. infect. Dis.*, **30**, 623.

KEYES, E. C. (1912) *Amer. J. med. Sci.*, **143**, 107.

KOLMER, J. A. and BROWN, C. P. (1914) *J. infect. Dis.*, **15**, 6.

KRISTJANSEN, A. (1931) *Arch. Derm. Syph.*, Berl., **164**, 239, 472.

LEES, D. (1919) *Lancet*, i. 1107.

LEYDEN, E. (1893) *Dtsch. med. Wschr.*, **19**, 909.

MCLEOD, J. W., COATES, J. C., HAPPOLD, F. C., PRIESTLEY, D. P., and WHEATLEY, B. (1934) *J. Path. Bact.*, **39**, 221.

MAGNER, W. (1920) *Lancet*, ii. 123.

MEINICKE, E. (1931) *Klin. Wschr.*, **10**, 1757.

MÜLLER, R. (1932) *Klin. Wschr.*, **11**, 1916.

MÜLLER, R. and OPPENHEIM, M. (1906) *Wien. klin. Wschr.*, **19**, 894.

NEISSER, A. (1879) *Zbl. med. Wiss.*, **17**, 497 ; (1894) *Dtsch. med. Wschr.*, **20**, 335.

OSMOND, T. E. and OLIVER, J. O. (1929) *Brit. J. ven. Dis.*, **5**, 281.

PRICE, I. N. O. (1933) " The complement fixation Test for Gonorrhoea." London County Council.

PRIESTLEY, A. H. (1919) *Lancet*, i. 787.

Report. (1918) *Spec. Rep. Ser. med. Res. Coun., Lond.*, No. 19.

ROBINSON, G. H. and MEADER, P. D. (1920) *J. Urol.*, **4**, 551.

ROGERS, J. (1906) *J. Amer. med. Ass.*, **46**, 263.

RUBENSTEIN, M. and GAURAN, M. (1923) *C. R. Soc. Biol.*, **89**, 893.

SCHOLTZ, W. (1900) *Zbl. Bakt.*, **27**, 162.

SCHRÖPL, E. (1934) *Arch. Derm. Syph.*, Berl., **170**, 162.

SCHWARTZ, H. J. and MCNEILL, A. (1911) *Amer. J. med. Sci.*, **141**, 693 ; (1912) *Ibid.*, **144**, 815.

SMITH, J. D. and WILSON, M. A. (1920) *J. Immunol.*, **5**, 499.

STEINSCHNEIDER and SCHÄFFER. (1895) *Berl. klin. Wschr.*, **32**, 984.

STRONG, T. J. (1904) *J. Amer. med. Ass.*, **42**, 1288.

STRUMIA, M. M. and KOHLHAS, J. J. (1933) *J. infect. Dis.*, **53**, 212.

THAYER, W. S. and LAZEAR, J. W. (1899) *J. exp. Med.*, **4**, 81.

THJØTTA, T. and WAALER, E. (1933) *Norsk Mag. Lægevidensk.*, **94**, 286.

THOMSON, D. (1919) *Lancet*, i. 1102.

TORREY, J. C. (1906) *J. Amer. med. Ass.*, **46**, 261.

TORREY, J. C. and BUCKELL, G. T. (1922) *J. Immunol.*, **7**, 305.

TORREY, J. C., WILSON, M. A., and BUCKELL, G. T. (1922) *J. infect. Dis.*, **31**, 148.

TULLOCH, W. J.   (1929) " A System of Bacteriology," **2,** 239.   *Med. Res. Coun., Lond.*
WALKER, A. S.   (1922) *Med. J. Aust.,* **11,** 634.
WARREN, S. L. and WILSON, K. M.   (1932) *Amer. J. Obstet. Gynœc.,* **24,** 592.
WASSERMANN, A.   (1898) *Z. Hyg. InfektKr.,* **27,** 298.
WATABIKI, T.   (1910) *J. infect. Dis.,* **7,** 159.
WERTHEIM, E.   (1891) *Dtsch. med. Wschr.,* **17,** 1351.
WITTE, P.   (1900) *Zbl. Bakt.,* **27,** 162.
WRIGHT, H. D.   (1929) *J. Path. Bact.,* **32,** 203 ;   (1933) *Ibid.,* **37,** 257.
WYNN, W. H.   (1905) *Lancet,* i. 352.

CHAPTER LXIII

SCARLET FEVER, AND OTHER DISEASES DUE TO HÆMOLYTIC STREPTOCOCCI

SCARLET FEVER

OUR present conception of the mechanism of infection and resistance in scarlet fever affords an excellent example of the solution of a bacteriological problem by the convergence of evidence obtained along many different lines of investigation.

The fact that long-chained streptococci are frequently present in the throat during the early stages of scarlatinal infection has been known since the early days of bacteriology. Baginsky and Sommerfeld, in 1900, recorded their presence in each of 700 cases. As soon as the differentiation of streptococci into hæmolytic and non-hæmolytic types had been established, it became clear that the species so constantly associated with scarlet fever was *Str. pyogenes*. The streptococcal infection appears not to be strictly confined to the tonsils, or fauces ; Hektoen, in 1903, reported the isolation of streptococci from the blood in 12 per cent. of the cases which he studied, and noted that this evidence of bacteræmia was not necessarily of bad prognostic significance. In spite of such observations as these, there was great hesitation in accepting the undoubted association between hæmolytic streptococci and scarlet fever as one of cause and effect ; and this hesitation was natural. *Str. pyogenes* was already known as the essential cause of various acute suppurative and septicæmic infections in man ; and there seemed no means of differentiating between the strains isolated from scarlet fever, and those isolated from such conditions as cellulitis or erysipelas. A septic form of scarlet fever was well recognized by clinicians, in which hæmolytic streptococci were by general consent accorded the principal causative rôle, and it was commonly agreed that these organisms were the most frequent causative agents in such complications as otitis media ; but the general trend of opinion was to regard *Str. pyogenes* as an important secondary invader, playing a part similar to that of *Str. pneumoniæ*, or of *Str. pyogenes* itself, in the secondary pneumonia of measles, influenza, or whooping cough. Moreover, the bacteriological findings had, in some directions, an appearance of inconsistency. Jochmann (1905), for instance, reported his failure to isolate streptococci from the blood, or tissues, of patients dying within a few days from a malignant form of the disease.

The suspicion remained, that the association might be closer than that implied by the dominant view ; and, whenever a new method of bacterial differentiation was applied to the *Streptococcus* group, an attempt was made to compare scarlatinal strains with those derived from other sources. The use of fermentation tests failed to distinguish any group which was constantly associated with scarlet fever ; though some observers recorded a high frequency of particular fermentative types in association with this disease. The introduction of serological methods of differentiation seemed to offer a better hope of solving this problem, and Moser and Pirquet (1902), Meyer (1902) and Rossiwall and Schick (1905) reported that scarlatinal strains of hæmolytic streptococci could be differentiated by agglutination tests. These findings were, however, not confirmed by other observers (Neufeld 1903, Aronson 1903, Hasenknopf and Salge 1903) ; and the problem remained unsolved. In the light of our present knowledge we can hazard the guess that, along these lines alone, it would have remained insoluble. It is true that the renewed interest in the antigenic analysis of the hæmolytic streptococci which followed on the studies of Dochez, Avery and Lancefield (1919) led to the collection of important new data, and that the results recorded by Bliss (1920, 1922), Gordon (1921), Eagles (1924), and Stevens and Dochez (1926*a* and *b*) went far to confirm and extend the earlier observations of Moser and von Pirquet ; but the more detailed studies, which have been undertaken in the last few years by Griffith (1926, 1927, 1928, 1934, 1935), Smith (1926, 1927*a*), James (1926), Gunn and Griffith (1928), McLachlan and Mackie (1928) and others (see Chapter XXIII), have revealed a high degree of antigenic heterogeneity among the hæmolytic streptococci, and have made it abundantly clear that there is no one antigenic type to which the name *Str. scarlatinæ* or *Str. pyogenes var. scarlatinæ* can be applied, though some types are far more commonly associated with scarlatinal infections than others, just as some types of pneumococci are more frequently isolated than others from cases of lobar pneumonia. With one exception, all strains of hæmolytic streptococci that have been isolated from cases of scarlet fever have been found to belong to Lancefield's Group A (*Streptococcus pyogenes*), the strains falling within this group being characteristically pathogenic for man (see Lancefield 1928, and, for further details of antigenic structure, Chapter XXIII).

Of the 27 types of hæmolytic streptococci differentiated by Griffith (1934), Types 1, 2 and 3 are those most frequently isolated from cases of scarlet fever. Type 4 has been isolated less frequently. Types 8, 11, 12 and 23 have been associated with particular outbreaks. Types 5, 6, 13, 15, 19, 22, 26 and 27 have been isolated from sporadic cases. Type 21, which was originally isolated from a case of scarlet fever, has been shown by Hare (1935) to belong to Lancefield's Group C which comprises mainly animal-pathogenic strains of hæmolytic streptococci. This strain, which forms the single exception referred to above, cannot therefore be regarded as a strain of *Str. pyogenes*, as that species is defined in Chapter XXIII.

Once it had been shown that *Str. pyogenes* was constantly associated with scarlet fever it was natural to inquire whether this organism would reproduce the disease in any experimental animal. The results obtained when the usual laboratory animals were inoculated with cultures of hæmolytic streptococci, from any source, showed that the guinea-pig, rabbit and mouse differed in their resistance to this bacterial species, and that the type of infection produced varied in relation to the virulence of the particular strain inoculated, and the route of inoculation ; but there was no indication of any correlation between a particular type of experimental infection and the source from which the infecting strain was obtained ; nor did any of the inoculated animals develop lesions which bore any obvious relation to scarlet fever in man.

More recently Dochez and Sherman (1922) have recorded the production in the guinea-pig of an infective syndrome showing certain points of resemblance to human scarlatina ; the method employed in these experiments consisted in the inoculation into the subcutaneous tissues of a small quantity of melted agar, and the subsequent inoculation, into the agar-mass, of a scarlatinal strain of *Str. pyogenes*. The animals so infected developed fever and an erythematous rash, followed by desquamation especially marked on the pads of the feet. Similar results were obtained with young swine.

It is, however, clear that rodents, and most other animal species which have been tested in this respect, are unsuitable for the experimental reproduction of scarlet fever ; and in this there is nothing surprising, since we have long learned that the clinical picture presented by any infective disease is a product of the reaction between a particular parasite and a particular host species.

Here, as elsewhere, it was natural to suppose that anthropoid apes would offer more suitable material. A series of experiments by Landsteiner, Levaditi and Prasek (1911) showed that scarlet fever could be reproduced in the higher apes by inoculating the throat with the faucial exudate removed from human cases of the disease. From the throats of the animals so infected, *Str. pyogenes* was constantly recovered, and it was sometimes found in the blood ; but the strains so isolated failed to reproduce the disease in other monkeys.

The proof that scarlet fever is caused by infection with hæmolytic streptococci rests on a series of observations that have been made on man himself, and these observations have elucidated the pathogenesis of the disease, as well as its causation.

Among the earlier observations there are some which gain added significance in the light of our present knowledge. Gabritschewsky (1907) prepared a vaccine from killed cultures of hæmolytic streptococci isolated from cases of scarlet fever, and with it attempted the immunization of a considerable series of human subjects. He noted, among the reactions produced, a number of manifestations which resembled those present in the natural disease. In addition to the local erythematous reaction, a proportion of the inoculated subjects developed a general reaction, including fever, malaise and, in some cases, a transient generalized erythema. Occasionally this was associated with an inflammatory reaction in the fauces, and in the tongue, the latter resembling the " strawberry-tongue " of scarlet fever. It was noted that persons, who had previously passed through an attack of scarlet fever, failed to develop either a local or general reaction.

Some years before, Moser (1902) had prepared an anti-scarlatinal serum by the immunization of horses with scarlatinal strains of streptococci, and had reported excellent results from its therapeutic use in the human disease. Gabritschewsky found that the administration of Moser's serum, before the inoculation of his vaccine, prevented both the local and general reaction. Other sera, prepared by other workers, gave far less favourable results (Dochez 1925) ; and for this reason the serum treatment of scarlet fever was never generally adopted.

In 1914 Krumwiede, Nicoll and Pratt recorded an instance in which a laboratory worker was accidentally infected by sucking into her mouth a suspension of living streptococci. After an incubation period of three days she passed through a typical attack of scarlet fever.

In 1921 Dick and Dick attempted to reproduce scarlet fever in a series of human volunteers by inoculating the throat with various organisms isolated from scarlatinal patients, including hæmolytic streptococci ; none of these volunteers developed the typical disease, though some developed tonsillitis. In 1923 the same observers carried out another series of experiments, using a strain of *Str. pyogenes* which had been isolated from the finger of a nurse who was suffering from surgical scarlatina. Of five volunteers, who were inoculated by swabbing the fauces with a broth culture of this organism, three showed no reaction, one developed a sore throat with fever, but without rash, and one passed through a typical attack of scarlet fever. Five other volunteers, who were swabbed with filtrates from these cultures, showed no reaction.   When these were later swabbed with living cultures, one of them developed scarlet fever.   Toyado and others (1931) record the production of scarlet fever in three volunteers by swabbing the throat with hæmolytic streptococci from scarlatinal patients.

It has thus been shown that certain strains of *Str. pyogenes* are capable of causing typical scarlet fever in susceptible human beings ; but these susceptible individuals are in a minority among any random sample of the adult population.

The explanation of this unequal distribution of resistance has emerged from a series of studies carried out along somewhat different lines.   In 1918 Schultz and Charlton recorded a phenomenon which has played an important part in the subsequent study of the disease.   They found that 1 c.c. of normal human serum, injected into the skin of a patient displaying a characteristic scarlatinal rash, produced a blanching of the rash in the immediate neighbourhood of the injection. This property was shared by the serum from a patient who was convalescent from scarlet fever, but not by serum withdrawn from a patient during the height of an attack.   It has since been shown that the Schultz-Charlton phenomenon is given by about 60 per cent. of normal sera (Dochez 1925).   This reaction was originally regarded as the result of the presence, in normal serum, of some substance which was removed from it during an attack of scarlet fever ; but Mair (1923) recorded an instance in which he was able to demonstrate that the serum of a child gave a negative Schultz-Charlton reaction before an attack of scarlet fever, and a positive reaction after convalescence.   He noted that sera obtained from young children, who have not had scarlet fever, give a much higher proportion of negative reactions than sera from a random sample of adults ; and he put forward the view that the positive reaction is the result of the development of a specific antitoxin, which neutralizes the toxin present in the skin of a scarlet fever patient.   According to this view the rash, and probably other features of the scarlatinal syndrome, are to be regarded as toxæmic in origin.

It had long been known that certain strains of hæmolytic streptococci yielded filtrates which, in large doses, were toxic for laboratory animals ; but the susceptibility of these animals was so slight that little or no progress was made in the study of such toxic filtrates before the investigation by Dick and Dick (1924*a*, *b*, 1925*a*, *b*) of their action in man.   Their results showed that Berkefeld filtrates of broth cultures of scarlatinal strains of *Str. pyogenes* contained a toxic substance which produced a typical erythematous reaction, when injected intradermally, in a proportion of normal persons who had not suffered from scarlet fever (see p. 459). This local reaction was induced by the injection of 0·1 c.c. of a 1 : 1,000 dilution of the particular toxic filtrate employed.   This test, which is more fully described on p. 1162, has since been applied to large samples of the normal population ; and the distribution of positive and negative reactors, which is closely analogous to that revealed by the application of the Schick test in the case of diphtheria, is in full accord with the view that the great majority of young children are susceptible to the erythrogenic toxin, but, with advancing years, acquire an active antitoxic immunity, either by passing through an attack of the clinical disease, or, more commonly, by an immunizing infection with a toxin-producing streptococcus without the production of the characteristic scarlatinal syndrome (see Chapter XLVI and Zingher 1924).

The administration of larger doses of erythrogenic toxin to susceptible persons has yielded even more demonstrative results.   In a number of cases such doses have induced a generalized reaction with fever, nausea, vomiting and a transient scarlatiniform rash. Most of the recorded instances of this " miniature scarlet fever " were observed during the earlier stages of the study of the erythrogenic toxin ; but it still occurs occasionally, when a particularly susceptible person is undergoing immunization with doses of the ordinary size (see p. 1167). This reaction is clearly analogous to that recorded by Gabritschewsky (1907).

Additional evidence has been contributed by the studies of Trask and Blake (1924), who record the following significant observations. A toxic substance can be demonstrated in the serum of patients acutely ill with scarlet fever, which produces a typical skin reaction when injected intracutaneously into persons who have not had scarlet fever, and whose serum gives a negative Schultz-Charlton reaction (*i.e.* contains no antitoxin). Such injections produce no reaction in persons whose serum gives a positive Schultz-Charlton reaction. This toxic substance is not neutralized by a human serum which gives a negative blanching test, but is readily neutralized by a human serum which gives a positive blanching test. It is not neutralized by normal horse serum, but it is readily neutralized by a horse anti-scarlatinal serum.

Taking this evidence as a whole, there seems little doubt as to its import. Scarlet fever in man is a disease caused by infection with *Str. pyogenes*. The causative organisms are, for the most part, localized in the throat, though there may be a transient bacteræmia in some cases. The clinical manifestations of the disease result from the action of a soluble toxin, which is absorbed from the local lesion and carried to the susceptible cells and tissues. The varying susceptibility of children and adults, and of the same age groups in different social environments, depends upon the presence or absence of circulating antitoxin. Animals other than man, and perhaps certain anthropoid apes, do not reproduce the disease, even when experimentally infected, because of their much greater resistance to the scarlatinal toxin.

Only one other point requires consideration at this stage, the unity or diversity of the toxins produced by different strains of *Str. pyogenes*. In much of the earlier work there was an overt or implicit suggestion that the scarlatinal toxin was a characteristic and distinctive product of those races of hæmolytic streptococci which were associated with scarlet fever. Subsequent studies have shown that this is not the case. Omitting any detailed descriptions of the results recorded by individual investigators (Park and Spiegel 1925, Lash 1926, Kirkbride and Wheeler 1926, Eagles 1926, Smith 1927*b*, McLachlan 1927, Okell and Parish 1928), the evidence at present available tends to support the following conclusions. The production of a soluble exotoxin, giving typical skin reactions in man, is characteristic of *Str. pyogenes* in general, and not of scarlatinal strains in particular. There is, however, some evidence that toxigenicity is a more constant character in scarlatinal than in non-scarlatinal strains. There is no conclusive evidence of any qualitative difference between the toxins produced by different antigenic types of *Str. pyogenes*. The majority of such toxins, whatever the source of the cultures from which they were derived, are neutralized by a single antitoxin. Whether an erythrogenic toxin is produced by any other species, or group, of hæmolytic streptococci is as yet uncertain (see Chapter XXIII).

The Diagnosis of Scarlet Fever.

Scarlet fever, in its characteristic clinical form, is a disease in which a throat infection with *Str. pyogenes* is associated with a rash produced by the erythrogenic toxin, and a syndrome that is, in the main, toxæmic in origin. A diagnosis of a throat infection caused by *Str. pyogenes* is not therefore a diagnosis of scarlet fever ; indeed, a clinician will frequently be concerned in differentiating a throat infection of this type from a case that, because of other criteria, would fall into the scarlet fever category. A throat swab has not, under these conditions, any great diagnostic value. We should expect to isolate *Str. pyogenes* from every case of scarlet fever ; but we should also expect to isolate it from many cases to which that diagnosis would not be applicable.

The Diagnosis of Susceptibility or Immunity to Scarlet Fever.

For this purpose we use the Dick test, in which a small dose of toxin is injected into the skin of one arm, and a dose of inactivated toxin into the skin of the other, to serve as a control. The amount of toxin injected is 0·2 c.c. containing one skin-test dose, and the method of performing the test is essentially the same as in the Schick reaction (see p. 1081). The following differences should, however, be noted.

The erythrogenic toxin is far more heat resistant than diphtheria toxin. The filtrate that is to serve as a control must therefore be heated at 96° C. for 45 minutes.

The skin reaction to the erythrogenic toxin occurs more rapidly than the reaction to diphtheria toxin. A bright red flush appears within 6 to 12 hours, attains its maximum in about 24 hours, and then fades rapidly, so that it may be almost invisible on the third day. The pseudo-reaction, when it occurs, is smaller and less intense than the true positive reaction and fades more slowly. In this last respect, the time relations of the positive and pseudo-reactions in the Dick test are the reverse of those in the Schick test, and the times of reading the Dick test must be adjusted accordingly.

The interpretation of the test does not differ from that of the Schick reaction. A positive reaction (positive on the test arm and negative on the control) or a combined reaction (positive and pseudo on the test arm and pseudo on the control) indicates susceptibility. A negative reaction (negative on both arms), or a pseudo-reaction (pseudo on both arms), indicates immunity.

We can safely assume that, except in the case of young infants (see p. 846), a negative reaction indicates the presence of circulating antitoxin ; this has been shown to be the case in many instances, and the Schultz-Charlton reaction affords further proof of the presence of antitoxin in the serum of resistant persons. Because of the difficulty of titrating scarlatinal antitoxin, to which we shall refer in a later section, we have, however, much less information in regard to the level of antitoxin that confers an effective immunity than we have in the case of diphtheria.

Although the reactions to the Schick and Dick tests have the same general significance, experience has shown that they are not equally reliable. It is, for instance, extremely rare for any Schick-negative person to develop diphtheria, while almost every case of diphtheria is found to be Schick-positive at the onset of the disease. In the case of the Dick test the figures, though tending quite clearly in the same direction, are of a different order.

Thus Toyada and his colleagues (1929) note that 41 of 305 cases of scarlet fever (14 per cent.) were known to be Dick-negative shortly before infection, They give the proportion of cases that are Dick-negative during the early stages of the disease as 23–59 per cent., according to different observers, and the proportion negative during convalescence as 82·3–91·7 per cent.

Okell (1932) records similar observations—22 Dick-positive reactors among 119 cases of scarlet fever 3 to 12 weeks after the onset of the disease—and notes that a considerable proportion of persons who have had scarlet fever in early life and are almost certainly immune give positive reactions.

It would seem a just conclusion, from the evidence at present available, that a Dick-negative reactor is much less likely to contract scarlet fever than a Dick-positive reactor, but that the odds against his doing so are not nearly so high as the odds against a Schick-negative reactor developing diphtheria, and that similarly a Schick-positive reaction is a more reliable indication of susceptibility to diphtheria than is a Dick-positive reaction to scarlet fever.

The Standardization of Erythrogenic Toxin.—One of the great difficulties of the Dick reaction is that involved in the standardization of the erythrogenic toxin (see Okell 1932, Friedman *et al.* 1935). The skin test dose is defined as the smallest amount of toxin that will, on the average, produce an erythematous reaction, 1 cm. in diameter, in the skin of a susceptible person within 24 hours. This dose, in fact, often corresponds approximately to 0·2 c.c. of a 1 : 1,000 dilution of a toxic broth culture. Its accurate measurement is, however, almost impossible ; in part, because the assumption that any sample of human beings are fully, or equally, susceptible, even when all react positively to a particular dilution of toxin, is quite unjustified ; in part, because an adequate supply of susceptible persons on whom the tests can be performed is not easy to obtain. When several fully susceptible persons are available for the titrations, an erythrogenic toxin can be measured with an approximation to accuracy—a filtrate of strength x can, for instance, be differentiated from a filtrate of strength $2x$—but it is not always easy to do even as well as this (see, for instance, James, Joe and Swyer 1929, O'Brien 1930). This question will be discussed in more detail when we are considering the standardization of antitoxin.

The Treatment of Scarlet Fever with Antitoxic Sera.

Clearly, the demonstration that a high-titre antitoxic serum can be obtained by immunizing a horse against erythrogenic toxin raises the question of the value of such antisera in the treatment of the disease in man.

It seems reasonable to suppose that a specific antitoxic serum will exert an effect on those manifestations of scarlet fever that are directly toxic in origin. We might expect a saving of life in severe toxæmic cases, a diminution in the rash and a more rapid subsidence of the fever in the milder type of infection. There would seem no *a priori* reason to expect any effect on those complications, such as otitis and cervical adenitis, that are caused by the invasive spread of the hæmolytic streptococci.

Figures in regard to death or recovery are not easy to obtain because the prevalent type of scarlet fever is very mild and the case fatality very low. Such figures as are available support the view that there is a significant saving of life in severe toxæmic cases when these occur.

Toyada and his colleagues (1929) record 8 deaths in 33 serum-treated cases of severe scarlet fever against 15 deaths in 33 untreated cases of the same order of severity ; and, so far as data with regard to death or recovery are forthcoming, other records are in general conformity with these observations. Thus, Mersol (1929) during an epidemic of scarlet fever in Jugoslavia, associated with a high case-fatality rate, records 4 deaths among 117 serum-treated patients (3·4 per cent.) as against 84 deaths among 377 untreated patients (22·3 per cent.).

In regard to the diminution in severity of the rash, the subsidence of fever, and the general alleviation of toxic symptoms, the consensus of opinion clearly supports the view that antiscarlatinal serum has a beneficial effect (see Benson and Maciver 1926, Harries

1927, Discussion 1927, Kinloch and others 1927, Husler 1927, Lenthe 1927, Eley 1928, Scott 1928, Bröcker 1928, Friedemann and Deicher 1928, Toyada and others 1929, Veldee and others 1931). It should be noted that Veldee and his collaborators, almost alone among those who have reported on this point, failed to demonstrate any significant effect on the temperature although there was a striking effect on the rash.

The data recorded by several of the observers referred to above are in accord with the view that antiscarlatinal serum has little effect on the frequency of complications ; but two important exceptions must be noted.

Harries (1927) reports on 100 cases treated with antitoxin and 100 untreated controls. The cases for treatment were selected by alternate admissions in order to obtain a random sample. Among the control groups there were 15 cases with complications, among the treated group 7 ; and this difference was almost entirely accounted for by the different frequency of otitis media—9 cases in the control group, 2 in the treated. Veldee and others (1931) record a careful study of 112 serum-treated patients and 84 controls, the allocation of the patients to the serum and no-serum groups again being by alternation of admission. The difference in the frequency of complications was striking, that in the control group being higher in each case—cervical adenitis, 19·5 per cent. as against 0·4 per cent. : otitis media, all types, 17·1 per cent. as against 7·3 per cent. : suppurative otitis, 7·3 per cent. as against 3·6 per cent., and so on. Those complications that are probably due to toxæmic rather than invasive processes showed the same wide differences—nephritis, 12·2 per cent. in the controls as against 0·9 per cent. in the treated : arthritis, 6·1 per cent. as against 0·0 per cent.

Summing up, we may say that there is clear evidence that antitoxic serum has a significant therapeutic effect on the toxic manifestations of scarlet fever, and suggestive evidence that it may—contrary to our *a priori* expectations—lessen the frequency of those complications that are due to the invasive action of the streptococci.

The Standardization of Scarlatinal Antitoxin.—As in the case of all other antisera, the standard of reference is an arbitrarily selected sample of serum. It happens that the unit of this serum was defined as 10 times the amount that, in the skin-neutralization test, will protect against the " test dose " of toxin ; while the " test dose " is defined as five " skin test doses," and a " skin test dose " as the least amount of toxin that, in a majority of susceptible persons, gives rise to a local skin reaction of not less than 10 mm. in diameter (see Dyer 1928). But there is nothing exact or binding about this definition. The Standard American serum was adopted by the Standardization Committee of the League in 1928, not as an agreed International Standard and Unit, but as a provisional standard for further study.

The great difficulty, which may be on its way to solution, has been the absence of any suitable experimental animal on which the toxin-antitoxin mixtures can be titrated.

Kirkbride and Wheeler (1926) have described characteristic skin reactions in the goat, and Ando and Kurauchi (1930) in white pigs ; but these observations have not been generally confirmed.

Until recently the most hopeful approach to an animal test appeared to be that devised by Parish and Okell (1927). Rabbits are injected intravenously with varying doses of the serum under test, and, 4 to 6 hours later, with 5 c.c. of a young broth culture of a virulent strain of a hæmolytic streptococcus. The effect of the antitoxin is to prevent the acute septicæmic death that occurs in controls. Most of the rabbits that have received the antitoxin die eventually of a subacute streptococcal infection associated with arthritis, pericarditis, etc. ; but death seldom occurs before the 6th day, and this is taken as the end-point (see also O'Brien, Okell and Parish 1929).

In 1930, however, Fraser and Plummer described a method of titrating scarlatinal toxin and antitoxin in the skin of Chinchilla rabbits ; and further experience with this test suggests that, with certain modifications, it gives results as accurate as those obtained in the human skin, or by the method of Parish and Okell (see Kolchin 1933, Plummer 1934, Buttle and Lowdon 1935). If further experience proves equally satisfactory this test will clearly take precedence of others, and we shall be in a much better position to attack the problems of antiscarlatinal immunity on a quantitative basis.

The Epidemiology of Scarlet Fever.

There is every reason to suppose that the epidemiology of scarlet fever is closely analogous to that of diphtheria. In both cases we have diseases characterized by primary throat lesions and a characteristic clinical syndrome that is determined, in the main, by the effects produced by the diffusion of a soluble toxin from the primary lesion. In both, carriers of the causative organism greatly outnumber the clinical cases. In both, the population at large is undergoing, from early childhood onwards, an active immunization resulting from latent or atypical infections (see, for instance, Okell and Parish 1928, Stocks 1930, Allison and Gunn 1932, Okell 1932).

The change in the percentage of Dick-positive reactors with age, and under varying environmental conditions, has been considered in Chapter XLVI, to which reference may be made. We may note here a few additional facts with regard to the frequency of the causative organism among the population at large and in convalescent cases.

Almost all the evidence available refers to the incidence of hæmolytic streptococci in general, not of *Str. pyogenes* in particular. Many of the relevant observations are recorded in Chapter LXXXVI, in relation to the normal flora of the human body ; but we may here give a few illustrative examples.

In an investigation conducted in Manchester over the period July, 1925, to July, 1927, in which the throats of 100 normal adults were swabbed once each month, the carrier rate of hæmolytic streptococci fluctuated between zero and 36·4 per cent., the more usual figure at any monthly swabbing ranging from 5 to 20 per cent. (see Report 1930).

In a similar (unpublished) study, carried out for several years past by Dr. Edith Straker in the authors' laboratory, the carrier rate for normal adults has varied from 0 to 20 per cent., but has usually fallen between 5 and 10 per cent. Throat swabs taken periodically from a boys' public school have given figures varying from between 6 and 19 per cent. ; while a single swabbing of a home for young children gave a figure of 18 per cent.

These figures, as has been said, refer to hæmolytic streptococci, actually to hæmolytic streptococci that form a soluble hæmolysin (see Chapter XXIII). The only figures of which we are aware by which they can be converted into a probable carrier rate for *Str. pyogenes*, *i.e.*, for hæmolytic streptococci belonging to Lancefield's Group A, are those recorded by Hare (1935). Among 100 strains of hæmolysin-forming streptococci isolated from normal human throats, he found 63 to be *Str. pyogenes*, as here defined. So far as we can accept this figure as generally applicable we should therefore multiply the figures given above by about 0·6 to obtain the *Str. pyogenes* carrier rate ; but it is probable that the proportion of *Str. pyogenes* among samples of hæmolytic streptococci isolated from normal throats would be found to vary as widely as the frequency of hæmolytic streptococci as a class, so that any manipulation of this kind will only give a very rough approximation to truth.

In any community, such as a school, where overt infections such as tonsillitis or scarlet fever are occurring, even though the number of such cases is small, the carrier rate for hæmolytic streptococci tends to be far higher. Under such conditions, Straker (unpublished) has found rates of 43 per cent. and 54 per cent. among the normal boys.

We have described on p. 1091 the way in which diphtheria bacilli disappear from the throat during convalescence, and reference to Table CV will show that about 50 per cent. of diphtheria convalescents have ceased to carry by the 20th day, and 90 per cent. by the 50th day. It has become quite clear that the disappearance of hæmolytic streptococci from the throat during convalescence from scarlet fever is much slower (see Nicholls 1927, Gordon 1927, Gunn and Griffith 1928, Allison and Gunn 1932) ; and it would seem that the carrier rate among convalescents on discharge from hospital is usually of the order of 50 per cent.

Even if these figures were more favourable we should not, in a disease in which the carriers among the general population largely outnumber the cases, expect isolation in fever hospitals, to exert any appreciable effect on the frequency of the disease among the population at large ; and we may note that Woods (1928), in a statistical study of the incidence of scarlet fever in various districts in this country over a period of 25 years, could find no evidence that isolation had any effect on the prevalence of the disease.

In the great majority of cases, the disease is spread by droplet infection ; and, as in diphtheria, the source of infection is probably more often a carrier than a case. Hæmolytic streptococci have been isolated by some observers from the desquamation scales from scarlet fever patients (see Allison and Gunn 1932) ; but it is unlikely that this is an important source of natural infection.

Apart from personal contact, one of the most important factors in the epidemic spread of scarlet fever would appear to be the occasional contamination of a milk supply. There have been accounts of milk-borne epidemics since the classical Hendon outbreak of 1885. An account of recent outbreaks in Massachusetts, with full bacteriological details, is given by Williams and his colleagues (1932). In Great Britain there have been within recent years several outbreaks of scarlet fever or septic sore throat, of which one, at Hove, involved over 1,000 families and caused 65 deaths (see Wilkinson 1931). (See also Chapter LXXXIX.)

As we have seen in Chapter XXIII, the hæmolytic streptococci that are natural pathogens of the cow, giving rise to mastitis, can be differentiated, antigenically and in other ways, from *Str. pyogenes*. It is probable that, in all milk-borne outbreaks of scarlet fever or of tonsillitis, the ultimate source of infection is a human carrier. The milk may be infected at any stage on its journey from the cow to the consumer ; or the cow's udder may occasionally be infected by a human type of hæmolytic streptococcus derived from a milker who is a carrier (see, for instance, Jones and Little 1928*a*, *b*).

The history of scarlet fever provides an excellent example of an infective disease which has exhibited variations in its behaviour during the past half-century. We have already noted the mildness of the type of infection now prevalent ; but this mildness is a relatively recent development. In 1861–5 the death rate from scarlet fever, in England and Wales, was 982 per million living ; twenty years later it had dropped to half this value ; and in the quinquennium 1921–5 it had fallen to 29 per million. This decrease in mortality has, during recent years, been associated with a shift in the age incidence of the disease. The morbidity in the 5–10 age group has increased at the expense of that in the 0–5 age group ; while the maximum mortality now tends to fall on older children and young adults.

Active Immunization against Scarlet Fever.

The reagent used for this purpose is a broth filtrate of a culture of a suitable strain of *Str. pyogenes*, containing the erythrogenic toxin. This toxin is not converted into toxoid before use. Though some observers (see Veldee 1931, 1933) have reported favourably on the immunizing value of a formol toxoid, similar to that employed in diphtheria immunization, most observers have found such preparations to be relatively inactive (Okell 1932, Dick and Dick 1934). Moreover, unlike diphtheria toxin, the erythrogenic toxin is relatively harmless. The use of the unmodified toxin for immunization rarely leads to any severe local reactions though troublesome reactions are more numerous than in diphtheria immunization. Generalized reactions of the " miniature scarlet fever " type can be avoided by decreasing the initial dose, and working it up very gradually, in those subjects whose reaction to the Dick test shows them to be unusually susceptible.

From our knowledge of the pathogenesis of the disease we should expect that immunization with the erythrogenic toxin would produce an effective immunity against that part of the total scarlatinal syndrome to which it gives rise—the characteristic rash and probably many of the other toxic symptoms. We should not expect any antibacterial immunity. There is no reason to suppose that the filtrate injected contains an effective dose of bacterial antigen ; and, even if it did, the resulting increase in resistance would only be operative against a single antigenic type of hæmolytic streptococcus, while a variety of types may give rise to typical scarlet fever. There is therefore no *a priori* reason to suppose that this method of immunization will protect against the local proliferation of hæmolytic streptococci in the throat, or their possible spread to other regions ; though it might have such an effect if the erythrogenic toxin played a part in damaging the tissues and allowing the streptococci to proliferate.

Extensive field trials have been made and the results are in general accord with expectation, though it seems doubtful whether the immunity induced is as effective as that obtained in immunization against diphtheria.

It would appear (Benson 1928) that the total dose of toxin required to induce immunity may be relatively large—20,000 skin test doses. For persons who give mildly positive Dick reactions 1,000 skin test doses usually form a safe initial dose, but in those who give a vivid and extensive Dick reaction it is wiser to commence with the injection of 500 skin test doses, or even less. Injections may then be given at weekly intervals, increasing the dose 2 to 5 times at each successive injection until a total of 20,000 skin test doses has been given in the course of 3 to 4 weeks. Dick and Dick (1929) have recommended even larger doses, commencing with 500 and working up to 80,000 to 100,000 skin test doses.

The evidence with regard to the proportion of susceptibles that can be rendered Dick-immune by active immunization is less extensive and less concordant than that available in the case of antidiphtheria immunization. It has been the experience of many observers that the proportion of cases in which a Dick-positive is converted into a Dick-negative reactor is lower and the relapse rate higher, than the corresponding figures for the change in the Schick reaction induced by diphtheria immunization (see Heller 1927, Toyada *et al.* 1929, Okell 1932) ; but it is possible that these results may be improved by large total dosage and a prolonged course of immunization.

The records of the incidence of scarlet fever in the immunized and non-immunized are as yet too few to afford a safe basis for any final conclusion as to the effectiveness of the procedure under different conditions ; but they clearly suggest that it has considerable value. Toyada and others (1929) record a scarlet fever incidence of 1 per 1,000 among fully immunized persons, 18·1 per 1,000 among those partially immunized, and 62·5 per 1,000 among non-immunized controls. As in diphtheria immunization, the most significant results have been reported from fever hospitals or other institutions in which the risk of contracting scarlet fever is unusually high.

Benson (1928) records the effect of Dick-testing and immunization on the incidence of scarlet fever among the nursing staff of the Edinburgh City Fever Hospital. His figures are set out in Table CXVIII, including the comparable figures for diphtheria.

TABLE CXVIII

ANNUAL INCIDENCE OF DIPHTHERIA AND SCARLATINA AMONG THE NURSING STAFF OF THE
EDINBURGH CITY FEVER HOSPITAL.

Year.	Total Staff.	Diphtheria Incidence Per cent.	Scarlatina Incidence Per cent.
1919	145	10·34	4·82
1920	148	6·75	9·46
1921	146	9·58	10·27
1922 [1]	147	8·84	6·12
1923	137	3·65	4·38
1924	128	3·12	8·59
1925 [1]	161	3·10	9·31
1926	153	1·30	3·52
1927	148	0·67	0·67

[1] Schick-testing and immunization commenced September, 1922. Dick-testing and immunization commenced October, 1925.

The figures for 1928, 1929, 1930 and 1931, as given in the Annual Reports of the Medical Officer of Health for Edinburgh, show that the very low incidence of diphtheria and scarlet fever among the staff has been maintained.

Dick and Dick (1929), summarizing their records, state that among 11,584 immunized persons in institutions where scarlet fever was epidemic, no case of scarlet fever occurred, and that of 1,191 nurses or interns immunized before commencing work in fever hospitals none contracted the disease.

It may be noted that the experience of active immunization in man is in general accord with the view that the protection afforded is less effective against the invasive than against the toxæmic effects of hæmolytic streptococcal infection. Thus Kinloch and others (1927) note an increase in the frequency of streptococcal tonsillitis among the nursing staff of a fever hospital after immunization, suggesting that the typical scarlatinal syndrome had been replaced by an infection confined to the throat. Benson (1928), on the other hand, has recorded a slight diminution in the incidence of tonsillitis among the nursing staff after immunization ; but the diminution was insignificant in comparison with the much greater decrease in the incidence of scarlet fever among the staff over the same period.

Other Infections with Hæmolytic Streptococci.

Tonsillitis

If we accept the view that scarlet fever is simply one of the clinical manifestations of infection with *Str. pyogenes*, it becomes necessary to inquire a little more closely into its relation to other types of infection with the same bacterial species.

With one of these, acute tonsillitis, the relation is certainly very close. It has been the common experience of epidemiologists that cases of tonsillitis, without the rash or other characteristic signs of scarlet fever, occur side by side with cases showing the fully developed syndrome, in any considerable epidemic of the latter disease. Butler (1909) has called attention to the frequency with which a history of sore throat is obtained among other members of a household, of which one member has contracted a typical attack of scarlatina ; and he notes that a sore throat in one member often precedes an attack of scarlatina in another, indicating that scarlatinal infection may be transmitted by those who never display the disease in its typical form. This epidemiological evidence has been greatly strengthened during recent years by the studies of Griffith and others (see Glover and Griffith 1931, Griffith 1934) which have shown that a single antigenic type of *Str. pyogenes*, spreading in a closed community such as a school, will produce scarlet fever in some cases and tonsillitis in others. It seems probable that the alternative clinical manifestations of tonsillitis and scarlet fever are determined mainly by the ratio between the toxigenicity of the infecting strain, and the antitoxic immunity of the host (see Okell and Parish 1928, Okell 1932).

The acceptance of this view involves the assumption of wide differences in the toxigenicity of different strains of *Str. pyogenes*, or at least in their capacity for producing the erythrogenic toxin *in vivo*. In some outbreaks, traceable to an infected milk supply, the prevailing clinical disease was recognizable scarlatina : in other milk-borne epidemics, such as those recorded by Davis and Rosenow (1912), by Stokes and Hachtel (1912) and by Coleman and Wheeler (1926), the prevailing type of infection was a sore throat, without the rest of the scarlatinal syndrome. We may suppose that each of these outbreaks was caused by a single strain of *Str. pyogenes* conveyed by milk ; and our knowledge of the distribution of antitoxic immunity, as revealed by the Dick test, renders it unlikely that differences in the average resistance of the various communities affected can have differed so widely as to account for the marked difference in clinical manifestations.

We should not, in such a conception of *Str. pyogenes* infections, interpret the term " toxigenicity " too literally. It is very probable that invasiveness, and perhaps the capacity to multiply freely in the tissues at the original focus of infection, are at least equally involved. The determining factor will be the ability of any given strain to produce toxin plentifully and rapidly in the tissues, and this involves many factors that are not concerned in the production of toxin by an organism growing under optimal cultural conditions in the laboratory. We may recall the fact that the undoubted differences in virulence between the *gravis, intermediate* and *mitis* types of the diphtheria bacillus are not paralleled by differences in toxigenicity as judged by growth *in vitro*.

It may, perhaps, be added that the studies of Griffith and his colleagues on epidemics of hæmolytic streptococcal infection, particularly in schools, supply some of the strongest evidence in support of the view that there exist, within any given pathogenic bacterial species, particular " epidemic strains " endowed with a heightened power of spreading naturally among the population at risk. Reference to Chapter LIII will show that this view is also supported by the results obtained in experimental epidemics.

Before leaving the question of tonsillitis, we may note that in this disease, as in scarlet fever, one of the more serious and common complications is a streptococcal infection of the middle ear.

Erysipelas

This classical example of acute streptococcal infection may, for our present purposes, be shortly dismissed.   As an experimental disease it has been discussed in some detail in Chapter L, in connection with the general problem of local immunity.   Its interest, in relation to the question of streptococcal immunity in general and scarlatinal immunity in particular, lies in the well-attested fact that a single attack of the disease confers no protection against subsequent infection ; indeed, some persons appear to possess a marked predisposition to the disease, and suffer from many attacks throughout their lives.   The striking contrast, in this respect, between erysipelas and scarlet fever, suggests an essential difference in the mechanism of infection and resistance, and it would seem reasonable to accept, as a purely provisional hypothesis, the view that the antitoxic immunity, which is the essential factor in resistance to scarlet fever, is relatively ineffective as a protection against the invasion of the skin by *Str. pyogenes*, which is the essential feature of erysipelas.

This does not of course involve the view that the erythrogenic toxin plays no part in erysipelas ; indeed, there are several reasons for believing that it may be responsible for certain features of the disease (see Okell 1932).   It means only that a degree of antitoxic immunity that will protect against scarlet fever will not protect against an erysipelatous infection of the skin.

Puerperal Fever

In discussing the problem of puerperal infection it has become customary, among those who are concerned with this problem from the clinical aspect, to adopt some arbitrary standard of pyrexia and to include in the febrile category all cases which show a rise in temperature beyond this limit of duration.   Such a classification, however useful it may be from the clinical point of view, can have little relation to ætiological factors ; and it is probable that the milder degrees of puerperal pyrexia include a miscellany of bacterial infections, which cannot, at the moment, be classified on any bacteriological basis.

As a cause of puerperal septicæmia, however, there can be no doubt that the hæmolytic streptococcus holds a pre-eminent position (London and N. England Committee 1925, Fitzgibbon and Bigger 1925, Colebrook, L., 1926, Kinloch *et al.* 1928, Colebrook, Dora C., 1935, and others).   Colebrook, D. C. (1935), for instance, in reviewing the results recorded by various workers, notes that among the fatal cases of puerperal fever the proportion due to infection with hæmolytic streptococci varied from 68 to 96 per cent.   The recent advances in our knowledge of the antigenic, and other, relationships of hæmolytic streptococci (see Chapter XXIII) clearly raise the question of the character of the strains associated with puerperal fever.   This question is discussed in a later section, in relation to the epidemiology of the disease ; but that discussion may here be anticipated by stating that, with very rare exceptions, the hæmolytic streptococci isolated from severe cases of puerperal fever have been found to be typical *Str. pyogenes*.

It will be convenient to consider the part played by antitoxic immunity, especially immunity to the erythrogenic toxin, before discussing the very important problem of the probable sources of infection.   If an antitoxic immunity of this type conferred any increased resistance to puerperal infection with hæmolytic streptococci we might reasonably hope to induce a significant decrease in maternal mortality by antitoxic immunization, carried out during pregnancy. In view, however, of our general knowledge of the relation of antitoxic to antibacterial immunity, we should hardly expect an immunity to the erythrogenic toxin to afford any significant protection against an invasive infection of the uterine tissues, leading to septicæmia ; and the facts are in accord with our expectations. Burt-White, Colebrook and others (1930), Stent (1930) and Baird and Cruickshank (1930) have shown that severe puerperal infections are just as common in women with a negative Dick reaction as in those who react positively.

It does not of course follow that the other toxins produced by hæmolytic streptococci, the hæmolysin, leucocidin and so on (see Chapter XXIII) and the corresponding antibodies play no significant part in puerperal infection ; but it may be stated that the balance of evidence at present available is in favour of the view that the decisive factor in attack is the invasiveness of the organism, and that defence depends, in the main, on an anti-bacterial immunity that is type-specific. We shall return to this question in relation to prophylaxis and treatment.

Sources of Infection.—The most important question from this point of view is as to whether the majority of puerperal infections with hæmolytic streptococci are intrinsic or extrinsic. These terms are usually employed to differentiate between those cases in which the hæmolytic streptococcus is present in the female genital passages before labour, and those in which it is introduced from without during labour or the puerperium. The problem at issue therefore narrows down to the presence or absence of hæmolytic streptococci in the cervix or vagina during the later periods of pregnancy. If it is frequently present under normal conditions, we should lay particular stress on host susceptibility, and on the extent of tissue injury during labour, as factors determining the occurrence of puerperal fever ; if it is usually absent, we should regard infection from without as the essential factor, and stress the vital importance of asepsis and antisepsis in handling maternity cases.

Fromme (1908) found streptococci in the vaginal secretions of 46 of 136 pregnant women, but none were hæmolytic. On the other hand he cultivated hæmolytic streptococci from almost every case of severe infection during the puerperium. Lüdke and Polano (1909) found no hæmolytic streptococci in 30 cases during a normal puerperium. Kanter and Pilot (1924) examined 96 cases during pregnancy, and found hæmolytic streptococci in one case only. Lockhart (1925) in a careful study of 100 cases, during which swabs were taken before and after labour, found hæmolytic streptococci in one case only before labour occurred, though streptococci of other types were frequent. One other case showed the presence of this organism in a swab taken immediately after labour ; and in four other cases, in each of which a single swab before labour and two taken in the first few days of the puerperium were negative, a copious growth of hæmolytic streptococci was obtained from a third swab, taken immediately the temperature began to rise. Taylor and Wright (1930) isolated 32 strains of hæmolytic streptococci from vaginal swabs taken from 1,123 pregnant women immediately after labour (2·7 per cent.). Rose (1933) records very similar figures.

It may then be stated with some confidence that hæmolytic streptococci are very infrequent in the genital passages during pregnancy, being present in something under 3 per cent. of cases. In the early days of the puerperium they are rather more frequent, being found in about 5 to 6 per cent. of all cases (see Hare 1934). If the observation of these cases showed that those women who were harbouring hæmolytic streptococci in their genital passages before labour were particularly liable to suffer from puerperal fever the hypothesis of intrinsic infection would receive strong support ; but this is not so. There is general agreement that the great majority of them pass through a perfectly normal puerperium and that this is also true of a high proportion of those women from whose genital passages hæmolytic streptococci are isolated during the puerperium itself.

These findings clearly raise the question as to whether the hæmolytic streptococci isolated under these conditions are *Str. pyogenes* (see Chapter XXIII). The balance of evidence is strongly in favour of the view that they are not.

Taylor and Wright (1930) raise this point in their report and note that, on the basis, of the fermentation of such substrates as salicin, mannitol and lactose only 18 of their 32 strains of hæmolytic streptococci would be classified as *Str. pyogenes*. Hare and Cole-brook (1934), using the additional biochemical tests described in Chapter XXIII, found that only 5 of 52 strains of hæmolytic streptococci isolated from the cervix or vagina during the early days of a normal puerperium behaved as *Str. pyogenes*, while a high pro-portion of the remainder (25 strains) gave the reactions of the bovine type, *Str. agalactiæ*. Hare (1934) also found that strains of hæmolytic streptococci isolated from afebrile cases were readily killed by human whole-blood, while strains from febrile cases were not.

Finally, Lancefield and Hare (1935) examined a large number of strains by the precipitin test (see Chapter XXIII) with the following results. Of 46 strains of hæmolytic strepto-cocci isolated from women suffering from puerperal fever, 45 fell into Lancefield's Group A (*Str. pyogenes*). Of 18 strains isolated after labour from women with mild puerperal infec-tions none were *Str. pyogenes*. Of 65 strains isolated during an afebrile puerperium one was *Str. pyogenes*. Of 13 strains isolated before labour, none was *Str. pyogenes*.

It may be added that Colebrook, Maxted and Johns (1935) failed to detect *Str. pyogenes* on the perineal or peri-anal skin of 160 women attending an antenatal depart-ment, and that Hare and Maxted (1935) failed to isolate *Str. pyogenes* from the fæces of 100 normal women during the first stage of labour.

There can then be very little doubt that *Str. pyogenes* is a very infrequent in-habitant of the normal genital passages either before or after labour. In Lancefield and Hare's series, for instance, the 13 strains of hæmolytic streptococci isolated before labour were obtained as the result of swabbing 855 women, and none of them were *Str. pyogenes*. The hypothesis of intrinsic puerperal infection receives very little support from such studies as these.

If we accept the view that infection is usually extrinsic in origin it is clearly of importance to determine its source. An obvious working hypothesis is that the hæmolytic streptococci are derived from those in attendance on the patient, or at least in her immediate entourage. Until recent years it was extremely difficult to test this hypothesis by observation. The normal carrier rates quoted earlier in this chapter will show that, if 5 to 10 persons have come into contact with a patient during labour in the early days of the puerperium, there is a very good chance of one or other of them carrying a hæmolytic streptococcus in the throat. It would be quite unjustifiable to assume on such a basis that the carrier in question had infected any particular case of puerperal fever.

The division of *Str. pyogenes* into 24 or more distinct serological types has, how-ever, entirely altered the position.

Taking an average figure of 10 per cent. for the normal carrier rate, in the throat, of hæmolytic streptococci, and multiplying this by 0·6 (see above) to obtain the rate for *Str. pyogenes*, we should expect about one person in seventeen who came into contact with a parturient woman to be a possible source of danger. But if this person may be harbouring any one of the 24 or more different types, and the patient may also be suffering from infection with any one of these types, the odds against the type isolated from the contact being identical with the type isolated from the patient become very high indeed, unless the patient has derived her infection from the contact, or *vice versa*. We cannot multiply 24 by 24 to get the exact odds, because that would assume that the carrier rate for each type of streptococcus was equal, which is almost certainly not the case ; but the odds are certainly high enough for an established identity of type to be significant.

Two series of observations are on record in which this method has been applied, using the technique of agglutination and agglutinin absorption for the antigenic analysis of the strains isolated. Smith (1931, 1933) was able to show that, in 39 of 49 cases of puerperal fever due to *Str. pyogenes*, a strain antigenically identical with that derived from the patient could be demonstrated in the throat or nose of the midwife, or doctor, or some other person in attendance on the patient, or, more rarely, in the throat or nose of the patient herself. In Smith's series the latter event occurred in 8 cases as opposed to 31 cases in which a contact was the probable source of infection.

Dora Colebrook (1935) has recorded a very careful and detailed study along similar lines, involving the examination of 63 cases of puerperal fever and their contacts. In 38·1 per cent. of these cases a hæmolytic streptococcus, antigenically identical with that derived from the blood or uterine discharges of the patient was also isolated from the patient's throat or nose. In 57·1 per cent. of the cases a strain antigenically identical with that causing the infection in the patient was isolated from the throat or nose of one or more persons in contact with the patient. In a proportion of these cases (22·2 per cent.) both the patient and a contact were carrying a strain identical with the infecting strain. Thus in 73 per cent. of the cases a strain identical with the infecting strain was isolated either from a contact or from a patient or from both.

We may conclude that, in a very high proportion of cases, the most probable source of uterine infection with *Str. pyogenes* during labour and the puerperium is from the throat or nose of some person in contact with the patient, or from the throat or nose of the patient herself. We must regard this transfer from outside sources to the genital passages as probable rather than certain, because we cannot exclude the possibility that transfer sometimes occurs in the reverse direction.

In regard to the mode of transfer a recent observation of Colebrook, Maxted and Johns (1935) is of considerable interest. They were able to isolate *Str. pyogenes* from the skin of the hand in 7 of 181 normal persons (3·8 per cent.). Taking the normal carrier rate in the throat as about 6 per cent., and regarding this as the most probable source of hæmolytic streptococci found on the hands, an obvious alternative is provided to direct droplet infection.

Prophylaxis.—If an effective method of active immunization were available the conditions for applying it would be peculiarly favourable, since we should be protecting against a risk occurring at a predictable time, with several months at our disposal during which immunity could be induced. Unfortunately no such method is at our disposal, nor is the immediate outlook hopeful. An antitoxic immunity, if effective, in this disease, would confer protection against all types of *Str. pyogenes*, since all form the same toxins. As we have seen, however, there is no evidence that such an immunity confers resistance against the invasive powers of the streptococcus. Such antibacterial immunity as we can induce by the injection of a bacterial vaccine will be type-specific, and it would therefore be necessary to include in our vaccine all the antigenic types that are responsible for puerperal infection. When we know more than we do now in regard to the actual frequency of these various types in puerperal fever it may be possible to prepare a vaccine that will protect against the types that are most often met with ; but our present data contain no indications that any particular type, or any small group of types, will be found to cover a large proportion of cases.

In the absence of an effective measure of active immunization we are forced to rely, in the main, on methods designed to prevent *Str. pyogenes* gaining access to the genital passages of parturient women. The lines along which such methods should be developed are sufficiently obvious from the observations outlined in the preceding section and their details do not concern us here.

Reference may be made to Chapter LI for a description of the attempts that have been made to increase the general resistance of pregnant women by adding Vitamin A to the diet.

Serum Treatment.—It is obvious that the factors that apply in prophylactic active immunization apply also to passive immunization in an established case by the injection of a specific antiserum. We should not expect that an antiscarlatinal serum, the principal effect of which is to neutralize the erythrogenic toxin, would confer any appreciable benefit, and in fact it does not do so. Nor is there any immunological reason to suppose that any of the ordinary antistreptococcal sera on the market will prove effective. We cannot, of course, exclude the possibility that antihæmolysin, antileucocidin, or antifibrinolysin, may exert some beneficial effect ; but we have no evidence that they will protect against the invasive action of *Str. pyogenes*, nor are the ordinary antisera standardized as to their content in these antibodies. If we desire an antibacterial effect we must ensure that the antibody in our serum corresponds to the surface antigen of our infecting bacterium, as we do in the treatment of lobar pneumonia (see Chapter LXXI) ; and this we cannot do. The results of adequate clinical trials are as unsatisfactory as these considerations would lead us to expect (see Colebrook, L., 1935).

At present, then, there is no method of serum treatment in puerperal fever that is founded on a scientific basis. When we have at our disposal type-specific antibacterial sera, can ascertain the type of the infecting streptococcus, and select the corresponding antiserum for treatment, we shall be in a position to carry out clinical trials with some hope of success.

The Rôle of Anaerobic Streptococci in Puerperal Fever.—Although we are concerned in this chapter with diseases caused by hæmolytic streptococci, it will be convenient to complete our summary of the bacteriological aspects of puerperal fever by a brief discussion of the part played by other organisms.

So far as severe and fatal infections are concerned, the organisms most frequently isolated, apart from *Str. pyogenes*, are the anaerobic streptococci described in Chapter XXIII.

Colebrook and Hare (1933), for instance, record that, among 100 positive blood cultures from a series of unselected cases of severe puerperal infections 60 yielded *Str. pyogenes*, 38 anaerobic streptococci, and 2 both types of organism. Although the case fatality of the bacteræmic type of puerperal fever due to anaerobic streptococci is high—about 40 per cent. (Colebrook, L., 1930)—the infections are of a less fulminating type than those due to *Str. pyogenes*. It seems probable, in view of the figures given above for the observed proportions of *Str. pyogenes* infections in different samples of fatal cases of puerperal infection, that the frequency of anaerobic streptococcal infections observed by Colebrook and Hare at Queen Charlotte's Hospital will prove to be rather above the average figure ; but that these organisms rank second only to *Str. pyogenes* as a bacterial cause of maternal mortality there can be no question. A point of some interest (see Colebrook and Hare 1933) is that mixed infections are relatively common, two or more different types of anaerobic streptococci being isolated from the blood in over 50 per cent. of the cases. The occurrence of these mixed infections has also been noted by Brown (1930).

The epidemiology of these anaerobic streptococcal infections forms an interesting contrast to that of puerperal fever caused by *Str. pyogenes*. It has been shown by many observers (see Natvig 1905, Wegelius 1909, Roskowsky 1912, Soule and Brown 1932, White 1933) that anaerobic streptococci form part of the normal flora of the female genital tract ; and the observations of White (1933) suggest that this may be their principal natural habitat. In this case therefore there can be little doubt that puerperal infection is largely intrinsic. (For other references in relation to anaerobic streptococci and their rôle in puerperal fever, see Chapter XXIII.)

Other Types of Puerperal Infection.—It remains to add that a few cases have been reported in which a fatal pyæmic infection due to *Staph. aureus* has developed during the puerperium ; but these are rarities.

In regard to the less severe and fatal types of puerperal infection, which are for the most part localized to the pelvis, a variety of bacteria may be responsible. Many cases are due to a localized infection with *Bact. coli*, and these are not infrequently associated with an infection of the urinary tract. Another group of cases are due to pelvic infections with the gonococcus, and so on.

Other Infections due to Hæmolytic Streptococci.

Cellulitis and other forms of suppuration due to *Str. pyogenes* are discussed in Chapter LXIV, the part played by this organism in acute respiratory infections is considered in Chapter LXXI, and its relation to acute rheumatism in Chapter LXV.

The Use of Specific Antisera in Infections with Str. pyogenes other than Scarlet Fever and Puerperal Fever.

The considerations outlined above in the discussion of the use of antistreptococcal sera in the treatment of puerperal fever clearly apply to all other infections with *Str. pyogenes*. With the single exception of scarlet fever, and the usefulness in that disease of a serum containing the specific antitoxin that neutralizes the erythrogenic toxin, there is no immunological evidence that any of the available antisera are likely to exert a specific curative effect.

Chemotherapy in Infections with Str. pyogenes.

As in other bacterial infections, chemotherapy has, until very recently, given disappointing results. Within the past year, however, an azo-dye containing a sulphonamide group (" Prontosil ") has been found to exert a significant curative effect, both in animal experiments and in natural human infections, including puerperal fever. It would appear that the sulphonamide group is the effective agent, and that the diazo linkage is not essential. It is, of course, impossible as yet to reach any definite conclusion as to the value of this new drug ; but the results so far recorded are at least promising (see Domagk 1935, Tréfouël *et al.* 1935, Levaditi and Vaisman 1936, Colebrook and Kenny 1936, Buttle *et al.* 1936).

REFERENCES

ANDO, K. and KURAUCHI, K. (1930) *J. Immunol.*, **18**, 341.
ALLISON, V. D. and GUNN, W. (1932) *Proc. R. Soc. Med.*, **25**, *Sect. Epidem.*, 927.
ARONSON, H. (1903) *Dtsch. med. Wschr.*, **29**, 439.
BAGINSKY, A. and SOMMERFELD, P. (1900) *Berl. klin. Wschr.*, **37**, 588.
BAIRD, D. and CRUICKSHANK, R. (1930) *Lancet*, ii. 1009.
BENSON, W. T. (1928) *Edin. med. J.*, **35**, 617.
BENSON, W. T. and MACIVER, D. P. (1926) *Edin. med. J.*, **33**, 701.
BLISS, W. P. (1920) *Johns Hopk. Hosp. Bull.*, **31**, 173 ; (1922) *J. exp. Med.*, **36**, 575.
BRÖCKER, W. (1928) *Münch. med. Wschr.*, **75**, 944.
BROWN, T. K. (1930) *Amer. J. Obstet. Gynaec.*, **20**, 300.
BURT-WHITE, H., COLEBROOK, L., MORGAN, G., JERVIS, B. J. W., and HARRE, G. E. (1930) *Brit. med. J.*, i. 240.
BUTLER, W. (1909) *Proc. R. Soc. Med.*, **2**, *Sect. Epidem.*, 69.
BUTTLE, G. A. H., GRAY, W. H., and STEPHENSON, D. (1936) *Lancet*, i. 1286.
BUTTLE, G. A. H. and LOWDON, A. S. R. (1935) *J. Path. Bact.*, **41**, 107.
COLEBROOK, DORA C. (1935) *Spec. Rep. Ser. med. Res. Coun., Lond.*, No. 205.
COLEBROOK, L. (1926) *Proc. R. Soc. Med.*, **19**, 31 ; (1930) *Brit. med. J.*, ii. 134 ; (1935) *Lancet*, i. 1085.
COLEBROOK, L. and HARE, R. (1933) *J. Obstet. Gynaec.*, **40**, 609.
COLEBROOK, L. and KENNY, M. (1936) *Lancet*, i. 1279.
COLEBROOK, L., MAXTED, W. R., and JOHNS, A. M. (1935) *J. Path. Bact.*, **41**, 521.
COLEMAN, MARION B. and WHEELER, M. W. (1926) *J. Lab. clin. Med.*, **11**, 1180.
DAVIS, D. J. and ROSENOW, E. C. (1912) *J. Amer. med. Ass.*, **58**, 773.
DICK, G. F. and DICK, G. H. (1921) *J. Amer. med. Ass.*, **77**, 782 ; (1924a) *Ibid.*, **82**, 265 ; (1924b) *Ibid.*, **83**, 84 ; (1925a) *Ibid.*, **84**, 802 ; (1925b) *Ibid.*, **84**, 1477 ; (1929) *Amer. J. Dis. Child.*, **38**, 905 ; (1934) *J. Amer. med. Ass.*, **103**, 1362.
Discussion. (1927) *Proc. R. Soc. Med.*, **20**, 1171.
DOCHEZ, A. R. (1925) *Medicine*, **4**, 251.
DOCHEZ, A. R., AVERY, O. T., and LANCEFIELD, R. C. (1919) *J. exp. Med.*, **30**, 159.
DOCHEZ, A. R. and SHERMAN, L. (1922) *J. Amer. med. Ass.*, **82**, 542.
DOMAGK, G. (1935) *Dtsch. med. Wschr.*, **61**, 250.
DYER, R. E. (1928) *Publ. Hlth Rep., Wash.*, **43**, 1659.
EAGLES, G. H. (1924) *Brit. J. exp. Path.*, **5**, 199 ; (1926) *Ibid.*, **7**, 286.
ELEY, R. C. (1928) *Amer. J. Dis. Child.*, **35**, 14.
FITZGIBBON, G. and BIGGER, J. W. (1925) *Brit. med. J.*, i. 773.
FRASER, F. H. and PLUMMER, H. (1930) *Brit. J. exp. Path.*, **11**, 291.
FRIEDEMANN, U. and DEICHER, H. (1928) *Dtsch. med. Wschr.*, **54**, 813, 863.
FRIEDMAN, E., ESSERMAN, A. L., and GINSBURG, M. M. (1935) *J. Amer. med. Ass.*, **105**, 956.
FROMME, F. (1908) *Arch. Gynäk.*, **85**, 154.
GABRITSCHEWSKY. (1907) *Berl. klin. Wschr.*, **44**, 556.
GLOVER, J. A. and GRIFFITH, F. (1931) *Brit. med. J.*, ii. 521.
GORDON, J. E. (1927) *J. prev. Med., Baltimore*, **1**, 289.
GORDON, M. H. (1921) *Brit. med. J.*, i. 632.
GRIFFITH. (1926) *J. Hyg., Camb.*, **25**, 385 ; (1927) *Ibid.*, **26**, 363 ; (1928) *Ibid.*, **27**, 113 ; (1934) *Ibid.*, **34**, 542 ; (1935) *Ibid.*, **35**, 23.
GUNN, W. and GRIFFITH, F. (1928) *J. Hyg., Camb.*, **28**, 250.
HARE, R. (1934) *J. Path. Bact.*, **38**, 129 ; (1935) *Ibid.*, **41**, 499.
HARE, R. and COLEBROOK, L. (1934) *J. Path. Bact.*, **39**, 429.
HARE, R. and MAXTED, W. R. (1935) *J. Path. Bact.*, **41**, 513.
HARRIES, E. H. R. (1927) *Ann. Rep. med. Offr Hlth, Birmingham*, p. 59.
HASENKNOPF and SALGE. (1903) *Jb. Kinderheilk.*, **58**, 218.
HEKTOEN, L. (1903) *J. Amer. med. Ass.*, **40**, 685.
HELLER, S. (1927) *Med. Klin.*, **23**, 320.
HUSLER, J. (1927) *Münch. med. Wschr.*, **74**, 707.
JAMES, G. R. (1926) *J. Hyg., Camb.*, **25**, 415.
JAMES, G. R., JOE, A., and SWYER, R. (1929) *J. Hyg., Camb.*, **29**, 347.
JOCHMANN, G. (1905) *Z. klin. Med.*, **56**, 316.
JONES, F. S. and LITTLE, R. B. (1928a) *J. exp. Med.*, **47**, 945 ; (1928b) *Ibid.*, **47**, 957.
KANTER, A. E. and PILOT, I. (1924) *Surg. Gynec. Obstet.*, **38**, 96.
KINLOCH, J. P., SMITH, J., and STEPHEN. (1928) "Maternal Mortality in Aberdeen, etc.," *Scot. Bd. Hlth. Edin.*
KINLOCH, J. P., SMITH, J., and TAYLOR, J. S. (1927) *J. Hyg., Camb.*, **26**, 327.
KIRKBRIDE, MARY B. and WHEELER, M. W. (1926) *J. Immunol.*, **11**, 477.
KOLCHIN, B. S., VLADIMIR, F. B., SHAPIRO, R., and FEIG, I. (1933) *J. Immunol.*, **24**, 397.

KRUMWIEDE, C., NICOLL, M., and PRATT, J. S. (1914) *Arch. intern. Med.*, **13**, 909.
LANCEFIELD, R. C. (1928) *J. exp. Med.*, **47**, 91, 469, 481, 843, 857.
LANCEFIELD, R. C. and HARE, R. (1935) *J. exp. Med.*, **61**, 335.
LANDSTEINER, K., LEVADITI, C., and PRASEK, E. (1911) *Ann. Inst. Pasteur*, **25**, 754.
LASH, A. F. (1926) *J. Amer. med. Ass.*, **86**, 1427.
LENTHE, H. (1927) *Dtsch. med. Wschr.*, **53**, 313.
LEVADITI, C. and VAISMAN, A. (1936) *C. R. Soc. Biol.*, **121**, 803.
LOCKHART, L. P. (1925) *J. Obstet. Gynaec.*, **32**, 49.
LONDON AND N. ENGLAND COMMITTEE. (1925) *Brit. med. J.*, i. 779.
LÜDKE and POLANO. (1909) *Münch. med. Wschr.*, **56**, 7.
MCLACHLAN, D. G. S. (1927) *J. Hyg.*, Camb., **26**, 84.
MCLACHLAN, D. G. S. and MACKIE, T. J. (1928) *J. Hyg.*, Camb., **27**, 225.
MAIR, W. (1923) *Lancet*, ii. 1390.
MERSOL, V. (1929) *Zbl. Bakt.*, **112**, 32.
MEYER. (1902) *Dtsch. med. Wschr.*, **28**, 751.
MOSER. (1902) *Wien. klin. Wschr.*, **15**, 1053.
MOSER and PIRQUET, VON. (1902) *Wien. klin. Wschr.*, **15**, 1053.
NATVIG, H. (1905) *Arch. Gynäk.*, **76**, 701.
NEUFELD, F. (1903) *Z. Hyg. InfektKr.*, **44**, 161.
NICHOLLS, E. E. (1927) *Amer. J. Hyg.*, **7**, 84.
O'BRIEN, R. A. (1930) *J. Hyg.*, Camb., **29**, 357.
O'BRIEN, R. A., OKELL, C. C., and PARISH, H. J. (1929) *Brit. J. exp. Path.*, **10**, 83.
OKELL, C. C. (1932) *Lancet*, i. 761, 815, 867.
OKELL, C. C. and PARISH, H. J. (1928) *Lancet*, i. 748.
PARISH, H. J. and OKELL, C. C. (1927) *J. Path. Bact.*, **30**, 521.
PARK, W. H. and SPIEGEL, R. G. (1925) *J. Immunol.*, **10**, 829.
PLUMMER, H. (1934) *Brit. J. exp. Path.*, **15**, 80.
Report. (1930) *Rep. publ. Hlth med. Subj.*, Lond., No. 58.
ROSE, J. K. (1933) *J. Obstet. Gynaec.*, **40**, 273.
ROSKOWSKY, A. (1912) *Zbl. Gynäk.*, **36**, 4.
ROSSIWALL, E. and SCHICK, B. (1905) *Wien. klin. Wschr.*, **18**, 3.
SCHULTZ and CHARLTON. (1918) *Z. Kinderheilk.*, **17**, 328.
SCOTT, J. A. (1928) *Lancet*, i. 124.
SMITH, J. (1926) *J. Hyg.*, Camb., **25**, 165 ; (1927a) *Ibid.*, **26**, 420 ; (1927b) *J. Path. Bact.*, **30**, 651 ; (1931) "Causation and Source of Infection in Puerperal Fever," H.M. Stat. Off., Lond. ; (1933) *J. Obstet. Gynaec.*, **40**, 991.
SOULE, S. D. and BROWN, T. K. (1932) *Amer. J. Obstet. Gynaec.*, **23**, 532.
STENT, L. (1930) *Lancet*, i. 1066.
STEVENS, F. A. and DOCHEZ, A. R. (1926a) *J. exp. Med.*, **43**, 379 ; (1926b) *Ibid.*, **44**, 439.
STOCKS, P. (1930) *Proc. R. Soc. Med.*, **23**, Sect. Epidem., 65.
STOKES, W. R. and HACHTEL, F. W. (1912) *Publ. Hlth Rep.*, Wash., **27**, 1923.
TAYLOR, J. and WRIGHT, H. D. (1930) *J. Obstet. Gynaec.*, **37**, 213.
TOYADA, T., FUTAGI, Y., and OKAMOTO, M. (1931) *J. infect. Dis.*, **48**, 350.
TOYADA, T., MORIWAKI, J., FUTAGI, Y., and HOSHIZAKI, M. (1929) "Exper. Res. on Etiology of Scarlet Fever." Darien, Manchuria.
TRASK, J. D. and BLAKE, F. G. (1924) *J. exp. Med.*, **40**, 381.
TRÉFOUËL, J., NITTI, F., and BOVET, D. (1935) *C. R. Soc. Biol.*, **120**, 756.
VELDEE, M. V. (1931) *Publ. Hlth Rep.*, Wash., **45**, 693 ; (1933) *Ibid.*, **48**, 549.
VELDEE, M. V., STEVENSON, F. E., and MITCHELL, A. G. (1931) *Publ. Hlth Rep.*, U.S. Treas. Dept., **46**, 3023.
WEGELIUS, W. (1909) *Arch. Gynaek.*, **88**, 249.
WHITE, E. (1933) *J. Obstet. Gynaec.*, **40**, 630.
WILKINSON, E. (1931) *Brit. med. J.*, ii. 494.
WILLIAMS, A. W., GURLEY, C. R., SOBEL, E., and CASTELDA, M. (1932) *J. Bact.*, **23**, 241.
WOODS, H. (1928) *J. Hyg.*, Camb., **28**, 147.
ZINGHER, A. (1924) *J. Amer. med. Ass.*, **83**, 432.

CHAPTER LXIV

PYOGENIC INFECTIONS

We have dealt in other chapters with many diseases which are associated with acute inflammatory or suppurative conditions in various parts of the body. There remain a number of infections which are characterized by the local formation of pus, by a spreading inflammatory reaction, associated with the formation of a purulent exudate, or by a septicæmic or pyæmic invasion of the blood stream. The bacteriology of some of the more important of these conditions is briefly discussed in the present chapter. It should be emphasized that the separation of bacterial infections, or of the bacteria which cause them, into pyogenic and non-pyogenic groups is largely arbitrary, and depends on the observation of the relative frequency of frankly suppurative lesions, among all those reactions which together characterize the association between a particular bacterial parasite and a particular animal host, the host species usually being man. It is quite easy to select some bacterial species, such as *Staph. aureus* or *Str. pyogenes*, as frankly pyogenic, and some others, such as *Myco. lepræ*, *C. diphtheriæ*, or *Cl. tetani* as non-pyogenic, in the usual sense ; but there are very many pathogenic bacteria which cannot be assigned definitely to one class or the other. The reaction of acute inflammation, associated with the formation of a serous, or sero-fibrinous exudate, and with the diapedesis and accumulation of polymorphonuclear cells, is a fundamental defence mechanism, which is brought into play in response to a great variety of stimuli ; and there are few bacterial species which are not pyogenic, in the sense that their presence may call forth this particular reaction in certain situations, and in certain circumstances. The characteristic reaction to the tubercle bacillus, for instance, takes the form of a non-suppurative granuloma, with giant cell formation and caseation ; but in the pleural cavity, in the meninges, or in the urinary bladder, the same bacillus may cause the formation of an inflammatory exudate containing a considerable portion of polymorphonuclear cells. Similarly, the typhoid bacillus is not, in the usual sense, a pyogenic organism ; but it may cause a suppurative cholecystitis. All we can do, in discussing pyogenic infections in general, is to indicate in a few instances the bacteria which are most commonly associated with these conditions.

Septicæmia.

Bacteræmia, in the sense of the mere presence of bacteria in the blood stream, has been described in several earlier chapters. Septicæmia is here used as a designation for a clinical syndrome associated with a severe bacteræmic infection. We may note that, among those organisms which tend to produce pyogenic lesions terminating in a fatal septicæmia, *Str. pyogenes* is by far the most important. The pneumococcus, belonging to the same genus, is a frequent cause of the same type of infection, either invading the blood stream directly from the lung, or from some suppurative focus such as an empyema. *Staph. aureus* may produce a purely septicæmic infection, following a localized infection, or an acute lymphangitis, but the generalization of a staphylococcal infection more commonly takes the form which is described in the following section. The occurrence of a transitory invasion of the blood stream by streptococci of the viridans type in cases of oral sepsis will be referred to in Chapter LXV (p. 1195). Attention may be drawn to the occurrence of septicæmia due to the non-sporing anaerobe *Fusiformis fusiformis*. This type is particularly liable to follow anginal infections, though it sometimes occurs after appendicitis or endometritis (see Lemierre 1936). Anaerobic streptococci are also liable to be overlooked. The great majority of bacteria which produce suppurative lesions may on occasion give rise to a secondary septicæmia ; and in almost all fatal cases of this type such an invasion of the blood stream occurs during the terminal stages of the disease. Thus a septicæmia occurs during the later stages of meningococcal meningitis, in cases of acute peritonitis, in rare cases of acute gonococcal infection, and so on. The balance of evidence suggests that actual multiplication of organisms in the circulating blood is a rare event, except as an immediately *ante-mortem* phenomenon. The septicæmic phase of any bacterial infection is probably the expression of a rapid and continuous invasion of the blood stream from the tissues, either from a single focus which is active and extensive, or from the multiple foci which have been established earlier in the disease. In the case of the frankly suppurative diseases, in which the primary or secondary foci are accessible to surgical interference, the results of adequate drainage testify to the efficiency of the clearing mechanism of the blood stream, if continuous re-invasion can be prevented.

Pyæmia.

This term is employed clinically to designate a type of generalization the mechanism of which differs, to some extent, from that referred to above. In some bacterial infections, and particularly in the more severe forms of infection with *Staph. aureus*, such as acute osteomyelitis, metastatic abscesses may occur in such situations as the kidney, the brain, or the pericardium. In rare cases of appendicitis, or of other suppurative lesions in the abdominal cavity, multiple abscesses may occur in the liver, in direct relation to the portal vein—a condition known as " portal pyæmia," and usually due to infection with *Bact. coli*. In either case the dissemination appears to depend on the occurrence of a suppurative phlebitis at the site of the primary lesion. This extends directly as a progressive thrombosis ; and particles of the infected thrombus, becoming detached, are carried by the blood stream until they reach some situation in which the anatomy of the blood vessels determines their impaction, where they give rise to the formation of secondary abscesses.

Staphylococcal Infections of the Skin and Subcutaneous Tissues.

Many of the localized pustular lesions of the skin are caused by staphylococci. The milder forms, such as acne pustules, are usually associated with a white staphylococcus (see Chapter XXIV). The more severe forms, such as boils or carbuncles, are almost always due to *Staph. aureus*. It may be noted that, in the acne pustule, the white staphylococcus is usually accompanied by the acne bacillus, which Fleming (1909) regards as the primary ætiological agent of the disease.

Infection of the sebaceous follicles in acne, and of the hair-follicles in superficial boils, appears to take place directly from the skin, without trauma. A more serious type of staphylococcal infection sometimes follows an insignificant traumatic infection with a virulent strain of *Staph. aureus*, taking the form of a rapidly spreading lymphangitis, with involvement of the regional lymph glands, and often terminating as an acute septicæmia. *Staph. aureus* may also give rise to suppurative mastitis in nursing mothers ; at times this may assume epidemic proportions in maternity homes (see Editorial 1936).

Streptococcal Infections of the Skin and Subcutaneous Tissues.

Erysipelas, an acute spreading infection of the true dermis, has been considered in Chapters L and LXIII.

Cellulitis is an acute spreading infection of the subcutaneous tissue, characterized by the formation of a sero-purulent, often blood-stained exudate, with no evidence of localization. Rapid lymphatic spread, and septicæmic generalization, are far more frequent than in the case of the localized staphylococcal infections. In very acute infections, such as those which may follow post-mortem wounds, the local manifestations may be minimal, the spread being so rapid that an acutely fatal septicæmia dominates the clinical picture from the first.

In these conditions the streptococcus involved is almost always *Str. pyogenes*.

It may be noted that a comparison of the modal types of staphylococcal and streptococcal infection affords an excellent example of the importance of differences in the biological characters of bacteria, in determining the type of lesion which they produce when they gain access to the tissues.

We may perhaps mention here the condition of *epizootic lymphadenitis* in guinea-pigs, which appears to be due to a capsulated β-hæmolytic streptococcus (see Cunningham 1929). The cervical glands are mainly affected. They are converted into large, thick-walled, fluctuating abscesses containing grumous, pale yellow pus of granular consistency. The disease is generally chronic, and may be confused with pseudotuberculosis (see Chapter LXX).

Botriomycosis.—In the past the term botriomycosis has been limited mainly to a disease of horses characterized by the occurrence of chronic abscesses in the skin, subcutaneous tissue, udder, spermatic cord, and less often the viscera. Of recent years, however, a disease of cattle and swine referred to as actinomycosis of the udder, has attracted considerable attention (see Magnusson 1928, Albiston 1930). Bacteriological study has rendered it clear that both the disease in the horse and the udder disease in cattle and swine are caused by *Staph. aureus*. There is therefore no longer any justification for calling two ætiologically identical diseases by different names, particularly since the term actinomycosis is applied to a disease of entirely different origin. We propose to use the term botriomycosis to cover all chronic granulomatous infections in animals due to *Staph. aureus*. A word of caution, however, is necessary. In swine, though not in cattle, true actinomycosis of the udder, due to infection with *Actinomyces bovis* or a closely related organism, does occur, and the differential diagnosis between this condition and botriomycosis has to be made by pathological and bacteriological methods. Again, *Staph. aureus* not infrequently gives rise in cows to an acute mastitis ; this disease must not be referred to as botriomycosis.

In the horse the abscesses are single or multiple, have thick fibrous walls, and are liable to break down with the production of sinuses and fistulæ containing a gelatinous discharge. On section, the interior of the abscess is seen to consist of soft nodes of granulation tissue situated in a network of fibrous strands. Embedded in the granulation tissue are small yellowish-white granules about the size of a grain of sand. These consist of grape or mulberry-like clusters of Gram-positive micrococci surrounded by a zooglœal substance. The granules are sometimes referred to as Bollinger's granules, and the organism has been called *M. ascoformans*, though there is little doubt that it is in fact *Staph. aureus*. A similar picture is seen in mammary botriomycosis of swine. In cattle, however, the colonies are surrounded by definite clubs instead of by an undifferentiated mass, and thus bear a close resemblance to true actinomycosis. In all three animals the disease may be reproduced by experimental inoculation of *Staph. aureus* under suitable conditions.

Mastitis in Cattle.—This important disease can only be touched on briefly here. Those who are interested in obtaining further information are referred to the series of papers by Minett and his colleagues in this country (Minett, Stableforth, and Edwards 1929, 1930, 1932, 1933, Minett and Stableforth 1931, Minett 1932, 1935, 1936, Stableforth 1930, 1932, Edwards 1932, 1933, 1934, Stableforth, Edwards, and Minett 1935), to Klimmer and Haupt (1930) and Seelemann (1932) in Germany, and to Rosell (1933) in Canada.

The disease is very prevalent among milch cows both in Europe and in the United States (see Brigham *et al.* 1929, Hucker *et al.* 1932), and constitutes one of the most serious economic problems confronting the dairy farmer. It is moreover of some public health importance, since occasionally streptococci of a type pathogenic for human beings may be excreted in the milk and give rise to scarlet fever or septic sore throat in those consuming it in the raw condition (see Chapter LXXXIX).

The bacteriology of mastitis is varied. Minett, Stableforth, and Edwards (1929), who investigated 113 cases of mastitis, found that 82 were due to streptococci, 21 to *C. pyogenes*, 6 to staphylococci, 3 to coliform bacilli, and 1 to *F. necrophorus*. We may briefly consider these different types.

Streptococcal Mastitis.—The streptococci causing mastitis may be divided on cultural, biochemical, and serological grounds into three groups.

Group I streptococci—the typical *Str. agalactiæ* (see Chapter XXIII)—are responsible for the common condition of chronic mastitis. The incidence of this disease increases with the age of the animal, and is high in cows over 5 years of age. Usually more than one quarter of the udder is attacked. Infection probably occurs through abrasions on the teats or *via* the teat canal, and is spread by the hands of the milker. The condition is very chronic, and it is doubtful whether complete recovery ever occurs.

Group II streptococci give rise usually to acute or subacute mastitis, which is much less common than the chronic form just described. The distinguishing features of Group II streptococci are absence of hæmolysis, reduction of methylene blue in milk, failure to ferment salicin, mannitol, inulin, or æsculin, and poor production of acid in glucose broth. Contagion from the hands of the milker plays no obvious part in this type of mastitis. Usually only one quarter of the udder is affected. The condition is, however, often very acute, and may lead to the partial or complete destruction of the quarter involved.

Minett (1936) also includes in this group the sorbitol-positive trehalose-negative sub-group of Lancefield's Group C strains of hæmolytic streptococci (see p. 450).

Group III streptococci are a much less important cause of disease. They are characterized by absence of hæmolysis, production of acid in litmus milk at 10° C., reduction of methylene blue in milk, and fermentation of salicin, mannitol, and inulin.

Streptococcus pyogenes.—This organism is occasionally isolated from cows suffering from mastitis. The udder is probably infected from the nasopharynx of the milker or other human carrier. Its presence in the milk is likely to be followed by outbreaks of sore throat or scarlet fever in persons consuming it in the raw state (see p. 449 and Chapter LXXXIX).

MASTITIS DUE TO C. PYOGENES.—This organism is responsible for so-called " summer mastitis." The disease in this country occurs during the second half of the year. It is far commoner in dry cows than in cows in milk, and usually develops shortly before calving. One or more quarters of the udder are affected. Constitutional symptoms, sometimes accompanied by swelling of the hock joints, are not uncommon. The condition is often chronic, and abscesses in the udder tissue may break through the skin. Microscopical examination of the udder secretion reveals enormous numbers of Gram-positive diphtheroid bacilli, which, when cultivated on coagulated blood serum, give the typical pitted appearance due to liquefaction.

STAPHYLOCOCCAL MASTITIS.—This form usually occurs a few days after calving. One or more quarters of the udder are affected. The condition is subacute or acute, and not infrequently proves fatal. The local invasion of the udder may be so severe as to give rise to gangrene. The discharge from the affected quarters contains large numbers of hæmolytic staphylococci. As has already been mentioned, staphylococci may also give rise to a chronic infection of the udder, which is usually referred to as actinomycosis but is more properly termed botriomycosis.

Diagnosis of Mastitis.—In its more severe forms mastitis can be detected by clinical means alone, but the chronic streptococcal types of infection usually call for laboratory assistance. Individual quarter samples of milk are required for examination, the fore-milk being the most suitable. In well-marked cases of the streptococcal disease flakes in the fore-milk are visible against a dark background ; the reaction of the milk is more alkaline than normal ; on centrifugation of the milk the cellular sediment is found to be increased and to exceed 1 part per 1,000 ; by the Breed Smear method the cells usually number more than 3 million per c.c. ; microscopical examination of the centrifugal deposit reveals the presence of fairly long-chained streptococci ; and cultivation of the centrifuged deposit shows the presence of streptococci which, on further examination, are found to belong to one of the mastitis groups. There is no question that cultivation of the centrifuged deposit —preferably in deep blood agar containing æsculin and crystal violet (Edwards 1933)—is much the most delicate test ; it should always be used when herd examinations are being made.

Prevention and Treatment of Mastitis.—The most satisfactory method of dealing with chronic streptococcal mastitis seems to be by a modification of the eradication plan. The milk of every cow in the herd is examined culturally, and the affected animals are either sold out, segregated on another part of the farm, or, if neither of these courses is possible, milked last. Strict attention must, of course, be paid to the general hygiene of milking, and every precaution taken to prevent infection of the clean herd. In this way it is possible to build up a non-infected herd, and to keep it free from infection indefinitely.

Little is yet known of the actual value of the therapeutic measures that have been proposed for treating animals suffering from the disease. Infusion of the udder with a suitable bactericidal agent, and vaccine treatment, are both regarded with some favour by practising veterinarians.

Conjunctivitis.—One of the commonest causes of acute conjunctivitis is the Koch-Weeks bacillus, which seems to be identical with *H. influenzæ* (see Chapter XXX). This condition appears to be widespread, occurs in epidemic form, and shows a definite seasonal prevalence in different countries. It is particularly common in Egypt, where the bacillus was first isolated by Koch. Another, less common, cause of conjunctivitis is the pneumococcus. This type of infection, which is more severe than that due to the Koch-Weeks bacillus, is irregular in distribution, is confined chiefly to children, and may occur in localized epidemics. It is more common in Eastern than in Western countries. Subacute, or angular, conjunctivitis is due to the Morax-Axenfeld bacillus (see Chapter XXXIV). Gonococcal conjunctivitis—ophthalmia neonatorum—is described in Chapter LXII. (For a general account of the bacteriology of conjunctivitis see Axenfeld 1928.)

Suppurative Lesions in Bones and Joints.—Acute osteomyelitis, occurring independently of a compound fracture, is almost always due to infection with *Staph. aureus*. It occurs mainly in children, in whom it not infrequently develops after a simple blow, or similar trauma. The infection is blood-borne. Acute suppurative periostitis is rare. When it occurs, it is usually a streptococcal infection. A subacute, or chronic, periostitis occasionally occurs as a sequel of typhoid, or paratyphoid fever, and is caused by the bacillus responsible for the primary infection. Such abscesses occur most commonly over the ribs, or the cranium.

A metastatic purulent arthritis may occur as a sequel to infection with any pyogenic bacterium ; though the pneumococcus is the organism most frequently isolated in such cases. Other bacteria are rarely isolated from true suppurative arthritis in man, except in those cases which follow wounds entering the joint. In animals other bacteria are often responsible for this condition, as, for instance, the diphtheroid bacillus *C. pyogenes* (see Chapter XVI).

Suppurative Lesions of the Alimentary Tract.

Appendicitis.—The bacteriology of acute appendicitis, and of the associated appendix abscesses, is very confused. It is possible that the primary lesion occurs in the wall of the appendix, and that it is due to a blood-borne infection with a streptococcus of the viridans type (see Rosenow 1915). The complex bacterial flora of this part of the intestine ensures a rapid secondary invasion of the damaged tissue with a host of different bacteria, among which *Bact. coli* is prominent ; and the bacteriology of the lesion found at operation is correspondingly complex. Veillon and Zuber (1898), using a combination of aerobic and anaerobic methods, examined 22 cases of appendicitis. From 19 cases they isolated anaerobic bacilli associated with rare streptococci and coliform bacilli ; from 2 of the cases anaerobic bacilli alone were recovered. Usually 5 or 6 different species were found together, and never less than two. Of the anaerobic bacilli the majority belonged to the Gram-positive non-sporing group, described in Chapter XVII ; amongst these *Fusiformis fragilis*, *F. ramosus*, *F. fusiformis*, and *F. furcosus* were the commonest.

Cl. welchii was also found very frequently. Recently Weinberg and his colleagues (1926, 1928) have examined 150 cases of acute appendicitis, a great number of which were of the gangrenous type. Of the aerobic bacteria the frequency was *Bact. coli* 128, enterococcus 41, *Proteus* 14, *Staphylococcus* 12, and *Streptococcus* 10 ; a few other species of organisms were found occasionally. Of the anaerobic bacteria the frequency was *Cl. welchii* 49, Gram-negative rod-shaped organisms 60, cocci and *Streptococci* 40, *F. ramosus* 16, *Cl. fallax* 5, *Cl. septique* 2, *Cl. histolyticum* 2, and other organisms in smaller numbers. Essentially similar results have been recorded by Schmitz (1930) and Buttiaux and Tiprez (1933). It is clearly impossible on the present evidence to assess the rôle played by each of these organisms in the ætiology of appendicitis, but it would appear not improbable that the organisms responsible for the gangrene and the general toxæmia in severe cases belong mainly to the anaerobic groups. Weinberg and his co-workers (1928) are so impressed with the importance of the anaerobes that they are using antitoxic serum prepared against these organisms in the treatment of appendicitis.

Cholecystitis.—The frankly suppurative form of cholecystitis appears to be due, in the majority of cases, to infection with *Bact. coli*, sometimes associated with streptococci. Acute cholecystitis may follow infection with *Bact. coli*, with *Bact. typhosum*, or with bacilli of the paratyphoid group. The relation between infection of the gall-bladder and the carrier-state in typhoid fever, will be discussed in Chapter LXVI. It may be noted that infections of the gall-bladder provide an interesting example of the importance of local conditions, of a semi-mechanical nature, in originating or perpetuating bacterial infection. Bacteria, and particularly members of the coli-typhoid group, have frequently been isolated from the interior of gall-stones. It is highly probable that a mild bacterial infection so alters the local conditions in the gall-bladder as to favour the formation of gall-stones, and that the cholesterol and bile salts of which these are composed may be deposited on a central nidus of desquamated cells, or fibrin, containing bacteria. There are also good reasons for believing that the presence of gall-stones greatly increases the liability to bacterial infection ; so that we have a vicious circle, each abnormality tending to promote, or perpetuate, the other. The bacteriology of gall-bladder infections is also of interest, in that it provides an example of the selective action of certain body fluids on bacteria, and illustrates the necessity for making due allowance for such fa tors in interpreting bacteriological findings. We have noted elsewhere that some authorities believe that the typhoid bacillus gains access to the gall-bladder *via* the blood vessels of the wall of the viscus, and not by the bile ducts. It has been suggested by many observers that the same is true in the majority of cases of cholecystitis, and that the primary lesion is a focus of infection beneath the epithelial lining. Rosenow (1916) has suggested that streptococci, with a special tendency to localize in the gall-bladder wall, play an important part in the production of cholecystitis in man. Wilkie (1928) has recorded an interesting series of observations, which tend to support this view. In 50 cases of cholecystitis, mainly chronic, he took cultures from the bile, the gall-bladder wall including all coats, the submucosa, and the small lymphatic gland situated near the junction of the cystic duct and the gall-bladder. From the bile, and from the pieces of gall-bladder wall which were contaminated with bile, he isolated streptococci on two occasions, *Bact. coli* three times, and *Cl. welchii* once. From the submucosal cultures, in which special care had been taken to prevent contamination with bile, he isolated streptococci in 21 cases, and *Cl. welchii* once. From the cystic gland he isolated streptococci in 43 cases, *Bact. coli* once, and *Cl. welchii* once. He concludes that cultures taken from the bile give an entirely misleading picture of the essential bacteriology of cholecystitis, owing to the inhibitory action of the bile salts on the streptococcus, which is the cause of the primary infection. These observations clearly suggest that *Bact. coli* may, in many cases, play the part of an important secondary invader, favoured by the selective action of the bile, rather than that of a primary agent.

Peritonitis.—Some cases of peritonitis are primary, for example, certain cases in children due to infection with the pneumococcus ; but the great majority of cases are secondary to some primary intra-abdominal lesion, such as appendicitis, perforated gastric or duodenal ulcer, or some type of intestinal obstruction. The species of bacteria involved in the primary invasion of the peritoneum depends in part on the nature of the primary lesion, in part on the flora of the section of the intestinal tract involved. In intestinal obstruction the bacteria from within the intestine tend to make their way through the intestinal wall, and to produce a mixed infection. In such cases, and in the later stages of any infection of the general peritoneal sac, other than those which are acutely fatal, the bacteriological picture is usually dominated by the colon bacillus.

Fatal post-operative peritonitis is often due to infection with a hæmolytic streptococcus, and a similar infection may occur as part of a septicæmic infection. Pelvic peritonitis, following salpingitis, is usually due to the gonococcus. Other bacteria which may be found in the peritoneal exudate include *Staph. albus*, bacilli of the *Proteus* group, and *Ps. pyocyanea* (see Dudgeon and Sargent 1905). In those cases in which free transit has occurred from the interior of some part of the lower intestine, anaerobes of the *Fusiformis* and *Clostridium* groups may be present. Cazzamali and Miglierina (1933), who examined 81 cases of acute peritonitis, found that aerobic organisms accounted for about two-thirds and anaerobic for about one-third of the total number isolated. In point of time the aerobic organisms preceded the anaerobic. *Bact. coli* seemed to be able to diffuse more rapidly through the peritoneal cavity than any other organism, while streptococci persisted for the longest time. In cases of perforated gastric or duodenal ulcer no organisms could be detected for 6, or even 12 hours, but after this time the peritoneal cavity was always infected, the commonest organism being a non-hæmolytic streptococcus. From a prognostic point of view, excluding infections with *Str. pyogenes*, the fewer organisms and the fewer species there are present, the more favourable is the outlook (see also Meleney *et al.* 1931).

Suppurative Lesions of the Respiratory Tract.

Suppurative lesions of the accessory sinuses of the nose usually arise by direct extension from the nares or nasopharynx, and the bacteria most frequently responsible are the potentially pathogenic constituents of the nasopharyngeal flora—*Str. pneumoniæ*, *Str. pyogenes*, and *H. influenzæ*. Another organism frequently isolated from cases of suppurative sinusitis is *Staph. aureus* ; while acute infection of the nasal sinuses with the meningococcus has been described, and is believed by some observers to play a part in the genesis of cerebrospinal meningitis (see Chapter LXI).

Under this heading, we may, for convenience, include otitis media. The great majority of cases in man are caused by *Str. pyogenes*, *Str. pneumoniæ*, or *Staph.*

aureus (Fisher 1929). Middle-ear disease is very common in rats, particularly in adult animals ; the main organisms involved appear to be *Actinobacillus actinoides*, streptococci, and diphtheroids (Nelson and Gowen 1930).

The bacteriology of infections of the lungs is discussed in Chapter LXXI. Suppurative inflammation of the pleural cavity arises by direct extension from the pulmonary lesion, and is due to the same infecting agent—in most cases of lobar pneumonia to *Str. pneumoniæ*, of secondary broncho-pneumonia to *Str. pneumoniæ*, *Str. pyogenes*, or occasionally to some other organism.

Pneumonia is common in adult rats and appears to be due to very much the same organisms as those responsible for otitis media. It may be noted that Jowett (1930, 1931) has described a *chronic pyobacillosis of sheep*, met with in the abattoir, which is characterized by multiple small abscesses in the lungs and sometimes other parts of the body. The causative organism is a Gram-negative ovoid bacillus, said to be identical with the *Bact. purifaciens* of Christiansen.

Acute Suppurative Lesions of the Urinary Tract.

Acute suppurative infections of the urinary tract leading to pyelitis, pyelonephritis, and cystitis are caused most frequently by *Bact. coli*. Dudgeon, Wordley, and Bawtree (1921, 1922–23) have drawn attention to the frequency with which hæmolytic types of *Bact. coli* are found in such infections, and have noted that these hæmolytic strains are particularly frequent in males. In a series of 44 *coli* infections in males, 72·7 per cent. were due to the hæmolytic and 27·3 per cent. to the non-hæmolytic type ; in 116 female cases, on the other hand, only 31 per cent. were due to the hæmolytic, and 69 per cent. to the non-hæmolytic type. More recently Dudgeon and Pulvertaft (1927) have described a particular type of acute urinary infection, associated as a rule with acute pyelitis or pyelonephritis, and caused by a hæmolytic, slow-lactose-fermenting type of coliform bacillus. The general symptoms at the onset are so severe that the urinary affection is often masked, and the true nature of the disease is not manifest for 2 or 3 days, when pus is found in the urine. In most cases recovery occurs, and the urine clears up completely, contrasting in this respect with infections due to the typical non-hæmolytic *Bact. coli*, in which chronic bacilluria is the rule.

Bact. aerogenes is said to be frequently present in infections of the genito-urinary tract (Hill *et al.* 1929). Another common invader is *Proteus vulgaris* (Taylor 1928) ; in acute cases this organism can be isolated from the blood stream, and may be present in pure culture in the urine. *Proteus vulgaris*, fæcal streptococci, *Ps. pyocyanea* and staphylococci are not infrequent secondary invaders in infections of the urinary tract. Infection of the urine with the gas-producing *Cl. welchii* may occur in cases of carcinoma of the rectum or bladder, associated with a recto-vesical fistula. Cystitis is a not uncommon complication of gonorrhœa, and is then due to the gonococcus, alone or in association with other organisms. Tuberculous cystitis or pyelonephritis, which is itself associated with pyuria, is frequently complicated during its later stages by a secondary infection with *Bact. coli*, staphylococci, or other organisms.

Infections of the bladder and of the pelvis of the kidney provide another illustration of the importance of local mechanical factors in promoting bacterial infection. Renal or vesical calculi, enlarged prostate, urethral stricture, vesical papilloma or carcinoma, are all conditions which, sooner or later, are associated with an infective cystitis.

Pyelonephritis is sometimes observed in *cattle* and is characterized by a membranous necrotic inflammation, which attacks principally the papillæ and leads to progressive destruction of the kidney ; there is an accompanying inflammation of the capsule, and often considerable fibrosis of the pelvis of the kidney, the ureter, and the bladder. The ætiology of this condition is still uncertain. By some it is said to be due to a Gram-positive diphtheroid bacillus, *C. pyogenes* ; by others to a mixed infection with *C. pyogenes*, streptococci, coliform bacilli, and other organisms (Glage 1928, Jones and Little 1930).

Treatment of Pyogenic Infections

Surgical.—Although the discussion of surgical methods of treatment takes us beyond our proper ground, it is permissible to point out that general bacteriological principles indicate the paramount importance of judicious surgical interference in those acute suppurative infections which are accessible to such measures. The removal, or adequate drainage, of a localized focus of infection will usually enable the defence mechanisms of the body to deal satisfactorily with the remaining bacteria. We have emphasized above the importance of mechanical factors in many cases of acute or chronic pyogenic infections ; and the rectification of these abnormalities by surgical means frequently results in a bacteriological cure. It may be noted that other factors, in addition to the removal of living bacteria, are involved in the successful drainage or removal of an infected focus. Reference to the discussion on " aggressins " in Chapter XLV will indicate that the antigenic constituents liberated in such a focus may play a significant part in extending the area of infection, or in favouring its local persistence.

Chemotherapy.—The early failure of such well-known disinfectants as carbolic acid and mercuric chloride to influence the course of infections in the animal body, even when introduced in amounts greater than those necessary to prevent growth of the organisms *in vitro*, led to a virtual abandonment by the bacteriologist of the field of chemotherapy. It is only in recent years, following on the demonstration of the value of drug treatment in protozoal infections, that workers have again entered this field. New organic compounds, mainly of the aniline group, have been prepared, and are now undergoing trial. The difficulty of assessing their value in the laboratory is considerable, for, as Browning (1933) points out, the results of *in vitro* experiments may throw very little light on occurrences in the living body. Acriflavine has proved to be one of the most suitable of the new synthetic products, combining a very low toxicity for the tissues with a high toxicity for most microorganisms. Its judicious use has met with considerable success in the control of infections occurring under both experimental and natural conditions, and it seems to be of particular value in the treatment of wounds, and of septic infections of the mouth. For these purposes a concentration of 1/1000–1/5000 is generally used. Nothing short of direct contact between the dye and the infecting organisms is likely to be successful. The destruction of organisms in the centre of masses of necrotic tissue or blood clot is probably beyond the power of any disinfectant (Browning 1933). The therapeutic action of acriflavine and similar substances appears to depend, not on the rapid destruction of the organisms, but on a more gradual effect leading to a diminution of their virulence and vitality, and so rendering them more suitable for ingestion by phagocytic cells.

Serotherapy.—The probability, now supported by experimental evidence, that staphylococci exert their deleterious action on the tissues by means of toxins, holds out some hope of the value of serum treatment.   Antitoxic serum, capable of neutralizing the hæmolytic, skin-necrosing, lethal, and leucocidic properties of the toxin, can be prepared by inoculation of horses with formolized, and later with pure, toxin.   Its antitoxin content can be titrated in one or other of the following ways.

(1) By testing mixtures of toxin and antitoxin for their hæmolytic activity towards rabbit red blood corpuscles.   In practice the test dose of toxin (LH) is determined which, when mixed with one provisional unit of antitoxin, causes partial hæmolysis ;   this test dose is then used for titrating the unknown antitoxin ;   (2) by inoculating toxin-antitoxin mixtures in 0·2 c.c. quantities intracutaneously into guinea-pigs of 300–400 grams.   The test dose $\frac{Lr}{10}$ is the quantity of toxin which, when mixed with 0·1 provisional unit of antitoxin, causes a small but characteristic necrotic lesion in 24–48 hours ;   (3) by inoculating toxin-antitoxin mixtures in 0·5 c.c. quantities intravenously into mice.   The test dose employed is that quantity of toxin which, when mixed with one provisional unit of antitoxin, causes death of half the mice within three days ;   (4) by inoculating toxin-antitoxin mixtures in 0·5 c.c. quantities intraperitoneally into mice.   The procedure is similar to method (3).   The international unit is now defined as the specific antitoxic activity contained in 0·5 mgm. of the dry standard preparation preserved at the National Institute for Medical Research, London.   (See Hartley and Smith 1935.)

The use of antistaphylococcal serum is of recent introduction, and little information is yet available about its value.   Favourable results have, however, been recorded on small series of cases (Dolman 1934a, b).   It seems probable that its main sphere of usefulness will be in the treatment of severe local or generalized infections accompanied, or likely to be followed by, septicæmia.   In such cases the intravenous inoculation of large doses should be tried.   If a favourable reaction results, serum treatment may be followed by a course of active immunization with toxoid.

Antiscarlatinal (antitoxic) and the ordinary type of antistreptococcal serum, which have already been described in relation to the treatment of scarlet fever and puerperal sepsis (Chapter LXIII), have on the whole given disappointing results in cases of septicæmia.

Vaccination.—Examination of the blood serum of man and animals has shown the presence in small amounts of natural antitoxin to staphylococci (see Parish, O'Meara, and Clark 1934, Murray 1935, Nélis and Poncelet 1935).   In normal human adults and new-born babies the antitoxin titre expressed in terms of international units is generally about 0·25–0·75 units per c.c.   In patients suffering from superficial staphylococcal infections, such as acne, blepharitis, furunculosis, and sycosis, the average titre is very slightly higher or practically unaltered.   In cases of carbuncles the titre is often slightly raised, while in cases of chronic osteomyelitis it is generally high, though not always so (see Blair and Hallman 1935–36), and may reach 15 units or more per c.c.   Experimentally and clinically it has been found that treatment of animals and patients suffering from chronic staphylococcal infections with formolized toxin—toxoid—but not with staphylococcal vaccines, is often followed by a rise in the antitoxin titre and considerable improvement in the local condition ;   though there seems to be no definite relationship between the absolute titre attained and the retrogression of the infection.   The preparation of the toxoid requires care, and strict precautions must be taken to ensure its innocuity and its antigenic potency (Dolman and Kitching 1935).   The dosage recommended by different workers varies somewhat.   Dolman (1933, 1935) starts with a dose of

0·05 c.c. increases by 0·05 c.c. weekly, till at the eighth injection 0·5 c.c. is given. If a second course of injections is needed, it is probably wise to rest the patient for a month or two. There seems to be fairly general agreement now that toxoid is of considerably more value than vaccines of whole staphylococci. Cases of boils and of chronic osteomyelitis are particularly benefited by toxoid treatment. In cases of acne, staphylococcal toxoid may well be combined with a vaccine of *C. acnes*. (For reports on this method of treatment see Dolman 1933, 1935, Dolman and Kitching 1935, Connor and McKie 1934, Parish, O'Meara, and Clark 1934, and Murray 1935, Whitby 1936).

Vaccines of *Bact. coli* and of *Proteus vulgaris* are sometimes of use in urinary infections. For further discussion of the value of vaccine treatment the reader is referred to the monograph by Dudgeon (1927).

REFERENCES

ALBISTON, H. E. (1930) *Aust., vet. J.*, **6,** 2.
AXENFELD, T. (1928) Kolle and Wassermann's " Hdb. path. Mikroorg.," 3te Abt., 1928–9, **6,** 281.
BLAIR, J. E. and HALLMAN, F. A. (1935–36) *Proc. Soc. exp. Biol., N.Y.*, **33,** 382.
BRIGHAM, G. D., McALPINE, J. G., and ANDERSON, E. O. (1929) *Bull. Storrs agric. Exp. Sta.*, No. 158.
BROWNING, C. H. (1933) *Brit. dent. J.*, **54,** 389.
BUTTIAUX, R. and TIPREZ, J. (1933) *C. R. Soc. Biol.*, **114,** 133.
CAZZAMALI, P. and MIGLIERINA, R. (1933) *Arch. ital. Chir.*, **34,** 573.
CONNOR, J. I. and McKIE, M. (1934) *Brit. J. Derm.*, **46,** 20.
CUNNINGHAM, J. S. (1929) *J. infect. Dis.*, **45,** 474.
DOLMAN, C. E. (1933) *J. Amer. med. Ass.*, **100,** 1007 ; (1934a) *Canad. med. Ass. J.*, **30,** 601 ; (1934b) *Ibid.*, **31,** 130 ; (1935) *Lancet*, i. 306.
DOLMAN, C. E. and KITCHING, J. S. (1935) *J. Path. Bact.*, **41,** 137.
DUDGEON, L. S. (1927) " Bacterial Vaccines and their Position in Therapeutics." London.
DUDGEON, L. S. and PULVERTAFT, R. J. V. (1927) *J. Hyg., Camb.*, **26,** 285.
DUDGEON, L. S. and SARGENT, P. W. G. (1905) " The Bacteriology of Peritonitis." London.
DUDGEON, L. S., WORDLEY, E., and BAWTREE, F. (1921) *J. Hyg., Camb.*, **20,** 137 ; (1922–3) *Ibid.*, **21,** 168.
Editorial. (1936) *Lancet*, ii. 91.
EDWARDS, S. J. (1932) *J. comp. Path.*, **45,** 43 ; (1933) *Ibid.*, **46,** 211 ; (1934) *Ibid.*, **47,** 49.
FISHER, J. H. (1929) *J. infect. Dis.*, **44,** 33.
FLEMING, A. (1909) *Lancet*, i. 1035.
GLAGE, F. (1928) Kolle and Wassermann's " Hdb. path. Mikroorg.," 3te Abt., 1928–9, **6,** 563.
HARTLEY, P. and SMITH, M. L. (1935) *Quart. Bull. Hlth. Org. L. of N. Spec. No. Biol. Standardisation*, Extract D. Jan. No., p. 68.
HILL, J. H., SEIDMAN, L. R., STADNICHENKO, A. M. S., and ELLIS, M. G. (1929) *J. Bact.*, **17,** 205.
HUCKER, G. J., TRUDELL, F., and JENNINGS, W. S. (1932) *N.Y. St. agric. Exp. Sta. Tec. Bull*, No. 199.
JONES, F. S. and LITTLE, R. B. (1930) *J. exp. Med.*, **51,** 909.
JOWETT, W. (1930) *J. comp. Path.*, **43,** 109 ; (1931) *Ibid.*, **44,** 202.
KLIMMER, M. and HAUPT, H. (1930) *Ergebn. Hyg. Bakt.*, **11,** 354.
LEMIERRE, A. (1936) *Lancet*, i. 701.
MAGNUSSON, H. (1928) *Acta path. microbiol. scand.*, **5,** 170.
MELENEY, F. C., HARVEY, H. D., and JERN, H. Z. (1931) *Arch. Surg.*, **22,** 1.
MINETT, F. C. (1932) *Bull. Off. int. Épizooties*, **6,** 124 ; (1935) *Proc. 12th int. vet. Congr.*, p. 511 ; (1936) *J. Hyg., Camb.*, **35,** 504.
MINETT, F. C. and STABLEFORTH, A. W. (1931) *J. comp. Path.*, **44,** 114.
MINETT, F. C., STABLEFORTH, A. W., and EDWARDS, J. S. (1929) *J. comp. Path.*, **42,** 213; (1930) *Ibid.*, **43,** 163 ; (1932) *Ibid.*, **45,** 1 ; (1933) *Ibid.*, **46,** 131.
MURRAY, D. S. (1935) *Lancet*, i. 303.
NÉLIS, P. and PONCELET, F. (1935) *C. R. Soc. Biol.*, **118,** 312.
NELSON, J. B. and GOWEN, J. W. (1930) *J. infect. Dis.*, **46,** 53.
PARISH, H. J., O'MEARA, R. A. Q., and CLARK, W. (1934) *Lancet*, i. 1054.
ROSENOW, E. C. (1915) *J. Amer. med. Ass.*, **65,** 1687 ; (1916) *J. infect. Dis.*, **19,** 527.

Rossel, J. M.   (1933) " La Mammite Streptococcique de la Vache," Ministère de L'Agriculture de la Province de Quebec.
Schmitz, H.   (1930) *Zbl. Bakt.*, **117,** 378.
Seelemann, M.   (1932) " Die Streptokokkeninfektionen des Euters."   M. & H. Schaper, Hanover.
Stableforth, A. W.   (1930) *J. comp. Path.*, **43,** 22 ;   (1932) *Ibid.*, **45,** 185.
Stableforth, A. W., Edwards, S. J., and Minett, F. C.   (1935) *J. comp. Path.*, **48,** 300.
Taylor, J. F.   (1928) *J. Path. Bact.*, **31,** 897.
Veillon and Zuber.   (1898) *Arch. Méd. exp.*, **10,** 517.
Weinberg, M., Prévot, A. R., Davesne, J., and Renard, C.   (1928) *C. R. Soc. Biol.*, **98,** 749, 752.
Weinberg, M., Renard, C., and Davesne, J.   (1926) *C. R. Soc. Biol.*, **94,** 813.
Whitby, L. E. H.   (1936) *Lancet*, i. 1454.
Wilkie.   (1928) *Brit. J. Surg.*, **15,** 450.

CHAPTER LXV

THE BACTERIOLOGY OF RHEUMATIC INFECTIONS AND OF ENDOCARDITIS

THE attempts which have been made to solve the problem of the ætiology of acute and chronic rheumatism are legion, and the literature is correspondingly extensive. An adequate review is impossible, and would indeed serve no useful purpose ; for the whole subject is at the moment too confused and obscure to allow of any systematic presentation. It may be said that, while most of the earlier observations that yielded positive results tended to inculpate one or another type of streptococcus, the present position of this problem is that interest is focussed on the relation of hæmolytic streptococci to acute rheumatic infection, and on the possibility that this disease is caused by a filtrable virus. The earlier studies have, for the moment at least, mainly a historical interest, and may therefore be very briefly summarized.

Westphal, Wassermann and Malkoff (1899) isolated a streptococcus from the blood of a patient suffering from rheumatic endocarditis, associated with chorea. In the following year Poynton and Paine (1900, 1913) published the first of their series of papers, in which, on the basis of extensive bacteriological studies in man and numerous experiments on the rabbit, they reached the conclusion that acute rheumatism is the result of infection with a particular variety of streptococcus, or with a closely allied group of streptococcal strains. Since the appearance of their reports, the bacteriologist has been mainly concerned with repeated attempts to determine the real nature of the association between certain types of streptococci and this particular disease. The observations of Poynton and Paine, with regard to the isolation of streptococci from the blood, exudates, or tissues of patients with acute rheumatism have been repeatedly confirmed (Beaton and Walker 1903, Walker and Ryffel 1903, Loeb 1908, Camisa 1910, Beattie and Yates 1912, Rosenow 1914, Lyall 1914, Swift and Kinsella 1917, Quigly 1918, Clawson 1925, Birkhaug 1927, Small 1927, Zinsser and Yu 1928, Kreidler 1928). The distribution of these streptococci in the body is not, however, such as one would expect on the assumption that the rheumatic manifestations are the result of a bacteræmic infection, associated with, or followed by, a localized proliferation in particularly susceptible tissues. In very few instances have the streptococci been cultivated from the joint fluid in acute rheumatic arthritis. Isolation from the blood during life has been successful in a somewhat larger proportion of cases ; but a considerable number of the strains described by various authors have been cultivated at autopsy, from the blood, from the pericardial fluid, or sometimes from the spleen. Moreover, the presence of streptococci in the blood, exudates or internal tissues is by no means a constant feature of acute rheumatic infection. In a large proportion of cases cultures obtained during life remain uniformly sterile, and careful bacteriological examinations carried out at autopsy on patients who have died from an acute attack may give entirely negative results (Bulloch 1912). The report by Cecil, Nicholls and Stainsby (1929a, b) that streptococci could be isolated from the blood of a high proportion of rheumatic patients by the use of a special technique gave a fresh impetus to work along these lines ; but there has been an almost entire failure to confirm their results (see Nye and Seegal 1929, Nye and Waxelbaum 1930, Margolis and Dorsey 1930, Cooley 1932, Dawson, Olmstead and Boots 1932*a*, Lichtman and Gross 1932, Steinfeld 1932).

To summarize : it is seldom possible to cultivate any bacteria from the local lesions during life ; blood cultures remain sterile in a large proportion of cases during the febrile stage of the disease ; but, in either case, when any bacterium has been isolated, it has almost invariably been a streptococcus ; cultures obtained at autopsy have, as would be expected, given growth in a higher proportion of cases, though by no means in all, and here again a streptococcus has been the predominating organism, either in pure culture or in association with those bacteria which occur as common, non-specific contaminants of cultures taken under these conditions.

With regard to the particular type of streptococcus concerned, the great majority of the strains isolated have been definitely described as non-hæmolytic, that is, as not giving rise to true hæmolysis.   In many cases, probably in the majority, the organism has been identified as *Str. viridans* by the green coloration given on blood agar ; in others, and particularly in some recent reports, the strains described are recorded as being without action on red blood corpuscles.

From the experiments of Poynton and Paine onwards, the study of the lesions produced in rabbits by the intravenous inoculation of streptococci has played a large part in the bacteriological attack on the problem of rheumatic infection.   The results of these extensive series of observations may be very shortly summarized.   Many of those lesions which are characteristic of rheumatic infection in man have been reproduced in the rabbit as the result of such inoculations.   The experimental lesions include endocarditis, nonsuppurative myocarditis, and arthritis of all degrees of severity, sometimes associated with extensive, secondary bony changes (Poynton and Paine 1900, 1913, Cole 1904, Wächter 1908, Bracht and Wächter 1909, Coombs *et al.* 1912, Jackson 1912, Rosenow 1914, Topley and Weir 1921, Birkhaug 1927, Small 1927, Gross *et al.* 1929, Clawson 1930, Moon and Stewart 1931).   But although the analogy between experimental rheumatism in the rabbit and the natural infection in man is very close, it is not exact.   This applies particularly to the myocardial lesions.   Aschoff (1904) described in detail characteristic nodular collections of cells in rheumatic myocarditis, and his observations have been fully confirmed by later workers (Geipel 1905, 1909, Fraenkel 1912).   In spite of a certain resemblance between some of the myocardial lesions in rabbits and the typical Aschoff nodule (Coombs *et al.* 1912, Jackson 1912), it is very doubtful whether the rabbit lesions can be regarded as pathognomonic (Wächter 1908, Bracht and Wächter 1909, Topley and Weir 1921, Gross *et al.* 1931).

However closely experimental streptococcal infection in the rabbit simulates acute rheumatism in man, it is quite certain that the ability to produce these lesions on intravenous inoculation cannot be regarded as evidence that a particular variety of streptococcus is ætiologically related to the human disease ; for many of the streptococcal strains which have produced the most characteristic lesions in the rabbit have been derived from sources quite unconnected with rheumatic infection, and some of them have been actively hæmolytic (Cole 1904, Jackson 1912, Topley and Weir 1921).   It is clear that experimental rheumatism in the rabbit is a characteristic reaction of that animal species to the intravenous inoculation of a variety of different streptococci.

Before leaving the problem of the possible relation of these heterogeneous strains of streptococci to rheumatic diseases it should be noted that many observers have suggested the possibility that some forms of rheumatism, at least, are allergic manifestations.   This view has, for instance, been developed by Zinsser and Yu

(1928) and it receives some support from the relative frequency of allergic skin reactions to killed cultures of streptococci of various types (see, for instance, Swift, Wilson and Todd 1929). It will be recalled in this connection that serum sickness in man is often associated with minor rheumatic manifestations.

Much of the confusion in regard to this problem is without doubt due to the difficulty of defining, or recognizing, rheumatism as a clinical entity, or series of entities. We have, in the previous discussion, been mainly concerned with acute rheumatic fever, where the clinical diagnosis is not in doubt, and it is to the ætiology of this condition that the following sections refer.

The Rôle of Hæmolytic Streptococci in Acute Rheumatism.—The possibility that acute rheumatism is one of the manifestations of infection with hæmolytic streptococci has been raised in a definite and categorical form by the recent studies of Coburn (Coburn 1931, Coburn and Pauli 1932a, b, c, 1935a, b, c, d, e, f, g).

The starting-point of these studies was the observation of a close epidemiological relationship, in place and time, between hæmolytic streptococcal infection of the throat and the incidence of acute rheumatic infection. It was also found that, in individual cases, a relapse was frequently associated with the reappearance of hæmolytic streptococci in the throat in large numbers. In instances in which this point was particularly studied, it was found that acute rheumatic symptoms tended to develop 1 to 5 weeks after the appearance of hæmolytic streptococci in the throat.

These observations have been amply confirmed by other workers. Thus Collis (1931) notes that an outbreak of tonsillitis in a ward occupied by children suffering from rheumatic heart disease led to a relapse in 9 of 11 children who developed this throat infection and from whose throats a hæmolytic streptococcus was isolated ; and Glover and Griffith (1931) describe outbreaks of tonsillitis in schools due to hæmolytic streptococcal infection in which a proportion of the infected boys developed all the symptoms of acute rheumatic fever (see also Schlesinger 1930, Sheldon 1931, Thomson 1934). The association between tonsillitis and acute rheumatism is, as Glover and Griffith emphasize, quite an old observation in its purely clinical aspect, and Newsholme in 1895 called attention to the similarity in epidemiological behaviour between rheumatism, erysipelas, puerperal fever and scarlet fever. As in the case of scarlet fever, the effect of recent studies has been to add precision to this observation by establishing the fact that the true relationship is between acute rheumatism and infection with hæmolytic streptococci. There are many indications that an important genetic factor is concerned, and that certain individuals have a special tendency to respond to infection with hæmolytic streptococci in this particular way.

The significance of these epidemiological relationships was greatly increased by the observation by Todd (1932) that the acute rheumatic process is almost constantly associated with a wide fluctuation in the titre of antistreptolysin in the blood of the patient. This fluctuation is of a rather peculiar kind, in that the rise in titre occurs during the acute rheumatic attack, and particularly during a relapse, while quiescent or recovered cases tend to show titres that are not greatly above the normal. These observations have been confirmed by Coburn and Pauli (1932c, 1935a, c, f). Wilson, Wheeler and Leask (1934), on the other hand, record divergent results.

Coburn and Pauli (1932c) also record positive agglutination and complement-fixation reactions with hæmolytic streptococci during an acute rheumatic attack, and—although this is not germane to the immediate problem at issue—Dawson, Olmstead and Boots

(1932*b*), and Dawson, Olmstead and Jost (1934) have reported the occurrence to high titre of agglutinins acting on hæmolytic streptococci as a group in the sera of patients suffering from rheumatoid arthritis.

Gibson, Thomson and Stewart (1933) record a higher proportion of skin reactions to extracts of hæmolytic streptococci among 140 rheumatic cases than among 145 controls, whereas there was no significant difference between the skin reactions of these groups to extracts of non-hæmolytic streptococci. On the other hand the Dick reaction was positive in only 16 per cent. of the rheumatic cases as compared with 28 per cent. of the controls.

It may be noted that Coburn and Pauli (1935*a*) report that immunization with streptococcus toxin fails to prevent the development of acute rheumatism.

Taking this evidence as a whole, it establishes a strong case for a significant association between acute rheumatism and hæmolytic streptococcal infection. The exact nature of this association is very difficult to determine. It may be that it is of the same nature as the relation between hæmolytic streptococci and scarlet fever, the organisms producing a primary lesion in the throat and there forming a soluble toxin that diffuses into the blood stream, is carried throughout the tissues, and gives rise, in specially susceptible subjects, to the characteristic lesions in the joints, heart and elsewhere. But the available evidence seems definitely against the view that the erythrogenic toxin acts in this way, and it seems at least as doubtful whether this rôle can be ascribed to the streptococcal hæmolysin, in spite of the fluctuations in the titre of antistreptolysin that undoubtedly occur. If, on the other hand, one postulates an allergic mechanism, it is not obvious why the hæmolytic streptococcus should play so predominant a part in inducing the disease. The problem has been further complicated by the observations that are recorded in the following section.

Is Acute Rheumatism a Virus Infection ?—Schlesinger, Signy and Amies (1935) have recorded observations on the basis of which they would answer this question in the affirmative. They find that the deposits obtained by high-speed centrifugation of specimens of pericardial fluid from cases of acute rheumatism contain bodies which, in their size and general morphology, closely resemble virus particles. Barnard (see reference above) contributes to their paper a note which includes photomicrographs of the particles in question. Relatively pure suspensions of these particles in formol saline were agglutinated by sera from patients suffering from, and successfully resisting, an acute rheumatic infection, while they were not agglutinated by normal sera, or by sera obtained from patients suffering from non-rheumatic infections.

The authors do not dispute the importance of hæmolytic streptococcal infections in relation to acute rheumatism ; but conclude that such infection in some way lowers resistance to invasion with the virus, or reactivates it if it is already present (see also Schlesinger, Signy and Payne 1935).

Subacute Bacterial Endocarditis

Although this disease bears no immediate, or necessary relationship to acute rheumatism, it is convenient to consider it in this chapter, if only because the isolation of non-hæmolytic streptococci from the blood stream in cases of this kind has perhaps done something to confuse the issue in regard to the causation of simple rheumatic endocarditis.

There can be no question that this fatal disease is due in the great majority of cases to the infection of a previously damaged, or congenitally abnormal, valve with streptococci, either of the viridans or of the enterococcus type, though other organisms may occasionally be concerned (see, for instance, Horder 1908–9, Schottmüller 1910, Kreidler 1926 and various references given in Chapter XXIII).

Our knowledge of the pathogenesis of this condition has been greatly advanced within recent years by the important studies of Lewis and Grant (1923), Grant (1924), and Grant, Wood and Jones (1928) on the pathological side, and by Okell and Elliott (1935) in regard to the probable mechanism of infection.

Lewis and Grant (1923) found that, in an unselected series of cases of subacute bacterial endocarditis, 26 per cent. had a congenitally bicuspid aortic valve ; and they calculate, on the basis of their experience, that of these persons with congenitally bicuspid aortic valves who reach adult life, some 23 per cent. die of subacute endocarditis. Grant (1924) and Grant, Wood and Jones (1928) have described the lesions of this disease in considerable detail, and have given reasons for believing that they are usually produced by direct infection of the endocardium from the blood stream, and not from embolism of the smaller vessels, where these are present. Small platelet thrombi on the surface of the valves themselves would, however, seem to be of major importance in providing a nidus for infection.

Okell and Elliott (1935), approaching this problem from a different angle, endeavoured to find a source from which the infecting streptococci might be derived. They took blood cultures from a series of persons in whom tooth extractions were carried out, in most cases because of the existence of oral sepsis, taking their samples immediately before extraction and immediately afterwards. They found that, of 40 persons who had extensive disease of the gums, 30 showed the presence of streptococci in the general circulation within 5 minutes after tooth extraction. Of 60 persons with moderate gum infection 42 gave a similar result ; while of 38 persons without detectable gum disease, but from whom one or more teeth had been extracted, 12 yielded streptococci from their blood. In a few cases in which a positive blood culture was obtained immediately after extraction a further specimen of blood was examined at an interval varying from 10 minutes to 8 hours after operation. These were all sterile, so that the bacteræmia following extraction would appear to be quite transitory. In 9 of the 100 cases with moderate or extensive gum disease streptococci were isolated from the sample of blood taken immediately before tooth extraction. In 10 further cases of pyorrhœa, in which only one blood culture was taken, and that before extraction, 3 yielded a growth of streptococci. In all, therefore, 12 of 110 cases of moderate or severe oral sepsis yielded streptococci from the blood, apart from the trauma associated with tooth extraction. On the other hand, blood cultures taken before extraction from the 38 persons without detectable gum disease, and from 30 healthy young adults with no evidence of dental disease all proved negative. It may be noted that none of the streptococci isolated during this investigation were hæmolytic, and that most were of the viridans type.

It would seem, therefore, that in any case of oral sepsis, there is likely to be an occasional leak of streptococci into the blood stream, leading to a transitory bacteræmia, this leak being temporarily intensified as the result of tooth extraction. These streptococci are, in a normal person, rapidly removed from the blood stream and cause no serious damage to the tissues ; but if they come in contact with a congenitally defective heart valve, or a valve already damaged as the result of rheumatic infection, they may set up a lasting and slowly fatal infection.

REFERENCES

ASCHOFF. (1904) *Verh. dtsch. path. Ges.*, **8**, 46.
BEATON, R. M. and WALKER, E. W. A. (1903) *Brit. med. J.*, i. 237.
BEATTIE, J. M. and YATES, A. G. (1912) *J. Path. Bact.*, **17**, 538.
BIRKHAUG, K. E (1927) *J. infect. Dis.*, **40**, 549.
BRACHT, E. and WÄCHTER. (1909) *Dtsch. Arch. klin. Med.*, **96**, 493.
BULLOCH, W. (1912) " System of Medicine," **2**, Part I, 606, Allbutt & Rolleston. London.
CAMISA, G. (1910) *Zbl. Bakt.*, **57**, 99.
CECIL, R. L., NICOLLS, E. E., and STAINSBY, W. J. (1929a) *J. exp. Med.*, **50**, 617 ; (1929b) *Arch. intern. Med.*, **43**, 571.
CLAWSON, B. J. (1925) *J. infect. Dis.*, **36**, 444 ; (1930) *Arch. Path.*, **9**, 1141.
COBURN, A. F. (1931) " The Factor of Infection in the Rheumatic State." Williams & Wilkins Co., Baltimore.
COBURN, A. F. and PAULI, R. H. (1932a) *J. exp. Med.*, **56**, 609 ; (1932b) *Ibid.*, **56**, 633 ; (1932c) *Ibid.*, **56**, 651 ; (1935a) *Ibid.*, **62**, 129 ; (1935b) *Ibid.*, **62**, 137 ; (1935c) *Ibid.*, **62**, 159 ; (1935d) *J. clin. Invest.*, **14**, 755 ; (1935e) *Ibid.*, **14**, 763 ; (1935f) *Ibid.*, **14**, 769 ; (1935g) *Ibid.*, **14**, 783.
COLE, R. I. (1914) *J. infect. Dis.*, **1**, 714.
COLLIS, W. R. F (1931) *Lancet*, i. 1341.
COOLEY, L. E. 1932) *J. infect. Dis.*, **50**, 330.
COOMBS, C., MILLER, R., and KETTLE, E. H. (1912) *Lancet*, ii. 1209.
DAWSON, M. H., OLMSTEAD, M., and BOOTS, R. H. (1932a) *Arch. intern. Med.*, **49**, 173. (1932b) *J. Immunol.*, **23**, 187.
DAWSON, M. H., OLMSTEAD, M., and JOST, E. L. (1934) *J. Immunol.*, **27**, 355.
FRAENKEL. (1912) *Beitr. path. Anat.*, **52**, 597.
GEIPEL, P. (190) *Dtsch. Arch. klin. Med.*, **85**, 75 ; (1909) *Münch. med. Wschr.*, **56**, 2469.
GIBSON, H. J., THOMSON, W. A. R., and STEWART, D. (1933) *Arch. Dis. Child.*, **8**, 57.
GLOVER, J. A. and GRIFFITH, F. (1931) *Brit. med. J.*, ii. 521.
GRANT, R. T. (1924) *Heart*, **11**, 9.
GRANT, R. T., WOOD, J. E., and JONES, T. D. (1928) *Heart*, **14**, 247.
GROSS, L., LOEWE, L., and ELIASOPH, B. (1929) *J. exp. Med.*, **50**, 41.
HORDER, T. J. 1908–9) *Quart. J. Med.*, **2**, 289.
JACKSON, L. (1912) *J. infect. Dis.*, **11**, 243.
KREIDLER, W. I (1926) *J. infect. Dis.*, **39**, 186 ; (1928) *Ibid.*, **43**, 415.
LEWIS, T. and GRANT, R. T. (1923) *Heart*, **10**, 21.
LICHTMAN, S. S. and GROSS, L. (1932) *Arch. intern. Med.*, **49**, 1078.
LOEB, L. M. (1908) *Arch. intern. Med.*, **2**, 266.
LYALL, H. W. (1914) *J. med. Res.*, **30**, 487.
MARGOLIS, H. M. and DORSEY, A. H. E. (1930) *J. infect. Dis.*, **46**, 442.
MOON, V. H. and STEWART, H. L. (1931) *Arch. Path.*, **11**, 190.
NEWSHOLME, A. (1895) *Lancet*, i. 589.
NYE, R. N. and SEEGAL, D. (1929) *J. exp. Med.*, **49**, 539.
NYE, R. N. and VAXELBAUM, E. A. (1930) *J. exp. Med.*, **52**, 885.
OKELL, C. C. and ELLIOTT, S. D. (1935) *Lancet*, ii. 869.
POYNTON, F. J. and PAINE, A. (1900) *Lancet*, ii. 861 ; (1913) " Researches on Rheumatism." London.
QUIGLY, W. J. 1918) *J. infect. Dis.*, **22**, 198.
ROSENOW, E. C. (1914) *J. infect. Dis.*, **14**, 61.
SCHLESINGER, B. (1930) *Arch. Dis. Child.*, **5**, 411.
SCHLESINGER, B. SIGNY, A. G., and AMIES, C. R. (1935) *Lancet*, i. 1145.
SCHLESINGER, B. SIGNY, A. G., and PAYNE, W. W. (1935) *Lancet*, i. 1090.
SCHOTTMÜLLER, H. (1910) *Münch. med. Wschr.*, **57**, 617, 697.
SHELDON, W. P. H. (1931) *Lancet*, i. 1337.
SMALL, J. C. (1927) *Amer. J. med. Sci.*, **173**, 101.
STEINFELD, F. (1932) *Zbl. Bakt.*, **123**, 414.
SWIFT, H. F. and KINSELLA, R. A. (1917) *Arch. intern. Med.*, **19**, 381
SWIFT, H. F., WILSON, M. G., and TODD, E. W. (1929) *Amer. J. Dis. Child.*, **37**, 98.
THOMSON, W. A. R. (1934) *Brit. med. J.*, i. 1162.
TODD, E. W. (1932) *Brit. J. exp. Path.*, **13**, 248.
TOPLEY, W. W. C. and WEIR, H. B. (1921) *J. Path. Bact.*, **24**, 333.
WÄCHTER. (1908) *Münch. med. Wschr.*, **55**, 1101.
WALKER, E. W. A. and RYFFEL, J. H. (1903) *Brit. med. J.*, ii. 659.
WESTPHAL, WASSERMANN, and MALKOFF. (1899) *Berl. klin. Wschr.*, **36**, 638.
WILSON, M. G., WHEELER, G. W., and LEASK, M. M. (1934) *Proc. Soc. exp. Biol., N.Y.*, **31**, 1001.
ZINSSER, H. and YU, H. (1928) *Arch. intern. Med.*, **42**, 301.

CHAPTER LXVI

ENTERIC INFECTIONS

AMONG the clinical records left by medical writers from Hippocrates onwards, we have little difficulty in recognizing cases which can, with reasonable certainty, be identified as instances of enteric fever. The separation of this type of infection from the mass of continued fevers was, however, a slow process ; and it was only during the first half of the nineteenth century that typhoid or enteric fever finally emerged as a clinical entity, from among the mass of continued fevers with which it had previously been confused. Various differences in behaviour between typhoid fever and the prevalent typhus, gaol, or famine fever had indeed been noted at much earlier dates. Among these pioneers were Willis (1659) and Huxham (1739) ; but their descriptions were not sufficiently detailed or complete to carry general conviction. As noted by Creighton (1894), the final recognition of enteric fever in this country resulted from the elaborate analysis of the symptoms of the different types of continued fever carried out by Sir William Jenner between 1849 and 1851. In Germany, the differentiation of typhus from typhoid was clearly recognized by Schoenlein (1839), under the names " Typhus exanthematicus " and " Typhus abdominalis," which have maintained their position in German literature. In France, the observations of Prost (1804), and particularly of Petit and Serres (1813), afforded what was probably the first accurate description of the intestinal lesions ; though many earlier records of post-mortem findings are in existence. These observations were confirmed and extended by Bretonneau (1826), Louis (1829), and Chomel (1834)—(see Gay 1918).

The most striking contribution to our knowledge of the natural history of typhoid fever, before the opening of the bacteriological era, is undoubtedly that made by William Budd (1856, 1873) of North Tawton in Devon. Budd had studied under Louis at the La Pitié hospital, and was therefore in a position to identify typhoid fever with considerable confidence. He insisted on its spread by contagion, on the fact that the infective agent was excreted in the fæces, on the rôle played by the contamination of water and milk in the epidemic spread of the disease, and on the possibility that infection might be derived from the excretions of a convalescent patient. His writings afford an admirable example of the value of accurate observations, carried out in the spirit of the field naturalist.

With the description of the typhoid bacillus by Eberth in 1880, and its isolation by Gaffky in 1884, it became possible to attack the problems of enteric infection by the methods devised by the bacteriologist. The subsequent isolation and study of the various species of paratyphoid bacilli showed that enteric fever, though a clinical entity, might result from infection with several distinct, though nearly related, bacterial species. For a description of these species reference may be made to Chapter **XXVII.**   The studies of recent years have yielded a considerable mass of data with regard to the distribution, in place and time, of the various bacterial types of enteric infection ; and this point will be discussed later in this chapter.   For the moment we may consider the results obtained in the detailed study of typhoid infection, in man and animals, taking them as representative of the behaviour of enteric infection as a whole, and noting certain exceptions for purposes of comparison or illustration.

Bacteriology.

During an attack of typhoid fever, the causative bacilli can be isolated from the fæces (Pfeiffer 1885), from the urine (Hueppe 1886), from the rose spots of the eruption (Neuhaus 1886), and from the blood (Vilchur 1887).   It may be noted that the intensive study of enteric infection in particular samples of the population, to which we shall refer later, has resulted in the demonstration that

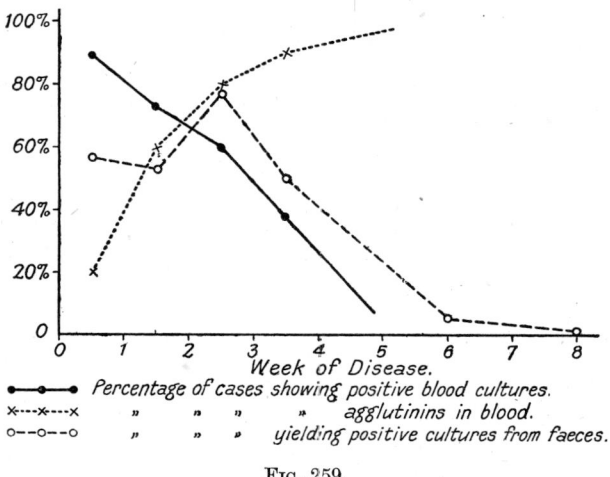

Percentage of cases showing positive blood cultures.
x---x---x   „   „   „   „   *agglutinins in blood.*
o--o--o   „   „   „   *yielding positive cultures from faeces.*

FIG. 259.

Bact. typhosum may occasionally be cultivated from the fæces during the incubation period, or even from the blood of an apparently healthy person, who may soon after develop the d i s e a s e (Conradi 1907, Mayer 1910).   The demonstration of specific agglutinins in the blood, usually attributed to Widal (1896) (since Grünbaum (1896), who noted their appearance earlier, recorded his observations later), has made it possible to study the progress of this particular response to infection, and to correlate the results with those obtained in attempts to isolate the causative organism.

A very instructive picture of the usual course of events during an attack of typhoid fever may be obtained by charting, for the successive weeks of the disease, the average frequency with which *Bact. typhosum* can be isolated from the blood, or from the fæces, and the frequency with which the serum gives the diagnostic agglutinin reaction.   In preparing Fig. 259 along these lines, we have employed for the fæces the figures of Gaehtgens and Brückner (1909), extrapolating by taking values beyond the 4th week intermediate between those recorded by Semple and Greig (1908), and those suggested by the findings of Lentz (1905) ; for the blood the figures recorded by Coleman and Buxton (1907), again extrapolating beyond the 4th week ; and for the agglutinins the figures given by Park and Williams (1925).

As indicated in the figure, the onset of symptoms is associated with a bacteræmia.   From the 1st week onwards the frequency with which *Bact. typhosum* can be isolated from the blood falls, at first slowly, then more rapidly.   By the end of the 3rd week it can be found in about half the cases ; after the 4th week its isolation is infrequent. It must be remembered that we are dealing with a frequency chart, not with the course of events in any individual case. It may be taken that the frequencies noted for the results of blood culture after the 4th week refer to cases which were febrile at that period, since such patients would naturally be selected for investigation. In any given case, it will usually be found that the decline of fever is associated with the disappearance of bacteria from the blood. In cases which terminate fatally as the result of the primary infection, apart from the secondary accidents of hæmorrhage and perforation, the severity of the bacteræmia usually increases until death (Jochmann 1914).

The frequency of *Bact. typhosum* in the fæces, on the other hand, increases from the 1st to the 3rd week and then falls somewhat slowly. The frequency curves for blood and fæces cross somewhere about the end of the 2nd week. Before that time, the bacilli are isolated more frequently from the blood than from the fæces ; after it, the position is reversed. In attempting deductions from such figures as these, we must remember that differences in technique may have an important influence on our results. There are certain technical difficulties associated with blood culture, and with the isolation of pathogenic bacteria from the fæces ; but they are different in kind, and the technical error involved may be quite different in degree. The significant point is the decreasing frequency of detectable bacteræmia, and the increasing frequency of *Bact. typhosum* in the intestine, during the first 2 to 3 weeks. This clearly suggests that the main direction of invasion during this period of the infection is from the blood stream to the intestine, not from the intestine to the blood. In the 1st week about 20 per cent. of the cases give a positive agglutination test. The curve then rises sharply, crossing the blood-culture curve just before the end of the 2nd week, and still rising attains a value of 90 per cent. or more by the 4th week ; after which it remains at a high level for several weeks.

Data are available which enable us to describe with considerable accuracy the course of the agglutination curve in an individual case of typhoid fever, plotting titre against time. The most extensive records, however—those of Dreyer and his colleagues—refer to results obtained with formolized broth cultures, which react chiefly to the H (flagellar) agglutinins (Dreyer *et al.* 1915, 1916, 1917). We have no such detailed information for the rise and fall of O (somatic) agglutinins ; but such evidence as is available suggests that the general form of the curve, at least over the earlier part of its course, is very similar to that followed by the H agglutinins. This question will be discussed more fully in relation to diagnosis. For our immediate purpose we may take it that agglutinins usually appear in the blood between the 3rd and 7th day of disease, rise, first slowly, then more steeply to a maximum between the 16th and 22nd days, and then fall, at first steeply, later (at least in the case of the flagellar agglutinins) very slowly, so that they are detectable for weeks or months after convalescence (Figs. 236, 237, p. 879).

The rise in agglutinins is usually associated with a decreasing bacteræmia, and the time at which the agglutinin titre reaches its maximum coincides approximately with an amelioration in the patient's general condition, as indicated by a gradual fall in temperature. In this connection the agglutinin curve, so far as it is described in terms of H agglutinins, should be regarded as an indication of a general antibody response, not as deriving its significance from the fluctuation in flagellar agglutinins themselves. There are many reasons for believing that these particular antibodies have little if any protective value, while the O agglutinins, and apparently the Vi antibody of Felix and Pitt (1934b), are of decisive importance from this point of view (see Chapter XLIV and later sections).

As Fig. 259 indicates, the bacilli do not disappear from the intestine so quickly, or so completely, as from the blood. There is a lag, which is relatively constant over the early part of the falling frequency curve, but which becomes more pronounced later. A considerable proportion of cases are still excreting *Bact. typhosum* in their fæces at a time when positive blood cultures can no longer be obtained; and some cases continue excreting well into convalescence or beyond it.

The results obtained in an extensive series of investigations, at the bedside, on post-mortem material, and by direct experiments on animals, have indicated the probable sequence of events during an attack of enteric fever.

If cultures are taken from various situations during a post-mortem examination, the distribution of typhoid bacilli is usually found to be as follows. In the intestine itself almost pure cultures are frequently obtained from the duodenum and upper part of the jejunum. At lower levels the bacilli become less and less numerous in proportion to the other intestinal bacteria; and, below the ileocæcal valve, they may be so outnumbered by *Bact. coli*, and by other organisms, as to escape detection in artificial culture (von Drigalski 1904). Outside the intestine, there are four situations in which *Bact. typhosum* is almost constantly present, and from which it can often be isolated in pure culture: the spleen, the enlarged mesenteric glands, the bone marrow, and the gall-bladder. It has been pointed out by Levy and Gaehtgens (1908) that, while the mesenteric glands are always enlarged and cultures from them almost constantly positive, other glands are frequently unaffected. It is of interest to note (Mallory 1898) that the enlargement of the mesenteric lymph nodes is associated with marked proliferation of the endothelial cells of the lymph sinuses, while the lymphoid cells are but little affected.

The intravenous inoculation of typhoid bacilli into rabbits or guinea-pigs is followed by their deposition in the liver, spleen, lymph glands, and bone marrow; but there is, in this case, no selective localization in the mesenteric glands. Lüdke (1909) noted the persistence of typhoid bacilli in the lymphatic glands and bone marrow of the guinea-pig, following intravenous inoculation, and their proliferation in these situations after their disappearance from the blood. Gay (1918) finds that typhoid bacilli persist in the bone marrow of infected rabbits after they have disappeared from the blood, lymph nodes and spleen. Reference to Chapter XLIV will afford additional data with regard to the fate of typhoid bacilli after intravenous or intraperitoneal inoculation (Buxton 1907a, b, Bull 1915).

The presence of typhoid bacilli in the gall-bladder is of particular interest, as will later appear. Von Fütterer (1888) was apparently the first to demonstrate that *Bact. typhosum* could be isolated from the gall-bladder in fatal cases of the disease. Gilbert and Girode (1890) confirmed its presence in this organ and Chiari (1894) noted its frequency. Pratt (1901) isolated *Bact. typhosum* from the gall-bladder in 21 of 30 fatal cases of typhoid fever, and Scott (1915) from 24 of 28 cases. The evidence for the occasional persistence of typhoid bacilli in the gall-bladder long after convalescence is equally conclusive. Droba (1889) isolated *Bact. typhosum* from the gall-bladder contents, and from the interior of the gallstones removed at operation 17 years after an attack of typhoid fever. Findlay and Buchanan (1906) isolated the bacillus from the gall-bladder 25 years after an attack, and at the same time demonstrated it in the fæces. In some cases, as in that reported by Dudgeon (1908), *Bact. typhosum* has been isolated from the gall-bladder in a case of cholelithiasis, in the absence of any history of typhoid fever. The literature contains many instances of a similar kind (see Ledingham and Arkwright 1912, Gay 1918).

The mechanism by which the gall-bladder becomes infected has been studied experimentally in rabbits. Blachstein (1891) found that bacilli could be isolated from the gall-bladder of these animals for days, or weeks, after an intravenous inoculation of living culture. Richardson (1899) recorded similar observations, and noted that some of the rabbits developed gall-stones, an observation which has been repeatedly confirmed (Gay 1918). The bacilli may reach the gall-bladder very rapidly after intravenous injection, according to Blumenthal (1910) within 10 minutes. They may persist in this situation over long periods (Morgan 1911, Johnston 1912, Gay and Claypole 1913). Weinfurter (1915) records an instance in which they were still present after 9 months.

The most generally accepted view, as regards the route by which the bacilli reach the gall-bladder from the blood, is that they travel from the liver capillaries to the bile canaliculi, and thence down the bile ducts (Doerr 1905, Lemierre and Abrami 1907, Nichols 1916). It has, on the other hand, been stated (Koch, J., 1909, Chiarolanza 1909) that they rapidly reach the gall-bladder even after ligation of the cystic duct, and that nests of bacilli may be found in the capillaries of the gall-bladder wall, suggesting that they pass directly into the viscus by this route. It is probable, as suggested by Gay (1918), that either route may be traversed.

Route of Infection.—We have not yet considered the question of the route by which the bacilli gain access to the tissues and the blood stream, during the initial stages of naturally occurring infection. Our knowledge of the epidemiology of enteric fever, and of its mode of spread, makes it quite clear that the bacilli enter the body by the alimentary tract ; the point at issue is the situation at which penetration of the mucosa occurs. It was originally believed that the bacilli passed through the stomach, proliferated in the intestine, and thence invaded the blood stream. This view has been very generally discarded ; since it seems clear that the heavy intestinal infection which occurs during the 2nd and 3rd weeks of an attack of typhoid is due, in large part, to the passage of bacilli into the intestine from the gall-bladder, and perhaps from the Peyer's patches and lymphoid follicles. Some authors (Förster 1908) insist that there is no reason to suppose that *Bact. typhosum* ever multiplies within the intestinal canal. It has been suggested that the bacilli usually gain access to the tissues *via* the tonsils and lymphoid tissue of the pharynx, rather than through the intestinal wall (Brion and Kayser 1906) ; and von Drigalski (1904) has reported an epidemic in which 40 per cent. of the cases suffered from an initial faucial angina. In many of these cases he obtained a pure culture of *Bact. typhosum* from the tonsils. Whether or not this route may be followed in some cases, there seems no adequate reason for discarding the traditional view that the usual portal of entry to the tissues is through the intestinal lymphatics ; and this appears to be supported by the constant involvement of the mesenteric glands.

We have already referred, in Chapter XLIV, to experiments recorded by Ørskov, Jensen and Kobayashi (1928), who noted the following sequence of events in experimental mouse typhoid, after infection *per os* with *Bact. typhi-murium* : the destruction, in the intestinal tract, of the greater part of the ingested bacteria, as evidenced by a transitory excretion of bacilli followed by a period during which none could be recovered from the fæces : the passage of some bacilli to the mesenteric glands, and their further passage to the blood stream, probably *via* the thoracic duct : a transitory bacteræmia, rapidly brought to an end by the removal of the bacilli by the reticulo-endothelial cells, particularly those of the liver and the spleen : a phase during which active proliferation is proceeding in the liver and spleen, as evidenced by the recovery of increasing numbers of bacilli from these organs, but during which the blood remains sterile : a phase of secondary bacteræmia, associated with a generalization of bacteria throughout the tissues, and a secondary invasion of the intestine, principally *via* the gall-bladder and bile duct.

It seems likely that a similar sequence of events occurs in natural infection in man. If so, it may well be that the incubation period in typhoid fever corresponds to the phases which precede the secondary invasion of the blood stream from the sites of primary proliferation in the liver, spleen and mesenteric glands, the occurrence of this secondary bacteræmia marking the onset of the actual illness. Such a conception receives some support from the occasional isolation of *Bact. typhosum* from the fæces and from the blood during the incubation period of the disease.

We have already considered in some detail the course of events during the later stages of the illness, and the factors which determine, in some cases, the persistence of bacilli in the tissues over long periods of time, and their persistent, or intermittent, excretion in the fæces. A few points remain to be discussed. The characteristic lesions in Peyer's patches appear to result from an initial hyperplasia of the endothelial cells in response to the bacterial invasion, followed by necrosis and sloughing, caused in part by the toxic action of some bacterial product, in part by interference with the blood supply. Perforation and hæmorrhage are in the nature of occasional associated accidents. The gall-bladder is one of the most frequent sites of persistent infection ; and is, from the epidemiological point of view, the most important, because of the ease with which bacilli escape thence to the intestine, to be excreted in the fæces ; but it is by no means the only situation in which the bacilli may remain latent over long periods of time. Experience with mice (Topley 1926) suggests that the spleen may form a persistent focus of infection ; and the well-known typhoid periostitis affords an example of a lesion which may occur long after convalescence from the original illness.

It should be noted that relapses may occur during convalescence, although they are relatively infrequent. They are usually milder and of shorter duration than the original attack ; and the mortality is low (Gay 1918). They are undoubtedly due to a re-invasion of the blood stream from the tissues in which typhoid bacilli are still proliferating at the time when the bacteræmic phase of the primary attack is brought to a close. They are milder, and of shorter duration, presumably because specific antibodies are already present, and because the tissues respond promptly to the secondary stimulus.

The Toxins of the Typhoid Bacillus and of Other Bacteria of the Salmonella Group.

These have been described in Chapter XXVII. We need only note here that they belong to the general class of endotoxins, and that some of them, at least, appear to be identical with the O antigens, in their natural complex form.

The Diagnosis of Enteric Fever.

So far we have dealt with typhoid fever as the classical example of enteric infections in general. Before discussing the laboratory methods available for diagnosis we must consider briefly the question as to which members of the Salmonella group, other than *Bact. typhosum*, give rise to a continued fever of the enteric type. In Chapter XXVII we have given a summarized description of the species, or types, that fall within this group, including the type of case from which they have been isolated. Here we may confine our attention to those organisms that have been isolated, at least with some frequency, from cases of continued fever. The rôle of the various members of this group in the causation of acute gastro-enteritis (bacterial food poisoning) is considered in Chapter LXIX.

The organisms that share with *Bact. typhosum* in the causation of enteric fever are *Bact. paratyphosum A*, *Bact. paratyphosum B*, *Bact. paratyphosum C*, and *Bact. choleræ-suis* var. *kunzendorf*. *Bact. paratyphosum C* is often known as " Hirschfeld's bacillus," or as the " Eastern European type of *Bact. paratyphosum C*," while *Bact. choleræ-suis* var. *kunzendorf* is often known as the " Western European type of *Bact. paratyphosum C*." In much of the literature the name " *Bact. suipestifer* " will be found in place of *Bact. paratyphosum C* or *Bact. choleræ-suis*. It may be noted that the disease caused by these two species differs from that due to infection with *Bact. typhosum*, *Bact. paratyphosum A* or *Bact. paratyphosum B*, in that the typical picture of an enteric infection is not infrequently complicated by lesions of a septic or suppurative type. It may also be noted that infection with *Bact. choleræ-suis* var. *kunzendorf* frequently takes the form of an acute gastro-enteritis instead of a continued fever. Certain recently identified species, or types, for instance *Bact. enteritidis* var. *chaco* and *Bact. enteritidis* var. *moscow*, have been isolated from cases of continued fever, the former in South America, the latter mainly in Russia.

Several other species within the Salmonella group, though usually causing an acute gastro-enteritis, occasionally give rise to a continued fever of the enteric type. This, for instance, is true of *Bact. typhi-murium*, perhaps better known as *Bact. aertrycke* ; it is possibly true of *Bact. enteritidis*. The element of doubt is introduced by the fact that *Bact. enteritidis* var. *dublin*, which is a natural pathogen of cattle, is certainly capable of causing a continued fever in man (see Smith and Scott 1930) ; and, since the differentiation of this variety is of recent date, it is possible that the earlier reports of isolated cases of enteric fever caused by *Bact. enteritidis* may have been instances of infection with the dublin variety.

For our present purpose we may confine our attention to the five species that are frequently implicated in the causation of enteric fever, noting that, from this point of view, *Bact. choleræ-suis* var. *kunzendorf* appears to occupy a position of relatively minor importance. Another fact of great significance from the point of view of diagnosis is that the frequency distribution of these various Salmonella types is very different in different parts of the world. This point will be elaborated in a later section.

The methods of diagnosis that are available and their relative value at different stages of the disease will be obvious from the time-relations shown in Fig. 259 and from the discussion of these relations in the text.

Cultural Methods in Diagnosis.—It should be emphasized that the actual isolation and identification of the infecting organism is always the method of choice. A positive agglutination reaction may be highly suggestive, and in some cases practically conclusive ; but it should not be accepted as satisfactory evidence of enteric infection, except in those rare cases in which bacteriological examination of the blood and excreta is impossible.

Reference to Fig. 249 will indicate the frequency with which a positive result may be expected in cultures made from the blood or fæces, at different stages of the disease. During the 1st week blood culture is the method of choice, and this procedure should be adopted in any case which is seen by the bacteriologist during the febrile period. At least 10 c.c. of blood should be withdrawn with a syringe from a vein—the median basilic vein of the arm, or some prominent vein in the bend of the elbow being usually selected—and this should be transferred to a flask containing 50—100 c.c. of some suitable medium, or distributed among a number of test tubes, containing a similar amount of medium in aggregate. Various media may be employed, two highly satisfactory forms being peptone water, or broth, containing 0·5 per cent. of sodium taurocholate.

A practical difficulty that often arises in this connection is that the laboratory worker may have no access to the case, and a properly taken blood culture may be an impossibility. In such cases, where the only material available is clotted blood that has been sent to the laboratory for an agglutination test, it is good practice to transfer the clot to some suitable medium, such as bile-salt broth, and examine the culture for the causative organism. A surprisingly high proportion of successful isolations may be secured in this way ; and in cases, where a sample of blood has been sent to the laboratory early in the disease the clot culture may be positive while the agglutination test is negative (see for instance Soman 1932, 1934, Downie and Fairbrother 1934).

In cases in which the causative organism has not been isolated from the blood, a positive or suspicious agglutination reaction should, wherever possible, be confirmed by the isolation of the causative organism from the urine or the fæces.

Isolation from the urine presents no great technical difficulties, since when the causative organism is present in this situation it is almost always present in large numbers, and frequently in pure culture. A typhoid or paratyphoid bacilluria is, however, not a sufficiently frequent character of this disease for us to attach any importance to a negative finding ; and cultivation from the fæces thus forms the most useful method of isolation in those cases where blood culture has failed. This method, moreover, is of primary importance in the detection of carriers.

Since the fæces contain a rich and varied bacterial flora, the isolation of the particular organism for which we are searching will depend in large part on the use of selective and differential media. For selection it is customary to employ a fluid medium containing substances that will inhibit the growth of bacteria other than typhoid or para-typhoid bacilli. For differentiation we use a solid medium containing lactose, and an indicator that enables us to differentiate between lactose-fermenting and non-lactose-fermenting organisms.

A method that has been very commonly employed is to use peptone water containing brilliant green in concentrations between 1 : 100,000 and 1 : 500,000 as a selective medium (see Chapter XXVII), and MacConkey's neutral-red-bile-salt-lactose agar as a differential medium. Within recent years, however, several workers have reported unfavourably on MacConkey's medium in comparison with others (see Horgan 1935, Jones 1936), and there seems little doubt that more satisfactory methods are available.

Among the selective media that have proved most successful is broth containing sodium tetrathionate, either alone (see Muller 1923, Silberstein 1929, Schäfer 1935, Jones 1936) or with the addition of brilliant green and bile (see Kauffmann 1930–31, 1935–36a, Boecker 1935, Waldhecker 1935).

In regard to the differential media used for plating from the primary enrichment culture, the Endo medium, containing lactose, sodium sulphite and basic fuchsin, is largely employed in many countries and has given satisfactory results. Teague and Clurman (1916, 1916–17) and Meyer and Stickel (1918) recommend an agar medium containing lactose, brilliant green and eosin ; and this has been found by Jones (1936) to give far better results than those obtained with MacConkey's medium.

The agar medium of Wilson and Blair (1927) containing glucose, bismuth sulphite and iron, or its later modifications (Wilson and Blair 1927, 1931), the differential value of which depends on the blackening of the colonies of typhoid or paratyphoid bacilli, also gives excellent results (see Horgan 1935, Jones 1936). But Jones (1936) finds that it has no advantage, so far as the examination of fæces is concerned, over the brilliant-green-eosin medium, while the characteristic black colonies take longer to develop than the characteristic translucent, faintly tinted colonies that appear on the brilliant-green-eosin medium. The Wilson and Blair medium has, it may be noted, proved of the greatest value in isolating typhoid or paratyphoid bacilli from sewage, or from an infected water supply (see Chapter LXXXVIII).

Whatever selective and differential media are employed, the frequency of isolation of typhoid and paratyphoid bacilli will be significantly increased by making repeated platings from the primary enrichment culture. Topley and Fielden (1922) pointed out that, in an ordinary broth culture from a specimen of fæces, various bacterial species succeed one another as the dominant viable organisms, and that it is a relatively common event to obtain a pure culture of *Bact. coli* on a plate seeded after 24 hours, and a pure culture of *Bact. typhosum* on a plate seeded after several days' incubation. In a selective medium, on the other hand, typhoid bacilli tend to develop before *Bact. coli* ; thus Waldhecker (1935) notes that plating from a tetrathionate-brilliant-green-bile selective medium after 5 hours' and 10 hours' incubation, instead of after 20 hours' only, considerably increased the percentage of positive results (see also Boecker 1935).

It must, in particular, be emphasized that the isolation of typhoid or paratyphoid bacilli from a specimen of fæces depends more on the relative numbers of these bacteria in the particular specimen examined than on any detail of technique. No reliance can be placed on a single negative result, whatever method of examination is employed ; and in carriers or convalescents, where the excretion of these organisms may be intermittent, many specimens may have to be examined before a positive result is obtained.

The Agglutination Reaction in Diagnosis.—In applying the agglutination reaction in the diagnosis of enteric infections we must first decide which of the possible causative organisms we shall include in our test. This obviously depends on the actual frequency of the different types of infection in the particular part of the world in which we happen to be working. In Great Britain, for instance, the very great majority of enteric infections are, at the present time, caused by infection with either *Bact. typhosum* or with *Bact. paratyphosum B*. In British Guiana, on the other hand, *Bact. typhosum* and *Bact. paratyphosum C* are the dominant species (see Giglioli 1930). This problem of the relative frequency of different types of infection also arises in connection with the interpretation of agglutination tests, and will be considered more fully under that head. For the moment we may suppose that we desire to include in our test all the species that usually cause a continued fever of the enteric type, but to exclude those that usually give rise to an acute gastro-enteritis.

This leaves us with *Bact. typhosum*, *Bact. paratyphosum A*, *Bact. paratyphosum B*, *Bact. paratyphosum C*, and *Bact. choleræ-suis* var. *kunzendorf*. All these species contain both flagellar and somatic antigens (see Chapter XXVII), and many observations that have been recorded during recent years have shown quite clearly that the agglutinins acting on both these antigens must be considered.

It has been shown, for instance, that some cases of enteric infection fail to develop H (flagellar) agglutinins while developing O (somatic) agglutinins to relatively high titre (Felix 1924a, b, 1930, Stuart and Krikorian 1928, Felix and Olitzki 1928, Pijper 1930, Gardner et al. 1930, Horgan 1932, Flis and Rosenberg 1934, Bole 1935). A test carried out with formolized broth cultures alone, and thus revealing only H agglutinins, would miss a varying proportion of positive results.

It would appear that the proportion of cases showing O agglutinins only is much higher in some localities than in others. Thus Pijper in South Africa (see Felix and Olitzki 1928) noted 34 persistently negative reactions in 120 cases of undoubted typhoid fever, when testing for H agglutinins only. Some cases of this type, at least, are infected with O variants of the typhoid bacillus (Olitzki 1928, Gardner et al. 1930).

It is equally true that particular samples of serum obtained from typhoid or paratyphoid cases may show flagellar but not somatic agglutinins. Smith (1932) records that 6 of 28 cases of typhoid fever showed H but not O agglutinins when the cases were first examined, while 11 of 42 cases of paratyphoid B fever gave a similar result (see also Downie and Fairbrother 1934, Soman 1934, Flis and Rosenberg 1934, Bole 1935).

Whether a case ever passes through all its stages developing H but no O agglutinins is as yet uncertain, though it seems unlikely. In any event the lesson is clear —both H and O agglutinins should be searched for in each specimen of blood examined.

A curious feature of the somatic agglutinins in typhoid and paratyphoid fever is that they fail to show the specificity that would be expected from the antigenic structure of *Bact. typhosum*, *Bact. paratyphosum A*, and *Bact. paratyphosum B* as determined by analysis with antisera prepared in the rabbit (see Table XLII, p. 551). Thus Felix (1924a) records that, of 28 cases of typhoid fever proved by the isolation of *Bact. typhosum* from the blood or fæces, 10 gave somatic agglutination with *Bact. paratyphosum A* and 21 with *Bact. paratyphosum B*, as well as with *Bact. typhosum*. Of 8 proved cases of infection with *Bact. paratyphosum A*, 6 gave somatic agglutination with *Bact. typhosum* and 6 with *Bact. paratyphosum B*. Of 11 proved cases of infection with *Bact. paratyphosum B*, 6 gave somatic agglutination with *Bact. typhosum* and 2 with *Bact. paratyphosum A*. Several other workers have recorded similar results. Thus, Smith (1932) found that the sera of 21 of 28 cases of typhoid fever showed O agglutinins for *Bact. typhosum* (the sera were collected at all stages in the disease, sometimes very early). Six cases showed O agglutinins for *Bact. paratyphosum B* (1 case was not tested against this organism). Of 42 cases of paratyphoid B fever, 25 showed O agglutinins for *Bact. paratyphosum B* and 20 showed O agglutinins for *Bact. typhosum*.

In general it has been found that the O titre for the infecting organism is higher than for the heterologous organism ; and Gardner and Stubington (1932) have shown that, using standardized suspensions and applying an appropriate reduction factor to the observed titres, it is possible in a majority of cases to form a correct opinion with regard to the type of infecting organism. This problem needs much fuller investigation before we can draw any detailed and definite conclusions with regard to the relationships between the somatic antigens of bacilli of the enteric group as a whole and the corresponding antibodies in the blood of infected persons.

For the moment we must note that, while the detection and measurement of O agglutinins is a valuable and often necessary step in the diagnosis of enteric infection, it appears to be of much less value in differentiating between one type of enteric infection and another, and that the present evidence suggests that it may be sufficient to include a single O suspension in our test, relying on our H suspensions to differentiate between one type of enteric fever and another. For the detection of O agglutinins, it is customary to employ either an alcoholized suspension, in which the H antigens have been inactivated, or a formolized broth culture of an O variant possessing no flagella.

We may note also that, in the case of the typhoid bacillus, it is not necessary to include a strain that is sensitive to the Vi antibody (see below), since it would appear that no case of typhoid fever develops Vi agglutinins without at the same time developing H or O agglutinins or both (see Kauffmann 1935).

In selecting our formolized broth suspensions for the detection of flagellar agglutinins, we must remember that two of the species that we are including in our list, *Bact. paratyphosum B* and *Bact. paratyphosum C*, are diphasic, that is, their flagellar antigens may assume one of two alternative forms, specific or group (see Chapter XXVII). Another species, *Bact. cholerœ-suis* var. *kunzendorf*, though monophasic, is permanently in the group phase. If therefore we include in our formolized broth cultures *Bact. typhosum*, *Bact. paratyphosum A*, *Bact. paratyphosum B* in the specific phase, *Bact. paratyphosum C* in the specific phase, and some diphasic species in the group phase, or, alternatively, a formolized culture of *Bact. cholerœ-suis* var. *kunzendorf*, and add to them one " O " suspension, we shall be in a position to diagnose, and differentiate, an infection due to any of these species, and to obtain an indication of an infection caused by any one of several other Salmonella species, though, in the latter case, we may not be able to determine the actual infecting species without additional examinations. In practice it will usually be possible to omit one or more of these specific H suspensions, according to the locality in which we happen to be working, while in other cases it will be necessary to add, or substitute, additional species or types.

So far we have been considering qualitative results, the mere presence or absence of agglutinins acting on particular antigens ; but we actually need to know the concentration in which each of these agglutinins is present in any given specimen of serum.

The results of agglutination tests are commonly expressed as titres, *i.e.*, as the highest dilution of a given serum that will produce agglutination of a given bacterial suspension under specified conditions of time and temperature. We shall, in all cases, wish to determine the real end-point ; so that we must specify conditions that will allow this end-point to be obtained. Somatic agglutination, for instance, is slower than flagellar flocculation. Tests with O suspensions should be read after 4 hours' incubation in a water-bath at 55° C., and again overnight. Tests with H suspensions may be read after 2–4 hours under the same conditions. It is usual to employ a geometrical series of dilutions, such as 1 : 20, 1 : 40, 1 : 80, 1 : 160 and so on, and the observed titre is thus subject to a wide margin of error unless some additional precautions are taken. A rough approximation may be made by noting the last tube to show detectable flocculation of the bacilli. By adopting an arbitrary degree of agglutination as a standard, and applying an interpolation table to the actual readings obtained, a much greater degree of accuracy can be attained (see Dreyer and Inman 1917).

But our difficulties do not end here. All suspensions of the same bacterial species are not equally sensitive to agglutination ; and if we tested a single sample of serum against a dozen suspensions of *Bact. typhosum* prepared from different strains in different ways we might get widely divergent answers. If there were no gross antigenic variations in our strains there would be a limit to such divergence— we should not often find that the titre given by any one suspension was more than, say, two or four times that given by another ; but this is a wide margin of technical error.

A valuable lead was given by the work of Dreyer and his colleagues during the late War (Dreyer, Walker and Gibson 1915, Dreyer and Walker 1916, Dreyer and Inman 1917), and the Standards Laboratory instituted in the Department of Pathology at Oxford under the auspices of the Medical Research Council has since performed an important service in preparing and issuing standard agglutinable suspensions, not only of the flagellated bacilli of the enteric group, but of non-flagellated variants of the same species, and of various other bacteria that are commonly employed in agglutination tests (see Gardner 1920, 1921, 1929). A sensitive suspension of a particular bacterium is adopted as a standard, and any subsequent suspension is compared with this by duplicate testing against an agglutinating serum. The new suspension is then labelled with a number that allows the titre observed with any given serum to be reduced to the titre that would have been observed had the " standard " suspension been employed.

This brings us to the question as to whether any particular titre, and if so what, can be regarded as a reliable indication of infection with one or other of this group of organisms. The answer is quite definite. *No arbitrary titre can be selected at, or above, which an agglutination can be regarded as " positive " in the diagnostic sense, and below which it can be regarded as " negative ". An observed titre for any one of these organisms constitutes one item of evidence which must be considered in relation to all the other evidence available.*

Among the more important ancillary data on which the interpretation of a single agglutination reaction depends are the following :—

(1) The natural level of agglutinins among a random sample of the population in the particular area in which the test is being made.

(2) The stage in the disease at which the sample of blood has been taken.

(3) The state of the patient in regard to previous inoculation with typhoid, or T.A.B., or T.A.B.C. vaccine.

We may discuss these various factors in sequence ; but we should note that the average level of agglutinins in a given population, as well as their titre in any particular person, may sometimes be affected by the results of prophylactic immunization.

We shall discuss the available evidence under (1) in some detail, since it has an important bearing on the epidemiology of the disease, as well as on diagnosis. It will be convenient to deal separately with H and O agglutinins and to start with the former.

(1) A valuable record of the London population in 1921 is given by Rosher and Fielden (1922), who examined 1,000 samples of serum sent to the laboratory for a Wassermann test, *i.e.*, from patients in whom there was no suspicion of an existing typhoid infection.

These sera were tested against formolized suspensions of *Bact. typhosum*, *Bact. paratyphosum A*, *Bact. paratyphosum B* and certain other members of the Salmonella group at dilutions ranging from 1 : 20 to 1 : 640 or more. Since our present knowledge with regard to the diphasic variation of the flagellar antigens was not then available it is impossible to be certain which type of agglutinin was concerned in the flocculation of the diphasic species. Taking the results for the three more important species, with this reservation as regards *Bact. paratyphosum B*, we obtain the figures set out in Table CXIX.

TABLE CXIX
LONDON

Bacterial Suspension.	Percentage of Sera Agglutinating at 1 : 20 or over.
Bact. typhosum	29
Bact. paratyphosum A	17
Bact. paratyphosum B	23

In 330 instances it was possible to obtain a reliable history as to whether the person had or had not been inoculated. The figures for this sub-sample, again taking the titres of 1 : 20 or over, are set out in Table CXX.

TABLE CXX
LONDON

Bacterial Suspension.	Inoculated.		Uninoculated.	
	No. of Sera.	Per cent. +	No. of Sera.	Per cent. +
Bact. typhosum	149	89	181	3
Bact. paratyphosum A	149	58	181	0
Bact. paratyphosum B	149	71	181	4

Since many more males than females were inoculated during the War it was to be expected that the figures for the two sexes would differ widely, and this was found to be the case. Thus, among 276 unselected male sera 42 per cent. agglutinated *Bact. typhosum* at a titre of 1 : 20 ; 28 per cent. *Bact. paratyphosum A* ; and 39 per cent. *Bact. paratyphosum B*. Among 165 female sera, 5 per cent. agglutinated *Bact. typhosum* ; 2 per cent. agglutinated *Bact. paratyphosum A* ; and 7 per cent. agglutinated *Bact. paratyphosum B*.

It is clear that the relatively high proportion of agglutinating sera among the London population as a whole was, in 1921, determined by the presence of a large number of recently inoculated persons.

A similar study was carried out in Manchester a few years later by Smith, MacVie and Newbold (1930) ; 302 specimens of sera sent to the laboratory for Wassermann tests during the years 1925 and 1926 were tested against formolized suspensions of various bacteria of the Salmonella group. In this case type suspensions of the diphasic species were employed, together with a single group suspension to detect the group agglutinins, so that a complete picture of the flagellar agglutinins was obtained over the range of types examined.

Taking first the Manchester population as a whole—and including the results with the type phase of *Bact. paratyphosum C*, and the group suspension—the percentages giving agglutination at 1 : 20 or over are set out in Table CXXI.

TABLE CXXI
MANCHESTER

Organism.	Percentage of Sera Agglutinating.
Bact. typhosum	14·9
Bact. paratyphosum A	5·9
Bact. paratyphosum B (type)	5·9
Bact. paratyphosum C (type)	0·3
" Group " Suspension	6·3

Comparing these figures with those of Rosher and Fielden they show a drop to about a half in the case of *Bact. typhosum*, to about a third in the case of *Bact. paratyphosum A* and to about a quarter in the case of *Bact. paratyphosum B*. Agglutinins for the type phase of *Bact. paratyphosum C* appear to be very uncommon in the normal English population. No information was available with regard to the state of inoculation of the persons from whom these blood samples were obtained ; but a division into males and females (see Table CXXII) affords highly suggestive evidence.

TABLE CXXII

MANCHESTER

Organism.	Percentage of Sera Agglutinating.	
	Males.	Females.
Bact. typhosum	23·3	4·7
Bact. paratyphosum A	11·6	0
Bact. paratyphosum B (type).	9·7	2·0
Bact. paratyphosum C (type)	0·0	0·6
" Group " Suspension	7·0	4·7

It will be noted that the figures of Smith, MacVie and Newbold for females agree fairly closely with those of Rosher and Fielden for uninoculated persons of both sexes, or for unselected female sera, so far as *Bact. typhosum, Bact. paratyphosum A* and *Bact. paratyphosum B* are concerned. In the case of the latter organism Rosher and Fielden's figure of 4·0 per cent. must be compared with both the paratyphoid B and group figures of Smith, MacVie and Newbold.

The fall in the frequency of flagellar agglutinins among the population as a whole is almost certainly due to a wearing-off of the effect of inoculation. Thus, in the case of *Bact. typhosum* Rosher and Fielden found 42 per cent. of agglutinating sera among adult males, compared to the 23·3 per cent. noted by Smith, MacVie and Newbold some six years later.

When we consider titres, as well as the mere presence or absence of agglutinins, the figures provided by Smith, MacVie and Newbold for females (see Table CXXIII) afford a useful guide to the titres we may expect to find in uninoculated adults. The figures under each titre give percentage of sera reacting at that titre, or over. Titres of over 1 : 160 are clearly very exceptional. Below this level there are considerable differences in the frequency of flagellar agglutinins for the different organisms.

TABLE CXXIII

MANCHESTER (Females)

Organism.	Percentage of Sera Agglutinating at, or above					
	1 : 20	1 : 40	1 : 80	1 : 160	1 : 320	1 : 640
Bact. typhosum	4·7	2·7	0·7	0·7	0	0
Bact. paratyphosum A	0	0	0	0	0	0
Bact. paratyphosum B (type) . .	2·0	1·3	0	0	0	0
Bact. paratyphosum C (type) . .	0·6	0·6	0·6	0	0	0
" Group " Suspension	4·7	2·0	1·4	1·4	0·7	0

An extremely interesting contrast to these English figures is afforded by those recorded by Giglioli (1933*a*) for a population of native labourers in British Guiana. Table CXXIV has been constructed from his data for 350 uninoculated persons, taking the figures for males and females together.

TABLE CXXIV

BRITISH GUIANA (Males and Females)

Organism.	Percentage of Sera Agglutinating at, or above					
	1 : 20	1 : 40	1 : 80	1 : 160	1 : 320	1 : 640
Bact. typhosum	24·6	16·0	8·3	4·0	1·7	0
Bact. paratyphosum A	9·4	6·9	3·7	1·7	0	0
Bact. paratyphosum B (type) . .	6·0	3·1	2·3	1·1	0	0
Bact. paratyphosum C (type) . .	14·3	11·4	7·1	6·0	2·6	0·6
" Group " Suspension	29·4	20·0	12·9	8·9	2·6	0·9

The figures for H agglutinins acting on *Bact. typhosum*, *Bact. paratyphosum A*, *Bact. paratyphosum C* or the " Group " suspension are all much higher than the corresponding figures for London or Manchester. The discrepancy is greatest in the case of *Bact. paratyphosum C*, and this clearly arises from the fact that this type of infection is, as Giglioli (1930) has shown, endemic in British Guiana.

As another contrast we may take the figures given by Alves (1936) for H agglutinins acting on *Bact. typhosum*, *Bact. paratyphosum A* and *Bact. paratyphosum B* among 530 sera from uninoculated natives in Southern Rhodesia. The lowest titre recorded in this series was 1 : 50. At this titre 5·1 per cent. of the sera agglutinated *Bact. typhosum* ; at 1 : 125 the percentage was 3·8, at 1 : 250 it was 2·2, and at 1 : 500 it was 1·5. No serum agglutinated *Bact. paratyphosum A* or *Bact. paratyphosum B* at the titres tested. Lewin (1934), working in South Africa, records the titres for typhoid H agglutinins among 442 sera from probably uninoculated persons. Of these sera 10·6 per cent. gave agglutination at 1 : 25, 2·9 per cent. at 1 : 100, 1·1 per cent. at 1 : 200, and 0·4 per cent. at 1 : 400— figures which are in near agreement with those of Alves over a similar range.

When we turn to O agglutinins we find our evidence rather less detailed.

So far as English figures are concerned, we have those recorded by Gardner and Stubington (1932) for 50 normal uninoculated persons. These are shown in Table CXXV.

TABLE CXXV

OXFORD

Organisms.	Percentage Agglutinating at, or above		
	1 : 25	1 : 50	1 : 100
Bact. typhosum O.	38	6	2
Bact. paratyphosum A O.	0	0	0
Bact. paratyphosum B * O.	12	2	0

* The suspension actually employed in this case was from an O variant of *Bact. typhi-murium*, which has the same O antigens as *Bact. paratyphosum B*.

Giglioli (1933*a*) included O agglutinins in his survey among the native labourers in British Guiana (Table CXXVI). It will be noted that the O agglutinins among

TABLE CXXVI
BRITISH GUIANA

Organism.	Percentage of Sera Agglutinating at, or above					
	1 : 20	1 : 40	1 : 80	1 : 160	1 : 320	1 : 640
Bact. typhosum O.	16·3	3·7	0·9	0·3	0·3	0
Bact. paratyphosum B O . .	20·3	5·7	2·0	0·3	0·3	0
Bact. paratyphosum C O . .	19·4	9·4	3·1	2·0	0·9	0·3

this sample of the population show no excess, where comparison is possible, over the English figures, in striking contrast to the marked excess shown with H agglutinins.

Horgan (1932) has tested 70 sera from Sudanese with no evidence of enteric infection, and no history of inoculation. At a titre of 1 : 25, 7·1 per cent. agglutinated an O suspension of *Bact. typhosum*, 4·3 per cent. agglutinated an O suspension of *Bact. paratyphosum* B, while no serum agglutinated an O suspension of *Bact. paratyphosum A*.

Lewin (1934) gives the following percentages for typhoid O agglutination at various titres among the 442 sera examined by him : 45·0 per cent. agglutinated at 1 : 25, 4·5 per cent. at 1 : 100, 2·0 per cent. at 1 : 200, and 1·8 per cent. at 1 : 400.

Alves (1936) gives figures for typhoid O agglutinins among 300 sera from normal uninoculated natives in Southern Rhodesia ; 9·33 per cent. gave agglutination at 1 : 50, 2·67 per cent. at 1 : 100, 2 per cent. at 1 : 250 and 1 per cent. at 1 : 500.

Where comparison is possible these figures are not widely discrepant ; and they suggest that the frequency and concentration of O agglutinins in different parts of the world differ much less than the frequency and concentration of H agglutinins. This is not surprising in view of the fact that the antibody response to specific stimulation with the O antigens is known to be more transitory than the response to the H antigens. There are many reasons for believing that the normal O agglutinins, when present to low titre only, represent normal antibodies of the type that have not arisen in response to infection (see Chapter XLVI).

Further surveys of this type are badly needed. We should have an accurate knowledge of the level of H and O agglutinins among the normal population in all those parts of the world in which the laboratory diagnosis of enteric infections is undertaken. Moreover, these surveys should be carried out by a standardized technique, and with standard reagent The figures quoted above are not, indeed, strictly comparable with one another because these requirements were not always fulfilled.

(2) The next factor that we have to consider in a diagnostic agglutination test is the stage of the disease at which the sample of blood was taken.

Reference to Fig. 259, p. 1198 and to Figs. 236, 237, p. 879, will indicate that the significance of a positive or negative agglutination test, or of a positive result to any given titre, varies according to the stage of the disease at which the sample of blood was taken.

It is clear that little importance can be attached to a negative agglutination test on a sample of blood taken during the first week of illness. It does *not* follow that a test made at this time is useless. It is often of the greatest value since, taken in conjunction with tests made at a later period, it often enables us to demonstrate that a significant rise in agglutinins has occurred ; the demonstration of such a rise has far more diagnostic significance than the demonstration that any particular sample of serum gives agglutination to a particular titre, unless that titre is a very high one.

As an illustrative example, bearing in mind our evidence with regard to the distribution of normal agglutinins, let us suppose that we find that a sample of serum, taken from a patient in the first week of the disease, gives an H titre of 1 : 20 against the typhoid bacillus. If the sample had been taken in British Guiana, this finding would have almost no significance, since about 1 normal person in 5 would give this titre. If it had been taken in South Africa, it would have been more suggestive. If it had been taken in England it would have been still more suggestive ; only about 1 normal person in 20 would give this titre. If we found, in addition, an O titre of 1 : 50, the significance of the H titre of 1 : 20 would be greatly increased, since in England a 1 in 20 chance and a 1 in 16 chance would both have come off in the same person. Similarly, a 1 : 20 H titre against *Bact. paratyphosum C* in England would be very suggestive of infection. In British Guiana it would have almost no significance.

If, however, we found these titres in a specimen of serum taken from a patient towards the end of the second week of the disease, or in the beginning of the third, their significance would be entirely altered. By that time a patient has usually developed an H titre well above 1 : 20, and an O titre well above 1 : 50. If we found such low titres at so late a period we should be inclined to suspect that they were due to some cause other than active infection.

Clearly we should like to have figures for the average H and O titres against the causative organism at each period of infection, and for each type of enteric infection ; but we have to be satisfied with something much less than this, because records that afford all the necessary data are by no means plentiful. Such figures as we have however give us a very useful lead.

Gardner and Stubington (1932) in 40 cases of typhoid fever record H titres of which all but 3 were above 1 : 125, 30 were 1 : 250 or over, and 14 were 1 : 1,000 or over. Of the O titres all were over 1 : 125, 37 were over 1 : 250, and 13 were over 1 : 1,000. In 40 cases of enteric fever caused by *Bact. paratyphosum B* the level of H agglutinins tended to be rather higher, but the level of O agglutinins, either for *Bact. typhosum* or *Bact. paratyphosum B*, definitely lower. Twenty-two of the 40 sera showed an O typhoid titre of less than 1 : 125, and 17 showed an anti-paratyphosum B O titre below this limit. Somewhat similar results are recorded in several of the papers referred to above, and in others not quoted.

In most instances it is not possible from the records to determine the day of disease on which the different specimens were taken ; but it seems a fair conclusion from the data that the great majority of typhoid infections will, during the 3rd week of the disease, show an H titre well over 1 : 100, and usually over 1 : 200, and an O titre of 1 : 100 or over. With paratyphoid infections the H titre against the causative organism will tend to be at least as high as that observed in typhoid fever, but the O titre, particularly if an O typhoid suspension is employed, may be somewhat lower.

(3) Let us now turn to the third factor that may influence the interpretation of our results, the effect of previous inoculation with a typhoid, or T.A.B. vaccine. This factor is particularly important in the diagnosis of enteric infections among troops in war time, or in countries where the risk of enteric infection is so high that many of the white or native population are inoculated.

Considerable assistance is gained, in the solution of this technical difficulty, by the difference in the nature of the antibody response to the H and O antigens. Felix (see above), who first emphasized the value of this method, originally stated that O agglutinins were not formed in response to antityphoid inoculation, and that hence O agglutination had the same diagnostic value in the inoculated as in the uninoculated. This, however, is not the case.

Thus Gardner (1929) found that of 6 persons with a history of inoculation in past years 1 gave O agglutination with *Bact. typhosum* at a titre of over 1 : 200 and of 11 persons inoculated 4 weeks before testing 3 gave titres of this order. To check these findings a healthy adult, who had been inoculated some 14 years earlier, was given 2 inoculations of T.A.B. vaccine and his agglutinins were determined at frequent intervals during the following month. The flagellar agglutinins were raised from a titre of 1 : 185 to a titre of 1 : 1,500 ; the O agglutinins were raised from zero to 1 : 50 ; both thereafter sank. Mudd (1932) showed that sera collected 10 days after the third injection of a T.A.B. vaccine contained O agglutinins to a significantly higher titre (1 : 80 to 1 : 320) than the average normal uninoculated controls ; and Horgan (1932) and Giglioli (1933*b*) record similar results.

As compared with these O titres, however, the H titres developed after typhoid and paratyphoid inoculation are very high. They usually attain a level of 1 : 500 or more, and often well over 1 : 1,000. What is much more important the O agglutinins disappear from the circulation far more rapidly than the H agglutinins.

Smith (1932) examined the sera of 17 normal persons who had been injected with typhoid vaccine between the years 1915 to 1929. All 17 showed flagellar agglutinins for *Bact. typhosum* at titres varying from 1 : 50 to 1 : 200 ; two of them showed O agglutinins, one at a titre of 1 : 50, the other at a titre of 1 : 200. Wyllie (1932) examined the sera of 22 persons who had received prophylactic injections of typhoid vaccine between 1928 and 1931 ; 13 showed no O agglutinins at 1 : 25, 9 reacted at or above this titre, the highest titre reached being 1 : 100 (see also Giglioli 1933*b* and others).

There are, then, good grounds for Felix's contention that O agglutinins are of more significance than H agglutinins in inoculated persons, though the difference is not so great as was originally suggested. This is particularly true of persons who have not been very recently inoculated, and who show moderate H titres. When very high H titres are encountered they become significant even in an inoculated person, provided the inoculation is not very recent. It is, for instance, very unusual to find an H titre of much over 1 : 1,000 for *Bact. typhosum*, or much over 1 : 500 for *Bact. paratyphosum A* or *Bact. paratyphosum B* at any period later than 6 months after an injection of T.A.B. vaccine.

There is another way in which this problem may be attacked. By taking several samples of blood from the same patient at different periods of the disease we may construct an " agglutinin curve " and base our diagnosis on fluctuations in titre rather than on the titre obtained with any one sample (see Dreyer, Walker and Gibson 1915, Dreyer and Walker 1916, Dreyer and Inman 1917, and also Perry 1918, Topley, Platt and Imrie 1920).

As regards the flagellar agglutinins reference to Chapter XLVII will show the time relations of the response to the inoculation of a killed culture and the response to active infection. When an inoculated person becomes infected, the response to infection is superimposed on the residual effect of the earlier response to inoculation, and we get the usual " infection " curve, starting not from the zero line, but from a base line representing the residual " inoculation " agglutinins. Since the rise in titre is more rapid than the fall, the most significant information will be obtained by repeated tests carried out during the first 3 weeks of infection ; but the early part of the fall from the maximal titre attained is usually steep enough to show a significant drop in titre during the early weeks of convalescence.

An H titre of 1 : 50, or of 1 : 250, in an inoculated person is of no significance. But an H titre of 1 : 50 on the 5th day of the disease followed by an H titre of 1 : 250 on the 10th day of the disease is highly suggestive of an active infection. We must not, however, in this connection forget the possibility of the non-specific stimulation of antibody production—the fresh output of typhoid agglutinins in response to some quite different infection (see Chapter XLVII).

The evidence on this point is conflicting. As regards the effect of enteric infection itself, it would appear that a person who has been inoculated with T.A.B. vaccine and subsequently develops typhoid fever usually responds by a renewed production of typhoid agglutinins, while the titres of agglutinins for *Bact. paratyphosum A* and *Bact. paratyphosum B* remain quite steady, or show trivial fluctuations. In some cases, however, a person who has been inoculated with triple vaccine and subsequently develops an infection due to one of the three organisms against which he has been vaccinated produces agglutinins not only against that organism but also against one or both of the heterologous species.

In regard to other diseases there is a conflict of opinion. Felix (1924*b*) considers that this non-specific response is of frequent occurrence—particularly as the result of infection with exanthematic typhus, but also with many other infections—and that the demonstration of a rise or fall in agglutinin titre in an inoculated subject suffering from a febrile disease has thus no diagnostic significance. It is quite certain (see Perry 1918, Topley, Platts and Imrie 1920) that inoculated persons may suffer from febrile infections of many kinds without showing any detectable fluctuations in the titre of flagellar agglutinins, and the application of the " agglutinin curve " as a diagnostic criterion during the War indicated its usefulness. But, in view of Felix's findings a rise or fall in titre cannot be regarded as certainly diagnostic of active enteric infection. We badly need more detailed information of such changes in titre as may occur in the course of various infective diseases.

In summary, it is only when a high titre of H agglutinins is found in an un-inoculated person, or a very high titre in a not-very-recently inoculated person, or an O titre well above the normal level in the uninoculated or not-very-recently inoculated, that a diagnosis of enteric fever can be based with reasonable safety on a single agglutination test. In all other cases the agglutination result must be regarded as offering an indication rather than as giving an answer. It must be considered in relation to all other available evidence ; and, if necessary, the test must be repeated once or more. Nor is it very useful to try to define " high " or " very high." If we call an H titre of 1 : 250 " high " and 1 : 1,000 " very high " and an O titre of 1 : 250 " well above the normal level " we shall usually be safe ; but many typhoid or paratyphoid patients will show lower titres than these, and the fixing of any arbitrary level tends to confuse the real issue rather than to clarify it.

The Treatment of Typhoid Fever with Antityphoid Sera.

There are various references in the literature to the treatment of typhoid fever by the injection of antisera prepared by immunizing horses with cultures, or extracts, of typhoid bacilli. This method has not, in the past, ever attained wide or general usage, though Grasset (1930, 1931) has recently reported favourable results from South Africa.

The question as to whether such a serum will exert any significant therapeutic effect in an established case of the disease is clearly ripe for re-examination in the light of our recently acquired knowledge of the antigenic structure of the typhoid bacillus, and of the rôle of different antibodies in antibacterial immunity (see Chapter XLIV). We have seen that it is the antibody acting on the surface O antigen of the typhoid bacillus that renders the ordinary smooth form of this organism sensitive to the phagocytic and lytic mechanisms of the tissues, and it has been noted that these O antigens, in the state in which they occur naturally in organisms of the Salmonella group, are themselves highly toxic, so that an O antibody might be expected to exert both an antibacterial and an anti-endotoxic effect, and it would be in no way surprising if a serum with a high anti-O titre exerted an effect on both the bacteræmia and the toxæmia that are associated with enteric infection.

The Vi Antigen of the Typhoid Bacillus, and the Vi Antibody.

The position in regard to this problem has, however, been greatly modified during recent years by a series of observations recorded by Felix and his colleagues.

Felix and Pitt (1934*a*) found that, when different smooth strains of typhoid bacilli were compared with one another in regard to their sensitiveness to agglutination by an O antiserum, they differed very widely, and that this sensitivity was inversely related to the virulence of the strains as judged by the intraperitoneal injection of mice. Thus three strains that were very slightly agglutinable by an O antiserum killed 10 of 10, 10 of 10 and 8 of 10 mice when injected in a dose of 100×10^6 bacilli; while three strains that were freely agglutinable by an O antiserum failed to kill a single mouse when injected in this dose. A high proportion of strains freshly isolated from cases of typhoid fever have been found to be of the mouse-virulent type.

In a later paper Felix and Pitt (1934*b*) showed that the virulence of the former strains, and their inagglutinability by an O antiserum, were due to the presence of a special antigenic component, which Felix called the " Vi " antigen. This antigen, it may be noted, is heat labile; so that agglutination tests to detect its presence, or absence, must be carried out with living suspensions at a temperature of 37° C. Rabbits immunized with living cultures of highly virulent typhoid bacilli produce, in addition to the usual O antibodies, a Vi antibody which agglutinates the virulent strains; while rabbits immunized with avirulent smooth strains, or with heat-killed virulent smooth strains, produce O antibodies alone. An antiserum prepared against virulent strains may be deprived of its O antibodies by absorption with avirulent bacilli, thus providing a pure anti-Vi serum. A Vi antiserum gives effective passive protection in mice against living virulent typhoid bacilli, while an O antiserum is almost or quite ineffective. An O antiserum will, however, protect mice against the toxic effects of a massive dose of killed typhoid bacilli.

These observations have been extended by Felix and his colleagues in a series of subsequent experiments (see Felix, Bhatnagar and Pitt 1934, Felix and Pitt 1935, Bhatnagar 1935, Felix and Bhatnagar 1935); and various peculiarities in the behaviour of the Vi antigen and Vi antibody have come to light, some of which are, at the moment, extremely difficult to explain, or to fit into our general picture of antityphoid immunity. Thus, a serum prepared in the rabbit by the injection of a formolized broth culture of typhoid bacilli contains Vi antibody, as shown by its ability to agglutinate virulent typhoid bacilli, but it has very feeble protective powers in mice, and is relatively ineffective in promoting phagocytosis of virulent typhoid bacilli *in vitro*. A serum prepared against living typhoid bacilli, on the other hand, exerts a protective and opsonic effect against virulent bacilli as well as agglutinating them. This question will be referred to again when discussing the problem of active immunization against enteric fever.

We may note that the essential findings of Felix and his colleagues in relation to the typhoid bacillus have been confirmed by other workers (see Kauffmann 1935). Whether the claim of Felix and Pitt (1936) to have established the presence in other Salmonella organisms of a Vi antigen, possessing a similar significance, is well founded, seems much more doubtful, especially when their findings are compared with those of Kauffmann (1935–36*b*, 1936).

Returning to the problem of the possible therapeutic effect of an antityphoid serum in man, it is clearly of importance to determine whether the O antibody or the Vi antibody, or both, are required to ensure an optimal result.

A clinical trial, carried out in Palestine, has been recorded by Felix (1935), with suggestive and promising results ; though the scale of the trial was quite inadequate to establish more than a case for further inquiry. The serum used in this trial contained both O and Vi antibodies to high titre, the control cases, of which there were very few, being treated with normal horse serum. It is therefore impossible to differentiate between the effect of O and Vi antibody. The report of those who observed the cases, that the main effect of the serum was in diminishing the toxæmia, suggests that the O antibody was not without effect.

The Epidemiology of Enteric Fever.

It would take us altogether beyond the scope of this book to discuss in any detail the extensive literature bearing on the epidemiology of enteric fever. It will, however, be useful to summarize the conclusions to be drawn from the available evidence, quoting certain illustrative records and reports, many of which must, of necessity, be arbitrarily selected from the numerous examples available.

The main conclusions which emerge quite clearly from the mass of evidence on record are that the single important source of enteric infection consists in typhoid or paratyphoid bacilli which are living, or proliferating, within the bodies of infected persons ; and that the whole problem of prevention, neglecting for the moment the possibility of active immunization, consists in stopping the various routes by which the bacilli may pass from the intestine of one individual to the mouth of another.

Moreover, the evidence obtained during surveys of H agglutinins among the normal population in different parts of the world, where different types of enteric infection are endemic, shows quite clearly that in this, as in other diseases, the frequency of infection is far greater than the frequency of the clinical disease, so that infection from carriers is almost certainly more important in its total effect than infection from cases (see Chapter LIII and discussion below).

One obvious route of epidemic spread is provided by the fæcal pollution of water supplies, and enteric fever shares with cholera a pre-eminent position among the water-borne diseases. It may be noted that the evidence inculpating a particular water supply is almost always circumstantial ; partly because the isolation of typhoid or paratyphoid bacilli from water is beset with technical difficulties, resulting from high dilution and the presence in an infected water of other intestinal bacteria in preponderating numbers ; partly because the effective pollution is in most cases temporary or intermittent, and has usually ceased by the time the water supply falls under suspicion. The evidence is, none the less, convincing enough. Water-borne epidemics are characterized by a typically explosive onset ; the curve of notifications rises suddenly and steeply, the majority of the cases developing within a relatively few days. The curve, for the whole epidemic, is often characteristically skew, the primary cases due to direct infection from the water supply being followed by secondary crops of contact cases. Where, as is often the case, different parts of a large town are supplied with water from different sources, the area primarily affected may be obviously related to a particular source of supply. Among classical epidemics, those at Worthing (1897) and at Lincoln (1905) afford good illustrative examples. Among recent epidemics, that at Hanover (1926) provides an instance in which an infection of the water supply seems to provide the most rational explanation, though the origin of spread, and its subsequent course, have not been established with certainty (Hahn 1926, Knorr 1927*b*).

Milk follows close on water as an important source of sudden and massive herd infection. Ballard, in pre-bacteriological days, adduced good circumstantial evidence for inculpating a polluted milk supply in a localized epidemic at Islington. Schüder (1901), who studied the records of 640 epidemics, attributed 110 to contaminated milk. The most serious epidemic traceable to an infected milk supply is that which occurred at Montreal in 1927, and involved, in the two waves which occurred between the beginning of March and the middle of July, 4,849 cases with 489 deaths (see Report 1927, Boucher 1927). McMaster (1926) has reported a small outbreak of paratyphoid B infection at Dover, traceable to a similar source, while Bullough (1931) has described a larger outbreak involving 312 persons with 8 deaths at Epping. Small outbreaks of typhoid or paratyphoid fever may often be traced to milk which has been utilized for the preparation of some form of food which is consumed uncooked. Ice-cream holds a pre-eminent position in this category. The source from which the milk itself is usually contaminated will be considered in a later section.

Among other food-stuffs, shell-fish and particularly oysters are an important source of infection. They are often bred, or fattened, in the sewage-polluted waters of tidal estuaries, and they are usually consumed uncooked. Numerous epidemics are on record which can be directly traced to this source (see Gay 1918). The relation between the incidence of typhoid fever in a large city, and the consumption of shell-fish, has been considered in some detail by Niven (1910) in connection with the seasonal prevalence of typhoid fever in Manchester.

Human hands are probably the principal agents in the conveyance of typhoid or paratyphoid bacilli from fæces to food ; but there is another agent, the fly, which may be of considerable importance as a carrier when allowed access to infected excreta. Its activities in this direction are particularly dangerous in tropical countries, and under the imperfect sanitary conditions which often prevail among armies on active service. Reed, Vaughan and Shakespeare (1899) drew attention to the clear association between the prevalence of typhoid fever among the American troops in the Spanish-American War, and the exposure of excreta ; and suggested that flies played an important part in the spread of the disease.

The mechanism involved in the carriage of *Bact. typhosum* by flies has been studied experimentally by Firth and Horrocks (1902), Ficker (1903) and Graham-Smith (1910). The danger of contamination from the soiled feet, or proboscis, appears to be of relatively short duration ; but the observations of Ficker and of Graham-Smith suggest that a far more important source of infection is provided by the fly which itself becomes infected, and carries the bacilli for some days in its intestinal canal. The observations of Faichnie (1909), who examined flies caught in infected areas, and isolated typhoid bacilli on several occasions from the crushed bodies of the insects after the exterior had been sterilized by flaming, point in the same direction.

The Typhoid and Paratyphoid Carrier.—As has been indicated above, the ultimate source of enteric infection would appear, in all cases, to be the excreta of an infected human being, and this source is seldom remote. There is little evidence that typhoid or paratyphoid bacilli survive for any length of time outside the human body under natural conditions. The mode of survival of the bacilli throughout non-epidemic times, and the starting-point of outbreaks in localities which had long been free from the disease, remained in doubt until the early years of the present century, when the problem was solved during the intensive investigation undertaken in S.W. Germany under the auspices of Robert Koch. Horton-Smith (1900) had previously recorded the case of a urinary carrier of *Bact. typhosum*, but the full significance of the chronic carrier was not appreciated until the results of the German campaign were reported. (For an excellent description and discussion of these results see Ledingham and Arkwright 1912.) Koch's thesis, that the convalescent carrier would probably be found to be the main source of the persistence of infection within a community, was soon established on a firm basis by the findings of the Commission (Frosch 1903, von Drigalski 1904) ; and von Drigalski established the fact that the typhoid bacillus might lead a prolonged existence within the human body, and be excreted in the fæces. Lentz (1905) found that 4·5 per cent. of 400 typhoid convalescents excreted *Bact. typhosum* for more than 10 weeks, and 3 per cent. for longer than 13 months. Brückner (1910) found 12 carriers among 316 persons who had suffered from typhoid fever in previous years ; and Gill (1927) records 9·48 per cent. of carriers among a similar sample of 348 persons. Kayser (1907) carried out a re-examination of specimens of urine and fæces from 101 persons who had passed through an attack of typhoid fever at least 1 year earlier, and had been discharged as free from bacilli ; three of these were found to be again excreting the bacilli. These findings established a point which has now become a commonplace : that the excretion of bacilli by a chronic carrier is frequently intermittent, and that several negative examinations towards the end of convalescence by no means ensure that no latent focus of infection remains. Once established, such a focus may remain latent during a prolonged period. There are several examples in which there is every reason to believe that the attack of typhoid fever, from which the infection arose, occurred 25 years or more before the time at which the carrier was found to be still excreting bacilli.

Klinger (1909), in summarizing the results obtained to that date, gives records of 431 carriers ; 211 of these were regarded as transitory carriers, as defined by their failure to excrete the bacilli for more than 3 months ; 220 were regarded as chronic carriers, in that they excreted the bacilli over some longer period. The distribution of these carriers, according to sex, and according to the presence or absence of a history of an attack of typhoid fever, was as follows :

	Males.	Females.
Transitory carriers :		
(a) History of attack	31	61
(b) No history of attack	58	61
Chronic carriers :		
(a) History of attack	33	143
(b) No history of attack	5	39

Two points of interest emerge from this distribution : (*a*) the large number of transitory carriers in which there was no history of a previous attack, and (*b*) the striking preponderance of females among the chronic carriers. The latter point is of particular importance ; and it may be noted that the difference between the sexes in this respect is of the same order as the difference in the occurrence of gall-stones. Klinger's data also show that the transitory carriers occurred mainly among children and young adults, the chronic carriers among those in middle or later life.

With regard to the frequency of typhoid carriers among atypical cases, contacts, non-contacts in epidemic or endemic areas, and the population at large, our direct information is somewhat scanty, but it is sufficient to indicate that the distribution is of the general type discussed in Chapter LIII.

Billet and others (1910) record the isolation of *Bact. typhosum* from a high proportion of clinically atypical cases, during an outbreak of typhoid in an infantry regiment. The bacillus was isolated from the blood in 7 of 39 suspects, and from the fæces in 13 of 64 (20·3 per cent.). Semple and Greig (1908) isolated *Bact. typhosum* from the fæces of two nursing orderlies, in typhoid wards, who had never shown any clinical evidence of the disease. Klinger (1906) examined the excreta of 1,700 persons, living in an area in which typhoid fever was endemic, and isolated *Bact. typhosum* in 15 cases. Eleven of these presented no clinical symptoms, either before or after the isolation of the bacilli. In 9 cases the bacilli were found once only. In 2 they were found 3 times; but in no case did they persist longer than 14 days. The other 4 carriers were of the chronic type. Two had passed through an attack of typhoid fever in previous years; from the remaining 2 no history could be obtained. Gill (1927) reports the discovery of 39 carriers of *Bact. typhosum*, and 16 carriers of *Bact. paratyphosum A* or *Bact. paratyphosum B*, among 1,076 persons engaged in the milk trade, in an area in which enteric fever had been prevalent for several years. This carrier rate (3·1 per cent.) is exceptionally high, even for an endemic centre.

Among the population at large the carrier rate is probably very low. Minelli (1906) discovered one carrier among 250 inmates of the town prison of Straszburg—0·4 per cent. Prigge (1909) records 0·29 per cent. of carriers among a sample of 10,841 persons in Saarbrücken. Rosenau, Lumsden and Kastle (1909) found 3 carriers among 993 persons in Washington. These figures are curiously similar, but the actual variation in the frequency of carriers among the general population is probably wide, and all we can safely conclude is that the average frequency is well under 1 per cent. In many localities it is probably considerably less.

On the main point at issue the evidence leaves no doubt. Within any community, in which enteric fever is endemic, there will be found transient or chronic carriers, who are acting as foci of infection; the isolation of every overt case of illness would not suffice to stamp out the disease.

With regard to contact cases Klinger (1909) records some interesting observations on the period of the disease at which infection is transmitted to the contact. In an investigation of 812 such cases he reached the conclusion that the distribution, in time, of the contact infections was as shown in Table CXXVII.

TABLE CXXVII

Period of Disease.	No. of Contact Cases.	Period of Disease.	No. of Contact Cases.
Incubation period :			
1st week	33	4th week	59
2nd ,, ...	150	5th ,,	34
Illness :		6th ,,	22
1st week	187	7th ,,	14
2nd ,, ...	158	8th ,,	16
3rd ,, ...	116	9th ,,	15
		10th ,,	8

It is obvious that the evidence on which such figures are based must be largely circumstantial. If they are correct it would appear that 183 of 812 contact cases, or more than 20 per cent., were infected during the incubation period of the primary case—at a time when the disease could not have been diagnosed, and when opportunities for its spread would be increased by the fact that the infected person would not be confined to bed. To such primary carriers (*i.e.*, those in the incubation stage of the disease) must be added the relatively numerous ambulatory cases of mild and atypical infection which occur during any extensive epidemic.

In regard to the danger of the chronic carrier, it is only necessary to say that the literature contains numerous and well-authenticated records of their activities. For accounts of such classical instances as the case of the Straszburg Master-Baker's Wife, the case of the Folkestone Milker, or the case of " Typhoid Mary," the student is referred to the excellent monograph of Ledingham and Arkwright. It need only be noted that in these, as in almost all subsequent cases, the carrier who has achieved publicity has been in some way concerned with the handling of food, and that a large proportion of milk-borne epidemics, or small outbreaks due to the consumption of such food-materials as ice-cream, have been traced to a carrier who has been concerned in their handling or transport.

It may be added that, in searching for a typhoid carrier among a given sample of the population, much help will be obtained by testing the serum of all suspects for agglutinins before proceeding to the cultural examination of fæces and urine. A carrier almost always shows the presence of H or O agglutinins, or both, if only to a relatively low titre, especially if repeated tests are made. It is not safe to assume that absence of agglutinins in the blood excludes the carrier state ; but an agglutinin survey seldom fails to narrow the field that has to be explored by cultural methods. For a recent review of the carrier problem, including possible methods of treatment, see Browning and others (1933).

The Effect of General Sanitation on the Prevalence of Typhoid Fever.

Having discussed the part played by the chronic carrier of enteric infection it will be convenient to consider briefly the changes in the incidence of typhoid fever which have occurred during the last 50 years, and their relation to the improvements which have taken place, during the same period, in the sanitary organization of civilized communities.

One of the most striking phenomena in the public health annals of this period has been the steady decline of enteric fever as an important item in the mortality statistics. In 1870 there were 388 deaths from enteric fever per million living in England and Wales, and 233 deaths registered as " ill-defined." In 1880 the enteric deaths had fallen to 261 per million, and the " ill-defined " deaths to 58, the latter probably as the result of better diagnosis. In 1890 the enteric deaths had fallen to 179 per million, and the " ill-defined " to 13. In Table CXXVIII, for which we are indebted to Miss Woods, are set out the death rates at ages from enteric fever in England and Wales, during the first 27 years of the present century. It will be noted that, for the first decade (1901–10), the death rate for males at the most susceptible age period (20–25) is no higher than for the population as a whole in 1890. Since 1910 the mortality from enteric fever has fallen rapidly; and in 1927 it had reached almost negligible proportions—less than 10 per million living.

This fall has not, however, been equally rapid in all Western countries. Gay (1918) points out that the mortalities in European cities during the decade 1901–10 varied from 17 per million in Stockholm to 337 per million in St. Petersburg. The average figure for the 33 largest European cities during this period was 65 per million, while the average figure for the 57 largest American cities during the last year of the decade was 195·9 per million.

These variations in place and in time are associated with characteristic differences in sanitary organization. As Gay points out, prior to 1880 or thereabouts, typhoid fever was a disease of cities, the incidence varying directly as the density of population, as exemplified by the figures for Munich and the surrounding district ; these show the highest incidence in the city garrison, a somewhat lower incidence in the city as a whole, and a still lower incidence in the surrounding rural area. After this time, however, the sanitation of large cities rapidly and steadily improved, especially with regard to the provision of a pure water supply, and the efficient disposal of excreta and sewage. This improvement in sanitation has more than compensated for the density of population, and the result has been a shift in the incidence of enteric fever from the populations of large towns to rural communities, living under more primitive sanitary conditions.

Godfrey (1928) records some interesting figures with regard to the present incidence of enteric fever in New York City and State. In New York City itself the cases—not deaths—number about 23 per 100,000 living. In towns with populations of 10,000–20,000 the incidence is about 70 per 100,000, in towns with populations of 5,000–10,000 it is about 63, in towns under 2,000 about 48, and in very small towns and villages about 42. Thus, while enteric fever is less frequent in New York City than elsewhere in the State, it is at the present time a disease of the small town, rather than a rural disease in the strict sense of that term. This is probably due to the fact that the small town has failed to keep its sanitary organization abreast of its growth ; so that the water supply, sewage disposal, and milk control are inadequate to protect a community rapidly increasing in density of population.

TABLE CXXVIII

ENTERIC FEVER: ENGLAND AND WALES. DEATH RATES PER MILLION

	0–	5–	10–	15–	20–	25–	35–	45–	55–	65–	75 and up
Males :											
1901–10 .	32	52	71	137	179	178	142	104	80	40	17
1921–24 .	3	6	10	20	19	20	17	16	16	13	3
1925 .	6	5		16		14	10	9	11	9	4
1926 .	2	5		11		16	14	15	10	11	7
1927 .	2	8		12		11	12	14	12	5	—
Females :											
1901–10	30	59	81	100	99	97	86	67	50	29	10
1921–24	3	9	11	19	18	16	15	13	7	9	3
1925 .	1	8		12		12	13	11	12	7	7
1925 .	2	5		12		7	12	11	11	4	7
1927 .	4	3		11		9	10	14	12	6	4

Godfrey includes a valuable table showing the incidence of enteric fever at ages, and the percentage fatality in each age group. Information of this kind is not available for many communities, and we reproduce his figures in Table CXXIX.

TABLE CXXIX

<small>INCIDENCE AND FATALITY OF ENTERIC FEVER IN DIFFERENT AGE GROUPS (after Godfrey).</small>

Age Group.	Incidence (percentage of cases at all ages).	Case Fatality Percentage.
Under 5	4·5	8·4
5–9	13·8	4·4
10–14	14·3	6·4
15–19	14·2	10·2
20–24	12·0	12·5
25–29	9·7	13·5
30–34	7·7	16·4
35–39	6·3	15·2
40–44	5·4	15·2
45–49	3·9	19·9
50–54	3·3	22·9
55–59	2·0	22·8
60 and over	2·9	36·5

Enteric fever, at the present time, is thus a disease with its maximum incidence in adolescence ; but the case fatality increases throughout life, save that children under 5 show a higher case mortality than children between 5 and 15.

In addition to the striking fall in the incidence of enteric fever as a whole, there was during the post-war years a change in the sex incidence, and in the prevalent bacteriological type of infection. Thus it was noted by Chauffard and his colleagues (1921), Weigmann (1926) and Knorr (1927a) that after the middle period of the War the incidence of enteric fever was higher among women than among men, thus reversing the normal sex incidence, as universally experienced before the War. There can be little doubt that this shift was the result of the experience undergone by the male sex between 1914 and 1918. Thus, in an epidemic at Pforzheim in 1919 (Knorr 1927a), the lower incidence among males than among females commenced at age 19 and ended at age 50, indicating very clearly the effect of military service. It seems probable that some part, at least, of the present advantage of the male sex was referable to the antityphoid vaccination of the troops during the War period ; but there are facts which suggest that this is not the whole story. In Schleswig-Holstein, for instance, during the period 1914–24, the advantage of the males extended to enteric fever caused by *Bact. paratyphosum B*, while the German troops, unlike the French and English, were immunized only against *Bact. typhosum*. It is possible that this heightened average resistance of the male may have been due to mild or atypical infection while on War service, but the question must for the moment remain an open one.

Prophylactic Immunization against Enteric Fever.

Antityphoid vaccination in man was initiated by Wright in 1897 (see Wright and Semple 1897, Wright 1902, 1908)—though the observations of Pfeiffer and Kolle (1896) have been held by some to establish a claim to priority—and has since been tried under field conditions on the largest scale. The recorded results strongly support the view that it significantly reduces the incidence of enteric infection in environments in which such infection is particularly likely to occur.

The most impressive figures are those collected by the Antityphoid Committee (Report 1913), referring to the incidence of typhoid fever among inoculated and uninoculated troops stationed abroad. These figures have been analysed in a valuable paper by Greenwood and Yule (1915), to which reference should be made by all those who are interested in the general question of the interpretation of data of this kind. Employing the method of the fourfold table, and including as inoculated all those who had received typhoid vaccine at the time of the last available return, the data are set out in Table CXXX.

TABLE CXXX

	Not Attacked.	Attacked.	Total.
Inoculated . .	10,322	56	10,378
Not inoculated .	8,664	272	8,936
Total	18,986	328	19,314

$$\chi^2 = 180 \cdot 38.$$
$$P = \text{less than } 0 \cdot 0001.$$

The value χ^2 is a measure, devised by Pearson, of the probability that the distribution actually observed might have arisen as the result of chance ; as χ^2 increases, this probability decreases. The value P gives this probability in the usual numerical form (*i.e.*, in this particular case the odds are greater than 9,999 to 1—actually they are much greater —against the observed distribution having arisen as the result of chance).

War conditions provide an admirable breeding ground for typhoid and paratyphoid infections ; and it might have been expected that 1914–18 would have yielded a final proof of the efficacy of antityphoid inoculation, and a close measure of its exact protective value. They did, in truth, greatly strengthen the presumptive evidence in its favour —we cannot reasonably suppose that the whole of the vast difference between the deadly rôle of typhoid in the Boer War (105 cases per year per 1,000 of strength) and its relative insignificance among the huge armies on the Western Front 15 years later (2·35 cases per year per 1,000 of strength—see Harvey 1929) was wholly due to better sanitary conditions. But the exigencies of war, the impossibility of getting complete figures for the inoculated and the uninoculated exposed to risk, and the fact that the proportion of inoculated men rose, in the British Army, to well over 90 per cent. by the end of 1915, rendered impossible the collection of mass figures of a kind suitable for detailed statistical analysis. The general trend of the evidence is not, however, in doubt. Thus (see Harvey 1929) the year 1915 provides figures for the percentage of inoculated men in the Army in France and the cases of typhoid in the inoculated and the uninoculated, from which the incidence in each group can be calculated. The incidence among the inoculated was 9·5 per 10,000, among the uninoculated 103·52 per 10,000. During this period the men were inoculated against typhoid only. The incidence rates for paratyphoid fever were, among the inoculated 21·53 per 10,000, among the uninoculated 39·84 per 10,000. This suggests some degree of group protection against paratyphoid infection—a result that would hardly have been expected on immunological grounds—but the wide difference in the incidence ratios (10·90 : 1 in favour of the inoculated in the case of typhoid and 1·85 : 1 in the case of paratyphoid) provides additional support for the view that the recorded figures do in fact represent a saving in morbidity due to the typhoid vaccine.

There is evidence, as might reasonably be expected, that the decrease in morbidity was associated with a decrease in case fatality, at least so far as typhoid fever was concerned. The case-fatality rate among 1,728 inoculated and infected men in the British armies in France was 4·57 per cent. ; among 703 uninoculated men it was 18·35 per cent. Curiously enough this finding was not paralleled in paratyphoid infection : among 1,357 infected men who had been inoculated with T.A.B. vaccine the case-fatality rate was 1·25 per cent. ; among 2,694 men who had not been inoculated with T.A.B. vaccine it was 1·34 per cent. The difference in the case fatality of typhoid in inoculated and uninoculated men is borne out by the figures recorded by Pfeiffer (1922) for the German Army ; 12–20 per cent. among the uninoculated, 2–3 per cent. among the inoculated.

Ancillary evidence which may perhaps be adduced in support of the efficacy of anti-

typhoid vaccination, is provided by the curious change in the sex incidence of enteric infection in the years following the War that has been referred to on p. 1223.

In the chapter on herd immunity we described experiments on mice ; and arguing, with the necessary caveat, from mice to men, we drew the tentative conclusion that antityphoid inoculation, carried out by the best technique at present available, would form a poor substitute for the ordinary methods of sanitary control as applied to a population exposed to a severe and continuous risk of infection. There seems no reason to modify this view in the light of the recorded results on man. Inoculated men appear to do much better than inoculated mice, but they are never exposed to such severe and continuous risk. Even with their advantages in this respect there is no evidence that the inoculation of all those at risk will stamp out the disease, though it will greatly reduce both its incidence and its fatality. As a method of decreasing the chances of infection or death run by persons who are exposed to a serious but not overwhelming risk for a limited period of time, antityphoid inoculation must be regarded as a very valuable prophylactic measure.

The typhoid vaccine employed for active immunization consists of a suspension of typhoid bacilli, killed by heating to 55°–60° C. for 30 minutes to one hour, and preserved by the addition of 0·5 per cent. phenol. Usually, in order to protect against infection with *Bact. paratyphosum A* and *Bact. paratyphosum B*, these bacteria are added to the suspension, constituting the ordinary T.A.B. vaccine. A usual bacterial content is 1,000 million *Bact. typhosum*, 750 million *Bact. paratyphosum A* and 750 million *Bact. paratyphosum B* per c.c., and a usual dose is 0·5 c.c. subcutaneously, followed by 1 c.c. after an interval of 7–14 days.

It is not yet possible to standardize a bacterial vaccine in the same way as we standardize an antitoxic or antibacterial serum. We noted, in connection with the testing of diphtheria prophylactics, that the statistical difficulties involved in assessing the efficacy of any reagent used to induce an active immunity are so great that it is impracticable to make an accurate comparison with any arbitrarily selected standard preparation. In the case of diphtheria toxoid it is, however, possible to prescribe limits, assessed by a suitable animal test, within which the activity of the immunizing reagent must fall. In dealing with bacterial vaccines, it has not yet proved possible to ensure even this degree of standardization. We must, therefore, be content for the moment to state the strength of our vaccines in terms of the number of bacteria they contain ; but it will be obvious, from the experimental data recorded in earlier chapters, that we should at least insist that the strains of bacteria used in the preparation of vaccines should contain, in full measure, the antigenic components on which immunizing capacity is known to depend.

Grinnell (1932), for instance, has examined twelve cultures of the " Rawlings " strain of typhoid bacillus—a classical laboratory strain that is widely used for the preparation of typhoid vaccine—and has compared their antigenic potency with that of several recently isolated strains. Although the Rawlings cultures were not rough in the ordinarily accepted sense, several of them showed intermediate characters as judged by the ordinary cultural tests. Their virulence for mice was definitely lower than that of the recently isolated completely smooth strains. Mice were immunized by the injection of killed cultures of the Rawlings strains or of the smooth strains and were subsequently tested for resistance. In one experiment 28 of 32 mice immunized with Rawlings strains and 1 of 31 mice immunized with the completely smooth strains died as the result of the test inoculation.

In a second experiment the deaths were 55 of 60 mice immunized with the Rawlings strains and 2 of 37 mice immunized with the smooth strains (see also Grinnell 1930).

In view of the recent observations of Felix and his colleagues, however, we clearly cannot rest content with the use of smooth strains for the preparation of our vaccines ; and if we accepted all the suggestions offered by passive protection experiments in mice we might doubt whether any killed vaccine, even if prepared from a highly virulent smooth strain, would afford an effective immunity. The experiments recently recorded by Perry and his colleagues (Perry, Findlay and Bensted 1933, 1934) lead, however, to a less gloomy conclusion.

In an extensive series of experiments on mice the finding of Felix and Pitt (1934a) that smooth strains of the *Bact. typhosum* vary in their virulence, and that highly virulent strains are relatively inagglutinable by an anti-O serum, was amply confirmed. On testing the immunizing power of these strains in mice they found that it was closely related to virulence. A virulent smooth strain would induce an active immunity against infection with a similar strain, but immunization with an avirulent smooth strain was almost as ineffective as immunization with a frankly rough strain variant. So far then the findings of Perry and his colleagues are in accord with those of Felix and Pitt ; but, in the induction of active immunity in mice, no evidence was found of the extreme lability of the effective antigen. So long as the strain employed was of the fully virulent smooth type, an ordinary heat-killed vaccine proved fully effective (see also Report 1936).

It would seem, therefore, that all typhoid and paratyphoid vaccines should be prepared from strains that are (a) completely smooth, and (b) of maximum virulence for a suitable laboratory animal. It will be wise to watch the latter proviso very closely, and to take every opportunity to check the results of laboratory tests by field trials in man. We certainly cannot assume that " mouse-virulent " and " man-virulent " will in all cases be interchangeable terms, though they seem to be so in regard to the typhoid bacillus.

The Administration of Typhoid Vaccine by the Mouth.—Following the observations of Besredka (see Chapter L), several attempts have been made to induce an effective immunity in man by giving a typhoid vaccine by the mouth, usually in the form of capsules or pills, in which bile is incorporated with the bacillary bodies to ensure the passage of the latter through the mucous membrane. We know that the administration *per os* of flagellated bacilli of the typhoid-paratyphoid group leads to the appearance in the serum of O agglutinins, though the formation of H agglutinins is either entirely suppressed or very greatly reduced (see Pijper and Dau 1930, Krause-Shimkin 1931, Greenwood, Topley and Wilson 1931). Since the O antibodies are important in the production of immunity, while the H antibodies are not, effective immunization by this route would seem to be possible, though very large amounts of bacillary substances have to be given as compared with the dose necessary to stimulate antibody formation when administered by subcutaneous injection. In view of recent work we should, perhaps, consider the effect of administration by the mouth on the response to the Vi antigen.

An account of a field trial, carried out in Portuguese India, is recorded by de Mello and his colleagues (1931). Among 339 persons vaccinated by mouth 13 developed typhoid (3·25 per cent.). Among 58 unvaccinated controls 2 developed typhoid (3·45 per cent.). Such numbers, as the authors are careful to emphasize, are far too small to allow of any definite conclusion ; but the results are not encouraging. It would, at least, be unwise to abandon the ordinary subcutaneous route in favour of vaccination *per os* until we have far more extensive data from the field.

Enteric Infection in Animals.

It is impossible to consider in any detail the numerous varieties of enteric infection which are known to occur among the lower animals under natural conditions. References to the relation of the different species or types, within the typhoid-paratyphoid group, to various forms of animal infection will be found in Chapter XXVII. It may be noted that the bacterial species with which we have so far been concerned in this chapter are not natural pathogens of animals ; while the species and types which produce enteric infection in swine, rats, mice, etc., usually give rise to acute gastro-enteritis when ingested by man (see Chapter LXIX).

The rôle played by *Bact. choleræ-suis* in hog cholera is discussed in Chapter LXXXIV.

Bacillary White Diarrhœa of Chicks.—References to several papers dealing with *Bact. pullorum*, the causative organism of this disease, and with the lesions which it produces in chicks and adult fowls, will be found in Chapter XXVII. A useful review of the literature is included in a paper by Rice (1926) ; and a recent account of the epidemiology of the disease, and its control in flocks, is given by Dalling, Mason and Gordon (1928). Apart from its great economic importance, the disease is of interest in that it affords an example of congenital infection *via* the egg, and an illustration of the application of bacteriological principles in the control of infective disease among live-stock.

The first cases of disease among an infected brood usually occur soon after hatching, and the outbreak often assumes epidemic proportions within a few days or weeks. Susceptibility to the natural spread of infection, in its severe form, would seem to be confined to the first few days after hatching. The incubation period is stated to vary from 4 to 10 days, though Rice records experiments in which it was as long as 28 days. Birds which survive the first few weeks seldom contract the disease in its acutely fatal form. Apart from the whitish diarrhœa, from which the disease derives its name, but which is by no means invariably present, the symptoms consist in drowsiness, thirst, and lack of appetite. The average duration of the disease is 2 or 3 days ; and the mortality is high—on the average about 70 per cent. At necropsy the lungs may be congested : the liver is enlarged, and may, according to some observers, show an unusual degree of mottling ; the intestine usually shows well-marked catarrhal enteritis.

Birds which survive the acute attack, and probably others which have never suffered from the typical disease, frequently develop a persistent ovarian infection ; and it is carrier birds of this type which perpetuate infection from one breeding season to another. A considerable proportion of the eggs laid by such birds are infected with *Bact. pullorum* ; Kaup (quoted by Rice) records nearly 20 per cent. of infected yolks among 3,510 fresh eggs examined. Thus, in an infected flock, each year's hatchings produce a high proportion of infected chicks, and the cycle is repeated from year to year.

The problem of control clearly resolves itself into the elimination of the carrier hens and this has been rendered possible by the application of the agglutination test. Blood is obtained from the wing vein, and the serum tested against suspensions of *Bact. pullorum*. This organism is non-flagellated, and contains only O antigens : the conditions must therefore be adjusted to reveal agglutination of this type. It is customary to use living suspensions, but it seems likely that alcoholized suspensions would prove as sensitive and could more readily be standardized. Incubation should be prolonged for 24 hours, though the results are usually readable after 4 hours at 55° C. The titre usually taken as diagnostic of infection is 1 : 40 to 1 : 50. Adopting this standard, it would appear that some 90 per cent. of carrier hens can be detected (Rice 1926). Such tests may be carried out at any time, and the detected carriers should be killed. The essential point, in preventing the perpetuation of infection from one season to another, is the elimination of all carriers among the birds preserved for breeding. The whole flock should be tested when the hatching season is over ; those which show agglutinins should be killed, and those which give negative reactions should be retested. Only birds which have twice reacted negatively, and whose previous history gives no reason to suspect infection, should be retained for breeding in the following year.

REFERENCES

ALVES, W. D. (1936) *S. Afr. med. J.*, **10**, 7.
BHATNAGAR, S. S. (1935) *Brit. J. exp. Path.*, **16**, 375.
BILLET, LE BIHAN, THÉRAULT, LAMANDÉ, LUTROT, and LOUIS. (1910) *Arch. Méd. Pharm. milit.*, **55**, 259.
BLACHSTEIN. (1891) *Johns Hopk. Hosp. Bull.*, **2**, 96.
BLUMENTHAL, E. (1910) *Zbl. 'Bakt.*, **55**, 341.
BOECKER, E. (1935) *Z. Hyg. InfektKr.*, **117**, 161.
BOLE, ROSEMARY. (1935) *J. Lab. clin. Med.*, **20**, 638.
BOUCHER, S. (1927) *Med. Offr*, **38**, 8.
BRION, A. and KAYSER, H. (1906) *Dtsch. Arch. klin. Med.*, **85**, 525.
BROWNING, C. H., with COULTHARD, H. L., CRUICKSHANK, R., GUTHRIE, K. J., and SMITH, R. P. (1933) *Spec. Rep. Ser. med. Res. Coun., Lond.*, No. 179.
BRÜCKNER. (1910) *Arb. ReichsgesundhAmt.*, **33**, 435.
BUDD, W. (1856) *Lancet*, ii. 618, 694 ; (1873) "Typhoid Fever." London.
BULL, C. G. (1915) *J. exp. Med.*, **22**, 475.
BULLOUGH, W. A. (1931) *Rep. med. Offr Hlth, Essex*, for year 1931, pp. 14–19.
BUXTON, B. H. (1907a) *J. med. Res.*, **16**, 17 ; (1907b) *Ibid.*, **16**, 250.
CHAUFFARD, A., ACHARD, and SERGENT. (1921) *Bull. Acad. Méd., Paris*, **85**, 84, 89, 182, 445.
CHIARI, H. (1894) *Zbl. Bakt.*, **15**, 648.
CHIAROLANZA, R. (1909) *Z. Hyg. InfektKr.*, **62**, 11.
COLEMAN, W. and BUXTON, B. H. (1907) *Amer. J. med. Sci.*, **133**, 896.
CONRADI. (1907) *Klin. Wschr.*, **17**, 273.
CREIGHTON, C. (1894) "A History of Epidemics in Britain." Camb. Univ. Press.
DALLING, T., MASON, J. E., and GORDON, W. S. (1928) *Vet. J.*, **83**, 555.
DOERR, R. (1905) *Zbl. Bakt.*, **39**, 624.
DOWNIE, A. W. and FAIRBROTHER, R. W. (1934) *Brit. med. J.*, i. 55.
DREYER, G. and INMAN, A. C. (1917) *Lancet*, i. 365.
DREYER, G. and WALKER, E. W. A. (1916) *Lancet*, ii. 419.
DREYER, G., WALKER, E. W. A., and GIBSON, A. G. (1915) *Lancet*, i. 324.
DRIGALSKI, VON. (1904) *Zbl. Bakt.*, **35**, 776.
DROBA. (1889) *Wien. klin. Wschr.*, **12**, 1141.
DUDGEON, L. S. (1908) *Lancet*, ii. 1651.
EBERTH, C. J. (1880) *Virchows Arch.*, **81**, 58.
FAICHNIE, N. (1909) *J. R. Army med. Cps*, **13**, 580, 672.
FELIX, A. (1924a) *Z. ImmunForsch.*, **39**, 127 ; (1924b) *J. Immunol.*, **9**, 115 ; (1930) *Lancet*, i. 505 ; (1935) *Ibid.*, i 799.
FELIX, A. and BHATNAGAR, S. S. (1935) *Brit. J. exp. Path.*, **16**, 422.
FELIX, A., BHATNAGAR, S. S., and PITT, R. M. (1934) *Brit. J. exp. Path.*, **15**, 346.
FELIX, A. and OLITZKI, L. (1928) *J. Hyg., Camb.*, **28**, 55.
FELIX, A. and PITT, R. M. (1934a) *J. Path. Bact.*, **38**, 409 ; (1934b) *Lancet*, ii. 186 ; (1935) *J. Hyg., Camb.*, **35**, 428 ; (1936) *Brit. J. exp. Path.*, **17**, 81.
FICKER, M. (1903) *Arch. Hyg.*, **46**, 274.

FINDLAY, J. W. and BUCHANAN, R. M. (1906) *Glasg. med. J.*, **65**, 177.
FIRTH, R. H. and HORROCKS, W. H. (1902) *Brit. med. J.*, ii. 936.
FLIS, S. and ROSENBERG, J. (1934) *C. R. Soc. Biol.*, **117**, 538.
FÖRSTER. (1908) *Münch. med. Wschr.*, **55**, 1.
FROSCH. (1903) *Festsch. 60 Geburtst. R. Koch*, p. 691. Jena.
FÜTTERER, VON. (1888) *Münch. med. Wschr.*, **35**, 316.
GAEHTGENS, W. and BRÜCKNER, G. (1909) *Zbl. Bakt.*, **53**, 559.
GAFFKY. (1884) *Mitt. ReichsgesundhAmt.*, **2**, 372.
GARDNER, A. D. (1920) *Lancet*, ii. 494 ; (1921) *J. Hyg., Camb.*, **19**, 333 ; (1929) *Ibid.*, **28**, 376.
GARDNER, A. D. and STUBINGTON, E. F. (1932) *J. Hyg., Camb.*, **32**, 516.
GARDNER, A. D., HOBSON, F. G., and STENHOUSE, G. (1930) *Lancet*, i. 182.
GAY, F. P. (1918) " Typhoid Fever." New York.
GAY, F. P. and CLAYPOLE, E. J. (1913) *Arch. intern. Med.*, **12**, 621.
GIGLIOLI, G. (1930) *J. Hyg., Camb.*, **29**, 273 ; (1933a) *Ibid.*, **33**, 379 ; (1933b) *Ibid.*, **33**, 387.
GILBERT, A. and GIRODE, J. (1890) *Sem. méd.*, **10**, 481.
GILL, D. G. (1927) *J. Amer. med. Ass.*, **89**, 1198.
GODFREY, E. S. (1928) *Amer. J. publ. Hlth.*, **18**, 616.
GRAHAM-SMITH, G. S. (1910) *Rep. loc. Govt Bd publ. Hlth*, **16**, 9.
GRASSET, E. (1930) *J. med. Ass. S. Afr.*, **4**, 380 ; (1931) *C. R. Soc. Biol.*, **106**, 810.
GREENWOOD, M., TOPLEY, W. W. C., and WILSON, J. (1931) *J. Hyg., Camb.*, **31**, 484.
GREENWOOD, M. and YULE, G. U. (1915) *Proc. R. Soc. Med.*, **8**, Sect. Epidem., 113.
GRINNELL, F. B. (1930) *J. Immunol.*, **19**, 457 ; (1932) *J. exp. Med.*, **56**, 907.
GRÜNBAUM, A. S. (1896) *Lancet*, ii. 806, 1747.
HAHN, M. (1926) *Mon. epidem. Rep. Hlth. Sect., L.o.N.*, **5**, 740.
HARVEY, D. (1929) "A System of Bacteriology," *Med. Res. Coun., Lond.*, **4**, 1.
HORGAN, E. S. (1932) *J. Hyg., Camb.*, **32**, 523 ; (1935) *Ibid.*, **35**, 38.
HORTON-SMITH, P. (1900) *Brit. med. J.*, i. 827.
HUEPPE. (1886) *Fortschr. Med.*, **4**, 447.
HUXHAM, J. (1739) " Essay on Fevers." London.
JOCHMANN. (1914) " Lehrbuch der Infektionskrankheiten." Berlin.
JOHNSTON, J. A. (1912) *J. med. Res.*, **27**, 177.
JONES, E. R. (1936) *J. Path. Bact.*, **42**, 455.
KAUFFMANN, F. (1930–31) *Zbl. Bakt.*, **119**, 148 ; (1935) *Quart. Bull. Hlth Org. L. of N., Geneva*, **4**, 482 ; (1935–6a) *Z. Hyg. InfektKr.*, **117**, 26 ; (1935–6b) *Ibid.*, **117**, 778 ; (1936) *Ibid.*, **118**, 318.
KAYSER, H. (1907) *Arb. ReichsgesundhAmt.*, **25**, 223.
KLINGER, P. (1906) *Arb. ReichsgesundhAmt.*, **25**, 223 ; (1909) *Ibid.*, **30**, 584.
KNORR, M. (1927a) *Münch. med. Wschr.*, **74**, 1761 ; (1927b) *Ibid.*, **74**, 1945.
KOCH, J. (1909) *Z. Hyg. InfektKr.*, **62**, 1.
KRAUSE-SHIMKIN, ESTHER. (1931) *Zbl. Bakt.*, **121**, 277.
LEDINGHAM, J. C. G. and ARKWRIGHT, J. A. (1912) " The Carrier Problem in Infectious Diseases." London.
LEMIERRE, A. and ABRAMI, P. (1907) *C. R. Soc. Biol.*, **63**, 252.
LENTZ. (1905) *Klin. Jb.*, **14**, 475.
LEVY, E. and GAEHTGENS, W. (1908) *Arb. ReichgesundhAmt.*, **28**, 168.
LEWIN, W. (1934) *S. Afr. med. J.*, **8**, 731.
LÜDKE. (1909) *Münch. med. Wschr.*, **56**, 57.
McMASTER, A. B. (1926) *Publ. Hlth.*, **39**, 177.
MAYER, G. (1910) *Zbl. Bakt.*, **53**, 234.
MALLORY, F. B. (1898) *J. exp. Med.*, **3**, 611.
MELLO, F. DE et al. (1931) *Arquivas da Escola Méd. Cirurg. de Nova Goa*. Ser. A., No. 6, p. 767.
MEYER, K. F. and STICKEL, J. E. (1918) *J. infect. Dis.*, **23**, 48.
MINELLI, S. (1906) *Zbl. Bakt.*, **41**, 406.
MORGAN, H. DE R. (1911) *J. Hyg., Camb.*, **11**, 202.
MUDD, S. (1932) *J. Immunol.*, **23**, 81.
MULLER, L. (1923) *C. R. Soc. Biol.*, **89**, 434.
NEUHAUS. (1886) *Berl. klin. Wschr.*, **23**, 89.
NICHOLS, H. J. (1916) *J. exp. Med.*, **24**, 497.
NIVEN, J. (1910) *Proc. R. Soc. Med.*, **3**, Sect. Epidem., 131.
OLITZKI, L. (1928) *Z. ImmunForsch.*, **55**, 445.
ØRSKOV, J., JENSEN, K. A., and KOBAYASHI, K. (1928) *Z. ImmunForsch.*, **55**, 34.
PARK, W. H. and WILLIAMS, A. W. (1925) " Pathogenic Organisms." New York.
PERRY, H. M. (1918) *Lancet*, i. 593.
PERRY, H. M., FINDLAY, H. T., and BENSTED, H. J. (1933) *J. R. Army med. Cps*, **60**, 241 ; (1934) *Ibid.*, **63**, 1.

PETIT and SERRES. (18_3) "Traité de la fièvre entéromésentérique." Paris.
PFEIFFER, R. (1885) *Dts-h. med. Wschr.*, **11**, 500 ; (1922) *Hdb. ärztl. Erfahrung. Weltkriege*, **7**, 327.
PFEIFFER, R. and KOLLE, W. (1896) *Dtsch. med. Wschr.*, **22**, 735.
PIJPER, A. (1930) *J. Hyg.*, *Camb.*, **29**, 380.
PIJPER, A. and DAU, H. (1930) *Brit. J. exp. Path.*, **11**, 112.
PRATT. (1901) *Amer. J. med. Sci.*, **122**, 584.
PRIGGE, R. (1909) *Klin. Jb.*, **22**, 245.
PROST, P. A. (1804) " Médicine éclairée par l'observation et l'ouverture des corps." Paris.
REED, VAUGHAN, and SHAKESPEARE. (1899) *Abs. Rep. Typhoid Fever in U.S. military Camps—Spanish War* 1898. Wash.
Reports. (1913) *Antityphoid Com.. G.B.*, London ; (1927) *Mon. epidem. Rep. Hlth. Sect. L. of N.*, **6**, 451 ; (1935) *Amer. J. publ. Hlth.*, **26**, 219.
RICE. (1926) *Ann. Rep. nat. vet. med. Ass.*, *G.B.I.*, p. 57.
RICHARDSON, M. W. (1899) *J. Boston Soc. med. Sci.*, **3**, 79.
ROSENAU, M. J., LUMSDEN, L. L., and KASTLE, J. H. (1909) *Bull. U.S. hyg. Lab.*, No. 52.
ROSHER, A. B. and FIELDEN, H. A. (1922) *Lancet*, i. 1088.
SCHÄFER, W. (1935) *Zbl. Bakt.*, **133**, 458.
SCHOENLEIN, J. L. (1839) " Allgemeine und specielle Pathologie und Therapie." Freiburg.
SCHÜDER. (1901) *Z. Hyg. InfektKr.*, **38**, 343.
SCOTT, H. H. (1915) *Ann. trop. Med. Parasit.*, **9**, 239.
SEMPLE, D. and GREIG, F. D. W. (1908) *Sci. Mem. med. sanit. Dep. India*, No. 32.
SILBERSTEIN, W. (1929) *Z. Hyg. InfektKr.*, **110**, 129.
SMITH, J. (1932) *J. Hyg.*, *Camb.*, **32**, 143.
SMITH, J. and SCOTT, W. M. (1930) *J. Hyg.*, *Camb.*, **30**, 32.
SMITH, M. M., McVIE, M H., and NEWBOLD, E. (1930) *J. Hyg.*, *Camb.*, **30**, 55.
SOMAN, D. W. (1932) *Indian med. Gaz.*, **67**, 15 ; (1934) *Ibid.*, **69**, 572.
STUART, G. and KRIKORIAN, K. S. (1928) *J. Hyg.*, *Camb.*, **28**, 105.
TEAGUE, O. and CLURMAN, A. W. (1916) *J. infect. Dis.*, **18**, 647 ; (1916–17) *J. med. Res.*, **35**, 107.
TOPLEY, W. W. C. (1920) *Lancet*, i. 477, 531, 645.
TOPLEY, W. W. C. and FIELDEN, H. A. (1922) *Lancet*, ii. 1164.
TOPLEY, W. W. C., PLATTS, S. G., and IMRIE, C. G. (1920) *Spec. Rep. Ser. med. Res. Coun.*, *Lond.*, No. 48.
VILCHUR. (1887) " Etiology and Clinical Bacteriology of Typhoid Fever." St. Petersb.
WALDHECKER, M. (1935) *Z. Hyg. InfektKr.*, **117**, 679.
WEIGMANN, F. (1926) *Z. Hyg. InfektKr.*, **106**, 650.
WEINFURTER, F. (1915) *Zbl. Bakt.*, **75**, 379.
WIDAL, F. (1896) *Bull. mém. Soc. Hôp.*, *Paris*, **6**, 26.
WILLIS, T. (1659) " De Febribus." London.
WILSON, W. J. and BLAIR, E. M. McV. (1927) *J. Hyg.*, *Camb.*, **26**, 374 ; (1931) *Ibid.*, **31**, 138.
WRIGHT, A. E. (1902) *Lancet*, ii. 651 ; (1908) *Zbl. Bakt.*, **46**, 188.
WRIGHT, A. E. and SEMPLE, D. (1897) *Brit. med. J.*, i. 256.
WYLLIE, J. (1932) *J. Hyg.*, *Camb.*, **32**, 375.

CHAPTER LXVII

BACILLARY DYSENTERY

INTRODUCTORY

TOGETHER with plague, cholera, and influenza, dysentery has been one of the great scourges of the world. Though rapidly growing less common, it was at one time a fatal epidemic disease, dogging the footsteps of armies in the field, present in camp, gaol, and hospital, and decimating the white races in the tropics. " Wherever the general hygienic conditions are bad, wherever the soil is much fouled by excreta . . . , wherever many people are crowded together in one building or camp, where the food is coarse, monotonous or unsound, there, especially in tropical and sub-tropical climates," dysentery is liable to break out (Manson 1914).

Before the last quarter of the nineteenth century dysentery was regarded as a single, well-defined disease. In 1875, however, Loesch demonstrated the presence of parasitic amœbæ in the stools of dysenteric patients, and in 1883 Robert Koch observed these amœbæ in the intestinal wall of patients dying of dysentery in Egypt. The subsequent demonstration of amœbæ in liver abscesses of patients who were then suffering, or who had at some previous time suffered, from dysentery left little doubt that at any rate one of the causal agents of this disease was the *Entamœba histolytica*. In 1898–1901 Shiga in Japan, Flexner in the Philippines, and Kruse in Germany brought evidence to show that another type of the disease was due to a bacillus which was closely allied to *Bact. typhosum*. Yet another type has been referred to infection with the *Balantidium coli*—one of the Infusoria.

In this chapter we shall deal exclusively with bacillary dysentery, referring our readers to textbooks on tropical medicine and protozoology for descriptions of the amœbic and balantidial types.

Historical.—Dysentery affords an illuminating example of a case in which the agglutination reaction was successfully employed to discover the causative agent of a disease.

Studying the epidemic of dysentery in Japan in 1896, Shiga (1898) isolated from the fæces and intestinal wall of dysenteric patients a Gram-negative, non-gelatin-liquefying coliform bacillus. This organism, which was cultivated from 34 patients, differed from the common *Bact. coli* in its failure to coagulate milk, and in certain other cultural properties. At the same time nine other organisms were cultivated. To ascertain which of them, if any, was causally related to the disease, Shiga tested the action of the patient's serum on each one of them. Only one of the types was agglutinated. This type was, moreover, never found in the fæces of patients suffering from other intestinal diseases such as typhoid or simple diarrhœa, nor was it agglutinated by the serum of such patients, or by the serum of healthy persons. In the acute stage of dysentery it was present in almost pure

1231

culture in the blood-and-mucus stools ; but during convalescence its isolation was difficult or impossible. This bacillus he called *Bact. dysenteriæ*. Though fatal to laboratory animals injected parenterally, it did not reproduce the characteristic symptoms of dysentery when given by the mouth.

In 1900 Flexner (1900*a*, *b*), then a member of the Commission sent out by the Johns Hopkins University to study the diseases prevailing in the Philippine Islands, reported the discovery of a bacillus closely resembling Shiga's.

A similar organism was discovered, also in 1900, by Strong and Musgrave working at Manila. In the same year Kruse (1900) in Germany described a bacillus that he had isolated from the fæces of 23 out of 24 patients suffering from dysentery.

There was at first considerable confusion with regard to the relation of these various strains to one another. This was finally elucidated by the investigations of Martini and Lentz (1902), who found that a serum prepared by the injection of a goat with Shiga's strain agglutinated Shiga, Kruse, and one of Flexner's strains (New Haven), but failed to react with Flexner's other strains (1 and Manila) or with Strong's bacillus. On the other hand, a serum prepared against Flexner I agglutinated Flexner I and Flexner Manila, but not Strong, Flexner New Haven, Shiga or Kruse. They likewise found that all of these bacilli were non-motile and non-flagellated. On a serological basis, therefore, they concluded that Shiga, Kruse, and Flexner New Haven were identical, and differed from Flexner I, Flexner Manila, and Strong ; these two Flexner strains likewise differed from Strong's bacillus. This conclusion received striking confirmation from the further work of Lentz (1902) ; testing the sugar reactions of the dysentery bacilli, he was struck by the observation that Flexner I, Flexner Manila, and Strong all produced acid in mannitol, whereas Shiga, Kruse, and Flexner New Haven did not.

Lentz's work served to divide the dysentery bacilli into (1) the non-mannitol-fermenters—Shiga and Kruse ; and (2) the mannitol-fermenters—Flexner I and Manila, and Strong. The former group was called the Shiga or the Shiga-Kruse group, the latter the Flexner group. (It is clear that Flexner isolated both the Shiga and Flexner types in the Philippines ; but the one that bears his name is exclusively the mannitol-fermenting type.)

It will be noted that without the agglutination reaction it would have been extremely difficult to prove the ætiological rôle of the dysentery bacillus. This organism, unlike *Bact. typhosum*, does not invade the blood stream, and cannot therefore be cultured from the blood. It does not reproduce the disease on injection into animals ; and by cultural properties alone it is not easily distinguishable from closely allied organisms. The agglutination reaction, in conjunction with the invariable presence of this bacillus in the acute stages of epidemic dysentery, sufficed to differentiate it from other organisms and to indicate its pathogenicity to man.

Besides the Shiga-Kruse and the Flexner group, numerous other organisms have been found capable of giving rise to dysentery, such as *Bact. sonnei*, Schmitz's bacillus (*Bact. ambiguum*), and the Newcastle bacillus (see pp. 1235–1237 and Chapter XXVII).

Epidemiology.

Bacillary dysentery is primarily an epidemic disease ; but like most epidemic diseases it frequently occurs endemically. At the present time it is more common in tropical than in temperate climates, but this is largely due to the lack of adequate sanitation. In former times, when sanitary measures were not so well enforced as they are now, dysentery was widespread all over Europe ; and in our own times it needed only a war with its accompanying indifferent sanitation to allow it to become rampant again. Wherever large numbers of men are in close contact for any length of time under poor hygienic conditions, dysentery is liable to break out. Thus it has always been, and to a certain extent still is, a disease of armies, gaols, hospitals, and asylums. Amœbic dysentery, on the other hand, occurs sporadically, and is mainly confined to tropical countries.

Epidemic Dysentery.—According to Rogers (1913) bacillary dysentery in India shows a characteristic seasonal incidence. During the cold months of January and February, the incidence is at a minimum. With the onset of the hot weather in March there is a small rise, followed, however, by a fall during the very hot months of May and June. The maximum increase follows closely the commencement of the heavy monsoon rains in July, rising to its highest point in August and September. With the cessation of the rains late in October and the fall of temperature, the incidence steadily declines. It is of interest to note that the months when dysentery is most common are also the months when flies are most abundant.

Working in Fiji, Manson-Bahr (see Bahr 1912) obtained evidence that infection was carried to some extent by the horse fly. The fly population was at its maximum when dysentery was most prevalent. Ample opportunity existed for contamination of the food ; and *Bact. shigæ* was actually isolated from the lower intestinal tract of two flies caught on the bed of a patient suffering from acute dysentery. This suggestion received confirmation from the careful work of Taylor (1919) during the War. In the Salonika Expeditionary Force the maximum incidence of dysentery corresponded closely to the maximum prevalence of flies. The conditions of temperature and humidity most favourable for fly breeding occurred between the middle of April and the middle of June, and again between the middle of September and the end of October. Corresponding to this, the peak of the dysentery curve was reached at the end of May and at the end of October. During the hot dry weather of July, August, and early September, both the fly prevalence and the dysentery incidence curves fell practically to zero (Fig. 260). Experiments made to test the ability of flies to carry dysentery bacilli showed that these insects, after feeding on milk cultures or on dysenteric fæces, might remain infective for 24 hours. Of 1,670 flies caught under natural conditions, 1 from a hospital kitchen was carrying *Bact. shigæ*, and 8 were carrying Flexner's bacillus. Manson-Bahr (1919) likewise isolated *Bact. shigæ* from the lower intestine of flies in Palestine.

From this and other evidence it would appear that flies constitute an important agency in the epidemic spread of bacillary dysentery. Though organisms may be found occasionally in the intestinal contents of these insects, they do not appear to survive for more than a few days, and the probability is that flies act mainly by carrying infective material on their feet rather than in their intestine.

Important as they are, flies are not the only method by which epidemic spread is occasioned. Infection may be carried by milk, and several well-authenticated outbreaks due to this method of transit have now been recorded in different countries. Under exceptionally favourable conditions, it is possible that the disease may be water-borne, but the evidence does not suggest that large outbreaks are often determined by this means.

It may be noted that in every outbreak of dysentery there are a number of cases of simple diarrhœa. Many of these are really mild infections with the dysentery bacillus (Graham 1918, Fitz-Gerald 1921).

In different outbreaks of dysentery both the morbidity and the mortality rates are subject to great variation. Amako (1908) mentions that in 1893 the incidence of dysentery in the town of Kobe in Japan was 12·12 per 1,000 ; in 1905 it had dropped to 2·3 per 1,000. The case-mortality rate in Japan in 1895 was 24·5 per cent. ; in 1900 it was 22·1 per cent. (Shiga 1901) ; in well-treated cases in Europe

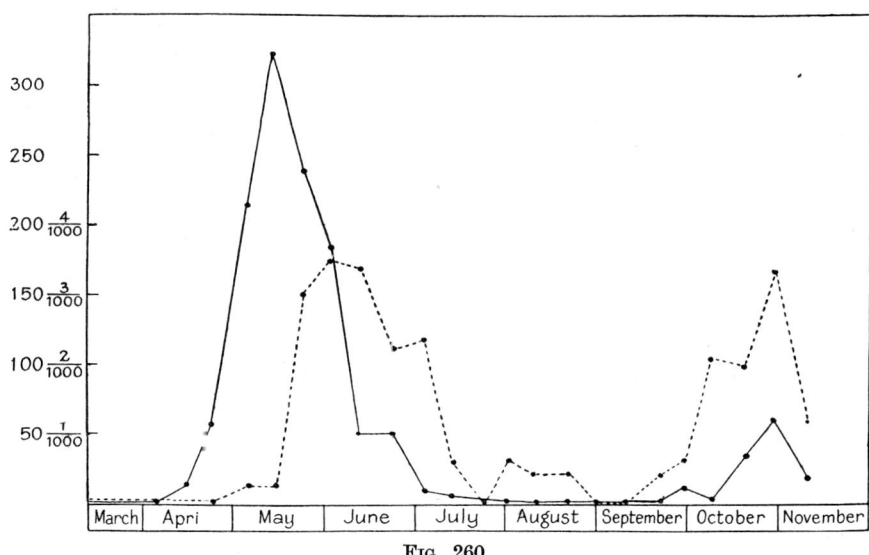

FIG. 260.

Showing the relationship between the prevalence of flies and the incidence of dysentery in the Salonika Expeditionary Force.

Continuous curve = Number of flies trapped *per diem.*
Interrupted curve = Incidence of dysentery cases per 1,000 *per diem.*
(After Taylor.)

it is as low as 0·3 per cent. (Graham 1918). Though detailed statistics are not available, there appears to be a consensus of opinion that dysentery due to *Bact. shigœ* is more fatal than that due to Flexner's or Sonne's bacillus.

Endemic and Asylum Dysentery.—Endemic dysentery occurs not only in tropical regions, but in many countries of the temperate zone. Its frequency is difficult to assess, and its very presence, as Bojlén (1934) has pointed out, may be almost entirely overlooked. The careful study carried out by Bojlén in Denmark seems to show that in that country the disease is widespread and of frequent occurrence. It may occur in any month of the year, though it is commonest between May and August. The sexes are attacked equally, but there is a very definite age distribution, the disease being most frequent in children of 1 to 10 years. The case mortality is about 2 per cent. Of the patients who recover, 2·7 per cent. are said to suffer from chronic colitis. The evidence suggests that infection is spread by means of convalescent carriers, by mild cases of dysentery, and perhaps by chronic dysentery carriers.

Asylum dysentery is a particular form of the endemic disease occurring in a closed community. It is to Kruse (1901) that its recognition as an infectious disease was mainly due. In this country Mott (1901–02) made a careful study of the condition from its clinical and epidemiological aspects. More recently Bojlén (1934) has carried out an extensive series of observations in Denmark. He finds that, in contrast to endemic dysentery in the general population, asylum dysentery is characterized by a high case mortality, varying from about 10 to 20 per cent. Relapses, and probably re-infections, are very common, and as many as 50 per cent. of the inmates may suffer from chronic dysentery. Persistent carriers are met with, and together with the numerous patients suffering or recovering from dysentery, they provide a continual source of infective material which is responsible for the further propagation of the disease. Spread of infection by carriers is of course rendered particularly easy owing to the lack of personal hygiene among the insane.

Bacteriological Findings in Different Epidemics.—One of the striking features of the bacteriology of dysentery is that in any large epidemic it is almost invariable to find bacilli of more than one type. A pure *shigæ* or a pure *flexneri* epidemic on a large scale appears to be a rarity, though in small outbreaks a single type may alone be isolated (Kruse *et al.* 1907). Not only so, but in any large outbreak, besides the well-defined Shiga and Flexner bacilli, it is usual to isolate a number of other organisms. In the past these have been referred to as para-Shiga, in-agglutinable Flexner, or more generally para-dysentery bacilli. Our increasing knowledge has served to classify many of these organisms into Schmitz, Sonne, and Newcastle types. There remain, however, a number of strains whose exact classification is at present doubtful, and whose rôle in the causation of dysentery still awaits elucidation. Where the disease is endemic, only one or two types may be involved, and in institutions only a single type may be found.

In different epidemics, in different countries, and at different times, the proportion of cases due to different bacillary types varies considerably; and even in the same epidemic the results of different observers may show a marked dissimilarity in this respect. In the British Salonika Force, Dudgeon (1919) and his co-workers obtained the following distribution of organisms in bacteriologically positive cases of dysentery (Table CXXXI):

TABLE CXXXI

	No. of Cases.	Percentage.
Bact. shigæ	335	38·3
Bact. flexneri Y . . .	503	57·6
Other Types	36	4·1

That is to say, Flexner's bacillus was half as common again as *Bact. shigæ*. But Graham (1918) and his co-workers, who investigated 2,500 cases of dysentery and diarrhœa in the British Salonika Force at much the same time—June, 1916, to the end of 1917—found that of the bacillary dysenteries 75 per cent. were due to *Bact. shigæ* and only 25 per cent. to *Bact. flexneri* Y.

Clinically the disease due to Shiga's bacillus is much more severe than that due to Flexner's; as well as the abdominal pain, diarrhœa and tenesmus, there is often a profound toxæmia ending in collapse. Complications such as arthritis (Graham 1919, Report 1919) and iridocyclitis, when they do occur, are almost invariably associated with the Shiga type of infection. Moreover, recovery from dysentery due to *Bact. shigæ* is a slow process ; frequently the patients remain debilitated for months, and on attempting to resume work are liable to relapse (Fletcher and Mackinnon 1919). This corresponds with the result of animal experiments, which show that Shiga's bacillus is much the more toxic organism of the two.

Besides the historically well-known Shiga and Flexner types, a number of other types have been recognized of late years. Some of these play a very important part in the causation of dysentery, particularly of the endemic and institutional variety. Three of these require attention.

Schmitz's Bacillus.—This was described by Schmitz (1917), and called *B. ambiguus* by Andrewes (1918). It was first encountered (with the possible exception of an American outbreak, see Park and Carey 1903) as the cause of an epidemic of dysentery in a Roumanian Prisoners of War Camp. The morbidity rate was high —10 per cent.—but the deaths were few. The bacillus, which, it will be remembered, differs from *Bact. shigæ* in producing indole, was isolated from a number of the patients. It was agglutinated by their serum to a titre of 1/500 to 1/1,000 ; Shiga's bacillus was likewise agglutinated to much the same titre, but Flexner's bacillus only to between 1/200 and 1/500. Apparently the bacillus was able to give rise to the production of group agglutinins, which were especially active towards *Bact. shigæ*. Incidentally it is interesting to remark that the epidemic occurred in the depth of the very severe winter of 1916–17, and indeed reached its maximum in January of the latter year. There is little doubt from Schmitz's account that the insanitary conditions prevailing in the camp were sufficient to explain the spread of the disease. This bacillus has now been found in other countries (see Mandry 1935, Boyd 1936). It is rarely responsible for more than a minority of the cases in any given area.

Sonne's Bacillus.—This is a more important organism. Though it had undoubtedly been previously observed in the United States and Germany, it was Sonne's description in 1915 that drew serious attention to it. From a number of sporadic cases of dysentery in Denmark Sonne cultivated a bacillus differing from *Bact. flexneri* in its late fermentation of lactose, in its marked production of acid in litmus milk during the second week of incubation, and in its different serological reactions. In an investigation of dysentery in Norway, Thjøtta (1919) found that 25 out of 65 strains isolated conformed to the Sonne type. More recent work in Denmark (Bojlén 1934) has shown that *Bact. sonnei* is as common as *Bact. flexneri* in the causation of endemic and institutional dysentery. In this country the organism has been often encountered (see Channon 1926, Kerrin and Cruickshank 1926, Fyfe 1927, Hay 1930, Cann and de Navasquez 1931, MacGill and Downie 1932, Pickles 1932). It seems to be very common in the United States and Canada (see Johnston and Brown 1930, Nelson 1930, Leahy 1931, Nabarro and Signy 1932, Felsen and Osofsky 1934), and has been observed in several other parts of the world. It is most frequently met with in endemic dysentery, particularly in asylums, children's hospitals, and nurses' homes. In infants it may give rise to an acute toxic form of dysentery, which in Japan is known as *Ekiri*. The disease may, however, occur in epidemic form, and several milk-borne outbreaks have been described (see Sylvest 1933, Bojlén 1934, Felsen and Osofsky 1934). Leuchs and Heim (1930) report an outbreak involving 51 persons due to infected cheese. Clinically, Sonne dysentery is said by some observers to be less severe than Flexner dysentery, but Bojlén (1934) disputes this. Mild and atypical cases of the disease are common in any reasonably large outbreak. Bacteriologically, the organisms are found in the fæces, while agglutinins are often demonstrable in the blood serum of patients suffering from the acute disease. The closely related organism, *Bact. dispar*, has so far not been definitely incriminated as a cause of dysentery, but further observations are required (see Forsyth 1933). The fact that some indole-positive strains were isolated by Felsen and Osofsky (1934) from a hospital outbreak of dysentery suggests that this organism cannot be dismissed as a possible cause of the disease.

Newcastle Bacillus.—This organism was first recognized as a cause of dysentery by Clayton and Warren (1929*a*, *b*) in Newcastle ; it has been since found in other parts of England, in Nigeria, and in India (see Downie, Wade, and Young 1933, Whitehead and Scott 1934, Boyd 1936). Owing to the facts that it usually forms gas, though only in very small quantity, and that it may be motile on first isolation, it has probably been overlooked or discounted in the past as a possible cause of dysentery.

Another organism of which mention must be made is *Bact. alkalescens*. Whether this organism is capable of giving rise to real dysentery is doubtful. Since, however, it has been isolated from the blood stream of a woman with puerperal fever (Smith and Fraser 1928), and has been found in an institutional outbreak of food-poisoning (Welch and Mickle 1934), its occasional pathogenicity for man must probably be accepted.

The rôle of Morgan's No. 1 bacillus—*Proteus morgani*—is likewise doubtful. Douglas and Colebrook (1917) found it in 29 per cent. of patients who had contracted dysentery in Gallipoli, while Candler and Dean (1911) isolated it from 5 out of 16 patients suffering from asylum dysentery. It seems to be an organism that is capable of multiplying in the intestine under suitable conditions, but it can hardly be ranked along with the Shiga, Flexner, and Sonne types as a primary cause of dysentery.

In an examination of 6,217 strains of dysentery bacilli isolated in India during the years 1932–34, Boyd (1936) observed the following distribution :

Bact. flexneri .	55·0 per cent.
Bact. shigæ .	14·9 ,,
Bact. sonnei .	9·4 ,,
Bact. ambiguum	5·4 ,,
Newcastle bacillus .	4·4 ,,
Other types and inagglutinable strains .	11·0 ,,

Dysentery Carriers.—Patients recovering from an acute attack of dysentery may continue to excrete the bacilli in their stools. Generally this excretion lasts for only a week or so, but a small proportion become persistent carriers. Fletcher and Mackinnon (1919), who during the War had unrivalled opportunities for studying the carrier condition in a depot for dysentery convalescents, found that of 935 patients 71 or 7·59 per cent. were carriers, and that 26 or 2·78 per cent. were persistent carriers. (They defined " persistent carrier " as one who carried the bacilli for more than 3 months after the beginning of the disease.) Of the 71 carriers 58 were carriers of Flexner's and 13 of Shiga's bacillus. Between these two classes there were striking differences. All the *shigæ* carriers belonged to the persistent group, whereas only 13 of the *flexneri* carriers were persistent excreters. The *shigæ* carriers excreted the bacilli with greater constancy than did the *flexneri* carriers ; thus out of 469 samples of fæces from *shigæ* carriers the bacillus was isolated 207 times, or once in every 2·26 specimens ; whereas of 1,803 samples from *flexneri* carriers the bacillus was found only 330 times, or once in every 5·46 specimens. The *flexneri* carriers had a tendency to be intermittent ; the bacillus was excreted for one or two days in succession, and then not again for a month or more ; it was then excreted once more, only to disappear again after a few days. Even more striking was the clinical difference between the two series. The *shigæ* carriers looked ill and suffered from chronic dysentery and extreme mental depression ; the *flexneri* carriers, on the other hand, were in moderately good health and were comparatively cheerful. This is to be attributed in part at least to the frequent relapses to which the *shigæ* carriers were subject ; no sooner had their diarrhœa ceased and their general condition improved, than the slightest dietetic indiscretion or resumption of exercise or work brought on again an acute attack of the disease. The conclusions to be drawn from these observations are that dysentery due to *Bact. shigæ* is altogether a more serious condition than that due to *Bact. flexneri,* and that its liability to become chronic renders it a source of prolonged invalidity. Both classes of carriers are, however, a danger to the community, and every practicable step should be taken to avoid their spreading the disease.

Studying institutional dysentery in Denmark due to *Bact. flexneri* and *Bact. sonnei,* Bojlén (1934) was struck by the frequency of persistent carriers. Some patients, whose stools were systematically examined, were found to excrete the bacilli for years. It seems probable that chronic carriers are not infrequent, and play an important part in maintaining the endemic state of the disease.

In conclusion it is worth while comparing dysentery with other enteric infections, notably typhoid. Dysentery has a short incubation period, about 48 hours as a rule. It is essentially a local disease ; the bacilli remain confined to the intestine and to the mesenteric glands ; they do not invade the blood stream, nor are they, except occasionally, found in the spleen or liver. In this respect dysentery—of the *shigæ* type—has been compared to diphtheria ; the bacilli produce a necrosis of the intestinal mucosa, often with pseudo-membrane formation, and their toxic products are absorbed, giving rise to profound systemic disturbance. The disease may also run a chronic course. Typhoid fever, on the other hand, has a long incubation period—up to 21 days ; it is primarily a septicæmic disease with secondary localization in the intestine ; the bacilli do not produce a soluble exotoxin ; and the disease has little tendency to become chronic.

Laboratory Infection in Man.—It has been pointed out in Chapter XXVII that, with the possible exception of monkeys, dysentery cannot be reproduced in laboratory animals. There are, however, a few definite cases recorded in the literature of experimental infection in human beings. Kruse (1901) mentions the case of Dr. Stöcker, an assistant in his laboratory at Bonn, who apparently infected himself while working with cultures of Shiga's bacillus. He suffered from a mild attack of the disease ; the bacilli were isolated from his stools ; and a typical rise and subsequent fall were observed in his blood agglutinins. For several years previously there had been no dysentery in the town. Flexner (1900b) likewise records the case of a laboratory assistant at Baltimore, who aspirated a fluid culture of the Flexner Manila strain into his mouth. He spat it out and rinsed his mouth with weak phenol, but within 48 hours he had severe diarrhœa, pain, and tenesmus, with blood and mucus in his stools. Unfortunately no cultures were made.

since it is probable that these are responsible for spreading infection. Dysentery bacilli, however, are often excreted intermittently, and the detection of all carriers is notoriously difficult. It seems necessary, if success is to be obtained, to isolate all patients with diarrhœa, dysentery, or chronic colitis, independent of the bacteriological findings (see Bojlén 1934).

Vaccination.—Owing to the great toxicity of *Bact. shigæ* the preparation of a suitable vaccine is very difficult. Even small doses of dead bacilli excite a severe reaction lasting for a week or more. Several workers have attempted to modify the toxicity by the addition of tricresol (Gay 1902), eusol (Dean and Adamson 1916), hydrogen peroxide (Dean and Adamson 1916), or other chemical substances, but so far as we know these vaccines have not been employed on a large scale in human beings.

Olitsky (1918), employing the principle of the lipo-vaccine introduced by Le Moignic and Pinoy (1916) for typhoid and paratyphoid, recommended the use of heat-killed bacilli suspended in neutral almond oil. The main advantage is that the rate of absorption is slower than with a watery vaccine, and the reaction of the patient is correspondingly less.

Iguchi, Ohstubo, and Eguchi (1933) have tried oral vaccination. Pills were prepared containing 30 mgm. of bacillary substance, representing three different local strains. Three pills were given at 3-day intervals. In 1930, 11,553 vaccinated infants showed an incidence rate of acute enteritis of 35·49 per 10,000, while the rate in 22,757 control infants was 80·85 per 10,000. The corresponding figures for 1931 were : 44·6 cases per 10,000 among 119,904 vaccinated, and 105·7 cases per 10,000 among 430,499 control children. The decrease in morbidity was therefore considerable. The difference in case-mortality rate, however, was less striking, being 41·5 per cent. in the vaccinated and 55·7 per cent. in the control subjects in 1930, and 41·5 per cent. and 49·1 per cent. respectively in 1931. Further observations are clearly required in confirmation of these results.

Shiga (1903) used a sero-vaccine. He injected 0·5 c.c. of a suspension of killed bacilli, mixed with 0·5 c.c. of immune serum, subcutaneously into the back ; 3 or 4 days later double the dose of bacilli was given without the serum. Antibodies were demonstrable in the blood of inoculated persons when examined 3 to 4 weeks later. During the years 1898–1900 Shiga inoculated 10,000 persons in Japan. Unfortunately no statistics of the results are given ; but it is stated that, whereas the morbidity rate was approximately the same in both vaccinated and unvaccinated, the mortality rate was appreciably altered. Thus of the uninoculated 30–40 per cent. are said to have died ; of the vaccinated patients hardly any died.

More recently Dumas, Ramon and Bilal (1926) have recommended the use of dysentery anatoxin—formolized toxin—prepared in a manner similar to that used for diphtheria anatoxin. Its injection into human beings causes only a slight local reaction ; 3 weeks after the second injection the blood of vaccinated persons contained enough antitoxin per c.c. to neutralize 5–20 M.L.D. for a rabbit.

Vaccines containing *Bact. flexneri* have been widely used, but no adequate data of their value are available.

Serotherapy.—Todd (1904) working in London, and Rosenthal (1903, 1904) working in Moscow, showed independently that the soluble toxin contained in cultures of *Bact. shigæ* was able to give rise on injection into animals to a true neutralizing antitoxin. Todd found that the serum had definite protective properties ; if it was injected intravenously into a rabbit, it protected the animal against a lethal dose of toxin or of dead bacilli, given simultaneously or half an hour later. A horse serum that he prepared contained sufficient antitoxin per c.c.

to neutralize 20,000 lethal doses of toxin for a rabbit. The union of toxin and antitoxin is said to conform to the law of multiple proportions (Pfeiffer and Ungermann 1909, Kolle *et al.* 1924). Since, however, complete neutralization occurs only when the toxin and the serum are intimately mixed, some authors have cast doubt on the antitoxic powers of the serum ; they would refer its protective effect to antibacterial rather than to antitoxic properties (Pfeiffer and Ungermann 1909, Bessau 1911). There seems to be little doubt that the serum does contain a true, specific antitoxin (Kraus and Dörr 1905). This is most effective when mixed directly with the toxin ; when injected before or afterwards its efficacy is diminished.

Antiserum is prepared by the intravenous injection of horses, first with heat-killed and later with living bacilli (Flexner and Amoss 1915). More recently dysentery anatoxin has been used for the production of serum (Dumas *et al.* 1926).

The titration of the serum is best carried out on the mouse, using intravenous inoculation (Kolle *et al.* 1924, Sudmersen *et al.* 1924). O'Brien and Runge (1925) suggested as a provisional standard that the unit of antitoxin should be that amount of serum which would neutralize the test dose—0·2 mgm.—of a standard toxin ; the test dose was approximately 10 lethal doses for the mouse. An improved method was described by Blake and Okell (1929), which according to Trevan (1929) leads to an increased accuracy in titration. Zozaya (1932) has used the polysaccharide precipitation test for the antibacterial standardization of serum, but Kurauchi and Nagata (1935) have reported unfavourably on this method.

Under the Therapeutic Substances Act one unit of Shiga antiserum is contained in 1/200 c.c. of a 1 per cent. solution of a standard dry (Copenhagen) serum.

In practice the results of serum treatment are not very convincing. Shiga (1901), in Japan, tested the therapeutic effect of an antidysentery serum, the method of preparation of which is not recorded ; from his report we have constructed the following tables (Tables CXXXIII, CXXXIV).

TABLE CXXXIII

SHOWING TOTAL MORTALITY OF DYSENTERY IN JAPAN. CONTROL TABLE.

Year.	No. of Cases.	Died.	Mortality.
			Per cent.
1895	52,711	12,959	24·5
1896	85,876	22,356	26·0
1897	91,077	23,189	25·4
1898	90,976	22,392	24·6
1899	108,713	23,763	21·8
1900	42,236	10,265	24·3

TABLE CXXXIV

SHOWING MORTALITY OF PATIENTS IN HOSPITAL TREATED WITH MEDICINE ALONE OR WITH SERUM.

Year	Hospital.	Mode of Treatment.	No. Treated.	Died.	Mortality.
					Per cent.
1895–99 . . .	Municipal	Medicine	2,565	929	36·2
1899	,,	Serum	88	11	12·5
1897	Infectious	Medicine	34	8	23·5
1898–1900 . .	,,	Serum	210	20	9·5

Unfortunately the figures of the serum-treated cases are few ; moreover the comparison, so far as individual hospitals are concerned, has been made between the mortality of cases treated with serum in one year and that of cases treated without serum in previous years. Shiga concludes, however, that serum treatment reduced the mortality to about one-third of its former value. (For records of results obtained by other authors previous to 1907 see Deane 1907.)

During the War, Graham (1918) treated a number of cases of dysentery occurring in the British Salonika Force. The serum with which he obtained his best results was prepared against both Shiga and Flexner strains, but it seems probable that its effect depended on its concentration in *shigæ* antitoxin ; 60–80 c.c. were injected intravenously, followed by 150–300 c.c. of normal saline ; this was repeated twice daily for the first two days, and once daily for the next two. Clinically, the serum relieved abdominal pain and tenesmus, and often reduced the number of stools. Patients infected with *Bact. shigæ* reacted better than those infected with Flexner's bacillus. Unfortunately no figures are given to substantiate the value of the serum treatment ; the mortality of patients treated in this way was apparently about 0·3 per cent. Summarizing, we may say that the evidence in favour of anti-shigæ serum is sufficient to justify its use in all cases of dysentery in which there is reason for suspecting that an acute infection is due to Shiga's bacillus.

Treatment with bacteriophage has been tried, but the results are not sufficiently conclusive to demand detailed attention (see Riding 1930).

REFERENCES

AMAKO, T. (1908) *Z. Hyg. InfektKr.*, **60**, 93.
ANDREWES, F. W. (1918) *Lancet*, i. 560.
BAHR, P. H. (1912) " Dysentery in Fiji during the year 1910." *Rep. Lond. School trop. Med.*
BESSAU, G. (1911) *Zbl. Bakt.*, **57**, 27.
BLAKE, A. V. and OKELL, C. C. (1929) *J. Path. Bact.*, **32**, 121.
BOJLÉN, K. (1934) " Dysentery in Denmark." Bianco Lunos Bogtrykkeri A/S, Copenhagen.
BOYD, J. S. K. (1936) *J. R. Army med. Cps*, **66**, 1.
CANDLER, J. P. and DEAN, G. (1911) *Arch. Neurol. Psychiat.*, **5**, 74.
CANN, L. W. and NAVASQUEZ, S. DE. (1931) *J. Hyg., Camb.*, **31**, 361.
CHANNON, H. A. (1926) *J. Path. Bact.*, **29**, 496.
CLAYTON, F. H. A. and WARREN, S. H. (1929*a*) *J. Hyg., Camb.*, **28**, 355 ; (1929*b*) *Ibid.*, **29**, 191.
DEAN, H. R. and ADAMSON, R. S. (1916) *Brit. med. J.*, i. 611.
DEANE, G. (1907) *J. R. Army med. Cps*, **9**, 572.
DOUGLAS, S. R. and COLEBROOK, L. (1917) *Spec. Rep. Ser. med. Res. Coun., Lond.*, No. 6.
DOWNIE, A. W., WADE, E., and YOUNG, J. A. (1933) *J. Hyg., Camb.*, **33**, 196.
DUDGEON, L. S. (1919) *Spec. Rep. Ser. med. Res. Coun., Lond.*, No. 40.
DUMAS, J., RAMON, and BILAL, S. (1926) *Ann. Inst. Pasteur*, **40**, 134.
FELSEN, J. and OSOFSKY, A. G. (1934) *J. Amer. med. Ass.*, **103**, 966.
FITZ-GERALD, W. E. (1921) *Lancet*, ii. 1051.
FLETCHER, W. and MACKINNON, D. L. (1919) *Spec. Rep. Ser. med. Res. Coun., Lond.*, No. 29.
FLEXNER, S. (1900*a*) *Zbl. Bakt.*, **28**, 625 ; (1900*b*) *Bull. Johns Hopk. Hosp.*, **11**, 231.
FLEXNER, S. and AMOSS, H. L. (1915) *J. exp. Med.*, **21**, 515.
FORSYTH, W. L. (1933) *J. trop. Med. Hyg.*, **36**, 65.
FYFE, G. M. (1927) *J. Hyg., Camb.*, **26**, 271.
GAY. (1902) *Univ. Pa. med. Bull.*, **15**, 307.
GRAHAM, D. (1918) *Lancet*, i. 51.
GRAHAM, G. (1919) *Lancet*, ii. 1030.
HAY, H. R. (1930) *J. Hyg., Camb.*, **30**, 25.
HISS, P. H. (1904) *J. med. Res.*, **13**, 1.
IGUCHI, J., OHSTUBO, I., and EGUCHI, C. (1933) *Bull. Off. int. Hyg. publ.*, **25**, 639.
JOHNSTON, M. M. and BROWN, A. (1930) *Canad. publ. Hlth J.*, **21**, 394.
KERRIN, J. C. and CRUICKSHANK, J. (1926) *J. Path. Bact.*, **29**, 315.

KOLLE, W., SCHLOSZBERGER, H., and PRIGGE, R. (1924) *Dtsch. med. Wschr.*, **50**, 1105.
KRAUS, R. and DÖRR, R. (1905) *Wien. klin. Wschr.*, **18**, 1077.
KRUMWIEDE, C. and PRATT, J. S. (1914) *J. exp. Med.*, **19**, 501.
KRUSE, W. (1900) *Dtsch. med. Wschr.*, **26**, 637 ; (1901) *Ibid.*, **27**, 370, 386.
KRUSE, RITTERSHAUS, KEMP, and METZ. (1907) *Z. Hyg. InfektKr.*, **57**, 417.
KURAUCHI, K. and NAGATA, S. (1935) *J. Immunol.*, **29**, 435.
LEAHY, A. D. (1931) *Amer. J. publ Hlth.*, **21**, 1126.
LENTZ. (1902) *Z. Hyg. InfektKr.*, **41**, 559.
LEUCHS, J. and HEIM, E. (1930) *Z. Medizinalbeamte*, Nr. 19, 587.
MACALISTER, G. H. K. (1910) *Brit. med. J.*, ii. 1506.
MACGILL, J. S. and DOWNIE, A. W. (1932) *Lancet*, ii. 29.
MANDRY, O. C. (1935) *Puerto Rico J. publ. Hlth.*, **10**, 308.
MANSON, P. (1914) " Tropical Diseases," 5th edit. London.
MANSON-BAHR, P. (1919) *J. R. Army med. Cps*, **33**, 117.
MARTINI, E. and LENTZ, O. (1902) *Z. Hyg. InfektKr.*, **41**, 540.
MOIGNIC LE and PINOY. (1916) *C. R. Soc. Biol.*, **79**, 201, 352.
MOTT. (1901–02) *Trans. Epidemiol. Soc., London*, **21**, 18.
MYERS, E. M. and KOSER, S. A. (1932) *J. prev. Med., Baltimore*, **6**, 101.
NABARRO, D. and SIGNY, A. G. (1932) *Arch. Dis. Child.*, **7**, 327.
NELSON, R. L. (1930) *J. Bact.*, **20**, 183.
O'BRIEN, R. A. and RUNGE, B. F. (1925) *Brit. J. exp. Path.*, **6**, 84.
OLITSKY, P. K. (1918) *J. exp. Med.*, **28**, 69.
PARK, W. H. and CAREY, H. W. (1903) *J. med. Res.*, **9**, 180.
PFEIFFER, R. and UNGERMANN, E. (1909) *Zbl. Bakt.*, **50**, 534.
PICKLES, W. N. (1932) *Lancet*, ii. 31.
Report. (1919) *Spec. Rep. Ser. med. Res. Coun., Lond.*, No. 40 ; (1920) *Ibid.*, No. 51.
RIDING, D. (1930) *J. Hyg., Camb.*, **30**, 387.
ROGERS, L. (1913) " Dysenteries, their Differentiation and Treatment." London.
ROSENTHAL, L. (1903) *Zbl. Bakt., Ref.*, **33**, 793 ; (1904) *Ibid.*, **34**, 503.
SCHMITZ, K. E. F. (1917) *Z. Hyg. InfektKr.*, **84**, 449.
SHIGA, K. (1898) *Zbl. Bakt.*, **24**, 817, 870, 913 ; (1901) *Dtsch. med. Wschr.*, **27**, 741, 765, 783 ; (1903) *Zbl. Bakt.*, **29**, 327.
SMITH, J. and FRASER, A. M. (1928) *J. Path. Bact.*, **31**, 511 ; (1930) *J. Hyg., Camb.*, **30**, 216.
SONNE, C. (1915) *Zbl. Bakt.*, **75**, 408.
STRONG, R. P. and MUSGRAVE, W. E. (1900) *J. Amer. med. Ass.*, **35**, 498.
SUDMERSEN, H. J., RUNGE, B. F., and O'BRIEN, R. A. (1924) *Brit. J. exp. Path.*, **5**, 100.
SYLVEST, E. (1933) *Ugeskr. Laeg.*, **95**, 309.
TAYLOR, J. F. (1919) *Spec. Rep. Ser. med. Res. Coun., Lond.*, No. 40.
THJØTTA, T. (1919) *J. Bact.*, **4**, 355.
TODD, C. (1904) *J. Hyg., Camb.*, **4**, 480.
TREVAN, J. W. (1929) *J. Path. Bact.*, **32**, 127.
VAILLARD, L. and DOPTER, C. (1903) *Ann. Inst. Pasteur*, **17**, 463.
WELCH, H. and MICKLE, F. L. (1934) *Amer. J. publ. Hlth.*, **24**, 219.
WHITEHEAD, H. and SCOTT, W. M. (1934) *Lancet*, ii. 248.
WU, J. P. and SIA, R. H. P. (1936) *Chin. med. J.*, Suppl. No. 1., 179.
ZOZAYA, J. (1932) *Brit. J. exp. Path.*, **13**, 28.

CHAPTER LXVIII

SUMMER DIARRHŒA

UNTIL the classical study made by Ballard in 1887 (1889), diarrhœa in infants was regarded as a symptom common to a number of heterogeneous disturbances of the alimentary tract ; Ballard was the first to recognize the disease as a clinical entity and to point out its close analogy with those diseases caused by infective micro-organisms.

Epidemiology.

The disease of which we are speaking, both in Europe and in America, is essentially an epidemic disease of the summer and autumn. Deaths from diarrhœa occur at other times of the year, though in much smaller numbers ; but whether they are a manifestation of the same disease or are due to some other cause is unknown ; in this chapter we shall not consider them.

Summer diarrhœa attacks the population at all ages ; it is commonest in the second year of life, and is commoner in old people than in adolescents. Peters (1910), studying the disease at Mansfield in 1908, found that less than 20 per cent. of the cases were in infants under 2 years of age. On the other hand, the mortality of the disease is confined almost entirely to infants ; about 90 per cent. of the deaths at Mansfield were in infants under 2 years of age. Similarly Niven (1904) records that in 1903 there were 507 deaths in Manchester from summer diarrhœa, of which 480 were in patients under 5 years old. The period of maximum mortality is from 3 to 6 months after birth, when it may reach a figure of 30–40 per cent. Breast-fed infants are remarkably exempt from the disease, especially from fatal attack. Of 88 infants under 1 year of age with diarrhœa, all but four were artificially fed (Niven 1904).

In 1911 Dudfield (1912) in Paddington estimated the attack rate of breast-fed infants at 28·3 per cent., and of those artificially fed at 58·6 per cent. ; but of the former infants not a single one died. It is probable that during the first year of life many infants owe their escape from the disease to breast-feeding. There is evidence to show that infants in the 1st year are more susceptible to the disease when artificially fed than those in the 2nd year (Peters 1910) ; we may therefore conclude that breast-feeding is responsible for delaying the onset of the disease. Further evidence of the protective effect of breast-feeding is contributed by Grulee, Sanford, and Schwartz (1935), who analysed the morbidity and mortality statistics relating to 20,000 infants, and found that the incidence of gastro-intestinal disorders was considerably higher in the artificially than in the breast-fed group.

Social factors also determine to some extent the incidence of summer diarrhœa. Broadly speaking, the lower the social class, the greater the degree of overcrowding in the homes, and the dirtier the domestic environment, the more widespread is the disease.

In favour of the infectious nature of the disease is the occurrence of multiple cases in the same household. Of the numerous inquirers who have investigated this point, Niven (1904) records 2 or more cases in 36 out of 111 families; Hutt (1914) in 19 out of 67 families; Peters (1910) in 83 out of 174 families; and Sandilands (1910) in 16 out of 35 houses attacked. That is to say, multiple cases occur in about 25 to 50 per cent. of families during the height of an epidemic. Moreover the onset of the cases in any one family is generally consecutive, the secondary cases succeeding the primary ones at an average interval of 8 days (Hutt 1914). Not only is the disease capable of spreading in the family; it may also spread amongst children, and occasionally nurses, in hospitals (Sandilands 1910). It is difficult therefore to avoid the conclusion that the disease is infectious.

Effect of Temperature.—One of the striking features of summer diarrhœa is its relation to temperature. Ballard (1889) made the following statements : " The summer rise of diarrhœal mortality does not commence until the mean temperature recorded by the 4-foot earth thermometer has attained somewhere about 56° F., no matter what may have been the temperature previously attained by the atmosphere or recorded by the 1-foot earth thermometer." Moreover, " the maximum diarrhœal mortality of the year is usually observed in the week in which the temperature recorded by the 4-foot earth thermometer attains its mean weekly maximum." " The decline of the diarrhœal mortality . . . coincides with the decline of the temperature recorded by the 4-foot earth thermometer, which temperature declines very much more slowly than the atmospheric temperature, or than that recorded by the 1-foot earth thermometer ; so that the epidemic mortality may continue (although declining) long after the last-mentioned temperatures have fallen greatly, and may extend some way into the fourth quarter of the year."

These conclusions of Ballard's have been quoted in full, because they have greatly influenced the views held by subsequent observers on the activity of the disease. Peters (1910) regarded the influence of temperature as, in a sense, all-powerful. According to him, failure of the summer temperature to reach a certain height for a certain time will inhibit the epidemic altogether ; the epidemic invariably ceases a fortnight after the weekly air temperature has passed in a decided way below 50° F. Although Ballard regarded the 4-foot earth temperature as the important factor, while Peters confined his attention to the atmospheric temperature, both observers agreed fundamentally in the view that for the genesis of an epidemic there must be a certain critical accumulation of heat.

Dudfield (1912), who made a statistical analysis of the relation between the temperature and attack rate, found that the correlation coefficient between air temperature and diarrhœal attacks was 0·55, and between earth temperature (3 ft. 2 in.) and diarrhœal attacks was 0·68. The recent examination, however, by Brownlee and Young (1922) has not altogether substantiated the results of previous workers. While admitting that a certain degree of accumulated temperature seems essential to provide the necessary impulse for the development of the epidemic, and that some degree of permanence of the excess of temperature is required to maintain a high epidemic level, they were unable to find any obvious or definite relationship between the occurrence of the maximum temperature and the maximum fatality from diarrhœa.

The effect of rainfall is apparently indirect, working through its action on the temperature. Excessive rainfall, especially if prolonged, is sometimes followed by a decline in the epidemic, but analysis renders it probable that this action can be explained best by the lowering of the temperature that results (Brownlee and Young 1922).

It is natural to inquire how the temperature influences the epidemic spread of diarrhœa. Ballard (1889) held that the essential cause of the disease resides ordinarily in the superficial layers of the earth, where it is intimately associated with the life processes of some micro-organism. He supposed that a rise in the earth temperature was followed by a multiplication of the organism, which infected the food, and thus gained access to the alimentary canal. The tendency of later workers has been to regard the influence of temperature in a more indirect light. Niven (1910), who studied the prevalence of flies in the years 1904–09 in Manchester, found a close correspondence between the number of flies captured week by week and the incidence and mortality of diarrhœa. The incidence curve began to ascend when the flies reached a certain number, and continued to rise when the flies had attained a maximum. The deaths, however, diminished more rapidly than the flies in the middle part of the decline. This he explained by assuming that in years of high incidence the more susceptible and exposed infants were killed off or rendered immune ; and by the fact that towards the close of the fly season the flies are hampered in their movements by the oncoming cold and by the attack of a fungus—*Empusa muscæ*—which renders them less effective in transmitting the active agent of the disease. Hamer (1908) partly confirmed Niven's findings. In London he found that the 4-foot earth temperature, the fly prevalence, and the diarrhœal incidence rose almost simultaneously (Fig. 261). The fly and the diarrhœal curves followed one another closely, showing not only a parallel rise, but synchronous fluctuations ; the diarrhœa curve, however, began to fall slightly earlier than the fly curve, and declined more rapidly. This fact is not satisfactorily explained by Niven's hypothesis ; for it occurs in years of slight as well as of extensive prevalence, showing that it cannot be due to exhaustion of the susceptible population. On further investigation, Hamer noticed discrepancies that rendered doubtful the relationship of flies to diarrhœa. Thus in 1908 the deaths from diarrhœa were far more numerous than in 1907 ; yet the number of flies was not correspondingly excessive. Moreover, comparison of the 1907 and 1908 curves showed that from mid-August until the end of the first week of October in 1907, and from September 4 to October 5 in 1908, the flies were practically stationary in numbers. Yet during the stationary period of 1907, diarrhœa was steadily increasing, while during the stationary period of 1908 it was steadily declining. These observations, of course, do not disprove the fly hypothesis ; they may be explained by assuming that the amount of infective material to be conveyed may vary independently of the number of flies. When the amount of infective material is large, comparatively few flies may transmit as much as a greater number of flies may transmit when it is small. If the available infective material is small, the frequency of flies will have little appreciable effect.

This assumption receives some support from a study of the curves obtained by Hope (1920) in Liverpool. In some years the maximum of the diarrhœal mortality was attained before the maximum prevalence of flies. Further in the years 1916, 1917, and 1918, the two curves agreed closely ; but in 1919, while the fly curve was as well marked as in the three previous years, the curve of diarrhœal mortality was very low, and presented no agreement or parallelism with the curve of fly prevalence (Fig 262).

Arnold (1928) has suggested that the effect of summer temperature in decreasing the secretory activity of the stomach, and hence interfering with the gastro-

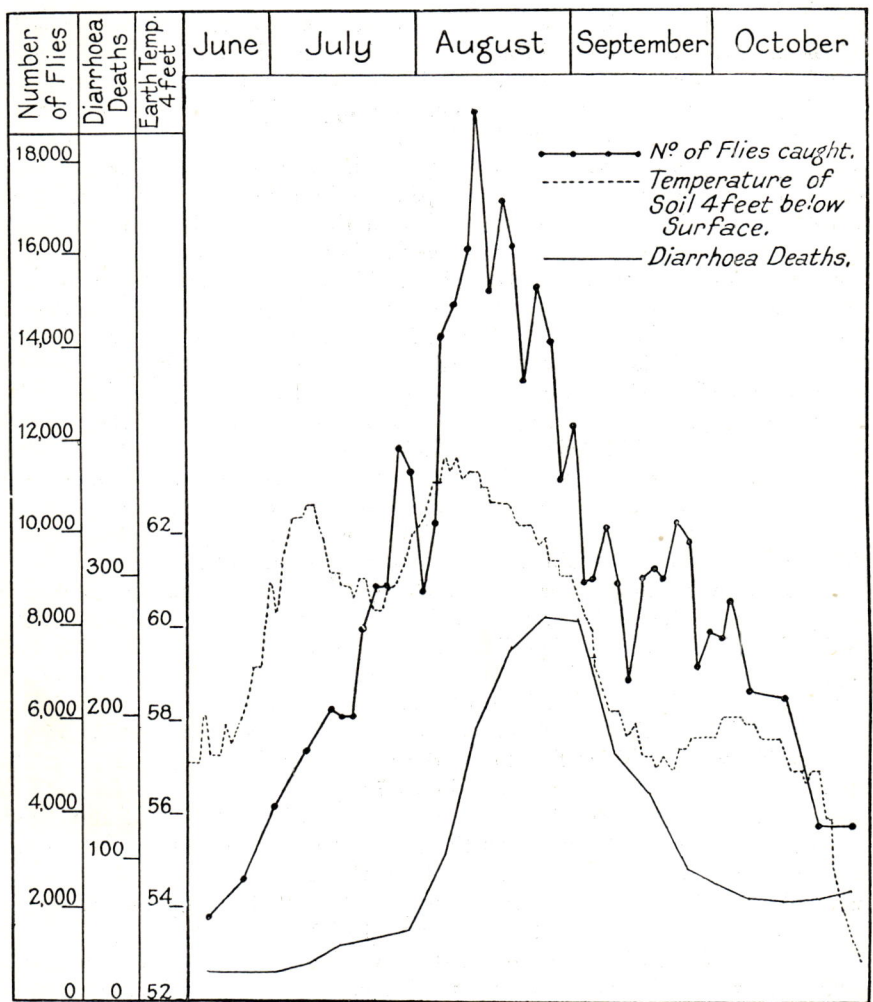

FIG. 261.

Showing the relationship between the prevalence of flies, the soil temperature, and the mortality from summer diarrhœa in London in 1908.   (After Hamer.)

duodenal auto-disinfecting mechanism, may play an important part in determining the occurrence of summer diarrhœa, the higher incidence among infants being due to the greater instability of their digestive mechanism.

Another factor, which may well play some part in the prevalence of infantile diarrhœa, is the effect of high temperature on the rate of multiplication of bacteria

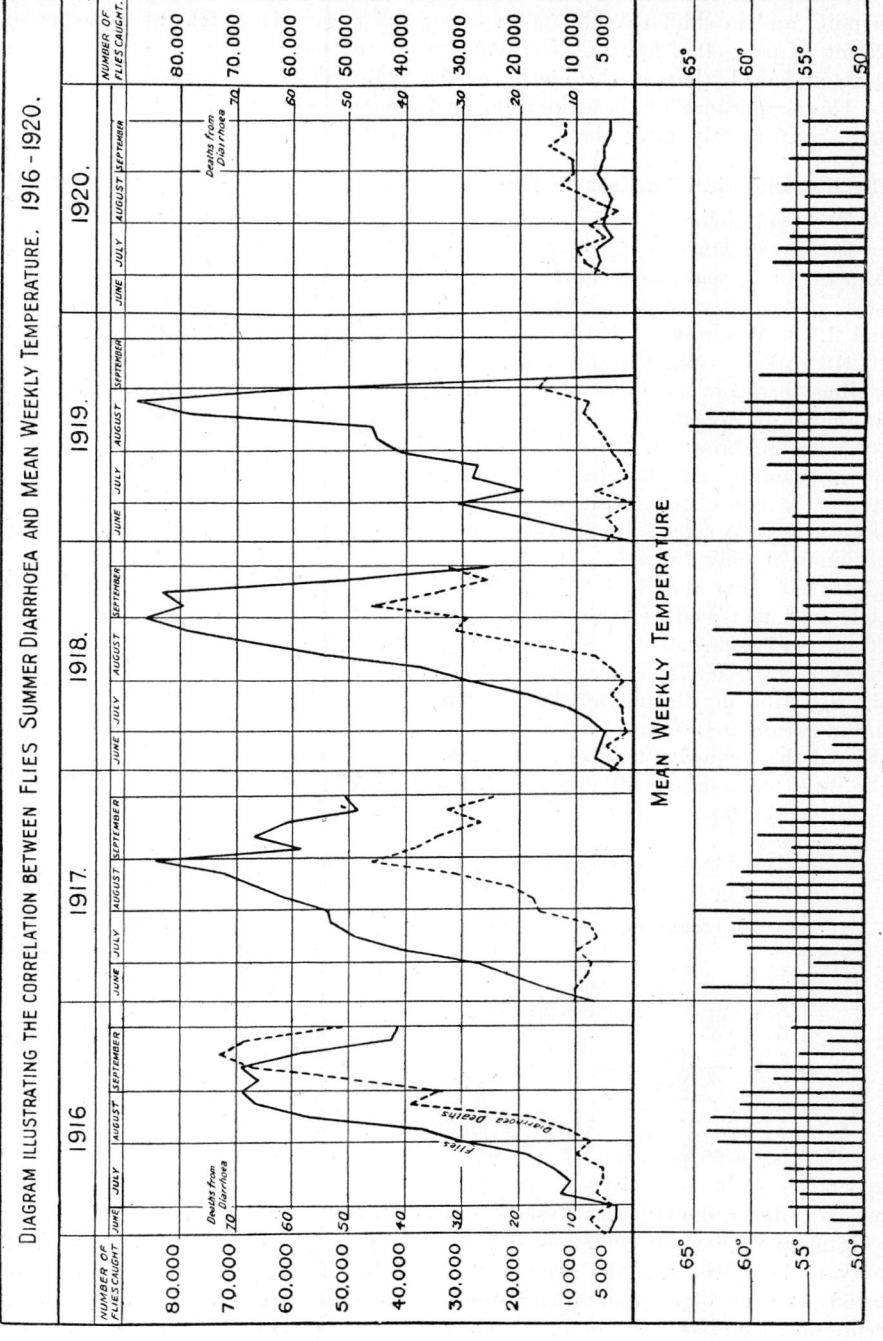

DIAGRAM ILLUSTRATING THE CORRELATION BETWEEN FLIES SUMMER DIARRHOEA AND MEAN WEEKLY TEMPERATURE. 1916 - 1920.

FIG. 262.—AFTER HOPE.

in milk, and in similar foods. This factor will clearly be operative to a greater extent in poor-class houses, ill-provided with the means for keeping food-stuffs clean and cool, than in the houses of the well-to-do.

The significance of the epidemiological evidence as a whole can be discussed more conveniently after the bacteriological data have been considered.

The Bacteriological Findings in Summer Diarrhœa.

The bacteriological findings in summer diarrhœa are extremely conflicting.

Booker, in America (1896), who was one of the first to investigate the intestinal flora in this disease, reported a general increase in the numbers of certain organisms, particularly *Proteus* and streptococci. Several years later, between 1909 and 1913, Metchnikoff (1914) in Paris isolated *Proteus vulgaris* from 204 out of 218 cases of infantile diarrhœa. He produced diarrhœa in chimpanzees by feeding them on the fæces of affected infants, and found that *Proteus vulgaris* subsequently appeared in their fæces. Though admitting that this organism is often an inhabitant of the normal intestinal tract, he concluded that it was the specific cause of infantile diarrhœa. Bertrand (1914), one of Metchnikoff's pupils, studied 55 cases of the disease in London Hospitals in the summer of 1912, and isolated *Proteus vulgaris* from every case ; while in the stools of 24 normal children he found it only twice.

In 1903 Hiss and Russell in America cultivated a bacillus from the colon of a child who had died of acute diarrhœa ; this proved to belong to the dysentery group, and was called the Y-bacillus. Duval and Bassett (1904), Duval and Shorer (1904), Wollstein and Dewey (1904), and a number of other workers under the direction of Flexner at the Rockefeller Institute, carried out an extensive investigation in 1902 and 1903 into the ætiology of summer diarrhœa. The results showed the frequent presence of dysentery bacilli in the fæces during life, and in the intestinal mucosa after death (Table CXXXV).

TABLE CXXXV
DYSENTERY BACILLI IN STOOLS OF INFANTS WITH SUMMER DIARRHŒA.

No. of Cases studied.	*Bact. shigæ.*	*Bact. flexneri.*	*Bact. shigæ* and *Bact. flexneri* Mixed.
412	23	256	6
No. of Cases with Dysentery Bacilli. 285	8·1%	89·8%	2·1%

That is, in 69 per cent. of patients dysentery bacilli were found ; these were generally—in 90 per cent.—of the Flexner type. Examination of the fæces of normal infants showed that dysentery bacilli were quite uncommon.

Similar results were obtained in Boston 11 years later by Tenbroeck and Norbury (1915, 1916). In the summer of 1914 they found Flexner's bacillus in 54 or 68 per cent. of 79 infants with summer diarrhœa, and in 1915 in 51 or 68 per cent. of 75 infants. Again in 1919, 69 per cent. of cases of summer diarrhœa investigated by Davison (1919*a*, *b*) in Birmingham, U.S.A., were found to be due to the dysentery bacillus, Flexner's bacillus being twice as common as Shiga's.

In Baltimore 82 per cent. of the cases were due to dysentery bacilli ; in this series Flexner's was the only type found.

In this country the findings have been entirely different. Flexner's bacillus has hardly ever been isolated from cases of summer diarrhœa. On the contrary the organisms that have been found most frequently are the Morgan No. 1 bacillus (*Proteus morgani*) and Sonne's bacillus. In the summer of 1905 Morgan (1906), working at the Lister Institute, London, isolated his bacillus from 28 out of 58 cases ; in the fæces of 20 normal children it was not found once. He continued his work for the next three years ; the results he obtained are summarized in Table CXXXVI (Morgan and Ledingham 1909).

TABLE CXXXVI

FREQUENCY OF MORGAN NO. 1 BACILLUS IN SUMMER DIARRHŒA.

Year.	Cases examined.	Percentage of Positive Cases.
1905	58	48·2
1906	54	55·8
1907	191	16·2
1908	166	53·0

It will be noticed that, except in 1907, in which the incidence of summer diarrhœa was low, the bacillus was isolated from about half the cases. During the epidemic of 1908 it was isolated from 12 per cent. of normal children ; it was likewise found in flies coming from infected houses. Morgan and Ledingham (1909), in summing up the evidence, regard this bacillus as an important factor in the causation of summer diarrhœa. Attempts to reproduce the disease in animals were not successful ; but the oral administration of large doses to rats, young rabbits, and monkeys sometimes proved fatal.

Investigations made by Ross (1910–11) in Manchester, and O'Brien (1910–11) in London in the summer of 1910, showed that there was an increase in the number of non-lactose-fermenting bacilli in the stools of patients with diarrhœa. Morgan's bacillus was comparatively infrequent—5 per cent. and 14 per cent. respectively. Orr (1910–11) at Shrewsbury did not find it once in an examination of 19 cases. It is to be noted, however, that the incidence of summer diarrhœa in 1910 was very low. In the summer of 1911 Lewis (1911–12) at Birmingham likewise noted an increase in the number of non-lactose-fermenting colonies in diarrhœal stools. Morgan's bacillus was found in 101 out of 140 cases, or 72·1 per cent., and in 17 of 100 normal children under 5 years of age, or 17 per cent. He found that of 20 strains isolated from diarrhœal children, 14 proved fatal to rats or mice on feeding. Further, he was successful in isolating the organism from 5 out of 18 samples of milk from houses in which there were at the time, or had recently been, cases of diarrhœa. Graham-Smith (1911–12), examining flies collected in Cambridge and in Birmingham in the summer of 1911, isolated bacilli of the Morgan type (86 per cent. of which were Morgan No. 1) from 5·3 per cent. of flies captured in diarrhœa-infected houses, and from only 0·6 per cent. of flies captured in houses free from diarrhœa. During the 3rd week of August the proportion of flies infected with *Proteus morgani* reached 15·6 per cent. at Cambridge and 12·0 per cent. at Birmingham.

In the same year, however, Alexander (1911–12) at Liverpool encountered

Morgan's No. 1 bacillus in only 23 out of 174 cases, or 13·2 per cent. ; moreover he found it in 5 out of 75 normal children, or 6·7 per cent.

Of recent years Morgan's bacillus does not appear to have been isolated so frequently in this country. Nabarro (1923), in an examination of the fæces of 68 cases of summer diarrhœa during the epidemic of 1921, did not encounter it once ; on the other hand he isolated from 21 of the cases an organism which, in the light of subsequent work (Nabarro 1927), was probably Sonne's dysentery bacillus.

In Germany the findings have been diverse. Gildemeister and Baerthlein (1913) examined the fæces of 70 infants suffering from diarrhœa in the summer of 1912. Flexner's dysentery bacillus was found in 9, *Bact. enteritidis* in 1, other bacilli of the Salmonella group in 4, and the so-called Dahlem bacillus (resembling the Voldagsen bacillus) in 22. The following year Baerthlein and Huwald (1914) found *Bact. flexneri* in 21, Salmonella bacilli in 7, and the Dahlem bacillus in 24 out of 72 cases.

In Australia Patterson and Williams (1922) have found the Sonne dysentery bacillus in 3 cases of acute diarrhœa in babies. Harper (1932) stated that Tidswell, who carried out a bacteriological examination of her cases, found non-lactose-fermenters in a large proportion of the specimens examined. Of 206 non-lactose-fermenters isolated from different patients, 69 belonged to the dysentery, and 137 to the Salmonella, group—the latter organisms being mainly *Bact. paratyphosum A* and *B* and *Bact. typhi-murium.*

Other organisms, such as *Cl. welchii* and *Ps. pyocyanea*, have been inculpated by different workers.

There is general agreement that in summer diarrhœa the non-lactose-fermenting organisms in the fæces are increased. How far this is significant it is difficult to say, since the presence of non-lactose-fermenters in the fæces is associated not only with diarrhœa, but with the type of food supplied. The fæces of infants fed on cows' milk contain more of these organisms than those of breast-fed infants. For example, from 38 specimens of fæces from normal breast-fed infants, Lewis isolated non-lactose-fermenters only 4 times, but from 27 specimens from normal infants fed on cows' milk he isolated them 22 times. It is therefore not justifiable to compare the percentage of non-lactose-fermenters in diarrhœal children fed on cows' milk with that of normal breast-fed infants.

The exact species of non-lactose-fermenter that is preponderant varies in different countries. In America it is chiefly Flexner's dysentery bacillus, and in this country *Proteus morgani* and *Bact. sonnei.* Metchnikoff found *Proteus vulgaris* to be predominant ; others have been struck by the increased frequency of *Ps. pyocyanea*, members of the Salmonella group, or *Cl. welchii.*

Before forming any opinion on the ætiological significance of these organisms it is well to remember that, epidemiologically, summer diarrhœa is a disease that is widespread in every part of Europe and America. It may be difficult to believe that a disease which reaches its maximum about the 32nd to the 36th week in London, Paris, Berlin, Moscow, Chicago, and New York, which produces a clinical syndrome of diarrhœa, vomiting, and collapse, with the passage of fæces containing frequently mucus and sometimes blood, and which is specially fatal to infants under 2 years of age, can be determined by a diversity of bacterial species. It may be difficult to believe that one and the same disease is due to the Flexner and Shiga dysentery bacilli in America, to *Proteus vulgaris* in France, to the Dahlem bacillus in Germany, and to *Proteus morgani* and *Bact. sonnei* in this country. Yet we are faced with the alternatives either that the disease is due to a different agent in each of these countries, or that it is uniform and is due to a primary agent with which we are at present unacquainted.

It is not justifiable to assume that because summer diarrhœa is an epidemiological entity, it is necessarily a bacteriological entity. It may be caused by a number of different organisms, in much the same way as dysentery is caused by a number of different organisms. Presumably the conditions that favour the growth and transference of one of these organisms likewise favour the growth and transference of the others. The finding of a number of different organisms in a disease that appears to be epidemiologically uniform is not incompatible with our present knowledge of bacteriology.

Brownlee and Young (1922) have made the suggestion that summer diarrhœa is a mixed disease consisting mainly of two separate components. On analysing the data for London during the last 60 years they found not only that the mortality from diarrhœa had diminished considerably from 1890 onwards, but that the maximum of the annual epidemic had gradually become later and later. Previous to 1899 the maximum fell about the 30th to the 33rd week of the year; in 1899 there was a change, the epidemic reaching its acme later. From 1907 onwards the maximum did not occur till the 35th to the 40th week, and with the single exception of 1911 the number of deaths was comparatively small. Further analysis showed that the curve of the annual mortality from diarrhœa could be split up into an early and a late epidemic; the early one, which reached its maximum about the 31st week, had a steep ascent and a rapid decline, and levied a heavy toll on life; the second, which reached its maximum about the 36th week, had a more gradual slope throughout, and was less fatal. During the present century the early epidemic has become less and less evident, and has been replaced largely by the late epidemic. The composite nature of the diarrhœal mortality curve was substantiated by examination of the records for other English cities, and also Paris, Berlin, Moscow, Chicago, and New York. Each of the annual curves could be analysed into two symmetrical curves, the means of which were separated by an interval of about 5 weeks.

During the past 20 or 30 years, diarrhœa in this country has gradually assumed smaller and smaller proportions. The better disposal of garbage, the diminution of dust, the replacement of horse by motor traffic, the decrease in the number of flies, the improvement in cleanliness of the milk supply, and the greatly increased use of pasteurized and dried milk in the feeding of infants and children have probably all aided in lessening the chances of bacterial contamination of food.

Summing up the epidemiological evidence, it would seem probable that summer diarrhœa is a bacterial infection, the prevalence of which is determined by a number of factors, varying to some extent independently, but all conditioned directly or indirectly and to a greater or less extent by the prevailing temperature. Among these factors, it is highly probable that fly prevalence holds an important place; but it is not likely that its rôle is as decisive as that of the flea in the case of plague, or of the louse in the case of typhus fever. The available bacteriological evidence suggests that no one organism can be regarded as the specific cause of summer diarrhœa, but that any one of a number of potentially pathogenic species, either alone or in combination, may be capable of giving rise to the disease.

Diagnosis and Treatment.

It follows from our ignorance of the exact ætiology of summer diarrhœa that bacteriological examination is of little help. The clinical picture is generally sufficiently defined to enable a diagnosis to be made. From an academic point of view, however, it is desirable to obtain as much information as possible on the bacterial flora of the fæces. These should be collected and examined as soon as possible for non-lactose-fermenting organisms. It is generally useless to take a blood culture, since these organisms rarely give rise to a bacteræmia (Tenbroeck 1915, Tenbroeck and Norbury 1915). At autopsy, cultures should be made from the liver, spleen, mesenteric glands, and intestinal mucosa ; it is uncommon, however, for the bacilli to penetrate beyond the mesenteric glands. Agglutinins in the patient's serum to *Bact. flexneri* or *Proteus morgani* are irregular and infrequent, and are of little help in determining the nature of the infection.

The prophylaxis of summer diarrhœa is similar to that of enteric fever. Particular care should be taken of the infant's food, and all disturbances of digestion attended to immediately. Breast-feeding is strongly recommended for infants during their first summer. In the treatment of the disease, anti-dysentery serum has been employed in America, but with what results it is difficult to say.

REFERENCES

ALEXANDER, D. M. (1911–12) *41st Rep. loc. Govt Bd M.O.'s Suppl.*, p. 288.
ARNOLD, L. (1928) *Amer. J. Hyg.*, **8**, 604.
BAERTHLEIN, K. and HUWALD, W. (1914) *Dtsch. med. Wschr.*, **40**, 478.
BALLARD, E. (1889) *17th Rep. loc. Govt Bd M.O.'s Spec. Suppl.*, 1887.
BERTRAND, D. M. (1914) *Ann. Inst. Pasteur*, **28**, 121.
BOCKER, W. D. (1896) *Rep. Johns Hopk. Hosp.*, **6**, 159.
BROWNLEE, J. and YOUNG, M. (1922) *Proc. R. Soc. Med.*, **15**, Epidem. Sect., p. 55.
DAVISON, W. C. (1919c) *Abstr. Bact.*, **4**, 15 ; (1919b) *Ibid.*, **4**, 324.
DUDFIELD, R. (1912) *Proc. R. Soc. Med.*, **5**,, Part 2, p. 99.
DUVAL, C. W. and BASSETT, V. H. (1904) *Studies Rockefeller Inst. med. Res.*, **2**, 7.
DUVAL, C. W. and SHORER, E. H. (1904) *Studies Rockefeller Inst. med. Res.*, **2**, 42.
GILDEMEISTER, E. and BAERTHLEIN, K. (1913) *Dtsch. med. Wschr.*, **39**, 982.
GRAHAM-SMITH, G. S. (1911–12) *41st Rep. loc. Govt Bd M.O.'s Suppl.*, p. 304.
GRULEE, C. G., SANFORD, H. N., and SCHWARTZ, H. (1935) *J. Amer. med. Ass.*, **104**, 1986.
HAMER, W. H. (1908) *Rep. loc. Govt Bd M.O.'s.*, Nos. 1138, 1207.
HARPER, M. (1932) *Med. J. Aust.*, **1**, 538.
HISS, P. H. and RUSSELL, F. F. (1903) *Med. News*, **82**, 289.
HOPE, E. W. (1920) *Lpool ann. Hlth Rep.*, p. 49.
HUTT, C. W. (1914) *J. Hyg., Camb.*, **13**, 422.
LEWIS, C. J. (1911–12) *41st ann. Rep. loc. Govt Bd M.O.'s Suppl.*, p. 265.
METCHNIKOFF, E. (1914) *Ann. Inst. Pasteur*, **28**, 89.
MORGAN, H. DE R. (1906) *Brit. med. J.*, i. 908.
MORGAN, H. DE R. and LEDINGHAM, J. C. G. (1909) *Proc. R. Soc. Med.*, **2**, Epidem. Sect., p. 133.
NABARRO, D. (1923) *Brit. med. J.*, ii. 857 ; (1927) *J. Path. Bact.*, **30**, 176.
NIVEN, J. (1904) *Ann. Rep. City of Manchester*, p. 168 ; (1910) *Proc. R. Soc. Med.*, **3**, Part 2, p. 131.
O'BRIEN, R. A. (1910–11) *40th ann. Rep. loc. Govt Bd M.O.'s Suppl.*, p. 367.
ORR, T. (1910–11) *40th ann. Rep. loc. Govt Bd M.O.'s Suppl.*, p. 374.
PATTERSON, S. W. and WILLIAMS, F. E. (1922) *J. Path. Bact.*, **25**, 393.
PETERS, O. H. (1910) *J. Hyg., Camb.*, **10**, 602.
ROSS, S. M. (1910–11) *40th ann. Rep. loc. Govt Bd M.O.'s Suppl.*, p. 347.
SANDILANDS, J. E. (1910) *Proc. R. Soc. Med.*, **3**, Part 2, p. 95.
TENBROECK, C. (1915) *Boston med. surg. J.*, **173**, 284.
TENBROECK, C. and NORBURY, F. G. (1915) *Boston med. surg. J.*, **173**, 280 ; (1916) *Ibid.*, **174**, 785.
WOLLSTEIN and DEWEY. (1904) *Studies Rockefeller Inst. med. Res.*, **2**, 55.

CHAPTER LXIX

BACTERIAL FOOD POISONING AND BOTULISM

FOOD POISONING

Definition.—The consumption of unwholesome food or drink may give rise not only to well-known bacterial infections such as enteric fever, dysentery, cholera, tuberculosis, undulant fever, scarlet fever, septic sore throat, and so on, in which the food serves as a vehicle for the specific infective organism, but also to such diverse conditions as those due to the ingestion of inherently poisonous substances —for example deadly nightshade, hemlock, poisonous fish, toadstools, and ergot-infected grain—and those in which the food has become contaminated directly with such poisons as arsenic, tin, or other heavy metals. The term " food poisoning," however, is conventionally restricted to acute gastro-enteritis due to the bacterial infection of food or drink. So defined, it is divided into two groups : (1) that following the multiplication within the body of pathogenic organisms contained in the food ; this may be referred to as the " infection " type, (2) that following the ingestion of food in which poisonous substances have been formed as the result of bacterial proliferation ; this may be referred to as the " toxin " type.

Botulism, which is also a consequence of bacterial proliferation in food, differs from either of the types just described in the character of the symptoms and in the nature of the toxin involved ; though, for convenience, it will be discussed in this chapter in a separate section (p. 1269). Those interested in chemical food poisoning may be referred to the works of Jordan (1931) and Tanner (1933).

It will be noted that the definition given above excludes food idiosyncrasy and food allergy—conditions in which the food itself is wholesome but the patient's reaction is abnormal.

Symptomatology.

In the *infection* type of food poisoning, after an incubation period varying from half an hour to 3 days, but generally between 6 and 24 hours, the illness commences with severe headache, followed by nausea, vomiting, diarrhœa and abdominal pain. Fever is usually present ; the temperature may rise to 102° F. In favourable cases the symptoms gradually abate so that the patient is better within a week, but in very severe cases restlessness occurs, followed by extreme thirst, cramp, coma, and death. At autopsy the mucosa of the stomach and intestines is swollen and often intensely congested. Peyer's patches are not particularly involved. Minute ulcers may be seen. Microscopic examination reveals fatty degeneration of the liver. The causative bacilli can be isolated from the heart's blood, spleen, and other viscera in a considerable proportion of fatal cases.

In the *toxin* type of food poisoning, the general symptoms resemble those of the infection type, but the incubation period is usually shorter—half an hour to 4 hours—vomiting tends to be more violent, prostration is greater, there is less fever, and recovery is more rapid, the patient often being well again within 24–48 hours. These cases are rarely fatal, so that adequate information about the postmortem findings is lacking.

Epidemiology.

Incidence.—It is difficult, in the absence of compulsory notification, to estimate the frequency of food poisoning in this country. From January, 1921, to October, 1923, Savage and White (1925*b*) collected details of 86 outbreaks in Great Britain, involving about 2,300 persons with 24 deaths. But it is probable that a number of other outbreaks occurred which were not sufficiently important to attract attention. In America, Jordan calculated in 1917 that about 15,000 to 20,000 persons a year were attacked. The country that suffers most severely is Germany, probably on account of the large amount of uncooked meat that is consumed. The following figures (Table CXXXVII) refer only to outbreaks that were due to meat or meat products. The number of outbreaks from all causes was probably much higher.

TABLE CXXXVII

INCIDENCE OF FOOD POISONING IN GERMANY FOLLOWING THE CONSUMPTION OF MEAT AND MEAT PRODUCTS.

(Meyer 1929)

Year.	No. of Outbreaks.	Cases.	Deaths.
1923	76	3,746	28
1924	62	1,712	21
1925	83	1,905	22
1926	84	2,679	17
1927	110	3,548	27
1928	78	977	18

Solitary cases of food poisoning, in which one member only of a family consuming similar food is attacked, are apt to escape diagnosis, the symptoms being ascribed to indigestion, chill, or some other cause, unless a bacteriological examination is made. Such cases are being detected with increasing frequency.

Season.—In this country food poisoning is commoner during the summer than the winter. Savage and White (1925*b*) found that about 72 per cent. of outbreaks occur between May and October. This is probably due to the greater rapidity with which bacteria are able to multiply under warm conditions. But the seasonal incidence depends to a certain extent on the proportion of canned to fresh food that is eaten. In America, for example, it appears to be customary for the housewife to can her vegetable produce in the summer months and to consume it during the winter ; since the process of home canning is not altogether satisfactory, outbreaks of poisoning due to the consumption of this food are fairly common in the winter months. Many of these outbreaks, however, are of the botulism type.

Morbidity and Mortality.—One of the striking facts is the high morbidity rate of most outbreaks. Often all who eat the affected food are attacked. Geiger

(1923) estimates it at 75–100 per cent. An exception may be made in the case of milk ; Savage and White (1925*b*) state that in Salmonella infections conveyed by milk the morbidity rate is only 40–50 per cent. Another striking characteristic is the low mortality rate ; this is estimated by Geiger (1923) in America as less than 0·5 per cent., by Savage (1920) in England as 1·5 per cent., and by Lentz (1924) in Germany as 4·5 per cent. This last figure probably included cases of botulism, and is therefore too high. Mayer (1913) in Germany, dealing purely with Salmonella outbreaks, recorded a mortality rate of only 1 per cent. Taking milk outbreaks alone, Savage and White (1925*b*) find the mortality rate to be less than 0·2 per cent. Sex has apparently little influence. As regards age, the disease seems to be more fatal in the very young, and in the old.

General Bacteriology of Food Poisoning

Before discussing in detail the various factors concerned in the production of bacterial food poisoning, it may be well to take a brief view of the subject as a whole. Towards the end of last century, largely owing to the work of Brieger (1889), food poisoning came to be regarded as due to the presence in the food of toxic amines or *ptomaines* that had been formed as the result of protein decomposition. The work of Vaillard (1902), Fornario (1906), Cathcart (1906*b*), Savage (1921), and others, however, showed that these bodies were relatively non-toxic to laboratory animals, except when given in doses larger than were ever likely to be ingested under natural conditions. The fact, moreover, that the ptomaines did not appear till protein decomposition had reached an advanced stage, when the food would be repugnant to the normal senses, taken in conjunction with the observation that food poisoning usually results from food which is quite sound in appearance, rendered it doubtful whether these bodies played any part in the causation of the type of illness we are considering.

Belief in ptomaine poisoning received its death-blow, so far as scientific bacteriology was concerned, when it was found that in many outbreaks the food contained organisms of the Salmonella, or occasionally the dysentery, group. As the result of the work of Savage in this country, and of Jordan in the United States, food poisoning came to be regarded almost as synonymous with food-borne Salmonella infection. Further work, however, failed to reveal the presence of these organisms in a considerable proportion of the outbreaks in which an adequate investigation was carried out, particularly in outbreaks following the consumption of canned food. To meet this difficulty Savage (1920, 1923, 1932) (see also Savage and White 1925*a*, *b*) put forward the attractive hypothesis that these outbreaks were due to the ingestion by the patient not of the living Salmonella organisms, but of their toxins. It was supposed that the organisms had multiplied in the food prior to its consumption, and had formed thermostable toxic substances. The subsequent cooking to which the food was exposed destroyed the organisms themselves, but did not seriously affect their toxic products, which were therefore able to give rise to food poisoning on ingestion. No adequate confirmatory evidence of the formation of specific exotoxins by members of the Salmonella group was forthcoming, and the balance of evidence appeared to be against this view (but see p. 1265).

While bacteriologists were speculating about the causation of the non-Salmonella food-poisoning outbreaks, Dack, Jordan, and their colleagues in Chicago (see p. 1263) drew attention to certain outbreaks of poisoning which were proved to be due to the presence in the food of a toxin formed by staphylococci. By observations made on human volunteers, it was shown that certain strains of staphylococci were able to form toxic substances endowed with some degree of thermostability. These findings were of special interest in that they afforded conclusive proof of the formation of bacterial toxins in the food prior to its consumption. Hitherto the only known instance of this was that of botulism—a condition to be described later, in which the anaerobic bacillus, *Cl. botulinum*, gives rise to an extremely potent specific exotoxin with an action, not on the gastro-intestinal mucosa, but on the central nervous system.

Other observations by Jordan and by various continental workers cast serious suspicion on food in which there had been inordinate bacterial multiplication of any type. The inference to be drawn from these observations was that many organisms, non-pathogenic in themselves, such as *Bact. coli*, *Proteus vulgaris*, *Proteus morgani*, milk streptococci and others when allowed to multiply under favourable conditions in suitable types of food-stuffs, led to the appearance of toxic substances having an irritating effect on the human gastro-intestinal mucosa. Many workers had toyed with this idea of non-specific toxin formation, but had abandoned it in the absence of adequate evidence. The epidemiological, and more recently the bacteriological, evidence seems to us, however, to be becoming increasingly strong in favour of this view. The pendulum is in fact slowly swinging in the direction of the old " ptomaine " theory, with the distinction that the poisons now regarded as responsible are not the result of advanced protein decomposition, but are products of the growth in the food of those bacteria which are able to proliferate enormously without greatly altering the appearance and taste of the food. These products are most probably the autolysed bacterial bodies themselves (see Jordan 1931, Jordan and Burrows 1935, Savage 1933, Report 1934).

Summing up, we may say that bacterial food poisoning may be due (1) to infection with living Salmonella, or occasionally dysentery, bacilli, (2) to intoxication with substances, whose nature and mode of origin is as yet imperfectly understood, which are formed as the result of undue bacterial multiplication in the food.

Bacteriology and Epidemiology of the " Infection " type of Food Poisoning

In 1888 Gaertner isolated an organism known as *Bact. enteritidis*, from the meat of an emergency-slaughtered cow, at Frankenhausen in Germany. The meat had been consumed by 58 persons, all of whom developed food poisoning. One man who had eaten about $1\frac{1}{2}$ lb. died in 36 hours. At autopsy, the same bacillus was isolated from the organs of the cadaver as from the meat. In 1898, Durham in England and de Nobele in Belgium described another organism, which they had isolated simultaneously from patients suffering from meat poisoning and from the meat that they had consumed. This organism was known until recently as *Bact. aertrycke*—Aertrycke being the name of the Belgian village where the outbreak occurred. It is now, however, called *Bact. typhi-murium*, this being the name given to an organism which was isolated by Loeffler in 1892 from a mouse epizoötic, and which was subsequently found to be identical with *Bact. aertrycke*.

The intensive study of the Salmonella group during the past few years has brought to light a number of other organisms concerned in the production of food poisoning. Of these the most important are *Bact. choleræ-suis* var. *kunzendorf*,

Bact. thompson, Bact. newport, Bact. bovis-morbificans, Bact. potsdam, and *Bact. enteritidis* var. *dublin.* Other types occasionally met with comprise *Bact. senftenberg, Bact. senftenberg* var. *newcastle, Bact. stanley, Bact. reading, Bact. derby, Bact. london, Bact. newport* var. *kottbus, Bact. bareilly, Bact. aberdeen, Bact. cholerœ-suis, Bact. panama, Bact. virchow, Bact. oranienburg,* and *Bact. heidelberg* (see Savage 1920, 1932, Savage and White 1925b, Elkeles 1930, Lovell 1932a, b, Report 1933, 1934, 1935, Smith 1933, 1934, Habs 1933, Anderson *et al.* 1935, Jones and Wright 1936, and Chapter XXVII).

So far as this country is concerned, the commonest type is undoubtedly *Bact. typhi-murium.* Thus during the years 1923–34 Scott (Report 1933, 1934, 1935) obtained the following distribution of Salmonella types in food-poisoning outbreaks that were brought to the notice of the Ministry of Health (Table CXXXVIII).

TABLE CXXXVIII

FREQUENCY OF SALMONELLA TYPES IN BRITISH FOOD-POISONING OUTBREAKS, 1923–3

Type.	Number of Outbreaks.
Bact. typhi-murium	110
Bact. enteritidis	19
Bact. thompson	16
Bact. newport	13
Bact. cholerœ-suis *Bact. cholerœ-suis* var. *kunzendorf*	8
Bact. bovis-morbificans	4
Bact. enteritidis var. *dublin*	3
Bact. potsdam	3
Bact. senftenberg var. *newcastle*	2
Bact. eastbourne	2
Bact. derby	1
Unidentified	5

Besides members of the Salmonella group, certain organisms of the dysentery group, particularly *Bact. sonnei* and *Bact. flexneri,* may be concerned in the production of food poisoning. More usually these organisms give rise to dysentery, but occasionally their ingestion in food is followed by typical gastro-enteritis (Clayton and Hunter 1928, Sowden 1933, Scott 1936).

The proportion of total food-poisoning outbreaks constituted by Salmonella infections is difficult to assess accurately. In 112 outbreaks in the British Isles recorded by Savage (1920), 39 were shown to be due to bacilli of this group. In 100 later outbreaks recorded by Savage and White (1925b), these bacilli were isolated in only 20 instances. Scott's (1936) experience at the Ministry of Health suggests that about 30 per cent. of the severer outbreaks are due to Salmonella infections.

Type of Food.—In Salmonella outbreaks the incriminated food has generally been meat, milk, fish, or other animal protein such as eggs ; vegetables and cereals are less commonly, and fruits rarely, implicated. Moreover the meat has often been made up into pâtés, pies, brawn, jellies, sausages, or other similar products—a process that involves imperfect cooking and liability to contamination. Fresh meat that has been responsible for poisoning will on investigation generally be found to have been stuffed, or re-cooked, or otherwise treated ; or it may prove to be ham that has been imperfectly pickled or cooked.

In some outbreaks the food has been prepared and allowed to stand for a time before being eaten ; in others it has been heated up again on the 2nd or 3rd days ; in others, especially in hot weather, it has been placed in the oven for an hour or so "to prevent its going bad," and not cooked and eaten till the following day.

It is important to remember that the food may, and generally does, appear quite normal to ordinary inspection. To illustrate this, van Ermengem (1896) tells a graphic story of a meat inspector in Belgium who was asked to give his opinion on some suspected sausages. Judging from their excellent appearance, their good smell, and their rosy colour, he pronounced them suitable for consumption, and to demonstrate their harmlessness he ate three slices himself. He developed acute gastro-enteritis, and died in 5 days. From his viscera at autopsy, and from the sausages, *Bact. enteritidis* was isolated. This story illustrates another point of importance—namely, that the distribution of bacilli in an article of food may be quite uneven. Though a large number of sausages were made from the same meat on the same day, only four of them were infected. This is a frequent observation, particularly in relation to canned foods ; only one or two cans of a large batch may prove harmful, showing that either the original contamination was localized, or that in the process of sterilization one or two cans, through bad packing or some other cause, failed to be raised to the temperature required to kill the bacilli.

Of recent years considerable attention has been directed towards poisoning by *eggs*. These have been derived most frequently from ducks, less often from hens and pigeons (Clarenburg and Dornickx 1932, Lovell 1932a, Scott 1933, Seligmann 1935, Hohn and Herrmann 1935, Jansen 1936). Salmonella infection of ducks, mainly by *Bact. typhi-murium* and *Bact. enteritidis* or one of its varieties, seems to be not uncommon. Beller and Reinhard (1934), in Germany who examined 1,500 duck's eggs from 34 farms, found that about 1 per cent. of them contained Salmonella organisms. Infection was present on seven of the farms, and about 2–8 per cent. of the eggs from these farms were infected. Examination of 531 fowls revealed only one that was infected with *Bact. typhi-murium* (Beller and Zeki 1934). In this country Doyle (1927) has described an epizoötic in chicks due to *Bact. typhi-murium*. It is well known, of course, that fowls often suffer from bacillary white diarrhœa due to *Bact. pullorum*, and ducks from keel disease due to *Bact. anatum*, but neither of these organisms appears to be pathogenic to human beings. On the other hand, infection with *Bact. typhi-murium* or *Bact. enteritidis* is less common, but is of considerably greater public health importance. The disease caused by these two organisms is often fairly acute and accompanied by a bacteræmia. The eggs are probably infected during their formation in the oviduct, though the organisms may gain access through the intact shell (see Scott 1933). The frequency of this form of food poisoning is peculiarly difficult to ascertain, because unless the infected egg is used for preparing a custard, mayonnaise, or some similar dish, infection is restricted to individuals, and so does not usually come to the notice of the public health authorities.

In 68·8 per cent. of the 112 British outbreaks recorded by Savage (1920), in which animal food was the vehicle, the meat was derived from the pig or the ox. Experience in other countries has been much the same. Meyer (1929), for example, reports that, in Germany between the years 1923 and 1928, out of a total of 281 outbreaks in which the animal source of origin was determined, 168 were due to cattle, 60 to pig, and 49 to horse flesh. In 137 other outbreaks sausage meat was the cause, and in a further 75 outbreaks meat of various types had been used.

Mode of Infection of the Food.—Briefly, the meat may come from an animal infected during life with a specific organism, or it may come from a healthy animal and be contaminated during the course of preparation for eating.

In the early days of bacteriology Bollinger maintained that the flesh of animals suffering from septic and pyæmic diseases was dangerous for human beings. This thesis provided the basis of our present system of meat inspection. The diseases which Bollinger had in mind were:

(1) Polyarthritis septica of calves following navel infection.
(2) Hæmorrhagic enteritis of calves and cattle.
(3) Septic metritis and mastitis of cows.
(4) Septic peritonitis, pleuritis, and pericarditis.
(5) Osteomyelitis.
(6) Septic wounds and injuries.
(7) Pyæmia following swine fever and septic pneumonias.

Whether or not the flesh of such animals is dangerous to man is disputable. Many authors (Müller 1926) deny it, maintaining that these infections bear little, if any, relation to food poisoning in man. There appears to be no doubt, however, that animals, especially cattle and pigs, may suffer from intestinal and other diseases caused by organisms of the Salmonella group (Uhlenhuth and Hübener 1913). In 1910 Zwick and Weichel (1910*b*) examined 21 cases of acute mastitis in cattle; from 19 of them they isolated a coliform organism fermenting lactose, from one *Bact. enteritidis*, and from another a paratyphoid bacillus.

Bact. enteritidis var. *dublin* is known to be responsible for the calf dysentery of Denmark, and this organism has been isolated from calves in other countries. *Bact. choleræ-suis* is frequently found in the intestine of pigs suffering from swine fever. Both *Bact. typhi-murium* and *Bact. enteritidis* have been isolated by various workers of recent years from sick animals (see Gheorghiu and Costin 1927, Lachenschmid 1931, Edwards 1934, Lovell and Hughes 1935, Hohn and Herrmann 1935, Ferrario 1935). It may be concluded, therefore, that both cattle and pigs are susceptible to infection with the various types of Salmonella organisms of the food-poisoning group: though it must be noted that neither the *dublin* nor the *choleræ-suis* type is often associated in this country with acute food poisoning; more usually the *Dublin* type gives rise to a paratyphoid-like fever, and *choleræ-suis* to an acute septicæmic or pyogenic infection.

There is ample scope for a thorough inquiry into the various types of Salmonella capable of infecting domestic animals, and of the type of disease to which they give rise. Our present knowledge suggests that the disease is usually of an acute, and often fatal, type. Elkeles (1930), who has reviewed the subject, quotes figures from Standfusz which show that in Salmonella infections of animals, 22–47 per cent. are characterized by gastro-intestinal symptoms, 11–21 per cent. by septicæmia, 11–19 per cent. by disturbances occurring at parturition, and 19–48 per cent. by other types of clinical manifestations. Whether the disease often runs a mild or sub-clinical course, and whether the animals continue to excrete the specific organisms in the fæces or urine for any considerable length of time, are questions that still await an answer. The observations of Lovell (1932*c*) on cattle, pigs, horses, and sheep do not suggest, however, that chronic carriers are common.

These findings agree with the epidemiological evidence, which shows that in most instances of food poisoning due to the consumption of meat from an infected animal, the animal has been " emergency-slaughtered." In Germany such animals afford a frequent source of human infection. No fewer than 120 of the German outbreaks recorded by Meyer (1929) between the years 1923 and 1928 were due to this cause. In this country, on the other hand, the consumption of food from obviously sick animals is uncommon, and most Salmonella meat-poisoning outbreaks are due to contamination of the meat from a healthy animal after slaughter. An exception must, however, be made for certain milk-borne outbreaks in which, either the udder of the cow is infected, or in which the milk becomes contaminated from the infected fæces of the animal. A large outbreak of the former type was recorded by Kinloch, Smith and Taylor (1926) and outbreaks of the latter type have been recorded by McAllan and Howie (1931).

Passing on to the second method of infection, we may note that opportunities for sound meat to be contaminated during the course of preparation for food are numerous, though it is notoriously difficult to detect the way in which any given article has been infected. The main sources are rats and mice, and human carriers. Both *rats* and *mice* suffer naturally from infection with *Bact. typhi-murium* and *Bact. enteritidis*.

Savage and White (1923) examined 96 rats from two slaughter houses. From 6 of them—all from one slaughter house—*Bact. enteritidis* was isolated ; 3 of them were harbouring the organism in their intestines and had presumably been excreting it before death. Moreover, 20 out of 66 rats examined contained agglutinins in their blood serum for *Bact. enteritidis*, varying in titre from 1/40 to 1/800 or higher, probably indicative either of an old or a recent infection. They quote the findings of Savage and Read, who isolated this organism from 5 out of 41 rats examined in 1913. There is evidence that outbreaks of food poisoning in man are not infrequently associated with infection of rodents with organisms of the Salmonella group (see Bainbridge 1912, Willführ and Wendtlandt 1921, Spray 1926). It is possible that other domestic animals may harbour Salmonella bacilli.

The frequency of rodent typhoid varies in different countries, and in different parts of the same country, and is often increased locally by the use of " virus " preparations. It is well known that infected animals, while suffering from a chronic disease, or showing no obvious symptoms of illness, may excrete the causative organism in the fæces for weeks or months (Topley and Ayrton 1924). Food prepared in unsanitary premises is liable to be contaminated from the droppings of these animals. A number of outbreaks are on record in which infection has been traced directly or indirectly to the use of " virus " preparations (see Jordan 1931, Report 1933, Tanner 1933, Jones and Wright 1936).

The part played by the *human carrier* is difficult to define. There are numerous instances in which Salmonella organisms have been found in the fæces of persons not suffering from food poisoning.

Thus Fletcher (see Perry 1920) found *Bact. typhi-murium* in the fæces of three soldiers who were convalescing from dysentery or enteric fever. Trommsdorf, Rajchman and Porter (1911), in their investigations of the Wrexham outbreak of 1910 due to pork pies, found that the head cook was a chronic carrier, and was excreting an organism of the Salmonella group in her fæces. Sporadic cases of infection with organisms of the Salmonella group are not uncommon (Rosher and Wilson 1921). A large outbreak of food poisoning in France during the War due to the Newport bacillus was ascribed by Perry and Tidy

(1919) to a human carrier in the cook-house. Both Jordan (1917) and Geiger (1923) in America are convinced of the importance of the human carrier.

In spite of these findings, certain workers, notably Savage (1932), deny that the human carrier plays more than a quite insignificant part in the causation of food poisoning. In 121 outbreaks investigated by Savage there were only 5 in which a human carrier seemed to have been responsible for infection of the food. Other workers, however, such as Jordan (1917) and Geiger (1923), would ascribe more importance to this mode of infection. Considering how difficult it is to trace the exact source of infection, we shall probably be wise to reserve our judgment on this issue. That chronic Salmonella carriers, analogous to chronic typhoid carriers, are uncommon, there seems to be little doubt ; but considering the frequency of rodent typhoid, it would be surprising if sporadic infections of human beings, particularly those used to handling food, did not occur fairly often. Such infections are likely to be characterized by gastro-intestinal disturbance lasting a few days, and to be accompanied by excretion of the causative organism in the fæces. Temporary carriers of this type must always be a danger to the human population. Their detection by bacteriological methods is bound to be difficult, since their carrier condition will often have cleared up before suspicion is cast upon them. The frequency of Salmonella bacilli in sewage (Scott 1936) rather suggests that human carriers are more common than is generally supposed.

Finally, it may be noted that in food-poisoning outbreaks due to food derived from a sick animal, *Bact. enteritidis* or one of its varieties is most frequently found, while in outbreaks due to sound meat contaminated during its course of preparation for food, *Bact. typhi-murium* is the predominant organism (see Bainbridge 1912, Mayer 1913, Jordan 1917).

Bacteriology and Epidemiology of the "Toxin" Type of Food Poisoning

The clinical manifestations of this type of food poisoning, which come on after a very short incubation period, have already been described. The type of food involved varies considerably. Usually it is some form of canned or potted meat or fish, but other articles such as pickled or pressed beef, tongue or ham, cheese or milk, may be incriminated (Report 1935).

Up till recently little was known about the causation of these outbreaks, but the work of Dack and Jordan and their associates in the United States has afforded a definite pointer towards the probable mechanism involved. In 1914 Barber, working in the Philippines, reported a very clear instance of a "toxin" outbreak due to the growth of a white staphylococcus in the milk of a certain cow. Immediately after withdrawal from the udder, the milk could be consumed with impunity, but if it was allowed to stand for a few hours at room temperature, 28°–30° C., it gave rise within about 2 hours to nausea, vomiting, abdominal pain, diarrhœa, cramps, and faintness. Similar symptoms were produced in human volunteers by the consumption of pure milk cultures of the strain of *Staph. albus* isolated from the cow in question, though kittens, puppies, and monkeys proved refractory. This report furnished in its general outlines an almost complete picture of the causative factors responsible for a "toxin" outbreak. Unfortunately, however, no particular attention seems to have been paid to it, and it was not till the rediscovery several years later by Dack and his colleagues (1930) of staphylococcal food poisoning that the subject attracted the attention it deserved. Since that time numerous outbreaks caused by the production of a toxic substance elaborated by staphylococci in the food have been described (Dack *et al.* 1930, 1935, Jordan 1931, Jordan and Hall 1931, McBurney 1933, Jordan and Burrows 1934, Report 1934). Most of the outbreaks have followed the consumption of milk products, particularly cakes and éclairs filled with cream or custard, though some have been traced to gravy or to canned meat or fish. The circumstances have invariably been such as to favour the multiplication of the organisms in the food prior to its consumption. No one type of staphylococcus has been involved, and no method at present exists, apart from the feeding of broth filtrates to human volunteers, of determining whether a given strain is toxigenic (Stritar and Jordan 1935). The observations of Dolman (1934) suggest that this particular property is possessed by very few staphylococcal strains. Their source of origin is still in doubt, but considering the frequency of staphylococci in the cow's udder, the human throat, and skin, contamination of food with these organisms must be relatively common. Only, however, when the conditions are favourable for their growth in the food, is their presence likely to be of danger. Little is yet known about the nature of the toxin produced. It is clearly distinct from the hæmolytic and necrotic toxins of the staphylococci (see Chapter XXIV); it is comparatively heat resistant, not being completely destroyed by boiling even for 30 minutes; it gives rise to acute gastro-enteritis with severe collapse when consumed by human volunteers in doses of 2–10 c.c. ; it appears to be relatively non-toxic when fed to most laboratory animals, though young *rhesus* monkeys may be affected after a dose of 25–50 c.c. ; it is of doubtful antigenicity, and little tolerance to it seems to be developed in the human subject as the result of repeated dosage (see Jordan 1930, Jordan, Dack, and Woolpert 1931, Dack, Jordan, and Woolpert 1931*a*, Dack *et al.* 1931*b*, Jordan and Burrows 1933).

The occurrence of staphylococcal food-poisoning outbreaks has suggested an explanation for many of the other " toxin " outbreaks. For several years banal organisms such as *Proteus vulgaris* and *Bact. coli* have been found in suspected food, but their importance has generally been discounted on the basis of their non-pathogenicity to laboratory animals. It is now becoming increasingly clear, both on epidemiological and bacteriological grounds, that a number of organisms, many of them non-pathogenic, when allowed to grow in food under suitable conditions, are able to give rise to toxic substances having a highly irritating effect on the human gastro-intestinal mucosa.

Jansen and Dooren de Jong (1930) record a highly suggestive outbreak of this type. Several hundred persons, who had attended a festive dinner in Rotterdam and afterwards proceeded to the theatre, were seized within 1–2 hours of the meal with acute gastro-enteritis. The symptoms comprised general malaise, severe vomiting, offensive diarrhœa, pallor, cold sweats, gastric oppression, faintness, and sometimes unconsciousness. After thorough evacuation most of the patients recovered in about 12 hours and were able to resume their work. Bacteriological examination of the 22 articles of food that had been consumed at the dinner was begun in the early hours of the next morning. Chief suspicion fell on a potato purée, which, after its preparation had been left for 8 hours on a rack above the oven. At the time of examination this article contained about 200 million organisms per gram, of which 50 million were *Bact. coli*. In spite of an intensive search, no organisms of the Salmonella group were found, and chemical examination of the food for heavy metals, arsenic, and alkaloids was negative. The inference, which was supported by epidemiological inquiry, that the potato purée contained a toxin that had been formed during its incubation period above the stove, is very strong, though in the absence of experiments on human volunteers, it must still remain an inference.

Similar outbreaks apparently due to the inordinate growth of coliform organisms in milk, or of streptococci in fish, cheese, or cream pies have been recorded by Aoki and Sakai (1926), Gustafson (1932), Linden, Turner, and Thom (1926), and Jordan and Burrows (1934). In the last outbreak viridans streptococci were shown to produce in culture a filtrable toxin capable of causing acute gastro-enteritis when administered to monkeys in a dose of 25 c.c. Outbreaks associated with *Proteus vulgaris* or *Proteus morgani* have been described by Glücksmann (1899), Silberschmidt (1899), Pfuhl (1900), Demnitz (1926) and several others, while Tanner and Ramsey (1932) have recorded an outbreak of poisoning due to the multiplication of a micrococcus in milk.

The more recent work of Jordan and Burrows (1935) has lent added support to this conception of food poisoning. These workers find that freshly isolated bacteria of various types, such as staphylococci, streptococci, *Proteus*, *Bact. coli*, *Bact. œrogenes*, and *Bact. typhi-murium*, when grown under suitable conditions, are capable of producing substances that cause vomiting and other symptoms of gastro-intestinal irritation in monkeys. The exact conditions necessary to the production of these substances have not yet been defined, but growth in a custard medium, or in a medium to which starch has been added, appears to be particularly favourable.

By successive transfers on a starch medium Jordan and Burrows were able to restore the property of enterotoxin production to strains that had lost it, and to induce this property in strains in which it had never previously been demonstrated.

A discussion on the nature of these toxic substances would serve no useful purpose at the moment, since our knowledge of them is far too fragmentary. We would rather pose a question to be answered by further work. Are these bodies formed as the result of the synthetic activities of the bacteria, or are they the product of simple protein disintegration? There is a good deal of evidence that certain organisms, notably members of the Salmonella group, contain in their bodies thermostable toxic substances which are soluble in water, and are precipitated by alcohol or concentrated acetic acid (Brieger and Fraenkel 1890, Cathcart 1906a, Ecker 1917, Savage and White 1925a, Menten 1926, Bahr and Dyssegaard 1927, Meyn 1930). The method of extracting these bodies has been described by Raistrick and Topley (1934), who have found that they are of polysaccharide nature. Injected intravenously into rabbits, they give rise to great weakness and prostration, often accompanied by tremors, diarrhœa, and hyperglycæmia (Delafield 1934), while their injection intraperitoneally into mice in a dose of about 0·5 mgm. proves fatal (Martin 1934). Whether these bodies, which appear to represent part of the normal somatic structure of the organisms, are identical with the enterotoxic substances found free in starch medium cultures put up by Jordan and Burrows' (1935) method, and whether the enterotoxic substances formed by different organisms have the same general chemical structure, are questions that still await an answer. There seems to be a considerable field of inquiry open for a study of these bodies along chemical and biological lines.

Summarizing, we may say that evidence has been accumulating in the past few years to show that many of the "toxin" outbreaks of food poisoning are due to the production of toxic substances in the food prior to its consumption. These substances, the exact nature of which is still unknown, are formed under suitable conditions by a number of different bacteria, of which staphylococci, streptococci, coliform, *Proteus*, and possibly Salmonella, organisms appear to be the most important.

The frequency of the " toxin " type of outbreak varies in different countries. In Great Britain probably about one-third of the reported outbreaks are due to staphylococcal intoxication (Scott 1936). Another third may be due to toxic substances formed by other species of bacteria, but our information is as yet too scanty to enable us to make any definite statement. One factor that greatly hinders exact knowledge on this subject is the absence of any simple laboratory method for detecting the presence of toxic substances in the food or in filtrates of broth cultures of suspected organisms. For this reason many bacteriological reports are completely negative, and no further attention is paid to the outbreaks. One fact does seem clear, namely that poisoning due to canned beef is becoming much less common in this country, owing apparently to the improvements made during recent years in processing. Another interesting fact is the comparative infrequency now of summer diarrhœa of infants. Though this condition is usually of an infectious nature, there is a good deal of evidence to suggest that milk in which inordinate bacterial growth has been allowed to occur may contain substances having an irritating effect on the gastro-intestinal mucosa, particularly of infants. Attention was drawn to this possibility many years ago by Park and Holt (1903). There is reason to believe that one factor in the diminution of summer diarrhœa of late years has been the much greater care exercised in the production of milk, and the frequency with which it is now submitted to pasteurization or other forms of heat treatment.

Diagnosis and Investigation of Outbreaks.

The diagnosis of food poisoning is primarily clinical. For the full investigation of an outbreak the reader is referred to textbooks of Hygiene, but the general procedure is briefly as follows : (1) Secure a complete list of cases. (2) Obtain particulars of individual cases. (3) Ascertain the vehicle of infection. (4) Study the history of the implicated food. (5) Search for evidence pointing to the source of infection of the food.

Materials collected for examination should include (1) the actual food consumed ; it is most important that this should be obtained : (2) the vomit and fæces of patients, and the blood for agglutination : (3) the blood, spleen, liver and intestine of fatal cases : (4) the fæces and blood of suspected carriers who may have contaminated the food. The material should be sent to the laboratory packed in ice. A bacteriological examination should first be made, and if this is negative, search should be made for chemical poisons or preservatives in the food.

In Salmonella outbreaks the organisms can frequently be demonstrated in the food, and in the fæces of the patient ; vomited matter is much less satisfactory. In their isolation the general plan should be to plate suspensions of the suspected material on to suitable selective and differential media (see Chapter LXVI), both directly and after incubation in brilliant green peptone water, to pick off likely colonies, to identify them roughly by the slide agglutination method using special group sera, and to complete their identification later by cultural, biochemical, and more detailed serological methods. For a description of the general method of investigating food-poisoning outbreaks and of identifying Salmonella types, reference should be made to a Memorandum by the Ministry of Health (Memo. 1935). Attention must also be paid to the possible presence of *Bact. sonnei* and *Bact. flexneri*. The length of time during which Salmonella organisms can be isolated varies considerably. Perry and Tidy (1919), reporting on a large outbreak in France affecting over 1,000 men, found that 50 per cent. of the patients ceased to excrete the organisms by the end of the 4th week ; one patient, however, was still excreting them after 14 weeks.

Suspected material may be inoculated into mice or guinea-pigs, but this procedure is attended by grave danger. Laboratory rodents often suffer from natural infection with the very types of Salmonella that are most likely to be found in cases of food poisoning. In consequence, bacilli may be isolated from the tissues other than those contained in the inoculum. Many careful workers have fallen victim to this type of occurrence (Holth 1909, Mühlens *et al.* 1909, Zwick and Weichel 1910*a*). A similar technique applied to the fæces of healthy animals such as cattle and pigs has also been responsible, it may be noted, for grossly misleading reports on the frequency of Salmonella bacilli in normal excreta. Unless therefore a stock of animals is available which is known to be free from this type of infection, it is advisable not to use the animal inoculation method.

An indirect method, which may sometimes be of help in ascertaining the nature of the infecting organism, is afforded by the use of the agglutination test on the sera of the patients. The value of this method, however, is seriously diminished (1) by the fact that the agglutinin response in infected persons is generally poor, and (2) by the fact that agglutinins to organisms of the Salmonella group are not infrequently present in the sera of healthy persons. In patients with a previous history of enteric fever, and in those who have received typhoid-paratyphoid inoculation, the titre is often comparatively high (see Chapter LXVI). For this reason, if any attention is to be paid to the agglutination test in the diagnosis of food poisoning, it is desirable to examine the serum of each patient at the earliest possible moment, and again 10 days or so later. Unless a considerable rise in titre occurs during this interval, no definite conclusions should be drawn from the result. If this method is employed, the range of antigens selected for testing should be representative of the organisms most commonly found in the area in which the outbreak has occurred. In this country, such a series might include the following organisms (Table CXXXIX).

TABLE CXXXIX

SHOWING THE ANTIGENS TO BE EMPLOYED IN THE EXAMINATION OF THE PATIENTS' SERA FOR AGGLUTININS.

Group.	Species.	O antigen.	H antigen. Specific.	H antigen. Non-specific.
A	{ *Bact. senftenberg* var. *newcastle* O .	I, III	—	—
	{ *Bact. senftenberg* var. *newcastle* H .	—	g s	—
B	{ *Bact. typhi-murium* O	IV, V	—	—
	{ *Bact. typhi-murium* H	—	i	1, 2, 3
C	{ *Bact. choleræ-suis* O	VI, VII	—	—
	{ *Bact. choleræ-suis* H	—	c	1, 3, 4, 5
D	{ *Bact. enteritidis* O	IX	—	—
	{ *Bact. enteritidis* H	—	g o m	—
E	{ *Bact. london* O	X, III	—	—
	{ *Bact. london* H	—	l v	1, 4, 6

In practice, however, it usually suffices at first to test the patient's blood serum against the *typhi-murium*, the *enteritidis*, and the *newport* types, choosing preferably chloroformed suspensions giving both H and O agglutination (Scott 1936). A positive result, while indicating the probable group to which the infecting organism belong, does not of course enable the exact species to be defined. The only satisfactory method of doing this is to isolate the actual organism involved.

In the absence of demonstrable evidence of Salmonella or dysentery infection, an endeavour should be made, particularly in outbreaks of the " toxin " type, to discover the presence of toxic substances of bacterial origin in the food or of organisms capable of forming such substances. The investigation of this type of outbreak is remarkably difficult. Often the only way of demonstrating the presence of these toxic bodies is to administer the suspected material to young *rhesus* monkeys. Organisms of any one type isolated from the food in large numbers, especially such organisms as staphylococci, streptococci, coliform and *Proteus* bacilli, should be cultivated under the conditions known to be favourable for toxin production (see Jordan and Burrows 1935), and broth filtrates should be tested on monkeys or human volunteers. It is clear that the mere presence of potential toxin-producing organisms in the food is not sufficient evidence of their actual guilt, since food may be undoubtedly contaminated with these organisms without becoming poisonous. In many of these outbreaks even a careful review of all the evidence, epidemiological and bacteriological, will justify no more than a cautious expression of opinion as to their mode of origin. As has already been pointed out, there is ample scope for investigation of this type of outbreak, and it is to be hoped that in the future an attempt will be made to ascertain the chemical nature of the bacterial toxins found in the food.

The examination of canned foods should be conducted on the same principles as that of fresh food, but there are a number of technical details to be attended to ; for a description of these the reader is referred to articles by Esty and Stevenson (1925), Savage (1923), and Esty (1935).

Prophylaxis.

The hygienic precautions necessary to prevent food poisoning concern the whole course of the food from the slaughter of the animal to the final preparation for consumption. A thorough system of meat inspection is essential. The meat of animals that are ill or are emergency-slaughtered should as a rule be condemned. To this precaution alone Meyer (1916) attributes the comparative infrequency of meat poisoning in California, where it is known that calves are infected with *Bact. enteritidis*. The laxity of the meat inspection in Germany since the War appears to have resulted in a great increase in the number of poisoning outbreaks. The measures to be taken to ensure the cleanliness of premises where made-up meat is prepared are dealt with fully in textbooks of Hygiene. It is particularly important not to employ cooks who have previously suffered from enteric infections. Everything should be done to prevent the access of rats, mice, or other animals to food destined for human consumption.

Meat should be used fresh whenever possible, and should be thoroughly cooked before it is eaten. Cooking, it must be understood, does not necessarily sterilize the meat. The penetration of heat into a large joint is slow, and the interior may not reach, or may not be maintained long enough at, a temperature sufficient to kill all the organisms. This is especially true of food contained in cans, which, even after heating to above the boiling-point for an hour or more, may yet contain living organisms—generally thermophilic or spore-bearing bacilli or resistant micrococci. Several workers have shown that about 70 per cent. of samples of canned foods are not sterile (Vaillard 1902, Bushnell 1922, Savage 1923). On the other hand, food poisoning is far less often caused by canned foods than by made-up foods. This is to be attributed partly to the greater heating that the former receive, but largely to the much greater care that is used in their preparation. But cooking is a wise precautionary measure ; even if it fails to kill all organisms, it probably succeeds in diminishing their numbers. If the food is not to be eaten immediately after it has been cooked, it should be placed in a cool situation, preferably in an ice-chest ; otherwise organisms that have escaped destruction may multiply abundantly. That this is true is manifested by the Chesterfield outbreak, which was due to the consumption of pork pies. In persons who ate them 2 days after they had been cooked, the incubation period was 22 hours ; in those who ate them 4 days after cooking it was 20 hours ; 6 days after cooking it was 14 hours, and 7 days after it was only $2\frac{1}{4}$ hours, showing that the organisms had multiplied abundantly since the preparation of the pies (see also Baars 1931). This precaution applies to all foods, especially milk. After pasteurization or boiling the milk should be rapidly cooled. In the preparation of ice-cream Buchan (1910) found that an enormous increase of bacteria occurred during the process of slow cooling that is employed after the preliminary heating.

The consumption of any animal food in the raw condition is attended by a certain amount of risk. This is particularly true of milk and cream. There is general agreement that, for the prevention of food poisoning and other milk-borne diseases, these articles should be submitted to pasteurization or other adequate form of heat treatment.

BOTULISM

INTRODUCTORY

Botulism (from Latin *botulus*, a sausage), sometimes known as allantiasis, or ichthyosismus, is a disease that was first described in 1820 by the German poet and medical writer Justinus Kerner (Jordan 1917). The causative bacterium was isolated and described by van Ermengem in 1896 (1896, 1897). Following on a festive gathering of a music club at the village of Ellezelles in Belgium, several of the members were taken ill, and three of them died within a week. The disease was confined to those who had partaken of a certain piece of raw ham ; the other ham and the remainder of the animal had been previously consumed without causing trouble. The contaminated ham, which was paler and softer than normal and smelt rancid, had during the process of pickling been placed at the bottom of the vessel and had come into contact with the brine. When fed to cats it caused mydriasis, partial paresis, secretory disturbances, aphonia, and other symptoms. From it van Ermengem cultivated a strictly anaerobic organism, which secreted a powerful toxin, giving rise to the same symptoms in cats as those caused by the original ham.

Since that date several outbreaks of botulism have been recorded, some in Germany, but more in America, where of late years the disease has attracted general attention. In this country only three small outbreaks have been described. (See p. 1271.)

Symptomatology and Pathology.

The incubation period is generally under 24 hours after consumption of the affected food, but may be prolonged to 72 hours. Prominent among the symptoms are vomiting, constipation, ocular pareses, thirst, pharyngeal paralysis, the secretion of thick, viscid saliva, and sometimes aphonia. General consciousness and sensibility remain intact till near the end, which is preceded by coma or delirium. The temperature is generally subnormal—96–98° F. Later in the illness it may rise owing to the onset of broncho-pneumonia (Dickson 1918). Death may occur within 24 hours from the time of onset, or may be delayed for a week. In cases that survive, complete recovery, particularly of the ocular movements, may not take place for 6 or 8 months.

At autopsy the kidneys, liver, and meninges are congested. Histological examination of the organs may reveal the presence of thrombosis. Kempner and Pollack (1897), Marinesco, and several of the earlier workers, found changes in the nerve cells of the brain and spinal cord of animals dying from *botulinum* poisoning, but recent work (Dickson and Shevky 1923, Cowdry and Nicholson 1924) suggests that the main effect of the toxin is exerted on the peripheral nerve endings, possibly those of the autonomic system. Contrary to the findings in tetanus, there appears to be no fixation of the toxin by the brain tissue (Coleman 1924).

Bacteriology.

Botulism is an intoxication, not an infection. The causative organism, *Cl. botulinum*, multiplies in the food before it is consumed, and produces a powerful soluble toxin, which on ingestion is absorbed by the mucosa of the stomach and upper part of the intestine, and gives rise to the characteristic disease. The potency of this toxin is such that the fatal dose for an adult man, calculated on the basis of animal experiments, might be as small as 1/100 mgm. or even less (Bengston 1924). The smallest lethal dose of the strongest tetanus toxin that has yet been prepared is about 25 times as great as this. Its ability to pass through the gastric mucosa unchanged differentiates it from tetanus or diphtheria toxin, both of which are harmless when given by the mouth. This may be due partly to its resistance to acids ; in an alkaline medium, such as prevails throughout the greater part of the small intestine, it is unstable. Of the two types of *Cl. botulinum* that have been encountered in human botulism (see p. 678), Type A is much commoner than Type B ; thus in 23 outbreaks occurring recently in America, 19 were due to Type A, and only 4 to Type B (Editorial 1926).

Though the disease is essentially an intoxication, evidence has been accumulating that under certain conditions the organism may multiply to a limited extent in the animal body. It is not necessary to examine this evidence in detail, but briefly it has been found (Edmondson *et al.* 1920*b*, Orr 1920, 1922, Coleman and Meyer 1922, Graham and Eriksen 1922, Coleman 1923, Hall and Davis 1923, Starin and Dack 1925) that if spores, which have been freed of their toxin by repeated washing or by heating to 80° C. for half an hour, are injected subcutaneously into guinea-pigs in large doses—500 million or so—or are given by the mouth in still larger doses—about 2,000 million—they may give rise to fatal disease ; from the spleen, liver, kidneys, or mesenteric glands the bacilli may be recovered in pure culture after death. The experiments on which these findings are based are not very convincing ; doubtless after such massive doses the spores are disseminated throughout the body. But it is doubtful whether germination of the spores occurs or whether the resultant bacilli multiply and form toxin. Since it is extremely difficult to free spores completely from all traces of toxin, especially by washing, and since very small quantities are required to kill a guinea-pig—1/10,000 mgm. or less—it is not surprising that some animals injected with so-called toxin-free spores succumb to the disease.

Even if it is possible experimentally to reproduce a true infection with *Cl. botulinum*, there is no evidence that under natural conditions the disease in man is other than a pure intoxication. In this view the majority of authors strongly concur (van Ermengem 1897, Römer 1900, Armstrong *et al.* 1919, Burke *et al.* 1921, Geiger *et al.* 1922).

A disease closely simulating botulism in man can be reproduced by the experimental inoculation or feeding of cats, monkeys, and certain other animals with toxic material (see Chapter XXXIII).

Epidemiology.

Botulism is due to the consumption of food in which *Cl. botulinum* has been growing. It occurs therefore in sporadic outbreaks limited to those who have partaken of the contaminated food. Since the disease is an intoxication, not an infection, secondary cases do not occur, but it is common for cats, dogs, and especially chickens that are fed on the remnants of the food to develop symptoms of poisoning.

Botulism is not a common disease. From 1899 to 1925, 146 outbreaks were reported in the U.S.A. and Canada, affecting 504 persons ; of these 337 died—a case mortality of 67 per cent. (Editorial 1926). Bacteriological evidence of the nature of the disease was available in 53 of these outbreaks. These figures probably underestimate the incidence of the disease ; at any rate it appears to have become commoner during the last few years when greater attention has been focussed upon it. During the 8 years 1918–25 in the U.S.A. there were about 13 outbreaks per annum.

In Germany 24 outbreaks of suspected botulism were reported between 1907 and 1923, but in only one of these was *Cl. botulinum* isolated. In the British Isles only 3 outbreaks have been recorded, the largest of which occurred in 1922 at Loch Maree in Scotland, when 8 persons were attacked after eating potted duck paste ; all the patients died within a week. *Cl. botulinum* Type A was cultivated from the remnants of the paste (Leighton 1923). The remaining two were in London (see Lane and Jone-Davies 1935, Annotation 1935). In America the disease is commoner during the winter months—the season of preserved food consumption.

Morbidity and Mortality Rate.—In any outbreak the morbidity rate is high. As a rule all who partake of the contaminated food develop the disease. The mortality rate varies in different outbreaks. In Germany it is said to be not more than 25 per cent. (Mayer 1913), but in America it is 60–70 per cent. (Burke *et al.* 1921). The earlier the symptoms appear, the higher is the mortality rate; of those that develop symptoms in 24 hours 84 per cent. die ; of those that develop symptoms in 72 hours 55 per cent. die ; and of those that are alive after the 8th day 20 per cent. die (Burke *et al.* 1921).

Type of Food.—Nearly all the reported outbreaks of botulism have been caused by food that has been smoked, pickled, or canned, allowed to stand for a time, and eaten before cooking, or after inadequate cooking (Jordan 1917). No cases have yet followed the consumption of fresh food, cooked or uncooked. In several instances those who have consumed the affected food after cooking have escaped, whereas those who have consumed it prior to cooking have been attacked (Geiger *et al.* 1922). There is a difference between Europe and America in the type of food responsible for poisoning. In Europe most cases have been due to sausages, ham, preserved meats, game pâtés, potted goose or duck, and brawn ; a few, especially in Russia, have been ascribed to salted fish, such as salmon and sturgeon (van Ermengem 1897, Nitta 1919). In America, on the other hand, the contaminated foods have generally been canned fruits and vegetables, such as olives (Armstrong *et al.* 1919, Edmondson *et al.* 1920*a*), string beans (Geiger *et al.* 1922, Geiger 1924, Stricker and Geiger 1924), corn (Geiger *et al.* 1922, Geiger 1924), spinach (Geiger 1920), and peas (Editorial 1926). A few have been due to cooked meat or fish (Editorial 1926), and some to cheese (Nevin 1921). Home-canned string beans alone accounted for 19 out of 55 recent outbreaks in America (Editorial 1926).

In the majority of instances, the preserved foods have been noticeably spoiled. The cans are often blown and show numerous gas bubbles on opening ; the solid part of the food has a mushy or disintegrated appearance, and smells like rancid butter or cheese (Burke 1919*c*). In the case of ham the flesh is often paler and softer than normal, and has a rancid odour (van Ermengem 1897, Savage and White 1925*b*). The food, however, may be well preserved.

Mode of Infection of the Food and Distribution of Cl. botulinum in Nature.

The most extensive investigations on the distribution of *Cl. botulinum* in nature have been conducted by Meyer and his colleagues in America. It is abundantly clear that the organism is a normal inhabitant of the surface layers of the soil, from which it may obtain access to vegetables, fruits, hay, silage, and other cultivated produce. It may be transported by insects, and it may be eaten by horses, cattle, and other animals. In America it is common in the soils of the Western States of the Cordilleran system. It is less frequent in the Atlantic States, and is relatively rare in the Middle States, the Great Plains, and the Mississippi valley. The following tables (Tables CXL and CXLI), taken from Meyer and Dubovsky (1922*b*), illustrate the frequency with which it is encountered in different types of soils, and in vegetables and fodder.

In a similar study made of the soil and vegetable produce in California, 624 samples were examined ; 206 yielded toxic cultures (Meyer and Dubovsky 1922*a*). Taking together the figures for the U.S.A. including California, Meyer and Dubovsky found that 581 of 2,162 samples examined showed the presence of *Cl. botulinum*, *i.e.* 26·8 per cent. Three hundred and ninety-five strains were typed ; 250 or 63·3 per cent. were Type A, 138 or 34·9 per cent. were Type B, and 7 or 1·8 per cent. were mixed A and B.

From Table CXL it will be noticed that *Cl. botulinum* was commoner in virgin soils and pasture than in cultivated soils and manure. This has been held to indicate that the organism is a natural inhabitant of the soil and not merely a contaminant derived from animal fæces. Indeed the older view that the organism is a natural inhabitant of the intestine of animals, and is spread by their fæces, must be abandoned.

Meyer and Dubovsky (1922*c*) likewise examined specimens of soil from Belgium, Denmark, the Netherlands, England, and Switzerland. *Cl. botulinum* Type B was demonstrated in a variable proportion of soils from the different countries, but in not a single instance was Type A found. From this country 64 specimens were examined, and 9 of them yielded toxic cultures ; the counties furnishing the positive results were Durham, Derbyshire, Middlesex, Hereford and Sussex, thus indicating a widespread distribution of the organism. In Scotland, Leighton and Buxton (1928), in an examination of 100 samples of soil, encountered *Cl. botulinum* four times ; two of the cultures belonged to

TABLE CXL. Modified from Meyer and Dubovsky (1922*b*).

DISTRIBUTION OF *Cl. botulinum* IN DIFFERENT TYPES OF SOILS IN ALL STATES OF AMERICA, WITH THE EXCEPTION OF CALIFORNIA AND VIRGINIA.

	Specimens Examined.	Toxic Cultures.	Weak Toxin.	Type A.	Type B.	Types A and B.
Virgin soil	335	105	22	59	22	2
Cultivated soils	274	47	13	18	16	—
Garden soils	142	41	12	23	6	—
Soil and manure from animal corrals and yards .	161	20	9	6	5	—
Pasture	51	19	5	3	11	—

Type A, one to Type B, while the remaining one contained both Types A and B. Both types of *Cl. botulinum* have been demonstrated in the soils of Canada, China, and at least one of the Pacific Islands (Dubovsky and Meyer 1922*b*, Schoenholz and Meyer 1922).

TABLE CXLI. Modified from Meyer and Dubovsky (1922*b*).

DISTRIBUTION OF *Cl. botulinum* IN DIFFERENT VEGETABLES AND FODDER IN ALL STATES OF AMERICA, WITH THE EXCEPTION OF CALIFORNIA AND VIRGINIA.

	Total No. Examined.	Positive Cultures.	Percentage of Positive Cultures.
Mouldy hay	44	7	15·9
String beans, pods and stalks . . .	44	14	31·8
Decayed vegetation	29	6	20·6
Ensilage	15	3	20·0
Corn husks, leaves and stalks . . .	80	6	7·5
Beets, roots and tops	37	6	16·2
Tomato plant and roots	24	2	8·3

Meyer and Dubovsky's results have not as yet received general confirmation; some of their conclusions may have to be modified (Geiger and Benson 1923, Bachmann and Haynes 1924), and more work must be carried out before the relationship of the two types to environmental conditions can be definitely determined.

Cl. botulinum is present occasionally in the fæces of animals such as pigs, cattle, and horses (Burke 1919*a*, Tanner and Dack 1922, Easton and Meyer 1924), which feed on soil produce, but there is no evidence that it is a natural intestinal inhabitant. It is rarely present in the fæces of healthy human beings; Easton and Meyer (1924) failed to find it in 88 specimens examined, even though it was known that the spores were being ingested on raw fruits and vegetables used as food. Kahn (1924) likewise obtained negative results when examining the anaerobic flora of the stools of 72 persons.

Factors influencing the Development of Cl. botulinum in Canned Foods.—It is difficult to understand why, with such a wide distribution of *Cl. botulinum* in the soil and on fruits and vegetables, botulism itself is so uncommon. The organism is unable to grow in the animal body and give rise to infection; fresh foods, cooked or uncooked, may therefore be eaten with impunity. For botulism to result, the organism must multiply and form its toxin in the food before consumption. But even so one would expect the incidence of the disease from canned foods to be far greater than it is. We know that the spores of *Cl. botulinum* may withstand boiling for from half an hour to 22 hours (Bigelow and Esty 1920, Weiss 1921, Esty and Meyer 1922, Tanner and Twohey 1926), and a temperature of 120° C. for as long as 20 minutes. In the Loch Maree outbreak the potted duck paste had been heated during the process of manufacture at three different stages, the temperature in one stage approximating to 115° C. for 2 hours. Heat alone is therefore not sufficient to explain why the majority of canned foods are innocuous. Other factors must be involved.

The hydrogen-ion concentration of the food has an important bearing on the efficacy of sterilization. Esty and Meyer (1922) found that at pH 7·0 the spores were destroyed in 330 minutes at 100° C.; at pH 5·05 in 45 minutes, and at pH 3·7 in 10 minutes. The higher the hydrogen-ion concentration, the shorter is the time required for destruction (Bigelow and Esty 1920, Weiss 1921). The presence of sodium chloride in the food lowers the thermal resistance, which decreases with increasing concentration of the salt (Weiss 1921). The smaller the number of spores in the food the shorter is the time necessary to kill them (Bigelow and Esty 1920). Spores from young cultures are said to be more resistant to heat than those from old (Weiss 1921, Esty and Meyer 1922, Tanner and Dack 1922). These are some of the factors influencing the sterilization of the food.

It has also been found that spores of *Cl. botulinum* may remain dormant for days, weeks or months before germinating (Dickson *et al.* 1925). The type of food influences the development of the bacilli; string beans, spinach, corn, peas, and salmon appear to be specially favourable for growth; acid fruits and vegetables are less so (Koser *et al.* 1921, Geiger and Benson 1923, Schoenholz *et al.* 1923, Bachmann 1924). The presence of other organisms, such as *Cl. sporogenes*, apparently interferes with development (Jordan and Dack 1924). Finally, not all strains of *Cl. botulinum* form toxin (Bengtson 1922*b*) though the majority appear to do so (Starin 1924).

It is probable that a large number of factors determine the survival, germination, multiplication, and toxin production of *Cl. botulinum* in canned food. Unless these factors are favourably combined the food remains innocuous. The most important of these appear to be (1) the presence of spores in suitable numbers, (2) insufficient heating, (3) anaerobic conditions, (4) too slow cooking, (5) the use of the food without final cooking. The records make it clear that the danger from home-canned food is far greater than from that which is commercially prepared.

Diagnosis.

The symptoms of botulism in man are generally so characteristic as to render the disease capable of being diagnosed on clinical grounds. To confirm this diagnosis the following procedure should be adopted.

A. Demonstration of Botulinum Toxin in the Suspected Food.—For rapid diagnosis the food is suspended in saline, and injected intraperitoneally into three mice. A few hours before the injection, one mouse is given subcutaneously a small dose of antitoxin Type A and another Type B. Alternatively the food suspension may be added to the antitoxin, and the mixture injected subcutaneously. If the control mouse and one of the protected mice die, it may be provisionally concluded that *botulinum* toxin was present in the food, corresponding to the type of antitoxin which was given to the surviving mouse.

Meanwhile the food should be seeded into 2 per cent. glucose broth, Hitchens' medium (0·2 per cent. dextrose infusion broth containing 0·1 per cent. agar), beef heart peptic digest liver broth, peptonized bullock's heart broth (de Lavergne and Abel 1925), or cooked meat medium, and incubated anaerobically for 10 days at 35° C. The culture is then filtered, and the filtrate tested by intraperitoneal injection of mice or subcutaneous injection of guinea-pigs ; antiserum Type A and B should be administered to two of the animals in order to determine the type of toxin present.

B. Isolation of the Bacillus from the Food.—Pure cultures may be obtained by heating broth cultures to 80° C. for half an hour to destroy contaminating non-sporing bacilli, and seeding into deep agar cultures, which are incubated anaerobically. The characteristic colonies should be picked off, grown in liquid medium, and tested for toxin production (Burke 1919*b*). Single colonies may likewise be obtained by plating the broth culture, after heating, on 5 per cent. horse blood extract agar plates incubated anaerobically (Wheeler and Humphreys 1924).

C. Isolation of Cl. botulinum from the Patient's Fæces or Vomit.—It is worth while attempting to culture the organism from the patient's fæces or vomit ; the same method should be employed as for culturing it from food. Wheeler and Humphreys (1924) obtained pure cultures from the fæces of a woman on the 6th day of disease. Positive results have also been reported on fæces taken from the 6th to the 12th day of the disease (Dubovsky and Meyer 1922*a*).

D. Isolation of Cl. botulinum from the Intestinal Contents and Viscera at Autopsy.—*Cl. botulinum* does not usually invade the body, but it may occasionally be isolated from the liver (Dubovsky and Meyer 1922*a*) or spleen (Stricker and Geiger 1924).

E. Other Methods of Examination.—In patients that recover, antitoxin corresponding to the type of the organism concerned may sometimes be demonstrated in the serum. Thus Stricker and Geiger (1924) found antitoxin present in the serum of two patients on the 14th day after the consumption of the affected food ; 0·25 c.c. of the serum protected mice against 15,000 M.L.D. of Type A toxin, but not against Type B toxin.

Prophylaxis.

We are at present too ignorant of the factors determining the growth and toxin production of *Cl. botulinum* in foods to lay down an effective method of preventing the disease. Home-canning is generally acknowledged to be fraught with danger, since the temperature attained in heating is as a rule too low to destroy the spores. Even fractional sterilization, which is possible in the home, is unreliable, because the spores may not develop in the meantime (Burke 1919*c*). On the other hand, commercially canned food is far less likely to be dangerous. In most outbreaks the food has been abnormal in appearance and odour. Bulging of the tin, the presence of gas bubbles on opening, a disintegrated appearance of the food, and a rancid smell, should be sufficient to condemn the food. On no account should such food be eaten, even after cooking (Tanner and Twohey 1926). But in some toxin-containing cans no evidence of spoiling is detectable (Schoenholz *et al.* 1923).

Prevention of botulism due to the consumption of made-up meat foods is particularly difficult. Van Ermengem (1897) lays emphasis on the necessity in pickling hams of using strong brine, which is unfavourable to the development of the organism.

In handling suspected food care should be taken not to allow it to come in contact with cuts ; Geiger (1924) states that the toxin may be absorbed from broken skin areas, mucous surfaces, and fresh wounds.

Treatment.

The toxins produced by Types A and B of *Cl. botulinum* are antigenically distinct. Antitoxic sera can be prepared by the injection of rabbits (Nevin 1921), goats (Kempner 1897, Forssman 1905) and horses (Leuchs 1910) with each type of toxin. The antitoxin neutralizes the toxin according to the law of multiple proportions (Kempner 1897). Injected before or simultaneously with the toxin it is protective for guinea-pigs and mice. Its therapeutic properties are limited. Kempner (1897) found that 300,000 neutralizing doses, given 24 hours after the injection of the toxin, saved the life of a guinea-pig. Similar results were obtained by Kempner and Pollack (1897). Toxin-antitoxin mixtures given by the mouth are said to be dissociated in the stomach (Leuchs 1910). No international standard has yet been laid down for the antitoxin, but the intravenous inoculation of mice with toxin-antitoxin mixtures appears to be a promising method of titration (Glotowa and Dankerowitz 1935).

In the treatment of human cases antiserum has not yet been proved to be effective. Some favourable results have, however, been reported (McCasky 1919, Geiger 1920). Large doses, 50 c.c. or more, of polyvalent serum, or of monotypical serum if the type of the intoxicating organism is known, should be given intravenously every day till the patient recovers, or all hope is abandoned. A prophylactic dose of 10 c.c. should be given intramuscularly to all who have partaken of the poisonous food, and who have not yet developed symptoms of the disease. The antitoxin unit in the U.S.A. is that amount which prevents death within 4 days of guinea-pigs weighing 250 gm. injected with 1,000 M.L.D. of toxin.

Burke, Elder and Pischel (1921) state that liquid soap neutralizes the toxin, and that olive oil prevents its absorption from the gut. They advise therefore the use of high enemas of soap and olive oil. Iodine and potassium permanganate are both able to destroy the toxin *in vitro*, and might reasonably be given by the mouth. Alcohol precipitates the toxin (Armstrong *et al.* 1919) ; and it is possible that frequent small doses of brandy might prove beneficial.

Botulism in Animals

Of recent years considerable attention has been devoted to a study of diseases of domestic animals characterized as a rule by fairly sudden onset, paralytic symptoms and often death. In many instances it has been possible to demonstrate a relationship between the type of fodder used and the occurrence of the outbreak. Organisms of the *botulinum* type have frequently been isolated from the animals and from the fodder, and the toxin produced in culture has been shown to be capable of reproducing the symptoms of the disease when given by the mouth or inoculated subcutaneously. The complete chain of evidence necessary to incriminate these organisms in the causation of the disease has often been lacking, but there seems to be little question that in many outbreaks the diagnosis of botulism has been essentially correct.

Great confusion exists about the exact identity of the various organisms isolated. Because some of them differ in their toxin production from the classical *Cl. botulinum* A or B types, the names *Cl. parabotulinum*, *Cl. parabotulinum bovis*, or *Cl. parabotulinum equi* have been suggested, and the disease caused by them has been termed parabotulism. This is not the place to discuss bacteriological nomenclature, but we are in entire agreement with Weinberg and Ginsbourg (1927) that for the moment these organisms should be regarded as varieties of *Cl. botulinum* and referred to as *Cl. botulinum* Type C, D, or E. Their relationship to each other and to the two classical types is very uncertain, and apart from slight differences in the nature of the toxin produced, there seems to be nothing that would justify their elevation to specific rank. Moreover, since some of the recorded outbreaks have been traced to toxin produced by the classical A or B types, and others in the same species of animal to toxin of the C, D, or E types, there seems to be no justification in referring to the former group as instances of botulism and to the latter as instances of parabotulism.

A complete study of the immunological behaviour of the toxins produced by these various organisms has not yet been made. The limited information available seems to show that the toxin of Types A and B is lethal, when given *per os*, to monkeys, ducks, horses, and laboratory animals, but probably not to goats. Type C_α is toxic by the mouth to ducks, slightly so to laboratory animals, but non-toxic to monkeys and goats. Type C_β is toxic by the mouth to monkeys, goats, ducks, and slightly so to laboratory animals. Type D is toxic by the mouth to goats, horses, and slightly so to laboratory animals, but not to monkeys. Type E is toxic by the mouth to horses. Both types D and E seem to be very closely related to type C (see Theiler *et al.* 1926–1927, Theiler 1928, Robinson 1929*a, b*, Gunnison and Meyer 1930, Gunnison and Coleman 1932).

Forage Poisoning in Horses.—Forage poisoning is a very common disease in America, affecting several thousand horses annually ; numerous cases have been recorded in Europe and in Egypt. Buckley and Shippen in 1917 observed that experimentally induced botulism in horses closely simulated naturally occurring forage poisoning. From toxic oat-hay and ensilage they isolated a bacillus resembling *Cl. botulinum* ; experimental intoxication with this organism could be prevented by the administration of anti-botulinum serum. Graham and Brueckner (1919) isolated an organism like *Cl. botulinum* from a corn ensilage that had been responsible for an outbreak of forage poisoning. Horses fed with 2 c.c. of a broth culture of this organism manifested clinical symptoms of forage poisoning—difficulty in mastication, ptyalism, muscular weakness, pharyngeal paresis, recumbency, dyspnœa, protruding and pendulous tongue, mucous discharge from the nostrils, marasmus and enuresis—and died in a week. At necropsy lesions similar to some of the gross lesions occurring in forage poisoning were observed. Horses given a prophylactic dose of *botulinum* antiserum on the previous day recovered. On the other hand, Gaiger (1924) in this country has found that horses are comparatively insusceptible to *Cl. botulinum*, whether the culture is given by mouth or inoculated into the tissues. In view of the widespread distribution of *Cl. botulinum*, it is obviously insufficient to demonstrate its presence in the fodder, or in the intestinal canal of the animal ; it must be shown that the contents of the intestine are definitely toxic.

In South Africa Theiler (1928) made some interesting observations on forage poisoning in mules. Circumstances surrounding the death of two mules in the same manger suggested that the food had become contaminated. Examination revealed the presence of a semi-decomposed rat in the hay, and bacteriological investigation left no doubt that the carcass of the animal contained *botulinum* toxin which had contaminated the hay.

The part played by rats in the spread of botulism in horses and cattle is dealt with by Theiler and Robinson (1927) and Robinson (1929a). The organism isolated in South Africa is referred to as the E type, but it is closely related to the C_β type of America and Australia.

Forage poisoning is a wide term covering a number of different conditions, and it is not to be thought that it is uniformly due to poisoning with the toxin of *Cl. botulinum*. According to Walker (1929), the grass disease of this country is almost certainly different from botulism, while according to Gordon (1934) some outbreaks of grass sickness result from intoxication with products of *Cl. welchii* (see Chapter XXXIII).

Botulism in Cattle.—Forage poisoning in cattle is commonest between the ages of 6 months and 2 years ; the mortality is 2–10 per cent. (Graham and Schwarze 1921b). From a corn silage that was shown to have been responsible for an outbreak in cattle on two different occasions, Graham and Schwarze (1921b) isolated *Cl. botulinum* Type B. Whether the organism had any causal relationship to the poisoning was not definitely ascertained.

Dubovsky and Meyer (1922a) isolated *Cl. botulinum* from the liver and mesenteric glands of two cows suffering from ictero-hæmoglobinuria. In Australia Seddon (1922) has investigated an epizootic disease of cattle known by the names of Midland cattle disease, impaction paralysis, or dry bible ; this disease appears to be identical with the *lamziekte* of South Africa. From animals dying of the disease he isolated an organism, which he called *B. parabotulinus* ; this organism is now referred to as the C type of *Cl. botulinum*. Experimentally its toxin gave rise to bulbar paralysis in cattle.

Our knowledge of botulism in cattle has been extended by Theiler and his colleagues (1926–27) working on lamziekte in South Africa. This disease, which is characterized by paresis and paralysis, principally of the locomotor system, but sometimes of the muscles of mastication and deglutition, occurs in areas where the phosphorus content of the soil, and hence of the pasturage, is deficient. According to Theiler, the affected animals have a craving for phosphorus. This they endeavour to satisfy by eating the debris of carcasses, especially bones, which they find on the veld. Some of these carcasses, or the remains of muscle around the bones, happen to be infected with *Cl. botulinum*, and if sufficient toxin has been produced by the multiplication of this organism, the animals are liable to develop the characteristic symptoms of lamziekte (see also Seddon 1927). The disease can be prevented by feeding bone-meal to the animals ; this satisfies their craving for phosphorus, and so prevents their indulging in the so-called practice of " osteophagia." The infecting organism appears to be mainly of the D type, but, as already noted, it is closely related to the C_β type found in Australia by Seddon. According to Scheuber (1929), it is found in the soil near decomposing carcasses, and often in the intestinal contents of both sick and healthy animals.

Limberneck in Chickens and Duck Disease.—In 1918 Dickson made the following statement : " In the series of outbreaks (of botulism) which I have investigated it has been the rule to find that varying numbers of chickens have died from limberneck." This disease is characterized by weakness, muscular incoordination, a drooping neck, anorexia, prostration, and coma. Death frequently follows. Geiger, Dickson and Meyer, writing in 1922, were able to collect records in the U.S.A. of 103 outbreaks since 1910 with 3,500 deaths. Evidence that limberneck is an avian type of botulism is rapidly accumulating.

The toxin of *Cl. botulinum* has been demonstrated in the crop and intestinal contents of fowls dying of the disease (Graham and Schwarze 1921*a*, Graham and Boughton 1923*a*, Geiger *et al.* 1922). Experimentally it has been found that the feeding of toxic material gives rise to symptoms of limberneck (Dickson 1918). The disease has frequently followed the consumption of home-canned string beans (Meyer and Dubovsky 1922*b*). Most of the outbreaks investigated have been due to Type A, but there is evidence that Type B may be toxic to chickens (Geiger *et al.* 1922).

In 1920 Wilkins and Dutcher concluded from their experiments that limberneck was a disease resulting from paralysis following the ingestion of fly larvæ (*Lucilia cæsar*). Two years later Bengtson (1922*a*, 1923) isolated from the larvæ an organism similar in many respects to *Cl. botulinum*, which in large doses reproduced the symptoms of limberneck. This organism she called *Cl. botulinum* Type C (1923). These findings were confirmed by Graham and Boughton (1923*a*, *b*). It would appear therefore that chickens may develop limberneck from ingestion of fly larvæ containing *Cl. botulinum*; the evidence, however, is as yet insufficient to establish this conclusively.

A disease of **ducks** has been reported in different parts of the world (see Gunnison and Coleman 1932) which appears to be a form of botulism. The organism, known as *Cl. botulinum* Type C_α, has been isolated from the liver, and the corresponding toxin has been demonstrated in the bodies of ducks dying of this disease. The intoxication appears to be due to the consumption of food material in which the organisms have been multiplying, or to ingestion of infected fly larvae.

Sporadic cases of botulism have been reported in a number of *other animals and birds* (see Robinson 1929*b*). Outbreaks of poisoning in cats, dogs, and goats have followed the consumption of home-canned string beans (Geiger *et al.* 1922). Experimentally, Graham and Eriksen (1922) found dogs to be resistant to feeding with *botulinum* toxin, but to be susceptible to Type A, not to Type B, toxin on subcutaneous injection.

REFERENCES

ANDERSON, C. W., McSWEENEY, C. J., MORGAN, W. P., SUGDEN, J. H., and PICKEN, R. M. F. (1935) *Lancet*, i. 285.
Annotation. (1935) *Lancet*, ii. 639.
AOKI, K. and SAKAI, K. (1926) *Zbl. Bakt.*, **98**, 145.
ARMSTRONG, C., STORY, R. V., and SCOTT, E. (1919) *Publ. Hlth Rep., Wash.*, **34**, 2877.
BAARS, G. (1931) *Z. Fleisch- u. Milchhyg.*, **41**, 521.
BACHMANN, F. M. (1924) *J. infect. Dis.*, **34**, 129.
BACHMANN, F. M. and HAYNES, E. (1924) *J. infect. Dis.*, **34**, 132.
BAHR, L. and DYSSEGAARD, A. (1927) *Zbl. Bakt.*, **102**, 268.
BAINBRIDGE, F. A. (1912) *Lancet*, i. 705, 771, 849.
BARBER, M. A. (1914) *Philipp. J. Sci.*, B, **9**, 515.
BELLER, K. and REINHARD, H. (1934) *Berl. tierärztl. Wschr.*, **5**, 226.
BELLER, K. and ZEKI, M. (1934) *Arb. ReichsgesundhAmt.*, **67**, 265.
BENGSTON, I. A. (1922*a*) *Publ. Hlth Rep., Wash.*, **37**, 164; (1922*b*) *Ibid.*, **37**, 2252; (1923) *Ibid.*, **38**, 340; (1924) *Bull. U.S. hyg. Lab.*, No. 136.
BIGELOW, W. D. and ESTY, J. R. (1920) *J. infect. Dis.*, **27**, 602.
BRIEGER, L. (1889) *Virchows Arch.*, **115**, 483.
BRIEGER, L. and FRAENKEL, C. (1890) *Berl. klin. Wschr.*, **27**, 242, 268.
BUCHAN, G. F. (1910) *J. Hyg., Camb.*, **10**, 93.
BUCKLEY, J. S. and SHIPPEN, L. P. (1917) *J. Amer. vet. med. Ass.*, **50**, 809.
BURKE, G. S. (1919*a*) *J. Bact.*, **4**, 541; (1919*b*) *J. Bact.*, **4**, 555; (1919*c*) *J. Amer. med. Ass.*, **72**, 88.
BURKE, V., ELDER, J. C., and PISCHEL, D. (1921) *Arch. intern. Med.*, **27**, 265.
BUSHNELL, L. D. (1922) *J. Bact.*, **7**, 283.

CATHCART, E. P. (1906a) *J. Hyg., Camb.*, **6**, 112 ; (1906b) *J. Hyg., Camb.*, **6**, 248.
CLARENBURG, A. and DORNICKX, C. G. J. (1932) *Nederl. Tijdschr. Geneesk.*, **76**, 1579.
CLAYTON, F. H. A. and HUNTER, J. W. (1928) *Lancet*, ii. 649.
COLEMAN, G. E. (1923) *J. infect. Dis.*, **33**, 384 ; (1924) *J. infect. Dis.*, **34**, 614.
COLEMAN, G. E. and MEYER, K. F. (1922) *J. infect. Dis.*, **31**, 622.
COWDRY, E. V. and NICHOLSON, F. M. (1924) *J. exp. Med.*, **39**, 827.
DACK, G. M., BOWMAN, G. W., and HARGER, R. N. (1935) *J. Amer. med. Ass.*, **105**, 1598.
DACK, G. M., CARY, W. E., WOOLPERT, O., and WIGGERS, H. (1930) *J. prev. Med., Baltimore*, **4**, 167.
DACK, G. M., JORDAN, O., and WOOLPERT, O. (1931a) *J. prev. Med., Baltimore*, **5**, 151.
DACK, G. M., WOOLPERT, O., NOBLE, I., and HALLIDAY, E. G. (1931b) *J. prev. Med., Baltimore*, **5**, 391.
DELAFIELD, M. E. (1934) *Brit. J. exp. Path.*, **15**, 130.
DEMNITZ, A. (1926) *Zbl. Bakt.*, **98**, 141.
DICKSON, E. C. (1918) *Monogr. Rockefeller Inst. med. Res.*, No. 8.
DICKSON, E. C. and SHEVKY, R. (1923) *J. exp. Med.*, **37**, 711.
DICKSON, E. C., BURKE, G. S., BECK, D., and JOHNSTON, J. (1925) *J. infect. Dis.*, **36**, 472.
DOLMAN, C. E. (1934) *J. infect. Dis.*, **55**, 172.
DOYLE, T. M. (1927) *J. comp. Path.*, **40**, 71.
DUBOVSKY, B. J. and MEYER, K. F. (1922a) *J. infect. Dis.*, **31**, 501 ; (1922b) *Ibid.*, **31**, 595.
EASTON, E. J. and MEYER, K. F. (1924) *J. infect. Dis.*, **35**, 207.
ECKER, E. E. (1917) *J. infect. Dis.*, **21**, 541.
Editorial. (1926) *J. Amer. med. Ass.*, **86**, 482.
EDMONDSON, R. B., BORD, G. G. DE, and THOM, C. (1920a) *Abstr. Bact.*, **4**, 10.
EDMONDSON, R. B., GILTNER, L. T., and THOM, C. (1920b) *Arch. intern. Med.*, **26**, 357.
EDWARDS, P. R. (1934) *J. infect. Dis.*, **54**, 85.
ELKELES, G. (1930) *Ergebn. Hyg. Bakt.*, **11**, 68.
ERMENGEM, E. VAN. (1896) *Rev. Hyg.*, **18**, 761 ; (1897) *Z. Hyg. InfektKr.*, **26**, 1.
ESTY, J. R. (1935) *Amer. J. publ. Hlth.*, **25**, 165.
ESTY, J. R. and MEYER, K. F. (1922) *J. infect. Dis.*, **31**, 650.
ESTY, J. R. and STEVENSON, A. E. (1925) *J. infect. Dis.*, **36**, 486.
FERRARIO, J. C. (1935) *Folia biol.*, Nos. 49–51, p. 217.
FORNARIO. (1906) *Ann. Igiene (sper.)*, **16**, 215.
FORSSMAN, J. (1905) *Zbl. Bakt.*, **38**, 463.
GAIGER, S. H. (1924) *J. comp. Path.*, **37**, 163.
GEIGER, J. C. (1920) *Publ. Hlth Rep., Wash.*, **35**, 2858 ; (1923) *J. Amer. med. Ass.*, **81**, 1275 ; (1924) *Amer. J. publ. Hlth.*, **14**, 309.
GEIGER, J. C. and BENSON, H. (1923) *Publ. Hlth Rep., Wash.*, **38**, 1611.
GEIGER, J. C., DICKSON, E. C., and MEYER, K. F. (1922) *Publ. Hlth Bull.*, No. 127.
GHEORGHIU, I and COSTIN, G. (1927) *C. R. Soc. Biol.*, **97**, 1025.
GLOTOWA, E. W. and DANKEROWITZ, A. K. (1935) *Zbl. Bakt.*, **133**, 155.
GLÜCKSMANN, S. (1899) *Zbl. Bakt.*, **25**, 696.
GORDON, W. S. (1934) *Vet. Rec.*, **14**, 1016.
GRAHAM, R. and BOUGHTON, I. B. (1923a) *Abstr. Bact.*, **7**, 29 ; (1923b) *Ibid.*, **7**, 30.
GRAHAM, R. and BRUECKNER, A. L. (1919) *J. Bact.*, **4**, 1.
GRAHAM, R. and ERIKSEN, S. (1922) *J. infect. Dis.*, **31**, 402.
GRAHAM, R. and SCHWARZE, H. (1921a) *J. infect. Dis.*, **28**, 317 ; (1921b) *J. Bact.* **6**, 69.
GUNNISON, J. B. and COLEMAN, G. E. (1932) *J. infect. Dis.*, **51**, 542.
GUNNISON, J. B. and MEYER, K. F. (1930) *J. infect. Dis.*, **46**, 335.
GUSTAFSON, F. (1932) *Z. Fleisch- u. Milchhyg.*, **42**, 203.
HABS, H. (1933) *Zbl. Bakt.*, **130**, 367.
HALL, I. C. and DAVIS, N. C. (1923) *J. exp. Med.*, **37**, 585.
HOHN, J. and HERRMANN, W. (1935) *Zbl. Bakt.*, **133**, 183.
HOLTH, H. (1909) *Zbl. Bakt.*, **49**, 611.
JANSEN, J. (1936) *Tijdschr. Diergeneesk.*, **63**, 140.
JANSEN, J. D. and DOOREN DE JONG, L. E. DEN. (1930) *Zbl. Bakt.*, **117**, 193.
JONES, E. R. and WRIGHT, H. D. (1936) *Lancet*, i. 22.
JORDAN, E. O. (1917) " Food Poisoning," Chicago ; (1930) *J. Amer. med. Ass.*, **94**, 1648 ; (1931) "Food Poisoning and Food-borne Infection," Univ. Chicago Press, Chicago.
JORDAN, E. O. and BURROWS, W. (1933) *Proc. Soc. exp. Biol., N.Y.*, **30**, 448 ; (1934) *J. infect. Dis.*, **55**, 363 ; (1935) *Ibid.*, **57**, 121.
JORDAN, E. O. and DACK, G. M. (1924) *J. infect. Dis.*, **35**, 576.
JORDAN, E. O., DACK, G. M., and WOOLPERT, O. (1931) *J. prev. Med., Baltimore*, **5**, 383.
JORDAN, E. O. and HALL, J. R. (1931) *J. prev. Med., Baltimore*, **5**, 387.
KAHN, M. C. (1924) *J. infect. Dis.*, **35**, 423.
KEMPNER, W. (1897) *Z. Hyg. InfektKr.*, **26**, 481.
KEMPNER, W. and POLLACK, B. (1897) *Dtsch. med. Wschr.*, **23**, 505.

KINLOCH, J. P., SMITH, J., and TAYLOR, J. S. (1926) *J. Hyg., Camb.*, **25**, 434.
KOSER, S. A., EDMONDSON, R. B., and GILTNER, L. T. (1921) *J. Amer. med. Ass.*, **77**, 1250.
LACHENSCHMID, B. (1931) *Z. InfektKr. Haustiere*, **39**, 94.
LANE, C. R. and JONES-DAVIES, T. E. (1935) *Lancet*, ii. 717.
LAVERGNE, V. DE, and ABEL, E. (1925) *Rev. Hyg.*, **47**, 950.
LEIGHTON, G. R. (1923) *Rep. Scot. Bd Hlth*, H.M. Stat. Off.
LEIGHTON, G. and BUXTON, J. B. (1928) *J. Hyg., Camb.*, **28**, 79.
LENTZ, O. (1924) *Z. Hyg. InfektKr.*, **103**, 321.
LEUCHS, J. (1910) *Z. Hyg., InfektKr.*, **65**, 55.
LINDEN, B. A., TURNER, W. R., and THOM, C. (1926) *Publ. Hlth Rep., Wash.*, **41**, 1647.
LOVELL, R. (1932a) *Nat. vet. med. Ass. G.B., 50th Ann. Congr.* ; (1932b) *Bull. Hyg., Lond.*, **7**, 405 ; (1932c) *J. comp. Path.*, **45**, 27.
LOVELL, R. and HUGHES, D. L. (1935) *J. comp. Path.*, **48**, 267.
MCCASKY, G. W. (1919) *Amer. J. med. Sci.*, **158**, 57.
MARTIN, A. R. (1934) *Brit. J. exp. Path.*, **15**, 137.
MCALLAN, J. and HOWIE, G. (1931) *Nat. vet. med. Ass. G.B., 49th Ann. Congr.*
MCBURNEY, R. (1933) *J. Amer. med. Ass.*, **100**, 1999.
MAYER. (1913) *Dtsch. Vjschr. öff. GesundhPfl.*, **45**, 58.
MEMORANDUM. (1935) *Min. Hlth., Lond.*, No. 188 Med.
MENTEN, M. L. (1926) *J. infect. Dis.*, **38**, 354.
MEYER, K. F. (1916) *J. infect. Dis.*, **19**, 700.
MEYER, R. (1929) *Reichsgesundheitsblatt*, **4**, 725.
MEYER, K. F. and DUBOVSKY, B. J. (1922a) *J. infect. Dis.*, **31**, 541 ; (1922b) *Ibid.*, **31**, 559 ; (1922c) *Ibid.*, **31**, 600.
MEYN, A. (1930) *Zbl. Bakt.*, **115**, 168.
MÜHLENS, DAHM, and FÜRST. (1909) *Zbl. Bakt.*, **48**, 1.
MÜLLER, M. (1926) *Z. Hyg. InfektKr.*, **105**, 524.
NEVIN, M. (1921) *J. infect. Dis.*, **28**, 226.
NITTA, N. (1919) *J. comp. Path.*, **32**, 122.
ORR, P. F. (1920) *Abstr. Bact.*, **4**, 10 ; (1922) *J. infect. Dis.*, **30**, 118.
PARK, W. H. and HOLT, L. E. (1903) *Med. News, N.Y.*, **83**, 1066.
PERRY, H. M. (1920) *J. R. Army med. Cps*, **35**, 267.
PERRY, H. M. and TIDY, H. L. (1919) *Spec. Rep. Ser. med. Res. Coun., Lond.*, No. 24.
PFUHL, A. (1900) *Z. Hyg. InfektKr.*, **35**, 265.
RAISTRICK, H. and TOPLEY, W. W. C. (1934) *Brit. J. exp. Path.*, **15**, 113.
Report. (1933) *Ann. Rep. Chief med. Offr., Min. of Hlth*, for year 1932 ; (1934) *Ibid.*, for year 1933 ; (1935) *Ibid.*, for year 1934.
ROBINSON, E. M. (1929a) *15th Rep., Director vet. Educ. Res., S. Africa*, Section iii, p. 97 ; (1929b) *Ibid.*, p. 111.
RÖMER, P. (1900) *Zbl. Bakt.*, **27**, 857.
ROSHER, A. B. and WILSON, G. S. (1921) *Lancet*, i. 16.
SAVAGE, W. G. (1920) " Food Poisoning and Food Infections," Cambridge ; (1921) *J. Hyg., Camb.*, **20**, 69 ; (1923) " Canned Foods in Relation to Health," Cambridge ; (1932) *J. prev. Med., Baltimore*, **6**, 425 ; (1933) *J. Hyg., Camb.*, **33**, 233.
SAVAGE, W. G. and WHITE, P. B. (1923) *J. Hyg., Camb.*, **21**, 258 ; (1925a) *Spec. Rep. Ser. med. Res. Coun., Lond.*, No. 91 ; (1925b) *Ibid.*, No. 92.
SCHEUBER, J. R. (1929) *15th Rep., Director vet. Educ. Res., S. Africa*, Section iii. p. 223.
SCHOENHOLZ, P. and MEYER, K. F. (1922) *J. infect. Dis.*, **31**, 610.
SCHOENHOLZ, P., ESTY, J. R., and MEYER, K. F. (1923) *J. infect. Dis.*, **33**, 289.
SCOTT, W. M. (1933) *Bull. Off. int. Hyg. publ.*, **25**, 828 ; (1936) *Pers. Comm.*
SEDDON, H. R. (1922) *J. comp. Path.*, **35**, 147 ; (1927) *Aust. vet. J.*, **3**, 136.
SELIGMANN, E. (1935) *Schweiz. med. Wschr.*, **65**, 550.
SILBERSCHMIDT, W. (1899) *Z. Hyg. InfektKr.*, **30**, 328.
SMITH, J. (1933) *J. Hyg., Camb.*, **33**, 224 ; (1934) *Ibid.*, **34**, 351.
SOWDEN, G. (1933) *Brit. med. J.*, ii. 836.
SPRAY, R. S. (1926) *J. Amer. med. Ass.*, **86**, 109.
STARIN, W. A. (1924) *J. infect. Dis.*, **34**, 148.
STARIN, W. A. and DACK, G. M. (1925) *J. infect. Dis.*, **36**, 383.
STRICKER, F. D. and GEIGER, J. C. (1924) *Publ. Hlth Rep., Wash.*, **39**, 655.
STRITAR, J. and JORDAN, E. O. (1935) *J. infect. Dis.*, **56**, 1.
TANNER, F. W. (1933) " Food-borne infections and intoxications." Twin City Printing Co., Champaign, Ill.
TANNER, F. W. and DACK, G. M. (1922) *J. infect. Dis.*, **31**, 92.
TANNER, F. W. and RAMSEY, R. J. (1932) *Amer. J. med. Sci.*, **184**, 80.
TANNER, F. W. and TWOHEY, H. B. (1926) *Zbl. Bakt.*, **98**, 136.
THEILER, A. (1928) *13th and 14th Rep., Director vet. Educ. Res., S. Africa*, Part I, p. 47.
THEILER, A. and ROBINSON, E. M. (1927) *Z. InfekKr. Haustiere*, **31**, 165.

THEILER, A., VILJOEN, P. R., GREEN, H. H., TOIT, P. J. DU, MEIER, H., and ROBINSON, E. M. (1926–27) 11*th and* 12*th Rep., Director vet. Educ. Res., S. Africa,* Part II, p. 821.

TOPLEY, W. W. C. and AYRTON, J. (1924) *J. Hyg., Camb.,* **22,** 234.

TROMMSDORF, R., RAJCHMAN, L., and PORTER, A. E. (1911) *J. Hyg., Camb.,* **11,** 89.

UHLENHUTH, P. and HÜBENER, E. (1913) See Kolle & Wassermann's " Hdb. path. Mikroorg.,'' 2te Abt., 1912–13, **3,** 1005.

VAILLARD, L. (1902) *Rev. Hyg.,* **34,** 17, 109.

WALKER, A. B. (1929) *Brit. J. exp. Path.,* **10,** 352.

WEINBERG, M. and GINSBOURG, B. (1927) " Données récentes sur les microbes anaérobies et leur rôle en pathologie.'' Masson & Cie., Paris.

WEISS, H. (1921) *J. infect. Dis.,* **28,** 70.

WHEELER, M. W. and HUMPHREYS, E. (1924) *J. infect. Dis.,* **35,** 305.

WILKINS and DUTCHER. (1920) *J. Amer. vet. med. Ass.,* **57,** 653.

WILLFÜHR and WENDTLANDT. (1921) *Z. Hyg. InfektKr.,* **94,** 192.

ZWICK and WEICHEL. (1910*a*) *Arb. ReichsgesundhAmt.,* **33,** 250 ; (1910*b*) *Ibid.,* **34,** 391.

CHAPTER LXX

PLAGUE, PASTEURELLOSIS, AND PSEUDOTUBERCULOSIS

PLAGUE

INTRODUCTORY

PLAGUE has been one of the greatest scourges of the human race. From time to time it has swept over the world in relentless waves, exacting a toll of life probably unequalled by that of any other epidemic disease. In the 5th and 6th chapters of the 1st Book of Samuel there is an unmistakable account of bubonic plague. Before the Christian era 41 epidemics are on record ; during the 1,500 years following the birth of Christ there are records of 109 epidemics, including the great plague of Justinian's reign, and the Black Death of the fourteenth century. Between 1500 and 1720 there were 45 pandemics of plague (Editorial 1925a). During the eighteenth and the nineteenth centuries it was comparatively quiescent, being confined almost entirely to endemic foci in various parts of Asia ; but at the close of the last century it sprang once more into activity. Starting in Hong-Kong in 1894, it invaded India, Japan, Asiatic Turkey, and European Russia in 1896 ; the following year it reached Madagascar and Mauritius. In 1899 Arabia, Persia, the Straits Settlements, Austria, Portugal, British South Africa, Egypt, the French Ivory Coast, Portuguese Africa, the Argentine, Brazil, Paraguay, and the Hawaiian Islands were affected. There was a small outbreak at Glasgow in 1900, and in the same year the disease appeared at Sydney in Australia and at San Francisco, California. Undoubtedly the brunt of the disease was borne by India, where in the 20 years 1898–1918 more than $10\frac{1}{4}$ million deaths were recorded (White 1918–19).

At the present time plague is spread widely but unevenly throughout the world. One of the most disturbing features is the progressive infection of rodents that is occurring in America, South Africa, and apparently certain other countries ; these animals form a reservoir for the conservation of the virus.

The causative organism was isolated independently and almost simultaneously by Kitasato (1894) and by Yersin (1894), at Hong-Kong in 1894. Numerous workers, particularly Ogata (1897), Simond (1898), and Gauthier and Raybaud (1902, 1903) were responsible for showing that the disease is primarily one of rodents, and that it is spread to man by the agency of infected fleas. This conception was criticized by several workers (Nuttall 1898, Galli-Valerio 1900, 1903), but was definitively proved to be correct by the English Plague Commission (Report 1906).

Epidemiology.

There are certain parts of the world from which plague never dies out ; these constitute permanent endemic foci, and serve as starting-points for epidemics.

The maintenance of infection in these areas depends on the rodent population. In the South-Western Himalayas it is the rats that are infected, in the Kirghiz Steppes it is the spermophiles, in Transbaikalia the tarbagans, in California the ground squirrels, and in South Africa the gerbilles. Periodically epidemics of plague break out amongst these rodents, exterminating a large proportion of them. For some time infection lies dormant, manifesting itself only by isolated deaths. Then later, as the animals breed and a fresh susceptible population arises, another wave occurs, leading again to decimation of the herd (Elton 1925).

Man is infected from these animals either directly or, more often, by the intermediation of fleas. Year by year, single cases of plague, or groups, occur, small in themselves but sufficient to show that the disease is still smouldering. So long as these foci remain secluded they are of little importance; but once communication is set up with the surrounding country, there is a danger that plague may take on epidemic spread.

An epidemic starting in this way runs a characteristic course. In the pre-epidemic phase there are a few cases separated by considerable intervals of time. This is succeeded by the epidemic phase in which a rapid succession of cases occurs constituting the major portion of the outbreak. Finally there is a decline resembling the commencement, but not so long drawn out. Infection does not occur by direct contact with the sick; it spreads by contiguity from place to place, so that an increasing number of small foci are established. Often the infection seems to be localized to buildings, particularly grain stores, warehouses, or shops; in these, many cases of plague are contracted by people who have no immediate relation to each other. Plague has a predilection for dirty, insanitary dwellings, and more particularly for their ground floors; it attacks the lowest class of the population living under the worst conditions.

Infection may also occur *per saltum*. A focus of plague suddenly appears several miles—sometimes hundreds of miles—from the primary focus, and serves in its turn as the centre from which infection may spread to the surrounding localities. The contiguous mode of spread is dependent on the gradual dissemination of plague amongst the rats; *per saltum* infection results either from the transportation of rats or rat fleas by railways, ships, or other means of communication, or by human beings infested with rat fleas. It is probably due to importation of plague from cities that villages are infected. Greenwood (see Report 1911, p. 47) obtained evidence that villages situated near railways were more liable to plague than villages not so situated.

Though bubonic plague has occurred in nearly every part of the globe, it is confined chiefly to the warmer latitudes (Robertson 1923). Extreme heat and dryness of the atmosphere are inimical to its spread; thus in India it occurs during the colder months of the year, when the mean temperature is between 50° F. and 85° F., and the air has a high relative humidity, or, as it is sometimes expressed, a low saturation deficiency. According to White (1918–19), humidity is the most important factor in the spread of plague in India; the years of maximum mortality have been the years with a high mean relative humidity. This was particularly true of the Punjab and Northern India (White 1918–19).

The case mortality of bubonic plague is about 60–90 per cent., of pneumonic plague 100 per cent.

In Bombay the English Plague Commission (Report 1907, p. 724) determined that prior to the annual outbreak of human plague there was an epidemic amongst the rats. First the rats belonging to the species *Rattus norvegicus* (*Mus decu-manus*) were affected. After an interval of about 10 days an epizootic appeared in the rats of the species *Rattus rattus* (*Mus rattus*) ; and after a further interval of 10 days the human epidemic broke out. From this they inferred that *R. rattus* was infected from *R. norvegicus*, and subsequently conveyed the disease to man. It was further observed that plague persisted in *R. norvegicus* during the off-season—in Bombay from June to December—and flared up at the onset of the colder weather (Fig. 263, p. 1286).

The transference of plague from rat to rat and from rat to man occurs almost exclusively by fleas. Chief amongst these are *Xenopsylla cheopis* and *Ceratophyllus fasciatus*—the rat fleas. It has been shown that in the absence of their specific hosts, both of these types of flea will bite human beings. Plague is essentially a septicæmic disease ; towards the end of an attack the bacilli are present in the blood in enormous numbers, and are readily imbibed by the fleas that infest the rat. When the animal dies, the fleas leave the corpse and wait for a suitable opportunity to attach themselves to a fresh host. Meanwhile the bacilli multiply in the proventriculus, often to such an extent as to block it completely, and pre-vent access of food to the stomach. A flea in this condition is hungry, and when it succeeds in finding a new host, attacks it with vigour. The act of sucking, however, only distends the already contaminated œsophagus, and on the cessation of the pumping act some of the blood is forced back into the wound (Bacot and Martin, see Report 1914). Sometimes a temporary passage is cleared through the mass of obstructing bacilli ; this fails, however, to restore the lost valvular function to the proventriculus ; it merely leaves a passage through which the blood can flow out of the stomach as freely as it enters. Hence after a full meal, blood extends from the posterior portion of the stomach to the anterior chamber of the pharyngeal pump. Such a flea is probably more dangerous than one whose proventriculus is completely blocked, since the contents of the stomach can be regurgitated into the wound with greater freedom (Report 1915c).

The length of time that a flea can remain infected depends on several factors, chief of which are temperature and humidity. During the epidemic season in Bombay rat fleas remained infective for about 15 days, but during the non-epidemic season this period was reduced to 7 days. Under laboratory conditions *C. fasciatus* harboured virulent bacilli for 47 days (Report 1915b). For survival of the bacilli in the flea a low temperature—about 50° F.—and a nearly saturated atmosphere are most favourable. A temperature over 80° F., or even a lower temperature with a dry atmosphere, are adverse to survival (Liston 1924).

It has been suggested that the bacilli in the flea's stomach may be attacked by the phagocytes in the rat's blood which has been ingested ; when the tem-perature rises the phagocytes become more active. This may explain why a flea clears itself more quickly at a high than at a low temperature, and also why, if it is fed on healthy blood after being infected, it clears itself more quickly than when it is starved. The clearance is said to be still more rapid when the flea is fed on the blood of immunized animals (Report 1908, p. 260). It is possible that in this manner the increasing proportion of immune rats towards the close of an epidemic exercises an inhibitory effect on the spread of the disease.

Plague in Rats.

In India the two species mentioned above are chiefly involved in the spread of plague. *Rattus norvegicus* is the large grey rat ; it lives in sewers, stables, and garbage.

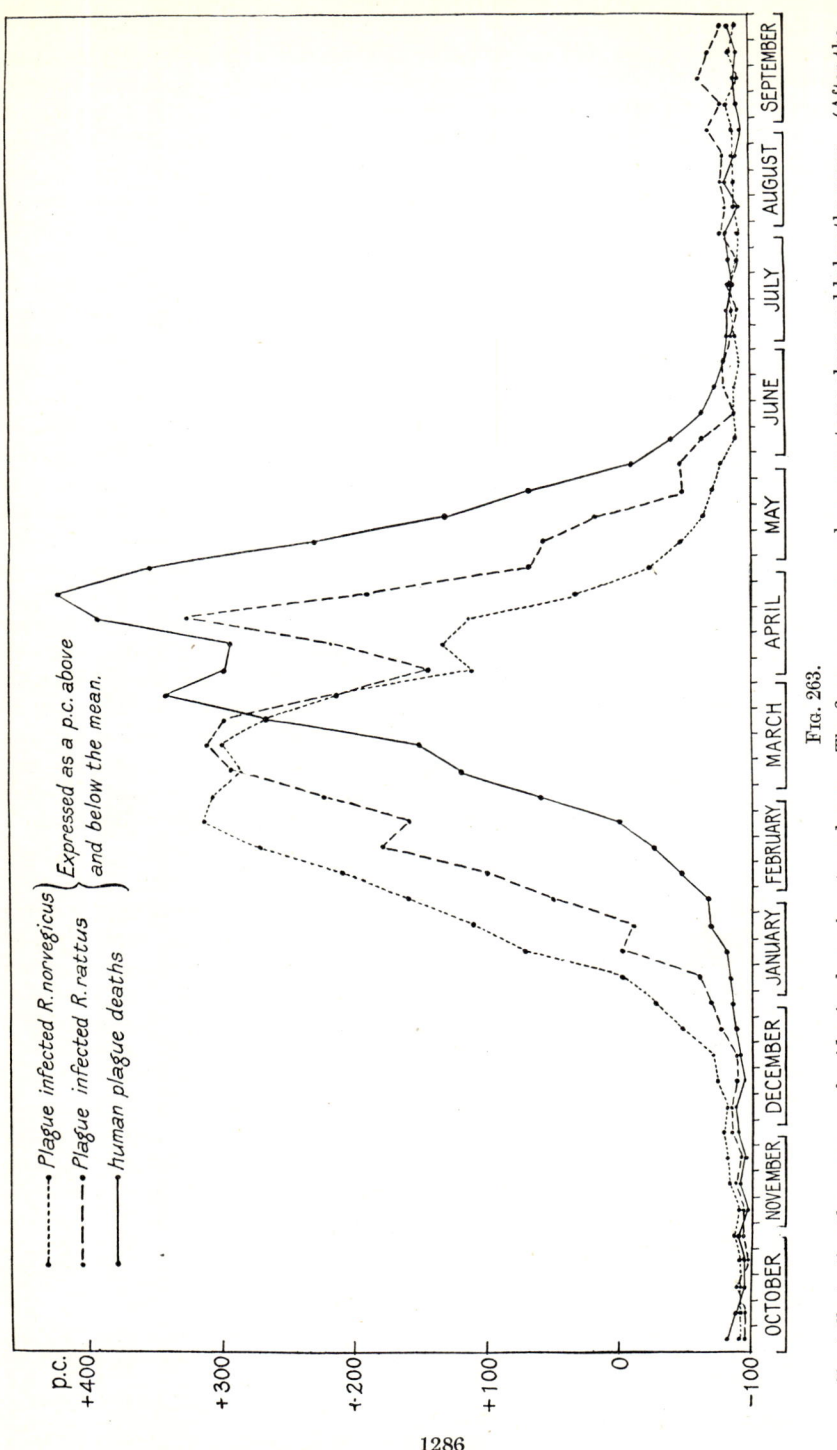

p.c.
+400
+300
+200
+100
0
-100

OCTOBER | NOVEMBER | DECEMBER | JANUARY | FEBRUARY | MARCH | APRIL | MAY | JUNE | JULY | AUGUST | SEPTEMBER

••••••• Plague infected R. norvegicus ⎫ Expressed as a p.c. above
– – – – Plague infected R. rattus   ⎬ and below the mean.
———— human plague deaths   ⎭

FIG. 263.

Chart illustrating the sequence of epidemic plague in rats and man. The figures are expressed as percentages above and below the mean. (After the English Plague Commission in India.)

Rattus rattus is the black rat ; it is smaller and less fierce than the grey rat, and, living in houses or their immediate neighbourhood, it comes into closer contact with the human population. The natural mode of infection of rats appears to be almost entirely by fleas. It is possible that animals may acquire the disease by devouring their dead companions ; but considering that it is not easy to infect rats by feeding on plague material, and that the post-mortem appearances in rats dying naturally of plague are different from those of rats experimentally infected by feeding, it is doubtful whether this is more than a rare occurrence.

In Bombay, of the dead rats examined during 1905–06, 22·2 per cent. of *R. norvegicus,* and 16·7 per cent. of *R. rattus* were infected with plague. Of the live rats the figures were 0·85 per cent. and 0·37 per cent. respectively. Thus plague was commoner in *R. norvegicus* than in *R. rattus* (Report 1907, p. 724). The susceptibility of the two species to experimental inoculation with plague was almost identical. In Sydney during $2\frac{3}{4}$ years ending December 31, 1904, 125,872 rats and mice were caught and examined ; plague was identified in 0·37 per cent. (Thompson 1906).

During the height of the epizootic the lesions are those of acute plague, but during and subsequent to the decline, a number of healthy rats are encountered with atypical lesions. One of the commonest of these is a large abscess in the spleen or liver, containing plague bacilli. The rats, though infected, have evidently been able to withstand the attack. Whether these rats act as chronic carriers of the disease and are responsible for keeping alive the infection, it is difficult to say. The English Plague Commission discountenanced this view, but were unable to disprove it.

More recently Bordas, Dubief and Tanon (1922) in an examination of 5,000 rats in the neighbourhood of Paris, found a number of animals with atypical lesions containing plague bacilli of lowered virulence. They are disposed to regard such rats as chronic carriers of the disease, serving to keep alive the infection from one epizootic to the next. They would explain the occurrence of a fresh outbreak as contingent on an increase in virulence of the bacillus.

Experimental Transmission of Plague in Rats.—It has been abundantly demonstrated by different workers that plague does not spread from rat to rat by contact in the absence of fleas. On the other hand infection spreads readily in the presence of fleas, even though the animals have no immediate contact with each other. Two experiments of the English Plague Commission will illustrate this.

Experiment 1.—(Report 1910.) Bombay rats were inoculated with plague and mixed with normal rats in godowns. In one set of godowns fleas were excluded, but

TABLE CXLII

EFFECT OF FLEAS ON THE MORTALITY OF RATS IN EXPERIMENTAL EPIDEMICS.

	Flea-free Godowns.	Flea Godowns.
Inoculated rats put in	84	70
,, ,, died of plague	73 or 86·9%	63 or 90%
Normal rats put in	125	125
,, ,, died of plague	0	57 or 45·6%
Plague rats eaten	3	1
Fleas present	None	About 24 per rat

in the other set they were permitted to multiply. In the flea-free godowns none of the normal rats, which were in continuous contact with the infected rats, developed plague, whereas in the others infection spread rapidly (Table CXLII).

The rats dying of plague in the flea godowns nearly all showed cervical buboes, indicating that the site of infection had been on the head or neck ; this is the situation on which the fleas chiefly congregate.

EXPERIMENT 2.—(Report 1906, p. 421). This was a repetition of an experiment performed by Gauthier and Raybaud (1902, 1903). Two wire-mesh cages were employed, each standing in a shallow tray filled with dry earth or sand. The cages were enclosed in a single glass box, the roof of which was covered with fine muslin impervious to fleas (see Fig. 264). Rats were introduced through the lids of the cages, and the lids themselves were covered with fine muslin. Into Cage X was placed a rat, inoculated with plague, together with 10 to 20 fleas. As soon as the rat was dead, a healthy rat was placed in Cage Y. The carcass of the first rat was allowed to remain in X for 8 to 12 hours after

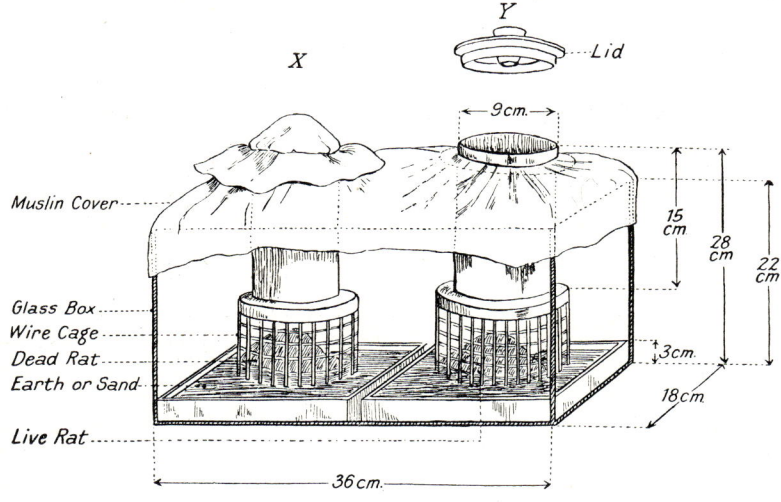

FIG. 264.

The wire-mesh employed was 3 mm. ; in the figure it is shown much larger, for the sake of clearness.

the animal's death. During that time fleas transferred themselves to the new rat through the wire mesh of the cages. Immediate contact between the two rats was absolutely prevented. This experiment was repeated several times, and in 69 per cent. of instances in which healthy, presumably non-immune, rats were used, the rat in Cage Y contracted plague.

Experiments were also carried out on guinea-pigs (Report 1906, p. 421). A series of 6 godowns were specially constructed by the Commission. The walls were of brick and mortar, 9 inches thick ; the floors were of concrete on top of a high plinth. Each godown measured internally 7 ft. × 6 ft. Leading into the interior were double doors, lined with wire netting, between which was an inspection chamber. The essential difference in the structure of the godowns was in the roofs. Nos. 1 and 2 were roofed with country tiles, placed in four layers on the top of wooden laths. On the inside of this roof there was a wire netting on a wooden framework in Godown 2, and two layers of wire netting, 10 inches apart, in No. 1. So that while rats could build their nests in the tiles of the roof, they were completely shut off from the interior of the godowns. Mangalore tiles were used for roofing Godowns 3 and 4 ; these do not afford so good a shelter for rats as country tiles ; a single layer of wire netting separated the tiles from the interior. Godowns 5 and 6 were roofed with a single layer of corrugated iron fastened down with cement to the tops of the walls, so that no rats could nest at all. Godowns Nos. 1 and 3 had a small roof light ; the rest were in darkness (Fig. 265).

By allowing 3 guinea-pigs to run about in each godown for 6 days, and making flea counts every day, it was ascertained that the number of fleas varied in each instance with the accessibility of the roof to rats. Thus in No. 1, 54 fleas ; in No. 2, 228 ; in No. 3, 40 ; and in No. 4, 70 fleas were caught in 6 days. In Nos. 5 and 6 fleas were few or absent. Incidentally this experiment brings out the importance of darkness in favouring infestation by fleas.

In these godowns a series of experimental epidemics was initiated amongst guinea-pigs, generally by introducing a number of animals experimentally infected

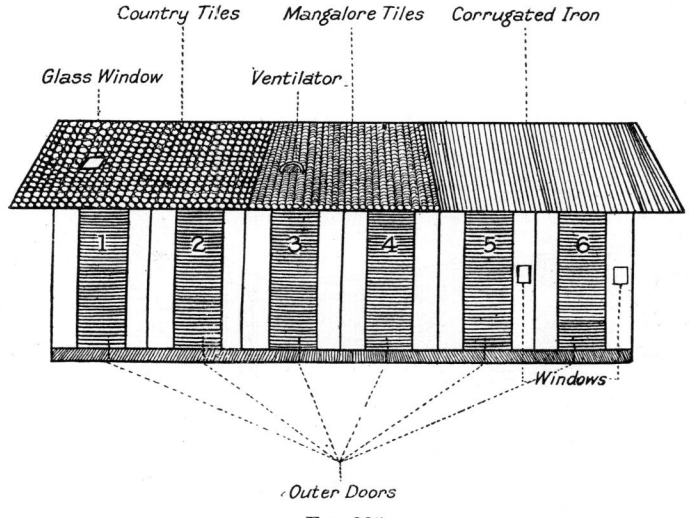

FIG. 265.

The doors opened into the left-hand side of each godown, not in the middle as indicated in the figure.

with plague and adding normal animals to them. For the detailed results, reference must be made to the Commission's Report (1906) ; the conclusions that were drawn from them were as follows :

(1) Close contact of plague-infected with healthy animals, if fleas were excluded, did not lead to the production of an epizootic. Since the godowns were never cleaned out, close contact involved contact with fæces, urine, and discharges of infected animals, and the eating of contaminated food.

(2) Close contact of the young with the infected animals failed to infect the former ; even the suckling of young animals by infected mothers proved ineffectual.

(3) If fleas were present, then an epizootic broke out, the rate of progress being in direct proportion to the number of fleas present.

(4) Infection can take place without any contact with contaminated soil. Thus, in one experiment, guinea-pigs placed in wire cages 2 inches above the ground developed plague. But when the cages were suspended 2 feet above the ground, none of them became ill, indicating that aerial infection does not occur.

In another experiment 2 monkeys were placed in Godown No. 2, in which 3 guinea-pigs had recently died of plague. Each monkey was in a separate cage of the same pattern, the only difference being that one was surrounded by a layer of tanglefoot (an adhesive substance) 6 inches wide, while the other one was unprotected. (A rat flea cannot jump farther than about 5 inches.) The roof of each cage was impervious to fleas, and the bottom was of teak wood, which prevented contact of the animal with the ground. After two nights in the godown the monkeys were removed and segregated. Two fleas were caught on the unprotected monkey, and five fleas were found stuck on the tanglefoot. The unprotected monkey soon became ill, developing a bubo in the right axilla, which contained plague bacilli. The protected monkey remained well.

Equally suggestive were the experiments in the plague houses of Bombay. Guinea-pigs were allowed to run about in these houses to act as traps for fleas ; the usual number of fleas—mostly rat fleas—caught in this way was about 20 per room. In 29 per cent. of

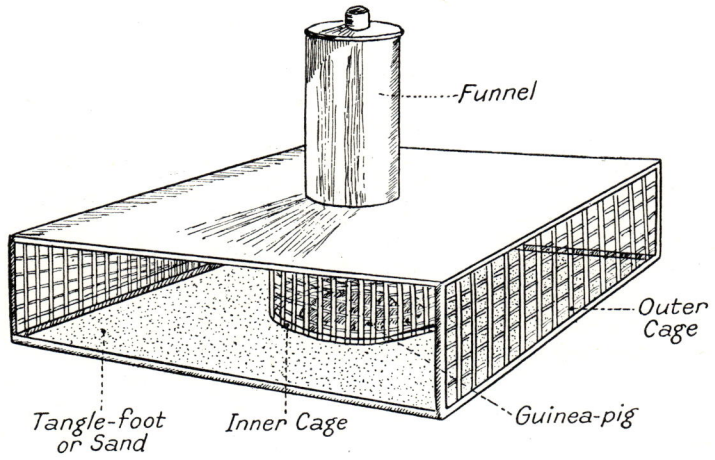

Fig. 266.

The outer large mesh wire netting, which has been omitted from one side of the outer cage, was to prevent the tanglefoot from being destroyed, and to prevent rats from coming into close contact with the guinea-pig. The tanglefoot prevented the access of fleas to the inner cage ; the sand did not.

instances guinea-pigs left in these rooms for from 18 to 40 hours contracted plague. The situation of the bubo was usually in the cervical region—explicable by the habit that fleas have of collecting round the under surface of the neck.

In other experiments guinea-pigs were placed in cages, of the pattern shown in Fig. 266. One of the cages was surrounded by a 6-inch boundary of tanglefoot ; the other by a layer of sand. When left in plague-infected houses, 24 per cent. of the animals in the unprotected cages developed plague whereas not one of the animals in the protected cages did so.

Mode of Spread of Plague in Bombay.—The conclusions drawn from these experiments receive support from epidemiological observations in the field. Plague in man predominates amongst the lowest classes, particularly those in dirty and insanitary dwellings, where rats and fleas are numerous. The higher classes, such as the Parsees and the Europeans, suffer very slightly. The presence of an initial bubo renders it highly probable that infection occurs by the skin, and the predominant selection of the inguinal region for the development of the bubo suggests that the bacilli gain entrance through the skin of the leg. In confirmation of this it has been noted by several observers that in about 5 per cent. of cases the first sign of plague is a small vesicle, surrounded by an area of redness (Simond 1898). This is found generally on the leg, and is undoubtedly due to the bite of a flea. Living plague bacilli are said to be uniformly present in these vesicles.

Though rats in Bombay breed throughout the year, both *R. rattus* and *R. norvegicus* breed most freely from June to October. The largest proportion of young rats in relation to the total population is reached in November and December.

Rat fleas are most prevalent during the months of February, March, April, and May. The infestation of *R. norvegicus* is more than double that of *R. rattus*. Thus the number of fleas per rat during these months is about 5 for *R. rattus* and 12 for *R. norvegicus*. In this connection it will be remembered that plague is commoner in *R. norvegicus* than in *R. rattus*. The epidemic season for rats and man lasts from January or February till April or May, the maximum prevalence being either in March or April. The sequence of events would appear to be as follows. During the hot season the rats breed freely, and a large susceptible population is produced. As the colder weather arrives, the fleas increase in numbers, and plague breaks out in *R. norvegicus*. This is rapidly followed by an epizootic in *R. rattus*, and this in its turn by the human epidemic. At the onset of the hot weather in May or June the flea population decreases rapidly, and plague in rats and man comes to an end for the year. The subsidence of the epidemic is accounted for partly by the increasing proportion of immune rats, and partly by the decrease in the number of fleas. With regard to the former it was found by the English Commission that Bombay rats captured towards the end of the epizootic were more resistant to experimental inoculation with *Past. pestis* than those at the beginning. Whether the rats that had survived the epizootic were more resistant *ab initio*, or had acquired immunity during the progress of the epizootic, it was impossible to say.

During the off-season sporadic plague occurs in rats, particularly *R. norvegicus*, and in man ; but the conditions are obviously unsuitable for its spread on any but a small scale.

We have dealt at some length with the conditions prevailing in Bombay, because they have been investigated so thoroughly. In other parts of India much the same sequence of events has been observed, with, however, variations dependent on climatic and other factors. It is curious that 75 per cent. of the plague cases in India are distributed over the Punjab, the Bombay Presidency, and the United Provinces, when it is remembered that these areas contain less than a third of the total human population (Low 1920). This anomaly is explicable largely by the favourable climatic conditions existing in these areas for multiplication of fleas. Where these conditions are unsuitable, plague either does not occur or runs a diminutive course. Madras, for example, though bordering on the highly infected Bombay Presidency, is relatively free from plague. The probable reason for this difference is that the predominating rat flea in the Madras Presidency is *X. astia*, which as Liston (1924) and Hirst (1926, 1927) have shown, is considerably less effective in carrying plague from rat to rat than *X. cheopis*. A supplementary, but probably less important reason, is that during about 7 months of the year the climatic conditions in certain parts of Madras are unfavourable both to flea reproduction and to the transmission of infection by rat fleas. It is noteworthy that in Madras and Colombo plague seems to be confined to areas in which *X. cheopis* is prevalent. While *X. astia* is indigenous to Southern India, *X. cheopis* has only been recently introduced—mainly by the grain and cotton trade. It is still spreading, or attempting to spread, in these new areas, and the incidence and severity of plague epidemics appear to be associated directly with the number of *cheopis* present (King and Pand t 1931).

The conclusions advanced by the English Commission (Report 1908, p. 266) on the seasonal prevalence of plague in Bombay and the Punjab were as follows : The *rise* of the rat epizootic, and therefore of the human epidemic, depends on (1) a suitable mean temperature, somewhat below 85° F. and in general over 50° F. ; (2) a sufficient number of susceptible rats ; (3) a sufficient number of rat fleas.

The *fall* of the rat epizootic and of the human epidemic depends on (1) a high mean temperature, 85° F. or over ; (2) a diminution in the total number of rats and an increase in the proportion of immune to susceptible animals ; (3) a diminution in the number of rat fleas.

In Egypt, Petrie and Todd (1924) were able to determine the influence of season on the spread of the disease. In the Southern Provinces the maximum incidence was in February or March ; in Northern Egypt, at Alexandria and Port Said, it was in July. The optimum temperature for epidemic spread was 68°–77° F., and the optimum vapour pressure deficiency 1–10 millibars. These, too, were the optimum conditions for the development of fleas. There was a lag period of 4 to 6 weeks between the onset of favourable atmospheric conditions and epidemic prevalence of the disease in man ; this was apparently taken up by the development and multiplication of *X. cheopis*. The two rodents chiefly concerned in the spread of plague were *Rattus rattus* and the Cairo spiny mouse (*Acomys cahirinus*). *X. cheopis* constituted from 90–100 per cent. of the fleas on these animals trapped in houses.

In the mountainous districts of Java, according to Otten (1932) fleas reach their maximum in October and November, and human plague reaches its maximum in December. The flea index follows the rise and fall of the saturation deficiency—just the opposite to what occurs in India.

It will be gathered that the conditions determining the epidemic spread of plague are very stringent. The links in the rat-flea-man chain must be delicately adjusted ; a slight fault in one link is sufficient to impair the efficiency of the whole chain, or even to break it altogether. This is doubtless the reason why in countries where the conditions are not so favourable as in India, plague often has great difficulty in spreading (Robertson 1923). Several times during the present century it has been introduced into England, chiefly at the ports, yet it has uniformly failed to take hold. In East Suffolk, it is true, it is endemic in the rats (Bulstrode 1910-11, Eastwood and Griffith 1914, Macalister and Brooks 1914), having been imported probably in grain ; but apart from attacking one or two persons it has shown no potentialities for spreading to the human population (see Greenwood 1935). Likewise in America, though the rats and the ground squirrels are endemically infected, human cases of the disease have been uncommon (Boyd and Kemmerer 1921).

Plague in other Rodents.

GROUND SQUIRRELS.—Plague first appeared at San Francisco in 1900. By 1904 it had spread from the rats to the ground squirrels—*Citellus beecheyi* (Editorial 1925a). In 1909–10, 150,000 squirrels were examined from different parts of California ; of these 402 were infected with plague (McCoy 1910). The fleas infesting squirrels are *Ceratophyllus acutus* Baker, and less frequently *Hoplopsyllus anomalus* Baker. In the former of these plague bacilli have been demonstrated (McCoy 1911). Both of them readily attack man. Several cases of human plague have been traced to contact with ground squirrels. It is interesting to note that the primary bubo has generally been in the axilla—probably from handling the squirrels.

Since the relation of man to squirrels is not nearly so close in California as the relation of man to rats is in India, it is not surprising that the cases traced to infection from squirrels have been mainly sporadic. A further point of interest is that the bacilli in squirrel plague appear to be less virulent for guinea-pigs than those from cases of rat plague in America and India (McCoy 1911).

GERBILLES AND MULTIMAMMATE MICE.—Plague was introduced into South Africa in 1900–02 by rats in forage vessels coming from South American ports. Since then isolated outbreaks have occurred in different parts of the country without any explanation being apparent of the mode of infection. In 1921, how-ever, a case of plague on a farm was traced to infected rodents. It was discovered that the gerbilles or Nachtmuis (*Gerbillus tateronia*) and the multimammate mice (*Rattus coucha*) in the locality were infected with plague (Mitchell 1921). Both of these animals come into fairly close contact with man. Plague spread rapidly in the rodents during 1923–24, and in that year there were 167 outbreaks of human plague in the Union, with 372 cases and 235 deaths. Large epizootics have occurred, killing off 80–90 per cent. of the veldt rodents and 30–40 per cent. of the associated small carnivora—mongoose and suricat. The rodents are not com-pletely exterminated by the disease ; the survivors breed freely, so that in time another large susceptible population appears, which is likewise decimated by plague (Kauntze 1926). It is estimated that plague is distributed over about 50,000 square miles (Editorial 1925b).

SPERMOPHILES AND FIELD MICE.—Endemic plague in the Steppes of South-west Russia has been traced to spermophiles—*Spermophilus musicus* and *Sp. rufescens*—and to field mice. In winter when the spermophiles are hibernating, cases of human plague appear to be due to infection from wandering field mice, which take refuge in the thatched roofs of the houses (Zabolotny 1923). A number of cases in winter, however, appear to be of the pneumonic type (Radcliffe 1879–80). In certain provinces, such as Saratow, Astrakhan, and the Don province, marmots are also infected (Tschurilina 1930).

TARBAGANS.—Numerous outbreaks of plague have occurred in Transbaikalia, Mongolia, and Manchuria. The origin of these has been traced to infected tar-bagans (Zabolotny 1923, Petrie 1924, Wu Lien Teh 1924). The tarbagan (*Arctomys bobac*) is a small rodent living in deep burrows. From September to April it hibernates, and the breeding season is in July and August. During April, May, June and September its skin is largely sought after by Russian and Chinese hunters for the manufacture of imitation sable. The tarbagan harbours fleas—*Ceratophyllus silantievi* Wagner—which will bite man when starved (Wu Lien Teh

1913). In its burrows there are certain passages used for the deposition of excrement, and the corpses of animals that have died during hibernation, as well as skin, bones, and other refuse. These passages are in absolute darkness, and are cool, moist, and of equable temperature ; it is probable that they afford suitable conditions for conservation of the pest virus during the winter (Jettmar 1923).

During the summer, sporadic cases of bubonic plague occur amongst the tarbagan hunters. In the winter pneumonic plague occurs in epidemic form.

Pneumonic Plague.

The epidemiology of pneumonic plague is different from that of the bubonic form, one of the chief differences being that the former is highly contagious, whereas the latter is not.

Provided the conditions are favourable, primary pneumonic plague may spread with great rapidity. In 1910–11 the outbreak in Manchuria and North China levied a toll of 60,000 lives ; in 1917–18 there were 16,000 deaths in South Mongolia and China, and in 1920–21 there were 9,000 deaths in Transbaikalia (Wu Lien Teh 1922). The epidemic is independent of rodents ; it spreads directly by droplet infection from one person to another. The closer the contact, the more likely is infection to spread ; this accounts for the prevalence of pneumonic plague in the winter, when overcrowding in insanitary dwellings is so common. This form of the disease appears to be uniformly fatal (Jettmar 1923).

In some countries, such as Manchuria, Transbaikalia, and the Kirghiz Steppes, bubonic plague occurs during the warm weather, and pneumonic plague during the winter. Under these conditions it seems probable that the outbreaks of pneumonic plague arise from cases of bubonic plague complicated by secondary pneumonia.

Bacteriology and Diagnosis of Plague in Man and Animals

Diagnosis of Natural Rat Plague.

During an epizootic the diagnosis of plague in rats can be made almost as well macroscopically as by microscopical examination. The signs and their frequency in *R. rattus* and *R. norvegicus* combined were as follows (Report 1907) :

		Per cent.
(1) Subcutaneous congestion, particularly in submaxillary region	.	30·5
(2) Subcutaneous hæmorrhages, particularly in submaxillary region or flank	.	40·5
(3) Cervical œdema	.	10·0
(4) Single bubo	.	73·05

(a) Cervical bubo	. 75 per cent. of cases of single bubo
(b) Axillary bubo	. 15·1 ,, ,, ,, ,, ,,
(c) Groin bubo .	. 6·1 ,, ,, ,, ,, ,,
(d) Sublumbar .	. 3·8 ,, ,, ., ,, ,,

(5) Multiple buboes	.	11·67
(6) Granular liver	.	55·5
(7) Pleural effusion	.	64·5
(8) Hæmorrhages in lungs and pleuræ	.	24·0
(9) Hæmorrhages in kidneys and suprarenals . . .	.	8·5
(10) Granular spleen	.	4·5

Without doubt the presence of a bubo is the most important single indication of plague. In the early stage the gland is enlarged, congested, and shows hæmorrhagic points on section. When fully developed, it contains an area of grey necrosis confined to the medulla, or occupying the whole gland. The bubo is hard, and can be moved about under the skin with ease. Microscopically, plague bacilli are found in about 99 per cent. of buboes ; in over half the buboes involution forms are present. The bacilli are best demonstrated by staining with carbol-thionin ; with this dye they are faintly coloured except at the poles, which stain deeply.

The liver frequently shows a patchy distribution of alternate red and yellow areas—best described as mottling. In many instances there are small, grey or whitish areas of necrosis, giving the organ a stippled appearance as if it had been dusted with grey pepper ; as a rule they do not project above the surface. The spleen is sometimes enlarged, and is firm and moulded over the stomach ; sometimes it contains granules or actual nodules, which may be discrete or confluent. Occasionally a wedge-shaped portion of the spleen is converted into a cheese-like mass. Pleural effusion is a very characteristic feature ; it is clear, abundant, and straw-coloured, less often blood-stained. The five most important signs of plague are : (1) bubo ; (2) subcutaneous and general congestion ; (3) granular liver ; (4) congested spleen ; (5) pleural effusion. Of these 1, 3, and 5 may persist in rats that have undergone putrefaction, and are then of great diagnostic value.

Microscopically, bacilli are most abundant in the bubo, then in the spleen, and least numerous in the heart's blood. Particular attention should be paid to the polar-stained barrel forms in fresh material, and to the characteristic rings and discs in putrefying material (Kister 1930). Cultures should be made from these three situations, single colonies picked off, and carefully studied.

Inoculation of guinea-pigs or mice should be made subcutaneously with a suspension of the bubo or spleen. If the animal has undergone putrefaction, and other organisms are likely to interfere with the inoculation test, pieces of the tissue should be rubbed on to the shaven abdomen of a guinea-pig. *Past. pestis* is able to penetrate the unbroken skin, whereas very few other organisms can do so. The Commission found that this test failed in only 2 per cent. of fresh and 10 per cent. of putrid rats.

In putrid animals the *thermoprecipitin test* is sometimes of value (Kraus 1897*b*, Piras 1913, Warner 1914, Philip and Hirst 1917). One part of the finely divided organ is mixed with 5 to 10 parts of distilled water, boiled for 5 minutes, filtered repeatedly through paper or asbestos wool under pressure till clear, and run on to the top of a specific serum in a small tube. In a positive reaction a precipitate appears in 5 minutes at 37° C., increasing to a maximum after 2 hours.

There are several other diseases that may be confused with plague.

Pasteurellosis in rats does not appear to be very common, but when it does occur it is most confusing (Smillie 1920, Wayson 1925 ; see also Mitchell 1930). The bacilli are smaller, more regular, and differ from plague chiefly in their sugar reactions and in their formation of indole.

Past. pseudotuberculosis (*rodentium*) gives rise to an infection in rats often accompanied by the formation of nodules in the spleen and liver. As a rule these nodules are larger than those of plague, and stand out more from the surface. One means of differentiation is the injection of the organisms into white rats ; these animals are said to be susceptible to plague but relatively resistant to pseudotuberculosis. *Past. pseudotuberculosis*, if examined in broth cultures after about 16 hours' incubation at 22° C., is generally found to be motile, whereas *Past. pestis* is uniformly non-motile. (For further differences between these organisms see Chapter XXIX.)

According to Levinthal (1931), buboes in both rats and guinea-pigs may be caused by *Bact. coli*. Differentiation is readily accomplished by growth on Mac-Conkey agar. Agglutination of the organisms with an anti-plague horse serum is not always reliable, because the serum may contain agglutinins to *Bact. coli*.

Infection of rats with *Trypanosoma lewisii* may readily be confused with plague (Macalister and Brooks 1914). Diagnosis is easy on microscopical examination, since trypanosomes are found in large numbers in the blood.

The lesions of plague in other rodents are similar to those in rats, and need not be described separately. In ground squirrels there is a disease called Tularæmia, which closely resembles plague ; cultivation is necessary to distinguish between them.

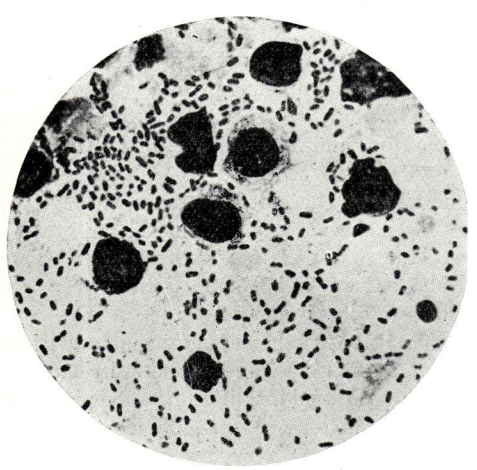

FIG. 267.—*Pasteurella pestis.*

Film from inguinal bubo of infected guinea-pig, showing the bipolar-stained ovoid bacilli (× 1000).

The diagnosis of epidemic plague in rats is comparatively simple, but great difficulties are met with in the sporadic form. The lesions are often atypical (Eastwood and Griffith 1914), buboes may be absent, and sometimes nothing characteristic may be noticed. Williams and Kemmerer (1923), in an examination of rats at Galveston, Texas, found 9 plague-infected rats, none of which showed any macroscopic signs of plague. The infection was discovered by gross or combined inoculations of the tissues of all rats in each day's catch. They advise that the rats should be divided into batches of 10, and the combined spleens or glands of each batch should be emulsified and injected into a guinea-pig. Even this method is not infallible, because at the decline of an epizootic or during an inter-epizootic period the virulence of the bacilli may be so low that the guinea-pig either does not die or dies with atypical lesions ; in this case a fresh inoculation should be made from the guinea-pig, and repeated in series till the virulence of the organism is sufficiently exalted to give rise to typical plague.

When a hitherto uninfected locality is invaded by plague, the rats may succumb rapidly to a septicæmic form of the disease, in which buboes are insignificant or absent (Philip and Hirst 1917). Such rats may appear almost normal to the naked eye, though the bacilli are seen microscopically in large numbers in the blood and viscera.

Towards the end of an epizootic, lesions of chronic or resolving plague may be found. The chief of these are : (1) chronic buboes ; (2) necrotic areas in the spleen ; (3) chronic abscesses in spleen, and more rarely in liver ; (4) perisplenitis ;

(5) scars in spleen ; (6) bisected or trisected spleen ; (7) adhesions of spleen to surrounding structures. In these lesions bacilli may or may not be found.

Diagnosis of Plague in Man.

During Life.—A small vesicle is sometimes present on the leg in the early stages of the disease corresponding to the flea-bite. Microscopical examination of the fluid will show the presence of plague bacilli. The bubo, which is generally in the inguinal region, should be aspirated, and the fluid examined microscopically, by culture, and by animal inoculation (Fig. 267).

In severe, and sometimes even in ambulant, cases plague bacilli may be demonstrated in the patient's blood, either microscopically or by culture. Septicæmia is not always present. It may appear early or late in the course of the disease, and is subject to marked fluctuations (Report 1908, p. 221).

The German Plague Commission (Report 1899) found that the patient's serum often agglutinated the plague bacillus, though usually to a low titre 1/2 to 1/40. A positive test is of value, a negative one meaningless. In mild or chronic cases, where the diagnosis is in doubt, and the bubo is small, hard, and difficult to aspirate, the bubo should be excised and injected into a guinea-pig (Uriarte 1925). In pneumonic plague large numbers of bacilli are found in the sputum.

The fæces of plague patients do not contain *Past. pestis* ; the urine often does (Ogata 1897)—in 19–30 per cent. of patients (Report 1908, p. 221).

After Death.—Microscopical, cultural, and animal inoculation tests should be relied on for diagnosis, the best material being the bubo or the spleen. If the cadaver is comparatively fresh, the tissue suspension should be injected subcutaneously or intraperitoneally into a guinea-pig ; the latter method is more reliable if the organisms are few. In putrid cadavers the organ should be rubbed on to the shaven abdomen of a guinea-pig or on to its nasal mucosa (Zlatogoroff 1904, Girard 1934) ; the thermoprecipitin test may likewise be used. In frozen cadavers *Past. pestis* can be cultivated from buboes up to 102 days (Zlatogoroff 1904).

Prophylaxis, Vaccination, and Serotherapy

Prophylaxis.—The aim of prophylaxis is to weaken or break the rat-flea-man chain by striking at one of its links. The rat constitutes the first link. Complete destruction of all rats and mice is, however, quite impracticable. The animals breed at such a rate as to render futile all attempts at extermination. According to the English Plague Commission the progeny of a single pair might number 858 in 16 months (Report 1911). Thompson in Sydney found that, in spite of an intensive campaign against rats and mice, the number caught each week was nearly uniform ; there was no evidence that the slaughter policy was making any real impression on the general horde. Again, complete destruction of rats on ships is impracticable ; if performed thoroughly it would cause more dislocation of the traffic than would be tolerated. It has been suggested by Rodier (1926) that a more efficacious method would be to kill all female rats caught, and liberate the males ; the resulting polyandry, he considers, would lead to practical extinction of the species.

Rats are comparatively harmless so long as they do not come into intimate contact with human beings. The most hopeful policy is to render all houses, granaries, shops, and such places unsuitable as rat habitations.

There is some evidence that plague in India is becoming less virulent (White 1918–19). This may possibly be due to the increasing proportion of immune rats. It has been shown that rats from a plague-infected area are more resistant to experimental inoculation than those from non-infected areas ; and the young of resistant animals are said to enjoy a high degree of natural immunity (Liston 1924). How far resistance is due to an increased genetic immunity in the strict sense, occurring as the result of natural selection, and how far it is due to the acquirement of active immunity by the young animals as the result of latent infection, occurring perhaps at a time when antibody derived from the placental circulation or the colostrum is still present in the animal's tissues, it is impossible to say, but readers who are interested in this fascinating problem will do well to consult the review of the subject by Hill (1934). Indiscriminate attempts to exterminate rats might interfere with this process of selection, and might perhaps do more harm than good. Incidentally this evolution of a race of immune rats may perhaps explain many of the gaps in the continuity of plague history (Liston 1924).

The second link in the chain—the flea—must be dealt with by strict personal hygiene and domestic cleanliness. In the absence of dirt and litter the fleas have nowhere to breed. The possibility that other insects—bugs, flies, ticks—may share in spreading the disease has been carefully considered (Nuttall 1897, 1898, Report 1915*d*). There is no doubt that these insects may be experimentally infected by sucking the blood of plague rats, but their rôle in nature as transmitters of the disease would appear to be negligible.

Man forms the third link. Two measures are usually advocated : (1) Case isolation, which is of little importance, since man plays but a small part in the spread of the disease. (2) Evacuation, which is sound in theory, since it removes the susceptible population from the infected localities, but is very difficult in practice—at any rate on a large scale. Undoubtedly the most satisfactory mode of combating plague in man, in endemic areas, would be efficient vaccination (Haffkine 1907–08). The value of the present methods of carrying this out will be dealt with below.

Against pneumonic plague we are as powerless as against influenza or other rapidly-spreading respiratory disease ; the most important measure is the prevention of overcrowding, especially at night.

Vaccines.—Animals have been vaccinated successfully against plague by numerous workers, using preparations of different kinds (Yersin *et al.* 1895, Report 1899, Report 1910, p. 536). Rats, mice, and rabbits are not difficult to immunize ; but guinea-pigs cannot be rendered completely resistant. In the past attenuated living cultures were tried (see Report 1915*a*), but all workers now use vaccines in which the organisms have been killed. In the prophylaxis of plague in man Haffkine's vaccine has been chiefly used. It is prepared from a 4-weeks' culture of *Past. pestis* at 27° C., in goat digest broth, killed by heat for 15 minutes at 55° C. and the subsequent addition of 0·5 per cent. phenol. According to Schütze (1934), it is desirable to neutralize the alkali in the culture before heating, in order not to destroy the envelope antigen of the bacillus. The vaccine is standardized by a mouse protection test (see Taylor 1933, Sokhey and Maurice 1935). The dosage for an adult is usually 4 c.c., given at a single inoculation. The protective value of this vaccine is difficult to assess. Most of the trials have been made in India, where exact collection of statistics is notoriously difficult. The selection of the groups for vaccination has in some instances not been above criticism. To give an adequate summary of the results obtained would necessitate more space than can here be spared ; the reader who wishes to examine the evidence is referred to the Indian Plague Commission's Report (1901). A synoptic table, however, giving the more important groups of figures is reproduced (Table CXLIII).

TABLE CXLIII

SHOWING INCIDENCE AND MORTALITY OF PLAGUE IN INOCULATED AND UNINOCULATED PERSONS
(Taylor 1933).

Outbreak.	Average Populations.		Inoculated.		Uninoculated.	
	Inoculated.	Unin-oculated.	Attacks.	Deaths.	Attacks.	Deaths.
House of Correction, By-culla	147	172	2	—	12	6
Lanowli	323	377	14	7	78	57
Umerkhadi Jail . . .	147	127	3	—	10	6
Undhera	71	64	8	3	27	26
Hubli	24,631	17,786	Not available	338	Not available	2,348
S.M.R. Hubli	1,260	760	11	2	35	21
Belgaum	4,842	4,558	78	40	506	346
Jewish Community, Aden	1,190	982	23	8	83	65
Nawashahr	2,648	2,141	9	5	41	32
Kahma	863	889	—	—	10	5
Khatkar Kalan . . .	1,040	338	6	2	6	5
Salem	27,489	27,181	434	226	1,693	1,495
Coimbatore	26,559	22,604	150	56	707	492
Baghdad	56,555	108,445	65	36	806	638
Average population . .	147,765	186,424	—	—	—	—
Attacks and deaths . .	—	—	803 *	723	4,014 *	5,542
Attack rate per 10,000 .			66		232	
Death rate per 10,000 .			49		297	
Case mortality . . .			48 per cent.		79 per cent.	

* Excluding Hubli, for which no attack rates were available.

These figures suggest that inoculation confers roughly a fourfold protection against attack, and a sixfold protection against death. The effect of the vaccine probably lasts for some months. (For experimental work on vaccination of animals against plague see Naidu and Sathe 1932, Otten 1933.)

Serum Treatment.—A number of sera have been used in the treatment of human plague. Rowland (see Report 1911, p. 11) stated that serum prepared by immunizing horses with a solution of nucleoproteins from the plague bacillus had definite curative properties in rats. But in practice no serum has yet given unequivocal results (McCoy and Chapin 1920). A report on the use of Yersin's, Haffkine's, Lustig's, Terni's, and Brazil's sera was published by the Government of India (Haffkine 1905) ; none of them affected the mortality of the disease. The English Plague Commission likewise obtained no evidence that serum treatment was beneficial (Report 1912, p. 326).

PASTEURELLOSIS OR HÆMORRHAGIC SEPTICÆMIA OF ANIMALS

The observations of Bollinger and of Kitt in 1878 on an epidemic disease affecting wild hogs, deer, and later cattle in the neighbourhood of Munich constitute the first work of importance on a group of diseases attacking several species of animals, and known collectively as Hæmorrhagic Septicæmia. Kitt was successful in isolating the causative organism and in transmitting the disease to mice and pigeons. A similar organism was obtained by Pasteur in 1880 from fowl cholera, by Loeffler in 1882 from swine plague, by Poels (1886) from septic pleuropneumonia of calves, and by numerous workers during the next few years from diseases in other animals. In 1901 Lignières proposed to unite all these affections into one group under the name of Pasteurellosis, and to call the infecting organisms *Pasteurella*. He divided this group into 6 sub-groups according to the species of animal attacked :

(1) Avian type, attacking hens (fowl cholera), other birds, and rabbits.

(2) Porcine type, giving rise to swine plague (*Schweineseuche, peste du porc*).

(3) Ovine type, affecting sheep (*pneumo-entérite, lombriz*), and infectious pneumonia of goats.

(4) Bovine type, attacking cattle (*Wild- und Rinderseuche, septicémie hémorragique des bovidés, pneumo-entérite du bœuf, barbone* of buffaloes, septic pleuropneumonia of calves, and *entiqué*).

The 5th and 6th sub-groups comprised equine influenza and canine distemper respectively, neither of which is actually due to *Pasteurella*.

This classification is incomplete and has little to recommend it ; there is no place in it for pasteurellosis of the mouse, the rat, the reindeer and other animals that suffer naturally from the disease. Moreover it has now become clear that all true *Pasteurella* infections are manifestations of one infective process—Septicæmia hæmorrhagica. The causative organism is apparently the same throughout ; and there is no means by which its animal origin can be ascertained with certainty.

So far as we know, hæmorrhagic septicæmia does not attack man. Several authors, it is true, have described diseases in man that they consider to be due to a member of the *Pasteurella* group (Lorey 1911, Brugnatelli 1913, Besredka 1915), but careful examination of their records has failed to convince us that they were dealing with this organism at all.

The clinical manifestations of pasteurellosis vary according to the animal attacked ; in some animals two or more forms of the disease have been recognized. Generally it runs an acute course with death in the space of a few hours to a few days. The mortality is high, 70–100 per cent. (Brimhall and Wilson 1900, Rice 1926). Post mortem, the main lesions are found in the viscera. Petechial hæmorrhages are common especially in the pleura, endocardium, and kidneys ; and larger hæmorrhages may be scattered through the submucous connective tissue and lymphatic glands (Brimhall and Wilson 1900). In the pulmonary form the mucosa of the trachea and bronchi is congested ; the lungs are hyperæmic and show diffuse or patchy consolidation ; the pleura is covered with coagulated fibrin, and there is a fibrinous or purulent exudate in the pericardium (Poels 1886). The peribronchial and mediastinal lymph glands are swollen, and on section are moist and red. Congestion of the kidneys is noticeable, particularly in swine ; microscopically there is epithelial necrosis of the tubules (Magnusson 1914). In the intestinal form the most noticeable feature is acute hæmorrhagic enteritis, with sometimes bloody mucus in the intestine (Rice 1926). The spleen and liver usually show little or no change (Voges 1896), but they are frequently covered with fibrino-purulent exudate, similar to that in the peritoneal cavity (Mørch and Krogh-Lund 1931). Microscopically the small, regular, oval, Gram-negative, bipolar-staining bacilli are found in enormous numbers in the blood and viscera.

The method by which the disease spreads is not altogether clear. Hueppe (1886) regarded it as a ground infection like anthrax, but the very low resistance of the organisms to inimical agencies would seem to exclude this. Magnusson (1914), who observed a large epidemic amongst reindeer in Sweden, suggested that it was spread by a sucking insect. This suggestion finds some support in the observations of Daubney, Hudson, and Roberts (1934), who brought evidence to show that the disease in cattle could be carried by the flea *Ctenocephalus felis* Bouche. Recently the belief has been gaining ground that it is primarily a respiratory infection. The organisms have been found on the mucosa of the mouth and in the nasopharynx of normal swine (Uhlenhuth and Haendel 1913). De Kruif (1921, 1922*a*, *b*, 1923), working with rabbits suffering from snuffles—a chronic form of the disease—observed the organism in the nose of a large proportion of normal animals. Webster (1924*a*, *b*) found that preceding an outbreak there was a rise in the normal carrier rate. The susceptibility of rabbits varied greatly, some being highly resistant, others succumbing with ease. Similar variation in the susceptibility of fowls to natural and experimental infection has likewise been noted by Rice (1926). These observations suggest that natural infection occurs through the nose, and that it is dependent on the presence of carriers.

Protection, Vaccination, and Serotherapy.

It was when working with chicken cholera that Pasteur observed a spontaneous diminution of virulence in a culture which he had left for some weeks at room temperature in contact with the air. This culture, on inoculation into fowls, proved harmless. When these fowls were re-inoculated shortly afterwards with a virulent culture, instead of dying of hæmorrhagic septicæmia they recovered rapidly after a brief indisposition.

The vaccines used at present for the prophylaxis of pasteurellosis are made chiefly from strains attenuated by heat or chemical agents. In some instances their use appears to have yielded satisfactory results (Brimhall and Wilson 1900, Chamberland and Jouan 1906, Hutyra and Marek 1912, Magnusson 1914). Immune sera prepared by injection of horses with living organisms or with body exudates are sometimes employed therapeutically (Schirop 1908). The most promising method appears to be combined active and passive immunization.

Other Diseases Associated with Pasteurella or Pasteurella-like Organisms.

Pasteurella is a common secondary invader in many diseases of animals. It has been found especially in swine fever, in which it gives rise to severe pulmonary complications, in influenza of horses (Lignières 1901), and occasionally in canine distemper (Lignières 1901), in roup (Bushnell 1923) and diphtheria of fowls (Chamberland and Jouan 1906).

The so-called " de Aar disease," described by Pirie (1929) and Mitchell (1930), affecting the veld rodents of South Africa, was probably due to a genuine *Pasteurella* infection. On the other hand the contagious pneumonia of sheep, recorded by Dungal (1931) in Iceland, was caused by an organism differing in several respects from *Past. septica* (see Chapter XXIX), as was also the pyogenic disease of sheep described by Jowett (1931).

A number of outbreaks in fowls (Higgins 1898), geese (Frosch and Bierbaum 1909), rabbits (Kraus 1897*a*, Kurila 1909, van Saceghem 1922), and guinea-pigs (Busson 1921) have been ascribed to infection with *Pasteurella*, which, from the records, were probably due to other organisms. There is still a disposition to treat the *Pasteurella* group as a convenient refuge for any small, Gram-negative bacillus whose identity has not been accurately ascertained.

PSEUDOTUBERCULOSIS

There are three or four diseases of animals known as pseudotuberculosis, which are caused by different organisms.

Pseudotuberculosis of Rodents.—In 1883 Malassez and Vignal described a disease in a guinea-pig that had been used for experimental inoculation, which was characterized by the presence of nodules histologically similar to those of tuberculosis, but containing zooglœal masses of coccoid bacilli. To this disease they gave the name zooglœal tuberculosis. A similar organism was found by Dor (1888), Charrin and Roger (1888), Nocard (1889), and Zagari (1890) in guinea-pigs dying either naturally or after inoculation with pathological material. Preisz (1894), who made a comparative study of these organisms, concluded that they were identical with a bacillus described by Pfeiffer in 1890 under the name *B. pseudotuberculosis rodentium*, now known as *Past. pseudotuberculosis*.

The disease attacks guinea-pigs chiefly, and to a less extent rats. In Germany cats appear to be not infrequently infected (Pallaske and Meyn 1932). Sporadic cases of the disease are observed in mice, rabbits, hares, pigeons, turkeys, and canaries (Pallaske 1933). Infection appears to occur by the alimentary tract. Post mortem in guinea-pigs, there are rounded greyish-white spherical nodules up to 2 or 3 mm. in diameter, distributed chiefly in the spleen, liver, and lungs. The nodules are well defined, often protrude from the surface, and on section appear creamy or caseous. Enlarged caseous mesenteric glands are generally present. Microscopically the lesions contain large numbers of short, coccoid or ovoid, bipolar-stained Gram-negative bacilli, which can be readily cultivated on agar (see Chapter XXIX). The disease can be reproduced experimentally in large numbers of different animals and birds (see Pallaske 1933). On injection into guinea-pigs, rabbits, rats, or mice the bacilli prove fatal in 1 to 3 weeks, depending on the dose used and the site of injection. At necropsy after intramuscular inoculation there is a caseous local lesion, enlargement of the regional lymphatic glands, and nodules in the spleen, liver, and lungs. Microscopically, the bacilli are numerous in the local lesion and glands.

Pseudotuberculosis of Mice.—This disease is due to a short Gram-positive diphtheroid bacillus, *C. murium*, described independently by Bongert (1901) and Kutscher (1894), (see Chapter XVI).

Pseudotuberculosis of Sheep.—This disease has been reported in Europe, America, and Australia. It is caused by a short, non-motile, Gram-positive diphtheroid organism, known as the Preisz-Nocard bacillus or *C. ovis* (Preisz 1894). The same organism appears to be responsible for ulcerative lymphangitis of horses and contagious acne of horses (Hutyra and Marek 1912), (see Chapter XVI).

REFERENCES

BESREDKA, A.   (1915) *C. R. Soc. Biol.*, **78**, 288.
BONGERT.   (1901) *Z. Hyg. InfektKr.*, **37**, 449.
BORDAS, DUBIEF, and TANON.   (1922) *Pr. méd.*, **30**, Part II, p. 831.
BOYD, M. F. and KEMMERER, T. W.   (1921) *Publ. Hlth Rep., Wash.*, **36**, 1754.
BRIMHALL, S. D. and WILSON, L. B.   (1900) *J. comp. Med.*, **21**, 722.
BRUGNATELLI, E.   (1913) *Zbl. Bakt.*, **70**, 337.
BULSTRODE, H. T.   (1910–11) *40th Ann. Rep. loc. Govt Bd M.O.'s Suppl.*, p. 36.
BUSHNELL, L. D.   (1923) *Abstr. Bact.*, **7**, 30.
BUSSON, B.   (1921) *Zbl. Bakt.*, **86**, 101.
CHAMBERLAND and JOUAN.   (1906) *Ann. Inst. Pasteur*, **20**, 81.
CHARRIN and ROGER, G. H.   (1888) *C. R. Soc. Biol.*, **5**, 272.
DAUBNEY, R., HUDSON, J. R., and ROBERTS, J. I.   (1934) *J. comp. Path.*, **47**, 211.
DOR, L.   (1888) *C. R. Soc. Biol.*, **5**, 449.
DUNGAL, N.   (1931) *J. comp. Path.*, **44**, 126.
EASTWOOD, A. and GRIFFITH, F.   (1914) *J. Hyg., Camb.*, **14**, 285.
Editorial.   (1925a) *Publ. Hlth Rep., Wash.*, **40**, 51 ; (1925b) *Brit. med. J.*, i. 851.
ELTON, C. S.   (1925) *J. Hyg., Camb.*, **24**, 138.
FROSCH, P. and BIERBAUM, K.   (1909) *Zbl. Bakt.*, **52**, 433.
GALLI-VALERIO, B.   (1900) *Zbl. Bakt.*, **27**, 1 ; (1903) *Ibid.*, Ref. **33**, 753.
GAUTHIER, J.-C. and RAYBAUD, A.   (1902) *C. R. Soc. Biol.*, **54**, 1497 ; (1903) *Rev. Hyg.*, **25**, 426.
GIRARD, G.   (1934) *C. R. Soc. Biol.*, **117**, 601.
GREENWOOD, M.   (1935) " Epidemics and Crowd-Diseases," Williams & Norgate Ltd., Lond.
HAFFKINE, W. M.   (1905) *Sci. Mem. med. sanit. Dep. India*, New. Ser., No. 20 ; (1907–8) *Proc. R. Soc. Med.*, **1**, Part I, Epidem. Sect., p. 71.
HIGGINS, C. H.   (1898) *J. exp. Med.*, **3**, 651.
HILL, A. B.   (1934) *Spec. Rep. Ser. med. Res. Coun., Lond.*, No. 196.
HIRST, P.   (1926) *Ceylon J. med. Sci.*, Sect. D, **1**, 155 ; (1927) *Ibid.*, **1**, 273.
HUEPPE, F.   (1886) *Berl. klin. Wschr.*, **23**, 753, 776, 794.
HUTYRA, F. and MAREK, J.   (1912) " Special Pathology and Therapeutics of the Diseases of Domestic Animals," **1**, 77.   Chicago and London.
JETTMAR, H. M.   (1923) *Z. Hyg. InfektKr.*, **97**, 322.
JOWETT, W.   (1931) *J. comp. Path.*, **44**, 202.
KAUNTZE, W. H.   (1926) *Bull. Hyg., Lond.*, **1**, 66.
KING, H. H. and PANDIT, C. G.   (1931) *Indian. J. med. Res.*, **19**, 357.
KISTER.   (1930) *Zbl. Bakt.*, **117**, 433.
KITASATO, S.   (1894) *Lancet*, ii. 428.
KRAUS, R.   (1897a) *Z. Hyg. InfektKr.*, **24**, 396 ; (1897b) *Wien. klin. Wschr.*, **10**, 736.
KRUIF, P. H. DE.   (1921) *J. exp. Med.*, **33**, 773 ; (1922a) *Ibid.*, **35**, 561 ; (1922b) *Ibid.*, **36**, 309 ; (1923) *Ibid.*, **37**, 647.
KURILA, S.   (1909) *Zbl. Bakt.*, **49**, 508.
KUTSCHER.   (1894) *Z. Hyg. InfektKr.*, **17**, 327.
LEVINTHAL, W.   (1931) *Z. Hyg. InfektKr.*, **112**, 433.
LIGNIÈRES, M. J.   (1901) *Ann. Inst. Pasteur*, **15**, 734.
LISTON, W. G.   (1924) *Brit. med. J.*, i. 900, 950, 997.
LOREY, A.   (1911) *Z. Hyg. InfektKr.*, **68**, 49.
Low.   (1920) *Rep. Minist. Hlth*, No. 3.   H.M. Stat. Off.
MACALISTER, G. H. and BROOKS, R. ST. J.   (1914) *J. Hyg., Camb.*, **14**, 316.
McCoy, G. W.   (1910) *J. Hyg., Camb.*, **10**, 589 ; (1911) *Publ. Hlth Bull.*, No. 43.
McCoy, G. W. and CHAPIN, C. W.   (1920) *Publ. Hlth Rep., Wash.*, **35**, 1647.
MAGNUSSON, H.   (1914) *Z. InfektKr. Haustiere*, **15**, 61.
MALASSEZ, L. C. and VIGNAL, W.   (1883) *Arch. Phys. norm. path.*, 3rd Ser., **2**, 369.
MITCHELL, J. A.   (1921) *J. Hyg., Camb.*, **20**, 377 ; (1930) *J. Hyg., Camb.*, **29**, 394.
MØRCH, J. R. and KROGH-LUND, G.   (1931) *Z. Hyg. InfektKr.*, **112**, 471.
NAIDU, B. P. B. and SATHE, R. G.   (1932) *Indian J. med. Res.*, **19**, 987.
NOCARD.   (1889) *C. R. Soc. Biol.*, **1**, 608.
NUTTALL, G. H. F.   (1897) *Zbl. Bakt.*, **22**, 87 ; (1898) *Ibid.*, **23**, 625.
OGATA, M.   (1897) *Zbl. Bakt.*, **21**, 769.
OTTEN, L.   (1932) *J. Hyg., Camb.*, **32**, 396 ; (1933) *Meded. Dienst. Volksgezondh. Ned.-Ind.*, Part II, 61.
PALLASKE, G.   (1933) *Z. InfektKr. Haustiere*, **44**, 43.
PALLASKE, G. and MEYN, A.   (1932) *Dtsch. tierärztl. Wschr.*, **40**, 577.
PETRIE, G. F.   (1924) *J. Hyg., Camb.*, **22**, 397.
PETRIE, G. F. and TODD, R. E.   (1924) *J. Hyg., Camb.*, **23**, 117.
PFEIFFER, A.   (1890) *Zbl. Bakt.*, **7**, 219.

PHILIP, W. M. and HIRST, L. F.   (1917) *J. Hyg., Camb.*, **15**, 527.
PIRAS, L.   (1913) *Zbl. Bakt.*, **71**, 69.
PIRIE, J. H. H.   (1929) *Publ. S. Afr. Inst. med. Res.*, **4**, 218.
POELS, J.   (1886) *Fortschr. Med.*, **4**, 388.
PREISZ, H.   (1894) *Ann. Inst. Pasteur*, **8**, 231.
RADCLIFFE, J. N.   (1879–80) *9th Rep. loc. Govt Bd*, M.O.'s Suppl., p. 1.
Report.   (1899) *German Plague Comm., Arb. ReichsgesundhAmt.*, **16**, 1 ; (1901) *Indian
    Plague Comm.*, **5**, 181, H.M. Stat. Off. ; (1906) *English Plague Comm., J. Hyg., Camb.*,
    6, 421 ; (1907) *Ibid.*, **7**, 324 ; (1908) *Ibid.*, **8**, 162 ; (1910) *Ibid.*, **10**, 315 ; (1911) *Ibid.*, **11**,
    Suppl. ; (1912) *Ibid.*, **12**, Suppl. ; (1914) *Ibid.*, **13**, Suppl., p. 423 ; (1915a) *Ibid.*, **14**,
    Suppl., p. 756 ; (1915b) *Ibid.*, **14**, Suppl., p. 770 ; (1915c) *Ibid.*, **14**, Suppl., p. 774 ; (1915d)
    Ibid., **14**, Suppl., p. 777.
RICE, J. P.   (1926) *Ann. Cong. Nat. vet. med. Ass. G.B.I.*, p, 57.
ROBERTSON, H. McG.   (1923) *Publ. Hlth Rep., Wash.*, **38**, 1519.
RODIER, W.   (1926) *Bull. Hyg., Lond.*, **1**, 312.
SACEGHEM, R. VAN.   (1922) *C. R. Soc. Biol.*, **86**, 281.
SCHIROP, H.   (1908) *Zbl. Bakt.*, **47**, 307.
SCHÜTZE, H.   (1934) *Brit. J. exp. Path.*, **15**, 200.
SIMOND, P.-L.   (1898) *Ann. Inst. Pasteur*, **12**, 625.
SMILLIE, W. G.   (1920) *J. infect. Dis.*, **27**, 378.
SOKHEY, S. S. and MAURICE, H.   (1935) *Bull. Off. int. Hyg. publ.*, **27**, 1534.
TAYLOR, J.   (1933) *Indian J. med. Res.*, No. 27.
THOMPSON, J. A.   (1906) *J. Hyg., Camb.*, **6**, 537.
TSCHURILINA, A. A.   (1930) *Z. Hyg. InfektKr.*, **111**, 198.
UHLENHUTH, P. and HAENDEL, L.   (1913) See Kolle & Wassermann's " Hdb. path. Mikroog.,"
    2te Abt., 1912–13, **6**, 325.
URIARTE, L.   (1925) *C. R. Soc. Biol.*, **92**, 901.
VOGES, O.   (1896) *Z. Hyg. InfektKr.*, **23**, 149.
WARNER, C. E.   (1914) *J. Hyg., Camb.*, **14**, 360.
WAYSON, N. E.   (1925) *Publ. Hlth Rep., Wash.*, **40**, 1975.
WEBSTER, L. T.   (1924a) *J. exp. Med.*, **39**, 837, 843, 857 ; (1924b) *Ibid.*, **40**, 109, 117.
WHITE, F. N.   (1918–19) *Indian J. med. Res.*, **6**, 190.
WILLIAMS, C. L. and KEMMERER, T. W.   (1923) *Publ. Hlth Rep., Wash.*, **38**, 1873.
WU LIEN TEH.   (1913) *J. Hyg., Camb.*, **13**, 237 ; (1922) *Ibid.*, **21**, 62 ; (1924) *Ibid.*, **22**, 329.
YERSIN.   (1894) *Ann. Inst. Pasteur*, **8**, 662.
YERSIN, CALMETTE, and BORREL.   (1895) *Ann. Inst. Pasteur*, **9**, 589.
ZABOLOTNY, D.   (1923) *Ann. Inst. Pasteur*, **37**, 618.
ZAGARI.   (1890) *Zbl. Bakt.*, **8**, 208.
ZLATOGOROFF, S. J.   (1904) *Zbl. Bakt.*, **36**, 559.

CHAPTER LXXI

ACUTE RESPIRATORY INFECTIONS

ONE at least of the diseases dealt with in this chapter—epidemic influenza—would be more correctly placed among the virus diseases considered in Chapter LXXXIV ; and it is highly probable that the same applies to the common cold. Both these infections are, however, so closely connected from the clinical point of view with other respiratory diseases that it is convenient to take them out of their proper order.

The Common Cold

Studies that have been recorded in recent years, and particularly those of Dochez and his colleagues (Shibley, Mills and Dochez 1929, Dochez, Shibley and Mills 1930, Dochez, Mills and Kneeland 1931a, b, 1932, 1933, 1936) have greatly strengthened the view advanced by Foster (1917) that the infectious common cold is a virus disease (see also Long et al. 1931, Powell and Clowes 1931).

Since we have as yet no satisfactory evidence that any of the ordinary laboratory animals are susceptible to infection with this virus, resort has been made to the higher apes, or to human volunteers ; and this has seriously limited the scope of the experiments. One of the great difficulties that has to be overcome in work of this kind is to eliminate the risk of natural contact infection.

Dochez, Shibley and Mills (1930) recorded the transmission of the common cold to anthropoid apes, and to human volunteers, by the intranasal instillation of filtered washings from cases of the disease. Long and others (1931), using human volunteers, succeeded in several instances in inducing an acute cold with filtered nasal washings, and in transmitting it from one subject to another in series. Dochez, Mills and Kneeland (1931a, b) recorded the cultivation of the virus in Tyrode solution containing minced chick embryo, and the production of a cold in two of three volunteers with a fifteenth subculture (see also Dochez, Mills and Kneeland 1936) ; and Powell and Clowes (1931) have recorded similar findings.

It is probable that many points in the problem of the ætiology of the common cold—the existence of one or more types of virus, the relation of the cold virus to the influenza virus, and so on—will await the discovery of a more convenient experimental animal than man, or the anthropoid ape. In the meantime we seem justified in accepting the view that the infectious common cold is a virus disease, at least as the best working hypothesis ; and, for this reason, earlier observations that sought to trace a causal relationship between various bacterial inhabitants of the nasopharynx and this particular disease have become of minor interest, and may be briefly summarized.

The available records are indeed by no means consistent (see Williams, Nevin and Gurley 1921, Shibley, Hanger and Dochez 1926, Noble, Fisher and Brainard 1928, Shibley,

Mills and Dochez 1929, Burky and Smillie 1929). Taking them as a whole it may fairly be said that they fail to establish any case for a consistent significant change in the bacterial flora of the nasopharynx in association with the onset of an acute cold.

In an investigation undertaken in Manchester during the period 1926–28 (see Report 1930) a nasopharyngeal swab was taken each month from 100 persons who volunteered to assist in the inquiry. Additional swabbings were taken from these persons whenever they contracted a cold. Data were thus available for a considerable number of swabbings, taken from the same persons at times when they were suffering from a cold, and at other times when they were not. The figures referring to the frequency of *H. influenzæ*, hæmolytic streptococci and the pneumococcus, are set out in Table CXLIV. They refer only to those persons who contracted a cold during the period of observation ; and they do not include the results obtained in cases which, on clinical grounds, were diagnosed as influenza.

TABLE CXLIV

	With Colds (110 Swabs).		Without Colds (1,731 Swabs).	
	Number +.	Per cent.+.	Number +.	Per cent. +.
H. influenzæ	52	47·27	984	56·85
Hæmolytic streptococci .	19	17·27	229	13·23
Pneumococci	30	27·27	446	25·77

It will be noted that, while pneumococci and hæmolytic streptococci were slightly more frequent in those that had colds, than in those that had not, the difference is slight and insignificant ; *H. influenzæ* was more frequently isolated at times when no sign of a cold was present. It should be added that most of these colds were trivial ; and it is probable that the factors of type and severity of infection are largely responsible for the divergent findings recorded by different workers. The " common cold " is, in fact, not a clinical entity, and it defies definition on clinical grounds. If attention is confined to severe catarrhs, associated with a definite mucopurulent discharge, it is the common experience of bacteriologists that the organisms most frequently isolated are pneumococci, *H. influenzæ*, and, less frequently, hæmolytic streptococci. This is particularly true when the local reaction in the nose and nasopharynx is associated with definite suppurative sinusitis. In a proportion of such cases *Staph. aureus* may be found. In the particular case of the influenza bacillus, Dochez, Mills and Kneeland (1932) have noted the replacement of the ordinary " rough " type by the " smooth " virulent type of Pittmann (see Chapter XXX) following the induction of acute colds in apes with a filtrable virus.

Prophylactic Immunization against the Common Cold.

No virus-containing preparation is as yet available for active immunization. In view of what has been said above we should not expect that the injection of a bacterial vaccine, containing pneumococci, influenza bacilli, hæmolytic streptococci and so on, would have any effect on the incidence of colds, since the causal organism is not included in it. There is scarcely more reason to suppose that it would in any way diminish the severity of colds or lessen the chances of secondary infection, since the bacterial species of which it is composed are antigenically highly heterogeneous, and only a few arbitrarily selected types of each species can be included. The results of adequate clinical trials are in accord with immunological expectations.

Von Sholly and Park (1921), using a mixed vaccine of the ordinary type, inoculated 1,327 persons and kept them under observation, together with 3,025 uninoculated controls, from September 1919 to May 1920 ; during this period 57·7 per cent. of the inoculated and 38·2 per cent. of the uninoculated developed colds. Jordan and Sharp (1921) observed 448 inoculated persons and 461 uninoculated controls from November 1919 to June 1920 ; 54·9 per cent. of the inoculated and 51·6 per cent. of the uninoculated developed colds. Ferguson, Davey and Topley (1927) observed 138 inoculated persons and 148 uninoculated controls from November 1924 to May 1925 ; 78·3 per cent. of the inoculated and 70·3 per cent. of the uninoculated developed colds. Brown (1932) observed 80 inoculated persons and 82 uninoculated controls from November 1929 to June 1930 ; the inoculated contracted 1·85 colds per person during this period, the uninoculated 2·17.

It may be added that, with very few exceptions, the results of properly conducted trials are equally unfavourable to the suggestion that immunization with an " anti-catarrhal " vaccine diminishes the severity of colds, or lessens the frequency of secondary infections.

Epidemic Influenza

The recent solution of the problem of the ætiology of influenza by Laidlaw and his colleagues (see Smith, Andrewes and Laidlaw 1933) will certainly stand as one of the important landmarks in the history of preventive medicine.

This disease has presented the epidemiologist with one of his most fascinating and provoking problems. It has a long and puzzling history ; and, within recent years, it has been the reigning killing disease of adult life ; nor is there any likelihood that its reign will end apart from some effective method of prophylaxis. The pandemic of 1918–19 was one of the great pestilences of mankind, destroying more lives in a few months than did the Great War in 4 years. Those who are interested in that pandemic and in the lessons to be learned from it may be referred to the report issued by the Ministry of Health (Report 1920). We may note that influenza is one of those diseases that seems to confer only a transitory immunity, in the sense that repeated attacks are common. We may also note that its epidemiological study has, up to the present time, been rendered unusually difficult by the lack of precision in its clinical diagnosis. There is little difficulty in telling when we are faced with an *epidemic* of influenza ; but sporadic cases, and even minor outbreaks, of acute febrile diseases are very apt to receive this particular label without any very definite reason. The clinical syndrome that justifies a diagnosis of influenza is, indeed, singularly difficult to define. It seems extremely probable that, with the knowledge we now possess, the clinician and bacteriologist between them will be able to place this problem on a far more satisfactory footing.

The Ætiology of Influenza.

In view of our present knowledge the long controversy as to whether epidemic influenza was, or was not, caused by *H. influenzæ*, described by Pfeiffer in 1892, has lost all but historical interest.

Those interested may be referred to the monograph by Kristensen (1922). We may summarize the extensive bacteriological literature by noting that, while there is ample evidence that the influenza bacillus is very frequently present in the nasopharynx of those suffering from the disease (see for instance Pritchett and Stillman 1919, McClelland 1919, Park 1919, Duval and Harris 1919, Schorer 1919, Medalia 1919, Dick and Murray 1919, McIntosh 1922), and though its distribution in the tissues, as revealed by post-mortem examination, makes it clear that it often plays a part in the disease as it appears in man (see Fildes and McIntosh 1920, McIntosh 1922), its curious absence in certain epidemics, particularly in the summer of 1918, had raised serious doubts as to its primary ætiological rôle before the view that influenza was a virus disease had been clearly established (see Mandelbaum 1918, Selter 1918, Messerschmidt *et al.* 1919, Leichtentritt 1918, Kristensen 1922).

The virus theory of influenza was, of course, held quite widely as a possible working hypothesis, before the problem was attacked by Laidlaw and his colleagues, and there had been occasional reports of the transmission of an influenza-like disease to apes or to human volunteers with filtered washings from influenzal patients ; but none of these experiments were on such a scale as to establish any definite conclusion.

The most important contribution to the influenza problem, prior to the original report of Smith, Andrewes and Laidlaw (1933) was the work of Shope on influenza in swine, and this will be considered in a later section.

In view of their great importance the observations of Laidlaw and his colleagues must be discussed in some detail.

In their original communication Smith, Andrewes and Laidlaw (1933) showed that a characteristic febrile disease could be induced in ferrets by the intranasal instillation of filtered nasal washings from a human case of epidemic influenza. This disease was transmissible in series, from ferret to ferret, either by natural contact or by the intranasal instillation of filtered material. Ferrets that had recently recovered from the disease were resistant to re-infection, and their serum contained protective antibodies in high concentration. In this report it was also noted that Shope's swine influenza virus produced in ferrets a disease indistinguishable from that produced by the human virus, and that there appeared to be an immunological relationship between the two types. These observations were later confirmed and extended (see, also, Shope 1935, Francis and Shope 1936). Shope (1934b), who had successfully repeated the experiments of Smith, Andrewes and Laidlaw, found that the swine influenza virus when injected intranasally into ferrets under ether anæsthesia produced pneumonic lesions in the lungs, and Andrewes, Laidlaw and Smith (1934), using a similar technique, were able to induce a fatal pneumonia in mice, both with the human and swine viruses. Francis (1934) isolated a strain of the human virus from cases of influenza in Puerto Rico, and this virus and other strains isolated later in New York and Philadelphia were found to be immunologically identical with the original English strain, and with other strains isolated in England during the winter and early spring of 1934–35 (Laidlaw 1935, Andrewes, Laidlaw and Smith 1935, Francis and Magill 1935). An immunologically identical virus has since been isolated from epidemics of influenza in Australia (Burnet 1935a) and in Alaska (Pettit, Mudd and Pepper 1936). Laidlaw (1935) suggests that the swine influenza virus may represent the 1918–19 human virus which has become acclimatized to swine. This tentative hypothesis is based in part on the proved immunological relationship, but not identity, of the two viruses, in part on the fact that, while neutralizing antibodies to the human virus were found in most human sera, antibodies to the swine influenza virus were regularly present in adult human sera, but were wholly absent from the sera of a small sample of children (Andrewes, Laidlaw and Smith 1935). Similar findings have recently been recorded by Francis and Magill (1936), and by Shope (1936). This frequent presence of neutralizing antibodies in adult human sera is a serious difficulty in performing the crucial experiment of the transmission of influenza from an infected ferret to a human volunteer. There are, however, a few recorded instances of influenza in man following contact with infected ferrets which are, at least, highly suggestive.

It may be noted that the sizes of the viruses of human and swine influenza have recently been determined by Elford, Andrewes and Tang (1936) and found to fall within the range 80–120 $m\mu$; while Burnet (1935*b*) has recorded the successful cultivation of the virus on the chorio-allantoic membrane of the hen's egg.

Immunization.—The problem of immunization against the influenza virus is clearly of primary importance. If we could induce an effective active immunity in man we should be in a position to eliminate the disease, or reduce it to negligible proportions. It is possible that passive immunization, by the injection of an anti-body-containing serum, might exert some therapeutic effect in an established case ; but this method, even if successful, should clearly be regarded as a second and subsidiary line of defence.

This problem, as it has developed experimentally in the hands of Laidlaw and his colleagues, has reached a stage at which definite progress can be reported (see Smith, Andrewes and Laidlaw 1935).

It has already been noted that ferrets that have recovered from an attack of the virus disease are, for a time, completely resistant to infection. This solid immunity persists for about 3 months, and then gradually wanes. Ferrets with a waning immunity still show the presence of protective antibodies in their blood, although the nasal mucosa has become susceptible to re-infection ; and, when it is re-infected, the circulating antibodies fail to protect the animal against a general febrile reaction. The position in regard to active immunization, apart from the production of an attack of the disease, is curious and interesting. The ferret is not susceptible to the injection of the living virus otherwise than by the intranasal instillation or by some other method of introduction directly into the respiratory tract. Animals inoculated subcutaneously, intradermally, intraperitoneally, intramuscularly, intratesticularly or intracerebrally show no sign of illness. Such injections, particularly if frequently repeated, lead to the appearance of protective antibodies in the circulating blood ; but the appearance of these antibodies is not associated with any effective resistance to infection by the intranasal route. This clearly suggests that the local conditions in the nasal mucosa are of predominating importance ; but, so far, attempts to induce immunity by the intranasal injection of killed or inactivated virus have failed.

If, however, a ferret that is in the stage of waning immunity is injected subcutaneously with living virus, its immunity may be reinforced, so that it becomes again completely resistant to intranasal infection. Immunization by the subcutaneous route is not therefore completely without effect ; and this is also shown by the fact that the injection of living or formolized virus into normal ferrets, although it induces no effective immunity to re-infection by the intranasal route, lessens the frequency of lung lesions. A similar effect may be observed in mice. It would appear then that the most that has been accomplished at the moment, on the lines of active immunization, is the production of a partial immunity of a relatively low grade (see Chapter **XXXIX**). The observations recorded in this section may usefully be considered in relation to the discussion of local immunity in Chapter **L**.

In regard to passive immunization, it has proved possible to produce an anti-influenzal horse serum that contains neutralizing antibodies to relatively high titre (see Laidlaw, Smith, Andrewes and Dunkin 1935).

This serum, when injected intraperitoneally into mice in relatively large doses, significantly increases their resistance to the intranasal injection of virus, under light ether anæsthesia, 45 minutes later. It also leads to a reduction in percentage mortality when injected intravenously or intraperitoneally into mice 24–48 hours after the intranasal instillation of virus.

The protective antibodies in an anti-influenzal horse serum are contained in the pseudoglobulin fraction, and the greater part are precipitated in the fraction salted out between 12 and 16 per cent. sodium sulphate.

In the past many attempts have been made to induce an immunity to influenza by the injection of a vaccine containing *H. influenzæ*. Clearly, such a procedure has no scientific justification and it is sufficient to note that, here again, adequate field trials are in accord with immunological expectations (see von Sholly and Park 1921, Jordan and Sharp 1921).

Swine Influenza

We have referred above to Shope's observations on swine influenza (see Shope 1931*a*, *b*, 1932, 1934*a*, *b*, 1935, Lewis and Shope 1931). This disease first appeared, or was first recognized, in the United States in the autumn of 1918. It occurred in epidemic form in close association with the human pandemic of influenza, and it was at once suggested that there was some causal relation between them.

Shope (1931*a*, *b*) was able to show that the swine disease, in its characteristic clinical form, was caused by the associated effects of a filtrable virus and a hæmophilic bacillus, closely resembling the human influenza bacillus, to which he gave the name of *H. influenzæ-suis* (see Chapter XXX). The virus alone caused a relatively trivial infection, unassociated with the pulmonary complications of the natural epidemic disease. The bacillus alone caused no detectable illness. As in the infection of ferrets with human influenza virus, the swine virus must be injected intranasally in order to produce any symptoms of disease ; injected intramuscularly it has no effect, either in inducing the mild virus disease or in rendering the animal sensitive to the intranasal instillation of *H. influenzæ-suis* (Shope 1932). The intramuscular injection of the virus does, however, render swine immune both to the mild virus disease and to the severe disease caused by the associated effect of the virus and the hæmophilic bacillus. Injections of *H. influenzæ-suis*, on the other hand, induce no immunity either to the virus or to the associated action of the virus and bacillus (Shope 1932).

As noted above, Shope (1934*b*) has shown that the swine virus, acting alone, will produce in ferrets a disease that is indistinguishable from that produced by the human influenza virus. He has also (Shope 1935) transmitted the virus to mice. The immunological relationship of the human and swine viruses, and its possible significance, have been discussed above.

Influenza in other Animals.

There are several other animal diseases, occurring in sporadic or epidemic form, to which the label " influenza " has been attached ; " horse influenza " is an example. In the particular instance of the horse disease there is suggestive, if not conclusive, evidence that it is caused by a filtrable virus ; and it is altogether probable that we shall find that several animal diseases are in fact due to infection with a virus of the influenzal type (see Discussion 1935). The work of Shope and of Laidlaw and his colleagues has rendered possible a detailed study of these problems along sound immunological lines, and the solution of many of them can reasonably be expected.

Whooping Cough

H. pertussis, the causative organism of this disease, was first isolated and described by Bordet and Gengou (1906) (see Chapter XXX). Its ætiological rôle is shown by the following observations. It can be isolated in the great majority of cases during the first 2 weeks of the disease by the cough-plate method, or from the lungs at autopsy. It has very rarely been isolated from normal persons, or from persons suffering from other diseases. In the later stages of the disease and during convalescence specific complement-fixing antibodies make their appearance in the blood.

It may be added that Macdonald and Macdonald (1933) record the experimental production of whooping cough in two children with a culture of *H. pertussis*, and that Shibley and Hoelscher (1934) have reported the successful reproduction of the disease in the chimpanzee. The infections produced in ordinary laboratory animals, which bear no resemblance to the disease in man, are described in Chapter XXX.

Diagnosis.

Cultural.—As has been stated, *H. pertussis* can almost always be isolated from the sputum during the early stages of the disease (see Wollstein 1909, Chievitz and Meyer 1916). During recent years the cough-plate method has been extensively used for diagnostic purposes, and has given satisfactory results. The patient is induced to cough directly on to a plate of Bordet-Gengou medium, and this is examined for the characteristic colonies after 48–72-hours' incubation (see Chapter XXX).

Among the reports on the results obtained by this are the following. Madsen (1925), in 914 cases, records 75 per cent. of positive isolations during the initial catarrhal stage, 61 per cent. during the 2nd week, 45 per cent. during the 3rd, 40·5 per cent. during the 4th, and 9 per cent. during the 5th. Sauer (1933c), in 400 cases, records 88 per cent. of positive isolations in the early catarrhal stage, 64 per cent. in the paroxysmal stage, and none in the late stages. Gardner and Leslie (1932), in 47 cases, record 67–75 per cent. of positive results in the first 3 weeks, 25 per cent. in the 4th and none thereafter. Kendrick and Elderling (1934), in 207 cases, record 78–84 per cent. of positive results during the first 3 weeks, 39 per cent. in the 4th and none in the 6th (see also Sugare and McLeod 1929, Sauer and Hambrecht 1930, Kristensen 1933). It may be added that Kristensen (1933) records his failure to isolate *H. pertussis* from 500 healthy persons, and from 202 persons suffering from other respiratory diseases. Among 301 contacts, *H. pertussis* was isolated in 9 instances, and all these 9 persons subsequently developed whooping cough. Kendrick and Elderling (1934) and Wilcox (1934) also record their failure to isolate the bacillus from any condition other than whooping cough.

Complement Fixation.—The demonstration that specific complement-fixing antibodies appeared in the blood was first made by Bordet and Gengou (1906, 1907). The antigen employed is a suspension of *H. pertussis*.

These observations were confirmed by Winholt (1915) and by Chievitz and Meyer (1916), who showed that the reaction first becomes positive in the 3rd or 4th week, the proportion of cases reacting positively increasing up to the 8th or 10th week. The reaction usually becomes negative again in the course of a few months. Similar observations have since been reported by many observers (see Madsen 1925, Gundel and Schlüter 1933a, b). There is general agreement that a small proportion of cases fail to develop a positive reaction at any stage in the disease.

It will be seen, therefore, that attempted cultivation by the cough plate is the diagnostic method of choice during the early stage of the disease, and before the characteristic paroxysmal cough has developed. It is at this stage that a bacteriological method of diagnosis is most helpful. In those cases in which the diagnosis remains in doubt for 3–4 weeks both the cough-plate and the complement-fixation tests may be employed. Where a laboratory diagnostic method is sought in a case of more than 4 weeks' standing the complement-fixation test should be used.

Prophylactic Vaccination against Whooping Cough.

Reference to Chapter XXX will show that *H. pertussis* is antigenically of a single type. The conditions are, therefore, particularly favourable for active immunization with a vaccine of this organism. It has been noted, however, in the same chapter that this organism is very liable to undergo variation in the laboratory, and that the variant strains are of low virulence for laboratory animals and fail to produce an effective immunity (see Leslie and Gardner 1931). It is therefore of the greatest importance that strains used for immunization should be fully virulent (Phase I of Leslie and Gardner) ; and the fact that this necessity has not always been allowed for must be borne in mind in assessing the published records of immunization in the field. Among the large-scale trials that have so far been reported are the following :

Madsen (1933) records trials made in the Faroe Islands during an epidemic in 1923–24, and in another epidemic in 1929. In the first epidemic the experience of 2,094 vaccinated subjects was compared with that of 627 unvaccinated controls. The incidence of the disease was the same in the vaccinated and unvaccinated, but it was milder and the death rate was lower among the vaccinated. In the preparation of the vaccine used in this trial several recent strains were used. In the epidemic of 1929, the vaccinated numbered 1,832, the unvaccinated 466. The experience in this epidemic was more favourable, 458 of the 1,832 vaccinated subjects escaped attack, as compared with 8 of the 466 unvaccinated controls. The vaccine used in this trial was prepared from a freshly isolated strain of *H. pertussis*. In the second trial, as in the first, the disease was less severe and the deaths proportionately fewer among the vaccinated than among the unvaccinated. Taking both epidemics together, the mortality among the vaccinated was 0·15 per cent., as compared with 2·4 per cent. among the unvaccinated. These trials suggested that prophylactic immunization with an *H. pertussis* vaccine is only moderately effective in preventing the disease, but is of very real value in decreasing severity and mortality.

Extensive trials have recently been carried out in the United States particularly by Sauer (see Sauer and Hambrecht 1928, Sauer 1933*a*, *b*, *c*, 1935) and these have given far more promising results. The method adopted in these trials, in which the vaccine employed was made from a freshly isolated strain of *H. pertussis*, was to keep a careful record of the exposure of the vaccinated children, whose average age at the time of vaccination was 18 months, and to see how many of them developed the disease. Taking Sauer's experience (Sauer 1933*b*, 1935), among 394 children 30 were subsequently exposed to intimate family contact, and 169 were exposed to occasional contact—in all on 360 occasions during 7 years. None of these children developed whooping cough. Although we have no dependable index of the exact contagiousness of the disease it is certainly very high (see the Faroe Island experience above), and it is probable that some 70–75 per cent. of unprotected children contract the disease when intimately exposed to it. Sauer's results are therefore impressive. Sauer (1935) also records the results obtained by various other workers, using a commercial vaccine prepared from a freshly isolated strain. Among 2,945 vaccinated children there were 130 known exposures. Of these 21 contracted the disease. These figures, though less impressive than those recorded by Sauer himself, are definitely encouraging.

Another very convincing record is that of Kendrick and Elderling (1936). In this case the experience of the vaccinated children was compared with that of unvaccinated controls. Most of the children vaccinated were in the 1st or 2nd year of life. The controls belonged to the same age groups ; and, where possible, a vaccinated child was controlled by another in the same family. Among 712 vaccinated children there had, at the time the report was published, been 60 known exposures to infection, and 4 of these exposed children had contracted the disease. Among 882 unvaccinated controls there had been 84 known exposures to infection, and of these exposed unvaccinated children 63 had contracted the disease.

Since whooping cough is now a major, almost *the* major, killing disease of childhood, it seems eminently desirable, in view of such figures as these, that active immunization should be practised on the largest possible scale. Since it is a disease of early childhood, every effort should be made to vaccinate children towards the close of the 1st year of life, or early in the 2nd. The vaccine must be prepared from a fully virulent, preferably freshly isolated, strain of *H. pertussis* ; and the available evidence suggests that large doses are necessary. The vaccine is usually prepared to contain 10,000 million bacilli per c.c., and of this four injections should be given in doses of 1 c.c., 1·5 c.c., 1·5 c.c., and 3 c.c. The injections are given subcutaneously ; and, to avoid a local reaction, the last dose of 3 c.c. should be injected at two sites, 1·5 c.c. at each.

Secondary Broncho-Pneumonia

Influenza, whooping cough, measles, and to a less extent certain other specific infective diseases, are peculiarly liable to be associated with a secondary infection of the lungs ; and it is this fact which is answerable for the high mortality associated with such diseases. The case mortality during an epidemic of influenza, for instance, is almost entirely determined by the frequency of pulmonary complications. Without entering into the pathology of these pulmonary lesions we may note that the distribution is usually of the broncho-pneumonic type ; and that the pneumonias associated with influenza are frequently characterized by certain features, which serve to distinguish them from those which follow measles or whooping cough. Thus, in cases of influenzal pneumonia, the lesions of the bronchi are often unusually severe ; hæmorrhages into the alveoli, into the bronchi, or around the bronchioles, are frequently encountered ; and localized areas of necrosis, or suppuration, are not uncommon (see Opie *et al.* 1921).

The bacteriology of secondary broncho-pneumonia in general, and of influenzal pneumonia in particular, differs from that of primary lobar pneumonia (see next section) in the fact that the pneumococcus plays a far less predominant rôle ; and that, among the pneumococcal cases, the three main serological types are found to be responsible for only a small minority of the infections. In influenzal pneumonia, *H. influenzæ* may play a dominant rôle. Hæmolytic streptococci, which play a negligible rôle in primary lobar pneumonia, frequently invade the lung during an influenzal attack, and give rise to a particularly fatal type of infection. In whooping cough it is probable that *H. pertussis* itself plays a large, but not an exclusive, part in the production of lung lesions.

The species of bacteria isolated from the sputum, blood, or empyema fluid during life, and from the lungs or other tissues at autopsy, vary from place to place and from time to time. There is definite evidence, in the records, of a secondary local prevalence of a particular bacterial species, imposed on the primary

P.B. U U

prevalence of influenza, or of measles ; so that one observer may record a high incidence of streptococcal pneumonia, another a considerable series of secondary pneumococcal infections, and a third may note the occurrence of numerous pulmonary infections due to *Staph. aureus*. It is clear that pneumococci, influenza bacilli and hæmolytic streptococci are the chief offenders, and together account for the great majority of fatal infections. The figures recorded by Dwinell (1919), in 69 autopsies on fatal cases of influenzal pneumonia, may be regarded as typical of an outbreak in which hæmolytic streptococci are playing a predominant part. The frequency of the various bacterial species in this series of cases was as follows.

		Per cent.
Hæmolytic streptococci	41 cases	= 59·4
Pneumococcus (all types)	8 ,,	= 11·6
Non-hæmolytic streptococci	17 ,,	= 24·6
Staphylococci	13 ,,	= 18·9
H. influenzæ	34 ,,	= 49·3

The predominance of pneumoccal types other than I, II, and III in any outbreak of influenzal pneumonia in which *Str. pneumoniæ* is the principal secondary agent is illustrated by the following figures, giving the type of pneumococcus isolated from 105 cases of influenzal pneumonia (Opie *et al.* 1921).

	Per cent.
Type I	7·6
Type II	3·8
Type II (atypical)	18·1
Type III	5·7
Other Types	64·8

The fact that these secondary pneumonic infections play a large part in determining the case-mortality rate in any outbreak of influenza, measles or whooping cough, raises a point of the first importance in regard to the effective control of these diseases. It is probable that the secondary bacterial invader, responsible for the fatal issue, is in many cases leading a vegetative existence in the upper part of the respiratory tract of the host, at the time when the primary infection is contracted. In other cases the host may receive the secondary invader from the same source, and at the same time, as the primary infecting agent. There is, however, little doubt that a considerable proportion of fatal secondary infections result from the implantation, on a case of primary influenza or measles, of a virulent streptococcus or pneumococcus ; and the records contain instances of waves of secondary infection, due to a particular bacterial species, passing through hospital wards, or concentration camps (see Opie *et al.* 1921). The conditions which, in the aggregate, make up the environmental factor known as " hospitalization," are capable of playing the same part to-day, in the case of secondary respiratory disease, as they played in the past, in the case of surgical or puerperal sepsis. The patient with influenza or measles should be regarded as peculiarly liable to acute respiratory infection, and should be carefully guarded from secondary infection. There is, for instance, ample evidence that overcrowding in hospital wards, or in military camps, may seriously increase the mortality during an outbreak of influenza or of measles.

There seems little hope that any form of prophylactic immunization, apart from immunization against the primary disease, will reduce the liability to such secondary infections. As will be obvious, we are faced with a multiplicity of heterogeneous bacterial antigens, and it seems scarcely reasonable to expect that we can ever induce immunity to all the bacterial species and types, to which a person with some primary predisposing infection may become a prey.

The same heterogeneity of infecting agents severely limits the opportunities for the use of specific serum therapy.

Primary Pneumococcal Pneumonia

We need not here consider the clinical or pathological aspects of pneumonia as it occurs in man, nor discuss the vexed question of the classification of acute inflammatory lesions of the lungs. Excluding the broncho-pneumonias of young children, and the secondary pneumonias to which we have already referred, there remain a group of cases in which a severe pyrexial illness, with sudden onset and a tendency towards recovery by crisis in non-fatal cases, is associated with signs and symptoms of pulmonary involvement ; and in which bacteræmia is frequently present during the initial phase of infection, and is a constant feature in severe and fatal cases. Infections of this type are, with very few exceptions, caused by the pneumococcus ; and it is with such primary pneumococcal pneumonias that we are here concerned.

The Experimental Disease.—We have referred, in some detail, to the experimental study of pneumococcal infections in laboratory animals, when discussing the general problems of infection and resistance ; and we may at this point confine our attention to certain experimental evidence which directly concerns the mechanism of pneumonic infection in man.

Blake and Cecil (1920a, b, c, Cecil and Blake 1920a, b, c, d) have carried out an extremely instructive series of studies on experimental pneumonia in the monkey. They found that lobar pneumonia could consistently be produced in these animals by inoculating minute amounts of pneumococcal cultures directly into the trachea. The disease so produced was identical with lobar pneumonia in man : in its clinical manifestations ; in its tendency to terminate by crisis ; in the presence of a bacteræmic phase, which was transitory in cases that recovered, but progressive in cases that succumbed ; and in the lesions found at necropsy in fatal cases. Inoculation, by swabbing, of the nose and throat, never resulted in pneumonic infection. Monkeys which were inoculated intravenously, or subcutaneously, either died of pneumococcal septicæmia, without pulmonary lesions, or recovered without any involvement of the lungs. Blake and Cecil conclude that the normal route of infection in lobar pneumonia is *via* the bronchi, and discuss (Blake and Cecil 1920b) the route by which infection spreads through the pulmonary tissue. A detailed and valuable account of experimental Type III pneumonia in the monkey has recently been recorded by Francis and Terrell (1934).

As noted elsewhere, Gaskell (1927) has carried out a large series of intratracheal inoculations in rabbits, and has brought evidence to show that the type of infection produced in these animals is mainly determined by the virulence of the strain of pneumococcus injected, ranging, as virulence decreases, from a rapidly fatal septicæmia without pulmonary changes, through lobar and lobular pneumonia, and through lesions confined almost entirely to the bronchi and bronchioles, to a complete absence of reaction.

If we collate the available experimental evidence with the numerous observations which have been carried out on the natural disease as it occurs in man (Dochez 1912, Sia, Robertson and Woo 1928, Finland and Sutliff 1931a), we can construct a picture of the sequence of events in lobar pneumonia, which, however incomplete it may be, will aid us in the discussion of the results obtained in serum treatment, and in prophylactic vaccination.

It would appear that the initial phase of the infection is marked by a progressive invasion of the lung tissue, frequently associated with a detectable bacteræmia. The inflammatory reaction in the lung progresses through its successive stages ; and the bacteræmia may, or may not, increase in severity. At some time between the 4th and 7th days, in favourable cases, specific antibodies begin to appear in the blood ; and, coincidently with their appearance, the temperature falls by crisis, the pneumococci disappear from the blood if they were ever present in detectable numbers, and the clinical condition of the patient undergoes a striking amelioration, though abnormal signs in the lungs may persist for several days, or even weeks.

There are good grounds for believing that the degree and persistence of bacter- æmia, rather than the local condition in the lungs, is the main factor in determining death or recovery. The most virulent of Gaskell's strains produced in rabbits rapid septicæmic death without pneumonic consolidation. In acutely fatal cases of pneumonia in man the lung changes at autopsy may be relatively slight ; but blood cultures taken during life are, in such cases, almost always positive. The prognostic significance of a positive blood culture is one of the best-attested facts which have emerged from the bacteriological study of this disease.

In a series of 448 cases, studied at the Hospital of the Rockefeller Institute, 136 gave positive blood cultures, and of these 76 died, a mortality of 55·8 per cent. ; 312 gave negative blood cultures, and of these 26 died, a mortality of 8·3 per cent. (Avery et al. 1917). In a smaller series recorded by Cecil (1928), of 37 patients with positive blood cultures 29 died, a mortality of 78·3 per cent. ; while of 70 patients with negative blood cultures 7 died, a mortality of 10 per cent.

In such series as these the figures given for positive or negative blood cultures must not be taken as an accurate index of the presence or absence of bacteræmia, but rather of its severity. The precise amount of blood withdrawn and, to a less extent, the method employed in cultivation will make a significant difference in the proportion of negative and positive results ; and different observers have, in fact, recorded very different figures. But any one technique, employed over a considerable series of cases, will place in the positive category those patients who are suffering from a bacteræmia in excess of some limiting range, and in the negative category those whose blood is infected, less heavily, or not at all.

The Frequency of the Different Serological Types of Pneumococci in Lobar Pneumonia.—The antigenic structure of the pneumococci has been described in Chapter XXIII, where it is noted that the recent studies of Cooper and her colleagues (Cooper, Edwards and Rosenstein 1929, Cooper et al. 1932, Cooper and Walter 1935) have resulted in the sub-division of the old " Group IV," composed of un- differentiated strains, into 29 new types ; so that the differentiated and labelled types of pneumococci now run from Type I to Type XXXII, the classical Types I, II and III retaining their priority. Many of the studies on the relative frequency of the different pneumococcal types, in lobar pneumonia and in the nose and throat of healthy persons, was made before " Group IV " was subdivided, and it will be convenient to consider these records before dealing with the recently differentiated types.

The figures recorded by Avery, Chickering, Cole and Dochez (1917) for the incidence of the various types in pneumonic infection, and among normal persons, in New York during the few years prior to 1917, are set out in Table CXLV. This table indicates that, at that time, some 80 per cent. of all cases of lobar pneumonia in adults were caused by infection with one or other of the three classical types, regarding Type II and its sub-groups as constituting a single type. It will be noted that Type I was very rare in normal persons, Type II relatively rare, and Type III relatively common.

TABLE CXLV

FREQUENCY OF DIFFERENT TYPES OF PNEUMOCOCCI IN LOBAR PNEUMONIA AND IN THE MOUTHS OF NORMAL PERSONS IN NEW YORK (Avery and others).

Type.	Lobar Pneumonia.		Normal Mouths.	
	No.	Frequency Percentage.	No.	Frequency Percentage.
I	151	33·3	1	0·8
II	133	29·3	0	0·0
IIa	6	1·3	1	0·8
IIb	4	0·9	7	5·8
IIx	9	2·0	14	11·6
III	59	13·0	34	28·1
Group IV	92	20·3	64	52·9

The relative frequency of the different types observed in New York in 1917 has not been maintained at other times and in other places.

Glynn, Digby and Jones (1923) have collected from the literature a large series of records, adding the results obtained in their own examination of 96 cases. In Table CXLVI we summarize certain of these figures, with the addition of a few others which have been reported at later dates. Most observers have not differentiated between the sub-groups of Type II, and we have included all varieties of this type under a single heading.

TABLE CXLVI

FREQUENCY OF THE DIFFERENT SEROLOGICAL TYPES OF PNEUMOCOCCI IN LOBAR PNEUMONIA, AS RECORDED BY VARIOUS OBSERVERS.

Observers.	Country or District.	Period.	No. of Cases examined.	Frequency percentage.			
				Type I.	Type II.	Type III.	Group IV.
Schorer, Clark and others	U.S.A.	1917–18	101	30·7	14·9	17·8	36·6
Thomas	U.S.A.	1917–21	239	25·1	10·9	14·6	49·4
Cecil, Baldwin and Larsen	U.S.A.	1921–26	1,913	33·6	19·1	13·3	33·3
Griffith	England	1920–22	150	30·6	32·7	6·7	30·0
Glynn, Digby and Jones .	England (Liverpool)	1919–21	96	45·8	24·0	2·1	28·1
Ferguson and Lovell . .	England (Manchester)	1925–27	116	43·1	4·3	0·0	52·6

These figures are sufficient to indicate that the incidence of the various types may vary fairly widely from place to place and from time to time ; and it will be noted that Type III pneumonia appears to be relatively infrequent in England, at least during recent years. Cecil, Baldwin and Larsen (1927), during their 5-years' study of the frequency distribution of the three types, noted a marked variation in frequency from year to year. Thus the frequency of Type I varied from 21·0 per cent. to 45·2 per cent., that of Type II from 15·9 per cent. to 20·6 per cent., that of Type III from 7·9 to 17·2 per cent., and that of Group IV from 23·5 per cent. to 41·0 per cent.

In his study of lobar pneumonia among the mine-workers on the Rand, Lister (1917) carried out a serological analysis of 148 strains, 143 of which he allocated to 11 groups, labelled by letters, leaving 5 unclassified. The three major groups, A, B, and C, accounted for 31·0 per cent., 16·2 per cent., and 21·6 per cent. of the strains respectively, leaving 31·2 per cent. in the minor groups. Subsequent investigations have shown that Lister's Group C is identical with the American Type I, and his Group B with the American Type II ; but his Group A, which was the type most frequently isolated in South Africa prior to 1916, is not identical with any of the three classical American types.

It is of interest to note the case-fatality rates of primary pneumococcal pneumonia, tabulated according to the various infecting types. Table CXLVII gives these rates (*a*) for various American experiences, (*b*) for various English experiences, as collected by Glynn, Digby and Jones (1923), (*c*) for an American experience recorded by Cecil (1928), (*d*) for an American experience recorded by Rosenblüth (1928), and (*e*) for an English experience recorded by Ferguson and Lovell (1928). These percentage figures are of unequal value, in the different series and for the different types, since the total numbers under each head are in some cases small, but taken together they give an informative picture of the fatality of the infections due to the different types, and bring out the significant points : that Type III infections show a high fatality rate ; that the case fatality of Type II pneumonia tends to be intermediate between that of Type III and Type I. The figures given for the case mortality of " Group IV " infections have, of course, little value, since they represent infections due to a heterogeneous collection of different types.

TABLE CXLVII

CASE-FATALITY RATES, PER CENT., OF PRIMARY PNEUMONIA DUE TO THE DIFFERENT TYPES OF PNEUMOCOCCI, AS RECORDED BY VARIOUS OBSERVERS.

Series.	Fatality Percentage.			
	Type I.	Type II.	Type III.	Group IV.
A	21·2	34·7	54·1	19·1
B	27·1	36·3	—[1]	11·5
C	22·2	40·3	40·0	24·0
D	37·0	40·0	33·0	11·0
E	26·0	20·0	—[2]	24·6

[1] Only 4 cases of Type III pneumonia recorded, 1 death.
[2] No case of Type III pneumonia recorded.

In regard to the frequency of the more recently differentiated types our information is as yet more scanty.

In lobar pneumonia in adults (Cooper *et al.* 1932) Types IV, V, VII and VIII show the highest frequencies among the newly differentiated types, followed by Types VI, XVIII, XIII and IX ; but there is no predominance of any one type of the same order as that of the three classical types among the whole group of pneumococci isolated from lobar pneumonia ; and almost every type is represented by one or more cases. Smillie (1933) also found that cases of lobar pneumonia, other than those caused by Types I, II and III, were due to infection with a wide variety of types, of which Types V, VII, VIII and XVIII were the most frequent.

In the pneumonia of children, it may be noted, the distribution of the various types differs widely from that in adults, particularly in that the three classical types are responsible for a much smaller proportion of cases.

Raia, Plummer and Shultz (1931), for instance, recording the types of pneumococci isolated from pneumonia in children in Bellevue Hospital, New York, report that during the year 1928–29 only 13·5 per cent. of the cases were due to infection with Type I, II, or III, while during the year 1929–30 the corresponding figure was 16·8 per cent. Some 80 per cent. of cases were due to infection with one or other of Cooper's newly differentiated types, the remainder being caused by other organisms such as hæmolytic streptococci. Of the new types, Type VI and Type XIV were most prominent ; but sera were not available for all the 32 types, and a proportion of strains remained unclassified. Cooper and others (1932) found Types VI, XIV and V to be most frequent among the strains isolated in children ; but, here again, almost every type was represented.

The Treatment of Pneumonia with Antipneumococcal Serum.

The sera employed in the treatment of pneumonia are prepared by injecting horses with whole cultures of pneumococci of one or more of the different serological types. All the laboratory evidence suggests that anti-pneumococcal immunity is type-specific ; and we should not therefore expect a serum prepared against any one type to exert a curative effect on an infection caused by any other. Many of the early trials in man were, in fact, carried out with a " polyvalent " serum prepared by immunizing horses against Types I, II and III. It will be convenient to consider the results obtained in trials with this, and other, sera before discussing the question of how such antisera should be standardized and utilized.

We have quoted numerous experiments that establish the protective action of a type-specific antiserum as tested in the rabbit or mouse, and a few that indicate a curative action when the serum is injected shortly after the establishment of an experimental bacteræmia. In either case it has been shown that the serum increases the efficiency of the normal clearing mechanism and suppresses, or cuts short, the bacteræmic phase.

Of particular interest, from our present point of view, are the following observations.

Cecil and Blake (1920e) studied the effect of serum treatment on experimental lobar pneumonia in monkeys, induced by the intratracheal inoculation of virulent Type I pneumococci. They found that the intravenous injection of the specific antiserum exerted a prompt therapeutic effect, freeing the circulating blood from pneumococci, shortening the infection and greatly reducing its severity. Of 5 treated monkeys all recovered while the controls died. Curphey and Baruch (1932) infected rabbits by the intradermal injection of virulent Type I pneumococci, and studied the effect of the subsequent injection of a Type I antipneumococcal serum by the intravenous or intramuscular route. With the intravenous injection of 400 units 24 hours after infection, 1 of 13 animals survived ; with 800 units 12 of 32 animals survived ; with 2,500 units 14 of 19 animals survived. With shorter intervals between infection and the administration of serum smaller doses sufficed to ensure the survival of a considerable proportion of the animals.

This method of treatment has since 1915 received an extensive clinical trial in man, particularly in America. It is, however, only within the last few years that its value has been established with an approach to certainty, and a serious attempt been made to assess its effect in terms of a percentage reduction in mortality.

Even now we can only offer approximate estimates, and some few observations are hard to fit into the general picture. The history of the serum treatment of pneumonia affords an illuminating example of the neglect of a useful therapeutic measure that may follow a failure to plan early trials in such a way as to allow significant but undramatic effects to be measured with some approach to accuracy.

The earliest considerable series of cases are those recorded by Avery and his colleagues (Avery *et al.* 1917). In 107 cases of serum-treated pneumonia there were 8 deaths, a mortality of 7·5 per cent. There were no controls; but a favourable conclusion with regard to the influence of serum on mortality was based on the contrast between the observed case-fatality rate and the rates of 25–30 per cent. recorded by these workers before they commenced the use of serum, and by other observers elsewhere. This method of comparison is, however, not valid. The variability of the case-mortality rates in different outbreaks of pneumonia is well known; and the records of serum-treated cases show a similar variability, though, for the most part, over a lower range. Thus Wadsworth (1924), commenting on a series of collected figures, notes case-fatality rates in serum-treated patients varying from 6·0 to 18·0 per cent., and reference to the tabulated results that follow will show higher figures. Clearly the only satisfactory way of assessing the effect of serum is to compare treated with untreated cases in the same place and at the same time. Within recent years a considerable series of trials have been carried out along these lines. It may be noted that they refer, in each case, to patients treated with concentrated polyvalent antipneumococcal sera containing antibodies for Types I, II and III, the Type III antibody being present in relatively low concentration.

In a series recorded by Cecil (1928) the data were collected as follows. During the winters of 1920, 1921 and 1922 six medical wards were set aside as " antibody wards," all cases of pneumonia admitted to these wards were treated with Huntoon's polyvalent antibody solution, while all cases of pneumonia admitted to six other wards were treated on ordinary medical lines without serum therapy. The type of infecting pneumococcus was determined in each case. The results are recorded in Table CXLVIII.

TABLE CXLVIII

Comparison of Case-Fatality Rates in Treated and Untreated Cases of Lobar Pneumonia (Cecil).

Type of Pneumococcus.	Antibody Wards.			Control Wards.			Difference.	Diff./S.E. Diff.
	Cases.	Deaths.	Deaths Percentage.	Cases.	Deaths.	Deaths Percentage.		
I	158	21	13·3	162	36	22·2	8·9 ± 4·27	2·09
II . . .	83	23	27·7	67	27	40·3	12·6 ± 7·74	1·63
III	73	29	39·7	60	24	40·0	0·3 ± 8·5	—
Group IV . .	110	18	16·4	121	29	24·0	7·6 ± 5·2	1·46

It will be noted that there is a clear suggestion that Type I and Type II pneumonias were benefited by the serum, while Type III pneumonias were not. Only in the case of Type I pneumonia does the difference between the treated and untreated groups as compared with its standard error attain a value that would be conventionally regarded as statistically significant. The suggestion that some therapeutic effect was exerted on pneumonias due to infection with strains belonging to the antigenically heterogeneous Group IV is not in accord with our expectations; but the difference in this case falls short of statistical significance.

A very valuable record is that provided by Park, Bullowa and Rosenblüth (1928). The serum employed was Felton's concentrated polyvalent antipneumococcal serum, and random sampling was ensured, as far as possible, by giving serum to alternate cases in order of admission. The relevant figures are set out in Table CXLIX.

TABLE CXLIX

Type.	Hospital.	Treated.		Untreated.		Difference Percentage.	Diff./S.E. Diff.
		Cases.	Deaths Percentage.	Cases.	Deaths Percentage.		
I	[1] Combined	266	19	249	33	14 ± 3·8	3·7
	Bellevue	144	19	132	33	14 ± 5·3	2·6
	Harlem	114	20	109	34	14 ± 5·8	2·4
II . . .	Combined	176	35	165	45	10 ± 5·3	1·9
	Bellevue	107	39	95	53	14 ± 6·9	2·0
	Harlem	61	30	63	32	2 ± 8·3	0·2
III . . .	Combined	82	33	92	29	− 4 ± 7·0	0·6
	Bellevue	32	38	52	27	− 11 ± 10·6	1·0
	Harlem	47	32	38	32	0 ± 10·2	—
Group IV .	Combined	313	24	324	26	2 ± 3·4	0·6
	Bellevue	131	30	128	40	10 ± 5·2	1·9
	Harlem	171	20	190	15	− 5 ± 4·0	1·2

[1] The combined figures include a small series of cases treated at the New York Hospital.

Taking the combined experience it will be noted that the concentrated serum exerted a significantly beneficial effect on Type I pneumonia. In Type II pneumonia the effect is more doubtful. The combined experience clearly suggests a beneficial effect ; but this is due almost entirely to the results obtained in Bellevue Hospital. In Harlem Hospital over the same period of time serum-treated Type II pneumonias showed no advantage, a fact that emphasizes the danger of putting trust in small numbers or in single trials. The Type III cases received no benefit from the serum. The Group IV cases were unaffected as judged by the combined experience. In Bellevue they seemed to receive some benefit. In Harlem they fared worse than the controls. We need not then attach much importance to the apparent therapeutic effect in Group IV cases noted by Cecil.

More recently Cecil and Plummer (1930) have recorded a series of Type I pneumonias treated with Felton's serum between 1924 and 1929. Of 239 treated cases 20·1 per cent. died ; of 234 untreated cases 31·2 per cent. died, giving a difference of 11·1 ± 4·01 per cent. The experience of the same observers with Type II pneumonia is curious (see Cecil and Plummer 1932). During the seasons 1924–25, 1926–27 and 1927–28 (the records for 1925–26 were incomplete) the serum-treated cases did better than the controls, the case mortalities during these 3 years being 33·3 per cent. as against 48·3 per cent., 41·1 per cent. as against 48·4 per cent. and 38·4 per cent. as against 53·5 per cent. During the two following seasons the position was reversed : in 1928–29 the serum-treated patients showed a case mortality of 46·8 per cent. as against 39·3 per cent. in the untreated : in 1929–30 a case mortality of 39·3 per cent. as against 24·5 per cent. Over the whole period of trial 252 treated patients showed a case mortality of 40·5 per cent., 253 untreated patients showed a case mortality of 45·8 per cent. During the season 1930–31 the trial was continued on the alternate case method, limiting the treated and control groups to cases of Type II pneumonia admitted within 72 hours of onset. Of 21 treated cases 3 died ; of 20 control cases 13 died.

Under the auspices of the Therapeutic Trials Committee of the Medical Research Council a study has recently been made of the effect of Type I and Type II antisera in the corresponding types of pneumonia in London, Edinburgh and Aberdeen. The sera employed had almost all been concentrated, and the routine dose was 20,000 units, repeated eight-hourly, the total dosage varying from 50,000 to 120,000 units. The results obtained, while confirming the earlier findings in regard to the beneficial effects of these antisera, suggest that their therapeutic value depends, at least in part, on the age of the patients treated. Thus, of 140 serum-treated Type I patients, aged between 20 and 40, 5·7 per cent. died. Of 224 untreated patients in the same group 11·2 per cent. died. Of 44 Type I serum-treated cases aged 40 to 60, 22·7 per cent. died. Of 77 untreated cases in the same age group 26·0 per cent. died. Of 111 Type II serum-treated cases in the younger age group 12·6 per cent. died. Of 194 untreated cases 22·7 per cent. died. Of 53 Type II serum-treated cases in the older age group 35·8 per cent. died. Of 111 untreated cases in the same group 34·2 per cent. died.

Antisera against a few of the other types of pneumococci are already available in the United States for therapeutic purposes ; and a few preliminary trials have been recorded. Bullowa (1933) reports favourably on a small series of Type VII and Type VIII cases treated with specific antisera. In later communications (Bullowa 1934, 1935a) he gives the result of further experience with the Type VIII antiserum. Of 37 non-bacteræmic serum-treated cases, 2 died. Of 85 non-bacteræmic untreated cases, 14 died. Of 10 treated bacteræmic cases, 2 died. Of 15 untreated bacteræmic cases, 5 died. In another small series of cases the mortalities were higher, but the serum-treated patients still showed an advantage. Type XIV antiserum has also been tested on a small scale during the period 1928–34 (see Bullowa 1935b), many of these cases being in children. Among 21 serum-treated cases, 3 died ; among 107 untreated cases, 26 died.

In summarizing these trials it seems a fair conclusion that a case has been established for the use of a Type I antiserum in the treatment of Type I pneumonia, and, rather more doubtfully, for the use of a Type II antiserum in Type II cases. The Type III antisera at present available seem quite ineffective, and there seems no immediate prospect of improving this position (see Cecil et al. 1936). The scanty evidence at present available suggests that antisera against several of the other types will prove to be of therapeutic value; but we are not yet in a position to form definite conclusions in regard to these.

The results of clinical trials are in entire accord with the view, based on laboratory experience, that the therapeutic effect of each of these sera is type-specific, depending in the main on the content of the antibody acting on the capsular, type-specific, polysaccharide antigen.

If, then, we intend to use an antipneumococcal serum we must determine the type of infecting pneumococcus at the earliest possible moment ; though we may if we choose administer a dose of a polyvalent Type I and Type II serum at once, discontinuing it if the infecting pneumococcus is found not to belong to either of these types.

The method of typing usually employed is to inject a specimen of sputum into the peritoneum of a mouse, to kill the animal after 6 to 8 hours, and to carry out agglutination and precipitation tests with the sediment and supernatant fluid of the peritoneal washings. This method can be made more rapid by using slide agglutination followed by staining (Sabin 1929), and noting the swelling of the capsule that results from the action of the antiserum, as well as the agglutination itself. This capsular-swelling reaction, which was first described by Neufeld (1902), can be applied to specimens of sputum direct (see Armstrong 1932, Logan and Smeall 1932, Sabin 1933, Beckler and MacLeod 1934, Cooper and Walter 1935, Bullowa 1935c, Mulder 1935) ; and, in experienced hands, appears to yield reliable results.

As regards the dose of serum and the number and frequency of the injections that should be administered, there are good reasons for believing that these factors are of primary importance. We might suppose from our knowledge of passive protection in the rabbit or mouse that a comparatively small dose of serum would suffice to render the pneumococci sensitive to phagocytosis. But the experiments of Curphey and Baruch show that, with antibacterial as with antitoxic sera, the effective curative dose is a high multiple of the protective dose. It is highly probable that this is due to the fact that the specific antigen, or hapten, accumulates in the blood in considerable quantities during a pneumococcal infection and exerts an aggressive effect, combining with the corresponding antibody and so diverting it from the living pneumococci (see Chapter XLV).

Thus, Park and Cooper (1928) note that, when an antipneumococcal serum is injected into a normal person, the specific antibody disappears relatively slowly from the circulating blood ; so that one-quarter to one-half of the amount administered is still present 24 hours after an intravenous injection. In severe cases of pneumonia the course of events is quite different ; the specific antibody is rapidly neutralized. If a polyvalent serum is administered it will be found that the antibodies corresponding to types other than that responsible for the infection can be detected in the circulating blood for relatively long periods, as in normal persons. In order to estimate the amount of antibody that might be required to neutralize the circulating antigen, Park and Cooper titrated samples of blood from cases of severe pneumonia against the corresponding antipneumococcal sera. In two Type I cases they found that 1 c.c. of the patient's blood neutralized one unit of antibody, and in one Type I case 1 c.c. neutralized 5 units of antibody. In two Type II cases 1 c.c. of blood neutralized 50 units of antibody. This means that several thousand units of antibody would be required to neutralize the circulating antigen.

Park and Cooper recommend that every pneumonia patient should, on admission to hospital, receive 10,000 units of Type I and Type II antibody administered intravenously. So long as the temperature remains high, the injections should be continued every 8 to 12 hours. When the type of the infecting pneumococcus has been determined a monovalent serum may be substituted for the polyvalent preparation. If the infection is found to be due to a type of pneumococcus against which no specific serum is available, the injections should be discontinued.

The Standardization of Antipneumococcal Sera.

In the original attempts to measure the potency of such a serum (see Neufeld and Händel 1909, Neufeld and Schnitzer 1927–28) titrations were made in mice both with a constant dose of serum and a varying dose of pneumococci, and with a constant dose of pneumococci and a varying dose of serum.

These and later experiments (see Felton 1930a) have made it clear that the relation between the number of pneumococci injected and the dose of serum necessary to protect against them is not of a simple linear kind, i.e., if x c.c. of serum will protect against y pneumococci it does not follow that nx c.c. of serum will protect against ny pneumococci. Felton's experiments suggested that, under optimal conditions, this linear relationship held over a limited range ; but the results obtained by Smith (1932) indicate that it is very unsafe to assume that if one serum in a particular dose gives a certain degree of protection against n pneumococci, and another serum in the same dose gives the same degree of protection against 2n pneumococci, the second serum is twice as potent as the first. He found, for instance, that with a constant dose of a particular serum and varying doses of pneumococci, the death rate in a group of 50 mice receiving 12,500 cocci was greater than that in another group of 50 mice receiving 125,000 pneumococci, while in another experiment a hundredfold increase in the number of pneumococci, keeping the dose of serum constant, failed to cause any significant increase in the percentage mortality.

It happened, however, for reasons that are not altogether clear, that the method of varying the dose of pneumococci was at first adopted in testing antipneumococcal sera (see Prausnitz 1929). Sera were not titrated in terms of units, but a limit of potency was laid down which had to be attained before a serum was regarded as satisfactory for issue. In Germany this limit was protection by 0·2 c.c. of serum against 0·1 c.c. of a culture of such virulence that 0·000,001 c.c. was fatal for untreated mice. In America it was protection by 0·2 c.c. of serum against 0·1 c.c. of a culture of such virulence that 0·000,000,1 c.c. was fatal for untreated mice. A method that does not assign a value in terms of units to each batch of serum issued is clearly unsatisfactory from the clinical point of view, and within recent years attempts have been made to improve the method of standardization, though no international agreement has yet been reached.

Felton (1925, 1928, 1930a, b, 1931) has carried out extensive studies on this problem, adopting the method of testing varying doses of the serum to be standardized against a constant dose of pneumococci and defining the unit of serum as the least amount that will protect mice against 1,000,000 lethal doses of a virulent pneumococcal culture. His studies, and those of Parish (1930), Trevan (1930), Falk et al. (1931) and Smith (1932), make it clear that the unit value of a serum cannot be accurately determined by direct titration against any particular pneumococcal culture. Smith, for instance, in repeated titrations of a particular serum against a particular strain of pneumococcus found that the amount of serum necessary to protect 50 per cent of mice against the test dose of culture employed varied between 0·000,9 c.c. and 0·003,4 c.c. Felton (1930a) would ascribe such divergent results, particularly when different strains of pneumococci are employed, to independent variation of virulence and of capacity to unite with antibody.

This difficulty may in any case be avoided by comparing an unknown serum with a standard serum, and assigning a value to the former, not in terms of the particular dose of pneumococci against which it protects, but in terms of the arbitrary unit value assigned to the standard preparation. Any variation in the culture will presumably affect the neutralizing power of the standard and the unknown serum to the same extent; and it is probably a fair assumption that, if n c.c. of the standard and $2n$ c.c. of the unknown serum each give a mortality of 50 per cent. when injected into an adequate sample of mice together with the same dose of the same pneumococcal culture, the unknown serum contains half as many units of protective antibody as the standard.

The titration curves recorded by Parish (1930), Trevan (1930) and Smith (1932) make it clear that this method allows an assay within a reasonable degree of accuracy provided that an adequate sample of mice is injected with each dose. Actually the standardization of an antipneumococcal serum to within a margin of error of $\pm$ 30 per cent. demands the use of 40 mice for each dose of the unknown serum tested, and another 40 mice for each dose of the standard serum with which it is to be compared.

It may be added that the common practice is now to inject the serum and culture simultaneously into the peritoneum and to use 0·0025–0·1 c.c. of culture as the test dose, according to its virulence and bacterial content. The virulence should be maximal, so that 10 pneumococci or less will kill untreated mice, and the inoculum should correspond to 500,000–5,000,000 lethal doses.

An important saving in mice would obviously be effected if we could substitute an *in vitro* for an *in vivo* test. The type-specificity of the protective action clearly suggests that the effective antibody is that which corresponds to the type-specific polysaccharide; but, equally clearly, we must establish this identity by direct experiment before we can accept an *in vitro* estimation of this antibody as affording an adequate measure of protective value.

Certain of the earlier observers (see for instance Wadsworth 1917) reported a complete and puzzling lack of correlation between agglutinin titre and protective power. It seems likely that some particularly unfavourable conditions must have affected such results as these ; since Falk *et al.* (1931) and Felton (1931) record a close parallelism between agglutinin titre and protective power in mice. Felton, testing 39 sera by both methods, reports a correlation coefficient of $+ 0.80$; but his protocols show a few markedly divergent results.

Since the isolation of the type-specific polysaccharide hapten of Heidelberger and Avery (1923) attempts have naturally been made to correlate precipitin content with protective power, and these have, on the whole, given better correlation than the agglutinin estimations (see Sobotka and Friedlander 1928, Friedlander *et al.* 1928, Zozaya *et al.* 1930, Heidelberger *et al.* 1930, Falk *et al.* 1931, and Felton 1931). Few of these comparative titrations can, however, be regarded as an adequate test, since the method of optimal proportions was not followed in determining the precipitin content of the serum.

More recently Smith (1932) has carried out a series of careful comparative titrations along these lines. Using the optimal-proportion method of Dean and Webb (1926) in the precipitin estimations, and injecting adequate samples of mice (40 for each dose of serum) in the protection tests, he has compared several Type I antipneumococcal sera with a particular serum taken as a standard. His results have been extremely encouraging. With four unconcentrated sera the protective power, measured in terms of the standard serum, corresponded almost exactly to the figure obtained by comparing the precipitin content. Three concentrated sera did not, however, give such close agreement. In each case the protective power was greater than would have been indicated by the precipitin content, and in one instance the discrepancy was considerable. If this difficulty can be surmounted, it seems likely that the precipitin test will afford an accurate and relatively simple method of standardization (see also Hartley *et al.* 1933, Smith *et al.* 1934).

Felton and Stahl (1935) have advocated using the precipitin-test standardization, testing falling doses of antiserum against a constant amount of polysaccharide, and determining the point of equivalence by testing the supernatant fluids for residual polysaccharide. It is not easy to see what advantage this technique has over the method of optimal proportions.

There seems little doubt that precipitin tests, using chemically purified antigens, will come into extended use for standardization purposes, and will perhaps eventually replace the laborious and expensive mouse-protection tests. But we shall have to watch this transition very carefully, and retain our *in vivo* titrations until we are quite sure that our *in vitro* methods give us entirely reliable answers. The main danger in any hasty acceptance of the *in vitro* tests lies in the possible effect of slight differences, or modifications, in the chemical structure of the antigenic components concerned. The relation of the natural acetylated form of the Type I pneumococcal polysaccharide to the non-acetylated form that is obtained by certain chemical methods of isolation (see p. 444) provides a case in point.

Other Possible Methods of Specific Treatment.

In view of the apparent impossibility of obtaining a satisfactory Type III antipneumococcal serum, and the relative frequency of this type of infection, it is perhaps worth noting that an alternative method of treating this type of infection is available ; though, so far as we are aware, no trials in man have yet been made (see Cecil *et al.* 1936). This method, which depends on entirely new principles and is, for that reason, of great theoretical interest, depends on an observation made by Dubos and Avery (1931). These workers recorded the isolation of a bacterium which, when grown in a synthetic medium containing the specific polysaccharide of Type III pneumococcus as the source of carbon, elaborates an enzyme that specifically attacks this hapten, and that can be obtained apart from the organism that produces it by filtration of a partly autolysed culture. This enzyme has no bactericidal action on Type III pneumococci, but it attacks the polysaccharide hapten as it is produced by the growing bacterial cells. When mice are injected with the specific enzyme together with a fatal dose of virulent Type III pneumococci they are effectively protected (Avery and Dubos 1931). This protection is sharply type-specific; it is quite ineffective against Type I and Type II pneumococci. In addition to its protective effect the enzyme exerts a curative action in mice if injected during the earlier stages of infection. Goodner, Dubos and Avery (1932) have studied the curative action of this enzyme on Type III infections in the rabbit, induced by the intradermal injection of a virulent strain. This type of infection, which starts as a spreading local lesion and leads, in untreated controls, to an acute bacteræmia fatal on about the 3rd or 4th day, offers obvious advantages for studies of this kind as compared with the acutely fatal peritoneal infection in the mouse. The enzyme, injected intravenously in adequate dosage 24 hours after the intradermal injection of pneumococci, was found to have a striking curative effect. In one series of tests, for instance, one of 19 treated animals died as compared with 36 of 38 untreated controls. Goodner and Dubos (1932) have studied the quantitative relationship between the degree of bacteræmia 24 hours after infection and the curative dose of enzyme. Of 10 rabbits showing 3–10 pneumococci per c.c. of blood and receiving 2·5–100 " units " of enzyme all survived. Of 11 rabbits showing 103–630 cocci per c.c. of blood 5 that received 4–10 units died, 6 that received 20–100 units recovered. Of 9 rabbits showing over 13,000 cocci per c.c. of blood and receiving 5–100 units of enzyme all died. Francis, Terrell, Dubos and Avery (1934) record a series of observations on the curative effect of this enzyme on experimental Type III pneumonia in the monkey. In 68 untreated monkeys the mortality was 50 per cent.; in 40 treated monkeys it was 20 per cent. (see also Dubos 1932, 1935, Dubos and Bauer 1935).

Prophylactic Immunization against Pneumonia.

The records of antipneumococcal immunization in laboratory animals are copious, and their significance is unequivocal. It is clear that susceptible animals, such as mice and rabbits, can be immunized with almost uniform success against infection by the usual routes. More immediately pertinent, perhaps, are the observations of Cecil and Blake (1920a, b, c) and Cecil and Steffen (1923, 1925), which showed that monkeys could be immunized with a considerable measure of success against intratracheal infection with Type I or Type II pneumococci, though the results with Type III were less promising.

As in serum treatment, however, all the evidence suggests that the immunity acquired is strictly type-specific; and it is clear that, with so heterogeneous a species as the pneumococcus, this factor will seriously limit the usefulness of mass immunization. It is possible that vaccination against a few prevalent types might produce a significant decrease in the incidence of the disease, even though it failed to eliminate it, or to reduce it to negligible proportions; but this we can only tell by experience.

The records of field trials on man tell a rather puzzling story. The frequency of lobar pneumonia, though very high in the aggregate, is not concentrated on particular age groups or confined in considerable part, as are diphtheria and scarlet fever, to schools and institutions. There are, however, certain environments that entail a particularly high risk of infection; and, in some of them, trials have been carried out on a considerable scale.

The most extensive data are those provided by the report of Lister (1917) on the result of vaccination against pneumonia among the native labourers on the Rand mines.

The numbers at risk were large ; but over the greater part of the period of trial the natives were not divided into inoculated and uninoculated groups. An earlier trial (see Orenstein 1931), in which 55,900 natives of various tribes had been divided into two equal groups, one inoculated and the other uninoculated, had shown a pneumonia incidence of 16·4 per 1,000 among the inoculated, 20·6 per 1,000 among the controls. As a result, wholesale inoculation was commenced in many mines, and the only basis of comparison available is that between the incidence of pneumonia in a particular mine before and after the institution of active immunization. As we have seen, this method of comparison is always liable to error. There was, in fact, a definite fall in the incidence of pneumonia following these mass inoculations ; but the pneumonia death rate on the Rand had fallen sharply from the high level of 1907–11 before mass immunization was instituted, and there is no need to assume that the fall in death rate from 1916–20 was other than a continuation of the trend that was already well marked over the period 1911–14. Orenstein (1931) would attribute the whole downward trend to circumstances other than immunization, in particular to the decrease in the recruitment of tropical natives since 1911. If, as seems probable, we can attach little significance to the secular change in incidence or mortality we are left with ancillary evidence concerning the prevalence of particular infecting types in the pre- and post-inoculation periods. Lister had previously classified the strains of pneumococci isolated from the Rand miners into a series of types which he labelled A, B, C, D, E, F, G, H, J and K, with a further undifferentiated group. Of these types A, B and C accounted for more than 70 per cent. of cases. Subsequent investigations have shown that Lister's Type C is identical with the classical Type I, and his Type B with Type II. The vaccine he employed for his earlier immunizations was prepared from these three strains, and three subcutaneous injections were given each containing 2,000,000,000 cocci of each type —in some series even larger doses were employed. In a particular trial 82 cases of pneumonia occurred among some 10,000 inoculated natives ; but none of these were due to infection with Type A, B or C. The subsequent history of events on the Rand is, however, very difficult to interpret. In 1917 a change was made in the constitution of the vaccine, each dose containing 1,000,000,000 cocci of each of eight different types (see Ordman 1931). The pneumonia death rate continued to fall till about 1920–22 but since then it has risen ; and this rise, though not great, has been most marked in the last 3 years of the period under review—1927, 1928 and 1929. Orenstein (1931) notes that, in 1929, inoculation was discontinued in certain mines, and the subsequent experience in these was compared with the experience in others in which inoculation was continued. The mines in which inoculation was continued had a higher attack rate in 1930 than in 1928, while the mines in which inoculation had been stopped had a lower attack rate. It may be, as Ordman (1931) has suggested, that this recent failure in immunization is due to a change in the type of infection, not only in the prevalent types of pneumococci but in the rôle played by other bacterial species. In so far as this is the case, it illustrates the difficulty of immunizing against the clinical entity " pneumonia," which after all is the practical problem to be faced.

Environmental conditions particularly favourable to the occurrence of lobar pneumonia were provided in some of the concentration camps and depôts during the War. Cecil (1925) reviews the results of a considerable series of mass inoculations carried out in America during the period 1918–19. As in so many of the medical records of the War, military exigencies often prevented the fulfilment of the conditions needed for a satisfactory statistical comparison. At Camp Upton, among 12,519 vaccinated men no case of pneumonia due to Type I, II or III pneumococci occurred during the trial period, while 26 cases occurred among 20,000 unvaccinated controls ; but the incidence in the controls is very low, and the significance of the difference is rendered doubtful by the fact that pneumonias due to other types of pneumococci, and streptococcal pneumonia, were also more frequent among the controls than among the inoculated, a result that can hardly be attributed to the inoculation. At another depôt 38 cases of pneumonia were recorded among 48,849 vaccinated men, an incidence of 83·5 per 100,000 ; and 83 cases among 49,463 unvaccinated men, an incidence of 168 per 100,000. The types of infecting pneumococci in this series are not specified.

A third large-scale trial has been recorded by Malone (1925) and by King (1925). This was carried out on Indian troops in the Baluchistan district. The vaccine employed contained Type I and Type II pneumococci, 2,500,000,000 of each, and two injections were given. Among 2,996 inoculated men the pneumonia incidence was 9·346 per 1,000 ; among 5,227 uninoculated controls it was 10·714 per 1,000, a quite insignificant difference. The lack of protection cannot be ascribed to a difference in the incidence of the different pneumococcal types among the inoculated and uninoculated. Of 16 cases of pneumonia among the inoculated, in which the type of infecting organism was determined, 3 were due to Type I, 1 to Type II and 12 to the undifferentiated Group IV. Of 18 cases among the uninoculated, 5 were infected with Type I, 2 with Type II and 11 with Group IV. It is, of course, true that the local prevalence of types was not such as to afford much hope of any great reduction in incidence—23 of 34 typed cases were caused by types against which the vaccine could not be expected to afford protection—but there is no significant evidence of protection against Types I and II.

In summary, it would seem fair to conclude that there is presumptive evidence, based on animal experiments, that immunization with particular types of pneumococci will afford some increase in resistance to infection with these types. This evidence has not been strengthened by the results of recorded trials in man ; and it would seem that, with our present methods, the increase in resistance attained is slight at best.

Skin Reactions in Pneumonia.

We may close this section by noting certain observations which, though not immediately applicable to the practical control of the disease, have considerable theoretical significance.

Tillett and Francis (1929) tested the effect of intradermal injections of purified pneumococcal polysaccharide, and of pneumococcal protein, into patients suffering from pneumonia. They found that convalescent patients reacted to the injection of the polysaccharide by developing a wheal-and-erythema reaction which appeared within 30–60 minutes and then rapidly faded. This reaction was type-specific. Injection of pneumococcal protein, on the other hand, produced a delayed erythematous reaction reaching its height in 18–24 hours. This reaction was not type-specific. Finland and Sutliff (1931a, b) confirmed these observations, noting that the wheal-and-erythema reaction appears at or about the time of the crisis in patients who recover, while it is usually absent in cases that end fatally. In certain groups of subjects in whom repeated tests were carried out, they found that skin-sensitivity to the later injections appeared to develop as the result of the earlier ones. They also observed (Finland and Sutliff 1931a) that skin sensitivity was induced by the intravenous administration of an antipneumococcal serum. Francis (1933) records an extended experience of the occurrence of the immediate wheal-and-erythema reaction in 53 cases of Type I pneumonia, 48 of which were treated with Type I antipneumococcal serum. The results confirmed his previous finding that the appearance of the reaction has a favourable prognostic significance, and that its absence is suggestive of a fatal issue. The appearance of the reaction is correlated with the presence of specific antibodies in the blood, in the sense that the skin reaction is never present if antibodies are absent ; but the skin test may be negative though circulating antibodies are present, and its absence, even in such cases, seems to retain its bad prognostic significance. Finland and Dowling (1935) record a further study of the response to the intradermal injection of pneumococcal polysaccharide, in which they were able to show that the injection of purified polysaccharide, prepared by two different methods, induced characteristic skin sensitivity and, in addition, led to the appearance of specific antibodies in the serum.

These observations are of interest in that they seem to provide an example of an immunizing response to a purified polysaccharide, and also in the indication they give that a specific cell activity, associated with, but not entirely determined by, the presence of antibodies in the blood, is an important factor in the protective mechanisms of the tissues. Their significance is clearly not confined to the particular case of pneumonia.

REFERENCES

ANDREWES, C. H., LAIDLAW, P. P., and SMITH, W.   (1934) *Lancet*, ii. 859 ; (1935) *Brit. J. exp. Path.*, **16,** 566.

ARMSTRONG, R. R.   (1932) *Brit. med. J.*, i. 187.

AVERY, O. T. and DUBOS, R.   (1931) *J. exp. Med.*, **54,** 73.

AVERY, O. T., CHICKERING, H. T., COLE, R., and DOCHEZ, A. R.   (1917) *Monogr. Rockefeller Inst. med. Res.*, No. 7.

BECKLER, E. and MACLEOD, P.   (1934) *J. clin. Invest.*, **13,** 901.

BLAKE, F. G. and CECIL, R. L.   (1920a) *J. exp. Med.*, **31,** 403 ; (1920b) *Ibid.*, **31,** 445 ; (1920c) *Ibid.*, **31,** 499.

BORDET, J. and GENGOU, O.   (1906) *Ann. Inst. Pasteur*, **20,** 731 ; (1907) *Ibid.*, **21,** 720.

BROWN, W. E.   (1932) *Amer. J. Hyg.*, **15,** 36.

BULLOWA, J. G. M.   (1933) *N.Y. St. J. Med.*, **33,** 13 ; (1934) *J. Amer. med. Ass.*, **102,** 1560 ; (1935a) *Amer. J. med. Sci.*, **190,** 65 ; (1935b) *J. clin. Invest.*, **14,** 373 ; (1935c) *J. Amer. med. Ass.*, **105,** 1512.

BURKY, E. L. and SMILLIE, W. G.   (1929) *J. exp. Med.*, **50,** 643.

BURNET, F. M.   (1935a) *Med. J. Aust.*, **2,** 651 ; (1935b) *Ibid.*, **2,** 687.

CECIL, R. L.   (1925) *Medicine*, **4,** 395 ; (1928) *Arch. intern. Med.*, **41,** 295.

CECIL, R. L., BALDWIN, H. S., and LARSEN, N. P.   (1927) *Arch. intern. Med.*, **40,** 253.

CECIL, R. L. and BLAKE, F. G.   (1920a) *J. exp. Med.*, **31,** 518 ; (1920b) *Ibid.*, **31,** 657 ; (1920c) *Ibid.*, **31,** 685 ; (1920d) *Ibid.*, **32,** 1 ; (1920e) *Ibid.*, **32,** 719.

CECIL, R. L. and PLUMMER, N.   (1930) *J. Amer. med. Ass.*, **95,** 1547 ; (1932) *Ibid.*, **98,** 779.

CECIL, R. L., PLUMMER, N., and MCCALL, M.   (1936) *Amer. J. med. Sci.*, **191,** 305.

CECIL, R. L. and STEFFEN, G. I.   (1923) *J. exp. Med.*, **38,** 149 ; (1925) *Bull. U.S. hyg. Lab.*, No. 141.

CHIEVITZ, I and MEYER, A. H.   (1916) *Ann. Inst. Pasteur*, **30,** 503.

COOPER, GEORGINA, EDWARDS, M., and ROSENSTEIN, C.   (1929) *J. exp. Med.*, **49,** 461.

COOPER, GEORGINA, ROSENSTEIN, C., WALTER, A., and PEIZER, L.   (1932) *J. exp. Med.*, **55,** 531.

COOPER, GEORGINA and WALTER, A. W.   (1935) *Amer. J. publ. Hlth.*, **25,** 469.

CURPHEY, T. J. and BARUCH, H. B.   (1932) *J. exp. Med.*, **55,** 925.

DEAN, H. R. and WEBB, R. A.   (1926) *J. Path. Bact.*, **29,** 473.

DICK, G. H. and MURRAY, E.   (1919) *J. infect. Dis.*, **25,** 6.

Discussion.   (1935) *Proc. R. Soc. Med.*, **28,** 941.

DOCHEZ, A. R.   (1912) *J. exp. Med.*, **16,** 665.

DOCHEZ, A. R., MILLS, K. C., and KNEELAND, Y.   (1931a) *Proc. Soc. exp. Biol., N.Y.*, **28,** 513 ; (1931b) *Ibid.*, **29,** 64 ; (1932) *Ibid.*, **30,** 314 ; (1933) *Ibid.*, **30,** 1017 ; (1936) *J. exp. Med.*, **63,** 559.

DOCHEZ, A. R., SHIBLEY, G. S., and MILLS, K. C.   (1930) *J. exp. Med.*, **52,** 701.

DUBOS, R.   (1932) *J. exp. Med.*, **55,** 377 ; (1935) *Ibid.*, **62,** 259.

DUBOS, R. and AVERY, O. T.   (1931) *J. exp. Med.*, **54,** 51.

DUBOS, R. and BAUER, J. H.   (1935) *J. exp. Med.*, **62,** 271.

DUVAL, C. W. and HARRIS, W. H.   (1919) *J. infect. Dis.*, **25,** 384.

DWINELL, W. G.   (1919) *Amer. J. med. Sci.*, **158,** 216.

ELFORD, W. J., ANDREWES, C. H., and TANG, F. F.   (1936) *Brit. J. exp. Path.*, **17,** 51.

FALK, K. G., MCGUIRE, G., VALENTINE, E., and WITNEY, E.   (1931) *J. Immunol.*, **19,** 199.

FELTON, L. D.   (1925) *J. infect. Dis.*, **37,** 199, 309 ; (1928) *Ibid.*, **43,** 531, 543 ; (1930a) *J. Immunol.*, **19,** 485 ; (1930b) *Ibid.*, **19,** 511 ; (1931) *Ibid.*, **21,** 341.

FELTON, L. D. and STAHL, H. J.   (1935) *Publ. Hlth Rep., Wash.*, **50,** 1730.

FERGUSON, F. R., DAVEY, A. F. C., and TOPLEY, W. W. C.   (1927) *J. Hyg., Camb.*, **26,** 98.

FERGUSON, F. R. and LOVELL, R.   (1928) *Quart. J. Med.*, **22,** 85.

FILDES, P. and McINTOSH, J. (1920) *Brit. J. exp. Path.*, **1**, 119, 159.
FINLAND, M. and DOWLING, H. F. (1935) *J. Immunol.*, **29**, 285.
FINLAND, M. and SUTLIFF, W. D. (1931a) *J. exp. Med.*, **54**, 637 ; (1931b) *Ibid.*, **54**, 653.
FOSTER, G. B. (1917) *J. infect. Dis.*, **21**, 451.
FRANCIS, T. (1933) *J. exp. Med.*, **57**, 617 ; (1934) *Science*, **80**, 457.
FRANCIS, T. and MAGILL, T. P. (1935) *J. exp. Med.*, **62**, 505 ; (1936) *Ibid.*, **63**, 655.
FRANCIS, T. and SHOPE, R. E. (1936) *J. exp. Med.*, **63**, 645.
FRANCIS, T. and TERRELL, E. E. (1934) *J. exp. Med.*, **59**, 609.
FRANCIS, T., TERRELL, E. E., DUBOS, R., and AVERY, O. T. (1934) *J. exp. Med.*, **59**, 641.
FRIEDLANDER, M., SOBOTKA, H., and BANZHAF, E. J. (1928) *J. exp. Med.*, **47**, 79.
GARDNER, A. D. and LESLIE, P. H. (1932) *Lancet*, i. 9.
GASKELL, J. F. (1927) *Lancet*, ii. 951.
GLYNN, E. E., DIGBY, L., and JONES, H. W. (1923) *Spec. Rep. Ser. med. Res. Coun., Lond.* No. 79.
GOODNER, K. and DUBOS, R. (1932) *J. exp. Med.*, **56**, 521.
GOODNER, K., DUBOS, R., and AVERY, O. T. (1932) *J. exp. Med.*, **55**, 393.
GUNDEL, M. and SCHLÜTER, W. (1933a) *Klin. Wschr.*, **12**, 1633 ; (1933b) *Z. ImmunForsch.*, **81**, 218.
HARTLEY, P., PARISH, H. J., PETRIE, G. F., and SMITH, W. (1933) *Lancet*, ii. 91.
HEIDELBERGER, M. and AVERY, O. T. (1923) *J. exp. Med.*, **38**, 73.
HEIDELBERGER, M., SIA, R. H. P., and KENDALL, F. E. (1930) *J. exp. Med.*, **52**, 477.
JORDAN, E. O. and SHARP, W. B. (1921) *J. infect. Dis.*, **28**, 357.
KENDRICK, P. and ELDERLING, G. (1934) *Amer. J. publ. Hlth.*, **24**, 309 ; (1936) *Ibid.*, **26**, 8.
KING, H. H. (1925) *Indian J. med. Res.*, **12**, 571.
KRISTENSEN, B. (1933) *J. Amer. med. Ass.*, **101**, 204.
KRISTENSEN, M. (1922) " Haemoglobinophilic Bacteria." Copenhagen.
LAIDLAW, P. P. (1935) *Lancet*, i. 1118.
LAIDLAW, P. P., SMITH, W., ANDREWES, C. H., and DUNKIN, G. W. (1935) *Brit. J. exp. Path.*, **16**, 275.
LEICHTENTRITT, B. (1918) *Dtsch. med. Wschr.*, **44**, 1419.
LESLIE, P. H. and GARDNER, A. D. (1931) *J. Hyg., Camb.*, **31**, 423.
LEWIS, P. H. and SHOPE, R. (1931) *J. exp. Med.*, **54**, 361.
LISTER, F. S. (1917) *Publ. S. Afr. Inst. med. Res.*, No. 10.
LOGAN, W. R. and SMEALL, J. T. (1932) *Brit. med. J.*, i. 189.
LONG, P. H., DOULL, J. A., BOURN, J. M., and McCOMB, E. (1931) *J. exp. Med.*, **53**, 447.
McCLELLAND, J. E. (1919) *Amer. J. med. Sci.*, **158**, 80.
MACDONALD, H. and MACDONALD, E. J. (1933) *J. infect. Dis.*, **53**, 328.
McINTOSH, J. (1922) *Spec. Rep. Ser. med. Res. Coun., Lond.*, No. 63.
MADSEN, T. (1925) *Boston med. surg. J.*, **192**, 50 ; (1933) *J. Amer. med. Ass.*, **101**, 187.
MALONE, R. H. (1925) *Indian J. med. Res.*, **12**, 565.
MANDELBAUM. (1918) *Münch. med. Wschr.*, **65**, 812.
MEDALIA, L. S. (1919) *Boston med. surg. J.*, **180**, 323.
MESSERSCHMIDT, T., HUNDESHAGEN, K., and SCHEER, K. (1919) *Z. Hyg. InfektKr.*, **88**, 552.
MULDER, J. (1935) *Nederl. Tijdschr. Geneesk.*, **79**, 4353.
NEUFELD, F. (1902) *Z. Hyg. InfektKr.*, **40**, 54.
NEUFELD, F. and HÄNDEL, L. (1909) *Z. ImmunForsch.*, **3**, 159.
NEUFELD, F. and SCHNITZER, R. (1927–8) *Arb. ReichsgesundhAmt.*, 3te Aufl., **4**, 913.
NOBLE, W. C., FISHER, E., and BRAINARD, D. H. (1928) *J. prev. Med., Baltimore*, **2**, 105.
OPIE, E. L., BLAKE, F. G., SMALL, J. L., and RIVERS, T. M. (1921) " Epidemic Respiratory Diseases." London.
ORDMAN, D. (1931) *J. med. Ass. S. Afr.*, **5**, 108.
ORENSTEIN, A. J. (1931) *J. med. Ass. S. Afr.*, **5**, 108.
PARISH, H. J. (1930) *J. Path. Bact.*, **33**, 729.
PARK, W. H. (1919) *J. Amer. med. Ass.*, **73**, 318.
PARK, W. H., BULLOWA, J. G. M., and ROSENBLÜTH, M. B. (1928) *J. Amer. med. Ass.*, **91**, 1503.
PARK, W. H. and COOPER, G. (1928) *J. Amer. Med. Ass.*, **90**, 1349.
PETTIT, H., MUDD, S., and PEPPER, D. S. (1936) *J. Amer. med. Ass.*, **106**, 890.
PFEIFFER, R. (1892) *Dtsch. med. Wschr.*, **18**, 28.
POWELL, H. M. and CLOWES, G. H. A. (1931) *Proc. Soc. exp. Biol., N.Y.*, **29**, 332.
PRAUSNITZ, C. (1929) Mem. Standardization Therap. Sera., etc., L. of Nat. Hlth. Organ. Geneva.
PRITCHETT, IDA W. and STILLMAN, E. G. (1919) *J. exp. Med.*, **29**, 259.
RAIA, ANTOINETTE, PLUMMER, N., and SHULTZ, S. (1931) *Amer. J. Dis. Child.*, **42**, 57.
Reports. (1920) *Min. Hlth Rep. publ. Hlth med. Subj., Lond.*, No. 5 ; (1930) *Ibid.*, No. 58.
ROSENBLÜTH, M. B. (1928) *J. Amer. med. Ass.*, **90**, 1351.
SABIN, A. B. (1929) *Amer. J. publ. Hlth.*, **19**, 1148 ; (1933) *J. Amer. med. Ass.*, **100**, 1584.

SAUER, L. W.   (1933a) *J. Amer. med. Ass.*, **100**, 239 ;   (1933b) *Ibid.*, **101**, 1449 ;   (1933c)
    J. Pediat., **2**, 740 ;   (1935) *Amer. J. publ. Hlth.*, **11**, 1226.
SAUER, L. W. and HAMBRECHT, L.   (1928) *J. Amer. med. Ass.*, **91**, 1861 ;   (1930) *Ibid.*,
    95, 263.
SCHORER, E. H.   (1919) *N.Y. med. J.*, **110**, 97.
SELTER, H.   (1918) *Dtsch. med. Wschr.*, **44**, 932.
SHIBLEY, G. S., HANGER, F. M., and DOCHEZ, A. R.   (1926) *J. exp. Med.*, **43**, 415.
SHIBLEY, G. S. and HOELSCHER, H.   (1934) *J. exp. Med.*, **60**, 403.
SHIBLEY, G. S., MILLS, K. C., and DOCHEZ, A. R.   (1929) *Proc. Soc. exp. Biol., N.Y.*, **27**, 59.
SHOLLY, A. I. VON and PARK, W. H.   (1921) *J. Immunol.*, **6**, 103.
SHOPE, R. E.   (1931a) *J. exp. Med.*, **54**, 349 ;   (1931b) *Ibid.*, **54**, 373 ;   (1932) *Ibid.*, **56**, 575 ;
    (1934a) *Ibid.*, **59**, 201 ;   (1934b) *Ibid.*, **60**, 49 ;   (1935) *Ibid.*, **62**, 561.
SHOPE, R. E.   (1936) *J. exp. Med.*, **63**, 669.
SIA, R. H. P., ROBERTSON, O. H., and WOO, S. T.   (1928) *J. exp. Med.*, **48**, 513.
SMILLIE, W. G.   (1933) *J. Amer. med. Ass.*, **101**, 1281.
SMITH, W.   (1932) *J. Path. Bact.*, **35**, 509.
SMITH, W., ANDREWES, C. H., and LAIDLAW, P. P.   (1933) *Lancet*, ii. 66 ;   (1935) *Brit. J.
    exp. Path.*, **16**, 291.
SMITH, W., FISCHER, W., and SMITH, M. L.   (1934) *Lancet*, ii. 155.
SOBOTKA, H. and FRIEDLANDER, M.   (1928) *J. exp. Med.*, **47**, 57.
SUGARE, H. and MCLEOD, J. W.   (1929) *Lancet*, ii. 165.
TILLETT, W. S. and FRANCIS, T.   (1929) *J. exp. Med.*, **50**, 687.
TREVAN, J. W.   (1930) *J. Path. Bact.*, **33**, 739.
WADSWORTH, A.   (1917) *J. exp. Med.*, **25**, 629 ;   (1924) *Amer. J. Hyg.*, **4**, 119.
WILCOX, HARRIET L.   (1934) *J. infect. Dis.*, **55**, 199.
WILLIAMS, A. W., NEVIN, M., and GURLEY, C. R.   (1921) *J. Immunol.*, **6**, 5.
WINHOLT, W.   (1915) *J. infect. Dis.*, **16**, 389.
WOLLSTEIN, M.   (1909) *J. exp. Med.*, **11**, 41.
ZOZAYA, J., BOYER, J., and CLARK, J.   (1930) *J. exp. Med.*, **52**, 471.

CHAPTER LXXII

UNDULANT FEVER, CONTAGIOUS ABORTION OF CATTLE, AND ALLIED INFECTIONS. TULARÆMIA

UNDULANT FEVER

EVER since the time of Hippocrates a low type of fever characterized by fairly regular remissions or intermissions has been recognized along the Mediterranean littoral. Several names have been applied to it, of which Malta fever and Mediterranean fever are the two best known. In 1887 Bruce reported the discovery of a small micro-organism, which he called *Micrococcus melitensis*, in the spleen of patients dying of the disease. Its injection into monkeys gave rise to a remittent fever, sometimes terminating fatally, and the organism was recovered in pure culture from the liver and spleen. Nearly 20 years later Zammit (1905) of the Malta Board of Health showed that the organism also infected goats. Further work rendered it evident that the goat was in fact the natural host of *Br. melitensis*, and that infection was carried to man by the consumption of raw milk.

In 1918 Evans drew attention to the similarity between the organism isolated from Malta fever and that described by Bang (1897) as the cause of a widespread disease in cattle known as contagious abortion. Her observations were soon confirmed, and in honour of Sir David Bruce the generic name *Brucella* was proposed for the two organisms. The close similarity between *Br. melitensis* and *Br. abortus* suggested the possibility that this latter organism might be pathogenic for human beings. It was not long before Bevan (1921–22) brought evidence to prove the correctness of this surmise. He drew attention to the occurrence in Southern Rhodesia of cases of undulant fever affecting persons who had apparently had no direct or indirect contact with goats. In the areas concerned epizootic abortion of cattle was prevalent, and it appeared probable that infection was being transferred to man by raw cow's milk. Numerous investigators turned their attention to this subject, and before long cases of undulant fever due to *Br. abortus* had been reported from practically every country in the world.

A third causal agent of this disease is *Brucella suis*—an organism originally described by Traum (1914) in the United States. Its natural habitat is the pig. Man becomes infected chiefly by contact with diseased carcasses, and undulant fever due to this organism has therefore a very definite occupational incidence.

These findings have necessitated a reconsideration of the nomenclature of the disease. Since all three organisms give rise to very much the same symptoms in man, and since *Brucella* infections are now known to be widespread over the globe, the term Malta fever is no longer generally applicable. It is being gradually replaced by the term undulant fever, which is free from any geographical connotation. Though this term is satisfactory for febrile infections, it is rather misleading if used in reference to non-febrile infections with *Brucella* organisms, which are now being recognized as increasingly common. Hence the term Brucellosis has been suggested on analogy with tuberculosis, to apply to all types of *Brucella* infections, febrile or non-febrile, overt or latent, in animals or in man. This term has little to recommend it, since these considerations apply almost equally to diseases caused by other infective agents. We prefer ourselves to use instead the term " Brucella infection."

For the sake of clarity we propose to give a separate description of the epidemiology of undulant fever in man due to the three type organisms. We shall deal first with infections caused by *Br. melitensis*, including in our description the general symptomatology and bacteriology of the disease.

Undulant Fever due to Br. melitensis

Synonyms : Malta fever, Mediterranean fever, Neapolitan fever, Country fever of Constantinople, New fever of Crete, Rock fever of Gibraltar. French : *Mélitococcie.*

Quoting from the classical monograph of Hughes (1897) : " Clinically, the fever has a peculiarly irregular temperature curve, consisting of intermittent waves or undulations of pyrexia, of a distinctly remittent character. These pyrexial waves or undulations last, as a rule, from 1 to 3 weeks, with an apyrexial interval, or period of temporary abatement of pyrexial intensity between, lasting for 2 or more days. . . . This pyrexia is usually accompanied by obstinate constipation, progressive anæmia, and debility. It is often complicated with, and followed by, neuralgic symptoms referred to the peripheral or central nervous system ; arthritic effusions ; painful inflammatory conditions of certain fibrous structures, of a localized nature ; or swelling of the testicles." Numerous clinical types are recognized, such as the malignant, the undulatory, the intermittent, and the irregular type. In addition, there are subclinical infections, which can be diagnosed only by bacteriological methods, and infections that may remain latent for weeks or months before flaring up or retrogressing. For a description of these the reader is referred to Marston (1863), who first differentiated Malta fever from other fevers, to Hughes (1897), whose clinical study has never been improved upon, and more recently to Rainsford (1935) and Lisbonne and Janbon (1935). Several complications may occur, beyond those already mentioned, including osteomyelitis, which usually takes the form of localized bone abscesses, bronchitis, and acute inflammation of one or other of the visceral organs.

The commonest symptoms are probably asthenia, fever, muscular and articular pains, nocturnal sweats—often drenching—anorexia, constipation, nervous irritability, and chills or rigors (Taylor and Hazemann 1932).

The incubation period is variable. It may be as short as a week or as long as several months. Most commonly it is 10–30 days. The duration of the illness varies from a few days to over a year, 3 months being the usual time.

Bacteriology.

Bacteriologically, the work of Bruce (1887, 1888, 1893), of Hughes (1893, 1897), and of the Mediterranean Fever Commission (Report 1905–07) showed that the disease was a septicæmia. Working in Malta, Bruce (1893) was able on two occasions to grow the organism from the juice obtained by splenic puncture, and subsequent observers showed that, in the early stages of the disease, *Br. melitensis* could frequently be isolated from the peripheral blood. The post-mortem appearances agreed with this interpretation ; there was an increase of pericardial fluid, congestion and enlargement of the liver, and great hypertrophy of the spleen. The presence of small areas of congestion in the mucosa and submucosa of the intestine, and the enlargement of the mesenteric glands, the interior of which often consisted of semi-purulent material, were suggestive of an alimentary mode of infection. Cultures taken post mortem from the spleen, liver, and lymphatic glands were positive in 100 per cent. of cases, from the kidney in 85 per cent., and from the heart blood, pericardial fluid and bone marrow in about 50 per cent. (Kennedy 1906). *Br. melitensis* was never found in the saliva nor in the sweat of patients, but it was shown to be quite commonly excreted in the urine. Kennedy (1905), who made a special study of this point, examined no fewer than 1,974 specimens of urine from 61 different patients. In 186 of the samples from 33 of the cases he obtained positive cultures. In a series of 43 cases, in which 20 or more samples from each patient were examined, the organism was isolated from 31. Often the organism could be detected for only 1 day ; sometimes it was excreted daily for 2 or 3 weeks. From these figures it may be concluded that, at some time or another, probably at least 75 per cent. of patients suffering from Malta fever pass the specific agent in their urine ; this excretion may be sudden and transitory, or it may last for weeks, extending onwards into convalescence.

As the organism is not infrequently found post mortem in the gall-bladder, it is reasonable to suppose that it must be excreted in the fæces. This is probably so, but the technical difficulties of isolating it are considerable. Eyre (1908), however, obtained a positive culture from the colon of a case which came to autopsy.

Outside the body, the organism was found to be fairly resistant ; dried on cloth, it remained alive for 17 days, in dust for 44 days, and in sterile tap-water for 20 days (Kennedy 1905).

Epidemiology in Malta.—The epidemiology of undulant fever due to *Br. melitensis* varies in different countries. Since it has been studied most fully in Malta, we may review briefly the findings of the Mediterranean Fever Commission (Report 1905–07) in this island. The maximum incidence rate in Malta was found to occur in July and August. Generally speaking, it varied directly with the atmospheric temperature and inversely with the rainfall. The most susceptible age was between 11 and 30 years, but the disease occurred at any time of life. The upper classes of the civilian population and the officers of the services suffered more heavily than the lower classes and the non-commissioned ranks respectively. During the 33 years 1859–91 the incidence of the disease varied between 269·5 per 1,000 in 1859 and 91·2 per 1,000 in 1888. In spite of this comparatively high rate of morbidity, the mortality rate was low—about 2 per cent. But the duration of the fever and the prolonged disability following its actual termination combined to render it a potent cause of invalidity.

At the time of the Commission's appointment the mode of infection was still unknown. Several ways were suggested, but little evidence was produced in favour of any particular one. Johnstone (1905), who conducted an epidemiological inquiry into the disease, reported that neither food nor drink appeared to have any marked connection with the spread of the fever ; nor did dust infection or direct personal contagion play a part. Similarly Davies (1906) concluded that neither water, milk, nor any other articles of food seemed to be responsible in any way ; he favoured a theory of contagion, either direct or through the agency of mosquitoes.

It was left to Zammit of the Malta Board of Health, and a member of the Commission on Mediterranean Fever, to indicate the true path of infection. In his first communication (1905) he reported that 5 out of 6 goats which he had examined gave a positive agglutination reaction to *Br. melitensis*. From the blood of two of these animals, he succeeded in cultivating the actual organism itself. Horrocks (1905) rapidly confirmed this, and further demonstrated the frequent presence of *Br. melitensis* in the milk and the urine of apparently healthy goats. Kennedy (1905c), who examined the blood serum of 161 goats from 8 different herds, demonstrated the presence of specific agglutinins in no fewer than 84 or 52·2 per cent. of specimens. This high incidence of infection was found to exist not only in the public herds, but in those animals that were kept privately under special care.

As it was evident that *goats' milk* was probably the main source of infection, it was desirable to ascertain on a large scale the proportion of infected animals. For this purpose, Zammit's test was found to be of great value. It consists in observing the presence of agglutinins, not in the blood serum, but in the milk of the goats. The proportion of infected goats judged by this test is definitely lower than that given by the serum agglutination test, since only 60–85 per cent. of the animals showing blood agglutinins also contain agglutinins in their milk. Zammit (1906) examined 710 samples of milk, and obtained 133 positive reactions. From every milk giving a strong reaction he was able to isolate *Br. melitensis* in culture. Horrocks and Kennedy (1906), who made numerous investigations both by the serum and by the milk agglutination test, came to the conclusion that 41 per cent. of the goats in Malta were infected, and that 10 per cent. of those that supplied milk were excreting *Br. melitensis*. It was found difficult to recognize the infected animals on clinical grounds ; they did not suffer from a true fever, and though some showed loss of weight, a thinning of the coat, and a short hacking cough, others remained perfectly well and displayed no sign of illness. The amount of milk secreted was likewise no criterion, for the infected animals frequently yielded as much and more than the non-infected ones.

From these investigations it was apparent that the goats of Malta were heavily infected with *Br. melitensis*, and that about 10 per cent. of the milch goats were excreting this organism in their milk. As the majority of milk consumed in the island was goats' milk—cows are few owing to insufficient pasturage—it was easy to see how the disease might be transmitted to human beings.

Steps were taken by both the Navy and the Army, in 1906, to stop the supply of goats' milk to the troops. The result was most striking. Within a year the disease had been practically eradicated, only a few easily explained cases occurring. Amongst the civil population, such radical steps could not be taken ; the gradually decreasing incidence observed during the following years was largely due to the killing off of many of the infected goats (Table CL).

This method, however, afforded no permanent protection, and the disease continued to exact a heavy toll. Of recent years it has been increasing in extent and severity among the civil population. There has, in fact, been a steady rise from 1926, when there were 596 cases with 27 deaths, till 1934, when there were 1,909 cases with 88 deaths.

TABLE CL (taken from Eyre 1908, 1912).

	Civil.		Navy.		Army.	
	Cases.	Deaths.	Cases.	Deaths.	Cases.	Deaths.
1901 . . .	642	54	252	3	253	9
1902 . . .	624	45	354	2	155	6
1903 . . .	589	48	339	6	404	9
1904 . . .	573	59	333	8	320	12
1905 . . .	663	88	270	7	643	16
1906 . . .	822	117	145	4	163	2
1907 . . .	714	78	12	0	9	1
1908 . . .	502	?	6	—	5	?
1909 . . .	456	?	10	—	1	?
1910 . . .	318	?	3	—	1	?

Consumption of goats' milk was not the only method of infection, though it was undoubtedly the most important for the troops and naval ratings on the island. Contamination of the skin or mucosæ with infective material—particularly common in laboratory workers—afforded another method. Occasionally infection appeared to be insect-borne, or transmitted by sexual congress (Eyre, McNaught, Kennedy, and Zammit 1907).

The history of Malta fever is instructive. In the first place, it affords an excellent example of a disease whose incidence was not immediately affected by the discovery of the causative agent. In order to prevent a disease, it is not necessary to know the causative agent, so long as we know the way in which it spreads. Once this is known, the steps necessary for limiting it may be considered. In some cases, as in that of milk-borne disease, the steps may be relatively simple ; stop the supply of milk, or insist on its adequate heat treatment, and the infection can no longer be transmitted to human beings. In other cases, notably the respiratory diseases, the problem is more difficult. No satisfactory method for preventing the inhalation of infected material has yet been devised ; and until this proves possible, measures against these diseases will be more profitably directed towards increasing the host resistance than to interfering with the spread of infection.

The second point of interest is that, in an epidemiological inquiry, it is harder to assess the importance of a given factor when it operates more or less uniformly throughout a population, than when it is distributed in such a way as to affect different sections unevenly. Both the epidemiologists who investigated the disease in Malta (Johnstone 1905, Davies 1906) reported that there was no evidence to suggest that infection was conveyed by food. Both of them overlooked the fact that a disease spread by an article of almost universal consumption, such as goats' milk, would show little preference for any one class of the population, if the contamination of the milk were widespread and frequent, rather than local and occasional. The clue to the problem was furnished by the bacteriologist. It was this second discovery, that a large proportion of goats contained agglutinins in their blood for *Br. melitensis*, which complemented the first discovery, that of the organism itself, and pointed out the way by which the spread of the disease might be checked.

(For an excellent account of the epidemiology of Malta fever in the Royal Navy, see Dudley 1931.)

Epidemiology in Other Countries.—The next most important bacteriological and epidemiological study of the disease has been made by Taylor and his colleagues in the South of *France*, working at the Undulant Fever Centre established at Montpellier by the Rockefeller Foundation (see Taylor and Hazemann 1932, Taylor, Lisbonne, and Roman 1932, Taylor, Lisbonne, and Vidal 1935). The disease was found to be widespread in the south-east of France, where sheep and goats are common and cattle are relatively few. The incidence in males was 2–3 times that in females, and was highest in the 15–45 age group. The occupational incidence was very striking, the majority of the cases occurring in the agricultural community, especially among those engaged in rearing sheep and goats. The seasonal prevalence was at its maximum in the spring, corresponding to the time of lambing and abortion. Though the consumption of goats' milk, and of fresh cheese made from goats', or ewes' milk, undoubtedly played some part in infection (see Carrieu and Lafenêtre 1932, Veloppé and Jaubert 1935), the evidence on the whole suggested that infection most frequently resulted from direct contact with infected animals and manure. In a population, however, living under such primitive conditions, and exposed to so many sources of infection, it was difficult to ascertain with certainty which was the most important route by which the organisms gained access to the body. The very interesting observation was made (Taylor, Vidal and Roman 1934) that cows in close contact with sheep and goats might become infected with *Br. melitensis*, excrete this organism for months in the milk, and give rise to undulant fever in human beings consuming it in the raw condition.

The disease affects several other countries, including Italy, Spain, Greece, Transcaucasia, Algeria, Tunis, Palestine, Arabia, India, South Africa, China, and various parts of South America. Like Malta, Corsica and Sicily are seriously affected. In this country, owing to the absence of *melitensis* infection in sheep and goats, disease due to this organism does not occur. In the United States there is a certain amount of undulant fever due to *Br. melitensis* in the goat-raising areas, but most of it is due to *Br. abortus* and *Br. suis*.

Undulant Fever due to Br. abortus

In its general symptomatology and bacteriology this disease resembles that caused by *Br. melitensis*. Though, as will be pointed out later, the ability of *Br. abortus* to give rise to undulant fever is less than that of *Br. melitensis*, once the typical disease has developed, it seems to pursue its course more or less independently of the type of the causative organism. The average duration is 3 months, and the case mortality about 2 per cent. Besides typical cases, however, a considerable number of so-called subclinical infections occur, characterized by only slight pyrexia and by a variety of different symptoms. Evans (1934) draws attention to the frequency in these patients of exhaustion, insomnia, irritability, and subjective disturbances, leading to a diagnosis of neurasthenia. Sometimes there is an acute influenza-like illness lasting for not more than a week, while at others a low chronic intermittent fever persists for months or even years. Acute abdominal symptoms are not uncommon, and in several patients an appendicectomy or cholecystectomy has been performed before the real nature of the disease was recognized (Simpson 1930).

Infection during pregnancy is sometimes, but not often, followed by abortion. The organism may be isolated from the placenta and uterus of the mother and from the stomach contents of the fœtus (see Kristensen and Holm 1929, Spengler 1929, Simpson 1930, Alessandrini and Pacelli 1932, Habs 1933*a*, Lauda 1934, Menzani and de Zanche 1934).

Frequency.—Though the disease is widespread throughout the world, its frequency is difficult to assess. As in tuberculosis, the reported cases may bear very little relation to the real incidence of infection. The reason for this is partly that the disease is still unknown to many practitioners, partly that it is impossible to diagnose with certainty except by bacteriological methods, and partly that in several countries, including Great Britain, the disease is not reportable. The so-called reported cases often refer to mere collections by private persons. The nearest approach we can make to ascertaining the incidence of the disease is by indirect methods, particularly by noting the proportion of sera from patients with undiagnosed pyrexia which agglutinate *Br. abortus* to a significant titre. In some countries, such as Denmark, where serological examination of pyrexial patients is common, and where all sera are examined under standard conditions in one central laboratory, it is easy by this means to obtain a fair estimate of the frequency of active infection with *Br. abortus*. In other countries, such as our own, where serological examination, especially in rural areas, is more restricted, and where sera are examined in multiple scattered laboratories, collection and integration of the data are very much harder. With reservations to be made later for certain occupational classes which are exposed to frequent infection with *Br. abortus*, a titre of 1/80 or over in febrile patients can be regarded as probably indicative of active infection. Having ascertained the proportion of Widal sera agglutinating *Br. abortus*, the probable number of cases of infection can be calculated, either directly if the total number of Widal sera examined in the whole country is known, or indirectly by a method described elsewhere (Wilson 1932*a*). The results obtained (see Table CLI) are essentially estimates, and probably err on the conservative side. (For references to figures used, see Kristensen and Holm 1929, Holl 1930, Weigmann 1931, Bijl and v.d. Hoeden 1931, Süpfle and Hofmann 1932, Bach 1932, Fried 1932, Grumbach and Grilichess 1932, Messer 1932, Dettling 1932, Wade 1933, Hall 1933, Russ 1934, Kalbfleisch and Kalbfleisch 1935.) It will be seen that the incidence of the disease, calculated per million of the population, is much the same in Great Britain, Germany, Austria, Holland, and Sweden, but

TABLE CLI

PROPORTION OF WIDAL SERA AGGLUTINATING *Br. abortus* TO 1/80 OR OVER, AND ESTIMATED ANNUAL NUMBER OF UNDULANT FEVER CASES ABOUT 1930.

(Data compiled from several papers in different countries ; for references, see text.)

Country.	No. of Sera Examined.	No Positive.	Percentage Positive.	Estimated Annual Number of Undulant Fever Cases.	No. of Cases per 1,000,000 Population.
Great Britain . . .	3,175	101	3·18	440	11
Germany	9,397	323	3·44	600	10
Austria	9,693	177	1·83	50	8
Switzerland	1,503	91	6·1	340	84
Holland	4,500	50	1·11	90	12
Denmark	4,623	500	10·82	500	147
Sweden	—	—	—	120	20

that it is considerably higher in Switzerland and Denmark. In the United States undulant fever is known to be very prevalent, but as some of the cases are due to infection with *Br. suis*, and the antigenic structure of this organism is closely related to that of *Br. abortus* (see Chapter XXXI), figures based on agglutination results are not strictly comparable with those just given. There is evidence to suggest that the different incidence in different countries is dependent to some extent on the frequency of contagious abortion in cattle, and the degree of exposure of the human population, though other factors undoubtedly play a part (Henricsson 1932, Olin 1935). Some of the difference is almost certainly more apparent than real, and is due to the much better diagnostic facilities available in certain countries than others.

Latent Infections.—Besides definite clinical disease, *Br. abortus* gives rise to a considerable amount of latent infection. Examination of Wassermann sera in this country and in Germany shows that about 1·5 per cent. agglutinate *Br. abortus* to a titre of 1/40 or over. The titre is generally less than 1/160, and high titres, such as those yielded by the majority of sera from patients with undulant fever, are uncommon. A certain proportion of these sera are derived from patients actually suffering from the disease. The majority, however, come from persons with no clinical evidence of undulant fever. The probability is that these agglutinins are due to latent infections with *Br. abortus*. This interpretation is supported by two facts. The first is that agglutinins, even in a titre of 1/20, are rarely present in the sera of persons who do not drink raw milk or cream, and who are not exposed to contact with infected animals. The second is that agglutinins are present in quite a high proportion of persons who drink considerable quantities of infected raw milk or cream, or whose duties bring them into close contact with infected animals (Table CLII). (For references to figures used, see Lentze 1930, Martin and Myers 1931, Maclean 1932, Wilson 1932b, Starr and Maxcy 1933, Molinelli, 1933, 1934, Hermann *et al.* 1934, v. Berkessy and Simon 1934, v. Berkessy

TABLE CLII

PROPORTION OF SERA AGGLUTINATING *Br. abortus* TO 1/40 OR OVER IN PERSONS EXPOSED TO
INFECTION.

(Data compiled from several papers in different countries ; for references, see text.)

Occupational Class.	Country.	No. of Sera.	No. Positive.	Percentage Positive.
Milk and Farm Employees	Germany	220	31	14·1
	Hungary	63	10	15·9
	New Zealand	104	17	16·4
	Argentine	136	16	11·8
Slaughterers	Great Britain	206	27	13·1
	Hungary	93	21	22·6
	U.S.A.	452	62	13·7
	Argentine	1,776	191	10·8
Veterinarians	Great Britain	63	13	20·6
	France	28	7	25·0
	Denmark	94	22	23·4
	U.S.A.	715	92	12·9
	Argentine	110	29	26·4

1935, Zimmermann 1935, Rossi 1935.)   The figures given in the table include the United States and the Argentine, in both of which countries there is some infection with *Br. suis*, but it will be seen that in all countries about 10–20 per cent. of persons in these special occupational classes contained agglutinins to *Brucella*. Investigation showed that some of these persons were suffering from undulant fever at the time of examination, or had recently recovered from it, but most of them had no symptoms indicative of active infection.   An exception should perhaps be made for veterinary surgeons, several of whom suffered from an allergic condition, which manifested itself in the form of a rash on the arm developing after " cleansing," *i.e.*, evacuation of the cow's uterus (see Huddleson and Johnson 1930, Haxthausen and Thomsen 1931, Wilson 1932*b*).

The conclusion seems to be that infection with *Br. abortus* resembles in many respects infection with the tubercle bacillus.   Both organisms have a fairly high degree of infectivity enabling them to establish themselves, at least temporarily, in the tissues.   Neither of them, however, has a high pathogenicity, so that in the majority of persons the infection remains latent or retrogresses.   Only in a small proportion of infected persons are the conditions favourable for the production of clinically detectable disease.   It is probable that latent infections often lead to latent immunization, thus explaining why undulant fever does not occur more often than it apparently does in veterinarians.   There is also evidence to suggest that persons who are exposed to heavy infection for the first time, or after a long interval of freedom from exposure, are more likely to develop the disease than those who are exposed to mild infection more or less continuously.   It would be idle to pretend, however, that we have any exact knowledge of the factors determining the course of infection in any given individual, and those who deny the pathogenicity of *Br. abortus* for man, because not every exposed person develops the disease, must be wholly unaware of the complexity of the equilibrium existing between host and parasite.   The possibility that strains of *Br. abortus* vary in virulence must be considered, but so far there is no evidence to support it (see Birch and Gilman 1935, Olin 1935).

Mode of Infection.—The mode of infection varies in different countries and in different parts of the same country.   The main source is obviously cattle, and man becomes infected by consumption of raw milk or cream, or by contact with infected animals, either alive or dead.   Generally speaking, the town population is exposed to infection from milk, while the country population is exposed to both milk-borne and direct contact infection.

Numerous records in different countries show that a considerable proportion of samples of raw milk coming from infected herds contain living *abortus* bacilli. In Great Britain about 20–30 per cent. of herd samples are infected.   Experience has shown that *consumption of raw infected milk* is attended by a certain risk of contracting the disease, whereas consumption of the same milk after pasteurization or other effective heat treatment is harmless.   In London, where about 95 per cent. of the milk is heat-treated, and in the large cities of the United States where most of the milk is pasteurized, undulant fever is practically unknown. The cases that do occur are mostly among those who drink Certified or other types of raw milk, either at home or on a visit to the country.

Several careful studies made in institutions and small communities supplied with infected raw milk have shown that a considerable proportion of the population develop serum agglutinins, that a small proportion suffer from subclinical and clinical forms of undulant fever, while, in a larger proportion, the infection remains completely latent. Removal of the infected animals, or pasteurization of the milk supply, is followed by cessation of clinical illness and by a gradual disappearance of agglutinins from the sera of latently infected persons (see King and Caldwell 1929, Hasseltine and Knight 1931, Sasano, Caldwell and Medlar 1931, Dooley 1932, Johns, Campbell and Tennant 1932, Wilcox 1932, Carpenter and Boak 1933, Welch and Mickle 1933, Hall and Learmonth 1934, Cameron and Wells 1934, Stone and Bogen 1935).

It may be pointed out here that alimentary infection is almost always due to the consumption of raw milk or cream. Butter and cheese, except when made from untreated milk and consumed within a week, are probably inoffensive, since the organisms die out very rapidly as the result of lactic fermentation (Mazé and Césari 1931). Moreover, a large proportion of manufactured butter is made from pasteurized cream in which the organisms are destroyed (see Smith, J., 1934a, Pullinger 1935).

Contact infections are mainly occupational, occurring in towns among slaughterers, and in the country among the farming population. Since the latter class, in particular, is usually exposed to infection from raw milk, the parts played by the two sources of infection are very difficult to determine. In countries with a large agricultural population, such as Denmark, it follows that the incidence of undulant fever is greater in rural than in urban districts, whereas in countries such as our own, where about 80 per cent. of the population is concentrated in towns, the reverse holds true. Contact infection is mainly from cattle, but horses and even dogs may at times constitute the source of infection (Menzani 1932). In both town and country the brunt of the disease is generally borne by *adult males*. The incidence is usually highest in the 15–45 age group, and is two to three times as high in males as in females. The age and sex incidence in country districts seems readily understandable, because of the predominance of male workers in contact with cattle, but in towns it is more puzzling. There is some evidence that in towns latent infections are commoner in women than in men, but that overt infections are commoner in men than in women (Harrison and Wilson 1928). The suggestion is that the greater consumption of raw milk in females confers on them an immunity which is often lacking in males, so that when the latter are exposed to infection, they prove more susceptible. Much the same argument has been used by Henricsson (1932) to explain why, in Sweden, more cases occur in the town than the country, namely, that the rural becomes better immunized than the urban population as the result of more frequent exposure to infection. Some workers (Hardy *et al.* 1931) have found that in towns males and females are affected more evenly than in the country, but there are numerous other observations to show that even in towns the adult male population provides the bulk of the cases.

Laboratory infections, though less common than with *Br. melitensis*, are by no means infrequent, and probably occur through contamination of the abraded skin or the conjunctiva with infective material (see Meyer 1933). The incidence in veterinary surgeons seems to be definitely higher than in the general population, but the information available from different countries is rather conflicting (see Spengler 1929, Huddleson and Johnson 1930, Knoth 1930a, Makkawejsky and Karkadinowsky 1930, Thomsen 1932a, Wilson 1932b, Herrmann *et al.* 1934, Khaum and Liedl 1935). Quite a high proportion of those engaged in " cleansing " develop the peculiar skin rash to which allusion has already been made. Both infants and children suffer from the disease, but very much less frequently than adults.

(For general epidemiological studies and reviews of the disease, in addition to those already quoted, see Simpson and Fraizer 1929, Dalrymple-Champneys 1929, 1931, 1934, 1935 ; Darsin 1930, Wallace 1930, Atwood and Hasseltine 1930, Zeller 1931, Tebbutt and Marsh 1931, Cruickshank and Barbour 1931, Smith 1932a, Schittenhelm 1932, Hardy, Jordan and Borts 1932, Mackie 1933, Habs 1933b, 1935, Steyrer 1934, Meyer *et al.* 1934a, McNabb 1934, Report 1934, Giltner 1934, Beattie, Smith and Tulloch 1935, Wilson 1935.)

Undulant Fever due to Br. suis

Probably the first diagnosed case of this disease was that described by Keefer (1924) in 1922 in the United States, though it was some time before the identity of the causative organism was realized. Clinically and bacteriologically the disease is similar to undulant fever caused by the *melitensis* and *abortus* types. Like *Br. melitensis, Br. suis* can be demonstrated more frequently in the blood stream than *Br. abortus*—possibly because of its greater ease of cultivation.

Epidemiologically, this disease is very much less extensive than the types already described. It is essentially an occupational disease, occurring among slaughterers and packers who handle the infected carcasses of pigs. The studies of Hardy and his colleagues (1931, 1932), of Huddleson, Johnson, and Hamann (1933a), and of Heathman (1934) in the middle western states of North America, have shown that a small amount of overt and a large amount of latent infection occurs in these workers. The organism apparently gains access through the abraded skin. Adult males are almost solely affected (Hasseltine 1930). Occasionally *Br. suis* infects cattle, and milk-borne outbreaks of undulant fever, without any special occupational incidence, are likely to occur (see Beattie and Rice 1934, Horning 1935). Brucella infection of pigs is far less common than contagious abortion of cattle. In consequence undulant fever due to *Br. suis* has hitherto been restricted mainly to the middle west of North America, to Brazil, and to the Argentine.

Diagnosis of Undulant Fever

The occurrence of subclinical and atypical infections renders the clinical diagnosis of undulant fever peculiarly difficult, and all observers are agreed on the fact that large numbers of cases are missed. The final diagnosis can be made only by bacteriological examination. In practice it is well to regard every case of pyrexia of undiagnosed origin as possibly due to *Brucella* infection, and to bear this disease in mind during the investigation of acute and chronic inflammatory conditions in which the diagnosis remains doubtful. Help is sometimes afforded by a blood count, which usually shows a secondary anæmia, a mild leucopenia, and a relative lymphocytosis.

Blood Culture.—In the febrile stages of the disease, an attempt should be made to isolate the causative organism from the blood stream.

The patient's blood should be withdrawn while the temperature is elevated, and preferably during the rise of a pyrexial wave. It should be distributed in 5–10 c.c. quantities into two flasks containing 20–100 c.c. of glucose broth, serum broth, or liver extract broth. One of the flasks should be incubated aerobically, the other in an atmosphere in which 10 per cent. of the air has been replaced by CO_2. Subcultures should be made every 3–5 days on to a solid medium, and these should be incubated in the same atmosphere as the parent culture. Growth is often slow, and no culture should be discarded in less than 4–8 weeks. (For alternative methods of blood culture, see Elkeles and Fried 1932, Rainsford 1933, Hauptmann 1935a, Stewart *et al.* 1935.)

Though blood culture is positive in a high proportion of *melitensis* and *suis* infections, not more than 10–20 per cent. of *abortus* infections prove positive by this method. In *melitensis* infections the organism can often be isolated from the urine, provided repeated samples are examined (Kennedy 1905). Occasionally *Br. abortus* can be demonstrated in the bile (Amoss and Poston 1930, Leavell and Amoss 1931a), stools (Smith 1932b, Beattie *et al.* 1935) and tonsil (Carpenter and Boak 1932, Poelma and Pickens 1932).

Agglutination Test.—The most generally useful method is the agglutination test, first introduced by Wright and Smith in 1897.

Final dilutions of the serum should be put up ranging from 1/20–1/5120, and the tubes should be incubated for 18 hours in a 37° C. or 55° C. water bath. Though there is a considerable degree of cross-agglutination between *Br. abortus* and *Br. suis* on the one hand, and *Br. melitensis* on the other, it is advisable to use as agglutinating antigens strains corresponding to the prevailing type of infection. In countries such as Great Britain, Germany, Denmark, Sweden, Canada, and New Zealand, where practically all infections are due to the *abortus* type, this organism alone is necessary. Similarly in countries such as Malta, Corsica, Sicily, Southern Italy, Algeria, Tunis, Greece, and Palestine, where nearly all infections are due to the *melitensis* type, this organism suffices. But in countries or areas where two or three types of infecting organism are known to occur, such as France, Northern Italy, the United States, and parts of South America, it is advisable to use both a *melitensis* and an *abortus* antigen. Great attention must be paid to the preparation of the agglutinating suspension. Only strains that are absolutely smooth, as judged by the thermoagglutination and trypaflavine tests, should be used. Any given suspension should be made up from a number of strains. The organisms should be grown on liver extract or glycerol agar for 2–3 days, washed off with saline, and heated to 55° C. for 1 hour. The suspension should be standardized to match an opacity tube containing 1,000 million *Bact. coli* per c.c., and preserved with 0·2 per cent. formol or 0·5 per cent. phenol. Suspensions prepared in this way will generally remain satisfactory for 3 months, but the moment signs of commencing stringiness appear, they should be discarded. For survey work, where large numbers of sera have to be examined, the slide method of agglutination may be used (see Huddleson and Abell 1928, Huddleson 1932, Welch and Mickle 1933).

The interpretation of the agglutination test is not always easy, and demands a knowledge of the clinical history and the occupation of the patient. Very much the same considerations affect the interpretation of this test as of that used in the diagnosis of enteric fever, and the reader may well refer back to Chapter LXVI in which the relevant factors are discussed in some detail. The propositions we lay down must not be regarded as more than suggestions, applying particularly to this country. Each of them will necessarily be subject to exceptions. (1) A titre of 1/80 or less, in the absence of clinical symptoms, is indicative either of a latent *Brucella* infection, or of a past infection—not necessarily attended by definite disease. (2) A titre of 1/80 or over, in the absence of clinical symptoms or of a recent pyrexial attack, is suggestive of frequent infections, usually occurring in persons drinking large quantities of infected raw milk or exposed to contact with infected animals or carcasses. (3) A titre of 1/80 or over in the presence of pyrexia and other symptoms of disease, occurring in a person whose occupation or habits do not expose him to special risk, is very suggestive of active infection with a member of the *Brucella* group. In persons belonging to the occupational classes referred to, in whom a latent infection is not uncommon, a titre of 1/80 is too low to be of diagnostic significance. On the other hand, a titre of 1/1000 or over is rarely met with except as the result of an active infection, and may usually be regarded as evidence of undulant fever. (4) A titre of 1/20–1/80, in the presence of clinically undulant fever, may likewise be considered as practically diagnostic of this disease. (5) The complete absence of agglutinins from a patient's serum does not exclude the diagnosis of *Brucella* infection. Cases are on record in which a positive blood culture has been obtained in the presence of a negative agglutination reaction (see Gilbert and Dacey 1932, Heathman 1934). Agglutinins are generally present in a suggestive titre by the end of the 2nd week, and in frank cases of undulant fever they generally rise to a titre of 1/640 or over. After the attack is over they tend to fall fairly rapidly, and may sink to a low level within 3 months. There is evidence that in chronic cases they may fall even during the period of active infection, so that too much stress must not be laid on a negative agglutination reaction in patients whose pyrexia has lasted for some months.

Attention must be called to the not infrequent occurrence of a prozone, sometimes extending to even 1/640 in high-titre sera. For this reason a wide range of dilutions should always be put up (see Spencer 1930, Priestley 1931, Hirsch 1935).

Several observers have stated that the agglutinin titre to *Brucella* may be high in patients suffering from enteric fever, tuberculosis, and other febrile conditions. The evidence for this statement is not very satisfactory. Apart from the anamnestic reaction, which is not likely to account for more than a slight raising of the titre (see Amoia 1933), the most common cause of non-specific agglutination is the use of a suspension made from strains that are not absolutely smooth. Such strains are often agglutinated by normal serum, and apparently even more often by the sera of febrile patients. Their use in the past has been very common and has given rise to much confusion in the literature. Provided smooth strains only are used, it is justifiable to conclude that an elevated titre to *Brucella* is indicative of infection—latent, active, or past—with an organism of the *Brucella* group. (For recent references see Bayne-Jones 1930, Ranque and Senez 1932, Magliulo 1933, Morellini 1933, Sanfilippo 1933, Wilson 1930, 1934, Mohr 1935, Hauptmann 1935*b*.) We may add that there is no evidence that circulating agglutinins result from the alimentary absorption of milk containing antibodies (see Boak and Carpenter 1929, Peterson 1935).

The type of infecting organism may often be determined by use of the quantitative agglutinin absorption test, described in Chapter XXXI, carried out on the patient's serum (see Habs and Sievert 1935).

The *complement-fixation reaction* may be used to confirm the agglutination test, or in suggestive cases when the latter test is negative. Complement-fixing bodies are said to appear later in the serum than agglutinins, and to persist longer (see Sasano, Caldwell, and Medlar 1931, Morales-Otero and Monge 1932, Laun and Heide 1934). A precipitation reaction has also been described (Schlesmann 1932).

Brucellin Test.—In 1922 Burnet drew attention to an allergic skin test, performed by the intradermal inoculation into the arm of 0·05–0·1 c.c. of a filtrate of a 20-day-old broth culture of *Br. melitensis* (*melitin*) or *Br. abortus* (*abortin*). A positive reaction is characterized by the appearance in 6 hours of a slightly raised, sometimes tender, œdematous plaque, 2–6 cm. in diameter, distinguished in colour from the surrounding skin. The reaction may disappear within 48 hours, or a central nodule may develop lasting for several days. Pseudo-reactions generally appear rapidly, and disappear within 24 hours. We have no space for an adequate discussion of this test. Its interpretation and value are rendered difficult by the fact that numerous preparations of brucellin (abortin or melitin) are in use. The potency of these is subject to considerable variation, and some of them give rise to reactions in normal persons. Not until a standard preparation and standard dose are used, will it be possible to assess the value of this test, Generally speaking, however, the reaction resembles the tuberculin test in denoting the occurrence of infection, without giving any clear indication as to its activity. In undulant fever it may not become positive for some weeks, but subsequently it remains positive, often for years. Its chief value will probably be found to lie in the diagnosis of chronic cases with a negative agglutination reaction, and in survey work for detecting the prevalence of *Brucella* infection (see Giordano 1929, Simpson 1930, Levin 1930, Leavell and Amoss 1931b, Straube 1932, Dubois and Sollier 1932a, Yeckel and Chapman 1933, Rainsford 1933, Huddleson *et al.* 1933b, Heathman 1934, Arbatskaia and Moroskin 1934, Goldstein 1934, Sarnowiec 1934, Olin 1935, Favorite and Culp 1935, Taylor, Lisbonne and Vidal 1935, Chiucini 1935).

The difficulty of interpreting the skin reaction has led Huddleson, Johnson, and Hamann (1933b) to introduce the so-called *opsono-cytophagic test*. Briefly, this consists in incubating the citrated blood of the patient with a *Brucella* suspension for 30 minutes at 37° C., making films, and counting the number of organisms in 25 leucocytes. It is said that a weak or negative reaction in conjunction with a negative skin test is evidence of susceptibility, that a negative reaction in conjunction with a positive skin reaction points to active *Brucella* infection, and that a positive reaction to both tests is indicative of immunity. These conclusions must await confirmation (see also Meyer *et al.* 1934b, Veazie and Meyer 1935).

For *post-mortem diagnosis*, cultures should be made from the spleen, liver, kidney, and mesenteric glands, and incubated aerobically and in 10 per cent. CO_2.

Prophylaxis and Treatment

The prevention of the disease in human beings consists ideally in the complete abolition of contact, direct or indirect, with infected animals or their products. Where infection is chiefly milk-borne, this may be comparatively easy. Either complete avoidance of milk, or its consumption only after pasteurization, boiling or sterilization, has been found in practice to be highly effective. Where, however, infection occurs mainly by contact, prevention becomes much more difficult. Vaccination of specially exposed persons may be tried, but there is as yet little evidence to show how far this method is likely to be successful.

Treatment of the disease itself is very unsatisfactory, and in spite of all measures the fever may continue for months or even years. The oral administration of dyes has been recommended by Leavell, Poston, and Amoss (1930). Several workers have claimed success by the use of intramuscular inoculation of autogenous or stock *Brucella* vaccines, given in a dose sufficient to evoke a smart febrile reaction and repeated every 3–7 days (see Schilling *et al.* 1931, Poppe 1933, Bianchi 1934). Di Guglielmo (1933) is supported by numerous observers in his claim for the therapeutic efficacy of intravenous administration of a *Brucella* vaccine. After one or two doses of about a million organisms to test the patient's sensitivity, doses increasing from 5 to 100 million are given every 3–4 days, till the temperature finally falls. Usually 7 injections, lasting over a month, are said to be required to bring about this end. Much the same results appear to be obtainable by protein shock therapy. Huddleson and Johnson (1933) in the United States, and Debono

(1935) in Malta, have both reported favourably on the intramuscular inoculation of brucellin. As with vaccine treatment, a dose sufficient to arouse a smart febrile reaction is chosen, and repeated every 3 or 4 days. Similar success is claimed by Montel (1932, 1933) for a formolized non-toxic preparation of brucellin. Serum treatment has been advocated (Hilgermann 1935), but judged by animal experiments, its efficacy is doubtful (Mitchell *et al.* 1935).

BRUCELLA INFECTION OF SHEEP AND GOATS

Reference has already been made, under the section dealing with undulant fever due to *Br. melitensis*, to infections of sheep and goats with this organism, and to the diagnosis of the disease by examination of the blood serum and milk serum for agglutinins. The disease exists particularly in countries along the Mediterranean littoral, in South Africa, and in some parts, notably Arizona, of the United States. When first introduced into a herd, particularly during pregnancy, infection is frequently followed by a considerable number of abortions, but unless fresh animals are added, it dies down, and subsequent abortions are uncommon. The infection, however, usually becomes chronic, and may persist for months or years. In this stage it is often difficult to diagnose. The agglutination reaction may be negative. Some help is afforded by the intradermal melitin test. A suitable preparation, preferably a bacterial extract such as that described by Huddleson and Johnson (1933) or Taylor, Lisbonne, and Vidal (1935), is inoculated into one of the skin folds between the base of the tail and the margin of the anus. Readings are made after 24 and 48 hours. A positive reaction is characterized by œdema. Generally speaking, it may be said that a positive skin test indicates that the animal has been or is infected, while a positive agglutination test indicates that the infection is active. At post-mortem examination the organisms can be isolated most easily from the udder and the supramammary lymphatic glands. During life the organisms are often excreted in enormous numbers in the milk and the urine, while after abortion the vaginal discharge may remain highly infective for some days. Infection probably occurs mainly by contamination of the skin and mucosæ, though possibly the alimentary route may play some part.

Experimentally, the disease can be reproduced in both sheep and goats by feeding and by cutaneous, subcutaneous, intravenous, and intraperitoneal inoculation with virulent cultures of *Br. melitensis*. The disease so produced is often afebrile and, in spite of a septicæmia, symptoms may be lacking. Many of the animals, however, are unthrifty ; their coats become thin ; their weight diminishes ; and a short hacking cough develops. Mastitis and arthritis are not uncommon ; male animals may suffer from orchitis, while females, if infected during pregnancy, may abort. Death rarely occurs. Bacteriologically, the organisms are found in the blood for a variable time after infection. They then disappear, first from the peripheral blood and most of the viscera, then from the spleen and kidneys, then from the superficial lymph glands, and last of all from the mammary glands. The milk does not usually become infective for 2–3 months after inoculation or feeding. Agglutinins, sometimes reaching a high titre, are demonstrable in the blood serum, usually within a fortnight or so of infection (see Shaw 1906, Horrocks and Kennedy 1906, Zammit 1906, Eyre *et al.* 1907).

Experimentally, disease can also be produced in sheep and goats by *Br. abortus*, though natural infections with this organism seem to be rare. Bang (1897) induced abortion in a pregnant ewe by intravaginal injection of a pure culture of *Br. abortus*. Intravenous inoculation gave rise to uterine inflammation. Zwick (1910) found that both feeding and intravenous inoculation were successful in establishing infection in sheep. Infected ewes may go to term, yet the specific organisms may be found in large numbers in the vaginal discharge. Intravenous inoculation of *Br. abortus* into goats may give rise to abortion (Reinhardt and Gauss 1915). Zwick and Krage (1913) found that goats injected subcutaneously on intravenously might excrete the organism in their milk 24 hours later; the excretion was sometimes maintained for 8 weeks or more. Goats are also susceptible to conjunctival infection with *Br. abortus* (van der Hoeden 1933).

The control of the disease is beset with difficulties of an economic and social nature. Prophylactic vaccination, though recommended by Zammitt and Debono (1933), has so far not proved very successful. The ideal method is a policy of eradication (see p. 1354). All animals should be subjected to an agglutination and a skin test, positive reactors should be slaughtered, and breeding should be carried out only from apparently uninfected animals. Herd tests should be made at 3-monthly intervals till no further reactors appear. If this policy is impracticable, the spread of infection should be limited as far as possible by elimination of all animals excreting the organism in the milk, and by the provision of separate boxes at the time of lambing or abortion. (For references to the general epizootiology and bacteriology of the disease see Report 1905–07, Segni 1931, Ananiadés and Miaoulis 1931, Dubois and Sollier 1932*b*, Pérès 1934, Moreno 1934, Meyer and Eddie 1935.)

It may be noted that abortion of sheep and goats is sometimes due to infection with *Bact. abortus-ovis*, a member of the Salmonella group (see Chapter XXVII).

CONTAGIOUS ABORTION IN CATTLE

Avortement épizoötique (French). *Seuchenhaftes Verwerfen* (German).

Contagious abortion in cattle is an infectious disease, due in the majority of cases to *Br. abortus* of Bang, and characterized by inflammatory changes of the uterine mucosa and fœtal membranes, resulting as a rule in the premature expulsion of the fœtus. Though regarded as contagious by Hutrel d'Arboval (1826) and Youatt (1834), (see Hutyra and Marek 1922), its infective nature was not shown definitely till 1878, when Lehnert transmitted the disease by intravaginal inoculation of pregnant cows with the vaginal discharge and placental tissue of aborting animals. In 1897 Bang, working with Stribolt, demonstrated microscopically a small Gram-negative bacillus in the uterine exudate of a cow with impending abortion, and succeeded in isolating it in pure culture. The intravaginal injection of this organism into two pregnant cows gave rise to abortion, and from the uterine exudate the organism was recovered in each case. Bang's work was confirmed by Preisz (1903) and Nowak (1908) on the Continent, by M'Fadyean and Stockman (1909) in this country, and by MacNeal and Kerr (1910) in America.

Epidemiology and Bacteriology

The disease is widespread throughout Europe, the United States of America, and most other countries of the world where there is a large cattle population. Its exact frequency is difficult to ascertain, but in this country Priestley (1934) estimates that 20 per cent. of the cows are infected. Similar high estimates have also been made for certain areas in the United States (Cotton 1931, Thomson 1932,

Birch 1934). Large herds are more often infected than small. On account of the heavy loss from abortions, the frequent subsequent sterility of the animals, and the diminution in the milk yield, it is economically one of the most important diseases affecting cattle. The fact, moreover, that infection may be transmitted to man renders the disease of public health interest.

Though clearly it is only pregnant animals that can display the typical symptom of abortion, infection may be conveyed by natural channels to cattle of any age and either sex. There is no distinct seasonal incidence. The commonest time for abortion to occur is from the 5th to the 8th month of pregnancy ; 35·4 per cent. of cases occur in the 7th month alone (Wall 1911). Judged from experimental work, the incubation period is variable ; according to Mohler and Traum (1911) it may last from 1 to 33 weeks.

Introduced into a fresh herd the disease may spread rapidly, assuming epidemic proportions. Provided that no new animals are imported, it loses its initial severity, passing into an endemic state in which, if no preventive measures are taken, it remains for some years. A pregnant animal becoming infected for the first time generally aborts at an early stage ; at its next pregnancy abortion occurs either not at all, or not till a later period ; and though abortion may be repeated on a third occasion it is much commoner for the calf to be delivered at full term. Bang (1897) reports that of 83 cows only 30 aborted in 2 successive years, and only 6 three times in succession. From this it may be gathered that an immunity is acquired which is usually sufficient to protect the animal against further attacks of the disease.

The bacillus may, however, remain alive in the tissues of the cow for a considerable length of time. Bang (1897) found it in the uterus of a cow 9 months after the foetus had died and become mummified. As a rule the uterus frees itself quickly, and the specific organism takes refuge in the udder and often in the supra-mammary and pelvic lymphatic glands, where it may persist for months or even years (see Doyle 1935). Under favourable conditions it may be demonstrated in the blood stream, and occasionally in the urine and faeces (see Fitch, Bishop, and Boyd 1932c). Its frequency in the circulating blood is a little doubtful. Soule (1930) isolated it from about 10 per cent. of cows containing serum agglutinins, and Lübke, in a much smaller series, from 22 per cent. Other workers, on the contrary, have failed to find it at all, or have found it in only a small proportion of animals (Fitch et al. 1932a, Krüger 1932, Doyle 1935, and numerous others). Probably the stage of the disease is important, and positive cultures are more likely in the early acute than the late chronic stage. Infection occurring in non-pregnant animals, particularly before sexual maturity is reached, may remain latent or may actually retrogress. In cows the organism frequently settles in the udder ; abortion may or may not occur at the next pregnancy. In calves and young heifers there is some evidence that the organism disappears completely from the tissues, but further observations are required, particularly to ascertain whether such animals develop any substantial degree of immunity. In the udder *Br. abortus* gives rise to small subacute or chronic inflammatory foci situated in the alveoli, the interalveolar connective tissue, and along the lactiferous ducts (Runnels and Huddleson 1925). The lesions are too small to be detectable by clinical examination.

From the udder the organisms are excreted in the *milk*. This important fact was first demonstrated by Schroeder and Cotton in 1911. Karsten (1932) found that the proportion of aborting cows in which the milk was subsequently shown to be infected varied on different farms from 24 to 70 per cent., while in infected herds 19–33 per cent. of cows that did not abort excreted the organisms in their milk. Sheather (1923) observed that 34 per cent. of cows giving a positive blood serum agglutination reaction were yielding infected milk. Numerous similar observations have been made by different workers. For example, Pröscholdt (1932) found that 53 per cent. of cows with a blood serum agglutinin titre of 1/100 or over were excreting *Br. abortus* in the milk. The same author observed that, of 208 cows whose milk was infected, 145 had aborted, while 63 had calved normally. Lerche (1931) gives very similar figures. The organisms may appear in the milk within 1 or 2 days of abortion, and are usually demonstrable within a week, though in some animals as long as 5 months may elapse before excretion commences (Wall 1930). Many cows cease excreting the organism after a few weeks, but others may remain infected for a year or two, or even permanently. In Pröscholdt's series, out of 145 aborting animals whose milk was infected, 22 had aborted 1–2 years previously. The excretion is irregular and often intermittent. The number of organisms present fluctuates from day to day. It is usually highest at the commencement of lactation, and gradually falls. Except in the first week or two of lactation, when there may be as many as 200,000 per c.c., it is uncommon for the milk on withdrawal to contain more than 30,000 per c.c. (Bang and Bendixen 1932a, Stockmayer 1936) ; the usual number is 10–2000 per c.c. (Karsten 1932). Infection is often confined to one or two quarters of the udder. The hind-quarters are more often affected than the fore, and the right hind-quarter seems to be affected more often than the left (Bang and Bendixen 1931, Thompson 1934, Doyle 1935).

Though the organism commonly responsible for the disease is *Br. abortus*, numerous observations have shown that cattle in close contact with infected goats or sheep may become infected with *Br. melitensis* (see Taylor, Vidal, and Roman 1934, Benussi 1935). The infection seems to be localized mainly in the udder, and abortion is uncommon. Similarly in large hog-raising districts, cattle may become infected with *Br. suis* and excrete this organism in the milk (see Beattie and Rice, 1934, Molinelli and Ithurrat 1934).

Mode of Infection and Experimental Reproduction of the Disease.—There has been a long dispute over the commonest mode of infection. Cattle are so easy to infect experimentally, not only by direct inoculation into the tissues, but also by the natural passages, that it is very difficult to decide on the route usually followed in the natural spread of disease. The three main portals are :

(1) THE MOUTH.—Bang (1906) and others have shown that it is possible to reproduce the disease in pregnant heifers and cows by feeding them with infective material, and have therefore suggested that infection probably occurs through contaminated fodder. It is known that the uterine exudate which is voided at the time of the abortion is extremely infective, that the bacilli may remain alive in it for some time—for 7 months if kept in the ice-chest (Bang 1897)—and that unless strict isolation of the cows is practised, there is ample opportunity for contamination of the pasture and other food-material. It must also be remembered that as the milk of aborting cows is frequently infective, this may serve as a further source of virus.

(2) THE VAGINA.—In his original experiments Bang (1897) demonstrated the possibility of infecting pregnant cows by intravaginal inoculation of pure cultures. This has been confirmed frequently (Report 1909, M'Fadyean *et al.* 1913, Seddon 1919). It seems, therefore, not improbable that contamination of the vagina with infected soil or litter may

be responsible for naturally acquired infection. A second method by which vaginal infection may occur is sexual intercourse. Bulls may be infected by subpreputial injection of pure cultures (M'Fadyean *et al.* 1913). Injected intravenously, the organisms may lodge in the testicles and be excreted in the seminal fluid (Seddon 1919). Experimentally these facts are sufficient to indicate that the bull may play an active part in conveying the disease to cows. There is still stronger evidence from the epidemiological side, sufficient without doubt to incriminate it (Bang 1897). Moreover the agglutination test shows that bulls are not infrequently infected by *Br. abortus* ; Holth (1911) found agglutinins in the blood of 3 out of 28 bulls which he examined.

(3) THE SKIN AND CONJUNCTIVA.—Attention has been drawn to these routes of infection by Bang (1931), Bang and Bendixen (1932b), Cotton and Buck (1932), and Cotton, Buck and Smith (1933a). Experimentally it has been found possible to infect animals fairly readily with *Br. abortus* by means of an infected compress left for a variable length of time in contact with the abraded, or even intact, skin. Infection has also followed simple conjunctival instillation of an *abortus* suspension.

Which of these three routes is the most important in practice, we have at present no exact means of telling. The Departmental Committee set up by the Board of Agriculture to investigate the disease considered that feeding was the most common method, that vaginal infection held second place, while sexual infection probably played quite an insignificant part. Contamination of mucosal and skin surfaces must almost certainly be responsible at times for infection, but on the whole the prevalent opinion still seems to favour the alimentary route (see Mieszner 1931). Considering the frequency with which *Br. abortus* is excreted in the milk, and the ease with which animals can be infected by the udder (Schmidt 1932), it seems probable that infection must at times be transmitted from infected to normal cows at the actual time of milking. Unless the normal animals are milked first, contaminated milk must be rubbed into the teats, thus giving the organisms an opportunity to penetrate the skin or to enter the teat canal. There is still a wide field open for investigation. *The aim must be, not to ascertain whether a given route of infection is ever taken under natural conditions, but what the frequency distribution of the possible routes of infection really is.* Exact knowledge of this type may prove of immense service in controlling the spread of infection in the field.

That the experimental reproduction of the disease can be readily accomplished by oral and parenteral inoculation was shown by the earlier workers. The interest of these experiments is now centring on the effect produced at different stages in the animal's life history, mainly with a view to the possible exploitation of living vaccines. It is abundantly clear that inoculation during pregnancy is frequently followed by abortion, and by permanent infection of the udder and lymphatic system, but it is not so clear what happens when infection is induced in the non-pregnant state, particularly in young animals. Lübke (1935), on the basis of limited observations, regards *abortus* infection of cattle as primarily a disease of the reticulo-endothelial system, capable of establishing itself at any age. Infection of the uterus and udder, in his view, merely occurs secondarily as the result of extreme hyperæmia of these organs. Other workers regard the disease as primarily an affection of the reproductive system. The difference is of importance. If Lübke is right, immunization during calfhood with a living vaccine may be possible. If he is wrong, and *Br. abortus* is unable to establish itself in the tissues of the young animal, then hopes of natural immunization or of producing an effective immunity with a living vaccine during calfhood are very much slenderer. Experimental observations are very much needed on the location and degree of persistence of *Br. abortus* in the tissues during early life.

We may add that cattle may be infected, not only with *Br. abortus*, but also with *Br. melitensis* and *Br. suis*. These organisms settle readily in the udder, but less frequently give rise to abortion (see Zeller and Beller 1934, Thomsen 1934). Provided freshly isolated smooth strains are used, *Br. abortus* from the blood of human patients suffering from undulant fever seems to be fully virulent for young heifers (Birch and Gilman 1935). There is no satisfactory evidence that *abortus* strains of human and bovine origin differ in virulence for man or animals, though few direct observations, with the necessary precautions, have yet been made on this point.

Diagnosis

In the yellow or dark-brown mucoid exudate found between the uterine mucosa and the chorion, large numbers of *Br. abortus* may be demonstrated microscopically, aggregated into clumps within the polymorphonuclear cells. The organism may likewise be seen in smears made from the gastro-intestinal contents of the fœtus. Provided the material sent for examination is fresh and uncontaminated, a provisional diagnosis may often be made microscopically ; as a rule, however, cultural or inoculation methods are required.

Cultivation.—The organism is best grown by seeding glycerine, or liver, agar slopes with the uterine exudate, or with the stomach contents of the fœtus, and incubating them in an atmosphere of air containing 5–10 per cent. of added CO_2 (Smith 1926, Huddleson *et al.* 1927). (See Chapter XXXI.) If uncontaminated, the organisms will form characteristic lenticular colonies in the course of 2 or 3 days (Fig. 153, p. 636). Their specificity should be confirmed by agglutination. The bacilli are sometimes found in the blood and in the liver of the fœtus, but less abundantly than in the stomach. If the material is not pure, it is best to resort immediately to guinea-pig inoculation. The material is ground up in Ringer's solution, and 0·5 c.c. injected intramuscularly into two or three guinea-pigs. The animals are killed after 4–8 weeks, the blood is examined for agglutinins, and cultures are made from the sublumbar glands and the spleen (see " Milk " below). At post-mortem examination of slaughtered animals the organisms are most likely to be found in the udder, and in the supramammary, iliac, and pharyngeal glands. They may be sought for by direct culture and by guinea-pig inoculation (see Doyle 1935). Any obvious lesions, such as hygroma of the knee (v. d. Hoeden 1932*a*), should also be examined.

Agglutination Reaction.—In practice this is the most widely used method of diagnosis. Although the agglutination test in cattle does not differ in principle from that in man, it is necessary to consider separately its interpretation in relation to the titre that may be observed.

The test may be carried out by the tube or the slide method (for technique, and preparation of antigens, see Huddleson and Abell 1928, Huddleson 1932, Welch and Mickle 1933, Fitch and Donham 1933, Donham and Fitch 1934*a*, *b*, 1935, Welch and Marsh 1935). Final serum dilutions of 1/10–1/2560 should be put up. Intermediate zone phenomena are frequently encountered (see Priestley 1931).

The interpretation of this test is often difficult, and is not rendered any easier by the fact that, owing to differences in technique, the titres of different workers may not be strictly comparable.

Calves, even those born of infected mothers, give a negative serum reaction at birth.

If, however, they are allowed to suck infected dams within the first 24 hours of life, agglutinins become demonstrable in their serum within about 2 hours. This appears to be due to the absorption through the alimentary tract of antibodies present in the colostrum. Calves passively immunized in this way lose their agglutinins very rapidly (McAlpine and Rettger 1925). Even calves that are actively infected and develop agglutinins some time after birth appear to lose them within 6 months, unless reinfection occurs (Thorp and Graham 1933).

In an animal that is infected during pregnancy the titre generally rises before abortion to 1/200–1/1000 or over. During the following 6 months it tends to fall. If the cow becomes a chronic carrier, the titre usually remains fairly high. About 80 per cent. of cows with a persistent titre of 1/200 or over are found to be excreting *Br. abortus* in the milk, while a titre of 1/1000 or over is almost diagnostic of udder infection. If animals are followed for any considerable length of time, the agglutinin titre of positive reactors will often be found to decline. This is particularly true of low reactors. Damon (1932), for example, who observed a herd with a mean complement of 225–250 animals over a period of 4 years, found that 27·7 per cent. of animals reacting at 1/25, 17 per cent. of those reacting at 1/50, and 5 per cent. of those reacting at 1/100 or over lost their agglutinins permanently (see also Hadley and Welsh 1931). Huddleson and Smith (1931), however, found that, of a total of 247 animals reacting at 1/25 or over, and followed up for a period of 1–8 years, only 4 became permanently negative. Animals that abort usually have a considerably higher titre than non-aborting animals. A few animals may fail to show any agglutinins at the time of abortion, and for a few days afterwards ; most of these become positive within 2–3 weeks, but there is some evidence that others may fail completely to develop agglutinins. Animals may certainly excrete *Br. abortus* in the milk and yet fail to show agglutinins in the blood serum or whey (Karsten 1932).

The interpretation of a single test is often difficult, and depends on whether infection is known to be present in the herd. Many workers regard a titre of 1/20 or 1/25 as strongly suggestive of infection, while others pay little or no attention to a titre of less than 1/100. Our own view is that a titre of 1/25 cannot be disregarded, particularly if occurring in an infected herd. The only satisfactory method, however, is to make monthly tests on all suspicious animals, so as to detect as soon as possible those that become definitely positive. It must always be remembered that, while a positive test is a practically certain indication of infection, a doubtful or negative test cannot be held to exclude infection. (For interpretation of reaction see also Zwick 1910, Grinstadt 1910, Wall 1911, M'Fadyean and Stockman 1912, Seddon 1919, Smillie, Little and Florence 1919, Mathews 1924, Jordan and McBroom 1932, White *et al.* 1933.)

Complement-Fixation Reaction.—The complement-fixation test gives results very similar to those of the agglutination test. Mohler and Traum (1911), who examined 400 sera by both methods, found close agreement between them ; in only five instances were the results at variance. Similar results were recorded by Wall (1911), Reinhardt and Gauss (1915), Zwick (1910), and others. Mitchell (1929) considers that both tests are desirable, while Lentz (1932) prefers the complement-fixation test. Holth (1911) demonstrated the value of the complement-fixation test in cases of abortion in which the products obtainable for examination were badly contaminated ; if the placenta is ground up in saline, heated to boiling-point and filtered, it can be used as an antigen.

The Abortin Reaction.—Abortin is a substance analogous to tuberculin, which was introduced by M'Fadyean and Stockman (1909) in an attempt to elaborate a diagnostic test based on the hypersensitiveness of infected animals. It is prepared from a 4 to 6 weeks' glucose glycerine broth culture, which is sterilized at 99° C. for 2 hours, filtered through a Berkefeld candle, evaporated to 1/10 of its bulk, and preserved with 0·5 per cent. phenol. The dark syrupy liquid thus obtained is suitably diluted before use, and injected subcutaneously. In a positive reaction the temperature rises to 104–106° F. As a method of diagnosis, this original abortin did not find favour ; the authors themselves after extensive trials were disappointed with it (Stockman 1914). Nor did Holtum's (1928) heat-killed suspension of *abortus* in phenolized saline meet with success. Probably a bacillary extract, such as that prepared by Huddleson and Johnson (1933) or Taylor, Lisbonne, and Vidal (1935) might be found satisfactory. Further observations are badly needed on the use of this test, preferably carried out by the intracutaneous inoculation of abortin into the caudal fold. A few promising reports of the test have been made of recent years (Dubois and Brune 1933, Dubois 1934, Rossi and Vigel 1934, Franco and Pezzi 1935), and it might prove valuable in the detection of agglutinin-negative animals. Mirri (1935) recommends a palpebral test.

Demonstration of Br. abortus in Milk.—Examination for the presence of *Br. abortus* in milk may be conducted by cultural or by animal inoculation methods.

Cultivation.—Cultural methods are satisfactory only with milk samples from individual cows collected under relatively aseptic conditions. Separate quarter samples should be taken, and either kept refrigerated, or preserved with 0·5–1·0 per cent. boric acid, till the time of examination. The whole milk, the gravity cream, or the deposit from high-speed centrifugation should be streaked on to a number of plates of liver extract agar, or 2 per cent. glycerol agar containing 10–15 per cent. of ox serum. Contaminating organisms may be partly suppressed by the addition to the medium of gentian violet and malachite green. The exact concentrations of these dyes vary according to their source of origin ; usually a final concentration of 1/100,000 to 1/200,000 is satisfactory. The plates should be incubated in 5–10 per cent. CO_2, and examined at intervals for ten days (see Huddleson *et al.* 1927, Hasley 1930, Traum and Henry 1930, Karsten 1932, Pröscholdt 1932, Karsten and Bischoff 1933, 1934, Stockmayer 1933*a*, 1935).

Animal Inoculation.—If the animal method is chosen, it is advisable to inoculate a mixture, composed of 2 c.c. of gravity cream and the deposit from 100 c.c. of milk after high-speed centrifugation, intramuscularly into the hind leg of each of two guinea-pigs. Alternatively 4 c.c. of whole milk may be injected, 2 c.c. into each thigh. The animals should be killed about 6 weeks later. At post-mortem examination the femoral and sublumbar glands will be enlarged and pale ; the spleen may be enlarged, its surface slightly irregular, and a few small greyish-yellow necrotic foci may be present. The liver may show two or three tiny necrotic foci. The macroscopic lesions are often inconspicuous, and must on no account be relied upon for diagnosis. The blood serum should be tested for agglutinins ; a titre of 1/25 or over is highly suggestive of infection. Cultures should be made from the sublumbar glands and spleen, and all suspicious organisms identified by agglutination and other methods. In not all animals containing serum agglutinins is it possible to isolate the organisms from the tissues. On the other hand, it is uncommon to isolate them in the absence of a positive agglutination reaction. Individual guinea-pigs vary considerably in their susceptibility to *Br. abortus*, and it is common to obtain positive results in one animal and negative in the other (see Smith 1932*b*, Plate 1934*a*). If tubercle bacilli are present in the milk simultaneously with *Br. abortus*, the guinea-pig will suffer from a double infection. The diagnosis of tuberculosis can be made on the basis of the macroscopic lesions and the demonstration of acid-fast bacilli in the organs. The diagnosis of *abortus* infection can be made on the basis of the agglutination reaction and the cultivation of the organisms from the tissues.

All workers are agreed that the animal inoculation method is more satisfactory for the demonstration of *Br. abortus* in milk than the direct cultural method. Plate (1934*b*) found that 90 per cent. of infected samples were positive by the animal and only 50 per cent. by the cultural method. Similarly Karsten and Bischoff (1934), who examined 466 milks by both methods, obtained 184 positive results by the guinea-pig and 101 by the cultural method. It is not uncommon to obtain occasional positive results by culture, when the animal inoculation results are negative, so that it is advisable to use both methods. In mixed milk, or in milk of single animals that has not been drawn aseptically and kept cold, the animal inoculation method is the only suitable means of demonstrating *Br. abortus.*

Serological Examination of Milk.—Indirect evidence of infection of the milk may be obtained by examination of the whey for agglutinins or complement-fixing bodies. The whey may be obtained by adding 1 drop of rennet to 5 c.c. of skim milk, incubating at 58° C. for 30 minutes, breaking up the clot, and centrifuging. Alternatively 5 c.c. of carbon tetrachloride may be added to 10 c.c. of milk, together with a small quantity of rennet. The milk is corked, and shaken for several minutes till the fat is extracted. It is then incubated for 1 hour, and centrifuged (Hall and Learmonth 1933). The advantage of 58° C. for incubation is that it destroys any complement present. The agglutination test is carried out in the usual way. Control tests must be put up, since non-specific reactions may occur. A whey agglutinin titre of 1/80 or over affords a high probability that the udder is infected and that *Br. abortus* is being excreted in the milk. The higher the titre, the more probable this is. Similarly, fixation of complement with 0·05 c.c. of whey is strongly suggestive of milk infection.

Examination of the whey for antibodies is sometimes used as a method of detecting infection of the animal with *Br. abortus.* Except as a preliminary means of investigation, this is unsatisfactory, because only about 20–80 per cent. of animals containing blood serum agglutinins give a positive whey reaction. (For references to use and interpretation of whey test, see M'Fadyean and Stockman 1909, Seddon 1915, Robinson 1919, Sheather 1923, Graham and Thorp 1930, Gilman 1930, Hasley 1931, Norton and Pless 1931, Berge and Ekrem 1932, 1934, Pröscholdt 1932, Karsten 1932, Karsten and Bischoff 1933, 1934, 1935, Plate 1934*a*, *b*, Caldwell, Parker, and Medlar 1934, Molinelli and Ithurrat 1934, 1935, Smith 1934*a*, *b*, van Oyen 1934.)

Prophylaxis and Treatment

At the time of abortion the uterine discharge is highly infectious ; the usual measures must therefore be taken for isolation of the animal, and subsequent disinfection of its stall. The fœtus and membranes should be burned, or buried in lime. Irrigation of the cow's vagina should be practised with an antiseptic solution for some days or weeks till all discharge has ceased, and not till some considerable time has elapsed since the complete cessation of the discharge should the cow be taken to the bull. If a bull has served an animal that has recently aborted, it is well to irrigate its penis and preputial sheath with an antiseptic solution, in order to prevent active infection of the bull, or passive carriage of the organism to another cow. Calves born of infected cows are better brought up on milk from another animal.

Eradication of Contagious Abortion.—The ideal policy is the complete eradication of infection. Various methods are recommended for doing this. The general principle consists in the detection of infected animals by the agglutination or complement-fixation reaction, the segregation or sale of positive reactors, and the building-up of a clean, non-infected herd. The degree of success attending this policy varies with a number of factors. With a small or medium-sized herd, particularly if self-contained and protected against infection from water, manure, and other animals, with provision of calving boxes, and re-testing of non-reactors every

2 months so as to eliminate all animals as soon as they become positive, it is often possible to eradicate the infection entirely and to maintain a healthy herd for several years. On the other hand, with very large herds, particularly if not self-contained, with flying herds, with farms on which adequate accommodation for segregation of infected, and quarantine of newly imported, animals is impossible, and with imperfect control over infection from other sources, the results are often disappointing. Generally speaking, if the conditions are favourable, and if the disease is not at the height of its activity, this policy should be adopted, since its success is followed by the improved general health of the herd, better and more regular breeding, and an increased milk supply. Success, however, cannot be guaranteed. One of the greatest problems at the moment is presented by the infected non-reactor, which may abort, or excrete *Br. abortus* in the milk, and so contaminate the other animals in the herd (see Bang 1906, M'Fadyean 1921, 1924, Giltner 1924, Thomsen 1928, Zeller 1931, Henricsson 1932, Kitselman 1932, Newsom and Cross 1932, Clark 1932, Mitchell *et al.* 1933, Fritz and Barnes 1933, Birch 1934, Birch *et al.* 1934, van Oyen 1934, Report 1935).

Vaccination.—In 1906 Bang reported that a certain amount of protection could be conferred on animals by intravenous injection of living *Br. abortus* some weeks before copulation. Dead bacilli were found to be valueless in this respect. Hopeful results were likewise obtained with living organisms by M'Fadyean and Stockman in 1909. Five years later Stockman (1914) reported the results of vaccination experiments on non-pregnant cattle with a living culture injected subcutaneously. In one herd of 201 animals injected 95·1 per cent. subsequently calved in the normal way, whereas of 243 controls only 79 per cent. did so. In two other herds the results were similar : 92·5 per cent. for vaccinated, 72·5 per cent. for control animals ; 93·5 per cent. for vaccinated and 62 per cent. for control animals. Experiments in which a heat-killed vaccine was used gave entirely negative results.

Since these early experiments there has been a considerable output of papers on the subject of vaccination. In very few instances has any serious attempt been made to include a proper control group, and the recorded results are therefore very difficult to interpret. There is a fairly general consensus of opinion that living vaccines, administered before, or in the very early stage of, pregnancy, do protect to some extent against actual abortion, and that dead vaccines are very much less effective in this respect. Vaccination, however, does not appear to diminish the *carrier rate* or to prevent the organisms being excreted in the milk, and therefore does not make this safe for human consumption. Moreover, living vaccines must be regarded as potentially dangerous for human beings (Merliac and Lisbonne 1936). They should never be used in clean herds. The real value of vaccination is difficult to assess. At the moment it is probably wisest to pursue the eradication policy whenever possible, and to reserve vaccination for herds in which more than 30 per cent. of the animals are infected. Vaccination, of course, interferes with the interpretation of the agglutination reaction, and should not therefore be undertaken in herds in which an eradication programme is likely to be introduced in the near future (see Smith and Little 1926, Zwick 1930, 1931, Karsten 1931, 1933, Schumann 1931, Jensen 1931, Delez 1932, Andrews 1932, Thomsen 1932*b*, Cotton 1932, Cotton and Buck 1934, Cotton, Buck and Smith 1933*b*, 1934, Wall 1933, M'Fadyean 1933, Zeller and Stockmayer 1935).

Experiments on guinea-pigs and mice with heat-killed organisms afford some evidence that vaccination improves the clearing mechanism of the body, and diminishes the residual infection of the tissues (Hagan 1922, Helms 1932, Guarna 1935). Whether by attention to antigenic structure, dosage, and time of vaccination, it is possible by dead vaccines to confer a significant increase of resistance on animals in the field is a question that is at present unanswerable.

BRUCELLA INFECTION OF SWINE

This disease has only recently been recognized, and is of limited distribution. It first attracted serious attention in the large hog-raising districts of the middle western States of North America. According to the observations of Boak and Carpenter (1930), Feldman and Olson (1934), and McNutt (1935) about 2 per cent. of animals destined for the abattoirs are infected in this area. Apart from Denmark, in which an epizoötic occurred during the years 1929–32, involving 240 herds, Europe seems to have suffered but little (Thomsen 1931, 1934, Knoth 1930*b*). A focus of infection has been found in White Russia (Makkawejski *et al.* 1933). The disease appears to be not uncommon in Brazil (see Neiva 1934) and the Argentine. It has been observed in New South Wales (King 1934). In this country it has not so far been detected (see Doyle 1934).

Bacteriologically, all outbreaks appear to have been due to *Br. suis*, and all of them, with the exception of the Danish epizoötic, to the American type (see Chapter **XXXI**), though complete information has not always been available on this point. The disease is essentially an infection of the reticulo-endothelial system, with the production of inflammatory disturbances in the glands, joints, and reproductive organs. Contrary to contagious abortion of cattle, in which the females are chiefly affected, the disease in swine attacks mainly the *boars*. Abortion, though it does occur, is much less frequent than in cattle. Abscess formation is met with in the submaxillary, cervical, inguinal, and popliteal lymph glands. The joints of the hind legs, particularly the knee and hock, are frequently affected ; they are swollen, painful, frequently contain fluid, and sometimes ankylose. Epididymo-orchitis is very common. In Makkewejski's series, no fewer than 269 out of 786 boars showed orchitis, usually bilateral. The affected testicles are sometimes of enormous size, reaching $6\frac{1}{2}$ lb. in weight, and purulent foci, which may undergo calcification, are not infrequent. Multiple foci may also be present in the vesiculæ seminales. *Br. suis* may, however, often be demonstrated in the tissues in the absence of macroscopic pathological changes.

In *sows* a condition for which Thomsen (1934) suggests the name " miliary brucellosis of the uterus " is frequently met with. The interior of the uterus is studded with small yellowish-white nodules located in the deeper layer of the mucosa and projecting slightly above the surface.

The disease can be readily reproduced by feeding and by conjunctival inoculation. According to Stockmayer (1933*b*), pigs are susceptible to *Br. abortus* as well as to *Br. suis*, though no outbreaks due to *Br. abortus* have yet been recorded in the field. Thomsen believes that natural infection is spread to a considerable extent by copulation, though this of course will account only for transmission of the disease to sows. Infection of the conjunctiva by urine, and alimentary infection probably play a part. Sucking pigs are readily infected. It is possible that infection occurs through the milk of the mother, though invasion of the udder is uncommon.

In the field, *diagnosis* is best made by the agglutination and complement-fixation tests on the blood serum. A titre of 1/100 is regarded as definitely positive, 1/50 as strongly suggestive, and 1/25 as doubtful. Some help may be given by the intradermal test (Thomsen 1934). In the abattoir, the blood serum should be examined, and a search made by culture and guinea-pig inoculation for *Br. suis* in the tissues. According to Johnson and Huddleson (1931) and Johnson, Huddleson, and Hamann (1933), the organisms are commonest in the spleen, gastric and supramammary lymph glands, and the liver. Numerous other organs may be infected, but less frequently.

The disease is of undoubted economic importance, owing particularly to impotence in the boars and abortion or sterility in the sows. But it is probably of even more importance in its effect on public health. Already large numbers of cases of undulant fever have been ascribed to it, and it affords a very real hazard for workers in abattoirs and packing houses. So far as reports go, it would seem to be fairly amenable to control by the eradication policy. In Denmark, by the institution of such a policy, involving slaughter of infected animals in lightly infected herds, and slaughter of all animals in heavily infected herds, it proved possible to stamp out the disease entirely within a very short time. Johnson, Huddleson, and Hamann (1933) in the United States have been successful with a less radical policy, involving blood testing once a month, followed by segregation and ultimate elimination of the positive reactors. The seasonal breeding of sows makes control of the disease considerably easier than in cattle. (For further information on this disease the reader is referred to the excellent monograph of Thomsen 1934.)

BRUCELLA INFECTION OF HORSES, DOGS, CATS, FOWLS AND RATS

Horses.—Following on the work of Rinjard and Hilger (1928) in France, *Brucella* infection of horses has now been recognized in a number of European countries (see van der Hoeden 1931, Makkawejsky *et al.* 1931, Panisset and Delbé 1932, Hieronymi and Gilde 1934), in the United States (Fitch, Delez, and Boyd 1930), and in Australia. In Holland van der Hoeden (1932*d*) found that 72 out of 482 horse sera, mostly taken from the slaughter-house, agglutinated *Br. abortus* to 1/100 or over. In this country Priestley (1934) obtained evidence that 5–15 per cent. of horses had specific antibodies in their blood. The incidence in males and females was much the same, but older horses seemed to be more often infected than younger. The disease may be contracted from other horses or from cattle. Though the infection frequently remains latent, in a certain proportion of animals it is accompanied by the appearance of suppurative lesions, particularly on the head and neck (poll-evil, fistulous withers), and less often of bone abscesses, arthritis, and tenosynovitis. Their appearance may be preceded by fever and weakness. No history of local trauma is usually obtainable. The inflammation is extremely painful, and lasts for a few days to several months. The abscess may disappear by absorption, but more often it breaks down at multiple points on the surface, and discharges a yellowish viscous fluid containing fibrinous clots. Bacteriologically *Br. abortus* can usually be isolated, or sometimes in the United States *Br. suis*, though secondary infection of the fistulæ readily occurs. Horses can be infected experimentally with *Br. abortus* by feeding or parenteral inoculation (v.d. Hoeden 1932*b*, *d*, Schneller 1934) ; but according to Fitch, Bishop, and Boyd (1932*b*) the local manifestations of the disease cannot be reproduced except by direct inoculation into the neck ligament.   The opinion is expressed by van der Hoeden (1932*b*, *d*) that poll-evil is essentially an allergic manifestation.   It was found, for example, that if dead *abortus* bacilli were injected subcutaneously into an infected animal, a local abscess formed from which living organisms could be cultivated.   Bacteriological diagnosis of infection is made by the serum-agglutinin test ; a titre of 1/100 may be regarded as positive, and 1/50 as suspicious.   An allergic test may also be used, the ophthalmic (v.d. Hoeden 1932*b*, *d*) or the intradermal (Rossi and Saunié 1934) route being chosen.   Horses may convey infection to cattle (White and Swett 1935), and in any eradication scheme the two animals should be kept separate.

Dogs.—*Brucella* infection of dogs appears usually to be of the inapparent type. Symptoms of disease are uncommon, and though occasionally metritis or local abscess formation may occur, the infection can usually be diagnosed only by examination of the blood serum for agglutinins and complement-fixing bodies. The disease seems to be not infrequent in both Europe and America.   In some surveys 2–10 per cent., or even more, of dogs have been found to be infected (v.d. Hoeden 1932*c*, Thomsen 1932*c*, Grandi 1933, Feldman, Mann, and Olson 1935), though caution must be observed in drawing conclusions on the frequency of infection from serological results alone.   The disease can be reproduced by feeding and by parenteral inoculation, and may be characterized by fever of an undulating type.   In both naturally and experimentally infected animals the organism may sometimes be demonstrated in the blood stream or urine (v.d. Hoeden 1932*c*, Thomsen 1932*c*, Feldman, Bollman, and Olson 1935, Olson and Feldman 1936). Most cases appear to be due to *Br. abortus*, but at least one *suis* infection has been described (Planz and Huddleson 1931).   Though dogs probably play little part in the general spread of *Brucella* infection, their possible rôle as carriers must be considered in attempts to eradicate the disease from cattle or other animals.

Little is known about the incidence of *Brucella* infection in *cats*, though considering their habit of drinking raw cows' milk it is difficult to believe that they are not frequently infected.   Experimentally, both *Br. abortus* and *Br. melitensis* may give rise to a severe disease with lesions in the joints and internal organs (Makkawejsky and Karkadinowskaja 1932).

Fowls.—The frequency of *Brucella* infection in fowls is still under discussion. Emmel and Huddleson (1929, 1930) brought evidence to suggest that the disease was very common in the United States, but their observations have not been altogether confirmed by subsequent workers (McNutt and Purwin 1930, v. Roekel *et al.* 1932).   It is noteworthy that their conclusions were based on the presence of agglutinins in the blood.   The isolation of the organisms from the tissues of naturally infected birds seems to have been very rarely accomplished.   Beller and Stockmayer (1933*a*) have shown that normal fowls frequently have agglutinins in their blood, and that no attention can be paid to a titre of less than 1/150 or 1/200. Most workers have found that experimental inoculation of fowls gives rise to an inapparent infection, having little or no effect on the health or egg-laying capacity of the birds (see McNutt and Purwin 1930, 1932, v. Roekel *et al.* 1932, Lombardo 1932, Beller and Stockmayer 1933*a*, *b*, and Chapter XXXI).   The natural infection seems to be more of epidemiological than clinical interest, though further observations are required, particularly to find out whether fowls may transmit infection to cattle.

Rats.—Little is known of the occurrence of natural infection in wild rodents, though, in view of the possible part played by these animals in the spread of infection among cattle, knowledge is urgently required. Karkadinovsky (1936) examined 34 wild grey rats on three farms infected with contagious abortion, and isolated *Br. abortus* from 11 of them. Most of the positive cultures were from the spleen and liver, but in two of the animals the blood was also found to be infected.

INFECTIOUS ABORTION IN CATTLE AND SHEEP DUE TO *Vibrio fetus*

In 1913 M'Fadyean and Stockman (Report 1913) described an enzootic abortion of sheep due to a spirillar organism, which was later called *Vibrio fetus* by Smith (1918). In this country, vibrionic abortion appears mainly to affect sheep, though the disease has been observed in cattle ; but in the United States it is responsible for a considerable proportion of cases in cattle. Smith (1919) found, for example, in 109 cases of abortion in which a relatively thorough examination of the fœtus and membranes was made, that 62 were due to *Br. abortus*, 26 to *V. fetus*, 2 to *C. pyogenes*, while in the remaining 19 no organisms were isolated or mixed cultures were obtained. The general epidemiology and bacteriology of vibrionic abortion are similar to those already described for the more common type of abortion. Thus infection appears to occur by feeding, and possibly by vaginal contamination : the vibrios are found in large numbers in the uterine exudate, in the placenta, and in the contents of the fœtal stomach : agglutinins are present in the serum of infected animals, active up to a dilution of 1/640 or even higher (Smith *et al.* 1920) : and pregnant cows can be infected by the mouth, though more certainly by intravenous inoculation.

An organism similar in many respects to *V. fetus*, and called *V. jejuni*, appears to be responsible for *autumn diarrhœa in cattle* in the United States (see Jones and Little 1931, Jones, Orcutt, and Little 1931, and Chapter XXI).

PNEUMONIA IN THE LOWER ANIMALS DUE TO *Br. bronchiseptica*

In 1911 M'Gowan isolated *Br. bronchiseptica* from the respiratory tract of a number of dogs, cats, rabbits, and guinea-pigs. He regarded the organism as a primary cause of canine distemper—a view that has since been disproved (see Chapter LXXXIV). *Br. bronchiseptica* is now known to be a frequent cause of infectious pneumonia in the lower animals, particularly in guinea-pigs (Smith 1913). It is present often in pure culture in the bronchi. Injected intraperitoneally into guinea-pigs in a dose of 0·5 c.c. of a 24-hours' broth culture it causes death in 24 to 48 hours ; post mortem there are small hæmorrhages on the peritoneum, and a viscid translucent exudate forming pseudo-membranes on the liver, spleen, and the less mobile parts of the intestine ; the bacilli are easily recovered from the peritoneal cavity, but with difficulty from the blood, liver or lungs. Subcutaneous injection produces a local lesion only ; feeding and inhalation are without effect. The organism is non-pathogenic to mice. It rapidly loses its virulence in culture outside the body.

TULARÆMIA

SYNONYMS : Deer-fly fever, Pahvant Valley fever, Ohara's disease.

In 1911 McCoy described a plague-like disease amongst the ground-squirrels (*Citellus beecheyi* Richardson) of California. The following year McCoy and Chapin (1912) isolated the causative organism—a very tiny Gram-negative bacillus—

from naturally infected animals, and reproduced the disease with pure cultures in guinea-pigs. They named it *Bact. tularense*—from Tulare, the county in which the disease was first observed. (This organism probably belongs to the *Brucella* group, see Chapter XXXI.) In 1921 the disease caused by this organism came to be known as tularæmia. It is apparently widespread amongst rodents in America, particularly in the Western States ; ground-squirrels and jack-rabbits are the two animals chiefly infected. The lesions found in animals dead of the disease are similar to those of plague ; there is a bubo, generally in the cervical, axillary, or inguinal region, containing dry, yellowish, caseous material ; the spleen is greatly enlarged, very dark in colour, and contains yellowish-white, discrete, caseous granules up to 1 mm. in diameter, projecting slightly above the surface ; there are numerous granules in the liver ; the lungs are rarely involved ; the organisms are present in enormous numbers in the spleen, in smaller numbers in the liver, bubo, and heart's blood (McCoy and Chapin 1912). Experimentally the disease can be reproduced in ground-squirrels, gophers, guinea-pigs, rabbits, mice, and monkeys ; rats are more resistant ; cats, dogs, and pigeons appear to be immune. Feeding, nasal instillation, cutaneous, subcutaneous, intraperitoneal, and conjunctival injection are all successful (see Chapter XXXI.) The disease appears to be spread by blood-sucking insects, especially ticks (McCoy and Chapin 1912, Francis 1921, Francis and Lake 1922, Parker *et al.* 1924, 1929). According to Parker and Spencer (1926*b*) the organism may be transmitted from infected female ticks to their progeny ; if this is true, it is one of the few examples known of the hereditary transmission of a bacterium by insects.

The first case of the disease in man was reported in 1914 by Wherry and Lamb in the United States. By 1930 notifications had been received of 420 cases from 43 States of the Union and the district of Columbia, though there is reason to believe that numerous other cases had occurred that were not diagnosed (see Francis 1921, Culpepper 1926, Dieter 1926, Freese *et al.* 1926, Lavan 1926, Maclachlan *et al.* 1926, Parker and Francis 1926, Cumming 1930). The disease has been met with in Japan, where it is known as Ohara's disease (see Ohara 1930), in Norway (see Wefring 1930), and in Soviet Russia (see Doubrowinsky 1930). The case mortality appears to be about 4 per cent.

Mode of Infection.—In the United States the three principal sources of infection for man are (1) the bites of ticks—mainly *Dermacentor andersoni* stiles and *Dermacentor occidentalis* Newmann—(2) the bites of flies (Francis 1921, Parker and Francis 1926), especially horse flies, and (3) the dressing of wild rabbits—jack, cottontail, and snowshoe. In Norway infection has been traced to hares (Thjøtta 1930, 1931*b*), and in Soviet Russia to water rats (Sarchi 1929, 1930), and to susliks (Tumansky and Kolesnikova 1935). The "lemming fever" of Norway, which follows the consumption of drinking water polluted by the bodies and excreta of the lemming, is thought to be related to tularæmia (Thjøtta 1931*a*). Whether infection of man occurs from sheep, which may occasionally suffer from tularæmia (Parker and Dade 1929, Philip and Jellison 1935), is not known. The incidence of the disease is mainly on those classes of the population who are brought into contact with infected animals, such as butchers, poultry-men, and trappers. Laboratory workers are often attacked (Parker and Spencer 1926*a*). Indeed there is probably no other organism that is so dangerous to work with in the laboratory. Unless scrupulous care is taken to avoid infection of the skin, nose, and conjunctiva, from fluid cultures and inoculated animals, the disease will almost certainly be contracted.

The way in which the organism enters the body is not known, but the evidence suggests that the site of infection is generally the skin of the fingers or the conjunctiva. It is known that in guinea-pigs the organism can pass through the intact skin (Lake and Francis 1922), and there is reason to believe that it may do so in human beings. In the usual glandular type of the disease, seen in butchers and poultry-men, after an acute onset with headache, rigors, pains and fever, a papule appears, generally on the back of the finger, which breaks down and leaves a ragged ulcer. The epitrochlear and axillary glands swell and become painful; they often break down and discharge purulent material. Fever is common for the first 2 or 3 weeks. Convalescence is very slow. When the organism gains entrance through the conjunctiva, ulcers may form on the inner surface of the eyelids, followed by swelling and tenderness of the preauricular and cervical glands. In the typhoid type of the disease there are no localizing symptoms. It is this type that is usually seen in laboratory workers (Lake and Francis 1922). In those patients who have been examined at post mortem, multiple small abscesses in the regional lymphatic glands, the spleen, liver, and lungs have often been found (see Francis and Callender 1927, Foulger *et al.* 1932).

Diagnosis and Treatment.—Diagnosis in animals is best made by macroscopic, microscopic, cultural, and pathogenicity tests. In the differential diagnosis from plague, account should be taken of the absence of pus at the site of infection, the greater variability in size of the granules in the spleen, the rarity with which the lungs are involved, and the failure of the organism to develop on ordinary media. In man, discharge from the local lesions or glands should be cultivated directly on to special media (see Shaw and Hunnicutt 1930), and injected into guinea-pigs (Francis 1923). The agglutination test is of special value. Curiously enough the organism does not often appear to be present in the blood (Lake and Francis 1922). An intradermal diagnostic test has been described (Foshay 1932).

Dead vaccines have been recommended for the prophylactic immunization of persons specially exposed to infection, while immune serum prepared by the inoculation of a goat has been tried on a small scale in the treatment of patients suffering from the disease (see Kudo 1934, Foshay 1934).

REFERENCES

ALESSANDRINI, A. and PACELLI, M. (1932) " Un pericolo sociale : Le Brucellosi." Publ. by Ann. Igiene, Rome.
AMOIA, R. (1933) *Boll. Sez. ital. Soc. int. Microbiol.*, **5,** 171.
AMOSS, H. L. and POSTON, M. A. (1930) *J. Amer. med. Ass.*, **95,** 482.
ANANIADÉS, B. and MIAOULIS, N. (1931) *Rev. gén. Méd. vét.*, **40,** 721.
ANDREWS, W. H. (1932) *Nat. vet. med. Ass. G.B.I.*
ARBATSKAIA, E. and MOROSKIN, H. (1934) *G. Batt. Immun.*, **12,** 979.
ATWOOD, G. E. and HASSELTINE, H. E. (1930) *Publ. Hlth Rep., Wash.*, **45,** 1343.
BACH, F. W. (1932) *Arch. Schiffs- u. Tropenhyg.*, **36,** 158.
BANG, B. (1897) *Z. Thiermed.*, **1,** 241 ; (1906) *J. comp. Path.*, **19,** 191.
BANG, O. (1931) *2me Congr. int. Path. comp.*, ii. 269.
BANG, O. and BENDIXEN, H. C. (1931) *Int. Milchwirtsch. Kongr.*, Proc., p. 117.
BANG, O. and BENDIXEN, H. C. (1932a) *Z. InfektKr. Haustiere*, **42,** 81 ; (1932b) *Medlemsbl. danske Dyrlaegeforen.*, Aug. 15, No. 1.
BAYNE-JONES, S. (1930) *Amer. J. publ. Hlth.*, **20,** 1313.
BEATTIE, C. P. and RICE, R. M. (1934) *J. Amer. med. Ass.*, **102,** 1670.
BEATTIE, C. P., SMITH, J., and TULLOCH, W. J. (1935) *Lancet*, i. 1427.
BELLER, K. and STOCKMAYER, W. (1933a) *Zbl. Bakt.*, **127,** 456 ; (1933b) *Dtsch. tierärztl. Wschr.*, **41,** 551.

Benussi, L.   (1935) *Ann. Igiene (Sper.)*, **45**, 28.
Berge, R. and Ekrem, A.   (1932) *Dtsch. tierärztl. Wschr.*, **40**, 844 ; (1934) *Ibid.*, **42**, 211.
Berkessy, L. von.   (1935) *Zbl. Bakt.*, **134**, 210.
Berkessy, L. von and Simon, I. B.   (1934) *Wien. klin. Wschr.*, **47**, 330.
Bevan, L. E. W.   (1921–22) *Trans. R. Soc. trop. Med. Hyg.*, **15**, 215.
Bianchi, L.   (1934) *Dtsch. med. Wschr.*, **60**, 788.
Bijl, J. P. and Hoeden, J. van der.   (1931) *Zbl. Bakt., Ref.*, **103**, 104.
Birch, R. R.   (1934) *J. Amer. vet. med. Ass.*, **84**, 854.
Birch, R. R. and Gilman, H. L.   (1935) *J. infect. Dis.*, **56**, 78.
Birch, R. R., Milks, C. H., and Gilman, H. L.   (1934) *J. Amer. vet. med. Ass.*, **84**, 341.
Boak, R. A. and Carpenter, C. M.   (1929) *J. Immunol.*, **17**, 65 ; (1930) *J. infect. Dis.*, **46**, 425.
Bruce, D.   (1887) *Practitioner*, **39**, 161 ; (1888) *Ibid.*, **40**, 241 ; (1893) *Ann. Inst. Pasteur*, **7**, 289.
Burnet, E.   (1922) *Arch. Inst. Pasteur Afrique nord.*, **2**, 187.
Caldwell, D. W., Parker, N. J., and Medlar, E. M.   (1934) *J. infect. Dis.*, **55**, 235.
Cameron, W. R. and Wells, N.   (1934) *Southern med. J.*, **27**, 907.
Carpenter, C. M. and Boak, R. A.   (1932) *J. Amer. med. Ass.*, **99**, 296 ; (1933) *Amer. J. med. Sci.*, **185**, 97.
Carrieu, M. and Lafenêtre, M.   (1932) *Le Lait*, **12**, 779.
Chiucini, G.   (1935) *G. Batt. Immun.*, **14**, 570.
Clark, C. F.   (1932) *J. Amer. vet. med. Ass.*, **81**, 54.
Cotton, W. E.   (1931) *Vet. Med.*, **26**, 66 ; (1932) *J. agric. Res.*, **45**, 705.
Cotton, W. E. and Buck, J. M.   (1932) *J. Amer. vet. med. Ass.*, **80**, 342 ; (1934) *J. Amer. vet. med. Ass.*, **84**, 329.
Cotton, W. E., Buck, J. M., and Smith, H. E.   (1933a) *J. Amer. vet. med. Ass.*, **83**, 91; (1933b) *J. agric. Res.*, **46**, 291, 315 ; (1934) *J. Amer. vet. med. Ass.*, **85**, 232, 389.
Cruickshank, R. and Barbour, W. J.   (1931) *Lancet*, i. 852.
Culpepper, M. B.   (1926) *Bull. Hyg., Lond.*, **1**, 531.
Cumming, H. S.   (1930) *Bull. Off. int. Hyg. publ.*, **22**, 1904.
Dalrymple-Champneys, W.   (1929) *Rep. publ. Hlth med. Subj., Min. Hlth, London*, No. 56 ; (1931) *Brit. med. J.*, ii. 604 ; (1934) *Lancet*, i. 95 ; (1935) *Ibid.*, ii. 1449.
Damon, S. R.   (1932) *Amer. J. Hyg.*, **16**, 798.
Darsin, E.   (1930) *Zbl. Bakt.*, **115**, 457.
Davies.   (1906) *Rep. Comm. medit. Fev.*, Part 4.
Debono, J. E.   (1935) *Lancet*, i. 374.
Delez, A. L.   (1932) *J. Amer. vet. med. Ass.*, **81**, 239.
Dettling, H.   (1932) *Arch. Hyg.*, **109**, 61.
Dieter, L. V.   (1926) *Publ. Hlth Rep., Wash.*, **41**, 1355.
Donham, C. R. and Fitch, C. P.   (1934a) *J. infect. Dis.*, **55**, 60 ; (1934b) *J. Amer. vet. med. Ass.*, **85**, 782 ; (1935) *Ibid.*, **87**, 188.
Dooley, P.   (1932) *Arch. intern. Med.*, **50**, 373.
Doubrowinsky.   (1930) *Bull. off. int. Hyg. publ.*, **22**, 1911.
Doyle, T. M.   (1934) *J. comp. Path.*, **47**, 134 ; (1935) *Ibid.*, **48**, 192.
Dubois, C.   (1934) *C. R. Soc. Biol.*, **115**, 1065.
Dubois, C. and Brune, C.   (1933) *C. R. Soc. Biol.*, **112**, 1297.
Dubois, C. and Sollier, N.   (1932a) *C. R. Soc. Biol.*, **109**, 359 ; (1932b) *C. R. Acad. Sci.*, **195**, 722.
Dudley, S. F.   (1931) *Lancet*, i. 683.
Elkeles, C. and Fried, R.   (1932) *Dtsch. med. Wschr.*, **58**, 1444.
Emmel, M. W. and Huddleson, I. F.   (1929) *J. Amer. vet. med. Ass.*, **75**, 578 ; (1930) *Ibid.*, **76**, 449.
Evans, A. C.   (1918) *J. infect. Dis.*, **22**, 580 ; (1934) *J. Amer. med. Ass.*, **103**, 665.
Eyre, J. W. H.   (1908) *Lancet*, i. 1677, 1747 ; (1912) *ibid.*, i. 88.
Eyre, J. W. H., McNaught, J. G., Kennedy, J. C., and Zammit, T.   (1907) *Rep. Comm. medit. Fev.*, Part 6, p. 3.
Favorite, G. O. and Culp, C. F.   (1935) *J. lab. clin. Med.*, **20**, 522.
Feldman, W. H., Bollman, J. L., and Olson, C.   (1935) *J. infect. Dis.*, **56**, 321.
Feldman, W. H., Mann, F. C., and Olson, C.   (1935) *J. infect. Dis.*, **56**, 55.
Feldman, W. H. and Olson, C.   (1934) *J. infect. Dis.*, **54**, 45.
Fitch, C. P. and Donham, C. R.   (1933) *J. Amer. vet. med. Ass.*, **82**, 46.
Fitch, C. P., Bishop, L. M., and Boyd, W. L.   (1932a) *Proc. Soc. exp. Biol., N.Y.*, **29**, 555 ; (1932b) *J. Amer. vet. med. Ass.*, **80**, 69.
Fitch, C. P., Delez, A. L., and Boyd, W. L.   (1930) *J. Amer. vet. med. Ass.*, **76**, 17.
Foshay, L.   (1932) *J. infect. Dis.*, **51**, 286 ; (1934) *Amer. J. Sci.*, **187**, 235.
Foulger, M., Glazer, A. M., and Foshay, L.   (1932) *J. Amer. med. Ass.*, **98**, 951.
Francis, E.   (1921) *Publ. Hlth Rep., Wash.*, No. 30, **36**, 1731 ; (1923) *Ibid.*, No. 25, **38**, 1391.

FRANCIS, E. and CALLENDER, G. R. (1927) *Arch. Path. lab. Med.*, **3**, 577.
FRANCIS, E. and LAKE, G. C. (1922) *Publ. Hlth Rep., Wash.*, **37**, 83.
FRANCO, E. and PEZZI, R. (1935) *Boll. Sez. ital. Soc. int. Microbiol.*, **7**, 58.
FREESE, H. L., LAKE, G. C., and FRANCIS, E. (1926) *Publ. Hlth Rep., Wash.*, **41**, 369.
FRIED, R. (1932) *Z. Hyg. InfektKr.*, **114**, 429.
FRITZ, B. S. and BARNES, M. F. (1933) *J. Amer. vet. med. Ass.*, **83**, 680.
GILBERT, R. and DACEY, H. G. (1932) *J. lab. clin. Med.*, **17**, 345.
GILMAN, H. L. (1930) *Cornell Vet.*, **20**, 106.
GILTNER, W. (1924) *J. Amer. vet. med. Ass.*, **64**, 469 ; (1934) " Brucellosis, A Public Health Problem." Agric. exp. Sta., East Lansing, Mich.
GIORDANO, A. S. (1929) *J. Amer. med. Ass.*, **93**, 1957.
GOLDSTEIN, J. D. (1934) *J. clin. Invest.*, **13**, 209.
GRAHAM, R. and THORP, F. (1930) *J. infect. Dis.*, **46**, 260.
GRANDI, G. (1933) *Nuova vet.*, **11**, No. 7, 29, No. 8, 14.
GRINSTADT. (1910) *J. comp. Path.*, **23**, 279.
GRUMBACH, A. and GRILICHESS, R. K. (1932) *Arch. Hyg.*, **109**, 147.
GUARNA, A. (1935) *Boll. 1st. sieroter. Milano*, **14**, 1009.
GUGLIELMO, G. DI. (1933) " La Cura specifica della Brucellosi." Officina Graphica moderna Impegnoso and Pulvirenti, Catania.
HABS, H. (1933a) *Zbl. ges. Hyg.*, **28**, 481 ; (1933b) *Ibid*, **30**, 369 ; (1935) Gundel, M., " Die ansteckenden Krankheiten," p. 135. Geo. Thieme, Leipzig.
HABS, H. and SIEVERT, L. (1935) *Dtsch. med. Wschr.*, **61**, 1398.
HADLEY, F. B. and WELSH, W. E. (1931) *Cornell Vet.*, **21**, 27.
HAGAN, W. A. (1922) *J. exp. Med.*, **36**, 711.
HALL, I. W. (1933) *Proc. R. Soc. Med.*, **26**, 1100.
HALL, I. C. and LEARMONTH, R. (1933) *J. infect. Dis.*, **52**, 27 ; (1934) *Ibid.*, **55**, 184.
HARDY, A. V., JORDAN, C. F., and BORTS, I. H. (1932) *Publ. Hlth Rep., Wash.*, **47**, 187.
HARDY, A. V., JORDAN, C. F., BORTS, I. H., and HARDY, G. C. (1931) *Nat. Inst. Hlth, Wash.*, Bull, No. 158.
HARRISON, H. and WILSON, G. S. (1928) *Lancet*, ii. 1338.
HASLEY, D. E. (1930) *J. infect. Dis.*, **46**, 430 ; (1931) *Amer. J. publ. Hlth.*, **21**, 515.
HASSELTINE, H. E. (1930) *Publ. Hlth Rep., Wash.*, **45**, 1660.
HASSELTINE, H. E. and KNIGHT, I. W. (1931) *Publ. Hlth Rep., Wash.*, **46**, 2291.
HAUPTMANN, W. (1935a) *Zbl. Bakt.*, **134**, 221 ; (1935b) *Med. Klin.*, **31**, 1174.
HAXTHAUSEN, H. and THOMSEN, A. (1931) *Arch. Derm. Syph., Berl.*, **163**, 477.
HEATHMAN, L. S. (1934) *J. infect. Dis.*, **55**, 243.
HELMS, T. (1932) *Z. ImmunForsch.*, **75**, 61.
HENRICSSON, E. (1932) " Epizootischer Abortus und Undulantfieber." Isaac Marcus Boktryckeri-Aktiebolag, Stockholm.
HERRMANN, E., MIRSABEKJAN, A., and MEGRABJAN, R. (1934) *Z. ImmunForsch.*, **81**, 500.
HIERONYMI, E. and GILDE, H. (1934) *Z. InfektKr. Haustiere*, **47**, 24.
HILGERMANN, R. (1935) *Münch. med. Wschr.*, **82**, 98.
HIRSCH, W. (1935) *Arch. Schiffs- u. Tropenhyg.*, **39**, 30.
HOEDEN, J. VAN DER. (1931) *Tijdschr. Diergeneesk.*, **58**, 1321 ; (1932a) *Ibid.*, **59**, 385 ; (1932b) *Ibid.*, **59**, 612 ; (1932c) *Ibid.*, **59**, 1383, 1446 ; (1932d) *Z. InfektKr. Haustiere*, **42**, 1 ; (1933) *J. comp. Path.*, **46**, 232.
HOLL, L. (1930) *G. Batt. Immun.*, **5**, 1.
HOLTH, H. (1911) *Z. InfektKr. Haustiere*, **10**, 207, 342.
HOLTUM, A. W. (1928) *J. comp. Path.*, **41**, 25, 79.
HORNING, B. G. (1935) *J. Amer. med. Ass.*, **105**, 1978.
HORROCKS, W. H. (1905) *Rep. Comm. Medit. Fev.*, Part 3, p. 84.
HORROCKS, W. H. and KENNEDY, J. C. (1906) *Rep. Comm. medit. Fev.*, Part 3, p. 37.
HUDDLESON, I. F. (1932) *Mich. agric. exp. Sta., Tec. Bull.*, No. 123.
HUDDLESON, I. F. and ABELL, E. (1928) *J. infect. Dis.*, **42**, 242.
HUDDLESON, I. F., HASLEY, D. E., and TORREY, J. P. (1927) *J. infect. Dis.*, **40**, 352.
HUDDLESON, I. F. and JOHNSON, H. W. (1930) *J. Amer. med. Ass.*, **94**, 1905 ; (1933) *Amer. J. trop. Med.*, **13**, 485.
HUDDLESON, I. F., JOHNSON, H. W., and HAMANN, E. E. (1933a) *J. Amer. vet. med. Ass.*, **83**, 16 ; (1933b) *Amer. J. publ. Hlth.*, **23**, 917.
HUDDLESON, I. F. and SMITH, L. H. (1931) *J. Amer. vet. med. Ass.*, **79**, 63.
HUGHES, M. L. (1893) *Ann. Inst. Pasteur*, **7**, 628 ; (1897) " Mediterranean, Malta or Undulant Fever," Macmillan & Co., London.
HUTYRA, F. and MAREK, J. (1922) " Special Pathology and Therapeutics of Diseases of Domestic Animals, 2nd Amer. edit., **1**, 780. Chicago and London.
JENSEN, C. O. (1931) *Dtsch. tierärztl. Wschr.*, **39**, 733.
JOHNS, E. P., CAMPBELL, F. J. H., and TENNANT, C. S. (1932) *Canad. med. Ass. J.*, **27**, 490.
JOHNSON, H. W. and HUDDLESON, I. F. (1931) *J. Amer. vet. med. Ass.*, **78**, 849.

JOHNSON, H. W., HUDDLESON, I. F., and HAMANN, E. E. (1933) *J. Amer. vet. med. Ass.*, **83**, 727.

JOHNSTONE. (1905) *Rep. Comm. Medit. Fev.*, Part 2.

JONES, F. S. and LITTLE, R. B. (1931) *J. exp. Med.*, **53**, 835, 845.

JONES, F. S., ORCUTT, M., and LITTLE, R. B. (1931) *J. exp. Med.*, **53**, 853.

JORDAN, E. O. and McBROOM, J. (1932) *J. Amer. vet. med. Ass.*, **81**, 401.

KALBFLEISCH, H. H. and KALBFLEISCH, E. (1935) *Wien. klin. Wschr.*, **48**, 523.

KARKADINOVSKY, J. A. (1936) *C. R. Soc. Biol.*, **121**, 1611.

KARSTEN. (1931) *Dtsch. tierärztl. Wschr.*, **39**, 385 ; (1932) *Ibid.*, **40**, 689 ; (1933) *Ibid.*, **41**, 358.

KARSTEN and BISCHOFF. (1933) *Dtsch. tierärztl. Wschr.*, **41**, 593 ; (1934) *Ibid.*, **42**, 465 ; (1935) *Ibid.*, **43**, 70.

KEEFER, C. S. (1924) *Bull. Johns Hopk. Hosp.*, **35**, 6.

KENNEDY, J. C. (1905) *Rep. Comm. Medit. Fev.*, Part 3, pp. 56, 71, 91 ; (1906) *Ibid.*, Part 4, p. 92.

KHAUM, A. and LIEDL, E. (1935) *Mitt. VolksgesundhAmt.*, Wien, No. 6, p. 55.

KING, M. J. and CALDWELL, D. W. (1929) *Amer. J. med. Sci.*, **178**, 115.

KING, R. O. C. (1934) *Aust. vet. J.*, **10**, 93.

KITSELMAN, C. H. (1932) *J. Amer. vet. med. Ass.*, **80**, 828.

KNOTH, M. (1930a) *Dtsch. tierärztl. Wschr.*, **38**, 822 ; (1930b) *Z. Fleisch- u. Milchhyg.*, **40**, 453.

KRISTENSEN, M. and HOLM, P. (1929) *Zbl. Bakt.*, **112**, 281.

KRÜGER, H. (1932) *Dtsch. tierärztl. Wschr.*, **40**, 481.

KUDO, M. (1934) *Jap. J. exp. Med.*, **12**, 377.

LAKE, G. C. and FRANCIS, E. (1922) *Publ. Hlth Rep., Wash.*, **37**, 392.

LAUDA, E. (1934) *Wien. klin. Wschr.*, **47**, 257.

LAUN, R. H. and HEIDE, E. (1934) *Z. Hyg. InfektKr.*, **116**, 315.

LAVAN, J. L. (1926) *J. Amer. med. Ass.*, **86**, 839.

LEAVELL, H. R. and AMOSS, H. L. (1931a) *Amer. J. med. Sci.*, **181**, 96 ; (1931b) *Arch. intern. Med.*, **48**, 1192.

LEAVELL, H. R., POSTON, M. A., and AMOSS, H. L. (1930) *J. Amer. med. Ass.*, **95**, 860.

LENTZ, W. (1932) *Dtsch. tierärztl. Wschr.*, **40**, 84.

LENTZE, F. A. (1930) *Zbl. Bakt.*, **118**, 360.

LERCHE. (1931) *Z. InfektKr. Haustiere*, **38**, 253.

LEVIN, W. (1930) *J. Lab. clin. Med.*, **16**, 275.

LISBONNE, M. and JANBON, M. (1935) " Encyclopédie Medico-chirurgicale."

LOMBARDO, F. (1932) *Ann. Igiene (sper.)*, **42**, 33.

LÜBKE, A. (1935) *Arch. wiss. prakt. Tierheilk.*, **68**, 233.

MACLACHLAN, W. W. G., FETTER, W. J., and CRATTY, A. R. (1926) *J. Amer. med. Ass.*, **86**, 749.

MACLEAN, F. S. (1932) *New Zealand med. J.*, **31**, 262.

MacNEAL, W. J. and KERR, J. E. (1910) *J. infect. Dis.*, **7**, 469.

McALPINE, J. G. and RETTGER, L. F. (1925) *J. Immunol.*, **10**, 811.

McCOY, G. W. (1911) *Publ. Hlth Bull., Wash.*, No. 43, p. 53.

McCOY, G. W. and CHAPIN, C. W. (1912) *J. infect. Dis.*, **10**, 61.

M'FADYEAN, J. (1921) *J. comp. Path.*, **34**, 48, 105 ; (1924) *Ibid.*, **37**, 192 ; (1933) *Ibid.*, **46**, 50.

M'FADYEAN, J., SHEATHER, A. L., and MINETT, F. C. (1913) *J. comp. Path.*, **26**, 142.

M'FADYEAN, J. and STOCKMAN, S. (1909) *Rep. Comm. on Epizootic Abortion*, Append. to Part I, London ; (1912) *J. comp. Path.*, **25**, 22.

M'GOWAN, J. P. (1911) *J. Path. Bact.*, **15**, 372.

McNABB, A. L. (1934) *Canad. publ. Hlth J.*, **25**, 10.

McNUTT, S. H. (1935) *J. Amer. vet. med. Ass.*, **86**, 183.

McNUTT, S. H. and PURWIN, P. (1930) *J. Amer. vet. med. Ass.*, **30**, 350 ; (1932) *Ibid.*, **81**, 641.

MACKIE, T. J. (1933) *Edin. med. J.*, **40**, Chir. 137.

MAGLIULO, L. (1933) *G. Batt. Immun.*, **10**, 284.

MAKKAWEJSKY, W. N. and KARKADINOWSKY, J. (1930) *Dtsch. tierärztl. Wschr.*, **38**, 369.

MAKKAWEJSKY, W. N. and KARKADINOWSKAJA, I. A. (1932) *Dtsch. tierärztl. Wschr.*, **40**, 229.

MAKKAWEJSKI, W. N., KARKADINOWSKAJA, I. A., and MICHEEW, N. I. (1933) *Dtsch. tierärztl. Wschr.*, **41**, 321.

MAKKAWEJSKY, W. N., KARKADINOWSKY, J. A., MICHEJEFF, N. J., GAWRILOFF, A. J., and DAWYDOWSKY, W. G. (1931) *Dtsch. tierärztl. Wschr.*, **39**, 86.

MARSTON, J. A. (1863) *Army med. Dep. statist. Rep.*, **3**, 486.

MARTIN, J. W. and MYERS, J. T. (1931) *J. prev. Med., Ba'timore*, **5**, 243.

MATHEWS, F. P. (1924) *J. infect. Dis.*, **35**, 498.

MAZÉ, P. and CÉSARI, E. (1931) *C. R. Soc. Biol.*, **108**, 630.

MENZANI, R. (1932) *Nuova vet.*, **10**, 37.

MENZANI, C. and ZANCHE, V. DE. (1934) *Ann. Igiene (sper.)*, **44,** 225.
MERLIAC, L. and LISBONNE, M. (1936) *Bull. Acad. Méd.*, **115,** 572.
MESSER, A. I. (1932) *Brit. med. J.*, i. 1030.
MEYER, K. F. (1933) *J. Bact.*, **29,** 43.
MEYER, K. F. and EDDIE, B. (1935) *J. Amer. vet. med. Ass.*, **86,** 286.
MEYER, K. F., EDDIE, B., VEAZIE, L., STEVENS, I. M., STEWART, B., and GEIGER, J. C. (1934*a*) *Arch. Gewerbepath. Gewerbehyg.*, **5,** 501.
MEYER, K. F., STEWART, B., VEAZIE, L., and EDDIE, B. (1934*b*) *Proc. Soc. exp. Biol., N.Y.*, **32,** 284.
MIESZNER, H. (1931) *Dtsch. med. Wschr.*, **57,** 286.
MIRRI, A. (1935) *Riv. sanit. sicil.*, **23,** 660, 665, 675, 681.
MITCHELL, C. A. (1929) *Canad. publ. Hlth J.*, **20,** 78.
MITCHELL, C. A., HUMPHREYS, F. A., and WALKER, R. V. L. (1933) *Canad. Dep. Agric. Rep. vet. Director gen.*, p. 46 ; (1935) *Canad. publ. Hlth J.*, **26,** 209.
MOHLER, J. R. and TRAUM, J. (1911) 28*th Ann. Rep. Bur. Anim. Indust.*, p. 147.
MOHR, W. (1935) *Z. ImmunForsch.*, **86,** 235.
MOLINELLI, E. A. (1933) *Semana méd.*, **40,** Part 2, 1919 ; (1934) *Ibid.*, **41,** Part 2, 1248.
MOLINELLI, E. A. and ITHURRAT, E. M. F. (1934) *Semana méd.*, **41,** Part 2, 176 ; (1935) *Rev. Hig. Sanid. pecuar.*, **25,** 358.
MONTEL, J. (1932) *Marseille méd.*, **69,** 537 ; (1933) *Ibid.*, **70,** 333.
MORALES-OTERO, P. and MONGE, G. (1932) *Porto Rico J. publ. Hlth.*, **8,** 193.
MORELLINI, M. (1933) *Riforma med.*, **49,** 1697.
MORENO, L. S. (1934) *Rev. Hig. Sanid. pecuar.*, **24,** 5.
NEIVA, C. (1934) *Brasil-Medico*, **48,** 421.
NEWSOM, I. E. and CROSS, F. (1932) *J. Amer. vet. med. Ass.*, **81,** 195.
NORTON, J. F. and PLESS, L. R. (1931) *Amer. J. publ. Hlth.*, **21,** 499.
NOWAK, J. (1908) *Ann. Inst. Pasteur*, **22,** 541.
OHARA, H. (1930) *Zbl. Bakt.*, **117,** 440.
OLIN, G. (1935) " Studien über das Undulantfieber in Schweden." Isaac Marcus Boktryckeri-Aktiebolag, Stockholm.
OLSON, C. and FELDMAN, W. H. (1936) *J. Amer. vet. med. Ass.*, **88,** 51.
OYEN, C. F. VAN. (1934) *Dtsch. tierärztl. Wschr.*, **42,** 457.
PANISSET, L. and DELBÉ, P. (1932) *Rev. gén. Méd. vét.*, **41,** 670.
PARKER, R. R. and DADE, J. S. (1929) *Publ. Hlth Rep., Wash.*, **44,** 126.
PARKER, R. R. and FRANCIS, E. (1926) *Publ. Hlth Rep., Wash.*, **41,** 1407.
PARKER, R. R. and SPENCER, R. R. (1926*a*) *Publ. Hlth Rep., Wash.*, **41,** 1341 ; (1926*b*) *Ibid.*, **41,** 1403.
PARKER, R. R., BROOKS, C. S., and HADLEIGH, M. (1929) *Publ. Hlth Rep., Wash.*, **44,** 1299.
PARKER, R. R., SPENCER, R. R., and FRANCIS, E. (1924) *Publ. Hlth Rep., Wash.*, **39,** 1057.
PÉRÈS, M. G. (1934) *Rev. gén. Méd. vét.*, **43,** 713.
PETERSON, C. E. (1935) *J. Lab. clin. Med.*, **20,** 727.
PHILIP, C. B. and JELLISON, W. L. (1935) *J. Amer. vet. med. Ass.*, **86,** 726.
PLANZ, J. F. and HUDDLESON, I. F. (1931) *J. Amer. vet. med. Ass.*, **79,** 251.
PLATE, G. (1934*a*) *Dtsch. tierärztl. Wschr.*, **42,** 537 ; (1934*b*) *Ibid.*, **42,** 768.
POELMA, L. J. and PICKENS, E. M. (1932) *J. Bact.*, **23,** 112.
POPPE, K. (1933) *Dtsch. med. Wschr.*, **59,** 913.
PREISZ, H. (1903) *Zbl. Bakt.*, **33,** 190.
PRIESTLEY, F. W. (1931) *J. Path. Bact.*, **34,** 81 ; (1934) *J. comp. Path.*, **47,** 181.
PRÖSCHOLDT, O. (1932) *Dtsch. tierärztl. Wschr.*, **40,** 673.
PULLINGER, E. J. (1935) *Lancet*, i. 1342.
RAINSFORD, S. G. (1933) *J. R. nav. med. Serv.*, **19,** 1 ; (1935) *Ibid.*, **21,** 81.
RANQUE, A. and SENEZ, C. (1932) *Marseille méd.*, **69,** 814.
REINHARDT and GAUSS. (1915) *Zbl. Bakt.*, **28,** 172.
Report. (1905–7) Mediterranean Fever Commission, Harrison & Sons, London ; (1909) *Rep. Dep. Comm. Epizootic Abortion*, Part I, *Bd Agric. Fish.*, H.M. Stat. Off., Lond. ; (1913) *Rep. Dep. Comm. Epizootic Abortion*, Part III, *Bd Agric. Fish*, H.M. Stat Off., Lond. ; (1934) *Reichsgesundheitsblatt*, **9,** 724 ; (1935) *Ibid.*, **10,** 243.
RINJARD, P. and HILGER, A. (1928) *Bull. Acad. vét. France*, **81,** 272.
ROBINSON, E. M. (1919) *J. comp. Path.*, **32,** 293.
ROEKEL, H. VAN, BULLIS, K. L., FLINT, O. S., and CLARKE, M. K. (1932) *J. Amer. vet. med. Ass.*, **80,** 641.
ROSSI, P. (1935) *C. R. Soc. Biol.*, **118,** 1053.
ROSSI, P. and SAUNIÉ, L. (1934) *C. R. Soc. Biol.*, **115,** 134, 137.
ROSSI, P. and VIGEL, F. (1934) *C. R. Soc. Biol.*, **115,** 248.
RUNNELS, R. A. and HUDDLESON, I. F. (1925) *Cornell Vet.*, **15,** 376.
RUSS, V. (1934) *Wien. klin. Wschr.*, **47,** 289.
SANFILIPPO, E. (1933) *G. Batt. Immun.*, **11,** 1.

SARCHI, G. J.   (1929) *Zbl. Bakt.*, **114**, 55 ;   (1930) *Ibid.*, **117**, 367.
SARNOWIEC, W.   (1934) *Ann. Inst. Pasteur*, **53**, 166.
SASANO, K. T., CALDWELL, D., and MEDLAR, E. M.   (1931) *J. infect. Dis.*, **48**, 576.
SCHILLING, G. S., MAGEE, C. F., and LEITCH, F. M.   (1931) *J. Amer. med. Ass.*, **96**, 1945.
SCHITTENHELM, A.   (1932) *Klin. Wschr.*, **11**, 905.
SCHLESMANN, C.   (1932) *Klin. Wschr.*, **11**, 1711.
SCHMIDT, W.   (1932) *Dtsch. tierärztl. Wschr.*, **40**, 702.
SCHNELLER.   (1934) *Tierärztl. Rdsch.*, **40**, 762.
SCHROEDER, E. C. and COTTON, W. E.   (1911) *28th Rep. Bur. Anim. Indust.*, p. 139.
SCHUMANN.   (1931) *Dtsch. tierärztl. Wschr.*, **39**, 567.
SEDDON, H. R.   (1915) *J. comp. Path.*, **28**, 20 ;   (1919) *J. comp. Path.*, **32**, 1.
SEGNI, G.   (1931) *Sperimentale*, **85**, lvi.
SHAW, E. A.   (1906) *Rep. Comm. Medit. Fev.*, Part IV, p. 16.
SHAW, F. W. and HUNNICUTT, T.   (1930) *J. Lab. clin. Med.*, **16**, 46.
SHEATHER, A. L.   (1923) *J. comp. Path.*, **36**, 255.
SIMPSON, W. M.   (1930) *Ann. intern. Med.*, **4**, 238.
SIMPSON, W. M. and FRAIZER, E.   (1929) *J. Amer. med. Ass.*, **93**, 1958.
SMILLIE, E. W., LITTLE, R. B., and FLORENCE, L.   (1919) *J. exp. Med.*, **30**, 341.
SMITH, T.   (1913) *J. med. Res.*, **29**, 291 ;   (1918) *J. exp. Med.*, **28**, 701 ;   (1919) *Ibid.*, **30**, 325 ;   (1926) *Ibid.*, **43**, 317.
SMITH, J.   (1932a) *Quart. J. Med.*, **25**, 303 ;   (1932b) *J. Hyg., Camb.*, **32**, 354 ;   (1934a) *Ibid.*, **34**, 242 ;   (1934b) *J. comp. Path.*, **47**, 125.
SMITH, T. and LITTLE, R. B.   (1926) *J. exp. Med.*, **43**, 327.
SMITH, T., LITTLE, R. B., and TAYLOR, M. S.   (1920) *J. exp. Med.*, **32**, 683.
SOULE, M. H.   (1930) *1st Int. Congr. Microbiol.*, Paris.
SPENCER, R. R.   (1930) *Publ. Hlth Rep., Wash.*, **45**, 2383.
SPENGLER, G.   (1929) " Die Bangsche Krankheit beim Menschen."   Urban and Schwarzenberg, Berlin.
STARR, L. E. and MAXCY, K. F.   (1933) *Virginia med. Monthly*, **60**, 218.
STEWART, B., EDDIE, B., PAXTON, F., and MEYER, K. F.   (1935) *Calif., West. Med.*, **43**, 112.
STEYRER, A.   (1934) *Münch. med. Wschr.*, **81**, 277.
STOCKMAN, S.   (1914) *J. comp. Path.*, **27**, 237.
STOCKMAYER, W.   (1933a) *Z. InfektKr. Haustiere*, **44**, 105 ;   (1933b) *Berl. tierärztl. Wschr.*, **49**, 741 ;   (1935) *Zbl. Bakt.*, **133**, 425 ;   (1936) *Z. InfektKr. Haustiere*, **49**, 46.
STONE, R. V. and BOGEN, E.   (1935) *Amer. J. publ. Hlth.*, **25**, 580.
STRAUBE, G.   (1932) *Med. Klin.*, **28**, 1501.
SÜPFLE, K. and HOFMANN, P.   (1932) *Arch. Hyg.*, **108**, 113.
TAYLOR, R. M. and HAZEMANN, R. H.   (1932) *Rev. Hyg.*, **54**, 481.
TAYLOR, R. M., LISBONNE, M., and ROMAN, G.   (1932) *Ann. Inst. Pasteur*, **49**, 284.
TAYLOR, R. M., LISBONNE, M., and VIDAL, L. F.   (1935) *Mouvement San.*, **12**, 51.
TAYLOR, R. M., VIDAL, L. F., and ROMAN, G.   (1934) *C. R. Soc. Biol.*, **116**, 132.
TEBBUTT, A. H. and MARSH, H. T.   (1931) *Med. J. Aust.*, **1**, 170.
THJØTTA, T.   (1930) *Bull. Hyg., Lond.*, **5**, 490 ;   (1931a) *Ibid.*, **6**, 355 ;   (1931b) *J. infect. Dis.*, **49**, 99.
THOMPSON, R.   (1934) *Canad. publ. Hlth. J.*, **25**, 229.
THOMSEN, A.   (1928) *Dtsch. tierärztl. Wschr.*, **36**, 768 ;   (1931) *Rev. gén. Méd. vét.*, **40**, 457 ;   (1932a) *Ibid.*, **41**, 597 ;   (1932b) *Dtsch. tierärztl. Wschr.*, **40**, 595 ;   (1932c) *Medlemsbl. danske Dyrlaegeforen.*, 15 Arg., Nr. 22 ;   (1934) " Brucella Infection in Swine," Levin and Munksgaard, Copenhagen.
THOMSON, W. M.   (1932) *J. Amer. vet. med. Ass.*, **81**, 348.
THORP, F. and GRAHAM, R.   (1933) *J. Amer. vet. med. Ass.*, **82**, 871.
TRAUM, J. E.   (1914) *Rep. Chief B. Anim. Industry*, p. 30.
TRAUM, J. and HENRY, B. S.   (1930) *J. infect. Dis.*, **47**, 380.
TUMANSKY, V. and KOLESNIKOVA, Z.   (1935) *Rev. Microbiol., Saratov*, **14**, 269.
VEAZIE, L. and MEYER, K. F.   (1935) *Proc. Soc. exp. Biol., N.Y.*, **32**, 1616.
VELOPPÉ and JAUBERT.   (1935) *Rev. gén. Méd. vét.*, **44**, 513.
WADE, E.   (1933) *Lancet*, i. 1342.
WALL, S.   (1911) *Z. InfektKr. Haustiere*, **10**, 23, 132 ;   (1930) *Proc. 11th int. vet. Congr., London* ;   (1933) *Acta. path. microbiol. scand.*, Suppl. 16, 543.
WALLACE, C. E.   (1930) *North-west Med.*, **29**, 566.
WEFRING, K. W.   (1930) *Bull. Off. int. Hyg. publ.*, **22**, 1908.
WEIGMANN, F.   (1931) *Dtsch. med. Wschr.*, **57**, 284.
WELCH, H. and MARSH, H.   (1935) *J. Amer. vet. med. Ass.*, **86**, 493.
WELCH, H. and MICKLE, F. L.   (1933) *J. Lab. clin. Med.*, **18**, 627.
WHERRY, W. B. and LAMB, B. H.   (1914) *J. infect. Dis.*, **15**, 331.
WHITE, G. C., JOHNSON, R. E., PLASTRIDGE, W. N., and REECE, R. P.   (1933) *Storrs agric. Exp. Sta., Bull.*, No. 185.

WHITE, G. C. and SWETT, P. P.   (1935) *J. Amer. vet. med. Ass.*, **87,** 146.
WILCOX, H. L.   (1932) *Amer. J. publ. Hlth.*, **22,** 1157.
WILSON, D. E.   (1935) *E. Afr. med. J.*, **12,** 108.
WILSON, G. S.   (1930) *Brit. med. J.*, ii. 679 ; (1932a) *Vet. Rec.*, **44,** 1226 ; (1932b) *Ibid.*,
   44, 1240 ; (1934) *J. Hyg., Camb.*, **34,** 361.
WRIGHT, A. E. and SMITH, F.   (1897) *Lancet*, i. 656.
YECKEL, H. C. and CHAPMAN, O. D.   (1933) *J. Amer. med. Ass.*, **100,** 1855.
ZAMMIT, T.   (1905) *Rep. Comm. Medit. Fev.*, Part III, p. 83 ; (1906) *Ibid.*, Part IV, p. 96.
ZAMMIT, T. and DEBONO, J. E.   (1933) *Lancet*, i. 134.
ZELLER, H.   (1931) *Bull. Off. int. Epizooties*, **5,** 84.
ZELLER, H. and BELLER, K.   (1934) *Münch. tierärztl. Wschr.*, **85,** 1.
ZELLER, H. and STOCKMAYER, W.   (1935) *Z. InfektKr. Haustiere*, **48,** 77.
ZIMMERMANN, E.   (1935) *Zbl. Bakt.*, **134,** 213.
ZWICK.   (1910) *Zbl. Bakt., Ref.* **47,** 219.
ZWICK, W.   (1930) 11*th Inter. vet. Congr., London* ; (1931) *Dtsch. tierärztl. Wschr.*, **39,** 705.
ZWICK and KRAGE.   (1913) *J. comp. Path.*, **26,** 59.

CHAPTER LXXIII

ANTHRAX

History

ANTHRAX is a disease that has been known from antiquity. In earlier days, however, it was not clearly separated from other affections closely simulating it. Maret (1752) and Fournier (1769) defined the clinical type of malignant pustule in man, and Chabert (1730) gave a clear description of anthrax in animals. In 1823 Barthelémy showed that it was transmissible by inoculation. Rayer (1850) described small, non-motile, filiform bodies in the blood of sheep dead of the disease, and confirmed its transmissibility by inoculation. (For references see Hutyra and Marek 1922.) In a series of papers, Davaine (1863a, b, c, 1864) showed that anthrax could be transmitted to sheep, horses, cattle, guinea-pigs, and mice, by the subcutaneous inoculation of infected but not of normal blood ; that in such animals the bacilli did not appear in the blood till 4 or 5 hours before death ; that in the blood they increased rapidly in numbers, and became filamentous ; and that after death they disappeared as soon as putrefaction commenced. He showed, moreover, that the blood of an infected animal, previous to its invasion with the bacilli, was non-infective, but that after invasion it was capable of conveying the disease ; that animals fed on infected viscera frequently became infected, but that animals fed on the putrefying organs of non-infected animals did not do so ; and that after death from anthrax the spleen, liver, kidneys, lungs, blood, and, to a less extent, other organs contained the bacilli in large numbers. In the same year, Tiegel and Klebs (see Koch 1881) showed that anthrax blood, if filtered through a clay candle, was deprived of its infectivity ; the filtrate was innocuous to animals, but the deposit on the filter remained active. These observations showed, as conclusively as could be expected in the absence of cultivation, that anthrax was caused by a living organism that multiplied in the body, invaded the blood stream, and produced death by septicæmia. To this organism Davaine gave the name of *Bactéridie*—a name by which it is still known among French writers. Subsequently Davaine and Raimbert (1864) found the same organism in a malignant pustule in man, thus demonstrating the ætiological identity of the disease in man and animals.

The final proof of the causative rôle of *B. anthracis* was produced by Koch (1877), who, in a classic masterpiece, which brought him suddenly into fame, gave a full account of the organism, described its formation of resistant spores, its cultivation *in vitro*, the reproduction of the disease by injection of pure cultures, and the recovery of the organism from the animals at necropsy.

The subsequent history of anthrax is largely connected with attempts at immunization, first made by Toussaint, and later with more success by Pasteur, by Sclavo, and by Sobernheim (see section on Vaccination).

Epidemiology

Anthrax in Animals.—Anthrax is primarily a disease of animals, from which man is secondarily infected. To understand the epidemiology of the disease in man, it is therefore necessary to consider first its incidence amongst animals.

Anthrax is a widespread disease occurring in nearly every country in the world. There are areas, such as the Beauce, Champagne and Auvergne in France, Eastern Prussia, the plains of the Danube, and parts of Siberia and Asia Minor in which it is specially prevalent, and from which it never dies out. As a rule, it is commoner in swampy, low-lying districts with warm, loose, moist soils, and in the great deltas, such as those of the Mississippi and the Brahmaputra. In warm countries its maximum incidence is in the months of June, July, August, and September, but in colder countries, such as Great Britain, the disease is commoner during the winter months. The most susceptible animals are the herbivora. Cattle, sheep, pigs, horses, and goats are the chief sufferers, but the disease may occur in dogs, cats, camels, buffaloes, deer, and even in beasts of prey. Algerian sheep are highly resistant (Chauveau 1880a).

In Europe the incidence is usually greater amongst cattle than amongst sheep, but in Australia and South America sheep are more frequently affected.

Since the Anthrax Order of 1910 came into force, the number of outbreaks in this country has been as follows (see Reports, 1914–1934):

1913	.	.	594 outbreaks	1925	.	.	669 outbreaks
1916	.	.	560 ,,	1928	.	.	536 ,,
1919	.	.	239 ,,	1931	.	.	465 ,,
1922	.	.	515 ,,	1934	.	.	395 ,,

In the year 1914, of the animals dying of anthrax 733 were cattle, 5 were sheep, 32 were swine, and 25 were horses. It is seen from this that rarely more than 1 or 2 animals were infected in any one outbreak. This is very different from the type of outbreak that still occurs in many continental areas, where whole herds may be decimated. A reason for this difference will be suggested under the section dealing with the mode of spread of the disease. Table CLIII gives an idea of the frequency of the disease in different parts of the globe (Page 1909).

TABLE CLIII

SHOWING THE AVERAGE ANNUAL NUMBER OF CASES OF ANTHRAX AMONGST ALL ANIMALS BETWEEN 1902 AND 1906.

United Kingdom	1,263
Italy	4,585
Germany	5,559
British India	29,398
European Russia, Finland and N. Caucasus . .	46,169

As a rule, anthrax in animals takes the form of a septicæmia, varying from a sudden apoplectic attack with death occurring in a few minutes after the appearance of the first symptoms, to a subacute type, manifested by fever, and frequently by intestinal disturbances, terminating fatally after about a week. In cattle and horses, circumscribed cutaneous swellings or carbuncles may sometimes appear, not unlike the malignant pustule of man ; in swine and dogs, localization is common on the mucosæ, particularly those of the pharynx and larynx. These forms with local manifestations are rarely so fatal as the general septicæmic disease.

MODE OF INFECTION AND SPREAD.—Anthrax is rarely spread directly from animal to animal. Infection generally occurs by the alimentary tract from ingestion of infected food. During the last stages of the disease in animals, the bacilli are excreted in the urine, fæces, and saliva. At the time of death and for some time afterwards, bloody infected fluid exudes from the openings of the body, and soils the neighbouring ground. The bacilli, which in the blood are invariably in the vegetative form, after being voided from the body soon produce spores under the influence of a suitable temperature and free access of oxygen. These spores are extremely resistant to inimical agencies and may remain alive on the surface of the ground for as long as 12 years (Pasteur 1881a). Cattle or sheep feeding on this ground are liable to be infected ; the spores are taken in by the mouth ; they probably pass through the stomach unharmed, multiply in the small intestine, invade the mucosa, and reach the blood stream.

This view, which was largely developed by Koch (1881) differed in some respects from that put forward by Pasteur (1880), who maintained that infection occurred through the mouth and pharynx. As evidence of this, he showed that if sheep were fed on spores, a certain proportion died of anthrax ; but that if to the infected food were added prickly substances, such as the pointed extremities of dried thistle leaves or barley spikes, which were able to cause erosions of the pharyngeal mucosa, the mortality amongst the sheep was increased. Pasteur, moreover, maintained that earth-worms played an important part in the actual contamination of the ground. He supposed that, when an animal was buried, the bacilli exuding from the openings of the body developed into spores, which were then brought by earth-worms to the surface of the soil, where they were deposited as casts. It is doubtful what importance is to be attributed to this view. Koch (1881), who examined a number of earth-worms placed in artificially infected soil, found that they rarely became infected ; and he brought indirect evidence to suggest that their rôle in the contamination of the ground was negligible in comparison with that caused by the exudation of infected body fluids from animals just before or after death.

The view that the infection of animals occurs chiefly by feeding on contaminated pasture land affords a possible explanation of the greater prevalence of anthrax in low-lying, marshy areas, and by the banks of streams, where grasses and decaying vegetable materials are abundant on which the bacillus may grow ; of the rise in incidence as soon as the weather becomes warm ; and of the absence of an æstival prevalence of the disease in cold countries.

In Great Britain, as already stated, the greatest number of cases occurs during the winter months. This fact alone is sufficient to suggest that the mode of infection is different from that in warmer climates. Though occasional infection may occur by contamination of the ground with the effluents from tannery and other industrial works, M'Fadyean (1903b) has brought evidence to show that soil infection plays little part in the spread of the disease in this country ; and that the majority of cases are traceable to imported food-stuffs. The evidence for this is, briefly, that anthrax occurs sporadically, not epidemically, as might be expected if the soil was the main source of infection ; that the disease is commonest during the winter months, when artificial food-stuffs are most used ; that it is more frequent amongst cattle, which receive artificial food-stuffs, than amongst sheep, which do not ; that 80 per cent. of outbreaks (Stockman 1911) occur on previously uninfected farms ; and that in most outbreaks there is a history of artificial feeding. (See also Jackson 1930.) This evidence, almost entirely circumstantial, has been supplemented by recent work abroad. In Germany in 1914, there were 7,181 cases of anthrax in animals ; in 1919 there were only 743. This tenfold decrease is attributed to the cessation, during the war, of the importation of artificial food-stuffs (Poppe 1922). That such food-stuffs may actually contain anthrax spores has been demonstrated for bone, fish and maize meal, for barley, and for oil-cake.

Another method of infection that may occur, though less commonly, is by flies. *Stomoxys calcitrans*, horse flies, and mosquitoes, for example, have been shown experimentally to convey anthrax (Poppe 1922). The transmission is mechanical (Morris 1918) ; there is no development of the bacilli in the insect's body.

Summarizing, we may say that in warm countries animals are infected chiefly by contaminated pasturage, less often by biting flies ; that in cold countries the chief mode of infection is apparently by artificial food-stuffs ; and that the most frequent mode of infection appears to be primarily or secondarily through the intestine. This last conclusion has been challenged by Besredka (1921) who believes that infection occurs through the skin (see Chapter L), and by Sanarelli (1925) and by Rovida and Schwarz (1928*a, b*), who were unable to demonstrate in laboratory animals the passage of anthrax bacilli through the intact intestinal mucosa.

Excluding very mild and latent cases, the mortality in animals seems to vary between 75 and 100 per cent.

Anthrax in Man.—Anthrax in man may be divided into (1) the non-industrial type, affecting shepherds, farmers, veterinary surgeons, knackers, butchers, pathologists, and others coming into close contact with infected animals ; and (2) the industrial type, arising from the manipulation of wool, animal hair and bristles, hides and skins, or occurring in other industries such as those dealing with harness, furniture, cutlery, boots, manure, rag-sorting, horn, or grain porterage. The epidemiology of these two types is so different that they must be treated separately.

The first type, which takes the form of malignant pustule, is due to contamination of the skin with material from infected animals. It is particularly common, therefore, in countries having a high incidence of anthrax amongst animals, and is relatively uncommon in countries, such as Great Britain, where the incidence amongst animals is low. Moreover, there is a close correlation between the seasonal incidence of anthrax in animals and in human beings. This is well seen in southern Italy, where the number of cases in man rises almost simultaneously during the summer months with the increased prevalence amongst animals (Page 1909). In the United States agricultural anthrax is on the increase (Report 1934–35).

The second type of anthrax, which may take the form of malignant pustule or pulmonary disease, is dependent on infection acquired during the industrial treatment of animal products, and shows no special seasonal incidence. For convenience of reporting, the cases in this country are divided into 5 groups (Table CLIV, p. 1372).

The total number of cases for the 12 years 1913 to 1924 was 743, of which 109, or 14·7 per cent. were fatal. This gives a yearly average of 62 cases with 9 deaths. Between the years 1896 and 1898, Legge (1905) calculated that the incidence amongst persons employed in the worsted and wool trades was 2·1 per 1,000, and amongst those employed in the horsehair industry 3·0 per 1,000, per annum.

In the woollen industries, anthrax occurs almost entirely round the Bradford

TABLE CLIV

Incidence of Industrial Anthrax in Great Britain.[1]

Year.	Wool.	Horsehair.	Hides and Skins.	Other Industries.	Dock Labourers.	Total.
1913 . . .	43 (5)	5 (1)	19 (2)	3	3	73 (8)
1914 . . .	29 (5)	5	15	6 (1)	7 (2)	62 (8)
1915 . . .	26 (2)	2	18 (3)	3 (1)	0	49 (6)
1916 . . .	80 (12)	6 (3)	18 (3)	2	2 (1)	108 (19)
1917 . . .	65 (11)	1	29 (2)	4 (1)	3 (1)	102 (15)
1918 . . .	49 (4)	4 (2)	14 (1)	1	3	71 (7)
1919 . . .	34 (5)	3 (1)	16 (1)	4 (2)	3 (2)	60 (11)
1920 . . .	25 (7)	5 (1)	17 (3)	1	4 (1)	52 (12)
1921 . . .	11 (3)	4 (1)	8 (1)	2 (1)	0	25 (6)
1922 . . .	19 (3)	9 (1)	16 (1)	1	1	46 (5)
1923 . . .	14 (1)	9 (2)	22 (1)	1 (1)	4 (3)	50 (8)
1924 . . .	19 (1)	4 (1)	16 (2)	4	2	45 (4)
Total . . .	414 (59)	57 (13)	208 (20)	32 (7)	32 (10)	743 (109)

The figures in brackets indicate mortality.

[1] For this Table, we are indebted to the kindness of Dr. S. A. Henry, H.M. Medical Inspector of Factories.

district of the West Riding and in Worcestershire ; the other centres are exempt. This can be explained by the fact that the dangerous classes of raw wool from Asia Minor and Persia are used in these districts. Amongst those engaged in the horsehair industry, the maximum incidence falls on those using the dangerous classes of hair from China, Russia, and Siberia. Among the dock porters, the incidence falls chiefly on those working in the ports of London and Liverpool (Legge 1905). (For incidence of human anthrax in Germany, Austria, and the United States during recent years, see Report 1934–35.)

In all but the woollen industry, the type of anthrax contracted is the malignant pustule. As infection occurs from contamination of the skin with the infected animal products, it is natural to expect that the uncovered parts of the body will suffer most severely. Legge (1905) gives the following table (Table CLV) showing the site of the pustule from figures collected by W. Koch (1886).

TABLE CLV

Location of Malignant Pustule.

Situation.	Number.	Per cent.
Head and face	108	43·5
Neck	103	41·5
Upper extremity . . .	31	12·5
Lower extremity . . .	3	1·2
Trunk	3	1·2

The site of the lesion varies, moreover, with the nature of the industry. Hide porters, for example, are frequently infected on the back of the neck, which is more open than other parts to excoriation. In butchers and others who have to handle carcasses, the arm is often affected. The face and neck are prone to attack in those using infected shaving brushes (Vincent 1922, Report 1921), and so on. In the woollen industries, infection occurs during the processes of sorting and combing. The worker inhales a large quantity of dust containing anthrax spores, and is hence liable to the pulmonary type of anthrax. Fifty years ago pulmonary infection was commoner than the malignant pustule, but improvements in factory legislation have diminished this type considerably.

The various products that are liable to give rise to anthrax in man come from regions where the disease is common in animals ; their danger is in proportion to the chance of their being infected. Hides and wool are frequently contaminated with blood ; horse hair and hog bristles are contaminated from various sources.

Owing to their greater exposure, anthrax is more common amongst men than women, but the disease is more fatal in women. The average case mortality for both sexes combined from 1899 to 1907 in Great Britain was 25·2 per cent.

Apart from the methods already mentioned, anthrax may be conveyed to man by the bites of insects that have just fed on the carcass of an infected animal. Contact infection in human beings is uncommon. Occasionally infection may occur by the food, and give rise to the intestinal form. The bacilli are destroyed by the gastric juice, but the spores escape and multiply in the intestine. Experimental evidence, based on findings in laboratory animals, suggests that for this mode of infection to occur in man, large numbers of spores must be present in the food. It is worth while mentioning that the milk of animals dying or just dead of the disease may contain the bacilli (M'Fadyean 1909) ; chances of infection by this method must in this country, at least, be rare.

It will be seen, therefore, that man is infected with anthrax only as a result of his dealings with animals or with animal products. Methods of prevention must be founded on an understanding of this fact.

Apart from malignant pustule, and the less common respiratory and intestinal forms of the disease in man, meningitis is not infrequently caused by the anthrax bacillus.

Bacteriology of Anthrax in Man and Animals.

Anthrax is a disease that, when fatal, invariably terminates in septicæmia. Whatever form the disease takes—the malignant pustule, respiratory, or intestinal —it is characterized by a primary local proliferation of the bacilli, with the formation of local lesions. The fate of the animal rests on the result of this local attack ; if it is resisted by the phagocytes and other defences of the body, recovery rapidly occurs ; if the bacilli prove too virulent, they invade the blood stream, and multiply abundantly. This invasion occurs late—generally not more than a few hours before death—and is accompanied by severe toxic manifestations. It is characteristic of anthrax that the bacilli remain confined almost entirely to the blood vessels ; they are found in maximum numbers in the capillaries of the liver, lung, kidney, spleen, intestine, and stomach, in smaller numbers in those of the brain, skin and muscle. Their distribution varies, however, with the animal attacked. In the blood of mice or rabbits, for example, there are few bacilli to be found ; in guinea-pigs there may be more bacilli than red blood corpuscles. In the larger animals they are usually plentiful, but pigs and horses may die before the organisms have proliferated sufficiently to be detected microscopically (Stockman 1911).

Experimental Production of Anthrax in Animals.—Under natural conditions, the disease is confined chiefly to the herbivora and to man, but occasionally other animals are attacked. Experimentally the disease can be reproduced in the herbivora, rodents, and the omnivora; birds, with the exception of sparrows, and to a less extent hens, ducks, and pigeons, are resistant. Reptiles and fish are insusceptible to infection.

Most of the early experiments on the larger animals were performed with the infected blood of other animals, and it was found that for transmission to be successful certain precautions had to be taken. Putrid blood, for example, often proved non-infective; as did blood that had been rapidly dried after removal from the body. On the other hand, blood or tissues that had been dried slowly were found to retain their infectivity for at least 4 years (Koch 1877). The occurrence of these anomalies was shown by Koch (1877) to be dependent on the presence or absence of spore formation. He found that whenever the bacilli had formed spores, and these spores were capable of being cultivated *in vitro*, the material containing them was infective to animals. The blood of a fœtus removed from a cow that had succumbed to anthrax proved innocuous, showing that the organisms had not passed the placental filter.

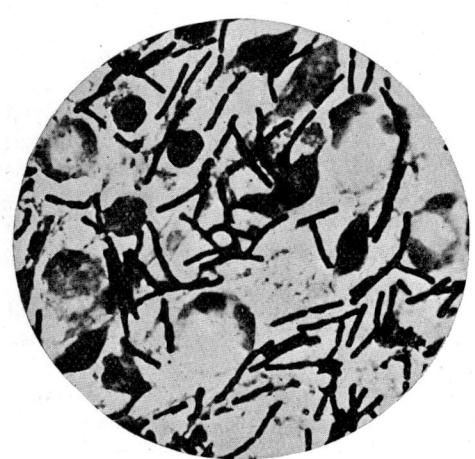

Fig. 268.—*Bacillus anthracis.*
Smear from spleen of experimentally infected guinea-pig, showing the bacilli in large numbers (× 1000).

The disease produced in the larger animals is similar to that occurring naturally. Certain points, however, deserve notice. Sheep can be infected equally well by whatever route the virus is introduced. Cattle, on the other hand, are resistant to subcutaneous inoculation, but are easily infected by the alimentary route (Koch *et al.* 1884). Subcutaneous inoculation in cattle may give rise to a severe spreading œdema, but never to a true malignant pustule; moreover, the animal generally recovers. Chauveau (1880*b*) found that the dose was of considerable importance. Large doses injected into sheep caused a 100 per cent. mortality; smaller doses caused a 50 per cent. mortality; whereas tiny doses of about 50–100 organisms were well supported, and were followed by immunity. In feeding experiments, the dose is very important. Oppermann (1906) was unable to infect sheep by this method with less than 100,000 spores. Koch, Gaffky and Loeffler (1884) found that sheep could be infected by feeding as certainly as by subcutaneous injection, provided large numbers of spores were given; with small numbers the results were irregular or completely negative. (For pathogenicity to small animals see p. 659.)

Diagnosis.

In animals suspected of having died of anthrax, it is important that a post-mortem examination should not be made, otherwise blood will be spilt on the neighbouring ground and will provide a source of infection for other beasts. In this country such post-mortems are now illegal. It is sufficient in cattle and sheep to cut off an ear and send it to the laboratory; or alternatively a swab should be soaked in the blood and several blood-films should be prepared for examination. In pigs and horses, however, as death may occur in the early stages of septicæmia when very few organisms are present in the blood, it is advisable to excise a superficial lymphatic gland, and to make smears of any œdematous fluid that may be present. Malignant pustule can often be diagnosed by bacteriological methods early in the disease, but anthrax of the respiratory and alimentary systems can rarely be diagnosed till late.

Microscopical Examination.—Microscopical examination of fresh material is generally sufficient to enable a provisional diagnosis to be made.

The blood or fluid should be spread on a slide and stained without fixation by Gram's method. A rather thicker film should be fixed imperfectly by three passages through the flame, and after being allowed to cool, stained for a few seconds with 1 per cent. aqueous methylene blue, washed thoroughly in water, and dried in air. By Gram's method the bacilli are stained violet; by the second method—described independently by Heim (1901) and by M'Fadyean (1903a, c, 1904)—they are stained blue, but are surrounded by a deposit of granular or amorphous material, coloured reddish-purple, probably representing the debris of the imperfectly fixed capsules. The bacilli are arranged singly or in pairs; usually they are about 4–6 μ long, but at times filamentous forms may be seen. They may be closely simulated by *Cl. welchii*, a large Gram-positive capsulated anaerobic

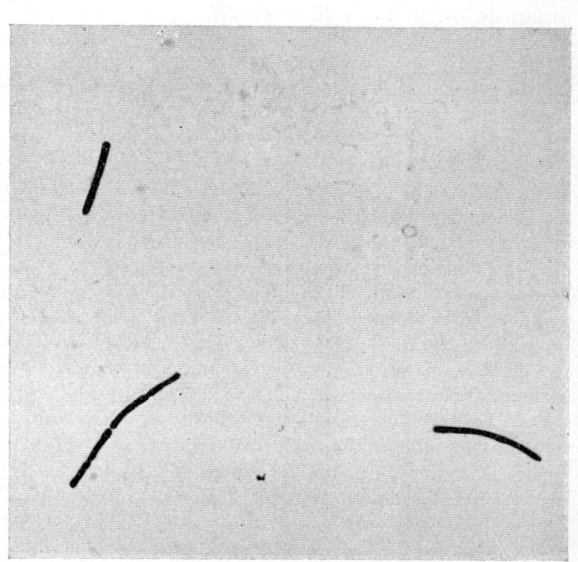

Fig. 269.—*Bacillus anthracis.*
Smear from a malignant pustule in man, showing the bacilli in small numbers ($\times$ 1000).

bacillus which may invade the blood stream in certain conditions. The exclusion of this organism must rest on cultural examination. Their number varies greatly. In the fluid taken from a malignant pustule in man, they may be so few as to escape observation; but if sections are made of a portion of excised tissue, embedded in paraffin, and stained by Gram, they can generally be found. Not too much attention should be paid to negative findings.

Cultural Examination.—Where possible, fresh material should be used. The blood or tissue juice may be taken on a swab, but unless it is to be examined at once it is better to collect it on a sterile thread or fragment of earthenware, or a piece of gypsum that has been soaked in broth and subsequently sterilized (Strassburg method). The drying of the material prevents the destruction of the bacilli by the bactericidal power of the serum (Eurich 1933), facilitates their rapid sporing, and prevents the growth of other organisms. Cultures are put up in the usual way on to agar plates and into broth, and the resulting growth carefully studied. It is important not to confuse *B. anthracis* with other members of the aerobic spore-bearing bacilli. To avoid this, it should be remembered that the anthrax bacillus is non-motile, and liquefies gelatin slowly, whereas most of the other members are motile, and liquefy gelatin rapidly. (For the further differentiation of *B. anthracis* from anthrax-like bacilli, see Chapter XXXII.)

If wool or hair is to be examined, it should be soaked in a weak solution of KOH, incubated for some hours, teased out, heated at 80° C. for 2 minutes, and seeded into 2 per cent. peptone agar, which is then poured into Petri dishes. Particular attention should be paid to the deep colonies, which, in cultures less than 24 hours old, have a characteristic opaque white filamentous appearance with sometimes a nebula at one end (Eurich 1912).

Pathogenicity Tests.—If possible, these should be carried out with the pure cultures that have been isolated. If the original material is used, particularly if this is old, putrid, or contaminated, the animal may die of infection with some organism other than *B. anthracis*. As a routine, the best animals to employ are the mouse and the guinea-pig.

About 0·5 c.c. of a 24-hours' broth culture should be injected subcutaneously into the thigh. Death generally occurs within 2 to 3 days ; post mortem, there is a hæmorrhagic gelatinous exudate at the site of inoculation, and a large, congested, dark-red spleen (see Chapter XXXII) ; microscopically, the bacilli are found in the blood and in smears made from the viscera (Fig. 268, p. 1374). Cultures should be put up for confirmation.

If the only available material is putrid, it is well to inoculate 3 or 4 mice by scratching the skin with a needle dipped in the fluid. As the anthrax bacillus can gain entrance through the abraded skin more easily than other organisms with which it is liable to be contaminated, death of one or more of the mice will probably occur from a pure anthracæmia. This method, first described by Koch, Gaffky and Loeffler (1884), is a good example of the method of purification of cultures by animal inoculation (see Chapter XI).

Wool, hair, or other industrial material should be suspended in water—if necessary after alkaline treatment in the way described under cultural examination—the suspension should be centrifuged, and the deposit inoculated into 2 or 3 guinea-pigs. The animal test is more delicate than the plate method. Using it, Glynn and Lewis (1912), to whom reference should be made for fuller particulars, isolated anthrax spores from 21·3 per cent. of 141 samples of industrial material—mainly hides, wool, hair and bones—supposed to have produced anthrax in Liverpool.

Serological Diagnosis.—Neither the agglutination nor the complement-fixation tests are of value for diagnosis. There is one test, however, depending on the presence in infected animal tissues of a substance—a precipitinogen—that reacts with a suitable immune serum to form a precipitate, which has been found of great value ; this is Ascoli's thermoprecipitin reaction.

Ascoli (1911) worked with saline extracts of tissues at room temperature, but he found that, for practical purposes, time could be saved by extraction at 100° C. For diagnosis, the organs or blood of the suspected animal are ground up and suspended in saline, boiled for 5 minutes, filtered through paper and allowed to cool. Of this extract, 0·5 c.c. is run very carefully on to the surface of a similar quantity of immune serum in a small tube. Within 15 minutes at room temperature, a definite ring-like precipitate forms at the junction of the two fluids. It is necessary to control the test very carefully with a known anthrax extract and with a normal serum. The method is a delicate one, and may give a positive result with material that has been kept for 2 years or more. A modification of the test has been recently described by Standfusz and Schnauder (1925), and an improved method of preparing high-titre precipitating sera by Rosenberg and Romanow (1929). The precipitable substance in the tissues is derived both from the capsular protein antigen and the somatic polysaccharide antigen. According to Tomcsik and Szongott (1933), most commercial sera contain precipitins only for the polysaccharide. Since there is more protein than polysaccharide antigen in the tissues (Tomcsik and Bodon 1934), it would probably be better to use a serum containing precipitins for both components.

Natural Immunity.

The investigation of the natural resistance of certain animals to anthrax played a prominent part in the controversy between the cellular and humoral schools of immunity, in the early days of bacteriology. Without attempting to adduce all the evidence that was brought forward during this controversy, we shall merely draw attention to some of the salient points. Von Behring (for references see Chapter XLIX) found that the blood serum of the rat—an animal that is fairly resistant to anthrax—possessed a remarkable destructive action on the bacillus and he was led to conclude that the immunity of this animal was dependent on the bactericidal content of its serum (see p. 918). On the other hand, Metchnikoff and his co-workers stated that, though the blood serum of the rat is bactericidal *in vitro* to the anthrax bacillus, the blood plasma *in vitro* does not possess this action. Furthermore, the spores are able to develop in the body of the rat, and to cause a symptomless infection (Kritschewski and Messik 1930) ; their further proliferation is restrained by the attack of the phagocytes, which ingest and destroy them. The serum of the rabbit, like that of the rat, has a bactericidal effect on the anthrax bacillus, yet the rabbit is susceptible to experimental inoculation with this organism.

The dog presents another interesting example. When young it is fairly susceptible ; when older it is more resistant to experimental injection. Nuttall (1888) found that the defibrinated blood of the dog readily destroyed the bacilli ; Metchnikoff was unable to confirm this, but demonstrated a close correlation between the phagocytic activity of the leucocytes and the resistance of the animal. Methods such as removal of the spleen, or intravenous injection of fine wood charcoal, which served to divert the leucocytes, destroyed this resistance.

Pasteur, Joubert and Chamberland (1878) found that the natural resistance of fowls to injection with anthrax could be destroyed by immersing them up to the thighs in cold water ; they concluded that the immunity of these birds depended on their high normal temperature (41–42° C.), which interfered with the development of the bacillus. That this explanation was incorrect was shown by Wagner (1890), who found that the bacillus developed readily in the blood and blood serum of fowls outside the body, even at a temperature of 43° C. Further experiments led to the conclusion that the immersion in cold water served to lower the phagocytic response, and thus allow the bacilli to proliferate. As a further illustration of this principle, we may quote the experiments of Charrin and Roger (1890), who stated that the natural resistance of rats could be broken down by excessive exercise, and of Preisz (1909), who found that frogs were resistant if kept at 18° C. but not at 30° C.

Weyl (1892) found that anthrax-infected threads, planted in the subcutaneous tissues of hens or pigeons, were rendered avirulent for mice in 4 days ; he satisfied himself that the bacilli were killed by the phagocytes as soon as the spores germinated.

Chauveau (1880c) stated that if anthrax bacilli were injected intravenously into vaccinated animals, the bacilli rapidly disappeared from the circulation, being filtered off by the lungs and spleen ; these bacilli, however, retained their vitality for some days. Sobernheim (1904) likewise found that the bacilli could live for weeks in the local infiltration produced in immunized sheep without undergoing any loss of virulence. From these experiments, it is clear that a number of bacilli may remain alive and virulent in the tissues without giving rise to disease.

The evidence that natural immunity to anthrax depends on the presence of

β lysins in the blood is unsatisfactory.   There is no correlation between the presence of these substances in different animal species and the natural resistance of these species to anthrax.   It would appear rather that the most important protective mechanism is phagocytosis.   Observations are at hand, however, that point to the presence of some other mechanism that prevents the proliferation of the organisms within the body.   The nature of this mechanism is at present unknown.

Prevention, Vaccination, and Serum Treatment.

The usual hygienic measures should be adopted on the occurrence of anthrax in a herd.   Every precaution should be taken to avoid contamination of the stall or pasture with blood or other fluid exuded from the animal.   The carcass should be buried at a depth of 6 feet, or cremated.   Other animals in the herd should be watched, and their temperatures should be taken before milking ; any animal showing rise of temperature should be isolated, and its milk withheld from distribution (M'Fadyean 1909).

Where the disease is epidemic, prophylaxis is best assured by vaccination.   In countries in which the cases are sporadic, close attention should be paid to the artificial food-stuffs, as these appear to be responsible for a large proportion of the outbreaks.

The prevention of industrial anthrax in man is directed partly to disinfection of the imported animal products, wool, hides, horsehair, and so on, and partly to diminishing the risk of contact with dangerous material in the factories.   For the various methods of disinfection, and for factory legislation, the reader is referred to textbooks of Hygiene.   Briefly, however, the disinfection of bales and fleeces may be accomplished by preliminary treatment with warm alkali, followed by exposure to a 2·5 per cent. solution of formaldehyde and drying in hot air (Memo. 1921).   Robertson (1932) recommends the use of H_2S for the disinfection of hides ; anthrax spores are destroyed in 7–16 days.

Vaccination.—In 1879, Chauveau (1880b) found that an animal which survived inoculation with anthrax was more resistant to subsequent inoculations.   The following year, Toussaint (1880a, b) successfully vaccinated sheep with defibrinated anthrax blood that had been heated for 10 minutes at 55° C.   In 1881, Pasteur (1881b, c) introduced a method of vaccination, founded on the same principle as that which had been successful in diminishing the virulence of the organism of chicken cholera.   He found that if the anthrax bacillus was cultivated in broth at 42–43° C., not only did it lose its power of forming spores, but it gradually decreased in virulence, till after 2 to 3 months it was no longer able to give rise to disease, even in the most susceptible animals.   Pasteur prepared two vaccines ; the first or *premier vaccin* was a subculture in broth from a strain that had been kept at 42–43° C. for 15 to 20 days ; its virulence was such that it could kill mice and young guinea-pigs, but was unable to kill adult guinea-pigs or rabbits.   The second or *deuxième vaccin* was a subculture after 10 to 12 days ; it was much more virulent, being able to kill mice, adult guinea-pigs and a certain proportion of injected rabbits.

Arrangements were made with the President of the Agricultural Society of Melun for a trial of this new method under field conditions.   Accordingly on May 5, 1881, on a farm at Pouilly-le-Fort, 24 sheep, 1 goat and 6 cows received their first vaccination, and on May 17 they were vaccinated a second time with the more virulent but still attenuated strain.   On May 31, Pasteur and his co-workers,

Roux and Chamberland, inoculated each of the vaccinated animals with a virulent culture of anthrax ; at the same time a series of control animals consisting of 24 sheep, 1 goat and 4 cows were similarly inoculated. Two days later, the vaccinated sheep and the goat were in perfect condition ; the control sheep and the goat were all dead. The 4 unvaccinated cows were suffering from severe œdema and fever ; the 6 vaccinated cows had neither fever nor œdema. The following day one of the vaccinated sheep died, but at necropsy it was found to be carrying a fœtus that had been dead for about a fortnight.

The success of this experiment led to the vaccination on a large scale of cattle and sheep in Europe, in South America, and in other countries. In 1894 Chamberland collected the statistics that were available for the years 1882 to 1893 inclusive (Table CLVI).

TABLE CLVI
RESULTS OF VACCINATION BY PASTEUR'S METHOD.

No. of sheep vaccinated	1,788,677
Mortality after 1st vaccine	5,668, or 0·32 per cent.
Mortality after 2nd vaccine	4,406, or 0·24 ,,
Mortality during the rest of the year	6,798, or 0·38 ,,
Total mortality	16,872, or 0·94 ,,
No. of oxen and cows vaccinated	200,962
Mortality after 1st vaccine	177, or 0·09 ,,
Mortality after 2nd vaccine	82, or 0·04 ,,
Mortality during rest of year	432, or 0·21 ,,
Total mortality	691, or 0·34 ,,

Before vaccination, the mean mortality of sheep was 10 per cent., of cattle 5 per cent. Chamberland calculated that vaccination had effected a saving of 5 million francs on sheep, and of 2 million francs on cattle.

In Germany, from 1901 to 1908, the total mortality of vaccinated cattle was 0·03 per cent., of horses 0·05 per cent., and of sheep 0·06 per cent. (Klimmer 1911).

At first sight these figures seem impressive, but further consideration suggests suspension of judgment. The method of comparing the mortality in vaccinated animals, during a given period, with the mortality amongst unvaccinated animals in a preceding period, is fallacious ; there is no evidence to show that the conditions of the two sets of animals were identical. Large numbers of the vaccinated animals were never subsequently exposed to any risk of anthrax at all ; hence no conclusions relative to their immunity can be drawn. Moreover, it would appear that anthrax in France is nearly as prevalent as it was before the vaccination era (Page 1909).

There have been many unfavourable reports on the Pasteurian method of vaccination. One of the chief objections is that it is impossible to standardize the virulence of the two vaccines exactly. Sometimes the virulence is too high, so that large numbers of animals die of the injection alone ; sometimes it is too low and confers no protection. Pasteur stated that the decrease in virulence at 42–43° C. occurred gradually, so that at any moment it was possible to fix the virulence at a given point. It is fairly clear now that this statement was incorrect. Preisz (1911), in an illuminating article, showed that in a culture maintained at 42–43° C. bacillary variants appear, some of which possess no capsules and are avirulent, while others possess capsules and are highly virulent ; intermediate forms, some spore-bearing, others non-spore-bearing, may appear, and may also differ in virulence. One and the same culture, therefore, may contain both highly virulent and quite avirulent varieties, besides a number of intermediate forms. Moreover, there is no strict relation between the length of incubation and the appearance of the different variants (see Chapter XXXII). These observations serve to explain the anomalous results of different workers, and show the impossibility of obtaining vaccines of fixed virulence by Pasteur's method.

CIENKOWSKY'S METHOD.—Two vaccines are prepared containing spore-bearing bacilli attenuated by heat, and standardized in virulence by repeated passage through gophers (*Zieselmaus*). The first vaccine, which is only one-tenth as strong as the second, is stated to kill mice but not guinea-pigs; the second vaccine kills guinea-pigs but not rabbits. The dose is 0·6 gm. for horses, 1·0 gm. for cattle, and 0·2 gm. for sheep, of vaccine I; the dose of vaccine II is half that of the first vaccine. This method has been used chiefly in Russia. The mortality of vaccinated horses is 0·1–0·3 per cent., of cattle 0·02–0·07 per cent., and of sheep 0·1 per cent. Favourable reports have been issued from Hungary and from North America; in Japan it has superseded Pasteur's method (Poppe 1922). It is clear that the objections raised by Preisz to the Pasteurian method apply equally to this method of vaccination.

SOBERNHEIM'S COMBINED METHOD.—This is a method of combined active and passive immunization. Sobernheim (1902, 1904, 1906) prepares an immune serum by injection of cattle or sheep with cultures of increasing virulence. For his vaccine, he uses a culture slightly attenuated by growth at 42·5° C. In practice, simultaneous injections are made, beneath the skin, of 10–16 c.c. of immune serum and 0·5–1·0 c.c. of vaccine. This method has been extensively adopted in Germany and South America, where it appears to have given good results. It has the merit of requiring only one injection instead of two; of conferring a passive immunity which protects the animal while an active immunity is developing; and of being attended by very little danger. It can be employed after an epidemic has broken out, without fear of rendering the animals more susceptible to infection.

None of the methods in use confers an immunity for more than 9 months or a year; hence vaccination must be repeated annually. It is extremely difficult to gather from the imperfect figures that have been reported what the value of vaccination really is. Instead of vaccinating alternate animals, and comparing the mortality of the vaccinated with the control animals in the same herd, the experiments have nearly all been made by vaccination of the entire herd, and comparing the mortality of the vaccinated animals with that of the non-vaccinated animals during previous years. The evidence is therefore circumstantial, and cannot be considered satisfactory.

On the whole, however, vaccination does seem to be of value in districts in which the disease is rife. It should never be employed in countries where merely sporadic cases occur, for the living bacilli that are injected may actually help to spread rather than to restrict the disease. Of the three methods given, the balance of evidence is in favour of Sobernheim's combined sero-vaccination.

Serum Treatment.—Several workers have prepared an immune serum by injection of animals with cultures of increasing virulence, and have found it capable of conferring passive immunity on rabbits. Sobernheim, in particular, has obtained satisfactory results both for protective and for therapeutic purposes with immune sheep and cattle serum, but speaking generally the serum treatment of animals has never been employed on a large scale.

In man, on the other hand, serum treatment is of great importance, and Sclavo's serum appears to have given excellent results. Sclavo (1895) first immunized sheep, but later (1896, 1898, 1901) he found that the ass gave the most satisfactory results. For use in man, 40–60 c.c. should be given intravenously and repeated in smaller doses subcutaneously. In 1903 Sclavo collected 164 cases of anthrax treated with serum in Italy ; there were 10 deaths or a mortality of £ 6·09 per cent. compared with a mortality of 24·1 per cent. for the whole of Italy (see Page 1909). Legge (1905) states that the mortality of cases treated early varies in different series from 7·1 per cent. to 15·4 per cent., as against 25 per cent. for untreated cases. In this country Hodgson (1928) has reported a series of 31 cases treated, with only two deaths. From 1 to 7 injections were given intravenously, the total dosage varying between 90 and 645 c.c. of serum. Eurich (1933) has had a mortality of only 5 per cent. in his last 200 cases of cutaneous anthrax. His treatment consists in never excising the pustule, except when it is in a site, such as the neck, where rapid extension is common, in immobilizing the part, in giving 80 c.c. of Sclavo's serum intravenously or subcutaneously on the 1st day and 60 c.c. on the 2nd, and in combining serum treatment with a moderately large dose of salvarsan on the 1st and 2nd days. This treatment is similar to that advocated in the United States (Report 1934–35).

The way in which the serum acts is unknown. It contains neither bactericidins nor antitoxins ; the agglutinin content is said to be no higher than that of normal serum ; but Cler (1906) states that it contains opsonins and complement-fixing bodies. Sobernheim (1904) found that immune serum could be heated to 60–70° C., could be kept for $2\frac{1}{2}$ years without any precautions, or could be frozen and thawed, without suffering any diminution of its protective power.

REFERENCES

Ascoli, A. (1911) *Zbl. Bakt.*, **58**, 63.
Besredka, A. (1921) *Ann. Inst. Pasteur*, **35**, 421.
Chamberland, C. (1894) *Ann. Inst. Pasteur*, **8**, 161.
Charrin, A. and Roger, G. H. (1890) *Arch. phys. norm. Path.*, **22**, 273.
Chauveau, A. (1880*a*) *C. R. Acad. Sci.*, **91**, 33 ; (1880*b*) *Ibid.*, **91**, 648 ; (1880*c*) *Ibid.*, **91**, 680.
Cler, E. (1906) *Zbl. Bakt.*, **40**, 241.
Davaine, C. (1863*a*) *C. R. Acad. Sci.*, **57**, 220 ; (1863*b*) *Ibid.*, **57**, 351 ; (1863*c*) *Ibid.*, **57**, 386 ; (1864) *Ibid.*, **59**, 393.
Davaine, C. and Raimbert. (1864) *C. R. Acad. Sci.*, **59**, 429.
Eurich, F. W. (1912) *J. Path. Bact.*, **17**, 249 ; (1933) *Brit. med. J.*, i. 50.
Glynn, E. E. and Lewis, F. C. (1912) *J. Hyg., Camb.*, **12**, 227.
Heim, L. (1901) *Arch. Hyg.*, **40**, 55.
Hodgson, A. E. (1928) *Lancet*, ii. 594.
Hutyra, F. and Marek, J. (1922) " Special Pathology and Therapeutics of the Diseases of Domestic Animals," 2nd Amer. edit., **1**, 1. Chicago and London.
Jackson, R. (1930) *J. comp. Path.*, **43**, 95.
Klimmer. (1911) " Handbuch der Serumtherapie und Serumdiagnostik in der Veterinär-medizin." Leipzig (Quoted from Hutyra and Marek, 1922.)
Koch, R. (1877) *Cohns Beitr. Biol. Pflanz.*, **2**, 277 ; (1881) *Mitt. ReichsgesundhAmt.*, **1**, 49.
Koch, R., Gaffky, and Loeffler. (1884) *Mitt. ReichsgesundhAmt.*, **2**, 147.
Koch, W. (1886) " Milzbrand und Rauschbrand " in Billroth and Lucke's Dtsch. Chir., Stuttgart.
Kritschewski, I. L. and Messik, R. E. (1930) *Z. ImmunForsch.*, **65**, 420.
Legge, T. M. (1905) *Lancet*, i. 689, 765, 841.
Memorandum. (1921) " Prevention of Anthrax among Industrial Workers." Home Office, London.

M'FADYEAN, J. (1903a) *J. comp. Path.*, **16**, 35 ; (1903b) *Ibid.*, **16**, 346 ; (1903c) *Ibid.*, **16**, 360 ; (1904) *Ibid.*, **17**, 58 ; (1909) *Ibid.*, **22**, 148.
MORRIS, H. (1918) *J. comp. Path.*, **31**, 134.
NUTTALL, G. (1888) *Z. Hyg. InfektKr.*, **4**, 353.
OPPERMANN. (1906) *J. comp. Path.*, **19**, 264.
PAGE, C. H. W. (1909) *J. Hyg., Camb.*, **9**, 279, 357.
PASTEUR, L. (1880) *C. R. Acad. Sci.*, **91**, 209 ; (1881a) *Ibid.*, **92**, 209 ; (1881b) *Ibid.*, **92**, 429 ; (1881c) *Ibid.*, **92**, 666.
PASTEUR, JOUBERT, and CHAMBERLAND. (1878) *Bull. Acad. Méd.*, 2nd Ser., **7**, 432.
POPPE, K. (1922) *Ergebn. Hyg. Bakt.*, **5**, 597.
PREISZ, H. (1909) *Zbl. Bakt.*, **49**, 341 ; (1911) *Ibid.*, **58**, 510.
Reports. (1914–1934) *Bd Agric. Fish., Lond.* ; (1921) *Min. Hlth Circ.*, No. 172 ; (1934–35) *Amer. publ. Hlth Ass. Year Book*, Suppl. *Amer. J. publ. Hlth.*, 1935, **25**, No. 2.
ROBERTSON, M. E. (1932) *J. Hyg., Camb.*, **32**, 367.
ROSENBERG, R. and ROMANOW, D. (1929) *Zbl. Bakt.*, **110**, 102.
ROVIDA, G. and SCHWARZ, E. (1928a) *Sperimentale*, **81**, 569 ; (1928b) *Ibid.*, **82**, 173, 765.
SANARELLI, G. (1925) *Ann. Inst. Pasteur*, **39**, 209.
SCLAVO, A. (1895) *Zbl. Bakt.*, **18**, 744 ; (1896) *Riv. Igiene Sanit. pubbl.*, **7**, 705, 745 ; (1898) *Ibid.*, **9**, 200, 814 ; (1901) *Ibid.*, **12**, 212, 247 ; (1903) *Ibid.*, **14**, 519.
SOBERNHEIM, G. (1902) *Berl. klin. Wschr.*, **39**, 516 ; (1904) *Dtsch. med. Wschr.*, **30**, 948, 988 ; (1906) *J. comp. Path.*, **19**, 249.
STANDFUSZ, R. and SCHNAUDER, F. (1925) *Zbl. Bakt.*, **95**, 61.
STOCKMAN, S. (1911) *J. comp. Path.*, **24**, 97.
TOMCSIK, J. and BODON, G. (1934) *Z. ImmunForsch.*, **83**, 426.
TOMCSIK, J. and SZONGOTT, H. (1933) *Z. ImmunForsch.*, **78**, 86.
TOUSSAINT, H. (1880a) *C. R. Acad. Sci.*, **91**, 135 ; (1880b) *Ibid.*, **91**, 303.
VINCENT, C. (1922) *J. infect. Dis.*, **31**, 499.
WAGNER, K. E. (1890) *Ann. Inst. Pasteur*, **4**, 570.
WEYL, T. (1892) *Z. Hyg. InfektKr.*, **11**, 381.

CHAPTER LXXIV

TETANUS

History

THIS disease was described by Hippocrates, Aretæus, and others, but its nature remained obscure till Carle and Rattone in 1884 demonstrated its transmissibility to animals. They injected a number of rabbits with a suspension of an acne pustule, which had been the starting-point of a fatal attack of tetanus. The injections, which were made into the sciatic nerve or into the back muscles, were followed in 2 or 3 days by tetanus. The disease could be transmitted to fresh animals by injection of a suspension of nerve tissue.

In the same year Nicolaier (1884, 1886), working at Göttingen, found that the inoculation of earth into mice, guinea-pigs, or rabbits was frequently followed by a disease closely simulating human tetanus. In the pus at the site of inoculation, besides cocci and other organisms, he noticed long, thin bacilli, resembling, but rather larger than, Koch's bacillus of mouse septicæmia (*Ery. muriseptica*). Though he was unable to isolate this organism in pure culture, he grew it in deep coagulated serum for seven generations, and reproduced the disease by injection of the last culture. In animals dying of the experimental disease Nicolaier was unable to find these bacilli microscopically except in the local lesion and, occasionally, in the sciatic nerve sheath and spinal cord. Their limited distribution led him to suggest that the organisms multiplied locally and produced a strychnine-like poison, which, on absorption, reproduced the disease. In 1886 Rosenbach observed a similar bacillus with a round terminal spore in a human case of tetanus, and the pus proved infective to animals. The final demonstration of the ætiological rôle of the tetanus bacillus was furnished in 1889 by Kitasato, who isolated it in pure culture from pus. This he accomplished by heating the pus to 80° C. for 45 to 60 minutes to destroy non-sporing organisms, plating out on gelatin, and incubating in an atmosphere of hydrogen. The inoculation of pure cultures into animals was successful in reproducing the disease.

Epidemiology.

A. Incidence.—Tetanus is an infective disease resulting generally from the contamination of a wound or raw surface, and characterized by a series of tonic muscular spasms usually commencing in the neighbourhood of the site of infection. The frequency with which the masseter muscles are involved has given rise to the popular term lockjaw. In mild cases the spasms may remain localized, but as a rule they become general and involve the whole of the somatic muscular system. In infants the cut surface of the umbilical cord may afford an entrance to the bacilli—tetanus neonatorum. Infections of the face or head give rise to a peculiar form—cephalic tetanus—characterized by facial paralysis and dysphagia. Visceral tetanus is an uncommon form, in which infection appears to originate from the bacilli in the intestinal tract.

In this country the disease is comparatively uncommon. From 1915 to 1924 the mean annual number of civilian deaths in England and Wales was 157·7, of which 123·2 were in men and 34·5 were in women. But in other countries, particularly the tropics, the disease is more widespread. In 1909 there were 1,373 deaths from tetanus amongst 732,528 deaths from all causes in 18 states of North America ; of these 30·7 per cent. were in children under 1 year (Osler 1920). At one time the 4th July celebrations were followed by a large number of cases, usually resulting from blank cartridge wounds (Smith 1908).

Tetanus has followed the administration of gelatin for the control of hæmostasis, of vaccine lymph, of antitoxic sera, of bacterial vaccines, and the insertion of catgut (Smith 1908).

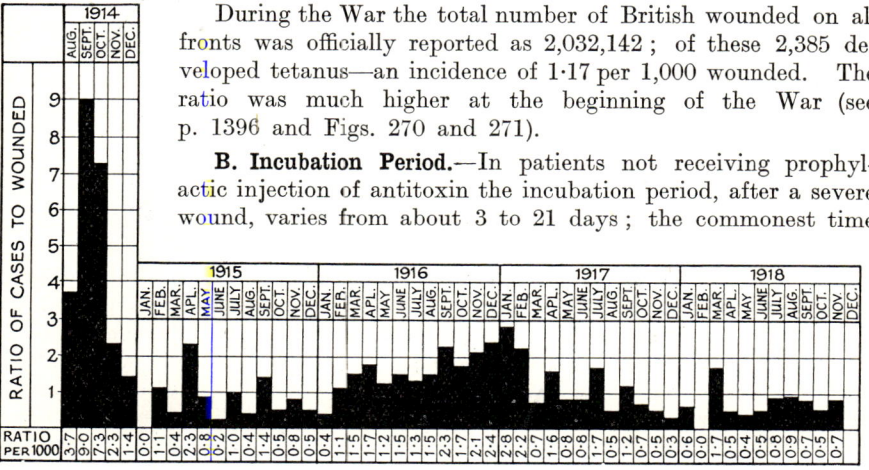

During the War the total number of British wounded on all fronts was officially reported as 2,032,142 ; of these 2,385 developed tetanus—an incidence of 1·17 per 1,000 wounded. The ratio was much higher at the beginning of the War (see p. 1396 and Figs. 270 and 271).

B. Incubation Period.—In patients not receiving prophylactic injection of antitoxin the incubation period, after a severe wound, varies from about 3 to 21 days ; the commonest time

Fig. 270.

The ratio per 1,000 of cases of tetanus to wounded. (After Bruce.)

of onset is about the 7th day. During the War the incubation period increased enormously—partly on account of the use of antitoxin prophylactically ; thus in cases treated in home hospitals, the incubation period increased from an average of 11·8 days in 1914 to 50 days in 1918–19 (Bruce 1920).

C. Mortality.—This depends on the nature of the wound, the site of infection, and the treatment accorded. Severe wounds, especially if deep, lacerated, or badly soiled, are characterized by a high mortality. Wounds of the upper extremities are more dangerous than those of the trunk or lower extremities (Bruce 1920). Tetanus neonatorum is very fatal.

The earlier the onset of symptoms, the more likely is death to occur (Table CLVII, opposite) (Bruce 1920).

In pre-serum days the case mortality was about 85 per cent. (Bruce 1920). Bruce (1915, 1916, 1917b, c, d, 1919, 1920) reports on 1,458 cases of tetanus that were treated in home hospitals during the War. After 1914 almost every

TABLE CLVII

SHOWING THE RELATION BETWEEN THE LENGTH OF THE INCUBATION PERIOD AND THE MORTALITY IN TETANUS.

Length of Incubation Period.	No. of Cases.	Case Mortality per cent.
2–10 days	294	58·1
11–22 days	477	35·3
Over 22 days	579	17·3

patient had received one or more prophylactic inoculations of antitoxin ; the majority had also been treated therapeutically with antiserum. The mortality from tetanus of these cases was as follows (Table CLVIII) :

TABLE CLVIII

MORTALITY OF CASES OF TETANUS IN THE WAR.[1]

Year.	No. of Cases.	Died of Tetanus.	Recovered.	Percentage Mortality.
1914 . . .	182	101	81	55·5
1915 . . .	138	78	60	56·5
1916 . . .	451	170	281	37·7
1917 . . .	376	76	294	20·5
1918 . . .	291	73	204	26·4
1919 . . .	20	3	16	15·8

[1] 21 cases dying from causes other than tetanus have been excluded.

Amongst cases of tetanus developing in France or Belgium and treated abroad the mortality was very much higher. In the spring of 1915 amongst 179 cases there were 140 deaths—78·2 per cent. case mortality. Between July and October, 1916, Leishman and Smallman (1917) reported on 160 cases with a mortality of 73·7 per cent. And between November, 1916, and December, 1917, Cummins and Gibson (1919) reported on 376 cases with a mortality of 67·0 per cent. The higher mortality in France was no doubt due to the fact that cases of tetanus with a short incubation period were treated abroad, whereas those in which this period was longer were generally evacuated to England.

D. Distribution of Tetanus Bacilli.

SOIL.—Nicolaier (1884) demonstrated the presence of tetanus bacilli in 12 out of 18 samples of earth. Some of the specimens—from Leipzig and Berlin—had been kept for years. In this country Fildes (1925a) examined 70 specimens of soil from waste and cultivated lands, and found *Cl. tetani* 33 times.

ANIMAL FÆCES.—Toledo (Toledo and Veillon 1891) demonstrated the presence of *Cl. tetani* in horse and in cow dung. Noble (1915) found it in 18 per cent. of 61 samples of horse fæces examined, but not in any of 21 samples of cow fæces. Sanfelice (1893) demonstrated it in 7 out of 23 samples of normal guinea-pig fæces. Fildes (1925a) isolated it from 34 out of 200 samples of normal horse fæces from London stables. Kerrin (1929) found it in 8 out of 53 samples of horse fæces, 4 out of 21 samples of cow, 6 out of 23 samples of sheep, 17 out of 37 samples of dog, 52 out of 141 samples of rat, and 6 out of 34 samples of hen fæces.　Approximately half of the strains proved to be atoxic.

HUMAN FÆCES.—Pizzini (1898) demonstrated the presence of *Cl. tetani* in human fæces ; he found it in 3 out of 10 samples from ostlers, and in 2 out of 90 samples from peasants.　On the basis of these results, it has been generally assumed that contact with horses strongly predisposes to the carrier condition in man, but we doubt if this assumption is justified.　In this country Tulloch (1919–20) found the tetanus bacillus in 5 out of 31 specimens of fæces, and Fildes (1925a) only twice in 200 specimens, while Kerrin (1928, 1929) failed to find it once in an examination of 304 samples of adult stools.　Similarly Scheunemann (1931) in Germany was unable to isolate it from 50 samples of human fæces.　The tetanus bacillus must be ingested frequently with raw food, but the evidence suggests that it is an organism of passage, which does not find a natural habitat in the human intestine.

Reproduction of the Disease in Animals.

Tetanus can be reproduced by the inoculation of pure cultures, or of the toxin, into mice, rats, guinea-pigs, rabbits, goats, horses, and monkeys.　Cats and dogs are more resistant ; birds and cold-blooded animals are highly resistant.　The most susceptible animal, calculated on the amount of toxin per gram of body weight necessary to prove fatal on injection, is the horse.　This is about 12 times as susceptible as the mouse ; the guinea-pig is 6 times, and the monkey 4 times, as susceptible as the mouse (von Lingelsheim 1912, Sherrington 1917).　On the other hand, the rabbit is twice, the dog 50 times, the cat 600, and the hen 30,000 times as resistant as the mouse (Kitasato 1891, von Lingelsheim 1912).　For a description of the lesions produced in laboratory animals reference should be made to Chapter XXXIII.

Mode of Infection in Tetanus.

Vaillard and Rouget in 1892 found that, if tetanus cultures were heated to 65–67° C. for half an hour to destroy the vegetative bacilli and the toxin, the toxin-free spores remaining could be injected in large numbers into a guinea-pig without giving rise to the disease.　Microscopical examination showed that the spores did not germinate in the tissues, but were rapidly taken up by the phagocytes, so that in 2 or 3 days they were completely ingested.　If, however, the spores were protected from the phagocytes by being wrapped in filter paper, they germinated and gave rise to fatal tetanus.　The same results could be obtained by inflicting a trauma at the site of injection, sufficient to cause tissue necrosis or effusion of blood, or by creating a simple fracture.　In the damaged tissue the spores were able to germinate, whereas in clean, aseptic wounds they were unable to do so.　The presence of other organisms, particularly aerobic, in the wound also permitted the germination of the spores.　From these observations it appears that toxin-free spores are innocuous, but that they can be activated by injuring the tissues or by a secondary infection.

These observations were extended by several workers, of whom, for the sake of convenience, we may quote one of the latest.　Francis (1924) found that toxin-free spores were rendered pathogenic for guinea-pigs by the simultaneous injection of staphylococci, or of a tissue debilitant such as quinine.　He also observed that if either of these agents was inoculated some time after the injection of the spores, tetanus frequently developed.

The result depended on the time elapsing between the two injections. When the spores and the accessory agent were given simultaneously into the same site, all the animals died ; when the accessory agent was given into the same site 9 to 30 days after the spores, 11 out of 24 of the animals died ; and when the interval was between 30 and 90 days, only 2 out of 20 died. These experiments show clearly that the spores may survive in the tissues for some time. This confirms the work of Vaillard and Rouget (1892), who found that though the spores were rapidly ingested by phagocytes, they were not necessarily destroyed, but might remain latent within the cells, and spontaneously give rise to tetanus some months afterwards (idiopathic tetanus). Francis concluded that in guinea-pigs they nearly all perished within 30 days, but that in mice they remained latent for at least 4 months.

During the War, renewed interest was taken in the mode of infection in tetanus. Numerous observations showed the presence of the tetanus bacillus in the wounds of men who manifested no symptoms of the disease. Thus in an examination of 100 soldiers not suffering from tetanus, Tulloch (1919–20) found the bacillus 19 times. Observation also showed that tetanus might not develop for weeks or months after the wound had healed, and might then appear suddenly after an operation, perhaps on another part of the body.

Repeating the experiments of previous workers, Tulloch (1919–20) found that toxin-free tetanus spores injected into animals could be stimulated to activity by the simultaneous inoculation of tissue debilitants, such as lactic acid, saponin, and trimethylamine. The results were not always satisfactory ; moreover the type of debilitant necessary to prove effective varied with the species of the animal. He then tried the action of *Cl. welchii* and *Cl. septique* toxins, and found that the addition of a sublethal dose of toxin to tetanus spores enabled the latter to germinate and give rise to a fatal disease.

Bullock (Gye) and Cramer (1919) made an important contribution to the subject when they discovered that the injection of small quantities of ionizable calcium salts together with toxin-free spores invariably led to the development of tetanus. About 2–3 mgm. of $CaCl_2$ was sufficient for a mouse, and about double this quantity for a guinea-pig. Using washed bacilli—but not spores—the same result was obtained whether the bacilli and the salt were injected into different sites at the same time, or into the same site at different times. Further examination led them to conclude that the effect of the calcium ions was not to alter the virulence of the bacteria or the potency of the toxin, but to produce a local change in the tissues at the site of injection. When the calcium salt and the bacilli were injected at different sites, the lesion occurred at the site of injection of the salt ; here, it is stated, the organisms were present in large numbers and were not ingested by phagocytes, whereas at the site of injection of the bacilli they underwent lysis and rapid phagocytosis.

It was further observed that soil had much the same action as that of the pure calcium salt. When, however, the calcium salts in the soil were precipitated by sodium carbonate, the watery extract no longer proved effective. They therefore came to the conclusion that one of the factors in allowing the germination of tetanus spores in a wound is the presence of ionizable calcium salts. Under natural conditions these are frequently introduced with the earth contaminating the wound. The fact that calcium salts are more abundant in cultivated than in waste soil, and that tetanus was far commoner at the beginning of the War, when the fighting was mainly on the highly cultivated soil of Flanders, than towards the end, when the soil had largely become waste, led them to suggest that there might be a causal relationship between the diminution of the calcium salts in the soil and the decrease in the incidence of tetanus.

More recent investigations by Fildes (1927) and Russell (1927) suggest very strongly that the germination of tetanus spores in the tissues is dependent chiefly upon the oxidation-reduction potential of the tissues. Histological examination of the tissues of guinea-pigs inoculated with spores revealed the fact that phagocytosis was always incomplete, and could not therefore be held responsible for the failure of the spores to germinate. It was observed that germination never occurred when the heated spores alone were injected ; and that when a mixture of spores and earth was injected, germination occurred only in the small areas of necrosis produced by the earth. Calcium chloride was found to produce a widespread necrosis ; spores inoculated at the same time germinated over the whole of the necrotic area. Fildes considers that in the normal tissues the O—R potential is sufficiently high to prevent the spores from germinating ; but that in areas of necrosis the potential falls to a point sufficiently low to permit of their germination. He would ascribe in fact the same importance to the O—R potential in determining the germination of spores *in vivo* as *in vitro*.

Further observations by Fildes (1929a, b) and his colleagues (Knight and Fildes 1930, Campbell and Fildes 1931), have greatly strengthened this view. It was found that tetanus spores were unable to germinate in a medium of pH 7·0–7·6 unless the oxidation reduction potential was reduced to Eh + 0·01 volt or below. The Eh of the subcutaneous tissue of the guinea-pig was found to be above this level. If, however, the partial pressure of oxygen in the tissues was lowered by keeping the animals in an atmosphere containing only 7 per cent., instead of the normal 21 per cent., of oxygen, then the Eh was reduced to a level at which germination of the spores in the presence of a mild activating agent such as aleuronat was often rendered possible. (See also p. 942.)

The observations of Wámoscher and von Vásárhelyi (1933) also support Fildes' explanation. These workers found that one of the most successful activating agents was a small piece of sterile agar. This acts presumably, not by causing an area of focal necrosis in the tissues, but by furnishing a nidus, cut off from the blood supply, in which the Eh is sufficiently low to enable tetanus spores to germinate.

From these observations we may form a conception of the genesis of tetanus in the body. When tetanus spores are introduced into a wound by contamination with earth, horse fæces, or other material, their fate depends largely on the presence or absence of certain accessory factors. Many of these have been described— notably trauma, hæmorrhage, tissue necrosis ; chemicals such as lactic acid, saponin, trimethylamine, colloidal silicic acid, and ionizable calcium salts ; and biological substances such as the toxins of *Cl. septique* and *Cl. welchii*. Which of these factors is the more important it is impossible to say ; recent work tends to ascribe less importance to mechanical injury, and more to calcium salts and the toxins of other anaerobes. The presence of a suitable accessory factor enables the spores to germinate and multiply in the tissues ; it seems probable that this action is dependent on the production by tissue debilitants of an area of necrosis with a sufficiently low oxidation-reduction potential to permit the spores to germinate. In post-operative tetanus the spores may be derived either from infected catgut (see Mackie 1928, Mackie *et al.* 1929, Bulloch 1929), or from some other situation such as the intestinal or the respiratory tract (see Carbone and Perrero 1895, Motzfeldt 1912, Wright 1930).

Absorption and Mode of Action of Tetanus Toxin.

The absorption and mode of action of tetanus toxin has provided a problem of extraordinary interest to experimental workers. The field covered has been so wide that it is impossible to do more than give here an outline of some of the more important experiments. Those who are interested in the subject will do well to consult the recent papers of Abel and his colleagues (see p. 1390), which give a far more adequate historical survey than we can provide.

If a guinea-pig is injected with a culture of tetanus bacilli, and allowed to develop the disease and die, it is found that scrapings from the site of inoculation are very rich in toxin ; in fact, Francis (1924) calculated that the scrapings from a single animal would be sufficient to kill 4,800 mice. On the other hand the blood serum of the dead guinea-pig contains only a minimum amount of toxin, perhaps just sufficient in 1 c.c. to kill one mouse ; while the organs are completely non-toxic (Rosenbach 1886, Kitasato 1891). Even the central nervous system, in which the toxin might be suspected of accumulating, is harmless on injection into animals (Kitasato 1889, Meyer and Ransom 1903).

The toxin does not appear to be absorbed by the blood to any great extent, because in the first place the toxin content of the blood is very low, and secondly, in order to produce fatal tetanus, more toxin is required when given by the blood stream than when injected subcutaneously ; moreover, with a given dose of toxin the incubation period is longer after intravenous than after subcutaneous inoculation.

Bruschettini (1890, 1892) induced tetanus in rabbits by the injection of toxin beneath the skin or into the sciatic nerve ; suspensions of the organs were made and injected into fresh animals. The blood and kidneys proved toxic ; the lumbar enlargement of the cord was sometimes toxic after subcutaneous, and invariably after intraneural, injection. He concluded that part of the toxin found its way into the blood stream, whence it was excreted by the kidneys ; and that part was absorbed by the peripheral nerves and carried to the central nervous system.

In 1897 Marie found that the direct injection into the sciatic nerve of a sub-lethal dose of toxin was sufficient to provoke a fatal attack of tetanus in a rabbit. But if a lethal dose was injected into the forepaw of a rabbit, whose 2nd cervical nerve on that side had been cut, tetanus failed to develop. These observations suggested that the toxin was absorbed by the peripheral nerves and conveyed to the spinal cord ; if these nerves were cut, the toxin was unable to reach the cord, and hence tetanus did not occur.

This suggestion was confirmed by Meyer, who found that the sciatic nerve of an animal into whose foot an inoculation had been made, was toxic to other animals. Marie and Morax (1902) repeated this with similar results, and added further important information. Thus, they showed that the peripheral nerves can take up toxin only if their nerve endings are intact. The absorption occurs rapidly ; for example the sciatic nerve of a guinea-pig which has been injected in the foot is toxic to mice in a little more than an hour after the inoculation. Further experiments suggested that the toxin passed up the axis cylinders in a centripetal current towards the spinal cord. Thus if the sciatic nerve is cut at the popliteal space some time after inoculation of toxin into the calf, the central end rapidly loses its toxicity. If the toxin is injected directly into the lumbar cord, the sciatic nerves remain free from toxin, whereas both the lumbar and the dorsal cords contain considerable amounts.

Meyer and Ransom (1903), using somewhat different methods, came to very much the same conclusions as Marie and Morax. They injected antitoxin into the right sciatic nerve of a rabbit, and then injected toxin subcutaneously into both hind legs. Tetanus developed in 2 or 3 days, but commenced in the left leg ; the right leg remained unaffected. In other words, the antitoxin blocked the passage of the toxin up the sciatic nerve of the right side, and prevented its reaching the cord.

Again, they injected toxin intravenously into a cat, and on the same day injected the sciatic and femoral nerves with antitoxin; the cat developed general tetanus with the exception of the hind legs which appeared normal. Their experiments seemed to show that the toxin was absorbed by the motor nerves, up which it passed to the spinal cord, where it exerted its effect on the anterior horn cells. If this is so, then the direct injection of toxin into the anterior portion of the cord should be followed rapidly by tetanus. This deduction is correct. Meyer and Ransom, in fact, found that under these conditions the first symptoms of tetanus in a cat appeared in about 3 hours. It is therefore clear why, after injection of pure toxin into a limb, there is an incubation period before the disease manifests itself. This period is occupied in the absorption of the toxin by the nerve endings and its passage upwards to the cord. As a rule, the smaller the animal and the less the distance the toxin has to travel along the nerves, the shorter is the incubation period. In the mouse, for example, it is about 12 hours, in the rabbit 18 to 36 hours, in the dog 36 to 48 hours, and in the horse 5 days (Meyer and Ransom 1903). The dose of toxin administered is also a determining factor. The larger this is, the shorter is the incubation period.

It is necessary for the toxin to reach the anterior horn cells of the cord; this it does by passing up the motor nerves. If the toxin is injected into the posterior roots between the ganglion and the cord, tetanus, as it is generally understood, does not occur. Moreover, if the toxin is injected into a part of the body devoid of motor nerves such as the testicles or the peritoneum, a peculiar form of splanchnic tetanus develops, characterized by a longer incubation period, a more rapid illness, and an absence of muscular spasms (von Lingelsheim 1912).

Summarizing, we may say that *the evidence hitherto quoted* suggests that the toxin, when injected into a limb, is absorbed chiefly by the motor nerve endings; thence it passes up the axis cylinders to the anterior horn cells. Not until these have been reached, do symptoms of tetanus appear. At first the contractions are confined to the injected limb; but later, as the toxin diffuses through the cord, the opposite limb and finally the muscles over the whole body become affected. A small amount is probably absorbed by the lymph and carried to the blood stream. From this it is taken up by the motor nerve endings in different parts of the body. Hence the tetanus developing after intravenous injection of toxin is slower in its development, but is generalized from the first.

This conception of the genesis of tetanus has recently received very severe criticism from Abel (1934), and his colleagues (Abel and Hampil 1935, Abel *et al.* 1935*a*, *b*).

Briefly, these workers object to the hypothesis of axis cylinder carriage on the ground that (1) there is no evidence to show that the axis cylinders ever contain tetanus toxin; (2) there is no known mechanism that will explain how the toxin is transported in the axis cylinders, often for long distances, to the central nervous system; and (3) the injection of a sub-lethal dose of toxin directly into the sciatic nerve of the dog does not give rise to tetanus, provided measures are taken to prevent the escape of the toxin into the surrounding tissues. This last experiment, on which Abel lays great emphasis, is not very convincing. The supporters of the axis cylinder hypothesis maintain that the toxin is taken up by the motor nerve endings; it does not follow, as Abel assumes, that toxin inoculated directly into the nerve bundles will reach the axis cylinders, since these are presumably well insulated by the medullary sheaths.

The second hypothesis, which has been held by some workers, that the toxin is carried to the central nervous system by the endoneural and perineural lymphatic vessels, seems to be ruled out on anatomical grounds. There is no evidence to show that the neural lymphatics drain into the cerebrospinal fluid; on the contrary the evidence seems fairly conclusive that they drain directly into lymph glands, which in their turn drain into the thoracic duct.

Discounting these two hypotheses, as well as that of the transference of the toxin in the tissue spaces of the nerve trunks by molecular forces, Abel adopts the view that the toxin reaches the central nervous system by the arterial circulation. Contrary to the findings of certain previous workers, he has been able to show that a very high proportion of the toxin injected into the limb of a sheep may be demonstrated in the lymph-glandular and vascular systems. Indeed, he calculates that under certain conditions the proportion may be as high as 90 per cent. Secondly, Abel believes that tetanus toxin has a dual action on the central and on the peripheral nervous system. The evidence on which this belief is based has not yet been given in full, but one of the experiments that has influenced Abel most may be cited. If a sub-lethal dose of toxin is injected into the muscle of the hind limb of a dog, local tetanus results. Since Abel has already shown that injection of the same amount of toxin into the sciatic nerve does not produce local tetanus, he argues that the toxin must act directly on the motor nerve endings of the muscle. He denies the possibility that the toxin injected intramuscularly passes up the axis cylinders to the central nervous system, stimulates the anterior horn cells, and gives rise to descending local tetanus, because local tetanus does not follow direct injection of toxin into the sciatic nerve. We have already pointed out the possible fallacy of such an argument, and the interpretation of this experiment seems to us to be doubtful.

The necessity of postulating a dual action of tetanus toxin, namely on the anterior horn cells and on the motor nerve endings of the muscle, contravenes the fundamental principle enunciated by William of Occam : *Entia non sunt multiplicanda præter necessitatem.* Acceptance of the peripheral action of the toxin to explain the genesis of local tetanus merely raises another difficulty : Why, that is to say, should there be such a long incubation period in tetanus if the toxin acts directly on the motor nerve endings ? And acceptance of the arterial distribution of the toxin fails to explain the ordered spread of the disease which has been noted by so many observers.

Summarizing, we may say that we are still ignorant of the exact mechanism by which tetanus toxin is absorbed, and of the way in which it exerts its action on the body cells. The two main hypotheses are (1) that the toxin is absorbed by the motor nerve endings, and carried up the axis cylinders to the anterior horn cells of the central nervous system, which are then stimulated to produce muscular contractions ; (2) that the toxin is absorbed by the lymphatic vessels, carried to the general circulation, and distributed to the central nervous system by the arterial blood supply.

It is impossible to say which, if either, of these rival hypotheses is correct. Taking the experimental evidence on the whole, we are of the opinion that the former explains the facts most readily and demands the minimum of assumption. Recent work on the axis cylinder carriage of some of the neurotropic viruses lends it additional support, since the passage along the nerve fibres of bodies so closely similar in size as the poliomyelitis virus and the molecule of tetanus toxin is presumably accomplished by much the same means. If the axis cylinder carriage of the viruses is accepted, then we see no difficulty in accepting the same mechanism of transmission for tetanus toxin. The final solution of this problem, however, must await further experimental work.

Immunity to Tetanus.

Natural.—Mammals vary in their susceptibility to tetanus ; some, such as the mouse, the monkey, and the horse are highly susceptible ; others, such as the dog and the cat, are much less susceptible. Most birds and cold-blooded animals are extremely resistant. Examination of the blood of susceptible and partially susceptible animals shows that, while the majority of cattle contain more than 1/500 unit of antitoxin per c.c., no antitoxin is present in the blood of man, horses, dogs, pigs, monkeys, or rodents. Sheep and goats may contain small quantities (Coleman 1931, Coleman and Meyer 1926, Ramon and Lemétayer 1934, 1935). The frequent presence of antitoxin in the blood of ruminants may be causally associated with the comparative resistance of these animals to tetanus. It is suggested that in ruminants tetanus bacilli multiply and form toxin in the digestive reservoirs which precede the true stomach, and that the toxin so formed, partly modified perhaps by the products of bacterial fermentation, is absorbed and gives rise to the production of antitoxin. Examination of the blood of naturally resistant animals has proved it to be devoid of antitoxin (Vaillard 1892) ; hence their immunity cannot be attributed to the presence of this antibody.

Marie (1897) injected a rabbit intravenously with 1,000,000 M.L.D. of toxin for a mouse. Blood was removed at frequent intervals, defibrinated, and injected in 1 c.c. quantities into mice. For the first 17 hours the blood proved toxic, but after this time it became innocuous ; the toxin had disappeared therefore from the circulation in less than a day. Vaillard (1892), on the other hand, who injected a hen with 20 c.c. of toxin, found that it persisted in the blood stream for several days. In the susceptible rabbit the toxin is supposed to be absorbed from the blood by the motor nerve endings, and carried to the cord, where it gives rise to disease. In the non-susceptible hen the toxin does not appear to be absorbed at all, or only slowly ; hence tetanus fails to develop.

An interesting contribution to the study of natural immunity was made by Wassermann and Takaki (Wassermann 1898, Wassermann and Takaki 1898), who found that the brain, and to a less extent the spinal cord, of normal animals was able to neutralize tetanus toxin. A mixture of toxin and brain suspension proved harmless on injection into animals. The amount that could be neutralized depended partly on the animal ; a guinea-pig's brain, for example, could neutralize completely 10 M.L.D. of toxin, and incompletely 60 M.L.D. They found moreover that the neutralization could occur in the body ; a mouse injected with a brain suspension, and 24 hours later given 3 to 5 M.L.D. of toxin, did not develop tetanus. From these experiments they concluded that the brain contained natural antitoxin.

As was to be expected, a number of workers immediately directed their attention to this interesting phenomenon (Marie 1898, Metchnikoff 1898a, b, Roux and Borrel 1898, Danysz 1899, Marie and Morax 1902). They all confirmed the original observation of the *in vitro* neutralization of toxin by a suspension of brain tissue, but differed from Wassermann and Takaki in their explanation of it. It was found that the cells of the cerebral cortex were most active ; that the brain of mammals was more powerful than that of birds and cold-blooded animals ; that the neutralizing agent was insoluble in saline ; that the union between the toxin and nerve cells was not permanent ; that there was no actual destruction of toxin ; and that for neutralization to occur there must be an intimate contact between the toxin and the cells. Protection experiments failed completely unless the two substances were inoculated at the same site. It is clear, therefore, that the brain does not act by virtue of its antitoxic content. The nervous tissue of the susceptible mammal has a strong affinity for tetanus toxin and, by combining with it, prevents its transference to the motor cells of the inoculated animal. On the other hand, the nervous tissue of the resistant hen, frog, and turtle (Metchnikoff 1898a) has little or no affinity for the toxin, and hence fails to anchor it. That this is the true explanation seems apparent from Roux and Borrel's work (1898), which showed that the lethal dose of toxin given directly into the brain of a rabbit was smaller than that necessary when given subcutaneously. The brain tissue of a susceptible animal resembles antitoxin in combining specifically with toxin, but with fatal effects to the animal concerned.

These observations also explain the fact that the central nervous system of animals dying of tetanus may appear to be devoid of toxin, when in reality it contains a considerable amount. To demonstrate the presence of the toxin it is only necessary to grind the brain up in 10 per cent. saline and to leave the suspension for some time, when the toxin will break away from the disintegrated cells and appear free in the fluid (Tizzoni and Cattani 1891a).

Acquired Immunity.—One of the most important advances in the progress of bacteriology was made by Behring and Kitasato (Behring and Kitasato 1890, Kitasato 1891, 1892, Behring 1892), when they discovered that the injection of a filtered culture of tetanus bacilli into an animal stimulated the production of an antibody which was able to neutralize the toxin and to preserve the life of animals injected with it. It protected not only against injections of toxin, but also against inoculation of the tetanus bacillus itself. Thus, if 0·2 c.c. of an antitoxic rabbit's serum was injected intraperitoneally into a mouse, and virulent tetanus bacilli were injected subcutaneously 24 hours later, the mouse remained perfectly well. The nature of the union between toxin and antitoxin has been discussed elsewhere (see Chapter XLIII). We may here confine ourselves to a consideration of its protective action in practical prophylaxis.

The antiserum acts, not by interfering with the germination of spores, nor with the multiplication of the bacilli in the tissues, but by neutralizing the toxin as fast as it is formed. If antitoxin is present in the circulating blood and lymph, it will neutralize the toxin before the latter has time to gain access to the nerves. If the antitoxin is not given till after the formation of toxin has begun, it will be too late to prevent the absorption by the nerves.

It follows that there are rigid conditions governing the usefulness of antitoxin. The most important of these is that it must be allowed to come into intimate contact with the toxin. Unless it does so it is valueless. It is known that the nervous tissue of mammals has a strong affinity for tetanus toxin ; it has no such affinity for tetanus antitoxin. Once the toxin has gained entrance to the nerves it can no longer be neutralized, unless the antitoxin is itself injected into the nerves. Meyer and Ransom (1903) injected antitoxin in large quantities intravenously into a cat, and at the same time injected a dose of toxin into the sciatic nerve ; the cat developed tetanus. The nerve tissue acts as a barrier separating the toxin from the antitoxin ; and nothing short of enormous doses of antitoxin in the blood stream can save the life of an animal if once the toxin has gained access to the nerves. We have, in fact, the anomaly of an animal, whose blood contains sufficient antitoxin to save the life of hundreds of mice, itself dying of tetanus. If the antitoxin is injected directly into the central nervous system, there is some evidence that it is able to neutralize the toxin and prevent further spread of the disease (Roux and Borrel 1898). This fact is, however, not yet clearly established, and Abel and Hampil (1935) offer an alternative explanation for Roux and Borrel's findings. Roux and Borrel, it may be noted, also showed that an actively immunized rabbit, capable of withstanding large doses of toxin subcutaneously or intravenously, yet succumbs as readily to the intracerebral injection of toxin as a normal rabbit.

Diagnosis.

The bacteriological diagnosis of tetanus is often difficult and sometimes impossible.

Microscopical Examination should be made where possible of the pus in the wound, and special note taken of bacilli with round, terminal spores. The organisms may be present in such small numbers that they may be altogether overlooked.

Cultural Methods are of more importance. The pus or wound scrapings are seeded into cooked meat medium, or into heart or liver digest broth containing a small portion of sterile rabbit kidney. After 5 days' anaerobic incubation at 37° C., if the typical bacilli are visible microscopically, the culture is heated to 70–75° C. for 20 minutes to destroy non-sporing bacilli, and plated out on liver or serum agar. To obtain a pure culture repeated platings may be necessary. Fildes (1925a) has drawn attention to the rapidly-spreading, effuse, proteus-like growth that occurs on an agar slope if the water of condensation is inoculated ; the bacilli grow over the whole slope and present a tenuous, jagged, fern-like edge at the top. From this a subculture may be made into the condensation water of a fresh tube, and a pure culture obtained after two or three transfers. Besides studying the cultural and biochemical reactions of the strain it is well to test it with a polyvalent agglutinating serum prepared against the common serological types of bacilli in the neighbourhood (Fildes 1925b).

Animal Inoculation.—Material from the wound should be suspended in saline and injected subcutaneously into mice or guinea-pigs. Though this procedure may give a positive result, it is not advisable to rely on it exclusively. Every effort should be made to obtain the organisms in pure culture before injection ; it is generally agreed that animal inoculation from a pure culture is more likely to be successful than from a mixed culture (McCoy and Bengtson 1918, Tenbroeck and Bauer 1922). The signs of tetanus in an animal are almost unmistakable, but a careful microscopical examination of the wound and the blood should be made to exclude the presence of other organisms. If a pure culture of the bacillus gives rise to the disease, then a broth filtrate should be injected into two mice, one of which has been given a prophylactic dose of antitoxin. In this way the toxicity of the strain can be determined.

Prophylaxis and Treatment.

The surgical treatment of wounds that are likely to be followed by tetanus lies outside our province, but clearly everything must be done to avoid the persistence of necrotic tissue, and to control bacterial proliferation within the wound. Attention must be drawn to the desirability of using properly prepared and disinfected catgut in the suturing of tissues at operation. The way to ensure this is described in the admirable monograph by Bulloch (1929) and his collaborators Lampitt and Bushill (1929).

Preparation, Standardization and Properties of Antitoxin.—The **preparation** of tetanus antitoxin, which plays so important a part in the prophylactic treatment of tetanus, has been the subject of research ever since its discovery. The pure toxin is too active to be injected directly into susceptible animals, and some method of decreasing its toxicity has to be employed.

Behring and Kitasato (1890) and Kitasato (1891) found that the injection into rabbits and mice of tetanus toxin, modified by treatment with a solution of iodine tri-chloride, rendered them immune ; their serum was found to contain an antitoxin capable of neutralizing the toxin. Later Behring (1892) immunized sheep and horses, and was thus able to obtain antitoxin in considerable quantities. Experiments on mice infected with splinters of wood dipped in a heated broth culture of *Cl. tetani* showed that the antitoxin was capable of protecting them if given before, simultaneously with, or 24 hours after the infection. The therapeutic dose required was very much greater than the prophylactic dose. Thus in one experiment the effective dose of serum was 0·001 c.c. when given 15 hours before, 0·1 c.c. when given at the same time as, and 0·4 c.c. when given 24 hours after, the infection (Kitasato 1892).

Vaillard (1892) confirmed the value of iodized toxin, and succeeded in immunizing rabbits by the injection of successive doses of filtered cultures heated at progressively lower temperatures ; finally the animals were able to withstand the intravenous injection of pure toxin. He likewise confirmed Behring's and Kitasato's work on the neutralizing and protective powers of the antitoxin, but was unable to satisfy himself of its curative power (Vaillard 1891). After a dose of 0·5 c.c. of antitoxic rabbit serum into a mouse, the animal resisted the injection of toxin during the next few days ; but after about a fortnight the passive immunity wore off and the animal regained its susceptibility to toxin. Serum injected some hours after the commencement of symptoms was without effect on the progress of the disease. Tizzoni and Cattani (1891a) were also unable to convince themselves of the curative power of antitoxin.

Antitoxin was later produced on a large scale by the injection of horses with toxin-antitoxin mixtures (Buxton and Glenny 1921). The toxin was over-neutralized, and a series of injections was given at intervals of a few days over a period of some months. Of recent years the preliminary treatment of toxin with formol has been widely adopted. The action of the formol is to deprive the toxin of its toxicity, while having little effect on its antigenic value. After a series of initial injections with this formolized product— sometimes referred to as anatoxin or formol toxoid—crude toxin itself can be injected. The actual technique of preparing the toxoid need not detain us here. Usually about 0·4 per cent. of formol is added to the toxin, and the mixture is incubated at 37°–39° C. till it is sufficiently detoxified. About 20 c.c. of formolized toxin should prove non-toxic to the guinea-pig on subcutaneous inoculation (Hosoya *et al.* 1931, Wilcox 1934). Some workers precipitate the toxoid with alum or zinc chloride, while some add tapioca or 0·5 per cent. $CaCl_2$ in an endeavour to increase its antigenic efficiency (see Glenny *et al.* 1926, Ramon *et al.* 1931, Ramon and Lemétayer 1932, Bergey 1934).

The **standardization** of tetanus antitoxin has presented considerable difficulties, due in part to the liability of tetanus toxin to deterioration. In the past three different units have been employed—a German, a French, and an American. Comparative observations made under the auspices of the Permanent Committee on Standardization of the Health Organization of the League of Nations showed that the relation of these units was as follows : 1 German unit = 66 American = 3,750 French units (see Prausnitz 1929). It was agreed that an international unit should be established equivalent to one-half the existing American unit, and that the standard antitoxin should be kept at the Serum Institute, Copenhagen. So defined, the unit of tetanus antitoxin represents the specific neutralizing activity for tetanus toxin contained in 0·1547 mgm. of the standard preparation. Antitoxin titrations are best carried out by the subcutaneous injection of toxin-antitoxin mixtures into mice, and the determination of that amount of toxin which just fails to produce tetanus by the 4th day (L0 dose). The L+ dose, *i.e.*, that dose which kills the animal on the 4th day, is much less satisfactory as a basis for standardization.

Properties.—Tetanus antitoxin remains fairly stable in a cold, dark place. If dried, powdered, and preserved in vacuum tubes in the presence of phosphorus pentoxide, and kept in the dark at 5° C., it remains unaltered for years (Rosenau and Anderson 1908). Exposure to sunlight or diffuse daylight gradually destroys it. It resists heat at 60° C. for half an hour, but is partly destroyed at 65° C., and completely at 68° C. (Tizzoni and Cattani 1891*b*). It·is non-dialysable, and is precipitated by ammonium sulphate with the globulin fraction. Hydrochloric and lactic acids, and caustic potash, destroy it.

Injected intravenously into animals, antitoxin circulates in the blood for some days. A very small amount may pass into the cerebrospinal fluid and into the milk of lactating animals (von Lingelsheim 1912). After subcutaneous injection the highest titre of antitoxin in the blood is reached in 1 to 3 days; from then on it diminishes till after a fortnight only a trace is left. Injected into the sub-arachnoid space it passes almost completely into the blood stream.

MacConkey and Homer (1917) found that the passive immunity conferred on guinea-pigs by the subcutaneous injection of 3½ units of antitoxin disappeared in about a fortnight. Increased dosage up to 40 units did not prolong this period; but when enormous doses were given—250 to 3,500 units—the animal remained immune for about a month. That is to say, passive immunity is at the best transient, and can be relied upon only for a short time.

Prophylactic Injection of Antitoxin.—In the prophylaxis of tetanus in man it is advisable to inject 500 units of antitoxin beneath the skin of the abdomen as soon after the receipt of the wound as possible. The type that calls for this treatment is the dirty lacerated wound, contaminated with street mud, earth, or animal fæces, especially if accompanied by severe bruising of the tissues or fracture of the bones. It is advisable to inject a portion of the serum in two

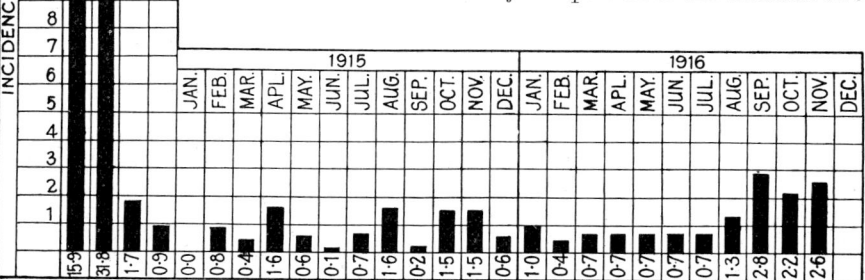

FIG. 271.

The incidence of tetanus per 1,000 wounded in Home Hospitals during 1914–16, showing the fall in incidence after Oct., 1914, when the use of antitetanic serum became generalized. (After Bruce.)

or three places around the actual lesion. The wound itself should preferably be excised; if this is impossible it should be cleansed and thoroughly drained. If the wound is severe and is likely to take some time to heal, it is well to repeat the injection every week. Should symptoms of tetanus develop, large doses—

30,000 units or more—must be given every day, partly around the wound and partly intrathecally.

From animal experiments there is not the least doubt of the protective value of antitoxin, but in man the evidence is necessarily indirect. This may be summarized as follows :

(1) The prophylactic injection of antitoxin within a few hours of the receipt of a wound appears to diminish greatly the chances of tetanus. The incidence during the Great War is recorded in Figs. 270 and 271. The sudden fall in November, 1914, can in all probability be ascribed to the prophylactic use of antitetanic serum that was introduced about the middle of the preceding month. The rise towards the end of 1916 may have been fictitious ; Bruce ascribes it to improved diagnosis, particularly of local tetanus, which was largely overlooked at the beginning of the War. The subsequent fall in 1917 and 1918 may perhaps be related to the more efficient prophylactic serum treatment which was commenced in June, 1917, but more probably to the practice of early excision of wounds which was introduced about the same time.

(2) When it does not prevent the development of tetanus it appears to lengthen its incubation period. This will be seen from Table CLIX, showing the average incubation period amongst wounded treated in home hospitals during the War.

TABLE CLIX

SHOWING THE AVERAGE INCUBATION PERIOD OF TETANUS IN DIFFERENT YEARS OF THE WAR.

Year.	Length of Incubation Period in Days.
1914	11·8
1915	27·3
1916	34·0
1917	48·0
1918–19	50·0

A direct comparison of the average incubation period in patients who have received, and those who have not received, a prophylactic injection of antitoxin after having been wounded leads to the same conclusion ; in the inoculated this period is 45·5 days, in the uninoculated 10·9 days. In this connection it must be remembered that the passive immunity conferred by a single injection of antitoxin wears off in about a fortnight or three weeks. During this period the patient is unlikely to develop tetanus. But once this is past, he is probably just as susceptible as a person who has never been inoculated at all. Hence if tetanus bacilli are still present in the wound, they are liable to give rise to disease. If all patients had been given repeated doses of antitoxin at intervals of a week till their wounds healed, it is possible that these late cases of tetanus would have been greatly reduced in number.

(3) Tetanus developing in persons who have received a prophylactic injection appears to be less fatal than in uninoculated persons (Bruce 1920). This is seen from Table CLX.

TABLE CLX

SHOWING THE MORTALITY OF TETANUS IN INOCULATED AND UNINOCULATED PATIENTS.

	No. of Cases.	Died.	Case Mortality.
			Per cent.
Inoculated.	899	203	22·6
Non-inoculated or unrecorded	559	298	53·3

It is interesting to note that the average mortality amongst the inoculated during the War fell far more rapidly than amongst the uninoculated. This can probably be accounted for by the more regular administration of serum, and by its repeated administration every 7 days for 4 weeks which was undertaken at the instigation of the Tetanus Committee in June, 1917.

(4) During the War the proportion of cases of local to general tetanus rose considerably (Bruce 1920) (Table CLXI).

TABLE CLXI

SHOWING THE PROPORTION OF CASES OF LOCAL AND GENERAL TETANUS.

	Percentages.				
	1914.	1915.	1916.	1917.	1918.
General	98·9	98·6	87·0	76·6	83·5
Local	1·1	1·4	13·0	23·4	16·5

This may be in part attributed to the more general and efficient use of antitoxin prophylactically, and partly to improved diagnosis of local tetanus.

Since the protection afforded by serum wears off in the course of 2 or 3 weeks —often before the wound is healed—there is a tendency nowadays to reinforce the passive immunity so conferred by means of active immunization. In the French Army, for example, the directions are that every wounded soldier in whom the development of tetanus is to be feared is to be inoculated subcutaneously with 1·5 c.c. of formolized toxin, followed some minutes later at a different site by a suitable dose of serum. A second dose of 2 c.c. of formol toxoid is to be given 20 days, and a third dose 30 days later when considered desirable (Sacquépée 1933). Alum-precipitated formolized toxoid appears to give more favourable results than the plain toxoid (Jones and Moss 1936).

Therapeutic Injection of Antitoxin.—Whether or not antitoxin is of any value in man when given subsequently to the development of tetanus is a question that has received no definite answer. The figures collected during the War were ambiguous, and we see no purpose in retailing them ; for their full examination the reader is referred to Bruce (1915, 1916, 1917*a, b, c, d*, 1919), Dean (1917), and Leishman and Smallman (1917). Experiments with the smaller animals have shown that it is difficult or impossible to interfere with the progress of the disease once the first symptoms have manifested themselves, unless enormous doses are given ; even then the issue is uncertain.

On monkeys, however—chiefly *Macacus rhesus* and *Callithrix*—Sherrington (1917) obtained perfectly unequivocal results. He injected batches of 25 with 8 M.L.D. of toxin into the outer head of the gastrocnemius muscle. From 47 to 78 hours later, when the early symptoms of tetanus had appeared, he injected 2,000 U.S.A. units of antitoxin per kilo of monkey, giving the serum by different routes to the separate batches. All the control animals receiving no antitoxin died ; the mortality amongst the inoculated was as follows (Table CLXII).

This experiment answered two questions. It showed first of all that antitoxin might be of considerable therapeutic value ; and secondly that the route by which it was given was of supreme importance. Whereas antitoxin administered subcutaneously or intramuscularly had but little effect, given intrathecally it saved the lives of over half the animals.

TABLE CLXII

Serum given by :	Deaths.	Recoveries.	Percentage Mortality.
			Per cent.
Subcutaneous route	23	2	92
Intramuscular route	22	3	88
Intravenous route	18	7	72
Lumbar intrathecal route . .	11	14	44
Bulbar intrathecal route. . .	7	13	35
Cerebral subdural route . . .	10	0	100

It is difficult to explain the discrepancy between Sherrington's experimental results and the results in clinical practice ; but two points may be noticed. Firstly the monkeys were injected with pure toxin, not with bacilli ; it is doubtful whether the results would have been so favourable if an active infection had been set up. Secondly the dose of antitoxin used was large—2,000 units per kilo of monkey. This corresponds in man to 120,000 units administered in a single dose. To give this, using a highly potent serum containing 800 units per c.c., would necessitate the injection of 150 c.c.—an amount far in excess of that which could be administered intrathecally at one time. The average daily dose given in human practice —often by two or three routes—has been from 1,000 to 30,000 units ; larger doses have not often been employed. If the quantities suggested by Sherrington's work are really necessary—and experience suggests that smaller doses are inadequate —then it would seem desirable to devote attention to the production of antitoxic sera of a higher degree of concentration than those which we now possess.

The conclusions from Sherrington's work find some support in the experience of clinical observers who have succeeded in curing severe tetanus by the use of very large doses of antiserum, sometimes administered by the cisterna magna (see Paterson 1930, O'Carroll 1931, Bell 1931, Nabarro 1932). Nabarro, for example, injected no fewer than 633,000 units of antitoxin within the space of 9 days, while Paterson reached nearly 2 million units.

Even more suggestive, however, are the figures reported by Yodh (1932) at the J.J. Hospital in Bombay. Before he took charge, tetanus patients were treated with sedatives, and were given antitoxin intravenously and intramuscularly in doses of about 20,000 units a day. After taking charge, Yodh continued this treatment for a time, using, however, slightly larger doses of sedatives and serum. Later, he increased the dose of antitoxin a little more, and injected part of it by the lumbar intrathecal route. Still dissatisfied with his results, he started giving serum intrathecally by the cisterna magna, as well as intravenously, intramuscularly, and subcutaneously around the wound. Usually only one cisternal injection was made, 20–30 c.c. of serum being injected. The total amount of serum administered to any given patient varied from 40,000 to over 400,000 units. The results are given in Table CLXIII.

The cases were not strictly consecutive. Of a total of 229 cases treated by Yodh himself, 15 were not given serum treatment for one reason or another, sometimes because they were moribund. Since the distribution of these cases in point of time is not stated, it is impossible to know how much allowance to make on the figures yielded by the serum-treated patients. The results, however, do suggest very strongly that the intrathecal administration of serum by the cisterna magna route

TABLE CLXIII

EFFECT OF ROUTE AND DOSE OF SERUM INJECTIONS IN HUMAN PATIENTS SUFFERING FROM
TETANUS (Yodh 1932).

Mode of Serum Treatment.	No. of Patients.	No. died.	Case mortality per cent.
20,000 units per diem by *im.* and *iv.* routes . .	49	38	77·6
30,000–40,000 units for 1st day, 20,000 units later, by *im.* and *iv.* routes	80	52	65·0
Larger doses of serum by *im.*, *iv.*, and lumbar intrathecal routes	22	14	63·6
Total of 40,000 to 400,000 units by *im.*, *iv.*, *sc.*, and cisterna magna routes	112	53	47·3

im. = intramuscular : *iv.* = intravenous : *sc.* = subcutaneous.

is definitely beneficial. Clinically, some improvement was generally noticeable within 24 hours of the cisterna injection.

From Sherrington's results on monkeys and Yodh's results on human beings, it would appear that intrathecal administration of serum is more beneficial than injection by any other route. Why this should be so, it is difficult to understand. On *a priori* grounds one would expect that antitoxin conveyed by the blood stream would come into more intimate contact with the affected nerve cells than when it was injected into the cerebrospinal fluid. The superiority of the intrathecal route is, however, not yet completely substantiated. Florey and Fildes (1927), for example, obtained no better results in the therapeutic treatment of rabbits by the intrathecal than by the intravenous method. Moreover, Paterson (1930), who treated 26 consecutive children suffering from tetanus with only 7 deaths, used the intravenous and intramuscular routes. It must be noted, however, that Florey and Fildes' experiments were carried out on so few animals that a small advantage possessed by the intrathecal route may quite well have been obscured, while Paterson used enormous doses of serum, varying from a total of 120,000 to one of 1,970,000 units. It is possible that his results might have been even more favourable had he in fact adopted the intrathecal route.

Summarizing, all the evidence goes to show that in the therapeutic treatment of tetanus large and repeated doses of serum are required. In practice it seems advisable to administer the serum by the intramuscular, intravenous, and intrathecal routes. There is evidence that injection into the cisterna magna is of more benefit than the lumbar puncture route, and this should be adopted whenever practicable.

Tetanus in Animals.

The natural disease attacks horses more frequently than other animals, and is especially common in warm and tropical countries. In Northern Europe the incidence is low ; thus in the years 1899–1908 in the Prussian Army the annual average of horses developing the disease was only 0·6 per 1,000 (Hutyra and Marek 1912).

Tetanus occurs less frequently in cattle, sheep and goats, and is uncommon in the pig and the dog.

Infection occurs by contamination of wounds of skin, or of raw surfaces ; nails in the hoof, castration, tail docking, harness galling, bone fractures, and imperfect treatment of the navel at birth, seem to be responsible for the majority of cases.

Prophylactic injection of antitoxin is recommended previous to operations on the horse. Nocard (see Mohler and Eichhorn 1911) reported that in 2,727 horses which were given serum after various operations not a single case of tetanus developed, whereas during the same period 259 cases developed in horses that were not inoculated (number not stated). As a rule 500 units is sufficient. The passive immunity so conveyed lasts longer in the horse than in other animals because the serum is homologous, and is therefore excreted more slowly (Mohler and Eichhorn 1911). Buxton and Glenny (1921) were able to render horses actively immune by 3 injections at intervals of 3 days of a toxin-antitoxin mixture. A month later the animals withstood 2,000 guinea-pig M.L.D. of crude toxin. They recommend this method for the immunization of army horses.

Therapeutic inoculation of serum has not been followed by satisfactory results (Mohler and Eichhorn 1911).

REFERENCES

ABEL, J. J. (1934) *Science*, **79**, 63, 121.
ABEL, J. J., EVANS, E. A., HAMPIL, B., and LEE, F. C. (1935a) *Bull. Johns Hopk. Hosp.*, **56**, 84.
ABEL, J. J. and HAMPIL, B. (1935) *Bull. Johns Hopk. Hosp.*, **57**, 343.
ABEL, J. J., HAMPIL, B., and JONAS, A. F. (1935b) *Bull. Johns Hopk. Hosp.*, **56**, 317.
BEHRING. (1892) *Z. Hyg. InfektKr.*, **12**, 45.
BEHRING and KITASATO, S. (1890) *Dtsch. med. Wschr.*, **16**, 1113.
BELL, D. (1931) *Brit. med. J.*, i. 75.
BERGEY, D. H. (1934) *J. infect. Dis.*, **55**, 72.
BRUCE, D. (1915) *Lancet*, ii. 901 ; (1916) *Ibid.*, ii. 929 ; (1917a) *Brit. med. J.*, i. 118 ; (1917b) *Lancet*, i. 986 ; (1917c) *Ibid.*, ii. 411 ; (1917d) *Ibid.*, ii. 925 ; (1919) *Ibid.*, i. 311 ; (1920) *J. Hyg., Camb.*, **19**, 1.
BRUSCHETTINI, A. (1890) *La Riform. med.*, **6**, 1346 ; (1892) *Ibid.*, **8**, 256.
BULLOCH, W. (1929) *Spec. Rep. Ser. med. Res. Coun., Lond.*, No. 138.
BULLOCK, W. E. and CRAMER, W. (1919) *Proc. R. Soc.*, B, **90**, 513.
BUXTON, J. B. and GLENNY, A. T. (1921) *Lancet*, ii. 1109.
CAMPBELL, J. A. and FILDES, P. (1931) *Brit. J. exp. Path.*, **12**, 77.
CARBONE, T. and PERRERO, E. (1895) *Zbl. Bakt.*, **18**, 193.
CARLE and RATTONE. (1884) *G. Accad. Med. Torino*, 3rd Ser., **32**, 174.
COLEMAN, G. E. (1931) *Amer. J. Hyg.*, **14**, 515.
COLEMAN, G. E. and MEYER, K. F. (1926) *J. infect. Dis.*, **39**, 332.
CUMMINS, S. L. and GIBSON, H. G. (1919) *Lancet*, i. 325.
DANYSZ, J. (1899) *Ann. Inst. Pasteur*, **13**, 156.
DEAN, H. R. (1917) *Lancet*, i. 673.
FILDES, P. (1925a) *Brit. J. exp. Path.*, **6**, 62 ; (1925b) *Ibid.*, **6**, 91 ; (1927) *Ibid.*, **8**, 387 ; (1929a) *Ibid.*, **10**, 151 ; (1929b) *Ibid.*, **10**, 197.
FLOREY, H. and FILDES, P. (1927) *Brit. J. exp. Path.*, **8**, 393.
FRANCIS, E. (1924) *Bull. U.S. hyg. Lab.*, No. 95.
GLENNY, A. T., POPE, C. G., WADDINGTON, H., and WALLACE, U. (1926) *J. Path. Bact.*, **29**, 31.
HOSOYA, S., TAKADA, M., and TERAO, S. (1931) *Jap. J. exp. Med.*, **9**, 33.
HUTYRA, F. and MAREK, J. (1912) " Special Pathology and Therapeutics of the Diseases of Domestic Animals." London.
JONES, F. G. and MOSS, J. M. (1936) *J. Immunol.*, **30**, 115.
KERRIN, J. C. (1928) *Brit. J. exp. Path.*, **9**, 69 ; (1929) *Ibid.*, **10**, 370.
KITASATO, S. (1889) *Z. Hyg. InfektKr.*, **7**, 225 ; (1891) *Ibid.*, **10**, 267 ; (1892) *Ibid.*, **12**, 256.
KNIGHT, B. C. J. G. and FILDES, P. (1930) *Biochem. J.*, **24**, 1496.
LAMPITT, L. H. and BUSHILL, J. H. (1929) *Spec. Rep. Ser. med. Res. Coun., Lond.*, No. 138.
LEISHMAN, W. B. and SMALLMAN, A. B. (1917) *Lancet*, i. 131.

LINGELSHEIM, VON. (1912) See Kolle and Wassermann's "Hdb. path. Mikroorg.," 2te Abt., 1912–13, **4**, 737.

MacCONKEY, A. T. and HOMER, A. (1917) *Lancet*, i. 259.

MACKIE, T. J. (1928) " An Inquiry into Post-operative Tetanus—A Report to the Scottish Board of Health, Edinburgh." H.M. Stat. Off.

MACKIE, T. J., McLACHAN, D. G. S., and ANDERSON, E. J. M. (1929) " Certain Factors that promote the Development of the Tetanus Bacillus in the Tissues, with Special Reference to Post-operative Tetanus—an Experimental Inquiry. A Report to the Department of Health for Scotland." Edinburgh. H.M. Stat. Off.

McCOY, G. W. and BENGTSON, I. A. (1918) *Bull. U.S. hyg. Lab.*, No. 115.

MARIE, A. (1897) *Ann. Inst. Pasteur*, **11**, 591 ; (1898) *Ibid.*, **12**, 91.

MARIE, A. and MORAX, V. (1902) *Ann. Inst. Pasteur*, **16**, 818.

METCHNIKOFF, E. (1898a) *Ann. Inst. Pasteur*, **12**, 81 ; (1898b) *Ibid.*, **12**, 263.

MEYER, H. and RANSOM, F. (1903) *Arch. Path. Pharm.*, **49**, 369.

MOHLER, J. R. and EICHHORN, A. (1911) *28th Ann. Rep. Bur. Anim. Ind.*, p. 185.

MOTZFELDT, K. (1912) *Zbl. Bakt.*, **65**, 60.

NABARRO, D. (1932) *Lancet*, i. 450.

NICOLAIER, A. (1884) *Dtsch. med. Wschr.*, **10**, 842 ; (1886) *Jber. Fortschr. path. Mikroorg.*, **2**, 270.

NOBLE, W. (1915) *J. infect. Dis.*, **16**, 132.

O'CARROLL, T. (1931) *Brit. med. J.*, i. 74.

OSLER, W. (1920) " The Principles and Practice of Medicine," 8th edit. London and New York.

PATERSON, A. E. (1930) *Med. J. Aust.*, **1**, 832.

PIZZINI, L. (1898) *Zbl. Bakt.*, **24**, 890.

PRAUSNITZ, C. (1929) " Memoranda on the International Standardization of Therapeutic Sera and Bacterial Products." League of Nations Health Organization.

RAMON, G., DESCOMBEY, P., and LEMÉTAYER, E. (1931) *Ann. Inst. Pasteur*, **46**, 444.

RAMON, G. and LEMÉTAYER, E. (1932) *C. R. Soc. Biol.*, **109**, 827 ; (1934) *Ibid.*, **116**, 275 ; (1935) *Rev. Immunol., Paris*, **1**, 209.

ROSENAU, M. J. and ANDERSON, J. F. (1908) *Bull. U.S. hyg. Lab.*, No. 43.

ROSENBACH. (1886) *Arch. klin. Chir.*, **34**, 306.

ROUX, E. and BORREL, A. (1898) *Ann. Inst. Pasteur*, **12**, 225.

RUSSELL, D. S. (1927) *Brit. J. exp. Path.*, **8**, 377.

SACQUÉPÉE, E. (1933) *Paris méd.*, **23**, 491.

SANFELICE, F. (1893) *Z. Hyg. InfektKr.*, **14**, 339.

SCHEUNEMANN, K. (1931) *Arch. Hyg.*, **105**, 287.

SHERRINGTON, C. S. (1917) *Lancet*, ii. 964.

SMITH, T. (1908) *Trans. Chicago path. Soc.*, **7**, No. 4.

TENBROECK, C. and BAUER, J. H. (1922) *J. exp. Med.*, **36**, 261.

TIZZONI, G. and CATTANI, G. (1891a) *Zbl. Bakt.*, **9**, 189 ; (1891b) *Ibid.*, **9**, 685.

TOLEDO, S. and VEILLON. (1891) *Zbl. Bakt.*, **9**, 18.

TULLOCH, W. J. (1919–20) *J. Hyg., Camb.*, **18**, 103.

VAILLARD, L. (1891) *C. R. Soc. Biol.*, **3**, 462 ; (1892) *Ann. Inst. Pasteur*, **6**, 224.

VAILLARD, L. and ROUGET, J. (1892) *Ann. Inst. Pasteur*, **6**, 224.

WÁMOSCHER, L. and VÁSÁRHELYI, J. VON. (1933) *Z. Hyg. InfektKr.*, **115**, 535.

WASSERMANN, A. (1898) *Berl. klin. Wschr.*, **35**, 4.

WASSERMANN, A. and TAKAKI, T. (1898) *Berl. klin. Wschr.*, **35**, 5.

WILCOX, H. L. (1934) *J. Immunol.*, **27**, 195.

WRIGHT, H. D. (1930) *Univ. Coll. Hosp. Mag.*, **15**, 64.

YODH, B. B. (1932) *Brit. med. J.*, ii. 589.

CHAPTER LXXV

GAS GANGRENE: ANAEROBIC INFECTIONS OF ANIMALS

GAS GANGRENE IN MAN

IN the pre-antiseptic days the formation of sloughs, the occurrence of massive necrosis, and the onset of gangrene, so frequently followed upon any extensive operative procedure that they were regarded as more or less inevitable features of surgical practice. With the advent of antiseptic surgery, and the consequent healing of wounds by first intention, these processes became less and less common, till eventually even the names by which they were described took on an archaic air. It was therefore not unnatural that when gas gangrene made its appearance in the early days of the War, many surgeons were confronted with it for the first time. It was the older surgeons, who had had experience of pre-Listerian methods, who recognized its true nature, and who pointed out the impossibility of preventing it by the modern aseptic methods. Nevertheless, though the disease was old, its study had to be taken up anew. The problems involved were attacked with such success that by the end of the War gas gangrene had ceased to be of more than minor importance. In peace time the disease is uncommon, but is occasionally met with after severe compound fractures, and during the puerperium, particularly when following illegal abortions (see Hill 1936).

In this chapter we can give only an outline of the bacteriological investigation of gas gangrene; for a full description the reader is referred to the monograph of Weinberg and Séguin (1918), and to the Report of the Anaerobic Committee (see Report 1919).

Bacteriology.—In 1914 the incidence of gas gangrene amongst the British Expeditionary Force amounted to over 12 per cent. of the number wounded; of these 20–25 per cent. died. By 1918, owing to earlier evacuation of the wounded, excision of wounds, the employment of an antiseptic technique, and other measures, the incidence had fallen to under 1 per cent. (Report 1919). Indeed, in the Base Hospitals in 1918, amongst a total of about 25,000 wounded reported on by Bowlby (1919), only 84 patients developed serious or massive gas gangrene—an incidence of 0·34 per cent. In the French and German armies the incidence appears to have been rather higher.

Examination of the wound of a man dying of gas gangrene revealed a number of organisms, aerobic and anaerobic; it was uncommon to meet with only one species of bacterium. Thus in an examination of 91 cases, Weinberg and Séguin (1918) found anaerobes in 24, and anaerobes plus aerobes in 67; in only 10 of the former group was a single species isolated—monomicrobial infection. The diversity of flora was so great that no fewer than 38 different combinations of anaerobic bacteria occurred in their 91 cases. To separate these different organisms and to estimate their particular rôle in the genesis of the disease was a heavy task ; the results obtained by the French and English workers, however, agreed sufficiently well for it to be possible to state definitely that certain anaerobes, alone or in combination, were primarily responsible for gas gangrene (Table CLXIV).

TABLE CLXIV

THE FREQUENCY OF DIFFERENT ANAEROBES IN GAS GANGRENE (Report 1919).

	Weinberg and Séguin.	McIntosh.	McIntosh.	Henry.
	91 Cases.	41 Cases.	52 Cases.	50 Cases.
	Per cent.	Per cent.	Per cent.	Per cent.
Cl. welchii (*B. perfringens*) . . .	77	43·9	67·3	80
Cl. œdematiens	34	—	4·0	10
Cl. sporogenes	27	36·5	38·7	—
Cl. fallax	16·5	—	—	6
Cl. septique	13	19·5	16·3	16

Numerous other anaerobic bacilli were also found, such as *Cl. histolyticum, Cl. aerofœtidum, Cl. putrificum, Cl. bifermentans,* and *Cl. tertium.* Of the aerobes commonly encountered the majority consisted of diplo-streptococci and organisms belonging to the *Proteus* group (Weinberg and Séguin 1918). In 37 of Weinberg and Séguin's cases only one species of anaerobe was isolated ; of these 29 were *Cl. welchii,* 5 *Cl. œdematiens,* 1 *Cl. septique,* 1 *Cl. fallax,* and 1 *Cl. aerofœtidum.*

The suggestion that each of these organisms was capable by itself of giving rise to gas gangrene was borne out by animal experiments. With the possible exception of *Cl. sporogenes,* these five organisms were the only ones that could reproduce in animals a disease simulating the condition in man. With regard to *Cl. sporogenes* it is not clear whether it is pathogenic by itself. The work of the English bacteriologists suggests that it plays a subsidiary but important rôle in assisting *Cl. welchii, Cl. œdematiens,* and *Cl. septique* in their attack on the tissues, but that by itself it is harmless. On the other hand, Weinberg and Séguin regard it as potentially though weakly pathogenic.

Summing up, we may say that gas gangrene is not a bacteriological entity ; it may be caused by a number of different anaerobic bacilli. Usually these are present either in combination with each other or with aerobic organisms. The three most important anaerobes are *Cl. welchii* (*B. perfringens*), *Cl. œdematiens,* and *Cl. septique* (*Vibrion septique*) ; of less importance are *Cl. fallax, Cl. aerofœtidum,* and *Cl. sporogenes.*

Reproduction of Gas Gangrene in Animals.

The experimental disease caused by *Cl. welchii, Cl. septique,* and *Cl. œdematiens* has already been described in Chapter XXXIII.

Each of these organisms, it will be remembered, forms a true exotoxin (Bull and Pritchett 1917*a, b,* Report 1919, Weinberg and Séguin 1918), which apparently possesses hæmolytic, leucocidal, and necrotic powers (Kamen 1904, Eisenberg 1907, Simonds 1915, Weinberg and Séguin 1918, Report 1919, Weinberg and Ginsbourg 1927). The most potent toxin is formed by *Cl. œdematiens* ; indeed the disease associated with this organism partakes more of an intoxication than a true infection.

Mode of Development of Gas Gangrene in Man.

We have already seen that the injection of a broth culture of *Cl. welchii* or *Cl. septique* into a guinea-pig will give rise to a disease simulating gas gangrene. If, instead of using a whole broth culture, we wash the organisms thoroughly to free them from toxin, no disease is set up. Likewise, saline suspensions washed off an agar slope are non-pathogenic. Large numbers of the bacilli can be injected without giving rise even to a local lesion. But if to the toxin-free bacilli a sub-lethal dose of toxin (broth filtrate) is added, the mixture proves intensely virulent. A protocol from De Kruif and Bollman's paper (1917) will illustrate this point :

Effect of intramuscular injection into guinea-pigs of—

1·0 c.c. *Cl. welchii* broth filtrate	.	Survived.
0·05 c.c. washed organisms + 0·5 c.c. sterile broth .	.	Survived.
0·1 c.c. ,, ,, + 0·5 c.c. ,, ,, .	.	Died 36 hrs.
0·000,01 c.c. ,, ,, + 0·5 c.c. broth filtrate .	.	Died 19 hrs.

It will be seen that a non-lethal dose of filtrate decreased the M.L.D. of the washed bacilli several thousand times.

The broth filtrate contains an aggressin, probably identical with the toxin, which enables the bacilli to proliferate in the tissues. Without this the bacilli are partly lysed by the tissue fluids and partly taken up by phagocytes ; with it neither lysis nor phagocytosis occurs, but the organisms divide, produce fresh toxin, and bring about the death of the animal. In other words, the bacilli apart from their toxin are powerless to overcome the resistance of the tissues. How the broth filtrate acts is not clear, but since both *Cl. welchii* and *Cl. septique* are known to bring about in culture a very steep fall in Eh, it is not improbable that there are reducing substances in the filtrate capable of establishing a sufficiently low O-R potential to enable the spores to germinate. Once germination has started, the organisms probably produce their own reducing system, which enables them to multiply even in the presence of healthy tissue.

Toxin is not the only substance, however, that can break down this resistance. Bullock (Gye) and Cramer (1919), whose work has been described in the last chapter, found that small quantities of ionizable calcium salts—notably calcium chloride —exerted a similar kataphylactic action. Colloidal silicic acid behaved in the same manner.

Since the organisms introduced into a wound are devoid of toxin, being frequently in the sporing stage, it is difficult to understand why they should multiply. In the opinion of Bullock and Cramer the determining factor is some kataphylactic substance that is carried into the wound with them. Earth containing calcium salts or silicic acid is suggested as the probable accessory agent. The work of Fildes (1927) and Russell (1927) renders it highly probable that such substances as earth or calcium chloride act by causing foci of necrosis, in which the oxidation-reduction potential becomes sufficiently reduced to enable the anaerobic bacterial spores to germinate (see Chapter LXXIV).

The possible importance of secondary infection is difficult to assess ; it may well be that highly proteolytic organisms such as *Cl. histolyticum, Cl. putrificum, Cl. bifermentans,* and *Proteus vulgaris,* by destroying the tissues, assist in preparing the way for the gas-gangrene bacteria. Similarly mechanical injury, crushing of the tissues, effusion of blood, and fracture of bone may have the same effect. But of the precise value of each of these agents we are entirely ignorant.

That some determining factor is necessary, however, is shown not only experimentally in animals, but by the observation in man that *Cl. welchii, Cl. septique* and *Cl. œdematiens* may all be present in a wound without setting up gas gangrene.

" The disease begins, not when a wound has become infected with the pathogenic anaerobes, but from the moment when a group of these bacteria have been enabled to surround themselves with a toxin sufficiently concentrated to abolish the local defences of the tissues " (Report 1919). Once this has occurred, the organisms multiply, produce more toxin, and rapidly invade the tissues. The toxin of *Cl. welchii*, in particular, has a deleterious action on the suprarenals, and it is partly owing to the consequent lack of adrenalin in the blood that exhaustion and death occur so quickly. This paralysis of the suprarenals is aided by hæmorrhage, exposure to cold, and absorption of the acids formed by growth of the bacilli in the tissues.

Diagnosis.

Material suitable for examination consists of exudates from infected wounds, fluid from hæmorrhagic bullæ, and muscle removed at operation. Blood cultures may be practised during life (Weinberg and Séguin 1918), and a full examination made after death, if desired. The isolation of the different anaerobes requires a high degree of technical skill. Numerous procedures are employed for the purification of cultures.

Briefly, the material should be seeded into cooked meat medium, which serves as a repository for the various organisms. A small part of the mixed culture is heated to 80° C. for 20 minutes in order to destroy aerobic and anaerobic non-sporing forms, and then plated out on serum or on blood agar. Single colonies are picked off into broth, and replated three or four times.

Advantage may be taken of the different cultural requirements of the anaerobes; thus glucose is more favourable to the growth of the saccharolytic than of the proteolytic organisms. In order to separate *Cl. welchii* from a mixed culture, a tube of glucose broth may be seeded, incubated for 3 to 6 hours, and subcultured into a fresh tube. Similarly for the concentration of *Cl. septique* salicin broth may be used. After half a dozen or more subcultures the organism may be present in such excess that single colonies can readily be obtained on plating. For *Cl. sporogenes* a medium made with tap water containing pieces of coagulated egg white is useful for concentration. Pathogenic may be separated from non-pathogenic organisms by animal inoculation. Moreover the individual species of pathogenic bacteria may be separated by injection into protected animals. Thus, if a mixture of *Cl. welchii, Cl. septique*, and *Cl. œdematiens* is inoculated into a guinea-pig that has received a dose of antiserum prepared against the latter two organisms, then *Cl. welchii* alone will proliferate and invade the blood stream. For a full description of the methods of isolation and purification of the anaerobes the reader is referred to Report (1919).

According to Hoyt (1933), a useful method of demonstrating the presence of *Cl. welchii* is to inoculate the culture intravenously into a mouse, kill the animal in a few minutes, and incubate it for 6 hours at 37° C. A very striking picture is then presented. The tissues are pale pink, dry, and friable, the liver is pale, dry, and shrunken, and the heart pale and friable ; capsulated Gram-positive rods are present in smears of the liver and heart blood.

Blood cultures during life are frequently positive (Weinberg and Séguin 1918). *Cl. welchii* and *Cl. septique* are especially liable to invade the blood ; *Cl. œdematiens*, which acts chiefly by virtue of its toxin, often remains confined to the local lesion.

By examining the local œdema fluid microscopically and by the agglutination test, by experimental inoculation of partly protected animals, and by a study of the primary cultures, Weinberg and Séguin were often able to make a tentative diagnosis of the infecting organisms in 24 to 36 hours.

Prophylaxis and Treatment.

Towards the end of the War, antitoxin and antibacterial sera were prepared against *Cl. welchii, Cl. septique,* and *Cl. œdematiens.* The Armistice came before they had been given an extensive trial, but the results obtained were suggestive.

Weinberg and Séguin (1918) injected 10–30 c.c. of a mixture of 2 or of all 3 of the sera prophylactically into soldiers with serious wounds 5 to 18 hours after the receipt of the injury. Of 50 patients treated, 25 died within a day from their wounds without showing gas gangrene ; of the other 25, whose after-histories were followed for from 1 to 4 weeks, not one developed gaseous infection.

Therapeutically serum treatment was given to 30 patients with gas gangrene ; 19 recovered. Of the 11 that died 7 were treated very late or by non-specific serum, or developed secondary infections. The mortality therefore was higher than might be expected in properly treated cases. At the same time, of 66 patients who received no serum treatment or who were given non-specific serum, 35 died.

The doses recommended are 80–100 c.c. of mixed serum given locally, subcutaneously, intramuscularly or intravenously. Later, according to the flora in the wound, the proportions of the sera in the mixture may be altered, or a monospecific serum given. The injections should be repeated every day, or even more frequently. In cases of advanced toxæmia the only hope lies in the intravenous injection of large quantities of specific antitoxic serum. Though gas gangrene occurs but rarely in civil practice, antiserum prepared against the gas-gangrene organisms is finding a place in the treatment of certain conditions associated with an anaerobic invasion of the tissues (Weinberg and Howard 1927, Weinberg *et al.* 1928).

The most satisfactory type of serum to use is still under discussion. Antitoxic serum, prepared by the inoculation of horses with formolized, and later with pure, toxin appears to be of most value in combating toxæmia. On the other hand, Robertson and Felix (1930) and Henderson (1934, 1935) have drawn attention to the advantage of using an antibacterial serum, prepared against the somatic antigen of the invading organism, for protection against infection. They have brought evidence, with *Cl. septique,* to show that such a serum is more powerful in preventing the development of gas gangrene induced in guinea-pigs by the inoculation of activated spores than is an antitoxic serum. In practice the ideal would appear to be a serum possessed of both antibacterial and antitoxic powers. It is to be noted that in antibacterial sera the O antibody alone is potent ; the H antibody seems to be without protective activity. Moreover, the O antibody is type-specific, so that if antibacterial sera are to be used, they must be prepared by inoculation of horses with representatives of each antigenic type.

Several different methods have been employed in the *standardization* of antiserum against gas gangrene (see Dalling *et al.* 1928, Buttle and Trevan 1928, Glenny, Llewellyn-Jones, and Mason 1931, Weinberg, Davesne, and Prévot 1932, Bengtson 1934, Hartley and White 1935, Walbum and Reymann 1935, Ssilanowa 1935). Hitherto attention has been concentrated on the measurement of the antitoxic potency of the serum. The problem of measuring the antibacterial potency has not yet been attacked. The two chief methods used for titrating the antitoxin content are intramuscular or intravenous inoculation of mice, and intracutaneous inoculation of guinea-pigs, with toxin-antitoxin mixtures. The international standards laid down by the League of Nations may be briefly defined.

For antiserum against *Cl. welchii* the dry stable specimen of antitoxin prepared at the National Institute of Health, Washington, is accepted as the international standard ; the specific antitoxic activity contained in 0·322 mgm. constitutes one international unit (see Hartley 1931).

For antiserum against *Cl. septique* the dry stable specimen of antitoxin prepared at the National Institute for Medical Research, London, is accepted as the international standard ; the specific antitoxic activity contained in 0·2377 mgm. of this preparation constitutes one international unit (see Hartley and White 1935).

For antiserum against *Cl. œdematiens* the dry stable specimen of antitoxin prepared at the State Serum Institute, Copenhagen, is accepted as the international standard ; the specific antitoxic activity contained in 0·2681 mgm. of this preparation constitutes one international unit (see Walbum and Reymann 1935).

ANAEROBIC INFECTIONS OF ANIMALS

Blackleg and Gas Gangrene

SYNONYMS : Symptomatic anthrax, quarter-evil, blackquarter.
French : *Charbon symptomatique.*   German : *Rauschbrand.*

Blackleg is a disease attacking cattle, sheep, and less often swine (Meyer 1915). It is characterized by the appearance of a crepitant, fluctuating swelling, generally on one of the quarters, followed rapidly by death. Calves are resistant for the first 6 months of life ; they then become susceptible and remain so till about 2 years of age. The disease is commoner in the summer than in the winter. It may follow shearing, docking, parturition, or castration in sheep, but more often appears spontaneously. Arloing, Cornevin and Thomas (1881) first showed that the disease could be transmitted to cattle by inoculation of infective material. From the lesions, they isolated an anaerobic spore-bearing bacillus—*Cl. chauvœi*. The washed bacilli are non-infective, but they can be activated by a small dose of broth filtrate, or by substances such as lactic acid, potassium chloride, or sand (Nocard and Roux 1887, Roux 1888, Leclainche and Vallée 1900).

The term *gas gangrene* or *malignant œdema* is sometimes reserved for anaerobic infections of the muscle consequent on trauma. The essential pathology of blackleg and gas gangrene appears to be the same, and the distinction between the terms seems of doubtful value.

Blackleg in cattle seems to be generally caused by *Cl. chauvœi*, and in sheep by *Cl. septique* (Heller 1920, Gaiger 1924, Weinberg and Mihailesco 1929, Roberts and McEwen 1931).

Vaccination has been practised for many years and has been attended by a considerable amount of success. Arloing, Cornevin and Thomas used two vaccines of different virulence ; the first was prepared by exposing the dried juice from a blackleg tumour to 100–104° C. for 6 hours ; the second by exposing it to 85–90° C. for the same time. Inoculation of cattle was practised subcutaneously on the under surface of the tail. Statistics compiled by Cornevin (1895) are given in Table CLXV.

TABLE CLXV

RESULTS OF VACCINATION AGAINST BLACKLEG IN CATTLE.

| | No. of Animals Vaccinated. | Mortality due to vaccination. | |
		Total.	Per 1,000.
1893	6,696	5	0·75
1894	8,222	8	0·97
1895 first 6 months . . .	6,936	5	0·72

The mortality in the vaccinated animals varied in different districts from 0–10 per 1,000 ; amongst the unvaccinated animals it varied from 20 to 250 per 1,000. Several other vaccines have been employed (Roux 1888, Nitta 1919, Dalling 1925. See also *J. comp. Path.* 1895, **8**, 166). McEwen (1926) has recommended the use of a formolized broth culture of *Cl. chauvœi* ; under experimental conditions, sheep injected with this vaccine appeared to derive a greater degree of immunity against subsequent inoculation with a living culture than sheep vaccinated with a non-formolized broth filtrate. Henderson's (1932) work suggests that the O antigen is likely to prove a powerful immunizing agent. For field use this can be conveniently dispensed in the form of steamed suspensions.

Sera for therapeutic use have been prepared against *Cl. chauvœi* and *Cl. septique.* Their intravenous administration in cases of the fully developed disease appears at times to give very favourable results.

Braxy

SYNONYMS : *Bradsot* = quick plague.

Braxy is the term used for a disease of sheep occurring mainly in the north-western part of Europe. Recent work has rendered it clear that more than one type of disease is called by this name. For descriptive purposes we propose to reserve the term braxy for the type of disease characterized by inflammation of the fourth stomach, and to refer to the so-called German braxy by the term black disease or infectious necrotic hepatitis.

The classical or northern braxy occurs on the western coast of Norway, in Iceland, the Faroe islands, and Scotland. Sheep are most susceptible during their first year. The disease breaks out in the late autumn and early winter months when the animals descend from the hills to the pastures of the lowlands. In Scotland the losses from braxy in some districts may amount to as much as 35 per cent. of the first year's sheep (Gaiger 1924). Clinically, in the usual acute form of the disease, death occurs before any symptoms have been noticed ; in the subacute form there is weakness, followed by coma, dyspnœa, and death. The duration of the disease is a matter of a few hours. Post mortem, there is severe inflammation of the fourth stomach and duodenum, with œdema and hæmorrhage—sometimes necrosis—of the mucosa and submucous tissue. The peritoneal fluid is often turbid and in excess ; there are degenerative changes in the visceral organs, and an acute parenchymatous nephritis.

P.B. Z Z

The causative organism was described by Nielsen in 1888, who found it in large numbers in the stomach wall. It was identified by Gaiger (1922) with *Cl. septique*. The mode of infection is obscure ; experimental feeding with pure cultures of the bacillus apparently fails to reproduce the disease ; Jensen was successful only 5 times in 1,545 attempts (Gaiger 1924). Subcutaneous injection produces black-leg ; post mortem, lesions may be present in the abomasum simulating those of the natural disease (Hamilton 1902, 1906) ; there is no evidence however that natural infection occurs by this route. Again we are forced to conclude that some accessory factor must be present before the bacillus is able to invade the tissues. Experimental work on guinea-pigs by Borthwick (1934) suggests that intestinal stasis and exposure of the animal to cold are important factors in determining the invasion of the tissues by *Cl. septique*. While the feeding of cultures to normal guinea-pigs rarely set up infection, inhibition of peristalsis by narcotine, or pre-liminary exposure to cold, resulted in the development of a fatal infection in a fairly high proportion of the animals.

A considerable degree of protection is afforded by the use of Jensen's sero-vaccine.

Gaiger (1922) obtained promising results by the use of a sterile filtrate of a culture of *Cl. septique*. Of 10,340 hoggs (1st year sheep) vaccinated, 2·39 per cent. died of braxy, while among 3,800 control animals the mortality from braxy was 9 per cent. (see Gordon 1934*a*).

Dalling (1925, Dalling *et al.* 1925, 1926) advocated a combined vaccine against blackleg and braxy in sheep. He used a culture filtrate of *Cl. chauvœi* and a mix-ture of *Cl. septique* toxin and antitoxin. During the winter of 1924, 549 sheep were inoculated, with a braxy mortality of 0·36 per cent. ; of 464 unvaccinated sheep on the same farms and under the same conditions 15·5 per cent. died of braxy. Satisfactory results were also obtained by Gordon (1934*a*) using a formo-lized whole culture of *Cl. septique*. Preliminary experiments on sheep showed this to be superior to Gaiger's filtrate vaccine, and it was therefore used for further trial. Of 3,588 vaccinated hoggs, 73 (0·8 per cent.) died of braxy, while of 1,886 control animals on the same farms, 158 (8·4 per cent.) died of this disease. The vaccine is prepared by adding 0·5 per cent. formol to a 15-hour horse flesh broth culture and incubating at 37° C. for 2 days. By this time it should be bacterio-logically sterile, and should prove non-toxic when inoculated intravenously into mice in a dose of 0·5 c.c. Dungal (1932) in Iceland also reported favourable results from the use of a formolized whole culture vaccine of *Cl. septique*. Comparison with Jensen's sero-vaccine yielded the following figures. Of 11,308 sheep given the sero-vaccine, the mortality from all causes was 2·44 per cent. whereas of 59,736 sheep given the formolized vaccine, it was only 0·84 per cent.

Black Disease

SYNONYMS : Infectious necrotic hepatitis ; German braxy.

This disease occurs in Australia, particularly Victoria, New South Wales, and Tasmania, and in certain parts of Germany, where it is termed braxy. In Germany two types are recognized : (1) Meadow braxy, affecting mainly ewes at pasture in well-watered valleys ; and (2) Stall braxy, affecting chiefly young castrated lambs that are being fattened for market (Miessner, Meyn, and Schoop 1931).

In Australia the meadow type alone seems to be common. Well-nourished animals are affected. Clinically the course in meadow braxy is usually very acute, and the animals are often found dead before suspicion of illness has been aroused, but in stall braxy symptoms may be present for 12 hours before death. Examination of fresh carcasses reveals the presence of subcutaneous venous engorgement, which gives the skin a dark colour—hence the term black disease—amber-coloured fluid in the pericardial and peritoneal cavities, and characteristic necrotic areas in the liver. Unlike true braxy the abomasum is slightly or not at all affected, and no obvious degenerative changes are present in the visceral organs. The liver lesions are most typical of the disease. Greenish bile-stained areas of necrosis, about 1 cm. in diameter, containing cavities filled with blood clot and immature liver flukes, are usually seen in small numbers. In addition to these non-specific foci, there are a few characteristic, irregularly circular, necrotic areas, 2–3 cm. in diameter, sharply defined, yellowish-white in colour, and surrounded by a wide zone of venous congestion. Bacteriologically the liver can be shown to contain large anaerobic bacilli, which are refered to by the Germans as *Cl. gigas*, but which appear to be identical with, or a variety of, *Cl. œdematiens*.

The pathogenesis of the disease has been elucidated by Dodd (1918, 1921), Albiston (1927), and particularly Turner (1930), whose monograph affords an excellent example of the intelligent application of general principles to the investigation of a particular problem. The work of Fildes on tetanus (see Chapter LXXIV) made it clear that toxin-free spores were unable to germinate in healthy tissue owing to the existence of too high an O-R potential, but that if a focus was provided for them by mechanical, chemical, or biological means in which a sufficiently low potential could be established, germination commenced, and the bacilli produced their fatal toxin. A review of the pathogenesis of gas gangrene seemed to leave little doubt that the conclusions drawn by Fildes on the necessity of suitable respiratory conditions for the development of the tetanus bacillus probably held true for most other spore-bearing anaerobic bacteria. Turner, by a careful series of observations and experiments, was able to show that in black disease the necessary conditions for growth of the causative organism were found in the necrotic areas produced by invasion of the liver with wandering immature liver flukes of the species *Fasciola hepatica*. In these areas the organisms multiplied, and gave rise to a toxin which was responsible for the main features of the disease. Many sheep were found to be latently infected with the spores of *Cl. œdematiens*, but not until suitable necrotic foci were established by invasion with liver flukes did the infection become active.

Consequent on this work Turner prepared a formolized broth vaccine with which very satisfactory results were obtained in field trials. The figures showed that when two doses were given, the mortality from black disease was reduced on an average by about half, as compared with control animals on the same farm. Even more favourable results attended the use of three doses of vaccine.

Infections due to Cl. welchii : Lamb dysentery ; " Struck " ; infectious enterotoxæmia ; pulpy kidney disease

A number of acute toxæmic diseases have been described in different parts of the world, mostly affecting sheep, in which the lesions appear to result from an intestinal infection with a variety of *Cl. welchii*. The pathogenesis of these diseases still remains obscure, but considerable progress is being made in their control by vaccination and serotherapy.

Lamb dysentery is a disease that takes a heavy toll of life among the lambs during their first 2 weeks of life (Gaiger and Dalling 1921). It is particularly prevalent in the border counties of England and Scotland. Pathologically it is characterized by an enteritis varying from a mild congestion of the intestinal mucosa to a condition in which extensive tracts of the small and large intestine become necrosed and ulcerated. On the surface of the inflamed mucosa and ulcerated areas a bacillus is found closely allied to *Cl. welchii*, but differing from it in certain cultural particulars and in its production of a more powerful toxin (Dalling *et al.* 1925, Dalling 1928*b*, 1931–32). This organism is sometimes referred to as the lamb dysentery bacillus, and sometimes as the *agni* variety of *Cl. welchii*. For the moment it is probably better to call it *Cl. welchii* Type B (see Chapter XXXIII). The organisms are confined mainly to the intestine, and the body tissues are not usually invaded.

Protection against the disease can be afforded in one of two ways : (1) the pregnant ewe may be immunized with an over-neutralized toxin-antitoxin mixture, or with a simple formolized culture. Both of these methods of inoculation appear to give satisfactory results. Thus in one field experiment, the mortality from lamb dysentery amongst 741 lambs born of ewes inoculated with the toxin-antitoxin mixture was 1·07 per cent. ; amongst 1,157 lambs born of ewes inoculated with a formolized culture it was 1·12 per cent. ; while amongst 2,530 control lambs born of uninoculated ewes on the same farms it was 13·09 per cent. (Dalling 1928*b*. For further records see Dalling 1926, Dalling, Mason, and Gordon 1928, 1929). The antibodies generated in the ewe by this method are transferred to the new-born lamb by means of the colostrum (Dalling 1928*a*, Mason, Dalling, and Gordon 1930). (2) The new-born lamb may be injected directly with antitoxin. This method likewise gives satisfactory results. Thus on 15 farms in 1927 the mortality from lamb dysentery amongst 1,122 lambs injected with serum was 0·44 per cent., while amongst 1,241 control lambs on the same farms it was 17·16 per cent. (Dalling 1928*b*).

" **Struck** " is the local name given to a disease of sheep occurring during the late winter and spring months on the Romney Marsh in Kent. Clinically the symptoms are of short duration, and the case mortality is high. In fresh carcasses the main lesions are those of an acute enteritis and peritonitis, but in animals that have been dead for some hours the subcutaneous and muscular tissues present a picture similar to that found in gas gangrene. The work of McEwen (1930) and McEwen and Roberts (1931) seems to show that the disease is essentially a toxæmia consequent on the multiplication in the intestinal canal, and perhaps the body tissues, of an organism resembling *Cl. welchii*. The name *Cl. paludis* has been suggested for it, but until we know more of the relationship between this organism and other closely allied members of the *welchii* type it is probably better to refer to it as *Cl. welchii* Type C. Vaccination with toxoid is apparently of value in protecting against the disease (McEwen 1935).

Infectious entero-toxæmia is a disease of sheep described by Bennetts (1932) in Western Australia, and apparently due to the absorption of toxin from the small intestine. The organism, for which the name *Cl. ovitoxicum* has been suggested, appears to be more or less identical with Wilsdon's (1931, 1933) *Cl. welchii* Type D, and is better referred to by this name. The same organism appears to be responsible for the condition known as **pulpy kidney disease of lambs,** which has been studied in New Zealand by Gill (1932) and in Wales by Montgomerie and Dalling (1933) and Montgomerie and Rowlands (1933, 1934). Gordon (1934b), who examined filtrates of intestinal contents from lambs, sheep, and horses that had apparently died of acute toxæmia, was able to demonstrate the presence of a toxin neutralizable by an antitoxin to *Cl. welchii* Type D. His work suggests that this organism may play a part in a number of diseases of sheep and lambs, as well as certain types of grass sickness in horses.

The conditions governing the formation of a toxin in the various diseases that we have been discussing are still obscure, and there is a considerable field open for an investigation of the type so successfully undertaken by Turner (1930) in black disease. It is interesting to reflect that whereas anaerobic infections in man and the carnivora are generally preceded by trauma, in herbivora they often occur spontaneously (Heller 1920).

In this connection we may refer to the suggestive results obtained by Bosworth and Glover (1935). These workers made the interesting observation that, when toxin of *Cl. welchii* type D, but not of types A, B, or C, was added to an intestinal filtrate of a normal sheep, guinea-pig, or rabbit, the mixture proved considerably more toxic to the mouse than could be accounted for by the quantity of toxin added. Exactly the same amount of antitoxin, it is stated, was required to neutralize the toxin, whether it was free or mixed with the intestinal filtrate, though it is very difficult to understand how this could occur. The activating substance in the filtrate was destroyed by exposure to 70° C. for 20 minutes, and could be precipitated out with 9 volumes of alcohol. This work, if confirmed, may open up a promising field for inquiry.

(For a recent account of the anaerobic toxæmias of animals, see Woodruff 1936.)

For **botulism** in animals see Chapter LXIX.

REFERENCES

ALBISTON, H. E. (1927) *Aust. J. exp. Biol. med. Sci.,* **4,** 113.
ARLOING, CORNEVIN, and THOMAS. (1881) *C. R. Acad. Sci.,* **92,** 1246.
BENGTSON, I. A. (1934) *Publ. Hlth Rep., Wash.,* **49,** 251.
BENNETTS, H. W. (1932) *Aust. Coun. sci. industr. Res., Bull.* No. 57.
BORTHWICK, G. R. (1934) *Brit. J. exp. Path.,* **15,** 153.
BOSWORTH, T. J. and GLOVER, R. E. (1935) *Proc. R. Soc. Med.,* **28,** 1004.
BOWLBY, A. (1919) *Brit. med. J.,* i. 205.
BULL, C. G. and PRITCHETT, I. W. (1917a) *J. exp. Med.,* **26,** 119 ; (1917b) *Ibid.,* **26,** 867.
BULLOCK, W. E. and CRAMER, W. (1919) *Proc. roy. Soc., B,* **90,** 513.
BUTTLE, G. A. H. and TREVAN, J. W. (1928) *Brit. J. exp. Path.,* **9,** 182.
CORNEVIN. (1895) *J. comp. Path.,* **8,** 233.
DALLING, T. (1925) *J. Path. Bact.,* **28,** 536 ; (1926) *J. comp. Path.,* **39,** 148 ; (1928a) *Vet. Rec.,* **8,** 841 ; (1928b) *Ann. Congr. Nat. Vet. Med. Ass. G.B.I.* ; (1931–32) *Proc. R. Soc. Med.,* **25,** 807.
DALLING, T., ALLEN, H. R., and MASON, J. H. (1925) *Vet. Rec.,* **5,** 561 ; (1926) *Ibid.,* **6,** 505.
DALLING, T., MASON, J. H., and GORDON, W. S. (1928) *Vet. J.,* **84,** 640 ; (1929) *Vet. Rec.,* **9,** 902.
DODD, S. (1918) *J. comp. Path.,* **31,** 1 ; (1921) *Ibid.,* **34,** 1.
DUNGAL, N. (1932) *J. comp. Path.,* **45,** 313.
EISENBERG, P. (1907) *C. R. Soc. Biol.,* **62,** 491, 537.
FILDES, P. (1927) *Brit. J. exp. Path.,* **8,** 387.
GAIGER, S. H. (1922) *J. comp. Path.,* **35,** 191, 235 ; (1924) *Ibid.,* **37,** 163.
GAIGER, S. H., and DALLING, T. (1921) *J. comp. Path.,* **34,** 79.
GILL, D. A. (1932) *New Zealand J. Agric.,* **45,** 332.
GLENNY, A. T., LLEWELLYN-JONES, M., and MASON, J. H. (1931) *J. Path. Bact.,* **34,** 201.
GORDON, W. S. (1934a) *Vet. Rec.,* **14,** 1 ; (1934b) *Ibid.,* **14,** 1016.

HAMILTON.   (1902) *Trans. Highland and Agricultural Soc. of Scotland* ; (1906) Rept. Depart-
    mental Committee of Bd. Agric. in Louping-ill and Braxy.   London.
HARTLEY, P.   (1931) *Hlth Organization, League of Nations, Rep.* C.H. 1056 (1).
HARTLEY, P. and WHITE, P. B.   (1935) *Quart. Bull. League Nations*, Jan. Spec. No., p. 13.
HELLER, H. H.   (1920) *J. infect. Dis.*, **27**, 385.
HENDERSON, D. W.   (1932) *Brit. J. exp. Path.*, **13**, 421 ; (1934) *Ibid.*, **15**, 166 ; (1935)
    Ibid., **16**, 393.
HILL, A. M.   (1936) *J. Obstet. Gynaec.*, **43**, 201.
HOYT, A.   (1933) *Proc. Soc. exp. Biol., N.Y.*, **30**, 875.
KAMEN, L.   (1904) *Zbl. Bakt.*, **35**, 686.
KRUIF, P. H. DE, and BOLLMAN, J. L.   (1917) *J. infect. Dis.*, **21**, 588.
LECLAINCHE, E. and VALLÉE, H.   (1900) *Ann. Inst. Pasteur*, **14**, 202.
McEWEN, A. D.   (1926) *J. comp. Path.*, **39**, 253 ; (1930) *Ibid.*, **43**, 1 ; (1935) *J. S.-E. agric.
    Coll. Wye*, No. 35, p. 45.
McEWEN, A. D. and ROBERTS, R. S.   (1931) *J. comp. Path.*, **44**, 26.
MASON, J. H., DALLING, T., and GORDON, W. S.   (1930) *J. Path. Bact.*, **33**, 783.
MEYER, K. F.   (1915) *J. infect. Dis.*, **17**, 458.
MIESSNER, H., MEYN, A., and SCHOOP, G.   (1931) *Zbl. Bakt.*, **120**, 257.
MONTGOMERIE, R. F. and DALLING, T.   (1933) *Vet. J.*, **89**, 223.
MONTGOMERIE, R. F. and ROWLANDS, W. T.   (1933) *Vet. J.*, **89**, 388 ; (1934) *Ibid.*, **90**, 399.
NITTA, N.   (1919) *J. comp. Path.*, **32**, 122.
NOCARD and ROUX.   (1887) *Ann. Inst. Pasteur*, **1**, 257.
Report.   (1919) *Spec. Rep. Ser. med. Res. Coun., Lond.*, No. 39.
ROBERTS, R. S. and McEWEN, A. D.   (1931) *J. comp. Path.*, **44**, 180.
ROBERTSON, M. and FELIX, A.   (1930) *Brit. J. exp. Path.*, **11**, 14.
ROUX, E.   (1888) *Ann. Inst. Pasteur*, **2**, 49.
RUSSELL, D. S.   (1927) *Brit. J. exp. Path.*, **8**, 377.
SIMONDS, J. P.   (1915) *Monogr. Rockefeller Inst. med. Res.*, No. 5.
SSILANOWA, I. W.   (1935) *Zbl. Bakt.*, **133**, 149.
TURNER, A. W.   (1930) *Aust. Coun. sci. industr. Res.*, Bull. No. 46.
WALBUM, L. E. and REYMANN, C.   (1935) *Quart. Bull. League Nations*, Jan. Spec. No.,
    p. 42.
WEINBERG, M., DAVESNE, J., and PRÉVOT, A. R.   (1932) *Ann. Inst. Pasteur*, **49**, 387.
WEINBERG, M. and GINSBOURG, B.   (1927) " Données récentes sur les microbes anaérobies
    et leur rôle en pathologie."   Masson & Cie, Paris.
WEINBERG, M. and HOWARD, A. F.   (1927) *C. R. Soc. Biol.*, **97**, 221.
WEINBERG, M. and MIHAILESCO, M.   (1929) *Ann. Inst. Pasteur*, **43**, 1408.
WEINBERG, M., PRÉVOT, A. R., DAVESNE, J., and RENARD, C.   (1928) *C. R. Soc. Biol.*,
    98, 749, 752.
WEINBERG, M. and SÉGUIN, P.   (1918) " La gangréne gazeuse."   Paris.
WILSDON, A. J.   (1931) *2nd Rep. Director, Inst. anim. Path., Camb.*, p. 53 ; (1933) *Ibid.*,
    3rd Rep., p. 46.
WOODRUFF, H. A.   (1936) *Brit. med. J.*, i. 406.

CHAPTER LXXVI

NECROBACILLOSIS, OZÆNA, RHINOSCLEROMA, SOFT CHANCRE, TRACHOMA, INFECTIOUS MONONUCLEOSIS, GLANDULAR FEVER, AND BARTONELLA INFECTIONS

NECROBACILLOSIS

THIS term may be used to cover a wide variety of conditions in man and animals due to infection with the non-sporing anaerobic bacillus known as *Fusiformis necrophorus* (see Chapter XVII).

In *man*, necrobacillosis does not seem to be a common disease. It usually takes the form of purulent or gangrenous inflammation of the skin, but abscesses of the joints and lungs have been described (see Shaw 1933). The mode of infection is not always clear, but a number of cases have followed bites, or injuries from the teeth, of animals. What relation the disease has to Vincent's angina (see Chapter LXXVII), and to the various necrotic stomatitis conditions in which the closely related organism *Fusiformis fusiformis* seems to play a part, is not clear.

In *animals*, necrobacillosis takes the form of calf diphtheria, necrotic stomatitis of cattle, foot-rot of sheep, gangrenous dermatitis of horses and mules, hepatic necrosis of cattle, pigs, and sheep, labial necrosis of rabbits, and a number of other conditions (see Beveridge 1934).

In **calf diphtheria,** which was studied by Loeffler (1884), a false membrane stretches from the throat down into the trachea ; the superficial parts are caseous and friable, the deeper parts firmly adherent. Microscopically the membrane consists of a superficial layer containing large numbers of micrococci ; a middle layer, amorphous and unstained ; and a deep layer containing granular detritus with some cells and the characteristic long wavy rows of bacilli ; these are separated by a narrow unstained zone from a dense infiltration of cells. The lungs contain pneumonic foci, in which much the same microscopical picture is evident. A similar disease to calf diphtheria is said to occur in lambs.

Labial necrosis of rabbits is characterized by a dark bluish-red discoloration of the under lip, accompanied by a tender swelling. The infiltration passes gradually down the under surface of the mouth and front of the neck, and in about 8 days reaches the upper opening of the thorax. Constitutional symptoms develop about the 5th day ; a thin watery discharge comes from the nose ; the respirations increase in rate ; the temperature rises 1–1·5° C. and the animals die in an emaciated condition with marked dyspnœa. Post mortem, section shows that the under lip is converted into a yellowish-white, compact, bacon-like, necrotic mass, which in places extends to the bone ; around the necrotic mass is a reddish-black border. The cervical glands are greatly swollen, juicy, and greyish-red ; sometimes they show small caseous foci. There is bloody, slightly turbid fluid in the pleural and pericardial cavities with some fibrin deposit on the surrounding serous membranes. A few pneumonic areas may be seen in the lungs, with yellowish-white streaks passing from the pleura into the dark red pulmonary tissue.

The spleen and other viscera appear normal. The disease was first described by Schmorl (1891), who observed an epidemic among his laboratory rabbits.

The diagnosis of necrobacillosis is made by morphological and cultural methods. In the lesions the organisms appear mostly as Gram-negative wavy non-branching filaments lying parallel to one another. Attempts to isolate them may be made directly by the inoculation of serum agar shake cultures, or by streaking plates of blood or potato extract agar containing 1/10,000–1/20,000 gentian violet and incubating anaerobically (Slanetz and Rettger 1933). Alternatively, a tissue suspension may be inoculated subcutaneously into rabbits, and cultures made from the blood a few hours before death (Scrivner and Lee 1934).

OZÆNA

Ozæna is a disease characterized by atrophy of the nasal mucosa, and the secretion of muco-pus, which dries into greenish-yellow crusts with a peculiarly foul and penetrating odour. It starts generally in childhood or adolescence, and persists throughout life. Though a great many workers have studied the disease, its ætiology still remains doubtful ; indeed, it is not clear whether it is an infective disease at all. For a long time there were, among those who supported the infective theory, two rival schools : one, following Loewenberg (1894) and Abel (1896), maintained that the disease was caused by the *B. mucosus ozænæ*—an organism belonging to the group of capsulated bacilli (see Chapter XXVII) ; the other maintained that the primary cause was Perez's bacillus (Perez 1899, 1901, 1913) (see Chapter XVIII). A fact in favour of the former group was the isolation of the Loewenberg-Abel bacillus from nearly every case of the disease ; in favour of the latter group was the reproduction of a chronic rhinitis by intravenous injection of Perez's bacillus into rabbits.

We do not propose to discuss the evidence for and against the claims of these rival schools ; it is sufficient to point out that most of the early workers entirely underestimated the difficulty of establishing the ætiological rôle of any organism isolated from such a situation as the nose. And since diseases such as ozæna and rhinoscleroma have not yet been reproduced with certainty in animals, it is impossible to make out a strong enough case in favour of any one organism to warrant belief in its specific ætiological rôle.

At the present day few workers would care to dogmatize about the causation of ozæna. The general trend of opinion is that the organisms described by Loewenberg, Perez, and others are merely secondary invaders, which are able to multiply abundantly in the altered conditions accompanying an atrophic rhinitis. (For further references see Fricke 1896, Page 1912, Hofer 1913a, b, Ward 1916, 1917, Shiga 1922, Busson 1923, Blanc and Pangalos 1925, Olinescu and Atineu 1925.)

RHINOSCLEROMA

Rhinoscleroma is a disease of the nose and upper part of the respiratory tract, characterized by proliferative lesions of the infective granuloma type. It is confined to man, and occurs endemically in Eastern Europe and sporadically elsewhere. Most of the reported cases have occurred in Slavs. It would appear to be either non-contagious or only slightly contagious (Perkins 1907). It has not been transmitted to animals.

Bacteriologically rhinoscleroma stands in much the same position as ozæna. In 1882 von Frisch cultivated a member of the group of capsulated bacilli from the lesions ; he called it *B. rhinoscleromatis*. By injecting cultures into the sub-mucous tissue of the nasal septum, he produced in rats a small tumour, which contained the organisms (Galli-Valerio 1911). Though Frisch and his followers regarded the disease as caused by this bacillus, there is very little evidence to show that this organism is primarily responsible for it. There is no means by which it can be distinguished with certainty from other members of the capsu-lated group ; and since we know that members of this group may be present in the nose of healthy persons, it is difficult to prove that they play any part in the production of rhinoscleroma. The probability is that they are mere secondary invaders, which grow freely in the nose of patients suffering from the disease.

Tomášek (1925), Quast (1926), and Kouwenaar, Maasland, and Wolff (1934) state that the majority of cases give a positive complement-fixation reaction with a suitable antigen prepared from the rhinoscleroma bacillus, whereas control cases of ozæna and other respiratory diseases fail to do so. The test appears to be of some value in epidemiological survey work.

SOFT CHANCRE OR ULCUS MOLLE

Soft chancre is a non-syphilitic lesion of the external genitals and neighbour-ing regions due to infection with a small Gram-negative bacillus first described by Ducrey (1889), and generally known by his name. For the differential diagnosis of this disease from syphilis by clinical methods textbooks on venereal diseases must be consulted.

There appears to be little doubt that Ducrey's bacillus is responsible for soft chancre, and for the buboes which are sometimes associated with the primary lesion. Tomaszewski (1903) was successful in reproducing the disease in human subjects with pure cultures. Ulcerative lesions have likewise followed the inocu-lation of monkeys and rabbits with cultures several generations removed from primary isolation (Reenstierna 1921, Nicolle, 1923). In the diagnosis of the disease, microscopical and cultural examinations should be made in the way already indicated in Chapter XXXIV. An intradermal reaction has been de-scribed, and is said to give a high percentage of positive results in infected subjects (Reenstierna 1923, Cole and Levin 1935). The growth from a blood-agar culture is washed off in 0·5 per cent. phenolized saline, and kept in the ice-chest till it is completely sterile. For the test, 0·2 c.c. of the suspension is inoculated into the skin. A positive reaction is characterized by the development of a large cir-cular papule with an inflamed border, reaching its maximum in about 48 hours.

Vaccine treatment, and treatment with an antiserum prepared by the inocu-lation of rams, have been stated to yield satisfactory results (Reenstierna 1923, Nicolle and Durand 1924, Hababou-Sala 1925).

TRACHOMA

Since Noguchi (1927, 1928) described the isolation of a very small Gram-negative bacillus, *Bact. granulosis* (see p. 708) from 4 out of 5 American Indians suffering from trachoma, extensive investigations on the ætiological significance of this organism have been carried out in different parts of the world, and a voluminous literature has sprung up. Noguchi found that the inoculation of pure cultures of this bacillus beneath the conjunctiva and on to the scarified conjunctiva of *rhesus* monkeys was followed in 2 to 4 weeks by a granular conjunctivitis, which slowly progressed till after 2 to 5 months the inoculated conjunctiva closely resembled the human trachomatous conjunctiva in the early stages of the disease. The lesions were follicular ; they extended over the tarsus, which became thickened ; and in one monkey definite scar formation occurred. Histologically the lesions were closely similar to those found in human trachoma. The disease could be passed in series from monkey to monkey, and the organism could be recovered from the experimental lesions produced. The organism had no effect when inoculated into the conjunctiva of the rabbit.

Attempts to confirm Noguchi's findings have met with a varied degree of success. Olitsky (1930) and Olitsky, Knutti, and Tyler (1931*a*, *b*, *c*) claim to have succeeded in isolating *Bact. granulosis* from natural trachoma in human beings and from monkeys infected with human trachomatous material, and to have conveyed the disease to *rhesus* monkeys by conjunctival inoculation with pure cultures of this organism. On the other hand several workers including Wilson (1931) in Egypt, Bengtson (1932) in the United States, Schuurman (1932) in Java, and Tang and Chou (1935) in China have failed to isolate this organism during the investigation of large numbers of cases.

Two factors contribute to this confusion. The first is the difficulty of giving an adequate definition of trachoma : the second is the spontaneous occurrence in monkeys of a follicular conjunctivitis simulating in certain respects trachoma in human beings (see Wilson 1928, Olitsky and Tyler 1933, Olitsky, Syverton, and Tyler 1933). Trachoma is a chronic disease progressing from early conjunctival inflammation to late hypertrophy and cicatricial changes. It may be, as Olitsky, Knutti, and Tyler (1931*a*) suggest, that certain of the changes are due to secondary infection with other organisms. We have no space here to discuss the subject further, but for the part played by *Bact. granulosis* in the causation of the disease readers are referred to critical reviews by Weiss (1930) and Bengtson (1932).

The occurrence of epithelial cell inclusions, described under the terms " Lindner's initial bodies " and the " von Prowazek-Halberstaedter inclusion bodies " (see Bengtson 1928) has suggested to many workers that trachoma is caused primarily by a filtrable virus. It seems doubtful whether these inclusion bodies are altogether similar to those found in known filtrable virus infections, and there is some evidence to suggest that they result from the disintegration of bacteria by lytic substances in the conjunctival fluids and tissues (Bengtson 1928). Attempts to convey trachoma to monkeys by filtered material have not met with much encouragement (see Olitsky, Knutti, and Tyler 1931*c*).

INFECTIOUS MONONUCLEOSIS AND GLANDULAR FEVER

In 1926 Murray, Webb, and Swann at Cambridge described a disease of rabbits characterized by a large mononuclear leucocytosis, and caused by a small Gram-positive bacillus to which they gave the name *Bact. monocytogenes* (see p. 708).

Young rabbits, between 1 and 3 months old, are chiefly affected. They are undersized, usually develop a very distended belly, undergo progressive emaciation, and often die suddenly. P.M. subcutaneous tissue is œdematous, looking like jelly. Clear serous fluid is abundant in the pericardium, pleura, and peritoneum. Lungs are usually œdematous, and contain one or more red infarcts, the result of infected emboli. Liver is congested, and sometimes contains small, round, pale-yellow or grey areas of focal necrosis—1·5 mm. or less in diameter. Spleen is generally small, shrunken, pale pink, and rather tough, but in acute cases, and in cases in which there is extensive necrosis of the liver, the spleen is normal or slightly enlarged, softer, and of a dark purple colour. Adrenals are sometimes soft and diffluent. Mesenteric lymph glands are always enlarged and œdematous. Cultures of the organism are not easy to obtain ; they are most frequently successful from the mesenteric glands ; the heart's blood is usually sterile.

Experimentally, a similar disease can be produced by the intravenous injection of 0·1 mgm. of culture per kilo of rabbit ; death occurs, as a rule, in 24 to 48 hours. P.M. the liver shows focal necroses, the spleen is large and dark purple ; there is often necrosis of the suprarenals, and focal necroses in the lymph glands. Intraperitoneal injection of rabbits gives rise to a sero-fibrinous peritonitis, with abscesses containing thick white pus in the rolled-up omentum ; otherwise the lesions are similar to those after intravenous inoculation. Infection is rarely possible by feeding. When inoculated in a sub-lethal dose into rabbits, the organism gives rise to a leucocytosis reaching its maximum on the 4th day ; the polymorphs and lymphocytes undergo little change, but the large mononuclears increase both relatively and absolutely ; relatively, they increase from about 5 per cent. to 40 per cent. in 3 to 4 days ; absolutely, they increase from 400 per c.mm. to 6,000 per c.mm. It is because of this power to stimulate the appearance of mononuclears in the blood that the organism has been called *Bact. monocytogenes*. Experimentally the organism is pathogenic also to guinea-pigs and mice. After intraperitoneal inoculation of mice the most striking lesions are the numerous focal necroses in the spleen ; organisms can generally be recovered from the heart's blood of mice, rarely from that of rabbits.

Similar organisms have been isolated from other animals and from man (see p. 708). All of them appear to have the power of giving rise to a mononucleosis on experimental injection into rabbits, guinea-pigs, and chickens.

There is a disease of human beings known as **glandular fever** or infectious mononucleosis which may be briefly referred to here. It is an acute infectious disease characterized by fever, enlargement of the lymphatic glands and spleen, and changes in the blood, especially lymphocytosis. Tidy (1934) divides it into three clinical types according to whether the glandular enlargement, the sore throat, or the fever is most marked. The total leucocyte count is not greatly altered, but there is a considerable increase, both relative and absolute, in the number of lymphocytes. Eruptions are common in the febrile type. The acute stage does not usually last for more than a few days, and the disease is practically never fatal. Its ætiology is still unknown (see Anton 1934). Some workers regard it as a virus infection. (References : Tidy 1934, McKinlay 1935.) The reported increase by Paul and Bunnell (1932) of agglutinins to sheep cells in the blood of the patients may be of diagnostic importance.

BARTONELLA INFECTIONS. OROYA FEVER. VERRUGA PERUVIANA. INFECTIOUS ANÆMIA OF RATS, DOGS, AND MICE

These diseases, which have attracted attention during recent years, are caused by minute micro-organisms intimately associated with the red blood corpuscles, and belonging either to the *Bartonella* or *Eperythrozoon* groups (see Chapter XXXIV).

Oroya fever and **verruga peruviana** occur in certain districts of Peru and appear to be two stages of the same disease. *Oroya fever* is characterized by fever and a severe progressive anæmia, the red cell count sometimes falling within a few days to 1 million per c.mm. Examination of the blood shows the presence in the red corpuscles of small rod, dumb-bell, and coccoid bodies, varying considerably in number and staining red or reddish-purple with Giemsa. The organisms can be cultivated on semi-solid nutrient media. Inoculated intravenously into young *rhesus* monkeys, pure cultures of *Bartonella bacilliformis*, but not infected blood, give rise to an irregularly remittent type of fever, sometimes accompanied by severe anæmia.

Verruga peruviana is an eruptive disease caused by the same organism, which can be cultivated from the verruga nodules. Pure cultures, or juice from the nodules, inoculated intradermally above the eyebrow of monkeys give rise after an incubation period of 9–20 days to a local verruga papule. Experimental infection is followed by immunity. In the monkey the spleen appears to play no part in the defence mechanism of the host, such as it does in the rat infected with *Bartonella muris*. Both Oroya fever and verruga appear to be carried by *Phlebotomus noguchi*. (For further description see Noguchi 1926, Kikuth 1931, 1934.)

Infectious Anæmia of rats, caused by *Bartonella muris*, is a disease that is precipitated by splenectomy. With the exception of certain breeds, such as the Wistar strain, a large proportion of adult rats, both wild and tame, appear to suffer from a latent infection with this organism. In such animals removal of the spleen is followed, usually in 4 or 5 days, by general illness, emaciation, and a severe progressive anæmia. Frequently hæmoglobinuria develops and the animal dies, generally within 14 days. Recovery may, however, occur, but it is liable to be followed by relapses at irregular intervals. Examination of the blood during the acute stage of the disease reveals a high proportion of red cells infected with *Bartonella* (Fig. 193, p. 711). The organisms have been cultivated successfully on leptospiral and other media. In animals that recover they disappear from the blood in 1–5 weeks. Splenectomy in young rats that have not yet become infected with *Bartonella* is without effect, but if a pure culture or infected blood is injected into a splenectomized animal then typical anæmia develops. Inoculation of a non-infected non-splenectomized animal produces only a mild anæmia. The disease can also be reproduced in young rabbits, guinea-pigs, and white mice by inoculation.

The part played by the spleen is decisive, though in what way it acts is still a matter of conjecture. A quarter of the spleen left *in situ* is sufficient to protect the animal against the disease (Perla and Marmorston-Gottesman 1930). Perla and Marmorston-Gottesman (1932) have prepared an aqueous lipoid extract of the spleen that neutralizes the effect of splenectomy. The same workers find that if rats are fed prior to splenectomy on a diet containing an adequate amount of iron and copper, a large proportion of them fail to develop anæmia. Sandberg and Perla (1934) have shown that splenectomy in non-infected albino rats is followed by an increased retention of iron but an increased elimination of copper. The suggestion is therefore that the spleen plays an important part in the utilization of copper, and that in animals on a normal diet the amount of this substance is insufficient to prevent the development of a severe anæmia if the spleen is removed. Certain trypanosome infections, poisons such as toluylenediamine, pyridine, and phenylhydrazine (Lauda and Marcus 1928), irradiation, and possibly some bacterial infections, may activate a latent *Bartonella* infection even in the presence of an intact spleen.

Natural infection is probably carried by rat lice. Neosalvarsan administered before splenectomy prevents the development of anæmia. Administered after the disease has developed, it has a marked therapeutic effect. Certain arsenic-antimony compounds are said to be even more effective. (References : Mayer 1921, Ford and Eliot 1928, Eliot and Ford 1929, Perla and Marmorston-Gottesman 1930, 1931, 1932, Marmorston-Gottesman and Perla 1930, 1931, 1932*a*, *b*, Lwoff and Vaucel 1931, Roth 1932, Kikuth 1934, McCluskie and Niven 1934.)

Infectious Anæmia of dogs is caused by *Bartonella canis*. The organisms were first observed by Kikuth (1929) in the blood of a splenectomized dog. The course of the disease resembles that in rats. The parasites multiply up to a certain point, then suddenly disappear from the peripheral blood, only to reappear after a few days and again work up to a maximum. Remissions of this type may occur for months. The length of the relapses and of the remissions varies from dog to dog (Regendanz and Reichenow 1932). The anæmia is seldom severe ; death is infrequent ; and spontaneous recovery leaves behind it a substantial degree of immunity. Infection appears to be transmitted from dog to dog by fleas. Neosalvarsan exercises a specific effect on the course of the disease. At the height of the disease *Bartonella canis* is present in very large numbers. It is said by Regendanz and Reichenow to be situated extracellularly. This may account for the fact that the parasites may suddenly disappear from the blood without any serious diminution occurring in the number of red blood corpuscles. The organisms are very pleomorphic, and may become agglutinated into characteristic masses or chains at the periphery of the cells. Cats, as well as dogs, are susceptible to experimental inoculation after splenectomy (see also Pérard 1929, Lwoff and Provost 1929, Kikuth 1934).

REFERENCES

ABEL, R. (1896) *Z. Hyg. InfektKr.*, **21**, 89.
ANTON, W. (1934) *Zbl. Bakt.*, **131**, 89.
BENGTSON, I. A. (1928) *Publ. Hlth Rep., Wash.*, **43**, 2210 ; (1932) *Ibid.*, **47**, 1914.
BEVERIDGE, W. I. B. (1934) *J. Path. Bact.*, **38**, 467.
BLANC, G. and PANGALOS, G. (1925) *C. R. Soc. Biol.*, **93**, 1267, 1268.
BUSSON, B. (1923) *Münch. med. Wschr.*, **70**, 426.
COLE, H. N. and LEVIN, E. A. (1935) *J. Amer. med. Ass.*, **105**, 2040.
DUCREY, A. (1889) *Mschr. prakt. Derm.*, **9**, 387.
ELIOT, C. P., and FORD, W. W. (1929) *Amer. J. Hyg.*, **10**, 635.
FORD, W. W. and ELIOT, C. P. (1928) *J. exp. Med.*, **48**, 475.
FRICKE, C. (1896) *Z. Hyg. InfektKr.*, **23**, 380.
GALLI-VALERIO, B. (1911) *Zbl. Bakt.*, **57**, 481.
HABABOU-SALA, J. (1925) *C. R. Soc. Biol.*, **92**, 498.
HOFER, G. (1913*a*) *Berl. klin. Wschr.*, **1**, 2413 ; (1913*b*) *Wien. klin. Wschr.*, **26**, 1011.
KIKUTH, W. (1929) *Zbl. Bakt.*, **113**, 1 ; (1931) *Z. ImmunForsch.*, **73**, 1 ; (1934) *Proc. R. Soc. Med.*, **27**, 1241.
KOUWENAAR, W., MAASLAND, J. H., and WOLFF, J. W. (1934) *Geneesk. Tijdschr. Ned.-Ind.*, **74**, 1447.
LAUDA, E. and MARCUS, F. (1928) *Zbl. Bakt.*, **107**, 104.
LOEFFLER, F. (1884) *Mitt. ReichsgesundhAmt.*, **2**, 421.
LOEWENBERG. (1894) *Ann. Inst. Pasteur*, **8**, 292.
LWOFF, A. and PROVOST, A. (1929) *C. R. Soc. Biol.*, **101**, 8.
LWOFF, A. and VAUCEL, M. (1931) *Ann. Inst. Pasteur*, **46**, 258.
MARMORSTON-GOTTESMAN, J. and PERLA, D. (1930) *J. exp. Med.*, **52**, 121 ; (1931) *Ibid.*, **53**, 877 ; (1932*a*) *Ibid.*, **56**, 763 ; (1932*b*) *Proc. Soc. exp. Biol., N.Y.*, **29**, 989.
McCLUSKIE, J. A. W. and NIVEN, J. S. F. (1934) *J. Path. Bact.*, **39**, 185.
McKINLAY, C. A. (1935) *J. Amer. med. Ass.*, **105**, 761.
MAYER, M. (1921) *Arch. Schiffs- u. Tropenhyg.*, **25**, 150.
MURRAY, E. G. D., WEBB, R. A., and SWANN, M. B. R. (1926) *J. Path. Bact.*, **29**, 407.

NICOLLE, C. (1923) *C. R. Soc. Biol.*, **88**, 871.
NICOLLE and DURAND. (1924) *Arch. Inst. Pasteur, Tunis*, **8**, 243.
NOGUCHI, H. (1926) *J. exp. Med.*, **44**, 533, 697, 715, 729 ; (1927) *J. Amer. med. Ass.*, **89**, 739 ; (1928) *Monograph on Trachoma, J. exp. Med.*, **48**, No. 2, Suppl. No. 2.
OLINESCU, R. and ATINEU, A. (1925) *C. R. Soc. Biol.*, **93**, 741.
OLITSKY, P. K. (1930) *Trans. 35th ann. Meeting Amer. Acad. Ophthal. Oto-Laryng.*, p. 225.
OLITSKY, P. K., KNUTTI, R. E. and TYLER, J. R. (1931a) *J. exp. Med.*, **53**, 753 ; (1931b) *Ibid.*, **54**, 31 ; (1931c) *Ibid.*, **54**, 557.
OLITSKY, P. K., SYVERTON, J. T., and TYLER, J. R. (1933) *J. exp. Med.*, **57**, 871.
OLITSKY, P. K. and TYLER, J. R. (1933) *J. exp. Med.*, **57**, 229.
PAGE, C. G. (1912) *J. med. Res.*, **26**, 489.
PAUL, J. R. and BUNNELL, W. W. (1932) *Amer. J. med. Sci.*, **183**, 90.
PÉRARD, C. H. (1929) *C. R. Soc. Biol.*, **100**, 1111.
PEREZ, F. (1899 *Ann. Inst. Pasteur*, **8**, 937 ; (1901) *Ibid.*, **15**, 409 ; (1913) *Berl. klin. Wschr.*, **1**, 2411.
PERKINS, R. G. (1907) *J. infect. Dis.*, **4**, 51.
PERLA, D. and MARMORSTON-GOTTESMAN, J. (1930) *J. exp. Med.*, **52**, 131 ; (1931) *Ibid.*, **53**, 869 ; (1932) *Ibid.*, **56**, 777, 783.
QUAST, G. (1920) *Zbl. Bakt.*, **97**, 174.
REENSTIERNA, J. (1921) *Acta derm.-venereol., Stockh.*, **2**, 1 ; (1923) *Arch. Inst. Pasteur, Tunis*, **12**, 275.
REGENDANZ, P. and REICHENOW, E. (1932) *Arch. Schiffs- u. Tropenhyg.*, **36**, 305.
ROTH, H. (1932 *Z. ImmunForsch.*, **74**, 483.
SANDBERG, M., and PERLA, D. (1934) *J. exp. Med.*, **60**, 395.
SCHMORL, G. (1891) *Dtsch. Z. Thiermed.*, **17**, 375.
SCHUURMAN, C. J. (1932) *Zbl. Bakt.*, **125**, 158.
SCRIVNER, L. H. and LEE, A. M. (1934) *J. Amer. vet. med. Ass.*, **85**, 360.
SHAW, F. W. (1933) *Zbl. Bakt.*, **129**, 132.
SHIGA, M. (1922 *Zbl. Bakt.*, **88**, 521.
SLANETZ, L. W. and RETTGER, L. F. (1933) *J. Bact.*, **26**, 599.
TANG, F. F. and CHOU, C. H. (1935) *J. infect. Dis.*, **56**, 264.
TIDY, H. L. (1924) *Lancet*, ii. 180, 236.
TOMASCZEWSKI, E. (1903) *Z. Hyg. InfektKr.*, **42**, 327.
TOMÁŠEK, V. (1925) *Zbl. Bakt., Ref.* **79**, 564.
WARD, H. C. (1916) *J. infect. Dis.*, **19**, 153 ; (1917) *Ibid.*, **21**, 338.
WEISS, C. (1930) *J. infect. Dis.*, **47**, 107.
WILSON, R. P. (1928) *3rd. ann. Rep. Giza mem. ophthal. Lab., Cairo*, p. 78 ; (1931) *Brit. J. Ophthal.*, **15** 433.

CHAPTER LXXVII

RELAPSING FEVER, AVIAN SPIROCHÆTOSIS, AND VINCENT'S ANGINA

RELAPSING FEVER

SYNONYMS : Famine fever ; tick fever.

RELAPSING fever is the name given to a disease the chief characteristic of which is the occurrence of one or more relapses following the subsidence of the primary febrile paroxysm. It would perhaps be more correct to define it as a general term for a group of closely allied diseases ; for relapsing fever differs in its symptomatology in different countries. The disease is widespread in Eastern Europe, in Asia, in Egypt, and along the North African coast, in Mexico, and in Central and South America. It used to occur in this country and in Ireland, particularly during times of famine ; the last epidemic was in 1868–71. There was an epidemic in 1869 in New York and Philadelphia, and another in 1874 amongst Chinese labourers in California ; with these exceptions the United States has suffered but little. The tick fever of Central Africa was shown simultaneously by Ross and Milne (1904) and Dutton and Todd (1905) to be a form of relapsing fever. The incubation period is from 2 to 10 days as a rule, sometimes as long as 14 days. The mortality is generally low—less than 6 per cent.—but in some epidemics it has been as high as 30 per cent. The causative organism of the disease was first observed by Obermeier in the Berlin epidemic of 1867–68 ; his observations were published in 1873 (Obermeier 1873). He noticed the presence of thread-like bodies in the blood of patients during the febrile stage of the disease, the disappearance of these bodies during the afebrile stage, and their reappearance during the relapse. By reason of their motility and their wave-like spiral form, he considered them to belong to the group of Spirochætes. In the blood they occurred as straight forms, S-forms, and even as circles ; towards the end of the paroxysm he noticed their tendency to aggregation in rosettes and their granular disintegration. The organisms occurred only in patients with relapsing fever ; they were never found in the blood of normal persons, or of patients suffering from other fevers. These observations are of considerable historical importance, because they were among the first to establish the microbial theory of infection.

The spirochæte described by Obermeier is known as *Treponema recurrentis*, and is the usual type found in European relapsing fever. Besides this, a number of other spirochætes have been described associated with relapsing fever in other countries ; and as these exhibit certain antigenic differences they have been regarded as different species and named accordingly. Thus we have *Trep. duttoni* of Central Africa, *Trep. novyi* of America, *Trep. kochi* of East Africa, *Trep. carteri* of India, and several others.

As seen by dark-ground illumination in the blood of patients during a febrile paroxysm, they are actively motile spiral organisms, with a series of five to ten fairly regular but loose primary waves ; during rest their axis is generally straight, but when in motion they momentarily assume various curved and bizarre forms. Their length is variable, and differs with different species ; generally it is 10–20 μ. The spirals are 2–3 μ long, and about 1 μ in amplitude. Division occurs by transverse fission ; during this process a constriction appears at the middle, and the two organisms draw apart, leaving a thin thread-like connection between them. After separation has occurred, this remnant of the periplast may often be seen attached to one end ; by many workers it has been described as a flagellum. Under suitable conditions the organisms are extremely motile, darting rapidly across the field ; but in ordinary wet blood films their motion is slower ; they move backwards and forwards over a distance of not more than two or three times their own length (Novy and Knapp 1906). Rotation occurs around the long axis. The numbers present in a blood film vary from case to case ; at the height of the first pyrexial attack they are often numerous—several organisms to a field—but they may be relatively few and difficult to find. During the decline of the fever their numbers diminish, the organisms become less motile, and not infrequently they assume irregular shapes or accumulate in rosettes (see Fig. 195, p. 719) ; these changes are regarded as indicative of lysis or agglutination due to the action of developing antibodies in the host. After the subsidence of the fever they can no longer be found microscopically in the blood ; there is evidence, however, to suggest that a few organisms may persist in the blood, since inoculation of blood into animals during the apyrexial interval may give rise to infection. At the onset of the relapse they again become demonstrable microscopically in the blood, though not always in such large numbers as in the first attack. During the interval between the pyrexial attacks the organisms remain latent in the tissues. Experiments conducted on mice suggest that the brain is one of the organs in which infection frequently persists (Heronimus 1928).

The spirochætes are best demonstrated by dark-ground illumination ; but they may be stained by methylene blue, or preferably by Leishman or Giemsa, with both of which they take on a bluish colour. If the blood films are made in the usual way and allowed to dry in air, the organisms undergo gross distortion and present irregular and coiled forms ; if their natural form is to be preserved, they should be wet-fixed.

Transmission of the Disease.

Relapsing fever is transmitted by blood-sucking insects. Dutton and Todd (1905) showed that the tick fever of the Congo Free State was spread by the tick *Ornithodorus moubata* ; infected ticks were able to transmit the disease to monkeys, and in one experiment young ticks, newly hatched in the laboratory from eggs laid by infected parents, successfully conveyed the disease to monkeys, showing that the infection could be transmitted hereditarily. In Uganda, Ross and Milne (1904) brought evidence to show that the disease was spread by the bite of the tick *Ornithodorus savingnyi*. In Panama it is spread by the tick *O. talaje*. The method by which the tick transmits infection is not known with certainty, but it is supposed that the infected fluid exuded by the coxal glands contaminates the wound made by the bite of the tick. While the disease in Central Africa and in Central and Southern America is spread by ticks, the disease in Europe, Asia, North Africa and North America is spread by lice (Wenyon 1926). According to Brumpt (1933), however, some cases in the United States result from infection carried by the tick *O. turicata*. The organisms may be demonstrated for 24 hours in the stomach of the louse following an infective feed ; after this time they can no longer be demonstrated ; but in about 6 or 8 days they reappear in the fluids of the body cavity, and spread to all parts of the body including the legs and antennæ. Infection is conveyed to human beings not by the bite of the louse, which appears to be harmless, but by contamination of the wounds, made by biting or by scratching, with the body fluids of the louse.

Immunity.

The disappearance of the spirochætes from the blood stream at the end of the first pyrexial attack has been regarded by many workers as due to the development of antibodies. This view has to some extent been substantiated by the work of Novy and Knapp (1906).

Working with the rat, they found that the organisms would live in defibrinated blood kept at room temperature for 30 or 40 days, provided the blood was removed from the animal during the early stage of infection ; if it was taken during the later stages, they died in 24 hours. When the organisms were examined *in vivo* during the decline phase of the infection they were observed to become sluggish, to show end-to-end agglutination, and even to form small tangles. This was even more marked when blood from an immune animal was inoculated into an infected rat ; half an hour later the spirochætes were accumulated in tangled masses of 10 to 20 members, and showed end-to-end agglutination ; 1 hour later they were agglutinated into perfect radiating rosettes, and 2 hours later they were very scarce and were mostly immobile. Blood serum from a rat, which had been hyperimmunized by a course of 26 injections of infective blood, had marked immobilizing and agglutinative properties, even when diluted to 1/100. In rats that had recovered naturally from infection Pfeiffer's phenomenon could be produced *in vivo*. Intraperitoneal injection of infective blood into such animals was followed by agglutination and granular degeneration of the spirochætes ; in 10 minutes no free spirochætes could be found. The altered organisms were rapidly ingested by phagocytes. In hyperimmunized rats the spirochætes completely disappeared from the peritoneal cavity in 2 minutes. In passively immunized rats the spirochætes were agglutinated into rosettes, but later these broke up, and free organisms once more became numerous ; the animals, however, did not contract infection. The course of antibody production in human beings seems to resemble that in experimental animals (see Cunningham and Fraser 1935).

From these and other experiments, it would appear that during the course of the natural disease immune bodies—chiefly agglutinins, spirochætocidins and lysins—are developed, which are sufficiently powerful to overcome the blood infection and lead to the disappearance of the spirochætes from the circulation. These organisms remain latent in the brain and other tissues, and when the circulating antibodies have decreased, they once more enter the blood and give rise to a relapse. This stimulates the production of fresh antibodies, which again lead to the disappearance of spirochætes from the blood. After one or more relapses, the active immunity developed by the host is sufficient to prevent further invasion of the blood by the spirochætes, and an apparent cure results. Whether a true cure results, in the sense that the body is completely rid of spirochætes, is doubtful. Animal experiments suggest rather that, even though the organisms give no token of their presence, they may yet remain alive in the tissues for weeks or months. Immunity in relapsing fever appears to be an infection-immunity ; this corresponds to a state of the host in which, together with a humoral immunity, there is a latent infection of the tissues, which is capable under certain conditions of breaking down the existent immunity (Heronimus 1928). It is a state in which a working equilibrium is established between host and parasite, and like other equilibria is liable to disturbance (see Chapter XLVIII).

There is a considerable amount of evidence to show that after the first attack the spirochætes in the tissues undergo an antigenic change which renders them insusceptible to the antibodies produced by the host against the original strain. This enables them to invade the blood a second time and give rise to a relapse. The production of antibodies to the so-called " relapse " or " serum-fast " strain is followed by the disappearance of the organisms from the blood once more. A further antigenic change may occur in the tissues enabling the organisms to invade the blood for a third time. In some instances it appears that the relapse strain reverts to the parent type, and if the circulating antibodies generated during the first attack have diminished sufficiently, another invasion of the blood may occur (Aristowsky and Wainstein 1929a).

It will be understood that the antigenic specificity of the relapsing fever spirochætes is highly developed. This accounts not only for the fact that patients who have been infected with one type of relapsing fever, for example the European, can be infected with another type, such as the Indian or African, but that, as just noted, a patient who has recovered from invasion with a given strain is liable to suffer from a relapse due to an antigenic variant of the same strain.

Reproduction of the Disease in Animals.

Infection can be transmitted to monkeys, rats, and mice, but not to rabbits or guinea-pigs. In monkeys the disease runs much the same course as in man ; 2 or 3 days after subcutaneous inoculation with the patient's blood a pyrexial attack occurs, lasting for 3 or 4 days ; two, three, or four relapses may occur at intervals of 2 to 8 days, each relapse lasting from 1 to 4 days (Norris *et al.* 1906). After intraperitoneal inoculation of mice the organisms appear in the blood within 24 hours, and persist for 3 to 4 days ; they then disappear for several days, after which a relapse may occur ; three or four relapses may follow each other, separated by an interval of about 7 days (Novy and Knapp 1906). As many as 10 to 50 organisms may be present per field during the first infection, but in the relapses only 1 or 2 organisms are seen as a rule. Intraperitoneal inoculation of white rats is followed by the appearance of spirochætes in the blood in about 40 hours ; they disappear about 2 days later. The spirochætes are found not only in the blood, but in all the organs of the body. Infection is never fatal. Novy and Knapp (1906) state that rats never relapse.

Prophylaxis and Treatment.

Inoculation of living cultures, or sometimes of cultures killed by heating to 60° C. for 30 minutes, is said to give rise to the production of lysins. Persons so vaccinated may apparently resist infection with small doses of living spirochætes (Aristowsky and Wainstein 1929a, b). Whether vaccination is likely to be of value in practice it is as yet impossible to say. Like most spirochætal diseases, relapsing fever is readily cut short by injection of salvarsan. A single suitable dose often suffices to cure the disease and prevent relapses (Wenyon 1926). However, just as " serum-fast " variants may develop during the course of the disease, so " arsenic-fast " strains may be encountered, which are little affected by salvarsan. Infections with such strains may be treated by sodium potassium bismuth tartrate (Todd 1930). The serum of convalescent patients may be used therapeutically, but little information is available about the value of this method of treatment.

AVIAN SPIROCHÆTOSIS

In 1891 Sakharoff described a disease of geese that appeared every year in certain stations on the Transcaucasian railway, and resulted in a high mortality —80 per cent. Examination of the blood revealed the presence of spirochætes closely resembling those of human relapsing fever. Clinically, the infected goose went off its feed, remained apathetic in a sitting-down posture, and died of exhaustion after a week or more ; sometimes it developed diarrhœa, and its joints became affected. Post mortem, there was fatty degeneration of the heart and liver ; the liver moreover showed miliary yellowish granules of caseous consistency ; the spleen was soft and friable. During life actively motile spirochætes were found in fairly large numbers in the blood at the beginning of the disease ; later they collected into ray-forms, and finally into tangled ball-like masses. Before death they disappeared from the blood and at post mortem they could be found neither in the blood nor in the organs. Subcutaneous inoculation of infected blood reproduced the disease in normal geese after an incubation period of 4 or 5 days.

Working with the spirochæte of goose septicæmia—*Treponema anserinum*—Gabritschewsky (1898) found that if the blood serum of a goose, which had recovered naturally from the disease, was mixed with the blood of an infected goose, the spirochætes were killed in a few minutes at 37° C. ; if no immune serum was added, they lived for 18 hours. When the serum was heated to 60° C., its bactericidal power was destroyed completely. Further experiments showed that, while blood serum from a peripheral vein or from the right side of the heart killed the spirochætes in half an hour or less, juice sucked from the viscera—spleen, liver, kidney, and bone-marrow—did not kill them for $2\frac{1}{2}$ to 9 hours. He also found that, in infected geese, spirochætes could still be demonstrated in the internal organs after they had disappeared from the blood. He concluded therefore that the spirochætes were destroyed in the blood by the spirochætocidins, but remained latent in the viscera where the antibodies appeared to be less concentrated. This conception of immunity is similar to that reached in the case of human relapsing fever.

As well as the spirochætocidins, there are also lysins present in the blood, and agglutinins, which are responsible for the clumping of the organisms. Phagocytosis occurs, apparently as a secondary phenomenon, after the death or immobilization of the spirochætes, though according to Himmelweit (1933) it plays an active part in the destruction of the living organisms. Gabritschewsky further showed that naturally recovered geese remained immune to further infection, as long as bactericidins were present in the blood. Antispirochætal serum, prepared by the inoculation of horses, had marked protective properties when injected into geese simultaneously with, or 24 hours after, injection of spirochætal blood ; but once the organisms had appeared in the blood stream, it had no effect. That is to say, the serum had prophylactic, but not therapeutic properties. By injection of normal geese with a single dose of immune serum, followed on the next day by injection of spirochætal blood, he succeeded—by active immunization under cover of a passive immunity—in rendering the birds highly resistant to the disease. This method he recommended for combating natural outbreaks of the disease.

More widespread than the disease in geese is **spirochætosis of fowls,** which was first described by Marchoux and Salimbeni (1903) in Brazil, and later by Balfour (1908) in the Sudan. The symptoms and general course of the disease appear to be much the same as in geese.

The disease can be transmitted by subcutaneous, intramuscular, or intraperitoneal injection of hens with infected blood ; the bird develops diarrhœa, the temperature rises to 43° C., and spirochætes appear in the blood in 24 hours. The temperature falls after 3 or 4 days to 40° or 41° C., but the organisms continue to increase in the blood. Later, however, they become aggregated into groups, their movements become slower, and they form figures of 0 and 8. At this stage the bird dies, though sometimes a chronic disease develops, lasting for about a fortnight, and followed by death. The disease can be transmitted to fowls, geese, ducks, guinea-fowls, and sparrows ; pigeons are fairly refractory, monkeys and guinea-pigs completely so (Marchoux and Salimbeni 1903). Neither in the goose nor in the fowl do relapses occur ; the bird either dies or recovers completely.

The natural disease is spread by ticks. In Brazil *Argas miniatus* was found to be responsible ; in the old world *Argas persicus* is the tick that has been chiefly incriminated. Marchoux and Salimbeni (1903) found that ticks might remain infective for 5 months after biting a diseased fowl. According to Hindle (1912) ticks may transmit the infection to their progeny, and these again to the next generation, without having had an infective feed in the meantime.

The disease occurs in **ducks** as well as in fowls and geese. It is probable that the causative organism is the same in each species ; its proper name therefore is *Treponema anserinum* (Wenyon 1926). Those anxious for further information on avian spirochætosis are referred to the monograph of Knowles, Gupta, and Basu (1932) who, besides giving a bibliographical review of the subject, have made a number of observations themselves, particularly on the mechanism by which immunity develops.

Blood Spirochætoses in other Animals.

Cattle suffer from a spirochætosis caused by *Treponema theileri* ; infection is conveyed, at least in South Africa, by the tick *Margaropus decoloratus*. A similar disease in horses and in sheep, probably due to the same organism, *Trep. theileri*, has also been reported by Theiler in South Africa. Spirochætes of the relapsing fever type have been observed in the blood of elephants, camels, antelopes, monkeys, and some other mammals (Wenyon 1926).

VINCENT'S ANGINA AND CERTAIN RELATED INFECTIONS

There are certain necrotic and gangrenous infective processes in human beings, such as ulcero-membranous angina, hospital gangrene, noma, fœtid bronchitis, and gangrenous laryngitis, in which spirochætes have frequently been demonstrated. Of these, one of the chief is the so-called spirillum described by Vincent (1896, 1899), now known as *Treponema vincenti* (see Chapter XXXV). It is not clear whether this organism is responsible for the necrotic lesions in human beings in which it is found, or whether it is a mere secondary invader. Since it may sometimes be demonstrated in the depths of the infected tissues, it is possible that it may possess actual invasive properties (Ellermann 1907). It is very frequently found in association with a characteristic fusiform bacillus, likewise described by Vincent

(1896, see Chapter XVII). It has been suggested (Tunnicliff 1906) that *Trep. vincenti* and the fusiform bacillus represent two phases of the same organism ; but the balance of evidence is definitely against this view.

Treponemata have also been isolated from the sputum of tuberculous patients (Bezançon and Etchegoin 1926), and from other bronchial and pulmonary lesions (Bacigalupo 1928) ; but we know nothing with regard to the relation of these organisms to each other or to *Trep. vincenti*.

REFERENCES

ARISTOWSKY, W. M. and WAINSTEIN, A. B. (1929a) *Z. ImmunForsch.*, **61**, 296 ; (1929b) *Ibid.*, **63**, 240.
BACIGALUPO, J. (1928) *C. R. Soc. Biol.*, **99**, 1622.
BALFOUR, A. (1908) *Rep. Wellcome res. Lab.*, **3**, 38.
BEZANÇON, F. and ETCHEGOIN, E. (1926) *C. R. Soc. Biol.*, **94**, 1056.
BRUMPT, E. (1933) *C. R. Soc. Biol.*, **113**, 1369.
CUNNINGHAM, J. and FRASER, A. G. L. (1935) *Indian J. med. Res.*, **22**, 595.
DUTTON, J. E. and TODD, J. L. (1905) *Brit. med. J.*, ii. 1259.
ELLERMANN, V. (1907) *Z. Hyg. InfektKr.*, **56**, 453.
GABRITSCHEWSKY, G. (1898) *Zbl. Bakt.*, **23**, 365, 439, 635, 721, 778.
HERONIMUS, E. S. (1928) *Zbl. Bakt.*, **105**, 394.
HIMMELWEIT, F. (1933) *Z. Hyg. InfektKr.*, **115**, 710.
HINDLE, E. (1912) *Proc. Camb. phil. Soc.*, **16**, Part 6, p. 457.
KNOWLES, R., GUPTA, B. M. D., and BASU, B. C. (1932) *Indian med. Res. Mem.*, No. 22.
MARCHOUX, E. and SALIMBENI, A. (1903) *Ann. Inst. Pasteur*, **17**, 569.
NORRIS, C., PAPPENHEIMER, A. M., and FLOURNOY, T. (1906) *J. infect. Dis.*, **3**, 266.
NOVY, F. G. and KNAPP, R. E. (1906) *J. infect. Dis.*, **3**, 291.
OBERMEIER. (1873) *Berl. klin. Wschr.*, **10**, 152, 378, 391, 455.
ROSS, P. H. and MILNE, A. D. (1904) *Brit. med. J.*, ii. 1453.
SAKHAROFF, N. (1891) *Ann. Inst. Pasteur*, **5**, 564.
TODD, J. (1930) *Brit. med. J.*, i. 312.
TUNNICLIFF, R. (1906) *J. infect. Dis.*, **3**, 148.
VINCENT, H. (1896) *Ann. Inst. Pasteur*, **10**, 488 ; (1899) *Ibid.*, **13**, 609.
WENYON, C. M. (1926) " Protozoology," II. London.

CHAPTER LXXVIII

SYPHILIS, RABBIT SYPHILIS, AND YAWS

SYPHILIS

THE origin of syphilis is not definitely known, but its presence in Europe is said to date from the end of the fifteenth century, when it was brought to Spain by Columbus's sailors returning from the New World. The disease spread rapidly over Europe, and was at first endowed with the malignancy that is characteristic of most infective diseases on first reaching virgin soil. Now, after centuries of endemic prevalence, the disease is much milder ; this is probably due in part to better and more rapid treatment, and in part to the development of a racial immunity, similar to that which appears to have developed against tuberculosis.

Edwin Klebs in 1875–77 was apparently the first to see spirochætal bodies in syphilitic material and to transmit the disease to monkeys (see A. C. Klebs 1932). Haensell in 1881 produced a local lesion in rabbits by inoculation of the eye. Metchnikoff and Roux (1903, 1904*a*, *b*, 1905) transmitted the disease to apes, and found that chimpanzees developed not only primary but also secondary lesions following inoculation with human syphilitic material. In 1905 Schaudinn and Hoffmann discovered the causative organism of the disease. In chancres and in the inguinal glands of syphilitic patients they demonstrated a spirochæte, now known as *Treponema pallidum*, which occurred both on the surface and in the depth of the tissue. They stained it by a modified Giemsa stain, and described its characteristic morphology and movements. In chancres it was frequently accompanied by another spirochæte—*Trep. refringens*—which was broader, less regular, and more refractile. But *Trep. refringens* was sometimes found in non-syphilitic lesions, such as gonorrhœal papillomata, whereas *Trep. pallidum* was never found except in syphilis. Though Schaudinn and Hoffmann did not decide whether *pallidum* and *refringens* were different species, it has since been shown that it is *Trep. pallidum* alone that is responsible for the causation of syphilis. (For further history see Schuberg and Schlossberger 1930, Stokes 1931, Klebs 1932.)

Bacteriology.

Syphilis is transmitted chiefly by direct, but sometimes by indirect contact. *Treponema pallidum* has the power of gaining entrance to the body through minute lesions of the skin or mucous membranes. It is, however, a very strict parasite, and its life outside the animal body is short ; if this were not so, syphilis of non-venereal origin would probably be very much more common than it is. Infection may likewise be transmitted from mother to child, causing the congenital type of syphilis ; this results from the passage of spirochætes through the placenta. Except in congenital syphilis, in which the disease is generalized from the

1430

start, infection is rendered evident by the development of a primary lesion or chancre. This appears within a month of infection, and is accompanied by enlargement of the focal lymphatic glands. From 6 to 12 weeks after the appearance of the primary chancre, the secondary stage of the disease sets in ; this is marked by constitutional symptoms, cutaneous lesions, enlargement of the lymph glands, and often affections of the bones, joints, eyes, and other organs. The secondary passes over insensibly into the tertiary stage, which may persist for years ; this is characterized by the development of ulcerating necrotic lesions of the skin and by gummata of the internal organs. Years after the contraction of the disease disorders of the nervous system may appear, such as tabes dorsalis and general paralysis ; these are sometimes referred to as quaternary or para-syphilitic affections.

Up to the commencement of the secondary stage, syphilis is clinically a localized disease ; bacteriologically, however, it appears probable that infection becomes generalized soon after infection. Kolle and Evers (1926*b*) infected rabbits by cutaneous or subcutaneous inoculation into the scrotum with syphilitic material, removed the inguinal glands after varying periods, and injected these into fresh animals. By this means they found that the glands were infective within 30 minutes of the scrotal inoculation. Working with guinea-pigs, they were able to show that the spirochætes reached the focal glands within 5 minutes of cutaneous inoculation of the scrotum. In apes the time elapsing between infection and invasion of the glands is probably longer ; Metchnikoff and Roux (1905), for example, found that chimpanzees anointed locally with calomel ointment, 1 to 2 hours after cutaneous inoculation, never developed syphilis. Taking this experi-mental evidence in conjunction with the fact that local disinfective measures in human beings are comparatively valueless unless practised within an hour or two after exposure to infection, we may conclude that the spirochætes rapidly invade the tissues, even though they give no clinical sign of their presence. During the primary stage of the disease, they are found in the local chancre, and can some-times be demonstrated in the blood. Thus, Uhlenhuth and Mulzer (1913) drew off the blood of patients with primary and secondary syphilis, defibrinated it, and injected it into the testicles and scrotum of rabbits ; the whole operation was completed within 10 minutes. Syphilis developed in 67 per cent. of the animals inoculated from patients with primary, and in 70 per cent. of those inoculated from patients with secondary syphilis. Spirochætes are present in all the secondary lesions, and may be excreted in the semen (Uhlenhuth and Mulzer 1913). In the tertiary lesions such as gummata they are demonstrable, but only in small numbers ; their virulence, however, appears to be maintained. Noguchi and Moore (1913) found them in the brain of patients dying of general paralysis ; they were seen in all the layers of the cortex with the exception of the outer or neuroglial layer. In congenital syphilis spirochætes are distributed in large numbers through-out the viscera, particularly the liver, lungs, spleen, and suprarenals. Both in congenital and acquired syphilis the organisms may remain latent for long periods of time without giving rise to any clinical manifestations of disease.

Immunity to Syphilis.

Immunity to syphilis resembles in many respects immunity to tuberculosis ; that is to say, it is an infection-immunity. So long as infection persists, and so long as living spirochætes are present in the tissues, the infected person is relatively resistant to further infection. It is possible for a patient to develop two primary chancres, provided the second infection occurs before the development of the first chancre ; but once a primary chancre has developed, further infections almost invariably fail to give rise to a primary lesion. There is evidence to suggest, however, that this resistance to superinfection is more apparent than real, in the bacteriological sense. Though the second infection gives rise to no obvious symptoms of disease, the spirochætes nevertheless appear to gain access to the body and to give rise to a latent infection of the tissues.

Experiments indicate that immunity to superinfection is limited by various factors. Truffi (1910), for example, was able in some rabbits to produce a chancre by inoculation made as late as 12 days after the primary chancre had developed. Kolle and Schloszberger (1926) found that, whereas rabbits reinfected with the same strain of spirochæte did not develop a second primary lesion, those infected with a heterologous strain frequently did so. And even when no second primary lesion developed, it was shown by inoculation experiments made with the lymphatic glands that the organisms had gained access to the tissues ; by the use of cross-protection experiments in two sets of rabbits, each of which was immunized against 1 strain only, it was shown that the homologous and the heterologous strains were present side by side in the same glands. According to Uhlenhuth and Groszmann (1928) the age and the virulence of the first infecting strain are of importance ; infection with a weakly virulent strain may not protect against subsequent infection with a more virulent strain. Working with apes Neisser (1906) succeeded in reinfecting 9 animals at periods varying from 44 to 301 days after the first inoculation. These and other experiments indicate that, though as a rule an infected animal is resistant to superinfection, in the sense that it does not develop clinical symptoms, it may on occasion prove susceptible ; and, even when it does not, it may yet allow the penetration of the organisms into its tissues ; its immunity to superinfection is largely a symptom-immunity.

Other experiments support the view that infection may occur without the production of symptoms.

Kolle and Evers (1926a) found, for example, that 10 out of every 100 rabbits inoculated into the scrotum failed to develop a primary chancre or to show glandular swelling. These animals were nevertheless infected ; the popliteal glands from 12 of these animals were inoculated into fresh animals from 82 to 199 days after infection, and in every instance they produced infection. In such animals the organisms generally lie latent in the glands, but occasionally they become active and give rise to lesions several months later. The same authors found that if rabbits containing a deposit of bismuth in their tissues were inoculated with syphilitic material, they developed no lesions whatever ; but if the bismuth was later removed by surgical means, typical syphilitic lesions developed 7 or 8 weeks later. It would appear that the effect of the bismuth was not to prevent infection but to suppress the development of lesions ; the spirochætes gained access to the tissues, but remained latent till the bismuth was removed. In some animals, such as mice, inoculation with syphilitic material is usually without result ; no lesions develop. Yet by inoculation experiments on rabbits it has been shown that spirochætes are present in their tissues—glands, spleen, and brain—for months after infection (Kolle and Schloszberger 1928). There is evidence that the organisms actually multiply in the tissues of the mouse ; thus for 6 to 8 weeks after infection the organs frequently prove negative, but after that time, and apparently for the remainder of the mouse's life, they are positive. Yet in spite of this development in the tissues, the organisms never give rise to symptoms of disease.

Whether a true immunity both to clinical disease and to infection ever develops in rabbits is not clear. There is evidence that it may, but only in animals that have been infected for a long time.

Brown and Pearce (1921) treated rabbits with arsphenamine shortly after the development of the primary chancre, and 5 days later reinoculated them with the same strain as was originally used. Nearly all the treated animals developed chancres, whereas the untreated controls did not. This indicates that animals treated in the early stage of the disease can be rendered fully susceptible again. Chesney and Kemp (1925) obtained evidence suggesting that if treatment was begun early the animals almost always became susceptible to a second infection, whereas if it was begun late they generally proved refractory to a second infection. Further experiments (Chesney and Kemp 1926, Chesney, Halley, and Kemp 1927), however, seemed to show that the immunity to reinfection of rabbits treated late in the disease was not as complete as was originally supposed. Kolle and Prigge (1927) treated their rabbits with neosalvarsan in the late stage of the disease —75 to 250 days after infection. Reinfection gave rise to no symptoms, but inoculation experiments showed that the spirochætes had gained access to the tissues; in non-reinfected controls the tissues proved sterile. This indicates that animals treated in the late stage of the disease, and cured of infection, remain clinically immune; they develop no symptoms of disease on reinfection, but they are not sufficiently resistant to prevent the organisms from gaining access to the tissues. Uhlenhuth and Groszmann (1928) treated their rabbits with neosalvarsan in the late stage of the disease—107 to 506 days after infection. Reinfection with the homologous strain performed 3 to 10 months after treatment gave rise to no symptoms; and in only 4 out of 11 rabbits were spirochætes demonstrated in the tissues. This indicates that a certain proportion of rabbits treated in the late stage of the disease remain both clinically and bacteriologically resistant to fresh infection. Similar results have been recorded by Breinl (1935).

Resuming the general findings, it may be said that untreated rabbits in the late stage of syphilis usually show a chancre-immunity to the homologous strain, even though there is no general immunity. That is to say, their immunity is sufficient to prevent the formation of a characteristic local lesion on reinfection, but is insufficient to prevent the development of the inoculated organisms in the tissues. Syphilitic rabbits treated with salvarsan within 45 days after infection only exceptionally develop a chancre-immunity; those treated 45–90 days after infection frequently do so, while those treated later than 90 days after infection almost invariably do so. The real divergence of opinion between different workers concerns the existence of a general spirochætocidal immunity in rabbits treated in the late stage of the disease. Uhlenhuth and Groszmann (1928) are convinced that such an immunity does in fact develop, while Kolle and Prigge (1927, 1929, 1934) are as equally convinced that it does not.

It would perhaps be sententious to suggest that the truth lies somewhere between the two, and that rabbits treated in the late stage of the disease are more immune than those treated in the early stage, though not always sufficiently immune to withstand completely invasion by fresh organisms. The discrepancy between the results of the two main protagonists is probably more apparent than real. Indeed, in a recent publication Groszmann (1933) himself brings evidence to show that, though a general immunity does develop as the result of long-standing infection, it is of comparatively short duration. (See also Chapter XLVIII.)

How closely the immunity of human beings to syphilis resembles the immunity of rabbits is not known. Judging from clinical observations it would appear that the two are not dissimilar. There is no satisfactory evidence that a spontaneous cure occurs either in rabbits or in man ; once the organisms have given rise to active symptoms of disease, they remain latent in the tissues for an indefinite period. Every now and again they may become active, or they may remain permanently in the latent condition. Both rabbits and man can be cured if they are treated by salvarsan in the early stage of the disease ; in the later stages a complete cure is very difficult to attain. Even though in man the Wassermann reaction may be rendered temporarily negative, it frequently becomes positive again after treatment is stopped.

It is very important to know whether patients with latent syphilis are infective, but unfortunately our knowledge on the subject is scanty. Animal experiments suggest that female rabbits suffering from latent syphilis may transmit the disease to healthy bucks ; but apparently no primary lesions develop as in the usual type of rabbit syphilis ; the spirochætes can however be demonstrated in the regional glands (Kolle 1928, Albrecht 1930). Kolle thinks that syphilis in human beings is often contracted in this way. Many persons are discovered in the course of routine examination to be suffering from syphilis who never suspected it, and who never showed evidence of a primary lesion. In Kolle's view such persons may have been infected by latent carriers of the disease, and have themselves acquired a latent infection without developing the usual primary lesions.

Another view has been put forward by Levaditi (Levaditi *et al.* 1928) and his collaborators. Starting from the observation that spirochætes can only rarely be found microscopically in the focal glands of rabbits infected by the scrotal route, even though these glands are almost invariably infective to fresh animals, he supposes that the virus of syphilis undergoes a development cycle of which *Treponema pallidum* is only one of the stages. In certain rabbit lesions, particularly those that were undergoing retrogression, he observed involution forms of the spirochæte, amongst which were minute granules only just visible by the microscope. He supposes that the spirochætes pass into a finely granular stage ; that these granules are more resistant to arsenic and its compounds ; and that they are responsible for latent infections in syphilis, and possibly for certain cases of tabes and general paralysis in which spirochætes cannot be demonstrated. Similar hypotheses have been put forward by other workers, but the evidence in their favour is unsatisfactory. van Haelst (1933), who has carefully studied the question, finds that the successful transmission of infection to rabbits is to a considerable extent determined by dosage. The inability to demonstrate spirochætes in tabes may quite possibly be due to the very small number present in the tissues. If there is an ultramicroscopic phase of the organism, then filtrates of virulent organs should prove infective ; but according to Levaditi's own findings they do not.

Diagnosis.

In the primary stage of the disease, *Trep. pallidum* may be demonstrated in the chancre. The superficial part of the lesion should be cleansed by gentle swabbing with saline, and exudate should be drawn from the base of the chancre for examination ; this may conveniently be obtained by applying a small suction-cup with the usual rubber-ball attachment. The serous exudate should be examined under dark-ground illumination. The morphology of *Trep. pallidum* is described on p. 721. The eye-piece micrometer devised by Barnard (1923), with which an approximate measurement of the spirals can be made with ease and rapidity, forms a most useful aid in the identification of this organism.

It cannot be too strongly emphasized that the identification of *Trep. pallidum* in a primary chancre requires the expert knowledge which comes only with long experience. It depends on the recognition of fine differences in morphology, without the assistance of characteristic differences in staining reaction, or of confirmatory tests on pure cultures. It is fortunate that the primary penile chancre provides the large majority of cases which the bacteriologist is called on to examine, since the spirochætal flora in such lesions is usually not copious, and consists mainly of species, such as *Trep. refringens*, which are readily differentiated from *Trep. pallidum*. Chancres in other situations, such as the lip, or primary genital chancres in the female, are far more likely to show a complex spirochætal flora, including species closely resembling *Trep. pallidum* ; and, in such cases, the greatest caution should be observed in basing a diagnosis of syphilis on a microscopical examination alone. It happens that a penile chancre usually leads to a suspicion of syphilis at an earlier stage than a genital chancre in the female, or an extra-genital chancre in either sex ; so that the latter lesions tend to be overlooked in the early stages, and, by the time they have attracted attention, the infection has usually reached the stage at which the Wassermann reaction is positive, thus providing a most valuable check on the result of the direct microscopical examination.

In the early stage of the disease it is possible to demonstrate spirochætes in excised lymph glands by inoculating them intratesticularly into rabbits, and following the progress of infection in these animals by the Kahn test and by dark-ground examination of the emulsified testicle. Negative results, however, are often obtained in treated cases and even in old untreated cases (Lake and Bryant 1930). The method is of academic rather than of practical interest.

Diagnostic Serum Reactions.

The serum reactions employed in the diagnosis of syphilis have, on account of their clinical importance, been submitted to detailed and extensive study, out of all proportion to their general immunological interest. The literature is correspondingly copious and diffuse, and it is quite impossible to review it here, or to attempt any discussion of the various points at issue. We can only give a brief description of some of the available tests and a short discussion of their interpretation.

The Wassermann Test.—Wassermann, Neisser and Bruck (1906), and Wassermann, Neisser, Bruck, and Schucht (1906) described a complement-fixation reaction, using as an antigen a watery extract of the liver of a syphilitic fœtus. This test was found to give positive results in persons suffering from syphilis, and negative results in normal controls. The syphilitic liver was selected as a convenient source of *Trep. pallidum*, which had not then been cultivated ; and the reaction was at first supposed to be specific in the bacteriological sense. It was soon found, however, that this was not the case (Marie and Levaditi 1907), since extracts of normal liver gave identical results. Still better results were obtained when watery extracts were replaced by alcoholic extracts of various tissues, and it was shown that the reacting substance was contained in the lecithin fraction of the lipoids, which is soluble in alcohol but insoluble in acetone (Porges and Meier 1908). This so-called " antigen " is rendered more sensitive, as regards its reaction with syphilitic sera, by the addition of an alcoholic solution of cholesterol (Browning and Mackenzie 1924). The antigen most commonly employed at the present time is an alcoholic extract of heart-muscle from the ox, calf, or man, from which the acetone-soluble fraction has been removed. To this alcoholic extract is added an alcoholic solution of cholesterol, so that the cholesterol content is 0·3–0·4 per cent. ; and the combined alcoholic solution is suitably diluted with saline. With this " antigen " a com-plement-fixation test is carried out in the usual way, and with the usual controls. The Wassermann reaction is, therefore, in no way specific in the bacteriological sense ; its basis is essentially empirical. It has been found in practice to be one of the most useful and reliable methods employed as laboratory aids to diagnosis ; but its diagnostic significance depends entirely on an observed correlation with clinical findings, for which there is, as yet, no satisfactory explanation. The methods of performing the test are legion (see Reports 1918*a*, 1924, 1929, 1934, Cumming *et al.* 1935) and many modifications have been suggested to increase its sensitivity. The principles are, however, in no way different from those outlined in Chapter VI, in connection with complement fixation in general.

Three reagents are involved in the actual reaction—antigen, patient's serum, and complement. When these have been allowed to react for a suitable period—1 hour at 37° C., or overnight in the ice-box—sensitized red cells are added, and the mixtures are incubated for 1 hour at 37° C. to determine the presence or absence of hæmolysis, indicat-ing the presence or absence of unabsorbed complement. To establish a positive reaction it must be shown (*a*) that the patient's serum alone absorbs no complement, or at most a small fraction of that present in the test mixture ; (*b*) that the same is true of the antigen ; and (*c*) that the mixture of serum and antigen absorbs an amount of comple-ment greatly in excess of the sum of the small amounts absorbed by each of these reagents separately. Thus the essential tubes in carrying out a Wassermann reaction are (1) the antigen control, (2) the serum control, and (3) the test proper. The first control will serve for the whole series of tests carried out on any one day, the second must be put up for each serum tested. It is, however, obviously desirable to obtain a more accurate measure of the strength of the reaction than is possible by such a simple method as this ; and most of the methods in actual use are designed to yield a roughly quantitative result, which will enable the reactions to be graded into strongly positive, positive, weakly positive, doubtful, and negative. We may consider briefly the possible ways in which such results may be obtained, and the lines along which some approach to standardization may be sought.

There are three variables involved in the reaction—antigen, serum, and complement ; clearly, we may obtain quantitative results by holding any two of these constant, and varying the third. Varying the antigen introduces factors which need careful recon-sideration in view of the recent advances in our knowledge of the importance of optimal relations in antigen-antibody reactions ; at the present time this method is seldom, if ever, adopted. With the amount of antigen held constant we may vary either the test serum, or the complement. The latter method is very commonly employed, the serum-antigen mixtures being allowed to react in the presence of 3 and 5 M.H.D., or of 2, 4, 6 and 8 M.H.D. In either case the serum and antigen controls are put up with the smallest amount of complement employed in the test. In this way we grade the strength of a reacting serum in terms of the amount of complement which is fixed when a con-stant amount of serum (usually 0·5 c.c. of a 1 : 5 dilution) is mixed with a constant amount of antigen (0·5 c.c. of a suitable dilution), and the same volume of the suitably diluted guinea-pig's serum is added to the mixture.

An alternative method, advocated by several workers, is to hold antigen and comple-ment constant, and vary the amount of patient's serum, testing it in progressive dilu-tions of, say, 1 : 2·5, 1 : 5, 1 : 10, 1 : 20, 1 : 40, though it is not usual to employ more than three dilutions. This method has the advantage of giving a direct measure of the concentration of the Wassermann-antibody in the serum under test. The serum control is, of course, put up with the largest amount of serum employed in the actual test.

In either case it is necessary to standardize the complement. For this purpose a preliminary titration is carried out, to determine the minimal hæmolytic dose. It is convenient to carry out this titration in duplicate. In the first series one volume of progressive dilutions of guinea-pig serum is added to two volumes of saline—0·5 c.c. is usually taken as " one volume " throughout ; in the second series the same dilutions of guinea-pig serum are added to one volume of saline and one volume of the antigen to be used in the test. After 1 hour's incubation at 37° C., or a longer time in the ice-chest, one volume of a 5 per cent. suspension of red cells and one volume of a hæmolytic serum, so diluted as to contain at least 5 M.H.D. of hæmolysin, are added to each tube ; and both series are then incubated for 1 hour at 37° C. In this way we are able to determine the M.H.D. of complement (guinea-pig serum), before and after it has been allowed to react with the antigen. This obviates the necessity for any further antigen control, and enables us to detect any excessive anti-complementary action of the antigen, or any tendency of a particular specimen of guinea-pig's serum to react with the antigen alone. If such a test shows any marked difference in the M.H.D. in the two series, it may be taken that either the complement or the antigen is unsuitable, and must be replaced by a more satisfactory sample. In the test itself it is usual to employ 3 M.H.D. of complement, if this reagent is to be held constant.

Precipitation Reactions, including the Kahn Test.—From our knowledge of the antigen-antibody reactions in general, we should expect that any reaction which gives complement fixation under a particular set of conditions will give visible precipitation if the conditions are properly adjusted. So far as the lipoid antigens and the serum antibodies involved in the Wassermann reaction are concerned, this is the case. The various methods for applying the precipitation test to the diagnosis of syphilis are scarcely less numerous than the modifications of the Wassermann reaction (Michaelis 1907, Meinicke 1907, Sachs and Georgi 1918, Dreyer and Ward 1921, Kahn 1922a, b, 1928, Report 1923, Report 1929, Cumming et al. 1935). A precipitation test possesses certain obvious advantages as compared with a complement-fixation reaction, for routine diagnostic purposes. It involves the use of two reagents only—serum and antigen. It is more easily standardized, and it is simpler to perform. The Kahn test, in particular, has been widely used during recent years.

The antigen employed in this test (Kahn 1928) is of the same general type as that used in the Wassermann test ; but the preliminary extraction of the dried heart muscle, to remove the residual lipoid components, is carried out with ether instead of with acetone. The ether-extracted heart muscle is then extracted with alcohol, and cholesterol is added to the alcoholic extract. In preparing the antigen for use in the test, saline is added until an opalescent colloidal suspension is obtained, which disperses to give a clear solution on the addition of further saline, or serum. When the concentrations of the reagents are correctly adjusted, and flocculation is assisted by shaking, such an antigen, in the presence of a syphilitic serum, yields an almost immediate precipitate, while in the presence of a normal serum the solution remains clear and translucent. In the standard test three tubes are used. The amount of serum is kept constant (0·15 c.c.), and the amount of antigen is varied (0·05 c.c., 0·025 c.c. and 0·0125 c.c.). The tubes are shaken for 3 minutes, 1 c.c. of saline is added to the first tube, 0·5 c.c. to the second and third, and the results are read. In a strong reaction precipitation appears only in the third tube, with perhaps a trace of opalescence in the second ; that is, with a serum which contains little " antibody," precipitation is inhibited by excess of antigen.

The Interpretation of the Diagnostic Serum Reactions.—This is a problem that requires the closest co-operation between the clinician and the clinical pathologist, and its full discussion is beyond the scope of this book. It is considered at length in many of the reports and papers referred to above. For our present purpose we need consider only the results obtained in the most recent and systematic surveys.

As a preliminary to any such discussion it is necessary to note the methods employed in recording and reporting results. The tests most frequently used do not permit a reading in terms of any titre, dilution or ratio, and their results cannot therefore be recorded numerically. The most common method of recording is to use an arbitrary combination of plus and minus signs. A strongly positive reaction may, for instance, be recorded as $++++$, a less strong reaction as $+++$, a moderate reaction as $++$, a positive but weak reaction as $+$, a doubtful reaction as $+-$, or $-+$, and a frankly negative reaction as $-$. Sometimes other conventions are used, the plus and minus signs being combined differently, or the strongest reaction being awarded only two, or three, plus signs. Such a notation has nothing to recommend it. The conventional signs used by one pathologist differ from those used by another, and confusion results. Alternatively, words may be used instead of signs; and we then have " strongly positive," " positive," " weakly positive," " doubtful " and " negative " reactions. This is a little better; but there is much to be said for the contention (see Cumming *et al.* 1935) that a division into " positive," " doubtful " and " negative " results gives the clinician all that he can gain, and simplifies the issue. Without some general agreement, these labels will of course be arbitrarily applied, and a proportion of the sera reported to be positive by one test, or one worker, will be returned as doubtful by another. The only way in which this difficulty could be reduced to a minimum would be to standardize the technique, and to issue standardized reagents from central laboratories (see Report 1934).

Taking things as they are, we may inquire what actually happens when sera from syphilitic and non-syphilitic cases are submitted to different kinds of tests. We may take first a trial that was carried out in Copenhagen in 1928, under the auspices of the Health Organization of the League of Nations. Sera from several hundred persons clinically diagnosed as suffering from syphilis, and several hundred diagnosed as non-syphilitic, were submitted to various serological tests carried out by skilled pathologists from different countries (see Report 1929).

The significant figures taken from this report are tabulated, in a slightly modified form, in Table CLXVI. The various modifications of the Wassermann reaction employed, or the various workers using this test, are designated as W.R.1, W.R.2, etc. The results obtained by the Kahn test are labelled Kahn 1 and Kahn 2. Other forms of precipitation tests are labelled P.1, P.2, etc. The results are recorded as " positive," " doubtful " or " negative." It will be seen that the reports on the clinically syphilitic cases vary rather widely, and that some of the workers recorded rather a high proportion of positive or doubtful reactions among the clinically non-syphilitic cases. Taking the results at their face value, and allowing for the fact that many of the clinically syphilitic cases were clearly not in a stage in which they would give a positive serum reaction, W.R.3 with 42·6 per cent. of negatives among the clinically syphilitic, and 97·2 per cent. among the non-syphilitic has given satisfactory results. Both series of Kahn tests do better than this, and so does P. 2.

The variability of the results with sera from clinically syphilitic patients, and the relatively high proportion of negative results, are not surprising; because all stages and types of syphilis were included, and it is well known that the proportion of positive reactions varies widely in different stages and types of the disease. Boas, for instance (see Reports 1918*b*, 1919), records 59 per cent. of positive results in primary syphilis, 90 per cent. in secondary syphilis, 84 per cent. in tertiary syphilis, 72 per cent. in tabes, and 99·3 per cent. in general paralysis of the insane.

TABLE CLXVI

RESULTS OF COMPARATIVE TRIALS OF DIFFERENT COMPLEMENT-FIXATION AND PRECIPITATION TESTS.

	Syphilitic.			Non-syphilitic.		
	Per cent.			Per cent.		
	Positive.	Doubtful.	Negative.	Positive.	Doubtful.	Negative.
W.R. 1 . .	28·2	15·6	56·2	3·3	8·6	88·2
,, 2 . .	53·7	2·9	43·4	10·7	1·6	87·7
,, 3 . .	41·8	15·5	42·6	—	2·8	97·2
,, 4 . .	52·8	12·9	34·3	6·7	8·3	85·0
,, 5 . .	51·9	13·0	35·1	5·5	9·2	85·3
,, 6 . .	43·9	11·2	44·9	1·4	5·8	92·8
,, 7 . .	38·8	11·4	49·8	—	3·0	97·0
Kahn 1 . .	58·6	5·4	36·0	0·7	1·4	97·9
,, 2 . .	61·1	6·6	32·3	—	1·2	98·8
P. 1 . . .	49·0	7·6	43·4	2·1	3·0	94·9
,, 2 . . .	63·5	9·0	27·5	0·2	2·3	97·5
,, 3 . . .	53·5	14·0	32·5	0·5	8·8	90·7
,, 4 . . .	43·0	4·7	52·3	—	0·2	99·8
,, 5 . . .	52·5	4·3	43·2	—	0·2	99·8
,, 6 . . .	51·2	15·1	33·7	1·4	8·1	90·5
,, 7 . . .	40·1	14·3	45·6	0·6	10·2	89·3

It is in the type of case that shows a relatively low proportion of positive reactions, and a relatively high proportion of doubtful reactions, that most discrepancies will occur.

A recent report by the Public Health Service of the United States (see Cumming *et al.* 1935) gives valuable figures.

Table CLXVII has been constructed from the data contained in this report

TABLE CLXVII

RESULTS OF COMPARATIVE TRIALS OF DIFFERENT COMPLEMENT-FIXATION AND PRECIPITATION TESTS

	Percentage of Sera reacting positively.			
	Untreated Primary Syphilis.	Untreated Secondary Syphilis.	Late Syphilis. Varying Treatment.	Normal. Non-syphilitic.
W.R. 1	53·7	100	66·6	0·0
,, 2	65·9	100	72·1	0·0
,, 3	82·5	100	86·4	0·7
,, 4	69·8	100	58·0	0·0
Kahn 1	76·7	100	76·9	0·0
,, 2*	82·9	100	84·3	3·3
,, 3*	80·5	100	83·0	0·7
P. 1	72·1	100	82·4	2·0
,, 2	81·0	100	84·5	0·7
,, 3	58·1	98·4	64·5	3·3
,, 4	74·4	100	71·5	0·0
,, 5	72·1	98·5	83·6	1·3
,, 6	70·7	98·4	63·1	0·7

* See text.

and records the percentage of positive results obtained by various tests, and by various workers, in the examination of sera from syphilitic patients in various stages of the disease, and from normal persons showing no evidence of syphilis. The notation used is the same as in Table CLXVI ; but it should be noted that Kahn 2 and Kahn 3 refer to modifications of the standard Kahn test, and that the W.R.1, P. 1, etc. of one table are not identical with the W.R. 1 and P. 1 of the other.

TABLE CLXVIII

RESULTS OF COMPARATIVE TRIALS OF DIFFERENT COMPLEMENT-FIXATION AND PRECIPITATION TESTS.

	Percentage of Sera giving positive reactions.						
	Syphilis all Stages.	Leprosy.	Malaria.	Tuberculosis.	Fever.	Pregnancy.	Normal.
W.R. 1 . . .	70·5	44·0	14·3	1·9	2·2	0·0	0·0
,, 2 . . .	75·9	64·0	19·4	2·0	2·2	0·0	0·0
,, 3 . . .	88·2	62·0	20·6	7·5	2·2	3·8	0·7
,, 4 . . .	65·8	42·0	17·1	1·9	0·0	0·0	0·0
Kahn 1 . . .	80·5	60·0	11·4	1·9	0·0	0·0	0·0
,, 2* . .	86·6	76·0	16·7	7·7	2·2	1·9	3·3
,, 3* . .	85·4	68·0	19·4	1·9	0·0	0·0	0·7
P. 1 . . .	84·1	72·0	12·1	1·9	0·0	0·0	2·0
,, 2	86·6	40·0	11·1	5·7	2·3	1·9	0·7
,, 3	69·0	58·0	11·4	5·7	4·3	3·7	3·3
,, 4	76·3	66·0	14·3	1·9	0·0	0·0	0·0
,, 5	84·7	70·0	11·1	7·5	8·9	0·0	1·3
,, 6	69·4	52·0	8·6	0·0	0·0	0·0	0·7

* See text.

It will be noted that the proportion of positive results is, on the average, far higher than in the Copenhagen trial ; but this may well be due in large part to the nature of the cases examined. Most of the workers recorded 100 per cent. of positives in the untreated secondary cases ; but the percentage of positives recorded in the untreated primary infections ranges from 53·7 per cent. to 82·9 per cent., and in the tertiary cases from 58·0 per cent. to 86·4 per cent.

More useful information is obtained by making a comparison, not between syphilitic and normal persons, but between persons suffering from syphilis, and persons suffering from some other disease. Very extensive studies have been made along these lines with results that may be summarized as follows. There is general agreement that yaws, which is closely related to syphilis in its ætiology, responds in much the same way to various serum tests. Cases of leprosy give a lower, but still relatively high, proportion of positive reactions. It has often been stated that patients suffering from malaria tend to give positive reactions ; but here there has been a considerable conflict of evidence. The same is true of sleeping sickness. Some observers have recorded a small proportion of positive reactions in tuberculosis, some in febrile conditions, and some in pregnancy. The trial carried out by the Public Health Service of the United States provides information on several of these points, and Table CLXVIII has been constructed from the relevant data, including all the syphilitic cases, and the normal persons, from Table CLXVII.

It will be noted that the frequency of a positive reaction in leprosy is amply confirmed, that malaria yields an appreciable proportion of positive results, and tuberculosis far less, while the figures for febrile conditions and pregnancy differ but little from the normal. Another point will be noticed. On the whole, though there are exceptions, a test that tends to give a high proportion of positive results with sera from syphilitic patients, tends also to give a relatively high proportion of positive results with sera from those suffering with other diseases (see, for instance, W.R.3, Kahn 2, P.2 and P.5), while a test that gives a low proportion of positives in one case tends to do so in the other (see W.R.4 and P.6). Here, again, the standard Kahn test gives satisfactory results.

It is clear that there is not a great deal to choose between diagnosis by complement fixation and diagnosis by a precipitin reaction, so far as reliability is concerned. By either method there will be a certain range of variation in the results recorded by different workers, unless one standardized technique carried out with standardized reagents is to be enforced. In any case, the onus of interpreting the test must rest with the clinician, when he has made due allowance for the stage of the disease, if the case is one of syphilis, and for the possible or probable existence of one of the infections that may sometimes induce similar changes in the serum.

As a general working rule, and excluding cases of yaws and leprosy, it may be stated that, in a suspected case of primary syphilis, in the period between the first appearance of the chancre and the development of the secondary rash, a positive reaction will confirm the diagnosis, but a negative reaction will by no means contradict it. The latter is particularly true during the first 2 or 3 weeks after the chancre appears. In a case which, on clinical grounds, is regarded as secondary syphilis, a negative reaction tells very strongly against the provisional diagnosis. In such cases the test should always be repeated ; and, if the second test is also negative, the diagnosis should be very carefully reconsidered. A persistently negative reaction, lasting through this stage, may be taken as practically excluding syphilitic infection. In tertiary syphilis, with the exception of general paralysis, and perhaps of syphilitic aneurysm, a negative reaction cannot be regarded as excluding the diagnosis, though it may tell definitely against it.

The use of the Wassermann reaction in the control of treatment is too complex to be considered here. Broadly, it may be stated that, in a case which comes under treatment early, and which is efficiently treated, the Wassermann reaction becomes negative and remains so ; while in a case which escapes treatment during the early stages, or which is inefficiently treated during this period, it is extremely difficult, if not impossible, to produce a permanently negative Wassermann reaction by treatment administered several years after infection has been contracted (Browning and Mackenzie 1924, Report 1926).

It may be added that the tests used in the examination of the blood serum may also be applied to the cerebrospinal fluid in suspected cases of neuro-syphilis ; though certain of the precipitin tests give rather poor results when used for this purpose (see Cumming *et al.* 1935).

Such examinations should, of course, be controlled by examination of the fluid for cells, proteins, type of colloidal-gold curve and so on.

Prophylaxis and Treatment.

We do not propose to discuss the various hygienic methods that have been advocated for the prevention of syphilis.

Bacteriological methods of prophylaxis do not exist. Animal experiments indicate that it is difficult or impossible to protect animals by vaccination with dead spirochætes against subsequent infection with living organisms (Uhlenhuth and

Mulzer 1913, Groszmann 1929). Immune bodies have been demonstrated in the blood of infected animals, but so far the transference of passive immunity has been unsuccessful. Metchnikoff and Roux (1904a) obtained some evidence that apes inoculated with a weakly virulent strain of syphilis were protected against subsequent inoculation with a fully virulent strain, but the results were not conclusive. Treatment with salvarsan is successful in curing the disease in the early stages, but once the secondary stage has passed, definitive cure appears to be impossible.

A new method of treatment is now on trial, namely, that of hyperpyrexia or pyrotherapy. *Trep. pallidum* is apparently more susceptible to heat than are the tissue cells, and evidence has been obtained that by raising the body temperature to 41·5°–42° C. it is possible in experimentally infected rabbits to destroy the spirochætes *in vivo* (see Carpenter, Boak, and Warren 1932). The hyperpyrexia may be produced either by simple heat, by short-wave radiation, or in certain other ways. It is too early yet to say what value the method is likely to have in practice, but promising results have been reported (see Simpson 1935).

Rabbit Syphilis.

Rabbit syphilis is a naturally occurring venereal disease of rabbits due to the spirochæte *Treponema cuniculi*. The disease was first described by Ross (1912) and the spirochætes were first observed by Bayon (1913). The incidence of the disease in wild rabbits varies considerably ; according to some authorities as many as 20–40 per cent. in this country are affected. In hutch rabbits the disease is less common ; Adams, Cappell, and McCluskie (1928) noticed it in 14 out of 228 rabbits. The lesions consist of small scaly patches, often slightly eroded and covered with a brownish crust, situated on the genitals or in the perineal region. Sometimes the nostrils or eyelids are affected. The spirochætes are found in large numbers in scrapings from the lesions and in sections ; they are confined apparently to the superficial layers. The disease can be reproduced in normal rabbits by inoculation of an infective tissue suspension on to the scarified skin of the genital region ; transmission can also be effected by mating, but with less constancy. The incubation period is from 2 to 8 weeks ; once established, infection persists for months. In males spontaneous cure usually occurs, but in females the disease is very chronic. Rabbits suffering from rabbit syphilis can be infected with human syphilitic material, indicating that the two diseases are not identical (Noguchi 1922). *Trep. cuniculi* is morphologically indistinguishable from *Trep. pallidum*, though Noguchi (1922) says it is perhaps a trifle thicker and longer than the average *pallidum*. Like *pallidum* it stains rose-red with Giemsa. The disease is readily cured by intravenous injection of salvarsan, or by local application of Unguentum hydrargyri. (For further information on the disease and the properties of the causative organism, see Bessemans 1928, and Bessemans and de Geest 1928.)

YAWS

Yaws is a contagious inoculable disease characterized by the appearance of papules, which generally develop into a fungating, encrusted, granulomatous eruption (Manson 1914). It is widely diffused throughout the tropics, and occurs in its typical form only amongst the dark-skinned races. The causative organism, *Treponema pertenue*, was discovered by Castellani in 1905. It is a spirochæte morphologically indistinguishable from *Trep. pallidum*. Yaws occurs particularly in childhood. The commonest site for the primary lesion is on the lower extremities. The secondary eruption usually appears 2–4 weeks later. The disease is not as a rule of venereal origin. Some observers believe that infection occurs through the skin and is carried by gnats. Patients with yaws give a positive Wassermann reaction. The disease is curable by salvarsan and is amenable to treatment with mercury and potassium iodide.

The main interest of yaws is its relationship to syphilis. Many experienced clinicians are of the opinion that yaws is syphilis modified by race and climate.

There is evidence that yaws protects against syphilis. Parham (1922), for example, never once observed syphilis in the Samoans, in spite of their close contact with Europeans ; since nearly all Samoans are stated to have yaws in childhood, he argues that the disease must protect them from syphilis in adult life. Similarly Wilson and Mathis (1930), who in a period of 9 years in Haiti saw 45,000 cases of yaws and 300 cases of syphilis, only once met with an undoubted case of syphilis in a patient who had previously suffered from yaws. Further evidence is necessary, however, to determine the relationship between these two diseases.

REFERENCES

ADAMS, D. K., CAPPELL, D. F., and McCLUSKIE, J. A. W. (1928) *J. Path. Bact.*, **31,** 157.
ALBRECHT, B. (1930) *Dtsch. med. Wschr.*, **56,** 93.
BARNARD, J. E. (1923) *Brit. J. exp. Path.*, **4,** 68.
BAYON, H. (1913) *Brit. med. J.*, ii. 1159.
BESSEMANS, A. (1928) *C. R. Soc. Biol.*, **99,** 331.
BESSEMANS, A. and GEEST, B. DE. (1928) *C. R. Soc. Biol.*, **99,** 334.
BREINL, F. (1935) *Z. ImmunForsch.*, **84,** 195.
BROWN, W. H. and PEARCE, L. (1921) *J. exp. Med.*, **33,** 553.
BROWNING, C. H. and MACKENZIE, I. (1924) " Recent Methods in the Diagnosis and Treatment of Syphilis." 2nd Edit., Lond.
CARPENTER, C. M., BOAK, R. A., and WARREN, S. L. (1932) *J. exp. Med.*, **56,** 751.
CASTELLANI, A. (1905) *Brit. med. J.*, ii. 1280.
CHESNEY, A. M., HALLEY, C. R. L., and KEMP, J. E. (1927) *J. exp. Med.*, **46,** 223.
CHESNEY, A. M. and KEMP, J. E. (1925) *J. exp. Med.*, **42,** 17, 33 ; (1926) *Ibid.*, **44,** 589.
CUMMING, H. S., HAZEN, H. H., SANFORD, A. H., SENEAR, F. E., SIMPSON, W. M., and VONDERLEHR, R. A. (1935) *J. Amer. med. Ass.*, **104,** 2083.
DREYER, G. and WARD, H. K. (1921) *Lancet*, i. 956.
GROSZMANN, H. (1929) *Z. ImmunForsch.*, **60,** 470 ; (1933) *Ibid.*, **79,** 495.
HAELST, J. VAN. (1933) *Arch. int. Méd. exp.*, **8,** 543.
HAENSELL, P. (1881) *v. Graefes Arch. Ophthal.*, **27,** 93.
KAHN, R. L. (1922a) *Arch. Derm. Syph.*, *N.Y.*, **5,** 570, 734 ; (1922b) *Ibid.*, **6,** 332 ; (1928) " The Kahn Test." Baltimore.
KLEBS, A. C. (1932) *Science*, **75,** 191.
KOLLE, W. (1928) *Zbl. Bakt.*, **106,** 134.
KOLLE, W. and EVERS, E. (1926a) *Dtsch. med. Wschr.*, **52,** 557 ; (1926b) *Ibid.*, **52,** 1075.
KOLLE, W. and PRIGGE, R. (1927) *Dtsch. med. Wschr.*, **53,** 1499 ; (1929) *Ibid.*, **55,** 985 ; (1934) *Med. Klinik*, **30,** 46.
KOLLE, W. and SCHLOSZBERGER, H. (1926) *Dtsch. med. Wschr.*, **52,** 1245 ; (1928) *Ibid.*, **54,** 129.
LAKE, G. C. and BRYANT, K. K. (1930) *Nat. Inst. Hlth, Wash., Bull.* No. 157.
LEVADITI, C., SCHOEN, R., and SANCHIS-BAYARRI, M. V. (1928) *Ann. Inst. Pasteur*, **42,** 475.
MANSON, P. (1914) " Tropical Diseases." London.
MARIE, A. and LEVADITI, C. (1907) *Ann. Inst. Pasteur*, **21,** 138.
MEINECKE. (1907) *Berl. klin. Wschr.*, **44,** 1477.
METCHNIKOFF, E. and ROUX, E. (1903) *Ann. Inst. Pasteur*, **17,** 809 ; (1904a) *Ibid.*, **18,** 1 ; (1904b) *Ibid.*, **18,** 657 ; (1905) *Ibid.*, **19,** 673.
MICHAELIS. (1907) *Berl. klin. Wschr.*, **44,** 1477.
NEISSER. (1906) " Die experimentelle Syphilisforschung." Berlin.
NOGUCHI, H. (1922) *J. exp. Med.*, **35,** 391.
NOGUCHI, H. and MOORE, J. W. (1913) *J. exp. Med.*, **17,** 232.
PARHAM, J. C. (1922) *Amer. J. trop. Med.*, **2,** 341.

PORGES, O. and MEIER, G.   (1908) *Berl. klin. Wschr.*, **45**, 731.
Reports.   (1918*a*) *Spec. Rep. Ser. med. Res. Coun., Lond.*, No. 14 ;   (1918*b*) *Ibid.*, No. 21 ;
    (1919) *Ibid.*, No. 23 ;   (1923) *Ibid.*, No. 78 ;   (1924) *L. of N. Hlth Organization*, C5M5, iii ;
    (1926) *Spec. Rep. Ser. med. Res. Coun., Lond.*, No. 107 ;   (1929) *L. of N. Publ.*, **3**, 3.   (2nd
    Lab. Confer. on Serodiag. Syphilis.) ;   (1934) *Amer. J. publ. Hlth.*, **24**, 727.
ROSS, E. H.   (1912) *Brit. med. J.*, ii. 1653.
SACHS, H. and GEORGI, W.   (1918) *Med. Klinik*, **14**, 805.
SCHAUDINN, F. and HOFFMANN, E.   (1905) *Arb. ReichsgesundhAmt.*, **22**, 527.
SCHUBERG, A. and SCHLOSSBERGER, H.   (1930) *Klin. Wschr.*, **9**, 499.
SIMPSON, W. M.   (1935) *J. Amer. med. Ass.*, **105**, 2132.
STOKES, J. H.   (1931) *Science*, **74**, 502.
TRUFFI, M.   (1910) *Zbl. Bakt.*, **54**, 337.
UHLENHUTH, P. and GROSZMANN, H.   (1928) *Z. ImmunForsch.*, **55**, 380.
UHLENHUTH, P. and MULZER, P.   (1913) *Arb. ReichsgesundhAmt.*, **44**, 307.
WASSERMANN, A., NEISSER, A., and BRUCK, C.   (1906) *Dtsch. med. Wschr.*, **32**, 745.
WASSERMANN, A., NEISSER, A., BRUCK, C., and SCHUCHT, A.   (1906) *Z. Hyg. InfektKr.*,
    55, 451.
WILSON, P. W. and MATHIS, M. S.   (1930) *J. Amer. med. Ass.*, **94**, 1289.

CHAPTER LXXIX

WEIL'S DISEASE, SPIROCHÆTAL JAUNDICE IN ANIMALS, SWAMP FEVER, SEVEN-DAY FEVER OF JAPAN, AND RAT-BITE FEVER

WEIL'S DISEASE OR SPIROCHÆTOSIS ICTEROHÆMORRHAGICA

WEIL's disease is a fairly widespread and not uncommon disease, which frequently assumes prominence in war time. During the War of Secession, 1861–65, over 70,000 men contracted infectious jaundice, that is between 2·0 and 2·5 per cent. of the total strength (Uhlenhuth and Fromme 1916). In the late War it was common on the Western front, affecting both German and Allied troops (Uhlenhuth and Fromme 1916, Stokes *et al.* 1917, Martin and Pettit 1919). The disease was reported in Scotland in 1923 amongst the coal-miners of the East Lothian district. It appears to be fairly common in South America. It is frequently met with in Sumatra (Sardjito and Zuelzer 1929), and has been observed in the Andaman Islands (Brown 1928, Taylor and Goyle 1931). It is very common in Japan, where in 1933 there were as many as 1,636 cases. The United States seems to suffer but little. In Europe, Holland and France appear to have the highest incidence rate, but statistics of the real prevalence of the disease are unobtainable (see Report 1934). In Great Britain it is endemic in sewer workers (Fairley 1934, Alston and Brown 1935) and in those engaged in washing fish (Davidson *et al.* 1934, Davidson and Smith 1936).

The incubation period of the disease is 5 to 7 days as a rule, rarely as long as 13 days (Inada 1917). In the first or febrile stage, which lasts for 6 or 7 days, there is high fever, conjunctival congestion, muscular pains, and albuminuria. In the second or icteric stage, which lasts from the 7th to the 13th day, jaundice appears, there is a tendency to hæmorrhage, and death may occur. The third stage, or stage of convalescence, is marked by the gradual subsidence of the jaundice and other symptoms; it may be interrupted, however, by a secondary fever (Inada 1917). The mortality of the disease varies in different epidemics; in Japan it varies from 4·6 to 32 per cent. (Inada *et al.* 1916, Report 1934); on the Western front it was under 6 per cent. amongst the British, and 13 per cent. amongst the German troops (Stokes *et al.* 1917, Uhlenhuth and Fromme 1918); in the Scottish outbreak it was about 25 per cent. (Buchanan 1927).

The disease is due to infection with a spirochæte that was first described in 1915 by Inada and his colleagues in Japan (Inada *et al.* 1916). The usual name for this organism is *Leptospira icterohæmorrhagiæ*, but in Germany it is generally referred to as *Spirochæta icterogenes* (see Chapter XXXV). A few cases appear to be caused by *Lepto. canicola*—a closely allied species that is normally a pathogenic parasite of the dog (Schüffner 1934).

In man the spirochætes are widely distributed in the body during the 1st week of the disease, and can generally be demonstrated in the blood by guinea-pig injection, and occasionally by microscopical examination. After the 7th to 9th day they leave the blood and appear in the urine, at first in very small numbers, but gradually increasing till during the 3rd and 4th weeks they can be found microscopically by dark-ground illumination in the majority of cases. They persist in the urine for a variable time, but can rarely be found after the end of the 5th week. In patients dying during the febrile stage of the disease spirochætes can be demonstrated microscopically in the kidney, liver, adrenals, spleen, testicle, lymphatic glands, voluntary and cardiac muscle, and arterial walls; less frequently in the lung, pancreas, intestine, nervous system, and skin (Inada *et al.* 1916). If death occurs during the 2nd week or later, the chief organ in which spirochætes are found is the kidney; in the other organs they are less numerous or absent.

Occupational Incidence.—Weil's disease occurs chiefly in damp, badly drained, rat-infested situations. Thus in Japan it was noticed that the disease occurred in coal mines; that only the miners who worked in a particular section of the mines were affected; that this section was under water; and that when the water was pumped out, no more cases occurred (Inada *et al.* 1916). Later, it was noticed that cases never occurred in coal mines when the soil was acid; on the other hand they were numerous in coal mines on an alkaline soil (Ido *et al.* 1917a). Experiments have shown, in this connection, that the organisms are rapidly killed by a weakly acid solution. On the Western front Stokes (Stokes *et al.* 1917) observed that the cases occurred almost exclusively amongst the troops in the trenches; at the base they were very uncommon. Most of the cases, moreover, occurred in small sections of trench that were particularly wet and badly drained. Rats taken from one of these sections were found to contain pathogenic leptospiræ in the kidneys. Similar observations were made in the German Army (Uhlenhuth and Zuelzer 1921). Again in Scotland, Buchanan (1927) observed the disease amongst coal miners in the East Lothian district; pathogenic leptospiræ were found in the roof slime of a mine, and similar leptospiræ, the pathogenicity of which was not worked out, were frequent in pit and surface waters; infected rats were likewise found in the mines. In the Andamans, cases are practically confined to adult males engaged in outdoor occupations that involve working in water and mud for prolonged periods, such as in the rice fields (Taylor and Goyle 1931). In Holland the majority of the cases are contributed by swimmers, bargemen, fishermen, slaughter-house workers, and persons who by accident or with suicidal intent fall into canals, and are nearly drowned after swallowing large quantities of water (Schüffner 1930, 1934). In this country, as has already been stated, sewer workers and those engaged in washing fish are specially liable to the disease.

One very instructive *water-borne outbreak* is on record (Jorge 1932). It occurred in the north-east quarter of Lisbon in 1931, and involved at least 126 persons in the space of a month. Infection was traced to a particular fountain, the water of which during its passage underground in an open conduit had apparently been contaminated by rats from a neighbouring sewer. The case mortality of this epidemic was 24·6 per cent.

Mode of Transmission.—The mode of transmission of Weil's disease is not known with certainty, but there is strong reason to believe that infection takes place directly or indirectly by contamination of the abraded skin or of a mucous membrane, such as that of the eye, nose, or mouth, with rats' urine. The occupational incidence, which has just been referred to, affords striking evidence in favour of this conclusion, since contact with presumably contaminated water or sewage seems to be common to all types of persons attacked. Further evidence is provided by consideration of the frequency with which leptospiræ are found in apparently normal rats.

Infection of Rats.—It has been established by numerous workers that the rat—particularly *Rattus norvegicus*—is a very frequent carrier of pathogenic leptospiræ.

In Japan 40·2 per cent. of 149 rats of this species were found infected (Ido *et al.* 1917*a*) ; in England 30 per cent. of 100 wild rats (Balfour 1922, Stevenson 1922) ; in Scotland 36·7 per cent. of 166 wild rats (Buchanan 1927) ; in Berlin 10 per cent. of rats (Uhlenhuth and Zuelzer 1921) ; in Toronto 37 per cent. (Cameron and Irwin 1929) ; in Freiburg 44 per cent. (Zimmermann 1930) ; in Moscow 12 per cent. (Ssinjuschina 1929) ; and in Kiew 31 per cent. (Basilewsky 1933). In Rotterdam, where cases of Weil's disease are fairly common, from 7 to 40 per cent. of all rats examined have proved to be infected (Schüffner 1934). The frequency of infection depends largely on the age of the rat. Young rats are seldom infected, while over 50 per cent. of adult rats may harbour the spirochætes. The black rat rarely acts as a carrier. Field-mice are not uncommonly infected (Ido *et al.* 1917*a*, Buchanan 1927).

The spirochætes are found in the kidney and the urine, not in the blood or liver. Intraperitoneal injection of rat's urine, even in small amounts, 0·1–0·2 c.c., into guinea-pigs may give rise to fatal hæmorrhagic jaundice. Not all specimens of rat's urine in which leptospiræ are visible microscopically prove infective ; this is probably dependent on the acidity of the rat's urine, which rapidly proves fatal to the organisms. The same applies to the effect of human urine ; only in one-third of cases of Weil's disease does the urine prove to be infective. Uhlenhuth and Zuelzer (1921) found that fresh human or rat's urine rapidly killed the spirochætes ; but if the urine was neutralized, the organisms remained virulent for 2 days.

Leptospiræ in Water.—Admitting the frequency of infection of rats' urine, it should be possible to demonstrate the presence of *Lepto. icterohæmorrhagiæ* in contaminated water. Spirochætes morphologically identical with *Leptospira icterohæmorrhagiæ* are widespread in water. They were first observed by Wolbach and Binger in 1914, and have since been found by numerous workers in different parts of the world. In this country and in America they are known as *Leptospira biflexa* and in Germany as *Spirochæta pseudoicterogenes* (see Chapter **XXXV**). As pointed out by Zuelzer (1928) they are generally found attached to other spirochætes and protozoa. They are especially prevalent in the slime of ponds, lakes, and rivers, in the slime that collects on the ends of water taps and pipes, and in the roof slime of mines. They are very susceptible to acid and are therefore confined to waters with a pH of over 6·8. Thus they are abundant along the east coast of Sumatra where the water is alkaline and practically absent from Java where the water is acid (Sardjito and Zuelzer 1929). They are also susceptible to salt, and are said to perish in 3 days in alkaline water containing 0·17 per cent., and in a few hours in water containing 1·7 per cent., of chlorine as chloride (Schüffner 1934).

These organisms have occasioned much discussion. For some time opinion was influenced by the experiments of Baermann and Zuelzer (1927, 1928). These workers brought evidence to suggest that, though on first isolation water leptospiræ were avirulent, by passage through guinea-pigs, or occasionally through human beings, they could be so raised in virulence as to give rise in the guinea-pig to typical hæmorrhagic jaundice. In fact Baermann and Zuelzer regarded *Lepto-biflexa* merely as an avirulent form of *Lepto. icterohæmorrhagiæ*. Extensive observations by various workers have failed to confirm these findings. Possibly Baermann and Zuelzer were working with a strain of *Lepto. icterohæmorrhagiæ* that had become avirulent by residence under saprophytic conditions, or they may have isolated from one of their guinea-pigs a naturally infective strain entirely different from their passage strain. Except in special conditions, where the locality is heavily rat-infested, it is uncommon to isolate a pathogenic leptospiral strain from water. Since *Lepto. biflexa* is widely distributed over the globe, while cases of Weil's disease are topographically and occupationally circumscribed, it is difficult to avoid the conclusion that *Lepto. biflexa* has no ætiological relationship to the disease. Most of the evidence suggests that water becomes contaminated with *Lepto. icterohæmor-rhagiæ* from rats' urine, and that even in favourable circumstances the organisms die out fairly rapidly. For this reason infection of human beings is unlikely except from water exposed to frequent and heavy contamination.

Summarizing, it may be said that the evidence points strongly in favour of infection occurring through contact, often close and prolonged, with water or sewage recently contaminated with the urine of rats. A few cases of laboratory infection by contamination of the conjunctiva or the abraded skin with infective guinea-pig material have been recorded (Uhlenhuth and Fromme 1916, Uhlenhuth and Zimmermann 1933).

Diagnosis.—According to Schüffner (1934), 60 per cent. of patients with Weil's disease show no jaundice. The true nature of the illness in these cases is suggested by the severe muscular pains at the onset, the heavily coated tongue, the albuminuria, the meningeal symptoms, the increase in the proportion of immature polymorphonuclear leucocytes, and probably most striking of all the flushed conjunctivæ due to dilatation of the episcleral capillaries. Cases without jaundice are not fatal.

The diagnosis has to be made finally by the bacteriologist. Several methods are available. In general the aim is to demonstrate the organisms in the blood during the 1st week of the disease and in the urine during the subsequent weeks, and to confirm the diagnosis by serological examination. Though leptospiræ can almost invariably be found by dark-ground illumination in the freshly drawn blood of infected guinea-pigs, they are rarely found by this method in human cases. Cultivation of the blood is much more successful, and in the hands of certain workers, such as Taylor and Goyle (1931), has yielded a high proportion of positive results ; over 80 per cent. of positive cultures were obtained when the blood was withdrawn on the 4th or 5th day of the disease. Fletcher's medium (see Chapter XXXV) is recommended. Alternatively, 2–3 c.c. of the blood may be inoculated intra-cardially or intraperitoneally into guinea-pigs (see p. 727) ; the success of this method seems to depend on the virulence of the infecting strain. After the 1st week or 10 days of the disease, the organisms usually disappear from the blood and must be sought for in the urine. This should be examined by dark-ground illumination and by guinea-pig inoculation. The microscopical diagnosis is not always easy or reliable, since leptospiræ in the urine are often atypical in shape and may be granular and degenerated (Buchanan 1927).

For ease and rapidity of diagnosis more and more attention is being paid to serological methods of examination. Agglutinins, lysins, and complement-fixing bodies appear about the end of the 1st week of the disease and increase to reach their maximum after 4–7 weeks (Kisker 1935, Wolff 1936).

Agglutination is best carried out on slides incubated at 32° C. for 3 hours and observed under dark-ground illumination, using a low-power objective and a compensating ocular. If living organisms are used, agglutination is seen to occur in the lower dilutions and lysis in the higher. With formolized and phenolized suspensions agglutination alone is seen. Two or three different strains should be used, including one of *Lepto. canicola*.

By the end of the first week of the disease the titre if often about 1/20; during the 2nd week it rises, and usually passes the 1/1000 level; sometimes it may reach even 1/50,000 at a later stage in the disease. The interpretation of the agglutination reaction must depend not only on the titre, but on the clinical findings, the occupation of the patient, and the frequency of latent infections in the locality. In cases of doubt, the first should be repeated to see whether a rise in titre occurs in a few days. Agglutinins persist for a long time, and a retrospective diagnosis may be made even years after the attack (see Schüffner 1930, 1932, 1934, Gaehtgens 1933, Bijl and Korthof 1930, Davidson *et al.* 1934). The *adhesion phenomenon* may be used instead of direct agglutination (Brown 1935). Agglutinins are often present in the urine in titres up to 1/250 (van der Hoeden 1935).

Spirochætocidal antibodies may be tested for by mixing 1–2 c.c. of the patient's serum with several lethal doses of the virus, allowing the mixture to stand at room temperature for 30 minutes, and then injecting it into guinea-pigs. If protective bodies are present the animals will survive, while control animals will die of spirochætosis.

The occurrence of a polymorphonuclear leucocytosis in Weil's disease is said to be of value in the differential diagnosis from catarrhal jaundice, in which a lymphocytosis is usually observed.

The demonstration of infection in *rats* may be accomplished by dark-ground examination and cultivation of the kidney and urine, inoculation of guinea-pigs with ground-up kidney tissue, and a search for antibodies in the blood serum; agglutinins and lysins are often present in a titre of 1/400–1/3000 (see Cameron and Irwin 1929, Zimmermann 1930). For demonstrating the presence of *Lepto. icterohæmorrhagiæ* in *water*, the method described by Appelman and van Thiel (1935) of scarifying the shaved abdominal skin of guinea-pigs, and immersing them in the water for an hour, seems to hold out most prospect of success.

Prophylaxis and Treatment.

The prevention of Weil's disease would seem to consist in the drainage of infected areas and the suppression or exclusion of rats.

Prophylactic vaccination of workers who are specially exposed to risk of infection has been tried on a considerable scale in Japan with very promising results. The figures of Wani (1933), in particular, are impressive. He used a phenolized vaccine and gave two doses. The morbidity rate in the vaccinated subjects was only about a quarter of that in the control population.

Treatment by salvarsan is unsatisfactory; Weil's disease is in fact the only spirochætal infection that does not yield to arsenic. The most promising line of treatment is by immune horse serum; according to Martin and Pettit (1919), 60 c.c. of serum should be injected subcutaneously on the 1st day, and 20–40 c.c. on each of the next 2 or 3 days. In severe cases it should be given intravenously. There is evidence that serum treatment lowers the mortality of the disease (see

Inada 1923). (For much useful information on Weil's disease the reader is referred to the monograph by Taylor and Goyle 1931.)

SPIROCHÆTAL JAUNDICE IN ANIMALS

We have already mentioned that about 20–30 per cent. or so of wild rats are infected with *Lepto. icterohæmorrhagiæ*. The organism apparently gives rise, however, to little systemic disturbance in these animals, and rarely causes jaundice.

A disease, similar to Weil's disease and accompanied by jaundice, is not infrequent in **dogs** (see Okell *et al.* 1925). It appears to be caused, as a rule, by *Lepto. icterohæmorrhagiæ*. More frequently, however, leptospiral infection in dogs is due to *Lepto. canicola*, and takes the form, not of jaundice, but of uræmia (Stuttgart dog plague, canine typhus of Lukes). The disease caused by *Lepto. icterohæmorrhagiæ* affects dogs up to 3 years of age, runs an acute course, is accompanied by jaundice, and has a case mortality of about 50 per cent. The disease caused by *Lepto. canicola* attacks older dogs, tends to run a more chronic course, is characterized by an azotæmic-uræmic syndrome, due to involvement of the kidneys, but not usually by jaundice, and has a case mortality of about 80 per cent. (see Dhont *et al.* 1934, Schüffner *et al.* 1935). Dogs may act as healthy carriers of leptospiræ ; Kouwenaar and Wolff (1930) in Sumatra found 5·7 per cent. of street dogs to be infected. Such dogs constitute a source of danger for man. Bacteriological diagnosis follows the general lines already laid down for the human disease ; demonstration of agglutinins and lysins in the dog's serum is a rapid and convenient method (van der Hoeden 1935).

Leptospiral infections have been encountered in foxes (Dunkin and Laidlaw 1924–25), in mice (Bessemans and Thiry 1929), and in certain other animals.

SWAMP FEVER. SCHLAMMFIEBER

Swamp fever resembles a short-lived attack of Weil's disease, and is due to an organism called *Leptospira grippo-typhosa* (see Chapter XXXV). It has been reported chiefly in Germany, and more recently in Russia (Tarassoff 1935). Field workers in swampy districts are attacked, particularly during the hay harvest. Epidemics of considerable magnitude occur ; during July and August of 1926 there were about 900 cases in one single district of Silesia (Kathe 1928). Young adult males constitute a considerable proportion of the cases, presumably because of their greater exposure to infection from contaminated water. Clinically the onset is sudden with rigors or chills, headache, pains in the back and limbs, often severe cramps in the calves, and sometimes nausea, vomiting, and diarrhœa. In a minority of the cases a macular eruption appears on the body and face on the 3rd or 4th day. Jaundice is uncommon. The disease lasts for 5–7 days, the temperature falling by lysis. There is sometimes a short relapse 1 or 2 days later. The case mortality is about 0·4 per cent. (Korthof 1932). The disease can be reproduced in human subjects by inoculation with pure cultures of the infecting organism. Leptospiræ can be demonstrated in the blood during the first 2 days of the disease. In practice bacteriological diagnosis is best made by examination of the blood serum for agglutinins, which often reach a titre of over 1/1000 by the 2nd week.

The disease in man is not to be confused with the *swamp fever* or *infectious anæmia of horses*, which is apparently due to a filtrable virus (Stein 1935) (see p. 1531).

SEVEN-DAY FEVER OF JAPAN

SYNONYMS : *Nanukayami ; sakushu fever ; autumn fever.*

Seven-day fever is an autumnal disease occurring in many rural districts of Japan. Jaundice is slight or absent, and the disease is never fatal ; otherwise it resembles Weil's disease. We owe our knowledge of its bacteriology to the Japanese workers, Ido, Ito, and Wani (1918, 1919). The causative agent is a leptospira, called *Lepto. hebdomadis* ; this closely resembles *Lepto. icterohœmorrhagiœ*, and can be separated from it only by serological reactions, and less certainly by its pathogenicity (Brown and Davis 1927). The organism is present in the patient's blood during the 1st week of the disease ; it is excreted in the urine from the beginning of the 2nd week up to the end of the 4th or 5th week, being most abundant from the 18th to the 25th days. Injection of the patient's blood intra-cardially or intraperitoneally into young guinea-pigs frequently gives rise to a febrile disease followed by death in about 6 to 15 days ; at post mortem the appearances resemble those of guinea-pigs dying after injection of *Lepto. icterohœ-morrhagiœ*, but the jaundice is usually less and the hæmorrhages are fewer and less extensive. Spirochætes can be demonstrated microscopically in the liver. Not all guinea-pigs are susceptible to the disease. Immune bodies—spirochætocidins and lysins—appear in the blood of patients at the end of the 1st week. The disease is apparently spread by the field-mouse, *Microtus montebelli*. About 3 per cent. of these animals were found to excrete the organism in their urine. Infection of man probably occurs by the skin. Rabbits and mice are slightly susceptible to injection with large doses ; spirochætes appear in their blood, but death does not usually occur.

There is a fever known as Autumn Fever or *Akiyami*, which occurs in certain districts of Japan, and which has been ascribed to a spirochæte—*Lepto. autumnalis*. Two types of this spirochæte have been found, A and B. According to Stéfano-poulo and Hosoya (1928) the A variety is closely allied to *Lepto. icterohœmorrhagiœ*, while the B variety is identical with *Lepto. hebdomadis*.

RAT-BITE FEVER

As has already been pointed out (p. 997), there appear to be two distinct diseases known as rat-bite fever, one due to *Spirillum minus*, the other to an organism generally referred to as *Streptothrix moniliformis*, but better called *Actinomyces muris*. We shall consider here merely the spirochætal type of infection.

Rat-bite fever, or *Sodoku* as it is called in Japan, is a disease that occasionally supervenes in man on the bite of a rat. The incubation period is generally about a fortnight, but it may extend to weeks or months. The disease is ushered in by a sharp febrile paroxysm accompanied by swelling of the lymph glands and dark-red eruptions on the skin. Redness and swelling are noticed at the site of the wound, which during the incubation period has generally healed satisfactorily. There are often pains in the limbs on the affected side. After 3 or 4 days the attack comes to an end, but is succeeded by another in a few days. These febrile paroxysms with intermittent afebrile periods may be repeated for months, or even years. The mortality of the disease varies from about 2 to 10 per cent. The causative organism of the disease is a *Spirillum*, which was described in

1916 by Futaki and his co-workers (Futaki *et al.* 1916) in Japan (see Chapter XXXV). Though this organism appears to be a *Spirillum* and not a spirochæte, it is convenient to consider here the disease to which it gives rise. It is sometimes referred to as *Spirochæta morsus muris*, the name first given to it by Futaki (Futaki *et al.* 1917), but according to Robertson (1924) its correct name is *Spirillum minus*. The organism has been found in cases of rat-bite fever in this country (Robertson 1924), in Italy, Turkey, India, Dutch East Indies, and America (Shattock and Theiler 1924). (For a review of the literature see Robertson 1924, Theiler 1926, McDermott 1927–28.) In the human patient the organism is present in the swollen local lesion, the focal lymph glands, and the blood, but it is very difficult to demonstrate except by animal inoculation ; at autopsy it can be found also in the kidneys (Kaneko and Okuda 1917). Microscopical examination of the blood is usually negative.

The bacteriological diagnosis is best made by subcutaneous or intraperitoneal inoculation of blood taken at the height of a febrile paroxysm, or of serum expressed from the local lesion, into mice, rats, and guinea-pigs (Francis 1932). Aspirated peritoneal fluid or blood should be examined daily from the 5th to the 15th day by dark-ground illumination.

Numerous strains of *Spirillum minus* have been isolated from mice, rats, and human patients ; according to Schockaert (1928) they are all similar, constituting a single species. In Japan about 3 per cent. of house rats appear to carry the organism (Futaki *et al.* 1917). In the serum of patients who have recovered from rat-bite fever spirochæticidal bodies have been found (Ido *et al.* 1917*b*). Salvarsan is the most satisfactory drug for treatment.

REFERENCES

ALSTON, J. M. and BROWN, H. C. (1935) *Brit. med. J.*, ii. 339.
APPELMAN, J. M. and THIEL, P. H. VAN. (1935) *Zbl. Bakt.*, **133**, 224.
BAERMANN, G. and ZUELZER, M. (1927) *Klin. Wschr.*, **6**, 979 ; (1928) *Zbl. Bakt.*, **105**, 345.
BALFOUR, A. (1925) *Parasitology*, **14**, 282.
BASILEWSKY, B. G. (1933) *Zbl. Bakt.*, **129**, 502.
BESSEMANS, A. and THIRY, U. (1929) *C. R. Soc. Biol.*, **101**, 486.
BIJL, J. P. and KOETHOF, G. (1930) *Arch. Hyg.*, **105**, 29.
BROWN, H. C. (1923) *Lancet*, i. 388 ; (1935) *Brit. med. J.*, i. 411.
BROWN, H. C. and DAVIS, L. J. (1927) *Brit. J. exp. Path.*, **8**, 397.
BUCHANAN, G. (1927) *Spec. Rep. Ser. med. Res. Coun., Lond.*, No. 113.
CAMERON, G. C. and IRWIN, D. A. (1929) *Canad. publ. Hlth J.*, **20**, 386.
DAVIDSON, L. S. P., CAMPBELL, R. M., RAE, H. J., and SMITH, J. (1934) *Brit. med. J.*, ii. 1137.
DAVIDSON, L. S. P. and SMITH, J. (1936) *Quart. J. Med.*, N.S. **5**, 263.
DHONT, C. M., KLARENBEEK, A., SCHÜFFNER, W. A. P., and VOET, J. (1934) *Ned. Tijdschr. Geneesk.*, **78**, 519 .
DUNKIN, G. W. and LAIDLAW, P. P. (1924–25) *Ann. Rep. med. Res. Coun., Lond.*, p. 31.
FAIRLEY, N. H. (1934) *Brit. med. J.*, ii. 10.
FRANCIS, E. (1932) *Trans. Ass. Amer. Phys.*, **47**, 143.
FUTAKI, K., TAKAKI, I., TANIGUCHI, T., and OSUMI, S. (1916) *J. exp. Med.*, **23**, 249 ; (1917) *Ibid.*, **25**, 33.
GAEHTGENS, W. (1933) *Z. ImmunForsch.*, **79**, 428.
HOEDEN, J. VAN DE. (1935) *Ned. Tijdschr. Geneesk.*, **79**, 1943.
IDO, Y., HOKI, R., ITO, H., and WANI, H. (1917*a*) *J. exp. Med.*, **26**, 341.
IDO, Y., ITO, H., WANI, H., and OKUDA, K. (1917*b*) *J. exp. Med.*, **26**, 377.
IDO, Y., ITO, H., and WANI, H. (1918) *J. exp. Med.*, **28**, 435 ; (1919) *Ibid.*, **28**, 199.
INADA, R. (1917) *J. exp. Med.*, **26**, 355.
INADA, R. (1923) *Trop. Dis. Bull.*, **20**, 141.
INADA, R., IDO, Y., HOKI, R., KANEKO, H., and ITO, H. (1916) *J. exp. Med.*, **23**, 377.
JORGE, R. (1932) *Bull. Off. int. Hyg. publ.*, **24**, 88.

KANEKO, R. and OKUDA, K. (1917) *J. exp. Med.*, **26**, 363.
KATHE. (1928) *Zbl. Bakt.*, **109**, 284.
KISKER, A. (1935) *Z. ImmunForsch.*, **85**, 383.
KORTHOF, G. (1932) *Zbl. Bakt.*, **125**, 429.
KOUWENAAR, W. and WOLFF, J. W. (1930) *Ned. Tijdschr. Geneesk.*, **74**, 376.
MCDERMOTT, E. N. (1927–28) *Quart. J. Med.*, **21**, 433.
MARTIN, L. and PETTIT, A. (1919) " Spirochétose ictérohemorragique." Paris.
OKELL, C. C., DALLING, T., and PUGH, L. P. (1925) *Vet. J.*, **81**, 3.
Report. (1934) *Bull. Off. int. Hyg. publ.*, **26**, 1747, 1749, 1757, 1763, 1765.
ROBERTSON, A. (1924) *Ann. trop. Med. Parasit.*, **18**, 157.
SARDJITO, M. and ZUELZER, M. (1929) *Zbl. Bakt.*, **110**, 180.
SCHOCKAERT, J. (1928) *C. R. Soc. Biol.*, **98**, 595.
SCHÜFFNER, W. (1930) *Arch. Hyg.*, **103**, 249 ; (1932) *Arch. Schiffs. -u. Tropenhyg.*, **36**, 239;
    (1934) *Trans. trop. Med. Hyg.*, **28**, 7.
SCHÜFFNER, W., KOTTER, G. F., and SCHULTSZ, D. (1935) *Geneesk. Tijdschr. Ned.-Ind.*,
    75, 534.
SHATTOCK, G. C. and THEILER, M. (1924) *Amer. J. trop. Med.*, **4**, 453.
SSINJUSCHINA, M. N. (1929) *Zbl. Bakt.*, **114**, 199.
STÉFANOPOULO, G. J. and HOSOYA, S. (1928) *C. R. Soc. Biol.*, **98**, 1317.
STEIN, C. D. (1935) *J. Amer. vet. med. Ass.*, **87**, 312.
STEVENSON, A. C. (1922) *Amer. J. trop. Med.*, **2**, 77.
STOKES, A., RYLE, J. A., and TYTLER, W. H. (1917) *Lancet*, i. 142.
TARASSOFF, S. (1935) *Bull. Off. int. Hyg. publ.*, **27**, 683.
TAYLOR, J. and GOYLE, A. N. (1931) *Indian med. Res. Mem.*, No. 20.
THEILER, M. (1926) *Amer. J. trop. Med.*, **6**, 131.
UHLENHUTH and FROMME. (1916) *Berl. klin. Wschr.*, **53**, 296 ; (1918) *Dtsch. med. Wschr.*,
    44, 705.
UHLENHUTH, P. and ZIMMERMANN, E. (1933) *Dtsch. med. Wschr.*, **59**, 1393.
UHLENHUTH and ZUELZER. (1921) *Zbl. Bakt.*, **85**, Beiheft, p. 141.
WANI, H. (1933) *Z. ImmunForsch.*, **79**, 1.
WOLBACH, S. B. and BINGER, C. A. L. (1914) *J. med. Res.*, **30**, 23.
WOLFF, J. W. (1936) *Ned. Tijdschr. Geneesk.*, *Feestbundel*, p. 499.
ZIMMERMANN, E. (1930) *Zbl. Bakt.*, **119**, 74.
ZUELZER, M. (1928) *Zbl. Bakt.*, **105**, 384.

CHAPTER LXXX

THE TYPHUS GROUP OF FEVERS

THERE must be few diseases about which our knowledge has increased so rapidly during the past decade as the typhus fever group. Though epidemic typhus had been known for centuries, and had played no small part in determining the course of history, it was not till 1909 that Nicolle and his colleagues (1911) first discovered that infection was spread by the body-louse, and not till 1916 that da Rocha-Lima demonstrated the ætiological agent of the disease, *Rickettsia prowazeki*. In 1907 Ricketts in the United States had succeeded in transmitting Rocky Mountain spotted fever to guinea-pigs, but the generic relationship of this disease to typhus fever remained obscure till Wolbach (1925) in 1916 demonstrated the rickettsial nature of the causative agent. During the War a new fever, referred to as Trench fever, was recognized ; this was likewise found to be due to a species of *Rickettsia*. A sporadic form of typhus fever known as Brill's disease had been recognized for a long time in New York, a severer form known as *Tabardillo* in Mexico, and a milder form in Manchuria and the Far East. Broadly speaking, however, up till 1925, typhus fever was regarded as one of the major epidemic diseases, which in certain areas might sometimes occur in a relatively mild sporadic form. Rocky Mountain spotted fever and Trench fever were regarded as rickettsial diseases due to entirely different species of *Rickettsia* from that causing typhus fever.

In 1925 Fletcher and Lesslar (1925, 1926) found that the endemic typhus fever of the Federated Malay States could be divided serologically and epidemiologically into two entirely different groups, one met with in the towns, the other occurring in country districts. Both differed in certain important respects from the classical type and from each other. These observations provided the main impetus for an extensive and detailed search in various parts of the world for other types of typhus fever. The result has been to reveal the existence in several different countries of endemic typhus fever or typhus-like fevers many of which had previously been unrecognized. Our present knowledge, though very considerable, is still in its infancy. A large bibliography has already accumulated, and papers are now appearing in such rapid succession that the summary to which we must necessarily restrict ourselves will inevitably require modification by the time this edition is published.

The relationship to each other of the various types of endemic typhus fever is still in doubt, so that our classification of these diseases must be largely tentative. For the sake of simplicity, we shall deal first of all with the classical epidemic louse-borne typhus fever, and then pass on to a brief review of the various endemic types.

EPIDEMIC TYPHUS FEVER

Typhus fever, though now uncommon in epidemic form in civilized countries, has been in the past one of the great scourges of the world. Like dysentery it appeared wherever large numbers of people were herded together under insanitary conditions ; for this reason it was common in gaols—hence the alternative name " gaol fever "—in military campaigns, and during times of famine. During the War it was specially prevalent in Russia and in Central Europe. The case mortality is usually about 12–20 per cent., but in some epidemics it may be much higher. Those who wish to realize something of the havoc the disease has wrought among the human population, and of the significant part it has played in determining the outcome of great military campaigns, will do well to refer to the fascinating account given by Zinsser (1935).

In 1909 Nicolle and his colleagues (1911), by experiments on man and on monkeys, showed that the disease was spread by the body-louse, *Pediculus corporis*. The louse becomes infected by ingesting the blood of the patient. Within a period varying from about 1 to 2 weeks after feeding, the louse becomes infective, and can transmit the disease to normal persons. The time during which lice may remain infective is not known with certainty, but da Rocha-Lima (1920a) has demonstrated their infectivity for at least 24 days, and he believes that they remain infective for the rest of their lives.

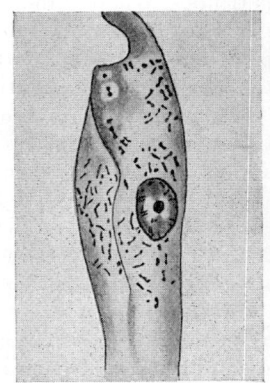

FIG. 272.—*Rickettsia prowazeki*, contained in an epithelial cell from the louse's mid-gut ; both coccal and bacillary forms can be seen. Magnification 1,200 diameters (approx.). (After Wolbach, Todd and Palfrey.)

Besides typical cases of typhus fever, there is reason to believe that atypical, and completely symptomless, cases of the disease may occur. These are probably commoner during inter-epidemic than during epidemic times, and are doubtless partly responsible for the maintenance of infection between one epidemic and the next (see Afanassiewa and Tretjak 1933, Kuteischikow *et al.* 1933, Isabolinski *et al.* 1934, Zinsser 1934).

Bacteriology.

The causative agent of the disease is *Rickettsia prowazeki*, first described by da Rocha-Lima in 1916, and later in the same year by Töpfer (1916b). Da Rocha-Lima observed this organism in the lice taken from 95 per cent. of typhus patients ; it was present in enormous numbers in the intestinal lumen and in the epithelial cells lining the gut wall (Fig. 272). The organisms stain a reddish-purple with Giemsa, are very small, of short elliptic or olive-shape, often in pairs, and are surrounded by a paler staining substance ; occasional very short and very long forms, up to $1\cdot5$–$2\ \mu$, may be seen. They were never found in lice fed on normal persons, or on typhus convalescents, but appeared regularly, and in enormous numbers, in lice fed on typhus patients. The time elapsing between feeding and the appearance of rickettsiæ in the gut depended on the temperature at which the lice were kept ; at 23° C. no rickettsiæ appeared at all, but at 32° C. they appeared in about 5 to 8 days, and persisted indefinitely. At about the same time as the rickettsiæ developed, the lice became infective for guinea-pigs. It is important to note that not every louse fed on a typhus patient develops rickettsiæ, or becomes infective. Wolbach, Todd and Palfrey (1922), for example, working in Poland in 1920, fed batches of 30 to 40 lice on typhus patients for an average period of 12 to 16 days, and found that, out of 52 experiments, in only 27 did the lice develop rickettsiæ. In a later series of experiments they also found that only a similar proportion of lice became infective for guinea-pigs. The actual proportion observed was very low, and is probably accounted for by imperfect technique in dealing with the lice ; during the latter part of their work the proportion of positive results was considerably higher. Arkwright, Bacot and Duncan (1919) similarly concluded that rickettsiæ do not appear regularly in the excreta of lice fed on typhus patients. Whether this is due to variation in the lice, or, as seems more probable, to the relatively low infectivity of typhus blood, is not known. The significant point is the general parallelism that exists between the presence of rickettsiæ in the louse, and the infectivity of the louse for guinea-pigs.

R. prowazeki has been cultivated by Wolbach and Schlesinger (1923–24) in tissue cultures. Small pieces of the brain of typhus guinea-pigs were seeded into normal guinea-pig plasma, and incubated in the usual way over hollow-ground slides. Rickettsiæ were found in the endothelial cells of the vessel walls ; primary cultures remained virulent for 8 to 15 days, second generation cultures up to 28 days. The rickettsiæ showed signs of multiplication within the cells ; they appeared as coccoid, bacillary, and filamentous forms similar to those found in lice.

Arkwright and Bacot (1923), using Weigl's technique, were able to infect lice by intra-rectal inoculation of a suspension of blood platelets from typhus patients and from infected guinea-pigs. To obtain regular results a thick suspension was required—platelets from 2 c.c. of blood suspended in 6 drops of saline. Similarly successful results were obtained by intra-rectal inoculation of lice with the excreta of infected lice.

The demonstration of *R. prowazeki* in human patients is not easy, but the organisms may be found in the vascular lesions, particularly those in the skin and brain (Wolbach 1925, Cowdry 1926).

As has already been described in Chapter XXXVI, a disease closely resembling typhus fever can be reproduced in monkeys, and a less typical but febrile disease in guinea-pigs. Microscopically, both in man and in guinea-pigs, the main lesions are found in the blood capillaries, especially those in the skin, skeletal muscles and central nervous system. They consist of thromboses with perivascular accumulations of cells, often accompanied by small hæmorrhages. In the central nervous system characteristic nodules are found, simulating tubercles. The primary lesion is in the endothelial cells lining the walls of the capillaries. Rickettsiæ have been demonstrated in the lesions of the skin, kidneys, testicles, brain, and other organs in man (Wolbach *et al.* 1922). The height and duration of the fever in guinea-pigs is variable. According to Arkwright and Bacot (1923) the most certain way of establishing that an attack of fever in the guinea-pig is really due to the typhus virus is to inject lice intra-rectally with a suspension of the guinea-pig's platelets, and observe the development of rickettsiæ in the excreta.

Relation of Rickettsia prowazeki to Typhus.—It may be well to set out the evidence on which the ætiological relationship of *Rickettsia prowazeki* to typhus is based.

(1) The occurrence of *R. prowazeki* in the characteristic perivascular nodules of typhus ; (2) its occurrence as the sole distinctive acquisition of lice fed on typhus ; (3) the failure to separate *R. prowazeki* from the virus of typhus by any method yet employed ; (4) the cultivation of *R. prowazeki* in lice by the intra-rectal inoculation of a platelet suspension from typhus patients or infected guinea-pigs, even after the virus has been passed several times through guinea-pigs (Atkin and Bacot 1922) ; and (5) the cultivation of *R. prowazeki* in tissue plasma cultures, using as a source of the virus a strain that had been maintained for 3 years by passage through guinea-pigs : all suggest that *R. prowazeki* is the ætiological agent of typhus (Wolbach 1925). To these we may add that both the typhus virus and *R. prowazeki* are destroyed by exposure to moist heat at 50°–55° C., and that neither is capable of passing through any but the coarsest bacterial filters, and then only irregularly. Against this view it may be said that rickettsiæ are sometimes found in lice taken from persons not suffering from typhus. For example, da Rocha-Lima (1920*a*) found rickettsiæ closely simulating *R. prowazeki* in lice that had been fed on trench-fever patients and on normal persons ; Arkwright and Bacot (1923) in Egypt had much the same experience ; in some of the lice taken from 2 out of 12 apparently healthy persons they found rickettsiæ simulating *R. prowazeki*. The lice in which they were found were not infective for guinea-pigs, and it is probable that the rickettsiæ were different from those associated with typhus. Da Rocha-Lima considers that the rickettsiæ found on persons not suffering from typhus belong to a different species—generally known as *R. rocha-limæ*. He distinguishes three types of *Rickettsia* in the louse : (1) very fine forms, predominantly intracellular, not very closely packed—*R. prowazeki* : (2) thicker, exclusively extracellular, but lying on the cells—*R. quintana* : and (3) thicker forms, grouped in compact masses, occurring both intra- and extra-cellularly—*R. rocha-limæ* ; these may perhaps be pathogenic organisms peculiar to the louse.

It will be seen that the cumulative evidence points very strongly to the ætiological rôle of *R. prowazeki* in typhus. Though rigid adherence to Koch's postulates demands that this conclusion must remain unproven till pure cultures, free from living cells, can be obtained, and used to reproduce the experimental disease in susceptible animals, we shall not depart from justifiable inference if we accept provisionally its essential truth. The onus now rests rather on those who would disprove it than on those who accept it.

Diagnosis of Epidemic Typhus Fever.

Though theoretically the demonstration of *R. prowazeki* in lice fed on typhus patients might be used for diagnosis of the disease, in practice it is far too lengthy a proceeding. The only diagnostic test of importance is the Weil-Felix reaction. In 1916 Weil and Felix, working in Eastern Galicia, cultivated from the urine of a patient with typhus a proteus-like organism that had the peculiarity of being agglutinated not only by the patient's serum but also by the sera of other patients suffering from typhus. Similar organisms were isolated from the urine or the blood of a number of other typhus patients ; these were called *Proteus X* strains ; the most highly agglutinable of them, and the most specific for typhus, was the *Proteus X* 19 strain (Felix 1916). This strain was agglutinated to a titre varying from 1/50 to 1/50,000 by typhus sera, and never above 1/25 by serum from non-typhus patients. Agglutinins appeared in the blood about the 4th day, and increased up to an acme about the end of the second or beginning of the 3rd week ; during convalescence they fell off rapidly, and after 5 months they had disappeared almost entirely. A positive reaction at 1/25 during the 1st week of the disease was regarded as a presumptive positive, though about 7–9 per cent. of persons not suffering from typhus were found to react at this titre. As a rule the titre rose rapidly, so that a positive diagnosis, 1/50 or higher, could generally be made by the 8th day.

The Weil-Felix reaction has now been employed on a large scale, and has been found remarkably valuable. As with many other serum reactions used in diagnosis, experience of it has brought to light certain anomalies and limitations that were not at first realized. Many workers have doubted its specificity, and have brought evidence to show that the reaction may be positive during the course of other infections, and even in healthy persons. Savoor, Castaneda, and Zinsser (1935), for example, in the United States, found that 25 out of 596 sera from various sources reacted positively in a titre of 1/80, and 4 in a titre of 1/160 (see also Peverelli 1930, Kraus *et al.* 1931, Isabolinski *et al.* 1934, Welch *et al.* 1934). In some of these instances it is probable that the patient had recently recovered from typhus fever, or was suffering from it in a mild or latent form. The titres already quoted as being regarded as diagnostic by Felix can probably be accepted during epidemic times, but during an inter-epidemic phase, and in countries in which the disease is known to exist in an endemic form, a titre of 1/50 should not be accepted as definite evidence of active infection without further investigation. A titre of 1/100 or 1/200 is, however, very strong presumptive evidence of typhus fever in a patient who has not recently recovered from this disease.

One very important fact must be borne in mind, namely, that it is only the agglutination of the O antigen that is diagnostic of typhus infection. Normal agglutinins to the H antigen of *Proteus* strains are not uncommon, and have no significance in the diagnosis of typhus fever. In practice, it is therefore desirable to work with suspensions prepared from a non-motile *Proteus X* 19 strain, so as to avoid the confusion caused by flagellar agglutinins. Formolized suspensions of such a strain appear to give satisfactory results. Agglutination of a non-motile strain, or agglutination of the small-flake type of a motile strain, is best referred to as agglutination of *Proteus OX* 19.

ENDEMIC TYPHUS AND TYPHUS-LIKE FEVERS

We may now consider the great range of typhus and typhus-like fevers that occur endemically in different parts of the world. Our brief survey may commence with the tropical typhus of Malay, which, though chronologically not the first to be recognized, nevertheless occupies a position of peculiar historical interest in the development of our knowledge of these diseases.

Tropical Typhus of Malay and the East Indies.

Fletcher and Lesslar (1925, 1926), studying the endemic typhus of the Federated Malay States, observed that the Weil-Felix reaction to *Proteus OX* 19 was positive in some cases but not in others. Wondering whether their strain of *Proteus X* 19 was losing its agglutinability, they sent home for a fresh strain, and received one from Dr. Kingsbury of the Middlesex Hospital. This strain, which may be referred to as *Proteus X* K, was found to be agglutinated by the sera of patients which failed to react with the *X* 19 type. It was further observed that sera which reacted to *OX* 19 did not agglutinate *OX* K. There was clearly some distinct serological difference between the two groups of typhus cases. The Kingsbury strain, it may be noted, was reputed to be a strain of *X* 19, but undoubtedly differed from this type antigenically. Further work (see also Fletcher 1930, 1932) showed that the typhus patients whose blood agglutinated *OX* 19 were to be found mainly in urban areas, particularly in shops and storehouses, while those whose blood agglutinated *OX* K came from country districts, especially places where rank grass and scrub had grown up on land which had been cleared of jungle. Fletcher referred to the former type of typhus as urban or *shop typhus,* and to the latter as rural or *scrub typhus.* Both diseases are endemic, non-contagious, and have a very low case mortality rate—usually less than 5 per cent. They are difficult or impossible to distinguish from each other on clinical grounds alone.

Shop typhus is apparently spread, not by lice, but by rat fleas—probably *Xenopsylla cheopis*—which it will be remembered plays so important a part in the transmission of plague. Rats appear to constitute the natural reservoir of the disease, and from them sporadic infections occur of the human population. The virus of shop typhus is mildly infective for monkeys. Injected intraperitoneally into male guinea-pigs, it gives rise to fever and a scrotal reaction, characterized by redness, tenderness, and swelling, similar to that described by Neill (1917) in guinea-pigs infected with Mexican typhus. Microscopical examination of the exudate in the tunica vaginalis reveals the presence of large numbers of rickettsial bodies in the endothelial cells (Lewthwaite and Savoor 1936b). The virus causes very little reaction when injected into the anterior chamber of the rabbit's eye. In rats it gives rise to a symptomless infection. The sera of infected monkeys agglutinate *Proteus OX* 19 but not *OX* K.

Scrub typhus is probably spread, not by lice or rat fleas, but by mites. This is not yet completely proven, but in infected areas—and scrub typhus is very largely a place disease—mites have been found infesting the dead flowers of palm trees as well as the ears of rats. The suggestion is that rats constitute the primary reservoir of infection, that they pass on the virus to mites, and that workers on plantations contract infection from the bites of these insects. In Sumatra the disease is generally referred to as *Mite Fever.* The virus of scrub typhus is practically non-infective for guinea-pigs and does not give rise to a scrotal reaction after intraperitoneal inoculation. In rats it produces a symptomless disease. Injected into the anterior chamber of the rabbit's eye, it gives rise after an incubation period of about 4–7 days to an acute irido-cyclitis ; microscopically rickettsial bodies can be demonstrated in large numbers in the endothelial cells of Descemet's membrane (Lewthwaite and Savoor 1936a). Intradermal inoculation into the monkey is followed in 5–10 days by a febrile disease, and by a local reaction at the site of injection, characterized by a papule which becomes necrotic and ulcerates ; a bubo of the regional lymphatic glands also develops. Sera of convalescent monkeys and rabbits agglutinate *OX* K but not *OX* 19. (For further description of tropical typhus see Anigstein 1933, Report 1933, 1934, 1935, Lewthwaite 1936.)

Mexican Typhus : Endemic Typhus of the United States.

In Mexico, and less frequently in the United States, two different types of typhus are seen. The one is epidemic, has its maximum prevalence in the winter, is associated with overcrowding, is most prevalent in the lower strata of society, has a fairly high case mortality, is contagious, is carried by lice, and resembles in every respect the classical epidemic louse-borne typhus of Europe. The other is endemic, occurs in the summer and autumn, is commonest in seaports, is not associated with overcrowding, has no predilection for the lower classes, has a case mortality of only 1 per cent., is non-contagious, and is carried by the rat flea *Xenopsylla cheopis*. The epidemic type is now uncommon in the United States, though it still occurs in Mexico. The credit for elucidating the rôle of the rat and the rat flea in the spread of the endemic type belongs to a group of Mexican and American workers, prominent amongst whom are Maxcy, Mooser, and Dyer (see Maxcy 1926, 1928, 1929, Mooser 1928, Mooser *et al.* 1931, Dyer *et al.* 1931*a*, *b*, *c*, *d*, 1932*a*, *b*, *c*, Ceder *et al.* 1931, Rumreich 1933).

The viruses of both the epidemic and the endemic types are infective for guinea-pigs. The *epidemic louse-borne* virus inoculated intraperitoneally into the male guinea-pig gives rise after about 9 days or more to a marked febrile attack, but to little or no scrotal reaction. Inoculation of the *endemic rat flea (murine)* virus gives rise to a less marked febrile attack, coming on as a rule in 4–6 days, and to a very marked scrotal reaction. Microscopical examination of the tunica vaginalis exudate shows the presence of numerous rickettsiæ, sometimes known as Mooser bodies, in the endothelial cells. The two diseases are further distinguished by the greater frequency of cerebral nodes in the epidemic type (see Lillie 1931, Pinkerton 1931). The viruses, however, are very much alike. Both give rise to agglutinins acting on *OX* 19, and cross-immunity experiments suggest their almost complete antigenic identity (see Zinsser and Castaneda 1930*a*, *b*, 1932, 1934, Zinsser and Batchelder 1930, Mooser and Dummer 1930, Weigl and Hertzig 1933, Mooser *et al.* 1934).

Endemic Rat Flea-borne Typhus of the Old World.

Following on the demonstration by American workers of the rôle played by the rat and the rat flea in the spread of endemic typhus, this disease has now been recognized in the other four continents. It is called by various local names, such as Toulon typhus, endemic typhus of Moscow, Manchurian typhus, and so on. Examination of wild rats in various areas has shown that these animals often give a positive Weil-Felix reaction to *OX* 19, and that they are latently infected with a murine typhus virus (Penfold and Corkill 1928, Marcandier *et al.* 1931, Kodama and Takahashi 1931, Kodama *et al.* 1932*a*, *b*, Brumpt 1932*c*, Netter 1932, Lépine 1932, Lawton and Murray 1933, Chao-Jen Wu 1933, Kritschewski and Solowiow 1934, Suzuki 1934, Nicolle and Sparrow 1934, Epstein and Silvers 1934 ; see also Tonking 1932–33).

Brill's Disease.

This is a very mild form of endemic typhus, which has been known for a long time. It occurs in the north-eastern coastal cities of the United States, and is almost entirely restricted to immigrant Russian and Polish Jews. The evidence, which has been carefully marshalled by Zinsser (1934), suggests that it is caused by the classical louse-borne virus, and that the patients have been infected before leaving Europe. The disease represents, in fact, the recrudescence of a latent infection acquired at some earlier time.

Tsutsugamushi Fever.

This disease, sometimes known as *Japanese River fever* or *Kedani*, occurs in Japan and the East Indies. It is commonest in the summer and autumn months ; it is confined to certain localities, particularly low-lying territory subject to flooding ; and it follows the bite of *Trombicula akamushi* Brumpt—a mite found on field mice and rats. These animals apparently constitute the reservoir of infection. The ætiological agent is *Rickettsia nipponica.* (Though this name was suggested for it by Sellards in 1923, and must be regarded as valid, recent workers have for some reason, which is not apparent, renamed this organism *R. tsutsugamushi, R. orientalis,* or *R. akamushi.*) The disease is characterized by fever, a local swelling at the site of the puncture wound, enlargement of the lymph glands and spleen, and a rash. The incubation period is about a week, and the case mortality is said to be 40 per cent. (Ogata 1931). Except for the local lesion and the bubo following the bite, and the high case mortality, the disease is very similar to the scrub typhus of Malay and the mite typhus of Sumatra, to both of which reference has already been made. The viruses of these diseases also closely resemble each other in being comparatively non-infective for guinea-pigs—though on this point there is some discrepancy of opinion—in causing a marked reaction in the rabbit's eye after intraocular injection, and in giving rise to a local necrotic lesion accompanied by fever on intradermal inoculation into the monkey. The sera of convalescent monkeys and rabbits agglutinate *Proteus* OX K but not OX 19. Cross-immunity experiments in the rabbit also indicate the very close relationship of these viruses to each other (see Nagayo *et al.* 1930, Kawamura and Imagawa 1931, Wolff 1931*b*, Report 1933, Kouwenaar and Wolff 1933, 1934, 1935, 1936, Wolff and Kouwenaar 1933, Lewthwaite and Savoor 1934, 1936*a, c*). The blood of patients suffering from tsutsugamushi fever agglutinates *Proteus* OX K, though not so constantly or to so high a titre as the blood of patients suffering from scrub typhus or mite fever (Wolff 1931*a*, Kawamura *et al.* 1935). For a general review of the disease and its bacteriology the reader is referred to Ogata (1931, 1935) and Nagayo and his colleagues (1931). It is difficult to assess the importance of the distinctions that have been pointed out between tsutsugamushi fever and scrub typhus. The evidence, on the whole, suggests that the two diseases are due to essentially the same virus (see Lewthwaite and Savoor 1936*c*).

Fièvre boutonneuse.

This disease, which was first described by Conor and Bruch (1910), occurs in Tunis and in certain other parts of the Mediteranean littoral. It appears to be identical with the *exanthematic fever of Marseille.* The name " boutonneuse " refers to the local nodule that is so frequently seen on the leg in the early stage of the disease. Infection is carried, not by the louse, the rat flea, or the mite, but by the dog tick, *Rhipicephalus sanguineus.* Dogs serve as the reservoir of the virus. As many as 30 per cent. of these animals may carry a latent infection. Dog ticks may remain infective for several months, and can transmit the virus hereditarily to their progeny. Patients suffering from the disease and infected dogs give a very weak Weil-Felix reaction ; both OX 19 and OX 2 (a strain differing in its antigenic structure from both OX 19 and OX K) are commonly agglutinated, though only in low titre. Rickettsiæ have been found in infected ticks, and the name *Rickettsia conori* has been suggested for the causative organism (Brumpt 1932*b*). Intraperitoneal inoculation of guinea-pigs often gives rise to a mild scrotal reaction (see Blanc and Caminopetros 1931, Durand 1931, 1932, 1933, Durand and Conseil 1931, Durand and Laigret 1932, Nicolle and Laigret 1932, Brumpt 1932*b*, Caminopetros and Contos 1932, 1933, Combiesco and Zotta 1932, Petzetakis and Karalis 1933, Combiesco 1934). A similar disease appears to occur in South Africa (Pijper and Dau 1935).

Other *tick-borne typhus fevers,* whose relationship to the types we have already described is not very clear, also occur in India and in Kenya (Megaw 1921, 1924, 1930, Roberts and Tonking 1933).

Rocky Mountain Spotted Fever.

This disease, which has been known for many years, occurs in North America. Two types are recognized : a Western type with a case mortality of 70 per cent. or so ; and an Eastern type occurring nearer the Atlantic border with a case mortality of only 20–25 per cent. (Badger 1933a). Both types appear to be mainly carried by ticks, the Western type by *Dermacentor andersoni* Stiles, the Eastern type by *Dermacentor variabilis* (Dyer *et al.* 1931e). The disease is due to *Rickettsia rickettsi.*

Ricketts (1907) was successful in transmitting infection to guinea-pigs and monkeys. Besides showing a febrile reaction, inoculated guinea-pigs often develop swellings and hæmorrhages of the scrotum and ears, which may go on to necrosis ; the spleen is considerably enlarged (see Munter 1928). The Western type often proves highly fatal to guinea-pigs. Rabbits also develop a febrile disease and sometimes a scrotal reaction. Introduction of the virus into the anterior chamber is less often followed by an acute reaction than occurs after inoculation with the scrub typhus or tsutsugamushi virus (Lewthwaite and Savoor 1936c). Rats and mice can be infected, but the disease pursues a symptomless course (Fukuda 1929).

In human and animal lesions the organisms are found with comparative ease. The lesions themselves resemble those of typhus, consisting of proliferative foci of vascular endothelial cells occurring in the smaller blood vessels, and accompanied later by necrosis and thrombosis. The blood vessels of the skin and reproductive organs are the most heavily infected. In the tick the organism presents three forms : (1) an intracellular bacillus-like form, without chromatoid granules, present only in the cytoplasm of the cells of the alimentary tract ; (2) a relatively small, rod-shaped form with chromatoid granules, present within the cells and the nuclei of many tissues ; (3) a relatively large lanceolate diploid form, which persists in the tissues, notably the salivary glands, long after the other forms have disappeared ; this lanceolate form is characterized by its chromatoid staining reaction ; it is the only form found in the eggs of infected ticks (see Wolbach 1925). It may be noted that ticks, once infected, are able to hand down infection to their progeny.

The Weil-Felix reaction in Rocky Mountain spotted fever is often weakly positive. Davis, Parker, and Walker (1934) found that 77 per cent. of sera taken between the 10th and 32nd days of illness agglutinated *Proteus OX* 19 to 1/160 or over ; when two samples were taken at suitable intervals, 95 per cent. of sera proved positive. *Proteus OX* 2 and *OX* K are also sometimes agglutinated, though only to low titre.

The relationship of *Rickettsia rickettsi* to other viruses of the typhus group is still undetermined. It is clearly different from the louse-borne and murine types, as well as from the scrub typhus and tsutsugamushi types. Cross-infection experiments with the fièvre boutonneuse virus have yielded conflicting results (Brumpt 1932a, Badger 1933b).

São Paulo Typhus.

This disease has recently attracted considerable attention. In its general symptomatology and high case mortality—70 per cent. or so—it resembles the Western type of Rocky Mountain spotted fever. The São Paulo virus, moreover, resembles the spotted fever virus in its peculiarly high pathogenicity for guinea-pigs and in the necrotic scrotal reaction to which it often gives rise in these animals and in rabbits. Inoculation into the anterior chamber of the rabbit's eye is not usually successful in causing an acute reaction ; the guinea-pig's eye, however, is very much more susceptible, and an inflammatory reaction associated with corneal opacity develops 2–5 days after inoculation (Monteiro 1931, Dyer 1933). Cross-immunity tests leave little doubt that the São Paulo virus is identical with the virus of Rocky Mountain spotted fever (Dyer 1933, Parker and Davis 1933). Infection appears to follow the bite of the tick *Amblyomma cajennense* (Monteiro *et al.* 1932). The Weil-Felix reaction may be positive, and both *OX* 2 and *OX* K may be agglutin-ated in low titre as well as *OX* 19. (For general account of disease see Piza *et al.* 1932, Fialho 1932.)

Trench Fever.—Synonyms : *Febris wolhynica : Febris quintana.*

Trench fever is a disease to which attention was first attracted in 1915, when it broke out in epidemic form amongst the troops in nearly every fighting area in Europe. Later it spread to Mesopotamia. The first account of it was given in this country by McNee, Renshaw and Brunt (1916), who called it Trench fever, and in Germany by Werner (1916) and His (1916), who called it Five-day fever and Wolhynian fever respectively. It was proved to be infective, because healthy men developed the disease when inoculated with the blood of patients suffering from it (McNee *et al.* 1916). The blood was found to be infective on the 1st day of the disease, and to remain so until at least the 51st day. Evidence was obtained that the virus was free in the blood plasma and was extra-corpuscular, but that, when the blood was allowed to clot, the virus was entangled in the fibrin and could not usually be demonstrated in the serum. Blood from trench fever patients generally gave rise to the disease in normal persons when inoculated intravenously or intramuscularly, but not when rubbed on to the scarified skin. Clinical and epidemiological evidence suggested that the disease was spread by body-lice, and experimentally it was found that if lice were allowed to feed on trench fever patients and subsequently transferred to normal persons, the latter developed the disease.

Lice fed on trench fever patients do not become infective for about 5 to 9 days, but once they have become infective, they remain so for at least 4 months. The virus is found to be present in the louse's excreta, and inoculation of these excreta is one of the best methods of transmitting the disease to man—much more certain than injection of blood. By this method the War Office Trench Fever Investigation Committee (see Bruce 1921) showed that patients suffering from trench fever might retain the power of infecting lice fed on them up to at least 443 days after the onset of the disease. The infectivity of the louse's excreta is very high ; 1/10 mgm. has sufficed to give rise to the disease when inoculated into man. The virulence of the excreta is destroyed by dry heat at 100° C. in 20 minutes, and by moist heat at 60° C. in 20 minutes.

It is very doubtful whether laboratory animals are susceptible to the disease ; a small proportion of guinea-pigs may develop a low undulating type of fever after inoculation with infective material, lasting fo several weeks, but infection cannot be transmitted by passage to fresh animals (da Rocha-Lima 1920*b*). On the other hand, human beings are almost all susceptible to the disease. One attack seems to produce only a partial and limited immunity ; a certain proportion of patients who have recovered from one attack may be reinfected by inoculation of blood or of louse excreta 4 or 5 months later (Bruce 1921).

In 1916 Töpfer (1916*a*) described the finding of small short rods, often arranged in pairs and often showing bipolar staining, in lice taken from trench fever patients. The rods were shorter and thicker than those seen in typhus, were present in enormous numbers, and were often arranged in heaps. Töpfer fed lice on 7 trench fever patients, and found these bodies in lice taken from 6 of them ; they did not appear till the 5th day after feeding, but from the 8th day onwards they were found in large numbers. They were never observed in lice fed on healthy persons. These bodies are now known by the name of *Rickettsia quintana*.

Töpfer's findings have been confirmed and amplified by a number of workers. Arkwright, Bacot and Duncan (1919–20) found that rickettsiæ appeared in lice 5 to 12 days after feeding on trench fever patients, and could be demonstrated in the excreta up to the death of the louse. Not all lice became infected at the same time ; after feeding on a patient, only a few lice were found to be infected by the end of the 1st week ; during the 2nd week the numbers infected and uninfected were about equal, while after the 2nd week the majority showed rickettsiæ. The organisms were found in large numbers crowding the region of the epithelial cells lining the gut ; they were always extracellular in position. In any given batch of lice rickettsiæ developed at about the same time as the louse's excreta became infective—as judged by human inoculation. Moreover a very close correspondence was found between the presence of rickettsiæ and the infectivity of the louse, and the absence of rickettsiæ and its non-infectivity. Rickettsiæ were almost invariably found in batches of lice fed on trench fever patients, but only very rarely when fed on normal persons—one positive result out of 245 specimens.

Rickettsia quintana has never been demonstrated satisfactorily in man, and until this has been done, and until the organism has been grown in pure cell-free cultures, it will be impossible to be certain that it is the cause of trench fever. But the observations just quoted on lice strongly suggest that this organism is responsible for the disease.

The remarkable observations made on himself by Bacot (1921) lend support to this view. Bacot went to Poland in February, 1920, with the Typhus Research Commission, taking his own stock of lice with him—a stock that had been under his personal observation and fed upon himself exclusively since November, 1915. During the whole of this time rickettsiæ had never been demonstrated in these lice. In April, after visiting a bathhouse in Warsaw, he contracted trench fever. Eight days later, he recommenced feeding his lice ; rickettsiæ indistinguishable from *R. quintana* began to appear, and from the 12th day onwards all the boxes of lice proved to be heavily infected. Bacot's blood remained infective for at least 3 months after the clinical termination of his attack. Of the lice collected at the bath-house 7 per cent. proved to be infected with rickettsiæ, which were situated extracellularly, and which were indistinguishable from *R. quintana*. Bacot considers that these lice had probably become infected from apparently healthy persons who had some time previously suffered from trench fever. The importance of this observation lies in the interpretation to be put on the discovery of extracellular rickettsiæ in lice which have had no apparent contact with trench fever patients. Are they to be regarded as a distinct species, peculiar to the louse—as da Rocha-Lima (1920*a*) thinks— and called *R. pediculi* or *R. rocha-limæ* ; or are they, in many cases, to be regarded as *R. quintana*, which has gained access to the louse from probably healthy carriers of trench fever ? Bacot clearly favours the latter view.

A few cases of trench fever have been recognized since the War, and there is some reason to believe that the disease is endemic in Poland and Russia (Laurell 1933, Braslawsky 1934). Little is yet known of the behaviour of the Weil-Felix reaction in cases of this disease.

Classification of the Typhus Fevers.

Attempts have been made to classify the typhus fevers on the nature of the transmitting vector. Besides breaking down at several points, such a classification is unsatisfactory for bacteriological purposes. We are entirely in agreement with Felix (1935) that the only sound classification is one based on the antigenic type of the causative virus. Unfortunately our knowledge is still too fragmentary to enable us to make more than a tentative subdivision on this basis, but the schema given in Table CLXIX may serve to indicate the main lines which such a classification should probably take.

TABLE CLXIX

Tentative Classification of the Typhus Group of Fevers. (Modified from Felix 1935.)

Sub-group.	Type X 19.	Type X K.	Type Undetermined.
Name of disease	Classical epidemic typhus. Mexican typhus—Tabardillo. Endemic typhus of U.S.A. Brill's disease. Toulon typhus. Endemic typhus of Manchuria, Moscow, Australia, etc. Shop typhus of Malay.	Tsutsugamushi fever. Scrub typhus of Malay. Mite fever of East Indies.	Rocky Mountain spotted fever. São Paulo typhus. Fièvre boutonneuse. Exanthematic fever of Marseille. Febbre errutiva. Tick-borne typhus of S. Africa. Tick-borne typhus of India. Tick-borne typhus of Kenya. Endemic typhus of S. Africa. Trench fever.
Vector	Lice and rat fleas.	Mites.	Ticks, lice and rat fleas.
Reservoir of virus .	Rats and man.	Field mice and rats.	Rodents, dogs, man.
Agglutination . .	OX 19 $+++$ OX 2 $+$ OX K $-$	OX 19 $-$ OX 2 $-$ OX K $+++$	OX 19 $+$ OX 2 $+$ OX K $+$

The relationship of the different types of typhus virus to each other is curiously reminiscent of that existing between the different types of *Brucella*. In both groups certain main types are distinguishable, but each main type contains a number of sub-types, often associated with a particular host or a particular locality. Epidemiological and bacteriological evidence suggests very strongly that both groups are labile, and are undergoing transformations in Nature under appropriate environmental conditions. So far, experimental workers have not been successful in converting one sub-type into another, though Mooser, Varela, and Pilz (1934) have recently claimed to be able to bring about a change of the classical louse-borne typhus virus into the murine type. It has been suggested by various workers that the murine typhus virus represents the original form, and that the epidemic type has been evolved from this by prolonged propagation in the louse-man-louse cycle.

Diagnosis of Endemic Typhus Fevers.

From what has already been said, and from Table CLXIX, it will be apparent that the Weil-Felix reaction is of considerable value in the diagnosis of fevers of the endemic typhus group. Its limitations are, however, greater than in the diagnosis of epidemic typhus, partly because the main antigen of the causative virus may not be represented in any available *Proteus X* strain, and partly because the frequency of latent and past infections in endemic areas often demands a considerably higher titre than would be regarded as diagnostic during an epidemic of classical typhus.

Discussion of the Weil-Felix Reaction.

The explanation of this reaction is still obscure. Earlier workers regarded it as an example of para-agglutination (Fairley 1919–20, Otto 1919), but later work rendered this explanation increasingly difficult to maintain. So long as only one antigenic type of *Proteus X* was known, para-agglutination afforded a satisfactory enough explanation, but now that we know of at least two antigenic types of *Proteus X*, namely, *OX* 19 and *OX* K, corresponding to two different types of *Rickettsia*, such an explanation is hardly tenable. If, that is to say, we regard *Rickettsia* and *Proteus X* as two entirely distinct groups of organisms, it is putting a strain on the imagination to expect that an antigenic variation in one organism should be accompanied by a corresponding antigenic variation in the other.

That the *Proteus X* bacilli are not themselves responsible for the disease is indicated by the following facts : (1) they are found in only a minority of typhus patients ; (2) they do not produce experimental typhus in the guinea-pig ; (3) they are never isolated from guinea-pigs infected with true typhus virus ; (4) guinea-pigs inoculated with *Proteus X* bacilli develop no immunity to the subsequent inoculation of typhus virus ; (5) guinea-pigs that have recovered after inoculation of typhus virus are as susceptible as normal guinea-pigs to a lethal dose of *Proteus X* bacilli (Otto 1919).

Felix himself has therefore come to the conclusion that the two organisms must be genetically related, and that *Proteus X* must be regarded as a variant of *Rickettsia*, differing from this organism in its morphological, cultural, and pathogenic properties, but resembling it in the possession of a common O antigen (see Chapter XXXVI and Felix and Rhodes 1931, Felix 1933*a*, *b*, 1935). If this is so, then *Proteus X* 19 may be looked upon as the variant of *R. prowazeki*, and *Proteus X* K as the variant of the *Rickettsia* of scrub typhus. *Proteus X* variants corresponding to *R. rickettsi* and *R. quintana* have not yet been discovered, though it is interesting to note that strains with a dual antigenic structure have been reported in Tunis (type *S* 24) and in São Paulo (type *X* L) (see Laigret and Durand 1934).

We should be unwise, however, to accept such an explanation without definite proof. Clearly, the most satisfactory evidence would be afforded by a direct demonstration of the change from *Rickettsia* to *Proteus*, either in tissue culture or in the louse's intestine. Attempts to prove the existence of a genetic relationship along these lines have not yet proved successful, though suggestive results have been recorded by Weigl (1923) and Anigstein (1933).

As a corollary it would be important to show that *Proteus X* strains were never encountered except in relation to *Rickettsia*. Our available information on this point is not very reassuring. A number of workers (see Sparrow and Roussel 1936, van Loghem 1936) have isolated *Proteus X* 19 strains from persons suffering from diseases other than typhus. Sparrow and Roussel themselves, working in Tunis where typhus is endemic, cultivated organisms of the *X* 19 type from the blood of about 50 per cent. of typhus patients, and about 9 per cent. of patients suffering from other diseases, such as undulant fever, typhoid fever, malaria, and pulmonary tuberculosis. It may further be noted that *Proteus* strains have been found in the blood and urine of typhus fever patients, which were not of the *X* 19 type (Schürer and Wolff 1919 ; see also Felix 1931).

Incidentally it may be remarked that infected guinea-pigs, unlike rabbits and monkeys, do not give a positive Weil-Felix reaction.

Prophylaxis and Treatment of the Typhus Fevers.

As in all other diseases which are purely insect-borne, the problem of preventing typhus fevers resolves itself into the control or elimination of the insect vector. In the particular instance of epidemic typhus fever the essential factor is the prevention of the frequent passage of the body louse from man to man ; and this is best attained by reducing louse infestation to a minimum, and by the prevention of overcrowding. Typhus is not a disease of which any cleanly and reasonably prosperous community need stand in dread during times of peace ; its whole history shows its close relation to poverty, overcrowding, dirt, wretchedness, and war. The control of endemic typhus fevers presents a more difficult problem, partly because of the widespread distribution of the various infecting agents, and partly because of the sporadic nature of the disease in human beings.

Vaccination.—Attempts to produce active immunity by vaccination have been made by a number of workers, particularly by Zinsser and his colleagues (Zinsser and Castaneda 1930*a*, 1931, 1933) and by Weigl (1933). The problem of obtaining a thick suspension of rickettsiæ can be solved, either (*a*) by Zinsser's method of intraperitoneal inoculation with a murine virus of guinea-pigs whose resistance has been lowered by injections of benzol, feeding on a vitamin-deficient diet, or best of all irradiation with X-rays (see also Macchiavello and Dresser 1935), or (*b*) by Weigl's method of intra-rectal inoculation of lice with the louse-borne virus. In the former method the peritoneal washings are used and treated with 0·2 per cent. formol ; in the latter method the louse's intestine is removed and ground up in 0·5 per cent. phenolized saline. It will be realized that neither of these methods can conveniently be used for the preparation of large quantities of vaccine. Weigl's vaccine, for example, which is given in 3 doses, necessitates the use of 120–175 lice for each subject. Vaccination has therefore to be restricted at present to persons whose occupation exposes them to an unusually high risk of infection—doctors and nurses in the case of epidemic typhus, field labourers, dock workers, or other classes in the case of endemic typhus. Guinea-pig experiments show that a considerable degree of immunity can be produced by inoculation with dead vaccines, and the preliminary results of Weigl (1933) on the vaccination of human beings appear hopeful.

Serum Treatment.

Nicolle, Conor and Conseil (1911) found that the serum of human patients or of monkeys convalescent from typhus fever possessed protective and curative properties, when tested on experimental infection in monkeys or the natural disease in man. The serum was most active on the 10th to the 12th day after defervescence ; after the 15th to the 20th day it had lost its activity completely, even though the monkey itself was resistant to a fresh inoculation of virus. Nicolle introduced the treatment of the disease by such serum. For *prophylactic* purposes he injects about 3 doses of blood serum, obtained by centrifugalization of the coagulated blood. According to his observations, persons treated by this method subsequently proved resistant to the inoculation of 3 c.c. of blood from a typhus guinea-pig. For *therapeutic* purposes the blood serum of convalescent patients may be injected in fairly large quantities. Little is as yet known of the value of this method of treatment.

REFERENCES

AFANASSIEWA, A. and TRETJAK. (1933) *Zbl. Bakt.*, **130**, 123.
ANIGSTEIN, L. (1933) " Researches on tropical typhus." *Studies Inst. med. Res., F.M.S.*, No. 22.
ARKWRIGHT, J. A. and BACOT, A. W. (1923) *Brit. J. exp. Path.*, **4**, 70.
ARKWRIGHT, J. A., BACOT, A., and DUNCAN, F. M. (1919) *Trans. Soc. trop. Med. Hyg.*, **12**, 61 ; (1919–20) *J. Hyg., Camb.*, **18**, 76.
ATKIN, E. E. and BACOT, A. (1922) *Brit. J. exp. Path.*, **3**, 196.
BACOT, A. (1921) *Brit. med. J.*, i. 156.
BADGER, L. F. (1933a) *Amer. J. publ. Hlth.*, **23**, 19 ; (1933b) *Publ. Hlth Rep., Wash.*, **48**, 507.
BLANC, G. and CAMINOPETROS, J. (1931) *Bull. Acad. Méd., Paris*, **105**, 884.
BRASLAWSKY, P. I. (1934) *Münch. med. Wschr.*, **81**, 172.
BRUCE, D. (1921) *J. Hyg., Camb.*, **20**, 258.
BRUMPT, E. (1932a) *C. R. Soc. Biol.*, **110**, 1197 ; (1932b) *Ibid.*, **110**, 1199 ; (1932c) *Bull. Acad. Méd., Paris*, **107**, 356.
CAMINOPETROS, J. and CONTOS, B. (1932) *C. R. Acad. Sci.*, **195**, 546 ; (1933) *C.R. Soc. Biol.*, **112**, 355.
CEDER, E. T., DYER, R. E., RUMREICH, A., and BADGER, L. F. (1931) *Publ. Hlth Rep., Wash.*, **46**, 3103.
CHAO-JEN WU. (1933) *Proc. Soc. exp. Biol., N.Y.*, **30**, 430.
COMBIESCO, D. (1934) *C. R. Soc. Biol.*, **115**, 672.
COMBIESCO, D. and ZOTTA, G. (1932) *C. R. Soc. Biol.*, **110**, 1222.
CONOR, A. and BRUCH, A. (1910) *Bull. Soc. Path. exot.*, **3**, 492.
COWDRY, E. V. (1926) *Arch. Path. Lab. Med.*, **2**, 59.
DAVIS, G. E., PARKER, R. R., and WALKER, M. E. (1934) *Publ. Hlth Rep., Wash.*, **49**, 298.
DURAND, P. (1931) *Arch. Inst. Pasteur, Tunis*, **20**, 56 ; (1932) *Ibid.*, **21**, 239 ; (1933) *Ibid.*, **21**, 484.
DURAND, P. and CONSEIL, E. (1931) *Arch. Inst. Pasteur, Tunis*, **20**, 54.
DURAND, P. and LAIGRET, J. (1932) *C. R. Acad. Sci.*, **194**, 798.
DYER, R. E. (1933) *Publ. Hlth Rep., Wash.*, **48**, 521.
DYER, R. E., BADGER, L. F., and RUMREICH, A. (1931e) *Publ. Hlth Rep., Wash.*, **46**, 1403.
DYER, R. E., CEDER, E. T., RUMREICH, A., and BADGER, L. F. (1932a) *J. infect. Dis.*, **51**, 137 ; (1931c) *Publ. Hlth Rep., Wash.*, **46**, 1869, 2415.
DYER, R. E., CEDER, E. T., LILLIE, R. D., RUMREICH, A., and BADGER, L. F. (1931d) *Publ. Hlth Rep., Wash.*, **46**, 2481.
DYER, R. E., RUMREICH, A., and BADGER, L. F. (1931a) *Publ. Hlth Rep., Wash.*, **46**, 334 ; (1931b) *J. Amer. med. Ass.*, **97**, 589.
DYER, R. E., WORKMAN, W. G., BADGER, L. F., and RUMREICH, A. (1932b) *Publ. Hlth Rep., Wash.*, **47**, 931.
DYER, R. E., WORKMAN, W. G., CEDER, E. T., BADGER, L. F., and RUMREICH, A. (1932c) *Publ. Hlth Rep., Wash.*, **47**, 987.
EPSTEIN, H. and SILVERS, I. L. (1934) *G. Batt. Immun.*, **12**, 593.
FAIRLEY, N. H. (1919–20) *J. Hyg., Camb.*, **18**, 203.
FELIX, A. (1916) *Wien. klin. Wschr.*, **29**, 873 ; (1931) *J. Hyg., Camb.*, **31**, 382 ; (1933a) *Trans. R. Soc. trop. Med. Hyg.*, **26**, 365 ; (1933b) *Ibid.*, **27**, 147 ; (1935) *Ibid.*, **29**, 113.
FELIX, A. and RHODES, M. (1931) *J. Hyg., Camb.*, **31**, 225.
FIALHO, A. (1932) *Rev. med.-cirurg., Brazil*, **40**, 183.
FLETCHER, W. (1930) *Proc. R. Soc. Med., Sect. Epidem. and State Med.*, **23**, 37 ; (1932) *Brit. med. J.*, ii. 1140.

FLETCHER, W. and LESSLAR, J. E. (1925) *Bull. Inst. med. Res., F.M.S.,* No. 2 ; (1926) *Ibid.,* No. 1.
FUKUDA, Y. (1929) *Zbl. Bakt.,* **111,** 408.
HIS. (1916) *Berl. klin. Wschr.,* **53,** 738.
ISABOLINSKI, M. P., SOBOLEWA, R. M., STRATANOWITSCH, N. J., RIWKINA, S. L., and MOSKALEWA, T. A. (1934) *Z. ImmunForsch.,* **81,** 405.
KAWAMURA, R. and IMAGAWA, Y. (1931) *Zbl. Bakt.,* **122,** 253.
KAWAMURA, R., IMAGAWA, Y., and ITO, T. (1935) *Kitasato Arch. exp. Med.,* **12,** 26.
KODAMA, M., KONO, M., and TAKAHASHI, K. (1932a) *Kitasato Arch. exp. Med.,* **9,** 91.
KODAMA, M. and TAKAHASHI, K. (1931) *Zbl. Bakt.,* **119,** 311.
KODAMA, M., TAKAHASHI, K., and KONO, M. (1932b) *Kitasato Arch. exp. Med.,* **9,** 97.
KOUWENAAR, W. and WOLFF, J. W. (1933) *Ned. Tijdschr. Geneesk.,* **77,** 3548 ; (1934) *J. infect. Dis.,* **55,** 315 ; (1935) *Geneesk. Tijdschr. Ned.-Ind.,* **75,** 34, 117 ; (1936) *Zbl. Bakt.,* **135,** 427.
KRAUS, R., AVILÉS, L. and CASTILLO, J. (1931) *Z. ImmunForsch.,* **70,** 363.
KRITSCHEWSKI, I. L. and SOLOWIOW, N. N. (1934) *Zbl. Bakt.,* **131,** 232.
KUTEISCHIKOW, A., DOSSER, E. M., and BERNHOFF, F. G. (1933) *Zbl. Bakt.,* **129,** 262.
LAIGRET, J. and DURAND, R. (1934) *Arch. Inst. Pasteur, Tunis,* **23,** 326.
LAURELL, A. (1933) *Klin. Wschr.,* **12,** 713.
LAWTON, F. B. and MURRAY, A. (1933) *Med. J. Aust.,* **20,** Part 1, 773.
LÉPINE, P. (1932) *C. R. Acad. Sci.,* **194,** 401.
LEWTHWAITE, R. (1936) *J. Path. Bact.,* **42,** 23.
LEWTHWAITE, R. and SAVOOR, S. R. (1934) *Trans. 9th. Congr. Far East Assoc. trop. med., Nanking,* **1,** 249 ; (1936a) *Brit. J. exp. Path.,* **17,** 1 ; (1936b) *Ibid.,* **17,** 23 ; (1936c) *Trans. R. Soc. trop. Med. Hyg.,* **29,** 561.
LILLIE, R. D. (1931) *Publ. Hlth Rep., Wash.,* **46,** 2840.
LOGHEM, J. J. VAN. (1936) *Ned. Tijdschr. Geneesk.,* **80,** 817.
McNEE, J. W., RENSHAW, A., and BRUNT, E. H. (1916) *Brit. med. J.,* i. 225.
MACCHIAVELLO, A. and DRESSER, R. (1935) *J. exp. Med.,* **62,** 297.
MARCANDIER, PLAZY, LE CHUITON, and PIROT, R. (1931) *Bull. Acad. Méd., Paris,* **105,** 1012.
MAXCY, K. F. (1926) *Publ. Hlth Rep., Wash.,* **41,** 1213, 2967 ; (1928) *Ibid.,* **43,** 3084 ; (1929) *Ibid.,* **44,** 589, 1735, 1935.
MEGAW, J. W. D. (1921) *Indian med. Gaz.,* **56,** 361 ; (1924) *Ibid.,* **59,** 68 ; (1930) *Bull. Off. int. Hyg. publ.,* **22,** 1527.
MONTEIRO, J. L. (1931) *C. R. Soc. Biol.,* **107,** 1161.
MONTEIRO, J. L., FONSECA, F. DA, and PRADO, A. (1932) *Brasil Med.,* **46,** 49.
MOOSER, H. (1928) *J. infect. Dis.,* **43,** 261.
MOOSER, H., CASTANEDA, M. R., and ZINSSER, H. (1931) *J. Amer. med. Ass.,* **97,** 231.
MOOSER, H. and DUMMER, C. (1930) *J. exp. Med.,* **51,** 189.
MOOSER, H., VARELA, G., and PILZ, H. (1934) *J. exp. Med.,* **59,** 137.
MUNTER, H. (1928) *Z. Hyg. InfektKr.,* **109,** 124.
NAGAYO, M., MIYAGAWA, Y., MITAMURA, T., TAMIYA, T., SATO, K., HAZATO, H., and IMAMURA, A. (1931) *Jap. J. exp. Med.,* **9,** 87.
NAGAYO, M., TAMIYA, T., MITAMURA, T., and SATO, K. (1930) *C. R. Soc. Biol.,* **104,** 637.
NEILL, M. H. (1917) *Publ. Hlth Rep., Wash.,* **32,** 1105.
NETTER, A. (1932) *Bull. Acad. Méd., Paris,* **107,** 408.
NICOLLE, C. and LAIGRET, J. (1932) *Arch. Inst. Pasteur, Tunis,* **21,** 251.
NICOLLE, C. and SPARROW, H. (1934) *Arch. Inst. Pasteur, Tunis,* **23,** 247.
NICOLLE, C., CONOR, A., and CONSEIL, E. (1911) *Ann. Inst. Pasteur,* **25,** 97.
OGATA, N. (1931) *Zbl. Bakt.,* **122,** 249 ; (1935) *Arch. Schiffs- u. Tropenhyg.,* **39,** 491.
OTTO, R. (1919) *Dtsch. med. Wschr.,* **45,** 817.
PARKER, R. R. and DAVIS, G. E. (1933) *Publ. Hlth Rep., Wash.,* **48,** 501, 839.
PENFOLD, W. J. and CORKILL, A. B. (1928) *Med. J. Aust.,* **15,** Part II, 304.
PETZETAKIS and KARALIS. (1933) *C. R. Soc. Biol.,* **114,** 470.
PEVERELLI, P. (1930) *Meded. Dienst Volksgezondh. Ned.-Ind,* **19,** 184.
PIJPER, A. and DAU, H. (1935) *J. Hyg., Camb.,* **35,** 116.
PINKERTON, H. (1931) *J. exp. Med.,* **54,** 181.
PIZA, J. DE T., MEYER, J. R., and GOMES, L. S. (1932) " Typho exanthematico de São Paulo." Sociedade Impressora, Paulista, São Paulo.
Report. (1933) *Ann. Rep. Inst. med. Res., F.M.S.,* for year 1932 ; (1934) *Ibid.,* for year 1933 ; (1935) *Ibid.,* for year 1934.
RICKETTS, H. T. (1907) *J. infect. Dis.,* **4,** 141.
ROBERTS, J. I. and TONKING, H. D. (1933) *E. Afr. med. J.,* **9,** 310.
ROCHA-LIMA, H. DA. (1916) *Berl. klin. Wschr.,* **53,** 567 ; (1920a) *Prowazek's Hdb. path. Protozoen,* **2,** 990 ; (1920b) *Ibid.,* **2,** 1031.
RUMREICH, A. S. (1933) *J. Amer. med. Ass.,* **100,** 331.

SAVOOR, S. R., CASTANEDA, M. R., and ZINSSER, H.   (1935) *Proc. Soc. exp. Biol., N.Y.*, **33,** 323.

SCHÜRER, J. and WOLFF, G.   (1919) *Zbl. Bakt.*, **82,** 517.

SELLARDS, A. W.   (1923) *Amer. J. trop. Med.*, **3,** 529.

SPARROW, H. and ROUSSEL, H.   (1936) *Arch. Inst. Pasteur, Tunis*, **25,** 58.

SUZUKI, K.   (1934) *Zbl. Bakt.*, **131,** 236.

TONKING, H. D.   (1932–33) *E. Afr. med. J.*, **9,** 152.

TÖPFER, H.   (1916a) *Münch. med. Wschr.*, **63,** 1495 ; (1916b) *Berl. klin. Wschr.*, **53,** 323.

WEIGL.   (1923) *Z. Hyg. InfektKr.*, **99,** 302.

WEIGL, R.   (1933) *Arch. Inst. Pasteur, Tunis*, **22,** 315.

WEIGL, R. and HERTZIG, A.   (1933) *Ann. Inst. Pasteur, Tunis*, **22,** 321.

WEIL, E. and FELIX, A.   (1916) *Wien. klin. Wschr.*, **29,** 33, 974.

WELCH, H., MICKLE, F. L., and BORMAN, E. K.   (1934) *Amer. J. publ. Hlth.*, **24,** 1157.

WERNER, H.   (1916) *Münch med. Wschr.*, **63,** 402.

WOLBACH, S. B.   (1925) *J. Amer. med. Ass.*, **84,** 723.

WOLBACH, S. B. and SCHLESINGER, M. J.   (1923–24) *J. med. Res.*, **44,** 231.

WOLBACH, S. B., TODD, J. L., and PALFREY, F. W.   (1922) *Rep. Typh. Res. Comm. League of Red Cross Soc. to Poland.* Cambridge, Mass.

WOLFF, J. W.   (1931a) *J. Hyg., Camb.*, **31,** 352 ; (1931b) *Geneesk. Tijdschr. Ned.-Ind.*, **71,** 35.

WOLFF, J. W. and KOUWENAAR, W.   (1933) *Ned. Tijdschr. Geneesk.*, **77,** 269.

ZINSSER, H.   (1934) *Amer. J. Hyg.*, **20,** 513 ; (1935) " Rats, Lice, and History." George Routledge & Sons, Ltd., London.

ZINSSER, H. and BATCHELDER, A. P.   (1930) *J. exp. Med.*, **51,** 847.

ZINSSER, H. and CASTANEDA, M. R.   (1930a) *J. exp. Med.*, **52,** 649 ; (1930b) *Ibid.*, **52,** 865 ; (1931) *Ibid.*, **53,** 325, 333, 493 ; (1932) *Ibid.*, **56,** 455 ; (1933) *Ibid.*, **57,** 381, 391 ; (1934) *Ibid.*, **59,** 471.

CHAPTER LXXXI

PLEUROPNEUMONIA AND CONTAGIOUS AGALACTIA

PLEUROPNEUMONIA OF CATTLE

PLEUROPNEUMONIA is an infectious disease of cattle characterized by an exudative inflammation of the interlobular lymph vessels and of the alveolar tissue of the lungs, with a simultaneous sero-fibrinous pleurisy. According to Nocard and Roux (1898), the essential lesion is a distension of the connective tissue layers between the lobules of the lungs with a large quantity of yellowish, limpid, albuminous, highly infective fluid. The disease is widespread throughout the world, with the exception of Western Europe, India, and North America (Walker 1930). It used to be common in Europe, but preventive measures have greatly decreased its incidence, while in the United States it has been completely eradicated. Epizootics are common in endemic areas ; the morbidity is high ; the case mortality varies considerably according to the severity of the disease. The mode of infection is not clear, but there is reason to believe that it is carried by droplets, and indirectly through dust particles contaminated with nasal discharge (Tang *et al.* 1935). The causative organism of the disease is characterized by a high degree of pleomorphism and by its filtrability. The disease can be reproduced experimentally by inoculation of cows with infective material or cultures of the filtrable organism (see Chapter XXXVII). Active immunization is practised by inoculation of tissue fluid, or preferably of a living, but not fully virulent strain of the organism, into the point of the tail. This results, as a rule, in a non-fatal disease, which leaves the animal immune for a year or more (see Bennett 1932). The serum of convalescent animals is used for passive immunization. Not all strains appear to be identical, and it is possible that an animal that has recovered from one attack may prove susceptible to later invasion by a different strain. In practice the slaughter policy is recommended for the control of the disease. (For pleuropneumonia of calves due to *Pasteurella septica*, see p. 1300.)

CONTAGIOUS AGALACTIA OF SHEEP AND GOATS

This disease is characterized by inflammatory lesions of the udder, eye, and joints. The milk yield in lactating animals is diminished, and instead of milk, a dirty yellow serous fluid containing small clots is secreted (Galloway 1930). Several outbreaks have occurred during the past hundred years in Europe, and more recently the disease has been encountered in North Africa. The case mortality is said to average about 15 per cent. The causative organism, which was first cultivated by Bridré and Donatien (1923, 1925), resembles the organism of pleuropneumonia in its pleomorphism and its filtrability. Natural infection usually appears to occur by ingestion. The disease can be reproduced by inoculation, especially of goats, with infected tissue suspensions, and with pure cultures (see Chapter XXXVII). Animals that have recovered naturally from an attack of the disease have a high degree of immunity. Active immunization is very difficult. Passive immunity may be conferred by the injection of immune sera prepared in sheep, goats, or horses (Bridré and Donatien 1925).

REFERENCES

BENNETT, S. C. J. (1932) *J. comp. Path.*, **45**, 257.
BRIDRÉ, J. and DONATIEN, A. (1923) *C. R. Acad. Sci.*, **177**, 841 ; (1925) *Ann. Inst. Pasteur*, **39**, 925.
GALLOWAY, I. A. (1930) " A System of Bacteriology," *Med. Res. Coun.*, **7**, 335.
NOCARD and ROUX. (1898) *Ann. Inst. Pasteur*, **12**, 240.
TANG, F. F., WEI, H., McWHIRTER, D. L., and EDGAR, J. (1935) *J. Path. Bact.*, **40**, 391.
WALKER, J. (1930) " A System of Bacteriology," *Med. Res. Coun.*, **7**, 322.

CHAPTER LXXXII

FILTRABLE VIRUS DISEASES

A. Group Characterized by Lesions of the Skin

In this and the following three chapters we describe the most important diseases of man and animals that are caused, or probably caused, by filtrable viruses. We are immediately faced with the problem of their classification. Numerous suggestions have been made by different workers for grouping these diseases according to the tissue attacked, the nature of the lesion produced, the presence of inclusion bodies, the transmissibility of infection, and so on (see Rivers 1932, Fine 1932, McKinley 1934, Fairbrother 1934, Hurst 1936). It is clear that the only satisfactory classification must rest on the nature and properties of the causative viruses themselves. Our knowledge, however, of the viruses is extremely meagre, and though tentative efforts at their classification are doubtless of value in research work, it is perhaps a little premature to reproduce them in what is primarily a textbook designed for teaching. We shall, therefore, omit any serious attempt at classification. The order in which we shall describe the various diseases will be determined partly by their public health importance, and partly by the nature of the organs or tissues mainly attacked. It may be noted that influenza and swine influenza have already been dealt with in the chapter on respiratory infections (Chapter LXXI).

VARIOLA AND VACCINIA

Variola, or smallpox, is a disease of great antiquity, of widespread distribution, affecting both sexes at all ages, and occurring both endemically and epidemically According to Rajchman (1928) there were over 300,000 cases of the disease in the world in 1927 ; in India alone it causes about 50,000 deaths annually. In recent years, however, smallpox has been characterized by an almost universal decrease in the case-mortality rate. There seems little doubt that this is due largely to the occurrence in many localities of a mild type of disease, usually referred to as " alastrim." There are in fact two entirely distinct types of the disease : (1) the classical type, with severe symptoms and a case-mortality rate of 10–30 per cent. : (2) the mild type or alastrim, with mild symptoms and a case-mortality rate of only 0·1–0·3 per cent. In some countries the two types may coexist side by side ; thus in 1922 there was an epidemic of the mild type in the Midlands and North of England, in which 895 cases were reported with only 3 deaths—a case-mortality rate of 0·3 per cent.—and a smaller epidemic of the classical type in London, in which 78 cases were reported with 24 deaths—a case mortality of 31 per cent.

The mode of infection in smallpox is not clear. It used to be thought that infection occurred from the inoculation of the skin with dried pustules and scabs, but this is now believed to be an unusual method. Epidemiological and experimental evidence points to infection by the nasopharyngeal route. The observations which indicate that infection is not usually carried by dried pustules and scabs are : (1) cases of smallpox occur without a rash which nevertheless prove infectious ; (2) experimental inoculation of the skin with variola seldom leads to more than a mild disease with imperfectly developed pocks. On the other hand, the virus is said to be generally present in the nasopharynx of patients, and to be sometimes demonstrable in this situation even during the incubation period. Von Wasielewski and Winkler (1925), who review the evidence, conclude that the virus is coughed out in droplets, and gives rise to infection of the mucosa of the upper respiratory tract ; from the infected mucosa the virus is then distributed to all parts of the body.

That variola is primarily caused by a filtrable virus, there is no doubt. Filtration experiments are not, however, always successful, probably because of the imperfect liberation of the virus from the cells, or its adsorption by particulate matter in the suspension (see Green and Eagles 1931). During the disease the virus appears to be widely distributed throughout the body ; it has been demonstrated in the blood stream (Ohtawara 1922, Parker and Nye 1925a, von Wasielewski and Winkler 1925, Haagen 1928). Though Levaditi (1924) maintains that the chief manifestations of the disease result from an affinity of the virus for the skin, there is now little doubt that the primary action of the virus is on the mesoderm ; for this reason it is now sometimes referred to as " viscerotropic " (see Ledingham 1924, Hurst 1936).

The cultivation of the virus of variola, and of the closely associated vaccinia virus, in the rabbit's testicle, in tissue cultures *in vitro*, and on the chorio-allantoic membrane of the developing chick embryo, has already been described (Chapter XXXVIII).

Animal Inoculation.—Smallpox cannot be reproduced in its typical form in any of the lower animals. In calves and rabbits only minimal lesions are produced ; and if material from these lesions is passed continuously through a series of animals, the virus is so altered that it gives rise to vaccinia or cow-pox, and reproduces this type of infection when again inoculated into a child.

The most susceptible animal to *variola* is the *monkey*. Intracutaneous inoculation of pus from a human patient gives rise to a papule after 5 days ; by the 8th day this is vesicular, and by the 10th day a typical pock is formed, with a raised congested edge surrounding a crateriform depression, partly filled with dark purulent material (Blaxall 1923, Gordon 1925). Intratesticular inoculation of the monkey with variola virus gives rise to an orchitis with the appearance of a rash on the scrotum. Passage from one monkey to another is almost uniformly successful. Cats and dogs are said to be less susceptible than monkeys, but more so than rabbits. Infection in the less susceptible animals may be of the " inapparent " type, in which immunity develops in the absence of any clinical manifestations of disease (Teissier *et al.* 1931). Pus from cases of alastrim gives rise to very much the same lesions as that from the classical type of smallpox.

Both calves and rabbits can be readily infected with *vaccinia*. Inoculation of the scarified skin of a *rabbit* with calf lymph causes a red swelling on the 3rd day, which increases until a red papule is formed, surrounded by a red areola ; the papules become vesiculated about the 5th day, and tend to coalesce and to become pustular ; scabbing follows on the 7th or 8th day. A good calf lymph should give a reaction in the rabbit when diluted 1/1000 ; sometimes a reaction occurs even in a 1/100,000 dilution. If vaccine lymph is inoculated intravenously into a rabbit, and a portion of the skin is thereafter shaved, vaccinial papules appear about the 3rd day on the shaved area (Calmette and Guérin 1901). If a very large dose of vaccine lymph is inoculated intravenously into a rabbit—1 to 2 c.c. of undiluted stock emulsion—or a highly virulent virus is employed, a generalized eruption occurs over the entire body surface, and lesions may develop in the internal organs (Noguchi 1918, Douglas *et al.* 1929, Armstrong and Lillie 1929). Subcutaneous inoculation may give rise to a local pustular eruption, but often

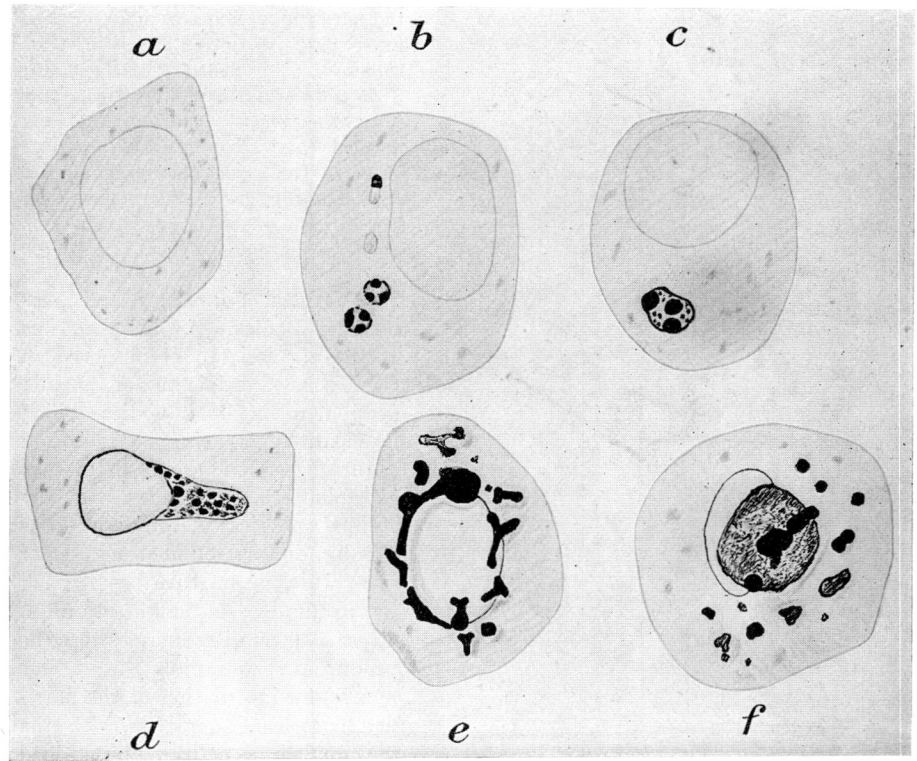

FIG. 273.

Guarnieri corpuscles in corneal cells of rabbit experimentally inoculated with vaccinia virus.

a = normal corneal cell.
b = cell one day after inoculation, containing small vaccine bodies.
c = cell 2 days after inoculation, containing a solitary vaccine body in which large and small droplets may be distinguished.
d = cell 4 days after inoculation, showing a vaccine body partly surrounding the nucleus.
e = cell 5 days after inoculation, showing vaccine bodies surrounding the nucleus.
f = cell 5 days after inoculation, containing numerous vaccine bodies.

(After Cowdry 1927.)

no superficial lesion appears at all. Intratesticular inoculation results in the development of an orchitis and œdema of the scrotum ; the animal dies about the 6th day. Inoculation on the scarified cornea gives rise to a keratitis and purulent conjunctivitis. Intracerebral inoculation of rabbits is followed by trembling, paralytic, and other nervous symptoms and by death on the 5th to the 8th day ; the brain and spinal cord of these animals prove infective to fresh rabbits, when inoculated on to the cornea or intracerebrally (Marie 1920).

In *mice* a vesiculo-pustular reaction may often be obtained by inoculation of the scarified foot pad or tail with vaccinia virus (Rosenau and Andervont 1931).

Histologically, the main lesion in the rabbit inoculated intracutaneously is a diffuse perivascular infiltration of the dermis ; the changes in the epidermis appear to be secondary to this. According to Ledingham (1924) the vaccinial lesion is essentially an acute infective granuloma in which the reticulo-endothelial system is primarily and dominantly involved. By continued passage through the brain of rabbits, the virus may acquire more or less fixed properties—like the virus of rabies—causing death regularly in 5 to 8 days (Marie 1920). To this fixed virus the term " neurovaccine " is applied by Levaditi and Nicolau (1923). The virus, though having a special affinity for the nervous tissue, is still able to produce typical lesions on cutaneous inoculation.

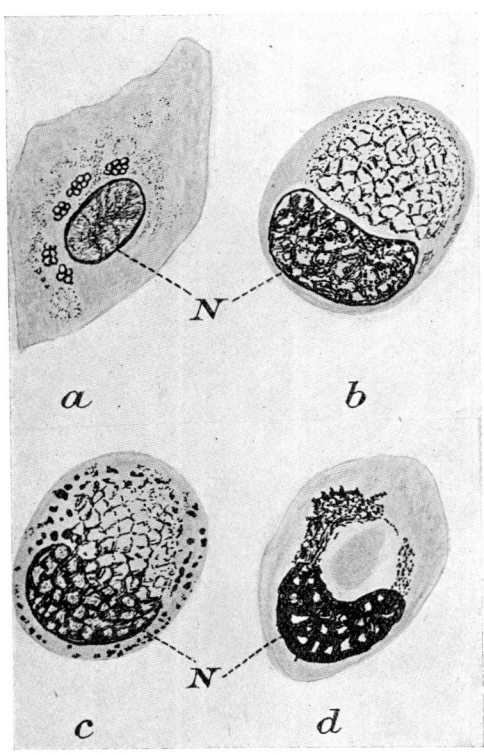

FIG. 274.

Guarnieri corpuscles in the cornea of an experimentally inoculated rat.

a = five small vaccine bodies in congeries.
b = fully developed vaccine body.
c = vaccine body showing reticulum breaking up into granules ; similar granules throughout cytoplasm.
d = vaccine body with central portion consisting of homogeneous material.
N = nucleus.

(After Ewing.)

Guarnieri Corpuscles and Elementary Bodies.—As long ago as 1892 Guarnieri (1894) observed in the lesions of variola and of vaccinia peculiar intracellular bodies, which he regarded as being of protozoal nature. When stained by methylene blue, the body shows a slightly stained spherical mass lying eccentrically, and surrounded by a clear area, which in its turn is encircled by a number of small granules. These Guarnieri corpuscles may be produced very rapidly—in a few hours—by inoculation of the scarified cornea of a rabbit with the vaccinia virus. Fixed, and stained with methylene blue and eosin, they appear as irregular pink and lilac masses, which indent the nuclei, and which may contain acidophilic or basophilic granules (Figs. 273, 274). Besides the Guarnieri corpuscles, which are always present at some stage in variolous and vaccinial lesions, very tiny intracellular bodies, $0 \cdot 1$–$0 \cdot 25$ μ in diameter, have been described ; they are generally called " Paschen's granules " (see Fig. 211, p. 749). The work of Ledingham and his colleagues, of Paschen, and of others (see Chapter XXXVIII) leaves no doubt that the Paschen granules, or elementary bodies as they are often called, constitute the actual causative virus of the disease. The Guarnieri corpuscles probably represent actual intracellular microcolonies of the virus. The microscopical demonstration of the virus particles *in situ* may be accomplished by suitable staining methods (see Taniguchi *et al.* 1932*a*, Haagen and Kodama 1934).

Laboratory Diagnosis of Smallpox.—The serological diagnosis of smallpox is made by mixing a suspension of ground-up variolous material with an antivaccinial rabbit serum, and incubating at 37° C. A positive reaction is marked by the appearance of a finely floccular precipitate, similar to that obtained with vaccinial material (Gordon 1925). Using this method, Tulloch (1928) has recently been able to make a rapid diagnosis of smallpox during the course of an epidemic in Dundee. The complement-fixation test may likewise be employed. The value of the flocculation test is becoming increasingly obvious. The careful studies of Burgess, Craigie and Tulloch (1929) and Craigie and Tulloch (1931) show that it constitutes an important practical method in the rapid diagnosis of doubtful cases of smallpox. For a description of the detailed technique reference should be made to the report by Craigie and Tulloch (1931). The serum of patients suffering from variola may also agglutinate suspensions of elementary bodies (Amies 1932). The reaction appears to be specific for variola and vaccinia. Some discussion has arisen over its real nature, but it is probably a mixed precipitation and agglutination reaction (see Craigie 1932, Gordon 1935*a*, *b*, Ledingham 1935*a*). Diagnosis may also be made by the complement-fixation test using a suspension of the crusts as antigen.

Tests depending on animal inoculation are less satisfactory. McKinnon and Defries (1928) and Defries and McKinnon (1928) find that the intracutaneous inoculation of variolous material into rabbits produces a reaction characterized by a red palpable swelling, commencing on the 2nd day and reaching its maximum about the 4th day, when it appears as a firm, elevated plateau, 10–20 mm. in diameter ; subsequently the central red area becomes straw-coloured, and desquamation or crust formation may occur ; the lesion disappears by the 12th day, leaving no scar. On the other hand, if the variolous matter is injected into vaccinated rabbits, either no reaction occurs at all, or there is an allergic reaction, characterized by the rapid appearance and disappearance of a red tense nodule (Blaxall 1923). Material from varicella, as a rule, gives rise to no reaction in either normal or vaccinated rabbits, though on this point the evidence is conflicting (Hull and Nauss 1926). Paul's test, which consists in the production of a keratitis by inoculation of the rabbit's cornea with variolous material, is sometimes used in diagnosis, but according to Defries and McKinnon (1928) it is positive in only 50 per cent. of cases.

Immunity.

Our whole knowledge of immunity may be said to have started with Jenner's discovery in 1796 that inoculation with cow-pox protects against subsequent inoculation with smallpox. He believed that cow-pox was really smallpox, modified by passage through the cow—a belief to which investigations of recent years have lent considerable support. Cutaneous inoculation of the calf with variolous material from man produces insignificant lesions ; but if the material from these lesions is passed through further calves in series, then after three or more passages a good vesiculo-pustular eruption appears on the inoculated skin. This experimentally produced disease is apparently identical with the naturally occurring cow-pox. If the pustules are scraped at the height of their development, ground up in a mortar, and mixed with glycerolated saline, the resulting product is indistinguishable from vaccine lymph. In practice it is found beneficial to pass the vaccinia virus from the calf to a rabbit, from the rabbit to a calf, from the calf to a child, and from the child back to a calf, or through some similar series ; in this way the activity of the virus seems to be better maintained than by continuous passage through one species of host.

Experimentally, rabbits that have been inoculated with vaccinia virus, either cutaneously, subcutaneously, or intravenously, become resistant to a second inoculation within about 10 days. If repeated injections are given, the rabbits become hyperimmunized, and in their serum neutralizing viricidal antibodies can be demonstrated, as well as agglutinins, precipitins, and complement-fixing bodies (Ledingham 1924, Gordon 1925, Sobernheim 1925). W. Smith (1929) has brought evidence to show that, in rabbits inoculated intravenously, the virus is rapidly taken up by the formed elements of the blood—probably the leucocytes—and remains in the circulation for at least 8 days. (See also Douglas and Smith 1930, Gildemeister and Hilgers 1930.) In order to demonstrate its presence, it is necessary, however, to fractionate the blood, and use only the washed cells for injection. If the whole blood is injected, the presence of the virus is masked by the antibodies, which become demonstrable in the plasma about the second day after infection, and increase up to the 6th or 7th day. This method of demonstrating the virus in material which, when injected in the original state, proves to be noninfective, may have an important bearing on future investigations into the distribution of the filtrable viruses within the body. (See also p. 958.)

By whatever route the virus is introduced, provided an active strain is used, a general immunity develops. There is a partial exception to this in the cornea ; a vaccinial keratitis renders the affected cornea resistant to further inoculation, but not necessarily the opposite cornea or the skin ; similarly cutaneous vaccination, though rendering the skin refractory, may yet leave the cornea susceptible (Levaditi and Nicolau 1923). According to Sobernheim (1925) this statement must be modified ; he brings evidence to show that after cutaneous inoculation the cornea does become immune to vaccinia, but the immunity develops more slowly in the cornea than in the skin—probably because of its poor blood supply. There seems little doubt, therefore, that immunity to vaccinia is a general and not a mere local immunity, and is dependent, to some extent at least, on the development of humoral antibodies.

Monkeys inoculated with vaccinia are completely protected against subsequent inoculation of variola (Gordon 1925) ; monkeys inoculated with variola or alastrim are either partly or completely protected against subsequent inoculation with vaccinia (Blaxall 1923, Gordon 1925). Immunologically the alastrim virus resembles the variola virus very closely, but minor differences are apparent in the degree of protection afforded by the different viruses against vaccinia. Generally speaking, vaccinia affords almost perfect protection against variola and alastrim, but the protection afforded by variola or alastrim against vaccinia is not so complete. The identity of alastrim with mild smallpox has been questioned, but the evidence of cross-immunity between the two diseases leaves little doubt that they are caused by essentially the same virus (see Leake and Force 1927, Diem 1930). Ledingham (1935b) has shown that, though the viruses of variola and vaccinia possess a common antigen, agglutination experiments reveal some difference between them. The precise nature of the antigenic change that takes place when variola becomes transformed into vaccinia has still to be determined. It must be mentioned, however, that there is a type of mild smallpox in Australia which affords practically no immunity either to variola or vaccinia, and to which vaccinia or variola affords only incomplete protection (Ledingham 1925).

Experiments in rabbits indicate that the highest immunity to vaccinia is produced by living virus. Gordon (1925) found that heat diminished the antigenic activity of the virus very considerably. Thus, to produce the same degree of protection as that afforded by raw virus, about 20 times as much virus heated to 55° C. for 30 minutes had to be employed ; lymph heated to 65° C. had only 1/100 of the immunizing power of the 55° C. lymph, while lymph heated to 100° or 120° C. had practically no immunizing effect at all. According to Nakagawa (1924), lymph heated to 100° C. for 40 minutes still has some immunizing power, but very large doses have to be employed to demonstrate it. Virus treated by exposure to 1 per cent. phenol for 24 hours at 37° C. had much the same immunizing power as the 55° C. lymph.

There is no question that the antigenic power of heated, phenolized, or formolized vaccinia virus is very much less than that of the untreated virus. Its power of stimulating antibody production, especially protective antibodies, seems to be very slight, though it can still serve as an efficient hapten in the demonstration of skin sensitivity in a sensitized human subject or animal (see Kaiser 1929, Zehnder 1929, Bussel and Maysner 1930, Andervont and Rosenau 1930, Kraus 1931, Hilgers 1931, Craigie and Wishart 1933, Parker and Rivers 1936). After vaccination of rabbits with raw lymph, immunity may be detectable about the 4th day ; during the next 2 days it increases rapidly, and by the 10th day a substantial immunity is attained.

Human Vaccination.—Inoculated cutaneously into human beings, the vaccinia virus produces only a localized pustular eruption, reaching its height about the 9th or 10th day, and followed as a rule by scarring and pitting—or foveation, as it is technically called. The size of the reaction is dependent on the concentration of virus in the lymph (von Gröer 1935). A second inoculation made some years later is generally followed by much the same reaction, but the development of the pustule is accelerated, so that in persons of 18 to 21 years of age, for example, who have not been vaccinated since infancy, the maximum reaction is reached about the 6th day (Report 1928a)—allergic reaction. There is evidence that the rate at which the pustule develops is an index of immunity resulting from the previous vaccination (McKinnon and Defries 1931).

For human vaccination, calf lymph is generally employed, but it has been shown that lymph taken from vaccinial lesions in other animals can be used satisfactorily.

Protective Effect of Vaccination.—The evidence that vaccination protects against smallpox is very strong, but unfortunately exact statistical evidence is difficult to obtain. This holds particularly with regard to protection against infection as opposed to death ; for, from the nature of the case, it is impossible in a diffuse population to be certain of the degree of risk to which the individual members have been exposed. On the other hand, a large body of statistical evidence has been accumulated to show that the case mortality from smallpox is greatly diminished by vaccination. This evidence is as follows :

(1) Vaccination diminishes the case mortality. Table CLXX gives the figures collected by Cameron (see Report 1928a) for the case mortality of smallpox in vaccinated and unvaccinated persons treated in the Metropolitan Asylums Board Hospitals during 1901–04.

TABLE CLXX

Year.	Vaccinated.			Unvaccinated or Doubtful.		
	Admitted.	Died.	Percentage Case Mortality.	Admitted.	Died.	Percentage Case Mortality.
1901 . . .	1,282	127	9·9	461	165	35·8
1902 . . .	5,663	578	10·2	2,253	759	33·6
1903 . . .	245	7	2·9	110	5	4·5
1904 . . .	289	14	4·8	160	13	8·1
Totals . .	7,479	726	9·7	2,984	942	31·57

It will be seen that the mortality amongst the unvaccinated was more than three times that amongst the vaccinated.   Macdonell (1901–02) found that in the outbreaks in Sheffield, Dewsbury, Leicester, and Warrington in the 1891–93 epidemic, the correlation between vaccination and mildness of disease was + 0·7935, and in Glasgow as high as + 0·9123.

(2) The greater the amount of foveation, the greater is the diminution of the case mortality (see Table CLXXI).

TABLE CLXXI

	Admitted.	Died.	Percentage Mortality.
With 4 scars or more . . .	3,139	171	5·4
„ 3 „	1,902	171	9·0
„ 2 „	1,442	184	12·8
„ 1 scar	930	168	17·9

(3) The greater the area of cicatrix left by the vaccination, the greater is the diminution of the case mortality (see Table CLXXII).

TABLE CLXXII

Area of Scar.	Admitted.	Died.	Percentage Mortality.
Area of $\frac{1}{2}$ sq. in. or more . .	5,564	388	7·0
„ > $\frac{1}{3}$ sq. in. but < $\frac{1}{2}$ sq. in.	889	138	15·5
„ < $\frac{1}{3}$ sq. in.	933	158	16·9

According to Turner (1905–06), among cases with equal total areas of vaccination scarring there is no difference in the amount of protection afforded by different numbers of scars.

(4) In vaccinated persons the mortality from smallpox increases with the length of time elapsing since vaccination.   Table CLXXIII affords a comparison, in this respect, between vaccinated and unvaccinated persons.   This table also shows a very different age-grouping of admissions in vaccinated and unvaccinated persons,

strongly suggesting that vaccination affords protection against infection as well as against death.

TABLE CLXXIII

Years.	Vaccinated.			Unvaccinated and Doubtful.		
	Admitted.	Died.	Percentage C.M.	Admitted.	Died.	Percentage C.M.
−10 . .	143	2	1·4	1,441	459	31·9
11–20 . .	1,218	23	1·9	761	166	21·8
21–30 . .	2,675	144	5·3	374	129	34·5
31–40 . .	1,861	247	13·3	180	80	44·4
41–50 . .	893	174	18·2	102	57	55·9
51–60 . .	311	55	17·7	73	31	42·5

A striking piece of evidence in favour of the value of vaccination is afforded by the fact that of the 4,406 cases of smallpox in vaccinated persons in England and Wales during the period 1921–26 only 3 were under 12 years of age. This observation is difficult to explain except on the hypothesis that vaccination during infancy confers a large measure of protection against the disease lasting for some years. Vaccination performed immediately prior to exposure to smallpox (the incubation period of which is 12 to 14 days) affords almost absolute protection against the disease. Vaccination performed during the incubation period of smallpox either prevents the development of the disease, or predisposes to a modified form of the disease. Similarly, recent successful revaccination is said to afford an almost absolute protection against smallpox (Brownlee 1905–06).

In the United States there is a very interesting relationship between the vaccination laws in the different states and the incidence of smallpox (Table CLXXIV).

TABLE CLXXIV

RELATION OF SMALLPOX MORBIDITY TO VACCINATION LAWS IN THE UNITED STATES, 1919–28. (Woodward and Feemster 1933.)

Vaccination Laws.	No. of States.	Population.	No. of Cases.	Incidence per 100,000
Compulsory vaccination	10	32,434,954	21,543	6·6
Local option	6	17,930,882	91,981	51·3
No vaccination laws	29	59,923,117	393,924	66·7
Compulsory vaccination prohibited .	4	4,002,888	46,110	115·2

The effect of vaccination appears to wear off with increasing age, as can be judged from Table CLXXIII; and it is therefore advisable, in countries where smallpox is rife, to perform revaccination at about 10, and again at about 20 years of age. (For general discussion of vaccination see Greenwood 1930, Report 1931.)

Complications of Vaccination.—Of the complications that may follow vaccination, suppuration is one of the commonest, and tetanus one of the most serious. Owing to the use of calf lymph, which cannot be satisfactorily sterilized, the introduction of micro-organisms into the wound is inevitable, but it is very difficult to say how often the calf lymph is responsible, and how often uncleanliness on the part of the operator, or during the after-treatment. Occasionally, as at Malmö, severe necrotic lesions may occur owing to the presence of pathogenic staphylococci in the lymph (Magnusson 1932, 1933). It may be noted that foot-and-mouth virus has been found occasionally in specimens of calf lymph, though there is no evidence that its presence had excited any unfavourable reaction in vaccinated children (see Gildemeister 1931, Gildemeister and Helm 1932*a, b*).

Tetanus is a very rare complication ; thus in 1904–13 in the United States, 31 million lymph doses were inoculated into human beings, and only 41 cases of tetanus were observed. Infection in these cases may be carried by the lymph ; but tetanus occurs only in those cases in which a protective shield or dressing strapped to the arm has been applied. Vaccination insertions treated openly have never been followed by tetanus (Armstrong 1927).

In recent years, a new complication has been observed, namely, *post-vaccinal encephalitis*. The first case studied in detail was observed by Turnbull in 1912 ; but it was not till the publication of Turnbull and McIntosh's report in 1926 that serious attention was drawn to the subject. Altogether in this country and abroad, some hundreds of cases have been observed, though the disease is now very much less frequent than formerly (Report 1936). Most of them have occurred after late primary vaccination. Vaccination during the 1st year of life rarely seems to be followed by encephalitis. Clinically, after an incubation period of 10 to 14 days, there is a rapid onset followed by an acute course, the symptoms being cerebral rather than spinal (Report 1928*a*). The mortality, among 62 cases recorded by the Committee on Vaccination, was 58 per cent. Histologically, the lesions are widely distributed in the grey and white matter of the brain and cord, and are characterized particularly by extra-vascular parenchymatous infiltration with large endothelial and glial cells, and by perivascular areas of softening or demyelination (McIntosh 1928). The ætiology of these cases is as yet unknown. Greenfield (1928) suggests that, as the lesions are similar in many respects to those seen in encephalomyelitis following measles and in disseminated sclerosis, the encephalitis is caused by some neurotropic virus which is capable of causing a latent infection, and may be stimulated into activity either by vaccination or by some exanthematous infection. This is the view favoured by the Committee on Vaccination (Report 1928*a*, 1930). McIntosh (1928), on the other hand, believes that post-vaccinal encephalitis is due to the vaccinia virus itself, because : (1) a similar encephalitis may occur in cases of smallpox ; (2) the vaccinia virus has been recovered from the brain of cases of post-vaccinal encephalitis ; (3) by the intracerebral injection of a neurotropic strain of the vaccinia virus, it is possible to produce in rabbits an encephalitis which he regards as essentially similar to that observed in human beings after vaccination. Each of these views has a substantial following (see Berger 1929, McIntosh 1930, McIntosh and Scarff 1930, Hurst and Fairbrother 1930, Clearkin 1930, Herzberg-Kremmer and Herzberg 1930, Eckstein 1931, Lucksch 1932, Armstrong 1932, Rivers *et al.* 1933, Ledingham 1934, Aldershoff 1935). (See also secondary encephalitis, p. 1503.)

Whichever view is correct, it would clearly be of advantage to avoid the severe generalized reactions that sometimes follow vaccination, and to do away with the danger of inoculating the patient with other organisms or other viruses contained in the vaccine lymph. Suggestions have been made for drying the lymph, diluting it, treating it with 0·25 per cent. phenol, or mixing it with an immune serum (Otten 1927, 1932, Gins 1929, Rhoads 1931). An even more satisfactory method would

probably be to do away with calf lymph altogether, and substitute a vaccine prepared from pure tissue or embryo cultures of the virus (Rivers 1931, Rivers and
Ward 1935, Herzberg 1935).

The production of potent antivaccinial sera has now been shown to be possible
(Ledingham *et al.* 1931, Fairbrother 1932), and there may be some call in the future
for such sera, or for sera prepared against the variola virus, in the treatment of
smallpox. So far serum treatment is still in the experimental stage (Yaoi 1935).

THE ANIMAL POXES, INCLUDING AVIAN DIPHTHERIA OR ROUP

Pox occurs in a number of animals, such as sheep, goats, cows, horses, swine,
fowls, and pigeons. The clinical manifestations vary ; in its typical form it occurs
as a vesico-pustular eruption on the skin, sometimes associated with very marked
epithelial proliferation ; on the other hand it may, as in horses, produce an eruption
in the mouth (contagious pustular stomatitis), as well as on the skin ; or, as in
fowls, diphtheritic pseudo-membranes in the throat (avian diphtheria or roup).
Histologically, inclusion bodies of the Guarnieri type are found in the lesions.

Whether the virus responsible for the animal poxes is identical with that
responsible for vaccinia in man, or whether each virus is specific for its particular
host is not yet clear, but evidence is rapidly accumulating to suggest that it is
the vaccinia virus itself or some variety of it. Thus it is usually possible, by rabbit
passage, to convert the mammalian pox viruses into a virus indistinguishable in
its action on rabbits and human beings from the vaccinia virus (Toyoda 1924).
Moreover animals inoculated with one variety of virus are more or less completely
protected against another variety (see also Borrel 1903, Bosc 1903, de Jong 1917,
Zwick 1924, von Wasielewski and Winkler 1925, Ledingham 1926).

Sheep-pox, known in France as *la clavelée*, is of some economic importance.
It was studied by Borrel in 1903 who noted the occurrence of distinctive cellular
bodies in the lesions, and showed that the causative virus was able to pass through
coarse Chamberland filters.

The disease, which runs an acute febrile course, is characterized by the development of a vesicular eruption, later becoming pustular, on the more exposed parts
of the body. Infection can readily be transmitted to normal sheep by inoculation
with the serous fluid contained in the loculated vesicles. The case mortality of
the natural disease is very low. Post-mortem examination of fatal cases reveals
the presence of generalized lesions. The lungs contain multiple, small, dense,
spherical nodules, hyaline in appearance with a central opaque spot ; they are
commonest near the pleural surface. Similar, but less obvious, lesions are also
seen in the liver and kidneys. Prophylactic inoculation with a sensitized vaccine
is widely practised in France (Bridré and Boquet 1923, 1933).

Rabbit-pox has recently been submitted to a careful experimental study by
Pearce and her colleagues (Pearce *et al.* 1936, Rosahn *et al.* 1936, Hu *et al.* 1936).
The virus is filtrable through Berkefeld V candles ; it is antigenically related to
the vaccinia virus, but not to Virus III (see p. 1494), or the virus of infectious
myxoma (see p. 1539) ; and it is able to infect guinea-pigs, mice, calves, and
probably rats.

Fowl-pox requires separate consideration. According to Doyle (1929) three
clinical forms may be recognized : (1) wart-like nodules on the comb, wattles, and
skin of the head ; (2) adherent, yellow, cheesy membranes in the mouth ; (3) a

watery or muco-purulent discharge from the eyes and nose ; this form is some-times referred to as " roup." One, or any combination, of these lesions, may be present in the same bird. These clinical forms have long been regarded as separate diseases, but the evidence now accumulating suggests that they are caused by one and the same filtrable virus, though the possibility that similar clinical con-ditions may be due to other agents cannot be excluded. Moreover, recent work suggests that the fowl-pox virus is related to the vaccinia virus. Thus Toyoda (1924) maintains that by passage through rabbits the fowl-pox virus can be con-verted into the vaccinia virus. Findlay (1928), however, has been unable to confirm this. The exact relationship between these two viruses must be left for the future to determine, but in any case the fowl-pox virus, both in its patho-genicity and in its serological reactions, seems to be less nearly related to the vaccinia virus than are the mammalian pox viruses. In the lesions of fowl-pox so-called Bollinger inclusion bodies, and Borrel elementary bodies, corresponding respectively to the Guarnieri corpuscles and the Paschen bodies in vaccinia, can be found (see Ludford and Findlay 1926).

Doyle and Minett (1927) found that pigeons were resistant to fowl-pox virus, but that fowls were susceptible to the virus of pigeon-pox. Moreover, they obtained evidence that pigeon-pox protected fowls against fowl-pox. Following on these observations, Doyle (1930) introduced the prophylactic vaccination of fowls with a vaccine consisting of dried pigeon-pox crusts suspended in glycerolated saline. This method is now being used on a wide scale with apparently very favour-able results. The relationship of the two viruses is not very clear, but according to Doyle (1930) repeated passage of the pigeon-pox virus through fowls leads to an increase in its virulence for the latter ; after 9 passages it may acquire all the characteristics of the typical fowl-pox virus.

Kikuth and Gollub (1932) have described a disease of canaries, which appears to be **canary-pox**. It has been studied by Burnet (1933), who notes that, though the clinico-pathological picture differs markedly from that of fowl-pox, the viruses of the two diseases resemble each other fairly closely.

One very interesting property of the pox viruses is their power to give rise in certain hosts—sheep and fowls particularly—to tumours characterized by epithelio-matous proliferation, superficially resembling neoplasms.

Contagious Pustular Dermatitis of Sheep

Contagious pustular dermatitis is a not infrequent malady amongst sheep in this country, and has been described by several workers on the Continent. (For refs. see Glover 1928.) It is probable that natural cases occur also amongst goats. The disease varies in severity : in the mild form there are pustular lesions on the lips and surrounding tissues ; in the severe form lesions occur on the oral mucosa, the vulva, the cornea, and on various other parts of the body, particularly the regions of the coronet and the tail. Sheep of any age may be attacked, but the disease is commonest in weaned lambs up to 1 year old. Experimentally vesico-pustular lesions can be produced by scarification of the thighs of normal lambs, or by intradermal inoculation of the lip with a suspension of dried crusts from the natural lesions ; the crusts generally prove active in a dilution of 1/50,000. All attempts to transmit the disease to laboratory animals have failed. Glover (1928) has brought evidence to suggest that the ætiological agent is a filtrable virus ; he was able to show that Berkefeld V filtrates of scrapings of these fresh lesions, autolysed at 37° C. for 3 hours before filtration, or of the dried crusts submitted to tryptic digestion, were infective for normal lambs. The virus in the dried crusts resists desiccation for at least 4 months. Under natural conditions the disease appears to be highly infectious. Animals that have recovered from the disease possess a high degree of immunity, sufficient to protect them against re-infection for at least 8 months.

HERPES

Herpes febrilis.—Herpes febrilis or simplex occurs in the form of small vesicles, which are almost always bilateral, on the muco-cutaneous borders of the mouth or nostrils of patients suffering from a variety of diseases, of which pneumonia is the commonest. Inoculation of the vesicular fluid on the scarified cornea of a rabbit is followed by a severe keratitis, which can be propagated indefinitely by passage. If fluid is taken from an early keratitis in the rabbit, it is possible to produce with it specific lesions in a number of different tissues, such as the skin, buccal mucosa, trachea, liver, adrenal, ovary, salivary glands, brain, and spinal cord (Goodpasture and Teague 1923–24a, Urbain and Schaefer 1927, Smith 1931a). Intracutaneous inoculation of human vesicular fluid produces in the rabbit an insignificant papular eruption, but once it has become adapted to the rabbit's tissues, the virus gives rise to a local herpetic lesion ; this method is of considerable value in the titration of infective material. Direct inoculation of human vesicular fluid on to the pad of the guinea-pig's foot is uniformly followed by the development of local vesicular lesions (Bedson 1934). A certain proportion of rabbits inoculated on the cornea develop, after a few days, a fatal encephalitis, characterized by widespread small-celled infiltrations, intense nerve-cell degeneration, and diffuse proliferative changes of some of the fixed elements of the tissue affected (da Fano 1923). Direct intracerebral or subdural inoculation of vesicular fluid into rabbits gives rise to a meningo-encephalitis which proves fatal in about 5 days, and which is transmissible in series to other rabbits by inoculation of the brain suspension. Experiments with monkeys have not given uniform results, but according to Teissier, Gastinel and Reilly (1925) cutaneous inoculation in *Callithrix* may result in the development of vesico-pustules, though often merely small papules appear. Corneal or intracerebral inoculations were without effect. Injected intracranially into mice, the herpes virus gives rise to a characteristic encephalitic syndrome appearing after about 3 days ; the virus can be maintained indefinitely by passage through mice (Andervont 1929).

The herpes virus can be grown easily in tissue cultures, one of the most suitable media being rabbit testis (Parker and Nye 1925b, Gildemeister *et al.* 1929, Smith 1931b). In the vesicular fluid it is present in the form of elementary bodies, which can be stained by suitable means (Taniguchi *et al.* 1934). Examination of the corneal lesions in rabbits during the first 24 hours reveals the presence of large numbers of inclusion bodies—called " α-bodies " by Lipschütz (1921) (Fig. 275). Though the virus may be demonstrated in the blood after intratesticular, and occasionally after intracutaneous, inoculation of rabbits (Gildemeister and Heuer 1929), the work of Goodpasture and Teague (1923–24b) seems to show that it may enter the peripheral nerves—sensory, motor, or sympathetic—from a local lesion and reach the central nervous system, where it is liable to give rise to a myelitis or encephalitis.

Rabbit brain is highly infective, but its infectivity can be increased by homogenization—a process which probably acts by disintegration of the cells and liberation of the virus particles in a free form. Freshly homogenized virus may prove fatal on intracerebral inoculation into rabbits in 12–30 hours, and even one ten-millionth of a gram of infected brain tissue may kill the animals within 5 days (Buggs and Green 1936).

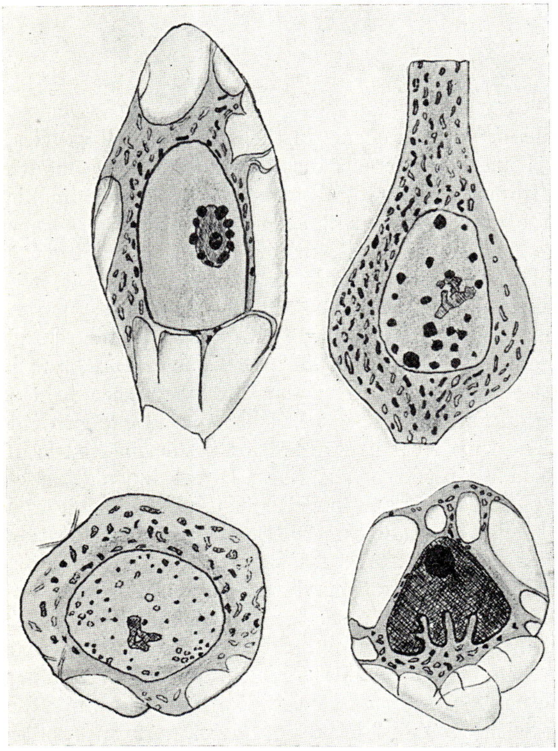

Rabbits that have passed through an attack of experimental keratitis possess a considerable degree of immunity to subsequent corneal, or even intracerebral, inoculation (Levaditi and Nicolau 1922). This immunity appears to depend largely on the development of humoral antibodies (Bedson and Crawford 1927, Schultz and Hoyt 1928). Bedson and Bland (1929) were able to obtain specific complement fixation with the herpes virus in the presence of serum from the hyper-immunized guinea-pig. Antibodies may also be demonstrated in a considerable proportion of children and adults, either by a specific neutralization test (Zinsser and Tang 1929, Andrewes and Carmichael 1930), or by complement fixation (Brain 1932). There is evidence that these antibodies result from a latent or overt infection with the virus. Recurrent attacks of herpes febrilis are not uncommon. Indeed, this disease constitutes one of the most striking exceptions to the general rule that filtrable virus infections usually leave behind them a solid and lasting immunity.

FIG. 275.

Intranuclear inclusion bodies in nerve cells of rabbits experimentally infected with herpes febrilis.
(After Cowdry and Nicholson 1924.)

Keratitis herpetica of human beings was shown by Grüter in 1912–14 to be transmissible to rabbits by inoculation of the scarified cornea. This observation was confirmed by Luger and Lauda (1921), who found, histologically, alterations in cellular structure similar to those in herpes febrilis. These consisted of giant-cell formation, the characteristic ballooning degeneration of Unna, and bodies which they considered to be due to a specific degenerative reaction of the nucleus, but which Lipschütz regards as inclusion bodies.

Herpes genitalis has likewise been shown to be transmissible to rabbits, but the keratitis set up by the genitalis virus is much less severe than that set up by the febrilis virus. Similarly, on subdural inoculation the genitalis virus is less virulent ; by this route the febrilis virus uniformly produces encephalitis in rabbits, fatal in 4 to 6 days ; the genitalis virus does not uniformly produce encephalitis, and, when it does, the rabbits do not die for 5 to 17 days (Blanc and Caminopetros 1924). Lipschütz (1921) succeeded in transferring genital herpes to human beings. Both in the human lesions and in the rabbit's cornea, he found nuclear inclusion bodies of the so-called β-type present in large numbers ; they are best looked for in the rabbit's cornea on the 3rd day after inoculation. He was unable to produce immunity to the genitalis virus by inoculation of the rabbit's cornea with the febrilis virus. He therefore regards the two viruses as biologically distinct.

Herpes zoster.

Herpes zoster differs clinically from herpes febrilis in forming large vesicles or bullæ, in occurring on the trunk, in being almost always unilateral, in being accompanied by sharp neuralgic pains, in being distributed along the course of sensory nerves, and in being non-recurrent. Experiments made to ascertain whether zoster is transmissible to animals have given most conflicting results.

Lipschütz (1921) claimed to have produced keratitis in rabbits with material from 3 out of 7 cases of zoster. Both in human lesions and in the rabbit's cornea, he found characteristic nuclear inclusion bodies, which he calls " zoster bodies." In the rabbit's cornea these bodies were present in greatest numbers on the 4th day after inoculation. The keratitis, when it did develop, was mild, and consisted of small round vesicles, which did not appear till the 4th day, and which after a few days tended to regress. Kundratitz (1924–25) claimed to have transmitted zoster to infants ; in contradistinction to herpes febrilis, in which the incubation period of the experimental human disease is only 24 to 48 hours, the incubation period in zoster was 12 to 15 days. Teague and Goodpasture (1923–24) obtained some evidence that the zoster virus differed from that of herpes febrilis mainly in its degree of virulence, but their experiments were not very satisfactory.

Cole and Kuttner (1925) failed to confirm the work of either Lipschütz, or Teague and Goodpasture. Using material from 9 cases of zoster, they performed corneal and intracerebral inoculations on rabbits ; they inoculated *rhesus* monkeys by the cerebral, cutaneous, neural, and corneal routes, and vervet monkeys by the testicular route ; and they rubbed the material on to the scarified tar-painted skin of rabbits and guinea-pigs —all with negative results. Since herpes febrilis can be easily transmitted to rabbits, while zoster either cannot be transmitted at all or only irregularly, they conclude that the two diseases are ætiologically distinct. Seidenberg (1931) was likewise unable to produce keratitis or orchitis in the rabbit with vesicular fluid from zoster patients ; and the cornea of rabbits inoculated with zoster virus was found to be still susceptible to the virus of herpes febrilis.

Elementary bodies may be demonstrated by suitable staining methods in zoster vesicles, particularly during the first 48 hours (Amies 1934, Taniguchi *et al.* 1934). It seems probable that they constitute the specific virus of the disease.

Summarizing, it would appear that the viruses of herpes febrilis, genitalis, and zoster all differ from each other ; the febrilis virus is the most virulent for the rabbit and the zoster virus the least. Whether they are to be regarded as distinct species of virus, or as varieties of the same species, it is at present impossible to say.

For the relation of herpes zoster to varicella see p. 1488.

VARICELLA

Chicken-pox appears to be due to a virus, which can be demonstrated by suitable staining methods in the vesicular fluid (Aragão 1911, Paschen 1919, Taniguchi *et al.* 1932*b*). The virus particles, or elementary bodies, are of coccoid form, and are arranged singly, in pairs, or in short chains. The virus is of very low infectivity for animals. Rivers and Tillet (1923, 1924*a*, *b*) however, succeeded by repeated passage in adapting a strain of virus to the rabbit's testicle. After a few generations the virus gave rise to an inflammatory reaction in the testicle, accompanied by œdematous swelling of the scrotum. A testicular suspension inoculated intradermally gave rise to a vesicular eruption. These findings were confirmed by Taniguchi and his colleagues (1932*b*), who also succeeded in cultivating the virus in rabbit lung and testicle tissue cultures inoculated with testicular suspension. Cross-immunization experiments on the rabbit's skin showed that the varicella virus was different from that of vaccinia. In the testicles of vervet monkeys inoculated intratesticularly with material from human varicella lesions eosinophilic nuclear inclusion bodies may be found (Rivers 1926, 1927).

Amies (1933) has described a specific agglutination reaction, using as antigen a 0·25 per cent. formolized suspension of elementary bodies prepared by the differential centrifugation of human vesicular fluid. Of 55 sera taken from patients 2–12 days after the onset of the attack, 35 contained agglutinins in a titre of 1/4–1/256, while 20 gave negative results. Antibodies appear about 5 days after the onset, and persist for some considerable time.

Relation between Herpes zoster and Varicella.

A large body of clinical evidence has been produced suggesting that zoster and varicella are closely allied diseases. The experimental evidence in favour of this conception has been summarized by Lipschütz and Kundratitz (1925) as follows : (1) In infants inoculated with zoster material, apart from the local vesicles that develop, a general varicella-like eruption may occur ; (2) children brought into contact with infants inoculated with zoster may develop chicken-pox ; (3) inoculation experiments with zoster, made on children who have recovered from varicella, prove negative ; (4) inoculation experiments with varicella, in children who have recovered from natural or experimental zoster, prove negative ; (5) the serum from patients convalescing from zoster has a protective action against varicella ; (6) both varicella and experimental zoster have the same incubation period ; (7) similar cytological appearances are found in both diseases. To these we may add that Netter and Urbain (1924, 1926, 1931) have reported the finding of identical antibodies, demonstrable by the complement-fixation test, in the serum of patients with zoster and varicella. These results have been confirmed by Brain (1933), who finds that zoster and varicella vesicular fluids give equally good fixation in the presence of zoster and varicella sera. It has further been shown that serum from convalescent zoster patients often agglutinates a suspension of varicella elementary bodies, though to a rather lower titre than a suspension of zoster elementary bodies. Conversely, serum from convalescent varicella patients often agglutinates zoster elementary bodies (Paschen 1933, Amies 1934). The virus of varicella appears to be slightly more infective for animals than that of zoster. Cross-immunization experiments on animals have as yet hardly been tried, and preliminary observations have not given very conclusive results (Rivers and

Eldridge 1929). Clinical experience, however, shows that an attack of varicella does not afford complete protection against herpes zoster. The evidence so far accumulated suggests that the two diseases are caused by the same virus, though possibly minor antigenic differences may exist between different strains.

LYMPHOGRANULOMATOSIS INGUINALE

SYNONYM : Climatic bubo

In 1913 Durand, Nicolas, and Favre of Lyon, drew attention to a bubonic disease, probably of venereal origin, which was characterized by a subacute inflammation of the inguinal lymphatic glands. In 1925 Frei reported the discovery of a specific intracutaneous test for the diagnosis of the disease. As a result of this means of differentiating lymphogranulomatosis from other diseases, several workers entered the field of investigation. In 1930 Hellerström and Wassén at the International Dermatological Congress in Copenhagen described the successful transmission of infection to monkeys by intracerebral inoculation, and concluded that the disease was of virus origin. Since then there has been a large outcrop of papers on various aspects of the subject, which it is impossible to summarize adequately in the space at our disposal. Those who are anxious for more detailed information are referred to monographs and papers by Stannus (1932), Koch (1933), Findlay (1933), Hellerström and Wassén (1934), Wassén (1935), Levaditi, Mollaret and Reinié (1935).

Though showing a preference for the tropics, the disease is widespread throughout the world. Males of 20–40 years of age are most often affected. The disease is contracted through sexual intercourse. After healing of the initial penile lesion, males cease to be infectious, whereas females, on account of the peculiar lymphatic distribution in the perineal region, remain infectious for months and years. In females particularly, the disease often involves the genito-ano-rectal tissues with the production of a stricture—a condition referred as *esthiomène*—though it is not yet established that all cases of esthiomène are caused by the lymphogranuloma virus.

Intracerebral inoculation of infective material into monkeys, gives rise, after an incubation period of 6–12 days, to meningo-encephalitis. The virus can be carried on indefinitely by passage. Mice are also susceptible to intracerebral inoculation. Guinea-pigs are fairly resistant. Infective monkey or mouse brain, when inoculated on to the prepuce, is able to reproduce the typical disease in human subjects (Levaditi *et al.* 1932, 1935, Wassén 1935).

The causative virus passes through Berkefeld N and Chamberland L3 candles, though the results are said to be inconsistent. According to Miyagawa and his colleagues (1935c) and to Broom and Findlay (1936), its probable diameter is about 0·125–0·175 μ. It is destroyed by exposure to a temperature of 56° C. for 10 minutes, and is readily inactivated by glycerol and by 0·1 per cent. formol. At 4° C. it remains virulent for about 3 weeks. Cultivation experiments have yielded rather ambiguous results. Elementary bodies, demonstrable by histological methods, have been described by Miyagawa and his colleagues (1935a, b) in infected mouse and monkey tissue.

In the diagnosis of the disease the Frei (1925) test is widely used. The antigen consists of pus from a bubo, heated to 60° C. for 2 hours on 1 day, and for 1 hour on the following day.   Intracutaneous inoculation of 0·1 c.c. gives rise in an infected subject to an infiltrated inflammatory area, at least 0·5 cm. across, with a small central zone of necrosis.   The reaction reaches its height after about 48 hours. Injected intravenously, the antigen gives rise to a febrile response ; according to Hellerström this method is more sensitive than the original intradermal test.

The blood serum of patients suffering from the disease is said to contain neutralizing bodies.

FOOT-AND-MOUTH DISEASE

Foot-and-mouth disease is a highly infectious disease of cloven-footed animals. Cattle, pigs, sheep, and goats are chiefly affected ; reindeer and camels are susceptible, and very exceptionally horses, dogs, and cats are attacked (Hutyra and Marek 1926).   Occasionally human beings contract the disease.   Epidemics occur from time to time in most countries, the disease remaining endemic in the intervening periods.   In this country the disease has been present in epidemic form during the past few years, culminating in 1923, when 1,854 separate outbreaks were reported involving the slaughter of 125,098 animals.   The disease itself is usually mild, causing a mortality in cattle of not more than 2–3 per cent., and a slightly higher mortality in sheep and pigs ; on the Continent, however, a malignant form sometimes occurs, causing a mortality of 50–70 per cent.   The incubation period is 2 to 7 days.   Infection usually occurs from animal to animal, the infective material coming into contact with the mucosa of the mouth, nose or conjunctiva, or with an abraded skin surface.   Cases of direct infection are easy to understand ; the real problem lies in explaining the origin of foot-and-mouth disease in animals that have not, so far as can be ascertained, been in contact with infected animals.   Numerous explanations have been offered of these cryptogenic cases. Thus it is supposed by some that infection is carried by contaminated hay, straw, milk, drinking water, clothes, and other objects.   In support of this, it has been found that the virus may survive on chopped hay at room temperature for at least 15 weeks, and on bran for at least 20 weeks (Report 1927).   Moreover, there is evidence that the virus may resist putrefaction for long periods (Report 1928*b*) In this way it is possible to understand how infection may lie dormant for months in dried discharges or in carcasses of infected animals.   That the virus may not only remain alive, but may keep its virulence under these conditions, was shown by the development of foot-and-mouth disease in a calf fed with hay that had been contaminated 1 month previously with infected saliva, and in pigs fed on crushed bones from the frozen carcasses of infected animals that had been killed several weeks previously (Report 1927).

Another explanation is that the virus is carried by human and animal agencies. Thus it has been suggested : (1) That birds may carry infectious material on their feet ; for this there is no direct evidence.   (2) That wild rodents may carry the disease and transmit it to cattle, sheep, and pigs coming into contact with them (see Beattie *et al.* 1928).   It has been shown that many of these rodents are susceptible to experimental infection, but practically all experiments designed to test the possibility of natural spread amongst them have given negative results.   The virus, however, has been demonstrated in hedgehogs.   (3) That the virus may gain access to, and persist on, the nasopharyngeal mucosa of human beings, who can then act as healthy carriers of the disease ; for this there is a certain amount of epidemiological, but no direct experimental evidence (Kling and Höjer 1926). (4) That infected cattle may remain as chronic carriers ; it has been found that infective material may persist on the hoofs for some time after recovery from the disease, but this appears to be an exceptional occurrence (Gins and Krause 1923). Animals that have recovered from the disease may excrete the virus in the urine, but the frequency of urinary carriers is still in doubt (Waldmann *et al.* 1931). The experimental evidence so far collected does not favour the view that chronic carriers are common.   On the other hand, there is a considerable amount of epidemiological evidence to suggest that infection is introduced into a herd by means of apparently healthy animals coming from another herd.   Moreover, if the virus could persist on the healthy mucosa of animals, or remain latent in their tissues, it would not be difficult to understand how outbreaks of the disease might occur in herds that had had no demonstrable contact with the disease.   At the present time it is impossible to come to any definite conclusion on the most common method of indirect infection ; but the Foot-and-mouth Disease Research Committee (Report 1928*b*) favour the view that the persistence of the virus in dried discharges on fodder, hair, and other materials, and in carcasses, is of greater epizootiological significance than its carriage in the body of recovered animals.

Experimental Reproduction of the Disease.—The disease can be experimentally reproduced in cattle, sheep, and pigs by rubbing infective material from the foot-and-mouth lesions into the scarified mucosa of the lip or mouth.   Intramuscular inoculation requires a larger dose, and the effect is less regular.

In *cattle* inoculated intramuscularly, the temperature rises in 1 to 3 days to about 104° F., and the characteristic lesions appear in 1 to 5 days.   Of 71 cattle that reacted to inoculation, foot and mouth lesions occurred together in 63 ; in the remaining 8, mouth lesions were absent (Report 1927).   Great differences in the severity of the disease occur as the result of inoculating different strains of virus.   Sheep inoculated intramuscularly generally show a rise of temperature to 104° or 105° F. in 18 to 48 hours.   Foot lesions are constant, appearing in 1 to 3 days or so, depending on the virulence of the strain.   Mouth lesions are uncommon.   Pigs inoculated intramuscularly show a rise of temperature in 20 to 48 hours ; foot lesions constantly develop, generally in 1 to 3 days ; mouth lesions are not quite so constant, and do not appear till after 3 days.

Waldmann and Pape (1920) showed that the disease could be reproduced experimentally in *guinea-pigs* by cutaneous or subcutaneous inoculation into the balls of the fore and hind feet, or into the hairless side of the metatarsus.

After intracutaneous inoculation of the foot pad, there is an incubation period lasting from 12 hours to 4 days.   The first signs of reaction are a rise of body temperature, and redness and swelling of the foot, followed by the development of small vesicles radiating from the line of inoculation.   The vesicles coalesce to form a large tense blister over the entire sole, containing as much as 0·1 c.c. of semi-transparent fluid, which is rich in virus. General symptoms of illness occur, and secondary vesicles develop on the uninoculated feet, and on the tongue, lips and gums.   About 2 days after their appearance, the vesicles become greyish-white and flattened, and then gradually dry up ; the whitish colour of the skin may remain for some time.   The vesicles usually heal completely in 10 to 14 days.   Though the animals are often ill, refuse food, and lose weight, only about 5 per cent. of them die.   The remainder recover, and are henceforth highly resistant to fresh inoculation.   The disease can be reproduced by intramuscular, intraperitoneal, and intravenous inoculation.   After intravenous injection, vesicles develop on the legs in 3 to 4 days ; mouth lesions are not usually observed (Waldmann and Pape 1920). Maitland (1928) has brought evidence to suggest that mechanical pressure is to some

extent responsible for the localization of the lesions on the pads of the feet after intramuscular injection of the virus. She found that if one foot was adequately protected
from pressure by being wrapped in cotton-wool, no lesions developed on this foot after
intramuscular injection, though typical vesicles appeared on the unprotected feet. Moreover, by exposing the feet to unusual pressure, as by keeping the animals in cages with
a coarse wire-mesh floor, she was able to induce the formation of vesicles on the toes,
and even on the dorsal parts of the feet—situations in which vesicles do not usually occur.
The disease can readily be passed from animal to animal by inoculation with infective
material.

Rabbits, rats and mice can all be infected, but the experimental disease is less severe
and less typical than in guinea-pigs ; dogs and cats sometimes prove susceptible ; fowls
and ducks are resistant. The disease practically never spreads from experimentally
inoculated to normal rodents. Even highly susceptible cattle placed in contact with
infected guinea-pigs rarely contract the disease.

Properties of the Virus.—The virus is present in great concentration in the
vesicle fluid of experimentally infected guinea-pigs ; even when diluted 1/1,000,000
times it is generally infective for normal guinea-pigs. In the blood, during the
febrile stage of the illness, the concentration is less, but even this is active in a
1/1,000 dilution (Report 1927). In cattle during the febrile stage of the disease,
the saliva, urine, milk and vesicular fluid are infective ; but in 3 to 6 days after
the appearance of the lesions they lose their infectivity completely. For diagnostic
purposes, it is therefore important to use fresh vesicular material, not more than
2 days old (Olitsky *et al.* 1928). The rapid disappearance of the virus from the
local lesion and blood of infected animals is one of the most remarkable features
of foot-and-mouth disease ; within the space of 3 or 4 days as a rule the virus,
from being present in large quantities, is reduced to such an extent that it is no
longer demonstrable by experimental methods.

Loeffler and Frosch (1898) in 1897 were the first to show that the foot-and-
mouth virus was filtrable. When present in diluted vesicle fluid, it will pass readily
through Berkefeld, Chamberland and Seitz filters. Experiments with gradocol
membranes suggest that the smallest particles are about 8–12 mμ in diameter,
but there is some evidence that considerably larger particles may occur, and that
the A, B, and C varieties are not identical in size (see Modrow 1929). The virus
was successfully cultivated by Maitland and Maitland (1931) in tissue cultures
containing guinea-pig embryo tissue and clotted guinea-pig plasma. Seventeen
successive generations were observed, and a titre as high as 1/100,000 was obtained
(see also Hecke 1930, Striegler 1933).

The virus is very resistant to certain methods of disinfection, though easily destroyed
by others. Thus when vesicle fluid from the guinea-pig is dried rapidly on a glass slide
at 37° C., it is often inactivated immediately ; but if dried slowly at room temperature,
and kept over H_2SO_4, it survives for 3 to 6 months. Filtered vesicle fluid is destroyed
by moist heat at 55° C. in 15 to 40 minutes. The virus when present in dilute vesicle
fluid is readily destroyed by high dilutions of chlorine, iodine, potassium permanganate,
caustic soda, and sulphuric acid, but in epithelial scrapings it is much more resistant.
Its apparent resistance to chemical disinfectants in the presence of organic matter is
probably due to the protective effect exerted by the protein coagula formed in the substrate (Olitsky *et al.* 1928). If coagulation is prevented, or if disinfectants are used that
do not coagulate protein, the virus is found to be very susceptible. In buffer solutions
the virus shows two zones of stability—an optimal zone at pH 6·5–10·0, and a less favourable zone at pH 2·5–3·5 (Galloway and Elford 1935). At a suitable pH it may survive
in the ice-chest for a year.

Plurality of Various Types.—Immunological experiments have shown that there are at least three different types of foot-and-mouth virus. Vallée and Carré (1922) met with two types, Virus O from the Department of the Oise, and Virus A from Germany (*origine allemande*). Both viruses were equally pathogenic for cattle, pigs, and sheep, and gave rise to the same clinical symptoms. Animals that had recovered from infection with one strain proved immune to further infection with the same strain, but were readily infected by the other strain. Waldmann and Trautwein (1926), in an examination of 30 strains of different origin in Germany, encountered three types ; 4 strains belonged to Type A, 4 to Type B, and 5 to Type C ; the remaining 17 strains were variants of the main types. Strains of different types were found in the same area. Oxen and guinea-pigs were infected experimentally with the three different types in succession. According to the Foot-and-mouth Disease Research Committee (Report 1928*b*), Vallée's Type A is the same as Waldmann's Type B, and Vallée's Type O the same as Waldmann's Type A ; Waldmann's Type C is a new type. The three types are said to be distinguishable by complement fixation (Ciuca 1929, Helm 1933).

Further observations, particularly by Manninger and von László (1930), Trautwein and Reppin (1932) and Daubney (1934), have cast considerable doubt on the fixity of these three types. Variant and intermediate types have been observed, and one intermediate strain was found to pass into an O type as the result of guinea-pig passage and into an A type as the result of storage in the cold. Daubney regards the bovine virus as a labile organism subject to spontaneous phase variations. The epidemiological importance of multiple types is obvious, since it renders possible the re-infection of animals that have already passed through one attack of the disease.

Immunity and Prophylactic Treatment.

An animal that has passed through an attack of foot-and-mouth disease is resistant to inoculation with the same strain for 6 to 12 months. The serum of immune animals contains antibodies capable of neutralizing the virus *in vitro*. Prophylactically, immunity may be produced by the injection of animals with a weakly virulent virus, given either alone or in combination with immune serum. The practice of using living virus is open to several objections.

Vallée, Carré and Rinjard (1926) succeeded in rendering cattle immune by the use of a formolized vaccine, prepared by exposing the virus to a concentration of 0·5 per cent. formol for 4 to 7 days at room temperature. Heifers inoculated subcutaneously with 10 c.c. of Virus A and 10 c.c. of Virus O vaccine were protected against subsequent infection with either strain, though one animal proved susceptible to Virus O. Immunity can likewise be produced in guinea-pigs by use of a formolized vaccine, but the immunity is only partial, and wears off in about 2 months ; moreover, antibodies are not demonstrable in the blood serum. Guinea-pigs may, however, be rendered highly resistant by the intramuscular injection of living virus, after preliminary immunization with formolized virus ; and in animals so treated antibodies may readily be demonstrated in the blood (Report 1927, 1928*b*). It remains true, however, that no satisfactory vaccine for the active immunization of cattle has yet been devised (Waldmann and Reppin 1935).

Immune serum may be used prophylactically or therapeutically ; in guinea-pigs the serum, though unable to protect completely against the disease, will yet prevent its generalization.

Vesicular Stomatitis of Horses

This disease is similar in many respects to foot-and-mouth disease. It has been observed chiefly in South Africa and the United States, and is characterized by the development of vesicles on the oral mucosa, particularly on that of the tongue. Though the disease is primarily one of equines, cattle may become infected naturally; the lesions in cattle resemble those of foot-and-mouth disease, but are less extensive, and do not usually affect the feet. Intramuscular injection of cattle with the vesicular stomatitis virus does not produce lesions, whereas injection with the foot-and-mouth virus does; in horses, on the other hand, inoculation of the scarified tongue with the stomatitis virus produces lesions, whereas the foot-and-mouth virus does not. Pigs do not contract vesicular stomatitis naturally, but can be infected experimentally. The guinea-pig is susceptible to experimental inoculation with the stomatitis virus. According to Olitsky, Traum and Schoening (1928) there is no cross-immunity between foot-and-mouth disease and vesicular stomatitis in cattle. The causative virus differs from that of foot-and-mouth disease in being larger, 70–100 mμ, and in multiplying readily on the chorio-allantoic membrane of the developing chick embryo (Galloway and Elford 1933, 1935). There are at least two antigenic types.

Virus III Infection of Rabbits

Virus III was the name given by Rivers and Tillett (1923, 1924*a, b*) to a filtrable virus encountered in rabbits during experimental work on chicken-pox. Injected intratesticularly into rabbits it produces a high fever and characteristic lesions in the cornea, testicles and skin; within the epithelial and endothelial cells of these lesions acidophilic nuclear inclusion bodies are found, similar to those seen in herpes and varicella. Injected intracerebrally it sometimes gives rise to a meningo-encephalitis, not unlike that of herpetic encephalitis (Rivers and Stewart 1928). Frozen and desiccated, and kept in sealed tubes on ice, it retains its virulence indefinitely; even after 15 months under these conditions it was still active. Its activity is also maintained for at least 6 weeks if infected testicular suspensions are mixed with equal amounts of glycerol, and stored on ice. It is destroyed by heat at 55° C. in 10 minutes. Rabbits injected with the virus develop an immunity to subsequent inoculation, which lasts for 6 months or more. The serum of immune rabbits contains antibodies capable of neutralizing the virus either *in vitro*, or locally in the rabbit's skin when the serum and virus are inoculated together. Attempts to confer passive immunity on rabbits, by intravenous injection of immune serum 24 hours previous to inoculation of the virus, proved negative. Rivers and Tillett found that about 15 per cent. of their young stock rabbits were refractory to infection with Virus III, indicating that they had suffered spontaneously from the disease. The same virus was met with in rabbits by Miller, Andrewes and Swift (1924). According to Andrewes (1929), it can be grown in tissue cultures prepared from adult rabbit testis. Typical intranuclear inclusion bodies are formed in these cultures.

INFECTIOUS ECTROMELIA

This is a highly infective disease of mice, which was first described by Marchal (1930) at Hampstead. It occurs in an acute form characterized by the presence of visceral lesions, in a chronic form characterized by necrosis of the feet, and in a latent symptomless form. In the chronic form one of the feet becomes swollen and œdematous, and serous fluid escapes from the surface, forming minute scabs. The disease may retrogress, in which case the foot becomes gangrenous and sloughs off leaving healthy tissue behind ; or infection may spread to another foot, the tail, or the mouth, and lead to the death of the animal. In the acute form the animals die without any external lesions. Post mortem the liver may be dirty grey in colour, or it may be red and mottled due to the presence of small white focal areas of necrosis. The spleen is slightly enlarged, and may show large white areas, especially in the more chronic cases. There is often an excess of pleural fluid. It must be emphasized, however, that mice may die of ectromelia without showing any definite macroscopic lesions. Histologically, the chief characteristic is necrosis of the mesoblastic tissues, and the presence in the epithelial cells of the skin and intestine of large acidophilic cytoplasmic inclusion bodies (see Figs. 213 and 214, p. 753). The disease can be readily transmitted to normal mice by contact, and by inoculation with infective material. Rats are susceptible, but develop only an " inapparent " infection (Burnet and Lush 1936).

The causative agent is a virus, 100–150 mμ in diameter, which can be demonstrated microscopically in the liver and cutaneous tissues (Barnard and Elford 1931). It is widely distributed throughout the body. It is destroyed by exposure to 55° C. for 30 minutes, but withstands the action of 50 per cent. glycerol in the ice-chest for several months. It can be grown in tissue culture (Downie and McGaughey 1935), and on the chorio-allantoic membrane of the chick embryo (Paschen 1936). The case mortality of the disease is generally fairly high.

In diagnosis, the chronic foot lesions must be distinguished from those caused by *Actinomyces muris*. This organism can be cultivated directly on serum agar. One of the best methods of demonstrating the presence of the virus in a suspected mouse is to filter a suspension of the liver and spleen through sand and paper pulp, to add 0·5 per cent. phenol, to leave it in the ice-chest till it is bacteriologically sterile, and to inoculate it intraperitoneally into normal mice. If the virus is present, the animals will die within 4-6 days, and macroscopic lesions will be demonstrable in the liver.

Animals that recover from the disease have a substantial immunity. Normal animals can be vaccinated with considerable success by means of a formolized liver suspension (Greenwood and Topley 1936). For a study of the epidemic spread of the disease, see Greenwood and Topley (1936).

REFERENCES

ALDERSHOFF, H. (1935) *Schweiz. med. Wschr.*, **65**, 510.
AMIES, C. R. (1932) *Lancet*, ii. 558 ; (1933) *Ibid.*, i. 1015 ; (1934) *Brit. J. exp. Path.*, **15**, 314.
ANDERVONT, H. B. (1929) *J. infect. Dis.*, **45**, 366.
ANDERVONT, H. B. and ROSENAU, M. J. (1930) *J. Immunol.*, **18**, 51.
ANDREWES, C. H. (1929) *Brit. J. exp. Path.*, **10**, 188.
ANDREWES, C. H. and CARMICHAEL, E. A. (1930) *Lancet*, i. 857.
ARAGÁO, H. DE B. (1911) *Mem. Inst. Osw. Cruz*, **3**, 309.
ARMSTRONG, C. (1927) *Publ. Hlth Rep., Wash.*, **42**, 3061 ; (1932) *Ibid.*, **47**, 1553.
ARMSTRONG, C. and LILLIE, R. D. (1929) *Publ. Hlth Rep., Wash.*, **44**, 2635.
BARNARD, J. E. and ELFORD, W. J. (1931) *Proc. roy. Soc.*, B, **109**, 360.
BEATTIE, J. M., MORCOS, Z., and PEDEN, D. (1928) *J. comp. Path.*, **41**, 353.
BEDSON, S. P. (1934) *Pers. comm.*
BEDSON, S. P. and BLAND, J. O. W. (1929) *Brit. J. exp. Path.*, **10**, 393.
BEDSON, S. P. and CRAWFORD, G. J. (1927) *Brit. J. exp. Path.*, **8**, 138.
BERGER, E. (1929) *Zbl. Bakt.*, **110**, 138.

BLANC, G. and CAMINOPETROS, J. (1924) *Ann. Inst. Pasteur*, **38**, 152.
BLAXALL, F. R. (1923) *Bull. Acad. Méd., Paris*, **89**, 146.
BORREL, A. (1903) *Ann. Inst. Pasteur*, **17**, 81, 123.
BOSC, F. J. (1903) *Zbl. Bakt.*, **34**, 413, 517, 666.
BRAIN, R. T. (1932) *Brit. J. exp. Path.*, **13**, 166 ; (1933) *Ibid.*, **14**, 67.
BRIDRÉ, J. and BOQUET, A. (1923) *Ann. Inst. Pasteur*, **37**, 229 ; (1933) *Ibid.*, **51**, 761.
BROOM, J. C. and FINDLAY, G. M. (1936) *Brit. J. exp. Path.*, **17**, 135.
BROWNLEE, J. (1905–06) *Biometrika*, **4**, 313.
BUGGS, C. W. and GREEN, R. G. (1936) *J. infect. Dis.*, **58**, 98.
BURGESS, W. L., CRAIGIE, J., and TULLOCH, W. J. (1929) *Spec. Rep. Ser. med. Res. Coun., Lond.*, No. 143.
BURNET, F. M. (1933) *J. Path. Bact.*, **37**, 107.
BURNET, F. M. and LUSH, D. (1936) *J. Path. Bact.*, **42**, 469.
BUSSEL and MAYSNER. (1930) *C. R. Soc. Biol.*, **103**, 411.
CALMETTE, A. and GUÉRIN, C. (1901) *Ann. Inst. Pasteur*, **15**, 161.
CIUCA, A. (1929) *J. Hyg., Camb.*, **28**, 325.
CLEARKIN, P. A. (1930) *Brit. J. exp. Path.*, **11**, 329.
COLE, R. and KUTTNER, A. G. (1925) *J. exp. Med.*, **42**, 799.
COWDRY, E. V. (1927) *J. exp. Med.*, **45**, 799.
COWDRY, E. V. and NICHOLSON, F. M. (1924) *J. Amer. med. Ass.*, **82**, 545.
CRAIGIE, J. (1932) *Brit. J. exp. Path.*, **13**, 259.
CRAIGIE, J. and TULLOCH, W. J. (1931) *Spec. Rep. Ser. med. Res. Coun., Lond.*, No. 156.
CRAIGIE, J. and WISHART, F. O. (1933) *Canad. publ. Hlth J.*, **24**, 72.
DAUBNEY, R. (1934) *J. comp. Path.*, **47**, 259.
DEFRIES, R. D. and McKINNON, N. E. (1928) *Amer. J. Hyg.*, **8**, 107.
DIEM, E. (1930) *Schweiz. med. Wschr.*, **60**, 1174.
DOUGLAS, S. R. and SMITH, W. (1930) *Brit. J. exp. Path.*, **11**, 96.
DOUGLAS, S. R., SMITH, W., and PRICE, L. R. W. (1929) *J. Path. Bact.*, **32**, 99.
DOWNIE, A. W. and McGAUGHEY, C. A. (1935) *J. Path. Bact.*, **40**, 147.
DOYLE, T. M. (1929) *Vet. Rec.*, **9**, 62 ; (1930) *J. comp. Path.*, **43**, 40.
DOYLE, T. M. and MINETT, F. C. (1927) *J. comp. Path.*, **40**, 247.
DURAND, M., NICOLAS, J., and FAVRE, M. (1913) *Bull. Soc. méd. Hôp. Paris*, **35**, 274.
ECKSTEIN, A. (1931) *Z. Hyg. InfektKr.*, **112**, 151.
FAIRBROTHER, R. W. (1932) *J. Path. Bact.*, **35**, 35 ; (1934) "Handbook of Filterable Viruses." William Heinemann, Ltd., London.
FANO, C. DA. (1923) *J. Path. Bact.*, **26**, 85.
FINDLAY, G. M. (1928) *Proc. roy. Soc., B*, **102**, 354 ; (1933) *Trans. R. Soc. trop. Med. Hyg.*, **27**, 35.
FINE, J. (1932) "Filterable Virus Diseases in Man." E. & S. Livingstone, Edinburgh.
FREI, W. (1925) *Klin. Wschr.*, **4**, 2148.
GALLOWAY, I. A. and ELFORD, W. J. (1933) *Brit. J. exp. Path.*, **14**, 400 ; (1935) *Ibid.*, **16**, 588.
GILDEMEISTER, E. (1931) *Zbl. Bakt.*, **120**, 83.
GILDEMEISTER, E., HAAGEN, E., and SCHEELE, L. (1929) *Zbl. Bakt.*, **114**, 309.
GILDEMEISTER, E. and HELM, R. (1932a) *Zbl. Bakt.*, **123**, 294 ; (1932b) *Ibid.*, **125**, 405.
GILDEMEISTER, E. and HEUER, G. (1929) *Dtsch. med. Wschr.*, **55**, 905.
GILDEMEISTER, E. and HILGERS, P. (1930) *Zbl. Bakt.*, **117**, 258.
GINS, H. A. (1929) *Z. Hyg. InfektKr.*, **110**, 581.
GINS, H. A. and KRAUSE, C. (1923) *Ergebn. allg. Path. path Anat.*, **20**, ii. 805.
GLOVER, R. E. (1928) *J. comp. Path.*, **41**, 318.
GOODPASTURE, E. W. and TEAGUE, O. (1923–24a) *J. med. Res.*, **44**, 121 ; (1923–24b) *Ibid.* **44**, 139.
GORDON, M. H. (1925) *Spec. Rep. Ser. med. Res. Coun., Lond.*, No. 98 ; (1935a) *Lancet*, i. 1527 ; (1935b) *Ibid.*, ii. 104.
GREEN, A. B. and EAGLES, G. H. (1931) *Brit. J. exp. Path.*, **12**, 202.
GREENFIELD, J. G. (1928) *Lancet*, ii. 1303.
GREENWOOD, M. (1930) *Brit. med. J.*, i. 398.
GREENWOOD, M. and TOPLEY, W. W. C. (1936) *Spec. Rep. Ser. med. Res. Coun., Lond.*, No. 209.
GRÖER, F. VON. (1935) *Z. ImmunForsch.*, **86**, 320.
GRÜTER. (1912–14) See LOWENSTEIN ; (1920) *Klin. Monatsbl. Augenheilk.*, **64**, 15.
GUARNIERI. (1894) *Zbl. Bakt.*, **16**, 299.
HAAGEN, E. (1928) *Zbl. Bakt.*, **109**, 31.
HAAGEN, E. and KODAMA, M. (1934) *Zbl. Bakt.*, **133**, 23.
HECKE, F. (1930) *Zbl. Bakt.*, **116**, 386.
HELLERSTRÖM, S. and WASSÉN, E. (1934) "Epidemiology and Etiology of Lymphogranuloma Inguinale." Masson & Cie, Paris.

HELM, R. (1933) *Zbl. Bakt.*, **130,** 305.
HERZBERG, K. (1935) *Z. ImmunForsch.*, **86,** 417.
HERZBERG-KREMMER, H. and HERZBERG, K. (1930) *Zbl. Bakt.*, **115,** 271.
HILGERS, P. (1931) *Zbl. Bakt.*, **123,** 178.
HU, C. K., ROSAHN, P. D., and PEARCE, L. (1936) *J. exp. Med.*, **63,** 353.
HULL, T. G. and NAUSS, R. W. (1926) *Amer. J. publ. Hlth.*, **16,** 101.
HURST, E. W. (1936) *Brain*, **59,** 1.
HURST, E. W. and FAIRBROTHER, R. W. (1930) *J. Path. Bact.*, **33,** 463.
HUTYRA, H. and MAREK, J. (1926) " Special Pathology and Therapeutics of the Diseases
    of Domestic Animals," 3rd Amer. Edit. Chicago and London.
JONG, D. A. DE. (1917) *Bull. Inst. Pasteur*, **15,** 237.
KAISER, R. (1929) *Z. ImmunForsch.*, **64,** 373.
KIKUTH, W. and GOLLUB, H. (1932) *Zbl. Bakt.*, **125,** 313.
KLING, C. and HÖJER, A. (1926) *C. R. Soc. Biol.*, **94,** 613, 615, 618.
KOCH, F. (1933) *Dermat. Z.*, **65,** 207.
KRAUS, R. (1931) *Z. ImmunForsch.*, **69,** 413.
KUNDRATITZ, K. (1924–25) *Mschr. Kinderheilk.*, **29,** 516.
LEAKE, J. P. and FORCE, J. N. (1927) *Bull. U.S. hyg. Lab.*, No. 149.
LEDINGHAM, J. C. G. (1924) *Brit. J. exp. Path.*, **5,** 332 ; (1925) *Lancet*, i, 199 ; (1926)
    J. State Med., **34,** 125 ; (1934) *Proc. R. Soc. Med.*, **27,** 881 ; (1935a) *Lancet*, ii. 45 ; (1935b)
    Bull. Johns Hopk. Hosp., **56,** 247, 337 ; **57,** 32.
LEDINGHAM, J. C. G., MORGAN, W. T. J., and PETRIE, G. F. (1931) *Brit. J. exp. Path.*,
    12, 357.
LEVADITI, C. (1924) *J. State Med.*, **32,** 151, 201, 251.
LEVADITI, C. and NICOLAU, S. (1922) *C. R. Soc. Biol.*, **86,** 228 ; (1923) *Ann. Inst. Pasteur*,
    37, 1.
LEVADITI, C., MOLLARET, P., and REINIÉ, L. (1935) *Bull. Acad. Méd.*, *Paris*, **113,** 439.
LEVADITI, C., RAVAUT, P., LÉPINE, P., and SCHOEN, R. (1932) *Ann. Inst. Pasteur*, **48,** 27.
LIPSCHÜTZ, B. (1921) *Arch. Derm. Syph.*, *Berl.*, **136,** 428.
LIPSCHÜTZ, B. and KUNDRATITZ, K. (1925) *Wien. klin. Wschr.*, **38,** 199.
LOEFFLER, F. and FROSCH, P. (1898) *Dtsch. med. Wschr.*, **24,** 80.
LUCKSCH, F. (1932) *Med. Klinik*, **28,** 1554.
LUDFORD, R. J. and FINDLAY, G. M. (1926) *Brit. J. exp. Path.*, **7,** 256.
LUGER, A. and LAUDA, E. (1921) *Wien. klin. Wschr.*, **34,** 132.
MACDONELL, W. R. (1901–02) *Biometrika*, **1,** 375.
McINTOSH, J. (1928) *Brit. med. J.*, ii. 334 ; (1930) *Lancet*, i. 618.
McINTOSH, J. and SCARFF, R. W. (1930) *J. Path. Bact.*, **33,** 483.
McKINLEY, E. B. (1934) *Puerto Rico J. publ. Hlth trop. Med.*, **9,** 299.
McKINNON, N. E. and DEFRIES, R. D. (1928) *Amer. J. Hyg.*, **8,** 93 ; (1931) *Canad. publ.
    Hlth J.*, **22,** 33.
MAGNUSSON, H. (1932) *Acta path. microbiol. scand.*, Suppl. 11, 204 ; (1933) *Ibid.*, **10,** 329.
MAITLAND, M. C. (1928) *J. comp. Path.*, **41,** 150.
MAITLAND, M. C. and MAITLAND, H. B. (1931) *J. comp. Path.*, **44,** 106.
MANNINGER, R. and LÁSZLÓ, S. VON. (1930) *Zbl. Bakt.*, **116,** 414.
MARCHAL, J. (1930) *J. Path. Bact.*, **33,** 713.
MARIE, A. (1920) *C. R. Soc. Biol.*, **83,** 476.
MILLER, C. P., ANDREWES, C. H., and SWIFT, H. F. (1924) *J. exp. Med.*, **40,** 773.
MIYAGAWA, Y., MITAMURA, T., YAOI, H., ISHII, N., NAKAJIMA, H., OKANISHI, J., WATANABE,
    S., and SATO, K. (1935a) *Jap. J. exp. Med.*, **13,** 1.
MIYAGAWA, Y., MITAMURA, T., YAOI, H., ISHII, N., and OKANISHI, J. (1935b) *Jap. J. exp.
    Med.*, **13,** 331 ; (1935c) *Ibid.*, **13,** 723.
MODROW, I. (1929) *Z. Hyg. InfektKr.*, **110,** 618.
NAKAGAWA, S. (1924) *Z. ImmunForsch.*, **39,** 563.
NETTER, A. and URBAIN, A. (1924) *C. R. Soc. Biol.*, **90,** 189 ; (1926) *Ibid.*, **94,** 98 ; (1931)
    Ann. Inst. Pasteur, **46,** 17.
NOGUCHI, H. (1918) *J. exp. Med.*, **27,** 425.
OHTAWARA, T. (1922) *Sci. Rep. Inst. infect. Dis. Tokyo Univ.*, **1,** 203.
OLITSKY, P. K., TRAUM, J., and SCHOENING, H. W. (1928) *Tec. Bull. U.S. Dep. Agric.*,
    No. 76.
OTTEN, L. (1927) *Z. Hyg. InfektKr.*, **107,** 677 ; (1932) *Meded. Dienst Volksgezondh. Ned.-
    Ind.*, **21,** 196.
PARKER, F. and NYE, R. N. (1925a) *Amer. J. Path.*, **1,** 325 ; (1925b) *Ibid.*, **1,** 337.
PARKER, R. F. and RIVERS, T. M. (1936) *J. exp. Med.*, **63,** 69.
PASCHEN, E. (1919) *Hyg. Rdsch.*, **9,** 314 ; (1933) *Zbl. Bakt.*, **130,** 190 ; (1936) *Zbl. Bakt.*,
    135, 445.
PEARCE, L., ROSAHN, P. D., and HU, C. K. (1936) *J. exp. Med.*, **63,** 241, 491.
RAJCHMAN, L. W. (1928) *Brit. med. J.*, ii. 521.

Report. (1927) 2nd *Prog. Rep. F. & M. Dis. Res. Comm. Min. Agric. Fish.* ; (1928*a*) *Rep. Comm. Vacc., Min. Hlth.*, Cd. 3148 ; (1928*b*) 3rd *Prog. Rep. F. & M. Dis. Res. Comm.* ; (1930) *Rep. Comm. Vacc. Min. Hlth*, Cd. 3738 ; (1931) *Rep. publ. Hlth med. Subj., Lond.*, No. 62 ; (1936) *Bull. Off. int. Hyg. publ.*, **28**, 513.

RHOADS, C. P. (1931) *J. exp. Med.*, **53**, 185.

RIVERS, T. M. (1926) *J. exp. Med.*, **43**, 275 ; (1927) *Ibid.*, **45**, 961. ; (1931) *Ibid.*, **54**, 453 ; (1932) *Arch. Neurol. Psych.*, **28**, 757.

RIVERS, T. M. and ELDRIDGE, L. A. (1929) *J. exp. Med.*, **49**, 899, 907.

RIVERS, T. M., SPRUNT, D. H., and BERRY, G. P. (1933) *J. exp. Med.*, **58**, 39.

RIVERS, T. M. and STEWART, F. W. (1928) *J. exp. Med.*, **48**, 603.

RIVERS, T. M. and TILLET, J. (1923) *J. exp. Med.*, **38**, 673 ; (1924*a*) *Ibid.*, **39**, 777 ; (1924*b*) *Ibid.*, **40**, 281.

RIVERS, T. M. and WARD, S. M. (1935) *J. exp. Med.*, **62**, 549.

ROSAHN, P. D., HU, C. K., and PEARCE, L. (1936) *J. exp. Med.*, **63**, 259, 379.

ROSENAU, M. J. and ANDERVONT, H. B. (1931) *Amer. J. Hyg.*, **13**, 728.

SCHULTZ, E. W. and HOYT, J. (1928) *J. Immunol.*, **15**, 411.

SEIDENBERG, S. (1931) *Z. Hyg. InfektKr.*, **112**, 134.

SMITH, W. (1929) *Brit. J. exp. Path.*, **10**, 93 ; (1931*a*) *J. Path. Bact.*, **34**, 493 ; (1931*b*) *Ibid.*, **34**, 747.

SOBERNHEIM, G. (1925) *Ergebn. Hyg. Bakt.*, **7**, 133.

STANNUS, H. S. (1932) *Proc. R. Soc. Med.*, **26**, 7.

STRIEGLER, E. (1933) *Zbl. Bakt.*, **128**, 332.

TANIGUCHI, T., HOSOKAWA, M., KUGA, S., and MASUDA, Z. (1934) *Jap. J. exp. Med.*, **12**, 101.

TANIGUCHI, T., HOSOKAWA, M., KUGA, S., KOMURA, Y. and NAKAMURA, F. (1932*a*) *Jap. J. exp. Med.*, **10**, 581.

TANIGUCHI, T., HOSOKAWA, M., KUGA, S., NAKAMURA, F., and MATSUMOTO, S. (1932*b*) *Jap. J. exp. Med.*, **10**, 599.

TEAGUE, O. and GOODPASTURE, E. W. (1923–24) *J. med. Res.*, **44**, 185.

TEISSIER, P., GASTINEL, P., and REILLY, J. (1925) *C. R. Soc. Biol.*, **92**, 1015.

TEISSIER, P., REILLY, J., RIVALIER, E., and STÉFANESCO, V. (1931) *C. R. Soc. Biol.*, **108**, 1039.

TOYODA, T. (1924) *Z. Hyg. InfektKr.*, **102**, 592.

TRAUTWEIN, K. and REPPIN, K. (1932) *Z. ImmunForsch.*, **73**, 347.

TULLOCH, W. J. (1928) *Commun. R. Soc. Med., Lond.* (Dec.).

TURNBULL, H. M. and McINTOSH, J. (1926) *Brit. J. exp. Path.*, **7**, 181.

TURNER, F. M. (1905–06) *Biometrika*, **4**, 483.

URBAIN, A. and SCHAEFER, W. (1927) *C. R. Soc. Biol.*, **97**, 1279.

VALLÉE, H. and CARRÉ, H. (1922) *C. R. Acad. Sci.*, **174**, 1498.

VALLÉE, H., CARRÉ, H., and RINJARD, P. (1926) *Rev. gén. Med. vét.*, **35**, 129.

WALDMANN, O. and PAPE, J. (1920) *Berl. tierärztl. Wschr.*, **36**, 519.

WALDMANN and REPPIN. (1935) *Z. InfektKr. Haustiere*, **47**, 283.

WALDMANN, O. and TRAUTWEIN, K. (1926) *Berl. tierärztl. Wschr.*, **42**, 569.

WALDMANN, O., TRAUTWEIN, K., and PYL, G. (1931) *Zbl. Bakt.*, **121**, 19.

WASIELEWSKI, T. VON and WINKLER, W. F. (1925) *Ergebn. Hyg. Bakt.*, **7**, 1.

WASSÉN, E. (1935) " Studies of Lymphogranuloma Inguinale from Etiological and Immunological Points of View." Levin and Munksgaard, Copenhagen.

WOODWARD, S. B. and FEEMSTER, R. F. (1933) *New Engl. J. Med.*, **208**, 317.

YAOI, H. (1935) *Jap. J. exp. Med.*, **13**, 307.

ZEHNDER, H. (1929) *Z. ImmunForsch.*, **64**, 365.

ZINSSER, H. and TANG, F. (1929) *J. Immunol.*, **17**, 343.

ZWICK. (1924) *Dtsch. tierärztl. Wschr.*, **32**, 643.

CHAPTER LXXXIII

FILTRABLE VIRUS DISEASES—*Continued*

B. Group characterized by Lesions of the Nervous System

ENCEPHALITIS

THERE are a number of diseases, many of them known to be caused by viruses, that affect the central nervous system and give rise to a picture of encephalitis, encephalomyelitis, or myelitis. The classification of these diseases is very difficult, and is generally made on the type of cell attacked. Since this is not a textbook of pathology, we do not wish to discuss the type of lesion produced in these diseases, particularly since there is still considerable disagreement among neuropathologists on this question. Those who wish for a classification along pathological lines may be referred to Rivers (1932) and Hurst (1936). We shall content ourselves with describing in sequence the more important diseases of man and animals in which the nervous system is primarily involved.

Human Encephalitis

Encephalitis Lethargica.

Different workers have recorded such conflicting results in regard to the ætiology of encephalitis lethargica that it is impossible to do more than summarize them, and discuss the conclusions that have been drawn from them.

In 1919 Loewe and Strauss (1919, 1920) in America claimed to have transmitted encephalitis lethargica to monkeys and rabbits by the inoculation of brain suspensions and nasopharyngeal washings from fatal cases ; the virus was recovered from the brain and nasopharynx of the inoculated animals, and appeared to consist of a small organism, which could be cultivated in Smith-Noguchi medium, and to cause when inoculated into rabbits a transmissible encephalitic disease. In 1921 Kling, Davide and Liljenquist (1921, 1924), working in Sweden, likewise claimed to have transmitted encephalitis lethargica to rabbits. Doerr and Zdansky (1923), working with material supplied by Kling, found in the brain of rabbits multiple granulomata, the size of a hemp-seed, containing small particles, 1·5–3·0 μ long, elongated or oval in shape, and staining with Ziehl-Neelsen. Levaditi, Nicolau and Schoen (1923), working with brains infected with Kling's virus, reported the finding of microscopical cysts of variable size, each one containing a number of spherical or ovoid bodies, 1–2 μ in diameter, having a brightly stained particle of chromatin ; they came to the conclusion that these bodies were probably forms of a protozoon, to which they gave the name *Encephalitozoon cuniculi.*

Meningo-encephalitis of Rabbits.—In 1922 Oliver described a spontaneous chronic meningo-encephalitis affecting 20 per cent. of her normal stock rabbits. Similar lesions in a few animals had been observed a few years previously by Bull

(1917), while working on streptococci isolated from poliomyelitis. In this country the disease was described independently by Twort (1922) and Twort and Archer (1923), who likewise met with it while investigating a different problem. McCartney (1924a) found that 55 per cent. of the stock rabbits at the Rockefeller Institute in New York were infected.

This disease may occur in epizootics ; symptoms are usually absent. Histologically, in the brain there are infiltrations with lymphocytes and plasma cells, occurring around the vessels, in the meninges, and in the cerebral substance itself, where the cells may form local aggregations or be widely diffused. In 15 per cent. of the rabbits there are, in addition, focal areas of necrosis, consisting of a necrotic centre surrounded by epithelioid cells, around which is a layer of mononuclear cells. In the centre of these necrotic lesions, there may be rounded or oval cyst-like bodies, containing numbers of small spherical, spindle- or pear-shaped particles, similar to those described by Levaditi under the name of *Encephalitozoon cuniculi*. These bodies generally consist of a thin structureless membrane, and a protoplasmic mass with regularly distributed chromatin particles ; on careful examination, it is found that the protoplasmic mass really consists of small spindle- or pear-shaped portions, each of which is provided with a particle of chromatin. This parasite appears to be a microsporidium belonging to the *Sporozoa* ; it has been found both in the brain and in the kidney lesions that occur in the disease. Under natural conditions this spontaneous meningo-encephalitis is spread by cage infection ; experimentally it can be transmitted by inoculation of nervous substance and the sedimented urine of infected animals. The parasite was described by Wright and Craighead in 1922, before Oliver had drawn attention to the spontaneous disease to which it gives rise. Cowdry and Nicholson (1924) have found a similar parasite in spontaneous encephalitis of mice (see also Pette 1928).

The discovery of this disease in rabbits was of great importance, because it immediately cast doubt on the claims of the American and Swedish workers to have transmitted encephalitis lethargica to rabbits. Since the lesions found in their experimental animals were very similar to those found in rabbits suffering from the spontaneous disease, and since in Kling's series only 50–60 per cent. of the inoculated rabbits showed these lesions—a figure agreeing closely with that found by McCartney to represent the frequency of the spontaneous disease —it seems probable that they had wrongly interpreted these lesions as evidence of experimental encephalitis lethargica.

A claim to have transmitted *encephalitis lethargica* to rabbits was likewise made by Levaditi and Harvier in 1920 (1922–23, see also Levaditi 1921, Levaditi *et al.* 1921a, b).

Working with the brains of patients who had succumbed to encephalitis, and with the nasopharyngeal secretions of patients during life, they were able to produce by intracerebral inoculation a fatal encephalitis in rabbits. By passage through a series of rabbits, a fixed virus was obtained, which produced encephalitis in 5 or 6 days when inoculated intracerebrally, and after 8 to 15 days when inoculated on to the cornea, into the anterior chamber of the eye, or on to the nasal mucosa. The properties of this virus were found to be similar to those of the *herpes febrilis* virus, and Levaditi concluded that the virus of encephalitis lethargica was identical with this virus, except that, on account of an increase in its virulence, it was able to attack the brain tissue. On the other hand, as one of the patients from whom the virus was obtained had suffered from an attack of herpes, it seems not unlikely that Levaditi was all the time working with a strain of herpes virus and not with that of encephalitis. This is the opinion arrived at by da Fano (1924), who gives a very able summary of the literature on the subject. Similar claims to those of Levaditi have been made by a number of other workers. According to da Fano, sufficient precautions were not taken to exclude the herpes virus, which appears to be widely diffused, and is not infrequently demonstrable in the saliva and nasopharynx not only of patients suffering from herpes, but also of apparently healthy carriers.

It is not clear, however, that the virus of encephalitis lethargica is distinct from that of herpes. Work by Perdrau (1925*a*, *b*), and by da Fano and Perdrau (1927), suggests that encephalitis lethargica may possibly be due to a modified herpes virus acting in the brain of a person who possesses a partial immunity to the virus. Working with herpes, Perdrau found that immunity in rabbits was best attained by intracutaneous inoculations of a passage virus which had developed fixed and neurotropic properties. The state of existing immunity of these animals was tested at intervals, and it was observed that the majority of immunized animals which finally succumbed to intracerebral inoculation of the passage virus showed symptoms similar to those of encephalitis lethargica in man ; the virus could not be recovered from the brain of these animals. The same type of disease could be produced in rabbits inoculated intracerebrally with a brain suspension from an encephalitis lethargica patient combined with a brain suspension of a rabbit immunized to herpes ; Perdrau suggests that the immune herpes brain contains an aggressin or some similar substance, which increases the virulence of the encephalitic virus. Histologically the lesions consisted of widespread meningeal, perivascular, and parenchymatous infiltrations of a subacute or chronic type, extensive atrophy of nerve cells, disintegration of the nerve tissue, accumulations of granulo-adipose cells, areas of true and pseudo-calcification, and reaction changes in the vascular and connective tissue. The lesions appear to be quite different from those seen in the spontaneous parasitic form of encephalitis of rabbits ; moreover this disease has never been reported in this country. Perdrau and da Fano regard the encephalitis produced by their passage virus as specifically herpetic ; moreover, they consider that clinically and histologically this chronic or subacute herpetic meningo-encephalitis of the rabbit closely resembles encephalitis lethargica in man.

Gay and Holden (1933) take the view that encephalitis lethargica is due to a modified or adapted neurotropic strain of herpes virus. They have been able by the inoculation of *Cebus* monkeys with this virus to produce a disease closely simulating human encephalitis. They also describe a case of encephalitis occurring in a laboratory worker after a monkey bite caused by a virus apparently identical with that of herpes.

Zinsser and Tang (1929) found that patients who had recovered from encephalitis lethargica more frequently contained herpetic antibody in their blood serum than normal persons. They were not disposed to pay much attention to these results, and, as Andrewes and Carmichael (1930) were unable to confirm them, it seems clear that the serological evidence cannot be taken to support the herpetic origin of encephalitis lethargica.

Both McIntosh (1923) and McCartney (1924*b*) in this country have reported the transmission of a fatal encephalitis to rabbits by the direct inoculation of brain suspensions from infected patients.

Summarizing, it may be said that the evidence available suggests that encephalitis lethargica may, on occasion, be transmitted by intracerebral inoculation to rabbits ; but that to avoid confusion care must be taken to use rabbits free from the spontaneous parasitic type of meningo-encephalitis. It appears possible that the encephalitic virus may bear some relation to the virus of herpes, but whether this is so or not cannot yet be definitely stated.

St. Louis Encephalitis.—A very remarkable outbreak of encephalitis occurred in St. Louis, Mo., during the late summer of 1933. The epidemic started at the beginning of August and finished about the end of October. Rather over a thousand persons were attacked—an incidence of approximately 1 per 1,000 of the population. The case-mortality rate, which had an average of 20 per cent., showed a striking increase in relation to the age of the patient ; thus, under 40 years of age it was less than 10 per cent. ; in the 40–50 age group it was 12 per cent., in the 50–60 group

21 per cent., in the 60–70 group 38 per cent., in the 70–80 group 56 per cent., and in the 80–90 group 80 per cent. Over half the fatal cases died in the 1st week. The incubation period was not ascertained with certainty, but appeared to be about 4–21 days. Pathologically, the lesions differed in several respects from those of encephalitis lethargica, particularly in the more extensive involvement of the meninges and spinal cord, the more widespread distribution of inflammatory foci through the brain, and the greater frequency of degenerative changes in the nerve cells and of neuronophagia.

Cultures of the blood and spinal fluid were sterile. Attempts to transmit the disease to rabbits proved a failure, but successful results were obtained by Muckenfuss, Armstrong, and McCordock (1933) with *Macacus rhesus* monkeys. Combined intracerebral and intraperitoneal inoculation of human brain suspension was followed in 8–14 days by a steadily rising temperature, drowsiness, intention tremor, muscular weakness and inco-ordination of the extremities, and increased pressure of spinal fluid. Most of the animals were killed, and it is not known whether the disease would have proved fatal spontaneously. The changes in the nervous system observed post mortem were similar to those in the human disease. Only about 40 per cent. of monkeys proved susceptible, and after 5 passages, experiments with these animals were discontinued.

The disease was also shown to be transmissible to *mice* (Webster and Fite 1935*a*). After intracerebral inoculation with human brain suspension these animals develop in 3–4 days a condition characterized by hyperæsthesia, coarse tremors, convulsions, prostration, and death in 4–6 days. The disease can be passed indefinitely through mice. Other animals, with the possible exception of the mule, appear to be refractory.

The virus is about 20–30 mμ in size (Webster and Fite 1935*b*, Elford and Perdrau 1935). It is present in great concentration in infected mouse brain; an intracerebral dose of even 3×10^{-8} gm. often proves fatal to mice. Mouse brain suspension remains virulent for at least 3 months when frozen; it withstands the action of 1 per cent. phenol for 25 days in the ice-chest, but is inactivated by 0·1 per cent. formol at room temperature in 12–18 hours (Brodie 1934*a*). Using the mouse protection test, in which the virus and the serum to be tested are mixed, incubated for 1 hour at 37° C., and inoculated intracerebrally into mice, it was found that the virus was neutralized by about 82 per cent. of sera from convalescent patients, but not by the serum of non-contacts or of patients who had suffered from herpes, encephalitis lethargica, or poliomyelitis (Webster, Fite and Clow 1935, Brodie 1934*a*). Wooley (1934), however, found that about 30 per cent. of sera from persons in different parts of the United States contained neutralizing bodies for the St. Louis virus. The virus is distinguished from the viruses of herpes, vaccinia, and Japanese encephalitis by its failure to provoke a response in rabbits, and from those of Rift Valley fever, louping-ill, poliomyelitis, equine encephalitis, and mouse encephalitis by its effects upon monkeys and mice. (For a general account of the disease, see Report 1935.)

Japanese Encephalitis.—Synonym: *B. encephalitis.*—In Japan several outbreaks of encephalitis have occurred during the past 70 years or so. They have been particularly common during the late summer months, and for this reason the disease is often referred to as " summer encephalitis." A large outbreak occurred in the summer and autumn of 1924, when there were over 7,000 cases with a fatality rate of 60 per cent. Another large epidemic, causing about 5,000 deaths, was witnessed in August and September 1935. A virus pathogenic to rabbits was isolated by Takaki (1926), and again by Taniguchi and his colleagues (1935). The latter virus gave rise to acute encephalitis on subdural inoculation into the rabbit and monkey. It proved to be different from the viruses of vaccinia, varicella and from Virus III, but its relationship to the herpes virus was doubtful. Kasahara and his colleagues (1936) also isolated a virus, which gave rise irregularly to fatal encephalitis in mice, which was non-infective to rabbits, but which could be passed intratesticularly through guinea-pigs. In many ways it resembled the St. Louis virus.

Australian X Encephalitis.—A disease simulating the Japanese encephalitis occurred in Australia in 1917 and again in 1918. It had a high fatality rate—70 per cent. This so-called X disease broke out again in New South Wales in 1922 and 1926. The virus is readily transmissible to monkeys, and the lesions to which it gives rise are very similar to those observed in sheep affected with louping-ill. The X disease may possibly be contracted from sheep (Perdrau 1936).

Secondary Encephalitis.—We have already (p. 1482) drawn attention to the encephalitis that occasionally follows vaccination against smallpox, and have discussed its ætiology. Similar cases of encephalitis sometimes occur during convalescence from other diseases such as measles, varicella, mumps, and influenza. The most striking characteristic of all these cases is the occurrence of perivascular demyelinization—a lesion which is not usually met with in primary encephalitis. Whether the production of secondary encephalitis is due to the virus causing the primary disease, or to a different virus lying latent in the tissues, or is a purely degenerative condition not determined by a virus at all, remains a subject for debate (see McIntosh 1928, McIntosh and Scarff 1928, Greenfield 1930, Rivers 1932, Ledingham 1935, Hurst 1936).

Encephalitis in Animals [1]

Borna Disease. Endemic Encephalo-myelitis of Horses, Cattle and Sheep.

Borna disease is the name given to an infectious encephalo-myelitis of horses. The name " Borna " is derived from the locality in Saxony where a severe epizootic occurred during the years 1894–96. The disease is widely distributed, and may occur in epidemic form with a mortality sometimes reaching 90 per cent. A similar encephalo-myelitis is likewise observed in cattle and sheep. Histologically, lesions are found in the central nervous system and in the peripheral nerves, and characteristic inclusions (Joest-Degen intranuclear corpuscles) are observed in the large ganglion cells of Ammon's horn. The disease is due to a filtrable virus, which appears to be the same in all three species of animal. The virus is resistant to glycerol, but sensitive to desiccation, ultra-violet light, and heat. Inoculated intracerebrally into rabbits it gives rise after an incubation period of 15 to 50 days to a disease characterized by cerebral symptoms and proving fatal in 5 to 17 days. The virus produces lesions in the central nervous system, and makes its way down the peripheral nerves, in which it sets up an interstitial neuritis. Monkeys, guinea-pigs, and rats are also susceptible. Rabbits may be immunized against the disease by the inoculation of suitably attenuated virus into the brain ; sometimes immunity is produced by multiple inoculations subcutaneously of large quantities of formolized vaccine. There is some evidence that the Borna virus is related to the virus of poliomyelitis. (For an excellent review of the disease, together with an account of original work, see Nicolau and Galloway 1928.)

[1] Meningo-encephalitis of rabbits has already been described on p. 1499.

American Encephalo-myelitis of Horses.—This is an endemic disease of the United States resembling the Borna disease of Europe, but differing from it in the histological character of the lesions and in the type of the causative virus (Hurst 1934, Howitt 1935). It has been observed along the Atlantic seaboard and in California. The Eastern type is a disease of late summer and autumn ; it is seen most often in the neighbourhood of salt marshes, and there is evidence to suggest that it is insect-borne (Tenbroeck *et al.* 1935). According to Kelser (1933), the Western type may be carried by *Aëdes ægypti.* The disease can be reproduced experimentally in the guinea-pig, rabbit, and mouse. The viruses of the Eastern and Western types differ in some respects, the Eastern type being more pathogenic to guinea-pigs and rabbits. Antigenically too there appears to be some difference between them, though cross-protection experiments have yielded slightly ambiguous results (see Howitt 1932, 1934, 1935, Records and Vawter 1935).

Encephalitis of Foxes.—This disease is endemic in certain parts of the United States, and at times assumes epidemic proportions. It is caused by a filtrable virus which invades the blood and may be demonstrated in various tissues. Clinically the disease is characterized by anorexia, hyperexcitability or lethargy, convulsions, paralysis, and not infrequently by death. Pathologically hæmorrhages in the brain and cord and in the viscera constitute the most striking feature of the disease ; perivascular infiltration with round cells is common in the cerebral nervous system, and the meninges are usually involved. Characteristic intranuclear inclusion bodies are found in the ependymal and endothelial cells of the central nervous system. The disease can be reproduced by intramuscular or intracranial inoculation of young foxes with homogenized brain and spinal cord. Unlike the natural disease, which seldom has a case mortality exceeding 20 per cent., the experimental disease is fatal in about 70 per cent. of cases. Infection can also be transmitted to dogs, though with some irregularity. (For an account of the disease see Green *et al.* 1930, 1931, 1933, 1934, Green 1931, Green and Shillinger 1934.)

Louping-ill.—This disease is an encephalo-myelitis of sheep characterized by cerebellar ataxia. The word " louping " is derived from an old Norse word meaning " leap," and refers to the peculiar gait of the animals which spring up and down when moving forwards. The disease seems to be limited to the border counties of England and Scotland and to the Western Highlands. It occurs in early spring, and is commonest on farms where there is rough hill grazing (Pool 1934). It has been studied mainly by workers in Scotland, who have shown (1) that the disease is caused by a virus which invades the blood stream and sometimes, but by no means always, affects the nervous system ; (2) that infection is carried by the tick *Ixodes ricinus* L., which is habitually present on louping-ill pastures ; (3) that infection can be transmitted by intracerebral inoculation to sheep, pigs, and mice ; (4) that the disease is often abortive ; (5) that recovery from the overt, abortive, or latent disease is followed by a substantial degree of immunity ; and (6) that some protection can be afforded by the use of formolized vaccine inoculated subcutaneously (see Pool *et al.* 1930, Alston and Gibson 1931, Brownlee and Wilson 1932, Gordon *et al.* 1932, MacLeod and Gordon 1932, Gordon 1934). The disease may also be transmitted to monkeys (Hurst 1931*a*) and to field voles (Findlay and Elton 1933). Both mice and monkeys can be infected by intranasal as well as by intracerebral inoculation (Elford and Galloway 1933, Galloway and Perdrau 1935). The virus can apparently reach the central nervous system from the nose without entering the blood stream. Rivers and Schwentker (1934) appear to have observed the disease in laboratory workers. Clinically the picture was that of an influenza accompanied by encephalitis. Recovery occurred, and neutralizing bodies were demonstrated in the patients' sera. The virus, however, was not isolated. According to Elford and Galloway (1933), the causative virus is about 15–20 mμ in diameter. Even after 40 mouse passages, it still remained infective for sheep.

POLIOMYELITIS

Poliomyelitis is principally a disease of young children, which occurs sporadically and epidemically. In the Northern hemisphere epidemics are commonest in the late summer and early autumn months, the maximum incidence of the disease being reached in August or September. The disease resembles cerebrospinal meningitis in attacking only a small proportion of the population ; though, as in meningitis, there is reason to believe that infection of a considerable proportion of the population occurs without giving rise to clinical evidence of disease. The case mortality of the declared disease is usually about 10–15 per cent., though it may reach a figure of even 40 per cent. The proportion of cases that show residual paralysis is difficult to estimate, because there is an increasing tendency among clinicians to diagnose the disease in the pre-paralytic stage. In this way a considerable number of abortive cases are included that do not develop paralysis at all. Probably not more than about 15–40 per cent. of the total cases show residual paralysis, and in many of these partial or even complete restoration of function ultimately occurs. Males are affected more often than females. The great majority of the cases occur within the first 10 years of life, though in the Danish outbreak of 1934 no fewer than 33·2 per cent. of the cases were persons aged 15 years or more (Jensen 1935). The incubation period is not known with certainty, but is probably about 4–7 days as a rule. The disease has been increasing in prevalence during the past 40 years or so ; and, though this country has suffered but little, severe epidemics have occurred in other parts of Europe and in North America.

The distribution of the cases in an epidemic is irregular. Wickman (1907), who investigated the big Swedish epidemic, found that the disease spread along the lines of communication, railways, roads, and so on. He brought evidence to show that infection was spread by carriers and by cases. Since it has been found that perfectly healthy persons may carry infection, and that patients may be infective in the incubation period, as well as for a week or two after the commencement of the disease, it is obvious that the prevention of infection by the isolation of cases or quarantining of contacts is not likely to be successful. The disease rarely becomes epidemic in schools or institutions, but it may attack a rural community in a characteristically epidemic form. Thus in the little village of Stokes Rivers, in Devonshire, 45 persons were attacked out of a total population of 119.

Infection most probably occurs by the respiratory tract. The virus has been demonstrated in the nasopharynx of patients suffering from the typical and from the abortive form of the disease, and occasionally of healthy carriers. It is probably expelled in droplets. In the nose the virus apparently invades the terminal processes of the olfactory nerves—the so-called olfactory hairs—and spreads along the axis cylinders to the brain, and thence to the anterior horn cells of the cord, where the chief lesions are produced (Fairbrother and Hurst 1930, Hurst 1930, Faber and Gebhardt 1933).

Further evidence that the virus travels along the axis cylinders is afforded by the observations of Leake (1935) on patients who had developed poliomyelitis after vaccination with an attenuated virus. In every instance in which the sequence was known, the level of the spinal cord first affected corresponded to the extremity in which the injection was made, paralysis beginning either in the same or the contra-lateral limb.

Infection by the gastro-intestinal tract has been suggested, and is supported by the occurrence of occasional outbreaks that appear to be carried by milk. Experimental evidence, however, does not support this view (see Flexner 1936), and it is probable that infection by this means is uncommon. Again, the suggestion has been made that infection is carried by insects, but the evidence in favour of this hypothesis is comparatively meagre ; moreover, the fact that the virus has never been demonstrated in the blood stream is difficult to reconcile with an insect-borne infection.

Transmission to Animals.—Poliomyelitis is transmissible to monkeys, but only with great difficulty, if at all, to other animals. Many workers have reported positive experiments in rabbits, but several others have completely failed ; moreover the disease produced in rabbits bears little clinical resemblance to human poliomyelitis.

Landsteiner and Popper (1909) were the first to transmit the disease to monkeys ; they injected the spinal cord from two fatal cases intraperitoneally into two monkeys. One animal became paralysed in the lower extremities, and died on the 6th day after inoculation ; the other was killed on the 19th day. At necropsy, lesions of the spinal cord, similar to those in man, were found in both monkeys. Later in the same year, Flexner and Lewis (1910), using cords from two human cases, succeeded in infecting monkeys by intracerebral, subcutaneous, intraperitoneal, intravenous, intrathecal and intraneural inoculation ; intratracheal inoculation and feeding proved unsuccessful. They were able, in addition, to carry over the disease from monkey to monkey by subdural injection of cord suspensions. Flexner and Lewis showed that the disease could be produced, not only by crude cord suspensions, but also by Berkefeld filtrates of these suspensions, and by filtrates of nasopharyngeal washings. Intranasal instillation is also successful (see Flexner 1935).

The disease in monkeys is similar to that in human beings. After intracerebral inoculation, there is an incubation period of about 6 to 10 days. During the prodromal period the monkey becomes excitable, the fur is ruffled, there is a high-pitched staccato cry, and the animal easily becomes tired. Within a few hours, ataxia develops, accompanied by tremor of the arms, legs or head. The ataxia rapidly merges into a flaccid paralysis, which extends to practically all the muscles of the body except those of the tail, jaws and diaphragm. The temperature drops to subnormal, the animal becomes weaker, and dies within 3 days after becoming prostrate (Amoss 1928). At necropsy, the lesions are similar to those in human beings, and may be briefly summarized as follows : (1) The lesions are chiefly in the grey matter of the cord ; the brain is only slightly affected. (2) There is a marked perivascular sheath infiltration, and a more diffuse infiltration of the grey matter of the cord ; the cells consist chiefly of lymphocytes, with a fair proportion of polymorphs and a small number of large cells with clear nuclei ; plasma cells and lymphoblasts are rare. (3) There is marked degeneration of the ganglion cells of the grey matter ; all stages of cellular degeneration, from a slight chromatolysis to complete neuronophagia can be seen. (4) Hæmorrhages are usually present in the grey matter of the cord (McIntosh and Scarff 1928, Hurst 1929). Characteristic intranuclear inclusion bodies have been described in the nerve cells of fatal human cases, though in monkeys they are less easy to demonstrate owing to the very rapid necrosis that these cells undergo (Hurst 1931*b*).

Properties of the Virus.—Flexner and Noguchi (1913) described the cultivation of minute globoid bodies, 0·15–0·3 μ in diameter, in an ascitic fluid rabbit kidney medium, and brought evidence to show that these bodies constituted the causative agent of the disease. The balance of evidence, however, is definitely against this conclusion (see Fairbrother 1929). More recent work has shown that the virus is probably much smaller—12–17 mμ according to Theiler and Bauer (1934), 8–12 mμ (Elford *et al.* 1935). It can be grown in tissue culture containing monkey serum and chick embryo brain (Gildemeister 1933). It is destroyed by heating to 50° C. for half an hour. It remains active in 0·5 per cent. phenol for 15 months, and can be preserved for 4 to 6 years in 50 per cent. glycerol (Amoss 1928). Little is yet known about its antigenic structure or its virulence, but there is a suggestion that not all strains are identical in these respects (Burnet and Macnamara 1931, Southby and McKie 1933, Paul and Trask 1933).

Immunity.—One attack of poliomyelitis produces a permanent immunity ; second attacks are very rare. Monkeys can be actively immunized against intra-cerebral inoculation by repeated intracutaneous inoculation with living virus, but complete protection is apparently not easy to obtain (Aycock and Kagan 1927, Stewart and Rhoads 1929). The serum of convalescent patients and monkeys, and of actively immunized monkeys, frequently but not always, contains sub-stances capable of inactivating the virus *in vitro*. Observations during the past few years have shown that neutralizing bodies are often present in the serum of persons who have never suffered from the clinical disease or been in known contact with infection. The test for these bodies is usually made by mixing the serum with a virus suspension, incubating at 37° C. for 2 hours and keeping in the ice-chest overnight, and injecting the mixture intracerebrally into *rhesus* monkeys (Aycock and Kramer 1930). Excluding new-born infants, whose blood often contains temporary antibodies, it is found that neutralizing bodies in the serum increase in frequency with age. In urban districts approximately 75 per cent. of children contain them by the age of 15 years. Most workers have concluded that these bodies represent specific antibodies resulting from latent infection and immuniza-tion. This view necessitates the belief that poliomyelitis infection is much more widespread than has hitherto been believed. The difficulty of accepting such a conclusion has led various workers, notably Jungeblut and his colleagues (Jungeblut 1933, Jungeblut and Engle 1933, 1934), to suppose that these antibodies are deve-loped as part of the normal physiological maturation of the individual and do not necessarily denote previous exposure to infection. More assumptions appear to be involved in this view than in supposing that active immunization is responsible. We do not wish, however, to discuss this question here, since reference has already been made to it in Chapter XLVI. Until we are in a better position to interpret the significance of the presence of neutralizing bodies in the serum, we shall be wise to refrain from drawing too far-reaching conclusions on the epidemiology of the disease.

Prophylaxis, Vaccination and Serum Treatment.—If our views on the frequency of latent infection are correct, it is clear that the detection and removal of carriers are as little likely to be successful in preventing poliomyelitis as they are in preventing cerebrospinal meningitis. General protective measures must therefore follow those common to all droplet-borne respiratory infections. Armstrong and Harrison (1935, 1936) have brought some evidence to suggest that the application to the nasal mucosa of a 2–4 per cent. solution of alum, or even better of a 0·32–0·64 per cent.

solution of picric acid, is capable of increasing the local resistance of monkeys to intranasal infection with poliomyelitis virus. So far, however, no data are available on the application of this method to human practice.

Attempts to vaccinate monkeys, and later children, against the disease have been numerous of late years, though it seems clear that mass immunization would be practicable only under quite exceptional conditions. Kolmer and his colleagues (Kolmer and Rule 1934a, b, Kolmer 1935, Kolmer et al. 1935) have used a 4 per cent. suspension of infected monkey cord in 1 per cent. sodium ricinoleate. The virus, though living, is said to be attenuated. Brodie (1934b) and Brodie and Park (1935), on the other hand, recommend a vaccine in which the virus has been inactivated by exposure to 0·1 per cent. formol at 37° C. for 8–12 hours. Both of these vaccines have been tried on a small scale in the United States. The demonstration, however, by Olitsky and Cox (1936) that Kolmer's vaccine may occasionally give rise to poliomyelitis in monkeys, and the even more serious development of poliomyelitis in children, occurring apparently as the result of prophylactic vaccination (Leake 1935), renders it very doubtful whether the continued use of living vaccines is justifiable.

As has already been pointed out, the blood serum of convalescent human patients often contains immune bodies capable of neutralizing the virus. During an epidemic, serum from such convalescent patients may be injected prophylactically into young children who have been exposed to infection, in a dose of 10 c.c. subcutaneously, the injection being repeated in a month if the epidemic persists. Serum from human convalescents may likewise be used for treatment. According to Aycock and Luther (1928), it should be given in the pre-paralytic stage of the disease. By giving intravenous and intraspinal injections of serum during this stage, they obtained evidence that the incidence and severity of the subsequent paralysis was decreased in comparison with untreated patients (Aycock et al. 1929). Further experience, however, of serum treatment, even in the pre-paralytic stage of the disease, has yielded disappointing results. Park (1932) collected figures referring to the treatment of 439 patients in the pre-paralytic stage of the disease with serum. The serum was given subcutaneously, intramuscularly, intravenously, intraspinally, or by two or more of these routes in combination. The total dosage amounted to 25–100 c.c. The results, which are given in Table CLXXV, failed

TABLE CLXXV

SHOWING THE CONDITION OF TREATED AND UNTREATED CASES OF POLIOMYELITIS AT THE END OF THREE WEEKS (After Park 1932).

	No. of Cases.	Died. Per cent.	Paralysis. Per cent.	Weakness. Per cent.	No Paralysis or Weakness. Per cent.
Treated	519	3·8	19·6	7·7	68·8
Controls	408	0·9	11·0	14·2	73·7

to show any advantage, as regards the development of paralysis, of the serum-treated over the control patients. Somewhat similar results are recorded by Fischer (1934), who compared 477 serum-treated patients in the pre-paralytic stage with 102 controls. Both as regards case mortality and the degree of paralysis the control group showed some slight, though probably insignificant, advantage over the serum-treated patients (see also Schultz and Gebhardt 1935, Jensen 1935).

Ascending Myelitis

We may note here that Sabin and Wright (1934) have recorded a human case of acute ascending myelitis, associated with focal necroses in the viscera, following the bite of an apparently normal *Macacus rhesus* monkey. By the inoculation of rabbits a strongly neurotropic filtrable virus was demonstrated in the patient's brain, cord, and spleen. In monkeys, however, the neurotropic tendency was not so evident. Intravenous inoculation of these animals was followed by a generalized disease not unlike that caused by vaccinia, and accompanied by a rash on the face, buccal mucosa, and conjunctiva (Sabin 1934). Antiviral bodies have been found in the blood of three normal *rhesus* monkeys, and it would therefore appear that these animals are liable to contract infection under natural conditions.

The occurrence of a primary myelitis following inoculation of rabbits with herpes virus has already been recorded (see also Koppisch 1935). We shall subsequently have occasion to refer to cases of acute ascending myelitis of the Landry type caused by the virus of rabies.

Infectious Paralysis of Guinea-pigs

This disease occurs sporadically in guinea-pigs, and closely resembles poliomyelitis. According to Römer (1911), who first described it, it can be transmitted to normal guinea-pigs by the intracerebral inoculation of filtered or unfiltered brain or cord suspensions. After an incubation period of 9 to 22 days, the animals become febrile and lose weight ; nervous disturbances develop, consisting of a gradually increasing muscular weakness, particularly of the hinder parts of the body ; paralysis of the hind legs develops, and occasionally of the bladder. The disease lasts from 3 days to 3 weeks. Pathologically, the lesions are those of a disseminated meningo-myeloencephalitis. They differ from those of poliomyelitis in showing greater meningeal infiltration, and in being most severe around the central canal of the cord. The virus is constantly present in the central nervous system ; it is also found in the prevertebral, inguinal, and mesenteric lymph glands, and occasionally in the liver and spleen.

Acute Lymphocytic Choriomeningitis

Synonym : Acute Aseptic Meningitis

The recognition of this disease is of very recent date, and little is yet known about it. Armstrong and Lillie (1934), while investigating a fatal case of St. Louis encephalitis, isolated a virus, quite different from the ordinary St. Louis virus, which gave rise in experimentally inoculated monkeys and mice to a lymphocytic choriomeningitis. An apparently identical virus was isolated by Scott and Rivers (1936) (see also Rivers and Scott 1936) from two benign cases of non-bacterial lymphocytic meningitis in adult males in the United States, and by Findlay, Alcock, and Stern (1936) in this country from the cerebrospinal fluid of two patients who exhibited vague nervous symptoms following a febrile attack. A similar or identical virus was isolated by Findlay and his colleagues from an irradiated mouse showing nervous phenomena, while Traub (1936) established the existence of an endemic infection with the same virus in a colony of apparently normal mice. The fact that certain animals may be endemically infected makes investigation of the human disease more difficult, but it will doubtless prove possible to establish non-infected stocks of mice, guinea-pigs, or monkeys for its further study.

According to Collis (1935), acute benign lymphocytic meningitis was first defined as a human disease by Wallgren in 1925 who described a small epidemic in Sweden. The main features are an acute onset, sometimes accompanied by inflammation of the upper respiratory tract, the development of symptoms of meningeal irritation, a benign course, absence of complications, and complete recovery within 10–14 days. The cerebrospinal fluid does not clot ; the sugar and chlorides remain normal ; and the fluid contains a considerable excess of lymphocytes.

The disease can be transmitted to monkeys, guinea-pigs, and mice. Five to twelve days after intracerebral inoculation mice become ill, develop tremors of the limbs, and die in 1–2 days with spastic convulsions of the hind legs. Guinea-pigs develop a marked febrile reaction after intracerebral, intranasal, or subcutaneous inoculation, lose weight, and often die, though not before the 12th day. In monkeys the virus has been shown to be widely disseminated throughout the tissues ; pathologically areas of lymphocytic infiltration are found in most of the organs (Armstrong *et al.* 1936, Lillie 1936). The virus appears to be fairly large. It has been cultivated successfully on the chorio-allantoic membrane of the developing chick embryo (Bengtson and Wooley 1936). It is neutralized by sera of monkeys and of human beings who have apparently suffered from infection at some previous date (Armstrong and Wooley 1935).

RABIES

Rabies is a disease of animals affecting particularly dogs, cats and carnivorous wild animals ; herbivora are less frequently attacked. The disease is transmissible to human beings by the bites of rabid animals, notably dogs, cats, wolves, and jackals. The incubation period varies according to the age of the animal, the situation of the bite, and the severity and nature of the bite. Generally speaking, it varies in animals from 2 to 8 weeks, and in human beings from 6 to 8 weeks ; it tends to be shorter in young animals and children, and after severe lacerated or deep punctured wounds about the head, face or neck. The disease does not uniformly appear after infection ; according to Hutyra and Marek (1926), only 30–40 per cent. of dogs bitten by rabid animals develop the disease ; and according to Cornwall (1923), only 35 per cent. of human beings bitten by rabid dogs die of rabies. The reasons for this are not clear ; it seems probable, however, that the body is able to withstand small doses of the virus, especially if the virus does not come into intimate contact with exposed nerves. Once the disease has developed, it is almost always fatal.

Sometimes the rabies virus gives rise in human beings to an acute *ascending myelitis*. The first case of this type was recorded by Knutti (1929), who based his diagnosis on the presence of Negri bodies in the ganglion cells of the spinal cord, and on the development of rabies in inoculated rabbits. A very remarkable outbreak of the disease was observed by Hurst and Pawan (1931) in Trinidad. Besides the occurrence of ascending myelitis in human beings, a form of paralytic rabies, erroneously diagnosed as botulism, was also met with in cattle. Investigation failed to disclose any history of a bite by a rabid animal, but evidence was brought to show that both the human and the cattle disease was due to vampire bats which conveyed the disease by sucking the blood of their victims. Further observations show that paralytic rabies is apparently widespread among animals in Brazil, where infection is carried by the vampire bat *Desmodus rufus* (de Verteuil and Urich 1936).

Animal Inoculation.—Rabies is transmissible to animals by subdural, intracerebral, or intravenous inoculation ; subcutaneous and cutaneous inoculations are less regular in their results. Pasteur and his colleagues (1881) found that dogs, when inoculated into the subarachnoid space over the brain with a suspension of the brain of a rabid dog, developed rabies after an incubation period of 1 to 2 weeks, and died within 3 weeks. If the virus is inoculated subdurally into a rabbit, the incubation period of the disease is about a fortnight ; but if the virus is passed in succession through a series of rabbits, the incubation period gradually falls, till after 20 to 25 passages it is only 8 days, and after a further 20 to 25 passages it is only 7 days (Pasteur 1885). The effect of passage is to convert the original " street virus " into a " fixed virus." These two viruses differ in certain respects. Thus, according to Levaditi, Nicolau and Schoen (1924), the fixed virus has a greater affinity for the nervous system of the rabbit than the street virus ; allied with this increased neurotropism, is the failure of the fixed virus to give rise to Negri corpuscles. Inoculated on to the scarified skin of the rabbit, both viruses give rise to rabies ; but if they are injected subcutaneously, the street virus alone proves virulent. It would appear that by passage through the rabbit's brain, the fixed virus has acquired a strong neurotropic affinity, which enables it to give rise to rabies in 7 days after subdural injection, but which usually renders it avirulent on subcutaneous inoculation. The street virus, on the other hand, takes about 14 days to produce rabies on subdural inoculation, and usually proves virulent when introduced subcutaneously. Fixed viruses can likewise be produced by passage through guinea-pigs, dogs, hens, and monkeys (Pasteur *et al.* 1884). Both street viruses, and the fixed viruses derived from them, show considerable variability in their virulence for animals ; some rarely produce infection when inoculated subcutaneously, others always do so (Marie *et al.* 1927). Pasteur (Pasteur *et al.* 1884) found that by passage through the brain of monkeys, the virus diminished in virulence for dogs, though when passed through rabbits or guinea-pigs it uniformly increased in virulence.

The virus is present in the saliva of rabid animals, and has sometimes been demonstrated in it 4 days before the onset of clinical symptoms. It is also found in the central nervous system, the peripheral nerves, and in the salivary glands, less regularly in the cerebrospinal fluid. Occasionally it may be demonstrated in the blood and the internal organs (Pasteur *et al.* 1884, Remlinger and Bailly 1931, 1932). The virus passes along the nerves from the local injury, and reaches the central nervous system ; this is shown by the fact that (1) the animal may live after resection of experimentally infected nerves ; (2) the resected nerves are themselves infective ; (3) the portion of the spinal cord in connection with the infected nerve becomes infective before other parts of the central nervous system (di Vestea and Zagari 1889, Marie *et al.* 1927). According to Nicolau and Galloway (1928), the virus, when introduced into the brain, may spread centrifugally, and be found in such nerves as the brachial and sciatic ; the passage of the virus along the nerves sets up an interstitial neuritis. It has been suggested that the salivary glands owe their infectivity to the presence in them of neurones, which may occur as single cells or as ganglionic aggregations, and which are situated just under the epithelium ; if the epithelium is abraded, the virus is set free from the neurones, and infects the saliva (Manouélian and Viala 1927, 1928, for refs. see McKendrick 1928*b*).

Properties of the Virus.—The rabies virus can pass through Berkefeld candles. Levaditi claims to have cultivated it in tissue cultures of the spinal ganglion cells of the monkey. Subcultures were made every 5 to 8 days ; the virus lived for 23 to 53 days, preserving its virulence for rabbits inoculated intracerebrally (see Marie *et al.* 1927). According to Sankaran, Iyengar, and Beer (1934), the virus can be separated from infected rabbit brain by electrophoresis. Little is known about its antigenic structure, but most strains seem to resemble each other fairly closely (Remlinger and Bailly 1930, Havens and Mayfield 1933). The fixed virus is very

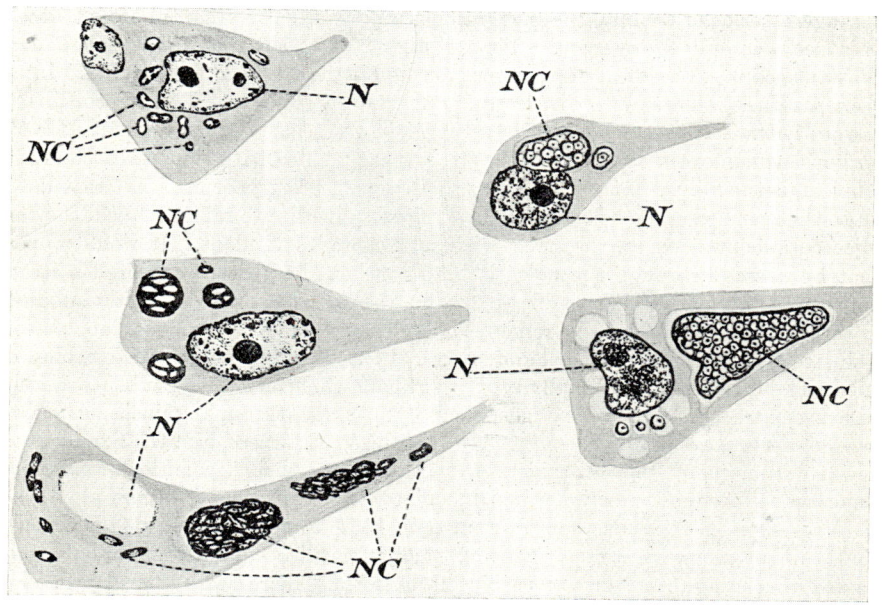

Fig. 276.

Negri corpuscles in Ammon's horn.   N = nucleus.   N.C. = Negri's corpuscle.
(After Manouélian, and Manouélian and Viala.)

sensitive to the photodynamic action of methylene blue, and this property may be made use of in the preparation of vaccines (Shortt and Brooks 1934, Galloway 1934).

One of the characteristic properties of the street virus is its power of giving rise to inclusion bodies in the nerve cells, known as Negri corpuscles (Negri 1903*a*, *b*) (Fig. 276). They are found most frequently in the cytoplasm and dendritic prolongations of the nerve cells, particularly in those of Ammon's horn. Usually they are about 3–10 μ in diameter, but they vary from 1 to 27 μ (Manouélian 1912). They generally conform in shape to their situation in the nerve cell, being rounded when in the cytoplasm, oval when compressed by the nucleus, and fusiform when in the dendrons. Each Negri body consists of a homogeneous mass containing clearer corpuscles, which may themselves contain one or more corpuscles, and sometimes short rods or granules. When stained by Giemsa, the homogeneous ground substance is lightish blue ; the larger corpuscles are pink, and the small corpuscles, rods, or granules are red or reddish-violet in colour. Fine blue-staining granules, which Negri regarded as forming a diffuse nucleus, are scattered throughout the body. In infections with fixed virus, Negri bodies are not usually present, but instead very fine granules, staining red with Mann's method, may be found in enormous numbers in the nerve cells (Manouélian 1912). The Negri bodies vary considerably in appearance. There is little doubt that they represent intracellular micro-colonies of the virus. Their presence in nervous tissue is diagnostic of infection, and their demonstration either directly, or indirectly by the mouse passage method (Webster and Dawson 1935), affords the most rapid means of determining the presence of infection in a suspected animal.

Prophylactic Treatment of Rabies.

Rabies is a fatal disease, and once symptoms have declared themselves, treatment is of no avail. But the disease is characterized by a long incubation period ; and it was Pasteur (1885) who realized the possibility of utilizing this period for carrying out specific vaccine treatment. Pasteur found that the spinal cords of rabbits dying of experimental rabies gradually lost their virulence when dried in air over KOH. By inoculating dogs with cords dried for varying periods, beginning with the least virulent and working up to the most virulent, he was able to immunize them to both natural and experimental rabies. His first human patient was a boy, Joseph Meister, aged 9 years, who had been bitten by a rabid dog in 14 places. Treatment was commenced 60 hours after the bite. Subcutaneous inoculation was performed, starting with a cord that had been dried for 14 days, and working up to a cord only 1 day old ; altogether 13 injections were given within 11 days. Rabbits inoculated with the cords 7 to 14 days old remained well ; rabbits inoculated with the cords 1 to 6 days old died after an incubation period increasing from 7 to 14 days. The cords first injected were therefore avirulent ; those used for the later injections were virulent. The treatment was a complete success, and formed the starting point of a system of preventive inoculation that is of world-wide distribution.

Pasteur's original method of inoculation is still used to-day, but a number of other methods have been developed by different workers. The most important of these are : (1) Högyes' method ; this consists of the subcutaneous injection of 1/100 to 1/10,000 dilutions of a 1 per cent. suspension of fixed virus of full virulence. This method has been used extensively with good results ; occasionally, however, the fixed virus may cause infection. (2) Babes' method ; in this the spinal cord is heated to 80°–60°–45° C. for 10 minutes, in order to attenuate the virus to varying degrees. (3) Semple's method ; the virus is killed with 1 per cent. carbolic acid. (4) Remlinger's method ; the virus is attenuated with ether. (5) Fermi's method of sero-vaccination. Fermi (1926) prepares his vaccine by exposing a 5 per cent. suspension of fixed living virus to 1 per cent. phenol for 1 to 10 days. The serum is prepared by the immunization of horses with the vaccine. The vaccine and the serum are mixed in varying proportions, and injected twice daily.

As adequate statistics of the results of treatment are not available, it is impossible to ascertain which of the different methods employed is of most value. Prausnitz (1927, see McKendrick 1928a), however, has extracted some figures put before the Paris Congress of 1927, which may be used for comparison (Table CLXXVI). (See also Stuart and Krikorian 1929–30, Cunningham and Malone 1930.)

P.B.   3 c*

TABLE CLXXVI

	Period.	Method.	No. Treated.	Mortality.	
				Total Percentage.	Reduced Percentage.[1]
Rome	1889–1919	Dried cords	9,930	1·08	0·37
	1920–1926	Phenolized living, attenuated	5,035	0·16	0·02
Kasauli (Europeans only)	1900–1907	Dried cords	1,935	0·41	—
	1907–1912	Högyes'	1,673	0·42	—
	1912–1926	Semple's	7,296	0·32	—
Jassy	1891–1896	Dried cords	631	1·11	0·32
	1896–1908	1% brain, 80° C. to unheated	3,300	0·36	0·12
	1908–1913	0·3–0·2% brain, 70° C. to unheated	3,940	0·1	0·0
	1914–1926	0·1% brain, 65° C. to unheated	22,377	0·13	0·04

[1] Reduced so as to exclude all cases not dying primarily of rabies.

Though the killed phenolized virus may undoubtedly give rise to a substantial degree of immunity when given in adequate dosage (Stuart and Krikorian 1929–30), there is evidence that it is inferior in practice to vaccines in which the virus is alive but attenuated. The figures of Cunningham and Malone (1930), in particular, to whose report reference should be made, seem to show the superiority of an etherized vaccine—prepared according to Alivisatos' (1922, 1926) method. While there are several objections to the use of live vaccines in the prophylaxis of most diseases, the facts that, in rabies, the case mortality is so high and the patient is already infected at the time of vaccination, do seem to warrant the taking of greater risks than would ordinarily be justifiable.

Occasionally, about once in every 3,538 persons treated, paralyses develop during or shortly after the treatment. The commonest time for them to appear is between the 11th and 30th days after the bite, that is to say, considerably before the onset of rabies in untreated persons. They are commonest in patients treated with dried cord, and least common in those treated with phenolized cord. They prove fatal in about 17 per cent. of cases. What they are due to is not yet known ; for a discussion of the subject see Remlinger (1927).

The Paris Conference on rabies recommended that prophylactic treatment should be applied to all human patients whenever they had been bitten, or whenever a mucosa had been contaminated with rabid saliva, even though no wound had been inflicted. The treatment should be commenced as soon as possible after the bite. In countries where rabies is common, they recommend that all dogs should be vaccinated with a single dose of killed or of fixed virus, and revaccinated every year. But a dog or other animal that has been bitten by a certainly rabid animal must be killed, whether vaccinated or not ; if bitten by a suspect animal, then the dog may be vaccinated therapeutically, and kept in quarantine for 6 months. The measures they recommend for the elimination of rabies consist in restricting all dogs not fitted with muzzles to the homes of their owners, and in destroying all stray dogs. In this country, where the muzzling orders and the strict supervision of all imported dogs have been carried out, when need has arisen, rabies is practically non-existent.

PSEUDORABIES

SYNONYMS : Mad itch : Infectious bulbar paralysis : Aujeszky's disease.

This disease, which was described by Aujeszky in 1902, has only recently attracted much attention. It appears to be an acute infection of the central nervous system affecting dogs, cats, cattle, horses, pigs, goats, sheep, rats, and mice, but not man. Though originally met with in Hungary, it has now been reported from a number of other European countries and from both North and South America. Unlike rabies the incubation period is very short—only a matter of hours—the onset is brusque, there is intense pruritus, which often completely dominates the clinical picture, the mental faculties are preserved, paralysis occurs very late and does not involve the lower jaw, the disease lasts only 24–48 hours, and sudden death is common (Remlinger and Bailly 1934). The fatality rate is usually very high. The mode of infection is still in doubt. According to Shope (1935), the disease in cattle is very fatal but non-contagious, whereas in pigs it is relatively mild but highly contagious. Shope believes that in pigs infection occurs by the nose, and that the abraded skin of cattle can probably be infected from contact with the pig's snout. A study of neutralizing bodies in the serum suggests that pseudorabies is a highly prevalent but unrecognized disease in the hogs of the Middle West. There is some evidence that the disease is spread by rats, and that pigs may become infected by feeding on contaminated material.

The disease can be reproduced experimentally in most animals, though monkeys appear to be fairly resistant. In the rabbit the disease exhibits a diverse and striking symptomatology. Infection is possible by practically any route. Intracerebral inoculation gives rise in 20–40 hours to a condition of wild excitement, accompanied by salivation, grinding of the teeth, blindness, and later coma and death. In rabbits injected subcutaneously the incubation period is 50–75 hours ; the animals then start scratching and biting the site of inoculation ; their efforts become increasingly savage till the skin is hairless, abraded, and bleeding ; feebleness sets in, and death occurs in a state of collapse 6–24 hours after the onset of pruritus (Shope 1931). The clinical picture, however, is very variable, and may assume an encephalitic, pseudo-herpetic, meningeal, paralytic, pruriginous, fulminating, or even abortive form (Remlinger and Bailly 1934). Some animals can be infected by feeding.

The causative virus is widely distributed in the body, being often demonstrable in the blood and internal organs as well as in the central nervous system. It is absent from the saliva, but in certain animals it may apparently be excreted in the urine (Bang 1932). It can pass through a Berkefeld W filter ; it survives for a considerable time in 50 per cent. glycerol, but is killed by exposure to a temperature of 55°–60° C. in 35 minutes (see McKinley 1929). It has been successfully grown in tissue culture and in a minced chick embryo medium (Traub 1933). Cross-immunity tests show that it is distinct from the virus of rabies (Gerlach and Schweinburg 1935). Immune sera that neutralize the virus can be prepared by inoculation of guinea-pigs (Shope 1931).

Pathologically, gross lesions are few. Hyperæmia of the meninges and small hæmorrhagic extravasations are seen. The histological changes vary considerably in different animals. According to Hurst (1933), in the rabbit and guinea-pig the virus gives rise to local inflammation and necrosis at the site of inoculation, passes up the peripheral nerves, as evidenced by the presence of inclusion bodies, and causes degeneration of the nerve and glial cells in the spinal ganglia and segments of the spinal cord corresponding to the peripheral nerve invaded.

We append brief descriptions of two animal diseases whose position in our rough scheme of classification is very doubtful.

SALIVARY GLAND VIRUS OF GUINEA-PIGS

Cole and Kuttner (1926) observed greatly swollen epithelial cells in the salivary glands of guinea-pigs; they were found in 84 per cent. of full-grown animals. Injection of a suspension of the affected submaxillary glands intracerebrally into young guinea-pigs was followed by fever, cerebral irritation, and death in 5 to 7 days, with diffuse subacute meningitis. In the exudate large numbers of cells were found similar to those in the salivary glands. Similar cells were also seen in the lesions resulting from inoculation of the same suspension into the testicle, lung, tongue, and submaxillary glands of young guinea-pigs. The virus is destroyed at 54° C. in 1 hour; it survives for 11 but not for 28 days in 50 per cent. glycerol. It passes through a Berkefeld N candle. The virus appears to give rise to no clinical symptoms in naturally infected guinea-pigs. Infected guinea-pigs are immune to the intracerebral inoculation of virus; in the serum of these animals neutralizing bodies can be demonstrated (Andrewes 1930). More recently Kuttner and Wang (1934) have described the presence of acidophilic intranuclear inclusion bodies in the submaxillary glands of hamsters, white mice, and wild rats; each of these animals appears to be infected by a specific virus. Similar inclusion bodies have also been noted in the salivary glands of human infants, but animal transmission experiments have proved unsuccessful.

PERIODIC OPHTHALMIA OF HORSES

This disease is characterized by a recurrent serous uveitis, with an acute onset, subsidence in 4–10 days, and a remission after 3–6 weeks. The symptoms can be reproduced in horses by inoculation of a Berkefeld N filtrate of infective material into the vitreous humour. Rabbits are also susceptible (Woods and Chesney 1930).

REFERENCES

ALIVISATOS, G. P. (1922) *Dtsch. med. Wschr.*, **48**, 295; (1926) *Zbl. Bakt.*, **98**, 394.
ALSTON, J. M. and GIBSON, H. J. (1931) *Brit. J. exp. Path.*, **12**, 82.
AMOSS, H. L. (1928) "Rivers' Filtrable Viruses." Baltimore and London.
ANDREWES, C. H. (1930) *Brit. J. exp. Path.*, **11**, 23.
ANDREWES, C. H. and CARMICHAEL, E. A. (1930) *Lancet*, i. 857.
ARMSTRONG, C. and HARRISON, W. T. (1935) *Publ. Hlth Rep.*, *Wash.*, **50**, 725; (1936) *Ibid.*, **51**, 203.
ARMSTRONG, C. and LILLIE, R. D. (1934) *Publ. Hlth Rep.*, *Wash.*, **49**, 1019.
ARMSTRONG, C. and WOOLEY, J. G. (1935) *Publ. Hlth Rep.*, *Wash.*, **50**, 537.
ARMSTRONG, C., WOOLEY, J. G., and ONSTOTT, R. H. (1936) *Publ. Hlth Rep.*, *Wash.*, **51**, 298.
AUJESZKY, A. (1902) *Zbl. Bakt.*, **32**, 353.
AYCOCK, W. L. and KAGAN, J. R. (1927) *J. Immunol.*, **14**, 85.
AYCOCK, W. L. and KRAMER, S. D. (1930) *J. prev. Med., Baltimore*, **4**, 189, 201.
AYCOCK, W. L. and LUTHER, E. H. (1928) *J. Amer. med. Ass.*, **91**, 387.

AYCOCK, W. L., LUTHER, E. H., McKHANN, C. F., SMITH, E. C., and KRAMER, S. D. (1929) *J. infect. Dis.*, **45**, 175.

BANG, O. (1932) *Acta path. microbiol., scand.*, Suppl. 11, p. 180.

BENGTSON, I. A. and WOOLEY, J. G. (1936) *Publ. Hlth Rep., Wash.*, **51**, 29.

BRODIE, M. (1934*a*) *Proc. Soc. exp. Biol., N.Y.*, **31**, 1227, 1229 ; (1934*b*) *Proc. Soc. exp. Biol., N.Y.*, **32**, 300.

BRODIE, M. and PARK, W. H. (1935) *J. Amer. med. Ass.*, **105**, 1089.

BROWNLEE, A. and WILSON, D. R. (1932) *J. comp. Path.*, **45**, 67.

BULL, C. G. (1917) *J. exp. Med.*, **25**, 557.

BURNET, F. M. and MACNAMARA, J. (1931) *Brit. J. exp. Path.*, **12**, 57.

COLE, R. and KUTTNER, A. G. (1926) *J. exp. Med.*, **44**, 855.

COLLIS, W. R. F. (1935) *Brit. med. J.*, ii. 1148.

CORNWALL, J. W. (1923) *Brit. med. J.*, ii. 298.

COWDRY, E. V. and NICHOLSON, F. M. (1924) *J. Amer. med. Ass.*, **82**, 545.

CUNNINGHAM, J. and MALONE, R. H. (1930) *Indian med. Res. Mem.*, No. 15.

DOERR, R. and ZDANSKY, E. (1923) *Schweiz. med. Wschr.*, **4**, 349, 1189.

ELFORD, W. J. and GALLOWAY, I. A. (1933) *J. Path. Bact.*, **37**, 381.

ELFORD, W. J., GALLOWAY, I. A., and PERDRAU, J. R. (1935) *J. Path. Bact.*, **40**, 135.

ELFORD, W. J. and PERDRAU, J. R. (1935) *J. Path. Bact.*, **40**, 143.

FABER, H. K. and GEBHARDT, L. P. (1933) *J. exp. Med.*, **57**, 933.

FAIRBROTHER, R. W. (1929) *J. Path. Bact.*, **32**, 435.

FAIRBROTHER, R. W. and HURST, E. W. (1930) *J. Path. Bact.*, **33**, 17.

FANO, C. DA. (1924) *Med. Sci.*, **10**, 355.

FANO, C. DA and PERDRAU, J. R. (1927) *J. Path. Bact.*, **30**, 67.

FERMI, C. (1926) *Seuchenbekämpf. exp. Ther. InfKr.*, **3**, 114.

FINDLAY, G. M., ALCOCK, N. S., and STERN, R. O. (1936) *Lancet*, i. 650.

FINDLAY, G. M. and ELTON, C. (1933) *J. comp. Path.*, **46**, 126.

FISCHER, A. E. (1934) *Amer. J. Dis. Child.*, **48**, 481.

FLEXNER, S. (1935) *J. exp. Med.*, **62**, 787 ; (1936) *Ibid.*, **63**, 209.

FLEXNER, S. and LEWIS, P. A. (1910) *J. exp. Med.*, **12**, 227.

FLEXNER, S. and NOGUCHI, H. (1913) *J. exp. Med.*, **18**, 461.

GALLOWAY, I. A. (1934) *Brit. J. exp. Path.*, **15**, 97.

GALLOWAY, I. A. and PERDRAU, J. R. (1935) *J. Hyg., Camb.*, **35**, 339.

GAY, F. P. and HOLDEN, M. (1933) *J. infect. Dis.*, **53**, 287.

GERLACH, F. and SCHWEINBURG, F. (1935) *Z. InfektKr. Haustiere*, **48**, 270.

GILDEMEISTER, E. (1933) *Dtsch. med. Wschr.*, **59**, 877.

GORDON, W. S. (1934) *Proc. R. Soc. Med.*, **27**, 701.

GORDON, W. S., BROWNLEE, A., WILSON, D. R., and MACLEOD, J. (1932) *J. comp. Path.*, **45**, 106.

GREEN, R. G. (1931) *Amer. J. Hyg.*, **13**, 201.

GREEN, R. G. and SHILLINGER, J. E. (1934) *Amer. J. Hyg.*, **19**, 362.

GREEN, R. G., KATTER, M. S., SHILLINGER, J. E., and HANSON, K. B. (1933) *Amer. J. Hyg.*, **18**, 462.

GREEN, R. G., ZIEGLER, N. R., DEWEY, E. T., and SHILLINGER, J. E. (1931) *Amer. J. Hyg.*, **14**, 353.

GREEN, R. G., ZIEGLER, N. R., GREEN, B. B., and DEWEY, E. T. (1930) *Amer. J. Hyg.*, **12**, 109.

GREEN, R. G., ZIEGLER, N. R., CARLSON, W. E., SHILLINGER, J. E., TYLER, S. H., and DEWEY, E. T. (1934) *Amer. J. Hyg.*, **19**, 343.

GREENFIELD, J. G. (1930) *J. Path. Bact.*, **33**, 453.

HAVENS, L. C. and MAYFIELD, C. R. (1933) *J. infect. Dis.*, **52**, 364.

HOWITT, B. F. (1932) *J. infect. Dis.*, **51**, 493 ; (1934) *Ibid.*, **55**, 138 ; (1935) *J. Immunol.*, **29**, 319.

HURST, E. W. (1929) *J. Path. Bact.*, **32**, 457 ; (1930) *Ibid.*, **33**, 1133 ; (1931*a*) *J. comp. Path.*, **44**, 231 ; (1931*b*) *J. Path. Bact.*, **34**, 331 ; (1933) *J. exp. Med.*, **58**, 415 ; (1934) *J. exp. Med.*, **59**, 529 ; (1936) *Brain*, **59**, 1.

HURST, E. W. and PAWAN, J. L. (1931) *Lancet*, ii. 622.

HUTYRA, H. and MAREK, J. (1926) " Special Pathology and Therapeutics of the Diseases of Domestic Animals," 3rd Amer. Edit. Chicago and London.

JENSEN, C. (1935) *Proc. R. Soc. Med.*, **28**, 1007.

JUNGEBLUT, C. W. (1933) *J. Immunol.*, **24**, 157.

JUNGEBLUT, C. W. and ENGLE, E. T. (1933) *J. Immunol.*, **24**, 267 ; (1934) *Ibid.*, **59**, 43.

KASAHARA, S., UEDA, M., OKAMOTO, Y., YOSHIDA, S., HAMANO, R., and YAMADA, R. (1936) *Kitasato Arch. exp. Med.*, **13**, 48.

KELSER, R. A. (1933) *J. Amer. vet. med. Ass.*, **82**, 767.

KLING, C., DAVIDE, H., and LILJENQUIST, F. (1921) *C. R. Soc. Biol.*, **84**, 815 ; (1924) *Med. Sci.*, **10**, 376.

KNUTTI, R. E. (1929) *J. Amer. med. Ass.*, **93**, 754.
KOLMER, J. A. (1935) *J. Amer. med. Ass.*, **105**, 1956.
KOLMER, J. A., KLUGH, G. F., and RULE, A. M. (1935) *J. Amer. med. Ass.*, **104**, 456.
KOLMER, J. A. and RULE, A. M. (1934a) *J. Immunol.*, **26**, 505 ; (1934b) *Amer. J. med. Sci.*, **188**, 510.
KOPPISCH, E. (1935) *Z. Hyg. InfektKr.*, **117**, 635.
KUTTNER, A. G. and WANG, S. H. (1934) *J. exp. Med.*, **60**, 773.
LANDSTEINER, K. and POPPER, E. (1909) *Z. ImmunForsch.*, **2**, 377.
LEAKE, J. P. (1935) *J. Amer. med. Ass.*, **105**, 2152.
LEDINGHAM, J. C. G. (1935) *Bull. Johns Hopk. Hosp.*, **56**, 247, 337 ; **57**, 32.
LEVADITI, C. (1921) *Bull. Inst. Pasteur*, **19**, 289.
LEVADITI, C. and HARVIER, P. (1922–23) *Med. Sci.*, **7**, 247.
LEVADITI, C., HARVIER, P., and NICOLAU, S. (1921a) *C. R. Soc. Biol.*, **84**, 524 ; (1921b) *Ibid.*, **85**, 213.
LEVADITI, C., NICOLAU, S., and SCHOEN, R. (1923) *C. R. Soc. Biol.*, **89**, 984 ; (1924) *C. R. Soc. Biol.*, **91**, 423.
LILLIE, R. D. (1936) *Publ. Hlth Rep., Wash.*, **51**, 303.
LOEWE, L. and STRAUSS, I. (1919) *J. Amer. med. Ass.*, **73**, 1056 ; (1920) *Ibid.*, **74**, 1373.
MACLEOD, J. and GORDON, W. S. (1932) *J. comp. Path.*, **45**, 240.
MCCARTNEY, J. E. (1924a) *J. exp. Med.*, **39**, 51 ; (1924b) *Brit. med. J.*, ii. 1159.
MCINTOSH, J. (1923) *Brit. J. exp. Path.*, **4**, 34 ; (1928) *Brit. med. J.*, ii. 334.
MCINTOSH, J. and SCARFF, R. W. (1928) *Proc. R. Soc. Med.*, **21**, 1.
MCKENDRICK, A. G. (1928a) *Trop. Dis. Bull.*, **25**, 187 ; (1928b) *Ibid.*, **25**, 706.
MCKINLEY, E. B. (1929) *Philipp. J. med. Sci.*, **39**, 1.
MANOUÉLIAN, Y. (1912) *Ann. Inst. Pasteur*, **26**, 973.
MARIE, A. C., REMLINGER, P., and VALLÉE, H. (1927) *Ann. Inst. Pasteur*, Suppl., April 25th–29th.
MUCKENFUSS, R. S., ARMSTRONG, C., and MCCORDOCK, H. A. (1933) *Publ. Hlth Rep., Wash.*, **48**, 1341.
NEGRI, A. (1903a) *Z. Hyg. InfektKr.*, **43**, 507 ; (1903b) *Ibid.*, **44**, 519.
NICOLAU, S. and GALLOWAY, I. A. (1928) *Spec. Rep. Ser. med. Res. Coun., Lond.*, No. 121.
OLITSKY, P. K. and COX, H. R. (1936) *J. exp. Med.*, **63**, 109.
OLIVER, J. (1922) *J. infect. Dis.*, **30**, 91.
PARK, W. H. (1932) *J. Amer. med. Ass.*, **99**, 1050.
PASTEUR, L. (1885) *C. R. Acad. Sci.*, **101**, 765.
PASTEUR, CHAMBERLAND, ROUX, and THUILLIER. (1881) *C. R. Acad. Sci.*, **92**, 1259.
PASTEUR, CHAMBERLAND, and ROUX. (1884) *C. R. Acad. Sci.*, **98**, 457, 1229.
PAUL, J. R. and TRASK, J. D. (1933) *J. exp. Med.*, **58**, 513.
PERDRAU, J. R. (1925a) *Brit. J. exp. Path.*, **6**, 41 ; (1925b) *Ibid.*, **6**, 123 ; (1936) *J. Path. Bact.*, **42**, 59.
PETTE, H. (1928) *Z. Hyg. InfektKr.*, **108**, 700.
POOL, W. A. (1934) *Proc. R. Soc. Med.*, **27**, 707.
POOL, W. A., BROWNLEE, A., and WILSON, D. R. (1930) *J. comp. Path.*, **43**, 253.
RECORDS, E. and VAWTER, L. R. (1935) *J. Amer. vet. med. Ass.*, **86**, 773.
REMLINGER, P. (1927) *Ann. Inst. Pasteur*, Suppl., April 25th–29th.
REMLINGER, P. and BAILLY, J. (1930) *Ann. Inst. Pasteur*, **45**, 376 ; (1931) *C. R. Soc. Biol.*, **107**, 201 ; (1932) *Ibid.*, **110**, 239 ; (1934) *Ann. Inst. Pasteur*, **52**, 361.
Report. (1935) " Report on the St. Louis Outbreak of Encephalitis." *Publ. Hlth Bull., Wash.*, No. 214.
RIVERS, T. M. and SCHWENTKER, F. F. (1934) *J. exp. Med.*, **59**, 669.
RIVERS, T. M. and SCOTT, T. F. MCN. (1936) *J. exp. Med.*, **63**, 415.
RÖMER. (1911) *Zbl. Bakt.*, **50**, Beiheft, p. 30.
SABIN, A. B. (1934) *Brit. J. exp. Path.*, **15**, 321.
SABIN, A. B. and WRIGHT, A. M. (1934) *J. exp. Med.*, **59**, 115.
SANKARAN, G., IYENGAR, K. R. K., and BEER, W. A. (1934) *Indian J. med. Res.*, **21**, 909.
SCHULTZ, E. W. and GEBHARDT, L. P. (1935) *J. Pediat.*, **7**, 332.
SCOTT, T. F. MCN. and RIVERS, T. M. (1936) *J. exp. Med.*, **63**, 397.
SHOPE, R. E. (1931) *J. exp. Med.*, **54**, 233 ; (1935) *Ibid.*, **62**, 85, 101.
SHORTT, H. E. and BROOKS, A. G. (1934) *Indian J. med. Res.*, **21**, 581.
SOUTHBY, R. and MCKIE, M. (1933) *Med. J. Aust.*, **2**, 404.
STEWART, F. W. and RHOADS, C. P. (1929) *J. exp. Med.*, **49**, 959.
STUART, G. and KRIKORIAN, K. S. (1929–30) *J. Hyg., Camb.*, **29**, 1.
TAKAKI, I. (1926) *Z. ImmunForsch.*, **47**, 441.
TANIGUCHI, T., KUGA, S., HOSOKAWA, M., MASUDA, Z., WADA, T., HORIMI, T., and HASHIDA, S. (1935) *Jap. J. exp. Med.*, **13**, 109.
TENBROECK, C., HURST, E. W., and TRAUB, E. (1935) *J. exp. Med.*, **62**, 677.
THEILER, M. and BAUER, J. H. (1934) *J. exp. Med.*, **60**, 767.

TRAUB, E.   (1933) *J. exp. Med.*, **58**, 663 ;   (1936) *Ibid.*, **63**, 533.
TWORT, C. C.   (1922) *Vet. J.*, **78**, 194.
TWORT, C. C. and ARCHER, H. E.   (1923) *Lancet*, i. 1102.
VERTEUIL, E. DE and URICH, F. W.   (1936) *Trans. R. Soc. trop. Med. Hyg.*, **29**, 317.
VESTEA, DI and ZAGARI.   (1889) *Zbl. Bakt.*, **6**, 25.
WEBSTER, L. T. and DAWSON, J. R.   (1935) *Proc. Soc. exp. Biol., N.Y.*, **32**, 570.
WEBSTER, L. T. and FITE, G. L.   (1935a) *J. exp. Med.*, **61**, 103 ;   (1935b) *Ibid.*, **61**, 411.
WEBSTER, L. T., FITE, G. L., and CLOW, A. D.   (1935) *J. exp. Med.*, **62**, 827.
WICKMAN, O. I.   (1907) "Beiträge zur Kenntniss der Heine-Medinschen Krankheit."   Berlin.
WOODS, A. C. and CHESNEY, A. M.   (1930) *J. exp. Med.*, **52**, 637.
WOOLEY, J. G.   (1934) *Publ. Hlth Rep., Wash.*, **49**, 1495.
WRIGHT, J. H. and CRAIGHEAD, E. M.   (1922) *J. exp. Med.*, **36**, 135.
ZINSSER, H. and TANG, F.   (1929) *J. Immunol.*, **17**, 343.

CHAPTER LXXXIV

FILTRABLE VIRUS DISEASES—*Continued*

C. Group Characterized by Catarrhal or Generalized Infection

MEASLES

Measles is a highly infectious disease of human beings, which occurs in epidemic form. Amongst civilized peoples it is chiefly a disease of childhood, but when introduced into localities that have not previously been infected, it attacks persons of all ages. By itself it is a relatively mild disease, but when complicated with respiratory infections—as it so frequently is—it is attended by a high mortality.

Anderson and Goldberger (1911) first recorded evidence indicating that measles could be experimentally transmitted to *monkeys*. The experiments of Nicolle and Conseil (1911, 1920) likewise suggested that monkeys were susceptible. The most convincing evidence, however, was brought by Blake and Trask (1921). These workers were able, by the intratracheal inoculation of filtered and unfiltered nasopharyngeal washings taken from measles patients 6 days before to 22 hours after the appearance of the rash, to produce in monkeys (*Macacus rhesus*) a disease closely simulating human measles. After an incubation period of 6 to 10 days, there developed a characteristic group of symptoms characterized by listlessness, drowsiness, leucopenia, catarrhal conjunctivitis, a rash on the labial mucosa, and a skin rash consisting of discrete red maculo-papules ; fever was inconstant. Recovery occurred after an illness of 7 to 10 days ; no respiratory complications were observed. The disease was carried on through monkeys for 6 generations, by intratracheal inoculation of tissue suspensions (chiefly skin and buccal mucosa) of monkeys killed from 2 to 6 days after the onset of the reaction. It was likewise produced by intravenous inoculation of monkeys with blood taken from experimentally infected monkeys 7 to 13 days after intratracheal inoculation. These experiments afford evidence for the belief that measles is due to infection with a filtrable virus.

Numerous workers (Nevin and Bittman 1921, Duval and D'Aunoy 1922, Scott and Simon 1924, 1925) have claimed to have transmitted measles to *rabbits*. Their work is criticized by Purdy (1925), who completely failed to obtain any significant reaction in rabbits—even with material that was shown to be infective for monkeys. Taniguchi and his colleagues (1935) have, however, recorded more convincing results. By the intratesticular inoculation of rabbits or guinea-pigs with nasopharyngeal washings from patients in the early stage of measles, they were successful in establishing five strains of the virus. The strains took some time to become adapted to the rabbit. When fully adapted they gave rise in 2–3 days to fever, leucopenia, and to a local swelling, congestion, and infiltration of the testicle, which reached its maximum in a week or 10 days. Intravenous inoculation of the rabbit virus into rabbits was followed in 2–4 days by fever, and a day later by papular eruptions on the lips, ears, and back. Inoculation on to the scarified cornea resulted in an acute kerato-conjunctivitis, occasionally followed by encephalitis ; in the corneal epithelium elementary bodies were found.

These experimental findings, taken as a whole, leave little doubt that the disease is caused by a filtrable virus.

Prophylaxis.—The prophylaxis of measles has lately been improved by the use of serum from convalescent patients or from normal adults who have previously suffered from the disease. In children under 3 years of age, in weakly debilitated children, and in children suffering from some other serious disease, it is advisable to prevent an attack completely by injecting a fairly large dose of serum within 5 days of exposure to infection. The injection should be made intramuscularly, preferably into the vastus externus. The duration of the resulting immunity is 3–4 weeks, and the patient is subsequently susceptible to infection. After the age of 3 years it is desirable to aim, not at complete protection, but at attenuation of the attack. This is achieved by injecting the same quantity of serum within 6–9 days, or half the quantity within 1–5 days, of exposure to infection. The immunity following a modified attack appears to be permanent. The requisite dosage of serum is given in Table CLXXVII.

TABLE CLXXVII

DOSAGE OF SERUM IN MEASLES PROPHYLAXIS. (After Brincker 1936.)

Nature of Serum.	Limiting Dosage in c.c.	Dosage Factor.	Route.	Prophylaxis.		Treatment.
				Protection.	Attenuation.	
Convalescent .	5–20	Age × 2	Intra-muscular	1–5 days	5–9 days	Within 6 days of onset.
Normal adult .	10–40	Age × 4	,,	1–3 ,,	3–9 ,,	Dosage factor : age × 4.
Whole blood .	Double its serum	Age × 4	,,	1–3 ,,	3–9 ,,	Route intra-venous.

Thus for a child under 3 years of age, 6 c.c. of convalescent, or 12 c.c. of normal adult, serum should be given for complete protection. For attenuation of the attack in a child of 6 years, 12 c.c. of convalescent serum should be given between the 6th and 9th days after exposure, or 6 c.c. between the 1st and 5th days. If adult serum is selected, double these quantities should be used. A fixed dose of 10 c.c. of adult serum is used by some workers in preference to an age-adjusted dose ; if protection is desired it is given within the first 5 days, if attenuation is desired within 6–9 days of exposure. Though this practice possesses the merit of simplicity, it is doubtful whether it is altogether satisfactory (Gunn 1936). Convalescent serum should preferably be withdrawn from the donor 7–10 days after defervescence. Whole blood is of value mainly in general practice, when blood may be withdrawn from the mother or other member of the household and inoculated directly into the child.

Owing to difficulty in obtaining suitable quantities of serum, use is now being made of placental extract. This appears to occupy in potency a position inter-mediate between convalescent and adult serum.

Statistical analysis of the data so far accumulated has shown the undoubted value of serum prophylaxis (Report 1933, 1936). Convalescent serum is found to be more effective than normal adult serum, but only when administered to children under 5 years of age at an interval of less than 3 days after exposure to infection. It must be understood that to secure an attenuated attack, it is necessary not only to give serum, but also to make reasonably sure that the child has been adequately exposed to infection.   Otherwise many children in whom it is desired to produce an attenuated attack resulting in lasting immunity may entirely fail to develop the disease and be left susceptible (Report 1936).   For this purpose it is probably desirable to leave the child in contact with infection for a day or two and to delay giving serum for 5–9 days.   (For further references to serum prophylaxis in measles see Richardson and Connor 1919, Degkwitz 1920, 1921, 1922, McNeal 1922, Debré and Ravina 1923, Méry *et al.* 1923, von Torday 1923*a*, *b*, Rolleston 1923–24, Weaver and Crooks 1924, Zingher 1924, Debré *et al.* 1925, 1926, 1930, Copeman 1925, Toomey 1926, Haas and Blum 1926, Park and Freeman 1926, Benson and Lawrie 1927, Karelitz and Levin 1927, Kingsbury 1927, Gunn 1928, Benson 1929, Morales and Mandry 1930, Barenberg *et al.* 1930, Nabarro and Signy 1931, Gunn 1932.)

MUMPS

Mumps is an infectious disease of human beings characterized by a non-suppurative enlargement of the parotid glands, and sometimes of the testicles.   Though Kermorgant (1925) brought some evidence to suggest that infection was caused by a spirochæte, there is now little doubt that the causative agent is a filtrable virus.   This conclusion, which was reached by Gordon in 1914 on the basis of monkey experiments, and by Wollstein in 1916 on the basis of experiments with cats, has received confirmation from the more recent experiments of Johnson and Goodpasture (1934, 1935), and Findlay and Clarke (1934).   Saliva taken from patients in the early stage of the disease and inoculated into Stenson's duct, gives rise in *Macacus rhesus* monkeys to a disease similar to mumps.   After an incubation period of 6–10 days or so, there is a rise of temperature, a leucopenia with a relative lymphocytosis, and a painful non-suppurative swelling of the parotid gland.   Passage experiments can be made with a suspension of the ground-up glands filtered through a Berkefeld N candle.   The intratesticular injection of such a filtrate gives rise in monkeys to a non-suppurative orchitis.   Johnson and Goodpasture (1935) were able to transmit the disease back to human volunteers after it had been maintained for several generations in the monkey.   The virus is resistant to freezing, drying, and glycerolation.   Monkeys that have recovered from one attack of the disease are actively immune.   Attempts to confer passive immunity to intraparotid infection by inoculation with the serum of persons who have recovered from mumps have so far proved a failure (Johnson and Goodpasture 1936).

PSITTACOSIS

This is primarily a disease of birds—especially parrots—which sometimes attacks man.   The first human case reported was by Ritter (1879–80) in Switzerland, who described the clinical and pathological features of the disease.   Little attention was paid to the condition till 1929–30 when psittacosis appeared in many places throughout the world.   In the United States alone 74 foci of infection were recognized, and 169 cases occurred with 33 deaths (Armstrong 1930).   The incubation period in man is usually about 6–15 days.   The disease resembles typhoid fever in many respects and is often complicated by pneumonia.   Infection occurs by the inhalation of infective material excreted by parrots, parrakeets, love-birds (budgerigars), or canaries. Case-to-case infection is rare. Workers in a laboratory where the virus is being handled are particularly prone to develop the disease (McCoy 1934).

In parrots the disease is characterized by diarrhœa, shivering, weakness, and apathy. Respiratory disturbances may develop, accompanied by croaking noises and the secretion of mucus. Recovery often occurs, and is followed by a considerable degree of immunity to fresh infection. Latent infection appears to be widespread among parrots, cockateels, lorikeets, budgerigars, and similar birds in their native countries, while in many aviaries in Europe and America the disease is endemic (Meyer and Eddie 1934, Burnet 1935). Pathologically the disease in parrots is essentially an infection of the liver and spleen with occasional involvement of the lungs. Multiple necrotic areas are found in the liver, and the infective agent is present in the blood, internal organs, nasal discharges, and fæces (Rivers *et al.* 1931). Infection can be transmitted experimentally to budgerigars, parrots, mice, rabbits, guinea-pigs, and monkeys by suitable methods of inoculation. In mice continuous passage of the virus is readily accomplished by intraperitoneal inoculation of infected liver and spleen suspensions. Injected intradermally into the shaved skin of the rabbit or guinea-pig, the virus gives rise to a local papular eruption similar to that caused by the virus of herpes. Intracerebral injection into monkeys, rabbits and guinea-pigs is followed by a meningo-encephalitis, but intranasal or intratracheal instillation produces in monkeys a pneumonic condition similar to that seen in man (see Bedson and Western 1930, Gordon 1930, Rivers and Berry 1931).

Ætiology.—The disease was first thought to be due to Nocard's bacillus (see Chapter XXVII), an organism apparently identical with *Bact. typhi-murium*, but the intensive work of the past few years has shown that it is caused by a virus or virus-like body. Bedson and his colleagues have been largely responsible for the ætiological investigation of this disease (Bedson *et al.* 1930, Bedson and Western 1930, Bedson 1932, 1936, Bedson and Bland 1932, 1934). They demonstrated the infectivity of human blood ; they transmitted the infection to budgerigars and mice ; they demonstrated the presence of virus-like bodies in infected tissues ; they grew these bodies in tissue culture ; and they showed that they were specifically agglutinated by psittacosis antiserum, and that they contained two different antigens, one heat-labile and one heat-stable, both of which were demonstrable by the complement-fixation reaction. Microscopical examination of suitable infective material, such as the tissues of mice suffering from the disease, reveals the presence of minute coccal and bacillary bodies, arranged singly and in pairs, and bearing a resemblance to rickettsiæ and to Paschen granules. They can be stained with Giemsa, and better still with Rivers' modification of Castaneda's rickettsial stain. They can be thrown down almost completely by centrifugation at 5,000 r.p.m. for 2 hours ; they are largely held back by a Chamberland L2 filter ; they survive in frozen mouse spleen for 2 months, but die out rapidly in 50 per cent. glycerol phosphate at 6° C. In tissue culture they increase rapidly in size, become embedded in a homogeneous ground substance, and are later replaced by smaller bodies (see Bland and Canti 1935). They can be cultivated in the developing chick embryo (Burnet and Rountree 1935), but they have not been grown in the absence of living tissue. The nature of these bodies is still in doubt, but in their general characteristics they seem to be more closely related to the filtrable viruses than to the bacteria or rickettsiæ.

Diagnosis and Immunity.—A rapid diagnostic test for the human disease, consisting of intraperitoneal injection of the patient's sputum into mice and the subsequent demonstration of elementary bodies in impression smears from the liver and spleen, has been described by Rivers and Berry (1935). The serum of convalescent patients contains complement-fixing bodies, but has little neutralizing power (Bedson 1933).

Vaccination experiments are still in the early stage. Bedson (1933) was able to produce some immunity by injection of 0·1–0·2 per cent. formolized mouse spleen virus, while Rivers and Schwentker (1934) found that unattenuated virus could be injected intramuscularly into monkeys and human beings without setting up serious disease. (For a general description of the disease and investigations on it, see also Sturdee and Scott 1930, Branham *et al.* 1930, Rivers 1934.)

It may be noted that Pacheco, Bier and Meyer (for references see Rivers and Schwentker 1932) have described another disease of parrots and parrakeets caused by a virus different from that responsible for psittacosis.

YELLOW FEVER

Little was known about the ætiology of this once-dreaded disease till the studies of the American and the French Commissions were undertaken in the early years of this century.

The American workers, Reed, Carroll, Agramonte and Lazear (1900–01), at the beginning of the century, first showed that the blood of patients was infective during the first 3 days of the fever ; that the infecting agent was able to pass through a Berkefeld filter ; that the virus was destroyed in the blood by heating to 55° C. for 10 minutes ; that infection was not spread by contagion ; that mosquitoes, *Aëdes ægypti* (also called *Aëdes argenteus*, and *Stegomyia fasciata*) fed on patients during the first 3 days of the fever, became, after an interval of about 12 days, capable of transmitting the disease to normal persons ; and that by the suppression of these insects, yellow fever could be brought under control.

Marchoux, Salimbeni and Simond (1903), likewise working with human volunteers, largely confirmed these results. They found, moreover, that the serum of patients during the first 3 days of the fever, but not later, proved infective to normal persons when injected subcutaneously in a dose of 0·1–1·0 c.c. ; that defibrinated blood kept at 24°–30° C. under a vaseline seal remained infective for 5, but not for 8 days ; that the injection of blood kept for 8 days under these conditions was apparently able to produce some degree of immunity in human beings ; and that the serum of convalescent patients appeared to be endowed with both prophylactic and therapeutic properties.

The natural outcome of these findings was to undertake an intensive anti-mosquito campaign. The result of this so far exceeded expectations that yellow fever was apparently wiped out of Central and South America. Ten years ago it was believed that the only serious remaining focus of infection was in West Africa. The work, however, of the past few years, carried out to a considerable extent under the auspices of the Rockefeller Foundation, has necessitated a complete revision of our ideas on the epidemiology of the disease. So far from having been wiped out in South America, it is now known that infection is widespread through large parts of the country, and that the disease occurs in an endemic form whose very existence had been previously unrecognized (Soper 1936). As has happened so often with other diseases, the more flagrant epidemic manifestations of the disease were allowed to obscure the less obvious but more persistent undercurrent of infection. The institution of routine post-mortem examinations of every person dying within 10 days of the onset of any disease—the so-called viscerotomy service —and the survey of different communities by the complement-fixation and the mouse-protection tests (see below) to ascertain the frequency of specific serum antibodies against the yellow fever virus, showed that infection was far more widely distributed than had been realized, and that many persons must have been infected without ever developing the characteristic symptoms of the disease. It was found that, besides the urban type of yellow fever, which is carried by *Aëdes ægypti*, another type existed—provisionally referred to as **jungle yellow fever**— which occurred in districts entirely free from this species of mosquito. It is too early yet to say very much about the epidemiology of this second type of the disease, but the evidence so far available suggests that man is infected, by various intermediary species of mosquito, from wild monkeys, which probably constitute the main reservoir of infection. Though there is reason to believe that rigid measures to keep down the prevalence of *A. ægypti* are likely to be successful in preventing the urban type of the disease, it is now clear that the eradication of infection by anti-mosquito measures alone is a hopeless task.

Animal Inoculation.—Stokes, Bauer and Hudson (1928), working in Nigeria, made a great advance when they found that Asiatic monkeys, in particular *Macacus rhesus*, could be experimentally infected with the virus of yellow fever, either by inoculation of virulent material, or by infected mosquitoes of the species *Aëdes ægypti*. Mosquitoes, when once infected, were found to be capable of transmitting the disease for the rest of their lives. It was shown that the bite of a single mosquito was sufficient to produce a fatal infection in a monkey. The virus in the circulating blood of monkeys was able to pass through Berkefeld V and N, but not through W, candles.

After subcutaneous inoculation of a *monkey* with infective material, there is an incubation period of 3 to 4 days, followed by a rise in temperature of about 3° F. ; this temperature persists for 36 to 48 hours, and then falls suddenly to subnormal; collapse occurs, and the monkey dies about 5 to 6 days after inoculation. Post mortem, jaundice is usually present in some part of the body, especially the laryngeal mucosa and the subcutaneous fat ; small hæmorrhages are frequently found, particularly in the lungs and alimentary canal, and in the wall of the stomach ; dark coffee-ground material is often seen in the stomach and small intestine ; the most constant feature, however, is the pale, mottled liver, which microscopically shows fatty degeneration and mid-zonal necrosis. The liver, when fresh, is highly infective for monkeys—in a dose of about 0·000,02 gm. When frozen, the liver remains virulent for about a fortnight ; when dried and frozen, it remains virulent for about 3 months (Hindle 1929). This forms a very useful method of preserving the virus.

White *mice* are also susceptible to infection (see Theiler 1930, Dinger 1931). The intracerebral inoculation of these animals with 0·05 c.c. of infective blood from a *rhesus* monkey gives rise, after an incubation period of 5 or 6 days, to an illness characterized by ruffling of the coat, inactivity, photophobia, paresis of the hind legs, tonic and clonic contractions of the whole body, and finally coma and death in 6–9 days. Post mortem there is an acute encephalitis, often with dilatation of the skin vessels, swelling of the lymph glands, hæmorrhages into the stomach, erosion of the gastric mucosa, fatty degeneration of the liver, and enlargement of the suprarenals. Infection can be carried on indefinitely by cerebral passage. According to Findlay and Clarke (1935a), an encephalitis may be set up in both monkeys and mice by the intranasal instillation of a neurotropic strain of virus (see also Findlay and Stern 1935). *Guinea-pigs* can be infected intracerebrally, provided a neurotropic strain is used (Dinger *et al.* 1930, Mathis 1934, Lloyd and Mahaffy 1935).

Properties of Virus.—There is now no doubt that yellow fever is caused by a filtrable virus. Using gradocol membranes, Findlay and Broom (1933) have found that the virus is probably about 17–28 mμ in diameter. Its survival in infected blood has already been referred to (see also Sawyer *et al.* 1929). Though it is borne by mosquitoes, there is no evidence to show that it can be hereditarily transmitted from one generation to the next (Philip 1929). Its successful *in vitro* cultivation in mouse embryo tissue has been reported by Lloyd, Theiler, and Ricci (1936), though it may be noted that the virus under these conditions gradually loses its power to infect monkeys. Animal experiments have shown that the virulence of the yellow fever virus is subject to alteration, and that neurotropic and viscerotropic strains may be established (see Sawyer *et al.* 1930, Findlay and Clarke 1935b).

Immunity and Vaccination.—The serum of convalescent patients and monkeys contains antibodies to the yellow fever virus, which may be demonstrated by the complement-fixation, the precipitation, or the mouse-protection test. This last test, which was elaborated by Sawyer and Lloyd (1931), consists in the intraperitoneal inoculation of mice with a fixed virus together with the serum to be tested ; a simultaneous injection of starch solution is made into the brain to localize the virus. If the serum contains no antibodies, the animal dies of encephalitis. These tests, alone or in combination, have now been widely used in the survey of indigenous populations, and their results, as already mentioned, have shown the widespread distribution of infection in South America and West Africa (see Hughes and Sawyer 1932, Soper *et al.* 1932, Mahaffy *et al.* 1933, Beeuwkes and Mahaffy 1934). The mouse-protection test is of particular value, since antibodies can often be demonstrated by its means several years after infection.

The inability to eradicate infection by anti-mosquito measures has rendered some form of vaccination of exposed populations desirable. Numerous vaccines have been prepared and are now undergoing trial in the field. Though Sellards and Laigret's (1932) (see also Laigret 1933) method of vaccination with attenuated mouse passage virus has been extensively employed, most workers are of the opinion that it is too dangerous for human use. Some form of serum-virus vaccine is now generally used. A suitable quantity—about 0·5 c.c. per kilo—of human serum, or a smaller quantity of hyperimmune monkey serum containing antibodies is inoculated a few hours before the injection of a strain of virus that has been maintained for several generations in mouse embryo tissue culture (see Findlay 1934, Theiler and Whitman 1935).

DENGUE FEVER

Dengue fever is a disease of warm climates, and is peculiar to man ; it occurs during the summer months, often in severe epidemic form, attacking a high proportion of the exposed population, and it is followed by a comparatively short-lived immunity. Ashburn and Craig (1907), working in the Philippines, brought evidence to show that infection was due to a filtrable virus carried by mosquitoes. By intravenous inoculation of volunteers with 20 minims of blood taken from dengue patients, they were able to reproduce the typical disease ; the incubation period was as a rule 3 to 4 days—similar to that of the natural disease. Inoculation of two volunteers with blood filtered through a diatomaceous candle likewise reproduced the disease successfully. One volunteer out of four subjected to experiment developed the disease after being bitten by *Culex fatigans* Wied.

Cleland and Bradley (1918) in Australia found that the mosquito *Aëdes ægypti* was capable of transmitting infection. This observation was confirmed by Siler, Hall and Hitchens (1925) in the Philippines, who found that the patient was infective for the mosquito during the first 3 days of the disease, and that the mosquito did not become infective for human beings till the 11th day after biting. Once infected, the mosquito apparently remained so for the rest of its life. The mosquito, *Aëdes albopictus*, which is widely disseminated in the Far East, is also said to serve as a vector (Simmons *et al.* 1930). Observations in Greece showed that the disease could be transmitted by direct inoculation of filtered or unfiltered blood. The virus persisted in the blood for at least 5 days. The serum of patients remained virulent in sealed tubes for at least 54 days at 15°–18° C. Human volunteers inoculated subcutaneously with the ground-up bodies of *Aëdes ægypti* captured a week previously in the rooms of dengue patients, developed the disease 7–9 days later (Blanc and Caminopetros 1930, Pontano 1930).

Harris and Duval (1924) found that guinea-pigs could be infected by intraperitoneal or intracardial injection of filtered blood. Monkeys develop an " inapparent " infection, and their blood is said to be virulent for man 5–8 days, but not 12 days, after inoculation. Immunity follows an attack of the disease, and lasts for at least 4 months. Little is known about the causation of the disease, beyond the fact that the virus can pass through an L2 candle. According to Duval and Harris (1924), it can be cultivated in Smith-Noguchi medium, but no confirmation of this statement is forthcoming.

Sandfly Fever

Synonym : Phlebotomus Fever.

This disease occurs in tropical and sub-tropical countries. It is characterized by an incubation period of 1–6 days, and a fever lasting about 3 days, accompanied by severe headache, pains in the back, bones, joints, and muscles, and followed by considerable prostration. It is rarely fatal. Second, and even third, attacks do occur, but are not very common. The causative agent appears to be a filtrable virus. This has recently been cultivated on the chorio-allantoic membrane of the developing chick embryo (Shortt *et al.* 1936). Infection is spread by the sandfly *Phlebotomus papatasii*, though possibly other species may act as vectors. The flies do not become infective for 7–10 days after biting a patient with the fever (Doerr 1908).

Rift Valley Fever. Enzootic Hepatitis

In 1931 Daubney and Hudson described a new virus disease affecting sheep, cattle, goats, and man in the Rift Valley of Kenya Colony. In very young lambs the disease causes a mortality of 90 per cent. or over ; but in ewes and cows the mortality is only 10–20 per cent. In man the disease resembles dengue fever, and is characterized by malaise, nausea, rigors, abdominal discomfort, violent headache, transient fever, severe pains in the back and joints, and a leucocytosis followed by a leucopenia. Fatal cases are uncommon. In animals examined post mortem the principal finding is focal necrosis in the liver. Acidophilic intranuclear inclusion bodies can be demonstrated in the liver cells (Findlay 1933). The mode of spread of the disease is still in doubt. Daubney and Hudson (1933) bring some evidence to show that infection is carried by mosquitoes, but it is possible that it can also gain access by the respiratory tract (Francis and Magill 1935). Laboratory workers are not infrequently attacked.

Experimentally the disease can be transmitted to susceptible animals, including mice, monkeys and ferrets, but not guinea-pigs or rabbits, by cutaneous, subcutaneous, or intranasal inoculation. Mice are peculiarly susceptible, most of the animals dying in 36–96 hours after inoculation (Findlay 1932).

The virus is widely distributed in the body, and can pass through the placenta to the fœtal organs. Its probable size is 23–35 mμ (Broom and Findlay 1933). In blood it is destroyed by exposure to a temperature of 56° C. for 40 minutes, but it survives contact with 0·5 per cent. phenol at 4° C. for 6 months. It can be cultivated in a minced chick embryo medium (Mackenzie 1933). An attack of the disease confers a high degree of immunity in sheep, and the serum of convalescent animals and human beings contains strong neutralizing and complement-fixing properties. Mice can be successfully immunized by a virus treated with formol or inactivated photodynamically with methylene blue (Mackenzie 1935).

An *epizootic hepato-enteritis* caused by a virus has been described in guinea-pigs (see Morcos 1933).

DISTEMPER

Distemper is an acute infectious disease of young carnivorous animals, most frequently observed in dogs. The disease in the dog is characterized by an incubation period of about 4 days, an initial coryza, fever of a peculiar type, severe gastro-intestinal disturbance, and a variable set of symptoms due to inflammation of the respiratory tract; in a small proportion of cases nerve symptoms due to an encephalitis are met with. The mortality in uncomplicated cases is low, but in those complicated with respiratory or nervous disturbances it may be as high as 50 or 80 per cent. The disease is said to be accompanied by an acute anæmia and hypoglycæmia (Wharton and Wharton 1934). The encephalo-myelitis that is sometimes observed is characterized by demyelination. The observations of Perdrau and Pugh (1930) suggest that it is caused by a virus different from the virus of distemper. It resembles in fact the encephalitis in man that occasionally follows vaccination or one of the acute exanthemata.

Distemper occurs naturally in the ferret, and is characterized by an incubation period of about 10 days, an initial coryza, and the formation of vesicles and pustules around the mouth just as in dogs, encephalitis may develop in a small proportion of cases. Distemper in the ferret is a very fatal disease, causing a mortality of about 90 per cent (Dunkin and Laidlaw 1926).

The disease has been studied to a limited extent in the cat (Hindle and Findlay 1933, Dalling 1934), the fitch (Dalling 1931b), and the fox (Dalling 1932a). Observations suggest that the disease in cats is caused by a different virus from that infecting dogs (Dalling 1932b).

Distemper can be experimentally reproduced in dogs or ferrets by the subcutaneous inoculation of infective material, such as blood or spleen. Carré (1905) was able to transmit the disease to young puppies by bacteria-free exudates and by bacteria-free filtrates of infective discharges. Though M'Gowan (1911) in Scotland, and Ferry (1911) and Torrey and Rahe (1913) in America, brought forward evidence to suggest that distemper was caused by *Br. bronchiseptica* (see Chapter XXXI), the recent work of Dunkin and Laidlaw (1926) and of Laidlaw and Dunkin (1928) leaves no doubt that the primary cause of distemper is a filtrable virus. These workers were able to transmit the disease to dogs and ferrets by infected blood and serum from which no bacteria could be cultivated, and by Mandler filtrates of ground-up ferret's spleen. The disease reproduced by these bacteriologically sterile inocula was identical with natural distemper. Laidlaw and Dunkin regard *Br. bronchiseptica* as a secondary infective agent responsible for the respiratory complications of the disease ; they draw attention to the fact that in natural distemper, in which pneumonia is not uncommon, *Br. bronchiseptica*, though readily cultivable from the lung, can rarely be cultivated from the blood, thus indicating that the organism is a secondary rather than a primary invader. Attempts to cultivate the virus have so far been unsuccessful. The natural disease is probably transmitted by infective secretions and discharges. The virus is present in the blood of ferrets during the first 4 days of the disease, and in the blood of dogs at the height of the first febrile period.

Vaccination.—Laidlaw and Dunkin (1928) were able to immunize ferrets and dogs by a specific formolized vaccine. They found that 2 c.c. of a 20 per cent. suspension of a ferret's spleen treated with 0·1 per cent. formol, when injected subcutaneously, would protect normal ferrets against a large dose of active virus given 2 weeks later. A similar formolized vaccine made from infected dog's liver, spleen, and lymph glands, when given in a single dose to dogs, and followed by the inoculation of an attenuated living strain of virus, produced complete immunity. It is noteworthy that vaccine made from ferret's tissues had little protective action on dogs, unless multiple injections were given ; and that vaccine made from dog's tissues had practically no protective action on ferrets, even when multiple injections were given. The vaccine has now been tested under field conditions and has given very satisfactory results. Experience has shown that the original " wet virus " used for the second dose is unsuitable for commercial distribution, and it has now been replaced by a stable dried form of virus (Dalling 1931*a*, 1932*b*). This vaccine, which is now made from the spleen and mesenteric lymph glands of dogs (Laidlaw and Dunkin 1932), appears to be almost uniformly successful. Immunization with a single dose of serum-virus mixture proved less satisfactory and was given up (Dalling 1932*b*). Perdrau and Todd (1933) introduced a vaccine in which the virus had been inactivated by the photodynamic action of methylene blue, but no results of its use in the field are yet available.

SWINE FEVER

SYNONYMS : Hog Cholera. *Schweinepest* (German). *Peste du porc* (French).

Swine fever or hog cholera is an infectious disease, peculiar to pigs, caused by a filtrable virus. The disease is primarily a septicæmia, but in a large proportion of cases intestinal complications develop due to *Bact. choleræ-suis* or other members of the animal paratyphoid group, or lung complications due to *Pasteurella suiseptica*. A great deal of confusion has occurred in the past with regard to this disease, which was originally believed by Salmon and T. Smith (1886, 1885–95) to be due to infection with *Bact. cholerœ-suis* ; but it now appears to be fairly certain that there are at least three infections which may occur singly or concurrently. (1) Swine fever ; this is due to a filtrable virus. (2) Paratyphoid of pigs ; this is an intestinal disease caused by *Bact. cholerœ-suis*. (3) Swine plague ; this is a pleuropneumonia caused by *Pasteurella suiseptica*. The confusion has resulted from the fact that in swine fever secondary invasion with *Bact. cholerœ-suis* or *Past. suiseptica* is very common.

The evidence that swine fever is primarily due to a filtrable virus was first advanced by de Schweinitz and Dorset (1903), and may be summarized as follows (Uhlenhuth and Haendel 1913) : (1) Filtered blood, serum, organ suspensions, bile, or urine, when inoculated in 1–2 c.c. doses, are able to give rise to the disease in normal pigs after an incubation period of about 8 to 10 days. (2) The disease may be carried over by passage from animal to animal by inoculation of filtered blood. (3) Animals that have withstood the inoculation of filtered blood are henceforward immune both to natural and experimental infection. (4) Swine that have passed through an attack of the natural disease are resistant to the inoculation of filtered blood. (5) Normal swine placed in contact with experimentally infected swine develop the disease. (6) Animals injected intravenously or fed with cultures of *Bact. cholerœ-suis* develop acute intestinal inflammation, similar to that occurring in swine fever, but the filtered blood of these animals is not infective to normal swine. (7) Normal animals placed in contact with animals infected with *Bact. cholerœ-suis* do not contract swine fever. (8) Animals that have overcome an infection with *Bact. cholerœ-suis* are not immune to swine fever. (9) *Bact. cholerœ-suis* is not demonstrable in more than a variable proportion of cases of swine fever.

Natural infection in swine fever appears to occur by ingestion of infective material, especially material contaminated with the urine of sick animals (Hutyra and Marek 1926). Animals that have recovered from the disease may continue to carry infection for weeks or months, the virus apparently persisting in the button ulcers of the intestine (Gibbs 1933).

The virus is fairly resistant to inimical agencies. In filtered blood it is said to withstand a temperature of 58° C. for 2 hours, but to be destroyed by a temperature of 78° C. maintained for 1 hour. Fluid material containing the virus retains its virulence at room temperature for 10 to 14 weeks. In serum the virus is destroyed by 2 per cent. formol in 15 days, and by 2·5 per cent. antiformin in 2 hours (Hutyra and Marek 1926).

Attempts to confer an active immunity on swine by the injection of killed virus have failed. In practice, immunity can be produced by the simultaneous injection of 20 c.c. immune serum, taken from an animal that has recovered from the disease, and 1–2 c.c. of defibrinated virulent blood. Animals treated by this method are immune for at least 6 months. (See also Donatien and Lestoquard 1929.)

RINDERPEST OR CATTLE PLAGUE

Rinderpest is an acute infectious disease of cattle, characterized by an incubation period of 3 to 9 days, acute fever lasting for 4 to 7 days, inflammation of the oral and gastric mucosa often attended by necrosis and ulceration, and a mortality varying from 15 to 75 per cent. The disease is prevalent in Southern Europe, Asia, and Africa. It also attacks buffaloes (Schein 1917). The existence of chronic carriers, with diphtheritic ulcers in the abomasum, has been recorded by Gibbs (1933).

Inoculation of normal animals with tissue fluids from an infected animal reproduces the disease. At the height of the disease the blood proves virulent in a dose of 1/1,000 to 1/25,000 c.c. (Schein 1917). Goats are susceptible to experimental infection, but continuous passage through these animals is said to be followed by a diminution in virulence of the virus. There is evidence that the virus is contained chiefly within the leucocytes. Thus in blood that is allowed to clot naturally the serum is avirulent; in defibrinated blood that is centrifuged the deposit alone is virulent; in blood laked with distilled water, and centrifuged, the deposit, which consists mainly of leucocytes, alone is virulent (Kolle, see Nicolle and Adil-Bey 1902; Schein 1917, Daubney 1928). Nicolle and Adil-Bey (1902) brought forward evidence to show that the virus, when present in diluted tissue fluids or suspensions, may pass through a Berkefeld N or a Chamberland F candle; the results however are inconstant—possibly because of the intracellular location of the virus. The virus has not yet been cultivated, but Minett (1923) found that it could remain alive for at least 6 days at 37° C. in citrated blood, and for at least 13 days at 39°–40° C. in a glucose ox blood peptone water medium layered with paraffin.

Cattle may be immunized against the disease by the simultaneous inoculation of immune serum and living virus. In buffaloes this method is unsatisfactory, unless a large amount of serum combined with the least possible amount of virus is used (Schein 1917). Daubney (1928) states that formolized vaccines prepared from spleen pulp confer a high degree of immunity upon inoculated animals, but field inoculations with these vaccines have not yet been carried out.

African Horse Sickness

African horse sickness is a highly infectious disease of horses and mules, characterized in the acute form by fever, general symptoms of illness, and pulmonary œdema; in the subacute form by fever, constitutional symptoms, and the development of subcutaneous œdematous swellings around the orbits, and not infrequently on the forehead, head, chest, abdomen, back, and extremities. The incubation period is about 6 to 7 days. In South Africa the disease occurs annually during the rainy, warmer months, January to March, especially in low moist localities, and is accompanied by a high mortality. Natural infection is probably carried by mosquitoes (Hutyra and Marek 1926). The disease can be reproduced experimentally in horses by the subcutaneous or intravenous inoculation of small quantities of blood taken from infected animals. Blood, when diluted with saline, and filtered through a Berkefeld or Chamberland candle, still proves infective. Prophylactic inoculation is apparently best accomplished by Theiler's method, which consists in the injection of large quantities of immune serum intravenously together with small quantities of virulent blood subcutaneously, followed by a second serum injection after the appearance of the febrile reaction.

Infectious Anæmia of Horses
Synonym: Swamp Fever.

This disease, which is not to be confused with the swamp fever of human beings caused by *Leptospira grippo-typhosa* (see Chapter LXXIX), has a wide geographical distribution, occurring in various parts of Europe, the United States, Canada, Japan, and South Africa. It is most prevalent in low-lying badly drained districts, and reaches its maximum incidence during the summer months. The disease is due to a filtrable virus, which is constantly present in the blood stream. Transmission probably occurs by biting flies—*Stomoxys calcitrans*. The disease can be reproduced experimentally by biting insects, but not by contact or feeding. Equines are alone susceptible ; laboratory animals are refractory. The disease may be acute or chronic. The acute form is characterized by fever, extreme weakness, and conjunctival hæmorrhages, the chronic form by general unthriftiness with extreme emaciation. Anæmia does not appear to be a prominent sign. Death may occur in acute cases. There is, as yet, no specific diagnostic test or therapeutic treatment for the disease (for references see Stein 1935).

Malignant Catarrh of Cattle

Synonym : *Snotsiekte.*

This disease occurs in various parts of the world, and is characterized by fever, catarrh of the oral, nasopharyngeal, and conjunctival membranes, general enlargement of the lymphatic glands, and often symptoms suggesting involvement of the brain or cord. The mortality is subject to considerable variation. Post mortem examination of fatal cases often reveals petechial hæmorrhages in the stomach, mottling of the liver and kidneys, congestion and petechiæ in the respiratory mucosa, œdema of the lungs, enlargement of the lymphatic glands, and sometimes plate-like extravasations of blood on the surface of the brain. The disease is apparently caused by a virus, which can be transferred to rabbits and back again to cattle (see Daubney and Hudson 1936).

Fowl Plague or Fowl Pest

This is an acute infectious disease of fowls, and exceptionally of geese, which was studied by Landsteiner (1906) and Russ (1906). The incubation period is 3–5 days ; the symptoms consist of depression and dullness, darkening of the comb and wattles, and inflammation of the buccal mucosa. The disease lasts 2–4 days, and is very frequently fatal (Hutyra and Marek 1926). The experimental disease may be produced in chickens by the inoculation of blood, nasal secretion, or cloacal secretion in minimal quantities. Pigeons are resistant. The minimal infecting dose of fowls' blood is seldom above 0·000,000,1 c.c. The virus is able to pass through porcelain candles, and according to Elford and Todd (1933) is 60–90 mμ in diameter. Todd (1928*a*) finds that in the centrifuged blood of infected fowls the virus is contained chiefly in the leucocytic layer, the concentration in this layer being roughly 100 times that in the clear plasma or washed red blood corpuscles. Doerr and Gold (1932), however, disagree with this, and bring evidence to show that the virus is adsorbed on to the red cells (see also Doerr and Seidenberg 1932). Attempts to cultivate the virus in defibrinated fowl blood have been unsuccessful, but Burnet and Ferry (1934) have grown it on the chorio-allantoic membrane of the developing chick embryo. Immunization experiments have been disappointing. Todd (1928*b*) was able to protect fowls against at least 300,000 lethal doses by giving three injections at weekly intervals of a phenolized vaccine, but his results still await confirmation. Heated or formolized vaccines both proved unsatisfactory.

NEWCASTLE DISEASE OF FOWLS

This disease, which was described by Doyle in 1927, was first observed on a poultry farm near Newcastle-on-Tyne, but has since been reported from many parts of the world. It is an acute, febrile, contagious disease of fowls, which resembles fowl plague, but differs from it in a number of particulars. In addition to general symptoms of sickness, there is an offensive watery diarrhœa, a mucous discharge from the nostrils and mouth, and, most characteristic of all, difficulty in respiration manifested by the long gasping inhalation through the half-opened beak. The incubation period is 4–11 days. The morbidity in infected flocks is very high, and the case mortality verges on 100 per cent. The disease can be readily transmitted not only to fowls, but also to pigeons, which it will be remembered are insusceptible to fowl plague. The causative agent is a virus, which, according to Burnet and Ferry (1934), is 80–120 mμ in diameter, and can be readily cultivated on the chorio-allantoic membrane of the developing chick embryo. It is found in the body fluids, organs, and excretions of affected birds. Cross-immunization tests show that the fowl plague and Newcastle viruses are distinct.

INFECTIOUS LARYNGO-TRACHEITIS OF FOWLS

This disease has so far been reported mainly from North America and Australia. It appears to have been first recognized and studied in the United States by May and Tittsler (1925), Beach (1931), and others. Hyperacute, acute, chronic and asymptomatic forms are recognized clinically (Seddon and Hart 1935). Affected birds suffer from difficulty in respiration. The head is elevated, the neck extended, and air is drawn in through the half-opened beak with a loud wheezing sound. During expiration the head is lowered, and violent fits of coughing may occur, accompanied by the expulsion of masses of clotted blood and mucus. Fowls of all ages are susceptible. The incubation period is 7–12 days. The morbidity in an infected herd is 50–90 per cent. The case mortality varies in different outbreaks from 5–90 per cent. averaging about 20 per cent. (Doyle 1933). The disease is contagious, and there is evidence that chronic carriers may play a part in keeping infection alive from one outbreak to the next (Gibbs 1933). Intratracheal inoculation of infective material into normal fowls readily sets up the disease, but pigeons are resistant (Seddon and Hart 1936). The causative agent appears to be a virus, which is said by Gibbs (1935) to pass through a membrane with an average pore diameter of 0·082 μ. This suggests that the virus is smaller than that of fowl plague or the Newcastle disease. Burnet (1936) has cultivated the virus on the chorio-allantoic membrane of the chick embryo, on which under suitable conditions it gives rise to pocks. By counting the number of pocks developing after inoculation with mixtures of virus and immune serum, he has been able to study the process of serum neutralization. The results suggest that epizootic strains are more readily neutralizable by serum than enzootic strains, even though no qualitative antigenic difference may be detectable between the two strains. Fowls may be actively immunized against the disease by inoculation of virulent material into the cloaca and bursa of Fabricius. The resulting lesions are not serious, and leave behind them a substantial degree of immunity (Beaudette and Hudson 1933). The best time to vaccinate is between the age of 16 and 20 weeks (Gibbs 1936). For the differential diagnosis of the disease from fowl-pox, coryza, and A-avitaminosis, the reader is referred to Seddon and Hart (1935).

REFERENCES

ANDERSON, J. F. and GOLDBERGER, J. (1911) *J. Amer. med. Ass.*, **57**, 1612.

ARMSTRONG, C. (1930) *Publ. Hlth Rep., Wash.*, **45**, 2013.

ASHBURN, P. M. and CRAIG, C. F. (1907) *Philipp. J. Sci.*, B, **2**, 93.

BARENBERG, L. H., LEWIS, J. M., and MESSER, W. H. (1930) *J. Amer. med. Ass.*, **95**, 4.

BEACH, J. R. (1931) *J. exp. Med.*, **54**, 801.

BEAUDETTE, F. R. and HUDSON, C. B. (1933) *J. Amer. vet. med. Ass.*, **82**, 460.

BEDSON, S. P. (1932) *Brit. J. exp. Path.*, **13**, 65 ; (1933) *Ibid.*, **14**, 162 ; (1936) *Ibid.*, **17**, 109.

BEDSON, S. P. and BLAND, J. O. W. (1932) *Brit. J. exp. Path.*, **8**, 461 ; (1934) *Ibid.*, **15**, 243.

BEDSON, S. P. and WESTERN, G. T. (1930) *Brit. J. exp. Path.*, **11**, 502.

BEDSON, S. P., WESTERN, G. T., and SIMPSON, S. L. (1930) *Lancet*, i. 235, 345.

BEEUWKES, H. and MAHAFFY, A. F. (1934) *Trans. R. Soc. trop. Med. Hyg.*, **28**, 39.

BENSON, W. T. (1929) *J. R. sanit. Inst.*, **49**, 108.

BENSON, W. T. and LAWRIE, J. D. H. (1927) *Edin. med. J.*, **34**, 216.

BLAKE, F. G. and TRASK, J. D. (1921) *J. exp. Med.*, **33**, 385, 413.

BLANC, G. and CAMINOPETROS, J. (1930) *Ann. Inst. Pasteur*, **44**, 367.

BLAND, J. O. W. and CANTI, R. G. (1935) *J. Path. Bact.*, **40**, 231.

BRANHAM, S. E., McCOY, G. W., and ARMSTRONG, C. (1930) *Publ. Hlth Rep., Wash.*, **45**, 2153.

BRINCKER, J. A. H. (1936) *Lancet*, i. 103.

BROOM, J. C. and FINDLAY, G. M. (1933) *Brit. J. exp. Path.*, **14**, 179.

BURNET, F. M. (1935) *J. Hyg., Camb.*, **35**, 412 ; (1936) *J. exp. Med.*, **63**, 685.

BURNET, F. M. and FERRY, J. D. (1934) *Brit. J. exp. Path.*, **15**, 56.

BURNET, F. M. and ROUNTREE, P. M. (1935) *J. Path. Bact.*, **40**, 471.

CARRÉ, H. (1905) *C. R. Acad. Sci.*, **140**, 689, 1489.

CLELAND, J. B. and BRADLEY, B. (1918) *J. Hyg., Camb.*, **16**, 317.

COPEMAN, W. S. C. (1925) *J. Hyg., Camb.*, **24**, 427.

DALLING, T. (1931a) *Vet. Rec.*, **11**, 617 ; (1931b). *Ibid.*, **11**, 1051 ; (1932a) *Ibid.*, **12**, 141-(1932b) *Ibid.*, **12**, 743 ; (1934) *Ibid.*, **14**, 1137.

DAUBNEY, R. (1928) *J. comp. Path.*, **41**, 228, 263.

DAUBNEY, R. and HUDSON, J. R. (1931) *J. Path. Bact.*, **34**, 545 ; (1933) *East Afr. med. J.*, **10**, 2 ; (1936) *J. comp. Path.*, **49**, 63.

DEBRÉ, R., BONNET, H., BROCA, R., FLORAND, J., and DECAM, C. (1930) *Bull. Soc. méd. Hôp. Paris*, 1055. June 13.

DEBRÉ, R., BONNET, H., and DECAM, C. (1926) *Rev. Hyg.*, **48**, 24.

DEBRÉ, R., JOANNON, P., BONNET, H., and DECAM, C. (1925) *Bull. Soc. méd. Hôp. Paris*, **49**, 682.

DEBRÉ, R. and RAVINA, J. (1923) *Bull. Soc. méd. Hôp. Paris*, **49**, 226.

DEGKWITZ, R. (1920) *Z. Kinderheilk.*, **25**, 134 ; (1921) *Ibid.*, **27**, 171 ; (1922) *Dtsch. med. Wschr.*, **48**, 26.

DINGER, J. E. (1931) *Zbl. Bakt.*, **121**, 194.

DINGER, J. E., SCHÜFFNER, W. A. P., and SNIJDERS, E. P. (1930) *Zbl. Bakt.*, **119**, 1.

DOERR, R. (1908) *Berl. klin. Wschr.*, **45**, 1847.

DOERR, R. and GOLD, E. (1932) *Z. Hyg. InfektKr.*, **113**, 645.

DOERR, R. and SEIDENBERG, S. (1932) *Z. Hyg. InfektKr.*, **114**, 269, 276.

DONATIEN, A. and LESTOQUARD, F. (1929) *Ann. Inst. Pasteur*, **43**, 1560.

DOYLE, T. M. (1927) *J. comp. Path.*, **40**, 144 ; (1933) *Ibid.*, **46**, 90.

DUNKIN, G. W. and LAIDLAW, P. P. (1926) *J. comp. Path.*, **39**, 201, 213.

DUVAL, C. W. and D'AUNOY, R. (1922) *J. exp. Med.*, **36**, 231.

DUVAL, C. W. and HARRIS, W. H. (1924) *J. exp. Med.*, **40**, 835.

ELFORD, W. J. and TODD, C. (1933) *Brit. J. exp. Path.*, **14**, 240.

FERRY, N. S. (1911) *J. infect. Dis.*, **8**, 399.

FINDLAY, G. M. (1932) *Trans. R. Soc. trop. Med. Hyg.*, **25**, 229.

FINDLAY, G. M. (1933) *Brit. J. exp. Path.*, **14**, 207.

FINDLAY, G. M. (1934) *Trans. R. Soc. trop. Med. Hyg.*, **27**, 437.

FINDLAY, G. M. and BROOM, J. C. (1933) *Brit. J. exp. Path.*, **14**, 391.

FINDLAY, G. M. and CLARKE, L. P. (1934) *Brit. J. exp. Path.*, **15**, 309; (1935a) *J. Path. Bact.*, **40**, 55 ; (1935b) *Trans. R. Soc. trop. Med. Hyg.*, **28**, 579.

FINDLAY, G. M. and STERN, R. O. (1935) *J. Path. Bact.*, **40**, 311.

FRANCIS, T. and MAGILL, T. P. (1935) *J. exp. Med.*, **62**, 433.

GIBBS, C. S. (1933) *J. infect. Dis.*, **53**, 169 ; (1935) *J. Bact.*, **30**, 411 ; (1936) *J. Amer. vet. med. Ass.*, **88**, 413.

GORDON, M. H. (1914) *Rep. loc. Govt Bd, New Ser.*, No. 96 ; (1930) *Lancet*, i. 1174.

GUNN, W. (1928) *Lancet*, ii. 690 ; (1932) *Brit. med. J.*, i. 183 ; (1936) *Pers. comm.*

HAAS, S. V. and BLUM, J. H. (1926) *J. Amer. med. Ass.*, **87**, 558.

HARRIS, W. H. and DUVAL, C. W. (1924) *J. exp. Med.*, **40**, 817.

HINDLE, E. (1929) *Trans. R. Soc. trop. Med. Hyg.*, **22**, 405.

HINDLE, E. and FINDLAY, G. M. (1933) *Proc. R. Soc. Med.*, **26**, 197.

HUGHES, T. P. and SAWYER, W. A. (1932) *J. Amer. med. Ass.*, **99**, 978.

HUTYRA, H. and MAREK, J. (1926) " Special Pathology and Therapeutics of the Diseases of Domestic Animals," 3rd Amer. Edit. Chicago and London.

JOHNSON, C. D. and GOODPASTURE, E. W. (1934) *J. exp. Med.*, **59**, 1 ; (1935) *Amer. J. Hyg.*, **21**, 46 ; (1936) *Ibid.*, **23**, 329.

KARELITZ, S. and LEVIN, S. (1927) *Amer. J. Dis. Child.*, **33**, 408.

KERMORGANT, Y. (1925) *Ann. Inst. Pasteur*, **39**, 565.

KINGSBURY, A. N. (1927) *Lancet*, i. 7.

LAIDLAW, P. P. and DUNKIN, G. W. (1928) *J. comp. Path.*, **41**, 1, 209 ; (1932) *Lancet*, ii. 1457.

LAIGRET, J. (1933) *Arch. Inst. Pasteur, Tunis*, **21**, 412.

LANDSTEINER, K. (1906) *Zbl. Bakt., Ref.*, **38**, 540.

LLOYD, W. and MAHAFFY, A. F. (1935) *Amer. J. trop. Med.*, **15**, 51.

LLOYD, W., THEILER, M., and RICCI, N. I. (1936) *Trans. R. Soc. trop. Med. Hyg.*, **29**, 481.

MACKENZIE, R. D. (1933) *J. Path. Bact.*, **37**, 75 ; (1935) *Ibid.*, **40**, 65.

MCCOY, G. W. (1934) *J. infect. Dis.*, **55**, 156.

MCNEAL, M. D. (1922) *J. Amer. med. Ass.*, **78**, 340.

M'GOWAN, J. P. (1911) *J. Path. Bact.*, **15**, 372.

MAHAFFY, A. F., LLOYD, W., and PENNA, H. A. (1933) *Amer. J. Hyg.*, **18**, 618.

MARCHOUX, SALIMBENI, and SIMOND. (1903) *Ann. Inst. Pasteur*, **17**, 665.

MATHIS, M. (1934) *C. R. Soc. Biol.*, **115**, 842.

MAY, H. G. and TITTSLER, R. P. (1925) *J. Amer. vet. med. Ass.*, **67**, 229.

MÉRY, H., GASTINEL, P., and JOANNON, P. (1923) *Bull. Acad. Méd., Paris*, **89**, 194.

MEYER, K. F. and EDDIE, B. (1934) *Klin. Wschr.*, **13**, 865.

MINETT, F. C. (1923) *J. comp. Path.*, **36**, 205.

MORALES, E. G. and MANDRY, O. C. (1930) *Amer. J. Dis. Child.*, **39**, 1214.

MORCOS, Z. (1933) *J. Bact.*, **25**, 239.

NABARRO, D. N. and SIGNY, A. G. (1931) *Brit. med. J.*, ii. 599.

NEVIN, M. and BITTMAN, F. R. (1921) *J. infect. Dis.*, **29**, 429.

NICOLLE, M. and ADIL-BEY. (1902) *Ann. Inst. Pasteur*, **16**, 56.

NICOLLE, C. and CONSEIL, E. (1911) *C. R. Acad. Sci.*, **153**, 1522 ; (1920) *C. R. Soc. Biol.*, **83**, 56.

PARK, W. H. and FREEMAN, R. G. (1926) *J. Amer. med. Ass.*, **87**, 556.

PERDRAU, J. R. and PUGH, L. P. (1930) *J. Path. Bact.*, **33**, 79.

PERDRAU, J. R. and TODD, C. (1933) *J. comp. Path.*, **46**, 78.

PHILIP, C. B. (1929) *J. exp. Med.*, **50**, 703.

PONTANO, T. (1930) *Z. ImmunForsch.*, **69**, 146.

PURDY, W. J. (1925) *Brit. J. exp. Path.*, **6**, 210.

REED, W., CARROLL, J., AGRAMONTE, A., and LAZEAR, J. W. (1900–01) See *Senate Documents, Wash.*, 1911, **66**, No. 822, p. 156.

Report. (1933) *Rep. med. Offr Hlth, School med. Offr on Measles Epidemic*, 1931–32, L.C.C. ; (1936) *Ibid.*, 1933–34.

RICHARDSON, D. L. and CONNOR, H. (1919) *J. Amer. med. Ass.*, **72**, 1046.

RITTER, J. (1879–80) *Dtsch. Arch. klin. Med.*, **25**, 53.

RIVERS, T. M. (1934) *The Harvey Lectures*, April 19th, p. 220.

RIVERS, T. M. and BERRY, G. P. (1931) *J. exp. Med.*, **54**, 105, 119, 129.

RIVERS, T. M. and BERRY, G. P. (1935) *J. exp. Med.*, **61**, 205.

RIVERS, T. M., BERRY, G. P., and SPRUNT, D. H. (1931) *J. exp. Med.*, **54**, 91.

RIVERS, T. M. and SCHWENTKER, F. F. (1932) *J. exp. Med.*, **55**, 911 ; (1934) *Ibid.*, **60**, 211.

ROLLESTON, J. D. (1923–24) *Med. Sci.*, **9**, 177.

RUSS, V. K. (1906) *Arch. Hyg.*, **59**, 286.

SALMON, D. E. and SMITH, T. (1886) *Amer. mon. micr. J.*, **7**, 204 ; (1885–95) *Rep. Bur. anim. Indust.*

SAWYER, W. A. and LLOYD, W. (1931) *J. exp. Med.*, **54**, 533.

SAWYER, W. A., LLOYD, W. D. M., and KITCHEN, S. F. (1929) *J. exp. Med.*, **50**, 1.

SAWYER, W. A., KITCHEN, S. F., FROBISHER, M., and LLOYD, W. (1930) *J. exp. Med.*, **51**, 493.

SCHEIN, H. (1917) *Ann. Inst. Pasteur*, **31**, 571.

SCHWEINITZ, DE and DORSET. (1903) *20th Ann. Rep. Bur. anim. Indust. Circ.*, No. 41.

SCOTT, J. M. and SIMON, C. E. (1924) *Amer. J. Hyg.*, **4**, 559, 725 ; (1925) *Ibid.*, **5**, 109.

SEDDON, H. R. and HART, L. (1935) *Aust. vet. J.*, **11**, 212 ; (1936) *Ibid.*, **12**, 13.

SELLARDS, A. W. and LAIGRET, J. (1932) *Arch. Inst. Pasteur, Tunis*, **21**, 229.

SHORTT, H. E., RAO, S. R., and SWAMINATH, C. S. (1936) *Indian J. med. Res.*, **23**, 865.

SILVER, J. F., HALL, M. W., and HITCHENS, A. P. (1925) *J. Amer. med. Ass.*, **84**, 1163.

SIMMONS, J. S., ST. JOHN, J. H., and REYNOLDS, F. H. K. (1930) *Philipp. J. Sci.*, **41**, 215.

SOPER, F. L.   (1936) *Lancet*, i. 510.
SOPER, F. L., FROBISHER, M., KERR, J. A., and DAVIS, N. C.   (1932) *J. prev. Med., Baltimore*, **6**, 341.
STEIN, C. D.   (1935) *J. Amer. vet. Med. Ass.*, **87**, 312.
STOKES, A., BAUER, J. H., and HUDSON, N. P.   (1928) *Amer. J. trop. Med.*, **8**, 103.
STURDEE, E. L. and SCOTT, W. M.   (1930) *Min. Hlth Rep. publ. Hlth med. Subj.*, No. 61.
TANIGUCHI, T., HOSOKAWA, M., KUGA, S., and TERADA, K.   (1935) *Jap. J. exp. Med.*, **13**, 577.
THEILER, M.   (1930) *Ann. trop. Med. Parasitol.*, **24**, 249.
THEILER, M. and WHITMAN, L.   (1935) *Amer. J. trop. Med.*, **15**, 347.
TODD, C.   (1928a) *Brit. J. exp. Path.*, **9**, 19 ; (1928b) *Ibid.*, **9**, 101.
TOOMEY, J. A.   (1926) *Amer. J. Dis. Child.*, **32**, 401.
TORDAY, F. VON.   (1923a) *Jb. Kinderheilk.*, **52**, 213 ; (1923b) *Ibid.*, **53**, 307.
TORREY, J. C. and RAHE, A. H.   (1913) *J. med. Res.*, **27**, 291.
UHLENHUTH, P. and HAENDEL, L.   (1913) See Kolle and Wassermann's " Hdb. path Mikroorg.," 2te Abt., 1912–13, **6**, 325.
WEAVER, G. H. and CROOKS, T. T.   (1924) *J. Amer. med. Ass.*, **82**, 204.
WHARTON, D. R. A. and WHARTON, M. W.   (1934) *Amer. J. Hyg.*, **19**, 189.
WOLLSTEIN, M.   (1916) *J. exp. Med.*, **23**, 353.
ZINGHER, A.   (1924) *J. Amer. med. Ass.*, **82**, 1180.

CHAPTER LXXXV

FILTRABLE VIRUS DISEASES—*Continued*

D. GROUP CHARACTERIZED BY TUMOUR FORMATION

FOWL LEUCÆMIA

This is an infectious disease of the blood-forming organs, associated with atrophy of the bone marrow and changes in the viscera.   The disease may be transmitted to normal fowls, but not to other birds, by intravenous inoculation with the citrated blood of infected fowls.   According to Ellermann (1921), the virus can pass through a Berkefeld candle.   Ellermann found that one strain of virus gave rise to three different types of leucæmia : (1) a myeloid type ; (2) a lymphatic type ; (3) an intravascular lymphoid type, characterized by intravascular deposits of lymphoid cells.   An increase of virulence was noted during its passage through fowls, shown by a shortening of the interval between inoculation and death, from 15 to 20 weeks, at the commencement, to 6 to 8 weeks at the end of the series of experiments.   In spite, however, of the increased rate of killing, the infecting power of the virus, as judged by the proportion of successful inoculations, remained approximately constant at 20–40 per cent.   Ellermann was unable to produce active immunity to the disease by subcutaneous inoculation of virulent material.

Furth (1932) found that infection could be transmitted by 0·000,001 c.c. of cell-free plasma, and that the virus could withstand drying for at least 54 days. He also (1933) described a new transmissible strain of chicken leucosis which gave rise to (1) lymphomatosis with or without tumour formation, (2) myelocytomatosis with or without leucæmia, (3) endothelioma.   The histology of the disease is beautifully illustrated in the monograph by Andersen and Bang (1928).

ROUS SARCOMA OF CHICKENS

Rous (1911, Rous *et al.* 1912, Rous and Murphy 1914) described three transplantable sarcomata of fowls.   Tumour I was a spindle-celled sarcoma that metastatized freely and caused death in a month ; Tumour VII was an osteochondrosarcoma ; and Tumour XVIII was a spindle-celled sarcoma with blood sinuses into which growth occurred.   Each of these three tumours could be transmitted to normal fowls by the inoculation of cell-free Berkefeld filtrates.   Gye (1925), who worked with the Rous Tumour I, has recorded evidence from which he concludes that the active agent is a living filtrable virus, which can be cultivated anaerobically in tubes of Hartley's broth to which 17 per cent. of rabbit serum, 0·2 per cent. KCl, and a fragment of chick embryo have been added.   He believes that the tumour-forming activity of this virus is dependent on the presence of another, non-living factor, which determines the type of cell which is infected, and hence the type of tumour which is produced. This second, auxiliary agent he calls the "specific factor." The evidence in favour of the dual nature of the active agent in tumour-filtrates consists in the differential action of aerobic incubation and of various chemical agents. In an extensive series of experiments Gye found that (a) primary "cultures" incubated aerobically at 37° C. for 3 days were inactive; (b) filtrates, obtained by passing the ground-up tumour through a mixture of paper pulp and sand, when treated with chloroform, were inactive; but that (c) the inactivated "cultures" and the chloroform-inactivated filtrates, when acting in combination, gave rise to typical tumours. He would regard the specific factor in the "cultures" as being destroyed by aerobic incubation, and the virus in the tumour filtrate as being destroyed by the chloroform. He would also extend the conclusions based on these results to malignant neoplasms in general. Gye's results have not yet been completely confirmed by other workers, and his hypothesis is still in the stage of discussion and experiment (Gye and Mueller 1929).

During the past two decades fresh filtrable tumours of fowls and other birds have been described, and considerable interest has centred around their ætiology. The demonstration by Ledingham and Gye (1935) of what appear to be elementary bodies in infective filtrates, and the immunological studies of Andrewes (1931, 1932, 1933), suggest more and more strongly that viruses, not differing in any important respect from those known to give rise to ordinary infectious diseases, play an essential part in the causation of these tumours (see Andrewes 1934).

Molluscum Contagiosum

This is a contagious skin disease of man characterized by the formation of small red masses, which later take on a warty appearance, undergo necrosis, and discharge caseous material. MacCallum (1892) described peculiar bodies in material taken from the disease, which he regarded as due to nucleolar extrusion. They were later described by Lipschütz (1907) as very small rounded bodies, about 0·25 μ in diameter, arranged singly or less often in pairs. They can be stained with Loeffler's flagellar stain or with Giemsa. These molluscum bodies were at one time considered to be parasites, but are now generally regarded as inclusion bodies (Goodpasture and King 1927). The disease is apparently caused by a filtrable virus, since positive inoculation experiments in man have been reported with Chamberland filtrates of the tumour (Juliusberg 1905).

Common Warts

Numerous workers have recorded evidence which suggests that common warts are infectious. Jadassohn (1896) found that they could be produced in human beings by experimental inoculation. More recently Wile and Kingery (1919), and Kingery (1921), in a small series of experiments, were able to produce warts by intracutaneous inoculation of human beings with a Berkefeld filtrate of a suspension of ground-up wart material. In one case the warts were carried over successfully for two generations. The incubation period varied from 4 weeks to 6 months.

INFECTIOUS MYXOMATOSIS OF RABBITS

Sanarelli (1898) described an infectious myxoma indigenous to rabbits of South America. The disease can be conveyed by inoculation of filtered material. Tumour masses appear quickly at the site of inoculation, and later at various other points in the subcutaneous tissue, as well as in the lymph glands and spleen. The disease is very malignant and kills rabbits in 7 to 15 days. Rivers (1926–27) finds that both epithelial and connective tissue are affected, the epithelial cells being destroyed, and certain of the connective-tissue cells undergoing proliferation. In the epidermal cells he describes small pink granular areas occupying the cytoplasm. They increase rapidly in size and form acidophilic masses often containing blue, round or rod-shaped, bodies. Lipschütz (1927), who has made similar observations, regards these round or rod-shaped bodies as micro-organisms. Their real nature is still obscure. The virus is widely distributed throughout the tissues, though most abundant in the swollen tissues and lymph glands. It is killed by heat at 50° C. in 15 minutes. It is quickly inactivated by a pH of less than 4·6. It withstands the action of glycerol for a year in the ice-chest. It is highly species-specific, and appears to be uniformly fatal for the domestic rabbit (see Rivers 1930, Findlay 1933, Hyde and Gardner 1933).

INFECTIOUS FIBROMATOSIS OF RABBITS

This disease, which was first observed by Shope (1932) (see also Shope 1936*a*) in cotton-tail rabbits, is of the nature of a filtrable fibroma, which occurs in the subcutaneous tissue. It can be transmitted by filtrates of the tumour suspension to wild and domestic rabbits, but not to other animals. Cytoplasmic inclusions are demonstrable in the cells. The condition is non-fatal, and undergoes spontaneous retrogression. The virus is resistant to glycerol, and is apparently different from that causing infectious myxomatosis. A very remarkable mutant strain has been derived from it which gives rise to acute inflammatory lesions instead of the usual proliferative changes (Andrewes 1936, Shope 1936*b*, Andrewes and Shope 1936, Editorial 1936).

INFECTIOUS PAPILLOMATOSIS OF RABBITS

This disease has been described by Shope and Hurst (1933). It affects cotton-tail rabbits, and is characterized by the presence of warty or horn-like protuberances on various parts of the body. Infection can be transmitted in series through cotton-tail rabbits. The virus is filtrable through a Berkefeld candle, resists the action of glycerol, and is killed by exposure to 70° C., but not 67° C., for 30 minutes. It exhibits a marked tropism for cutaneous epithelium. Rabbits with experimentally produced papillomata are partly or completely immune to re-infection, and their serum has neutralizing properties.

HODGKIN'S DISEASE

Little is known of the ætiology of this fatal disease, in which characteristic histological changes are usually found in the enlarged lymph glands and lymphoid deposits. Gordon (1933, 1934, 1936) has described the reproduction of meningo-encephalitis in rabbits by the intracerebral inoculation of autolysed gland suspensions. Elementary bodies are said to be distinguishable in human material and in impression preparations of infected rabbit's brain. The causative agent is said to pass through British Berkefeld and Seitz EK filters (van Rooyen 1934) ; to be inactivated by exposure to a temperature of 80° C. for 30 minutes ; to withstand 0·5 per cent. phenol at 37° C. for probably a week or longer ; and to be neutralized by the serum of a rabbit that has recovered from the infection. Until these findings are confirmed the ætiology of Hodgkin's disease must remain in doubt, particularly in view of the report by Friedemann and Elkeles (1933) that encephalitic symptoms can be produced in rabbits by intracerebral inoculation with bone marrow from cases of acute leukæmia and pernicious anæmia.

REFERENCES

ANDERSEN, C. W. and BANG, O. (1928) " La Leucémie ou Leucose transmissible des Poules." Festskrift. Bernard Bang, Særtryk.

ANDREWES, C. H. (1931) *J. Path. Bact.*, **34**, 91 ; (1932) *Ibid.*, **35**, 243 ; (1933) *Ibid.*, **37**, 17 ; (1934) *Lancet*, ii. 63, 117 ; (1936) *J. exp. Med.*, **63**, 157.

ANDREWES, C. H. and SHOPE, R. E. (1936) *J. exp. Med.*, **63**, 179.

Editorial. (1936) *Lancet*, i. 1125.

ELLERMANN, V. (1921) *J. exp. Med.*, **33**, 539.

FINDLAY, G. M. (1933) *Vet. J.*, **88**, 550.

FRIEDEMANN, U. and ELKELES, A. (1933) *Brit. med. J.*, ii. 1110.

FURTH, J. (1932) *J. exp. Med.*, **55**, 465, 479, 495 ; (1933) *Ibid.*, **58**, 253.

GOODPASTURE, E. W. and KING, H. (1927) *Amer. J. Path.*, **3**, 385.

GORDON, M. H. (1933) *Brit. med. J.*, i. 641 ; (1934) *Proc. R. Soc. Med.*, **27**, 1035 ; (1936) *Lancet*, ii. 65.

GYE, W. E. (1925) *Lancet*, ii. 109.

GYE, W. E. and MUELLER, J. H. (1929) *J. exp. Med.*, **49**, 195.

HYDE, R. R. and GARDNER, R. E. (1933) *Amer. J. Hyg.*, **17**, 446.

JADASSOHN. (1896) *Arch. Derm. Syph.*, *Wien*, **34**, 129.

JULIUSBERG, M. (1905) *Dtsch. med. Wschr.*, **31**, 1598.

KINGERY, L. B. (1921) *J. Amer. med. Ass.*, **76**, 440.

LEDINGHAM, J. C. G. and GYE, W. E. (1935) *Lancet*, i. 376.

LIPSCHÜTZ, B. (1907) *Wien. klin. Wschr.*, **20**, 253 ; (1927) *Ibid.*, **40**, 1101.

MACCULLUM. (1892) *J. cutan. Dis.*, **10**, 93.

RIVERS, T. M. (1926–27) *Proc. Soc. exp. Biol.*, *N.Y.*, **24**, 435 ; (1930) *J. exp. Med.*, **51**, 965.

ROOYEN, C. E. VAN. (1934) *Brit. med. J.*, i. 519.

ROUS, P. (1911) *J. exp. Med.*, **13**, 397.

ROUS, P. and MURPHY, J. B. (1914) *J. exp. Med.*, **19**, 52.

ROUS, P., MURPHY, J. B., and TYTLER, W. H. (1912) *J. Amer. med. Ass.*, **59**, 1793.

SANARELLI, G. (1898) *Zbl. Bakt.*, **23**, 865.

SHOPE, R. E. (1932) *J. exp. Med.*, **56**, 793, 803 ; (1936a) *Ibid.*, **63**, 33, 43 ; (1936b) *Ibid.*, **63**, 173.

SHOPE, R. E. and HURST, E. W. (1933) *J. exp. Med.*, **58**, 607.

WILE, U. J. and KINGERY, L. B. (1919) *J. Amer. med. Ass.*, **73**, 970.

CHAPTER LXXXVI

THE NORMAL FLORA OF THE HUMAN BODY

THE normal flora of the human and animal body has received relatively little attention from bacteriologists in the past, and it is only within recent years that any serious attempt has been made to study it in detail. Before describing the organisms met with in different parts of the body, it is necessary to realize certain general principles regulating their distribution. Firstly, our conception of the normal flora depends very largely on the technique that is employed. A survey based upon examination of stained smears frequently gives results quite different from a survey based on cultural examination. And the results obtained with one culture medium may differ widely from those obtained with another. The main reason for this difference is that every culture medium is more or less selective in its action ; it encourages the growth of some organisms and hinders or entirely prevents the growth of others. For example, very different pictures of the intestinal flora will be obtained on agar plates and on MacConkey plates ; on the latter medium the bile-salts will inhibit the growth of nearly all organisms except the Gram-negative coliform bacilli, whereas on agar numerous cocci, Gram-positive bacilli, and other organisms will develop as well. Similarly, very different pictures of the nasopharyngeal flora will be obtained if swabs from this region are plated (*a*) on ordinary agar, (*b*) on blood agar, and (*c*) on such a selective medium as Fildes' agar. The method of incubation is of great importance ; cultures incubated anaerobically will reveal a very different flora from those incubated aerobically. Incubation at 22° C. is unfavourable to the growth of many pathogenic species.

Having realized the importance of the technique employed, it is necessary to understand that the term "normal" flora may be misleading. It is possible to give a description of the intestinal or nasopharyngeal flora which will apply to the great majority of adult persons living under particular environmental conditions ; but this description may not be applicable, or may apply only in part, to another community, consuming a different diet, or exposed to a different climate. There are certain bacterial species which, so far as our information goes, are constantly present in particular situations. Thus, *Bact. coli* appears to be a normal intestinal parasite of man in all parts of the inhabited globe ; *Str. viridans* is, so far as we know, always present in the nasopharynx ; and *Staph. albus* seems always to be present on the normal skin. In addition to such constant constituents of the human bacterial flora, there are, however, very many species whose range is limited in space and time. Many of these species are potential pathogens, such, for instance, as the pneumococcus, the meningococcus, the influenza bacillus, and hæmolytic streptococci, among the nasopharyngeal flora ; but it is probable that many non-pathogenic species show a similarly localized distribution. If our knowledge were more extensive than it is, we should probably be able to describe a basal flora, characteristic of mankind under all conditions ; a supplementary flora, varying in frequency, but ranging widely as normal parasites of man ; and various species showing a restricted range or a temporary prevalence, conditioned by localized or transient environmental factors. This aspect of bacterial ecology has, however, received relatively little attention, except with regard to the incidence of a few important pathogenic species. If we include, among the normal flora of a particular region of the body, all those bacterial species which may be isolated from any considerable sample of apparently healthy persons, we must note that this flora varies widely, from time to time, and from place to place.

The nature of the intestinal flora, for example, depends on a number of factors, such as diet, gastric acidity, degree of peristalsis, external temperature, and so on. The predominant flora on a herbivorous differs from that on a carnivorous diet ; in the upper part of the small intestine it is more copious in persons with gastric hypoacidity than in normal persons. Again, the flora of the nasopharynx is constantly changing both in the same individual and in the same community. At one time, pneumococci and Pfeiffer's bacilli may be present in large numbers in apparently healthy persons, whereas at another time they may be far less frequent. It must be realized, therefore, that, in the account which follows, we can make no attempt to give a complete description of the organisms that may be found in different parts of the body, or to indicate more than roughly their frequency and relative proportions.

There is one additional point, which cannot be too strongly emphasized. None of those regions of the body, to which bacteria can gain entrance by the normal portals, provides a virgin soil in which any new-comer may flourish. It is just as impossible to ensure the proliferation of a particular bacterial species by introducing it into the mouth, as it is to ensure a crop of a particular plant by scattering seeds in a field already occupied by a pre-existing plant-association. The new-comer will have little chance of survival, unless it is adapted to occupy some definite place in its new environment. It is fairly certain that those pathogenic bacteria which spread readily from host to host owe their capacities in this direction to their ability to colonize on skin or mucous surfaces, or to escape from the superficial environment to the underlying tissues. This question, in relation to the upper part of the respiratory and alimentary tracts, has been studied in some detail by Bloomfield and his colleagues (Bloomfield 1919, 1921, 1922a, b, c, d, e, Bloomfield and Felty 1923a, b, c, Felty and Bloomfield 1923).

Normal Flora of the Alimentary Tract.

The bacteria present in the *mouth* are subject to great variation both in number and in kind. Even the relatively clean and healthy mouth contains a considerable amount of detritus and other organic matter derived from particles of food, desquamated epithelium, pharyngeal mucus, and other sources ; these provide nutriment for a diverse flora which is of necessity undergoing frequent change. Moreover, inflammatory processes of the teeth and gums are often present, favouring the growth of pyogenic bacteria. The saliva has apparently only a slight bactericidal effect, and it is perhaps surprising that, with so much organic matter in the mouth and so many organisms to grow in it, septic infections are not more common. There are probably three main reasons for this : firstly, the saliva, though lacking in bactericidal power, by its constant secretion tends to flush the mucous surfaces of the mouth, and wash off many of the adherent organisms, which, when swallowed, are rapidly killed by the gastric juice ; secondly, the mucosa of the mouth has a remarkably good blood supply, and it is a general rule that the better the blood supply of a tissue, the less liable it is to invasion by pyogenic bacteria ; thirdly, as Bloomfield (1922c) has shown, there is a highly efficient mechanism, apparently dependent on suction currents, by which any bacteria introduced into the mouth are drawn directly backwards towards the œsophagus, avoiding the tonsils and posterior wall of the pharynx. Of the great number of different organisms found in the mouth and saliva, among the commonest are (1) Micrococci, some of which form pigment and some of which do not ; the non-pigment-forming micrococci include some that are anaerobic (Ozaki 1915) ; (2) Staphylococci, especially a white pigmented type ; (3) Streptococci, either of the α-hæmolytic type, such as *Str. viridans*, or of the indifferent type ; (4) Gram-positive bacilli, often arranged in chains, and belonging to the group of aciduric bacilli, or of aerobic spore-bearing bacilli ; (5) Gram-negative bacilli, including organisms of the coliform and *Proteus* groups ; (6) Spirochætes ; these are almost invariably present between the gums and the teeth ; several types have been described, such as *Treponema buccalis*, *Treponema dentium*, *Treponema intermedium* (Dobell 1912), *Treponema microdentium*, *Treponema macrodentium* (Noguchi 1912), Vincent's spirillum, and Miller's spirillum. Organisms of the *Actinomyces* and *Fusiformis* groups appear to be not uncommon.

The *intestinal flora* of the breast-fed *infant* is relatively simple, consisting largely of *Lactobacillus bifidus* ; this bacillus in the early weeks of life may constitute 99 per cent. of the total organisms in the fæces (Cruickshank 1925). There are in addition a few enterococci and Gram-negative coliform bacilli (Tissier and Dreyfus 1925).

The intestinal flora of bottle-fed infants is not so simple. *L. bifidus* is uncommon ; on the other hand, another member of the aciduric group of bacteria —*Lactobacillus acidophilus*—is usually present in large numbers (Tissier 1900). Different types of coliform bacilli, enterococci, Gram-positive aerobic spore-bearing bacilli and anaerobic bacilli, occur more or less abundantly.

In the *adult*, numerous workers have found that the empty *stomach* is generally sterile. Immediately after a meal it contains numerous organisms, which have been ingested with the food ; but these, with the exception of acid-resistant vegetative bacilli and sporing bacteria, appear to be killed off rapidly. If, however, the motility of the stomach is excessive, or the acidity is below normal, this sterilizing effect of the gastric juice is probably incomplete. Thus in cases of gastric disease—particularly of carcinoma—sarcinæ, saprophytic bacilli, and other organisms may actually multiply in the stomach (Goodsir 1842, Oppler 1895). In the healthy adult there appear to be very few organisms in the duodenum and upper jejunum. Below this they increase, to reach their maximum in the large intestine.

The organisms present in the upper part of the *small intestine* appear to consist chiefly of enterococci. In the lower part numerous other organisms are found, and in much larger numbers ; amongst these are Gram-negative coliform bacilli, staphylococci, various gelatin-liquefying organisms, sarcinæ, yeasts, and sometimes aciduric bacilli (Niszle 1928). In the *large intestine* the flora is even more complex and numerous. The following organisms are commonly found : coliform bacilli of different types, enterococci, staphylococci of both the *aureus* and *albus* varieties, anaerobic spore-bearing organisms such as *Cl. welchii* and *Cl. putrificum*, aciduric bacteria including *L. acidophilus* and *L. acidophil-aerogenes*, thermophilic bacteria, spirochætes (Werner 1909), and yeasts ; less frequent are *Proteus* bacilli, *Ps. pyocyanea*, organisms of the Friedländer group, and aerobic spore-bearers such as *B. subtilis* and *B. mesentericus*. The proportion of anaerobic to aerobic bacilli in the intestine has probably been underestimated by most workers. Recent studies suggest that these organisms are very common in the fæces. Eggerth and Gagnon (1933) and Eggerth (1935), examining 65 specimens of normal stools, found that in nearly all of them the predominating organisms were obligate non-sporing anaerobes. The exact classification of these organisms was open to doubt ; some were Gram-positive and some Gram-negative. It is probable that they belonged partly to the *Fusiformis* and partly to the *Lactobacillus* groups. It may be noted that bacteria are said to make up 1/4–1/3 by weight of the fæces ; the greater part of them appear to be dead.

It is of interest to consider why the upper part of the small intestine contains so few living bacteria. Recent work, particularly in America, suggests that the " *auto-disinfecting mechanism* " of the duodenum—as described by Arnold and Brody (1926)—is dependent on the acid derived from the stomach. In normal persons the H-ion concentration of the duodenum and upper jejunum is about pH 5·5–6·3. The gastric contents entering the duodenum are saturated to their full buffer capacity, usually with an excess of free acid. The free acid is quickly neutralized by the bile, and by the pancreatic and intestinal juices ; the acid-buffered material is neutralized more slowly, and is chiefly responsible for maintaining the acidity of the contents of the upper part of the small intestine. In the presence of this degree of acidity few organisms are able to multiply ; but if, from gastric hypoacidity, the reaction of the duodenum becomes neutral or slightly alkaline, a rich bacterial flora develops. This can be imitated experimentally in dogs by injecting alkaline buffered solutions into the duodenum, by feeding with alkaline salts, or by raising the external temperature (Arnold and Brody 1926).

Dack and Woolpert (1932), working with monkeys not with dogs, obtained rather different results. They found that *Bact. prodigiosum* introduced by fistulæ into different parts of the intestine disappeared just as rapidly as when given by the mouth and made to pass through the stomach. Estimations of pH at different levels showed that the stomach contents had approximately a pH of 4–5, the duodenal of 6–7, the jejunal of 6–7·5, the ileal of 6–7, the cæcal of 5–7, and the descending colon of 5·5–7. In experiments *in vitro* a pH of about 4 was required to bring about a rapid reduction in the number of these organisms. This pH was met with only in the stomach. If, therefore, bacterial destruction occurs as rapidly in the intestine of the monkey as in the stomach, it is clear that acidity cannot be solely responsible. Whether the intestinal secretions themselves have any bactericidal action is doubtful, most of the evidence favours the view that they have none (Mylius and Sartorius 1926). It seems probable that the factors responsible for the auto-disinfecting mechanism of the gastro-intestinal tract are complex, and further work on this important aspect of bacterial ecology is urgently called for.

Provisionally we may conclude that in healthy persons the majority of the organisms ingested in the food and swallowed with the saliva are destroyed in the stomach by the gastric juice. The few surviving bacteria that pass through unharmed find the conditions in the duodenum and upper jejunum too acid to allow them to multiply. With their further passage down the intestine, they encounter neutral or even slightly alkaline conditions, and are able to proliferate abundantly (see Chapter XLII).

Origin of the Alimentary Flora.—Witkowski (1935), investigating the origin of the mouth flora, found that organisms could be demonstrated in the mouths of 49 out of 50 infants shortly after birth. These comprised mainly *Staph. albus*, coliform bacilli, Döderlein's bacillus, and streptococci. Examination of vaginal swabs from the mothers showed that these organisms were all present in the vagina in proportions corresponding fairly closely to those in the infant's mouth. It seems probable, therefore, that the initial flora of the infant's mouth is derived from the vagina of the mother. By 2–5 days after birth other organisms had appeared consisting, in decreasing order of frequency, of pneumococci, hæmolytic staphylococci, various types of streptococci, Friedländer bacilli, corynebacteria, sarcinæ, and Gram-negative cocci. Comparison of these findings with the mouth flora of the mother showed a considerable degree of correspondence, suggesting that the infant had derived these additional organisms from the nasopharyngeal tract of its mother and other persons in its environment.

The intestine at birth is sterile, but infection rapidly occurs, partly from above and partly from below. Schild (1895) found that the anus became contaminated with organisms from the air, bath-water, and other objects with which it came into contact. Organisms could be demonstrated in the meconium sometimes within 4 hours of birth, and usually within 10–17 hours. When the anus was disinfected and covered with a sterile towel, the meconium remained free from organisms for 20 hours—by which time infection had occurred from the food.

The Importance of Micro-organisms in the Intestine.

It was at one time widely believed that the presence of bacteria in the intestine was essential for the life of the host, that they assisted in the digestive processes, and that without them much of the food taken in would be passed out of the body again in an unassimilable condition. This belief arose as a very natural deduction from Pasteur's work on the microbial nature of fermentation. It was largely owing to Metchnikoff, who came to regard the intestinal flora with hostile suspicion, that the possibility of maintaining life with a sterile intestinal tract began to be seriously considered. Numerous workers had already devoted themselves to the realization of this possibility ; notable amongst them was Schottelius (1899, 1902, 1908), who spent several years endeavouring to rear chicks under sterile conditions, and failed. Nuttall and Thierfelder (1895–96) met with some success ; they removed an embryo guinea-pig by Cæsarean section, and maintained it uncontaminated for 8 days, after which the experiment had to be given up owing to technical difficulties. They convinced themselves, however, that bacteria in the intestinal canal are not necessary for life—so long, at least, as an animal diet is provided. It was Cohendy (1912) who finally succeeded in showing that prolonged life was possible under such conditions. By means of a specially constructed apparatus, he reared chicks under completely sterile conditions for from 12 to 40 days, and found that they developed and grew as well as control nonsterile chicks kept in a similar apparatus. The only difference noted was that the food of the sterile chicks was less perfectly digested than that of the control chicks ; but the sterile chicks made up for this by eating more. Cohendy concludes that life is possible with a sterile intestinal tract, but that the intestinal bacteria are probably of use in assisting digestion. How far the second part of this conclusion is applicable to man, whose diet contains very much less indigestible material than that of the chick, it is impossible to say. Cohendy states that his sterile chicks survived exposure to moisture, hunger, and thirst for several days ; whereas normal chicks proved extremely susceptible to such conditions. His explanation is that, as the chicks were free from all micro-organisms, they could not, however low their resistance might be, succumb to infection from the intestine or other parts of the body.

It is easy to pass from the conclusion that bacteria are unnecessary to the human organism to the conclusion that they are actively harmful. This is a transition that has been unjustifiably made. We have no space to discuss the question of *intestinal toxæmia.* The conception that numerous cases of ill-health and of actual well-defined disease processes are due to the absorption, from the intestine, of toxic products elaborated by proteolytic micro-organisms is a plausible one, but one that rests largely on unproven assumptions. It is the almost complete lack of experimental evidence that renders the discussion of this subject so fruitless at the present time (see Discussion 1913, Dudgeon 1926).

The earliest method attempted in efforts to prevent the possible absorption of toxins from the intestine, was the replacement of the putrefactive flora—anaerobic spore-bearers such as *Cl. sporogenes, Cl. putrificum,* and *Cl. histolyticum* ; aerobic spore-bearers such as *B. mesentericus* ; and organisms such as *Proteus vulgaris* and *Ps. pyocyanea*—by an organism of the aciduric group known as *Lactobacillus bulgaricus.* These attempts failed completely. It has since been found impossible to implant this bacillus in the normal intestine ; the conditions for its growth are unfavourable. Recent experimental work has shown that, in order to encourage the growth of a given type of organism in the intestine, it does not suffice to administer such an organism by the mouth, but that it is also essential to give by the mouth a sufficient quantity of a selective food material to enable it to flourish at the expense of other organisms. The replacement of a proteolytic by a saccharolytic flora—aciduric bacilli, *Cl. welchii,* and the enterococcus—can be largely accomplished by feeding on a high carbohydrate diet. In rats it has been found that by giving large quantities of lactose or dextrin in the diet, the intestinal flora can be so changed that it contains 90 per cent. or more of aciduric bacilli (Rettger and Cheplin 1921, Cannon and McNease 1923, Cruickshank 1928). These two carbohydrates are absorbed very slowly, and consequently pass into the large intestine. They are there acted upon by the aciduric bacilli—notably *L. acidophilus*—with the formation of a large amount of lactic acid ; the presence of this acid is unfavourable to the persistence of the proteolytic bacteria. Without the supply of lactose, dextrin or milk the aciduric bacilli cannot be successfully implanted in the intestine, even though pure cultures are given in large quantity daily. In infants 12 per cent. of lactose must be added to whole cow's milk or to lactic acid milk in order to convert the mixed intestinal flora into a lactobacillary flora similar to that found in the stools of breast-fed babies (Gerstley, Howell, and Nagel 1932). This is not the place to discuss the value of changing the intestinal flora in the treatment of constipation and other disorders, but we will refer our readers to the monograph by Rettger and his colleagues (1935). (See also Sanborn 1931a, b, Kopeloff et al. 1932.)

In the normal human adult, living on a mixed dietary, no sharp division into proteolytic and saccharolytic bacteria in the fæces can be made. As Dudgeon

(1926) points out, the term "proteolytic" is often used without any definite understanding of its connotation. Many workers include *Bact. coli* in the proteolytic flora, which is quite inadmissible ; *Proteus vulgaris,* and *Ps. pyocyanea,* both of which are proteolytic, are uncommon in the fæces ; anaerobic bacteria, such as *Cl. sporogenes* and *Cl. putrificum,* are demonstrable in only a small proportion of samples ; while the anaerobe that is most commonly present, *Cl. welchii,* has only weakly proteolytic powers. Dudgeon lays emphasis on the importance of diet in regulating the intestinal flora (see also Torrey 1930) ; he would regard, in fact, the normal flora as being determined largely by the number of organisms ingested, and by the favouring or inhibitory effect of various articles in the dietary on the multiplication of one or more types of bacterium already present in the intestine. In the practical examination of the intestinal flora, he considers it essential for the patient's diet to be rigidly controlled, and for several methods of investigation—microscopical observation of films stained by different methods, and aerobic and anaerobic cultivation in different media—to be employed.

The Normal Flora of the Respiratory Tract.

For our present purpose we may divide the respiratory tract into three sections : an upper part, including the anterior and posterior nares and the nasopharynx ; an intermediate zone, common to the respiratory and alimentary tracts, including the oropharynx and the tonsils ; and a lower part, including the larynx, trachea, bronchi and lungs.

The bacterial flora of the nasal passages differs in several respects from that of the nasopharynx. It is less copious : if swabs are taken from the nose and nasopharynx of a sample of normal persons, and plated on some suitable medium, the nasal swabs will give the lower colony counts, and the differences observed are often striking. Qualitatively, diphtheroid bacilli and staphylococci—especially *Staph. albus*—are far more frequent in the nose than in the nasopharynx, while *Str. viridans,* indifferent streptococci, and Gram-negative cocci of the *N. pharyngis* type, are far less frequent. These non-hæmolytic streptococci and Gram-negative cocci appear to constitute the basal normal flora of the nasopharynx in most communities, so far as this is revealed by the usual methods of cultivation ; and it would seem that the flora of the oropharynx is composed mainly of the same species (Neumann 1902, Shibley *et al.* 1926, Noble *et al.* 1928, personal observations).

It would appear (Calamida and Bertarelli 1902) that the accessory nasal sinuses are normally sterile. According to Thompson and Hewlett (1896), the trachea and bronchi contain few, if any, bacteria. It is, of course, clear that a certain number of bacteria must be drawn through the larynx with the inspired air ; but it would seem that the highly efficient filter provided by the tortuous nasal passages removes the great majority of the bacteria entering the nose. Those which penetrate beyond the vocal cords are promptly removed ; in part perhaps by being swept upwards again by the cilia of the lining epithelium ; in part by being caught up in the mucous secretion, and subsequently removed by expectoration ; in part by removal, *via* the lymphatics, to the regional lymphatic glands. In any case it would appear that, in healthy persons, and under normal conditions, there is no permanent bacterial colonization of the tracheal or bronchial mucosa (see Nenninger 1901, Paul 1902, Quesnil 1902).

The diphtheroid bacilli and staphylococci which are usually present in cultures from the nose, and the non-hæmolytic streptococci and Gram-negative cocci of the nasopharynx and tonsils, are seldom the only species isolated from swabs taken from these situations. Various other species, including many potential pathogens, are often recovered. The relative frequency of three such species— *Str. pneumoniæ*, hæmolytic streptococci and *H. influenzæ*—in the nose, nasopharynx, tonsils, and oral cavity in general, is indicated in the figures set out in Table CLXXVIII.

TABLE CLXXVIII

SHOWING THE FREQUENCY OF CERTAIN BACTERIAL SPECIES IN THE NASOPHARYNX, NOSE, TONSILS AND ORAL CAVITY AMONG A SAMPLE OF THE GENERAL POPULATION (Report 1930.)

Group.	No. of Swabs.		Pneumo-coccus.	*H. influ-enzæ.*	Hæmolytic Streptococci.	Gram-nega-tive Cocci.
			Per cent.	Per cent.	Per cent.	Per cent.
I and II .	412	Nasopharynx	40·98	59·01	7·77	97·09
		Nose	16·79	11·68	0·05	12·11
III . .	137	Nasopharynx	42·34	59·54	5·84	97·08
		Tonsil	44·53	54·89	5·11	98·54
IV . .	252	Nasopharynx	49·80	51·01	11·90	95·24
		Mouth-wash	25·70	25·10	11·95	94·82

These figures were obtained during an investigation carried out in Manchester between 1925 and 1927, and refer to a series of observations in which swabs were taken from the nasopharynx of a large number of persons over a total period of 2 years. In a proportion of these persons a second swab was taken at the same time, from the nose in two groups, and from the tonsils in a third group ; in a fourth group a general mouth-washing was collected and examined, at the same time as the nasopharyngeal swab was taken. Cultures were prepared on blood agar and Fildes' agar, and mice were inoculated intraperitoneally with each specimen. Figures showing the frequency of Gram-negative cocci are included for comparison. It will be noted that all these species were far less frequent in the nose than in the nasopharynx. This difference is particularly striking in the case of the normal Gram-negative cocci ; but it is clear that there is far less tendency for the pathogenic species to vegetate in the nose than in the nasopharynx. The figures for the swabs obtained from the tonsils, and from the nasopharynx, are practically identical. Mouth-washing, in this series of cases at least, appears to be a less effective method of isolating the pneumococcus or the influenza bacillus, but equally effective as regards the hæmolytic streptococci, or the Gram-negative cocci (see also Gundel and Linden 1931, Gundel and Okura 1933, Gundel 1933).

It must not be supposed that these are constant figures. They fluctuate rather widely from time to time and from place to place. Thus the nasopharyngeal carrier rate of hæmolytic streptococci may vary from zero to 20 per cent. in a sample of the normal adult population subjected to repeated swabbing. The fluctuations in pneumococci and influenza bacilli are usually smaller. Recent observations by Dr. Edith Straker (unpublished) in the authors' laboratory have shown that, in addition to the pathogenic or potentially pathogenic species referred to above, the nasopharyngeal carrier rate for meningococci may be much higher than has been supposed, fluctuating between 10 per cent. and 20 per cent. among a sample of normal adults (see also Dudley and Brennan 1934).

Such studies often show a striking tendency for any given individual to main tain a characteristic nasopharyngeal flora over a considerable period of time.

Gundel and Schwarz (1932), for instance, using antisera corresponding to the 32 types of pneumococci, were able to show that any one person tended to carry a single type of pneumococcus over a period of several months.

The characteristic nasopharyngeal flora, with its basic constituents such as streptococci of the viridans type and *N. pharyngis*, together with the fluctuating population of potentially more pathogenic bacteria, is established soon after birth ; and there is no doubt that the infant derives these organisms from the adults or older children in its immediate entourage.

Gundel and Schwarz (1932) have recorded an interesting study of this problem. They examined 426 nasopharygeal swabs from 51 mothers, 645 from their new-born infants, and 66 swabs from nurses in attendance. In accord with earlier observations they found that the nasopharynx was sterile at birth ; but in the first 2 days it became colonized by the usual viridans streptococci, Gram-negative cocci of the *pharyngis* type, occasional diphtheroid bacilli and a certain number of coliform bacilli. By the 2nd or 3rd day pneumococci and influenza bacilli were often present, and their frequency was found to depend on their distribution among the adults in immediate contact with the child, and particularly on their presence or absence in the mother. By serological typing it was often possible to establish the identity of the type of pneumococcus present in the child with that present in the mother (see also Kneeland 1930).

Within recent years various workers have described the presence of small Gram-negative, filter-passing, anaerobic bacilli, in suspensions obtained by washing out the nares, nasopharynx and oropharynx with sterile broth (Olitsky and Gates 1921*a*, *b*, Olitsky and McCartney 1923, Mills, Shibley and Dochez 1928, Garrod 1928, Burky and Freese 1931). The evidence suggests that these strains may be differentiated into several distinct types ; but they have not yet been submitted to detailed study from the systematic point of view. The so-called *Bacterium pneumosintes*, at one time regarded as a possible cause of epidemic influenza, apparently belongs to this group. The data at present available with regard to the relative frequency of these bacilli in normal persons, and in those suffering from colds, does not indicate that they play any significant rôle in such infections. Garrod (1928) has also described the isolation, by the same technique, of minute, Gram-negative, filter-passing, anaerobic cocci.

The Normal Flora of the Vagina.

An important distinction must be drawn between the flora of the vulva and vestibulum on the one hand and that of the vagina proper on the other. Except immediately after parturition and during the first few days of the puerperium, the vaginal flora is quite distinct from that of the vulval flora.

The *vulva* of the newly-born child is sterile ; organisms make their appearance in about 7 to 8 hours. The normal flora of the vulva is a rich and varied one, and depends largely on the organisms present in its immediate environment. According to Wegelius (1909) it consists of : (1) Obligatory aerobes and aerophilic bacteria, of which the chief types are pseudo-diphtheria bacilli and *M. tetragenus*. (2) Coliform bacilli. (3) Facultative anaerobes, usually more or less susceptible to acid. (4) Bacilli derived from the vagina, including yeasts. (5) Obligatory anaerobes. On agar plates incubated aerobically the commonest organisms to form colonies are staphylococci, diphtheroids, enterococci, sarcinæ, and coliform bacilli. Besides these organisms, yeasts—*Oidium* and *Saccharomyces*—are very common ; and the smegma bacillus is not infrequently demonstrable in smear preparations stained with Ziehl-Neelsen. Under anaerobic conditions of cultivation numerous colonies appear, consisting of organisms that have as yet been only imperfectly studied. Pathogenic bacteria are uncommon.

The normal flora of the *vagina* seems to depend largely on the glycogen content of the vaginal epithelium which, in its turn, is dependent on ovarian activity (Miura 1928, Cruickshank and Sharman 1934). The vagina of the newly born child is sterile ; organisms make their appearance in 12–24 hours. At first they consist of staphylococci, enterococci, and diphtheroids, but these are often replaced in 2 or 3 days by a practically pure culture of Döderlein's bacillus (see Chapter XXVIII). At this time glycogen is demonstrable in the vaginal epithelium, and the vaginal secretion itself is acid. The occurrence of glycogen appears to be due to the presence of œstrin derived from the maternal circulation. Soon this is excreted in the urine, glycogen is no longer demonstrable in the epithelium, Döderlein's bacillus disappears, and the vaginal secretion reverts towards alkalinity. From now on till puberty the vaginal secretion remains alkaline, and there is a varied flora of staphylococci, streptococci other than *Str. pyogenes*, coliform and diphtheroid bacilli. At puberty glycogen is again deposited in the vaginal wall, the secretion becomes acid, and Döderlein's bacillus establishes itself as the predominant organism. The flora, however, still remains mixed and Döderlein's bacillus is accompanied by many of the organisms that we have just mentioned, as well as by anaerobic streptococci, which appear to be commonly present in the female genital tract (see p. 463). At the menopause, when ovarian activity ceases, the conditions revert to those met with before puberty. Following parturition, and during the first few days of the puerperium, the vaginal flora resembles that of the vulva. At the time of parturition organisms ascend from the vulva to the uterus, where they may be demonstrated for several days (Wegelius 1909).

The vaginal secretion has a marked bactericidal action (see Küster 1929). To a large extent this may be ascribed to the presence of lactic acid, though other factors are probably involved. The lactic acid itself is derived from the glycogen, partly perhaps as the result of natural enzymes, but mainly on account of the fermentative activity of Döderlein's bacillus. (Further references : Döderlein 1892, Segre 1929, Cruickshank and Baird 1930, Pettit and Hitchcock 1933, Cruickshank 1934.)

The Normal Flora of the Urethra.

In the anterior urethra of males occasional white staphylococci and diphtheroids may be found, and a short Gram-negative diplobacillus, not to be mistaken for the gonococcus (Kutscher 1909). The female urethra is either sterile or contains a few non-pathogenic cocci. A saprophytic acid-fast bacillus, known as *Mycobacterium smegmatis*, is quite common in the preputial secretion both of males and females ; this organism may occasionally find its way into the urine, and be mistaken for the tubercle bacillus.

Normal Flora of the Skin.

Under this heading we shall exclude all the multifarious organisms that may at one time or another be found on the surface of the skin, the numbers and varieties of which depend largely on personal hygiene and environmental conditions. There are a few types of bacteria, however, that seem to multiply freely on the skin, and particularly in the sebaceous glands ; these can generally be cultivated without difficulty. The most important of these are the Gram-positive cocci. Of the numerous types that have been described much the commonest is the white pigmented variety called by Welch (1891) *Staphylococcus epidermidis albus* (see Chapter XXIV). Another variety, distinguished by its feebler biochemical activity, is found very frequently in scurf, and is known as Gordon's scurf staphylococcus. Occasionally yellow-pigmented staphylococci are found, and sometimes sarcinæ. The great majority of the cocci found on the skin are comparatively non-pathogenic both to human beings and to rabbits, but a few consist of the pathogenic golden variety known as *Staphylococcus aureus*. According to Koch (1908), this variety constitutes 3–5 per cent. of the total colonies developing on blood agar plates pressed against the normal skin, whereas the white staphylococci constitute 90 per cent. Amongst the other organisms met with are occasional coliform and *Proteus* bacilli, and diphtheroids. The healthy skin appears to have some natural self-disinfecting mechanism which is responsible for the rapid disappearance of living organisms implanted upon it (see Chapter XLII and Colebrook and Maxted 1933, Arnold and Bart 1934).

In the skin lining the external auditory meatus, as well as the usual staphylococci, diphtheroid bacilli are not uncommon, and sometimes saprophytic acid-fast bacilli, derived from the cerumen, are met with. In the conjunctival sac, organisms are comparatively scanty, and consist chiefly of diphtheroids, such as *C. xerosis*. The conjunctiva may owe its relative freedom from bacteria, in part, to a highly potent lytic enzyme, called by Fleming and Allison (1922) *lysozyme*. These workers found that tears have a high bactericidal power, capable of dissolving certain saprophytic cocci in a dilution of 1/40,000. Further study showed that, with the exception of cerebrospinal fluid, sweat, and urine, this enzyme is distributed to a greater or less extent in practically all the human secretions and tissues, as well as in animal and some vegetable tissues. Testing the bactericidal power against a large non-pathogenic coccus, called by them *M. lysodeikticus*, they found the blood serum active in a dilution of 1/270, nasal mucus and sputum in 1/13,500, and saliva in 1/300. Extracts of tissues made by grinding up 1 gm. of tissue with 20 c.c. of saline showed that the liver and the tonsil were active at a dilution of 1/400, the kidney and skin at about 1/100, while cartilage was active in 1/1,300. Lysozyme dissolves both dead and living organisms, and is more active as a rule against non-pathogenic than against pathogenic bacteria. Its range of activity appears, however, to be very limited, as judged by the number of bacterial species which it attacks (see Fleming and Allison 1927, Fleming 1929).

Bacteria in the Blood and Internal Organs.

We have unfortunately very little information as to the occurrence of bacteria in the blood and viscera in healthy persons. The technical limitations of the usual method of performing blood cultures are such that small numbers of organisms may quite easily escape detection. Even if a sufficiently large sample of blood is withdrawn, it is difficult to ensure that the few organisms contained in it will grow ; they may be destroyed by the bactericidal power of the blood or ingested by leucocytes. Moreover the blood that is examined is usually drawn from a peripheral vein, coming from one limited portion of the body, and not therefore so likely to contain bacteria as blood from, let us say, the pulmonary artery through which the blood from all parts of the body has to pass. It has been stated that bacteria frequently gain access to the blood stream under normal conditions, but are filtered off in such organs as the liver, lungs, and spleen, where they are destroyed by cellular and bactericidal action. We do not know how frequently this occurs, what the channels of transit are, or what bacterial species may be concerned. It is also stated that in the new-born infant the epithelial lining of the intestinal mucosa is deficient in places, and that passage of bacteria into the lymph stream and blood is very much more frequent during the first few days of life than it is subsequently. Whether the normal intestinal mucosa of the adult presents a constant barrier to the passage of bacteria is not definitely known ; nor is it known why some organisms are able to pass through it very much more easily than others. Experiments made by Arnold (1928) on dogs suggest that the permeability of the mucosa varies from time to time, and is influenced by such factors as the H-ion concentration of the intestinal contents and the amount of protein in the food. It is probable too that variations in the blood supply are of importance. That organisms, particularly streptococci, may pass into the blood stream of patients suffering from focal infections in different parts of the body seems evident from the work of Reith and Squier (1932) and Okell and Elliott (1935).

Examinations of normal mesenteric lymph glands have been few. It seems not improbable that bacteria of different types are frequently absorbed through the intestinal mucosa. Some of these are probably destroyed in the mesenteric glands or the liver ; a few may perhaps make their way to the blood stream, from which they will be removed by phagocytic cells. In support of this possibility is the observation that the muscles and viscera of apparently healthy cattle and pigs not infrequently contain bacteria (Zwick and Weichel 1911, Reith 1926). A wide field of experimental work is open to the student who is willing to study the distribution of living organisms in the tissues of apparently normal animals.

REFERENCES

ARNOLD, L. (1928) *Amer. J. Hyg.*, **8**, 604.
ARNOLD, L. and BART, A. (1934) *Amer. J. Hyg.*, **19**, 217.
ARNOLD, L. and BRODY, L. (1926) *Amer. J. Hyg.*, **6**, 672.
BLOOMFIELD, A. L. (1919) *Amer. Rev. Tuberc.*, **3**, 553 ; (1921) *Bull. Johns Hopk. Hosp.*, **32**, 33 ; (1922a) *Amer. Rev. Tuberc.*, **5**, 903 ; (1922b) *Bull. Johns Hopk. Hosp.*, **33**, 61 ; (1922c) *Ibid.*, **33**, 145 ; (1922d) *Ibid.*, **33**, 252 ; (1922e) *Amer. J. med. Sci.*, **164**, 854.
BLOOMFIELD, A. L. and FELTY, A. R. (1923a) *Arch. intern. Med.*, **32**, 386 ; (1923b) *Bull. Johns Hopk. Hosp.*, **34**, 393 ; (1923c) *Ibid.*, **34**, 414.
BURKY, E. L. and FREESE, H. L. (1931) *J. Bact.*, **22**, 309.
CALAMIDA, U. and BERTARELLI, E. (1902) *Zbl. Bakt.*, **32**, 428.
CANNON, P. R. and McNEASE, B. W. (1923) *J. infect. Dis.*, **32**, 175.
COHENDY, M. (1912) *Ann. Inst. Pasteur*, **26**, 106.
COLEBROOK, L. and MAXTED, W. R. (1933) *J. Obstet. Gynaec.*, **40**, 966.
CRUICKSHANK, R. (1925) *J. Hyg., Camb.*, **24**, 241 ; (1928) *Brit. J. exp. Path.*, **9**, 318 ; (1934) *J. Path. Bact.*, **39**, 213.
CRUICKSHANK, R. and BAIRD, D. (1930) *Edin. med. J.*, **37**, 135.
CRUICKSHANK, R. and SHARMAN, A. (1934) *J. Obstet. Gynaec.*, **41**, 190, 369.
DACK, G. M. and WOOLPERT, O. (1932) *J. prev. Med., Baltimore*, **6**, 129.
Discussion. (1913) *Proc. R. Soc. Med.*, **6**, Part i, Gen. Rep., p. 1.
DOBELL, C. (1912) *Arch. Protistenk.*, **26**, 117.
DÖDERLEIN, A. (1892) " Das Scheidensekret und seine Bedeutung für das Puerperalfieber." Leipzig.
DUDGEON, L. S. (1926) *J. Hyg., Camb.*, **25**, 119.
DUDLEY, S. F. and BRENNAN, J. R. (1934) *J. Hyg., Camb.*, **34**, 525.
EGGERTH, A. H. (1935) *J. Bact.*, **30**, 277.

EGGERTH, A. H. and GAGNON, B. H. (1933) *J. Bact.*, **25**, 389.
FELTY, A. R. and BLOOMFIELD, A. L. (1923) *Bull. Johns Hopk. Hosp.*, **34**, 379.
FLEMING, A. (1929) *Lancet*, i. 217.
FLEMING, A. and ALLISON, V. D. (1922) *Brit. J. exp. Path.*, **3**, 252 ; (1927) *Ibid.*, **8**, 214.
GARROD, L. P. (1928) *Brit. J. exp. Path.*, **9**, 155.
GERSTLEY, J. R., HOWELL, K. M., and NAGEL, B. R. (1932) *Amer. J. Dis. Child.*, **43**, 555.
GOODSIR. (1842) *Edin. med. surg. J.*, **57**, 430.
GUNDEL, M. (1933) *Z. Hyg. InfektKr.*, **114**, 659.
GUNDEL, M. and LINDEN, H. (1931) *Zbl. Bakt.*, **121**, 349.
GUNDEL, M. and OKURA, G. (1933) *Z. Hyg. InfektKr.*, **114**, 678.
GUNDEL, M. and SCHWARZ, F. K. T. (1932) *Z. Hyg. InfektKr.*, **113**, 411.
KNEELAND, Y. (1930) *J. exp. Med.*, **51**, 617.
KOCH, J. (1908) *Z. Hyg. InfektKr.*, **58**, 287.
KOPELOFF, N., BLACKMAN, N., and McGINN, B. (1932) *J. infect. Dis.*, **50**, 426.
KÜSTER, E. (1929) See Kolle and Wassermann's " Hdb. path. Mikroorg.," 3te Abt., **6**, 372.
KUTSCHER. (1909) *Berl. klin. Wschr.*, **66**, 2059.
MILLS, K. C., SHIBLEY, G. S., and DOCHEZ, A. R. (1928) *J. exp. Med.*, **47**, 193.
MIURA, H. (1928) *Mitt. med. Akad. Kioto*, **2**, 1.
MYLIUS, K. and SARTORIUS, F. (1926) *Zbl. Bakt.*, **99**, 565.
NENNINGER, O. (1901) *Z. Hyg. InfektKr.*, **38**, 94.
NEUMANN, R. O. (1902) *Z. Hyg. InfektKr.*, **40**, 33.
NISZLE, A. (1928) See Kolle and Wassermann's " Hdb. path. Mikroorg," 3te Abt., 1928–29, **6**, 391.
NOBLE, W. C., FISHER, E. A., and BRAINARD, D. H. (1928) *J. prev. Med., Baltimore*, **2**, 105.
NOGUCHI, H. (1912) *J. exp. Med.*, **15**, 81.
NUTTALL, G. H. and THIERFELDER, H. (1895–96) *Z. physiol. Chem.*, **21**, 109.
OKELL, C. C. and ELLIOTT, S. D. (1935) *Lancet*, ii. 869.
OLITSKY, P. K. and GATES, F. L. (1921a) *J. exp. Med.*, **33**, 713 ; (1921b) *Ibid.*, **34**, 1.
OLITSKY, P. K. and McCARTNEY, J. E. (1923) *J. exp. Med.*, **38**, 427.
OPPLER, B. (1895) *Dtsch. med. Wschr.*, **21**, 73.
OZAKI, Y. (1915) *Zbl. Bakt.*, **76**, 118.
PAUL, L. (1902) *Z. Hyg. InfektKr.*, **40**, 468.
PETTIT, H. and HITCHCOCK, C. H. (1933) *J. infect. Dis.*, **53**, 372.
QUESNIL, U. (1902) *Z. Hyg. InfektKr.*, **40**, 505.
REITH, A. F. (1926) *J. Bact.*, **12**, 367.
REITH, A. F. and SQUIER, T. L. (1932) *J. infect. Dis.*, **51**, 336.
Report. (1930) *Min. Hlth Rep. publ. Hlth med. Subj., Lond.*, No. 58.
RETTGER, L. F. and CHEPLIN, H. A. (1921) " A Treatise on the Transformation of the Intestinal Flora with Special Reference to the Implantation of Acidophilus." New Haven.
RETTGER, L. F., LEVY, M. N., WEINSTEIN, L., and WEISS, J. E. (1935) " L. acidophilus : Its therapeutic application." Yale Univ. Press, New Haven, Conn.
SANBORN, A. G. (1931a) *J. infect. Dis.*, **48**, 541 ; (1931b) *Ibid.*, **49**, 37.
SCHILD, W. (1895) *Z. Hyg. InfektKr.*, **19**, 113.
SCHOTTELIUS, M. (1899) *Arch. Hyg.*, **34**, 210 ; (1902) *Ibid.*, **42**, 48 ; (1908) *Ibid.*, **47**, 177.
SEGRE, G. V. (1929) *G. Batt. Immun.*, **4**, 26.
SHIBLEY, G. S., HANGER, F. M., and DOCHEZ, A. R. (1926) *J. exp. Med.*, **43**, 415.
THOMPSON, St. C. and HEWLETT, R. T. (1896) *Lancet*, i. 86.
TISSIER, H. (1900) " Recherches sur la flore intestinale des nourrissons." Paris.
TISSIER, H. and DREYFUS, S. (1925) *C. R. Soc. Biol.*, **92**, 476.
TORREY, J. C. (1930) *Proc. Soc. exp. Biol., N.Y.*, **28**, 295.
WEGELIUS, W. (1909) *Arch. Gynaek.*, **88**, 249.
WELCH, W. H. (1891) *Amer. J. med. Sci.*, **102**, 439.
WERNER, H. (1909) *Zbl. Bakt.*, **52**, 241.
WITKOWSKI, R. (1935) *Zbl. Bakt.*, **133**, 334.
ZWICK and WEICHEL. (1911) *Arb. ReichsgesundhAmt.*, **38**, 327.

CHAPTER LXXXVII

THE BACTERIOLOGY OF SOIL

HISTORY.—Up till the middle of the last century little was known of the chemical processes that go on in the soil. The production of humus—the black, sticky substance in farmyard manure or earth—was recognized to be due to decomposition of vegetable organic matter. It was known, too, that under certain conditions which could be experimentally controlled, it was possible for nitrates to be formed in the soil. But the exact significance for plant growth of humus, or of nitrates, or of any particular form of decomposition, was not clearly understood.

From 1840 onwards Liebig (see Russell 1923) published a series of papers in which he expounded the doctrine that plant nutrition was dependent on the presence of inorganic matter in the soil; that this was formed from organic matter by a slow process of oxidation—*eremacausis*; and that the direct addition of sulphates, phosphates, and carbonates would increase the fertility of the soil far more rapidly than the usual practice of adding manure.

A few years later Boussingault in France showed that plant nutrition was dependent on nitrification. How this process occurred was a mystery, but it was suggested by Pasteur that it was probably of a biological nature. This surmise was proved correct by Schloesing and Müntz (Schloesing 1889a, b, c, Schloesing and Müntz 1877a, b, 1878, 1879a, b). They took a glass tube 1 metre long, and filled it with quartz sand mixed with powdered chalk. Each day the sand was sprinkled with a constant amount of liquid sewage, which slowly percolated downwards, till after 8 days it reached the bottom of the tube. For the first 3 weeks the ammonia in the filtrate was present in the same concentration as in the crude sewage; but after this time nitrate made its appearance, and ammonia could no longer be found in the filtrate. When chloroform vapour was forced through the tube, nitrification ceased, and ammonia reappeared in the filtrate. Nitrification was not established again till all the chloroform vapour had been removed and fresh soil was added. Boiling for 1 hour likewise destroyed the nitrifying power of soils. If the sterilized soil was preserved from access of dust, it remained permanently incapable of nitrification; but when a little fresh vegetable soil was added, nitrification was once again established. There was little doubt from these experiments that nitrification was due to a living ferment.

Warington (see Russell 1923) at the Rothamsted Experimental Station found that the conversion of ammonia into nitrate took place in two stages; in the first, ammonia was oxidized to nitrite; in the second, nitrite was oxidized to nitrate. The organisms concerned in these processes escaped detection till Winogradsky (1890, 1891), working at Zürich, and later in Paris, succeeded, by the use of purely inorganic media, in isolating the two organisms concerned. The one, now known as *Nitrosomonas europœa,* converted ammonia into nitrite ; the other, now known as *Nitrobacter winogradskyi,* converted nitrite into nitrate.

These results made it clear that the ammonia which was formed by the decomposition of organic matter in soil could be oxidized to nitrates ; these could then be absorbed by growing plants, and built up again into organic nitrogen compounds. But since a portion of the nitrate was found to be washed out by rain before it had been absorbed, it was also clear that in course of time the nitrogen content of the soil would suffer gradual depletion, unless it could in some way be replenished. This idea led Berthelot to suggest that there must be a fixation of atmospheric nitrogen.

Hellriegel and Wilfarth (see Russell 1923) confirmed this suggestion. They noticed that leguminous plants behaved differently from other plants in being independent of the amount of nitrate in the soil. Sometimes they flourished in soils devoid of nitrate, and sometimes they failed to develop when nitrates were plentiful ; whenever they flourished, there were found to be nodules on the roots. Examination has shown that these nodules contain bacteria which are able to fix atmospheric nitrogen, and to convert it into nitrates ; these can then be assimilated by plants.

But it is not only the root organisms of leguminous plants that are capable of fixing nitrogen. Shortly afterwards, Winogradsky isolated a free-living anaerobic bacterium, *Clostridium butyricum,* and Beijerinck a free-living aerobic bacterium, *Azotobacter chroöcoccum,* both of which were found able to convert atmospheric nitrogen into ammonia and nitrate.

(For a more detailed account of the development of agricultural bacteriology, see Russell 1923, and for a discussion of some of the problems in soil microbiology, see Cutler and Crump 1935.)

The Soil Population.

The method employed by investigators has generally been to ascertain the nature of the chemical processes occurring in the soil, then to isolate the bacteria which are capable of bringing them about, and finally to determine the exact relation between bacterial activity and chemical change. The last step is difficult. Not only do soils vary in their porosity, humidity, reaction, degree of aeration, and colloidal condition, but they contain large numbers of different bacteria, protozoa, fungi, algæ, nematodes and other living organisms, each of which is contributing its metabolic activities, and altering the chemical bodies present in the soil. Experimental standardization of all these different factors cannot be obtained ; hence it is impossible to determine the exact changes brought about by any one species of organism. It is largely for this reason that agricultural research on the bacteriological side has progressed so slowly of late years.

In 1925 Winogradsky described a further method of investigation. The principle consists in examining the soil directly under the microscope, noting the different kinds of organisms present, then adding some nutritive substance, and observing the changes that occur in the microbial flora. He found, for instance, that the addition of mannitol caused organisms of the *Azotobacter* group to proliferate extensively ; addition of nitrite was followed by a reduction in the oligonitrophilic (nitrogen-fixing) organisms, and in the appearance of mycelial filaments ; peptone stimulated the spore-bearing bacilli, and so on. These changes were checked by chemical or by cultural examinations. By the further application of this method he hopes to obtain a better insight into the effect of simple alteration of conditions on the activity of the microbial flora. (See also Conn 1927, 1932, Conn and Darrow 1930.)

At Rothamsted much work has been done in determining the quantitative variations of living organisms in the soil. Two-hourly counts of the numbers of bacteria, protozoa and other organisms have been made continuously for 2 or 3 days, and the results correlated. It was found that the number of bacteria undergoes two diurnal variations, there being at least one maximum and one minimum each day. Seasonal, as well as daily, fluctuations were likewise found to occur. Table CLXXIX, taken from Russell's *Micro-organisms of the Soil* (1923), gives an idea of the population of the Rothamsted soil.

TABLE CLXXIX. (Modified from Russell 1923.)

SHOWING THE POPULATION OF ROTHAMSTED SOIL IN 1922.

	Nos. per gm. of Soil.	Approximate Wt. per Acre of Living Organisms.
Bacteria :		
High level	45,000,000	50 lbs.
Low level	22,500,000	25 ,,
Protozoa :		
(1) Ciliates—		
High level	1,000	—
Low level	100	—
(2) Amœbæ—		
High level	280,000	320 lbs.
Low level	150,000	170 ,,
(3) Flagellates—		
High level	770,000	190 lbs.
Low level	350,000	85 ,,
Algæ :		
Not blue-green	100,000 [1]	125 lbs.
Blue-green	Not known	—
Fungi :		
High level	1,500,000 [1]	1,700 lbs.
Low level	700,000	800 ,,

[1] = approximately.

Distribution of Organisms in the Soil.

No more than a brief résumé can be given here.

1. Moulds or Fungi.—These are ubiquitous. About 150 species have been isolated from different soils; *Mucor, Rhizopus, Aspergillus, Penicillium,* and *Monilia* are among the commonest. Their function is not known completely, but it is certain that they decompose organic matter with the production of ammonia, and that they are important agents in the destruction of cellulose. They are of special importance in acid soils, when bacterial activity is inhibited. They are not found below about 14 inches from the surface.

2. Algæ.—It is surprising that algæ containing chlorophyll, and therefore dependent on sunlight, should be found in the soil. They are distributed, however, chiefly near the surface, not descending much below 6 inches. As yet, little is known of their function.

3. Protozoa.—These are present in large numbers, the flagellates being the most numerous. Though some of the protozoa can derive their nourishment from substances in solution, the majority of them ingest solid food. The smaller species seem to live mainly off bacteria and yeasts, while the larger species, such as the ciliates and some of the amœbæ, consume in addition fungal spores, algæ, and even other protozoa (Cutler and Crump 1935). Most of them occur in the upper 4 inches ; below 12 inches their activity ceases.

4. Actinomyces.—Though these diminish absolutely in numbers with the depth of the soil, their relative numbers in relation to the bacteria increase, so that at a depth of 30 inches they form 40–80 per cent. of the total flora of the soil. They can decompose cellulose, and are probably of value in the oxidation of organic matter in the soil.

5. Bacteria.—The majority are found between 2 and 9 inches from the surface. In humid regions there are probably none below 2 to 3 feet, but in light, open, irrigated soils they may be carried down to 9 or 10 feet. Their numbers vary from about 3 to 200 million per gram of soil ; the average is about 20 million viable organisms. Conn (1918) has shown that there is a wide discrepancy between the number of organisms capable of developing on plates and the total number visible microscopically. Thus in one experiment he found 17 million viable to 175 million total bacilli ; in another, 14 million viable to 340 million total ; in another, 3 million viable to 133 million total. This does not mean that all the bacilli that fail to develop are dead ; it indicates rather that the nutrient conditions are unsuitable for a great number of them.

Winogradsky (1925), by direct examination of soil stained with " erythrosin extra," finds that the morphological types of bacteria are very much the same in all normal arable soils. Most of the organisms are cocci or cocco-bacilli ; there are, however, some very thin rods. Nearly all are arranged in groups of varying shapes—rounded masses, sometimes surrounded by a capsule, tetrads, layers and other forms ; isolated bacteria are uncommon. Sporing organisms, clostridia, filamentous, spiral, and mycelial forms are found only in very small numbers. It is interesting to note that the results obtained by direct microscopic examination of soil differ not only quantitatively but also qualitatively from those obtained by plating soil on nutrient agar or gelatin. By the latter method the spore-bearing aerobic bacteria, *B. subtilis*, *B. megatherium*, *B. vulgatus*, *B. mycoides* and others are predominant ; by the former method they are found only in small numbers. It is probable therefore that these organisms play only a small part in soil metabolism.

Numerous other organisms, belonging to the *Pseudomonas* and the *Proteus* groups, appear to be normal inhabitants of the soil. *Bact. aerogenes* is also found (Skinner and Murray 1926), and an acid-fast bacillus, not unlike *Myco. phlei*, is widely distributed in this country.

Bacteria are concerned to a greater or less extent in most of the chemical changes occurring in the soil. Their most important rôle, however, is to provide nitrogen to the growing plants. It is no exaggeration to say that practically the whole of the available nitrogen supply in the soil is dependent on bacterial activity. They serve a similar, but less important, purpose in rendering phosphorus suitable for plant nutrition.

The Effect of Environmental Conditions on the Soil Flora.

A. Moisture.—Soil consists of particles of mineral and organic matter separated by spaces that may be filled either with air or with water. The moisture content varies with the rainfall and with the nature of the soil. Since the food taken up by plants is largely in solution, it follows that a moist soil provides more available food than a dry soil. But if the moisture exceeds a certain limit, then the pores of the soil are clogged, and aeration is interfered with. There seems to be no constant relationship between the amount of moisture in a soil and the degree of bacterial proliferation ; but, in general, excessive dryness causes many organisms to perish, while excessive moisture interferes with the growth of the aerobic bacteria.

B. Aeration.—The amount of air is greater in open, sandy soils than in fine-grained, clay soils. Analysis shows that soil air contains about 2·5 per cent. CO_2 and 18·4 per cent. of oxygen. The increase in CO_2 compared with atmospheric air is due to the oxidation of the humus ; in this process oxygen is used up and CO_2 is given off. When the decomposition proceeds rapidly, as in sandy soils, the proportion of CO_2 may rise to 9 per cent. and the oxygen fall to 11 per cent. (Lipman 1916). In fine-grained, compact soils, especially when water-logged, the air circulation is so poor that the humus may accumulate more rapidly than it can be destroyed. Under these conditions the anaerobic bacteria flourish and produce characteristic chemical changes, converting the carbon partly into CO_2, partly into CH_4, and partly into humic acid.

C. Temperature.—The effect of temperature, like that of moisture, is erratic. There is no strict correlation between the temperature and the bacterial activity. Usually, when the soil warms up in spring or early summer, there is an increase in bacterial proliferation. Since sandy soils and sandy loams, being coarse-grained and containing a relatively small amount of water, warm up more rapidly than the fine-grained clay soils, which contain a relatively large amount of water, they are known as early soils ; bacterial activity in these soils begins earlier in the spring than in the late clay soils. Conn has found that freezing may also increase the number of viable bacteria ; this may be due to a lowering of the metabolic rate, thus increasing their average lifetime.

D. Reaction.—When a soil is cultivated the lime and other basic constituents are removed, leaving the organic acids in excess. Unless these are neutralized by the application of fresh lime, they will interfere with bacterial growth. Organisms of the *Azotobacter* group, for example, have a critical H-ion concentration about pH 6·0 (Gainey 1918) ; below this they will not grow. Acid soils therefore contain fewer bacteria than alkaline soils. If the acid is allowed to accumulate, bacterial activity is so interfered with that the decomposition of organic matter almost ceases ; this results in the formation of peat. When such a peat soil is drained, limed, and cultivated, the number of bacteria soon increases from a few thousands to several millions per gram of soil.

E. Food.—The bacteria in the soil are dependent for their food on organic matter—proteins, fats, carbohydrates, organic acids, alcohols and other compounds. Variations in the amount of these substances produce corresponding variations in the distribution of the different kinds of bacteria. For instance, small amounts of dextrose favour the nitrifying organisms ; larger quantities retard them, and encourage the moulds. Mineral salts have a profound effect.

Small doses of alkali salts stimulate the bacteria; large quantities prove toxic to them. Phosphates and potassium salts especially increase bacterial activity.

Numerous other factors, such as the colloidal condition of the soil, affect the soil flora. Bacteria increase in numbers in the spring and autumn; fluctuations occur from day to day, often in definite, short-period cycles (see Taylor 1936). In a given plot of land the numbers of bacteria may vary simultaneously throughout the whole area, or they may differ widely within the space of a few feet. The soil population must be considered as being in a state of fluctuating equilibrium; competition between the different kinds of bacteria and between the protozoa, moulds, *Actinomyces*, and other members of the soil flora is constantly in operation. This equilibrium may be upset by a change in the moisture, the temperature, the food supply, and by numerous other factors. The aim of the agricultural bacteriologist is to learn the effect on this equilibrium of alteration of the environmental conditions so as ultimately to be able to control it at will. (See an excellent account of the soil population by Russell 1923, and of the effect of environment on the soil population by Lipman 1921, from both of which we have drawn freely.)

Chemical Reactions dependent upon Bacterial Activity.

A. Destruction of Cellulose.—Cellulose $(C_6H_{10}O_5)_n$ is broken down by aerobic and anaerobic bacteria, by denitrifying bacteria, by moulds, and by *Actinomyces* (Lipman 1921). The products into which it is decomposed are not accurately known, but Omeliansky found two types of anaerobic bacteria, one of which could break it down with the liberation of methane and carbon dioxide, the other with the liberation of CO_2 and H_2. It is probable, however, that these gaseous compounds result from the action of secondary organisms in breaking down the compounds formed by the cellulose-decomposing bacteria. Söhngen (1906) has shown that *Methanomonas methanica* can oxidize CH_4 to CO_2 and H_2O, and that other organisms can oxidize hydrogen. Hutchinson and Richards (see Russell 1923) found that by treating a straw heap with ammonium sulphate, and thus providing the cellulose-decomposing bacteria with a suitable supply of nitrogen, the straw was decomposed with the formation of well-rotted manure.

B. Ammonification.—By this is meant the production of ammonia by bacteria from proteins or their cleavage products. Amino-acetic acid, for example, is oxidized with the formation of CO_2, water and ammonia; the process is accompanied by the liberation of heat.

$$NH_2CH_2COOH + 3O \longrightarrow 2CO_2 + H_2O + NH_3 + 152 \text{ calories.}$$

Since most bacteria can obtain their energy more easily from carbohydrates than from nitrogenous compounds, it follows that the rate of ammonification depends largely on the quantity of carbohydrate material in the soil. When this is present in considerable amount, it is utilized for food, so that little or no ammonia is produced. When the supply is exhausted, the nitrogenous matter is attacked, and ammonia is liberated. The addition of sugar or unrotted straw to the soil lowers the rate of ammonia production, and hence of nitrification. The process of ammonification is most active when the soil is moist and the temperature high. Which types of bacteria are responsible for the process is not known with certainty, but numerous species are apparently concerned, notably the spore-bearing aerobes, the *Pseudomonas* group, the *Chromobacteria*, and certain members of the coli-typhoid group, such as *Bact. aerogenes*.

Ammonia is also formed by the bacterial decomposition of urea and hippuric acid in manure. Several organisms may take part in this process, such as *Micrococcus ureæ* Cohn (1875), and *Sarcina ureæ* Beijerinck (1901) ; certain aerobic spore-bearing bacilli, such as *B. pasteurii* (described by Miquel as *Urobacillus pasteurii*), and *B. miquelii* (described by Beijerinck in 1901 as *Urobacillus miquelii*) ; and certain non-sporing rods, possibly belonging to the *Zopfius* group, such as the bacillus described by Beijerinck as *Urobacillus leubei*. (For references to these organisms, see Beijerinck 1901, Gibson 1934, 1935*a*, *b*.)

All these organisms secrete a ferment known as urease ; this is insoluble in water and does not diffuse out from the cell body. It acts best at a temperature of 45°–50° C., *i.e.* at a point higher than the optimum temperature of these bacteria, which varies between 23° and 32° C. The amount secreted varies considerably. Beijerinck found that *Bacillus pasteurii* when grown at 30° C. destroyed urea at the rate of 3·3 gm. per litre of medium per hour. The other organisms were less active. The urea is converted into ammonium carbonate.

Urea is also broken down, though by a different mechanism, by certain luminous bacteria found in the sea.

Many fungi appear to play an active part in ammonification.

C. Nitrification.—This process consists in the oxidation either of ammonia or of nitrites to nitrates, or broadly, the production of nitrates from decomposing organic matter. According to Schloesing (Schloesing and Müntz 1879*b*), it is most active at a temperature of 37° C. Oxygen is essential. The soil must be moist ; the more water it contains the better, provided the pores are not clogged so as to exclude air. A slight degree of alkalinity is required ; this is supplied by the addition of lime to the soil. A certain amount of organic matter is necessary for the supply of carbon, but too much organic matter has an inhibitory effect, apparently owing to the accumulation of carbon dioxide and ammonia formed as the result of its disintegration (Barritt 1933).

The reaction occurs in two stages. In the first ammonia is oxidized to nitrous acid ; this is neutralized by the bases in the soil with the formation of a neutral salt. In the second the nitrite is oxidized to nitrate. Orla-Jensen has represented the two reactions as follows :

$$(NH_4)_2CO_3 + 3O_2 = 2HNO_2 + CO_2 + 3H_2O + 148 \text{ cals.}$$
$$2KNO_2 + O_2 = 2KNO_3 + 22 \text{ cals.}$$

Nitrite is rapidly formed from the ammonia in the soil, and is in its turn rapidly oxidized to nitrate. Hence the addition of ammonium sulphate is quickly followed by the appearance of nitrate in the soil.

Which organisms are mainly responsible for nitrification is still uncertain. The views of Winogradsky, that the process is due entirely to autotrophic bacteria, such as *Nitrosomonas* and *Nitrobacter*, have long held sway, but there seems to be a growing feeling among soil bacteriologists that other organisms are also involved (Cutler and Crump 1935). *Nitrosomonas* requires an alkaline soil and the absence of organic matter. These conditions do not obtain everywhere, and it is noteworthy that at Rothamsted, in spite of intensive search, this organism has never yet been isolated. Instead, the presence of various bacteria capable of oxidizing ammonia to nitrite in the presence of organic matter has been demonstrated (Cutler and Mukerji 1931). A study of nitrifying filter beds has likewise revealed the occurrence of different species of bacteria capable of bringing about this oxidation (Cutler and Crump 1933). Cutler and Crump (1935) issue a warning against taking too specialized a view of bacterial activity in the soil. Among the ammonifying group of bacteria it is possible, they point out, to find species which, having produced ammonia from peptone, will then oxidize part of it to nitrite ; the same organisms under suitable conditions will further utilize nitrite, apparently for building up their own protoplasm. *Nitrobacter flavus* is credited with the ability to break down peptone to ammonia, and then to use this for the formation of nitrite, and ultimately of nitrate. The same authors remark that, granted suitable conditions, there must be very few bacteria in nature which are unable to interfere with the nitrite part of the nitrogen cycle. Either they can make small quantities of nitrite from ammonium salts, or they can remove nitrite, or they can perform both reactions according to the conditions prevailing at the time.

In culture in a synthetic medium, Bonazzi (1919) found that the total nitrogen oxidized to nitrite by *Nitrosomonas europœa* in 14 days amounted to 168·92 mgm. per litre. Boullanger and Massol (1904) found that this organism could oxidize 20 mgm. of ammonia-nitrogen to nitrite per litre per diem.

The process of nitrification is not continuous ; fluctuations are noticeable from time to time. Ploughing and working the soil increase the rate of nitrification, probably by bringing about thorough aeration, and by the provision of fresh food for the nitrifying bacteria.

D. Denitrification.—In this process nitrates are reduced by bacteria to nitrite, ammonia, or free nitrogen. Denitrification is chiefly in evidence in poorly-aerated, water-logged soils, where the bacteria are unable to obtain sufficient oxygen ; they therefore work under anaerobic conditions, obtaining their oxygen by the decomposition of nitrates. Winogradsky and Omeliansky (1899) state that the denitrifying bacteria can act only in the presence of organic matter ; hence if all of this has been used up, denitrification cannot occur. Schloesing (1889c) likewise showed that excess of ammonia in the soil led to denitrification. In practice it has been found that large additions of manure to the soil may increase denitrification ; it is therefore inadvisable to top-dress the soil with sodium nitrate shortly after large applications of manure or other organic material (Lipman 1916). In a well-aerated, well-drained soil denitrification is insignificant in amount. *Pseudomonas denitrificans* was the first organism found capable of completely reducing nitrates (Christensen 1904) ; but since then several others have been isolated, belonging to the spore-bearing aerobic bacteria, the coli-typhoid group, and the *Chromobacteria*.

E. Azotification or Fixation of Atmospheric Nitrogen.—The fixation of atmospheric nitrogen is a biological process ; soil by itself is incapable of fixing nitrogen (Schloesing 1889a). The organisms responsible for it may be divided into two groups : (1) the free-living group ; (2) the symbiotic group.

(1) Amongst the first group are numerous organisms that are capable of fixing nitrogen to a small extent (Fulmer and Fred 1917). The two that appear to be most active are *Clostridium butyricum* and the various species of *Azotobacter*. Both of these organisms are able to fix atmospheric nitrogen, and to convert it into ammonia, nitrite and nitrate, which can then be utilized by plants (Beijerinck

and van Delden 1902). It is probable that they frequently work together, organisms of the *Azotobacter* group using up the oxygen in the surroundings, and thus permitting the anaerobic *Clostridium butyricum* to proliferate. The process of azotification is endothermic ; the energy required to fix nitrogen must therefore be supplied by carbohydrates, alcohols, organic acids, or other easily decomposable substances. Unless such substances are available, fixation will not occur. The reaction of the soil is an important factor. When the H-ion concentration is greater than pH 6·0, the *Azotobacter* group ceases to function. It is best therefore to keep the soil slightly alkaline by the addition of lime. The amount of nitrate in the soil is also of importance. If this is present in considerable quantities, organisms of the *Azotobacter* group may utilize it, and nitrogen fixation may therefore be minimal ; if nitrate is small in amount or absent, then fixation is more liable to occur.

In a field left fallow at Rothamsted between 1882 and 1904, there was an annual average gain of 25 lbs. of nitrogen per acre. Not all of this can be ascribed to the action of bacteria ; it is probable that some of the nitrogen fixed is due to the activity of algæ (Schloesing and Laurent 1892). Fulmer and Fred (1917) have found numerous organisms in manure capable of fixing atmospheric nitrogen ; the chief of these they call *Bact. azophile.*

(2) The second group is represented by *Rhizobium leguminosarum.* On the roots of leguminous plants nodules are to be found, varying in shape and size from almost imperceptible enlargements to masses as large as haricot beans. If one of these nodules is crushed, it is found to contain large numbers of organisms, rod-shaped, oval or Y-forms, embedded in a hyaline matrix, replacing the cellular tissue of the plant (Klein 1894, Fremlin 1898). Hellriegel and Wilfarth (see Russell 1923) suggested that the fixation of nitrogen by the *Leguminosæ* was dependent on the activity of bacteria present in the root nodules. Beijerinck (1888), who first isolated *Rhiz. leguminosarum*, showed how this organism was able to infect plants, and to live in symbiosis with them. Later it was found to be responsible for the fixation of atmospheric nitrogen, and for supplying the plant on which it lived with an abundance of nitrates.

Infection of the plant occurs by the root hairs, down which the actively motile swarmers pass to invade the cellular tissue of the root itself. The organism multiplies, and stimulates a reaction on the part of the plant, the cells of which divide rapidly and push out the cortical tissue to form nodules. After a time a state of mutual toleration is established, characterized by the provision of nitrate to the plant in exchange for carbohydrates and salts. Since this state is of benefit to both parties, it may correctly be regarded as an example of symbiosis.

The invasive power of different strains of *Rhiz. leguminosarum* varies considerably. Some are easily resisted by the plant; others have no difficulty in penetrating. Artificial inoculation of soil with this organism is now practised when the conditions are suitable ; this is best accomplished by spraying the seeds with a culture preparatory to sowing. Acid soils are unfavourable to nodule formation ; thus leguminous plants grow best on limestone. Phosphates appear to increase it, and the amount of moisture is an important factor.

F. Other Chemical Reactions.—Apart from those we have already discussed, there are numerous other reactions in the soil dependent on bacterial activity.

Fats and waxes are decomposed by moulds, yeasts, and bacteria. Organic acids are formed by protein and carbohydrate decomposition.

There is an important group of bacteria, known as the sulphur bacteria, which derive their energy from the oxidation of sulphur, sulphides, and thiosulphates to sulphuric acid.

$$S + 3O + H_2O \rightarrow H_2SO_4 + 141 \text{ cals.}$$

On the other hand, anaerobic bacteria may obtain their energy by the reduction of sulphates (Russell 1923).

Another important group comprises the phenol-decomposing bacteria. Phenol and cresol bodies are formed in manured soil by the destruction of protein. Unless they were removed or destroyed they would act as antiseptics interfering with bacterial growth. Fortunately there are special bacteria that can break them down, utilizing them as their main source of energy.

Organic compounds are decomposed by bacteria with the liberation, amongst other bodies, of potassium and phosphorus. These two substances, which are so necessary for plant nutrition, can then be absorbed in the form of inorganic salts.

It will be seen that numerous reactions in the soil, resulting in the elaboration of substances beneficial to plant growth, are dependent on bacteria. The conclusion may be drawn that high plant fertility is dependent to a considerable extent on high bacterial activity. Other factors are probably concerned; but unless the nutritive substances necessary to plants are produced in adequate quantity by the bacterial population of the soil, comparative failure of the crops is to be expected.

The Cycle of the Elements in Nature.

Animal life is dependent on the elaboration by plants of complex organic substances—proteins, carbohydrates and fats—which can be utilized as food. Such substances are essential for animal nutrition, and they can be built up only by plants. This synthesis of organic matter is rendered possible by the presence of chlorophyll in the leaves. Under the influence of sunlight, which supplies the requisite energy, the carbon dioxide in the atmosphere is converted into carbohydrates, such as cellulose, starch or sugars, and, in combination with the inorganic nitrates, phosphates, sulphates and water absorbed by the roots, is ultimately used for the synthesis of the cellular protoplasm.

Animals are unable to perform this synthesis; they must be provided with complex organic substances, which are digested by enzymes. The split products are used partly for building up or replacing cellular protoplasm; most however are oxidized, and go to furnish the energy and heat requirements of the body. The waste substances resulting from these oxidations are excreted in the form of ammonia, urea or hippuric acid by the kidneys, as CO_2 by the lungs, and as water in the form of urine, sweat, and fæces.

It is a general law that plants live on inorganic, animals on organic substances. And since animals, owing to their incapacity to synthesize protoplasm from simple inorganic bodies, are necessarily dependent for their existence on the food supplied to them by plants, and since plants are unable to obtain the elements required except in the form of inorganic bodies, it follows that the continuance of life on the globe is ultimately dependent on the free supply of carbon dioxide, nitrates, phosphates, sulphates and water.

It is thus possible to trace cycles for each of the important elements, following it through its various phases of elaboration into organic, and its degradation into inorganic, matter.

The Carbon Cycle.—CO_2 is absorbed by green plants, transformed under the influence of chlorophyll and sunlight into carbohydrates, and is built up into cellular protoplasm. In this form it may be consumed by animals, which digest it, and liberate CO_2 into the air once more. If the plant dies, then the organic matter is destroyed by fungi and bacteria, and CO_2 is set free. Every carbon-containing product formed either in the decomposition of dead animal or vegetable matter is ultimately broken down with the liberation of CO_2.

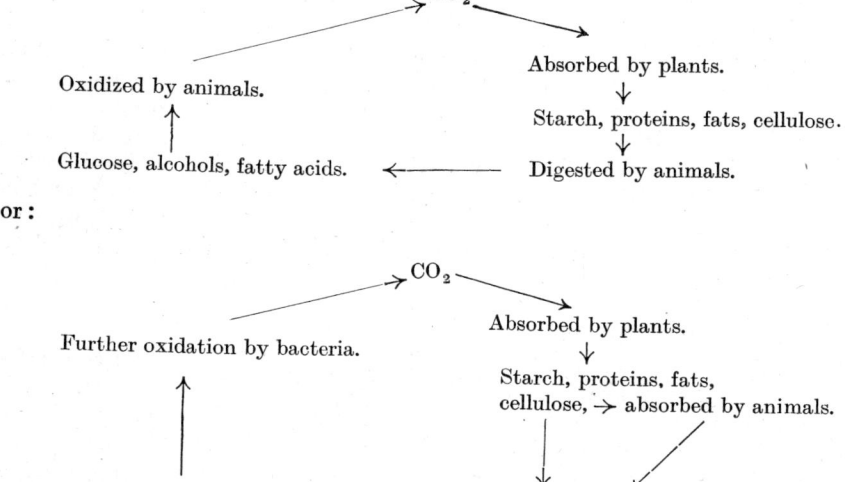

or :

Nitrogen Cycle.—Atmospheric nitrogen is fixed by bacteria and converted into ammonia, nitrites and nitrates; nitrates are absorbed by plants and built up into protoplasm. Plant tissue is consumed by animals and the nitrogenous compounds digested; ammonia, urea, or hippuric acid is excreted. Both the urea and the hippuric acid are decomposed into ammonia by bacteria.

The ammonia is oxidized by the nitrifying bacteria to nitrites and nitrates, which can then be absorbed again by plants. Dead animal or vegetable tissue is broken down by bacteria with the liberation of amino-acids and of ammonia. A certain amount of free nitrogen may be liberated in the process by denitrifying organisms.

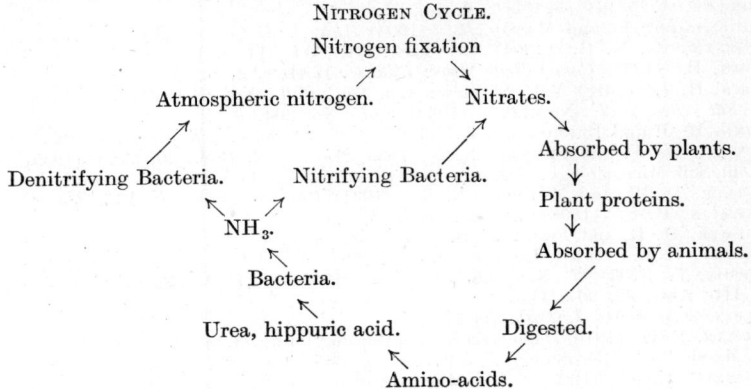

NITROGEN CYCLE.

or :

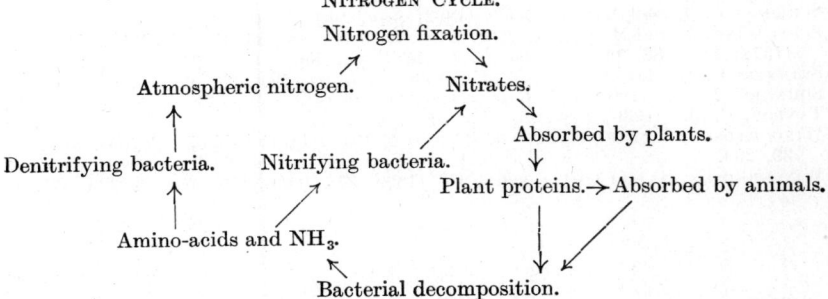

NITROGEN CYCLE.

Sulphur Cycle.—Sulphur is oxidized by bacteria to sulphates; these are absorbed by plants and built up into proteins. The proteins are taken in by animals, digested, and excreted as sulphates or as hydrogen sulphide. Hydrogen sulphide is oxidized by bacteria with the formation of sulphur.

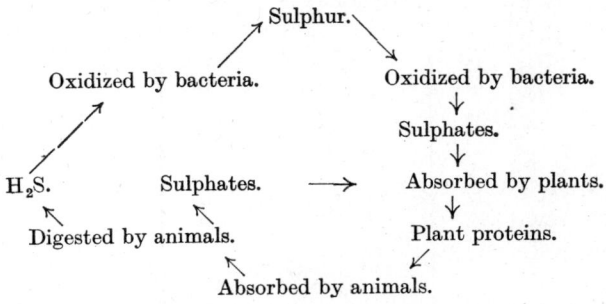

Similar cycles may be constructed for iron and for phosphorus.

REFERENCES

BARRITT, N. N. (1933) *Ann. appl. Biol.*, **20**, 165.
BEIJERINCK, M. W. (1888) *Bot. Ztg*, **46**, 724, 740, 756, 780, 796 ; (1901) *Zbl. Bakt.*, IIte Abt., **7**, 33.
BEIJERINCK, M. W. and DELDEN, A. VAN. (1902) *Zbl. Bakt.*, IIte Abt., **9**, 3.

BONAZZI, A. (1919) *J. Bact.*, **4**, 43.

BOULLANGER, E. and MASSOL, L. (1904) *Ann. Inst. Pasteur*, **18**, 181.

CHRISTENSEN, H. R. (1904) *Zbl. Bakt.*, IIte Abt., **11**, 190.

COHN, F. (1875) *Cohns Beitr. Biol. Pflanz.*, **1**, Heft. 2, p. 127.

CONN, H. J. (1918) *N.Y. St. agric. exp. Sta., Bull.*, No. 64 ; (1927) *N.Y. St. agric. exp. Sta., Tec. Bull.*, No. 129. ; (1932) *Ibid.*, No. 204.

CONN, H. J. and DARROW, M. A. (1930) *N.Y. St. agric. exp. Sta., Tec. Bull.*, No. 172.

CUTLER, D. W. and CRUMP, L. M. (1933) *Ann. appl. Biol.*, **20**, 291 ; (1935) " Problems in Soil Microbiology." Longmans, Green & Co., London.

CUTLER, D. W. and MUKERJI, B. K. (1931) *Proc. roy. Soc.*, B, **108**, 384.

FREMLIN, H. S. (1898) *J. Path. Bact.*, **5**, 389.

FULMER, H. L. and FRED, E. B. (1917) *J. Bact.*, **2**, 423.

GAINEY, P. L. (1918) *J. agric. Res.*, **14**, 265.

GIBSON, T. (1934) *J. Bact.*, **28**, 295, 313 ; (1935a) *J. Bact.*, **29**, 491 ; (1935b) *Zbl. Bakt.*, IIte Abt., **92**, 364, 414.

KLEIN, E. (1894) *J. Path. Bact.*, **2**, 205.

LIPMAN, J. G. (1916) " Bacteria in Relation to Country Life," 6th edit., New York ; (1921) Marshall's " Microbiology," 3rd edit., p. 345, London.

RUSSELL, E. J. (1923) " The Micro-organisms of the Soil." Longmans, Green & Co., London.

SCHLOESING, T. (1889a) *C. R. Acad. Sci.*, **109**, 210 ; (1889b) *Ibid.*, **109**, 423 ; (1889c) *Ibid.*, **109**, 883.

SCHLOESING, T. and LAURENT, E. (1892) *Ann. Inst. Pasteur*, **6**, 824.

SCHLOESING, T. and MÜNTZ, A. (1877a) *C. R. Acad. Sci.*, **84**, 301 ; (1877b) *Ibid.*, **85**, 1018 ; (1878) *Ibid.*, **86**, 892 ; (1879a) *C. R. Acad. Sci.*, **89**, 891 ; (1879b) *Ibid.*, **89**, 1074.

SKINNER, C. E. and MURRAY, T. J. (1926) *J. infect. Dis.*, **38**, 37.

SÖHNGEN, N. L. (1906) *Zbl. Bakt.*, IIte Abt., **15**, 513.

TAYLOR, C. B. (1936) *Proc. roy. Soc.*, B, **119**, 269.

WINOGRADSKY, S. (1890) *Ann. Inst. Pasteur*, **4**, 213 ; (1891) *Ibid.*, **5**, 92, 577 ; (1925) *Ibid.*, **39**, 299.

WINOGRADSKY, S. and OMELIANSKY, V. (1899) *Zbl. Bakt.*, IIte Abt., **5**, 329, 377, 429.

THE BACTERIOLOGY OF AIR, WATER, SHELL FISH, AND SEWAGE

AIR

WE do not propose to consider in detail the natural bacterial flora of air. Air undoubtedly serves as a medium for the transmission of many pathogenic organisms ; and there is scope for further investigation into the length of time that parasitic bacteria are able to remain alive in air under varying conditions of moisture, heat, and so on, and the distances they may be carried without losing their viability. Aeroplane surveys (see Proctor 1934, 1935) show that bacteria in the upper air consist largely of spore-bearing bacilli, and of organisms belonging to the *Coccaceœ* and *Achromobacterium* groups, suggesting that they are derived mainly from soil and surface dust. These organisms can be carried vertically for several miles into the air, and it is possible that they may also travel long distances horizontally. It is conceivable therefore that certain resistant pathogenic bacteria, like the anthrax bacillus, might be transmitted from one area or country to another, and serve, on again reaching the ground, as infective agents for man or animals. There is, however, no evidence to prove that this is more than a possibility. On the contrary, most of our observations suggest that infective material is rarely carried for more than short distances by air. The majority of droplet-borne infections seem to require fairly close contact between the infective and the exposed subject, while few pathogenic organisms seem to be able to withstand the almost complete desiccation under natural conditions that is probably necessary for their transportation by dust. Though autotrophic organisms may possibly undergo some multiplication in cloud areas, where moisture and traces of gases such as NH_3 and CO_2 are present, it seems extremely improbable that growth of parasitic organisms is likely to occur in air. For the medical bacteriologist the importance of the natural air flora or aeroplankton still remains to be demonstrated ; while as regards the persistence of parasitic organisms in air the intensive investigations of the earlier observers proved of such little value in the interpretation of epidemiological findings that they have been largely discontinued.

WATER

Bacterial Flora in Water.

It is convenient to divide the bacteria found in water into three groups :

A. NATURAL WATER BACTERIA.

In this group are included those organisms that are commonly found in waters free from gross pollution. They may be subdivided as follows :

Bacilli.

(1) Fluorescent {Gelatin liquefied.   *Ps. fluorescens liquefaciens.*
                {Gelatin not liquefied. *Ps. fluorescens non-liquefaciens.*

(2) Chromogenic {Red pigment. *Chr. prodigiosum, Chr. indicum.*
                {Orange „   *Chr. aurescens.*
                {Yellow „   *Chr. ochraceum.*
                {Violet „   *Chr. violaceum.*

(3) Non-chromogenic { These organisms belong mainly to the *Achromobacterium* group. They are sometimes divided up according to their reactions on gelatin and milk; but they have so far not received sufficient study to render their classification possible. Gram-positive, spore-bearing aerobes, which produce acid and gas in lactose, appear to be not uncommon (Greer 1928, Porter *et al.* 1935). Members of the coli-typhoid group are not natural inhabitants of entirely unpolluted waters.

Cocci.

(1) Chromogenic. Generally yellow pigment formed.
(2) Non-chromogenic. *M. candicans, M. aquatilis, M. coronatus.*

Sarcinæ.

Chiefly *Sarcina lutea.*

B. SOIL BACTERIA.

These organisms, though not normally inhabitants of water, are frequently washed into it during heavy rains. Most of them belong to the group of aerobic spore-bearing bacilli, such as *B. subtilis, B. vulgatus, B. megatherium,* and *B. mycoides.* Others, such as *Bact. ærogenes* and *Bact. cloacæ,* which appear to live most frequently on grain and plants, and which may conveniently be treated as soil organisms, are aerobic non-sporing bacilli. By the use of special media other organisms such as the nitrifying bacteria, may be isolated.

C. SEWAGE BACTERIA.

Many of the organisms in this group are normal inhabitants of the intestine of man and animals. Others live chiefly on decomposing organic matter of either animal or vegetable origin. Occasionally pathogenic organisms are included.

(1) *Intestinal Bacteria.*
    Bact. coli group.
    Streptococcus fæcalis.
    Cl. welchii.

    Pathogenic organisms, such as *Bact. typhosum* and *V. choleræ.*
(2) *Sewage Bacteria proper.*
    Proteus: Pr. vulgaris.
    Anaerobic spore-bearing bacilli: *Cl. sporogenes.*

(For the classification of water organisms see Fuller and Johnson 1899, Boyce and Hill 1900, Jordan 1903, Cornwall 1914.)

FACTORS DETERMINING THE KINDS AND NUMBERS OF BACTERIA IN WATER

A. Type of Water.—Waters may be divided according to their source into (1) surface and (2) deep waters. The former comprise all those that are found on or near the surface of the earth, and that have not been filtered through any considerable thickness of soil ; the latter comprise those which, in order to reach the underground stratum that they occupy, have percolated, often for several hundred feet, through porous layers of soil. Since surface waters are frequently exposed to contamination from dust, soil, sewage, factory wastes, and other decomposing organic matter, they may contain large numbers of bacteria, many of which are of intestinal origin. Deep waters, on the other hand, are generally pure, having had most of their surface contaminants filtered off on their downward passage through the soil ; and, though it is not unusual to find bacteria in larger numbers than one would expect, these are generally of a harmless type.

(1) SURFACE WATERS.

(a) *Rain.*—In falling to the earth, the raindrops come into contact with particles of suspended dust, and carry these down with them. The more dust there is in the atmosphere, the greater is the bacterial count. The figures in Table CLXXX have been recorded at the Montsouris Observatory at Paris.

TABLE CLXXX

	Bacteria per cubic metre of Air at Montsouris. Average for 10 Years.	Bacteria per litre of Rain Water at Montsouris. Average for 2 Years.
January	160	8,000
February	145	1,320
March	225	2,920
April	310	2,140
May	305	2,440
June	355	5,600
July	465	5,600
August	455	8,300
September	310	5,770
October	190	3,220
November	195	3,250
December	165	4,330
	Mean 275	Mean 5,300

From a comparison of these two columns, it will be seen that on the whole the greatest numbers of organisms in rain are found during the dusty months of June, July, August, and September. Montsouris is situated on the outskirts of Paris ; in the centre of the city the air was found to contain 6,040 bacteria per cubic metre, and the rain 19,000 bacteria per litre.

In the open country the organisms may not exceed 10 or 20 organisms per litre of rain.

(b) *Snow.*—This tends to be less pure than rain, probably because the snow-flakes have a greater surface on which to collect suspended particles in the atmosphere ; and also because their low temperature conduces to the survival of bacteria

3 E

In snow situated on the tops of high mountains, where it will be remembered that Pasteur found the air to be practically sterile, there are hardly any organisms.

(c) *Hail.*—Curiously enough, hail contains more bacteria than either rain or snow. Belli (1902) examined hail that fell in Padua during July, 1901, and found no fewer than 140,000 organisms per litre. Examination of the bacteria showed that they belonged to nine different types. During the formation of hail, it seems probable that rapidly ascending currents of air carry the raindrops up into a region of the atmosphere where they are solidified ; falling down they are melted, and again swept upwards and frozen. After they have been frozen and thawed a number of times the hailstones are thrown out on the periphery of the storm centre and finally come to earth (Mason 1902). It is suggested that the air currents carry up to the cloud region quantities of dust, which is thus incorporated in the hail. It is difficult to explain otherwise the presence in it of vegetable cells, and of fluorescent and soil bacteria.

(d) *Ice.*—The number of organisms in ice depends on the nature of the water from which the ice is formed. With the exception of the ice of glaciers, it is generally impure. Its low temperature is favourable to the survival of most bacteria ; hence the self-purification that occurs in waters on storage occurs hardly at all, or very slowly, in ice.

(e) *Shallow Wells.*—If protected from contamination in the immediate vicinity by brick sides, and if provided with a pump, shallow wells may contain relatively few bacteria ; but the water of an open draw-well, subject to the influx of dust and of surface washings, is generally very impure. In an examination of over 50 shallow wells, Savage (1906) found that the gelatin count at 20° C. varied from 100 organisms to 20,000 or more per c.c. ; and the agar count at 37° C. from less than 10 to over 100 per c.c.

(f) *Upland Surface Waters.*—If derived from open moorland that is protected from human and animal excretions, these waters are relatively pure. Most of the organisms they contain belong to the soil group of bacteria. The agar count is generally low, not more than 10 or 20 per c.c. The gelatin count is fairly high, up to 1,000 per c.c. ; after heavy rainfall it may rise to several thousands.

(g) *Rivers.*—In most countries rivers are heavily contaminated, and contain, not only the natural and the soil bacteria, but large numbers of organisms derived from sewage. In the raw Thames water taken at Hampton during 1906–11 Houston (1913) found the average number of colonies per c.c. on gelatin to be 4,310, and on agar 368 ; typical *Bact. coli* was found in 49·3 per cent. of samples of 0·1 c.c. and in 99·2 per cent. of samples of 100 c.c.

(h) *Lake Waters.*—Owing to the natural storage of water in lakes, there is a continuous process of self-purification occurring ; hence lake water is purer than the streams that feed it. Water taken from the middle of the lake contains fewer organisms than that taken near the shore. Lake Geneva contains as many as 150,000 bacteria per c.c. near the shore, but further out as few as 38 (Marshall 1921).

(i) *Sea Water.*—The number of bacteria in sea water is generally less than in fresh. Russell (1892) found that the water taken near the coast in the Gulf of Naples contained 70,000 organisms per c.c., but 4 kilometres out there were only 57. In deep sea the bacteria seem to be distributed evenly, there being almost as many near the bottom as on the surface. The ooze on the bed of the ocean is very rich in bacteria ; Russell found 20,000 organisms per c.c.

(*j*) *Mineral Springs.*—These tend to be relatively pure, and most of the organisms found in water derived from them come from imperfectly sterilized bottles (Duhot and Hutin 1933). The reaction of these waters varies considerably. Bance and Caillon (1929) give the following figures : Badoit pH 6·1, Vals pH 6·05–6·4, Vichy pH 6·4–6·9, Contrexéville pH 6·9–7·0, Vittel pH 7·1, Rubinat pH 7·3–7·6.

(2) DEEP WATERS.—Some of the purest waters that we know come from deep wells and springs. Fifteen driven wells in the neighbourhood of Boston, Mass., contained an average of only 18 colonies per c.c. (Prescott and Winslow 1913). In a period of 7 consecutive years, out of 1,565 samples of waters from the deep wells in Kent, Houston found *Bact. coli* in only 5·7 per cent., even when 100 c.c. were examined. The purity of springs depends mainly on their source and surroundings. In waters which have percolated through thick strata, the flora differs from that in surface waters ; the organisms develop slowly at room temperature, there are few liquefying colonies, and chromogenic organisms are relatively numerous (Prescott and Winslow 1913).

B. Nutrition.—The amount of available food supply is probably the most important factor of all in determining the number of bacteria in a given water. When organic matter is plentiful, organisms abound ; when it is scarce they are few, and tend to die out.

C. Temperature.—The effect of temperature varies with the amount of organic matter present. A rise of temperature in a water containing an ample food supply for the bacteria causes them to multiply rapidly : but when the organic matter is small in quantity, a rise in temperature has the reverse effect ; this is probably due to early exhaustion of the food supply, and the consequent diminution in rate of multiplication of the bacteria.

A low temperature, independent of the amount of organic matter present, favours the survival, though not the multiplication, of bacteria. Houston (1913) added typhoid bacilli to raw Thames water, and maintained the samples at temperatures varying from 0° C. to 37° C. The initial number added was 103,328 per c.c. of water. Table CLXXXI shows how much more rapid was the death of the organisms at 37° C. than at freezing-point. Hamilton (1935), who made observations on the Whangpoo river, found that in the short run from Shanghai to Woosung there was a diminution of 16 per cent. in the colon bacteria during the winter months, and of no less than 97–99 per cent. during the summer months.

TABLE CLXXXI

INFLUENCE OF TEMPERATURE. (Houston 1913.)

Degrees.	No. of Bacilli per c.c. surviving after weeks.								
	1.	2.	3.	4.	5.	6.	7.	8.	9.
0° C.	47,766	980	65	34	3	3	2	1	0·0
5° C.	14,894	26	6	3	0·3	0·1	0·0	—	—
10° C.	69	14	3	0·3	0·0	—	—	—	—
18° C.	39	3	0·4	0·0	—	—	—	—	—
27° C.	19	0·1	0·0	—	—	—	—	—	—
37° C.	5	0·0	—	—	—	—	—	—	—

D. Light.—It has been asserted that the ultra-violet rays of the sun play an effective part in destroying micro-organisms in water. Procaccini (1893) placed drain water, from which the coarser particles had been removed, in glass cylinders 50 cm. deep, and exposed them for 6 hours to the Italian sun in June. A control cylinder was protected from the light (Table CLXXXII).

TABLE CLXXXII

	Insolated Cylinder. Bacteria per c.c.	Darkened Cylinder. Bacteria per c.c.
Before Exposure :		
Surface	4,900	4,900
Middle	4,510	4,510
Bottom	6,781	6,781
After Exposure :		
Surface	0	7,261
Middle	2	9,051
Bottom	8	12,591

The water in the exposed cylinder was practically sterilized; that in the protected cylinder contained rather more organisms than at the start of the experiment.

It would appear that under laboratory conditions the actinic rays of the sun may exert a bactericidal effect. In nature, however, the conditions are altered. One of the main factors hindering the rays is the opacity of the water, which prevents their penetration for more than a short distance. Even in clear water, it is doubtful if they are active for more than a distance of 5 feet from the surface. Another factor is the movement of the water, which may prevent any single organism from being subjected to the rays for a sufficient time to kill it. In this country it is probable that sunlight has little, if any, effect in diminishing the bacterial content of waters. Ultra-violet rays generated from a mercury vapour lamp have, however, been used in the artificial purification of water (Thresh and Beale 1910, Foulds 1911); for this purpose it is essential for the water to be exposed in shallow layers.

E. Acidity.—Winslow and Lochridge (1906) showed that *Bact. coli* in tap water was destroyed by 0·0123 normal hydrochloric acid in 40 minutes. This corresponded to 12·8 parts per million of dissociated hydrogen. Organic acids were likewise bactericidal, but usually in a higher concentration; their effect appeared to be due, not only to the dissociated hydrogen, but also to the undissociated molecule or to the anion (see Chapter V).

Many natural waters have an acid reaction. In the moorland streams this acidity is due chiefly to the presence of peaty acids—the so-called humic and ulmic acids. Though it is difficult to estimate the effect of acidity on the destruction of bacteria and on the inhibition of their growth, there is little doubt that it does play a considerable part in purifying some waters.

F. Salinity.—The antiseptic and disinfectant action of salts has already been described in the chapter on Disinfection. It is not necessary here to do more than remind the reader of the inimical effects on bacterial growth and survival that certain salts may exercise. It is probably this factor that accounts for the difference both in the numbers and in the types of bacteria found in sea water.

G. Dissolved Oxygen.—Whipple and Mayer (1906) found that *Bact. typhosum* and *Bact. coli* remained viable in sterile water containing dissolved oxygen much longer than in water kept under anaerobic conditions. Thus, in one experiment, *Bact. typhosum* survived in filtered tap water exposed to the air at room temperature for nearly 2 months, but died in 4 days in an atmosphere of hydrogen. They suggest that this may partly explain why this organism dies more rapidly in polluted than in pure water, and why it survives for a shorter time in summer than in winter. The importance of oxygen in favouring the growth and survival of aerobic and facultative anaerobic organisms has also been stressed by Müller (1912).

H. Protozoal Content.—Huntemüller (1905) showed that flagellates contribute actively to the extermination of bacteria in water. River water naturally polluted by bacteria, or suspensions of *Bact. typhosum,* could be cleared in 4 days if flagellates—*Bodo saltans* or *Bodo ovatus*—were added (see also Kyriasides 1931). Stokvis and Swellengrebel (1911) demonstrated a similar action by infusoria—*Colpoda cucullus.* The bacterial destruction was preceded by a rise in the number of protozoa in the water, and was probably due to active ingestion, though this was not demonstrated conclusively. Aerobic conditions and a temperature between 10° and 30° C. were essential. König (quoted from Thresh and Beale 1925) found that in 1 c.c. of water from a well at the Hygienic Institute of Munich, 21 million added typhoid bacilli perished in 24 hours. This he attributed to the action of protozoa. In pure water the death rate in this time was trifling. Increasing attention is being paid to the action of predatory plankton in the self-purification of naturally polluted waters (Butterfield *et al.* 1931, Hoskins 1935). By keeping the bacterial population below the saturation point, it is suggested that the plankton favours the continuous multiplication of bacteria in the water, which results in its turn in a progressive oxidation of organic matter.

I. Rainfall.—The effect of rainfall on the bacterial content of a water is complicated. Rain falling after a drought washes large numbers of soil organisms into the water, and hence increases the numbers of bacteria. If the rain continues for some days, relatively few organisms may be carried in during the later period of rainfall, so that the stream is diluted with water purer than its own ; its bacterial content therefore sinks. Again, the nature of the water is of importance. A relatively pure stream may be contaminated by rain ; an impure stream may be benefited by dilution. As a rule, rivers and upland surface waters contain their greatest numbers of bacteria after heavy rainfall.

J. Season.—The monthly variation in the bacterial content of waters depends chiefly on the temperature and the rainfall. In this country, the highest counts are generally found in the winter months, when the temperature is low and the rainfall greatest. Rivers show more variation than upland surface waters (Tables CLXXXIII and CLXXXIV, p. 1574). The Thames in winter is swollen by heavy rain, and the quality deteriorates in consequence of the scouring effect over the whole drainage area. In summer many sources of pollution have dried up, and much of the water in the river is virtually stored or filtered water, derived from underground sources of supply ; hence the bacterial content falls (Houston 1917). In upland surface waters, a rise in the bacterial content is not infrequent during July and August ; the explanation of this is not clear, but it seems not unlikely that it is the result of dust and soil washings carried in by the summer rains (see Table CLXXXIV).

TABLE CLXXXIII

RAW THAMES WATER AT HAMPTON. (Houston 1913.)

Month.	Average No. of Colonies per c.c. on Gelatin at 20°–22° C. in 3 days.		
	1906.	1907.	1908.
January	2,075	5,246	13,454
February . . . . :	1,679	3,625	3,627
March	1,161	1,590	2,646
April	277	1,803	6,177
May	1,064	961	2,185
June	382	1,366	1,767
July	952	493	1,107
Augus	727	436	1,127
September	450	575	1,327
October	439	1,658	1,853
November	2,580	4,902	1,187
December	2,943	6,710	2,188

TABLE CLXXXIV

RESERVOIR IN PENNINES. UPLAND SURFACE WATER. MILLSTONE GRIT.

Month.	Average No. of Colonies per c.c. on Gelatin at 20°–22° C. in 3 days.		
	1921.	1922.	1923.
January	107	176	68
February	62	65	51
March	25	107	33
April	13	26	14
May	17	1	57
June	80	64	54
July	48	115	60
August	105	86	52
September	30	12	91
October	11	20	13
November	21	89	38
December	154	39	—

In countries in which the water supply is augumented by melting snows, the bacterial content rises considerably in spring time. Oslo obtains its water supply from a lake about 160 metres above sea level. During most of the year, Schmelck (1888) found that the number of organisms per c.c. was 10 to 60, rising up to 200 after heavy rain. But in the spring, when the snow was melting, the organisms increased to as many as 2,500 per c.c. It is probable that this increase was due to the large amount of earth and detritus which was brought down by the glacial streams.

K. Storage.—The simple storage of water in a reservoir suffices to decrease its bacterial content enormously. Houston (1913) found that after only 15 hours' storage the New River water showed a reduction in the agar count of 40 per cent. He maintains that storage acts in three ways : (1) Sedimentation : the organisms adherent to particles of suspended matter, and those in clumps or zoogloeæ, sink to the bottom, leaving the supernatant water purer. (2) Equalization : this factor comes into play only when several waters of different qualities are collected into one reservoir. It ensures a thorough mixing of the different waters, and prevents the excess distribution of a bad supply on any one day. Even in a river, the water may not be homogeneous ; samples taken from one side may be different in their bacterial content from those taken near the other side (see Table CLXXXVI, p. 1576). In a reservoir, natural or artificial, homogeneity is attained. (3) Devitalization : the organisms die in large numbers, probably from lack of food supply, and ingestion by protozoa. Houston added cholera vibrios to raw river water, and found that after 1 week's storage their numbers had been reduced by 99·9 per cent. ; after 3 weeks they could not be isolated even from 100 c.c. of water. Table CLXXXV shows the effect of storage on the London water.

TABLE CLXXXV

EFFECT OF STORAGE. 1907–08. AVERAGE RESULTS. (Houston 1913.)
Bacteria per c.c.

	Gelatin, 20°–22° C.	Agar, 37°C.	No. of Samples with *Bact. coli* in 0·01 c.c.
River Thames before storage	4,465	280	10·1%
River Thames after 15 days' storage at Chelsea	208	44	1·1%
Reduction	95·3%	84·3%	89·1%

The reduction occurs not only in pathogenic organisms and *Bact. coli*, but in organisms of all sorts, though not always equally. Houston states that even 1 week's storage would be more efficacious, in reducing the initial numbers of typhoid bacilli or cholera vibrios in a water, than sand filtration.

It is probably owing to storage that lake waters are so much purer than the streams that feed them. Some rivers with a very low gradient may offer conditions suitable for sedimentation.

L. Filtration.—Natural filtration occurs on a large scale, resulting in the accumulation of the underground deposits of water that are tapped by deep wells and main springs. Its efficacy in the removal of bacteria depends on the nature of the soil, and the depth of the strata penetrated. In loose, porous soils a greater depth must be traversed to ensure the same degree of purification that is attained by filtration through a more compact soil. Evidence suggests that, in a soil of moderate density, the greater part of the bacteria are removed in the first 10 or 15 feet. This is the reason why deep well water is so pure.

Artificially, sand filtration is used to remove bacteria from water in order to render it potable. Houston (1913) finds that this process, which in the case of the London waters follows storage for 30 days, removes 98 per cent. of the residual bacteria.

M. Other Factors.—It is known that certain rivers have a bactericidal effect on some of the intestinal organisms. Thus Arloing and Sempé (1924) state that the water of the Saône inhibits the growth of *Bact. coli* but not of *Bact. typhosum*. The water of the Isère inhibits the growth of *Bact. paratyphosum A* ; the Rhône *Bact. typhosum* ; and the sea at Havre *Bact. shigœ* (Arloing and Chavanne 1925; Arloing and Sempé 1926). In India the water of the Ganges is said to destroy the cholera vibrio (see Khan 1930). Arloing and Sempé (1926) and Bujanowski (1929) have recently advanced evidence to suggest that this inhibitory, and often highly specific action, is dependent on the presence in the water of a transmissible lytic agent, similar to that described by Twort and by d'Herelle. If this work is confirmed, it will be an interesting addition to our knowledge of the means by which waters undergo natural purification ; and it may serve to explain why certain regions are relatively immune to water-borne diseases—though this seems unlikely.

Self-Purification of Rivers.

From what has already been said, it is clear that the number of bacteria in a particular sample of water is determined by several factors, the precise effect of which it is difficult to assess. It is also clear that such factors as absence of organic matter, the presence of numerous protozoa, a high acidity, and the opportunity for sedimentation, are able to bring about a considerable reduction in the bacterial flora. It is not surprising, therefore, that rivers that have been heavily polluted by sewage may regain their natural purity after flowing for some distance. Jordan's (1900) observations on the Illinois river are of interest. The portion of the river that he examined was between Morris and Ottawa. Nine miles above Morris two tributaries unite, the relatively pure Kankakee, and the Desplaines, laden with Chicago sewage. During its flow of 24 miles from Morris to Ottawa the river improved in purity in spite of the absence of dilution with fresh water. The observations were made in October and November when there was neither sun nor rain (Table CLXXXVI).

TABLE CLXXXVI

	Distance from Morris.	No. of Colonies per c.c.			No. of Hourly Analyses.
		Right Bank.	Middle.	Left Bank.	
Upper station, Morris .	—	261,000	204,000	29,000	3
Middle station, Seneca .	12 miles (24 hours)	100,000	49,000	35,000	2
Lower station, Ottawa .	24 miles (48 hours)	11,500	10,700	13,500	2

The extraordinary degree of purification that occurred was accounted for partly by the slow movement of the river, which permitted sedimentation to occur, and partly by the absence of sufficient food-supply to support the large number of contaminating organisms. Jordan found between Morris and Ottawa a decrease in the albuminoid ammonia of 0·382 to 0·049 parts per million, and in the oxygen consumed of 2·3 to 2. This diminution was probably due to bacterial action.

There is no space to discuss more fully the self-purification of rivers. Enough has been said to indicate the most important factors controlling it. Moreover the importance of each factor varies with different rivers. The reader is referred to a study of the self-purification of the Spree below Berlin by Frank (1888), of the Danube below Vienna by Brezina (1906), and of the Whangpoo by Hamilton (1935).

Bacteriological Analysis

We do not propose to give a detailed description of the bacteriological analysis of water, since the Ministry of Health (Report 1934) in this country and the American Public Health Association (1933) in the United States have each described standard methods for its performance, to which reference should be made by those anxious for further knowledge. Great attention has to be paid to the sampling of the water (for details see Report 1934), and to the technical performance of the various procedures involved (for error of these see Wilson *et al.* 1935).

Plate Count.—In general, the analysis consists in an enumeration of the organisms or groups of organisms capable of forming colonies on a standard nutrient agar medium incubated aerobically at 20°–22° C. for 3 days or at 37° C. for 2 days. Since not all the organisms in water are viable ; since many viable organisms, such as those of the anaerobic and nitrifying groups, do not develop under the particular conditions provided ; and since some of the organisms occur in groups which give rise only to a single colony—it is clear that the colony count corresponds not to the total number of organisms or even to the number of viable organisms, but only to the number of bacterial units that are able to multiply under the nutritional, respiratory, and temperature conditions supplied. For this reason it should be reported either as the " number of colonies developing per c.c.," or more simply as the " plate count per c.c."

Coliform Count.—Besides a general bacterial enumeration, an attempt is made to estimate the number of coliform bacteria in the water, and often to ascertain the proportions of the various types of these organisms. The ideal method of doing this would be a direct plate count on a differential medium. So far, however, no medium has been devised that will differentiate with certainty between coliform and non-coliform organisms, or between the different types of coliform bacilli. The chief attempts made in this direction have been by Tonney and Noble (1930, 1931*a*, *b*, 1932*a*, *b*), who have devised a complex ferrocyanide citrate agar medium ; so far, however, the results of these workers have been only partially successful. The usual technique for estimating coliform bacilli is by the dilution method in a liquid medium, which allows of the observation of gas production—an important property serving to differentiate coliform from most non-coliform bacilli. In this country a series of MacConkey broths are inoculated with falling quantities of water, such as one 50 c.c. quantity, five 10 c.c., five 1 c.c., and five 0·1 c.c. quantities, incubated at 37° C. for 2 days, and the number of tubes showing acid and gas noted. The results are reported either in terms such as the following :

Coliform organisms present in 10 c.c., absent from 1 c.c.

or by means of a probability table (see Greenwood and Yule 1917, McCrady 1918, Hoskins 1934, Report 1934), in terms of the number of coliform organisms present per 100 c.c. The latter method is preferable, but it must be remembered that the figure yielded is only an approximation, since the error of counting by the dilution method is extremely high (see p. 66). Since other organisms, such as certain aerobic spore-bearers (see Greer 1928, Porter *et al.* 1935), may give rise to acid and gas in lactose broth, the count is best referred to as the " presumptive coliform count." If MacConkey medium is used, these organisms rarely cause confusion in water analysis, but if the American lactose broth is used, which is free from bile salt, a varying proportion of the presumptive positive tests will not be " confirmed " on further investigation. Besides MacConkey, several other media are used, but none of them seems to be superior to the lactose bile-salt neutral red broth or agar devised by MacConkey (see Raghavachari and Iyer 1936).

Differential Coliform Count.—Not infrequently it is desirable to ascertain the types of coliform organisms present. For this purpose it is usual to plate out on to MacConkey agar two or three of the positive tubes inoculated with the smallest quantities of water, to incubate for 24 hours, to pick off 2 or 3 lactose-fermenting colonies from each plate, and to test these in a series of media capable of differentiating between organisms of the coli, intermediate, and ærogenes-cloacæ types (see Chapter XXVII). This method, besides being tedious, suffers from two main objections. Firstly, if one type of organism is present in the original water in much smaller numbers than another type, it is liable to be diluted out during the preparation of the dilutions, so that plates inoculated from the positive tubes seeded with the smallest quantities of water will yield a culture of the commoner organism only. Secondly, even if the two types are present in approximately equal numbers, one type is liable to outgrow the other, so that again a pure, or almost pure, culture of one type develops on plating.

To obviate these errors, a method has been suggested (Wilson *et al.* 1935) which consists in subculturing *all* MacConkey broths showing acid and gas (1) into a fresh series of MacConkey broths, which are incubated at 43°–45° C. in a water-bath, and (2) into tubes of Koser's citrate, which are incubated at 37° C. The production of gas in MacConkey broth—but not necessarily in other media—at 44° C. seems to be characteristic of *Bact. coli* of fæcal origin, while the ability to grow in Koser's citrate is distinctive, in the coliform group, of the intermediate and ærogenes-cloacæ types. By making use of probability tables it is thus possible to obtain within 3 or 4 days a quantitative estimate of the organisms belonging to the coliform, the fæcal coli, and the intermediate-ærogenes-cloacæ groups. In this method, though the different types may be present in very unequal proportions in the fermented tubes, transference to highly selective liquid media will enable growth of even minimal numbers to occur.

Classification of Coliform Organisms in Water.—In Chapter XXVII we have discussed the classification of lactose-fermenting coliform bacilli according to the general principles of systematic bacteriology. In water analysis it is of greater advantage to classify these organisms in relation to their habitat, paying particular attention to their excretal or non-excretal origin. Such a classification is given in Table CLXXXVII.

TABLE CLXXXVII

CLASSIFICATION OF COLIFORM STRAINS MET WITH IN GREAT BRITAIN.

Type.	M.R.	V.P.	Growth in Citrate.	Indole.	Gas in MacConkey at 44° C.	Gelatin Liquefaction.	Probable Source of Origin.
Bact. coli, type I	+	−	−	+	+	−	Mammalian fæces
Bact. coli, type II	+	−	−	−	−	−	Non-excretal
Intermediate, type I	+	−	+	−	−	−	Dust and soil
Intermediate, type II	+	−	+	+	−	−	,, ,,
Bact. ærogenes, type I	−	+	+	−	−	−	Dust from grains and food-stuffs
Bact. ærogenes, type II.	−	+	+	+	−	−	,, ,,
Bact. cloacæ	−	+	+	−	−	+	,, ,,

It will be seen that coli I is apparently the only organism that finds its natural habitat in the mammalian intestine. Other coliform organisms are, of course, liable to be ingested with the food and to be found in the fæces, but the great mass of evidence suggests that these are not usually present except in relatively small numbers. The fact that coli I is the only type capable of forming gas in MacConkey broth at 44° C. is of special interest in that it enables this organism to be detected with great rapidity—if desirable by direct inoculation of the water into MacConkey broth followed by incubation at 44° C. for 18–24 hours. Coliform organisms, not conforming to any of the types recorded in Table CLXXXVII, are sometimes met with, though they rarely constitute more than a small proportion of the total. They are best referred to as *irregular* strains.

Examination for Fæcal Streptococci, Cl. welchii, and Pathogenic Organisms.—The plate and coliform counts constitute the usual water analysis. Sometimes, however, further information is required, and search may have to be made for special organisms.

In examining water for fæcal streptococci use is made of the partial heat resistance of these organisms, and of their ability to grow and form acid in MacConkey's medium (see Report 1934).

The search for *Cl. welchii* is conducted either by anaerobic incubation of litmus milk after preliminary heating to 80° C. for 10 minutes to destroy non-sporing organisms, or by use of W. J. Wilson's (1928) glucose sulphite iron agar medium.

Typhoid and paratyphoid bacilli are difficult to demonstrate in water, partly because of technical difficulties, and partly because, unless the contamination of the water is continual, these organisms will have died out by the time suspicion of their presence is aroused. Far and away the most satisfactory method is the use of the bismuth sulphite brilliant green medium devised by W. J. Wilson and B air (1931). When the difficulties of making this medium have been overcome, the results are highly successful, and typhoid and paratyphoid bacilli can be isolated even from crude sewage (see Houston 1930).

In the demonstration of *V. choleræ* advantage may be taken of its rapid growth in alkaline peptone water under aerobic conditions, and of the various differential media available (see Chapter XXI).

Interpretation of the Bacteriological Analysis.—Before attempting to give an opinion on the results of a bacteriological analysis, it is essential to gather particulars of the nature of the water, the method by which it was collected, the time of collection, and the amount of recent rainfall. It is sound practice, though not always possible, for the bacteriologist to make a topographical survey of the gathering ground, so as to ascertain the extent and the kind of pollution to which it is subject. If he is unable to do this personally, he should consult a map in which the source of the water and the immediate environment are indicated.

The whole aim of the bacteriological analysis of water is to find evidence of excretal pollution. Since we can rarely isolate directly specific pathogenic organisms, such as *Bact. typhosum*, we resort to estimating first of all the number of living bacteria of all sorts in the water, and secondly the number of living bacteria of intestinal origin. The greater the number of bacteria, the greater, presumably, is the amount of decomposing organic matter. The more bacteria of intestinal origin there are, the more likely are pathogenic species to be amongst them. Our evidence therefore is circumstantial, and is frequently open to doubt in its interpretation.

Unfortunately we cannot lay down absolute standards for all waters ; but we can lay down a standard for any one water.   This is possible by frequent and regularly repeated examinations, which teach us the range of normal variation. We become acquainted, in fact, with the bacterial character of the water.   Any marked deviation from the norm is at once regarded with suspicion.   On a water which we examine for the first time and for which we have no absolute standards, it is often difficult to express more than a tentative opinion.   A high agar count at 22° C., for example, may be significant or it may not ; and though the sanitary survey may assist us on this point, it may not be till several examinations under different conditions have been made that we can offer a definite opinion.

The agar count at 22° C. gives us information on the amount of decomposing organic matter in the water available for bacterial nutrition.   The more food there is, the greater is the number of organisms in the water.   Most of the bacteria that develop at 20° C. are non-pathogenic to human beings, and it might therefore be thought that their number was immaterial.   On the other hand they afford some indication of the amount of extraneous organic matter available for bacterial nutrition that has gained access to the water from various sources.   On general grounds the greater the amount of organic matter present, the more likely is the water to be contaminated with parasitic and potentially pathogenic organisms.

The agar count at 37° C. is a far more important index of dangerous pollution. Most of the natural and harmless bacteria in water do not grow readily at 37° C. ; the organisms developing at this temperature are chiefly of soil, sewage, or intestinal origin.   Hence our standards must be more stringent than at 22° C.

A high 37°C. agar count is often sufficient to condemn a water, though there are a number of exceptions to this rule.   For example, recently sunk wells and bores are liable for some time to give an unduly high count, which later decreases as the well settles.   Moreover, in some waters a rise in the agar count may occur in the summer months due, not to external pollution, but to actual multiplication of the organisms themselves.   The 37° C. agar count is of particular value in the control of filtration.   With slow sand filters the count on the filtered water should show a 95–98 per cent. reduction on that of the raw water.   A rise in the colony count is the usual signal of defect in the filter beds, demanding instant attention.

It is generally found that in a pure water about ten times as many organisms develop at 22° C. as at 37° C. ; in a polluted water this ratio is often less.   Some workers place more weight on the value of this ratio than on the individual counts.   This, we consider, is a mistake.   The ratio may vary within wide limits, quite independently of the amount of fæcal contamination.   Table CLXXXVIII brings out this point.   Moreover, in a water treated with chlorine, the number of colonies at 22° C. and 37° C. may be almost equal. This is doubtless accounted for by the susceptibility of the natural water bacteria, and the resistance of the spore-bearing soil bacteria ; both counts are lowered absolutely, but the 22° C. far more than the 37° C.

Just as the 37° C. is of greater significance than the 22° C. agar count, so the number of coliform bacilli is a more reliable index of excretal pollution than the 37° C. plate count.   It is also easier to lay down an absolute standard for *Bact. coli* than for either of the other two counts.   For example, this organism should not exceed 1 per 100 c.c. in deep well water, or 5 per 100 c.c. in a shallow well or upland surface water.   Its presence in greater numbers is strongly suggestive of pollution.

TABLE CLXXXVIII

Modified from Thresh and Beale (1925).

Source of Water.	Colonies per c.c.		Ratio of Gelatin to Agar.
	Gelatin 20° C.	Agar 37° C.	
Unpolluted deep well in chalk	61	3	20 : 1
Do.	161	13	12 : 1
Do.	9	3	3 : 1
Unpolluted spring water	51	3	17 : 1
Do.	34	6	6 : 1
Polluted deep well in chalk	84	4	21 : 1
Do.	260	72	4 : 1
Polluted shallow well	1,560	38	41 : 1
Do.	151	4	36 : 1
Polluted river water	6,300	140	45 : 1
Do.	29,600	3,300	9 : 1

A distinction should be drawn between the typical coli I, which is usually of excretal origin, and the other types of coliform bacilli, which are more often derived from other sources (see Table CLXXXVII). There is no question that coli I—the fæcal coli type—is the most delicate index we have of recent excretal pollution. With regard to the importance of the intermediate and ærogenes-cloacæ types, opinion is divided. There are those who maintain that, because these organisms are found in fæces—though only in small numbers—their presence cannot be neglected. There are those who draw attention to the fact that organisms of the ærogenes type are often present in infected urine (Hill *et al.* 1929, Burke-Gaffney 1933), and may constitute the dominant type of coliform bacilli in human fæces (Parr 1936). There are others who point out that, if recent excretal pollution has occurred, fæcal coli will undoubtedly be found too, so that the presence of other types in the absence of fæcal coli can generally be ignored.

The interpretation is to some extent affected by the rate at which these different organisms die out after gaining access to water. Here again our data do not provide us with a clear answer.

The vitality of these organisms in water varies with several factors. Houston (1913) found that storage of water for 15 days reduced the number of *Bact. coli* by 80–90 per cent. Gray (1932) and Burke-Gaffney (1933) bring evidence to show that *Bact. coli* dies out more rapidly than *Bact. ærogenes*. Ruchhoft and his colleagues (1933) find that both organisms disappear at about the same rate, while Platt (1935) finds that this rate depends to some extent on the temperature, *Bact. ærogenes* surviving longer than *Bact. coli* at 18°–20° C., but not at 0° C. or 37° C. Hamilton (1935), in China, finds that in the summer months *Bact. ærogenes* may actually multiply in water under favourable conditions.

On the whole, the evidence suggests that organisms of the ærogenes-cloacæ group tend to be rather more resistant to environmental conditions than fæcal coli. Their presence in water, in the absence of fæcal coli, may indicate either that contamination has occurred with non-polluted dust or soil, or that excretal contamination has occurred at a time sufficiently distant to permit the disappearance of all fæcal coli organisms.   Which of these explanations is correct it is impossible to say on any one sample of water without further examination.

In *this country* a high proportion of waters giving a positive presumptive coliform test actually contain fæcal coli (Bardsley 1934), and it is often therefore unnecessary to proceed to a differentiation of the coliform types.   On this point the Ministry of Health (Report 1934) recommends that if there are less than 2 coliform bacilli per 100 c.c. or more than 10, differentiation is usually unnecessary.   The former result indicates that the water is sufficiently pure for drinking purposes, the latter that it is almost certainly polluted.   If the numbers are intermediate, between about 2 and 10 per 100 c.c., the presumptive coliform organisms may usefully be submitted to the differential tests already described.   A result showing that they are exclusively of the intermediate or ærogenes-cloacæ types may be regarded with tolerance ;   and though it is wise in such circumstances to keep a close watch on the water lest further deterioration should occur, no immediate steps need be taken to ensure greater purity of the supply.

In the *tropics* a fairly high proportion of coliform organisms in water are often found to be of the intermediate or ærogenes-cloacæ types.   Since careful sanitary surveys have shown that such waters may be free from exposure to excretal contamination, it is clear that reliance on the presumptive coliform count in the tropics will result in the unnecessary condemnation of a number of unpolluted waters. Differentiation will generally be necessary, and attention should be devoted mainly to the numbers of fæcal coli.

In cases where the probable origin of coliform bacilli is doubtful, use may be made of the tests for fæcal streptococci and *Cl. welchii*.   Both of these organisms are commonly present in mammalian fæces.   If they are found in significant numbers in the water, they may be regarded as indicating that the doubtful coliform bacilli were probably of excretal origin.   Their absence, on the contrary, points to the reverse conclusion.   It is mainly as an aid to the interpretation of the coliform result that a test for these organisms finds its real value.   It must be pointed out, however, that both fæcal streptococci and *Cl. welchii* probably survive longer in water than fæcal coli, so that their presence in the absence of this organism is generally indicative of remote rather than of recent excretal contamination.   (For further information on the coliform group of organisms in relation to water supply in the tropics reference should be made to papers by Pawan 1925, 1926, 1931, Raghavachari 1926, Hicks 1927, Taylor 1927, and Burke-Gaffney 1932, 1933.)

Standards.—Having discussed briefly the interpretation of the results of the bacteriological analysis, we shall give for the student's guidance some standards that may be applied in determining the potability of a given water.   We cannot emphasize too strongly that these standards are not absolute ;   a good water may fail to conform to them, and a polluted water may come well within them.   But it is necessary for the student to have some basis on which to work.

It will be obvious that the larger the population is to which the water is distributed, the more stringent must our standards be.   The occurrence of typhoid fever in the inmates of a cottage drawing water from a polluted well is unfortunate, but its occurrence in the population of a large town is a catastrophe.   The standards that we suggest here are for *unpurified* water destined for consumption by a small population.   Though the deep well and main spring water would be safe for a town supply, the second water we quote would have to be purified before its delivery to a large number of consumers would be justified.

Deep Well and Main Spring Waters

Plate count, agar 3 days at 22° C. . . .	10–200 per c.c.
Plate count, agar 2 days at 37° C. . . .	1–10 per c.c.
Bact. coli fæcal type I	Less than 1 per 100 c.c.
Fæcal streptococci	Less than 1 per 100 c.c.
Cl. welchii	Less than 1 per 1,000 c.c.

Shallow Well, Land Spring, and Upland Surface Waters

Plate count, agar 3 days at 22° C. . . .	50–500 per c.c.
Plate count, agar 2 days at 37° C. . . .	5–30 per c.c.
Bact. coli fæcal type I	Less than 5 per 100 c.c.
Fæcal streptococci	Less than 5 per 100 c.c.
Cl. welchii	Less than 5 per 1,000 c.c.

A filtered river water should conform to the standard of a good shallow well water. If chlorination has been used in addition, then the coli standard should equal that of a deep well water.

One or two further points may be noted.

Occasionally in unpolluted deep well waters, there may be a high agar count at 22° C. This is found, as a rule, to result from the presence of a single species of organism that has apparently gained access from the air, and multiplied abundantly. Its presence is of no importance.

The effect of rainfall on the water should be noted carefully. Speaking generally, the less the water is influenced by this factor the better. Though rain in itself contains relatively few bacteria, it may carry in large numbers of undesirable organisms from the soil. A large increase in the number of organisms, especially if attended by a rise in the coli count, should always be regarded with suspicion.

Finally we repeat that judgment on the potability of a water can be given only after a careful weighing of all the evidence available. It must be remembered that the mere absence of evidence indicating fæcal pollution does not necessarily indicate that pollution has not taken place. All it does show is that at the time the sample was examined, there was no detectable evidence of pollution. It is partly for this reason that frequent examinations are desirable.

The interpretation of the bacteriological analysis is greatly facilitated by a concurrent chemical analysis, which supplies information on the amount of organic matter in the water. The results obtained by the two methods of examination should be carefully correlated. As a rule, they are in substantial agreement, but discrepancies are occasionally found which show the need for caution in the report, and perhaps for the desirability of a further examination.

Water-borne Disease.—The main diseases carried by water are enteric fever, dysentery, and cholera. For a description of these reference should be made to Chapters LX, LXVI, LXVII. In this country the incidence of water-borne disease is very low, but in some parts of Europe it is fairly high. The American continent also suffers badly. Gorman (1932) records an analysis of 282 outbreaks in the United States and Canada occurring during the years 1920–29, in which there were 12,203 cases of typhoid with 775 deaths, and 84,345 cases of dysentery. It was found that the outbreaks were due almost as much to carelessness in the transport of the water from its source to the consumer as in the use of water from polluted sources.

The access of sewage to a water supply is sometimes followed by gastro-enteritis, the exact causation of which is not always easy to ascertain (see Kathe and König-shaus 1932).

SHELL FISH

The chief importance of shell fish from a public health point of view is their liability to give rise to enteric fever. In France alone it is estimated that during the past 15 years more than 100,000 cases of typhoid fever due to the consumption of shell fish have occurred, of which 25,000 ended fatally (Belin 1934).

Shell fish become infected by being laid down in polluted water. According to Eyre (1924), about 2 litres of water enter and leave the shell of an oyster every hour. Large volumes of water also pass through mussels every 24 hours. The bacterial flora of these shell fish is largely determined by the nature of the water in which they are immersed. This is often subject to rapid changes. It is quite possible, for example, for mussels to be heavily polluted on an ebb tide and to clean themselves on a flood tide. The only satisfactory way of ensuring their purity is to lay them down for some days in non-polluted water.

An attempt is often made to control the suitability of shell fish for human consumption by bacteriological methods. The general principles of such an analysis are similar to those we have just discussed in the examination of water, particular attention being paid to the numbers of coliform bacilli. The difficulties, however, of obtaining an exact bacterial enumeration are considerably greater with shell fish than with water. The chief reason for this is the extraordinary variation in numbers from one oyster or mussel to another, and the gross irregularity in distribution of organisms within the individual shell fish themselves. There is in this country no standard method of analysis or standard of interpretation laid down for the examination of shell fish, with the result that many workers have evolved their own technique. Since the methods of different workers often differ in major points, we shall refrain from describing any one in detail. Those who are interested may be referred to papers by Eyre (1924, 1933), Dodgson (1928), Perry (1928, 1929), Bigger (1934), Beard and Meadowcroft (1935).

Eyre considers that 100 coliform organisms are permissible per oyster, while Dodgson (1934) maintains that, after they have been laid down in clean sterile water at a temperature above 55° F.—below which they will not open—there should be not more than 5 coliform bacilli per gram of oyster.

SEWAGE

In this country crude sewage contains about 10 million organisms per c.c. capable of developing on gelatin at 20° C., and from 1 to 5 million per c.c. on agar at 37° C. In America the numbers appear to be lower. There is often a marked rise in the summer months. The organisms making up these numbers are of many different kinds, and vary from one sewage to another. Prominent amongst them are the *Proteus* group, the coliform bacilli, streptococci, aerobic spore-bearing bacilli, natural water bacteria, and the denitrifying bacilli. *Bact. coli* may number 100,000 per c.c., *Streptococcus fœcalis* 1,000 to 10,000 per c.c., and *Cl. welchii* 100 to 1,000 per c.c. The process of purification is accompanied not so much by a diminution in the numbers of organisms, as by a change in the distribution of different organisms. Thus in the septic tank, the anaerobic liquefying bacteria are prominent ; on the contact beds the aerobic liquefying and the denitrifying bacteria gain the upper hand. It is evident that enormous numbers of bacteria must perish in the process ; by a comparison of the microscopic and the gelatin counts, Winslow (1905) found that the ratio of the total to viable organisms was about 20 to 1 in crude sewage, 40 to 1 in the septic tanks and filter beds, and 70 to 1 in the sand filter effluents. Table CLXXXIX illustrates the numerical changes occurring during biological purification.

TABLE CLXXXIX

BOSTON SEWAGE. (Modified from Winslow 1905.)

	Microscopic Count.	Gelatin.	Agar.	Microscopic ÷ Gelatin.	Agar × 100 ÷ Gelatin.
Crude sewage . .	29,000,000	1,690,000	1,400,000	17	83
Septic tanks . .	30,000,000	787,000	504,000	38	64
Contact filters .	24,000,000	521,000	432,000	46	83
Trickling filters .	17,000,000	451,000	284,000	39	63
Sand filters . .	65,000	9,160	10,800	7	120

It will be seen that no marked fall occurs in the number of living organisms till the sand filter stage is reached.

A method of sewage disposal that is now widely used is the Activated Sludge Process. Briefly this consists in treating the sewage with about 15 per cent. of bacterially active liquid sludge, in the presence of an ample supply of atmospheric oxygen. As a result of this treatment, a large proportion of the colloidal material undergoes coagulation, and subsequent sedimentation. The activated sludge itself results from the aeration of successive portions of sewage (see Martin 1927, Buswell 1928).

REFERENCES

ARLOING, F. and CHAVANNE. (1925) *C. R. Soc. Biol.*, **92**, 257.
ARLOING, F. and SEMPÉ. (1924) *C. R. Soc. Biol.*, **91**, 667 ; (1926) *Ibid.*, **94**, 191.
BANCE, J. and CAILLON, L. (1929) *Arch. Inst. Pasteur, Tunis*, **18**, 199.
BARDSLEY, D. A. (1934) *J. Hyg., Camb.*, **34**, 38.
BEARD, P. J. and MEADOWCROFT, N. F. (1935) *Amer. J. publ. Hlth.*, **25**, 1023.
BELIN, V. M. (1934) " Coquillages et fièvres typhoides. Un point d'histoire contemporaine." Les Presses universitaires de France, Paris.
BELLI, C. M. (1902) *Zbl. Bakt.*, IIte Abt., **8**, 445.
BIGGER, J. W. (1934) *J. Hyg., Camb.*, **34**, 172.
BOYCE, R. W. and HILL, C. A. (1900) *J. Path. Bact.*, **6**, 32.
BREZINA, E. (1906) *Z. Hyg. InfektKr.*, **53**, 369.
BUJANOWSKI, D. (1929) *Zbl. Bakt.*, **110**, 120.
BURKE-GAFFNEY, H. J. O'D. (1932) *J. Hyg., Camb.*, **32**, 85 ; (1933) *Ibid.*, **33**, 510.
BUSWELL, A. M. (1928) " The Chemistry of Water and Sewage Treatment." Chemical Catalog Co. Inc., New York.
BUTTERFIELD, C. T., PURDY, W. C., and THERIAULT, E. J. (1931) *Publ. Hlth Rep., Wash.*, **46**, 393.
CORNWALL, J. W. (1914) *Indian J. med. Res.*, **2**, 352.
DODGSON, R. W. (1928) *Min. Agric. Fish., Lond., Fish. Invest.*, Ser. 2, **10**, No. 1 ; (1934) *Pers. Comm.*
DUHOT, E. and HUTIN, A. (1933) *C. R. Soc. Biol.*, **112**, 195.
EYRE, J. (1924) *Publ. Hlth*, **38**, 6 ; (1933) *J. Hyg., Camb.*, **33**, 1.
FOULDS, M. (1911) *J. R. Army med. Cps*, **16**, 167.
FRANK, G. (1888) *Z. Hyg. InfektKr.*, **3**, 355.
FULLER, G. W. and JOHNSON, G. A. (1899) *J. exp. Med.*, **4**, 609.

Gorman, A. E. (1932) 6th Ann. Rep. Missouri Wat. Sewage Conf., p. 45.
Gray, J. D. A. (1932) J. Hyg., Camb., **32,** 132.
Greenwood, M. and Yule, G. U. (1917) J. Hyg., Camb., **16,** 36.
Greer, F. E. (1928) J. infect. Dis., **42,** 501.
Hamilton, W. (1935) " A Study of the Pollution of the River Whangpoo as affecting its Use as a Source of Water Supply." The Mercantile Printing Co., Ltd., Shanghai.
Hicks, E. P. (1927) J. Hyg., Camb., **26,** 357.
Hill, J. H., Seidman, L. R., Stadnichenko, A. M. S., and Ellis, M. G. (1929) J. Bact., **17,** 205.
Hoskins, J. K. (1934) Publ. Hlth Rep., Wash., **49,** 393 ; (1935) Ibid., **50,** 385.
Houston, A. C. (1913) " Studies in Water Supply," London ; (1917) " Rivers as Sources of Water Supply," London ; (1930) 25th ann. Rep. met. Water Bd, Lond.
Huntemüller, O. (1905) Arch. Hyg., **54,** 89.
Jordan, E. O. (1900) J. exp. Med., **5,** 271 ; (1903) J. Hyg., Camb., **3,** 1.
Kathe and Königshaus. (1932) Arch. Hyg., **109,** 1.
Khan, S. (1930) Indian J. med. Res., **18,** 361.
Kyriasides, K. (1931) Z. Hyg. InfektKr., **112,** 350.
McCrady, M. H. (1918) Canad. Publ. Hlth J., **9,** 201.
Marshall, C. E. (1921) " Microbiology," 3rd edit. London.
Martin, A. J. (1927) " The Activated Sludge Process." London.
Mason, W. P. (1902) " Water Supply," 3rd edit. New York.
Müller, A. (1912) Arb. ReichsgesundhAmt., **38,** 294.
Parr, L. W. (1936) Amer. J. publ. Hlth., **26,** 39.
Pawan, J. L. (1925) Ann. trop. Med. Parasit., **19,** 319 ; (1926) Ibid., **20,** 303 ; (1931) J. trop. Med. Hyg., **34,** 229, 267, 288, 310, 317, 345, 360, 380, 391, 413.
Perry, C. A. (1928) Amer. J. Hyg., **8,** 694 ; (1929) Ibid., **10,** 580.
Platt, A. E. (1935) J. Hyg., Camb., **35,** 437.
Porter, R., McCleskey, C. S., and Levine, M. (1935) Proc. Soc. exp. Biol., N.Y., **32,** 1032.
Prescott, S. C. and Winslow, C.-E. A. (1913) " Elements of Water Bacteriology," 3rd edit. New York.
Procaccini. (1893) Ann. Igiene (sper.), **3,** 437.
Proctor, B. E. (1934) Proc. Amer. Acad. Arts Sci., **69,** 315 ; (1935) J. Bact., **30,** 363.
Raghavachari, T. N. S. (1926) Indian J. med. Res., **14,** 47.
Raghavachari, T. N. S. and Iyer, P. V. S. (1936) Indian J. med. Res., **23,** 619.
Report. (1933) Amer. publ. Hlth Ass., " Standard Methods of Water Analysis," 7th edit. ; (1934) Rep. publ. Hlth med. Subj., No. 71.
Ruchhoft, C. C., Coulter, E. W., Adams, C. L., and Sotier, A. L. (1933) J. Bact., **25,** 143.
Russell, H. L. (1892) Z. Hyg. InfektKr., **11,** 165.
Savage, W. G. (1906) " The Bacteriological Examination of Water-Supplies." London.
Schmelck, L. (1888) Zbl. Bakt., **4,** 195.
Stokvis, C. S. and Swellengrebel, N. H. (1911) J. Hyg., Camb., **11,** 481.
Taylor, J. (1927) Indian J. med. Res., **14,** 801.
Thresh, J. C. and Beale, J. F. (1910) Lancet, ii. 1849 ; (1925) " The Examination of Waters and Water Supplies," 3rd edit. London.
Tonney, F. O. and Noble, R. E. (1930) J. Amer. Water Works Ass., **22,** 488 ; (1931a) J. infect. Dis., **48,** 413 ; (1931b) J. Amer. Water Works Ass., **23,** 1202 ; (1932a) Ibid., **24,** 1267 ; (1932b) J. Bact., **23,** 473.
Whipple, G. C. and Mayer, A. (1906) J. infect. Dis., Suppl. 2, p. 76.
Wilson, G. S., Twigg, R. S., Wright, R. C., Hendry, C. B., Cowell, M. P., and Maier, I. (1935) Spec. Rep. Ser. med. Res. Coun., Lond., No. 206.
Wilson, W. J. (1928) Final Rep. publ. Hlth Congr. and Exhibition, p. 203.
Wilson, W. J., and Blair, E. M. McV. (1931) J. Hyg., Camb., **21,** 138.
Winslow, C.-E. A. (1905) J. infect. Dis., Suppl. 1, p. 209.
Winslow, C.-E. A. and Lochridge, E. E. (1906) J. infect. Dis., **3,** 547,

CHAPTER LXXXIX

THE BACTERIOLOGY OF MILK

Sources of Bacteria in Milk

EVEN when drawn with aseptic precautions, milk always contains a certain number of bacteria which are derived from the milk ducts of the **cow's udder.** Their numbers vary considerably from quarter to quarter and from cow to cow, and are highest in the fore-milk and lowest in the strippings. The average plate count of aseptically drawn milk has been given by different workers as less than 10 per c.c. to several thousand. Many of the lower counts have probably under-estimated the true number owing to unsuitable technique in counting, while many of the higher counts have probably been made on milk derived from udders that were not strictly normal. Considering the extraordinary frequency of mastitis (see Minett 1932, Hucker *et al.* 1932, Diernhofer 1933), 50 per cent. of the animals in a herd often showing disease of one or more quarters, it is very difficult to arrive at any definite conclusion on the probable numbers of bacteria in milk coming from healthy udders. If the udder is diseased, streptococci, *Br. abortus*, tubercle bacilli, and other organisms may be excreted in the milk in large numbers —sometimes running into several thousands per c.c.

When aseptic precautions are not employed, the milk is liable to be contaminated with bacteria from the outside of the udder, the interior of milk vessels and utensils, and dust in the atmosphere of the milking shed. Of these various sources, far and away the most important is **unsterilized milking equipment**. The total number of organsims gaining access from the air and from dust is almost negligible compared with that derived from the surfaces of unsterilized pails, coolers, cans, strainers, clarifiers, and bottle fillers. Unless these utensils are actually sterilized—preferably by steam—their surfaces become coated with bacteria of various types, which may contribute enormous numbers of micro-organisms to the milk.

An additional source of contamination is the **human personnel.** If wet milking is practised, considerable numbers of organisms are liable to get washed into the milk from the milker's hands, as well of course as from the exterior of the udder and teats, unless these are thoroughly cleansed. Though numerically few, the organisms reaching the milk in this way may be of considerable public health importance, particularly if the milker happens to be an intestinal carrier of typhoid, paratyphoid, dysentery, or food-poisoning bacilli. The milker constitutes a further source of danger if he is carrying hæmolytic streptococci or diphtheria bacilli in his throat or nose, since these organisms may gain access to the milk *via* the cough spray.

Apart from initial contamination of the milk, **imperfect cooling** is often respon-sible for the presence of large numbers of bacteria in any given sample. However carefully milk is produced, sooner or later, provided it is kept at a suitable tempera-ture, it will go sour or putrid as the result of bacterial multiplication. If it is to remain sweet for more than a few hours, all milk should be cooled immediately after production to a temperature of 10° C. or below.

It may be noted that the **keeping quality** of the milk is determined partly by the degree of initial contamination and partly by the temperature at which it is kept. Milk produced under really cleanly conditions has a considerable bacteriostatic power, and shows little bacterial multiplication for several hours, even when incubated at a favourable temperature. On the other hand, the bacteriostatic effect of milk produced under dirty conditions is very slight, and bacterial multiplication sets in rapidly. For this reason it is much easier to distinguish between a milk produced under sanitary and one produced under insanitary conditions if the examination is delayed till the milks have stood at a temperature of 60° F. or so for 12–18 hours. After this time a milk produced under clean conditions will still have a low bacterial count, while a milk produced under dirty conditions will contain a large bacterial population.

The **production of clean milk** is largely a matter of technique, not of structural equipment or refinement. Provided all utensils are sterilized by steam, and the surface of the udder and the milker's hands are cleansed, it is possible to produce milk with a very low bacterial content even under unfavourable conditions. It is, however, not easy to maintain a satisfactory technique day in and day out unless suitable conditions and appliances are provided for the workers.

Types of Bacteria in Milk

The bacteria present in milk from healthy cows may be classified into the following groups :

1. Acid-forming Bacteria.—These organisms ferment the lactose in the milk with the production of acids, mainly lactic acid, which combine with the calcium caseinogenate, liberating free casein ; this, being insoluble in water, is precipitated in the form of a smooth, gelatinous curd, which shows little tendency to contract and squeeze out fluid. Lactic streptococci constitute some of the most important members of this group. One particular member is often referred to as *Str. lactis*, but as we have seen in Chapter XXIII the definition of this species is very difficult. Most of these organisms appear to be of vegetable origin, being found on corn, beans, peas, cabbage, etc. (Stark and Sherman 1935). Certain staphylococci, which are not infrequently found in the udder, are also active members of this group. We must further include the *Lactobacilli*, which, however, under ordinary conditions do not appear to proliferate very actively.

2. Gas-forming Bacteria.—These organisms ferment lactose with the production of both acid and gas. They produce a smooth, gelatinous curd, which is often riddled with gas bubbles. The acid produced is largely acetic, which imparts an unpleasant flavour to the milk. Coliform bacilli are among the commonest representatives of this group, which includes, however, certain anaerobic organisms such as *Cl. welchii* and *Cl. butyricum*.

3. Proteolytic Bacteria.—These organisms secrete one or other, or both, of two ferments—rennet and casease. Rennet acts in two stages ; in the first stage the calcium caseinogenate is converted into a soluble form of casein ; in the second stage this is precipitated in an insoluble form by the calcium salts present in the milk. The resulting clot gradually contracts, and squeezes out a more or less clear fluid, which is known as whey ; the whey contains the sugar, salts, and other proteins—lactalbumin and lactoglobulin—in the milk. Casease is a proteolytic enzyme, which digests the proteins present in the milk, breaking them down to proteoses, peptones, and amino-acids.

When the rennet predominates, a firm white curd is produced, which is slowly digested by the casease. When the casease is in excess, either no coagulation at all may occur, or a soft flocculent clot is formed, which is rapidly peptonized.

Many organisms fall under this heading : (*a*) spore-bearing aerobes, such as *B. subtilis* and *B. mesentericus* ; (*b*) *Proteus vulgaris* ; and (*c*) staphylococci and micrococci. Some of the organisms in this group also ferment lactose, so that the milk is rendered acid, besides being clotted and digested.

4. Alkali-forming Bacteria.—These organisms render the milk alkaline, presumably by acting on the proteins. Some of them also secrete lipase, and the combined effect is to saponify the fat, and convert the milk into a yellow translucent whey-like fluid. This action is not often seen, since the members of this group of bacteria are overgrown by members of other groups, which produce acid, coagulation, or peptonization. Organisms belonging to this group comprise *Bact. alkaligenes*, and some of the aerobic spore-bearers.

5. Inert Bacteria.—Many bacteria produce no visible change in milk and are hence called inert. Some of the udder cocci are included in this group. Members of the *Achromobacterium* group, most of which are probably derived from water, are also relatively inert. It may be noted that most of the pathogenic organisms which may be present in milk belong to this group.

Pathogenic Bacteria in Milk.—Apart from the organisms that we have described as being normally present in milk, there are others which are sometimes found in pathological conditions of the cow's udder, or which gain access to the milk from an infected water supply or from some person handling the milk.

Tubercle bacilli.—The presence of these organisms in milk depends on the frequency of bovine tuberculosis. In Great Britain this disease is very prevalent, about 40 per cent. of cattle reacting to the tuberculin test. Though it is true that tubercle bacilli may be excreted in the milk in the absence of any definite disease of the udder (Report 1909), some degree of tuberculous mastitis can generally be demonstrated—though not always clinically—in cows passing infected milk. It is probable that on an average about 0·5 per cent. of all milch cows in this country are excreting tubercle bacilli in the milk (see Chapter LVI). The proportion of market samples of raw milk containing these organisms depends to a considerable extent on the degree to which the milk is bulked, but an average figure of about 7 per cent. may be taken for the country as a whole (Report 1932). The numbers of tubercle bacilli excreted by a single cow are variable from animal to animal, and from day to day, but it is probable that they may reach several hundred per c.c. (see Pullinger 1934).

Br. abortus.—This organism is responsible for contagious abortion of cattle, which is probably even more prevalent in this country than tuberculosis. The udder is frequently infected, even in animals that have not aborted (see Chapter LXXII), though no lesions can be detected by clinical examination. The bacilli are excreted regularly or intermittently in the milk. Their numbers are usually greatest at the beginning of lactation, when they may reach as many as 200,000 per c.c., but in the later stages they diminish and rarely exceed 2,000 per c.c. (Stockmayer 1936). The udder may remain infected for years. About 30 per cent.

of samples of raw mixed milk offered for human consumption appear to contain this organism.

Streptococci.—Mastitis streptococci are of various types, the most important being *Str. agalactiæ* (see Chapter XXIII). They are excreted in variable numbers in the milk of cows suffering from mastitis. This disease is extremely common, and affects not only the poorer herds, but even herds producing high-grade milk. Pullinger (1935), for example, found that the milk from 10 out of 12 herds producing Certified milk and 12 out of 14 herds producing Grade A tuberculin-tested milk contained mastitis streptococci when examined at intervals over a period of 15 months. The majority of streptococci causing mastitis are probably non-pathogenic for man, but occasionally a strain of human type invades the udder, and may be responsible for outbreaks of scarlet fever or septic sore throat in persons consuming the milk. The milk may also be contaminated directly with these organisms from persons who are either suffering from streptococcal throat lesions, or who are carrying these organisms in their throat or nasopharynx.

Staph. aureus.—This organism is a not infrequent cause of mastitis. It is sometimes found in the healthy udder, but in cows suffering from acute mastitis it may be present in large numbers in the milk. Its public health importance lies in the fact that, under favourable conditions, it may multiply in the milk and give rise to a toxin capable of producing gastro-enteritis in human beings (see p. 1263).

C. diphtheriæ.—This organism occasionally finds its way into the milk from the throat or nasopharynx of a human carrier or case of diphtheria. Very occasionally it becomes implanted on ulcers on the cow's teats. Such an occurrence is peculiarly dangerous, since the milk is uniformly infected.

Typhoid, paratyphoid, food-poisoning, and dysentery bacilli.—These important pathogenic organisms, which may occasionally contaminate the milk, are usually derived from human or other extraneous sources (see p. 1597).

Quality in Milk. Cleanliness and Safety

Quality is a composite, not a single, attribute of milk. There are, for example, (1) the nutritive quality, (2) the cleanliness, (3) the keeping quality, (4) the pasteurizability, and (5) the safety of milk, to mention only five of its most important attributes. Leaving aside the nutritive quality, which can be determined only by chemical analysis and animal feeding experiments, we may consider for a moment what we mean by the other four properties.

By **cleanliness** is generally understood the freedom of the milk from extraneous matter, from blood, and from an undue number of leucocytes and bacteria. It is an unsatisfactory term, but by general usage it has come to bear this connotation.

The **keeping quality** of the milk refers, of course, to the length of time it will remain sweet, and free from odours and tastes that render it unpalatable.

The **pasteurizability** of the milk is a term devised to indicate the suitability of the milk for heat treatment. It is, of course, a mistaken idea that any milk can be pasteurized. A milk that is too acid will clot when the temperature is raised, and the resultant product will have to be discarded. Again, as Anderson and Meanwell (1933) have shown, some milks contain large numbers of heat-resistant bacteria, which are not destroyed by pasteurization, and which therefore prevent the pasteurized product from conforming to the legal standard.

The **safety** of milk is a term denoting its freedom from bacteria capable of giving rise to disease in man or animals.   It is by some writers confused with clean-liness, but there is no necessary or constant relationship between these two proper-ties.   Dirty milks, if free from pathogenic bacteria, may be quite safe, while very clean milks are not infrequently dangerous.

It has already been pointed out that pathogenic bacteria in milk may come from (1) the udder, such as the tubercle bacillus, *Br. abortus*, and some streptococci and staphylococci ; (2) the infected nasopharynx of human beings handling the milk, such as hæmolytic streptococci and diphtheria bacilli ; (3) excretal material gaining access either from the hands of human beings, or indirectly from water contaminated with urine or fæces—usually of human origin ; in one or other of these ways typhoid, paratyphoid, dysentery, and food-poisoning bacilli may be carried into the milk.   These are the organisms responsible for *dangerous* milk. Those responsible for *dirty* milk, on the other hand, come from various sources, particularly unsterilized milk utensils, caked mud and manure on the cow's udder, dirt on the milker's hands, and from the fore-milk in the teat canal.   Provided the cow is healthy, provided that none of the human beings handling the milk is a carrier of pathogenic bacteria, and provided that the water supply is pure, dirt and bacteria may gain access to the milk in considerable quantities without endan-gering the health of those consuming it.   On the other hand, if pathogenic bacteria find their way into the milk from one of the sources quoted above, no matter in how cleanly a manner the milk is produced, it is a potentially dangerous and unsafe milk.

These conclusions are borne out by epidemiological experience, which has shown that several outbreaks of disease have followed the consumption of milk of the highest standard of cleanliness.   Without discussing this subject further, we shall probably be wise to regard cleanliness and safety as two entirely separate attributes of milk.

For human consumption it is desirable, of course, that milk should be both clean and safe.   Clean milk is more æsthetically desirable, it has a better flavour, and it keeps longer.   Moreover, it is not likely to contain any of those toxic sub-stances resulting from undue bacterial proliferation, which have an irritating effect on the gastro-intestinal tract—particularly of infants (see Park and Holt 1903 and Chapter LXIX).   The fewer organisms there are in milk, and the more bacterial proliferation is checked, the less liable is the milk to give rise to digestive disturbance of this type.

As regards safety, it will be clear that *no raw milk can ever be regarded as com-pletely safe for human consumption*.   The frequency of disease in cattle, the risk of contamination from human and other sources, and the suitability of the milk itself as a medium for bacterial multiplication, combine to render the consumption of raw milk potentially dangerous.   The only satisfactory way of eliminating this danger is by pasteurization or some other form of heat treatment.

Bacteriological Grading of Milk

From a public health point of view it is usual to grade milk bacteriologically partly according to cleanliness and partly according to safety.   We may consider briefly the various methods available for these purposes.

Grading according to Cleanliness.

For a detailed description of the methods used and a study of their experi-mental errors, and for a critical discussion on the interpretation of their results, the reader is referred to the monograph by Wilson and his colleagues (1935).

Sampling.—Since the answer given by any test is determined so largely (*a*) by multiple factors involved in the production and subsequent handling of the milk ; (*b*) by the care with which the milk is sampled, and (*c*) by the time-temperature conditions under which the sample is taken and kept prior to analysis, it follows that it is unwise to pay too much attention to the results of any single examination. The most satisfactory procedure is to make frequent and regular examinations of the milk of any given producer throughout the year, and insist that a given proportion, for example 75 per cent., of the samples should come up to a given standard. In this way some allowance will be made for factors over which the producer is unable to exercise complete control, while at the same time ensuring that the conditions of production as a whole are kept at a reasonably high level.

Every endeavour should be made in the sampling of the milk to obtain a homogeneous distribution of organisms and fat. With regard to the subsequent treatment of the sample, two alternative procedures are available. If the intention is to test the cleanliness of production, it is desirable to expose the sample after collection to an agreed temperature for a given length of time, in order that the latent contamination in milk produced under bad conditions may have time to develop. When testing milk delivered to the consumer, on the other hand, it is desirable to ice the sample at once, so as to obtain information on the degree of bacterial contamination at the time of delivery by the distributor.

The sample may be examined by the following tests :

(1) **The Sediment Test.**—The amount of extraneous matter in the milk is determined either by filtration through a cotton pad, or by centrifugation. A simple sediment test of this sort is of value in controlling the gross dirt in milk and in education of the unhygienic farmer. Since, however, filtration through muslin gauze on the farm will remove dirt of this type, the absence of an obvious sediment must not be taken to mean that the conditions of production were satisfactory. Most of the bacteria in milk come, not from gross dirt, but from unsterilized utensils. Indeed, actual manure can be added to the milk without producing any marked increase in the bacterial content ; for this reason a sediment test is useful for the detection of gross particulate matter, the presence of which is not likely to be detected by purely bacteriological tests.

(2) **The Cellular Content.**—Normal milk contains various types of cells, the number of which is estimated by different workers as between about 200,000 and 1,000,000 per c.c. These estimates probably err on the high side. According to Prouty (1934), milk from absolutely normal udders contains, as a rule, less than 100,000 cells per c.c. But the perfectly normal udder is almost a curiosity, and for practical purposes, therefore, we must allow a considerable margin on this figure. An abnormally high cell count may be due to retention of the milk in the udder, which leads to desquamation of the epithelial cells in the alveoli and ducts, to acute or chronic inflammation, which brings about a rise in the polymorphonuclear leucocytes, or to some other cause. A mere count of the cells present affords little information about the quality of the milk, and it would be unwise to condemn a milk solely on account of an increased cell content. If long-chained streptococci are found in addition, the probability is that the cow is suffering from mastitis. Much more information can be obtained by a differential count, but the real value of this method lies in the help it gives to the veterinarian who is engaged in a study of the individual cow.

(3) **The Breed Smear Method.**—The general technique of this method is to spread 0·01 c.c. of the milk over 1 sq. cm. on a glass slide, to fix and de-fat, to stain with methylene blue, to count the number of individual organisms—the Breed " individual " count—or preferably the number of groups of organisms, individual organisms each being regarded as a group—the Breed " clump " count—in a given number of fields, and finally to calculate the number of organisms in 1 c.c. of the original milk. The result obtained affords an index of the total *stainable* organisms present, not necessarily of the total organisms. The chief value of this method lies in its rapidity, which enables an opinion to be formed on the bacterial cleanliness of a milk within a few minutes. It is particularly suitable for use in collecting stations to which milk from individual farms is brought before being mixed and sent up to towns in large rail or road tanks. Unsatisfactory milks, which would taint the rest, can be picked out quickly, and returned to the producer. With a little experience, a mere glance over a few fields is sufficient to indicate the general quality of the milk. The Breed Smear method is also of value to the farm inspector in indicating the probable nature of the defect in unsatisfactory milk. Thus the presence of large masses and clumps of bacteria suggests unsterilized milk utensils ; the presence of numerous organisms arranged in pairs or small units suggests inadequate cooling ; the presence of long-chained streptococci associated with a high leucocyte count suggests mastitis, and so on (see Breed 1929).

(4) **The Keeping Quality Test.**—The milk is kept in a special bottle at a given temperature, such as 60° F. or 70° F., and examined every 8 or 12 hours until it becomes sour or putrid. As a general method for controlling the hygienic quality of the milk, this test performs a useful function, but the fact that the end-point is entirely subjective necessarily exposes the result to a very large experimental error.

(5) **The Plate Count.**—This is one of the most widely used methods for the bacteriological grading of milk according to cleanliness. It is, however, exposed to criticism on so many grounds that it is doubtful whether its continued use is justifiable. Ostensibly the plate count measures the numbers of bacteria in the milk, but in fact it does not. The bacteria in raw milk are of many different kinds and come from varied sources. Often a large proportion are dead, while those that are alive differ in their nutritional, respiratory, and temperature requirements, so that no one medium incubated for a given length of time at a given temperature under aerobic conditions can possibly afford a true estimate even of the living organisms present. More important still, however, is the fact that many of the bacteria are distributed, not individually, but in chains and groups of varying sizes. The colonies developing on plates are derived therefore, not solely from individual organisms, but also from aggregates containing varying numbers of bacteria. In consequence the plate count merely registers the number of bacterial units capable of multiplying under the particular conditions selected. Since the average number of bacteria per clump is variable from one milk to another, and not constant from time to time even in milk of the same origin, it follows that the figures yielded by the plate count are arbitrary, are not strictly comparable, and have no absolute significance.

When it is further pointed out that these clumps of bacteria may disintegrate to a variable and quite uncontrollable extent during the process of dilution, leading in extreme instances to errors of 1,000 per cent. (Ward 1926), and that many of the individual steps in the technique of the count are very difficult to standardize, and even when standardized as nearly as possible are attended by a large experimental error, it will be realized that the figures yielded by the plate count are not merely arbitrary, but are also only approximate. (For a description and numerical assessment of the various errors of dilution, incubation, counting, personal bias and personal variability, sampling, overcrowding, and so on, see Wilson *et al.* 1935.)

Even were it possible to standardize the technique of the plate count, it would still be necessary to allow a margin of $\pm$ 50–90 per cent. on the result of any one milk, depending on the number of plates used for each dilution. Even this estimate would often fall short of the real variation met with in practice (Mattick *et al.* 1935). However accurate the plate count may be for the enumeration of bacteria in pure broth cultures, it is plainly unsuitable for this purpose when applied to milk. Because the results are expressed quantitatively in figures extending over a wide range, they afford a fictitious appearance of accuracy which leads, not only in laymen, but even in public health officials, to a wholly unjustifiable feeling of confidence in their value. It is not denied that the plate count can be used as a rough yard-stick for the grading of milk, but it is denied that it can be used as a millimetre rule. As scientific bacteriologists we can hardly condone a practice which is little short of bacteriological prostitution.

(6) **The Coliform Test.**—Like the plate count, this method has been extensively used in the past for the grading of milk without any real appreciation of the fundamental assumptions on which it rests. We have seen that in the analysis of *water* the coliform test affords us the most delicate index we have of excretal pollution. The main reasons for this are that (1) in this country something like 90 per cent. of waters giving a positive presumptive coliform reaction in MacConkey broth are proved on further examination to contain typical *Bact. coli* of excretal origin (Bardsley 1934) ; (2) organisms of the *Bact. coli* type in water in this country are very frequently derived from human excretal material, and since human fæces and urine may contain pathogenic bacteria, the presence of any excretal pollution, as indicated by the coliform test, must be regarded as potentially dangerous ; and (3) as a rule, coliform organisms do not seem to multiply in water under natural conditions ; on the contrary, they tend to die out rather rapidly (Houston 1913). In this country, therefore, the coliform count in water indicates the minimal amount of excretal pollution that has occurred.

When we turn to *milk* we find that (1) a considerable proportion—something like 50–70 per cent.—of raw milks in this country in which coliform bacilli are found contain not the true *Bact. coli* but organisms of the intermediate or ærogenes-cloacæ types. These organisms come mainly, not from fæces and urine, but from soil and grain, and their presence therefore in milk cannot be regarded as an index of excretal pollution ; (2) the true *Bact. coli* organisms that are found in milk appear to come either directly from cow-dung and manure, or indirectly from unsterilized milk utensils in which bacterial multiplication has occurred. If they are derived from the latter source, they clearly afford no index of *direct* excretal pollution. If they are derived from the first source, their presence may be considered objectionable on the ground that organisms pathogenic for man are sometimes present in the intestinal canal of the cow. The presence, however, in milk of excretal material of bovine origin must be regarded as very much less dangerous for man than that of human origin. (3) Unlike water, milk affords an admirable medium for the growth of coliform bacilli. If it is kept at a temperature of 50° F. or over, a great increase in their numbers may take place, a rise of several thousandfold often occurring at 60° F. within 24 hours (see Ayers and Clemmer 1918, Finkel-stein 1919, Sherman and Wing 1933). Unless, therefore, the milk has been kept at 40° F. or less, an estimation of the coliform bacilli affords only a very imperfect, and often entirely misleading, index of the extent of the original contamination. With a milk produced and kept under ordinary conditions, it is impossible to tell how many of the coliform bacilli gained access at the time of production, and how many are due to the multiplication of those originally present.

It will thus be seen that none of the three premises on which the scientific application of the coliform test to water in this country is based holds true for milk. Even a differentiation of the coliform group into its constituent types is not likely to help us, since (*a*) it is impossible to tell how many of the different types were original contaminants and how many have resulted from growth, and (*b*) organisms of the fæcal coli group are not necessarily derived directly from excretal material, but may come from unsterilized milk utensils on which they have been multiplying perhaps for several generations.

The presence of coliform bacilli in small numbers in water or milk is not in itself objectionable ; it is merely as an index of the possible accompanying presence of pathogenic organisms that it is of importance. In milk, the coliform test cannot be used as an index of direct excretal pollution, for though it is true that if manure gains access to milk, coliform organisms will probably be found, the reverse conclusion does not hold true. There are so many other sources on the farm for these organisms that their presence in milk cannot be held to justify the conclusion that the milk has necessarily been contaminated with excretal material. The coliform test on milk fails to provide us with that specific qualitative information which it supplies in the case of water, and as a general method of grading, therefore, it seems to be unsuitable. It may serve a useful purpose in the examination of the highest quality raw milk, since such milk often fails to show the presence of coliform bacilli in 1 c.c. quantities even several hours after production (Mattick and Williams 1925). Its use, however, in this connection is purely empirical, merely serving as an index of contamination of the milk from environmental sources. Again the test may be of some empirical value in the control of pasteurization, since the practical absence of coliform bacilli from pasteurized milk examined immediately after processing affords, except with very clean milks, a fairly good indication that pasteurization has been carried out efficiently.

(7) **The Modified Methylene Blue Reduction Test.**—The general technique of this test is to add 1 c.c. of a standard methylene blue solution to 10 c.c. of milk in a test tube, to insert a sterile rubber cork, to invert the tube once or twice so as to mix the dye with the milk, to incubate in a constant-temperature water-bath at 37°–38° C. in complete darkness, to invert the tube every half-hour, and to observe the time at which the dye is decolorized. If reduction has not occurred within a given time, then no further observations need be made (see Wilson *et al.* 1935).

Reduction depends partly on the absorption of oxygen and the production of reducing substances by the organisms, and partly on the presence of a natural reducing system in the milk itself. Since some of the reducing enzymes and some of the organisms are adsorbed on to the fat, and since the fat globules themselves play an important mechanical part in increasing the surface available for enzyme action and in affecting the visual depth of colour, the necessity of preventing an accumulation of cream at the surface will be realized ; hence the necessity of half-hourly inversion.

The rate at which methylene blue is reduced in milk depends partly on the number of organisms and partly on their metabolic activity. For this reason it affords a very good index, not only of the bacterial cleanliness of the milk, but also of its keeping quality. The test is unsuited for the milk of individual cows, and for freshly pasteurized milk. Its chief value lies in affording a fairly rapid means of assessing the general hygienic quality of raw mixed milk. Its technical simplicity, its cheapness, and its extremely small experimental error render it admirably suited for the routine control of this type of milk. The reduction time to be laid down must depend on the level of cleanliness desired. A milk of high quality, which has been kept for about 12 hours at atmospheric temperature in this country, should not reduce methylene blue in less than about 8 hours in the winter or 7 hours in the summer, while one of fairly good quality should not reduce the dye in less than about 6 and 5 hours respectively.

Besides the advantages already noted, the reduction test has certain scientific advantages over the plate count. The first is that the result does not appear to be affected to any considerable extent by the degree of aggregation of the bacteria, which is one of the most disturbing features of the plate count on milk. The second is that the test affords a much more delicate index of bacterial growth than the plate count. It will be remembered (Chapter IV) that during the lag phase bacteria increase in size for some time before they commence to divide. The plate count therefore remains approximately constant during this phase. The reduction time, on the other hand, falls rapidly, owing to the active metabolism of the organisms. It serves, in fact, as a remarkably sensitive index of growth, and is hence peculiarly fitted to gauge the keeping quality of the milk. The plate count yields a *static* picture of the bacterial population : the methylene blue reduction test affords a *dynamic* picture.

(8) **The Laboratory Pasteurization Test.**—This consists in making a plate count before and after pasteurization in the laboratory, and noting the numerical reduction that has occurred (Anderson and Meanwell 1933). Its main purpose is to detect the presence of heat-resistant and thermophilic bacteria in the milk, which may be present in such numbers as to prevent the pasteurized product from conforming to the official standards laid down. It is essentially a test for use in processing depots.

It will be realized that numerous tests are available for assessing the general cleanliness of milk, and that each of these tests affords an answer to a different question. Complete correspondence of the results of the different tests cannot therefore be expected. Experience has shown, however, that the Breed clump count, the plate count, and the modified methylene blue reduction test are all fairly highly correlated with each other. On individual milks, of course, the reduction test and the plate count may give widely different results, owing mainly to the extraordinary high experimental error of the plate count, but on an average the results of these tests are very similar. For practical purposes, therefore, there seems to be no advantage in using the complex, expensive, and highly inaccurate plate count in preference to the simple, inexpensive, and accurate reduction test. From a public health point of view, probably only two divisions need be made on the basis of *cleanliness*, namely (*a*) into milk that is suitable and (*b*) into milk that is not suitable for human consumption in the liquid state. We would again emphasize that a *clean* milk is not necessarily a *safe* milk.

Grading according to Safety.

The pathogenic organisms for which search is commonly made in milk are the tubercle bacillus, *Br. abortus*, and hæmolytic streptococci. The methods employed in searching for the first two organisms have already been described in Chapters LVI and LXXII respectively.

The presence of mastitis streptococci in milk may be demonstrated microscopically or by culture, but according to Minett (1935) the microscopic method detects only about half of the cases that are positive culturally. The cultural method is, therefore, the method of choice. Individual quarter samples of the fore-milk should be plated out on to a suitable blood agar medium, such as that recommended by Edwards (1933), and a study made of the colonies that develop. The differentiation of *Str. agalactiæ* from other closely related types has been discussed in Chapter XXIII.

Milk Designations.—The grades of milk in England and Wales have been newly defined in the Milk (Special Designations) Order 1936, which came into operation on 1st June, 1936. Briefly it lays down three main grades of milk—Tuberculin Tested, Accredited, and Pasteurized. For the full conditions regulating the production, testing, and distribution of these milks reference must be made to Order (1936) and Circular (1936). Some of the more important requirements, however, are set out in Table CXC.

It will be noted that (1) Tuberculin Tested milk may be pasteurized : (2) Accredited milk does not have to come from herds subjected to a tuberculin test, and hence cannot be guaranteed to be free from tubercle bacilli ; (3) There is no official designation for ordinary raw milk, and no bacteriological standard of cleanliness or safety are laid down for this type of milk. From the point of view of public health Tuberculin Tested (Pasteurized) and Pasteurized are the only two milks that can be relied upon as being free from the risk of causing disease. All other milks should be heated to the boiling-point before being consumed in the liquid state, if it is desired to ensure the destruction of pathogenic organisms.

Diseases borne by Milk.—From the description that has already been given of the pathogenic organisms that may be found in milk, it will be realized that milk serves as an important vehicle in the spread of disease to man. The frequency of tuberculosis of bovine origin and of undulant fever due to milk-borne organisms has been considered in Chapter LVI and LXXII respectively. In these diseases infection of the milk occurs in the udder of the cow itself. In scarlet fever, septic sore throat, and diphtheria, infection more usually occurs from the nasopharynx of some person handling the milk, while in typhoid fever, paratyphoid fever, dysentery, and food poisoning the causative organisms generally gain access to the milk from the infected hands of some human attendant, or probably less frequently from a contaminated water supply.

The true frequency of milk-borne disease is extremely difficult to estimate, partly because the disease is often insidious in its onset and suspicion of the milk supply is not aroused, and partly because isolated cases of milk-borne infections, even if they are recognized as such, are not usually recorded. In this country Savage (1912) has attempted to collect the data referring to milk-borne epidemics prior to 1912. Table CXCI summarizes the data for the subsequent 20 years 1912–31.

TABLE CXC

GRADES OF MILK LAID DOWN IN THE MILK (SPECIAL DESIGNATIONS) ORDER 1936, UNDER
SECTION 3 OF THE MILK AND DAIRIES (AMENDMENT) ACT, 1922.

Designation.	General Conditions.	Bacteriological [1] Requirements after 1st Jan., 1937.	Remarks.
Tuberculin tested.	Tuberculin test on herd at least every 6 months. Veterinary inspection every 6 months.	Must not reduce [2] methylene blue in 4½ hrs. 1st May to 31st Oct., or in 5½ hrs. 1st Nov. to 30th April. Coliform bacilli must be absent from 1/100 ml.	(i) If bottled on farm, may be labelled Tuberculin Tested (Certified). (ii) If pasteurized, must not contain more than 30,000 bacteria per ml.
Accredited.	Veterinary inspection every 3 months.	Same as for Tuberculin Tested milk.	If bottled on farm may be labelled Accredited (Farm Bottled).
Pasteurized.	Milk must be kept at a temperature of 145°–150° F. for at least 30 mins. and be immediately cooled to 55° F. or below.	Must not contain more than 100,000 bacteria per ml.	Pasteurizing plant must be approved by the licensing authority, and must be equipped with indicating and recording thermometers. Temperature records must be preserved for at least a month. The milk shall not be heated more than once.

[1] Before 1st Jan., 1937, Tuberculin Tested and Accredited milk must not contain more than 200,000 bacteria per ml., or coliform bacilli in 1/100 ml. After 1st Jan., 1937, the plate count is replaced by a modified methylene blue reduction test.

[2] If the sample is taken before the milk has been placed in bottles or other containers for delivery to the consumer (*i.e.*, producers' milk), it must be kept at atmospheric temperature till 6 p.m. if it is a morning milk, and until 10 a.m. on the following day if it is an evening milk, before it is tested bacteriologically. It is not necessary for every sample to be submitted to both reduction and coliform tests as a routine ; it will generally be found convenient in testing producers' milk to have most of the samples examined by the methylene blue test alone, reserving the coliform test for occasional use.

TABLE CXCI

OUTBREAKS OF MILK-BORNE DISEASE IN GREAT BRITAIN, 1912–31.   (Wilson 1933.)

Disease.	No. of Outbreaks.	No. of Outbreaks in which Number of Persons affected is stated.	No. of Persons affected in these Outbreaks.
Scarlet fever and septic sore throat	31	25	3,087
Diphtheria	13	12	732
Typhoid fever, paratyphoid fever, and dysentery	25	22	1,843
Gastro-enteritis	12	10	3,759
Total	81	69	9,421

These outbreaks merely represent those of which records are readily available, and almost certainly underestimate the real number. They pay no attention, of course, to sporadic cases of milk-borne infection, nor do they include the 6,000 cases of tuberculosis of bovine origin nor the 400–500 cases of undulant fever, in a large proportion of which infection is milk-borne, that occur annually in Great Britain.

In the United States Armstrong and Parran (1927) record data referring to 612 milk-borne epidemics occurring during the preceding 20 years (Table CXCII).

TABLE CXCII

Outbreaks of Milk-borne Disease in the United States, 1906–26. (Armstrong and Parran 1927.)

Disease.	No. of Outbreaks.	No. of Cases (incomplete).	No. of Deaths (incomplete).
Typhoid fever	479	14,968	219
Paratyphoid fever	7	434	15
Diarrhœa and dysentery . . .	6	92	5
Septic sore throat	42	21,045	139
Scarlet fever	40	3,939	20
Diphtheria	26	971	7
Miscellaneous diseases	12	878	5
Total	612	42,327	410

This table again affords merely a conservative estimate of the frequency of milk-borne epidemics, and there is reason to believe that many outbreaks are not recognized or are not recorded (Brooks 1933). It will be noted that the relative incidence of enteric fever is very much higher than in Great Britain.

We have no space to discuss the epidemiology of milk-borne disease. Apart from the explosive nature of the outbreak, it is interesting to note that in milk-borne scarlet fever and diphtheria the average age incidence is often very much higher than in non-milk-borne epidemics. The majority of the cases may occur in persons of 15 years and over (see Godfrey 1929, Clarke 1936).

Methods for increasing the Safety of the Milk Supply.

These fall into three main categories.

A. Control of Animal Disease.—Reference has already been made in Chapters LVI and LXXII to the methods available for diminishing the frequency of tuberculosis and contagious abortion in cattle, and in Chapter LXIV to the elimination of mastitis. The success attendant on these measures will depend very largely on the vigour with which they are prosecuted. The eradication of disease, however, from the animal population is essentially an agricultural and veterinary problem to be undertaken in the economic interests of the farmer, and the task, particularly in this country where cattle disease is so widespread, is bound to be a long one. However much, therefore, we may support our veterinary colleagues in their enterprise, we must remember that this mode of approach can afford only a tardy and a partial solution to the problems faced by the public health bacteriologist, namely, that of supplying a safe milk to the human population.

B. Control of the Human Personnel handling the Milk.—However healthy the animals producing the milk may be, there is always danger of its becoming infected directly or indirectly from the nasopharynx or fæces of human carriers of *Str. pyogenes, C. diphtheriæ, Bact. typhosum, Bact. paratyphosum A* and *B*, dysentery bacilli, and bacilli of the food-poisoning group. In the United States some attempt has been made to control the human personnel handling the milk. The most frequent examinations made comprise a physical inspection, a careful inquiry into the history of infectious disease, a series of fæcal and urinary examinations for organisms of the enteric and dysentery groups, and nose and throat swabs for streptococci and diphtheria bacilli (see Borman *et al.* 1935). There is no question that close supervision of milk operatives, particularly of those working in pasteurizing depots, is highly desirable. The procedure is, however, costly and is not free from administrative difficulties. Moreover, since the carrier state is often transient or intermittent, it is impossible without almost daily supervision to detect all dangerous persons.

C. Heat Treatment of the Milk : Pasteurization, Boiling, and Sterilization.—The dangers of infection of milk from cattle, from the human personnel, and from water are so great that we shall not be overstating the case if we assert that no raw milk can be regarded as perfectly safe for human consumption. Clearly we must interpret this axiom with discretion, remembering always that the stringency of our precautions must be commensurate with the size of the population at risk. It is very difficult to assess in any particular instance the real danger run by persons consuming a given milk supply, and our safest course is therefore to insist as far as possible that all pathogenic organisms shall be destroyed by some form of heat treatment.

Pasteurization is by far the most satisfactory method for this purpose. In this country the process consists in raising the milk to a temperature of 145°–150° F., holding it at this temperature for 30 minutes, and immediately cooling it to 55° F. or below. If this process is carried out in properly designed plant free from mechanical defects (see Scott and Wright 1935, Dalrymple-Champneys 1935), and supervised by intelligent and conscientious operatives, it can be relied upon to destroy all pathogenic organisms in the milk. The objections that have been raised to it are mainly economic. The farmer, particularly the producer-retailer, does not obtain such a high return for his milk if he has to pasteurize it himself or send it to a pasteurizing depot, as if he sells it directly to the customer in its original raw and possibly dangerous state. While appreciating the force of this objection, we cannot, of course, allow the public health of the nation to be sacrificed for the financial interests of a small section of the community.

Another objection that has been raised is that pasteurization lowers the nutritive value of the milk. The evidence brought to support this objection is negligible, while on the contrary there is a great deal pointing in the opposite direction (see Stirling and Blackwood 1933, Report 1934, 1936). There is no evidence that heat significantly lowers the food value of milk for man. " So far as is known, the only significant changes effected in the composition of milk are a partial loss of vitamin C and possibly of iodine. The amount of vitamin C in raw milk is in any case small and even in raw milk some loss usually occurs in the course of distribution. These deficiences can be made good in the diet of babies fed exclusively on cows' milk by the addition of fruit or vegetable juice and cod-liver oil, and in the diets of children and adults by the other items in a good mixed diet which should always contain potatoes or other vegetables or fresh fruit and some sea fish " (Report 1936).

From a public health point of view, therefore, there are strong reasons why all milk intended for consumption in the liquid state by a community of any size should be submitted to pasteurization, the process being, of course, adequately controlled by the appropriate supervising authorities. There is reason to believe that if pasteurization was rendered compulsory and universal, milk-borne disease would practically cease to exist.

If pasteurization is impracticable, then the milk should be *boiled* in the individual household. The most satisfactory way of doing this is to bring it to the boil in a closed vessel, preferably a double saucepan, and cool it immediately to as low a temperature as possible.

Sterilization is the term used for a process which is applied commercially, and which is intended to destroy all but the most resistant spore-bearing organisms. In some plants the temperature is not raised above boiling-point, but more usually the milk is heated under a slight pressure. It is distributed in hermetically sealed bottles. Bacteriologically the milk is perfectly safe, but the partial caramelization which it undergoes renders its flavour unpalatable to most persons.

REFERENCES

ANDERSON, E. B. and MEANWELL, L. J. (1933) *J. Dairy Res.*, **4**, 213.
ARMSTRONG, C. and PARRAN, T. (1927) *Publ. Hlth Rep., Wash.*, Suppl. No. 62.
AYERS, S. H. and CLEMMER, P. W. (1918) *U.S. Dep. Agric. Bull.*, No. 739.
BARDSLEY, D. A. (1934) *J. Hyg., Camb.*, **34**, 38.
BORMAN, E. K., WEST, D. E., and MICKLE, F. L. (1935) *Amer. J. publ. Hlth.*, **25**, 557.
BREED, R. S. (1929) *N.Y. St. agric. exp. Sta., Bull.* No. 566.
BROOKS, P. B. (1933) *Amer. J. publ. Hlth.*, **23**, 1165.
Circular. (1936) *Min. Hlth*, No. 1533. H.M. Stat. Off., Lond.
CLARKE, J. H. (1936) *Med. Offr*, **55**, 40.
DALRYMPLE-CHAMPNEYS, W. (1935) " The Supervision of Milk Pasteurising Plants." *Min. Hlth, Lond., Rep. publ. Hlth med. Subj.*, No. 77.
DIERNHOFER, K. (1933) *Zbl. Bakt., Ref.*, **108**, 382.
EDWARDS, S. J. (933) *J. comp. Path.*, **46**, 211.
FINKELSTEIN, R. (1919) *J. Dairy Sci.*, **2**, 460.
GODFREY, E. S. (1929) *Amer. J. publ. Hlth.*, **19**, 257.
HOUSTON, A. C. (1913) " Studies in Water Supply." Macmillan's Science Monographs, London.
HUCKER, G. J., TRUDELL, F., and JENNINGS, W. S. (1932) *N.Y. St. agric. exp. Sta., Tec. Bull.*, No. 199.
MATTICK, A. T. R. and WILLIAMS, R. S. (1925) *J. Hyg., Camb.*, **23**, 277.
MATTICK, A. T. R., McCLEMONT, J., and IRWIN, J. O. (1935) *J. Dairy Res.*, **6**, 130.
MINETT, F. C. (1932) *Off. int. Epizooties*, **6**, 124 ; (1935) *Proc. 12th int. vet. Congr.*, 511.
Order. (1936) *Milk (Special Designations) Order*, 1936, No. 356. H.M. Stat. Off., Lond.
PARK, W. H. and HOLT, L. E. (1903) *Med. News, N.Y.*, **83**, 1066.
PROUTY, C. C. (1934) *J. Dairy Sci.*, **17**, 75.
PULLINGER, E. J. (1934) *Lancet*, i. 967 ; (1935) *J. Dairy Res.*, **6**, 369.
Report. (1909) 3rd *interim Rep., roy. Comm. Tuberc.* H.M. Stat. Off., Lond. ; (1932) Rep. Spec. Comm. People's League of Hlth, " A Survey of Tuberculosis of Bovine Origin in Great Britain " ; (1934) *Econ. advis. Coun., Comm. Cattle Dis.*, H.M. Stat. Off., Lond. ; (1936) " The Nutritive Value of Milk." *Min. Hlth & Dept Hlth Scotland*, H.M. Stat. Off., Lond.
SAVAGE, W. G. (1912) " Milk and the Public Health." Macmillan & Co., Ltd, London.
SCOTT, A. W. and WRIGHT, N. C. (1935) " An Inquiry into the Design, Operation and Efficiency of Pasteurising Plants." *Hannah Dairy Res. Bull.*, No. 6.
SHERMAN, J. M. and WING, H. U. (1933) *J. Dairy Sci.*, **16**, 165.
STARK, P. and SHERMAN, J. M. (1935) *J. Bact.*, **30**, 639.

STIRLING, J. D. and BLACKWOOD, J. H. (1933) " The Nutritive Properties of Milk in relation to Pasteurisation." *Hannah Dairy Res. Bull.*, No. 5.

STOCKMAYER, W. (1936) *Z. InfektKr. Haustiere*, **49,** 46.

WARD, A. R. (1926) *Dairy Prod. Merchandising*, **6,** No. 5. March.

WILSON, G. S. (1933) *Lancet*, ii. 829.

WILSON, G. S., TWIGG, R. S., WRIGHT, R. C., HENDRY, C. B., COWELL, M. P., and MAIER, I. (1935) *Spec. Rep. Ser. med. Res. Coun., Lond.*, No. 206.

INDEX

All organisms are listed under the generic names given in the Classificatory Chart on p. 220. Since many rod-shaped organisms have in the past been known under the generic name of *Bacillus*, irrespective of whether or not they belonged to this genus, we have for the convenience of the reader included many of them under the heading Bacillus (non-italicized). Certain recent names, the claim of which to generic rank seems to us doubtful, such as *Escherichia*, *Eberthella*, *Klebsiella*, etc., are not indexed.

$9\frac{00}{\Lambda v}$ —